Seventh Edition — 1993

Voice for the Hobby

Baseball Card Price Guide

Jeff Kurowski, Editor

Library of Congress Catalog Number: 87-80033
ISBN: 0-87341-233-8

Krause Publications Inc.
700 E. State St.
Iola, Wis. 54990

Printed in the United States of America

ACKNOWLEDGEMENTS

Dozens of individuals have made countless valuable contributions which have been incorporated into the *Sports Collectors Digest Baseball Card Price Guide* While all cannot be acknowledged, special appreciation is extended to the following principal contributors who have exhibited a special dedication by creating, revising or verifying listings and technical data, reviewing market valuations or loaning cards for photography.

Johnny Adams, Jr.
Ken Agona
(Sports Cards Plus)
Gary Agostino
Lisa Albano
Dan Albaugh
Mark Anker
Steve Applebaum
Bill Ballew
John Beisiegel
Karen Bell
Cathy Black
Mike Bodner
Bill Bossert
(Mid-Atlantic Coin Exchange)
Brian Boston
Mike Boyd
Rich Bradley
Jon Brecka
John Brigandi
(Brigandi Coin Co.)
Lou Brown
Dan Bruner
(The Card King)
Greg Bussineau
(Superior Sports Cards)
Billy Caldwell
(Packman)
Len Caprisecca
Tony Carrafiell
(Delco Sports Cards)
Lee Champion
Dwight Chapin
Chriss Christiansen
Shane Cohen
(Grand Slam Sports Collectibles)
Rich Cole
Charles Conlon
Eric Cooper
(All Star Cards)
Bryan Couling
Clyde Cripe
Jim Cumpton
Robert Curtiss
Tom Daniels
(T&J Sports Cards)
Tom Day
Dick DeCourcy
Ken Degnan
(Georgia Music & Sports)
Mike Del Gado
(All American Sportscards)
Larry Dluhy
(Texas Trading Cards)
John Dorsey

Curtis Earl
Mark Elliott
Joe Esposito
(B&E Collectibles)
Doak Ewing
David Festberg
(Baseball and Hobby Shop)
Jay Finglass
Nick Flaviano
Jeff Fritsch
Larry Fritsch
Richard Galasso
Tom Galic
Tony Galovich
(American Card Exchange)
Frank Giffune
Richard Gilkeson
Gerald J. Glasser
Dick Goddard
Jack Goodman
Bill Goodwin
(St. Louis Baseball Cards)
Audre Gold
(Au Sports Memorabilia)
Mike Gordon
Howard Gordon
Bob Gray
Wayne Grove
(First Base)
Gerry Guenther
Don Guilbert
Tom Guilfoile
Julie Haddon
David, Joel & Walter Hall
(Hall's Nostalgia)
Gary Hamilton
Tom Harbin
Don Harrison
Rick Hawksley
Herbert Hecht
Bill Henderson
Kathy Henry
Gregg Hitesman
Jack Horkan
Jim Horne
Ron Hosmer
Marvin Huck
Robert Jacobsen
Donn Jennings
Scott Jensen
Jim Johnston
Stewart Jones
Larry Jordon
Judy Kay
(Kay's Baseball Cards)
Allan Kaye

Michael Keedy
Mark Kemmerle
Rick Keplinger
John King
John Kittleson
(Sports Collectibles)
Bob Koehler
David Kohler
Jay Kurowski
John Kurowski
Steve Lacasse
Lee Lasseigne
Mark K. Larson
William Lawrence
Morley Leeking
Rod Lethbridge
Paul Lewicki
Howie Levy
(Blue Chip Sportscard)
Rob Lifson
Jeff Litteral
Mark MacRae
Ken Magee
Paul Marchant
Bill Mastro
Tony McLaughlin
Don McPherson
John Mehlin
Bill Mendel
Blake Meyer
(Lone Star Sportcard Co.)
Dick Millerd
Minnesota Sports Collectibles
Keith Mitchell
J.A. Monaco
Joe Morano
Brian Morris
Mike Mowery
Peter Muldavin
Mark Murphy
(The Baseball Card "Kid")
David Musser
(D.M.B.'s Baseball Cards)
Frank Nagy
Chuck Nobriga
Mark Nochta
Wayne Nochta
Keith Olbermann
Joe Pasternack
(Card Collectors Co.)
Marty Perry
Tom Pfirrman
(Baseball Card Corner)
Dan Piepenbrok
(Uneeda Hobbie)
Stan Pietruska
(Pro Sports Investments)

Paul Pollard
Ed Ransom
Fred Rapoport
(Yesterday's Heroes)
Tom Reid
Bob Richardson
Gavin Riley
Ron Ritzler
Mike Rodell
Mike Rogers
Chris Ronan
Rocky Rosato
Alan Rosen
John Rumierz
Bob Rund
Jon Sands
(Howard's Coin Shop)
Kevin Savage
(The Sports Gallery)
Stephen Schauer
Dave Schwartz
(Dave's Sportscards)
Robert Scott
Corey Shanus
Dan Shedrick
Barry Sloate
Joe Smith
Mark Soltan
John Spalding
Kevin Spears
Gene Speranza
David Spivack
Don Steinbach
Dan Stickney
Larry Stone
Doug Stultz
Joe Szeremet
Erik Teller
K.J. Terplak
Dick Tinsley
Bud Tompkins
(Minnesota Connection)
Scott Torrey
Rich Unruh
Jack Urban
Pete Waldman
Eric Waller
Gary Walter
Ken Weimer
Dale Weselowski
E.C. Wharton-Tigar
Chris Williams
Charles Williamson
Kit Young
Ted Zanidakis

4

ROOKIE/FIRST CARD DESIGNATIONS

A player's name in italic type indicates a rookie card. An (FC) designation indicates a player's first card for that particular company. FCs will be found in 1981-90 Donruss, Fleer, Score and Topps sets. They will also be located in the Donruss Rookies, Fleer Update, Topps Traded and Score Traded sets.

BASEBALL CARD HISTORY

In 1887 — over 100 years ago — the first nationally distributed baseball cards were issued by Goodwin & Co. of New York City. The 1½" x 2½" cards featured posed studio photographs glued to stiff cardboard. They were inserted into cigarette packages with such exotic brand names as Old Judge, Gypsy Queen and Dog's Head. Poses were formal, with artificial backgrounds and bare-handed players fielding balls suspended on strings to simulate action.

Then, as now, baseball cards were intended to stimulate product sales. What could be more American than using the diamond heroes of the national pastime to gain an edge on the competition? It is a tradition that has continued virtually unbroken for a century.

Following Goodwin's lead a year later, competitors began issuing baseball cards with their cigarettes, using full-color lithography to bring to life painted portraits of the era's top players.

After a few short years of intense competition, the cigarette industry's leading firms formed a monopoly and cornered the market. By the mid-1980s there was little competition, and no reason to issue baseball cards. The first great period of baseball card issues came to an end.

The importing of Turkish tobaccos in the years just prior to 1910 created a revolution in American smoking habits. With dozens of new firms entering the market, the idea of using baseball cards to boost sales was revived.

In the years from 1909-1912, dozens of different sets of cards were produced to be given away in cigarette packages. There was a greater than ever variety in sizes, shapes and designs, from the extremely popular 1½" x 2⅝" color lithographed set of 500+ players which collectors call T206, to the large (5" x 8") Turkey Red brand cards. There were double folders, featuring two players on the same card, and triple folders, which had two player portraits and an action scene. Gold ink and embossed designs were also tried to make competing companies' cards attractive and popular.

It was this era that saw the issue of the king of baseball cards, the T206 Honus Wagner card, worth $400,000.

The zeal with which America's youngsters pursued their fathers, uncles, and neighbors for cigarette cards in the years just prior to World War I convinced the nation's confectioners that baseball cards could also be used to boost candy sales.

While baseball cards had been produced by candy companies on a limited basis as far back as the 1880s, by the early 1920s the concept was being widely used in the industry. The highly competitive caramel business was a major force in this new marketing strategy, offering a baseball card in each package of candy. Not to be outdone, Cracker Jack began including baseball cards in each box. The 1914-1915 Cracker Jack cards are important because they were the most popular of the candy cards to include players from a short-lived third major league, the Federal League.

Generally, candy cards of the era were not as colorful or well-printed as the earlier tobacco cards, due to the shortage of paper and ink-making ingredients caused by World War I.

The association of bubble gum and baseball cards is a phenomenon of only the past half-century. In the early 1930s techniques were developed using rubber tree products to give the elasticity necessary for blowing bubbles.

During this era the standard method of selling a slab of bubble gum and a baseball card in a colorfully wax-wrapped 1-cent package was developed. Bubble gum — and baseball card — production in this era was centered in Massachusetts, where National Chicle Co. (Cambridge) and Goudey Gum Co. (Boston) were headquartered.

Most bubble gum cards produced in the early 1930s featured a roughly square (about 2½") format, with players depicted in colorful paintings. For the first time, considerable attention was paid to the backs of the cards, where biographical details, career highlights and past season statistics were presented.

In 1939, a new company entered the baseball card market — Gum Inc., of Philadelphia. Its "Play Ball" gum was the major supplier of baseball cards until 1941, when World War II caused a shortage of the materials necessary both for the production of bubble gum and the printing of baseball cards.

Three years after the end of World War II baseball cards returned on a national scale, with two companies competing for the bubble gum market. In Philadelphia, the former Gum Inc. reappeared on the market as Bowman Gum Inc.

Bowman's first baseball card set appeared in 1948, very similar in format to the cards which had existed prior to the war, black-and-white player photos on nearly square (2" x 2½") cardboard. The 1948 Bowman effort was modest, with only 48 cards. The following year, color was added to the photos. For 1950, Bowman replaced the retouched photos with original color paintings of players, many of which were repeated a year later in the 1951 issue. Also new for 1951 was a larger card size, 2" x 3⅛".

Bowman had little national competition in this era. In 1948-1949, Leaf Gum in Chicago produced a 98-card set that is the only bubble gum issue of the era to include a Joe DiMaggio card.

While Bowman dominated the post-war era through 1951, in that year Topps began production of its first baseball cards, issuing three different small sets of cards and serving warning that it was going to become a major force in the baseball card field.

In 1952, Brooklyn-based Topps entered the baseball card market in a big way. Not only was its 407-card set the largest single-year issue ever produced, but its 2⅝" x 3¾" format was the largest-sized baseball card ever offered for over-the-counter sale. Other innovations in Topps' premiere issue for 1952 included the first-ever use of team logos in card design, and on the back of the card, the first use of line statistics to document the player's previous and career performance. By contrast, Bowman's set for 1952 remained in the smaller format, had 72 fewer cards and showed little change in design from 1951.

Just as clearly as Topps won the 1952 baseball card battle, Bowman came back in 1953 with what is often considered the finest baseball card set ever produced. For the first time ever, actual color photographs were reproduced on baseball cards in Bowman's 160-card set. To allow the full impact of the new technology, there were no other design elements on the front of the card and Bowman adopted a larger format, 2½" x 3¾".

And so the competition went for five years, with each

company trying to gain an edge by signing players to exclusive contracts and creating new and exciting card designs each year. Gradually, Topps became the dominant force in the baseball card market. In late 1955, Bowman admitted defeat and the company was sold to Topps.

Baseball cards entered a new era in 1957. After years of intense competition, Topps enjoyed a virtual monopoly that was rarely seriously challenged in the next 25 years. One such challenge in the opening years of the 1960s came from Post cereal, which from 1961-1963 issued 200-card sets on the backs of its cereal boxes.

In 1957, Topps' baseball cards were issued in a new size — 2½" x 3½" — that would become the industry-wide standard that prevails to this day. It was also the year that Topps first used full-color photographs for its cards, rather than paintings or retouched black-and-white photos. Another innovation in the 1957 set was the introduction of complete major/and or minor league statistics on the card backs. This feature quickly became a favorite with youngsters and provided fuel for endless schoolyard debates about whether one player was better than another.

In the ensuing five years, major league baseball underwent monumental changes. In 1958, the Giants and Dodgers left New York for California. In 1961-1962 expansion came to the major leagues, with new teams springing up from coast to coast and border to border.

The Topps baseball cards of the era preserve those days when modern baseball was in its formative stages.

In 1963, for the first time in seven years, it looked as if there might once again be two baseball card issues to choose from. After three years of issuing "old-timers" card sets, Fleer issued a 66-card set of current players. Topps took Fleer to court, where the validity of Topps' exclusive contracts with baseball players to appear on bubble gum cards was upheld. It was the last major challenge to Topps for nearly 20 years.

The 1960s offered baseball card collecting at its traditional finest. Youngsters would wait and worry through the long winter, watching candy store shelves for the first appearance of the brightly colored 5-cent card packs in the spring. A cry of "They're in!" could empty a playground in seconds as youngsters rushed to the corner store to see what design innovations Topps had come up with for the new year. Then, periodically during the summer, new series would be released, offering a new challenge to complete. As the seasons wore down, fewer and fewer stores carried the final few series, and it became a real struggle to complete the "high numbers" from a given year's set. But it was all part of the fun of buying baseball cards in the 1960s.

The early 1970s brought some important changes to the baseball card scene. The decade's first two Topps issues were stunning in that the traditional white border was dropped in favor of gray in 1970, and black in 1971. In 1972, Topps' card design was absolutely psychedelic, with brightly colored frames around the player photos, and comic book typography popping out all over. The design for the 1973 cards was more traditional, but the photos were not. Instead of close-up portraits or posed "action" shots, many cards in the 1973 Topps set featured actual game action photos. Unfortunately, too many of those photos made it hard to tell which player was which, and the set was roundly panned by collectors.

But most significantly, 1973 marked the last year in which baseball cards were issued by series through the course of the summer. On the positive side, this eliminated the traditional scarce "high numbers" produced toward the end of the season. On the negative side, it meant players who had been traded in the pre-season could no longer be shown in their correct uniforms, and outstanding new players had to wait a full year before their rookie cards would debut.

This marketing change made a significant impact on the hobby and helped spur a tremendous growth period in the late 1970s. By offering all of the cards at once, Topps made it easy for baseball card dealers to offer complete sets early in the year. Previously, collectors had to either assemble their sets by buying packs of cards, or wait until all series had been issued to buy a set from a dealer. It was in this era that many of today's top baseball card dealers got their start or made the switch to baseball cards a full-time business.

During this era, the first significant national competition to Topps' baseball card monopoly in many years was introduced. Hostess, a bakery products company, began distributing baseball cards printed on the bottoms of packages of its snack cakes, while the Kellogg's company distributed simulated 3-D cards in boxes of its cereals. The eagerness with which collectors gobbled up these issues showed that the hobby was ready for a period of unprecedented growth.

The baseball card hobby literally boomed in 1981. A federal court broke Topps' monopoly on the issue of baseball cards with bubble gum, and Fleer, from Philadelphia, and Donruss, of Memphis, entered the field as the first meaningful competition in nearly 20 years.

That same year also marked a beginning of the resurgence in the number of regional baseball card issues. Over the next few years, dozens of such sets came onto the market, helping to boost sales of everything from snack cakes to soda pop and police public relations. By 1984, more than half of the teams in the major leagues were issuing some type of baseball cards on a regional basis. The hobby had not enjoyed such diversity of issues since the mid-1950s.

While yet another court decision cost Fleer and Donruss the right to sell their baseball cards with bubble gum, both companies remained in the market and gained strength.

Topps' major contribution in this era was the introduction of annual "Traded" sets which offered cards of the year's new rookies as well as cards of traded players in their correct uniforms.

The mid-1980s showed continued strong growth in the number of active baseball card collectors, as well as the number of new baseball card issues. Topps, still the industry's leader, expanded the number and variety of its baseball issues with many different test issues and on-going speciality sets, including oversize cards, 3-D plastic cards, metal "cards" and much more.

After three years of over-production of its baseball card sets, Donruss, in 1984, significantly limited the number of cards printed, creating a situation in which demand exceeded supply, causing the value of Donruss cards to rise above Topps for the first time.

In 1984, Fleer followed Topps' lead and produced a season's-end "Update" set. Because the quantity of sets printed was extremely limited, and because it contains many of today's hottest young players, the 1984 Fleer Update set has become the most valuable baseball card issue produced in recent times.

In 1986, a fourth company joined the baseball card wars. Called "Sportflics," the cards were produced by a subsidiary of the Wrigley Gum Co., and featured three different photos on each card in a simulated 3-D effect. For 1987, a fourth national baseball card set, called Score, entered the scene. A fifth national baseball card set, Upper Deck, was created in 1989.

HOW TO USE THIS CATALOG

This catalog has been uniquely designed to serve the needs of beginning and advanced collectors. It provides

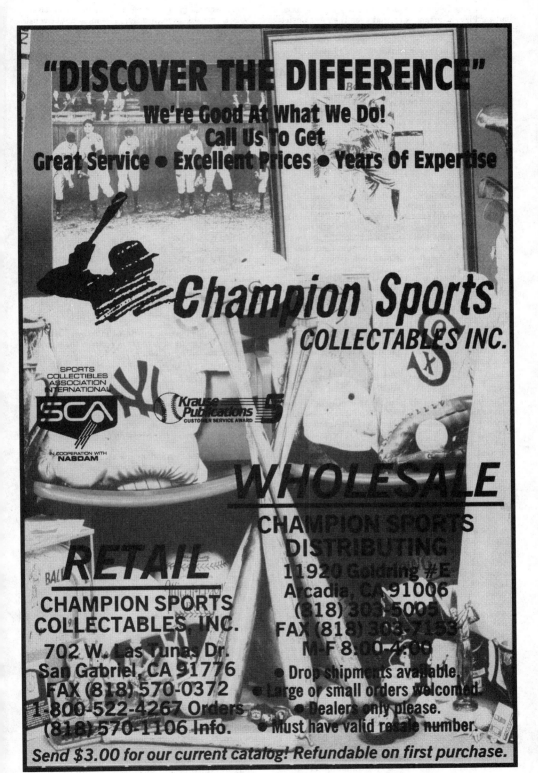

a comprehensive guide to more than 100 years of baseball card issues, arranged so that even the most novice collector can consult it with confidence and ease.

The following explanations summarize the general practices used in preparing this catalog's listings. However, because of specialized requirements which may vary from card set to card set, these must not be considered ironclad. Where these standards have been set aside, appropriate notations are incorporated.

ARRANGEMENT

Because the most important feature in identifying, and pricing, a baseball card is its set of origin, this catalog has been alphabetically arranged according to the name by which the set is most popularly known to collectors.

Those sets that were issued for more than one year are then listed chronologically, from earliest to most recent.

Within each set, the cards are listed by their designated card number, or in the absence of card numbers, alphabetically according to the last name of the player pictured.

IDENTIFICATION

While most modern baseball cards are well identified on front, back or both, as to date and issue, such has not always been the case. In general, the back of the card is more useful in identifying the set of origin than the front. The issuer or sponsor's name will usually appear on the back since, after all, baseball cards were first issued as a promotional item to stimulate sales of other products. As often as not, that issuer's name is the name by which the set is known to collectors and under which it will be found listed in this catalog.

Virtually every set listed in this catalog is accompanied by a photograph of a representative card. If all else fails, a comparison of an unknown card with the photos in this book will usually produce a match.

As a special feature, each set listed in this catalog has been cross-indexed by its date of issue. This will allow identification in some difficult cases because a baseball card's general age, if not specific year of issue, can usually be fixed by studying the biographical or statistical information on the back of the card. The last year mentioned in either the biography or stats is usually the year which preceded the year of issue.

PHOTOGRAPHS

A photograph on the front and back of at least one representative card from virtually every set listed in this catalog has been incorporated into the listings to aid in identification.

Photographs have been printed in reduced size. The actual size of cards in each set is given in the introductory text preceding its listing.

DATING

The dating of baseball cards by year of issue on the front or back of the card itself is a relatively new phenomenon. In most cases, to accurately determine a date of issue for an unidentified card, it must be studied for clues. As mentioned, the biography, career summary or statistics on the back of the card are the best way to pinpoint a year of issue. In most cases, the year of issue will be the year after the last season mentioned on the card.

Luckily for today's collector, earlier generations have done much of the research in determining year of issue for those cards which bear no clues. The painstaking task of matching players' listed and/or pictured team against their career records often allowed an issue date to be determined.

In some cases, particular cards sets were issued over a period of more than one calendar year, but since they are collected together as a single set, their specific year of issue is not important. Such sets will be listed with their complete known range of issue years.

NUMBERING

While many baseball card issues as far back as the 1880s have contained card numbers assigned by the issuer, to facilitate the collecting of a compete set, the practice has by no means been universal. Even today, not every set bears card numbers.

Logically, those baseball cards which were numbered by their manufacturer are presented in that numerical order within the listings of this catalog. The many unnumbered issues, however, have been assigned *Sports Collectors Digest Baseball Card Price Guide* numbers to facilitate their universal identification within the hobby, especially when buying and selling by mail. In all cases, numbers which have been assigned, or which otherwise do not appear on the card through error or by design, are shown in this catalog within parentheses. In virtually all cases, unless a more natural system suggested itself by the unique nature of a particular set, the assignment of *Sports Collectors Digest Baseball Card Price Guide* numbers by the cataloging staff has been done by alphabetical arrangement of the player's last names or the card's principal title.

Significant collectible variations of any particular card are noted within the listings by the application of a suffix letter within parentheses. In instances of variations, the suffix "a" is assigned to the variation which was created first.

NAMES

The identification of a player by full name on the front of his baseball card has been a common practice only since the 1920s. Prior to that, the player's last name and team were the usual information found on the card front.

As a standard practice, the listings in the *Sports Collectors Digest Baseball Card Price Guide* present the player's name exactly as it appears on the front of the card, if his full name is given there. If the player's full name only appears on the back, rather than the front of the card, the listing corresponds to that designation.

In cases where only the player's last name is given on the card, the cataloging staff has included the first name by which he was most often known for ease of

BILL HENDERSON'S CARDS
"King of the Commons"

"ALWAYS BUYING"
Call or Write
for Quote

2320 Ruger Ave.
Janesville, Wisconsin 53545
1-608-755-0922 ● FAX 1-608-755-0802

"ALWAYS BUYING"
Call or Write
for Quote

EX/MT TO MINT CONDITION HI # OR SEMI HI SCARCE SERIES	PRICE PER COMMON CARD	COMMON EACH	EX/MT TO MINT CONDITION OTHER SERIES	PRICE PER COMMON CARD	EX/MT TO MINT CONDITION GROUP LOTS FOR SALE MY CHOICE OF CARDS 50 Diff.	100 Diff.	200 Asst.	300 Asst.	500 Asst.	VG + TO EX Condition 50	100 Different	200
1948 Bowman (37-48)	$30.00	$25.00										
1949 Bowman (145-240)	90.00	18.00	(37-72)	20.00	850.					540.		
1950-51 Bowman 50 (1-72) 51 (253-324)	60.00	18.00	51 (2-36)	25.00	900.					600.		
1952 Topps (251-310)	60.00	30.00	(2-80)	60.00	1350.					900.		
1952 Bowman (37-72) 20.00 (217-252)	35.00	18.00	(2-36)	22.00	850.					540.		
1953 Topps (220-280)	100.00	30.00	(166-219)	20.00	900.					600.		
1953 Bowman (129-160)	45.00	35.00	(113-128)	55.00	1575.					950.		
1954 Topps		15.00	(51-75)	30.00	675.					450.		
1954 Bowman		10.00	(129-224)	15.00	450.	850.				270.	510.	
1955 Topps (161-210)	30.00	10.00	(151-160)	20.00	450.					270.		
1955 Bowman (225-320) 18.-30. Umps		8.00	(2-96)	8.50	360.	700.				210.	400.	
1956 Topps (101-180) $12.00 (261-340)	14.00	10.00	(181-260)	18.00	450.	850.				270.	510.	
1957 Topps (265-352)	25.00	7.50	(1-88)	8.50	350.	680.				225.	430.	
1958 Topps (111-198)	6.00	5.00	(1-110)	8.50	230.	450.	880.	1275.		140.	260.	
1959 Topps (507-572)	17.50	4.00	(1-110)	7.00	190.	370.	720.	1000.		115.	220.	430.
1960 Topps (441-506) $5.00 (507-572)	15.00	4.00	(1-110)	4.50	190.	370.	720.	1000.		115.	220.	430.
1961 Topps (447-522) $6.00 (523-589)	35.00	3.50	(371-446)	5.00	165.	320.	620.	900.		100.	190.	370.
1962 Topps (371-522) $6.00 (523-590)	15.00	3.00	(284-370)	4.00	140.	270.				85.	160.	310.
1963 Topps (447-522) $15.00 (523-573)	10.00	3.00	(284-446)	4.50	140.	270.				85.	160.	
1964 Topps (371-522) $5.00 (523)-587	10.00	2.50	(197-370)	3.50	115.	220.	430.			70.	130.	250.
1965 Topps (447-522) $6.00 (523-598)	6.50	2.50	(284-446)	5.00	115.	220.				70.	130.	
1966 Topps (447-522) $7.50 (523-598)	15.00	2.50	(371-446)	5.00	115.	220.	*340.			70.	130.	220.
1967 Topps (458-533) $7.50 (534-609)	20.00	2.00	(284-457)	4.00	90.	175.	*340.			60.	110.	210.
1968 Topps (534-598)	4.00	1.50	(458-533)	3.50	65.	125.	*240.			37.	70.	130.
1969 Topps (513-588) $2.00 (589-664)	2.50	1.50	(219-327)	2.50	65.	125.	*240.			37.	70.	150.
1970 Topps (547-633) 3.50 (634-720)	7.00	1.00	(460-546)	2.00	45.	88.	*170.	250.	400.	27.	52.	100.
1971 Topps (524-643) 4.00 (644-752)	7.00	1.00	(394-523)	2.00	45.	88.	*170.	250.	400.	27.	52.	100.
1972 Topps (526-656) 3.50 (657-787)	7.00	.75	(395-525)	1.50	35.	68.	*130.	*190.	300.	21.	40.	78.
1973 Topps (529-660)	3.00	.60	(397-528)	1.50	28.	54.	*105.	*150.	215.	18.	34.	65.
1974 Topps		.50			23.	45.	*85.	*125.	*170.		27.	50.
1975 Topps		.50			23.	45.	*85.	*125.			27.	50.
1976-77 Topps & 84 Donruss		.30			28.	*54.	*80.	*125.			16.	30.
1978-1980 Topps		.15			13.	*25.	*38.	*65.			8.	15.
1981 thru 1993 Topps 1981-1989 Fleer & Donruss except those listed below (specify year & co.)		.10			9. Per Yr.	*17. Per Yr.	*26. Per Yr.	*40. Per Yr.				
1985-86 Donruss, 1984-86 Fleer		.15			13.	*25.	*38.	*65.				

SPECIAL IN VG + TO EX
CONDITION-POSTPAID
Equal Distribution
of each year

250	58-62	450.00
500	58-62	850.00
250	60-69	350.00
500	60-69	650.00
1000	60-69	1,250.00
250	70-79	70.00
500	70-79	130.00
1,000	70-79	250.00
250	80-84	15.00
500	80-84	28.00
1,000	80-84	55.00

Special 1 Different from each year 1949-80 EX/MT - $160.00, VG-EX $110.00
Special 100 Different from each year 1956-80 EX/MT $4600.00, VG-EX $3000.00
Special 10 Different from each year 1956-80 EX/MT - $470.00, VG-EX $300.00

All lot groups are my choice only.

All assorted lots will contain as many different as possible.
Please list alternates whenever possible.
Send your want list and I will fill them at the above price for commons.
High numbers, specials, scarce series, and stars are priced at current Beckett.
You can use you Master Card or VISA to charge your purchases.
Minimum order $7.50 - Postage and handling .50 per 100 cards (minimum $2.50)

ANY CARD NOT LISTED ON PRICE SHEET IS PRICED AT CURRENT BECKETT MONTHLY HIGH COLUMN

* Group Lots are all different

SETS AVAILABLE
Topps 1988, 1989, 1990, 1991, 1992
$22.95 ea. + $2.50 UPS
6 for $22.95 ea. + $9.00 UPS
18 for $22.35 ea + $20.00 UPS
MIX OR MATCH

identification.

Cards which contain misspelled first or last names, or even wrong initials, will have included in their listings the incorrect information, with a correction accompanying in parentheses. This extends, also, to cases where the name on the card does not correspond to the player actually pictured.

GRADING

It is necessary that some sort of card grading standard be used so that buyer and seller (especially when dealing by mail) may reach an informed agreement on the value of a card. Each card set's listings are priced in the three grades of preservation in which those cards are most commonly encountered in the daily buying and selling of the hobby marketplace.

Older cards are listed in grades of Near Mint (NR MT), Excellent (EX) and Very Good (VG), reflecting the basic fact that few cards were able to survive for 25, 50 or even 100 years in close semblance to the condition of their issue. The pricing of cards in these three conditions will allow readers to accurately price cards which fall in intermediate grades, such as EX-MT, or VG-EX.

More recent issues, which have been preserved in top condition in considerable number, are listed in the grades of Mint (MT), Near Mint and Excellent, reflective of the fact that there exists in the current market little or no demand for cards of the recent past in grades below Excellent.

In general, although grades below Very Good are not priced in this catalog, close approximations of low-grade card values may figure on the following formula: Good condition cards are valued at about 50% of VG price, with Fair cards priced about 50% of Good. Cards in Poor condition have no market value except in the cases of the rarest and most expensive cards. In such cases, value has to be negotiated individually.

For the benefit of the reader, we present herewith the grading guide which was orginally formulated by *Baseball Cards* magazine and *Sports Collectors Digest* in 1981, and has been continually refined since that time. These grading definitions have been used in the pricing of cards in this) catalog, but they are by no means a universally accepted grading standard. The potential buyer of a baseball card should keep that in mind when encountering cards of nominally the same grade, but at a price which differs widely from that quoted in this book. Ultimately, the collector himself must formulate his own personal grading standards in deciding whether cards available for purchase meet the needs of his own collection.

No collector or dealer is required to adhere to the grading standards presented herewith — or to any other published grading standards — but all are invited to do so. The editors of the *Sports Collectors Digest Baseball Card Price Guide* are eager to work toward the development of a standardized system of card grading that will be consistent with the realities of the hobby marketplace. Contact the editors.

Mint (MT): A perfect card. Well-centered, with parallel borders which appear equal to the naked eye. Four sharp, square corners. No creases, edge dents, surface scratches, paper flaws, loss of luster, yellowing or fading, regardless of age. No imperfectly printed card — out of register, badly cut or ink flawed — or card stained by contact with gum, wax or other substances can be considered truly Mint, even if new out of the pack.

Near Mint (NR MT): A nearly perfect card. At first glance, a Near Mint card appears perfect; upon closer examination, however, a minor flaw will be discovered. On well-centered cards, three of the four corners must be perfectly sharp; only one corner shows a minor imperfection upon close inspection. A slightly off-center card with one or more borders being noticeably unequal — but still present — would also fit this grade.

Excellent (EX): Corners are still fairly sharp with only moderate wear. Card borders may be off center. No creases. May have very minor gum, wax or product stains, front or back. Surfaces may show slight loss of luster from rubbing across other cards.

Very Good (VG): Shows obvious handling. Corners rounded and/or perhaps showing minor creases. Other minor creases may be visible. Surfaces may exhibit loss of luster, but all printing is intact. May show major gum, wax or other packaging stains. No major creases, tape marks or extraneous markings or writing. Exhibit honest wear.

Good (G): A well-worn card, but exhibits no intentional damage or abuse. May have major or multiple creases. Corners rounded well beyond the border.

Fair (F): Shows excessive wear, along with damage or abuse. Will show all the wear characteristics of a Good card, along with such damage as thumb tack holes in or near margins, evidence of having been taped or pasted, perhaps small tears around the edges, or creases so heavy as to break the cardboard. Backs may show minor added pen or pencil writing, or be missing small bits of paper. Still, a basically complete card.

Poor: A card that has been tortured to death. Corners or other areas may be torn off. Card may have been trimmed, show holes from paper punch or have been used for BB gun practice. Front may have extraneous pen or pencil writing, or other defacement. Major portions of front or back design may be missing. Not a pretty sight.

In addition to these seven widely-used terms, collectors will often encounter intermediate grades, such as VG-EX (Very Good to Excellent), EX-MT (Excellent to Mint), or NR MT-MT (Near Mint to Mint). Persons who describe a card with such grades are usually trying to convey that the card has all the characteristics of the lower grade, with enough of the higher grade to merit mention. Such cards are usually priced at a point midway between the two grades.

VALUATIONS

Values quoted in this book represent the current retail market and are compiled from recommendations provided and verified through the author's daily involvement in the publication of the hobby's leading advertising periodicals, as well as the input of specialized consultants.

It should be stressed, however, that this book is intended to serve only as an aid in evaluating cards; actual market conditions are constantly changing. This is especially true of the cards of current players, whose on-field performance during the course of a season can greatly affect the value of their cards — upwards or downwards.

Publication of this catalog is not intended as a solicitation to buy or sell the listed cards by the editors, publishers or contributors.

Again, the values here are retail prices — what a collector can expect to pay when buying a card from a dealer. The wholesale price, that which a collector can expect to receive from a dealer when selling cards, will be significantly lower. Most dealers operate on a 100% mark-up, generally paying about 50% of a card's retail value. On some high-demand cards, dealers will pay up to 75% or even 100% or more of retail value, anticipating continued price increases. Conversely, for may low-demand cards, such as common player's cards of recent years, dealers may pay 25% or even less of retail.

It should also be noted that with several hundred thousand valuations quoted in this book, there are bound to be a few compilations or typographical errors which will creep into the final product, a fact readers should remember if they encounter a listing at a fraction of, or several times, the card's actual current retail price. The editors welcome the correction of any such errors discovered. Write: *Sports Collectors Digest Baseball Card Price Guide*, 700 E. State St., Iola, Wis. 54990.

SETS

Collectors may note that the complete set prices for newer issues quoted in these listings are usually significantly lower than the total of the value of the individual cards which comprise the set.

This reflects two factors in the baseball card market. First, a seller is often willing to take a lower composite price for a complete set as a "volume discount" and to avoid inventorying a large number of common player or other lower-demand cards.

Second, to a degree, the value of common cards can be said to be inflated as a result of having a built-in overhead charge to justify the dealer's time in sorting cards, carrying them in stock and filling orders. This accounts for the fact that even brand new baseball cards, which cost the dealer around 1 cent each when bought in bulk, carry individual price tags of 3 cents or higher.

ERRORS/VARIATIONS

It is often hard for the beginning collector to understand that an error on a baseball card, in and of itself, does not usually add premium value to that card. It is usually only when the correcting of an error in the subsequent printing creates a variation that premium value attaches to an error.

Minor errors, such as wrong stats or personal data, create a variation that premium value attaches to an error. Misspellings, inconsistencies, etc. — usually affecting the back of the card — are very common, especially in recent years. Unless a corrected variation was also printed, these errors are not noted in the listings of this book because they are not generally perceived by collectors to have premium value.

On the other hand, major effort has been expended to include the most complete listings ever for collectible variation cards. Many scarce and valuable variations — dozens of them never before cataloged — are included in these listings because they are widely collected and often have significant premium value.

COUNTERFEITS/REPRINTS

As the value of baseball cards has risen in the past 10-20 years, certains cards and sets have become too expensive for the average collector to obtain. This, along with changes in the technology of color printing, has given rise to increasing numbers of counterfeit and reprint cards.

While both terms describe essentially the same thing — a modern copy which attempts to duplicate as closely as possible an original baseball card — there are differences which are important to the collector.

Generally, a counterfeit is made with the intention of deceiving somebody into believing it is genuine, and thus paying large amounts of money for it. The counterfeiter takes every pain to try to make his fakes look as authentic as possible. In recent years, the 1963 Pete Rose, 1984 Donruss Don Mattingly and more than 30 superstar cards of the late 1960s-early 1980s have been counterfeited — all were quickly detected because of the differences in quality of cardboard on which they were printed.

A reprint, on the other hand, while it may have been made to look as close as possible to an original card, is made with the intention of allowing collectors to buy them as substitutes for cards they may never be otherwise able to afford. The big difference is that a reprint is generally marked as such, usually on the back of the card. In other cases, like the Topps 1952 reprint set, the replicas are printed in a size markedly different from the originals.

Collectors should be aware, however, that unscrupulous persons will sometimes cut off or otherwise obliterate the distinguishing word — "Reprint," "Copy," — or modern copyright date on the back of a reprint card in an attempt to pass it as genuine.

A collector's best defense against reprints and counterfeits is to acquire a knowledge of the look and feel of genuine baseball cards of various eras and issues.

UNLISTED CARDS

Readers who have cards or sets which are not covered in this edition are invited to correspond with the editor for purposes of adding to the compilation work now in progress. Address: *Sports Collectors Digest Baseball Card Price Guide*, 700 E. State St., Iola, Wis. 54990.

Contributors will be acknowledged in future editions.

COLLECTORS ISSUES

There exists within the hobby a great body of cards which do not fall under the scope of this catalog by virtue of their nature of having been issued solely for the collector market. Known as "collector issues," these cards and sets are distinguished from "legitimate" issues in not having been created as a sales promotional item for another product or service — bubble gum, soda, snack cakes, dog food, cigarettes, gasoline, etc.

By their nature, and principally because the person issuing them is always free to print and distribute more of the same if they should ever attain any real value, collector issues are generally regarded by collectors as having little or no premium value.

NEW ISSUES

Because new baseball cards are being issued all the time, the cataloging of them remains an on-going challenge. The editor will attempt to keep abreast of new issues so that they may be added to future editions of this book.

Readers are invited to submit news of new issues, especially limited-edition or regionally issued cards to the editors. Address: *Sports Collectors Digest Baseball Card Price Guide*, 700 E. State St., Iola, Wis. 54990.

Common Hobby Terms & Definitions

A

Airbrushing — An artist's technique used on baseball cards in which logos on uniforms or hats are altered or eliminated.

All-Star card (AS) — A card which denotes a player's selection to the previous year's All-Star Team.

Autographed card — Card which was personally autographed by the player depicted. Cards with facsimile signatures that are printed on many cards as part of the design, are not considered autographed cards.

Autograph guest — A current or former ball player or other celebrity who attends a card convention for the purpose of signing autographs for fans. Usually a fee is charged for the autograph, ranging from a few dollars to more than $30 for HOF players.

B

Baseball's Best — A set made by Donruss in 1988 and 1989. Also the name of a boxed set made by Fleer in 1987 and 1988, and the name of the set of insert cards made by *Baseball Cards* magazine in 1989 and 1990.

Bazooka cards — Cards issued with boxes of Bazooka Bubblegum (1959-1971, 1988-1990).

Big cards — Name for Topps' large, glossy-finish card issues produced in 1988-present. Cards reminiscent of Topps' cards from the 1950s.

Blank backs — A card that has a blank card back. Most collectors feel these cards are merely damaged, with a lower value than correctly-printed specimens, though some collectors will pay premiums on superstars or rookies.

Blanket — An early 20th-century collectible consisting of a square piece of felt or other fabric depicting a baseball player. Most popular are the 5" by 5" B-18 "blankets" from 1914, so-called because they were sometimes sewn together to form a blanket.

Blister pack — A blister pack is a method of card packaging in which cards are packaged in hard plastic on a cardboard backing, with three to four pockets of cards. Donruss (1987-present).

Borders — The portion of a card which surrounds the picture. They are usually white, but are sometimes other colors. Border condition is very important to the card's grade and value.

Bowman (B) — Sportscard manufacturer (1948-1955) bought out by Topps in 1956. Topps issued baseball sets under the Bowman name (1989-present).

Boxed sets — These are sets produced by one of the major card companies, usually in conjunction with a business, such as K-Mart or Walgreens. Boxed sets usually contain fewer than 60 cards, most of which are star players.

Box panel cards — Bonus cards which are featured on a panel of wax boxes of the major card companies. The idea was originated by Donruss in 1985. Complete sets range from four to 16 cards, and feature star players.

Brick — A "brick" of cards is any group of cards with similar characteristics, such as a 100-card brick of 1975 Topps cards. Bricks usually contain common cards.

Buy price — The price a dealer will to pay for cards or memorabilia.

Burger King cards (BK) — Cards issued in conjunction with Burger King (1977-1987).

C

Cabinet card — A large card from the 19th or early 20th centuries, usually issued on heavy cardboard.

Card lot — A "lot" of cards is the same card, such as a 1988 Topps Don Mattingly card, sold in a lot or "grouping" of five, 25, 50, 100 or whatever number of cards. A collector purchasing a "lot" of cards, gets the cards at a discounted price, as opposed to buying a single card. Example: a single Mattingly card costs $1, but 100 Mattingly cards cost $75 or 75-cents apiece.

Case — A sealed case containing wax boxes or other product units which card companies sell at wholesale to dealers or retail stores. For instance, a 1991 Topps "wax case" is made up of 20 "wax boxes."

Cello pack — A package of about 30 cards wrapped in a printed cellophane wrapper that allows you to see the top and bottom cards. There are usually 24 cello packs to a cello box, and 16 cello boxes to a cello case. Cello packs retail between for around $1. Issued by Topps, Fleer and Donruss.

Checklist (CL) — A list of every card in a particular set, usually with space allowing the collector to check whether or not he has the card. A checklist can appear on a card(s), in a book or elsewhere.

Classic cards — Baseball cards made by Game Time, Ltd., to go with its "Classic Baseball" trivia game (1987-present).

Coin — Can refer to an actual coin struck to commemorate an achievement made by a team or player; also, a collectible made soley from or with a combination of plastic, paper or metal, issued as a set, such as the 1988 Topps Coin set.

Collation — The act of putting cards in order, by hand or machine, usually numerically.

Collector issue — A set of cards produced primarily to be sold to collectors and not issued as a premium to be given away or sold with a commercial product.

Common card — A card which carries no premium value in a set. "Common" is a blunt way of saying the player depicted is not a star.

Convention — Also known as a "baseball card show" or "trading card show." A gathering of anywhere from one to 600 or more card dealers at a single location (convention center, hotel, school auditoriums or gymnasiums) for the purpose of buying, selling or trading cards.

Counterfeit cards — Cards made to look like original cards, and distributed with the intention of fooling a buyer. High-demand cards are the most likely to be counterfeited.

D

Dealer — A person who buys, sells and trades baseball cards and other memorabilia for profit. A dealer may be full-time, part-time, own a shop, operate a mail-order business from his home, deal at baseball card shows on weekends, or any combination of the above.

Die-cut card — A baseball card in which the player's outline has been partially separated from the background, enabling the card to be folded into a "stand-up" figure. Die-cut cards that have never been folded are worth more to collectors.

Disc — Circular-shaped card.

Donruss (D) — Baseball card manufacturer (1981-present).

Donruss Rookies (DR) — 56-card post-season set issued by Donruss which includes rookie players (1986-present). Sold exclusively through hobby dealers in separate box.

Double print (DP) — A card printed twice on the same sheet, making it twice as common as other cards on the sheet. Topps double-printed cards in virtually every set from 1952 to 1981. This was done to accomodate the year's set size on standard company printing sheets.

Drakes — Ohio-based bakery which made baseball cards in the 1950s, and again from 1981-1988.

E

Error — An error is usually found on card backs in the statistical or personal information, and sometimes on the card front (such as a reversed negative). If an error is not corrected, the error adds nothing to the value of the card. If the error is corrected, it is called a "variation" card.

Exhibit card — Postcard-size cards picturing baseball players and other celebrities and sold in penny-arcade machines. Exhibit cards were produced from the 1920s to the 1960s.

F

Factory set (F or FAC.) — A complete set collated (packaged) by the card producing company. Issued by all companies.

First card (FC) — Price guide designation which refers to the first appearance of a player in the major card sets.

Fleer (F) — Baseball card manufacturer (1959-1963, 1981-present).

Fleer Glossy Tin (FG) — Limited edition set produced by Fleer, which features the year's regular issue set in a high gloss finish and sold in a tin box (1987-present). Fleer Update sets also done in glossy style.

Fleer Update (FU) — 132-card post-season set from Fleer which includes players traded to other teams during the season, and rookies (1984-present). Sold exclusively through hobby dealers in its own separate box.

Food issue — A set of baseball cards or related memorabilia which was issued in conjunction with a food product, such as Post cereal or Hostess snack cakes.

G

Gallery of Champions — Trade name for a set of metallic reproductions of Topps cards made and sold by Topps from 1986-1988. The metals used were bronze, aluminum, pewter and silver.

Goudey — Baseball card manufacturer (1933-1936, 1938, 1941).

Grades — The physical state or condition of a card.

H

Hand collated set (H or HC) — A complete set put together by hand using cards from wax, cello, rack or vending boxes.

High-numbers — A term used to describe the final series in a particular set of cards. "High numbers" were generally produced in smaller quantities than other series and are, therefore, scarcer and more valuable.

Hall of Famer (HOFer) - A card picturing a member of the Baseball Hall of Fame, in Cooperstown, N.Y. Hall of Famer cards almost always command a premium over other cards.

Hartland statues — Wisconsin plastics company which produced, among other things, statues of baseball players in the late 1950s and early 1960s. Company reproduced the set in 1989 as Hartland's 25th Anniversary Commemorative Edition. Original statues very collectible.

I

In Action card (IA) — A card featuring a star player, designated with the words "In Action" on the card front. Most notably from the 1972 and 1982 Topps sets.

Inserts — A collectible included inside a regular pack of baseball cards to boost sales. Inserts have included posters, coins, stamps, tatoos, special cards, etc.

J

Jell-O cards — Cards sold as premiums with Jell-O packages (1962-1963).

K

Kellog's cards — Simulated three-dimensional cards given away in cereal boxes or via a mail-in offer (1970-1983).

Key cards — The most important (valuable) cards in a set, such as the Mickey Mantle card, a "key" card in the 1952 Topps set.

L

Last card — The final regular card issued for a player, such as Hank Aaron's "last" card was in the 1976 Topps set. No particular extra value is added for last cards.

Leaf-Donruss — Baseball cards produced by Donruss specifically for the Canadian market (1985-1988). Leaf issued its own set in 1990.

Legitimate issue — A card set issued as a premium with a commerical product to increase sales; not a "collector issue."

Letter of authenticity — A letter stating that a certain piece of memorabilia, like a uniform, is authentic.

Lithograph — A high-quality art print made in limited quantities.

M

MVP — Most Valuable Player award.

Mail-bid auction — An auction where bids are sent through the mail, with the highest bidder winning the merchandise.

Major set — A large, nationally-distributed set produced by a major card maker like Topps, Fleer, Donruss, Score, Sportflics or Upper Deck.

Megalot — A megalot describes a group of cards, usually 1,000 or more of the same player, purchased for investment or speculation.

Memorabilia — Refers to items other than cards, such as uniforms, bats, autographed baseballs, magazines, scorecards, pins, statues and the like.

Minis — Cards which resemble the regular issue cards in every way, except they are smaller in size. Most noteable are the 1975 Topps Minis.

Minor league cards — A card depicting a player from the minor leagues. Minor league sets are a fast-growing segment of the hobby.

Mother's cards — An Oakland, (Calif.)-based cookie company which produces popular high quality glossy finish regional sets (1982-present).

Multi-player card — A card picturing more than one player.

N

Non-sport card — A trading card or bubblegum card picturing a subject other than sports. Non-sports cards have depicted movie stars, television shows, moments in history and other subjects.

O

Obverse — The front of the card displaying the picture.

O-Pee-Chee (OPC) — Canadian card producing company (1965-present). O-Pee-Chee is Topps' official Canadian licensee, and O-Pee-Chee cards are almost identical to Topps' issues of the same year.

P

Panel — A strip of two or more uncut cards. Some card sets are issued in "panels."

Phone auction — An auction where bids for baseball cards or other memorabilia are taken over the phone, with the highest bidder getting the merchandise.

Plastic sheet — A polyethelyne or polyvinyl sheet designed to store baseball cards, the most common being the nine-pocket sheet (which fits today's standard-sized cards). The sheets have pre-punched holes on the left side which allows them to be placed in a three-ring binder.

Play Ball — Name of baseball cards produced by Gum, Inc., (1939-1941).

Police/Fire/Safety sets — Card sets sponsored by public law enforcement or fire fighting agencies and a major or minor league team. Card backs usually contain anti-drug messages, fire prevention tips or other safety messages.

Post cards — Cards sold as premiums on boxes of Post cereal (1960-1963, 1990).

Pre-rookie card — Name given to a major league player's minor league cards.

Price guide — A periodical or book which contains checklists of cards, sets and other memorabilia and their values in varying conditions.

Price on request (POR) — A dealer will advertise a card P.O.R. if he believes the card will fluctuate in price from the time he places his ad until the time the ad is seen by the public.

Promotional cards — Cards produced by the card companies which serve as a marketing tool for their upcoming cards. Promotional or "promo" cards are often sent to dealers to entice them to order cards. Promo cards have limited distribution and can be very expensive.

Proof card — A card produced by the card companies prior to printing their sets, which is "proofed" for errors, and checked for card design, photography, colors, statisical accuracy and so on. Proof cards are not distributed and a few of the older proof cards on the hobby market can be quite expensive.

PPD — Postage Paid.

R

Rack pack — A three-sectioned card package with about 14-16 cards per section. There are usually 24 rack packs to a rack box, and six rack boxes to a rack case. Topps, Fleer, Donruss, Score.

Rare — Difficult to obtain and limited in number. See "Scarce."

Rated Rookie (RR) — Donruss subset featuring young players the company feels are the top rookie players from a particular year (1984-present).

Record Breaker card (RB) — A special Topps card found in a regular issue set which commemorates a record-breaking performance by a player from the previous season.

Regional set — A card set distributed in one geographical area. Regional sets often depict players from one team.

Regular issue set — See "Major set."

Reprint cards — Cards reprinted to closely match original cards, made with the intention of allowing collectors to buy them as substitutes for cards they could not ever afford. Reprints are usually labled — but not always — "reprint."

Reverse — The back of a card.

Rookie card (R or RC) — The first appearance of a player in one of the major sets (Topps, Fleer, etc.), excluding update and traded sets. It may or may not be issued during the player's actual rookie season.

S

SASE — Self-Addressed Stamped Envelope.

Score (S or SC) — Brand name of sports cards (1988-present). Major League Marketing is the manufacturer.

Score Traded (ScTr) - 110-card post-season set issued by Score to include players traded during the season, as well as rookie players. Sold exclusively by hobby dealers in its own separate box.

Second-year card — The second card of a player issued in the major sets. Usually, a second-year card is the most expensive card of a player, next to the rookie card.

Sell price — The price a dealer sells a card.

Series — A group of cards that is part of a set, and was issued at one time. The term usually applied to Topps sets from 1952-1973, when sets were issued in various "series." Cards of different series are valued at different prices since some series are scarcer than others.

Set — A complete run of cards, including one number of each card issued by a particular manufacturer in a particular year; for example, a 1985 Fleer "set."

Set case — Companies sell their factory sets in sealed cases containing 8 to 16 sets per case, depending on the company. Issued by all major companies.

Skip-numbered — A set of cards not numbered in exact sequence. Some manufacturers have issued "skip-numbered" sets to trick collectors into buying more cards, looking for card numbers that didn't exist. Other sets became skip-numbered when one or more players were dropped from the set at the last minute and were not replaced with another.

Sleeve — A specially-designed, plastic wrapper used to house and protect individual baseball cards.

Special card — A card in a set that depicts something other than a single player; for example a checklist card, All-Star card, team card or leaders card.

Sportflics — Brand name of baseball cards (1986-present). Major League Marketing is the manufacturer.

SCD — *Sports Collectors Digest.*

Standard size card — A card which measures 2½" wide by 3½" tall. In 1957, Topps baseball cards were produced in the 2½" by 3½" size, which set the standard for modern baseball cards.

Star card — Card featuring a star player, but not one of "superstar" caliber. The term "minor star" may also be used to differentiate between levels of skill and popularity. In terms of value, "star" cards fall between "commons" and "superstars."

Starter lot — A group of cards from the same set, usually more than 100, which serves as a starting point for a hobbyist to begin putting a set together. Starter lots usually contain common players. Also known as a "starter set."

Starting Lineup — A line of plastic sports statues produced by Kenner (1988-present). Also, the name for a computer-based baseball game from Parker Brothers.

Sticker — An adhesive-backed baseball card. Stickers can be card-size or smaller. Topps, Fleer and Panini have issued major baseball sticker sets over the past years. Stickers are not overly popular with older collectors, though younger collectors seem to enjoy them.

Subset — A set of cards with the same theme within a larger set. Examples: Donruss Diamond Kings are a "subset" of the Donruss set; or Topps All-Star cards are a subset of the Topps set.

Super card — A designation referring to the physical size of a card. Generally, any card postcard-size or larger is referred to as a "super."

Superstar card — A card picturing a true "superstar," a player of Hall of Fame caliber, like Mike Schmidt.

Stock — Refers to the type of paper or cardboard used on a baseball card.

Swap Meet — Term used to describe early baseball card shows where most of the cards were traded between hobbyists.

T

Team card — Card which depicts an entire team.

Team set — A set which includes all cards relating to a certain team from a particular year, by a particular manufacturer.

Team issued set — A set produced to be sold or given away by a baseball team.

Test issue — A set of cards test-marketed on a small scale in a limited geographic areas of the country. Topps test-marketed a variety of items from the 1950s-1980s.

Tobacco cards — Cards issued in the late 19th and early 20th centuries as premiums with cigarettes or other tobacco products.

Topps (T) — Sports card company (1951-present).

Topps Tiffany (TTF) — Limited edition set produced by Topps, featuring the year's regular complete set in a high gloss finish (1984-present). Topps Traded sets also done in this style.

Topps Traded (TT or TTR) — 132-card post-season set which includes players traded to other teams during the year, as well as rookie players (1981-present). Sold mainly through hobby dealers.

Traded set — An auxiliary set of cards issued toward the end of the season to reflect trades made after the printing of the regular set. Also called "Update" sets, they may also include rookies not included in the regular set.

U

Uncut sheet — A full sheet of baseball cards that has never been cut into individual cards.

Upper Deck (UD) — Sportscard company (1989-present).

Upper Deck High Numbers (UDH) — 100-card set featuring players traded during the season, as well as rookie players. This set was sold through hobby dealers and in Upper Deck foil packs, similar to the way cards before 1974 were released.

V

Variation — A variation is the result of a card company correcting a previous mistake on a card, resulting in two or more variations of the same card. Some variations have increased in value, if they were produced in lesser quantities.

Vending box — Vending boxes contain 500 cards per box. There are 24 vending boxes per vending case, for a total of 12,000 cards. Topps.

W

Want list — A collector's or dealer's list of items he is wishing to buy. Often, a collector will send a dealer a "want" list, and the dealer will try to locate the items on the list.

Table of Contents

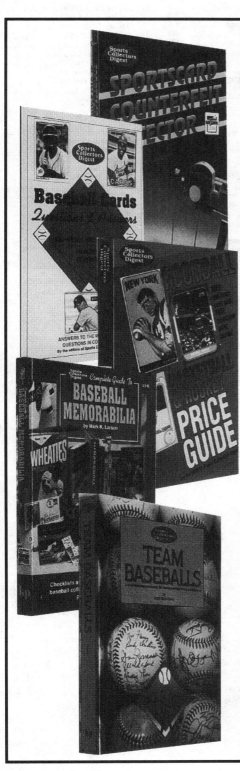

Sportscard Counterfeit Detector

Avoid worthless counterfeit cards using this new book that shows you how to detect more than 110 of the hobby's most dangerous, frequently encountered counterfeit cards. Includes detailed descriptions and more than 375 revealing, close-up photos. **$16.95**

Baseball Cards Questions & Answers

A virtual know-it-all on the subject of baseball card collecting. Packed with clear, concise answers to over 500 of the most frequently asked questions on America's hottest hobby, including all the whos, whats, whens, wheres, whys and hows of collecting baseball and other sports cards. **$5.95**

Football, Basketball & Hockey Price Guide

Packed with the most complete coverage of pricing for football, basketball and hockey cards produced since 1935. From cover to cover, this volume has more cards, more prices and more photos than any other single guide in this fast-growing field. **$14.95**

The Complete Guide To Baseball Memorabilia

Brings you collector prices along with checklisting information for many of the popular collectibles surrounding America's favorite sport. You'll find pricing and information for programs, magazines, statues, plates, books, uniforms, bats, cachets, autographs, pins, yearbooks, plus much, much more including auction results. **$14.95**

Team Baseballs

Provides hobbyists with vital information for maintaining, enhancing, preserving and evaluating baseballs autographed by players active from 1920 to the present. Includes essential information to help identify and date hundreds of autographed balls, and provides values for each entry. Over 100 photos are found throughout this fascinating book. **$19.95**

Note: Shipping & handling is $1.50 to $2.50 per book for U.S. addresses, $5.00 per book for foreign addresses. WI residents, please add 5.5% sales tax to total.

MasterCard & VISA Cardholders
SAVE TIME BY CALLING TOLL-FREE
(800) 258-0929
Department ZIC
Mon.-Fri. 6:30 am - 8 pm; Sat., 8 am - 2 pm, CST

1976 A & P Brewers

The Aaron and Yount cards from this regional issue support the set price. The set was sponsored by A & P grocery stores. The cards are oversized and were distributed by A & P only in 1976.

		NR MT	EX	VG
Complete Set:		25.00	12.50	7.50
Common Player:		.50	.25	.15
(1)	Henry Aaron	8.00	4.00	2.50
(2)	Pete Broberg	.50	.25	.15
(3)	Jim Colborn	.50	.25	.15
(4)	Mike Hegan	.50	.25	.15
(5)	Tim Johnson	.50	.25	.15
(6)	Von Joshua	.50	.25	.15
(7)	Sixto Lezcano	.50	.25	.15
(8)	Don Money	.50	.25	.15
(9)	Charlie Moore	.50	.25	.15
(10)	Darrell Porter	.50	.25	.15
(11)	George Scott	.50	.25	.15
(12)	Bill Sharp	.50	.25	.15
(13)	Jim Slaton	.50	.25	.15
(14)	Bill Travers	.50	.25	.15
(15)	Robin Yount	10.00	5.00	3.00
(16)	County Stadium	.50	.25	.15

1971 Allstate Insurance

This 4-card series was distributed as part of an internal sales promotion for Allstate Insurance. Graphic artist Ray Lending, an Allstate employee, created the 2-1/2" by 3-1/4" cards in duo-tone black and green on white. Card fronts show the players in batting stance, with the player name in one of the upper corners and the "Hall of Fame Series" logo printed across the bottom of the card. The card backs carry the player's full name and position,

followed by a brief career summary, biography, and Career Highlights chart listing major league totals. "1971 Charger" and "Hall of Fame Series" are printed at the bottom of the card back. 8,000 sets were distributed.

		NR MT	EX	VG
Complete Set:		50.00	35.00	17.50
Common Player:		10.00	7.50	3.75
(1)	Ty Cobb	10.00	7.50	3.75
(2)	Stan Musial	10.00	7.50	3.75
(3)	Babe Ruth	20.00	15.00	7.50
(4)	Ted Williams	10.00	7.50	3.75

1989 Ames 20/20 Club

This 33-card set was produced by Topps for the Ames toy store chain. As its name implies, the special boxed set highlights members of the 20/20 club, players who have recorded 20 home runs and 20 stolen bases in the same season. The glossy cards feature action or posed photos on the front with the player's name at the top and "Ames 20/20 Club" along the bottom. The Topps logo appears in the upper right corner.

		MT	NR MT	EX
Complete Set:		4.00	3.00	1.50
Common Player:		.09	.07	.04
1	Jesse Barfield	.09	.07	.04
2	Kevin Bass	.09	.07	.04
3	Don Baylor	.09	.07	.04
4	George Bell	.12	.09	.05
5	Barry Bonds	.40	.30	.15
6	Phil Bradley	.09	.07	.04
7	Ellis Burks	.20	.15	.08
8	Jose Canseco	.70	.50	.30
9	Joe Carter	.20	.15	.08
10	Kal Daniels	.09	.07	.04
11	Eric Davis	.20	.15	.08
12	Mike Davis	.09	.07	.04
13	Andre Dawson	.12	.09	.05
14	Kirk Gibson	.09	.07	.04
15	Pedro Guerrero	.12	.09	.05
16	Rickey Henderson	.50	.40	.20
17	Bo Jackson	.60	.45	.25
18	Howard Johnson	.20	.15	.08
19	Jeffrey Leonard	.09	.07	.04
20	Kevin McReynolds	.12	.09	.05
21	Dale Murphy	.09	.07	.04
22	Dwayne Murphy	.09	.07	.04
23	Dave Parker	.12	.09	.05
24	Kirby Puckett	.50	.40	.20
25	Juan Samuel	.09	.07	.04
26	Ryne Sandberg	.20	.15	.08
27	Mike Schmidt	.80	.60	.30
28	Darryl Strawberry	.25	.20	.10
29	Alan Trammell	.09	.07	.04
30	Andy Van Slyke	.09	.07	.04
31	Devon White	.09	.07	.04
32	Dave Winfield	.12	.09	.05
33	Robin Yount	.30	.25	.12

1990 Ames All-Stars

This 33-card set was the second consecutive issue produced by Topps for the Ames toy store chain. The cards measure 2-1/2" by 3-1/2" in size and feature baseball's top active hitters. Both the Ames and Topps logos appear on the cards.

		MT	NR MT	EX
Complete Set:		4.00	3.00	1.50
Common Player:		.08	.06	.03
1	Dave Winfield	.12	.09	.05
2	George Brett	.25	.20	.10
3	Jim Rice	.12	.09	.05
4	Dwight Evans	.12	.09	.05
5	Robin Yount	.25	.20	.10
6	Dave Parker	.10	.08	.04
7	Eddie Murray	.20	.15	.08
8	Keith Hernandez	.08	.06	.03
9	Andre Dawson	.20	.15	.08
10	Fred Lynn	.08	.06	.03
11	Dale Murphy	.15	.11	.06
12	Jack Clark	.08	.06	.03
13	Rickey Henderson	.50	.40	.20
14	Paul Molitor	.10	.08	.04
15	Cal Ripken	.25	.20	.10
16	Wade Boggs	.25	.20	.10
17	Tim Raines	.10	.08	.04
18	Don Mattingly	.40	.30	.15
19	Kent Hrbek	.08	.06	.03
20	Kirk Gibson	.10	.08	.04
21	Julio Franco	.12	.09	.05
22	George Bell	.12	.09	.05
23	Darryl Strawberry	.30	.25	.12
24	Kirby Puckett	.25	.20	.10
25	Juan Samuel	.08	.06	.03
26	Alvin Davis	.08	.06	.03
27	Joe Carter	.15	.11	.06
28	Eric Davis	.20	.15	.08
29	Jose Canseco	.50	.40	.20
30	Wally Joyner	.12	.09	.05
31	Will Clark	.50	.40	.20
32	Ruben Sierra	.25	.20	.10
33	Danny Tartabull	.15	.11	.06

Values for recent cards and sets are listed in Mint (MT), Near Mint (NM) and Excellent (EX), reflecting the fact that many cards from recent years have been preserved in top condition. Recent cards and sets in less than Excellent condition have little collector interest.

1991 Arena Holograms

Superstars from three sports are featured in this special hologram set. The cards were distributed through hobby dealers and are numbered on the back. The front of the card features the hologram, while the back features player information and a photo of the athlete in formal wear.

		MT	NR MT	EX
Complete Set:		15.00	11.00	6.00
Commom Player:		3.00	2.25	1.25
1	Joe Montana	3.00	2.25	1.25
2	Ken Griffey, Jr.	3.00	2.25	1.25
3	Frank Thomas	4.00	3.00	1.50
4	Barry Sanders	3.00	2.25	1.25
5	David Robinson	3.00	2.25	1.25

1948 Babe Ruth Story

The Philadelphia Gum Co., in 1948, created a card set about the movie "The Babe Ruth Story", which starred William Bendix and Claire Trevor. The set, whose American Card Catalog designation is R421, contains 28 black and white, numbered cards which measure 2" by 2-1/2". The Babe Ruth Story set was originally intended to consist of sixteen cards. Twelve additional cards (#'s 17-28) were added when Ruth died before the release of the film. The card backs include an offer for an autographed photo of William Bendix, starring as the Babe, for five Swell Bubble Gum wrappers and five cents.

		NR MT	EX	VG
Complete Set:		1200.00	600.00	360.00
Common Player: 1-16		13.00	6.50	4.00
Common Player: 17-28		40.00	20.00	12.00
1	"The Babe Ruth Story" In The Making	75.00	38.00	23.00
2	Bat Boy Becomes the Babe... William Bendix	13.00	6.50	4.00
3	Claire Hodgson...Claire Trevor	13.00	6.50	4.00
4	Babe Ruth and Claire Hodgson	13.00	6.50	4.00
5	Brother Matthias...Charles Bickford	13.00	6.50	4.00
6	Phil Conrad...Sam Levene	13.00	6.50	4.00
7	Night Club Singer...Gertrude Niesen	13.00	6.50	4.00
8	Baseball's Famous Deal...Jack Dunn (William Frawley)	13.00	6.50	4.00
9	Mr. & Mrs. Babe Ruth	13.00	6.50	4.00
10	Babe Ruth, Claire Ruth, and Brother Matthias	13.00	6.50	4.00
11	Babe Ruth and Miller Huggins (Fred Lightner)	13.00	6.50	4.00
12	Babe Ruth At Bed Of Ill Boy Johnny Sylvester (Gregory Marshall)	13.00	6.50	4.00
13	Sylvester Family Listening To Game	13.00	6.50	4.00
14	"When A Feller Needs a Friend" (With Dog At Police Station)	13.00	6.50	4.00

		NR MT	EX	VG
15	Dramatic Home Run	13.00	6.50	4.00
16	The Homer That Set the Record (#60)			
		13.00	6.50	4.00
17	"The Slap That Started Baseball's Famous			
	Career"	40.00	20.00	12.00
18	The Babe Plays Santa Claus	40.00	20.00	12.00
19	Meeting Of Owner And Manager	40.00	20.00	12.00
20	"Broken Window Paid Off"	40.00	20.00	12.00
21	Babe In A Crowd Of Autograph Collectors			
		40.00	20.00	12.00
22	Charley Grimm And William Bendix			
		40.00	20.00	12.00
23	Ted Lyons And William Bendix	50.00	25.00	15.00
24	Lefty Gomez, William Bendix, And Bucky			
	Harris	50.00	25.00	15.00
25	Babe Ruth and William Bendix	115.00	57.00	34.00
26	Babe Ruth And William Bendix	115.00	57.00	34.00
27	Babe Ruth And Claire Trevor	115.00	57.00	34.00
28	William Bendix, Babe Ruth, And Claire			
	Trevor	115.00	57.00	34.00

1987 Baseball
Super Stars Discs

Produced by Mike Schecter and Associates, the "Baseball Super Stars" disc set was released as part of a promotion for various brands of iced tea mixes in many parts of the country. Among the brands participating in the promotion were Acme, Alpha Beta, Bustelo, Key, King Kullen, Lady Lee, Our Own and Weis. The discs were issued in three-part folding panels with each disc measuring 2-1/2" in diameter. The disc fronts feature a full-color photo inside a bright yellow border. Two player discs were included in each panel along with a coupon disc offering either an uncut press sheet of the set or a facsimile autographed ball.

		MT	NR MT	EX
Complete Panel Set:		10.00	7.50	4.00
Complete Singles Set:		5.00	3.75	2.00
Common Panel:		.25	.20	.10
Common Single Player:		.05	.04	.02
	Panel	1.00	.70	.40
1	Darryl Strawberry	.20	.15	.08
2	Roger Clemens	.50	.40	.20
	Panel	.35	.25	.14
3	Ron Darling	.05	.04	.02
4	Keith Hernandez	.10	.08	.04
	Panel	1.00	.70	.40
5	Tony Pena	.05	.04	.02
6	Don Mattingly	.70	.50	.30
	Panel	1.00	.70	.40
7	Eric Davis	.35	.25	.14
8	Gary Carter	.08	.06	.03
	Panel	.80	.60	.30
9	Dave Winfield	.12	.09	.05
10	Wally Joyner	.20	.15	.08
	Panel	.50	.40	.20
11	Mike Schmidt	.25	.20	.10
12	Robby Thompson	.05	.04	.02
	Panel	1.00	.70	.40
13	Wade Boggs	.35	.25	.14
14	Cal Ripken Jr.	.40	.30	.15
	Panel	1.00	.70	.40

		MT	NR MT	EX
15	Dale Murphy	.15	.11	.06
16	Tony Gwynn	.15	.11	.06
	Panel	1.75	1.25	.70
17	Jose Canseco	.70	.50	.30
18	Rickey Henderson	.30	.25	.12
	Panel	.25	.20	.10
19	Lance Parrish	.08	.06	.03
20	Dave Righetti	.08	.06	.03

1988 Baseball
Superstars Discs

The "Second Annual Collector's Edition" of Baseball Super Stars Discs is very similar to the 1987 issue. A set of 20 discs (2-1/2" diameter) featuring full-color baseball player photos was inserted in specially marked cannisters of iced tea and fruit drinks. Each triple-fold insert consists of 2 player discs and one redemption card. Player discs are bright blue, yellow, red and green with a diamond design framing the player closeup. The player name appears upper left, the set logo appears upper right. Personalized disc series were issued for Tetley, Weis, Key Food and A&P supermarkets (untitled series were also sold at Lucky, Skaggs, Alpha Beta, Acme King Kullen, Laneco and Krasdale stores). The series name (i.e. Weis Winners) is printed below the player photo.

		MT	NR MT	EX
Complete Panel Set:		9.00	6.75	3.50
Complete Singles Set:		4.00	3.00	1.50
Common Panel:		.60	.45	.25
Common Single Player:		.05	.04	.02
	Panel	1.00	.70	.40
1	Wade Boggs	.35	.25	.14
2	Ellis Burks	.20	.15	.08
	Panel	1.00	.70	.40
3	Don Mattingly	.50	.40	.20
4	Mark McGwire	.25	.20	.10
	Panel	.70	.50	.30
5	Matt Nokes	.10	.08	.04
6	Kirby Puckett	.30	.25	.12
	Panel	.80	.60	.30
7	Billy Ripken	.05	.04	.02
8	Kevin Seitzer	.15	.11	.06
	Panel	.90	.70	.35
9	Roger Clemens	.30	.25	.12
10	Will Clark	.50	.40	.20
	Panel	.80	.60	.30
11	Vince Coleman	.10	.08	.04
12	Eric Davis	.30	.25	.12
	Panel	.70	.50	.30
13	Dave Magadan	.05	.04	.02
14	Dale Murphy	.15	.11	.06
	Panel	.80	.60	.30
15	Benito Santiago	.15	.11	.06
16	Mike Schmidt	.30	.25	.12
	Panel	.60	.45	.25
17	Darryl Strawberry	.20	.15	.08
18	Steve Bedrosian	.05	.04	.02
	Panel	.80	.60	.30
19	Dwight Gooden	.20	.15	.08
20	Fernando Valenzuela	.08	.06	.03

Values quoted in this guide reflect the retail price of a card — the price a collector can expect to pay when buying a card from a dealer. The wholesale price — that which a collector can expect to receive from a dealer when selling cards — will be significantly lower, depending on desirability and condition.

1990 Baseball Wit

This 108-card set was released in two printings. The first printing featured unnumbered cards and several errors. The second printing featured corrections and numbered cards. The set was available at several retail chains and feature trivia questions on the card backs. The set was dedicated to Little League baseball.

		MT	NR MT	EX
	Complete Set:	8.00	6.00	3.25
	Common Player:	.06	.05	.02
1	Orel Hershiser	.10	.08	.04
2	Tony Gwynn	.15	.11	.06
3	Mickey Mantle	.40	.30	.15
4	Willie Stargell	.15	.11	.06
5	Don Baylor	.06	.05	.02
6	Hank Aaron	.30	.25	.12
7	Don Larsen	.06	.05	.02
8	Lee Mazzilli	.06	.05	.02
9	Boog Powell	.06	.05	.02
10	Little League World Series	.06	.05	.02
11	Jose Canseco	.30	.25	.14
12	Mike Scott	.06	.05	.02
13	Bob Feller	.10	.08	.04
14	Ron Santo	.06	.05	.02
15	Mel Stottlemyre	.06	.05	.02
16	Shea Stadium	.06	.05	.02
17	Brooks Robinson	.10	.08	.04
18	Willie Mays	.30	.25	.12
19	Ernie Banks	.15	.11	.06
20	Keith Hernandez	.06	.05	.02
21	Bret Saberhagen	.06	.05	.02
22	Hall of Fame	.06	.05	.02
23	Luis Aparicio	.10	.08	.04
24	Yogi Berra	.15	.11	.06
25	Manny Mota	.06	.05	.02
26	Steve Garvey	.10	.08	.04
27	Bill Shea	.06	.05	.02
28	Fred Lynn	.06	.05	.02
29	Todd Worrell	.06	.05	.02
30	Roy Campanella	.15	.11	.06
31	Bob Gibson	.12	.09	.05
32	Gary Carter	.08	.06	.03
33	Jim Palmer	.15	.11	.06
34	Carl Yastrzemski	.12	.09	.05
35	Dwight Gooden	.10	.08	.04
36	Stan Musial	.20	.15	.08
37	Rickey Henderson	.25	.20	.10
38	Dale Murphy	.12	.09	.05
39	Mike Schmidt	.25	.20	.10
40	Gaylord Perry	.10	.08	.04
41	Ozzie Smith	.15	.11	.06
42	Reggie Jackson	.25	.20	.10
43	Steve Carlton	.15	.11	.06
44	Jim Perry	.06	.05	.02
45	Vince Coleman	.06	.05	.02
46	Tom Seaver	.25	.20	.10
47	Marty Marion	.06	.05	.02
48	Frank Robinson	.12	.09	.05
49	Joe DiMaggio	.35	.25	.14
50	Ted Williams	.35	.25	.14
51	Rollie Fingers	.12	.09	.05
52	Jackie Robinson	.30	.25	.12
53	Victor Raschi	.06	.05	.02
54	Johnny Bench	.20	.15	.08
55	Nolan Ryan	.40	.30	.15
56	Ty Cobb	.40	.30	.15
57	Harry Steinfeldt	.06	.05	.02

		MT	NR MT	EX
58	James O'Rourke	.06	.05	.02
59	John McGraw	.08	.06	.03
60	Candy Cummings	.06	.05	.02
61	Jimmie Foxx	.10	.08	.04
62	Walter Johnson	.10	.08	.04
63	1903 World Series	.06	.05	.02
64	Satchel Paige	.15	.11	.06
65	Bobby Wallace	.06	.05	.02
66	Cap Anson	.10	.08	.04
67	Hugh Duffy	.06	.05	.02
68	Buck Ewing	.06	.05	.02
69	Bobo Holloman	.06	.05	.02
70	Ed Delehanty	.06	.05	.02
71	Dizzy Dean	.15	.11	.06
72	Tris Speaker	.15	.11	.06
73	Lou Gehrig	.40	.30	.15
74	Wee Willie Keeler	.06	.05	.02
75	Cal Hubbard	.06	.05	.02
76	Eddie Collins	.06	.05	.02
77	Chris Von Der Ahe	.06	.05	.02
78	Sam Crawford	.06	.05	.02
79	Cy Young	.15	.11	.06
80	Johnny Vander Meer	.08	.06	.03
81	Joey Jay	.06	.05	.02
82	Zack Wheat	.06	.05	.02
83	Jim Bottomley	.06	.05	.02
84	Honus Wagner	.20	.15	.08
85	Casey Stengel	.12	.09	.05
86	Babe Ruth	.50	.40	.20
87	John Lindemuth	.06	.05	.02
88	Max Carey	.06	.05	.02
89	Mordecai Brown	.06	.05	.02
90	1869 Red Stockings	.06	.05	.02
91	Rube Marquard	.06	.05	.02
92	Horse Radbourne	.06	.05	.02
93	Hack Wilson	.08	.06	.03
94	Lefty Grove	.10	.08	.04
95	Carl Hubbell	.08	.06	.03
96	A.J. Cartwright	.06	.05	.02
97	Rogers Hornsby	.15	.11	.06
98	Ernest Thayer	.06	.05	.02
99	Connie Mack	.12	.09	.05
100	1939 Centennial Celebration	.06	.05	.02
101	Branch Rickey	.10	.08	.04
102	Dan Brouthers	.06	.05	.02
103	First Baseball Uniform	.06	.05	.02
104	Christy Mathewson	.15	.11	.06
105	Joe Nuxhall	.06	.05	.02
106	1939 Centennial Celebration	.06	.05	.02
107	President Taft	.06	.05	.02
108	Abner Doubleday	.06	.05	.02

1934 Batter-Up

National Chicle's 192-card "Batter-Up" set was issued from 1934 through 1936. The blank-backed cards are die-cut, enabling collectors of the era to fold the top of the card over so that it could stand upright on its own support. The cards can be found in black and white or a variety of color tints. Card numbers 1-80 measure 2-3/8" by 3-1/4" in size, while the high-numbered cards (#'s 81-192) measure 1/4" smaller in width. The high-numbered cards are significantly more difficult to find than the lower numbers. The set's ACC designation is R318.

		NR MT	EX	VG
Complete Set:		32500.00	16250.00	9750.
Common Player: 1-80		75.00	35.00	15.00
Common Player: 81-192		150.00	70.00	25.00
1	Wally Berger	150.00	50.00	15.00
2	Ed Brandt	75.00	35.00	15.00
3	Al Lopez	150.00	70.00	25.00
4	Dick Bartell	75.00	35.00	15.00
5	Carl Hubbell	200.00	100.00	35.00
6	Bill Terry	200.00	100.00	35.00
7	Pepper Martin	75.00	35.00	15.00
8	Jim Bottomley	150.00	70.00	25.00
9	Tommy Bridges	75.00	35.00	15.00
10	Rick Ferrell	125.00	50.00	15.00
11	Ray Benge	75.00	35.00	15.00
12	Wes Ferrell	75.00	35.00	15.00
13	Bill Cissell	75.00	35.00	15.00
14	Pie Traynor	175.00	80.00	30.00
15	Roy Mahaffey	75.00	35.00	15.00
16	Chick Hafey	150.00	75.00	25.00
17	Lloyd Waner	150.00	75.00	25.00
18	Jack Burns	75.00	35.00	15.00
19	Buddy Myer	75.00	35.00	15.00
20	Bob Johnson	75.00	35.00	15.00
21	Arky Vaughn (Vaughan)	125.00	55.00	28.00
22	Red Rolfe	75.00	35.00	15.00
23	Lefty Gomez	250.00	125.00	40.00
24	Earl Averill	125.00	55.00	20.00
25	Mickey Cochrane	150.00	75.00	30.00
26	Van Mungo	75.00	35.00	15.00
27	Mel Ott	275.00	125.00	50.00
28	Jimmie Foxx	300.00	150.00	50.00
29	Jimmy Dykes	75.00	35.00	15.00
30	Bill Dickey	275.00	125.00	55.00
31	Lefty Grove	250.00	125.00	35.00
32	Joe Cronin	150.00	75.00	28.00
33	Frankie Frisch	200.00	100.00	35.00
34	Al Simmons	150.00	70.00	25.00
35	Rogers Hornsby	400.00	200.00	75.00
36	Ted Lyons	175.00	80.00	25.00
37	Rabbit Maranville	175.00	80.00	25.00
38	Jimmie Wilson	75.00	35.00	15.00
39	Willie Kamm	75.00	35.00	15.00
40	Bill Hallahan	75.00	35.00	15.00
41	Gus Suhr	75.00	35.00	15.00
42	Charlie Gehringer	250.00	125.00	40.00
43	Joe Heving	75.00	35.00	15.00
44	Adam Comorosky	75.00	35.00	15.00
45	Tony Lazzeri	150.00	70.00	25.00
46	Sam Leslie	75.00	35.00	15.00
47	Bob Smith	75.00	35.00	15.00
48	Willis Hudlin	75.00	35.00	15.00
49	Carl Reynolds	75.00	35.00	15.00
50	Fred Schulte	75.00	35.00	15.00
51	Cookie Lavagetto	75.00	35.00	15.00
52	Hal Schumacher	75.00	35.00	15.00
53	Doc Cramer	75.00	35.00	15.00
54	Si Johnson	75.00	35.00	15.00
55	Ollie Bejma	75.00	35.00	15.00
56	Sammy Byrd	75.00	35.00	15.00
57	Hank Greenberg	250.00	125.00	40.00
58	Bill Knickerbocker	75.00	35.00	15.00
59	Billy Urbanski	75.00	35.00	15.00
60	Ed Morgan	75.00	35.00	15.00
61	Eric McNair	75.00	35.00	15.00
62	Ben Chapman	75.00	35.00	15.00
63	Roy Johnson	75.00	35.00	15.00
64	"Dizzy" Dean	650.00	300.00	100.00
65	Zeke Bonura	75.00	35.00	15.00
66	Firpo Marberry	75.00	35.00	15.00
67	Gus Mancuso	75.00	35.00	15.00
68	Joe Vosmik	75.00	35.00	15.00
69	Earl Grace	75.00	35.00	15.00
70	Tony Piet	75.00	35.00	15.00
71	Rollie Hemsley	75.00	35.00	15.00
72	Fred Fitzsimmons	75.00	35.00	15.00
73	Hack Wilson	300.00	150.00	50.00
74	Chick Fullis	75.00	35.00	15.00
75	Fred Frankhouse	75.00	35.00	15.00
76	Ethan Allen	75.00	35.00	15.00
77	Heinie Manush	125.00	50.00	18.00
78	Rip Collins	75.00	35.00	15.00
79	Tony Cuccinello	75.00	35.00	15.00
80	Joe Kuhel	75.00	35.00	15.00
81	Thomas Bridges	150.00	70.00	25.00
82	Clinton Brown	150.00	70.00	25.00
83	Albert Blanche	150.00	70.00	25.00
84	"Boze" Berger	150.00	70.00	25.00
85	Goose Goslin	400.00	200.00	65.00
86	Vernon Gomez	550.00	275.00	110.00
87	Joe Glen (Glenn)	150.00	70.00	25.00
88	"Cy" Blanton	150.00	70.00	25.00
89	Tom Carey	150.00	70.00	25.00
90	Ralph Birkhofer	150.00	70.00	25.00
91	Frank Gabler	150.00	70.00	25.00
92	Dick Coffman	150.00	70.00	25.00
93	Ollie Bejma	150.00	70.00	25.00
94	Leroy Earl Parmalee	150.00	70.00	25.00
95	Carl Reynolds	150.00	70.00	25.00
96	Ben Cantwell	150.00	70.00	25.00
97	Curtis Davis	150.00	70.00	25.00
98	Wallace Moses, Billy Webb	150.00	70.00	25.00
99	Ray Benge	150.00	70.00	25.00
100	"Pie" Traynor	400.00	200.00	75.00
101	Phil. Cavarretta	150.00	70.00	25.00
102	"Pep" Young	150.00	70.00	25.00
103	Willis Hudlin	150.00	70.00	25.00
104	Mickey Haslin	150.00	70.00	25.00
105	Oswald Bluege	150.00	70.00	25.00
106	Paul Andrews	150.00	70.00	25.00
107	Edward A. Brandt	150.00	70.00	25.00
108	Dan Taylor	150.00	70.00	25.00
109	Thornton T. Lee	150.00	70.00	25.00
110	Hal Schumacher	150.00	70.00	25.00
111	Minter Hayes, Ted Lyons	450.00	225.00	135.00
112	Odell Hale	150.00	70.00	25.00
113	Earl Averill	300.00	150.00	50.00
114	Italo Chelini	150.00	70.00	25.00
115	Ivy Andrews, Jim Bottomley	450.00	225.00	135.00
116	Bill Walker	150.00	70.00	25.00
117	Bill Dickey	550.00	275.00	115.00
118	Gerald Walker	150.00	70.00	25.00
119	Ted Lyons	300.00	150.00	50.00
120	Elden Auker (Eldon)	150.00	70.00	25.00
121	Wild Bill Hallahan	150.00	70.00	25.00
122	Freddy Lindstrom	350.00	175.00	65.00
123	Oral C. Hildebrand	150.00	70.00	25.00
124	Luke Appling	350.00	175.00	65.00
125	"Pepper" Martin	175.00	80.00	30.00
126	Rick Ferrell	350.00	175.00	65.00
127	Ival Goodman	150.00	70.00	25.00
128	Joe Kuhel	150.00	70.00	25.00
129	Ernest Lombardi	350.00	175.00	65.00
130	Charles Gehringer	450.00	225.00	135.00
131	Van L. Mungo	175.00	80.00	30.00
132	Larry French	150.00	70.00	25.00
133	"Buddy" Myer	150.00	70.00	25.00
134	Mel Harder	150.00	70.00	25.00
135	Augie Galan	150.00	70.00	25.00
136	"Gabby" Hartnett	350.00	175.00	65.00
137	Stan Hack	150.00	70.00	25.00
138	Billy Herman	350.00	175.00	65.00
139	Bill Jurges	150.00	70.00	25.00
140	Bill Lee	150.00	70.00	25.00
141	"Zeke" Bonura	150.00	70.00	25.00
142	Tony Piet	150.00	70.00	25.00
143	Paul Dean	250.00	125.00	50.00
144	Jimmy Foxx	700.00	300.00	115.00
145	Joe Medwick	350.00	175.00	65.00
146	Rip Collins	150.00	70.00	25.00
147	Melo Almada	150.00	70.00	25.00
148	Allan Cooke	150.00	70.00	25.00
149	Moe Berg	150.00	70.00	25.00
150	Adolph Camilli	150.00	70.00	25.00
151	Oscar Melillo	150.00	70.00	25.00
152	Bruce Campbell	150.00	70.00	25.00
153	Lefty Grove	600.00	275.00	115.00
154	John Murphy	150.00	70.00	25.00
155	Luke Sewell	150.00	70.00	25.00
156	Leo Durocher	350.00	175.00	65.00
157	Lloyd Waner	350.00	175.00	65.00
158	Guy Bush	150.00	70.00	25.00
159	Jimmy Dykes	150.00	70.00	25.00
160	Steve O'Neill	150.00	70.00	25.00
161	Gen. Crowder	150.00	70.00	25.00
162	Joe Cascarella	150.00	70.00	25.00
163	"Bud" Hafey	150.00	70.00	25.00
164	"Gilly" Campbell	150.00	70.00	25.00
165	Ray Hayworth	150.00	70.00	25.00
166	Frank Demaree	150.00	70.00	25.00
167	John Babich	150.00	70.00	25.00
168	Marvin Owen	150.00	70.00	25.00
169	Ralph Kress	150.00	70.00	25.00
170	"Mule" Haas	150.00	70.00	25.00
171	Frank Higgins	150.00	70.00	25.00
172	Walter Berger	150.00	70.00	25.00
173	Frank Frisch	400.00	200.00	75.00
174	Wess Ferrell (Wes)	150.00	70.00	25.00
175	Pete Fox	150.00	70.00	25.00
176	John Vergez	150.00	70.00	25.00
177	William Rogell	150.00	70.00	25.00
178	"Don" Brennan	150.00	70.00	25.00

		NR MT	EX	VG
179	James Bottomley	250.00	125.00	50.00
180	Travis Jackson	350.00	175.00	65.00
181	Robert Rolfe	175.00	80.00	30.00
182	Frank Crosetti	275.00	135.00	50.00
183	Joe Cronin	350.00	175.00	65.00
184	"Schoolboy" Rowe	175.00	80.00	30.00
185	"Chuck" Klein	350.00	175.00	65.00
186	Lon Warneke	150.00	70.00	25.00
187	Gus Suhr	150.00	70.00	25.00
188	Ben Chapman	200.00	90.00	30.00
189	Clint. Brown	180.00	85.00	35.00
190	Paul Derringer	250.00	125.00	40.00
191	John Burns	300.00	150.00	45.00
192	John Broaca	450.00	225.00	135.00

1959 Bazooka

The 1959 Bazooka set, consisting of 23 full-color, unnumbered cards, was issued on boxes of Bazooka one-cent bubble gum. The individually wrapped pieces of Bazooka gum were produced by Topps Chewing Gum. The blank-backed cards measure 2-13/16" by 4-15/16" Nine cards were first issued, with 14 being added to the set later. The nine more plentiful cards are #'s 1, 5, 8, 9, 14, 15, 16, 17 and 22. Complete boxes would command 75 percent over the prices in the checklist that follows.

		NR MT	EX	VG
Complete Set:		8500.00	4250.00	2550.
Common Player:		125.00	62.00	37.00
(1a)	Hank Aaron (name in white)	650.00	325.00	195.00
(1b)	Hank Aaron (name in yellow)	650.00	325.00	195.00
(2)	Richie Ashburn	400.00	200.00	120.00
(3)	Ernie Banks	650.00	325.00	195.00
(4)	Ken Boyer	300.00	150.00	90.00
(5)	Orlando Cepeda	200.00	100.00	60.00
(6)	Bob Cerv	200.00	100.00	60.00
(7)	Rocco Colavito	500.00	250.00	150.00
(8)	Del Crandall	125.00	62.00	37.00
(9)	Jim Davenport	125.00	62.00	37.00
(10)	Don Drysdale	650.00	325.00	210.00
(11)	Nellie Fox	350.00	175.00	105.00
(12)	Jackie Jensen	250.00	125.00	75.00
(13)	Harvey Kuenn	250.00	125.00	75.00
(14)	Mickey Mantle	2000.00	1000.00	600.00
(15)	Willie Mays	500.00	250.00	150.00
(16)	Bill Mazeroski	150.00	75.00	45.00
(17)	Roy McMillan	125.00	62.00	37.00
(18)	Billy Pierce	200.00	100.00	60.00
(19)	Roy Sievers	200.00	100.00	60.00
(20)	Duke Snider	800.00	400.00	250.00
(21)	Gus Triandos	200.00	100.00	60.00
(22)	Bob Turley	125.00	62.00	37.00
(23)	Vic Wertz	200.00	100.00	60.00

1960 Bazooka

Three-card panels were found on the bottoms of Bazooka bubble gum boxes in 1960. The blank-backed set is comprised of 36 cards with the card number located at the bottom of each full-color card. The individual cards measure 1-13/16" by

2-3/4"; the panels measure 2-3/4" by 5-1/2" in size. Prices, in the checklist that follows, are given for complete panels and individual cards.

		NR MT	EX	VG
Complete Panel Set:		1750.00	875.00	525.00
Complete Singles Set:		1200.00	600.00	360.00
Common Panel:		75.00	37.00	22.00
Common Single Player:		5.00	2.50	1.50
	Panel	100.00	50.00	30.00
1	Ernie Banks	50.00	25.00	15.00
2	Bud Daley	5.00	2.50	1.50
3	Wally Moon	5.00	2.50	1.50
	Panel	150.00	75.00	45.00
4	Hank Aaron	80.00	40.00	25.00
5	Milt Pappas	10.00	5.00	3.00
6	Dick Stuart	10.00	5.00	3.00
	Panel	200.00	100.00	60.00
7	Bob Clemente	100.00	50.00	30.00
8	Yogi Berra	50.00	25.00	15.00
9	Ken Boyer	12.00	6.00	3.50
	Panel	75.00	38.00	23.00
10	Orlando Cepeda	15.00	7.50	4.50
11	Gus Triandos	10.00	5.00	3.00
12	Frank Malzone	10.00	5.00	3.00
	Panel	80.00	40.00	25.00
13	Willie Mays	60.00	30.00	18.00
14	Camilo Pascual	5.00	2.50	1.50
15	Bob Cerv	5.00	2.50	1.50
	Panel	100.00	50.00	30.00
16	Vic Power	5.00	2.50	1.50
17	Larry Sherry	5.00	2.50	1.50
18	Al Kaline	50.00	25.00	15.00
	Panel	110.00	55.00	33.00
19	Warren Spahn	40.00	20.00	12.50
20	Harmon Killebrew	30.00	15.00	9.00
21	Jackie Jensen	12.00	6.00	3.50
	Panel	115.00	57.00	34.00
22	Luis Aparicio	25.00	12.50	7.50
23	Gil Hodges	30.00	15.00	9.00
24	Richie Ashburn	30.00	15.00	9.00
	Panel	110.00	55.00	33.00
25	Nellie Fox	30.00	15.00	9.00
26	Robin Roberts	30.00	15.00	9.00
27	Joe Cunningham	5.00	2.50	1.50
	Panel	110.00	55.00	33.00
28	Early Wynn	25.00	12.50	7.50
29	Frank Robinson	50.00	25.00	15.00
30	Rocky Colavito	15.00	7.50	4.50
	Panel	450.00	225.00	135.00
31	Mickey Mantle	300.00	150.00	90.00
32	Glen Hobbie	5.00	2.50	1.50
33	Roy McMillan	5.00	2.50	1.50
	Panel	75.00	37.00	22.00
34	Harvey Kuenn	12.00	6.00	3.50
35	Johnny Antonelli	5.00	2.50	1.50
36	Del Crandall	10.00	5.00	3.00

1961 Bazooka

Similar in design to the 1960 Bazooka set, the 1961 edition consists of 36 cards issued in panels of three on the bottom of Bazooka bubble gum boxes. The full-color cards, which measure 1-13/16" by 2-3/4" individually and 2-3/4" by 5-1/2" as panels, are numbered 1 through 36. The backs are blank.

		NR MT	EX	VG
	Complete Panel Set:	1500.00	750.00	450.00
	Complete Singles Set:	800.00	400.00	240.00
	Common Panel:	60.00	30.00	18.00
	Common Single Player:	5.00	2.50	1.50
	Panel	450.00	225.00	135.00
1	Art Mahaffey	10.00	5.00	3.00
2	Mickey Mantle	300.00	150.00	90.00
3	Ron Santo	12.00	6.00	3.50
	Panel	80.00	40.00	24.00
4	Bud Daley	5.00	2.50	1.50
5	Roger Maris	80.00	40.00	24.00
6	Eddie Yost	5.00	2.50	1.50
	Panel	65.00	32.00	19.50
7	Minnie Minoso	12.00	6.00	3.50
8	Dick Groat	12.00	6.00	3.50
9	Frank Malzone	10.00	5.00	3.00
	Panel	80.00	40.00	24.00
10	Dick Donovan	5.00	2.50	1.50
11	Ed Mathews	30.00	15.00	9.00
12	Jim Lemon	5.00	2.50	1.50
	Panel	60.00	30.00	18.00
13	Chuck Estrada	5.00	2.50	1.50
14	Ken Boyer	12.00	6.00	3.50
15	Harvey Kuenn	12.00	6.00	3.50
	Panel	60.00	30.00	18.00
16	Ernie Broglio	5.00	2.50	1.50
17	Rocky Colavito	15.00	7.50	4.50
18	Ted Kluszewski	15.00	7.50	4.50
	Panel	300.00	150.00	90.00
19	Ernie Banks	75.00	38.00	23.00
20	Al Kaline	75.00	38.00	23.00
21	Ed Bailey	5.00	2.50	1.50
	Panel	75.00	37.00	22.00
22	Jim Perry	5.00	2.50	1.50
23	Willie Mays	80.00	40.00	24.00
24	Bill Mazeroski	12.00	6.00	3.50
	Panel	80.00	40.00	24.00
25	Gus Triandos	5.00	2.50	1.50
26	Don Drysdale	25.00	12.50	7.50
27	Frank Herrera	10.00	5.00	3.00
	Panel	80.00	40.00	24.00
28	Earl Battey	5.00	2.50	1.50
29	Warren Spahn	35.00	17.50	10.50
30	Gene Woodling	10.00	5.00	3.00
	Panel	60.00	30.00	18.00
31	Frank Robinson	35.00	17.50	10.50
32	Pete Runnels	10.00	5.00	3.00
33	Woodie Held	5.00	2.50	1.50
	Panel	65.00	32.00	19.50
34	Norm Larker	5.00	2.50	1.50
35	Luis Aparicio	20.00	10.00	6.00
36	Bill Tuttle	5.00	2.50	1.50

1962 Bazooka

In 1962, Bazooka increased the size of its set to 45 full-color cards. The set is unnumbered and was issued in panels of three on the bottoms of bubble gum boxes. The individual cards measure 1-13/16" by 2-3/4" in size, whereas the panels are 2-3/4" by 5-1/2". In the checklist that follows the cards have been numbered by panel using the name of the player who appears on the left side of the panel. Panel #'s 1-3, 31-33 and 43-45 were issued in much shorter supply and command a higher price.

		NR MT	EX	VG
	Complete Panel Set:	3500.00	1750.00	1050.
	Complete Singles Set:	1800.00	900.00	540.00
	Common Panel:	30.00	15.00	9.00
	Common Single Player:	8.00	4.00	2.50
	Panel	1200.00	600.00	360.00
(1)	Bob Allison	150.00	75.00	45.00
(2)	Ed Mathews	350.00	175.00	105.00
(3)	Vada Pinson	150.00	75.00	45.00
	Panel	50.00	25.00	15.00
(4)	Earl Battey	8.00	4.00	2.50
(5)	Warren Spahn	30.00	15.00	9.00
(6)	Lee Thomas	8.00	4.00	2.50
	Panel	40.00	20.00	12.00
(7)	Orlando Cepeda	15.00	7.50	4.50
(8)	Woodie Held	8.00	4.00	2.50
(9)	Bob Aspromonte	8.00	4.00	2.50
	Panel	100.00	50.00	30.00
(10)	Dick Howser	10.00	5.00	3.00
(11)	Bob Clemente	50.00	25.00	15.00
(12)	Al Kaline	30.00	15.00	9.00
	Panel	100.00	50.00	30.00
(13)	Joey Jay	8.00	4.00	2.50
(14)	Roger Maris	40.00	20.00	12.00
(15)	Frank Howard	15.00	7.50	4.50
	Panel	70.00	35.00	21.00
(16)	Sandy Koufax	50.00	25.00	15.00
(17)	Jim Gentile	8.00	4.00	2.50
(18)	Johnny Callison	10.00	5.00	3.00
	Panel	30.00	15.00	9.00
(19)	Jim Landis	8.00	4.00	2.50
(20)	Ken Boyer	12.00	6.00	3.50
(21)	Chuck Schilling	8.00	4.00	2.50
	Panel	500.00	250.00	150.00
(22)	Art Mahaffey	10.00	5.00	3.00
(23)	Mickey Mantle	200.00	100.00	60.00
(24)	Dick Stuart	10.00	5.00	3.00
	Panel	100.00	50.00	30.00
(25)	Ken McBride	8.00	4.00	2.50
(26)	Frank Robinson	35.00	17.50	10.50
(27)	Gil Hodges	25.00	12.50	7.50
	Panel	100.00	50.00	30.00
(28)	Milt Pappas	10.00	5.00	3.00
(29)	Hank Aaron	70.00	35.00	21.00
(30)	Luis Aparicio	20.00	10.00	6.00
	Panel	1200.00	600.00	360.00
(31)	Johnny Romano	150.00	75.00	45.00
(32)	Ernie Banks	500.00	250.00	150.00
(33)	Norm Siebern	150.00	75.00	45.00
	Panel	40.00	20.00	12.00
(34)	Ron Santo	12.00	6.00	3.50
(35)	Norm Cash	10.00	5.00	3.00
(36)	Jim Piersall	10.00	5.00	3.00
	Panel	70.00	35.00	21.00
(37)	Don Schwall	8.00	4.00	2.50
(38)	Willie Mays	50.00	25.00	15.00
(39)	Norm Larker	8.00	4.00	2.50
	Panel	70.00	35.00	21.00
(40)	Bill White	10.00	5.00	3.00
(41)	Whitey Ford	30.00	15.00	9.00
(42)	Rocky Colavito	15.00	7.50	4.50
	Panel	1200.00	600.00	360.00
(43)	Don Zimmer	200.00	100.00	60.00
(44)	Harmon Killebrew	300.00	150.00	90.00
(45)	Gene Woodling	150.00	75.00	45.00

1963 Bazooka

The 1963 Bazooka issue reverted back to a 12-panel, 36-card set, but saw a change in the size of the cards. Individual cards measure 1-9/16" by 2-1/2", while panels are 2-1/2" by 4-11/16" in size. The card design was altered also, with the player's name, team and position situated in a white oval space at the bottom of the card. The full-color, blank-backed set is numbered 1-36. Five Bazooka All-Time Greats cards were inserted in each box of bubble gum.

		NR MT	EX	VG
	Complete Panel Set:	1500.00	750.00	450.00
	Complete Singles Set:	800.00	400.00	240.00
	Common Panel:	30.00	15.00	9.00
	Common Single Player:	5.00	2.50	1.50
	Panel	400.00	200.00	120.00
1	Mickey Mantle (batting righty)	300.00	150.00	90.00
2	Bob Rodgers	5.00	2.50	1.50
3	Ernie Banks	40.00	20.00	12.50
	Panel	50.00	25.00	15.00
4	Norm Siebern	5.00	2.50	1.50
5	Warren Spahn (portrait)	30.00	15.00	9.00
6	Bill Mazeroski	10.00	5.00	3.00
	Panel	115.00	57.00	34.00
7	Harmon Killebrew (batting)	30.00	15.00	9.00
8	Dick Farrell (portrait)	5.00	2.50	1.50
9	Hank Aaron (glove in front)	60.00	30.00	17.50
	Panel	150.00	75.00	45.00
10	Dick Donovan	5.00	2.50	1.50
11	Jim Gentile (batting)	5.00	2.50	1.50
12	Willie Mays (bat in front)	75.00	38.00	23.00
	Panel	70.00	35.00	21.00
13	Camilo Pascual (hands at waist)	5.00	2.50	1.50
14	Bob Clemente (portrait)	50.00	25.00	15.00
15	Johnny Callison (wearing pinstripe uniform)	8.00	4.00	2.50
	Panel	200.00	100.00	60.00
16	Carl Yastrzemski (kneeling)	100.00	50.00	30.00
17	Don Drysdale	70.00	35.00	20.00
18	Johnny Romano (portrait)	5.00	2.50	1.50
	Panel	30.00	15.00	9.00
19	Al Jackson	8.00	4.00	2.50
20	Ralph Terry	8.00	4.00	2.50
21	Bill Monbouquette	5.00	2.50	1.50
	Panel	95.00	47.00	28.00
22	Orlando Cepeda	15.00	7.50	4.50
23	Stan Musial	50.00	25.00	15.00
24	Floyd Robinson (no pinstripes on uniform)	5.00	2.50	1.50
	Panel	30.00	15.00	9.00
25	Chuck Hinton (batting)	5.00	2.50	1.50
26	Bob Purkey	5.00	2.50	1.50
27	Ken Hubbs	12.00	6.00	3.50
	Panel	60.00	30.00	18.00
28	Bill White	8.00	4.00	2.50
29	Ray Herbert	5.00	2.50	1.50
30	Brooks Robinson (glove in front)	35.00	17.50	10.50
	Panel	60.00	30.00	18.00
31	Frank Robinson (batting, uniform number doesn't show)	50.00	25.00	15.00
32	Lee Thomas	5.00	2.50	1.50
33	Rocky Colavito (Detroit)	10.00	5.00	3.00
	Panel	60.00	30.00	18.00
34	Al Kaline (kneeling)	35.00	17.50	10.50
35	Art Mahaffey	5.00	2.50	1.50
36	Tommy Davis (batting follow-thru)	8.00	4.00	2.50

1963 Bazooka All-Time Greats

Consisting of 41 cards, the Bazooka All-Time Greats set was issued as inserts (5 per box) in boxes of Bazooka bubble gum. A black and white head-shot of the player is placed inside a gold plaque within a white border. The card backs have black print on white and white and yellow and contain a brief biography of the player. The numbered cards measure 1-9/16" by 2-1/2" in size. The cards can be found with silver fronts instead of gold. The silver are worth double the values listed in the following checklist.

		NR MT	EX	VG
	Complete Set:	250.00	125.00	75.00
	Common Player:	3.00	1.50	.90
1	Joe Tinker	3.50	1.75	1.00
2	Harry Heilmann	3.00	1.50	.90
3	Jack Chesbro	3.00	1.50	.90
4	Christy Mathewson	5.00	2.50	1.50
5	Herb Pennock	3.00	1.50	.90
6	Cy Young	6.00	3.00	1.75
7	Big Ed Walsh	3.00	1.50	.90
8	Nap Lajoie	3.50	1.75	1.00
9	Eddie Plank	3.00	1.50	.90
10	Honus Wagner	8.00	4.00	2.50
11	Chief Bender	3.00	1.50	.90
12	Walter Johnson	8.00	4.00	2.50
13	Three-Fingered Brown	3.00	1.50	.90
14	Rabbit Maranville	3.00	1.50	.90
15	Lou Gehrig	40.00	20.00	12.00
16	Ban Johnson	3.00	1.50	.90
17	Babe Ruth	55.00	27.00	16.50
18	Connie Mack	5.00	2.50	1.50
19	Hank Greenberg	3.50	1.75	1.00
20	John McGraw	3.50	1.75	1.00
21	Johnny Evers	3.00	1.50	.90
22	Al Simmons	3.00	1.50	.90
23	Jimmy Collins	3.00	1.50	.90
24	Tris Speaker	3.50	1.75	1.00
25	Frank Chance	3.00	1.50	.90
26	Fred Clarke	3.00	1.50	.90
27	Wilbert Robinson	3.00	1.50	.90
28	Dazzy Vance	3.00	1.50	.90
29	Pete Alexander	3.50	1.75	1.00
30	Judge Landis	3.00	1.50	.90
31	Wee Willie Keeler	3.00	1.50	.90
32	Rogers Hornsby	5.00	2.50	1.50
33	Hugh Duffy	3.00	1.50	.90
34	Mickey Cochrane	3.50	1.75	1.00
35	Ty Cobb	40.00	20.00	12.00
36	Mel Ott	3.50	1.75	1.00
37	Clark Griffith	3.00	1.50	.90
38	Ted Lyons	3.00	1.50	.90
39	Cap Anson	3.50	1.75	1.00
40	Bill Dickey	3.50	1.75	1.00
41	Eddie Collins	3.50	1.75	1.00

1964 Bazooka

The 1964 Bazooka set is identical in design and size to the previous year's effort. However, different photographs were used from year to year by Topps,

1964 Bazooka Stamps

issuer of Bazooka bubble gum. The 1964 set consists of 36 full-color, blank-backed cards numbered 1 through 36. Individual cards measure 1-9/16" by 2-1/2"; three-card panels measure 2-1/2" by 4-11/16". Sheets of ten full-color baseball stamps were inserted in each box of bubble gum.

Occasionally mislabeled "Topps Stamps," the 1964 Bazooka Stamps set was produced by Topps, but was found only in boxes of 1¢ Bazooka bubble gum. Issued in sheets of ten, 100 color stamps make up the set. Each stamp measures 1" by 1-1/2" in size. While the stamps are not individually numbered, the sheets are numbered one through ten. The stamps are commonly found as complete sheets of ten and are priced in that fashion in the checklist that follows.

		NR MT	EX	VG
Complete Panel Set:		1500.00	750.00	450.00
Complete Singles Set:		750.00	375.00	225.00
Common Panel:		30.00	15.00	9.00
Common Single Player:		5.00	2.50	1.50
	Panel	250.00	125.00	75.00
1	Mickey Mantle (portrait)	200.00	100.00	60.00
2	Dick Groat	8.00	4.00	2.50
3	Steve Barber	5.00	2.50	1.50
	Panel	40.00	20.00	12.00
4	Ken McBride	5.00	2.50	1.50
5	Warren Spahn (head to waist shot)			
		30.00	15.00	9.00
6	Bob Friend	6.00	3.00	1.75
	Panel	115.00	57.00	34.00
7	Harmon Killebrew (portrait)	30.00	15.00	9.00
8	Dick Farrell (hands above head)	5.00	2.50	1.50
9	Hank Aaron (glove to left)	70.00	35.00	20.00
	Panel	70.00	35.00	21.00
10	Rich Rollins	5.00	2.50	1.50
11	Jim Gentile (portrait)	5.00	2.50	1.50
12	Willie Mays (looking to left)	50.00	25.00	15.00
	Panel	70.00	35.00	21.00
13	Camilo Pascual (pitching follow-thru)			
		5.00	2.50	1.50
14	Bob Clemente (throwing)	50.00	25.00	15.00
15	Johnny Callison (batting, screen showing)			
		8.00	4.00	2.50
	Panel	75.00	37.00	22.00
16	Carl Yastrzemski (batting)	50.00	25.00	15.00
17	Billy Williams (kneeling)	30.00	15.00	9.00
18	Johnny Romano (batting)	5.00	2.50	1.50
	Panel	55.00	27.00	16.50
19	Jim Maloney	5.00	2.50	1.50
20	Norm Cash	8.00	4.00	2.50
21	Willie McCovey	30.00	15.00	9.00
	Panel	30.00	15.00	9.00
22	Jim Fregosi (batting)	6.00	3.00	1.75
23	George Altman	5.00	2.50	1.50
24	Floyd Robinson (wearing pinstripe uniform)			
		5.00	2.50	1.50
	Panel	30.00	15.00	9.00
25	Chuck Hinton (portrait)	5.00	2.50	1.50
26	Ron Hunt (batting)	8.00	4.00	2.50
27	Gary Peters (pitching)	5.00	2.50	1.50
	Panel	60.00	30.00	18.00
28	Dick Ellsworth	5.00	2.50	1.50
29	Elston Howard (holding bat)	12.00	6.00	3.50
30	Brooks Robinson (kneeling with glove)			
		30.00	15.00	9.00
	Panel	110.00	55.00	33.00
31	Frank Robinson (uniform number shows)			
		40.00	20.00	12.00
32	Sandy Koufax (glove in front)	50.00	25.00	15.00
33	Rocky Colavito (Kansas City)	10.00	5.00	3.00
	Panel	65.00	32.00	19.50
34	Al Kaline (holding two bats)	30.00	15.00	9.00
35	Ken Boyer (head to waist shot)	10.00	5.00	3.00
36	Tommy Davis (batting)	8.00	4.00	2.50

		NR MT	EX	VG
Complete Sheet Set:		500.00	250.00	150.00
Common Sheet:		25.00	12.50	7.50
1	Max Alvis, Ed Charles, Dick Ellsworth, Jimmie Hall, Frank Malzone, Milt Pappas, Vada Pinson, Tony Taylor, Pete Ward, Bill White	25.00	12.50	7.50
2	Bob Aspromonte, Larry Jackson, Willie Mays, Al McBean, Bill Monbouquette, Bobby Richardson, Floyd Robinson, Frank Robinson, Norm Siebern, Don Zimmer	40.00	20.00	12.00
3	Ernie Banks, Bob Clemente, Curt Flood, Jesse Gonder, Woody Held, Don Lock, Dave Nicholson, Joe Pepitone, Brooks Robinson, Carl Yastrzemski	60.00	30.00	18.00
4	Hank Aguirre, Jim Grant, Harmon Killebrew, Jim Maloney, Juan Marichal, Bill Mazeroski, Juan Pizarro, Boog Powell, Ed Roebuck, Ron Santo	40.00	20.00	12.00
5	Jim Bouton, Norm Cash, Orlando Cepeda, Tommy Harper, Chuck Hinton, Albie Pearson, Ron Perranoski, Dick Radatz, Johnny Romano, Carl Willey	30.00	15.00	9.00
6	Steve Barber, Jim Fregosi, Tony Gonzalez, Mickey Mantle, Jim O'Toole, Gary Peters, Rich Rollins, Warren Spahn, Dick Stuart, Joe Torre	125.00	62.00	37.00
7	Felipe Alou, George Altman, Ken Boyer, Rocky Colavito, Jim Davenport, Tommy Davis, Bill Freehan, Bob Friend, Ken Johnson, Billy Moran	30.00	15.00	9.00
8	Earl Battey, Ernie Broglio, Johnny Callison, Donn Clendenon, Don Drysdale, Jim Gentile, Elston Howard, Claude Osteen, Billy Williams, Hal Woodeshick	35.00	17.50	10.50
9	Hank Aaron, Jack Baldschun, Wayne Causey, Moe Drabowsky, Dick Groat, Frank Howard, Al Jackson, Jerry Lumpe, Ken McBride, Rusty Staub	40.00	20.00	12.00
10	Ray Culp, Vic Davalillo, Dick Farrell, Ron Hunt, Al Kaline, Sandy Koufax, Ed Mathews, Willie McCovey, Camilo Pascual, Lee Thomas	50.00	25.00	15.00

1965 Bazooka

The 1965 Bazooka set is identical to the 1963 and 1964 sets. Different players were added each year and different photographs were used for those players being included again. Individual cards cut from the boxes measure 1-9/16" by 2-1/2". Complete three-card panels measure 2-1/2" by

4-11/16". Thirty-six full-color, blank-backed, numbered cards comprise the set. Prices are given for
individual cards and complete panels in the checklist
that follows.

		NR MT	EX	VG
	Complete Panel Set:	1300.00	650.00	390.00
	Complete Singles Set:	700.00	350.00	210.00
	Common Panel:	25.00	12.50	7.50
	Common Single Player:	5.00	2.50	1.50
	Panel	225.00	115.00	70.00
1	Mickey Mantle (batting lefty)	200.00	100.00	60.00
2	Larry Jackson	5.00	2.50	1.50
3	Chuck Hinton	5.00	2.50	1.50
	Panel	30.00	15.00	9.00
4	Tony Oliva	10.00	5.00	3.00
5	Dean Chance	5.00	2.50	1.50
6	Jim O'Toole	5.00	2.50	1.50
	Panel	110.00	55.00	33.00
7	Harmon Killebrew (bat on shoulder)	25.00	12.50	7.50
8	Pete Ward	5.00	2.50	1.50
9	Hank Aaron (batting)	50.00	25.00	15.00
	Panel	80.00	40.00	24.00
10	Dick Radatz	5.00	2.50	1.50
11	Boog Powell	10.00	5.00	3.00
12	Willie Mays (looking down)	40.00	20.00	12.00
	Panel	65.00	32.00	19.50
13	Bob Veale	5.00	2.50	1.50
14	Bob Clemente (batting)	40.00	20.00	12.00
15	Johnny Callison (batting, no screen in background)	8.00	4.00	2.50
	Panel	45.00	22.00	13.50
16	Joe Torre	8.00	4.00	2.50
17	Billy Williams (batting)	20.00	10.00	6.00
18	Bob Chance	5.00	2.50	1.50
	Panel	30.00	15.00	9.00
19	Bob Aspromonte	5.00	2.50	1.50
20	Joe Christopher	5.00	2.50	1.50
21	Jim Bunning	12.00	6.00	3.50
	Panel	80.00	40.00	24.00
22	Jim Fregosi (portrait)	8.00	4.00	2.50
23	Bob Gibson	25.00	12.50	7.50
24	Juan Marichal	20.00	10.00	6.00
	Panel	25.00	12.50	7.50
25	Dave Wickersham	5.00	2.50	1.50
26	Ron Hunt (throwing)	8.00	4.00	2.50
27	Gary Peters (portrait)	5.00	2.50	1.50
	Panel	80.00	40.00	24.00
28	Ron Santo	10.00	5.00	3.00
29	Elston Howard (with glove)	12.00	6.00	3.50
30	Brooks Robinson (portrait)	30.00	15.00	9.00
	Panel	110.00	55.00	33.00
31	Frank Robinson (portrait)	35.00	17.50	10.50
32	Sandy Koufax (hands over head)	40.00	20.00	12.00
33	Rocky Colavito (Cleveland)	10.00	5.00	3.00
	Panel	60.00	30.00	18.00
34	Al Kaline (portrait)	30.00	15.00	9.00
35	Ken Boyer (portrait)	10.00	5.00	3.00
36	Tommy Davis (fielding)	8.00	4.00	2.50

1966 Bazooka

The 1966 Bazooka set was increased to 48 cards.
Issued in panels of three on the bottoms of boxes of
bubble gum, the full-color cards are blank-backed and

numbered. Individual cards measure 1-9/16" by
2-1/2", whereas panels measure 2-1/2" by
4-11/16".

		NR MT	EX	VG
	Complete Panel Set:	1750.00	875.00	525.00
	Complete Singles Set:	1000.00	500.00	300.00
	Common Panel:	25.00	12.50	7.50
	Common Single Player:	5.00	2.50	1.50
	Panel	65.00	32.00	19.50
1	Sandy Koufax	50.00	25.00	15.00
2	Willie Horton	6.00	3.00	1.75
3	Frank Howard	8.00	4.00	2.50
	Panel	50.00	25.00	15.00
4	Richie Allen	10.00	5.00	3.00
5	Mel Stottlemyre	8.00	4.00	2.50
6	Tony Conigliaro	15.00	7.50	4.50
	Panel	275.00	137.00	82.00
7	Mickey Mantle	200.00	100.00	60.00
8	Leon Wagner	5.00	2.50	1.50
9	Ed Kranepool	6.00	3.00	1.75
	Panel	70.00	35.00	21.00
10	Juan Marichal	20.00	10.00	6.00
11	Harmon Killebrew	25.00	12.50	7.50
12	Johnny Callison	6.00	3.00	1.75
	Panel	55.00	27.00	16.50
13	Roy McMillan	5.00	2.50	1.50
14	Willie McCovey	25.00	12.50	7.50
15	Rocky Colavito	10.00	5.00	3.00
	Panel	65.00	32.00	19.50
16	Willie Mays	50.00	25.00	15.00
17	Sam McDowell	8.00	4.00	2.50
18	Vern Law	6.00	3.00	1.75
	Panel	55.00	27.00	16.50
19	Jim Fregosi	6.00	3.00	1.75
20	Ron Fairly	6.00	3.00	1.75
21	Bob Gibson	25.00	12.50	7.50
	Panel	70.00	35.00	21.00
22	Carl Yastrzemski	50.00	25.00	15.00
23	Bill White	8.00	4.00	2.50
24	Bob Aspromonte	5.00	2.50	1.50
	Panel	55.00	27.00	16.50
25	Dean Chance (California)	5.00	2.50	1.50
26	Bob Clemente	50.00	25.00	15.00
27	Tony Cloninger	5.00	2.50	1.50
	Panel	70.00	35.00	21.00
28	Curt Blefary	5.00	2.50	1.50
29	Milt Pappas	5.00	2.50	1.50
30	Hank Aaron	55.00	27.00	16.50
	Panel	60.00	30.00	18.00
31	Jim Bunning	12.00	6.00	3.50
32	Frank Robinson (portrait)	30.00	15.00	9.00
33	Bill Skowron	8.00	4.00	2.50
	Panel	60.00	30.00	18.00
34	Brooks Robinson	30.00	15.00	9.00
35	Jim Wynn	6.00	3.00	1.75
36	Joe Torre	8.00	4.00	2.50
	Panel	160.00	80.00	48.00
37	Jim Grant	5.00	2.50	1.50
38	Pete Rose	110.00	55.00	33.00
39	Ron Santo	10.00	5.00	3.00
	Panel	60.00	30.00	18.00
40	Tom Tresh	8.00	4.00	2.50
41	Tony Oliva	10.00	5.00	3.00
42	Don Drysdale	25.00	12.50	7.50
	Panel	25.00	12.50	7.50
43	Pete Richert	5.00	2.50	1.50
44	Bert Campaneris	8.00	4.00	2.50
45	Jim Maloney	5.00	2.50	1.50
	Panel	70.00	35.00	21.00

		NR MT	EX	VG
46	Al Kaline	30.00	15.00	9.00
47	Eddie Fisher	5.00	2.50	1.50
48	Billy Williams	20.00	10.00	6.00

1967 Bazooka

The 1967 Bazooka set is identical in design to the Bazooka sets of 1964-1966. Issued in panels of three on the bottoms of bubble gum boxes, the set is made up of 48 full-color, blank-backed, numbered cards. Individual cards measure 1-9/16" by 2-1/2"; complete panels measure 2-1/2" by 4-11/16" in size.

		NR MT	EX	VG
	Complete Panel Set:	1600.00	800.00	480.00
	Complete Singles Set:	900.00	450.00	270.00
	Common Panel:	25.00	12.50	7.50
	Common Single Player:	5.00	2.50	1.50
	Panel	25.00	12.50	7.50
1	Rick Reichardt	5.00	2.50	1.50
2	Tommy Agee	5.00	2.50	1.50
3	Frank Howard	8.00	4.00	2.50
	Panel	35.00	17.50	10.50
4	Richie Allen	10.00	5.00	3.00
5	Mel Stottlemyre	8.00	4.00	2.50
6	Tony Conigliaro	15.00	7.50	4.50
	Panel	250.00	125.00	75.00
7	Mickey Mantle	200.00	100.00	60.00
8	Leon Wagner	5.00	2.50	1.50
9	Gary Peters	5.00	2.50	1.50
	Panel	80.00	40.00	24.00
10	Juan Marichal	20.00	10.00	6.00
11	Harmon Killebrew	25.00	12.50	7.50
12	Johnny Callison	6.00	3.00	1.75
	Panel	50.00	25.00	15.00
13	Denny McLain	12.00	6.00	3.50
14	Willie McCovey	25.00	12.50	7.50
15	Rocky Colavito	10.00	5.00	3.00
	Panel	65.00	32.00	19.50
16	Willie Mays	40.00	20.00	12.00
17	Sam McDowell	6.00	3.00	1.75
18	Jim Kaat	12.00	6.00	3.50
	Panel	50.00	25.00	15.00
19	Jim Fregosi	6.00	3.00	1.75
20	Ron Fairly	6.00	3.00	1.75
21	Bob Gibson	25.00	12.50	7.50
	Panel	80.00	40.00	24.00
22	Carl Yastrzemski	40.00	20.00	12.00
23	Bill White	6.00	3.00	1.75
24	Bob Aspromonte	5.00	2.50	1.50
	Panel	60.00	30.00	18.00
25	Dean Chance (Minnesota)	5.00	2.50	1.50
26	Bob Clemente	40.00	20.00	12.00
27	Tony Cloninger	5.00	2.50	1.50
	Panel	80.00	40.00	24.00
28	Curt Blefary	5.00	2.50	1.50
29	Phil Regan	5.00	2.50	1.50
30	Hank Aaron	50.00	25.00	15.00
	Panel	60.00	30.00	18.00
31	Jim Bunning	12.00	6.00	3.50
32	Frank Robinson (batting)	25.00	12.50	7.50
33	Ken Boyer	10.00	5.00	3.00
	Panel	60.00	30.00	18.00
34	Brooks Robinson	30.00	15.00	9.00
35	Jim Wynn	6.00	3.00	1.75
36	Joe Torre	8.00	4.00	2.50

		NR MT	EX	VG
	Panel	160.00	80.00	48.00
37	Tommy Davis	6.00	3.00	1.75
38	Pete Rose	90.00	45.00	27.00
39	Ron Santo	10.00	5.00	3.00
	Panel	60.00	30.00	18.00
40	Tom Tresh	8.00	4.00	2.50
41	Tony Oliva	10.00	5.00	3.00
42	Don Drysdale	25.00	12.50	7.50
	Panel	25.00	12.50	7.50
43	Pete Richert	5.00	2.50	1.50
44	Bert Campaneris	6.00	3.00	1.75
45	Jim Maloney	5.00	2.50	1.50
	Panel	80.00	40.00	24.00
46	Al Kaline	30.00	15.00	9.00
47	Matty Alou	6.00	3.00	1.75
48	Billy Williams	20.00	10.00	6.00

1968 Bazooka

The design of the 1968 Bazooka set is radically different from previous years. The player cards are situated on the sides of the boxes with the box back containing "Tipps From The Topps." Four unnumbered player cards, measuring 1-1/4" by 3-1/8", are featured on each box. The box back includes a small player photo plus illustrated tips on various aspects of the game of baseball. The boxes are numbered 1-15 on the top panels. There are 56 different player cards in the set, with four of the cards (Agee, Drysdale, Rose, Santo) being used twice to round out the set of fifteen boxes.

		NR MT	EX	VG
	Complete Box Set:	3300.00	1650.00	990.00
	Complete Singles Set:	2000.00	1000.00	600.00
	Common Box:	120.00	60.00	36.00
	Common Single Player:	5.00	2.50	1.50
1	Box	200.00	100.00	60.00
	Maury Wills (Bunting)	20.00	10.00	6.00
(1)	Clete Boyer	9.00	4.50	2.75
(2)	Paul Casanova	7.00	3.50	2.00
(3)	Al Kaline	30.00	15.00	9.00
(4)	Tom Seaver	70.00	35.00	21.00
2	Box	150.00	75.00	45.00
	Carl Yastrzemski (Batting)	50.00	25.00	15.00
(5)	Matty Alou	9.00	4.50	2.75
(6)	Bill Freehan	9.00	4.50	2.75
(7)	Jim Hunter	20.00	10.00	6.00
(8)	Jim Lefebvre	7.00	3.50	2.00
3	Box	120.00	60.00	36.00
	Bert Campaneris (Stealing bases)	20.00	10.00	6.00
(9)	Bobby Knoop	7.00	3.50	2.00
(10)	Tim McCarver	12.00	6.00	3.50
(11)	Frank Robinson	25.00	12.50	7.50
(12)	Bob Veale	7.00	3.50	2.00
4	Box	90.00	45.00	27.00
	Maury Wills (Sliding)	20.00	10.00	6.00
(13)	Joe Azcue	7.00	3.50	2.00
(14)	Tony Conigliaro	15.00	7.50	4.50
(15)	Ken Holtzman	9.00	4.50	2.75
(16)	Bill White	9.00	4.50	2.75
5	Box	150.00	75.00	45.00
	Julian Javier (The Double Play)	20.00	10.00	6.00
(17)	Hank Aaron	50.00	25.00	15.00
(18)	Juan Marichal	20.00	10.00	6.00

		NR MT	EX	VG
(19)	Joe Pepitone	12.00	6.00	3.50
(20)	Rico Petrocelli	9.00	4.50	2.75
	Box	200.00	100.00	60.00
6	Orlando Cepeda (Playing 1st Base)			
		25.00	12.50	7.50
(21)	Tommie Agee	5.00	2.50	1.50
(22)	Don Drysdale	10.00	5.00	3.00
(23)	Pete Rose	70.00	35.00	21.00
(24)	Ron Santo	5.00	2.50	1.50
	Box	120.00	60.00	36.00
7	Bill Mazeroski (Playing 2nd Base)			
		20.00	10.00	6.00
(25)	Jim Bunning	12.00	6.00	3.50
(26)	Frank Howard	12.00	6.00	3.50
(27)	John Roseboro	9.00	4.50	2.75
(28)	George Scott	9.00	4.50	2.75
	Box	150.00	75.00	45.00
8	Brooks Robinson (Playing 3rd Base)			
		50.00	25.00	15.00
(29)	Tony Gonzalez	7.00	3.50	2.00
(30)	Willie Horton	9.00	4.50	2.75
(31)	Harmon Killebrew	25.00	12.50	7.50
(32)	Jim McGlothlin	7.00	3.50	2.00
	Box	120.00	60.00	36.00
9	Jim Fregosi (Playing Shortstop)	20.00	10.00	6.00
(33)	Max Alvis	7.00	3.50	2.00
(34)	Bob Gibson	20.00	10.00	6.00
(35)	Tony Oliva	12.00	6.00	3.50
(36)	Vada Pinson	12.00	6.00	3.50
	Box	120.00	60.00	36.00
10	Joe Torre (Catching)	25.00	12.50	7.50
(37)	Dean Chance	7.00	3.50	2.00
(38)	Tommy Davis	9.00	4.50	2.75
(39)	Ferguson Jenkins	15.00	7.50	4.50
(40)	Rick Monday	9.00	4.50	2.75
	Box	300.00	150.00	90.00
11	Jim Lonborg (Pitching)	25.00	12.50	7.50
(41)	Curt Flood	9.00	4.50	2.75
(42)	Joel Horlen	7.00	3.50	2.00
(43)	Mickey Mantle	150.00	75.00	45.00
(44)	Jim Wynn	7.00	3.50	2.00
	Box	150.00	75.00	45.00
12	Mike McCormick (Fielding the Pitcher's Position)	20.00	10.00	6.00
(45)	Bob Clemente	40.00	20.00	12.00
(46)	Al Downing	9.00	4.50	2.75
(47)	Don Mincher	7.00	3.50	2.00
(48)	Tony Perez	15.00	7.50	4.50
	Box	200.00	100.00	60.00
13	Frank Crosetti (Coaching)	35.00	17.50	10.50
(49)	Rod Carew	40.00	20.00	12.00
(50)	Willie McCovey	25.00	12.50	7.50
(51)	Ron Swoboda	7.00	3.50	2.00
(52)	Earl Wilson	7.00	3.50	2.00
	Box	150.00	75.00	45.00
14	Willie Mays (Playing the Outfield)	50.00	25.00	15.00
(53)	Richie Allen	12.00	6.00	3.50
(54)	Gary Peters	7.00	3.50	2.00
(55)	Rusty Staub	10.00	5.00	3.00
(56)	Billy Williams	20.00	10.00	6.00
	Box	200.00	100.00	60.00
15	Lou Brock (Base Running)	40.00	20.00	12.00
(57)	Tommie Agee	5.00	2.50	1.50
(58)	Don Drysdale	10.00	5.00	3.00
(59)	Pete Rose	70.00	35.00	21.00
(60)	Ron Santo	5.00	2.50	1.50

**Regional interest may affect
the value of a card.**

1969 Bazooka

Issued over a two-year span, the 1969-70 Bazooka set utilized the box bottom and sides. The box bottom, entitled "Baseball Extra," features an historic event in baseball. The bottom panels are numbered 1 through 12. Two "All-Time Great" cards were located on each side of the box. These cards are not numbered and have no distinct borders. Individual cards measure 1-1/4" by 3-1/8"; the "Baseball Extra" panels measure 3" by 6-1/4". The prices in the checklist that follows are for complete boxes only. Cards/panels cut from the boxes have a greatly reduced value - 25 per cent of the complete box prices for all cut pieces.

		NR MT	EX	VG
	Complete Box Set:	250.00	125.00	75.00
	Common Box:	15.00	7.50	4.50
1	No-Hit Duel By Toney And Vaughn (Mordecai Brown, Ty Cobb, Willie Keeler, Eddie Plank)	18.00	9.00	5.50
2	Alexander Conquers Yanks (Rogers Hornsby, Ban Johnson, Walter Johnson, Al Simmons)	15.00	7.50	4.50
3	Yanks Lazzeri Sets A.L. Hit Record (Hugh Duffy, Lou Gehrig, Tris Speaker, Joe Tinker)	18.00	9.00	5.50
4	Home Run Almost Hit Out Of Stadium (Grover Alexander, Chief Bender, Christy Mathewson, Cy Young)	15.00	7.50	4.50
5	Four Consecutive Homers By Gehrig (Frank Chance, Mickey Cochrane, John McGraw, Babe Ruth)	30.00	15.00	9.00
6	No-Hit Game By Walter Johnson (Johnny Evers, Walter Johnson, John McGraw, Cy Young)	15.00	7.50	4.50
7	Twelve RBI's By Bottomley (Ty Cobb, Eddie Collins, Johnny Evers, Lou Gehrig)	20.00	10.00	6.00
8	Ty Ties Record (Mickey Cochrane, Eddie Collins, Met Ott, Honus Wagner)	15.00	7.50	4.50
9	Babe Ruth Hits Three Homers In Game (Cap Anson, Jack Chesbro, Al Simmons, Tris Speaker)	25.00	12.50	7.50
10	Calls Shot In Series Game (Nap Lajoie, Connie Mack, Rabbit Maranville, Ed Walsh)	25.00	12.50	7.50
11	Ruth's 60th Homer Sets New Record (Frank Chance, Nap Lajoie, Mel Ott, Joe Tinker)	25.00	12.50	7.50
12	Double Shutout By Ed Reulbach (Rogers Hornsby, Rabbit Maranville, Christy Mathewson, Honus Wagner)	15.00	7.50	4.50

1971 Bazooka Unnumbered Set

This Bazooka set was issued in 1971, consisting of 36 full-color, blank-backed, unnumbered cards. Issued in panels of three on the bottoms of Bazooka bubble gum boxes, individual cards measure 2" by 2-5/8" whereas complete panels measure 2-5/8" by 5-5/16". In the checklist that follows, the cards have been numbered by panel using the name of the player who appears on the left portion of the panel.

		NR MT	EX	VG
	Complete Panel Set:	375.00	187.00	112.00
	Complete Singles Set:	225.00	112.00	67.00
	Common Panel:	10.00	5.00	3.00
	Common Single Player:	1.50	.70	.45
1	Panel	30.00	15.00	9.00
(1)	Tommie Agee	1.50	.70	.45
(2)	Harmon Killebrew	7.00	3.50	2.00
2	Panel	40.00	20.00	12.00
(3)	Reggie Jackson	20.00	10.00	6.00
3	Panel	25.00	12.50	7.50
(4)	Bert Campaneris	1.50	.70	.45
4	Panel	25.00	12.50	7.50
(5)	Pete Rose	25.00	12.50	7.50
5	Panel	15.00	7.50	4.50
(6)	Orlando Cepeda	3.00	1.50	.90
6	Panel	30.00	15.00	9.00
(7)	Rico Carty	2.00	1.00	.60
7	Panel	15.00	7.50	4.50
(8)	Johnny Bench	20.00	10.00	6.00
8	Panel	30.00	15.00	9.00
(9)	Tommy Harper	1.50	.70	.45
9	Panel	15.00	7.50	4.50
(10)	Bill Freehan	2.00	1.00	.60
10	Panel	10.00	5.00	3.00
(11)	Roberto Clemente	20.00	10.00	6.00
11	Panel	30.00	15.00	9.00
(12)	Claude Osteen	1.50	.70	.45
12	Panel	15.00	7.50	4.50
(13)	Jim Fregosi	2.00	1.00	.60
(14)	Billy Williams	6.00	3.00	1.75
(15)	Dave McNally	1.50	.70	.45
(16)	Randy Hundley	1.50	.70	.45
(17)	Willie Mays	20.00	10.00	4.50
(18)	Jim Hunter	6.00	3.00	1.75
(19)	Juan Marichal	6.00	3.00	1.75
(20)	Frank Howard	3.00	1.50	.90
(21)	Bill Melton	1.50	.70	.45
(22)	Willie McCovey	7.00	3.50	2.00
(23)	Carl Yastrzemski	12.00	6.00	3.50
(24)	Clyde Wright	1.50	.70	.45
(25)	Jim Merritt	1.50	.70	.45
(26)	Luis Aparicio	6.00	3.00	1.75
(27)	Bobby Murcer	3.00	1.50	.90
(28)	Rico Petrocelli	2.00	1.00	.60
(29)	Sam McDowell	2.00	1.00	.60
(30)	Clarence Gaston	1.50	.70	.45
(31)	Brooks Robinson	6.50	3.25	2.00
(32)	Hank Aaron	20.00	10.00	4.50
(33)	Larry Dierker	1.50	.70	.45
(34)	Rusty Staub	2.00	1.00	.60
(35)	Bob Gibson	7.00	3.50	2.00
(36)	Amos Otis	1.50	.70	.45

		NR MT	EX	VG
	Complete Panel Set:	1000.00	500.00	300.00
	Complete Singles Set:	550.00	275.00	165.00
	Common Panel:	10.00	5.00	3.00
	Common Single Player:	2.00	1.00	.60
	Panel	150.00	75.00	45.00
1	Tim McCarver	15.00	7.50	4.50
2	Frank Robinson	45.00	23.00	13.50
3	Bill Mazeroski	15.00	7.50	4.50
	Panel	45.00	22.00	13.50
4	Willie McCovey	12.00	6.00	3.50
5	Carl Yastrzemski	20.00	10.00	6.00
6	Clyde Wright	2.00	1.00	.60
	Panel	20.00	10.00	6.00
7	Jim Merritt	2.00	1.00	.60
8	Luis Aparicio	9.00	4.50	2.75
9	Bobby Murcer	5.00	2.50	1.50
	Panel	10.00	5.00	3.00
10	Rico Petrocelli	3.00	1.50	.90
11	Sam McDowell	3.00	1.50	.90
12	Clarence Gaston	2.00	1.00	.60
	Panel	150.00	75.00	45.00
13	Ferguson Jenkins	20.00	10.00	6.00
14	Al Kaline	45.00	23.00	13.50
15	Ken Harrelson	15.00	7.50	4.50
	Panel	45.00	22.00	13.50
16	Tommie Agee	2.00	1.00	.60
17	Harmon Killebrew	12.00	6.00	3.50
18	Reggie Jackson	20.00	10.00	6.00
	Panel	20.00	10.00	6.00
19	Juan Marichal	9.00	4.50	2.75
20	Frank Howard	5.00	2.50	1.50
21	Bill Melton	2.00	1.00	.60
	Panel	55.00	27.00	16.50
22	Brooks Robinson	15.00	7.50	4.50
23	Hank Aaron	30.00	15.00	9.00
24	Larry Dierker	2.00	1.00	.60
	Panel	20.00	10.00	6.00
25	Jim Fregosi	3.00	1.50	.90
26	Billy Williams	10.00	5.00	3.00
27	Dave McNally	2.00	1.00	.60
	Panel	30.00	15.00	9.00
28	Rico Carty	3.00	1.50	.90
29	Johnny Bench	18.00	9.00	5.50
30	Tommy Harper	2.00	1.00	.60
	Panel	60.00	30.00	18.00
31	Bert Campaneris	2.00	1.00	.60
32	Pete Rose	35.00	17.50	10.50
33	Orlando Cepeda	6.00	3.00	1.75
	Panel	45.00	22.00	13.50
34	Maury Wills	6.00	3.00	1.75
35	Tom Seaver	20.00	10.00	6.00
36	Tony Oliva	6.00	3.00	1.75
	Panel	30.00	15.00	9.00
37	Bill Freehan	3.00	1.50	.90
38	Roberto Clemente	25.00	12.50	7.50
39	Claude Osteen	2.00	1.00	.60
	Panel	20.00	10.00	6.00
40	Rusty Staub	3.00	1.50	.90
41	Bob Gibson	10.00	5.00	3.00
42	Amos Otis	2.00	1.00	.60
	Panel	125.00	62.00	37.00
43	Jim Wynn	10.00	5.00	3.00
44	Rich Allen	18.00	9.00	5.50
45	Tony Conigliaro	10.00	5.00	3.00
	Panel	40.00	20.00	12.00
46	Randy Hundley	2.00	1.00	.60
47	Willie Mays	30.00	15.00	9.00
48	Jim Hunter	9.00	4.50	2.75

GRADING GUIDE

Mint (MT): A perfect card. Well-centered with all corners sharp and square. No creases, stains, edge nicks, surface marks, yellowing or fading.

Near Mint (NM): A nearly perfect card. At first glance, a NM card appears to be perfect. May be slightly off-center. No surface marks, creases or loss of gloss.

Excellent (EX): Corners are still fairly sharp with only moderate wear. Borders may be off-center. No creases or stains on fronts or backs, but may show slight loss of surface luster.

Very Good (VG): Shows obvious handling. May have rounded corners, minor creases, major gum or wax stains. No major creases, tape marks, writing, etc.

Good (G): A well-worn card, but exhibits no intentional damage. May have major or multiple creases. Corners may be rounded well beyond card border.

1971 Bazooka Numbered Set

The 1971 Bazooka numbered set is a proof set produced by the company after the unnumbered set was released. The set is comprised of 48 cards as opposed to the 36 cards which make up the unnumbered set. Issued in panels of three, the nine cards not found in the unnumbered set are #'s 1-3, 13-15 and 43-45. All other cards are identical to those found in the unnumbered set. The cards, which measure 2" by 2-5/8", contain full-color photos and are blank-backed.

1988 Bazooka

This 22-card set from Topps marks the first

Bazooka issue since 1971. Full-color player photos are bordered in white, with the player name printed on a red, white and blue bubble gum box in the lower right corner. Flip sides are also red, white and blue, printed vertically. A large, but faint, Bazooka logo backs the Topps baseball logo, team name, card number, player's name and position, followed by batting records, personal information and brief career highlights. Cards were sold inside specially marked 59¢ and 79¢ Bazooka gum and candy boxes, one card per box.

		MT	NR MT	EX
Complete Set:		8.00	6.00	3.25
Common Player:		.20	.15	.08
1	George Bell	.25	.20	.10
2	Wade Boggs	.70	.50	.30
3	Jose Canseco	1.00	.70	.40
4	Roger Clemens	.60	.45	.25
5	Vince Coleman	.20	.15	.08
6	Eric Davis	.30	.25	.12
7	Tony Fernandez	.20	.15	.08
8	Dwight Gooden	.60	.45	.25
9	Tony Gwynn	.40	.30	.15
10	Wally Joyner	.40	.30	.15
11	Don Mattingly	1.50	1.25	.60
12	Willie McGee	.20	.15	.08
13	Mark McGwire	.40	.30	.15
14	Kirby Puckett	.50	.40	.20
15	Tim Raines	.30	.25	.12
16	Dave Righetti	.20	.15	.08
17	Cal Ripken	.50	.40	.20
18	Juan Samuel	.20	.15	.08
19	Ryne Sandberg	.50	.40	.20
20	Benny Santiago	.20	.15	.08
21	Darryl Strawberry	.60	.45	.25
22	Todd Worrell	.20	.15	.08

1989 Bazooka

This 22-card set marks the second consecutive year Bazooka has issued following a 17-year absence. Full color action and posed player shots are bordered by a white frame. Other features of this standard-size includes a "Shining Stars" logo across the top, a yellow stripe enclosing the player's name at the bottom, and the Topps/Bazooka logo in the bottom right corner. Flip sides are printed in red and blue, and contain a large but faint Bazooka logo, the Topps baseball logo, card number, team name, player's name and position, followed by batting or pitching records, personal information and brief highlights. Topps produced this 22-card set in 1989 to be included (one card per box) in specially-marked boxes of its Bazooka brand bubblegum. The player photos have the words "Shining Star" along the top, while the player's name appears along the bottom of the card, along with the Topps Bazooka logo in the lower right corner. The cards are numbered alphabetically.

	MT	NR MT	EX
Complete Set:	5.00	3.75	2.00
Common Player:	.15	.11	.06

		MT	NR MT	EX
1	Tim Belcher	.15	.11	.06
2	Damon Berryhill	.15	.11	.06
3	Wade Boggs	.60	.45	.25
4	Jay Buhner	.15	.11	.06
5	Jose Canseco	.80	.60	.30
6	Vince Coleman	.15	.11	.06
7	Cecil Espy	.15	.11	.06
8	Dave Gallagher	.15	.11	.06
9	Ron Gant	.35	.25	.14
10	Kirk Gibson	.15	.11	.06
11	Paul Gibson	.15	.11	.06
12	Mark Grace	.60	.45	.25
13	Tony Gwynn	.35	.25	.14
14	Rickey Henderson	.40	.30	.15
15	Orel Hershiser	.25	.20	.10
16	Gregg Jefferies	.50	.40	.20
17	Ricky Jordan	.25	.20	.10
18	Chris Sabo	.15	.11	.06
19	Gary Sheffield	.50	.40	.20
20	Darryl Strawberry	.50	.40	.20
21	Frank Viola	.20	.15	.08
22	Walt Weiss	.15	.11	.06

1990 Bazooka

For the second consecutive year, Bazooka entitled its set "Shining Stars." Full color action and posed player shots are featured on the card fronts. The flip sides feature player statistics in a style much like the cards from the previous two Bazooka issues. Unlike the past two releases, the cards are not numbered alphabetically. The cards measure 2-1/2" by 3-1/2" in size and 22 cards complete the set.

		MT	NR MT	EX
Complete Set:		7.00	5.25	2.75
Common Player:		.15	.11	.06
1	Kevin Mitchell	.30	.25	.12
2	Robin Yount	.20	.15	.08
3	Mark Davis	.15	.11	.06
4	Bret Saberhagen	.15	.11	.06
5	Fred McGriff	.20	.15	.08
6	Tony Gwynn	.20	.15	.08
7	Kirby Puckett	.30	.25	.12
8	Vince Coleman	.15	.11	.06
9	Rickey Henderson	.40	.30	.15
10	Ben McDonald	.50	.40	.20
11	Gregg Olson	.20	.15	.08
12	Todd Zeile	.30	.25	.12
13	Carlos Martinez	.20	.15	.08
14	Gregg Jefferies	.40	.30	.15
15	Craig Worthington	.15	.11	.06
16	Gary Sheffield	.40	.30	.15
17	Greg Briley	.15	.11	.06
18	Ken Griffey, Jr.	2.00	1.50	.80
19	Jerome Walton	.20	.15	.08
20	Bob Geren	.15	.11	.06
21	Tom Gordon	.20	.15	.08
22	Jim Abbott	.20	.15	.08

The values quoted are intended to reflect the market price.

1991 Bazooka

For the third consecutive year Bazooka entitled its set "Shining Stars." The cards are styled like the 1990 issue, but include the Topps "40th Anniversary" logo. The 1991 issue is considered much scarcer than the previous releases. The cards measure 2-1/2" by 3-1/2" in size and 22 cards complete the set.

		MT	NR MT	EX
Complete Set:		15.00	11.00	6.00
Common Player:		.30	.25	.12
1	Barry Bonds	.50	.40	.20
2	Rickey Henderson	.50	.40	.20
3	Bob Welch	.30	.25	.12
4	Doug Drabek	.40	.30	.15
5	Alex Fernandez	.80	.60	.30
6	Jose Offerman	.60	.45	.25
7	Frank Thomas	3.00	2.25	1.25
8	Cecil Fielder	.60	.45	.25
9	Ryne Sandberg	.60	.45	.25
10	George Brett	.40	.30	.15
11	Willie McGee	.30	.25	.12
12	Vince Coleman	.30	.25	.12
13	Hal Morris	.60	.45	.25
14	Delino DeShields	.50	.40	.20
15	Robin Ventura	.70	.50	.30
16	Jeff Huson	.30	.25	.12
17	Felix Jose	.50	.40	.20
18	Dave Justice	.60	.45	.25
19	Larry Walker	.35	.25	.14
20	Sandy Alomar, Jr.	.40	.30	.15
21	Kevin Appier	.30	.25	.12
22	Scott Radinsky	.30	.25	.12

1958 Bell Brand Dodgers

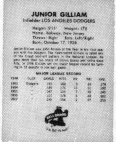

Celebrating the Dodgers first year of play in Los Angeles, Bell Brand inserted ten different unnumbered cards in their bags of potato chips and corn chips. The cards, which measure 3" by 4", have a sepia-colored photo inside a 1/4" green woodgrain border. The card backs feature statistical and biographical information and include the Bell Brand logo. Roy Campanella is included in the set despite a career-ending car wreck that prevented him from ever playing in Los Angeles.

		NR MT	EX	VG
Complete Set:		1200.00	600.00	360.00
Common Player:		40.00	20.00	12.00
1	Roy Campanella	150.00	75.00	45.00
2	Gino Cimoli	125.00	62.00	37.00
3	Don Drysdale	90.00	45.00	27.00
4	Junior Gilliam	40.00	20.00	12.00
5	Gil Hodges	90.00	45.00	27.00
6	Sandy Koufax	150.00	75.00	45.00
7	Johnny Podres	125.00	62.00	37.00
8	Pee Wee Reese	90.00	45.00	27.00
9	Duke Snider	300.00	150.00	90.00
10	Don Zimmer	40.00	20.00	12.00

1960 Bell Brand Dodgers

Bell Brand returned with a baseball card set in 1960 that was entirely different in style to their previous effort. The cards, which measure 2-1/2" by 3-1/2", feature beautiful, full-color photos. The backs carry a short player biography, the 1960 Dodgers home schedule, and the Bell Brand logo. Twenty different numbered cards were inserted in various size bags of potato chips and corn chips. Although sealed in cellophane, the cards were still subject to grease stains. Cards #'s 6, 12 and 18 are the scarcest in the set.

		NR MT	EX	VG
Complete Set:		700.00	350.00	210.00
Common Player:		20.00	10.00	6.00
1	Norm Larker	20.00	10.00	6.00
2	Duke Snider	70.00	35.00	21.00
3	Danny McDevitt	20.00	10.00	6.00
4	Jim Gilliam	25.00	12.50	7.50
5	Rip Repulski	20.00	10.00	6.00
6	Clem Labine	100.00	50.00	30.00
7	John Roseboro	20.00	10.00	6.00
8	Carl Furillo	25.00	12.50	7.50
9	Sandy Koufax	125.00	62.00	37.00
10	Joe Pignatano	20.00	10.00	6.00
11	Chuck Essegian	20.00	10.00	6.00
12	John Klippstein	80.00	40.00	25.00
13	Ed Roebuck	20.00	10.00	6.00
14	Don Demeter	20.00	10.00	6.00
15	Roger Craig	30.00	15.00	9.00
16	Stan Williams	20.00	10.00	6.00
17	Don Zimmer	25.00	12.50	7.50
18	Walter Alston	125.00	62.00	37.00
19	Johnny Podres	25.00	12.50	7.50
20	Maury Wills	30.00	15.00	9.00

1961 Bell Brand Dodgers

The 1961 Bell Brand set is identical in format to the previous year, although printed on thinner stock. Cards can be distinguished from the 1960 set by the 1961 schedule on the backs. The cards, which measure 2-7/16" by 3-1/2", are numbered by the player's uniform number. Twenty different cards

Norm Larker
INFIELDER — L.A. DODGERS

		NR MT	EX	VG
12	Tom Davis	12.00	6.00	3.50
16	Ron Perranoski	12.00	6.00	3.50
19	Jim Gilliam	15.00	7.50	4.50
20	Daryl Spencer	12.00	6.00	3.50
22	John Podres	15.00	7.50	4.50
24	Walter Alston	30.00	15.00	9.00
25	Frank Howard	15.00	7.50	4.50
30	Maury Wills	30.00	15.00	9.00
32	Sandy Koufax	80.00	40.00	25.00
34	Norm Sherry	12.00	6.00	3.50
37	Ed Roebuck	12.00	6.00	3.50
40	Stan Williams	12.00	6.00	3.50
51	Larry Sherry	12.00	6.00	3.50
53	Don Drysdale	50.00	25.00	15.00
56	Lee Walls	12.00	6.00	3.50

were inserted into various size potato chip and corn chip packages, each card being sealed in a cellophane wrapper.

		NR MT	EX	VG
Complete Set:		375.00	185.00	110.00
Common Player:		12.00	6.00	3.50
3	Willie Davis	15.00	7.50	4.50
4	Duke Snider	60.00	30.00	18.00
5	Norm Larker	12.00	6.00	3.50
8	John Roseboro	12.00	6.00	3.50
9	Wally Moon	12.00	6.00	3.50
11	Bob Lillis	12.00	6.00	3.50
12	Tom Davis	12.00	6.00	3.50
14	Gil Hodges	30.00	15.00	9.00
16	Don Demeter	12.00	6.00	3.50
19	Jim Gilliam	15.00	7.50	4.50
22	John Podres	15.00	7.50	4.50
24	Walter Alston	30.00	15.00	9.00
30	Maury Wills	30.00	15.00	9.00
32	Sandy Koufax	80.00	40.00	25.00
34	Norm Sherry	12.00	6.00	3.50
37	Ed Roebuck	12.00	6.00	3.50
38	Roger Craig	15.00	7.50	4.50
40	Stan Williams	12.00	6.00	3.50
43	Charlie Neal	12.00	6.00	3.50
51	Larry Sherry	12.00	6.00	3.50

1962 Bell Brand Dodgers

WALLY MOON
OUTFIELDER — L.A. DODGERS

The 1962 Bell Brand set is identical in style to the previous two years and cards can be distinguished by the 1962 Dodgers schedule on the back. The set consists of 20 cards, each measuring 2-7/16" by 3-1/2" and numbered by the player's uniform number. Printed on glossy stock, the 1962 set was less susceptible to grease stains.

		NR MT	EX	VG
Complete Set:		375.00	185.00	110.00
Common Player:		12.00	6.00	3.50
3	Willie Davis	15.00	7.50	4.50
4	Duke Snider	60.00	30.00	18.00
6	Ron Fairly	12.00	6.00	3.50
8	John Roseboro	12.00	6.00	3.50
9	Wally Moon	12.00	6.00	3.50

1951 Berk Ross

Entitled "Hit Parade of Champions," the 1951 Berk Ross set features 72 stars of various sports. The cards, which measure 2-1/16" by 2-1/2" and have tinted color photographs, were issued in boxes containing two-card panels. The issue is divided into four subsets with the first ten players of each series being baseball players. Only the baseball players are listed in the checklist that follows. Complete panels are valued 50 per cent higher than the sum of the individual cards.

		NR MT	EX	VG
Complete Set:		1200.00	600.00	360.00
Common Player:		12.00	6.00	3.50
1-1	Al Rosen	20.00	10.00	6.00
1-2	Bob Lemon	20.00	10.00	6.00
1-3	Phil Rizzuto	50.00	25.00	15.00
1-4	Hank Bauer	30.00	15.00	9.00
1-5	Billy Johnson	13.00	6.50	4.00
1-6	Jerry Coleman	13.00	6.50	4.00
1-7	Johnny Mize	30.00	15.00	7.50
1-8	Dom DiMaggio	30.00	15.00	9.00
1-9	Richie Ashburn	15.00	7.50	4.50
1-10	Del Ennis	13.00	6.50	4.00
2-1	Stan Musial	300.00	150.00	90.00
2-2	Warren Spahn	30.00	15.00	9.00
2-3	Tommy Henrich	15.00	7.50	4.50
2-4	Larry "Yogi" Berra	225.00	112.00	67.00
2-5	Joe DiMaggio	400.00	200.00	120.00
2-6	Bobby Brown	15.00	7.50	4.50
2-7	Granville Hamner	12.00	6.00	3.50
2-8	Willie Jones	12.00	6.00	3.50
2-9	Stanley Lopata	12.00	6.00	3.50
2-10	Mike Goliat	12.00	6.00	3.50
3-1	Ralph Kiner	30.00	15.00	9.00
3-2	Billy Goodman	12.00	6.00	3.50
3-3	Allie Reynolds	15.00	7.50	4.50
3-4	Vic Raschi	15.00	7.50	4.50
3-5	Joe Page	13.00	6.50	4.00
3-6	Eddie Lopat	15.00	7.50	4.50
3-7	Andy Seminick	12.00	6.00	3.50
3-8	Dick Sisler	12.00	6.00	3.50
3-9	Eddie Waitkus	12.00	6.00	3.50
3-10	Ken Heintzelman	12.00	6.00	3.50
4-1	Gene Woodling	15.00	7.50	4.50
4-2	Cliff Mapes	13.00	6.50	4.00
4-3	Fred Sanford	13.00	6.50	4.00
4-4	Tommy Bryne	13.00	6.50	4.00
4-5	Eddie (Whitey) Ford	125.00	62.00	37.00

		NR MT	EX	VG
4-6	Jim Konstanty	13.00	6.50	4.00
4-7	Russ Meyer	12.00	6.00	3.50
4-8	Robin Roberts	30.00	15.00	9.00
4-9	Curt Simmons	13.00	6.50	4.00
4-10	Sam Jethroe	30.00	15.00	9.00

1952 Berk Ross

Although the card size is different (2" by 3"), the style of the fronts and backs of the 1952 Berk Ross set is similar to the previous year's effort. Seventy-two unnumbered cards make up the set. Rizzuto is included twice in the set and the Blackwell and Fox cards have transposed backs. The cards were issued individually rather than as two-card panels like in 1951.

		NR MT	EX	VG
Complete Set:		4500.00	2250.00	1350.
Common Player:		12.00	6.00	3.50
(1)	Richie Ashburn	30.00	15.00	9.00
(2)	Hank Bauer	18.00	9.00	5.50
(3)	Larry "Yogi" Berra	100.00	50.00	30.00
(4)	Ewell Blackwell (photo actually Nelson Fox)	18.00	9.00	5.50
(5)	Bobby Brown	18.00	9.00	5.50
(6)	Jim Busby	12.00	6.00	3.50
(7)	Roy Campanella	125.00	56.00	35.00
(8)	Chico Carrasquel	12.00	6.00	3.50
(9)	Jerry Coleman	15.00	7.50	4.50
(10)	Joe Collins	15.00	7.50	4.50
(11)	Alvin Dark	15.00	7.50	4.50
(12)	Dom DiMaggio	18.00	9.00	5.50
(13)	Joe DiMaggio	700.00	350.00	200.00
(14)	Larry Doby	18.00	9.00	5.50
(15)	Bobby Doerr	35.00	17.50	10.50
(16)	Bob Elliot (Elliott)	12.00	6.00	3.50
(17)	Del Ennis	12.00	6.00	3.50
(18)	Ferris Fain	12.00	6.00	3.50
(19)	Bob Feller	75.00	38.00	23.00
(20)	Nelson Fox (photo actually Ewell Blackwell)	18.00	9.00	5.50
(21)	Ned Garver	12.00	6.00	3.50
(22)	Clint Hartung	12.00	6.00	3.50
(23)	Jim Hearn	12.00	6.00	3.50
(24)	Gil Hodges	50.00	30.00	15.00
(25)	Monte Irvin	30.00	15.00	9.00
(26)	Larry Jansen	12.00	6.00	3.50
(27)	George Kell	25.00	12.50	7.50
(28)	Sheldon Jones	12.00	6.00	3.50
(29)	Monte Kennedy	12.00	6.00	3.50
(30)	Ralph Kiner	40.00	20.00	12.00
(31)	Dave Koslo	12.00	6.00	3.50
(32)	Bob Kuzava	15.00	7.50	4.50
(33)	Bob Lemon	30.00	15.00	9.00
(34)	Whitey Lockman	12.00	6.00	3.50
(35)	Eddie Lopat	18.00	9.00	5.50
(36)	Sal Maglie	15.00	7.50	4.50
(37)	Mickey Mantle	1200.00	600.00	360.00
(38)	Billy Martin	50.00	30.00	15.00
(39)	Willie Mays	500.00	250.00	150.00
(40)	Gil McDougal (McDougald)	18.00	9.00	5.50
(41)	Orestes Minoso	15.00	7.50	4.50
(42)	Johnny Mize	40.00	20.00	12.00
(43)	Tom Morgan	15.00	7.50	4.50
(44)	Don Mueller	12.00	6.00	3.50
(45)	Stan Musial	400.00	200.00	120.00

		NR MT	EX	VG
(46)	Don Newcombe	18.00	9.00	5.50
(47)	Ray Noble	12.00	6.00	3.50
(48)	Joe Ostrowski	15.00	7.50	4.50
(49)	Mel Parnell	12.00	6.00	3.50
(50)	Vic Raschi	18.00	9.00	5.50
(51)	Pee Wee Reese	65.00	33.00	20.00
(52)	Allie Reynolds	18.00	9.00	5.50
(53)	Bill Rigney	12.00	6.00	3.50
(54)	Phil Rizzuto (bunting)	55.00	28.00	16.50
(55)	Phil Rizzuto (swinging)	55.00	28.00	16.50
(56)	Robin Roberts	30.00	15.00	9.00
(57)	Eddie Robinson	12.00	6.00	3.50
(58)	Jackie Robinson	200.00	100.00	60.00
(59)	Elwin "Preacher" Roe	15.00	7.50	4.50
(60)	Johnny Sain	15.00	7.50	4.50
(61)	Albert "Red" Schoendienst	30.00	15.00	9.00
(62)	Duke Snider	125.00	56.00	35.00
(63)	George Spencer	12.00	6.00	3.50
(64)	Eddie Stanky	15.00	7.50	4.50
(65)	Henry Thompson	12.00	6.00	3.50
(66)	Bobby Thomson	18.00	9.00	5.50
(67)	Vic Wertz	12.00	6.00	3.50
(68)	Waldon Westlake	12.00	6.00	3.50
(69)	Wes Westrum	12.00	6.00	3.50
(70)	Ted Williams	400.00	200.00	120.00
(71)	Gene Woodling	18.00	9.00	5.50
(72)	Gus Zernial	12.00	6.00	3.50

1986 Big League Chew

The 1986 Big Leaugue Chew set consists of 12 cards featuring the players who have hit 500 or more career home runs. The cards, which measure 2-1/2" by 3-1/2", were inserted in specially marked packages of Big League Chew, the shredded bubble gum developed by former major leaguer Jim Bouton. The set is entitled "Home Run Legends" and was available through a write-in offer on the package. Recent-day players in the set are shown in color photos, while the older sluggers are pictured in black and white.

		MT	NR MT	EX
Complete Set:		6.00	4.50	2.50
Common Player:		.40	.30	.15
1	Hank Aaron	.60	.45	.25
2	Babe Ruth	1.00	.70	.40
3	Willie Mays	.60	.45	.25
4	Frank Robinson	.40	.30	.15
5	Harmon Killebrew	.40	.30	.15
6	Mickey Mantle	1.25	.90	.50
7	Jimmie Foxx	.40	.30	.15
8	Ted Williams	.70	.50	.30
9	Ernie Banks	.40	.30	.15
10	Eddie Mathews	.40	.30	.15
11	Mel Ott	.40	.30	.15
12	500-HR Group Card	.50	.40	.20

1991 Bleachers Frank Thomas

This limited edition three-card set features 23-karat gold cards. The photos feature Frank Thomas at different stages of his baseball career before the big leagues. Production was limited to 10,000 sets and 1,500 uncut strips. All are numbered and feature a gold facsimile autograph on the back.

	MT	NR MT	EX
Complete Set:	30.00	22.00	12.00
Common Player:	8.00	6.00	3.25
1 Frank Thomas (Auburn Tigers)	8.00	6.00	3.25
2 Frank Thomas (Sarasota White Sox)			
	8.00	6.00	3.25
3 Frank Thomas (Birmingham Barons)			
	8.00	6.00	3.25

1992 Bleachers Ken Griffey, Jr.

Young superstar Ken Griffey, Jr. is honored in this three-card set featuring him at different stages of his baseball career. The 23-karat gold cards feature full-color photos and a facsimile autograph on the back. Production was limited to 10,000 cut sets and 1,500 uncut strips.

	MT	NR MT	EX
Complete Set:	30.00	22.00	12.00
Common Player:	8.00	6.00	3.25
1 Ken Griffey, Jr. (Moeller High School)			
	8.00	6.00	3.25
2 Ken Griffey, Jr. (Bellingham Mariners)			
	8.00	6.00	3.25
3 Ken Griffey, Jr. (San Bernadino Spirit)			
	8.00	6.00	3.25

1992 Bleachers David Justice

Atlanta Brave slugger David Justice is the subject of this three card 23-karat gold set. The cards depict Justice at different stages of his baseball career. Like the other Bleachers issues, production was limited to 10,000 cut card sets and 1,500 uncut strips.

	MT	NR MT	EX
Complete Set:	25.00	18.00	9.00
Common Player:	7.00	5.25	2.75

		MT	NR MT	EX
1	David Justice (Durham Bulls)	7.00	5.25	2.75
2	David Justice (Greenville Braves)	7.00	5.25	2.75
3	David Justice (Richmond Braves)	7.00	5.25	2.75

1987 Boardwalk And Baseball

The 33-card "Top Run Makers" set was produced by Topps for distribution by the recreation amusement park "Boardwalk and Baseball," located near Orlando, Fla. The cards, which measure 2-1/2" by 3-1/2", feature fronts which contain full-color player photos and the park's logo (B/B). The card backs are printed in black and pink on white stock and offer personal data and career statistics. The set was issued in a specially designed box.

		MT	NR MT	EX
Complete Set:		6.00	4.50	2.50
Common Player:		.09	.07	.04
1	Mike Schmidt	.50	.40	.20
2	Eddie Murray	.35	.25	.14
3	Dale Murphy	.40	.30	.15
4	Dave Winfield	.30	.25	.12
5	Jim Rice	.30	.25	.12
6	Cecil Cooper	.12	.09	.05
7	Dwight Evans	.15	.11	.06
8	Rickey Henderson	.40	.30	.15
9	Robin Yount	.35	.25	.14
10	Andre Dawson	.25	.20	.10
11	Gary Carter	.35	.25	.14
12	Keith Hernandez	.30	.25	.12
13	George Brett	.40	.30	.15
14	Bill Buckner	.09	.07	.04
15	Tony Armas	.09	.07	.04
16	Harold Baines	.15	.11	.06
17	Don Baylor	.12	.09	.05
18	Steve Garvey	.35	.25	.14
19	Lance Parrish	.20	.15	.08
20	Dave Parker	.15	.11	.06
21	Buddy Bell	.09	.07	.04
22	Cal Ripken	.60	.45	.25
23	Bob Horner	.12	.09	.05
24	Tim Raines	.30	.25	.12
25	Jack Clark	.15	.11	.06
26	Leon Durham	.09	.07	.04
27	Pedro Guerrero	.15	.11	.06
28	Kent Hrbek	.15	.11	.06

		MT	NR MT	EX
29	Kirk Gibson	.20	.15	.08
30	Ryne Sandberg	.60	.45	.25
31	Wade Boggs	.70	.50	.30
32	Don Mattingly	1.00	.70	.40
33	Darryl Strawberry	.60	.45	.25

1987 Bohemian Hearth Bread Padres

Bohemian Hearth Bread Company of San Diego issued a 22-card set highlighting the San Diego Padres. Produced in conjunction with Mike Schechter Associates, the cards are the standard 2-1/2" by 3-1/2" size. The card fronts contain a full-color photo encompassed by a yellow border. The Bohemian Hearth Bread logo is located in the upper left corner of the card. The card backs are printed in light brown ink on a cream color card stock and carry player personal and statistical information.

		MT	NR MT	EX
	Complete Set:	50.00	37.50	20.00
	Common Player:	.50	.40	.20
1	Garry Templeton	1.25	.90	.50
4	Jose Cora	.60	.45	.25
5	Randy Ready	.50	.40	.20
6	Steve Garvey	5.00	3.75	2.00
7	Kevin Mitchell	6.00	4.50	2.50
8	John Kruk	4.00	3.00	1.50
9	Benito Santiago	8.00	6.00	3.25
10	Larry Bowa	1.00	.70	.40
11	Tim Flannery	.50	.40	.20
14	Carmelo Martinez	.50	.40	.20
16	Marvell Wynne	.50	.40	.20
19	Tony Gwynn	12.00	9.00	4.75
21	James Steels	.50	.40	.20
22	Stan Jefferson	1.00	.70	.40
30	Eric Show	1.00	.70	.40
31	Ed Whitson	1.00	.70	.40
34	Storm Davis	1.00	.70	.40
37	Craig Lefferts	.80	.60	.30
40	Andy Hawkins	1.00	.70	.40
41	Lance McCullers	.50	.40	.20
43	Dave Dravecky	2.00	1.50	.80
54	Rich Gossage	2.25	1.75	.90

1948 Bowman

Bowman Gum Co.'s premiere set was produced in 1948, making it one of the first major issues of the post-war period. Forty-eight black and white cards comprise the set, with each card measuring 2-1/16" by 2-1/2" in size. The card backs, printed in black ink on grey stock, include the card number and the player's name, team, position, and a short biography. Twelve cards (#'s 7, 8, 13, 16, 20, 22, 24, 26, 29, 30 and 34) were printed in short supply when they were removed from the 36-card printing sheet to make room for the set's high numbers (#'s 37-48). These 24 cards command a higher price than the remaining

cards in the set.

		NR MT	EX	VG
	Complete Set:	3500.00	1750.00	1050.
	Common Player: 1-36	20.00	10.00	6.00
	Common Player: 37-48	25.00	12.50	7.50
1	Bob Elliott	100.00	35.00	15.00
2	Ewell (The Whip) Blackwell	25.00	12.50	7.50
3	Ralph Kiner	175.00	87.00	52.00
4	Johnny Mize	100.00	50.00	30.00
5	Bob Feller	200.00	100.00	60.00
6	*Larry (Yogi) Berra*	550.00	275.00	165.00
7	Pete (Pistol Pete) Reiser	50.00	25.00	15.00
8	Phil (Scooter) Rizzuto	225.00	112.00	67.00
9	Walker Cooper	20.00	10.00	6.00
10	Buddy Rosar	20.00	10.00	6.00
11	Johnny Lindell	20.00	10.00	6.00
12	Johnny Sain	25.00	12.50	7.50
13	Willard Marshall	30.00	15.00	9.00
14	Allie Reynolds	30.00	15.00	9.00
15	Eddie Joost	20.00	10.00	6.00
16	Jack Lohrke	30.00	15.00	9.00
17	Enos (Country) Slaughter	100.00	50.00	30.00
18	Warren Spahn	300.00	150.00	90.00
19	Tommy (The Clutch) Henrich	25.00	12.50	7.50
20	Buddy Kerr	30.00	15.00	9.00
21	Ferris Fain	20.00	10.00	6.00
22	Floyd (Bill) Bevins (Bevens)	40.00	20.00	12.00
23	Larry Jansen	20.00	10.00	6.00
24	Emil (Dutch) Leonard	30.00	15.00	9.00
25	Barney McCoskey (McCosky)	20.00	10.00	6.00
26	Frank Shea	40.00	20.00	12.00
27	Sid Gordon	20.00	10.00	6.00
28	Emil (The Antelope) Verban	30.00	15.00	9.00
29	Joe Page	50.00	25.00	15.00
30	"Whitey" Lockman	40.00	20.00	12.00
31	Bill McCahan	20.00	10.00	6.00
32	Bill Rigney	20.00	10.00	6.00
33	Bill (The Bull) Johnson	20.00	10.00	6.00
34	Sheldon (Available) Jones	30.00	15.00	9.00
35	George (Snuffy) Stirnweiss	20.00	10.00	6.00
36	Stan Musial	900.00	450.00	275.00
37	Clint Hartung	25.00	12.50	7.50
38	Al "Red" Schoendienst	150.00	75.00	45.00
39	Augie Galan	25.00	12.50	7.50
40	Marty Marion	80.00	40.00	25.00
41	Rex Barney	25.00	12.50	7.50
42	Ray Poat	25.00	12.50	7.50
43	Bruce Edwards	25.00	12.50	7.50
44	Johnny Wyrostek	25.00	12.50	7.50
45	Hank Sauer	25.00	12.50	7.50
46	Herman Wehmeier	25.00	12.50	7.50
47	Bobby Thomson	70.00	35.00	21.00
48	George "Dave" Koslo	70.00	20.00	10.00

Definitions for grading conditions are located in the Introduction of this price guide.

1949 Bowman

In 1949, Bowman increased the size of its issue to 240 numbered cards. The cards, which measure 2-1/16" by 2-1/2", are black and white photos overprinted with various pastel colors. Beginning with card #109 in the set, Bowman inserted the player's names on the card fronts. Twelve cards (#'s 4, 78, 83, 85, 88, 98, 109, 124, 127, 132 and 143), which were produced in the first four series of printings, were reprinted in the seventh series with either a

Definitions for grading conditions are located in the Introduction of this price guide.

card front or back modification. These variations are noted in the checklist that follows. Card #'s 1-3 and 5-73 can be found with either white or grey backs. The complete set of value in the following checklist does not include the higher priced variation cards.

		NR MT	EX	VG
Complete Set:		16000.00	8000.00	4750.
Common Player: 1-36		15.00	7.50	4.50
Common Player: 37-73		18.00	9.00	5.50
Common Player: 74-144		15.00	7.50	4.50
Common Player: 145-240		70.00	35.00	21.00
1	Vernon Bickford	100.00	30.00	15.00
2	Carroll "Whitey" Lockman	18.00	9.00	5.50
3	Bob Porterfield	18.00	9.00	5.50
4a	Jerry Priddy (no name on front)	18.00	9.00	5.50
4b	Jerry Priddy (name on front)	40.00	20.00	12.00
5	Hank Sauer	15.00	7.50	4.50
6	Phil Cavarretta	20.00	10.00	6.00
7	Joe Dobson	15.00	7.50	4.50
8	Murry Dickson	15.00	7.50	4.50
9	Ferris Fain	18.00	9.00	5.50
10	Ted Gray	15.00	7.50	4.50
11	Lou Boudreau	60.00	30.00	18.00
12	Cass Michaels	15.00	7.50	4.50
13	Bob Chesnes	15.00	7.50	4.50
14	*Curt Simmons*	30.00	15.00	9.00
15	Ned Garver	15.00	7.50	4.50
16	Al Kozar	15.00	7.50	4.50
17	Earl Torgeson	15.00	7.50	4.50
18	Bobby Thomson	30.00	15.00	9.00
19	*Bobby Brown*	50.00	25.00	15.00
20	Gene Hermanski	18.00	9.00	5.50
21	Frank Baumholtz	15.00	7.50	4.50
22	Harry "P-Nuts" Lowrey	15.00	7.50	4.50
23	Bobby Doerr	70.00	35.00	21.00
24	Stan Musial	500.00	250.00	150.00
25	Carl Scheib	15.00	7.50	4.50
26	George Kell	60.00	30.00	18.00
27	Bob Feller	150.00	75.00	45.00
28	Don Kolloway	15.00	7.50	4.50
29	Ralph Kiner	90.00	45.00	27.00
30	Andy Seminick	15.00	7.50	4.50
31	Dick Kokos	15.00	7.50	4.50
32	Eddie Yost	15.00	7.50	4.50
33	Warren Spahn	175.00	87.00	52.00
34	Dave Koslo	15.00	7.50	4.50
35	Vic Raschi	20.00	10.00	6.00
36	Harold "Peewee" Reese	200.00	100.00	60.00
37	John Wyrostek	18.00	9.00	5.50
38	Emil "The Antelope" Verban	18.00	9.00	5.50
39	Bill Goodman	18.00	9.00	5.50
40	George "Red" Munger	18.00	9.00	5.50
41	Lou Brissie	18.00	9.00	5.50
42	Walter "Hoot" Evers	18.00	9.00	5.50
43	Dale Mitchell	18.00	9.00	5.50
44	Dave Philley	18.00	9.00	5.50
45	Wally Westlake	18.00	9.00	5.50
46	*Robin Roberts*	250.00	125.00	70.00
47	Johnny Sain	18.00	9.00	5.50
48	Willard Marshall	18.00	9.00	5.50
49	Frank Shea	18.00	9.00	5.50
50	Jackie Robinson	800.00	400.00	250.00
51	Herman Wehmeier	18.00	9.00	5.50
52	Johnny Schmitz	18.00	9.00	5.50
53	Jack Kramer	18.00	9.00	5.50
54	Marty "Slats" Marion	20.00	10.00	6.00
55	Eddie Joost	18.00	9.00	5.50
56	Pat Mullin	18.00	9.00	5.50
57	Gene Bearden	18.00	9.00	5.50
58	Bob Elliott	18.00	9.00	5.50
59	Jack "Lucky" Lohrke	18.00	9.00	5.50
60	Larry "Yogi" Berra	300.00	150.00	90.00
61	Rex Barney	20.00	10.00	6.00
62	Grady Hatton	18.00	9.00	5.50
63	Andy Pafko	20.00	10.00	6.00
64	Dom "The Little Professor" DiMaggio			
		30.00	15.00	9.00
65	Enos "Country" Slaughter	75.00	37.00	23.00
66	Elmer Valo	18.00	9.00	5.50
67	Alvin Dark	30.00	15.00	9.00
68	Sheldon "Available" Jones	18.00	9.00	5.50
69	Tommy "The Clutch" Henrich	25.00	12.50	7.50
70	Carl Furillo	60.00	30.00	18.00
71	Vern "Junior" Stephens	18.00	9.00	5.50
72	Tommy Holmes	20.00	10.00	6.00
73	Billy Cox	20.00	10.00	6.00
74	Tom McBride	15.00	7.50	4.50
75	Eddie Mayo	15.00	7.50	4.50
76	Bill Nicholson	15.00	7.50	4.50
77	Ernie (Jumbo and Tiny) Bonham	15.00	7.50	4.50
78a	Sam Zoldak (no name on front)	18.00	9.00	5.50
78b	Sam Zoldak (name on front)	40.00	20.00	12.00
79	Ron Northey	15.00	7.50	4.50
80	Bill McCahan	15.00	7.50	4.50
81	Virgil "Red" Stallcup	15.00	7.50	4.50
82	Joe Page	20.00	10.00	6.00
83a	Bob Scheffing (no name on front)			
		18.00	9.00	5.50
83b	Bob Scheffing (name on front)	40.00	20.00	12.00
84	*Roy Campanella*	700.00	350.00	200.00
85a	Johnny "Big John" Mize (no name on front)			
		75.00	37.00	23.00
85b	Johnny "Big John" Mize (name on front)			
		125.00	62.00	37.00
86	Johnny Pesky	18.00	9.00	5.50
87	Randy Gumpert	15.00	7.50	4.50
88a	Bill Salkeld (no name on front)	18.00	9.00	5.50
88b	Bill Salkeld (name on front)	40.00	20.00	12.00
89	Mizell "Whitey" Platt	15.00	7.50	4.50
90	Gil Coan	15.00	7.50	4.50
91	Dick Wakefield	15.00	7.50	4.50
92	Willie "Puddin-Head" Jones	15.00	7.50	4.50
93	Ed Stevens	15.00	7.50	4.50
94	James "Mickey" Vernon	18.00	9.00	5.50
95	Howie Pollett	15.00	7.50	4.50
96	Taft Wright	15.00	7.50	4.50
97	Danny Litwhiler	15.00	7.50	4.50
98a	Phil Rizzuto (no name on front)	100.00	50.00	30.00
98b	Phil Rizzuto (name on front)	200.00	100.00	60.00
99	Frank Gustine	15.00	7.50	4.50
100	Gil Hodges	200.00	100.00	60.00
101	Sid Gordon	15.00	7.50	4.50
102	Stan Spence	15.00	7.50	4.50
103	Joe Tipton	15.00	7.50	4.50
104	Ed Stanky	18.00	9.00	5.50
105	Bill Kennedy	15.00	7.50	4.50
106	Jake Early	15.00	7.50	4.50
107	Eddie Lake	15.00	7.50	4.50
108	Ken Heintzelman	15.00	7.50	4.50
109a	Ed Fitzgerald (Fitz Gerald) (script name on back)			
		18.00	9.00	5.50
109b	Ed Fitzgerald (Fitz Gerald) (printed name on back)			
		40.00	20.00	12.00
110	Early Wynn	125.00	62.00	37.00
111	Al "Red" Schoendienst	80.00	40.00	25.00
112	Sam Chapman	15.00	7.50	4.50
113	Ray Lamanno	15.00	7.50	4.50
114	Allie Reynolds	30.00	15.00	9.00
115	Emil "Dutch" Leonard	15.00	7.50	4.50
116	Joe Hatten	18.00	9.00	5.50
117	Walker Cooper	15.00	7.50	4.50
118	Sam Mele	15.00	7.50	4.50
119	Floyd Baker	15.00	7.50	4.50
120	Cliff Fannin	15.00	7.50	4.50
121	Mark Christman	15.00	7.50	4.50
122	George Vico	15.00	7.50	4.50
123	Johnny Blatnick	15.00	7.50	4.50
124a	Danny Murtaugh (script name on back)			
		18.00	9.00	5.50
124b	Danny Murtaugh (printed name on back)			
		40.00	20.00	12.00
125	Ken Keltner	18.00	9.00	5.50
126a	Al Brazle (script name on back)	18.00	9.00	5.50
126b	Al Brazle (printed name on back)			
		40.00	20.00	12.00
127a	Henry "Heeney" Majeski (script name on back)			
		18.00	9.00	5.50
127b	Henry "Heeney" Majeski (printed name on back)			
		40.00	20.00	12.00
128	Johnny Vander Meer	20.00	10.00	6.00

		NR MT	EX	VG
129	Bill "The Bull" Johnson	20.00	10.00	6.00
130	Harry "The Hat" Walker	18.00	9.00	5.50
131	Paul Lehner	15.00	7.50	4.50
132a	Al Evans (script name on back)	18.00	9.00	5.50
132b	Al Evans (printed name on back)	40.00	20.00	12.00
133	Aaron Robinson	15.00	7.50	4.50
134	Hank Borowy	15.00	7.50	4.50
135	Stan Rojek	15.00	7.50	4.50
136	Henry "Hank" Edwards	15.00	7.50	4.50
137	Ted Wilks	15.00	7.50	4.50
138	Warren "Buddy" Rosar	15.00	7.50	4.50
139	Hank "Bow-Wow" Arft	15.00	7.50	4.50
140	Rae Scarborough (Ray)	15.00	7.50	4.50
141	Ulysses "Tony" Lupien	15.00	7.50	4.50
142	Eddie Waitkus	15.00	7.50	4.50
143a	Bob Dillinger (script name on back)	18.00	9.00	5.50
143b	Bob Dillinger (printed name on back)	40.00	20.00	12.00
144	Milton "Mickey" Haefner	15.00	7.50	4.50
145	Sylvester "Blix" Donnelly	70.00	35.00	21.00
146	Myron "Mike" McCormick	75.00	37.00	22.00
147	Elmer "Bert" Singleton	70.00	35.00	21.00
148	Bob Swift	70.00	35.00	21.00
149	Roy Partee	75.00	37.00	22.00
150	Alfred "Allie" Clark	70.00	35.00	21.00
151	Maurice "Mickey" Harris	70.00	35.00	21.00
152	Clarence Maddern	70.00	35.00	21.00
153	Phil Masi	70.00	35.00	21.00
154	Clint Hartung	70.00	35.00	21.00
155	Fermin "Mickey" Guerra	70.00	35.00	21.00
156	Al "Zeke" Zarilla	70.00	35.00	21.00
157	Walt Masterson	70.00	35.00	21.00
158	Harry "The Cat" Brecheen	70.00	35.00	21.00
159	Glen Moulder	70.00	35.00	21.00
160	Jim Blackburn	70.00	35.00	21.00
161	John "Jocko" Thompson	70.00	35.00	21.00
162	Elwin "Preacher" Roe	150.00	75.00	50.00
163	Clyde McCullough	70.00	35.00	21.00
164	Vic Wertz	110.00	55.00	33.00
165	George "Snuffy" Stirnweiss	70.00	35.00	21.00
166	Mike Tresh	70.00	35.00	21.00
167	Boris "Babe" Martin	70.00	35.00	21.00
168	Doyle Lade	70.00	35.00	21.00
169	Jeff Heath	70.00	35.00	21.00
170	Bill Rigney	75.00	37.00	22.00
171	Dick Fowler	70.00	35.00	21.00
172	Eddie Pellagrini	70.00	35.00	21.00
173	Eddie Stewart	70.00	35.00	21.00
174	Terry Moore	75.00	37.00	22.00
175	Luke Appling	125.00	62.00	37.00
176	Ken Raffensberger	70.00	35.00	21.00
177	Stan Lopata	70.00	35.00	21.00
178	Tommy Brown	75.00	37.00	22.00
179	Hugh Casey	75.00	37.00	22.00
180	Connie Berry	70.00	35.00	21.00
181	Gus Niarhos	70.00	35.00	21.00
182	Hal Peck	70.00	35.00	21.00
183	Lou Stringer	70.00	35.00	21.00
184	Bob Chipman	70.00	35.00	21.00
185	Pete Reiser	75.00	37.00	22.00
186	John "Buddy" Kerr	70.00	35.00	21.00
187	Phil Marchildon	70.00	35.00	21.00
188	Karl Drews	70.00	35.00	21.00
189	Earl Wooten	70.00	35.00	21.00
190	Jim Hearn	70.00	35.00	21.00
191	Joe Haynes	70.00	35.00	21.00
192	Harry Gumbert	70.00	35.00	21.00
193	Ken Trinkle	70.00	35.00	21.00
194	Ralph Branca	110.00	55.00	33.00
195	Eddie Bockman	70.00	35.00	21.00
196	Fred Hutchinson	75.00	37.00	22.00
197	Johnny Lindell	70.00	35.00	21.00
198	Steve Gromek	70.00	35.00	21.00
199	Cecil "Tex" Hughson	70.00	35.00	21.00
200	Jess Dobernic	70.00	35.00	21.00
201	Sibby Sisti	70.00	35.00	21.00
202	Larry Jansen	70.00	35.00	21.00
203	Barney McCosky	70.00	35.00	21.00
204	Bob Savage	70.00	35.00	21.00
205	Dick Sisler	70.00	35.00	21.00
206	Bruce Edwards	75.00	37.00	22.00
207	Johnny "Hippity" Hopp	70.00	35.00	21.00
208	Paul "Dizzy" Trout	75.00	37.00	22.00
209	Charlie "King Kong" Keller	100.00	50.00	30.00
210	Joe "Flash" Gordon	75.00	37.00	22.00
211	Dave "Boo" Ferris	70.00	35.00	21.00
212	Ralph Hamner	70.00	35.00	21.00
213	Charles "Red" Barrett	70.00	35.00	21.00
214	*Richie Ashburn*	550.00	275.00	165.00
215	Kirby Higbe	70.00	35.00	21.00

		NR MT	EX	VG
216	Lynwood "Schoolboy" Rowe	70.00	35.00	21.00
217	Marino Pieretti	70.00	35.00	21.00
218	Dick Kryhoski	70.00	35.00	21.00
219	Virgil "Fire" Trucks	75.00	37.00	22.00
220	Johnny McCarthy	70.00	35.00	21.00
221	Bob Muncrief	70.00	35.00	21.00
222	Alex Kellner	70.00	35.00	21.00
223	Bob Hoffman (Hofman)	70.00	35.00	21.00
224	*Leroy "Satchel" Paige*	1200.00	600.00	350.00
225	*Gerry Coleman*	100.00	50.00	30.00
226	Edwin "Duke" Snider	1000.00	500.00	300.00
227	Fritz Ostermueller	70.00	35.00	21.00
228	Jackie Mayo	70.00	35.00	21.00
229	Ed Lopat	125.00	60.00	40.00
230	Augie Galan	70.00	35.00	21.00
231	Earl Johnson	70.00	35.00	21.00
232	George McQuinn	70.00	35.00	21.00
233	*Larry Doby*	175.00	87.00	52.00
234	Truett "Rip" Sewell	75.00	37.00	22.00
235	Jim Russell	70.00	35.00	21.00
236	Fred Sanford	70.00	35.00	21.00
237	Monte Kennedy	70.00	35.00	21.00
238	Bob Lemon	225.00	112.00	67.00
239	Frank McCormick	70.00	35.00	21.00
240	Norman "Babe" Young (photo actually Bobby Young)	150.00	75.00	45.00

1949 Bowman
Pacific Coast League

One of the scarcest issues of the post-war period, the 1949 Bowman PCL set was issued only on the West Coast. Like the 1949 Bowman regular issue, the cards contain black and white photos overprinted with various pastel colors. Thirty-six cards, which measure 2-1/16" by 2-1/2", make up the set. It is believed that the cards may have been issued only in sheets and not sold in gum packs.

		NR MT	EX	VG
Complete Set:		5500.00	2750.00	1650.
Common Player:		150.00	75.00	45.00
1	Lee Anthony	150.00	75.00	45.00
2	George Metkovich	150.00	75.00	45.00
3	Ralph Hodgin	150.00	75.00	45.00
4	George Woods	150.00	75.00	45.00
5	Xavier Rescigno	150.00	75.00	45.00
6	Mickey Grasso	150.00	75.00	45.00
7	Johnny Rucker	150.00	75.00	45.00
8	Jack Brewer	150.00	75.00	45.00
9	Dom D'Allessandro	150.00	75.00	45.00
10	Charlie Gassaway	150.00	75.00	45.00
11	Tony Freitas	150.00	75.00	45.00
12	Gordon Maltzberger	150.00	75.00	45.00
13	John Jensen	150.00	75.00	45.00
14	Joyner White	150.00	75.00	45.00
15	Harvey Storey	150.00	75.00	45.00
16	Dick Lajeski	150.00	75.00	45.00
17	Albie Glossop	150.00	75.00	45.00
18	Bill Raimondi	150.00	75.00	45.00
19	Ken Holcombe	150.00	75.00	45.00
20	Don Ross	150.00	75.00	45.00
21	Pete Coscarart	150.00	75.00	45.00
22	Tony York	150.00	75.00	45.00
23	Jake Mooty	150.00	75.00	45.00

		NR MT	EX	VG
24	Charles Adams	150.00	75.00	45.00
25	Les Scarsella	150.00	75.00	45.00
26	Joe Marty	150.00	75.00	45.00
27	Frank Kelleher	150.00	75.00	45.00
28	Lee Handley	150.00	75.00	45.00
29	Herman Besse	150.00	75.00	45.00
30	John Lazor	150.00	75.00	45.00
31	Eddie Malone	150.00	75.00	45.00
32	Maurice Van Robays	150.00	75.00	45.00
33	Jim Tabor	150.00	75.00	45.00
34	Gene Handley	150.00	75.00	45.00
35	Tom Seats	150.00	75.00	45.00
36	Ora Burnett	150.00	75.00	45.00

1950 Bowman

The quality of the 1950 Bowman issue showed a marked improvement over the company's previous efforts. The cards are beautiful color art reproductions of actual photographs and measure 2-1/16" by 2-1/2" in size. The card backs include the same type of information as found in the previous year's issue but are designed in a horizontal format. Cards found in the first two series of the set (#'s 1-72) are the scarcest in the issue. The backs of the final 72 cards in the set (#'s 181-252) can be found with or without the copyright line at the bottom of the card, the "without" version being the less common.

		NR MT	EX	VG
Complete Set:		10000.00	5000.00	3000.
Common Player: 1-72		50.00	25.00	15.00
Common Player: 73-252		16.00	8.00	4.75
1	Mel Parnell	200.00	25.00	8.00
2	Vern Stephens	50.00	25.00	15.00
3	Dom DiMaggio	60.00	30.00	18.00
4	Gus Zernial	50.00	25.00	15.00
5	Bob Kuzava	50.00	25.00	15.00
6	Bob Feller	200.00	100.00	60.00
7	Jim Hegan	50.00	25.00	15.00
8	George Kell	90.00	45.00	27.00
9	Vic Wertz	50.00	25.00	15.00
10	Tommy Henrich	60.00	30.00	18.00
11	Phil Rizzuto	150.00	75.00	45.00
12	Joe Page	50.00	25.00	15.00
13	Ferris Fain	50.00	25.00	15.00
14	Alex Kellner	50.00	25.00	15.00
15	Al Kozar	50.00	25.00	15.00
16	*Roy Sievers*	50.00	25.00	15.00
17	Sid Hudson	50.00	25.00	15.00
18	Eddie Robinson	50.00	25.00	15.00
19	Warren Spahn	200.00	100.00	60.00
20	Bob Elliott	50.00	25.00	15.00
21	Harold Reese	200.00	100.00	60.00
22	Jackie Robinson	700.00	350.00	200.00
23	*Don Newcombe*	150.00	75.00	50.00
24	Johnny Schmitz	50.00	25.00	15.00
25	Hank Sauer	50.00	25.00	15.00
26	Grady Hatton	50.00	25.00	15.00
27	Herman Wehmeier	50.00	25.00	15.00
28	Bobby Thomson	70.00	35.00	21.00
29	Ed Stanky	50.00	25.00	15.00
30	Eddie Waitkus	50.00	25.00	15.00
31	Del Ennis	50.00	25.00	15.00
32	Robin Roberts	125.00	62.00	37.00
33	Ralph Kiner	125.00	62.00	37.00

		NR MT	EX	VG
34	Murry Dickson	50.00	25.00	15.00
35	Enos Slaughter	100.00	50.00	30.00
36	Eddie Kazak	50.00	25.00	15.00
37	Luke Appling	70.00	35.00	21.00
38	Bill Wight	50.00	25.00	15.00
39	Larry Doby	60.00	30.00	18.00
40	Bob Lemon	100.00	50.00	30.00
41	Walter "Hoot" Evers	50.00	25.00	15.00
42	Art Houtteman	50.00	25.00	15.00
43	Bobby Doerr	80.00	40.00	25.00
44	Joe Dobson	50.00	25.00	15.00
45	Al "Zeke" Zarilla	50.00	25.00	15.00
46	Larry "Yogi" Berra	350.00	175.00	100.00
47	Jerry Coleman	55.00	27.00	16.50
48	Leland "Lou" Brissie	50.00	25.00	15.00
49	Elmer Valo	50.00	25.00	15.00
50	Dick Kokos	50.00	25.00	15.00
51	Ned Garver	50.00	25.00	15.00
52	Sam Mele	50.00	25.00	15.00
53	Clyde Vollmer	50.00	25.00	15.00
54	Gil Coan	50.00	25.00	15.00
55	John "Buddy" Kerr	50.00	25.00	15.00
56	*Del Crandell (Crandall)*	60.00	30.00	18.00
57	Vernon Bickford	50.00	25.00	15.00
58	Carl Furillo	60.00	30.00	18.00
59	Ralph Branca	60.00	30.00	18.00
60	Andy Pafko	50.00	25.00	15.00
61	Bob Rush	50.00	25.00	15.00
62	Ted Kluszewski	70.00	35.00	21.00
63	Ewell Blackwell	50.00	25.00	15.00
64	Alvin Dark	50.00	25.00	15.00
65	Dave Koslo	50.00	25.00	15.00
66	Larry Jansen	50.00	25.00	15.00
67	Willie Jones	50.00	25.00	15.00
68	Curt Simmons	50.00	25.00	15.00
69	Wally Westlake	50.00	25.00	15.00
70	Bob Chesnes	50.00	25.00	15.00
71	Al Schoendienst	100.00	50.00	30.00
72	Howie Pollet	50.00	25.00	15.00
73	Willard Marshall	16.00	8.00	4.75
74	*Johnny Antonelli*	16.00	8.00	4.75
75	Roy Campanella	300.00	150.00	90.00
76	Rex Barney	16.00	8.00	4.75
77	Edwin "Duke" Snider	275.00	137.00	80.00
78	Mickey Owen	16.00	8.00	4.75
79	Johnny Vander Meer	16.00	8.00	4.75
80	Howard Fox	16.00	8.00	4.75
81	Ron Northey	16.00	8.00	4.75
82	Carroll Lockman	16.00	8.00	4.75
83	Sheldon Jones	16.00	8.00	4.75
84	Richie Ashburn	75.00	38.00	23.00
85	Ken Heintzelman	16.00	8.00	4.75
86	Stan Rojek	16.00	8.00	4.75
87	Bill Werle	16.00	8.00	4.75
88	Marty Marion	16.00	8.00	4.75
89	George Munger	16.00	8.00	4.75
90	Harry Brecheen	16.00	8.00	4.75
91	Cass Michaels	16.00	8.00	4.75
92	Hank Majeski	16.00	8.00	4.75
93	Gene Bearden	16.00	8.00	4.75
94	Lou Boudreau	50.00	25.00	15.00
95	Aaron Robinson	16.00	8.00	4.75
96	Virgil "Fire" Trucks	16.00	8.00	4.75
97	Maurice McDermott	16.00	8.00	4.75
98	Ted Williams	700.00	350.00	200.00
99	Billy Goodman	16.00	8.00	4.75
100	Vic Raschi	20.00	10.00	6.00
101	Bobby Brown	20.00	10.00	6.00
102	Billy Johnson	16.00	8.00	4.75
103	Eddie Joost	16.00	8.00	4.75
104	Sam Chapman	16.00	8.00	4.75
105	Bob Dillinger	16.00	8.00	4.75
106	Cliff Fannin	16.00	8.00	4.75
107	Sam Dente	16.00	8.00	4.75
108	Rae Scarborough (Ray)	16.00	8.00	4.75
109	Sid Gordon	16.00	8.00	4.75
110	Tommy Holmes	16.00	8.00	4.75
111	Walker Cooper	16.00	8.00	4.75
112	Gil Hodges	80.00	40.00	24.00
113	Gene Hermanski	16.00	8.00	4.75
114	Wayne Terwilliger	16.00	8.00	4.75
115	Roy Smalley	16.00	8.00	4.75
116	Virgil "Red" Stallcup	16.00	8.00	4.75
117	Bill Rigney	16.00	8.00	4.75
118	Clint Hartung	16.00	8.00	4.75
119	Dick Sisler	16.00	8.00	4.75
120	John Thompson	16.00	8.00	4.75
121	Andy Seminick	16.00	8.00	4.75
122	Johnny Hopp	16.00	8.00	4.75
123	Dino Restelli	16.00	8.00	4.75
124	Clyde McCullough	16.00	8.00	4.75

		NR MT	EX	VG
125	Del Rice	16.00	8.00	4.75
126	Al Brazle	16.00	8.00	4.75
127	Dave Philley	16.00	8.00	4.75
128	Phil Masi	16.00	8.00	4.75
129	Joe "Flash" Gordon	16.00	8.00	4.75
130	Dale Mitchell	16.00	8.00	4.75
131	Steve Gromek	16.00	8.00	4.75
132	James Vernon	16.00	8.00	4.75
133	Don Kolloway	16.00	8.00	4.75
134	Paul "Dizzy" Trout	16.00	8.00	4.75
135	Pat Mullin	16.00	8.00	4.75
136	Warren Rosar	16.00	8.00	4.75
137	Johnny Pesky	16.00	8.00	4.75
138	Allie Reynolds	60.00	30.00	18.00
139	Johnny Mize	60.00	30.00	18.00
140	Pete Suder	16.00	8.00	4.75
141	Joe Coleman	16.00	8.00	4.75
142	*Sherman Lollar*	16.00	8.00	4.75
143	Eddie Stewart	16.00	8.00	4.75
144	Al Evans	16.00	8.00	4.75
145	Jack Graham	16.00	8.00	4.75
146	Floyd Baker	16.00	8.00	4.75
147	*Mike Garcia*	16.00	8.00	4.75
148	Early Wynn	60.00	30.00	18.00
149	Bob Swift	16.00	8.00	4.75
150	George Vico	16.00	8.00	4.75
151	Fred Hutchinson	16.00	8.00	4.75
152	Ellis Kinder	16.00	8.00	4.75
153	Walt Masterson	16.00	8.00	4.75
154	Gus Niarhos	16.00	8.00	4.75
155	Frank "Spec" Shea	16.00	8.00	4.75
156	Fred Sanford	16.00	8.00	4.75
157	Mike Guerra	16.00	8.00	4.75
158	Paul Lehner	16.00	8.00	4.75
159	Joe Tipton	16.00	8.00	4.75
160	Mickey Harris	16.00	8.00	4.75
161	Sherry Robertson	16.00	8.00	4.75
162	Eddie Yost	16.00	8.00	4.75
163	Earl Torgeson	16.00	8.00	4.75
164	Sibby Sisti	16.00	8.00	4.75
165	Bruce Edwards	16.00	8.00	4.75
166	Joe Hatten	16.00	8.00	4.75
167	Elwin Roe	60.00	30.00	18.00
168	Bob Scheffing	16.00	8.00	4.75
169	Hank Edwards	16.00	8.00	4.75
170	Emil Leonard	16.00	8.00	4.75
171	Harry Gumbert	16.00	8.00	4.75
172	Harry Lowrey	16.00	8.00	4.75
173	Lloyd Merriman	16.00	8.00	4.75
174	Henry Thompson	16.00	8.00	4.75
175	Monte Kennedy	16.00	8.00	4.75
176	Sylvester Donnelly	16.00	8.00	4.75
177	Hank Borowy	16.00	8.00	4.75
178	Eddy Fitzgerald (Fitz Gerald)	16.00	8.00	4.75
179	Charles Diering	16.00	8.00	4.75
180	Harry Walker	16.00	8.00	4.75
181	Marino Pieretti	16.00	8.00	4.75
182	Sam Zoldak	16.00	8.00	4.75
183	Mickey Haefner	16.00	8.00	4.75
184	Randy Gumpert	16.00	8.00	4.75
185	Howie Judson	16.00	8.00	4.75
186	Ken Keltner	16.00	8.00	4.75
187	Lou Stringer	16.00	8.00	4.75
188	Earl Johnson	16.00	8.00	4.75
189	Owen Friend	16.00	8.00	4.75
190	Ken Wood	16.00	8.00	4.75
191	Dick Starr	16.00	8.00	4.75
192	Bob Chipman	16.00	8.00	4.75
193	Harold "Pete" Reiser	16.00	8.00	4.75
194	Billy Cox	16.00	8.00	4.75
195	Phil Cavaretta (Cavarretta)	16.00	8.00	4.75
196	Doyle Lade	16.00	8.00	4.75
197	Johnny Wyrostek	16.00	8.00	4.75
198	Danny Litwhiler	16.00	8.00	4.75
199	Jack Kramer	16.00	8.00	4.75
200	Kirby Higbe	16.00	8.00	4.75
201	Pete Castiglione	16.00	8.00	4.75
202	Cliff Chambers	16.00	8.00	4.75
203	Danny Murtaugh	16.00	8.00	4.75
204	Granville Hamner	16.00	8.00	4.75
205	Mike Goliat	16.00	8.00	4.75
206	Stan Lopata	16.00	8.00	4.75
207	Max Lanier	16.00	8.00	4.75
208	Jim Hearn	16.00	8.00	4.75
209	Johnny Lindell	16.00	8.00	4.75
210	Ted Gray	16.00	8.00	4.75
211	Charlie Keller	16.00	8.00	4.75
212	Gerry Priddy	16.00	8.00	4.75
213	Carl Scheib	16.00	8.00	4.75
214	Dick Fowler	16.00	8.00	4.75
215	Ed Lopat	20.00	10.00	6.00

		NR MT	EX	VG
216	Bob Porterfield	16.00	8.00	4.75
217	Casey Stengel	150.00	75.00	45.00
218	Cliff Mapes	16.00	8.00	4.75
219	*Hank Bauer*	70.00	35.00	20.00
220	Leo Durocher	50.00	25.00	15.00
221	Don Mueller	16.00	8.00	4.75
222	Bobby Morgan	16.00	8.00	4.75
223	Jimmy Russell	16.00	8.00	4.75
224	Jack Banta	16.00	8.00	4.75
225	Eddie Sawyer	16.00	8.00	4.75
226	Jim Konstanty	16.00	8.00	4.75
227	Bob Miller	16.00	8.00	4.75
228	Bill Nicholson	16.00	8.00	4.75
229	Frank Frisch	60.00	30.00	18.00
230	Bill Serena	16.00	8.00	4.75
231	Preston Ward	16.00	8.00	4.75
232	Al "Flip" Rosen	60.00	30.00	18.00
233	Allie Clark	16.00	8.00	4.75
234	*Bobby Shantz*	25.00	12.50	7.50
235	Harold Gilbert	16.00	8.00	4.75
236	Bob Cain	16.00	8.00	4.75
237	Bill Salkeld	16.00	8.00	4.75
238	Vernal Jones	16.00	8.00	4.75
239	Bill Howerton	16.00	8.00	4.75
240	Eddie Lake	16.00	8.00	4.75
241	Neil Berry	16.00	8.00	4.75
242	Dick Kryhoski	16.00	8.00	4.75
243	Johnny Groth	16.00	8.00	4.75
244	Dale Coogan	16.00	8.00	4.75
245	Al Papai	16.00	8.00	4.75
246	*Walt Dropo*	25.00	12.50	7.50
247	Irv Noren	16.00	8.00	4.75
248	*Sam Jethroe*	16.00	8.00	4.75
249	George Stirnweiss	16.00	8.00	4.75
250	Ray Coleman	16.00	8.00	4.75
251	John Lester Moss	16.00	8.00	4.75
252	Billy DeMars	100.00	50.00	30.00

1951 Bowman

In 1951, Bowman increased the numbers of cards in its set for the third consecutive year when it issued 324 cards. The cards are, like 1950, color art reproductions of actual photographs but now measured 2-1/16" by 3-1/8" in size. The player's name is situated in a small, black box on the card front. Several of the card fronts are enlargements of the 1950 version. The high-numbered series of the set (#'s 253-324), which includes the rookie cards of Mantle and Mays, are the scarcest of the issue.

		NR MT	EX	VG
Complete Set:		21000.00	15500.00	7000.
Common Player: 1-36		20.00	10.00	6.00
Common Player: 37-252		14.00	7.00	4.25
Common Player: 253-324		60.00	30.00	18.00
1	*Ed Ford*	1300.00	575.00	300.00
2	Larry "Yogi" Berra	400.00	200.00	120.00
3	Robin Roberts	80.00	40.00	25.00
4	Del Ennis	20.00	10.00	6.00
5	Dale Mitchell	20.00	10.00	6.00
6	Don Newcombe	35.00	17.50	10.50
7	Gil Hodges	90.00	45.00	27.00
8	Paul Lehner	20.00	10.00	6.00
9	Sam Chapman	20.00	10.00	6.00
10	Al "Red" Schoendienst	75.00	38.00	23.00

		NR MT	EX	VG			NR MT	EX	VG
11	George "Red" Munger	20.00	10.00	6.00	102	Emil "Dutch" Leonard	14.00	7.00	4.25
12	Hank Majeski	20.00	10.00	6.00	103	Andy Pafko	20.00	10.00	6.00
13	Ed Stanky	20.00	10.00	6.00	104	Virgil "Fire" Trucks	20.00	10.00	6.00
14	Alvin Dark	22.00	11.00	6.50	105	Don Kolloway	14.00	7.00	4.25
15	Johnny Pesky	20.00	10.00	6.00	106	Pat Mullin	14.00	7.00	4.25
16	Maurice McDermott	20.00	10.00	6.00	107	Johnny Wyrostek	14.00	7.00	4.25
17	Pete Castiglione	20.00	10.00	6.00	108	Virgil Stallcup	14.00	7.00	4.25
18	Gil Coan	20.00	10.00	6.00	109	Allie Reynolds	40.00	20.00	12.00
19	Sid Gordon	20.00	10.00	6.00	110	Bobby Brown	40.00	20.00	12.00
20	Del Crandall	20.00	10.00	6.00	111	Curt Simmons	20.00	10.00	6.00
21	George "Snuffy" Stirnweiss	20.00	10.00	6.00	112	Willie Jones	14.00	7.00	4.25
22	Hank Sauer	20.00	10.00	6.00	113	Bill "Swish" Nicholson	14.00	7.00	4.25
23	Walter "Hoot" Evers	20.00	10.00	6.00	114	Sam Zoldak	14.00	7.00	4.25
24	Ewell Blackwell	20.00	10.00	6.00	115	Steve Gromek	14.00	7.00	4.25
25	Vic Raschi	30.00	15.00	9.00	116	Bruce Edwards	20.00	10.00	6.00
26	Phil Rizzuto	100.00	50.00	30.00	117	Eddie Miksis	20.00	10.00	6.00
27	Jim Konstanty	20.00	10.00	6.00	118	Preacher Roe	40.00	20.00	12.00
28	Eddie Waitkus	20.00	10.00	6.00	119	Eddie Joost	14.00	7.00	4.25
29	Allie Clark	20.00	10.00	6.00	120	Joe Coleman	14.00	7.00	4.25
30	Bob Feller	125.00	62.00	37.00	121	Gerry Staley	14.00	7.00	4.25
31	Roy Campanella	260.00	130.00	78.00	122	Joe Garagiola	150.00	75.00	45.00
32	Duke Snider	250.00	125.00	75.00	123	Howie Judson	14.00	7.00	4.25
33	Bob Hooper	20.00	10.00	6.00	124	Gus Niarhos	14.00	7.00	4.25
34	Marty Marion	20.00	10.00	6.00	125	Bill Rigney	20.00	10.00	6.00
35	Al Zarilla	20.00	10.00	6.00	126	Bobby Thomson	30.00	15.00	9.00
36	Joe Dobson	20.00	10.00	6.00	127	Sal Maglie	50.00	25.00	15.00
37	Whitey Lockman	14.00	7.00	4.25	128	Ellis Kinder	14.00	7.00	4.25
38	Al Evans	14.00	7.00	4.25	129	Matt Batts	14.00	7.00	4.25
39	Ray Scarborough	14.00	7.00	4.25	130	Tom Saffell	14.00	7.00	4.25
40	*Dave "Gus" Bell*	20.00	10.00	6.00	131	Cliff Chambers	14.00	7.00	4.25
41	Eddie Yost	20.00	10.00	6.00	132	Cass Michaels	14.00	7.00	4.25
42	Vern Bickford	14.00	7.00	4.25	133	Sam Dente	14.00	7.00	4.25
43	Billy DeMars	14.00	7.00	4.25	134	Warren Spahn	110.00	55.00	33.00
44	Roy Smalley	14.00	7.00	4.25	135	Walker Cooper	14.00	7.00	4.25
45	Art Houtteman	14.00	7.00	4.25	136	Ray Coleman	14.00	7.00	4.25
46	George Kell	65.00	32.50	19.50	137	Dick Starr	14.00	7.00	4.25
47	Grady Hatton	14.00	7.00	4.25	138	Phil Cavarretta	20.00	10.00	6.00
48	Ken Raffensberger	14.00	7.00	4.25	139	Doyle Lade	14.00	7.00	4.25
49	Jerry Coleman	20.00	10.00	6.00	140	Eddie Lake	14.00	7.00	4.25
50	Johnny Mize	60.00	30.00	18.00	141	Fred Hutchinson	20.00	10.00	6.00
51	Andy Seminick	14.00	7.00	4.25	142	Aaron Robinson	14.00	7.00	4.25
52	Dick Sisler	14.00	7.00	4.25	143	Ted Kluszewski	40.00	20.00	12.00
53	Bob Lemon	40.00	20.00	12.00	144	Herman Wehmeier	14.00	7.00	4.25
54	Ray Boone	20.00	10.00	6.00	145	Fred Sanford	20.00	10.00	6.00
55	Gene Hermanski	20.00	10.00	6.00	146	Johnny Hopp	20.00	10.00	6.00
56	Ralph Branca	30.00	15.00	9.00	147	Ken Heintzelman	14.00	7.00	4.25
57	Alex Kellner	14.00	7.00	4.25	148	Granny Hamner	14.00	7.00	4.25
58	Enos Slaughter	60.00	30.00	18.00	149	Emory "Bubba" Church	14.00	7.00	4.25
59	Randy Gumpert	14.00	7.00	4.25	150	Mike Garcia	20.00	10.00	6.00
60	Alfonso Carrasquel	14.00	7.00	4.25	151	Larry Doby	25.00	12.50	7.50
61	Jim Hearn	14.00	7.00	4.25	152	Cal Abrams	20.00	10.00	6.00
62	Lou Boudreau	55.00	27.50	16.50	153	Rex Barney	20.00	10.00	6.00
63	Bob Dillinger	14.00	7.00	4.25	154	Pete Suder	14.00	7.00	4.25
64	Bill Werle	14.00	7.00	4.25	155	Lou Brissie	14.00	7.00	4.25
65	Mickey Vernon	20.00	10.00	6.00	156	Del Rice	14.00	7.00	4.25
66	Bob Elliott	14.00	7.00	4.25	157	Al Brazle	14.00	7.00	4.25
67	Roy Sievers	20.00	10.00	6.00	158	Chuck Diering	14.00	7.00	4.25
68	Dick Kokos	14.00	7.00	4.25	159	Eddie Stewart	14.00	7.00	4.25
69	Johnny Schmitz	14.00	7.00	4.25	160	Phil Masi	14.00	7.00	4.25
70	Ron Northey	14.00	7.00	4.25	161	Wes Westrum	20.00	10.00	6.00
71	Jerry Priddy	14.00	7.00	4.25	162	Larry Jansen	14.00	7.00	4.25
72	Lloyd Merriman	14.00	7.00	4.25	163	Monte Kennedy	14.00	7.00	4.25
73	Tommy Byrne	20.00	10.00	6.00	164	Bill Wight	14.00	7.00	4.25
74	Billy Johnson	20.00	10.00	6.00	165	Ted Williams	600.00	300.00	175.00
75	Russ Meyer	14.00	7.00	4.25	166	Stan Rojek	14.00	7.00	4.25
76	Stan Lopata	14.00	7.00	4.25	167	Murry Dickson	14.00	7.00	4.25
77	Mike Goliat	14.00	7.00	4.25	168	Sam Mele	14.00	7.00	4.25
78	Early Wynn	60.00	30.00	18.00	169	Sid Hudson	14.00	7.00	4.25
79	Jim Hegan	14.00	7.00	4.25	170	Sibby Sisti	14.00	7.00	4.25
80	Harold "Peewee" Reese	150.00	75.00	50.00	171	Buddy Kerr	14.00	7.00	4.25
81	Carl Furillo	40.00	20.00	12.00	172	Ned Garver	14.00	7.00	4.25
82	Joe Tipton	14.00	7.00	4.25	173	Hank Arft	14.00	7.00	4.25
83	Carl Scheib	14.00	7.00	4.25	174	Mickey Owen	14.00	7.00	4.25
84	Barney McCosky	14.00	7.00	4.25	175	Wayne Terwilliger	14.00	7.00	4.25
85	Eddie Kazak	14.00	7.00	4.25	176	Vic Wertz	20.00	10.00	6.00
86	Harry Brecheen	20.00	10.00	6.00	177	Charlie Keller	20.00	10.00	6.00
87	Floyd Baker	14.00	7.00	4.25	178	Ted Gray	14.00	7.00	4.25
88	Eddie Robinson	14.00	7.00	4.25	179	Danny Litwhiler	14.00	7.00	4.25
89	Henry Thompson	14.00	7.00	4.25	180	Howie Fox	14.00	7.00	4.25
90	Dave Koslo	14.00	7.00	4.25	181	Casey Stengel	100.00	50.00	30.00
91	Clyde Vollmer	14.00	7.00	4.25	182	Tom Ferrick	20.00	10.00	6.00
92	Vern "Junior" Stephens	20.00	10.00	6.00	183	Hank Bauer	40.00	20.00	12.00
93	Danny O'Connell	14.00	7.00	4.25	184	Eddie Sawyer	14.00	7.00	4.25
94	Clyde McCullough	14.00	7.00	4.25	185	Jimmy Bloodworth	14.00	7.00	4.25
95	Sherry Robertson	14.00	7.00	4.25	186	Richie Ashburn	60.00	30.00	18.00
96	Sandalio Consuegra	14.00	7.00	4.25	187	Al "Flip" Rosen	25.00	12.50	7.50
97	Bob Kuzava	14.00	7.00	4.25	188	*Roberto Avila*	20.00	10.00	6.00
98	Willard Marshall	14.00	7.00	4.25	189	Erv Palica	20.00	10.00	6.00
99	Earl Torgeson	14.00	7.00	4.25	190	Joe Hatten	20.00	10.00	6.00
100	Sherman Lollar	20.00	10.00	6.00	191	Billy Hitchcock	14.00	7.00	4.25
101	Owen Friend	14.00	7.00	4.25	192	Hank Wyse	14.00	7.00	4.25

		NR MT	EX	VG
193	Ted Wilks	14.00	7.00	4.25
194	Harry "Peanuts" Lowrey	14.00	7.00	4.25
195	Paul Richards	30.00	15.00	9.00
196	Bill Pierce	20.00	10.00	6.00
197	Bob Cain	14.00	7.00	4.25
198	*Monte Irvin*	100.00	50.00	30.00
199	Sheldon Jones	14.00	7.00	4.25
200	Jack Kramer	14.00	7.00	4.25
201	Steve O'Neill	14.00	7.00	4.25
202	Mike Guerra	14.00	7.00	4.25
203	*Vernon Law*	20.00	10.00	6.00
204	Vic Lombardi	14.00	7.00	4.25
205	Mickey Grasso	14.00	7.00	4.25
206	Conrado Marrero	14.00	7.00	4.25
207	Billy Southworth	14.00	7.00	4.25
208	Blix Donnelly	14.00	7.00	4.25
209	Ken Wood	14.00	7.00	4.25
210	Les Moss	14.00	7.00	4.25
211	Hal Jeffcoat	14.00	7.00	4.25
212	Bob Rush	14.00	7.00	4.25
213	Neil Berry	14.00	7.00	4.25
214	Bob Swift	14.00	7.00	4.25
215	Kent Peterson	14.00	7.00	4.25
216	Connie Ryan	14.00	7.00	4.25
217	Joe Page	20.00	10.00	6.00
218	Ed Lopat	20.00	10.00	6.00
219	Gene Woodling	40.00	20.00	12.00
220	Bob Miller	14.00	7.00	4.25
221	Dick Whitman	14.00	7.00	4.25
222	Thurman Tucker	14.00	7.00	4.25
223	Johnny Vander Meer	20.00	10.00	6.00
224	Billy Cox	20.00	10.00	6.00
225	Dan Bankhead	20.00	10.00	6.00
226	Jimmy Dykes	20.00	10.00	6.00
227	Bobby Schantz (Shantz)	20.00	10.00	6.00
228	Cloyd Boyer	14.00	7.00	4.25
229	Bill Howerton	14.00	7.00	4.25
230	Max Lanier	14.00	7.00	4.25
231	Luis Aloma	14.00	7.00	4.25
232	Nelson Fox	110.00	55.00	33.00
233	Leo Durocher	60.00	30.00	18.00
234	Clint Hartung	14.00	7.00	4.25
235	Jack "Lucky" Lohrke	14.00	7.00	4.25
236	Warren "Buddy" Rosar	14.00	7.00	4.25
237	Billy Goodman	14.00	7.00	4.25
238	Pete Reiser	20.00	10.00	6.00
239	Bill MacDonald	14.00	7.00	4.25
240	Joe Haynes	14.00	7.00	4.25
241	Irv Noren	14.00	7.00	4.25
242	Sam Jethroe	20.00	10.00	6.00
243	John Antonelli	20.00	10.00	6.00
244	Cliff Fannin	14.00	7.00	4.25
245	John Berardino	20.00	10.00	6.00
246	Bill Serena	14.00	7.00	4.25
247	Bob Ramazotti	14.00	7.00	4.25
248	*Johnny Klippstein*	20.00	10.00	6.00
249	Johnny Groth	14.00	7.00	4.25
250	Hank Borowy	14.00	7.00	4.25
251	Willard Ramsdell	14.00	7.00	4.25
252	Homer "Dixie" Howell	14.00	7.00	4.25
253	*Mickey Mantle*	8000.00	4000.00	2500.
254	*Jackie Jensen*	70.00	35.00	21.00
255	Milo Candini	60.00	30.00	18.00
256	Ken Silvestri	60.00	30.00	18.00
257	Birdie Tebbetts	60.00	30.00	18.00
258	*Luke Easter*	60.00	30.00	18.00
259	Charlie Dressen	60.00	30.00	18.00
260	Carl Erskine	90.00	45.00	27.00
261	Wally Moses	60.00	30.00	18.00
262	Gus Zernial	60.00	30.00	18.00
263	Howie Pollett (Pollet)	60.00	30.00	18.00
264	Don Richmond	60.00	30.00	18.00
265	Steve Bilko	60.00	30.00	18.00
266	Harry Dorish	60.00	30.00	18.00
267	Ken Holcombe	60.00	30.00	18.00
268	Don Mueller	60.00	30.00	18.00
269	Ray Noble	60.00	30.00	18.00
270	Willard Nixon	60.00	30.00	18.00
271	Tommy Wright	60.00	30.00	18.00
272	Billy Meyer	60.00	30.00	18.00
273	Danny Murtaugh	60.00	30.00	18.00
274	George Metkovich	60.00	30.00	18.00
275	Bucky Harris	60.00	30.00	18.00
276	Frank Quinn	60.00	30.00	18.00
277	Roy Hartsfield	60.00	30.00	18.00
278	Norman Roy	60.00	30.00	18.00
279	Jim Delsing	60.00	30.00	18.00
280	Frank Overmire	60.00	30.00	18.00
281	Al Widmar	60.00	30.00	18.00
282	Frank Frisch	80.00	40.00	25.00
283	Walt Dubiel	60.00	30.00	18.00

		NR MT	EX	VG
284	Gene Bearden	60.00	30.00	18.00
285	Johnny Lipon	60.00	30.00	18.00
286	Bob Usher	60.00	30.00	18.00
287	Jim Blackburn	60.00	30.00	18.00
288	Bobby Adams	60.00	30.00	18.00
289	Cliff Mapes	60.00	30.00	18.00
290	Bill Dickey	175.00	70.00	44.00
291	Tommy Henrich	70.00	35.00	20.00
292	Eddie Pellagrini	60.00	30.00	18.00
293	Ken Johnson	60.00	30.00	18.00
294	Jocko Thompson	60.00	30.00	18.00
295	Al Lopez	90.00	45.00	25.00
296	Bob Kennedy	60.00	30.00	18.00
297	Dave Philley	60.00	30.00	18.00
298	Joe Astroth	60.00	30.00	18.00
299	Clyde King	60.00	30.00	18.00
300	Hal Rice	60.00	30.00	18.00
301	Tommy Glaviano	60.00	30.00	18.00
302	Jim Busby	60.00	30.00	18.00
303	Marv Rotblatt	60.00	30.00	18.00
304	Allen Gettel	60.00	30.00	18.00
305	*Willie Mays*	3000.00	1500.00	900.00
306	*Jim Piersall*	110.00	55.00	33.00
307	Walt Masterson	60.00	30.00	18.00
308	Ted Beard	60.00	30.00	18.00
309	Mel Queen	60.00	30.00	18.00
310	Erv Dusak	60.00	30.00	18.00
311	Mickey Harris	60.00	30.00	18.00
312	Gene Mauch	60.00	30.00	18.00
313	Ray Mueller	60.00	30.00	18.00
314	Johnny Sain	60.00	30.00	18.00
315	Zack Taylor	60.00	30.00	18.00
316	Duane Pillette	60.00	30.00	18.00
317	*Forrest Burgess*	70.00	35.00	20.00
318	Warren Hacker	60.00	30.00	18.00
319	Red Rolfe	60.00	30.00	18.00
320	Hal White	60.00	30.00	18.00
321	Earl Johnson	60.00	30.00	18.00
322	Luke Sewell	60.00	30.00	18.00
323	*Joe Adcock*	90.00	45.00	27.00
324	Johnny Pramesa	110.00	40.00	15.00

1952 Bowman

Bowman reverted back to a 252-card set in 1952, but retained the card size (2-1/16" by 3-1/8") employed the preceding year. The cards, which are color art reproductions of actual photographs, feature a facsimile autograph on the fronts. Artwork for 15 cards that were never issued was uncovered several years ago and a set featuring those cards was subsequently made available to the collecting public.

		NR MT	EX	VG
Complete Set:		9000.00	4500.00	2750.
Common Player: 1-36		18.00	9.00	5.50
Common Player: 37-216		18.00	9.00	5.50
Common Player: 217-252		30.00	15.00	9.00
1	Larry "Yogi" Berra	600.00	250.00	100.00
2	Bobby Thomson	30.00	10.00	6.00
3	Fred Hutchinson	18.00	9.00	5.50
4	Robin Roberts	60.00	30.00	18.00
5	*Orestes Minoso*	100.00	50.00	30.00
6	Virgil "Red" Stallcup	18.00	9.00	5.50
7	Mike Garcia	18.00	9.00	5.50
8	Harold "Pee Wee" Reese	100.00	50.00	30.00
9	Vern Stephens	18.00	9.00	5.50

		NR MT	EX	VG			NR MT	EX	VG
10	Bob Hooper	18.00	9.00	5.50	101	Mickey Mantle	2000.00	1000.00	600.00
11	Ralph Kiner	60.00	30.00	18.00	102	Peanuts Lowrey	18.00	9.00	5.50
12	Max Surkont	18.00	9.00	5.50	103	Joe Haynes	18.00	9.00	5.50
13	Cliff Mapes	18.00	9.00	5.50	104	Hal Jeffcoat	18.00	9.00	5.50
14	Cliff Chambers	18.00	9.00	5.50	105	Bobby Brown	20.00	10.00	6.00
15	Sam Mele	18.00	9.00	5.50	106	Randy Gumpert	18.00	9.00	5.50
16	Omar Lown	18.00	9.00	5.50	107	Del Rice	18.00	9.00	5.50
17	Ed Lopat	32.00	16.00	9.50	108	George Metkovich	18.00	9.00	5.50
18	Don Mueller	18.00	9.00	5.50	109	Tom Morgan	15.00	7.50	4.50
19	Bob Cain	18.00	9.00	5.50	110	Max Lanier	18.00	9.00	5.50
20	Willie Jones	18.00	9.00	5.50	111	Walter "Hoot" Evers	18.00	9.00	5.50
21	Nelson Fox	50.00	25.00	15.00	112	Forrest "Smokey" Burgess	18.00	9.00	5.50
22	Willard Ramsdell	18.00	9.00	5.50	113	Al Zarilla	18.00	9.00	5.50
23	Bob Lemon	40.00	20.00	12.00	114	Frank Hiller	18.00	9.00	5.50
24	Carl Furillo	30.00	15.00	9.00	115	Larry Doby	30.00	15.00	9.00
25	Maurice McDermott	18.00	9.00	5.50	116	Duke Snider	200.00	100.00	60.00
26	Eddie Joost	18.00	9.00	5.50	117	Bill Wight	18.00	9.00	5.50
27	Joe Garagiola	80.00	40.00	25.00	118	Ray Murray	18.00	9.00	5.50
28	Roy Hartsfield	18.00	9.00	5.50	119	Bill Howerton	18.00	9.00	5.50
29	Ned Garver	18.00	9.00	5.50	120	Chet Nichols	18.00	9.00	5.50
30	Al "Red" Schoendienst	60.00	30.00	18.00	121	Al Corwin	18.00	9.00	5.50
31	Eddie Yost	18.00	9.00	5.50	122	Billy Johnson	18.00	9.00	5.50
32	Eddie Miksis	18.00	9.00	5.50	123	Sid Hudson	18.00	9.00	5.50
33	*Gil McDougald*	70.00	35.00	20.00	124	George Tebbetts	18.00	9.00	5.50
34	Al Dark	20.00	10.00	6.00	125	Howie Fox	18.00	9.00	5.50
35	Gran Hamner	18.00	9.00	5.50	126	Phil Cavarretta	18.00	9.00	5.50
36	Cass Michaels	18.00	9.00	5.50	127	Dick Sisler	18.00	9.00	5.50
37	Vic Raschi	18.00	9.00	5.50	128	Don Newcombe	30.00	15.00	9.00
38	Whitey Lockman	18.00	9.00	5.50	129	Gus Niarhos	18.00	9.00	5.50
39	Vic Wertz	18.00	9.00	5.50	130	Allie Clark	18.00	9.00	5.50
40	Emory Church	18.00	9.00	5.50	131	Bob Swift	18.00	9.00	5.50
41	Chico Carrasquel	18.00	9.00	5.50	132	Dave Cole	18.00	9.00	5.50
42	Johnny Wyrostek	18.00	9.00	5.50	133	Dick Kryhoski	18.00	9.00	5.50
43	Bob Feller	110.00	55.00	33.00	134	Al Brazle	18.00	9.00	5.50
44	Roy Campanella	200.00	100.00	60.00	135	Mickey Harris	18.00	9.00	5.50
45	Johnny Pesky	18.00	9.00	5.50	136	Gene Hermanski	18.00	9.00	5.50
46	Carl Scheib	18.00	9.00	5.50	137	Stan Rojek	18.00	9.00	5.50
47	Pete Castiglione	18.00	9.00	5.50	138	Ted Wilks	18.00	9.00	5.50
48	Vern Bickford	18.00	9.00	5.50	139	Jerry Priddy	18.00	9.00	5.50
49	Jim Hearn	18.00	9.00	5.50	140	Ray Scarborough	18.00	9.00	5.50
50	Gerry Staley	18.00	9.00	5.50	141	Hank Edwards	18.00	9.00	5.50
51	Gil Coan	18.00	9.00	5.50	142	Early Wynn	40.00	20.00	12.00
52	Phil Rizzuto	80.00	40.00	25.00	143	Sandalio Consuegra	18.00	9.00	5.50
53	Richie Ashburn	50.00	25.00	15.00	144	Joe Hatten	18.00	9.00	5.50
54	Billy Pierce	18.00	9.00	5.50	145	Johnny Mize	50.00	30.00	15.00
55	Ken Raffensberger	18.00	9.00	5.50	146	Leo Durocher	35.00	17.50	10.50
56	Clyde King	18.00	9.00	5.50	147	Marlin Stuart	18.00	9.00	5.50
57	Clyde Vollmer	18.00	9.00	5.50	148	Ken Heintzelman	18.00	9.00	5.50
58	Hank Majeski	18.00	9.00	5.50	149	Howie Judson	18.00	9.00	5.50
59	Murray Dickson (Murry)	18.00	9.00	5.50	150	Herman Wehmeier	18.00	9.00	5.50
60	Sid Gordon	18.00	9.00	5.50	151	Al "Flip" Rosen	30.00	15.00	9.00
61	Tommy Byrne	18.00	9.00	5.50	152	Billy Cox	18.00	9.00	5.50
62	Joe Presko	18.00	9.00	5.50	153	Fred Hatfield	18.00	9.00	5.50
63	Irv Noren	18.00	9.00	5.50	154	Ferris Fain	18.00	9.00	5.50
64	Roy Smalley	18.00	9.00	5.50	155	Billy Meyer	18.00	9.00	5.50
65	Hank Bauer	30.00	15.00	9.00	156	Warren Spahn	90.00	45.00	27.00
66	Sal Maglie	30.00	15.00	9.00	157	Jim Delsing	18.00	9.00	5.50
67	Johnny Groth	18.00	9.00	5.50	158	Bucky Harris	30.00	15.00	9.00
68	Jim Busby	18.00	9.00	5.50	159	Dutch Leonard	18.00	9.00	5.50
69	Joe Adcock	30.00	15.00	9.00	160	Eddie Stanky	18.00	9.00	5.50
70	Carl Erskine	30.00	15.00	9.00	161	Jackie Jensen	32.00	16.00	9.50
71	Vernon Law	18.00	9.00	5.50	162	Monte Irvin	50.00	25.00	15.00
72	Earl Torgeson	18.00	9.00	5.50	163	Johnny Lipon	18.00	9.00	5.50
73	Jerry Coleman	18.00	9.00	5.50	164	Connie Ryan	18.00	9.00	5.50
74	Wes Westrum	18.00	9.00	5.50	165	Saul Rogovin	18.00	9.00	5.50
75	George Kell	40.00	20.00	12.00	166	Bobby Adams	18.00	9.00	5.50
76	Del Ennis	18.00	9.00	5.50	167	Bob Avila	18.00	9.00	5.50
77	Eddie Robinson	18.00	9.00	5.50	168	Preacher Roe	32.00	16.00	9.50
78	Lloyd Merriman	18.00	9.00	5.50	169	Walt Dropo	18.00	9.00	5.50
79	Lou Brissie	18.00	9.00	5.50	170	Joe Astroth	18.00	9.00	5.50
80	Gil Hodges	70.00	35.00	21.00	171	Mel Queen	18.00	9.00	5.50
81	Billy Goodman	18.00	9.00	5.50	172	Ebba St. Claire	18.00	9.00	5.50
82	Gus Zernial	18.00	9.00	5.50	173	Gene Bearden	18.00	9.00	5.50
83	Howie Pollet	18.00	9.00	5.50	174	Mickey Grasso	18.00	9.00	5.50
84	Sam Jethroe	18.00	9.00	5.50	175	Ransom Jackson	18.00	9.00	5.50
85	Marty Marion	18.00	9.00	5.50	176	Harry Brecheen	18.00	9.00	5.50
86	Cal Abrams	18.00	9.00	5.50	177	Gene Woodling	30.00	15.00	9.00
87	Mickey Vernon	18.00	9.00	5.50	178	Dave Williams	18.00	9.00	5.50
88	Bruce Edwards	18.00	9.00	5.50	179	Pete Suder	18.00	9.00	5.50
89	Billy Hitchcock	18.00	9.00	5.50	180	Eddie Fitzgerald (Fitz Gerald)	18.00	9.00	5.50
90	Larry Jansen	18.00	9.00	5.50	181	Joe Collins	15.00	7.50	4.50
91	Don Kolloway	18.00	9.00	5.50	182	Dave Koslo	18.00	9.00	5.50
92	Eddie Waitkus	18.00	9.00	5.50	183	Pat Mullin	18.00	9.00	5.50
93	Paul Richards	18.00	9.00	5.50	184	Curt Simmons	18.00	9.00	5.50
94	Luke Sewell	18.00	9.00	5.50	185	Eddie Stewart	18.00	9.00	5.50
95	Luke Easter	18.00	9.00	5.50	186	Frank Smith	18.00	9.00	5.50
96	Ralph Branca	18.00	9.00	5.50	187	Jim Hegan	18.00	9.00	5.50
97	Willard Marshall	18.00	9.00	5.50	188	Charlie Dressen	15.00	7.50	4.50
98	Jimmy Dykes	18.00	9.00	5.50	189	Jim Piersall	18.00	9.00	5.50
99	Clyde McCullough	18.00	9.00	5.50	190	Dick Fowler	18.00	9.00	5.50
100	Sibby Sisti	18.00	9.00	5.50	191	*Bob Friend*	15.00	7.50	4.50

		NR MT	EX	VG
192	John Cusick	18.00	9.00	5.50
193	Bobby Young	18.00	9.00	5.50
194	Bob Porterfield	18.00	9.00	5.50
195	Frank Baumholtz	18.00	9.00	5.50
196	Stan Musial	500.00	250.00	150.00
197	Charlie Silvera	15.00	7.50	4.50
198	Chuck Diering	18.00	9.00	5.50
199	Ted Gray	18.00	9.00	5.50
200	Ken Silvestri	18.00	9.00	5.50
201	Ray Coleman	18.00	9.00	5.50
202	Harry Perkowski	18.00	9.00	5.50
203	Steve Gromek	18.00	9.00	5.50
204	Andy Pafko	18.00	9.00	5.50
205	Walt Masterson	18.00	9.00	5.50
206	Elmer Valo	18.00	9.00	5.50
207	George Strickland	18.00	9.00	5.50
208	Walker Cooper	18.00	9.00	5.50
209	Dick Littlefield	18.00	9.00	5.50
210	Archie Wilson	18.00	9.00	5.50
211	Paul Minner	18.00	9.00	5.50
212	Solly Hemus	18.00	9.00	5.50
213	Monte Kennedy	18.00	9.00	5.50
214	Ray Boone	18.00	9.00	5.50
215	Sheldon Jones	18.00	9.00	5.50
216	Matt Batts	18.00	9.00	5.50
217	Casey Stengel	125.00	67.00	37.00
218	Willie Mays	1000.00	500.00	300.00
219	Neil Berry	32.00	16.00	9.50
220	Russ Meyer	32.00	16.00	9.50
221	Lou Kretlow	32.00	16.00	9.50
222	Homer "Dixie" Howell	32.00	16.00	9.50
223	Harry Simpson	32.00	16.00	9.50
224	Johnny Schmitz	32.00	16.00	9.50
225	Del Wilber	32.00	16.00	9.50
226	Alex Kellner	32.00	16.00	9.50
227	Clyde Sukeforth	32.00	16.00	9.50
228	Bob Chipman	32.00	16.00	9.50
229	Hank Arft	32.00	16.00	9.50
230	Frank Shea	32.00	16.00	9.50
231	Dee Fondy	32.00	16.00	9.50
232	Enos Slaughter	90.00	45.00	25.00
233	Bob Kuzava	32.00	16.00	9.50
234	Fred Fitzsimmons	32.00	16.00	9.50
235	Steve Souchock	32.00	16.00	9.50
236	Tommy Brown	32.00	16.00	9.50
237	Sherman Lollar	32.00	16.00	9.50
238	*Roy McMillan*	32.00	16.00	9.50
239	Dale Mitchell	32.00	16.00	9.50
240	*Billy Loes*	40.00	20.00	12.50
241	Mel Parnell	32.00	16.00	9.50
242	Everett Kell	32.00	16.00	9.50
243	George "Red" Munger	32.00	16.00	9.50
244	*Lew Burdette*	70.00	35.00	21.00
245	George Schmees	32.00	16.00	9.50
246	Jerry Snyder	32.00	16.00	9.50
247	John Pramesa	32.00	16.00	9.50
248	Bill Werle	32.00	16.00	9.50
249	Henry Thompson	32.00	16.00	9.50
250	Ivan Delock	32.00	16.00	9.50
251	Jack Lohrke	32.00	12.50	7.50
252	Frank Crosetti	150.00	50.00	20.00

1953 Bowman Color

The first set of current major league players featuring actual color photographs, the 160-card 1953 Bowman Color set remains one of the most popular issues of the post-war era. The set is greatly appreciated for its uncluttered look; card fronts that

contain no names, teams or facsimile autographs. Bowman increased the size of their cards to a 2-1/2" by 3-3/4" size in order to better compete with Topps Chewing Gum. Bowman copied an idea from the 1952 Topps set and developed card backs that gave player career and previous year statistics. The high-numbered cards (#'s 113-160) are the scarcest of the set, with #'s 113-128 being exceptionally difficult to find.

		NR MT	EX	VG
Complete Set:		12000.00	6000.00	3500.
Common Player: 1-112		30.00	15.00	9.00
Common Player: 113-128		40.00	20.00	12.00
Common Player: 129-160		40.00	20.00	12.00
1	Davey Williams	100.00	25.00	12.00
2	Vic Wertz	30.00	15.00	9.00
3	Sam Jethroe	30.00	15.00	9.00
4	Art Houtteman	30.00	15.00	9.00
5	Sid Gordon	30.00	15.00	9.00
6	Joe Ginsberg	30.00	15.00	9.00
7	Harry Chiti	30.00	15.00	9.00
8	Al Rosen	40.00	20.00	12.00
9	Phil Rizzuto	110.00	55.00	33.00
10	Richie Ashburn	85.00	42.00	26.00
11	Bobby Shantz	30.00	15.00	9.00
12	Carl Erskine	50.00	30.00	15.00
13	Gus Zernial	30.00	15.00	9.00
14	Billy Loes	30.00	15.00	9.00
15	Jim Busby	30.00	15.00	9.00
16	Bob Friend	30.00	15.00	9.00
17	Gerry Staley	30.00	15.00	9.00
18	Nelson Fox	75.00	38.00	23.00
19	Al Dark	30.00	15.00	9.00
20	Don Lenhardt	30.00	15.00	9.00
21	Joe Garagiola	80.00	40.00	25.00
22	Bob Porterfield	30.00	15.00	9.00
23	Herman Wehmeier	30.00	15.00	9.00
24	Jackie Jensen	40.00	20.00	12.00
25	Walter "Hoot" Evers	30.00	15.00	9.00
26	Roy McMillan	30.00	15.00	9.00
27	Vic Raschi	40.00	20.00	12.00
28	Forrest "Smoky" Burgess	30.00	15.00	9.00
29	Roberto Avila	30.00	15.00	9.00
30	Phil Cavarretta	30.00	15.00	9.00
31	Jimmy Dykes	30.00	15.00	9.00
32	Stan Musial	500.00	250.00	150.00
33	Harold "Peewee" Reese	450.00	225.00	135.00
34	Gil Coan	30.00	15.00	9.00
35	Maury McDermott	30.00	15.00	9.00
36	Orestes Minoso	50.00	30.00	15.00
37	Jim Wilson	30.00	15.00	9.00
38	Harry Byrd	30.00	15.00	9.00
39	Paul Richards	30.00	15.00	9.00
40	Larry Doby	40.00	20.00	12.00
41	Sammy White	30.00	15.00	9.00
42	Tommy Brown	30.00	15.00	9.00
43	Mike Garcia	30.00	15.00	9.00
44	Hank Bauer, Yogi Berra, Mickey Mantle	400.00	200.00	125.00
45	Walt Dropo	30.00	15.00	9.00
46	Roy Campanella	250.00	125.00	75.00
47	Ned Garver	30.00	15.00	9.00
48	Hank Sauer	30.00	15.00	9.00
49	Eddie Stanky	30.00	15.00	9.00
50	Lou Kretlow	30.00	15.00	9.00
51	Monte Irvin	50.00	25.00	15.00
52	Marty Marion	30.00	15.00	9.00
53	Del Rice	30.00	15.00	9.00
54	Chico Carrasquel	30.00	15.00	9.00
55	Leo Durocher	60.00	30.00	18.00
56	Bob Cain	30.00	15.00	9.00
57	Lou Boudreau	50.00	25.00	15.00
58	Willard Marshall	30.00	15.00	9.00
59	Mickey Mantle	2200.00	1100.00	650.00
60	Granny Hamner	30.00	15.00	9.00
61	George Kell	30.00	15.00	9.00
62	Ted Kluszewski	50.00	25.00	15.00
63	Gil McDougald	50.00	25.00	15.00
64	Curt Simmons	30.00	15.00	9.00
65	Robin Roberts	70.00	35.00	21.00
66	Mel Parnell	30.00	15.00	9.00
67	Mel Clark	30.00	15.00	9.00
68	Allie Reynolds	50.00	25.00	15.00
69	Charlie Grimm	30.00	15.00	9.00
70	Clint Courtney	30.00	15.00	9.00
71	Paul Minner	30.00	15.00	9.00
72	Ted Gray	30.00	15.00	9.00
73	Billy Pierce	30.00	15.00	9.00

		NR MT	EX	VG
74	Don Mueller	30.00	15.00	9.00
75	Saul Rogovin	30.00	15.00	9.00
76	Jim Hearn	30.00	15.00	9.00
77	Mickey Grasso	30.00	15.00	9.00
78	Carl Furillo	50.00	25.00	15.00
79	Ray Boone	30.00	15.00	9.00
80	Ralph Kiner	80.00	40.00	25.00
81	Enos Slaughter	70.00	35.00	21.00
82	Joe Astroth	30.00	15.00	9.00
83	Jack Daniels	30.00	15.00	9.00
84	Hank Bauer	50.00	25.00	15.00
85	Solly Hemus	30.00	15.00	9.00
86	Harry Simpson	30.00	15.00	9.00
87	Harry Perkowski	30.00	15.00	9.00
88	Joe Dobson	30.00	15.00	9.00
89	Sandalio Consuegra	30.00	15.00	9.00
90	Joe Nuxhall	30.00	15.00	9.00
91	Steve Souchock	30.00	15.00	9.00
92	Gil Hodges	100.00	45.00	27.00
93	Billy Martin, Phil Rizzuto	200.00	100.00	60.00
94	Bob Addis	30.00	15.00	9.00
95	Wally Moses	30.00	15.00	9.00
96	Sal Maglie	45.00	23.00	13.50
97	Eddie Mathews	175.00	87.00	52.00
98	Hector Rodriquez	30.00	15.00	9.00
99	Warren Spahn	175.00	87.00	52.00
100	Bill Wight	30.00	15.00	9.00
101	Al "Red" Schoendienst	80.00	40.00	25.00
102	Jim Hegan	30.00	15.00	9.00
103	Del Ennis	30.00	15.00	9.00
104	Luke Easter	30.00	15.00	9.00
105	Eddie Joost	30.00	15.00	9.00
106	Ken Raffensberger	30.00	15.00	9.00
107	Alex Kellner	30.00	15.00	9.00
108	Bobby Adams	30.00	15.00	9.00
109	Ken Wood	30.00	15.00	9.00
110	Bob Rush	30.00	15.00	9.00
111	Jim Dyck	30.00	15.00	9.00
112	Toby Atwell	30.00	15.00	9.00
113	Karl Drews	40.00	20.00	12.00
114	Bob Feller	250.00	125.00	75.00
115	Cloyd Boyer	40.00	20.00	12.00
116	Eddie Yost	40.00	20.00	12.00
117	Duke Snider	600.00	300.00	175.00
118	Billy Martin	300.00	150.00	90.00
119	Dale Mitchell	40.00	20.00	12.00
120	Marlin Stuart	40.00	20.00	12.00
121	Yogi Berra	500.00	250.00	150.00
122	Bill Serena	40.00	20.00	12.00
123	Johnny Lipon	40.00	20.00	12.00
124	Charlie Dressen	45.00	23.00	13.50
125	Fred Hatfield	40.00	20.00	12.00
126	Al Corwin	40.00	20.00	12.00
127	Dick Kryhoski	40.00	20.00	12.00
128	Whitey Lockman	40.00	20.00	12.00
129	Russ Meyer	50.00	25.00	15.00
130	Cass Michaels	40.00	20.00	12.00
131	Connie Ryan	40.00	20.00	12.00
132	Fred Hutchinson	50.00	25.00	15.00
133	Willie Jones	40.00	20.00	12.00
134	Johnny Pesky	50.00	25.00	15.00
135	Bobby Morgan	50.00	25.00	15.00
136	Jim Brideweser	40.00	20.00	12.00
137	Sam Dente	40.00	20.00	12.00
138	Bubba Church	40.00	20.00	12.00
139	Pete Runnels	50.00	25.00	15.00
140	Alpha Brazle	40.00	20.00	12.00
141	Frank "Spec" Shea	40.00	20.00	12.00
142	Larry Miggins	40.00	20.00	12.00
143	Al Lopez	60.00	30.00	18.00
144	Warren Hacker	40.00	20.00	12.00
145	George Shuba	50.00	25.00	15.00
146	Early Wynn	125.00	62.00	40.00
147	Clem Koshorek	40.00	20.00	12.00
148	Billy Goodman	40.00	20.00	12.00
149	Al Corwin	40.00	20.00	12.00
150	Carl Scheib	40.00	20.00	12.00
151	Joe Adcock	40.00	20.00	12.00
152	Clyde Vollmer	40.00	20.00	12.00
153	Ed "Whitey" Ford	450.00	225.00	135.00
154	Omar "Turk" Lown	40.00	20.00	12.00
155	Allie Clark	40.00	20.00	12.00
156	Max Surkont	40.00	20.00	12.00
157	Sherman Lollar	50.00	25.00	15.00
158	Howard Fox	40.00	20.00	12.00
159	Mickey Vernon (Photo actually Floyd Baker)	40.00	17.50	10.50
160	Cal Abrams	90.00	30.00	15.00

1953 Bowman Black & White

The 1953 Bowman Black and White set is similar in all respects to the 1953 Bowman Color set, except that it lacks color. Purportedly, high costs in producing the color series forced Bowman to issue the set in black and white. Sixty-four cards, which measure 2-1/2" by 3-3/4", comprise the set.

		NR MT	EX	VG
Complete Set:		2500.00	1250.00	700.00
Common Player:		30.00	15.00	9.00
1	Gus Bell	125.00	55.00	35.00
2	Willard Nixon	32.00	11.00	6.50
3	Bill Rigney	32.00	16.00	9.50
4	Pat Mullin	30.00	15.00	9.00
5	Dee Fondy	30.00	15.00	9.00
6	Ray Murray	30.00	15.00	9.00
7	Andy Seminick	30.00	15.00	9.00
8	Pete Suder	30.00	15.00	9.00
9	Walt Masterson	30.00	15.00	9.00
10	Dick Sisler	30.00	15.00	9.00
11	Dick Gernert	30.00	15.00	9.00
12	Randy Jackson	30.00	15.00	9.00
13	Joe Tipton	30.00	15.00	9.00
14	Bill Nicholson	30.00	15.00	9.00
15	Johnny Mize	125.00	67.00	37.00
16	Stu Miller	30.00	15.00	9.00
17	Virgil Trucks	32.00	16.00	9.50
18	Billy Hoeft	30.00	15.00	9.00
19	Paul LaPalme	30.00	15.00	9.00
20	Eddie Robinson	30.00	15.00	9.00
21	Clarence "Bud" Podbielan	30.00	15.00	9.00
22	Matt Batts	30.00	15.00	9.00
23	Wilmer Mizell	30.00	15.00	9.00
24	Del Wilber	30.00	15.00	9.00
25	John Sain	60.00	30.00	18.00
26	Preacher Roe	60.00	30.00	18.00
27	Bob Lemon	125.00	67.00	37.00
28	Hoyt Wilhelm	125.00	67.00	37.00
29	Sid Hudson	30.00	15.00	9.00
30	Walker Cooper	30.00	15.00	9.00
31	Gene Woodling	50.00	25.00	15.00
32	Rocky Bridges	30.00	15.00	9.00
33	Bob Kuzava	32.00	16.00	9.50
34	Ebba St. Clair (St. Claire)	30.00	15.00	9.00
35	Johnny Wyrostek	30.00	15.00	9.00
36	Jim Piersall	50.00	25.00	15.00
37	Hal Jeffcoat	30.00	15.00	9.00
38	Dave Cole	30.00	15.00	9.00
39	Casey Stengel	300.00	150.00	90.00
40	Larry Jansen	30.00	15.00	9.00
41	Bob Ramazotti	30.00	15.00	9.00
42	Howie Judson	30.00	15.00	9.00
43	Hal Bevan	30.00	15.00	9.00
44	Jim Delsing	30.00	15.00	9.00
45	Irv Noren	32.00	16.00	9.50
46	Bucky Harris	50.00	25.00	15.00
47	Jack Lohrke	30.00	15.00	9.00
48	Steve Ridzik	30.00	15.00	9.00
49	Floyd Baker	30.00	15.00	9.00
50	Emil "Dutch" Leonard	30.00	15.00	9.00
51	Lou Burdette	50.00	25.00	15.00
52	Ralph Branca	40.00	20.00	12.00
53	Morris Martin	30.00	15.00	9.00
54	Bill Miller	32.00	16.00	9.50
55	Don Johnson	30.00	15.00	9.00

		NR MT	EX	VG
56	Roy Smalley	30.00	15.00	9.00
57	Andy Pafko	30.00	15.00	9.00
58	Jim Konstanty	30.00	15.00	9.00
59	Duane Pillette	30.00	15.00	9.00
60	Billy Cox	40.00	20.00	12.00
61	Tom Gorman	32.00	16.00	9.50
62	Keith Thomas	30.00	15.00	9.00
63	Steve Gromek	32.00	16.00	9.50
64	Andy Hansen	50.00	15.00	9.00
81	Joe Black	50.00	25.00	15.00

A player's name in italic indicates a rookie card. An (FC) indicates a player's first card for that particular card company.

1954 Bowman

Bowman's 1954 set consists of 224 full-color cards that measure 2-1/2" by 3-3/4". It is believed that contractual problems caused the pulling of card #66 (Ted Williams) from the set, creating one of the most sought-after scarcities of the post-war era. The Williams card was replaced by Jim Piersall (who is also #210) in subsequent print runs. The set contains over 40 variations, most involving statistical errors on the card backs that were corrected. Neither variation carries a premium value as both varieties appear to have been printed in equal amounts. The complete set price that follows does not include all variations or #66 Williams.

		NR MT	EX	VG
Complete Set:		4500.00	2250.00	1350.
Common Player: 1-112		8.00	4.00	2.50
Common Player: 113-224		10.00	5.00	3.00
1	Phil Rizzuto	150.00	50.00	21.00
2	Jack Jensen	15.00	7.50	4.50
3	Marion Fricano	8.00	4.00	2.50
4	Bob Hooper	8.00	4.00	2.50
5	William Hunter	8.00	4.00	2.50
6	Nelson Fox	25.00	12.50	7.50
7	Walter Dropo	8.00	4.00	2.50
8	James F. Busby	8.00	4.00	2.50
9	Dave Williams	8.00	4.00	2.50
10	Carl Daniel Erskine	12.00	6.00	3.50
11	Sid Gordon	8.00	4.00	2.50
12a	Roy McMillan (551/1290 At Bat)	8.00	4.00	2.50
12b	Roy McMillan (557/1296 At Bat)	8.00	4.00	2.50
13	Paul Minner	8.00	4.00	2.50
14	Gerald Staley	8.00	4.00	2.50
15	Richie Ashburn	35.00	17.50	10.50
16	Jim Wilson	8.00	4.00	2.50
17	Tom Gorman	8.00	4.00	2.50
18	Walter "Hoot" Evers	8.00	4.00	2.50
19	Bobby Shantz	8.00	4.00	2.50
20	Artie Houtteman	8.00	4.00	2.50
21	Victor Wertz	8.00	4.00	2.50
22a	Sam Mele (213/1661 Putouts)	8.00	4.00	2.50
22b	Sam Mele (217/1665 Putouts)	8.00	4.00	2.50
23	*Harvey Kuenn*	35.00	17.50	10.50
24	Bob Porterfield	8.00	4.00	2.50
25a	Wes Westrum (1.000/.987 Field Avg.)	8.00	4.00	2.50

		NR MT	EX	VG
25b	Wes Westrum (.982/.986 Field Avg.)	8.00	4.00	2.50
26a	Billy Cox (1.000/.960 Field Avg.)	8.00	4.00	2.50
26b	Billy Cox (.972/.960 Field Avg.)	8.00	4.00	2.50
27	Richard Roy Cole	8.00	4.00	2.50
28a	Jim Greengrass (Birthplace Addison, N.J.)	8.00	4.00	2.50
28b	Jim Greengrass (Birthplace Addison, N.Y.)	8.00	4.00	2.50
29	Johnny Klippstein	8.00	4.00	2.50
30	Delbert Rice Jr.	8.00	4.00	2.50
31	"Smoky" Burgess	8.00	4.00	2.50
32	Del Crandall	8.00	4.00	2.50
33a	Victor Raschi (no traded line)	12.00	6.00	3.50
33b	Victor Raschi (with traded line)	30.00	15.00	9.00
34	Sammy White	8.00	4.00	2.50
35a	Eddie Joost (quiz answer is 8)	8.00	4.00	2.50
35b	Eddie Joost (quiz answer is 33)	8.00	4.00	2.50
36	George Strickland	8.00	4.00	2.50
37	Dick Kokos	8.00	4.00	2.50
38a	Orestes Minoso (.895/.961 Field Avg.)	8.00	4.00	2.50
38b	Orestes Minoso (.963/.963 Field Avg.)	8.00	4.00	2.50
39	Ned Garver	8.00	4.00	2.50
40	Gil Coan	8.00	4.00	2.50
41a	Alvin Dark (.986/.960 Field Avg.)	8.00	4.00	2.50
41b	Alvin Dark (.968/.960 Field Avg.)	8.00	4.00	2.50
42	Billy Loes	8.00	4.00	2.50
43a	Robert B. Friend (20 shutouts in quiz question)	8.00	4.00	2.50
43b	Robert B. Friend (16 shutouts in quiz question)	8.00	4.00	2.50
44	Harry Perkowski	8.00	4.00	2.50
45	Ralph Kiner	40.00	20.00	12.00
46	Eldon Repulski	8.00	4.00	2.50
47a	Granville Hamner (.970/.953 Field Avg.)	8.00	4.00	2.50
47b	Granville Hamner (.953/.951 Field Avg.)	8.00	4.00	2.50
48	Jack Dittmer	8.00	4.00	2.50
49	Harry Byrd	8.00	4.00	2.50
50	George Kell	25.00	12.50	7.50
51	Alex Kellner	8.00	4.00	2.50
52	Myron N. Ginsberg	8.00	4.00	2.50
53a	Don Lenhardt (.969/.984 Field Avg.)	8.00	4.00	2.50
53b	Don Lenhardt (.966/.983 Field Avg.)	8.00	4.00	2.50
54	Alfonso Carrasquel	8.00	4.00	2.50
55	Jim Delsing	8.00	4.00	2.50
56	Maurice M. McDermott	8.00	4.00	2.50
57	Hoyt Wilhelm	30.00	15.00	9.00
58	"Pee Wee" Reese	70.00	35.00	21.00
59	Robert D. Schultz	8.00	4.00	2.50
60	Fred Baczewski	8.00	4.00	2.50
61a	Eddie Miksis (.954/.962 Field Avg.)	8.00	4.00	2.50
61b	Eddie Miksis (.954/.961 Field Avg.)	8.00	4.00	2.50
62	Enos Slaughter	40.00	20.00	12.00
63	Earl Torgeson	8.00	4.00	2.50
64	Ed Mathews	60.00	30.00	18.00
65	Mickey Mantle	900.00	450.00	275.00
66a	Ted Williams	4250.00	2125.00	1250.
66b	Jimmy Piersall	100.00	50.00	30.00
67a	Carl Scheib (.306 Pct. with two lines under bio)	8.00	4.00	2.50
67b	Carl Scheib (.306 Pct. with one line under bio)	8.00	4.00	2.50
67c	Carl Scheib (.300 Pct.)	8.00	4.00	2.50
68	Bob Avila	8.00	4.00	2.50
69	Clinton Courtney	8.00	4.00	2.50
70	Willard Marshall	8.00	4.00	2.50
71	Ted Gray	8.00	4.00	2.50
72	Ed Yost	8.00	4.00	2.50
73	Don Mueller	8.00	4.00	2.50
74	James Gilliam	15.00	7.50	4.50
75	Max Surkont	8.00	4.00	2.50
76	Joe Nuxhall	8.00	4.00	2.50
77	Bob Rush	8.00	4.00	2.50
78	Sal A. Yvars	8.00	4.00	2.50
79	Curt Simmons	8.00	4.00	2.50
80a	John Logan (106 Runs)	8.00	4.00	2.50
80b	John Logan (100 Runs)	8.00	4.00	2.50
81a	Jerry Coleman (1.000/.975 Field Avg.)	8.00	4.00	2.50
81b	Jerry Coleman (.952/.975 Field Avg.)	8.00	4.00	2.50
82a	Bill Goodman (.965/.986 Field Avg.)	8.00	4.00	2.50
82b	Bill Goodman (.972/.985 Field Avg.)	8.00	4.00	2.50

		NR MT	EX	VG
83	Ray Murray	8.00	4.00	2.50
84	Larry Doby	12.00	6.00	3.50
85a	Jim Dyck (.926/.956 Field Avg.)	8.00	4.00	2.50
85b	Jim Dyck (.947/.960 Field Avg.)	8.00	4.00	2.50
86	Harry Dorish	8.00	4.00	2.50
87	Don Lund	8.00	4.00	2.50
88	Tommy Umphlett	8.00	4.00	2.50
89	Willie May (Mays)	350.00	175.00	105.00
90	Roy Campanella	150.00	60.00	38.00
91	Cal Abrams	8.00	4.00	2.50
92	Kenneth David Raffensberger	8.00	4.00	2.50
93a	Bill Serena (.983/.966 Field Avg.)	8.00	4.00	2.50
93b	Bill Serena (.977/.966 Field Avg.)	8.00	4.00	2.50
94a	Solly Hemus (476/1343 Assists)	8.00	4.00	2.50
94b	Solly Hemus (477/1343 Assists)	8.00	4.00	2.50
95	Robin Roberts	40.00	20.00	12.00
96	Joe Adcock	8.00	4.00	2.50
97	Gil McDougald	15.00	7.50	4.50
98	Ellis Kinder	8.00	4.00	2.50
99a	Peter Suder (.985/.974 Field Avg.)	8.00	4.00	2.50
99b	Peter Suder (.978/.974 Field Avg.)	8.00	4.00	2.50
100	Mike Garcia	8.00	4.00	2.50
101	Don James Larsen	45.00	23.00	13.50
102	Bill Pierce	8.00	4.00	2.50
103a	Stephen Souchock (144/1192 Putouts)	8.00	4.00	2.50
103b	Stephen Souchock (147/1195 Putouts)	8.00	4.00	2.50
104	Frank Spec Shea	8.00	4.00	2.50
105a	Sal Maglie (quiz answer is 8)	8.00	4.00	2.50
105b	Sal Maglie (quiz answer is 1904)	8.00	4.00	2.50
106	"Clem" Labine	8.00	4.00	2.50
107	Paul E. LaPalme	8.00	4.00	2.50
108	Bobby Adams	8.00	4.00	2.50
109	Roy Smalley	8.00	4.00	2.50
110	Al Schoendienst	35.00	17.50	10.50
111	Murry Monroe Dickson	8.00	4.00	2.50
112	Andy Pafko	8.00	4.00	2.50
113	Allie Reynolds	12.00	6.00	3.50
114	Willard Nixon	12.00	6.00	3.50
115	Don Bollweg	12.00	6.00	3.50
116	Luscious Luke Easter	12.00	6.00	3.50
117	Dick Kryhoski	12.00	6.00	3.50
118	Robert R. Boyd	12.00	6.00	3.50
119	Fred Hatfield	12.00	6.00	3.50
120	Mel Hoderlein	12.00	6.00	3.50
121	Ray Katt	12.00	6.00	3.50
122	Carl Furillo	15.00	7.50	4.50
123	Toby Atwell	12.00	6.00	3.50
124a	Gus Bell (15/27 Errors)	12.00	6.00	3.50
124b	Gus Bell (11/26 Errors)	12.00	6.00	3.50
125	Warren Hacker	12.00	6.00	3.50
126	Cliff Chambers	12.00	6.00	3.50
127	Del Ennis	12.00	6.00	3.50
128	Ebba St Claire	12.00	6.00	3.50
129	Hank Bauer	20.00	10.00	6.00
130	Milt Bolling	12.00	6.00	3.50
131	Joe Astroth	12.00	6.00	3.50
132	Bob Feller	80.00	40.00	25.00
133	Duane Pillette	12.00	6.00	3.50
134	Luis Aloma	12.00	6.00	3.50
135	Johnny Pesky	12.00	6.00	3.50
136	Clyde Vollmer	12.00	6.00	3.50
137	Elmer N. Corwin Jr.	12.00	6.00	3.50
138a	Gil Hodges (.993/.991 Field Avg.)	50.00	25.00	15.00
138b	Gil Hodges (.992/.991 Field Avg.)	55.00	28.00	16.50
139a	Preston Ward (.961/.992 Field Avg.)	12.00	6.00	3.50
139b	Preston Ward (.990/.992 Field Avg.)	12.00	6.00	3.50
140a	Saul Rogovin (7-12 Won/Lost with 2 Strikeouts)	12.00	6.00	3.50
140b	Saul Rogovin (7-12 Won/Lost with 62 Strikeouts)	12.00	6.00	3.50
140c	Saul Rogovin (8-12 Won/Lost)	12.00	6.00	3.50
141	Joe Garagiola	45.00	23.00	13.50
142	Al Brazle	12.00	6.00	3.50
143	Puddin Head Jones	12.00	6.00	3.50
144	Ernie Johnson	12.00	6.00	3.50
145a	Billy Martin (.985/.983 Field Avg.)	50.00	25.00	15.00
145b	Billy Martin (.983/.982 Field Avg.)	60.00	30.00	18.00
146	Dick Gernert	12.00	6.00	3.50
147	Joe DeMaestri	12.00	6.00	3.50
148	Dale Mitchell	12.00	6.00	3.50
149	Bob Young	12.00	6.00	3.50

		NR MT	EX	VG
150	Cass Michaels	12.00	6.00	3.50
151	Patrick J. Mullin	12.00	6.00	3.50
152	Mickey Vernon	12.00	6.00	3.50
153a	Whitey Lockman (100/331 Assists)	12.00	6.00	3.50
153b	Whitey Lockman (102/333 Assists)	12.00	6.00	3.50
154	Don Newcombe	25.00	12.50	7.50
155	Frank J. Thomas	12.00	6.00	3.50
156a	Everett Lamar Bridges (320/467 Assists)	12.00	6.00	3.50
156b	Everett Lamar Bridges (328/475 Assists)	12.00	6.00	3.50
157	Omar Lown	12.00	6.00	3.50
158	Stu Miller	12.00	6.00	3.50
159	John Lindell	12.00	6.00	3.50
160	Danny O'Connell	12.00	6.00	3.50
161	Yogi Berra	175.00	87.00	52.00
162	Ted Lepcio	12.00	6.00	3.50
163a	Dave Philley (152 Games with no traded line)	12.00	6.00	3.50
163b	Dave Philley (152 Games with traded line)	25.00	12.50	7.50
163c	Dave Philley (157 Games with traded line)	12.00	6.00	3.50
164	Early "Gus" Wynn	40.00	20.00	12.50
165	Johnny Groth	12.00	6.00	3.50
166	Sandalio Consuegra	12.00	6.00	3.50
167	Bill Hoeft	12.00	6.00	3.50
168	Edward Fitzgerald (Fitz Gerald)	12.00	6.00	3.50
169	Larry Jansen	12.00	6.00	3.50
170	Edwin D. Snider	150.00	75.00	45.00
171	Carlos Bernier	12.00	6.00	3.50
172	Andy Seminick	12.00	6.00	3.50
173	Dee V. Fondy Jr.	12.00	6.00	3.50
174a	Peter Paul Castiglione (.966/.959 Field Avg.)	12.00	6.00	3.50
174b	Peter Paul Castiglione (.970/.959 Field Avg.)	12.00	6.00	3.50
175	Melvin E. Clark	12.00	6.00	3.50
176	Vernon Bickford	12.00	6.00	3.50
177	Edward Ford	100.00	50.00	30.00
178	Del Wilber	12.00	6.00	3.50
179a	Morris Martin (44 ERA)	12.00	6.00	3.50
179b	Morris Martin (4.44 ERA)	12.00	6.00	3.50
180	Joe Tipton	12.00	6.00	3.50
181	Lester Moss	12.00	6.00	3.50
182	Sherman Lollar	12.00	6.00	3.50
183	Matt Batts	12.00	6.00	3.50
184	Mickey Grasso	12.00	6.00	3.50
185a	Daryl Spencer (.941/.944 Field Avg.)	12.00	6.00	3.50
185b	Daryl Spencer (.933/.936 Field Avg.)	12.00	6.00	3.50
186	Russell Meyer	12.00	6.00	3.50
187	Verne Law (Vern)	12.00	6.00	3.50
188	Frank Smith	12.00	6.00	3.50
189	Ransom Jackson	12.00	6.00	3.50
190	Joe Presko	12.00	6.00	3.50
191	Karl A. Drews	12.00	6.00	3.50
192	Selva L. Burdette	12.00	6.00	3.50
193	Eddie Robinson	12.00	6.00	3.50
194	Sid Hudson	12.00	6.00	3.50
195	Bob Cain	12.00	6.00	3.50
196	Bob Lemon	35.00	17.50	10.50
197	Lou Kretlow	12.00	6.00	3.50
198	Virgil Trucks	12.00	6.00	3.50
199	Steve Gromek	12.00	6.00	3.50
200	C. Marrero	12.00	6.00	3.50
201	Bob Thomson	12.00	6.00	3.50
202	George Shuba	12.00	6.00	3.50
203	Vic Janowicz	12.00	6.00	3.50
204	Jack Collum	12.00	6.00	3.50
205	Hal Jeffcoat	12.00	6.00	3.50
206	Steve Bilko	12.00	6.00	3.50
207	Stan Lopata	12.00	6.00	3.50
208	Johnny Antonelli	12.00	6.00	3.50
209	Gene Woodling (photo reversed)	12.00	6.00	3.50
210	Jimmy Piersall	20.00	10.00	6.00
211	Alfred James Robertson Jr.	12.00	6.00	3.50
212a	Owen L. Friend (.964/.957 Field Avg.)	12.00	6.00	3.50
212b	Owen L. Friend (.967/.958 Field Avg.)	12.00	6.00	3.50
213	Dick Littlefield	12.00	6.00	3.50
214	Ferris Fain	12.00	6.00	3.50
215	Johnny Bucha	12.00	6.00	3.50
216a	Jerry Snyder (.988/.988 Field Avg.)	12.00	6.00	3.50
216b	Jerry Snyder (.968/.968 Field Avg.)	12.00	6.00	3.50

		NR MT	EX	VG
217a	Henry Thompson (.956/.951 Field Avg.)			
		12.00	6.00	3.50
217b	Henry Thompson (.958/.952 Field Avg.)			
		12.00	6.00	3.50
218	Preacher Roe	12.00	6.00	3.50
219	Hal Rice	12.00	6.00	3.50
220	Hobie Landrith	12.00	6.00	3.50
221	Frank Baumholtz	12.00	6.00	3.50
222	Memo Luna	12.00	6.00	3.50
223	Steve Ridzik	12.00	6.00	3.50
224	William Bruton	30.00	9.00	4.00

1955 Bowman

Bowman produced its final baseball card set in 1955, a popular issue which has player photographs placed inside a television set design. The set consists of 320 cards that measure 2-1/2" by 3-3/4" in size. The high-numbered cards (#'s 225-320) are scarcest in the set and include 31 umpire cards.

		NR MT	EX	VG
Complete Set:		5000.00	2500.00	1500.
Common Player: 1-224		9.00	4.50	2.75
Common Player: 225-320		25.00	12.50	7.50
1	Hoyt Wilhelm	100.00	20.00	12.00
2	Al Dark	10.00	5.00	3.00
3	Joe Coleman	9.00	4.50	2.75
4	Eddie Waitkus	9.00	4.50	2.75
5	Jim Robertson	9.00	4.50	2.75
6	Pete Suder	9.00	4.50	2.75
7	Gene Baker	9.00	4.50	2.75
8	Warren Hacker	9.00	4.50	2.75
9	Gil McDougald	12.00	6.00	3.50
10	Phil Rizzuto	50.00	25.00	15.00
11	Billy Bruton	9.00	4.50	2.75
12	Andy Pafko	10.00	5.00	3.00
13	Clyde Vollmer	9.00	4.50	2.75
14	Gus Keriazakos	9.00	4.50	2.75
15	*Frank Sullivan*	10.00	5.00	3.00
16	Jim Piersall	9.00	4.50	2.75
17	Del Ennis	10.00	5.00	3.00
18	Stan Lopata	9.00	4.50	2.75
19	Bobby Avila	9.00	4.50	2.75
20	Al Smith	9.00	4.50	2.75
21	Don Hoak	9.00	4.50	2.75
22	Roy Campanella	100.00	50.00	30.00
23	Al Kaline	150.00	75.00	45.00
24	Al Aber	9.00	4.50	2.75
25	Orestes "Minnie" Minoso	25.00	12.50	7.50
26	Virgil Trucks	10.00	5.00	3.00
27	Preston Ward	9.00	4.50	2.75
28	Dick Cole	9.00	4.50	2.75
29	Al "Red" Schoendienst	30.00	15.00	10.50
30	Bill Sarni	9.00	4.50	2.75
31	Johnny Temple	9.00	4.50	2.75
32	Wally Post	9.00	4.50	2.75
33	Nelson Fox	25.00	12.50	7.50
34	Clint Courtney	9.00	4.50	2.75
35	Bill Tuttle	9.00	4.50	2.75
36	Wayne Belardi	9.00	4.50	2.75
37	Harold "Pee Wee" Reese	70.00	35.00	21.00
38	Early Wynn	20.00	10.00	6.00
39	Bob Darnell	10.00	5.00	3.00
40	Vic Wertz	10.00	5.00	3.00
41	Mel Clark	9.00	4.50	2.75
42	Bob Greenwood	9.00	4.50	2.75

		NR MT	EX	VG
43	Bob Buhl	10.00	5.00	3.00
44	Danny O'Connell	9.00	4.50	2.75
45	Tom Umphlett	9.00	4.50	2.75
46	Mickey Vernon	10.00	5.00	3.00
47	Sammy White	9.00	4.50	2.75
48a	Milt Bolling (Frank Bolling back)	10.00	5.00	3.00
48b	Milt Bolling (Milt Bolling back)	25.00	12.50	7.50
49	Jim Greengrass	9.00	4.50	2.75
50	Hobie Landrith	9.00	4.50	2.75
51	Elvin Tappe	9.00	4.50	2.75
52	Hal Rice	9.00	4.50	2.75
53	Alex Kellner	9.00	4.50	2.75
54	Don Bollweg	9.00	4.50	2.75
55	Cal Abrams	9.00	4.50	2.75
56	Billy Cox	9.00	4.50	2.75
57	Bob Friend	10.00	5.00	3.00
58	Frank Thomas	9.00	4.50	2.75
59	Ed "Whitey" Ford	70.00	35.00	20.00
60	Enos Slaughter	30.00	15.00	9.00
61	Paul LaPalme	9.00	4.50	2.75
62	Royce Lint	9.00	4.50	2.75
63	Irv Noren	10.00	5.00	3.00
64	Curt Simmons	10.00	5.00	3.00
65	*Don Zimmer*	25.00	12.50	7.50
66	George Shuba	10.00	5.00	3.00
67	Don Larsen	20.00	10.00	6.00
68	*Elston Howard*	70.00	35.00	21.00
69	Bill Hunter	10.00	5.00	3.00
70	Lou Burdette	9.00	4.50	2.75
71	Dave Jolly	9.00	4.50	2.75
72	Chet Nichols	9.00	4.50	2.75
73	Eddie Yost	9.00	4.50	2.75
74	Jerry Snyder	9.00	4.50	2.75
75	Brooks Lawrence	9.00	4.50	2.75
76	Tom Poholsky	9.00	4.50	2.75
77	Jim McDonald	9.00	4.50	2.75
78	Gil Coan	9.00	4.50	2.75
79	Willie Miranda	9.00	4.50	2.75
80	Lou Limmer	9.00	4.50	2.75
81	Bob Morgan	9.00	4.50	2.75
82	Lee Walls	9.00	4.50	2.75
83	Max Surkont	9.00	4.50	2.75
84	George Freese	9.00	4.50	2.75
85	Cass Michaels	9.00	4.50	2.75
86	Ted Gray	9.00	4.50	2.75
87	Randy Jackson	9.00	4.50	2.75
88	Steve Bilko	9.00	4.50	2.75
89	Lou Boudreau	20.00	10.00	6.00
90	Art Ditmar	9.00	4.50	2.75
91	Dick Marlowe	9.00	4.50	2.75
92	George Zuverink	9.00	4.50	2.75
93	Andy Seminick	9.00	4.50	2.75
94	Hank Thompson	9.00	4.50	2.75
95	Sal Maglie	12.00	6.00	3.50
96	Ray Narleski	9.00	4.50	2.75
97	John Podres	20.00	10.00	6.00
98	James "Junior" Gilliam	12.00	6.00	3.50
99	Jerry Coleman	10.00	5.00	3.00
100	Tom Morgan	10.00	5.00	3.00
101a	Don Johnson (Ernie Johnson (Braves) on front)	10.00	5.00	3.00
101b	Don Johnson (Don Johnson (Orioles) on front)	25.00	12.50	7.50
102	Bobby Thomson	12.00	6.00	3.50
103	Eddie Mathews	60.00	30.00	18.00
104	Bob Porterfield	9.00	4.50	2.75
105	Johnny Schmitz	9.00	4.50	2.75
106	Del Rice	9.00	4.50	2.75
107	Solly Hemus	9.00	4.50	2.75
108	Lou Kretlow	9.00	4.50	2.75
109	Vern Stephens	9.00	4.50	2.75
110	Bob Miller	9.00	4.50	2.75
111	Steve Ridzik	9.00	4.50	2.75
112	Gran Hamner	9.00	4.50	2.75
113	Bob Hall	9.00	4.50	2.75
114	Vic Janowicz	9.00	4.50	2.75
115	Roger Bowman	9.00	4.50	2.75
116	Sandalio Consuegra	9.00	4.50	2.75
117	Johnny Groth	9.00	4.50	2.75
118	Bobby Adams	9.00	4.50	2.75
119	Joe Astroth	9.00	4.50	2.75
120	Ed Burtschy	9.00	4.50	2.75
121	Rufus Crawford	9.00	4.50	2.75
122	Al Corwin	9.00	4.50	2.75
123	Marv Grissom	9.00	4.50	2.75
124	Johnny Antonelli	10.00	5.00	3.00
125	Paul Giel	9.00	4.50	2.75
126	Billy Goodman	9.00	4.50	2.75
127	Hank Majeski	9.00	4.50	2.75
128	Mike Garcia	10.00	5.00	3.00
129	Hal Naragon	9.00	4.50	2.75

	NR MT	EX	VG
130 Richie Ashburn	25.00	12.50	7.50
131 Willard Marshall	9.00	4.50	2.75
132a Harvey Kueen (incorrect spelling on back)			
	10.00	5.00	3.00
132b Harvey Kuenn (correct spelling on back)			
	30.00	15.00	9.00
133 Charles King	9.00	4.50	2.75
134 Bob Feller	60.00	30.00	18.00
135 Lloyd Merriman	9.00	4.50	2.75
136 Rocky Bridges	9.00	4.50	2.75
137 Bob Talbot	9.00	4.50	2.75
138 Davey Williams	9.00	4.50	2.75
139 Billy & Bobby Shantz	9.00	4.50	2.75
140 Bobby Shantz	10.00	5.00	3.00
141 Wes Westrum	10.00	5.00	3.00
142 Rudy Regalado	9.00	4.50	2.75
143 Don Newcombe	25.00	12.50	7.50
144 Art Houtteman	9.00	4.50	2.75
145 Bob Nieman	9.00	4.50	2.75
146 Don Liddle	9.00	4.50	2.75
147 Sam Mele	9.00	4.50	2.75
148 Bob Chakales	9.00	4.50	2.75
149 Cloyd Boyer	9.00	4.50	2.75
150 Bill Klaus	9.00	4.50	2.75
151 Jim Brideweser	9.00	4.50	2.75
152 Johnny Klippstein	9.00	4.50	2.75
153 Eddie Robinson	10.00	5.00	3.00
154 *Frank Lary*	9.00	4.50	2.75
155 Gerry Staley	9.00	4.50	2.75
156 Jim Hughes	10.00	5.00	3.00
157a Ernie Johnson (Don Johnson (Orioles) picture on front)	10.00	5.00	3.00
157b Ernie Johnson (Ernie Johnson (Braves) picture on front)	18.00	9.00	5.50
158 Gil Hodges	40.00	20.00	12.00
159 Harry Byrd	9.00	4.50	2.75
160 Bill Skowron	25.00	12.50	7.50
161 Matt Batts	9.00	4.50	2.75
162 Charlie Maxwell	9.00	4.50	2.75
163 Sid Gordon	9.00	4.50	2.75
164 Toby Atwell	9.00	4.50	2.75
165 Maurice McDermott	9.00	4.50	2.75
166 Jim Busby	9.00	4.50	2.75
167 Bob Grim	10.00	5.00	3.00
168 Larry "Yogi" Berra	110.00	55.00	33.00
169 Carl Furillo	25.00	12.50	7.50
170 Carl Erskine	15.00	7.50	4.50
171 Robin Roberts	30.00	15.00	9.00
172 Willie Jones	9.00	4.50	2.75
173 Al "Chico" Carrasquel	9.00	4.50	2.75
174 Sherman Lollar	10.00	5.00	3.00
175 Wilmer Shantz	9.00	4.50	2.75
176 Joe DeMaestri	9.00	4.50	2.75
177 Willard Nixon	9.00	4.50	2.75
178 Tom Brewer	9.00	4.50	2.75
179 Hank Aaron	225.00	112.00	67.00
180 Johnny Logan	9.00	4.50	2.75
181 Eddie Miksis	9.00	4.50	2.75
182 Bob Rush	9.00	4.50	2.75
183 Ray Katt	9.00	4.50	2.75
184 Willie Mays	235.00	117.00	72.00
185 Vic Raschi	10.00	5.00	3.00
186 Alex Grammas	9.00	4.50	2.75
187 Fred Hatfield	9.00	4.50	2.75
188 Ned Garver	9.00	4.50	2.75
189 Jack Collum	9.00	4.50	2.75
190 Fred Baczewski	9.00	4.50	2.75
191 Bob Lemon	25.00	12.50	7.50
192 George Strickland	9.00	4.50	2.75
193 Howie Judson	9.00	4.50	2.75
194 Joe Nuxhall	10.00	5.00	3.00
195a Erv Palica (no traded line on back)	9.00	4.50	2.75
195b Erv Palica (traded line on back)	25.00	12.50	7.50
196 Russ Meyer	10.00	5.00	3.00
197 Ralph Kiner	35.00	17.50	10.50
198 Dave Pope	9.00	4.50	2.75
199 Vernon Law	10.00	5.00	3.00
200 Dick Littlefield	9.00	4.50	2.75
201 Allie Reynolds	25.00	12.50	7.50
202 Mickey Mantle	500.00	250.00	150.00
203 Steve Gromek	9.00	4.50	2.75
204a *Frank Bolling* (Milt Bolling back)	10.00	5.00	3.00
204b *Frank Bolling* (Frank Bolling back)	20.00	10.00	6.00
205 Eldon "Rip" Repulski	9.00	4.50	2.75
206 Ralph Beard	9.00	4.50	2.75
207 Frank Shea	9.00	4.50	2.75
208 Eddy Fitzgerald (Fitz Gerald)	9.00	4.50	2.75
209 Forrest "Smoky" Burgess	10.00	5.00	3.00
210 Earl Torgeson	9.00	4.50	2.75

	NR MT	EX	VG
211 John "Sonny" Dixon	9.00	4.50	2.75
212 Jack Dittmer	9.00	4.50	2.75
213 George Kell	25.00	12.50	7.50
214 Billy Pierce	10.00	5.00	3.00
215 Bob Kuzava	9.00	4.50	2.75
216 Preacher Roe	10.00	5.00	3.00
217 Del Crandall	10.00	5.00	3.00
218 Joe Adcock	10.00	5.00	3.00
219 Whitey Lockman	9.00	4.50	2.75
220 Jim Hearn	9.00	4.50	2.75
221 Hector "Skinny" Brown	9.00	4.50	2.75
222 Russ Kemmerer	9.00	4.50	2.75
223 Hal Jeffcoat	9.00	4.50	2.75
224 Dee Fondy	9.00	4.50	2.75
225 Paul Richards	16.00	8.00	4.75
226 W.F. McKinley (umpire)	25.00	12.50	7.50
227 Frank Baumholtz	15.00	7.50	4.50
228 John M. Phillips	15.00	7.50	4.50
229 Jim Brosnan	16.00	8.00	4.75
230 Al Brazle	15.00	7.50	4.50
231 Jim Konstanty	25.00	12.50	7.50
232 Birdie Tebbetts	15.00	7.50	4.50
233 Bill Serena	15.00	7.50	4.50
234 Dick Bartell	15.00	7.50	4.50
235 J.A. Paparella (umpire)	25.00	12.50	7.50
236 Murray Dickson (Murry)	15.00	7.50	4.50
237 Johnny Wyrostek	15.00	7.50	4.50
238 Eddie Stanky	16.00	8.00	4.75
239 Edwin A. Rommel (umpire)	25.00	12.50	7.50
240 Billy Loes	16.00	8.00	4.75
241 John Pesky	16.00	8.00	4.75
242 Ernie Banks	400.00	200.00	125.00
243 Gus Bell	16.00	8.00	4.75
244 Duane Pillette	15.00	7.50	4.50
245 Bill Miller	15.00	7.50	4.50
246 Hank Bauer	30.00	15.00	9.00
247 Dutch Leonard	15.00	7.50	4.50
248 Harry Dorish	15.00	7.50	4.50
249 Billy Gardner	15.00	7.50	4.50
250 Larry Napp (umpire)	25.00	12.50	7.50
251 Stan Jok	15.00	7.50	4.50
252 Roy Smalley	15.00	7.50	4.50
253 Jim Wilson	15.00	7.50	4.50
254 Bennett Flowers	15.00	7.50	4.50
255 Pete Runnels	16.00	8.00	4.75
256 Owen Friend	15.00	7.50	4.50
257 Tom Alston	15.00	7.50	4.50
258 John W. Stevens (umpire)	25.00	12.50	7.50
259 *Don Mossi*	25.00	12.50	7.50
260 Edwin H. Hurley (umpire)	25.00	12.50	7.50
261 Walt Moryn	16.00	8.00	4.75
262 Jim Lemon	16.00	8.00	4.75
263 Eddie Joost	15.00	7.50	4.50
264 Bill Henry	15.00	7.50	4.50
265 Albert J. Barlick (umpire)	80.00	40.00	25.00
266 Mike Fornieles	15.00	7.50	4.50
267 George (Jim) Honochick (umpire)	70.00	35.00	21.00
268 Roy Lee Hawes	15.00	7.50	4.50
269 Joe Amalfitano	15.00	7.50	4.50
270 Chico Fernandez	16.00	8.00	4.75
271 Bob Hooper	15.00	7.50	4.50
272 John Flaherty (umpire)	25.00	12.50	7.50
273 Emory "Bubba" Church	15.00	7.50	4.50
274 Jim Delsing	15.00	7.50	4.50
275 William T. Grieve (umpire)	25.00	12.50	7.50
276 Ivan Delock	15.00	7.50	4.50
277 Ed Runge (umpire)	25.00	12.50	7.50
278 *Charles Neal*	25.00	12.50	7.50
279 Hank Soar (umpire)	25.00	12.50	7.50
280 Clyde McCullough	15.00	7.50	4.50
281 Charles Berry (umpire)	25.00	12.50	7.50
282 Phil Cavarretta	16.00	8.00	4.75
283 Nestor Chylak (umpire)	25.00	12.50	7.50
284 William A. Jackowski (umpire)	25.00	12.50	7.50
285 Walt Dropo	16.00	8.00	4.75
286 Frank E. Secory (umpire)	25.00	12.50	7.50
287 Ron Mrozinski	15.00	7.50	4.50
288 Dick Smith	15.00	7.50	4.50
289 Arthur J. Gore (umpire)	25.00	12.50	7.50
290 Hershell Freeman	15.00	7.50	4.50
291 Frank Dascoli (umpire)	25.00	12.50	7.50
292 Marv Blaylock	15.00	7.50	4.50
293 Thomas D. Gorman (umpire)	25.00	12.50	7.50
294 Wally Moses	15.00	7.50	4.50
295 E. Lee Ballanfant (umpire)	25.00	12.50	7.50
296 *Bill Virdon*	30.00	15.00	9.00
297 L.R. "Dusty" Boggess (umpire)	25.00	12.50	7.50
298 Charlie Grimm	25.00	12.50	7.50
299 Lonnie Warneke (umpire)	25.00	12.50	7.50
300 Tommy Byrne	16.00	8.00	4.75

		NR MT	EX	VG
301	William R. Engeln (umpire)	25.00	12.50	7.50
302	*Frank Malzone*	30.00	15.00	9.00
303	J.B. "Jocko" Conlan (umpire)	100.00	50.00	30.00
304	Harry Chiti	15.00	7.50	4.50
305	Frank Umont (umpire)	25.00	12.50	7.50
306	Bob Cerv	25.00	12.50	7.50
307	R.A. "Babe" Pinelli (umpire)	25.00	12.50	7.50
308	Al Lopez	40.00	20.00	12.00
309	Hal H. Dixon (umpire)	25.00	12.50	7.50
310	Ken Lehman	16.00	8.00	4.75
311	Lawrence J. Goetz (umpire)	25.00	12.50	7.50
312	Bill Wight	15.00	7.50	4.50
313	A.J. Donatelli (umpire)	25.00	12.50	7.50
314	Dale Mitchell	15.00	7.50	4.50
315	Cal Hubbard (umpire)	100.00	50.00	30.00
316	Marion Fricano	15.00	7.50	4.50
317	Wm. R. Summers (umpire)	25.00	12.50	7.50
318	Sid Hudson	15.00	7.50	4.50
319	Albert B. Schroll	25.00	12.50	7.50
320	George D. Susce, Jr.	60.00	30.00	18.00

1989 Bowman

Topps, which purchased the Bowman Co. back in 1955, revived the Bowman name in 1989, issuing a 484-card set modeled after the 1953 Bowman cards. The cards are 2-1/2" by 3-3/4", slightly larger than a current standard-sized card. The fronts contain a full-color player photo, with facsimile autograph on the bottom and the Bowman logo in an upper corner. The unique card backs include a breakdown of the player's stats against each team in his league. A series of "Hot Rookie Stars" highlight the set. The cards were distributed in both wax packs and rack packs. Each pack included a special reproduction of a classic Bowman card with a sweepstakes on the back. The special cards said "reprint" on the front.

		MT	NR MT	EX
Complete Set:		8.00	6.00	3.25
Common Player:		.03	.02	.01
1	Oswald Peraza	.05	.04	.02
2	Brian Holton	.05	.04	.02
3	Jose Bautista	.05	.04	.02
4	Pete Harnisch	.10	.08	.04
5	Dave Schmidt	.03	.02	.01
6	Gregg Olson	.30	.25	.12
7	Jeff Ballard	.10	.08	.04
8	Bob Melvin	.03	.02	.01
9	Cal Ripken	.20	.15	.08
10	Randy Milligan	.08	.06	.03
11	Juan Bell	.15	.11	.06
12	Billy Ripken	.05	.04	.02
13	Jim Trabor	.03	.02	.01
14	Pete Stanicek	.03	.02	.01
15	Steve Finley	.20	.15	.08
16	Larry Sheets	.03	.02	.01
17	Phil Bradley	.05	.04	.02
18	Brady Anderson	.10	.08	.04
19	Lee Smith	.03	.02	.01
20	Tom Fischer	.15	.11	.06
21	Mike Boddicker	.03	.02	.01
22	Rob Murphy	.03	.02	.01
23	Wes Gardner	.03	.02	.01
24	John Dopson	.10	.08	.04
25	Bob Stanley	.03	.02	.01

		MT	NR MT	EX
26	Roger Clemens	.20	.15	.08
27	Rich Gedman	.03	.02	.01
28	Marty Barrett	.03	.02	.01
29	Luis Rivera	.03	.02	.01
30	Jody Reed	.05	.04	.02
31	Nick Esasky	.05	.04	.02
32	Wade Boggs	.40	.30	.15
33	Jim Rice	.10	.08	.04
34	Mike Greenwell	.15	.11	.06
35	Dwight Evans	.15	.11	.06
36	Ellis Burks	.25	.20	.10
37	Chuck Finley	.05	.04	.02
38	Kirk McCaskill	.05	.04	.02
39	Jim Abbott	.60	.45	.25
40	Bryan Harvey	.05	.04	.02
41	Bert Blyleven	.08	.06	.03
42	Mike Witt	.03	.02	.01
43	Bob McClure	.03	.02	.01
44	Bill Schroeder	.03	.02	.01
45	Lance Parrish	.05	.04	.02
46	Dick Schofield	.03	.02	.01
47	Wally Joyner	.10	.08	.04
48	Jack Howell	.03	.02	.01
49	Johnny Ray	.03	.02	.01
50	Chili Davis	.05	.04	.02
51	Tony Armas	.03	.02	.01
52	Claudell Washington	.03	.02	.01
53	Brian Downing	.03	.02	.01
54	Devon White	.10	.08	.04
55	Bobby Thigpen	.08	.06	.03
56	Bill Long	.03	.02	.01
57	Jerry Reuss	.03	.02	.01
58	Shawn Hillegas	.03	.02	.01
59	Melido Perez	.05	.04	.02
60	Jeff Bittiger	.05	.04	.02
61	Jack McDowell	.03	.02	.01
62	Carlton Fisk	.10	.08	.04
63	Steve Lyons	.03	.02	.01
64	Ozzie Guillen	.05	.04	.02
65	Robin Ventura	2.00	1.50	.80
66	Fred Manrique	.03	.02	.01
67	Dan Pasqua	.03	.02	.01
68	Ivan Calderon	.03	.02	.01
69	Ron Kittle	.03	.02	.01
70	Daryl Boston	.03	.02	.01
71	Dave Gallagher	.05	.04	.02
72	Harold Baines	.08	.06	.03
73	Charles Nagy	.20	.15	.08
74	John Farrell	.03	.02	.01
75	Kevin Wickander	.25	.20	.10
76	Greg Swindell	.15	.11	.06
77	Mike Walker	.15	.11	.06
78	Doug Jones	.05	.04	.02
79	Rich Yett	.03	.02	.01
80	Tom Candiotti	.03	.02	.01
81	Jesse Orosco	.03	.02	.01
82	Bud Black	.03	.02	.01
83	Andy Allanson	.03	.02	.01
84	Pete O'Brien	.05	.04	.02
85	Jerry Browne	.05	.04	.02
86	Brook Jacoby	.03	.02	.01
87	Mark Lewis	.40	.30	.15
88	Luis Aguayo	.03	.02	.01
89	Cory Snyder	.05	.04	.02
90	Oddibe McDowell	.05	.04	.02
91	Joe Carter	.15	.11	.06
92	Frank Tanana	.03	.02	.01
93	Jack Morris	.03	.02	.01
94	Doyle Alexander	.03	.02	.01
95	Steve Searcy	.08	.06	.03
96	Randy Bockus	.05	.04	.02
97	Jeff Robinson	.05	.04	.02
98	Mike Henneman	.05	.04	.02
99	Paul Gibson	.03	.02	.01
100	Frank Williams	.03	.02	.01
101	Matt Nokes	.05	.04	.02
102	Rico Brogna	.15	.11	.06
103	Lou Whitaker	.08	.06	.03
104	Al Pedrique	.03	.02	.01
105	Alan Trammell	.05	.04	.02
106	Chris Brown	.03	.02	.01
107	Pat Sheridan	.03	.02	.01
108	Gary Pettis	.03	.02	.01
109	Keith Moreland	.03	.02	.01
110	Mel Stottlemyre, Jr.	.15	.11	.06
111	Bret Saberhagen	.10	.08	.04
112	Floyd Bannister	.05	.04	.02
113	Jeff Montgomery	.05	.04	.02
114	Steve Farr	.05	.04	.02
115	Tom Gordon	.40	.30	.15
116	Charlie Leibrandt	.03	.02	.01

		MT	NR MT	EX				MT	NR MT	EX
117	Mark Gubicza	.08	.06	.03		208	Dave Valle	.03	.02	.01
118	Mike MacFarlane	.03	.02	.01		209	Scott Bradley	.03	.02	.01
119	Bob Boone	.05	.04	.02		210	Harold Reynolds	.08	.06	.03
120	Kurt Stillwell	.05	.04	.02		211	Tino Martinez	1.25	.90	.50
121	George Brett	.15	.11	.06		212	Rich Renteria	.03	.02	.01
122	Frank White	.05	.04	.02		213	Rey Quinones	.03	.02	.01
123	Kevin Seitzer	.08	.06	.03		214	Jim Presley	.03	.02	.01
124	Willie Wilson	.03	.02	.01		215	Alvin Davis	.10	.08	.04
125	Pat Tabler	.03	.02	.01		216	Edgar Martinez	.03	.02	.01
126	Bo Jackson	1.00	.70	.40		217	Darnell Coles	.03	.02	.01
127	Hugh Walker	.20	.15	.08		218	Jeffrey Leonard	.08	.06	.04
128	Danny Tartabull	.05	.04	.02		219	Jay Buhner	.08	.06	.03
129	Teddy Higuera	.08	.06	.03		220	Ken Griffey, Jr.	3.00	2.25	1.25
130	Don August	.03	.02	.01		221	Drew Hall	.03	.02	.01
131	Juan Nieves	.03	.02	.01		222	Bobby Witt	.03	.02	.01
132	Mike Birkbeck	.03	.02	.01		223	Jamie Moyer	.03	.02	.01
133	Dan Plesac	.05	.04	.02		224	Charlie Hough	.03	.02	.01
134	Chris Bosio	.05	.04	.02		225	Nolan Ryan	.70	.50	.30
135	Bill Wegman	.03	.02	.01		226	Jeff Russell	.05	.04	.02
136	Chuck Crim	.03	.02	.01		227	Jim Sundberg	.03	.02	.01
137	B.J. Surhoff	.05	.04	.02		228	Julio Franco	.15	.11	.06
138	Joey Meyer	.03	.02	.01		229	Buddy Bell	.03	.02	.01
139	Dale Sveum	.03	.02	.01		230	Scott Fletcher	.03	.02	.01
140	Paul Molitor	.08	.06	.03		231	Jeff Kunkel	.03	.02	.01
141	Jim Gantner	.03	.02	.01		232	Steve Buechele	.03	.02	.01
142	Gary Sheffield	.80	.60	.30		233	Monty Fariss	.25	.20	.10
143	Greg Brock	.03	.02	.01		234	Rick Leach	.03	.02	.01
144	Robin Yount	.25	.20	.10		235	Ruben Sierra	.40	.30	.15
145	Glenn Braggs	.03	.02	.01		236	Cecil Espy	.05	.04	.02
146	Rob Deer	.03	.02	.01		237	Rafael Palmeiro	.10	.08	.04
147	Fred Toliver	.03	.02	.01		238	Pete Incaviglia	.03	.02	.01
148	Jeff Reardon	.03	.02	.01		239	Dave Steib	.05	.04	.02
149	Allan Anderson	.05	.04	.02		240	Jeff Musselman	.03	.02	.01
150	Frank Viola	.15	.11	.06		241	Mike Flanagan	.03	.02	.01
151	Shane Rawley	.03	.02	.01		242	Todd Stottlemyre	.05	.04	.02
152	Juan Berenguer	.03	.02	.01		243	Jimmy Key	.05	.04	.02
153	Johnny Ard	.20	.15	.08		244	Tony Castillo	.10	.08	.04
154	Tim Laudner	.03	.02	.01		245	Alex Sanchez	.05	.04	.02
155	Brian Harper	.03	.02	.01		246	Tom Henke	.03	.02	.01
156	Al Newman	.03	.02	.01		247	John Cerutti	.03	.02	.01
157	Kent Hrbek	.08	.06	.03		248	Ernie Whitt	.03	.02	.01
158	Gary Gaetti	.08	.06	.03		249	Bob Brenly	.03	.02	.01
159	Wally Backman	.03	.02	.01		250	Rance Mulliniks	.03	.02	.01
160	Gene Larkin	.03	.02	.01		251	Kelly Gruber	.10	.08	.04
161	Greg Gagne	.03	.02	.01		252	Ed Sprague	.20	.15	.08
162	Kirby Puckett	.35	.25	.14		253	Fred McGriff	.50	.40	.20
163	Danny Gladden	.03	.02	.01		254	Tony Fernandez	.08	.06	.03
164	Randy Bush	.03	.02	.01		255	Tom Lawless	.03	.02	.01
165	Dave LaPoint	.03	.02	.01		256	George Bell	.10	.08	.04
166	Andy Hawkins	.03	.02	.01		257	Jesse Barfield	.05	.04	.02
167	Dave Righetti	.05	.04	.02		258	Sandy Alomar	.20	.15	.08
168	Lance McCullers	.03	.02	.01		259	Ken Griffey	1.00	.70	.40
169	Jimmy Jones	.03	.02	.01		260	Cal Ripken, Sr.	.15	.11	.06
170	Al Leiter	.03	.02	.01		261	Mel Stottlemyre	.15	.11	.06
171	John Candelaria	.03	.02	.01		262	Zane Smith	.03	.02	.01
172	Don Slaught	.03	.02	.01		263	Charlie Puleo	.03	.02	.01
173	Jamie Quirk	.03	.02	.01		264	Derek Lilliquist	.15	.11	.06
174	Rafael Santana	.03	.02	.01		265	Paul Assenmacher	.03	.02	.01
175	Mike Pagliarulo	.03	.02	.01		266	John Smoltz	.60	.45	.25
176	Don Mattingly	.40	.30	.15		267	Tom Glavine	.10	.08	.04
177	Ken Phelps	.03	.02	.01		268	Steve Avery	2.00	1.50	.80
178	Steve Sax	.08	.06	.03		269	Pete Smith	.05	.04	.02
179	Dave Winfield	.20	.15	.08		270	Jody Davis	.03	.02	.01
180	Stan Jefferson	.03	.02	.01		271	Bruce Benedict	.03	.02	.01
181	Rickey Henderson	.40	.30	.15		272	Andres Thomas	.03	.02	.01
182	Bob Brower	.03	.02	.01		273	Gerald Perry	.05	.04	.02
183	Roberto Kelly	.10	.08	.04		274	Ron Gant	.05	.04	.02
184	Curt Young	.03	.02	.01		275	Darrell Evans	.03	.02	.01
185	Gene Nelson	.03	.02	.01		276	Dale Murphy	.08	.06	.03
186	Bob Welch	.03	.02	.01		277	Dion James	.03	.02	.01
187	Rick Honeycutt	.03	.02	.01		278	Lonnie Smith	.08	.06	.03
188	Dave Stewart	.08	.06	.03		279	Geronimo Berroa	.05	.04	.02
189	Mike Moore	.08	.06	.03		280	Steve Wilson	.20	.15	.08
190	Dennis Eckersley	.08	.06	.03		281	Rick Suctcliffe	.05	.04	.02
191	Eric Plunk	.03	.02	.01		282	Kevin Coffman	.03	.02	.01
192	Storm Davis	.03	.02	.01		283	Mitch Williams	.10	.08	.04
193	Terry Steinbach	.10	.08	.04		284	Greg Maddux	.05	.04	.02
194	Ron Hassey	.03	.02	.01		285	Paul Kilgus	.03	.02	.01
195	Stan Royer	.15	.11	.06		286	Mike Harkey	.10	.08	.04
196	Walt Weiss	.15	.11	.06		287	Lloyd McClendon	.05	.04	.02
197	Mark McGwire	.40	.30	.15		288	Damon Berryhill	.05	.04	.02
198	Carney Lansford	.08	.06	.03		289	Ty Griffin	.10	.08	.04
199	Glenn Hubbard	.03	.02	.01		290	Ryne Sandberg	.15	.11	.06
200	Dave Henderson	.05	.04	.02		291	Mark Grace	.30	.25	.12
201	Jose Canseco	.40	.30	.15		292	Curt Wilkerson	.03	.02	.01
202	Dave Parker	.05	.04	.02		293	Vance Law	.03	.02	.01
203	Scott Bankhead	.05	.04	.02		294	Shawon Dunston	.08	.06	.04
204	Tom Niedenfuer	.03	.02	.01		295	Jerome Walton	.15	.11	.06
205	Mark Langston	.15	.11	.06		296	Mitch Webster	.03	.02	.01
206	Erik Hanson	.50	.40	.20		297	Dwight Smith	.15	.11	.06
207	Mike Jackson	.03	.02	.01		298	Andre Dawson	.15	.11	.06

#	Player	MT	NR MT	EX		#	Player	MT	NR MT	EX
299	Jeff Sellers	.03	.02	.01		390	Jeff Parrett	.05	.04	.02
300	Jose Rijo	.05	.04	.02		391	Mike Maddux	.03	.02	.01
301	John Franco	.05	.04	.02		392	Don Carman	.03	.02	.01
302	Rick Mahler	.03	.02	.01		393	Bruce Ruffin	.03	.02	.01
303	Ron Robinson	.03	.02	.01		394	Ken Howell	.03	.02	.01
304	Danny Jackson	.03	.02	.01		395	Steve Bedrosian	.05	.04	.02
305	Rob Dibble	.08	.06	.04		396	Floyd Youmans	.03	.02	.01
306	Tom Browning	.03	.02	.01		397	Larry McWilliams	.03	.02	.01
307	Bo Diaz	.03	.02	.01		398	Pat Combs	.25	.20	.10
308	Manny Trillo	.03	.02	.01		399	Steve Lake	.03	.02	.01
309	Chris Sabo	.15	.11	.06		400	Dickie Thon	.03	.02	.01
310	Ron Oester	.03	.02	.01		401	Ricky Jordan	.35	.25	.14
311	Barry Larkin	.15	.11	.06		402	Mike Schmidt	.40	.30	.15
312	Todd Benzinger	.05	.04	.02		403	Tom Herr	.03	.02	.01
313	Paul O'Neil	.05	.04	.02		404	Chris James	.03	.02	.01
314	Kal Daniels	.05	.04	.02		405	Juan Samuel	.08	.06	.03
315	Joel Youngblood	.03	.02	.01		406	Von Hayes	.08	.06	.03
316	Eric Davis	.25	.20	.10		407	Ron Jones	.15	.11	.06
317	Dave Smith	.05	.04	.03		408	Curt Ford	.03	.02	.01
318	Mark Portugal	.03	.02	.01		409	Bob Walk	.03	.02	.01
319	Brian Meyer	.03	.02	.01		410	Jeff Robinson	.03	.02	.01
320	Jim Deshaies	.05	.04	.02		411	Jim Gott	.03	.02	.01
321	Juan Agosto	.03	.02	.01		412	Scott Medvin	.03	.02	.01
322	Mike Scott	.10	.08	.04		413	John Smiley	.03	.02	.01
323	Rick Rhoden	.03	.02	.01		414	Bob Kipper	.03	.02	.01
324	Jim Clancy	.03	.02	.01		415	Brian Fisher	.03	.02	.01
325	Larry Andersen	.03	.02	.01		416	Doug Drabek	.03	.02	.01
326	Alex Trevino	.03	.02	.01		417	Mike Lavalliere	.03	.02	.01
327	Alan Ashby	.03	.02	.01		418	Ken Oberkfell	.03	.02	.01
328	Craig Reynolds	.03	.02	.01		419	Sid Bream	.03	.02	.01
329	Bill Doran	.03	.02	.01		420	Austin Manahan	.20	.15	.08
330	Rafael Ramirez	.03	.02	.01		421	Jose Lind	.03	.02	.01
331	Glenn Davis	.10	.08	.04		422	Bobby Bonilla	.30	.25	.12
332	Willie Ansley	.25	.20	.10		423	Glenn Wilson	.03	.02	.01
333	Gerald Young	.03	.02	.01		424	Andy Van Slyke	.10	.08	.04
334	Cameron Drew	.10	.08	.04		425	Gary Redus	.03	.02	.01
335	Jay Howell	.05	.04	.03		426	Barry Bonds	.30	.25	.12
336	Tim Belcher	.05	.04	.03		427	Don Heinkel	.03	.02	.01
337	Fernando Valenzuela	.05	.04	.03		428	Ken Dayley	.03	.02	.01
338	Ricky Horton	.03	.02	.01		429	Todd Worrell	.05	.04	.02
339	Tim Leary	.03	.02	.01		430	Brad DuVall	.20	.15	.08
340	Bill Bene	.15	.11	.06		431	Jose DeLeon	.03	.02	.01
341	Orel Hershiser	.20	.15	.08		432	Joe Magrane	.10	.08	.04
342	Mike Scioscia	.05	.04	.02		433	John Ericks	.20	.15	.08
343	Rick Dempsey	.03	.02	.01		434	Frank DiPino	.03	.02	.01
344	Willie Randolph	.03	.02	.01		435	Tony Pena	.05	.04	.02
345	Alfredo Griffin	.03	.02	.01		436	Ozzie Smith	.08	.06	.03
346	Eddie Murray	.08	.06	.03		437	Terry Pendleton	.03	.02	.01
347	Mickey Hatcher	.03	.02	.01		438	Jose Oquendo	.03	.02	.01
348	Mike Sharperson	.03	.02	.01		439	Tim Jones	.05	.04	.02
349	John Shelby	.03	.02	.01		440	Pedro Guerrero	.10	.08	.04
350	Mike Marshall	.03	.02	.01		441	Milt Thompson	.03	.02	.01
351	Kirk Gibson	.05	.04	.02		442	Willie McGee	.05	.04	.02
352	Mike Davis	.03	.02	.01		443	Vince Coleman	.05	.04	.02
353	Bryn Smith	.03	.02	.01		444	Tom Brunansky	.05	.04	.02
354	Pascual Perez	.03	.02	.01		445	Walt Terrell	.03	.02	.01
355	Kevin Gross	.03	.02	.01		446	Eric Show	.03	.02	.01
356	Andy McGaffigan	.03	.02	.01		447	Mark Davis	.10	.08	.04
357	Brian Holman	.05	.04	.02		448	Andy Benes	.60	.45	.25
358	Dave Wainhouse	.20	.15	.08		449	Eddie Whitson	.03	.02	.01
359	Denny Martinez	.03	.02	.01		450	Dennis Rasmussen	.03	.02	.01
360	Tim Burke	.03	.02	.01		451	Bruce Hurst	.03	.02	.01
361	Nelson Santovenia	.08	.06	.04		452	Pat Clements	.03	.02	.01
362	Tim Wallach	.05	.04	.02		453	Benito Santiago	.10	.08	.04
363	Spike Owen	.03	.02	.01		454	Sandy Alomar, Jr.	.50	.40	.20
364	Rex Hudler	.03	.02	.01		455	Garry Templeton	.03	.02	.01
365	Andres Galarraga	.08	.06	.03		456	Jack Clark	.05	.04	.02
366	Otis Nixon	.03	.02	.01		457	Tim Flannery	.03	.02	.01
367	Hubie Brooks	.03	.02	.01		458	Roberto Alomar	1.25	.90	.50
368	Mike Aldrete	.03	.02	.01		459	Camelo Martinez	.03	.02	.01
369	Rock Raines	.08	.06	.03		460	John Kruk	.03	.02	.01
370	Dave Martinez	.03	.02	.01		461	Tony Gwynn	.20	.15	.08
371	Bob Ojeda	.03	.02	.01		462	Jerald Clark	.05	.04	.02
372	Ron Darling	.05	.04	.02		463	Don Robinson	.03	.02	.01
373	Wally Whitehurst	.20	.15	.08		464	Craig Lefferts	.03	.02	.01
374	Randy Myers	.05	.04	.02		465	Kelly Downs	.03	.02	.01
375	David Cone	.05	.04	.02		466	Rick Rueschel	.05	.04	.02
376	Doc Gooden	.25	.20	.10		467	Scott Garrelts	.03	.02	.01
377	Sid Fernandez	.05	.04	.02		468	Wil Tejada	.03	.02	.01
378	Dave Proctor	.20	.15	.08		469	Kirt Manwaring	.10	.08	.04
379	Gary Carter	.03	.02	.01		470	Terry Kennedy	.03	.02	.01
380	Keith Miller	.05	.04	.02		471	Jose Uribe	.03	.02	.01
381	Gregg Jefferies	.20	.15	.08		472	Royce Clayton	.50	.40	.20
382	Tim Teufel	.03	.02	.01		473	Robby Thompson	.05	.04	.02
383	Kevin Elster	.03	.02	.01		474	Kevin Mitchell	.25	.20	.10
384	Dave Magadan	.03	.02	.01		475	Ernie Riles	.03	.02	.01
385	Keith Hernandez	.05	.04	.02		476	Will Clark	.40	.30	.15
386	Mookie Wilson	.05	.04	.02		477	Donnell Nixon	.03	.02	.01
387	Darryl Strawberry	.40	.30	.15		478	Candy Maldonado	.03	.02	.01
388	Kevin McReynolds	.10	.08	.04		479	Tracy Jones	.03	.02	.01
389	Mark Carreon	.05	.04	.02		480	Brett Butler	.05	.04	.02

		MT	NR MT	EX
481	Checklist	.05	.04	.02
482	Checklist	.05	.04	.02
483	Checklist	.05	.04	.02
484	Checklist	.05	.04	.02

Values quoted in this guide reflect the retail price of a card — the price a collector can expect to pay when buying a card from a dealer. The wholesale price — that which a collector can expect to receive from a dealer when selling cards — will be significantly lower, depending on desirability and condition.

1989 Bowman Inserts

Bowman inserted sweepstakes cards in its 1989 packs. Each sweepstakes card features a reprint Bowman card on the front. The cards were by no means scarce.

		MT	NR MT	EX
	Complete Set:	1.50	1.25	.60
	Common Player:	.10	.08	.04
(1)	Richie Ashburn	.10	.08	.04
(2)	Yogi Berra	.20	.15	.08
(3)	Whitey Ford	.10	.08	.04
(4)	Gil Hodges	.10	.08	.04
(5)	Mickey Mantle (1951)	.25	.20	.10
(6)	Mickey Mantle (1953)	.25	.20	.10
(7)	Willie Mays	.25	.20	.10
(8)	Satchel Paige	.15	.11	.06
(9)	Jackie Robinson	.20	.15	.08
(10)	Duke Snider	.15	.11	.06
(11)	Ted Williams	.25	.20	.10

1990 Bowman

Bowman followed up its 1989 release with 528-card set in 1990. The 1990 cards follow the classic Bowman style featuring a full color photo bordered in white. The Bowman logo appears in the upper left corner. The player's team nickname and name appear on the bottom border of the card photo. Unlike the 1989 set, the 1990 cards measure 2-1/2" by 3-1/2" in size. The card backs are horizontal and display the player's statistics against the teams in his respective league. Included in the set are special insert cards that feature a reproduction of a painting of a modern-day superstar done in the style of the 1951 Bowman cards. The paintings were produced for Bowman by artist Craig Pursley. The card backs contain a sweepstakes offer with a chance to win a complete set of 11 lithographs made from these paintings.

		MT	NR MT	EX
	Complete Set:	10.00	7.50	4.00
	Common Player:	.05	.04	.02
1	Tommy Greene	.25	.20	.10
2	Tom Glavine	.06	.05	.02
3	Andy Nezelek	.08	.06	.03
4	Mike Stanton	.20	.15	.08
5	Rick Lueken	.08	.06	.03
6	Kent Mercker	.25	.20	.10
7	Derek Lilliquist	.06	.05	.02
8	Charlie Liebrandt	.05	.04	.02
9	Steve Avery	.60	.45	.25
10	John Smoltz	.15	.11	.06
11	Mark Lemke	.08	.06	.03
12	Lonnie Smith	.06	.05	.02
13	Oddibe McDowell	.05	.04	.02
14	Tyler Houston	.10	.08	.04
15	Jeff Blauser	.05	.04	.02
16	Ernie Whitt	.05	.04	.02
17	Alexis Infante	.10	.08	.04
18	Jim Presley	.06	.05	.02
19	Dale Murphy	.10	.08	.04
20	Nick Esasky	.06	.05	.02
21	Rick Sutcliffe	.06	.05	.02
22	Mike Bielecki	.06	.05	.02
23	Steve Wilson	.10	.08	.04
24	Kevin Blankenship	.10	.08	.04
25	Mitch Williams	.10	.08	.04
26	Dean Wilkins	.10	.08	.04
27	Greg Maddux	.12	.09	.05
28	Mike Harkey	.20	.15	.08
29	Mark Grace	.20	.15	.08
30	Ryne Sandberg	.40	.30	.15
31	Greg Smith	.20	.15	.08
32	Dwight Smith	.15	.11	.06
33	Damon Berryhill	.05	.04	.02
34	Earl Cunningham	.15	.11	.06
35	Jerome Walton	.25	.20	.10
36	Lloyd McClendon	.05	.04	.02
37	Ty Griffin	.20	.15	.08
38	Shawon Dunston	.10	.08	.04
39	Andre Dawson	.10	.08	.04
40	Luis Salazar	.05	.04	.02
41	Tim Layana	.20	.15	.08
42	Rob Dibble	.10	.08	.04
43	Tom Browning	.05	.04	.02
44	Danny Jackson	.05	.04	.02
45	Jose Rijo	.06	.05	.02
46	Scott Scudder	.20	.15	.08
47	Randy Myers	.06	.05	.02
48	Brian Lane	.15	.11	.06
49	Paul O'Neill	.05	.04	.02
50	Barry Larkin	.10	.08	.04
51	Reggie Jefferson	.40	.30	.15
52	Jeff Branson	.20	.15	.08
53	Chris Sabo	.08	.06	.03
54	Joe Oliver	.10	.08	.04
55	Todd Benzinger	.05	.04	.02
56	Rolando Roomes	.05	.04	.02
57	Hal Morris	.30	.25	.12
58	Eric Davis	.15	.11	.06
59	Scott Bryant	.20	.15	.08
60	Ken Griffey	.06	.05	.02
61	Darryl Kile	.15	.11	.06
62	Dave Smith	.05	.04	.02
63	Mark Portugal	.05	.04	.02
64	Jeff Juden	.35	.25	.14
65	Bill Gullickson	.05	.04	.02
66	Danny Darwin	.05	.04	.02
67	Larry Andersen	.05	.04	.02
68	Jose Cano	.10	.08	.04
69	Dan Schatzeder	.05	.04	.02
70	Jim Deshaies	.05	.04	.02
71	Mike Scott	.06	.05	.02
72	Gerald Young	.05	.04	.02
73	Ken Caminiti	.05	.04	.02
74	Ken Oberkfell	.05	.04	.02
75	Dave Rhode	.20	.15	.08
76	Bill Doran	.06	.05	.02
77	Andujar Cedeno	.20	.15	.08
78	Craig Biggio	.08	.06	.03
79	Karl Rhodes	.15	.11	.06
80	Glenn Davis	.10	.08	.04
81	Eric Anthony	.30	.25	.12
82	John Wetteland	.20	.15	.08
83	Jay Howell	.06	.05	.02
84	Orel Hershiser	.10	.08	.04
85	Tim Belcher	.08	.06	.03
86	Kiki Jones	.25	.20	.10

		MT	NR MT	EX			MT	NR MT	EX
87	Mike Hartley	.20	.15	.08	178	Moises Alou	.25	.20	.10
88	Ramon Martinez	.30	.25	.12	179	Steve Carter	.08	.06	.03
89	Mike Scioscia	.06	.05	.02	180	Gary Redus	.05	.04	.02
90	Willie Randolph	.06	.05	.02	181	Barry Bonds	.10	.08	.04
91	Juan Samuel	.06	.05	.02	182	Don Slaught	.05	.04	.02
92	Jose Offerman	.30	.25	.12	183	Joe Magrane	.06	.05	.02
93	Dave Hansen	.30	.25	.12	184	Bryn Smith	.05	.04	.02
94	Jeff Hamilton	.05	.04	.02	185	Todd Worrell	.06	.05	.02
95	Alfredo Griffin	.05	.04	.02	186	Jose Deleon	.05	.04	.02
96	Tom Goodwin	.35	.25	.14	187	Frank DiPino	.05	.04	.02
97	Kirk Gibson	.06	.05	.02	188	John Tudor	.05	.04	.02
98	Jose Vizcaino	.20	.15	.08	189	Howard Hilton	.10	.08	.04
99	Kal Daniels	.06	.05	.02	190	John Ericks	.10	.08	.04
100	Hubie Brooks	.06	.05	.02	191	Ken Dayley	.05	.04	.02
101	Eddie Murray	.08	.06	.03	192	Ray Lankford	.80	.60	.30
102	Dennis Boyd	.05	.04	.02	193	Todd Zeile	.80	.60	.30
103	Tim Burke	.06	.05	.02	194	Willie McGee	.06	.05	.02
104	Bill Sampen	.20	.15	.08	195	Ozzie Smith	.10	.08	.04
105	Brett Gideon	.06	.05	.02	196	Milt Thompson	.05	.04	.02
106	Mark Gardner	.20	.15	.08	197	Terry Pendleton	.05	.04	.02
107	Howard Farmer	.15	.11	.06	198	Vince Coleman	.06	.05	.02
108	Mel Rojas	.15	.11	.06	199	Paul Coleman	.25	.20	.10
109	Kevin Gross	.05	.04	.02	200	Jose Oquendo	.05	.04	.02
110	Dave Schmidt	.05	.04	.02	201	Pedro Guerrero	.06	.05	.02
111	Denny Martinez	.06	.05	.02	202	Tom Brunansky	.06	.05	.02
112	Jerry Goff	.10	.08	.04	203	Roger Smithberg	.10	.08	.04
113	Andres Galarraga	.08	.06	.03	204	Eddie Whitson	.05	.04	.02
114	Tim Welch	.12	.09	.05	205	Dennis Rasmussen	.05	.04	.02
115	Marquis Grissom	.40	.30	.15	206	Craig Lefferts	.05	.04	.02
116	Spike Owen	.05	.04	.02	207	Andy Benes	.15	.11	.06
117	Larry Walker	.30	.25	.12	208	Bruce Hurst	.06	.05	.02
118	Rock Raines	.08	.06	.03	209	Eric Show	.05	.04	.02
119	Delino DeShields	.40	.30	.15	210	Rafael Valdez	.10	.08	.04
120	Tom Foley	.05	.04	.02	211	Joey Cora	.05	.04	.02
121	Dave Martinez	.05	.04	.02	212	Thomas Howard	.20	.15	.08
122	Frank Viola	.10	.08	.04	213	Rob Nelson	.05	.04	.02
123	Julio Valera	.15	.11	.06	214	Jack Clark	.06	.05	.02
124	Alejandro Pena	.05	.04	.02	215	Garry Templeton	.05	.04	.02
125	David Cone	.08	.06	.03	216	Fred Lynn	.05	.04	.02
126	Doc Gooden	.20	.15	.08	217	Tony Gwynn	.08	.06	.03
127	Kevin Brown	.20	.15	.08	218	Benny Santiago	.08	.06	.03
128	John Franco	.08	.06	.03	219	Mike Pagliarulo	.05	.04	.02
129	Terry Bross	.25	.20	.10	220	Joe Carter	.08	.06	.03
130	Blaine Beatty	.20	.15	.08	221	Roberto Alomar	.08	.06	.03
131	Sid Fernandez	.08	.06	.03	222	Bip Roberts	.05	.04	.02
132	Mike Marshall	.05	.04	.02	223	Rick Reuschel	.05	.04	.02
133	Howard Johnson	.10	.08	.04	224	Russ Swan	.20	.15	.08
134	Jaime Roseboro	.20	.15	.08	225	Eric Gunderson	.20	.15	.08
135	Alan Zinter	.20	.15	.08	226	Steve Bedrosian	.05	.04	.02
136	Keith Miller	.06	.05	.02	227	Mike Remlinger	.40	.30	.15
137	Kevin Elster	.05	.04	.02	228	Scott Garrelts	.05	.04	.02
138	Kevin McReynolds	.06	.05	.02	229	Ernie Camacho	.05	.04	.02
139	Barry Lyons	.05	.04	.02	230	Andres Santana	.25	.20	.10
140	Gregg Jefferies	.25	.20	.10	231	Will Clark	.35	.25	.14
141	Darryl Strawberry	.25	.20	.10	232	Kevin Mitchell	.25	.20	.10
142	Todd Hundley	.25	.20	.10	233	Robby Thompson	.05	.04	.02
143	Scott Service	.15	.11	.06	234	Bill Bathe	.06	.05	.02
144	Chuck Malone	.15	.11	.06	235	Tony Perezchica	.08	.06	.03
145	Steve Ontiveros	.05	.04	.02	236	Gary Carter	.05	.04	.02
146	Roger McDowell	.06	.05	.02	237	Brett Butler	.05	.04	.02
147	Ken Howell	.05	.04	.02	238	Matt Williams	.15	.11	.06
148	Pat Combs	.15	.11	.06	239	Ernie Riles	.05	.04	.02
149	Jeff Parrett	.05	.04	.02	240	Kevin Bass	.05	.04	.02
150	Chuck McElroy	.15	.11	.06	241	Terry Kennedy	.05	.04	.02
151	Jason Grimsley	.15	.11	.06	242	Steve Hosey	.30	.25	.12
152	Len Dykstra	.08	.06	.03	243	Ben McDonald	.40	.30	.15
153	Mickey Morandini	.15	.11	.06	244	Jeff Ballard	.05	.04	.02
154	John Kruk	.05	.04	.02	245	Joe Price	.05	.04	.02
155	Dickie Thon	.05	.04	.02	246	Curt Schilling	.05	.04	.02
156	Ricky Jordan	.10	.08	.04	247	Pete Harnisch	.06	.05	.02
157	Jeff Jackson	.10	.08	.04	248	Mark Williamson	.05	.04	.02
158	Darren Daulton	.05	.04	.02	249	Gregg Olson	.15	.11	.06
159	Tom Herr	.05	.04	.02	250	Chris Myers	.15	.11	.06
160	Von Hayes	.06	.05	.02	251	David Segui	.40	.30	.15
161	Dave Hollins	.35	.25	.14	252	Joe Orsulak	.05	.04	.02
162	Carmelo Martinez	.05	.04	.02	253	Craig Worthington	.05	.04	.02
163	Bob Walk	.05	.04	.02	254	Mickey Tettleton	.06	.05	.02
164	Doug Drabek	.08	.06	.03	255	Cal Ripken	.20	.15	.08
165	Walt Terrell	.05	.04	.02	256	Billy Ripken	.05	.04	.02
166	Bill Landrum	.05	.04	.02	257	Randy Milligan	.06	.05	.02
167	Scott Ruskin	.08	.06	.03	258	Brady Anderson	.05	.04	.02
168	Bob Patterson	.05	.04	.02	259	Chris Hoiles	.20	.15	.08
169	Bobby Bonilla	.10	.08	.04	260	Mike Devereaux	.05	.04	.02
170	Jose Lind	.05	.04	.02	261	Phil Bradley	.05	.04	.02
171	Andy Van Slyke	.08	.06	.03	262	Leo Gomez	.30	.25	.12
172	Mike LaValliere	.05	.04	.02	263	Lee Smith	.06	.05	.02
173	Willie Greene	.20	.15	.08	264	Mike Rochford	.06	.05	.02
174	Jay Bell	.06	.05	.02	265	Jeff Reardon	.06	.05	.02
175	Sid Bream	.05	.04	.02	266	Wes Gardner	.05	.04	.02
176	Tom Prince	.05	.04	.02	267	Mike Boddicker	.05	.04	.02
177	Wally Backman	.05	.04	.02	268	Roger Clemens	.25	.20	.10

		MT	NR MT	EX			MT	NR MT	EX
269	Rob Murphy	.05	.04	.02	360	Travis Fryman	1.25	.90	.50
270	Mickey Pina	.25	.20	.10	361	Ed Romero	.05	.04	.02
271	Tony Pena	.06	.05	.02	362	Lloyd Moseby	.06	.05	.02
272	Jody Reed	.06	.05	.02	363	Mark Gubicza	.08	.06	.03
273	Kevin Romine	.05	.04	.02	364	Bret Saberhagen	.10	.08	.04
274	Mike Greenwell	.08	.06	.03	365	Tom Gordon	.15	.11	.06
275	Maurice Vaughn	.80	.60	.30	366	Steve Farr	.05	.04	.02
276	Danny Heep	.05	.04	.02	367	Kevin Appier	.30	.25	.12
277	Scott Cooper	.25	.20	.10	368	Storm Davis	.05	.04	.02
278	Greg Blosser	.25	.20	.10	369	Mark Davis	.05	.04	.02
279	Dwight Evans	.06	.05	.02	370	Jeff Montgomery	.06	.05	.02
280	Ellis Burks	.08	.06	.03	371	Frank White	.06	.05	.02
281	Wade Boggs	.10	.08	.04	372	Brent Mayne	.20	.15	.08
282	Marty Barrett	.05	.04	.02	373	Bob Boone	.06	.05	.02
283	Kirk McCaskill	.06	.05	.02	374	Jim Eisenreich	.05	.04	.02
284	Mark Langston	.06	.05	.02	375	Danny Tartabull	.08	.06	.03
285	Bert Blyleven	.06	.05	.02	376	Kurt Stillwell	.05	.04	.02
286	Mike Fetters	.08	.06	.03	377	Bill Pecota	.05	.04	.02
287	Kyle Abbott	.20	.15	.08	378	Bo Jackson	.80	.60	.30
288	Jim Abbott	.10	.08	.04	379	Bob Hamelin	.20	.15	.08
289	Chuck Finley	.06	.05	.02	380	Kevin Seitzer	.08	.06	.03
290	Gary DiSarcina	.15	.11	.06	381	Rey Palacios	.05	.04	.02
291	Dick Schofield	.05	.04	.02	382	George Brett	.12	.09	.05
292	Devon White	.06	.05	.02	383	Gerald Perry	.05	.04	.02
293	Bobby Rose	.15	.11	.06	384	Teddy Higuera	.08	.06	.03
294	Brian Downing	.05	.04	.02	385	Tom Filer	.05	.04	.02
295	Lance Parrish	.06	.05	.02	386	Dan Plesac	.06	.05	.02
296	Jack Howell	.05	.04	.02	387	Cal Eldred	.20	.15	.08
297	Claudell Washington	.05	.04	.02	388	Jaime Navarro	.06	.05	.02
298	John Orton	.06	.05	.02	389	Chris Bosio	.05	.04	.02
299	Wally Joyner	.08	.06	.03	390	Randy Veres	.05	.04	.02
300	Lee Stevens	.30	.25	.12	391	Gary Sheffield	.20	.15	.08
301	Chili Davis	.05	.04	.02	392	George Canale	.10	.08	.04
302	Johnny Ray	.05	.04	.02	393	B.J. Surhoff	.06	.05	.02
303	Greg Hibbard	.15	.11	.06	394	Tim McIntosh	.15	.11	.06
304	Eric King	.06	.05	.02	395	Greg Brock	.05	.04	.02
305	Jack McDowell	.08	.06	.03	396	Greg Vaughn	.50	.40	.20
306	Bobby Thigpen	.08	.06	.03	397	Darryl Hamilton	.10	.08	.04
307	Adam Peterson	.05	.04	.02	398	Dave Parker	.10	.08	.04
308	Scott Radinsky	.20	.15	.08	399	Paul Molitor	.08	.06	.03
309	Wayne Edwards	.06	.05	.02	400	Jim Gantner	.05	.04	.02
310	Melido Perez	.06	.05	.02	401	Rob Deer	.05	.04	.02
311	Robin Ventura	.50	.40	.20	402	Billy Spiers	.15	.11	.06
312	Sammy Sosa	.30	.25	.12	403	Glenn Braggs	.06	.05	.02
313	Dan Pasqua	.05	.04	.02	404	Robin Yount	.15	.11	.06
314	Carlton Fisk	.08	.06	.03	405	Rick Aguilera	.05	.04	.02
315	Ozzie Guillen	.08	.06	.03	406	Johnny Ard	.15	.11	.06
316	Ivan Calderon	.08	.06	.03	407	Kevin Tapani	.25	.20	.10
317	Daryl Boston	.05	.04	.02	408	Park Pittman	.20	.15	.08
318	Craig Grebeck	.15	.11	.06	409	Allan Anderson	.05	.04	.02
319	Scott Fletcher	.05	.04	.02	410	Juan Berenguer	.05	.04	.02
320	Frank Thomas	3.00	2.25	1.25	411	Willie Banks	.40	.30	.15
321	Steve Lyons	.05	.04	.02	412	Rich Yett	.05	.04	.02
322	Carlos Martinez	.10	.08	.04	413	Dave West	.08	.06	.03
323	Joe Skalski	.08	.06	.03	414	Greg Gagne	.05	.04	.02
324	Tom Candiotti	.05	.04	.02	415	Chuck Knoblauch	1.00	.70	.40
325	Greg Swindell	.06	.05	.02	416	Randy Bush	.05	.04	.02
326	Steve Olin	.15	.11	.06	417	Gary Gaetti	.08	.06	.03
327	Kevin Wickander	.08	.06	.03	418	Kent Hrbek	.08	.06	.03
328	Doug Jones	.06	.05	.02	419	Al Newman	.05	.04	.02
329	Jeff Shaw	.10	.08	.04	420	Danny Gladden	.05	.04	.02
330	Kevin Bearse	.10	.08	.04	421	Paul Sorrento	.15	.11	.06
331	Dion James	.05	.04	.02	422	Derek Parks	.25	.20	.10
332	Jerry Browne	.06	.05	.02	423	Scott Leius	.20	.15	.08
333	Joey Belle	.40	.30	.15	424	Kirby Puckett	.20	.15	.08
334	Felix Fermin	.05	.04	.02	425	Willie Smith	.20	.15	.08
335	Candy Maldonado	.06	.05	.02	426	Dave Righetti	.08	.06	.02
336	Cory Snyder	.06	.05	.02	427	Jeff Robinson	.05	.04	.02
337	Sandy Alomar	.30	.25	.12	428	Alan Mills	.20	.15	.08
338	Mark Lewis	.12	.09	.05	429	Tim Leary	.05	.04	.02
339	Carlos Baerga	.40	.30	.15	430	Pascual Perez	.05	.04	.02
340	Chris James	.05	.04	.02	431	Alvaro Espinoza	.05	.04	.02
341	Brook Jacoby	.06	.05	.02	432	Dave Winfield	.12	.09	.05
342	Keith Hernandez	.06	.05	.02	433	Jesse Barfield	.06	.05	.02
343	Frank Tanana	.05	.04	.02	434	Randy Velarde	.05	.04	.02
344	Scott Aldred	.15	.11	.06	435	Rick Cerone	.05	.04	.02
345	Mike Henneman	.06	.05	.02	436	Steve Balboni	.05	.04	.02
346	Steve Wapnick	.15	.11	.06	437	Mel Hall	.05	.04	.02
347	Greg Gohr	.15	.11	.06	438	Bob Geren	.06	.05	.02
348	Eric Stone	.15	.11	.06	439	Bernie Williams	.40	.30	.15
349	Brian DuBois	.10	.08	.04	440	Kevin Maas	.40	.30	.15
350	Kevin Ritz	.10	.08	.04	441	Mike Blowers	.15	.11	.06
351	Rico Brogna	.10	.08	.04	442	Steve Sax	.08	.06	.03
352	Mike Heath	.05	.04	.02	443	Don Mattingly	.35	.25	.14
353	Alan Trammell	.08	.06	.03	444	Roberto Kelly	.08	.06	.03
354	Chet Lemon	.06	.05	.02	445	Mike Moore	.06	.05	.02
355	Dave Bergman	.05	.04	.02	446	Reggie Harris	.15	.11	.06
356	Lou Whitaker	.08	.06	.03	447	Scott Sanderson	.05	.04	.02
357	Cecil Fielder	.40	.30	.15	448	Dave Otto	.05	.04	.02
358	Milt Cuyler	.20	.15	.08	449	Dave Stewart	.08	.06	.03
359	Tony Phillips	.06	.05	.02	450	Rick Honeycutt	.05	.04	.02

		MT	NR MT	EX
451	Dennis Eckersley	.08	.06	.03
452	Carney Lansford	.06	.05	.02
453	Scott Hemond	.15	.11	.06
454	Mark McGwire	.20	.15	.08
455	Felix Jose	.15	.11	.06
456	Terry Steinbach	.06	.05	.02
457	Rickey Henderson	.25	.20	.10
458	Dave Henderson	.06	.05	.02
459	Mike Gallego	.05	.04	.02
460	Jose Canseco	.50	.40	.20
461	Walt Weiss	.06	.05	.02
462	Ken Phelps	.05	.04	.02
463	Darren Lewis	.40	.30	.15
464	Ron Hassey	.05	.04	.02
465	Roger Salkeld	.30	.25	.12
466	Scott Bankhead	.06	.05	.02
467	Keith Comstock	.05	.04	.02
468	Randy Johnson	.10	.08	.04
469	Erik Hanson	.10	.08	.04
470	Mike Schooler	.06	.05	.04
471	Gary Eave	.15	.11	.06
472	Jeffrey Leonard	.06	.05	.02
473	Dave Valle	.05	.04	.02
474	Omar Vizquel	.05	.04	.02
475	Pete O'Brien	.05	.04	.02
476	Henry Cotto	.05	.04	.02
477	Jay Buhner	.06	.05	.02
478	Harold Reynolds	.06	.05	.02
479	Alvin Davis	.08	.06	.03
480	Darnell Coles	.05	.04	.02
481	Ken Griffey, Jr.	2.00	1.50	.80
482	Greg Briley	.12	.09	.05
483	Scott Bradley	.05	.04	.02
484	Tino Martinez	.40	.30	.15
485	Jeff Russell	.06	.05	.02
486	Nolan Ryan	.40	.30	.15
487	Robb Nen	.20	.15	.08
488	Kevin Brown	.06	.05	.02
489	Brian Bohanon	.20	.15	.08
490	Ruben Sierra	.15	.11	.06
491	Pete Incaviglia	.06	.05	.02
492	Juan Gonzalez	2.00	1.50	.80
493	Steve Buechele	.05	.04	.02
494	Scott Coolbaugh	.15	.11	.06
495	Geno Petralli	.05	.04	.02
496	Rafael Palmeiro	.08	.06	.03
497	Julio Franco	.08	.06	.03
498	Gary Pettis	.05	.04	.02
499	Donald Harris	.20	.15	.08
500	Monty Fariss	.20	.15	.08
501	Harold Baines	.08	.06	.03
502	Cecil Espy	.05	.04	.02
503	Jack Daugherty	.08	.06	.03
504	Willie Blair	.15	.11	.06
505	Dave Steib	.06	.05	.02
506	Tom Henke	.06	.05	.02
507	John Cerutti	.05	.04	.02
508	Paul Kilgus	.05	.04	.02
509	Jimmy Key	.06	.05	.02
510	John Olerud	.40	.30	.15
511	Ed Sprague	.20	.15	.08
512	Manny Lee	.05	.04	.02
513	Fred McGriff	.08	.06	.03
514	Glenallen Hill	.10	.08	.04
515	George Bell	.08	.06	.03
516	Mookie Wilson	.06	.05	.02
517	Luis Sojo	.15	.11	.06
518	Nelson Liriano	.05	.04	.02
519	Kelly Gruber	.08	.06	.03
520	Greg Myers	.06	.05	.02
521	Pat Borders	.06	.05	.02
522	Junior Felix	.25	.20	.10
523	Eddie Zosky	.25	.20	.10
524	Tony Fernandez	.06	.05	.02
525	Checklist	.05	.04	.02
526	Checklist	.05	.04	.02
527	Checklist	.05	.04	.02
528	Checklist	.05	.04	.02

A player's name in italic indicates a rookie card. An (FC) indicates a player's first card for that particular card company.

1990 Bowman Inserts

Bowman inserted sweepstakes cards in its 1990 packs, much like in 1989. This 11-card set features current players displayed in drawings by Craig Pursley.

		MT	NR MT	EX
Complete Set:		1.00	.70	.40
Common Player:		.06	.05	.02
(1)	Will Clark	.10	.08	.04
(2)	Mark Davis	.06	.05	.02
(3)	Dwight Gooden	.08	.06	.03
(4)	Bo Jackson	.08	.06	.03
(5)	Don Mattingly	.08	.06	.03
(6)	Kevin Mitchell	.08	.06	.03
(7)	Gregg Olson	.08	.06	.03
(8)	Nolan Ryan	.15	.11	.06
(9)	Bret Saberhagen	.08	.06	.03
(10)	Jerome Walton	.06	.05	.02
(11)	Robin Yount	.10	.08	.04

NOTE: A card number in parentheses ( ) indicates the set is unnumbered.

1991 Bowman

The 1991 Bowman set features 704 cards compared to 528 cards in the 1990 issue. The cards feature the 1953 Bowman style. Special Rod Carew cards, slugger cards and foil cards are included. The set is numbered by teams. Like the 1989 and 1990 issues, the card backs feature a breakdown of performance against each other team in the league.

		MT	NR MT	EX
Complete Set:		15.00	11.00	6.00
Common Player:		.05	.04	.02
1	Rod Carew-I	.15	.11	.06
2	Rod Carew-II	.15	.11	.06
3	Rod Carew-III	.15	.11	.06
4	Rod Carew-IV	.15	.11	.06
5	Rod Carew-V	.15	.11	.06
6	Willie Fraser	.05	.04	.02
7	John Olerud	.10	.08	.04
8	William Suero	.15	.11	.06
9	Roberto Alomar	.10	.08	.04
10	Todd Stottlemyre	.06	.05	.02
11	Joe Carter	.10	.08	.04
12	Steve Karsay	.20	.15	.08
13	Mark Whiten	.20	.15	.08
14	Pat Borders	.05	.04	.02
15	Mike Timlin	.15	.11	.06
16	Tom Henke	.06	.05	.02
17	Eddie Zosky	.08	.06	.03
18	Kelly Gruber	.08	.06	.03
19	Jimmy Key	.06	.05	.02
20	Jerry Schunk	.12	.09	.05
21	Manny Lee	.05	.04	.02
22	Dave Steib	.08	.06	.03
23	Pat Hentgen	.12	.09	.05
24	Glenallen Hill	.08	.06	.03

		MT	NR MT	EX				MT	NR MT	EX
25	Rene Gonzales	.05	.04	.02		117	Phil Plantier	.80	.60	.30
26	Ed Sprague	.10	.08	.04		118	Roger Clemens	.15	.11	.06
27	Ken Dayley	.05	.04	.02		119	John Marzano	.05	.04	.02
28	Pat Tabler	.05	.04	.02		120	Jody Reed	.06	.05	.02
29	Denis Boucher	.12	.09	.05		121	Scott Taylor	.12	.09	.05
30	Devon White	.08	.06	.03		122	Jack Clark	.06	.05	.02
31	Dante Bichette	.05	.04	.02		123	Derek Livernois	.12	.09	.05
32	Paul Molitor	.08	.06	.03		124	Tony Pena	.05	.04	.02
33	Greg Vaughn	.08	.06	.03		125	Tom Brunansky	.05	.04	.02
34	Dan Plesac	.05	.04	.02		126	Carlos Quintana	.05	.04	.02
35	Chris George	.12	.09	.05		127	Tim Naehring	.10	.08	.04
36	Tim McIntosh	.08	.06	.03		128	Matt Young	.05	.04	.02
37	Franklin Stubbs	.05	.04	.02		129	Wade Boggs	.15	.11	.06
38	Bo Dodson	.15	.11	.06		130	Kevin Morton	.15	.11	.06
39	Ron Robinson	.05	.04	.02		131	Pete Incaviglia	.05	.04	.02
40	Ed Nunez	.05	.04	.02		132	Rob Deer	.05	.04	.02
41	Greg Brock	.05	.04	.02		133	Bill Gullickson	.05	.04	.02
42	Jaime Navarro	.06	.05	.02		134	Rico Brogna	.12	.09	.05
43	Chris Bosio	.05	.05	.02		135	Lloyd Moseby	.05	.04	.02
44	B.J. Surhoff	.06	.05	.02		136	Cecil Fielder	.15	.11	.06
45	Chris Johnson	.12	.09	.05		137	Tony Phillips	.05	.04	.02
46	Willie Randolph	.06	.05	.02		138	Mark Leiter	.05	.04	.02
47	Narciso Elvira	.10	.08	.04		139	John Cerutti	.05	.04	.02
48	Jim Gantner	.05	.04	.02		140	Mickey Tettleton	.06	.05	.02
49	Kevin Brown	.05	.04	.02		141	Milt Cuyler	.10	.08	.04
50	Julio Machado	.05	.04	.02		142	Greg Gohr	.10	.08	.04
51	Chuck Crim	.05	.04	.02		143	Tony Bernazard	.05	.04	.02
52	Gary Sheffield	.08	.06	.03		144	Dan Gakeler	.12	.09	.05
53	Angel Miranda	.12	.09	.05		145	Travis Fryman	.30	.25	.12
54	Teddy Higuera	.06	.05	.02		146	Dan Petry	.05	.04	.02
55	Robin Yount	.10	.08	.04		147	Scott Aldred	.08	.06	.03
56	Cal Eldred	.12	.09	.05		148	John DeSilva	.12	.09	.05
57	Sandy Alomar	.08	.06	.03		149	Rusty Meacham	.12	.09	.05
58	Greg Swindell	.06	.05	.02		150	Lou Whitaker	.06	.05	.02
59	Brook Jacoby	.06	.05	.02		151	Dave Haas	.06	.05	.02
60	Efrain Valdez	.08	.06	.03		152	Luis de los Santos	.05	.04	.02
61	Ever Magallanes	.12	.09	.05		153	Ivan Cruz	.12	.09	.05
62	Tom Candiotti	.05	.04	.02		154	Alan Trammell	.08	.06	.03
63	Eric King	.05	.04	.02		155	Pat Kelly	.35	.25	.14
64	Alex Cole	.05	.04	.02		156	Carl Everett	.35	.25	.14
65	Charles Nagy	.08	.06	.03		157	Greg Cadaret	.05	.04	.02
66	Mitch Webster	.05	.04	.02		158	Kevin Maas	.15	.11	.06
67	Chris James	.05	.04	.02		159	Jeff Johnson	.15	.11	.06
68	Jim Thome	.60	.45	.25		160	Willie Smith	.15	.11	.06
69	Carlos Baerga	.06	.05	.02		161	Gerald Williams	.20	.15	.08
70	Mark Lewis	.08	.06	.03		162	Mike Humphreys	.15	.11	.06
71	Jerry Browne	.05	.04	.02		163	Alvaro Espinoza	.05	.04	.02
72	Jesse Orosco	.05	.04	.02		164	Matt Nokes	.05	.04	.02
73	Mike Huff	.06	.05	.02		165	Wade Taylor	.12	.09	.05
74	Jose Escobar	.12	.09	.05		166	Roberto Kelly	.08	.06	.03
75	Jeff Manto	.06	.05	.02		167	John Habyan	.05	.04	.02
76	Turner Ward	.10	.08	.04		168	Steve Farr	.05	.04	.02
77	Doug Jones	.05	.04	.02		169	Jesse Barfield	.05	.04	.02
78	Bruce Egloff	.12	.09	.05		170	Steve Sax	.06	.05	.02
79	Tim Costo	.20	.15	.08		171	Jim Leyritz	.05	.04	.02
80	Beau Allred	.06	.05	.02		172	Robert Eenhoorn	.15	.11	.06
81	Albert Belle	.20	.15	.08		173	Bernie Williams	.15	.11	.06
82	John Farrell	.05	.04	.02		174	Scott Lusader	.05	.04	.02
83	Glenn Davis	.08	.06	.03		175	Torey Lovullo	.08	.06	.03
84	Joe Orsulak	.05	.04	.02		176	Chuck Cary	.05	.04	.02
85	Mark Williamson	.05	.04	.02		177	Scott Sanderson	.05	.04	.02
86	Ben McDonald	.15	.11	.06		178	Don Mattingly	.15	.11	.06
87	Billy Ripken	.05	.04	.02		179	Mel Hall	.06	.05	.02
88	Leo Gomez	.08	.06	.03		180	Juan Gonzalez	.30	.25	.12
89	Bob Melvin	.05	.04	.02		181	Hensley Meulens	.08	.06	.03
90	Jeff Robinson	.05	.04	.02		182	Jose Offerman	.15	.11	.06
91	Jose Mesa	.05	.04	.02		183	Jeff Bagwell (Foil)	1.50	1.25	.60
92	Gregg Olson	.08	.06	.03		184	Jeff Conine	.20	.15	.08
93	Mike Devereaux	.06	.05	.02		185	Henry Rodriguez (Foil)	.25	.20	.10
94	Luis Mercedes	.20	.15	.08		186	Jimmie Reese (Foil)	.15	.11	.06
95	Arthur Rhodes	.20	.15	.08		187	Kyle Abbott	.10	.08	.04
96	Juan Bell	.05	.04	.02		188	Lance Parrish	.06	.05	.02
97	Mike Mussina	.60	.45	.25		189	Rafael Montalvo	.12	.09	.05
98	Jeff Ballard	.05	.04	.02		190	Floyd Bannister	.05	.04	.02
99	Chris Hoiles	.08	.06	.03		191	Dick Schofield	.05	.04	.02
100	Brady Anderson	.05	.04	.02		192	Scott Lewis	.12	.09	.05
101	Bob Milacki	.05	.04	.02		193	Jeff Robinson	.05	.04	.02
102	David Segui	.06	.05	.02		194	Kent Anderson	.05	.04	.02
103	Dwight Evans	.06	.05	.02		195	Wally Joyner	.10	.08	.04
104	Cal Ripken	.12	.09	.05		196	Chuck Finley	.08	.06	.03
105	Mike Linskey	.12	.09	.05		197	Luis Sojo	.05	.04	.02
106	Jeff Tackett	.12	.09	.05		198	Jeff Richardson	.08	.06	.03
107	Jeff Reardon	.08	.06	.03		199	Dave Parker	.08	.06	.03
108	Dana Kiecker	.05	.04	.02		200	Jim Abbott	.08	.06	.03
109	Ellis Burks	.08	.06	.03		201	Junior Felix	.06	.05	.02
110	Dave Owen	.12	.09	.05		202	Mark Langston	.08	.06	.03
111	Danny Darwin	.05	.04	.02		203	Tim Salmon	.20	.15	.08
112	Mo Vaughn	.20	.15	.08		204	Cliff Young	.08	.06	.03
113	Jeff McNeely	.25	.20	.10						
114	Tom Bolton	.05	.04	.02						
115	Greg Blosser	.12	.09	.05						
116	Mike Greenwell	.10	.08	.04						

Please See pp. 782-783 for completion of
1991 Bowman

1993 EDITION FEATURES

SUBSETS ON:

◆ *"First Cards"— 43 Cards of Players who Have Never had a Baseball Card Made of Them*

◆ *"Game of the Century"— First All-Star Game*

◆ *"Spitballers" and "Accused Spitballers"*

◆ *Players Who Made It by "Beating the Odds"*

◆ *Native American Greats*

◆ *Great Catchers and Managers*

EXCLUSIVE COLOR CARD BONUS

◆ 8 color-enhanced Conlon Cards have been randomly inserted exclusively in Conlon Collection™ counter packs and blister packs.

◆ Very Limited. Only 100,000 of each have been printed.

FREE SEND-AWAY OFFER

◆ Send 20 proofs of purchase from Conlon foil packs with a self-addressed stamped envelope to get color enhanced Shoeless Joe Jackson and Jim Thorpe cards. These two cards are available only through this send-away offer.

≡MEGACARDS™

Megacards, Inc. • P.O. Box 1323 • Fairfield, IA 52556 • 515-472-4159
THE CONLON COLLECTION™ is a trademark of The Sporting News
Publishing Co.

		MT	NR MT	EX				MT	NR MT	EX
205	Scott Bailes	.05	.04	.02		296	Mike Boddicker	.06	.05	.02
206	Bobby Rose	.06	.05	.02		297	Joel Johnston	.12	.09	.05
207	Gary Gaetti	.06	.05	.02		298	Tim Spehr	.15	.11	.06
208	Ruben Amaro	.12	.09	.05		299	Hector Wagner	.12	.09	.05
209	Luis Polonia	.06	.05	.02		300	George Brett	.12	.09	.05
210	Dave Winfield	.10	.08	.04		301	Mike Macfarlane	.06	.05	.02
211	Bryan Harvey	.06	.05	.02		302	Kirk Gibson	.06	.05	.02
212	Mike Moore	.05	.04	.02		303	Harvey Pulliam	.15	.11	.06
213	Rickey Henderson	.15	.11	.06		304	Jim Eisenreich	.05	.04	.02
214	Steve Chitren	.15	.11	.06		305	Kevin Seitzer	.06	.05	.02
215	Bob Welch	.06	.05	.02		306	Mark Davis	.05	.04	.02
216	Terry Steinbach	.06	.05	.02		307	Kurt Stillwell	.05	.04	.02
217	Ernie Riles	.05	.04	.02		308	Jeff Montgomery	.06	.05	.02
218	Todd Van Poppel	1.25	.90	.50		309	Kevin Appier	.06	.05	.02
219	Mike Gallego	.05	.04	.02		310	Bob Hamelin	.10	.08	.04
220	Curt Young	.05	.04	.02		311	Tom Gordon	.06	.05	.02
221	Todd Burns	.05	.04	.02		312	Kerwin Moore	.12	.09	.05
222	Vance Law	.05	.04	.02		313	Hugh Walker	.12	.09	.05
223	Eric Show	.05	.04	.02		314	Terry Shumpert	.05	.04	.02
224	Don Peters	.15	.11	.06		315	Warren Cromartie	.05	.04	.02
225	Dave Stewart	.10	.08	.04		316	Gary Thurman	.05	.04	.02
226	Dave Henderson	.06	.05	.02		317	Steve Bedrosian	.05	.04	.02
227	Jose Canseco	.20	.15	.08		318	Danny Gladden	.05	.04	.02
228	Walt Weiss	.06	.05	.02		319	Jack Morris	.08	.06	.03
229	Dann Howitt	.06	.05	.02		320	Kirby Puckett	.15	.11	.06
230	Willie Wilson	.05	.04	.02		321	Kent Hrbek	.08	.06	.03
231	Harold Baines	.06	.05	.02		322	Kevin Tapani	.08	.06	.03
232	Scott Hemond	.06	.05	.02		323	Denny Neagle	.25	.20	.10
233	Joe Slusarski	.12	.09	.05		324	Rich Garces	.12	.09	.05
234	Mark McGwire	.10	.08	.04		325	Larry Casian	.10	.08	.04
235	Kirk Dressendorfer	.30	.25	.12		326	Shane Mack	.08	.06	.03
236	Craig Paquette	.15	.11	.06		327	Allan Anderson	.05	.04	.02
237	Dennis Eckersley	.10	.08	.04		328	Junior Ortiz	.05	.04	.02
238	Dana Allison	.12	.09	.05		329	Paul Abbott	.10	.08	.04
239	Scott Bradley	.05	.04	.02		330	Chuck Knoblauch	.30	.25	.12
240	Brian Holman	.06	.05	.02		331	Chili Davis	.08	.06	.03
241	Mike Schooler	.06	.05	.02		332	Todd Ritchie	.12	.09	.05
242	Rich Delucia	.12	.09	.05		333	Brian Harper	.06	.05	.02
243	Edgar Martinez	.08	.06	.03		334	Rick Aguilera	.06	.05	.02
244	Henry Cotto	.05	.04	.02		335	Scott Erickson	.60	.45	.25
245	Omar Vizquel	.05	.04	.02		336	Pedro Munoz	.30	.25	.12
246	Ken Griffey, Jr.	1.50	1.25	.60		337	Scott Leius	.10	.08	.04
247	Jay Buhner	.06	.05	.02		338	Greg Gagne	.05	.04	.02
248	Bill Krueger	.05	.04	.02		339	Mike Pagliarulo	.05	.04	.02
249	Dave Fleming	.50	.40	.20		340	Terry Leach	.05	.04	.02
250	Patrick Lennon	.15	.11	.06		341	Willie Banks	.10	.08	.04
251	Dave Valle	.05	.04	.02		342	Bobby Thigpen	.06	.05	.02
252	Harold Reynolds	.06	.05	.02		343	Roberto Hernandez	.15	.11	.06
253	Randy Johnson	.08	.06	.03		344	Melido Perez	.05	.04	.02
254	Scott Bankhead	.06	.05	.02		345	Carlton Fisk	.10	.08	.04
255	Ken Griffey	.08	.06	.03		346	Norberto Martin	.12	.09	.05
256	Greg Briley	.05	.04	.02		347	Johnny Ruffin	.12	.09	.05
257	Tino Martinez	.12	.09	.05		348	Jeff Carter	.12	.09	.05
258	Alvin Davis	.06	.05	.02		349	Lance Johnson	.05	.04	.02
259	Pete O'Brien	.05	.04	.02		350	Sammy Sosa	.10	.08	.04
260	Erik Hanson	.08	.06	.03		351	Alex Fernandez	.20	.15	.08
261	Bret Boone	.15	.11	.06		352	Jack McDowell	.10	.08	.04
262	Roger Salkeld	.15	.11	.06		353	Bob Wickman	.20	.15	.11
263	Dave Burba	.08	.06	.03		354	Wilson Alvarez	.15	.11	.06
264	Kerry Woodson	.12	.09	.05		355	Charlie Hough	.05	.04	.02
265	Julio Franco	.08	.06	.03		356	Ozzie Guillen	.06	.05	.02
266	Dan Peltier	.20	.15	.08		357	Cory Snyder	.05	.04	.02
267	Jeff Russell	.05	.04	.02		358	Robin Ventura	.15	.11	.06
268	Steve Buechele	.06	.05	.02		359	Scott Fletcher	.05	.04	.02
269	Donald Harris	.12	.09	.05		360	Cesar Bernhardt	.12	.09	.05
270	Robb Nen	.10	.08	.04		361	Dan Pasqua	.05	.04	.02
271	Rich Gossage	.06	.05	.02		362	Rock Raines	.08	.06	.03
272	Ivan Rodriguez	1.50	1.25	.60		363	Brian Drahman	.12	.09	.05
273	Jeff Huson	.06	.05	.02		364	Wayne Edwards	.05	.04	.02
274	Kevin Brown	.06	.05	.02		365	Scott Radinsky	.06	.05	.02
275	Dan Smith	.15	.11	.06		366	Frank Thomas	1.50	1.25	.60
276	Gary Pettis	.05	.04	.02		367	Cecil Fielder (AL Slugger)	.10	.08	.04
277	Jack Daugherty	.05	.04	.02		368	Julio Franco (AL Slugger)	.10	.08	.04
278	Mike Jeffcoat	.05	.04	.02		369	Kelly Gruber (AL Slugger)	.08	.06	.03
279	Brad Arnsberg	.06	.05	.02		370	Alan Trammell (AL Slugger)	.08	.06	.03
280	Nolan Ryan	.25	.20	.10		371	Rickey Henderson (AL Slugger)	.10	.08	.04
281	Eric McCray	.12	.09	.05		372	Jose Canseco (AL Slugger)	.15	.11	.06
282	Scott Chiamparino	.08	.06	.03		373	Ellis Burks (AL Slugger)	.08	.06	.03
283	Ruben Sierra	.15	.11	.06		374	Lance Parrish (AL Slugger)	.06	.05	.02
284	Geno Petralli	.05	.04	.02		375	Dave Parker (AL Slugger)	.08	.06	.03
285	Monty Fariss	.08	.06	.03		376	Eddie Murray (NL Slugger)	.08	.06	.03
286	Rafael Palmeiro	.08	.06	.03		377	Ryne Sandberg (NL Slugger)	.12	.09	.05
287	Bobb Witt	.06	.05	.02		378	Matt Williams (NL Slugger)	.08	.06	.03
288	Dean Palmer	.25	.20	.10		379	Barry Larkin (NL Slugger)	.08	.06	.03
289	Tony Scruggs	.12	.09	.05		380	Barry Bonds (NL Slugger)	.10	.08	.04
290	Kenny Rogers	.05	.04	.02		381	Bobby Bonilla (NL Slugger)	.10	.08	.04
291	Bret Saberhagen	.08	.06	.03		382	Darryl Strawberry (NL Slugger)	.10	.08	.04
292	Brian McRae	.40	.30	.15		383	Benny Santiago (NL Slugger)	.06	.05	.02
293	Storm Davis	.05	.04	.02		384	Don Robinson (NL Slugger)	.05	.04	.02
294	Danny Tartabull	.08	.06	.03		385	Paul Coleman	.10	.08	.04
295	David Howard	.12	.09	.05		386	Milt Thompson	.05	.04	.02

		MT	NR MT	EX			MT	NR MT	EX
387	Lee Smith	.06	.05	.02	478	D.J. Dozier	.10	.08	.04
388	Ray Lankford	.15	.11	.06	479	Kevin McReynolds	.06	.05	.02
389	Tom Pagnozzi	.06	.05	.02	480	Tom Herr	.05	.04	.02
390	Ken Hill	.06	.05	.02	481	Gregg Jefferies	.08	.06	.03
391	Jamie Moyer	.05	.04	.02	482	Pete Schourek	.12	.09	.05
392	Greg Carmona	.12	.09	.05	483	Ron Darling	.06	.05	.02
393	John Ericks	.10	.08	.04	484	Dave Magadan	.06	.05	.02
394	Bob Tewksbury	.05	.04	.02	485	Andy Ashby	.10	.08	.04
395	Jose Oquendo	.05	.04	.02	486	Dale Murphy	.08	.06	.03
396	Rheal Cormier	.30	.25	.12	487	Von Hayes	.06	.05	.02
397	Mike Milchin	.12	.09	.05	488	Kim Batiste	.08	.06	.03
398	Ozzie Smith	.10	.08	.04	489	Tony Longmire	.15	.11	.06
399	Aaron Holbert	.15	.11	.06	490	Wally Backman	.05	.04	.02
400	Jose DeLeon	.05	.04	.02	491	Jeff Jackson	.08	.06	.03
401	Felix Jose	.30	.25	.12	492	Mickey Morandini	.08	.06	.03
402	Juan Agosto	.05	.04	.02	493	Darrel Akerfelds	.05	.04	.02
403	Pedro Guerrero	.08	.06	.03	494	Ricky Jordan	.06	.05	.02
404	Todd Zeile	.08	.06	.03	495	Randy Ready	.05	.04	.02
405	Gerald Perry	.05	.04	.02	496	Darrin Fletcher	.06	.05	.02
406	Donovan Osborne	.12	.09	.05	497	Chuck Malone	.05	.04	.02
407	Bryn Smith	.05	.04	.02	498	Pat Combs	.06	.05	.02
408	Bernard Gilkey	.15	.11	.06	499	Dickie Thon	.05	.04	.02
409	Rex Hudler	.05	.04	.02	500	Roger McDowell	.06	.05	.02
410	Thomson/Branca (Foil)	.10	.08	.04	501	Len Dykstra	.06	.05	.02
411	Lance Dickson	.15	.11	.06	502	Joe Boever	.05	.04	.02
412	Danny Jackson	.05	.04	.02	503	John Kruk	.06	.05	.02
413	Jerome Walton	.06	.05	.02	504	Terry Mulholland	.06	.05	.02
414	Sean Cheetham	.12	.09	.05	505	Wes Chamberlain	.35	.25	.14
415	Joe Girardi	.05	.04	.02	506	Mike Lieberthal	.15	.11	.06
416	Ryne Sandberg	.15	.11	.06	507	Darren Daulton	.06	.05	.02
417	Mike Harkey	.06	.05	.02	508	Charlie Hayes	.06	.05	.02
418	George Bell	.08	.06	.03	509	John Smiley	.06	.05	.02
419	Rick Wilkins	.20	.15	.08	510	Gary Varsho	.05	.04	.02
420	Earl Cunningham	.06	.05	.02	511	Curt Wilkerson	.05	.04	.02
421	Heathcliff Slocumb	.12	.09	.05	512	Orlando Merced	.25	.20	.10
422	Mike Bielecki	.05	.04	.02	513	Barry Bonds	.12	.09	.05
423	Jessie Hollins	.12	.09	.05	514	Mike Lavalliere	.05	.04	.02
424	Shawon Dunston	.06	.05	.02	515	Doug Drabek	.06	.05	.02
425	Dave Smith	.05	.04	.02	516	Gary Redus	.05	.04	.02
426	Greg Maddux	.08	.06	.03	517	William Pennyfeather	.15	.11	.06
427	Jose Vizcaino	.05	.04	.02	518	Randy Tomlin	.06	.05	.02
428	Luis Salazar	.05	.04	.02	519	Mike Zimmerman	.12	.09	.05
429	Andre Dawson	.10	.08	.04	520	Jeff King	.06	.05	.02
430	Rick Sutcliffe	.05	.04	.02	521	Kurt Miller	.15	.11	.06
431	Paul Assenmacher	.05	.04	.02	522	Jay Bell	.06	.05	.02
432	Erik Pappas	.12	.09	.05	523	Bill Landrum	.05	.04	.02
433	Mark Grace	.08	.06	.03	524	Zane Smith	.05	.04	.02
434	Denny Martinez	.06	.05	.02	525	Bobby Bonilla	.10	.08	.04
435	Marquis Grissom	.10	.08	.04	526	Bob Walk	.05	.04	.02
436	Wilfredo Cordero	.30	.25	.12	527	Austin Manahan	.08	.06	.03
437	Tim Wallach	.06	.05	.02	528	Joe Ausanio	.12	.09	.05
438	Brian Barnes	.15	.11	.06	529	Andy Van Slyke	.08	.06	.03
439	Barry Jones	.05	.04	.02	530	Jose Lind	.05	.04	.02
440	Ivan Calderon	.08	.06	.03	531	Carlos Garcia	.12	.09	.05
441	Stan Spencer	.12	.09	.05	532	Don Slaught	.05	.04	.02
442	Larry Walker	.08	.06	.03	533	Colin Powell (Foil)	.25	.20	.10
443	Chris Haney	.12	.09	.05	534	Frank Bolick (Foil)	.25	.20	.10
444	Hector Rivera	.12	.09	.05	535	Gary Scott (Foil)	.30	.25	.12
445	Delino DeShields	.12	.09	.05	536	Nikco Riesgo (Foil)	.30	.25	.12
446	Andres Galarraga	.06	.05	.02	537	Reggie Sanders	.60	.45	.25
447	Gilberto Reyes	.06	.05	.02	538	Tim Howard (Foil)	.25	.20	.10
448	Willie Greene	.10	.08	.04	539	Ryan Bowen	.15	.11	.06
449	Greg Colbrunn	.12	.09	.05	540	Eric Anthony	.08	.06	.03
450	Rondell White	.30	.25	.12	541	Jim Deshaies	.05	.04	.02
451	Steve Frey	.06	.05	.02	542	Tom Nevers	.12	.09	.05
452	Shane Andrews	.15	.11	.06	543	Ken Caminiti	.05	.04	.02
453	Mike Fitzgerald	.05	.04	.02	544	Karl Rhodes	.12	.09	.05
454	Spike Owen	.05	.04	.02	545	Xavier Hernandez	.08	.06	.03
455	Dave Martinez	.05	.04	.02	546	Mike Scott	.06	.05	.02
456	Dennis Boyd	.05	.04	.02	547	Jeff Juden	.15	.11	.06
457	Eric Bullock	.06	.05	.02	548	Darryl Kile	.08	.06	.03
458	Reid Cornelius	.15	.11	.06	549	Willie Ansley	.10	.08	.04
459	Chris Nabholz	.15	.11	.06	550	Luis Gonzalez	.35	.25	.14
460	David Cone	.08	.06	.03	551	Mike Simms	.15	.11	.06
461	Hubie Brooks	.06	.05	.02	552	Mark Portugal	.05	.04	.02
462	Sid Fernandez	.06	.05	.02	553	Jimmy Jones	.05	.04	.02
463	Doug Simons	.10	.08	.04	554	Jim Clancy	.05	.04	.02
464	Howard Johnson	.10	.08	.04	555	Pete Harnisch	.06	.05	.02
465	Chris Donnels	.15	.11	.06	556	Craig Biggio	.08	.06	.03
466	Anthony Young	.15	.11	.06	557	Eric Yelding	.05	.04	.02
467	Todd Hundley	.12	.09	.05	558	Dave Rohde	.06	.05	.02
468	Rick Cerone	.05	.04	.02	559	Casey Candaele	.05	.04	.02
469	Kevin Elster	.05	.04	.02	560	Curt Schilling	.05	.04	.02
470	Wally Whitehurst	.06	.05	.02	561	Steve Finley	.06	.05	.02
471	Vince Coleman	.08	.06	.03	562	Javier Ortiz	.08	.06	.03
472	Doc Gooden	.08	.06	.03	563	Andujar Cedeno	.20	.15	.08
473	Charlie O'Brien	.05	.04	.02	564	Rafael Ramirez	.05	.04	.02
474	Jeromy Burnitz	.40	.30	.15	565	Kenny Lofton	.30	.25	.12
475	John Franco	.08	.06	.03	566	Steve Avery	.15	.11	.06
476	Daryl Boston	.05	.04	.02	567	Lonnie Smith	.05	.04	.02
477	Frank Viola	.08	.06	.03	568	Kent Mercker	.06	.05	.02

		MT	NR MT	EX
569	Chipper Jones	.40	.30	.15
570	Terry Pendleton	.06	.05	.02
571	Otis Nixon	.05	.04	.02
572	Juan Berenguer	.05	.04	.02
573	Charlie Leibrandt	.05	.04	.02
574	David Justice	.30	.25	.12
575	Keith Mitchell	.25	.20	.10
576	Tom Glavine	.08	.06	.03
577	Greg Olson	.05	.04	.02
578	Rafael Belliard	.05	.04	.02
579	Ben Rivera	.10	.08	.04
580	John Smoltz	.06	.05	.02
581	Tyler Houston	.05	.04	.02
582	Mark Wohlers	.40	.30	.15
583	Ron Gant	.30	.25	.12
584	Ramon Caraballo	.10	.08	.04
585	Sid Bream	.05	.04	.02
586	Jeff Treadway	.05	.04	.02
587	Javier Lopez	.12	.09	.05
588	Deion Sanders	.08	.06	.03
589	Mike Heath	.05	.04	.02
590	Ryan Klesko	1.25	.90	.50
591	Bob Ojeda	.05	.04	.02
592	Alfredo Griffin	.05	.04	.02
593	Raul Mondesi	.20	.15	.08
594	Greg Smith	.05	.04	.02
595	Orel Hershiser	.08	.06	.03
596	Juan Samuel	.06	.05	.02
597	Brett Butler	.06	.05	.02
598	Gary Carter	.06	.05	.02
599	Stan Javier	.05	.04	.02
600	Kal Daniels	.08	.06	.03
601	Jamie McAndrew	.15	.11	.06
602	Mike Sharperson	.05	.04	.02
603	Jay Howell	.05	.04	.02
604	Eric Karros	.30	.25	.12
605	Tim Belcher	.06	.05	.02
606	Dan Opperman	.12	.09	.05
607	Lenny Harris	.05	.04	.02
608	Tom Goodwin	.10	.08	.04
609	Darryl Strawberry	.15	.11	.06
610	Ramon Martinez	.12	.09	.05
611	Kevin Gross	.05	.04	.02
612	Zakary Shinall	.12	.09	.05
613	Mike Scioscia	.05	.04	.02
614	Eddie Murray	.08	.06	.03
615	Ronnie Walden	.15	.11	.06
616	Will Clark	.20	.15	.08
617	Adam Hyzdu	.15	.11	.06
618	Matt Williams	.08	.06	.03
619	Don Robinson	.05	.04	.02
620	Jeff Brantley	.05	.04	.02
621	Greg Litton	.05	.04	.02
622	Steve Decker	.25	.20	.10
623	Robby Thompson	.06	.05	.02
624	Mark Leonard	.12	.09	.05
625	Kevin Bass	.05	.04	.02
626	Scott Garrelts	.05	.04	.02
627	Jose Uribe	.05	.04	.02
628	Eric Gunderson	.08	.06	.03
629	Steve Hosey	.08	.06	.03
630	Trevor Wilson	.06	.05	.02
631	Terry Kennedy	.05	.04	.02
632	Dave Righetti	.06	.05	.02
633	Kelly Downs	.05	.04	.02
634	Johnny Ard	.08	.06	.03
635	Eric Christopherson	.12	.09	.05
636	Kevin Mitchell	.10	.08	.04
637	John Burkett	.05	.04	.02
638	Kevin Rogers	.12	.09	.05
639	Bud Black	.05	.04	.02
640	Willie McGee	.06	.05	.02
641	Royce Clayton	.15	.11	.06
642	Tony Fernandez	.06	.05	.02
643	Ricky Bones	.12	.09	.05
644	Thomas Howard	.06	.05	.02
645	Dave Staton	.15	.11	.06
646	Jim Presley	.05	.04	.02
647	Tony Gwynn	.10	.08	.04
648	Marty Barrett	.05	.04	.02
649	Scott Coolbaugh	.06	.05	.02
650	Craig Lefferts	.05	.04	.02
651	Eddie Whitson	.05	.04	.02
652	Oscar Azocar	.05	.04	.02
653	Wes Gardner	.05	.04	.02
654	Bip Roberts	.06	.05	.02
655	Robbie Beckett	.15	.11	.06
656	Benny Santiago	.06	.05	.02
657	Greg W. Harris	.05	.04	.02
658	Jerald Clark	.06	.05	.02
659	Fred McGriff	.10	.08	.04

		MT	NR MT	EX
660	Larry Andersen	.05	.04	.02
661	Bruce Hurst	.06	.05	.02
662	Steve Martin	.12	.09	.05
663	Rafael Valdez	.06	.05	.02
664	Paul Faries	.06	.05	.02
665	Andy Benes	.08	.06	.03
666	Randy Myers	.06	.05	.02
667	Rob Dibble	.08	.06	.03
668	Glenn Sutko	.12	.09	.05
669	Glenn Braggs	.05	.04	.02
670	Billy Hatcher	.05	.04	.02
671	Joe Oliver	.05	.04	.02
672	Freddie Benavides	.12	.09	.05
673	Barry Larkin	.08	.06	.03
674	Chris Sabo	.08	.06	.03
675	Mariano Duncan	.05	.04	.02
676	Chris Jones	.15	.11	.06
677	Gino Minutelli	.12	.09	.05
678	Reggie Jefferson	.12	.09	.05
679	Jack Armstrong	.06	.05	.02
680	Chris Hammond	.06	.05	.02
681	Jose Rijo	.08	.06	.03
682	Bill Doran	.05	.04	.02
683	Terry Lee	.06	.05	.02
684	Tom Browning	.06	.05	.02
685	Paul O'Neill	.08	.06	.03
686	Eric Davis	.10	.08	.04
687	Dan Wilson	.15	.11	.06
688	Ted Power	.05	.04	.02
689	Tim Layana	.05	.04	.02
690	Norm Charlton	.06	.05	.02
691	Hal Morris	.10	.08	.04
692	Rickey Henderson (Foil)	.20	.15	.08
693	Sam Militello (Foil)	.30	.25	.12
694	Matt Mieske (Foil)	.60	.45	.25
695	Paul Russo (Foil)	.25	.20	.10
696	Domingo Mota (Foil)	.25	.20	.10
697	Todd Guggiana (Foil)	.20	.15	.08
698	Marc Newfield	.40	.30	.15
699	Checklist	.05	.04	.02
700	Checklist	.05	.04	.02
701	Checklist	.05	.04	.02
702	Checklist	.05	.04	.02
703	Checklist	.05	.04	.02
704	Checklist	.05	.04	.02

1992 Bowman

Topps introduced several changes with the release of its 1992 Bowman set. The 705-card set features 45 special insert cards stamped with gold foil. The cards are printed with a premium UV coated glossy card stock. Several players without major league experience are featured in the set. Included in this group are 1991 MVP's of the minor leagues and first round draft choices.

		MT	NR MT	EX
Complete Set:		60.00	45.00	25.00
Common Player:		.07	.05	.03
1	Ivan Rodriguez	.20	.15	.08
2	Kirk McCaskill	.07	.05	.03
3	Scott Livingstone, Scott Livingstone			
		.10	.08	.04
4	Salomon Torres	.20	.15	.08
5	Carlos Hernandez	.20	.15	.08
6	Dave Hollins	.12	.09	.05
7	Scott Fletcher	.07	.05	.03

#	Name	MT	NR MT	EX	#	Name	MT	NR MT	EX
8	Jorge Fabregas	.20	.15	.08	99	David Zancanaro	.10	.08	.04
9	Andujar Cedeno	.12	.09	.05	100	Ken Griffey, Jr.	1.00	.70	.40
10	Howard Johnson	.12	.09	.05	101	Todd Hundley	.10	.08	.04
11	Trevor Hoffman	.20	.15	.08	102	Mike Trombley	.20	.15	.08
12	Roberto Kelly	.10	.08	.04	103	Ricky Gutierrez	.20	.15	.08
13	Gregg Jefferies	.12	.09	.05	104	Braulio Castillo	.20	.15	.08
14	Marquis Grissom	.12	.09	.05	105	Craig Lefferts	.07	.05	.02
15	Mike Ignasiak	.07	.05	.03	106	Rick Sutcliffe	.10	.08	.04
16	Jack Morris	.10	.08	.04	107	Dean Palmer	.10	.08	.04
17	William Pennyfeather	.20	.15	.08	108	Henry Rodriguez	.15	.11	.06
18	Todd Stottlemyre	.07	.05	.03	109	Mark Clark	.20	.15	.08
19	Chito Martinez	.12	.09	.05	110	Kenny Lofton	.30	.25	.12
20	Roberto Alomar	.15	.11	.06	111	Mark Carreon	.07	.05	.03
21	Sam Militello	.20	.15	.08	112	J.T. Bruett	.20	.15	.08
22	Hector Fajardo	.20	.15	.08	113	Gerald Williams	.20	.15	.08
23	Paul Quantrill	.20	.15	.08	114	Frank Thomas	1.50	1.25	.60
24	Chuck Knoblauch	.12	.09	.05	115	Kevin Reimer	.08	.06	.03
25	Reggie Jefferson	.12	.09	.05	116	Sammy Sosa	.08	.06	.03
26	Jeremy McGarity	.20	.15	.08	117	Mickey Tettleton	.10	.08	.04
27	Jerome Walton	.08	.06	.03	118	Reggie Sanders	.20	.15	.08
28	Chipper Jones	.50	.40	.20	119	Trevor Wilson	.07	.05	.03
29	Brian Barber	.20	.15	.08	120	Cliff Brantley	.20	.15	.08
30	Ron Darling	.07	.05	.02	121	Spike Owen	.07	.05	.02
31	Robert Petrone	.20	.15	.08	122	Jeff Montgomery	.07	.05	.02
32	Chuck Finley	.08	.06	.03	123	Alex Sutherland	.20	.15	.08
33	Edgar Martinez	.10	.08	.04	124	Brien Taylor	3.00	2.25	1.25
34	Napolean Robinson	.20	.15	.08	125	Brian Williams	.15	.11	.06
35	Andy Van Slyke	.10	.08	.04	126	Kevin Seitzer	.07	.05	.02
36	Bobby Thigpen	.08	.06	.03	127	Carlos Baerga	1.50	1.25	.60
37	Travis Fryman	.50	.40	.20	128	Gary Scott	.10	.08	.04
38	Eric Christopherson	.10	.08	.04	129	Scott Cooper	.10	.08	.04
39	Terry Mulholland	.08	.06	.03	130	Domingo Jean	.25	.20	.10
40	Darryl Strawberry	.15	.11	.06	131	Pat Mahomes	.25	.20	.10
41	Manny Alexander	.15	.11	.06	132	Mike Boddicker	.07	.05	.02
42	Tracey Sanders	.20	.15	.08	133	Roberto Hernandez	.20	.15	.08
43	Pete Incaviglia	.08	.06	.03	134	Dave Valle	.07	.05	.02
44	Kim Batiste	.10	.08	.04	135	Kurt Stillwell	.07	.05	.02
45	Frank Rodriguez	.40	.30	.15	136	Brad Pennington	.20	.15	.08
46	Greg Swindell	.10	.08	.04	137	Jermaine Swifton	.20	.15	.08
47	Delino DeShields	.12	.09	.05	138	Ryan Hawblitzel	.25	.20	.10
48	John Ericks	.20	.15	.08	139	Tito Navarro	.20	.15	.08
49	Franklin Stubbs	.07	.05	.02	140	Sandy Alomar	.10	.08	.04
50	Tony Gwynn	.12	.09	.05	141	Todd Benzinger	.07	.05	.03
51	Clifton Garrett	.20	.15	.08	142	Danny Jackson	.07	.05	.03
52	Mike Gardella	.20	.15	.08	143	Melvin Nieves	.50	.40	.20
53	Scott Erickson	.10	.08	.04	144	Jim Campanis	.20	.15	.08
54	Gary Caballo	.20	.15	.08	145	Luis Gonzalez	.10	.08	.04
55	Jose Oliva	.20	.15	.08	146	Dave Doorneweerd	.20	.15	.08
56	Brook Fordyce	.15	.11	.06	147	Charlie Hayes	.08	.06	.03
57	Mark Whiten	.10	.08	.04	148	Greg Maddux	.15	.11	.06
58	Joe Slusarski	.08	.06	.03	149	Brian Harper	.08	.06	.03
59	J.R. Phillips	.20	.15	.08	150	Brent Miller	.20	.15	.08
60	Barry Bonds	.15	.11	.06	151	Shawn Estes	.20	.15	.08
61	Bob Milacki	.07	.05	.02	152	Mike Williams	.20	.15	.08
62	Keith Mitchell	.10	.08	.04	153	Charlie Hough	.07	.05	.02
63	Angel Miranda	.20	.15	.08	154	Randy Myers	.07	.05	.02
64	Raul Mondesi	.50	.40	.20	155	Kevin Young	.30	.25	.12
65	Brian Koelling	.20	.15	.08	156	Rick Wilkins	.07	.05	.02
66	Brian McRae	.10	.08	.04	157	Terry Schumpert	.07	.05	.02
67	John Patterson	.12	.09	.05	158	Steve Karsay	.15	.11	.06
68	John Wetteland	.12	.09	.05	159	Gary DiSarcina	.07	.05	.03
69	Wilson Alvarez	.08	.06	.03	160	Deion Sanders	.20	.15	.08
70	Wade Boggs	.10	.08	.04	161	Tom Browning	.07	.05	.02
71	Darryl Ratliff	.20	.15	.08	162	Dickie Thon	.07	.05	.02
72	Jeff Jackson	.10	.08	.04	163	Luis Mercedes	.10	.08	.04
73	Jeremy Hernandez	.20	.15	.08	164	Ricardo Ingram	.20	.15	.08
74	Darryl Hamilton	.10	.08	.04	165	Tavo Alavarez	.20	.15	.08
75	Rafael Belliard	.07	.05	.02	166	Rickey Henderson	.20	.15	.08
76	Ricky Talicek	.20	.15	.08	167	Jaime Navarro	.10	.08	.04
77	Felipe Crespo	.20	.15	.08	168	Billy Ashley	.30	.25	.12
78	Carney Lansford	.08	.06	.03	169	Phil Dauphin	.20	.15	.08
79	Ryan Long	.15	.11	.06	170	Ivan Cruz	.20	.15	.08
80	Kirby Puckett	.25	.20	.10	171	Harold Baines	.08	.06	.03
81	Earl Cunningham	.10	.08	.04	172	Bryan Harvey	.08	.06	.03
82	Pedro Martinez	.20	.15	.11	173	Alex Cole	.07	.05	.02
83	Scott Hatteberg	.20	.15	.11	174	Curtis Shaw	.20	.15	.08
84	Juan Gonzalez	.30	.25	.12	175	Matt Williams	.10	.08	.04
85	Robert Nutting	.15	.11	.06	176	Felix Jose	.15	.11	.06
86	Calvin Reese	.12	.09	.05	177	Sam Horn	.07	.05	.03
87	Dave Silvestri	.10	.08	.04	178	Randy Johnson	.08	.06	.03
88	Scott Ruffcorn	.07	.05	.02	179	Ivan Calderon	.08	.06	.03
89	Rick Aguilera	.08	.06	.03	180	Steve Avery	.15	.11	.06
90	Cecil Fielder	.20	.15	.08	181	William Suero	.10	.08	.04
91	Kirk Dressendorfer	.10	.08	.04	182	Bill Swift	.10	.08	.04
92	Jerry Dipoto	.15	.11	.06	183	Howard Battle	.20	.15	.08
93	Mike Felder	.07	.05	.02	184	Ruben Amaro	.10	.08	.04
94	Craig Paquette	.15	.11	.06	185	Jim Abbott	.10	.08	.04
95	Elvin Paulino	.20	.15	.08	186	Mike Fitzgerald	.07	.05	.02
96	Donovan Osborne	.30	.25	.12	187	Bruce Hurst	.08	.06	.03
97	Hubie Brooks	.07	.05	.02	188	Jeff Juden	.10	.08	.04
98	Derek Lowe	.20	.15	.08	189	Jeromy Burnitz	.20	.15	.08

	MT	NR MT	EX			MT	NR MT	EX
190 Dave Burba	.07	.05	.03	281 Mo Sanford	.20	.15	.08
191 Kevin Brown	.08	.06	.03	282 Greg Perschke	.20	.15	.08
192 Patrick Lennon	.20	.15	.08	283 Kevin Flora	.20	.15	.08
193 Jeffrey McNeely	.20	.15	.08	284 Jeff Williams	.20	.15	.08
194 Wil Cordero	.30	.25	.12	285 Keith Miller	.08	.06	.03
195 Chili Davis	.08	.06	.03	286 Andy Ashby	.12	.09	.05
196 Milt Cuyler	.07	.05	.03	287 Doug Dascenzo	.07	.05	.03
197 Von Hayes	.07	.05	.03	288 Eric Karros	1.50	1.25	.60
198 Todd Revening	.20	.15	.08	289 Glenn Murray	.25	.20	.10
199 Joel Johnson	.15	.11	.06	290 Troy Percival	.20	.15	.08
200 Jeff Bagwell	.20	.15	.08	291 Orlando Merced	.10	.08	.04
201 Alex Fernandez	.10	.08	.04	292 Peter Hoy	.20	.15	.08
202 Todd Jones	.20	.15	.08	293 Tony Fernandez	.08	.06	.03
203 Charles Nagy	.10	.08	.04	294 Juan Guzman	.40	.30	.15
204 Tim Raines	.08	.06	.03	295 Jesse Barfield	.07	.05	.03
205 Kevin Maas	.08	.06	.03	296 Sid Fernandez	.08	.06	.03
206 Julio Franco	.10	.08	.04	297 Scott Cepicky	.20	.15	.08
207 Randy Velarde	.07	.05	.02	298 Garret Anderson	.20	.15	.08
208 Lance Johnson	.08	.06	.03	299 Cal Eldred	.50	.40	.20
209 Scott Leius	.08	.06	.03	300 Ryne Sandberg	.15	.11	.06
210 Derek Lee	.20	.15	.08	301 Jim Gantner	.07	.05	.03
211 Joe Sondrini	.20	.15	.08	302 Mariano Rivera	.20	.15	.08
212 Royce Clayton	.20	.15	.08	303 Ron Lockett	.20	.15	.08
213 Chris George	.20	.15	.08	304 David Nied, Jose Offerman	.08	.06	.03
214 Gary Sheffield	.20	.15	.08	305 Denny Martinez	.08	.06	.03
215 Mark Gubicza	.08	.06	.03	306 Luis Ortiz	.20	.15	.08
216 Mike Moore	.07	.05	.03	307 David Howard	.08	.06	.03
217 Rick Huisman	.10	.08	.04	308 Russ Springer	.10	.08	.04
218 Jeff Russell	.08	.06	.03	309 Chris Howard	.15	.11	.06
219 D.J. Dozier	.15	.11	.06	310 Kyle Abbott	.12	.09	.05
220 Dave Martinez	.07	.05	.03	311 Aaron Sele	.20	.15	.08
221 Al Newman	.07	.05	.03	312 David Justice	.15	.11	.06
222 Nolan Ryan	.30	.25	.12	313 Pete O'Brien	.07	.05	.03
223 Teddy Higuera	.08	.06	.03	314 Greg Hansell	.20	.15	.08
224 Damon Buford	.20	.15	.08	315 Dave Winfield	.20	.15	.08
225 Ruben Sierra	.20	.15	.08	316 Lance Dickson	.12	.09	.05
226 Tom Nevers	.20	.15	.08	317 Eric King	.07	.05	.03
227 Tommy Greene	.10	.08	.04	318 Vaughn Eshelman	.20	.15	.08
228 Nigel Wilson	2.00	1.50	.80	319 Tim Belcher	.08	.06	.03
229 John DeSilva	.20	.15	.08	320 Andres Galarraga	.08	.06	.03
230 Bobby Witt	.08	.06	.03	321 Scott Bullett	.25	.20	.10
231 Greg Cadaret	.07	.05	.03	322 Doug Strange	.08	.06	.03
232 John VanderWal	.25	.20	.10	323 Jerald Clark	.08	.06	.03
233 Jack Clark	.10	.08	.04	324 Dave Righetti	.08	.06	.03
234 Bill Doran	.07	.05	.03	325 Greg Hibbard	.08	.06	.03
235 Bobby Bonilla	.20	.15	.08	326 Eric Dillman	.20	.15	.08
236 Steve Olin	.10	.08	.04	327 Shane Reynolds	.20	.15	.08
237 Derek Bell	.30	.25	.12	328 Chris Hammond	.08	.06	.03
238 David Cone	.15	.11	.06	329 Albert Belle	.15	.11	.06
239 Victor Cole	.15	.11	.06	330 Rich Becker	.15	.11	.06
240 Rod Bolton	.20	.15	.08	331 Eddie Williams	.08	.06	.03
241 Tom Pagnozzi	.08	.06	.03	332 Donald Harris	.08	.06	.03
242 Rob Dibble	.08	.06	.03	333 Dave Smith	.08	.06	.03
243 Michael Carter	.20	.15	.08	334 Steve Fireovoid	.20	.15	.08
244 Don Peters	.15	.11	.06	335 Steve Buechele	.07	.05	.03
245 Mike LaValliere	.07	.05	.03	336 Mike Schooler	.07	.05	.03
246 Joe Perona	.20	.15	.08	337 Kevin McReynolds	.08	.06	.03
247 Mitch Williams	.08	.06	.03	338 Hensley Meulens	.08	.06	.03
248 Jay Buhner	.08	.06	.03	339 Benji Gil	.20	.15	.08
249 Andy Benes	.10	.08	.04	340 Don Mattingly	.15	.11	.06
250 Alex Ochoa	.20	.15	.08	341 Alvin Davis	.07	.05	.03
251 Greg Blosser	.08	.06	.03	342 Alan Mills	.07	.05	.03
252 Jack Armstrong	.07	.05	.03	343 Kelly Downs	.07	.05	.03
253 Juan Samuel	.07	.05	.03	344 Leo Gomez	.10	.08	.04
254 Terry Pendleton	.10	.08	.04	345 Tarrik Brock	.20	.15	.08
255 Ramon Martinez	.10	.08	.04	346 Ryan Turner	.50	.40	.20
256 Rico Brogna	.15	.11	.06	347 John Smoltz	.10	.08	.04
257 John Smiley	.08	.06	.03	348 Bill Sampen	.07	.05	.03
258 Carl Everett	.30	.25	.12	349 Paul Byrd	.20	.15	.08
259 Tim Salmon	.50	.40	.20	350 Mike Bordick	.10	.08	.04
260 Will Clark	.20	.15	.08	351 Jose Lind	.08	.06	.03
261 Ugueth Urbina	.20	.15	.08	352 David Wells	.07	.05	.03
262 Jason Wood	.20	.15	.08	353 Barry Larkin	.15	.11	.06
263 Dave Magadan	.07	.05	.03	354 Bruce Ruffin	.07	.05	.03
264 Dante Bichette	.07	.05	.03	355 Luis Rivera	.07	.05	.03
265 Jose DeLeon	.07	.05	.03	356 Sid Bream	.07	.05	.03
266 Mike Neill	.20	.15	.08	357 Julian Vasquez	.20	.15	.08
267 Paul O'Neill	.08	.06	.03	358 Jason Bere	.20	.15	.08
268 Anthony Young	.08	.06	.03	359 Ben McDonald	.10	.08	.04
269 Greg Harris	.07	.05	.03	360 Scott Stahoviak	.20	.15	.08
270 Todd Van Poppel	.30	.25	.12	361 Kirt Manwaring	.08	.06	.03
271 Pete Castellano	.20	.15	.08	362 Jeff Johnson	.10	.08	.04
272 Tony Phillips	.10	.08	.04	363 Rob Deer	.07	.05	.03
273 Mike Gallego	.07	.05	.03	364 Tony Pena	.07	.05	.03
274 Steve Cooke	.25	.20	.10	365 Melido Perez	.07	.05	.03
275 Robin Ventura	.15	.11	.06	366 Clay Parker	.07	.05	.03
276 Kevin Mitchell	.10	.08	.04	367 Dale Sveum	.07	.05	.03
277 Doug Linton	.15	.11	.06	368 Mike Scioscia	.07	.05	.03
278 Robert Eenhorne	.20	.15	.08	369 Roger Salkeld	.12	.09	.05
279 Gabe White	.25	.20	.10	370 Mike Stanley	.07	.05	.03
280 Dave Stewart	.10	.08	.04	371 Jack McDowell	.15	.11	.06

		MT	NR MT	EX				MT	NR MT	EX
372	Tim Wallach	.07	.05	.03		463	Scott Servais	.10	.08	.04
373	Billy Ripken	.07	.05	.03		464	Brian Jordan	.50	.40	.20
374	Mike Christopher	.20	.15	.08		465	Doug Drabek	.10	.08	.04
375	Paul Molitor	.10	.08	.04		466	Carl Willis	.07	.05	.03
376	Dave Stieb	.08	.06	.03		467	Bret Barberie	.08	.06	.03
377	Pedro Guerrero	.10	.08	.04		468	Hal Morris	.08	.06	.03
378	Russ Swan	.07	.05	.03		469	Steve Sax	.08	.06	.03
379	Bob Ojeda	.07	.05	.03		470	Jerry Willard	.07	.05	.03
380	Donn Pall	.07	.05	.03		471	Dan Wilson	.20	.15	.08
381	Eddie Zosky	.10	.08	.04		472	Chris Hoiles	.15	.11	.06
382	Darnell Coles	.07	.05	.03		473	Rheal Cormier	.08	.06	.03
383	Tom Smith	.15	.11	.06		474	John Morris	.07	.05	.03
384	Mark McGwire	.15	.11	.06		475	Jeff Reardon	.08	.06	.03
385	Gary Carter	.10	.08	.04		476	Mark Leiter	.07	.05	.03
386	Rich Amarel	.10	.08	.04		477	Tom Gordon	.07	.05	.03
387	Alan Embree	.15	.11	.06		478	Kent Bottenfield	.15	.11	.06
388	Jonathan Hurst	.15	.11	.06		479	Gene Larkin	.07	.05	.03
389	Bobby Jones	.10	.08	.04		480	Dwight Gooden	.15	.11	.06
390	Rico Rossy	.15	.11	.06		481	B.J. Surhoff	.10	.08	.04
391	Dan Smith	.15	.11	.06		482	Andy Stankiewicz	.10	.08	.04
392	Terry Steinbach	.08	.06	.03		483	Tino Martinez	.10	.08	.04
393	Jon Farrell	.07	.05	.03		484	Craig Biggio	.10	.08	.04
394	Dave Anderson	.07	.05	.03		485	Denny Neagle	.10	.08	.04
395	Benito Santiago	.10	.08	.04		486	Rusty Meacham	.10	.08	.04
396	Mark Wohlers	.10	.08	.04		487	Kal Daniels	.08	.06	.03
397	Mo Vaughn	.10	.08	.04		488	Dave Henderson	.08	.06	.03
398	Randy Kramer	.10	.08	.04		489	Tim Costo	.10	.08	.04
399	John Jaha	.25	.20	.10		490	Doug Davis	.15	.11	.06
400	Cal Ripken, Jr.	.50	.40	.20		491	Frank Viola	.10	.08	.04
401	Ryan Bowen	.15	.11	.06		492	Cory Snyder	.08	.06	.03
402	Tim McIntosh	.07	.05	.03		493	Chris Martin	.15	.11	.06
403	Bernard Gilkey	.08	.06	.03		494	Dion James	.07	.05	.03
404	Junior Felix	.08	.06	.03		495	Randy Tomlin	.08	.06	.03
405	Cris Colon	.20	.15	.08		496	Greg Vaughn	.10	.08	.04
406	Marc Newfield	.10	.08	.04		497	Dennis Cook	.07	.05	.03
407	Bernie Williams	.10	.08	.04		498	Rosario Rodriguez	.07	.05	.03
408	Jay Howell	.07	.05	.03		499	Dave Staton	.07	.05	.03
409	Zane Smith	.07	.05	.03		500	George Brett	.15	.11	.06
410	Jeff Shaw	.07	.05	.03		501	Brian Barnes	.08	.06	.03
411	Kerry Woodson	.08	.06	.03		502	Butch Henry	.08	.06	.03
412	Wes Chamberlain	.10	.08	.04		503	Harold Reynolds	.08	.06	.03
413	Dave Mulicki	.20	.15	.08		505	Lee Smith	.08	.06	.03
414	Benny Distefano	.08	.06	.03		506	Steve Chitren	.07	.05	.03
415	Kevin Rogers	.20	.15	.08		507	Ken Hill	.10	.08	.04
416	Tim Naehring	.10	.08	.04		508	Robbie Beckett	.15	.11	.06
417	Clemente Nunez	.20	.15	.08		509	Troy Afenir	.07	.05	.03
418	Luis Sojo	.07	.05	.03		510	Kelly Gruber	.08	.06	.03
419	Kevin Ritz	.07	.05	.03		511	Bret Boone	.50	.40	.20
420	Omar Oliveras	.07	.05	.03		512	Jeff Branson	.20	.15	.08
421	Manuel Lee	.07	.05	.03		513	Mike Jackson	.07	.05	.03
422	Julio Valera	.10	.08	.04		514	Pete Harnisch	.08	.06	.03
423	Omar Vizquel	.07	.05	.03		515	Chad Kreuter	.07	.05	.03
424	Darren Burton	.15	.11	.06		516	Joe Vitko	.15	.11	.06
425	Mel Hall	.08	.06	.03		517	Orel Hershiser	.10	.08	.04
426	Dennis Powell	.07	.05	.03		518	John Doherty	.10	.08	.04
427	Lee Stevens	.08	.06	.03		519	Jay Bell	.10	.08	.04
428	Glenn Davis	.08	.06	.03		520	Mark Langston	.10	.08	.04
429	Willie Greene	.12	.09	.05		521	Dann Howitt	.07	.05	.03
430	Kevin Wickander	.08	.06	.03		522	Bobby Reed	.10	.08	.04
431	Dennis Eckersley	.10	.08	.04		523	Roberto Munoz	.15	.11	.06
432	Joe Orsulak	.07	.05	.03		524	Todd Ritchie	.07	.05	.03
433	Eddie Murray	.08	.06	.03		525	Bip Roberts	.08	.06	.03
434	Matt Stairs	.10	.08	.04		526	Pat Listach	2.00	1.50	.80
435	Wally Joyner	.10	.08	.04		527	Scott Brosius	.08	.06	.03
436	Rondell White	.15	.11	.06		528	John Roper	.15	.11	.06
437	Rob Mauer	.10	.08	.04		529	Phil Pratt	.15	.11	.06
438	Joe Redfield	.15	.11	.06		530	Denny Walling	.07	.05	.03
439	Mark Lewis	.08	.06	.03		531	Carlos Baerga	.15	.11	.06
440	Darren Daulton	.10	.08	.04		532	Manny Ramirez	.80	.60	.30
441	Mike Henneman	.08	.06	.03		533	Pat Clements	.07	.05	.03
442	John Cangelosi	.07	.05	.03		534	Ron Gant	.10	.08	.04
443	Vince Moore	.20	.15	.08		535	Pat Kelly	.07	.05	.03
444	John Wehner	.08	.06	.03		536	Billy Spiers	.07	.05	.03
445	Kent Hrbek	.08	.06	.03		537	Darren Reed	.10	.08	.04
446	Mark McLemore	.07	.05	.03		538	Ken Caminiti	.08	.06	.03
447	Bill Wegman	.07	.05	.03		539	Butch Hosky	.15	.11	.06
448	Robby Thompson	.07	.05	.03		540	Matt Nokes	.07	.05	.03
449	Mark Anthony	.15	.11	.06		541	John Kruk	.08	.06	.03
450	Archi Cianfrocco	.20	.15	.08		542	John Jaha (Foil)	.35	.25	.12
451	Johnny Ruffin	.12	.09	.05		543	Justin Thompson	.20	.15	.08
452	Javier Lopez	.35	.25	.14		544	Steve Hosey	.08	.06	.03
453	Greg Gohr	.15	.11	.06		545	Joe Kmak	.10	.08	.04
454	Tim Scott	.15	.11	.06		546	John Franco	.08	.06	.03
455	Stan Belinda	.08	.06	.03		547	Devon White	.08	.06	.03
456	Darrin Jackson	.08	.06	.03		548	Elston Hansen (Foil)	.30	.25	.12
457	Chris Gardner	.12	.09	.05		549	Ryan Klesko	.30	.25	.12
458	Esteban Beltre	.10	.08	.04		550	Danny Tartabull	.08	.06	.03
459	Phil Plantier	.15	.11	.06		551	Frank Thomas (Foil)	2.00	1.50	.80
460	Jim Thome	.10	.08	.04		552	Kevin Tapani	.08	.06	.03
461	Mike Piazza	.30	.25	.12		553	Willie Banks	.08	.06	.03
462	Matt Sinatro	.07	.05	.03		554	B.J. Wallace (Foil)	.50	.40	.20

#	Name	MT	NR MT	EX
555	Orlando Miller	.20	.15	.08
556	Mark Smith	.20	.15	.08
557	Tim Wallach (Foil)	.20	.15	.08
558	Bill Gullickson	.08	.06	.03
559	Derek Bell (Foil)	.35	.25	.14
560	Joe Randa (Foil)	.25	.20	.10
561	Frank Seminara	.10	.08	.04
562	Mark Gardner	.08	.06	.03
563	Rick Greene (Foil)	.25	.20	.10
564	Gary Gaetti	.08	.06	.03
565	Ozzie Guillen	.08	.06	.03
566	Charles Nagy (Foil)	.35	.25	.14
567	Mike Milchin	.15	.11	.06
568	Ben Shelton (Foil)	.25	.20	.10
569	Chris Roberts (Foil)	.25	.20	.10
570	Ellis Burks	.08	.06	.03
571	Scott Scudder	.07	.05	.03
572	Jim Abbott (Foil)	.35	.25	.14
573	Joe Carter	.10	.08	.04
574	Steve Finley	.10	.08	.04
575	Jim Olander (Foil)	.15	.11	.06
576	Carlos Garcia	.20	.15	.08
577	Greg Olson	.08	.06	.03
578	Greg Swindell (Foil)	.25	.20	.10
579	Matt Williams (Foil)	.25	.20	.10
580	Mark Grace	.10	.08	.04
581	Howard House (Foil)	.30	.25	.12
582	Luis Polonia	.07	.05	.03
583	Erik Hanson	.08	.06	.03
584	Salomon Torres (Foil)	.25	.20	.10
585	Carlton Fisk	.10	.08	.04
586	Bret Saberhagen	.10	.08	.04
587	Chad McDonnell (Foil)	.25	.20	.10
588	Jimmy Key	.08	.06	.03
589	Mike MacFarlane	.08	.06	.03
590	Barry Bonds (Foil)	.30	.25	.12
591	Jamie McAndrew	.20	.15	.08
592	Shane Mack	.10	.08	.04
593	Kerwin Moore	.15	.11	.06
594	Joe Oliver	.07	.05	.03
595	Chris Sabo	.08	.06	.03
596	Alex Gonzalez	.15	.11	.06
597	Brett Butler	.08	.06	.03
598	Mark Hutton	.15	.11	.06
599	Andy Benes (Foil)	.20	.15	.08
600	Jose Canseco	.15	.11	.06
601	Darryl Kile	.08	.06	.03
602	Matt Stairs (Foil)	.25	.20	.10
603	Robert Butler (Foil)	.25	.20	.10
604	Willie McGee	.08	.06	.03
605	Jack McDowell	.10	.08	.04
606	Tom Candiotti	.08	.06	.03
607	Ed Martel	.15	.11	.06
608	Matt Mieske (Foil)	.25	.20	.10
609	Darrin Fletcher	.08	.06	.03
610	Rafael Palmeiro	.08	.06	.03
611	Bill Swift (Foil)	.20	.15	.08
612	Mike Mussina	.30	.25	.12
613	Vince Coleman	.08	.06	.03
614	Scott Cepicky (Foil)	.20	.15	.08
615	Mike Greenwell	.08	.06	.03
616	Kevin McGehee	.15	.11	.06
617	Jeffrey Hammonds (Foil)	2.00	1.50	.80
618	Scott Taylor	.15	.11	.06
619	Dave Otto	.07	.05	.03
620	Mark McGwire (Foil)	.50	.40	.20
621	Kevin Tatar	.20	.15	.08
622	Steve Farr	.07	.05	.02
623	Ryan Klesko (Foil)	.30	.25	.12
625	Andre Dawson	.15	.11	.06
626	Tino Martinez (Foil)	.20	.15	.08
627	Chad Curtis	.20	.15	.08
628	Mickey Morandini	.10	.08	.04
629	Gregg Olson (Foil)	.20	.15	.08
630	Lou Whitaker	.08	.06	.03
631	Arthur Rhodes	.15	.11	.06
632	Brandon Wilson	.20	.15	.08
633	Lance Jennings	.20	.15	.08
634	Allen Watson	.30	.25	.12
635	Len Dykstra	.08	.06	.03
636	Joe Girardi	.07	.05	.03
637	Kiki Hernandez (Foil)	.25	.20	.10
638	Mike Hampton	.20	.15	.08
639	Ai Osuna	.10	.08	.04
640	Kevin Appier	.10	.08	.04
641	Rick Helling (Foil)	.40	.30	.15
642	Jody Reed	.07	.05	.02
643	Ray Lankford	.15	.11	.06
644	John Olerud	.10	.08	.04
645	Paul Molitor (Foil)	.20	.15	.08
646	Pat Borders	.08	.06	.03

#	Name	MT	NR MT	EX
647	Mike Morgan	.07	.05	.02
648	Larry Walker	.15	.11	.06
649	Pete Castellano	.20	.15	.08
650	Fred McGriff	.15	.11	.06
651	Walt Weiss	.07	.05	.03
652	Calvin Murray	.60	.45	.25
653	Dave Nilsson	.30	.25	.12
654	Greg Pirkl	.20	.15	.08
655	Robin Ventura	.15	.11	.06
656	Mark Portugal	.07	.05	.03
657	Roger McDowell	.07	.05	.03
658	Rick Hirtensteiner (Foil)	.20	.15	.08
659	Glenallen Hill	.08	.06	.03
660	Greg Gagne	.07	.05	.03
661	Charles Johnson (Foil)	2.00	1.50	.80
662	Brian Hunter	.10	.08	.04
663	Mark Lemke	.07	.05	.03
664	Tim Belcher (Foil)	.20	.15	.08
665	Rich DeLucia	.07	.05	.03
666	Bob Walk	.07	.05	.03
667	Joe Carter (Foil)	.30	.25	.12
668	Jose Guzman	.10	.08	.04
669	Otis Nixon	.08	.06	.03
670	Phil Nevin (Foil)	2.00	1.50	.80
671	Eric Davis	.10	.08	.04
672	Damion Easley	.20	.15	.08
673	Will Clark (Foil)	.50	.40	.20
674	Mark Kiefer	.20	.15	.08
675	Ozzie Smith	.20	.15	.08
676	Manny Ramirez (Foil)	1.00	.70	.40
677	Gregg Olson	.10	.08	.04
678	Cliff Floyd	1.00	.70	.40
679	Duane Singleton	.20	.15	.08
680	Jose Rijo	.08	.06	.03
681	Willie Randolph	.08	.06	.03
682	Michael Tucker (Foil)	1.00	.70	.40
683	Darren Lewis	.08	.06	.03
684	Dale Murphy	.10	.08	.04
685	Mike Pagliarulo	.07	.05	.03
686	Paul Miller	.20	.15	.08
687	Mike Robertson	.20	.15	.08
688	Mike Devereaux	.10	.08	.04
689	Pedro Astacio	.35	.25	.14
690	Alan Trammell	.10	.08	.04
691	Roger Clemens	.20	.15	.08
692	Bud Black	.07	.05	.02
693	Turuk Wendell	.25	.20	.10
694	Barry Larkin (Foil)	.20	.15	.08
695	Todd Zeile	.08	.06	.03
696	Pat Hentgen	.15	.11	.06
697	Eddie Taubensee	.15	.11	.06
698	Guillermo Vasquez	.20	.15	.08
699	Tom Glavine	.15	.11	.06
700	Robin Yount	.15	.11	.06
701	Checklist	.07	.05	.03
702	Checklist	.07	.05	.03
703	Checklist	.07	.05	.03
704	Checklist	.07	.05	.03
705	Checklist	.07	.05	.03

GRADING GUIDE

Mint (MT): A perfect card. Well-centered with all corners sharp and square. No creases, stains, edge nicks, surface marks, yellowing or fading.

Near Mint (NM): A nearly perfect card. At first glance, a NM card appears to be perfect. May be slightly off-center. No surface marks, creases or loss of gloss.

Excellent (EX): Corners are still fairly sharp with only moderate wear. Borders may be off-center. No creases or stains on fronts or backs, but may show slight loss of surface luster.

Very Good (VG): Shows obvious handling. May have rounded corners, minor creases, major gum or wax stains. No major creases, tape marks, writing, etc.

Good (G): A well-worn card, but exhibits no intentional damage. May have major or multiple creases. Corners may be rounded well beyond card border.

1954 Briggs Meats

JAMES BUSBY, Outfielder
Born February 8, 1927, at Kenedy, Texas
THROWS RIGHT — BATS RIGHT

The Briggs Meat set was issued over a two-year span (1953-54) and features 26 players from the Washington Senators and 12 from the New York City area baseball teams. The set was issued in two-card panels on hot dog packages sold in the Washington, D.C. vicinity. The color cards, which are blank-backed and measure 2-1/4" by 3-1/2", are printed on waxed cardboard. The style of the Senators cards in the set differs from that of the New York players. Poses for the New York players can also be found on cards in the 1954 Dan-Dee Potato Chips and 1953-1955 Stahl-Meyer Franks sets.

		NR MT	EX	VG
Complete Set		8000.00	4000.00	2500.
Common Player		100.00	50.00	30.00
(1)	Hank Bauer	150.00	75.00	45.00
(2)	James Busby	100.00	50.00	30.00
(3)	Tommy Byrne	100.00	50.00	30.00
(4)	John Dixon	100.00	50.00	30.00
(5)	Carl Erskine	150.00	75.00	45.00
(6)	Edward Fitzgerald (Fitz Gerald)	100.00	50.00	30.00
(7)	Newton Grasso	100.00	50.00	30.00
(8)	Melvin Hoderlein	100.00	50.00	30.00
(9)	Gil Hodges	250.00	125.00	75.00
(10)	Monte Irvin	175.00	87.00	52.00
(11)	Whitey Lockman	100.00	50.00	30.00
(12)	Mickey Mantle	2200.00	1100.00	660.00
(13)	Conrado Marrero	100.00	50.00	30.00
(14)	Walter Masterson	100.00	50.00	30.00
(15)	Carmen Mauro	100.00	50.00	30.00
(16)	Willie Mays	1000.00	500.00	300.00
(17)	Mickey McDermott	100.00	50.00	30.00
(18)	Gil McDougald	150.00	75.00	45.00
(19)	Julio Moreno	100.00	50.00	30.00
(20)	Don Mueller	100.00	50.00	30.00
(21)	Don Newcombe	150.00	75.00	45.00
(22)	Robert Oldis	100.00	50.00	30.00
(23)	Erwin Porterfield	100.00	50.00	30.00
(24)	Phil Rizzuto	250.00	125.00	75.00
(25)	James Runnels	100.00	50.00	30.00
(26)	John Schmitz	100.00	50.00	30.00
(27)	Angel Scull	100.00	50.00	30.00
(28)	Frank Shea	100.00	50.00	30.00
(29)	Albert Sima	100.00	50.00	30.00
(30)	Duke Snider	500.00	250.00	150.00
(31)	Charles Stobbs	100.00	50.00	30.00
(32)	Willard Terwilliger	100.00	50.00	30.00
(33)	Joe Tipton	100.00	50.00	30.00
(34)	Thomas Umphlett	100.00	50.00	30.00
(35)	Gene Verble	100.00	50.00	30.00
(36)	James Vernon	125.00	62.00	37.00
(37)	Clyde Volmer (Vollmer)	100.00	50.00	30.00
(38)	Edward Yost	100.00	50.00	30.00

1977 Burger King Yankees

The first Topps-produced set for Burger King restaurants was issued in the New York area in 1977 and featured the A.L. champion New York Yankees.

Twenty-two players plus an unnumbered checklist were issued at the beginning of the promotion with card #23 (Lou Piniella) being added to the set at a later date. The Piniella card was issued in limited quantities. The cards, numbered 1 through 23, are 2-1/2" by 3-1/2" in size and have fronts identical to the regular 1977 Topps set except for the following numbers: 2, 6, 7, 13, 14, 15, 17, 20 and 21. These cards feature different poses or major picture-cropping variations. It should be noted that very minor cropping variations between the regular Topps sets and the Burger King issues exist throughout the years the sets were produced.

		NR MT	EX	VG
Complete Set:		45.00	22.00	13.50
Common Player:		.30	.15	.09
1	Yankees Team (Billy Martin)	1.00	.50	.30
2	Thurman Munson	7.00	3.50	2.00
3	Fran Healy	.30	.15	.09
4	Jim Hunter	2.00	1.00	.60
5	Ed Figueroa	.30	.15	.09
6	Don Gullett	.70	.35	.20
7	Mike Torrez	.70	.35	.20
8	Ken Holtzman	.50	.25	.15
9	Dick Tidrow	.30	.15	.09
10	Sparky Lyle	.50	.25	.15
11	Ron Guidry	1.00	.50	.30
12	Chris Chambliss	.50	.25	.15
13	Willie Randolph	1.00	.50	.30
14	Bucky Dent	1.00	.50	.30
15	Graig Nettles	1.00	.50	.30
16	Fred Stanley	.30	.15	.09
17	Reggie Jackson	8.00	4.00	2.50
18	Mickey Rivers	.50	.25	.15
19	Roy White	.50	.25	.15
20	Jim Wynn	.70	.35	.20
21	Paul Blair	.70	.35	.20
22	Carlos May	.30	.15	.09
23	Lou Piniella	25.00	12.50	7.50
---	Checklist	.10	.05	.03

1978 Burger King Astros

JESUS ALOU

Burger King restaurants in the Houston area

distributed a Topps-produced 23-card set showcasing the Astros in 1978. The cards are standard size (2-1/2" by 3-1/2") and are numbered 1 through 22. The checklist card is unnumbered. The card fronts are identical to the regular 1978 Topps set with the exception of card numbers 21 and 22, which have different poses. Although not noted in the following checklist, it should be remembered that very minor picture-cropping variations between the regular Topps issues and the 1977-1980 Burger King sets do exist.

		NR MT	EX	VG
Complete Set:		12.00	6.00	3.50
Common Player:		.35	.20	.11
1	Bill Virdon	.50	.25	.15
2	Joe Ferguson	.35	.20	.11
3	Ed Herrmann	.35	.20	.11
4	J.R. Richard	.60	.30	.20
5	Joe Niekro	.60	.30	.20
6	Floyd Bannister	.70	.35	.20
7	Joaquin Andujar	.60	.30	.20
8	Ken Forsch	.40	.20	.12
9	Mark Lemongello	.35	.20	.11
10	Joe Sambito	.40	.20	.12
11	Gene Pentz	.35	.20	.11
12	Bob Watson	.40	.20	.12
13	Julio Gonzalez	.35	.20	.11
14	Enos Cabell	.40	.20	.12
15	Roger Metzger	.35	.20	.11
16	Art Howe	.60	.30	.20
17	Jose Cruz	.80	.40	.25
18	Cesar Cedeno	.80	.40	.25
19	Terry Puhl	.40	.20	.12
20	Wilbur Howard	.35	.20	.11
21	Dave Bergman	.60	.30	.20
22	Jesus Alou	.60	.30	.20
-----	Checklist	.04	.02	.01

1978 Burger King
Rangers

FERGIE JENKINS

Issued by Burger King restaurants in the Dallas-Fort Worth area, this 23-card Topps-produced set features the Texas Rangers. The cards are standard size (2-1/2" by 3-1/2") and are identical in style to the regular 1978 Topps set with the following exceptions: #'s 5, 8, 10, 12, 17, 21 and 22. An unnumbered checklist card was included with the set.

		NR MT	EX	VG
Complete Set:		12.00	6.00	3.50
Common Player:		.35	.20	.11
1	Billy Hunter	.35	.20	.11
2	Jim Sundberg	.50	.25	.15
3	John Ellis	.35	.20	.11
4	Doyle Alexander	.50	.25	.15
5	Jon Matlack	.60	.30	.20
6	Dock Ellis	.35	.20	.11
7	George Medich	.35	.20	.11
8	Fergie Jenkins	1.75	.90	.50
9	Len Barker	.35	.20	.11
10	Reggie Cleveland	.60	.30	.20
11	Mike Hargrove	.40	.20	.12
12	Bump Wills	.60	.30	.20

		NR MT	EX	VG
13	Toby Harrah	.50	.25	.15
14	Bert Campaneris	.50	.25	.15
15	Sandy Alomar	.35	.20	.11
16	Kurt Bevacqua	.35	.20	.11
17	Al Oliver	1.00	.50	.30
18	Juan Beniquez	.35	.20	.11
19	Claudell Washington	.50	.25	.15
20	Richie Zisk	.40	.20	.12
21	John Lowenstein	.60	.30	.20
22	Bobby Thompson	.60	.30	.20
-----	Checklist	.04	.02	.01

1978 Burger King
Tigers

JACK MORRIS

Rookie cards of Morris, Trammell and Whitaker make the Topps-produced 1978 Burger King Detroit Tigers issue the most popular of the BK sets. Twenty-two player cards and an unnumbered checklist make up the set which was issued in the Detroit area. The cards measure 2-1/2" by 3-1/2", and are identical to the regular 1978 Topps issue with the following exceptions - card #'s 6, 7, 8, 13, 15 and 16. Collectors are reminded that numerous minor picture-cropping variations between the regular Topps issues and the Burger King sets appear from the 1977 through 1980. These minor variations are not noted in the following checklist.

		NR MT	EX	VG
Complete Set:		65.00	32.00	19.50
Common Player:		.40	.20	.12
1	Ralph Houk	.40	.20	.12
2	Milt May	.40	.20	.12
3	John Wockenfuss	.40	.20	.12
4	Mark Fidrych	1.00	.50	.30
5	Dave Rozema	.40	.20	.12
6	Jack Billingham	.40	.20	.12
7	Jim Slaton	.40	.20	.12
8	Jack Morris	15.00	7.50	4.50
9	John Hiller	.50	.25	.15
10	Steve Foucault	.40	.20	.12
11	Milt Wilcox	.40	.20	.12
12	Jason Thompson	.50	.25	.15
13	Lou Whitaker	15.00	7.50	4.50
14	Aurelio Rodriguez	.40	.20	.12
15	Alan Trammell	20.00	10.00	6.00
16	Steve Dillard	.40	.20	.12
17	Phil Mankowski	.40	.20	.12
18	Steve Kemp	.50	.25	.15
19	Ron LeFlore	.50	.25	.15
20	Tim Corcoran	.40	.20	.12
21	Mickey Stanley	.40	.20	.12
22	Rusty Staub	1.00	.50	.30
---)	Checklist	.10	.05	.03

1978 Burger King
Yankees

Produced by Topps for Burger King outlets in the New York area for the second year in a row, the 1978 Yankees set contains 22 cards plus an unnumbered checklist. The cards are numbered 1 through 22 and are the standard size of 2-1/2" by 3-1/2". The cards feature the same pictures found in the regular 1978 Topps set except for numbers 10, 11 and 16. Only those variations containing different poses or major picture-cropping differences are noted. Numerous minor picture-cropping variations, that are very insignificant in nature, exist between the regular Topps sets and the Burger King issues of 1977-1980.

		NR MT	EX	VG
Complete Set:		10.00	5.00	3.00
Common Player:		.30	.15	.09
1	Billy Martin	.80	.40	.25
2	Thurman Munson	3.00	1.50	.90
3	Cliff Johnson	.30	.15	.09
4	Ron Guidry	1.00	.50	.30
5	Ed Figueroa	.30	.15	.09
6	Dick Tidrow	.30	.15	.09
7	Jim Hunter	1.00	.50	.30
8	Don Gullett	.30	.15	.09
9	Sparky Lyle	.50	.25	.15
10	Rich Gossage	1.00	.50	.30
11	Rawly Eastwick	.70	.35	.20
12	Chris Chambliss	.50	.25	.15
13	Willie Randolph	.50	.25	.15
14	Graig Nettles	.80	.40	.25
15	Bucky Dent	.50	.25	.15
16	Jim Spencer	.70	.35	.20
17	Fred Stanley	.30	.15	.09
18	Lou Piniella	.80	.40	.25
19	Roy White	.50	.25	.15
20	Mickey Rivers	.50	.25	.15
21	Reggie Jackson	4.00	2.00	1.25
22	Paul Blair	.30	.15	.09
----	Checklist	.04	.02	.01

1979 Burger King
Phillies

Twenty-two Philadelphia Phillies players are featured in the 1979 Burger King issue given out in the Philadelphia area. The Topps-produced set, whose cards measure 2-1/2" by 3-1/2", also includes an unnumbered checklist. The cards are

identical to the regular 1979 Topps set except in seven instances. Card numbers 1, 11, 12, 13, 14, 17 and 22 have different poses. Very minor picture-cropping variations between the regular Topps issues and the Burger King sets can be found throughout the four years the cards were produced, but only those variations featuring major changes are noted in the following checklist.

		NR MT	EX	VG
Complete Set:		10.00	5.00	3.00
Common Player:		.20	.10	.06
1	Danny Ozark	.60	.30	.20
2	Bob Boone	.60	.30	.20
3	Tim McCarver	.60	.30	.20
4	Steve Carlton	3.00	1.50	.90
5	Larry Christenson	.20	.10	.06
6	Dick Ruthven	.20	.10	.06
7	Ron Reed	.20	.10	.06
8	Randy Lerch	.20	.10	.06
9	Warren Brusstar	.20	.10	.06
10	Tug McGraw	.40	.20	.12
11	Nino Espinosa	.60	.30	.20
12	Doug Bird	.20	.10	.06
13	Pete Rose	4.00	1.25	.90
14	Manny Trillo	.60	.30	.20
15	Larry Bowa	.50	.25	.15
16	Mike Schmidt	4.00	2.00	1.25
17	Pete Mackanin	.60	.30	.20
18	Jose Cardenal	.20	.10	.06
19	Greg Luzinski	.40	.20	.12
20	Garry Maddox	.30	.15	.09
21	Bake McBride	.20	.10	.06
22	Greg Gross	.20	.10	.06
----	Checklist	.04	.02	.01

1979 Burger King
Yankees

The New York Yankees were featured in a Topps-produced Burger King set for the third consecutive year in 1979. Once again, 22 numbered player cards and an unnumbered checklist made up the set. The cards, which measure 2-1/2" by 3-1/2", are identical to the 1979 Topps regular set except for card numbers 4, 8, 9 and 22 which included new poses. Only different poses or major picture-cropping variations between the regular Topps set and the Burger King issue are recognized in the checklist that follows. Numerous minor picture cropping variations between the regular Topps issue and the Burger King sets of 1977-1980 exist.

		NR MT	EX	VG
Complete Set:		10.00	5.00	3.00
Common Player:		.30	.15	.09
1	Yankees Team (Bob Lemon)	.50	.25	.15
2	Thurman Munson	2.00	1.00	.60
3	Cliff Johnson	.30	.15	.09
4	Ron Guidry	1.00	.50	.30
5	Jay Johnstone	.40	.20	.12
6	Jim Hunter	.90	.45	.25
7	Jim Beattie	.30	.15	.09

		NR MT	EX	VG
8	Luis Tiant	.80	.40	.25
9	Tommy John	1.00	.50	.30
10	Rich Gossage	.90	.45	.25
11	Ed Figueroa	.30	.15	.09
12	Chris Chambliss	.50	.25	.15
13	Willie Randolph	.50	.25	.15
14	Bucky Dent	.50	.25	.15
15	Graig Nettles	.70	.35	.20
16	Fred Stanley	.30	.15	.09
17	Jim Spencer	.30	.15	.09
18	Lou Piniella	.70	.35	.20
19	Roy White	.50	.25	.15
20	Mickey Rivers	.50	.25	.15
21	Reggie Jackson	3.00	1.50	.90
22	Juan Beniquez	.30	.15	.09
----	Checklist	.04	.02	.01

NOTE: A card number in parentheses ( ) indicates the set is unnumbered.

1980 Burger King Phillies

Philadelphia-area Burger King outlets issued a 23-card set featuring the Phillies for the second in a row in 1980. The Topps-produced set, whose cards measure 2-1/2" by 3-1/2", contains 22 player cards and an unnumbered checklist. The card fronts are identical in design to the regular 1980 Topps sets with the following exceptions - card numbers 1, 3, 8, 14 and 22 feature new poses. Collectors should note that very minor picture-cropping variations between the regular Topps issues and the Burger King sets exist in all years. Those minor differences are not noted in the checklist that follows. The 1980 Burger King sets were the first to include the Burger King logo on the card backs.

		NR MT	EX	VG
Complete Set:		8.00	4.00	2.50
Common Player:		.15	.08	.05
1	Dallas Green	.50	.25	.15
2	Bob Boone	.25	.13	.08
3	Keith Moreland	.60	.30	.20
4	Pete Rose	3.00	1.50	.90
5	Manny Trillo	.20	.10	.06
6	Mike Schmidt	3.00	1.50	.90
7	Larry Bowa	.40	.20	.12
8	John Vukovich	.50	.25	.15
9	Bake McBride	.15	.08	.05
10	Garry Maddox	.20	.10	.06
11	Greg Luzinski	.30	.15	.09
12	Greg Gross	.15	.08	.05
13	Del Unser	.15	.08	.05
14	Lonnie Smith	.50	.25	.15
15	Steve Carlton	1.75	.90	.50
16	Larry Christenson	.15	.08	.05
17	Nino Espinosa	.15	.08	.05
18	Randy Lerch	.15	.08	.05
19	Dick Ruthven	.15	.08	.05
20	Tug McGraw	.30	.15	.09
21	Ron Reed	.15	.08	.05
22	Kevin Saucier	.50	.25	.15
----	Checklist	.04	.02	.01

1980 Burger King Pitch, Hit & Run

In 1980, Burger King issued, in conjunction with its "Pitch, Hit & Run" promotion, a Topps-produced 34-card set featuring pitchers (card #'s 1-11), hitters (#'s 12-22), and base stealers (#'s 23-33). The card fronts, which carry the Burger King logo, are identical in nature to the regular 1980 Topps set except for numbers 1, 4, 5, 7, 9, 10, 16, 17, 18, 22, 23, 27, 28, 29 and 30, which feature different poses. The cards, which are numbered 1 through 33, measure 2-1/2" by 3-1/2" in size. An unnumbered checklist was included with the set.

		NR MT	EX	VG
Complete Set:		25.00	12.50	7.50
Common Player:		.20	.10	.06
1	Vida Blue	.50	.25	.15
2	Steve Carlton	1.00	.50	.30
3	Rollie Fingers	.30	.15	.09
4	Ron Guidry	.70	.35	.20
5	Jerry Koosman	.40	.20	.12
6	Phil Niekro	.40	.20	.12
7	Jim Palmer	1.50	.70	.45
8	J.R. Richard	.20	.10	.06
9	Nolan Ryan	8.00	4.00	2.50
10	Tom Seaver	1.50	.70	.45
11	Bruce Sutter	.25	.13	.08
12	Don Baylor	.25	.13	.08
13	George Brett	1.50	.70	.45
14	Rod Carew	.90	.45	.25
15	George Foster	.25	.13	.08
16	Keith Hernandez	.90	.45	.25
17	Reggie Jackson	2.25	1.25	.70
18	Fred Lynn	.70	.35	.20
19	Dave Parker	.40	.20	.12
20	Jim Rice	.80	.40	.25
21	Pete Rose	2.50	1.25	.70
22	Dave Winfield	1.50	.70	.45
23	Bobby Bonds	.40	.20	.12
24	Enos Cabell	.20	.10	.06
25	Cesar Cedeno	.20	.10	.06
26	Julio Cruz	.20	.10	.06
27	Ron LeFlore	.40	.20	.12
28	Dave Lopes	.40	.20	.12
29	Omar Moreno	.40	.20	.12
30	Joe Morgan	1.00	.50	.30
31	Bill North	.20	.10	.06
32	Frank Taveras	.20	.10	.06
33	Willie Wilson	.25	.13	.08
----	Checklist	.04	.02	.01

1982 Burger King Braves

A set consisting of 27 "Collector Lids" featuring the Atlanta Braves was issued by Burger King restaurants in 1982. The lids, which measure 3-5/8" in diameter, were placed on a special Coca-Cola cup which listed the scores of the Braves' season-opening 13-game win streak. A black and white photo plus the player's name, position, height, weight, and 1981 statistics are found on the lid front. The unnumbered, blank-backed lids also contain logos for Burger King, Coca-Cola, and the Major League Baseball Players Association.

		MT	NR MT	EX
	Complete Set:	40.00	30.00	16.00
	Common Player:	1.00	.70	.40
(1)	Steve Bedrosian	2.50	2.00	1.00
(2)	Bruce Benedict	1.00	.70	.40
(3)	Tommy Boggs	1.00	.70	.40
(4)	Brett Butler	2.50	2.00	1.00
(5)	Rick Camp	1.00	.70	.40
(6)	Chris Chambliss	1.25	.90	.50
(7)	Ken Dayley	1.00	.70	.40
(8)	Gene Garber	1.00	.70	.40
(9)	Preston Hanna	1.00	.70	.40
(10)	Terry Harper	1.00	.70	.40
(11)	Bob Horner	2.00	1.50	.80
(12)	Al Hrabosky	1.25	.90	.50
(13)	Glenn Hubbard	1.00	.70	.40
(14)	Randy Johnson	1.00	.70	.40
(15)	Rufino Linares	1.00	.70	.40
(16)	Rick Mahler	1.50	1.25	.60
(17)	Larry McWilliams	1.00	.70	.40
(18)	Dale Murphy	12.00	9.00	4.75
(19)	Phil Niekro	5.00	3.75	2.00
(20)	Biff Pocoroba	1.00	.70	.40
(21)	Rafael Ramirez	1.00	.70	.40
(22)	Jerry Royster	1.00	.70	.40
(23)	Ken Smith	1.00	.70	.40
(24)	Bob Walk	1.00	.70	.40
(25)	Claudell Washington	1.25	.90	.50
(26)	Bob Watson	1.00	.70	.40
(27)	Larry Whisenton	1.00	.70	.40

1982 Burger King Indians

The 1982 Burger King Indians set was sponsored by WUAB-TV and Burger Kings in the Cleveland vicinity. The cards' green borders encompass a large yellow area which contains a black and white photo plus a baseball tip. Manager Dave Garcia and his four coaches provide the baseball hints. The cards, which

measure 3" x 5", are unnumbered and blank-backed.

		MT	NR MT	EX
	Complete Set:	8.00	6.00	3.25
	Common Player:	.70	.50	.30
(1)	Dave Garcia (Be In The Game)	.70	.50	.30
(2)	Dave Garcia (Sportsmanship)	.70	.50	.30
(3)	Johnny Goryl (Rounding The Bases)	.70	.50	.30
(4)	Johnny Goryl (3rd Base Running)	.70	.50	.30
(5)	Tom McCraw (Follow Thru)	.70	.50	.30
(6)	Tom McCraw (Selecting A Bat)	.70	.50	.30
(7)	Tom McCraw (Watch The Ball)	.70	.50	.30
(8)	Mel Queen (Master One Pitch)	.70	.50	.30
(9)	Mel Queen (Warm Up)	.70	.50	.30
(10)	Dennis Sommers (Get Down On A Ground Ball)	.70	.50	.30
(11)	Dennis Sommers (Protect Your Fingers)	.70	.50	.30
(12)	Dennis Sommers (Tagging First Base)	.70	.50	.30

1986 Burger King

Burger King restaurants in the Pennsylvania and New Jersey areas issued a 20-card set entitled "All-Pro Series". The cards were issued with the purchase of a Whopper sandwich and came in folded panels of two cards each, along with a coupon card. The card fronts feature a color photo and contain the player's name, team and position plus the Burger King logo. Due to a licensing problem, the team insignias on the players' caps were airbrushed away. The card backs feature black print on white stock and contain brief biographical and statistical information.

		MT	NR MT	EX
	Complete Panel Set	9.00	6.75	3.50
	Complete Singles Set	6.00	4.50	2.50
	Common Panel	.75	.60	.30
	Common Single Player	.10	.08	.04
	Panel	.70	.50	.30
1	Tony Pena	.10	.08	.04
2	Dave Winfield	.20	.15	.08
	Panel	2.00	1.50	.80
3	Fernando Valenzuela	.20	.15	.08
4	Pete Rose	.50	.40	.20
	Panel	1.50	1.25	.60
5	Mike Schmidt	1.00	.70	.40
6	Steve Carlton	.30	.25	.12
	Panel	.70	.50	.30
7	Glenn Wilson	.10	.08	.04
8	Jim Rice	.20	.15	.08
	Panel	2.50	2.00	1.00
9	Wade Boggs	.80	.60	.30
10	Juan Samuel	.10	.08	.04
	Panel	1.50	1.25	.60
11	Dale Murphy	.40	.30	.15
12	Reggie Jackson	.30	.25	.12
	Panel	1.25	.90	.50
13	Kirk Gibson	.20	.15	.08
14	Eddie Murray	.30	.25	.12
	Panel	1.00	.70	.40
15	Cal Ripken, Jr.	.30	.25	.12
16	Willie McGee	.10	.08	.04

		MT	NR MT	EX
	Panel	1.75	1.25	.70
17	Dwight Gooden	.50	.40	.20
18	Steve Garvey	.25	.20	.10
	Panel	3.00	2.25	1.25
19	Don Mattingly	1.50	1.25	.60
20	George Brett	.40	.30	.15

1987 Burger King

The 1987 Burger King "All-Pro 2nd Edition Series" set was part of a giveaway promotion at participating Burger King restaurants. The set is comprised of 20 players on ten different panels. The cards measure 2-1/2" by 3-1/2" each with a three-card panel (includes a coupon card) measuring 7-5/8" by 3-1/2". The card fronts feature a full-color photo and the Burger King logo surrounded by a blue stars-and-stripes border. The backs contain black print on white stock and carry a brief player biography and 1986 career statistics. The set was produced by Mike Schecter Associates and, as with many MSA issues, all team insignias were airbrushed away.

		MT	NR MT	EX
Complete Panel Set:		8.00	6.00	3.25
Complete Singles Set:		4.00	3.00	1.50
Common Panel:		.25	.20	.10
Common Single Player:		.05	.04	.02
	Panel	1.25	.90	.50
1	Wade Boggs	.40	.30	.15
2	Gary Carter	.15	.11	.06
	Panel	1.00	.70	.40
3	Will Clark	.50	.40	.20
4	Roger Clemens	.20	.15	.08
	Panel	.50	.40	.20
5	Steve Garvey	.15	.11	.06
6	Ron Darling	.08	.06	.03
	Panel	.25	.20	.10
7	Pedro Guerrero	.08	.06	.03
8	Von Hayes	.05	.04	.02
	Panel	.60	.45	.25
9	Rickey Henderson	.25	.20	.10
10	Keith Hernandez	.12	.09	.05
	Panel	.60	.45	.25
11	Wally Joyner	.20	.15	.08
12	Mike Krukow	.05	.04	.02
	Panel	1.75	1.25	.70
13	Don Mattingly	8.00	6.00	3.25
14	Ozzie Smith	.08	.06	.03
	Panel	.50	.40	.20
15	Tony Pena	.05	.04	.02
16	Jim Rice	.15	.11	.06
	Panel	.80	.60	.30
17	Ryne Sandberg	.25	.20	.10
18	Mike Schmidt	.40	.30	.15
	Panel	.80	.60	.30
19	Darryl Strawberry	.12	.09	.05
20	Fernando Valenzuela	.20	.15	.08

A player's name in italic indicates a rookie card. An (FC) indicates a player's first card for that particular card company.

1985 Cain's Potato Chips Tigers

This 20-card set commemorating the 1984 World champion Tigers was issued by Cain's Potato Chips in the Michigan area in 1985. The yellow-bordered, unnumbered cards measure 2-3/4" in diameter and feature full-color oval photos inside a diamond. The word "Cain's" appears in the upper left corner, while the player's name appears in the lower left with his position directly below the photo. The words "1984 World Champions" are printed in the upper right corner. The backs include 1984 statistics. The cards were inserted in bags of potato chips.

		MT	NR MT	EX
Complete Set:		40.00	30.00	16.00
Common Player:		1.00	.70	.40
(1)	Doug Bair	1.00	.70	.40
(2)	Juan Berenguer	1.00	.70	.40
(3)	Dave Bergman	1.00	.70	.40
(4)	Tom Brookens	1.00	.70	.40
(5)	Marty Castillo	1.00	.70	.40
(6)	Darrell Evans	2.00	1.50	.80
(7)	Barbaro Garbey	1.00	.70	.40
(8)	Kirk Gibson	2.50	2.00	1.00
(9)	John Grubb	1.00	.70	.40
(10)	Willie Hernandez	1.25	.90	.50
(11)	Larry Herndon	1.00	.70	.40
(12)	Chet Lemon	1.25	.90	.50
(13)	Aurelio Lopez	1.00	.70	.40
(14)	Jack Morris	3.50	2.75	1.50
(15)	Lance Parrish	2.50	2.00	1.00
(16)	Dan Petry	1.00	.70	.40
(17)	Bill Scherrer	1.00	.70	.40
(18)	Alan Trammell	4.00	3.00	1.50
(19)	Lou Whitaker	3.50	2.75	1.50
(20)	Milt Wilcox	1.00	.70	.40

1986 Cain's Potato Chips Tigers

For the second year in a row, player discs of the Detroit Tigers were found in boxes of Cain's Potato Chips sold in the Detroit area. Twenty discs make up the set which is branded as a "1986 Annual Collectors' Edition." The discs, which measure 2-3/4" in diameter, have fronts which contain a color photo plus the player's name, team and position. The Cain's logo and the Major League Baseball Players Association's logo also appear. The backs, which display black print on white stock, contain player information plus the card number.

		MT	NR MT	EX
Complete Set:		40.00	30.00	16.00
Common Player:		1.00	.70	.40
1	Tom Brookens	1.00	.70	.40
2	Willie Hernandez	1.25	.90	.50
3	Dave Bergman	1.00	.70	.40
4	Lou Whitaker	3.50	2.75	1.50
5	Dave LaPoint	1.00	.70	.40
6	Lance Parrish	2.50	2.00	1.00
7	Randy O'Neal	1.00	.70	.40
8	Nelson Simmons	1.00	.70	.40
9	Larry Herndon	1.00	.70	.40
10	Doug Flynn	1.00	.70	.40
11	Jack Morris	3.50	2.75	1.50
12	Dan Petry	1.00	.70	.40
13	Walt Terrell	1.00	.70	.40
14	Chet Lemon	1.25	.90	.50
15	Frank Tanana	1.50	1.25	.60
16	Kirk Gibson	2.50	2.00	1.00
17	Darrell Evans	2.00	1.50	.80
18	Dave Collins	1.00	.70	.40
19	John Grubb	1.00	.70	.40
20	Alan Trammell	4.00	3.00	1.50

The values quoted are intended to reflect the market price.

1987 Cain's Potato Chips Tigers

Player discs of the Detroit Tigers were inserted in boxes of Cain's Potato Chips for the third consecutive year. The 1987 edition is made up of 20 round cards, each measuring 2-3/4" in diameter. The discs, which were packaged in a cellophane wrapper, feature a full-color photo surrounded by an orange border. The backs are printed in red on white stock. The set was produced by Mike Schecter and Associates.

		MT	NR MT	EX
Complete Set:		20.00	15.00	8.00
Common Player:		.60	.45	.25
1	Tom Brookens	.60	.45	.25
2	Darnell Coles	.60	.45	.25
3	Mike Heath	.60	.45	.25
4	Dave Bergman	.60	.45	.25
5	Dwight Lowry	.60	.45	.25
6	Darrell Evans	1.25	.90	.50
7	Alan Trammell	2.75	2.00	1.00
8	Lou Whitaker	2.00	1.50	.80
9	Kirk Gibson	2.00	1.50	.80
10	Chet Lemon	.75	.60	.30
11	Larry Herndon	.60	.45	.25
12	John Grubb	.60	.45	.25
13	Willie Hernandez	.75	.60	.30
14	Jack Morris	2.00	1.50	.80
15	Dan Petry	.60	.45	.25
16	Walt Terrell	.60	.45	.25

		MT	NR MT	EX
17	Mark Thurmond	.60	.45	.25
18	Pat Sheridan	.60	.45	.25
19	Eric King	.60	.45	.25
20	Frank Tanana	.75	.60	.30

1989 Cap'n Crunch

This 22-card set was produced by Topps for Cap'n Crunch cereal boxes. Two cards and a stick of gum were included in each cereal box while the offer was active. The fronts of these 2-1/2" by 3-1/2" cards feature red, white and blue borders. The card backs are horizontal and feature lifetime statistics. The set was not offered in any complete set deal.

		MT	NR MT	EX
Complete Set:		15.00	11.00	6.00
Common Player:		.50	.40	.20
1	Jose Canseco	1.00	.70	.40
2	Kirk Gibson	.50	.40	.20
3	Orel Hershiser	.60	.45	.35
4	Frank Viola	.70	.50	.30
5	Tony Gwynn	.60	.45	.35
6	Cal Ripken	.70	.50	.30
7	Darryl Strawberry	.80	.60	.30
8	Don Mattingly	.80	.60	.30
9	George Brett	.70	.50	.30
10	Andre Dawson	.60	.45	.25
11	Dale Murphy	.50	.40	.20
12	Alan Trammell	.50	.40	.20
13	Eric Davis	.80	.60	.30
14	Jack Clark	.50	.40	.20
15	Eddie Murray	.50	.40	.20
16	Mike Schmidt	1.00	.70	.40
17	Dwight Gooden	.80	.60	.30
18	Roger Clemens	1.00	.70	.40
19	Will Clark	1.00	.70	.40
20	Kirby Puckett	.70	.50	.30
21	Robin Yount	.60	.45	.25
22	Mark McGwire	.60	.45	.25

1984 Cereal Series

The Topps-produced 1984 Cereal Series set is identical to the Ralston Purina set from the same year in nearly all aspects. On the card fronts the words "Ralston Purina Company" were replaced by "Cereal Series" and Topps logos were substituted for Ralston checkerboard logos. The set is comprised of 33 cards, each measuring 2-1/2" by 3-1/2." The cards were inserted in unmarked boxes of Chex brand cereals.

		MT	NR MT	EX
Complete Set		13.00	9.75	5.25
Common Player		.20	.15	.08
1	Eddie Murray	.50	.40	.20
2	Ozzie Smith	.30	.25	.12
3	Ted Simmons	.20	.15	.08
4	Pete Rose	1.00	.70	.40
5	Greg Luzinski	.20	.15	.08
6	Andre Dawson	.50	.40	.20
7	Dave Winfield	.50	.40	.20
8	Tom Seaver	.50	.40	.20
9	Jim Rice	.50	.40	.20
10	Fernando Valenzuela	.40	.30	.15
11	Wade Boggs	1.00	.70	.40
12	Dale Murphy	.70	.50	.30
13	George Brett	.70	.50	.30
14	Nolan Ryan	2.00	1.50	.80
15	Rickey Henderson	.80	.60	.30
16	Steve Carlton	.50	.40	.20
17	Rod Carew	.60	.45	.25
18	Steve Garvey	.50	.40	.20
19	Reggie Jackson	.60	.45	.25
20	Dave Concepcion	.20	.15	.08
21	Robin Yount	.60	.45	.25
22	Mike Schmidt	1.00	.70	.40
23	Jim Palmer	1.00	.70	.40
24	Bruce Sutter	.20	.15	.08
25	Dan Quisenberry	.20	.15	.08
26	Bill Madlock	.20	.15	.08
27	Cecil Cooper	.20	.15	.08
28	Gary Carter	.30	.25	.12
29	Fred Lynn	.30	.25	.12
30	Pedro Guerrero	.30	.25	.12
31	Ron Guidry	.30	.25	.12
32	Keith Hernandez	.40	.30	.15
33	Carlton Fisk	.30	.25	.12

1987 Champion Phillies

This four card set is interesting in that the players are not identified on the card fronts or backs. The full-color cards, which measure 2-3/4" by 4-5/16", were produced by the Champion Spark Plug Co. as part of a contest held at participating Big A, Car Quest and Pep Boys auto parts stores. Entrants were advised to return the scratch-off coupon portion of the card for a chance to win a Blackbird Racer. Each card contains a scratch-off portion which may have contained an instant prize. Each card can be found with either a Big A, Car Quest or Pep Boys logo in the lower left corner on the card front. The contest was also sponsored in part by the Philadelphia Phillies and radio station WIP.

	MT	NR MT	EX
Complete Set:	20.00	15.00	8.00
Common Player:	1.00	.70	.40

		MT	NR MT	EX
(1)	Von Hayes (glove on knee)	3.00	2.25	1.25
(2)	Steve Jeltz (#30 on uniform)	1.00	.70	.40
(3)	Juan Samuel (laying on base)	4.00	3.00	1.50
(4)	Mike Schmidt (making throw)	12.00	9.00	4.75

1985 Circle K

Produced by Topps for Circle K stores, this 33-card set is entitled "Baseball All Time Home Run Kings". The cards, which measure 2-1/2" by 3-1/2", are numbered on the back according to the player's position on the all-time career home run list. Joe DiMaggio, who ranked 31st, was not included in the set. The set is skip-numbered from 30 to 32. The glossy card fronts contain the player's name in the lower left corner and feature a color photo, although black and white photos were utilized for a few of the homer kings who played before 1960. The card backs have blue and red print on white stock and contain the player's career batting statistics. The set was issued with a specially designed box.

		MT	NR MT	EX
Complete Set:		8.00	6.00	3.25
Common Player:		.15	.11	.06
1	Hank Aaron	.60	.45	.25
2	Babe Ruth	2.00	1.50	.80
3	Willie Mays	.60	.45	.25
4	Frank Robinson	.25	.20	.10
5	Harmon Killebrew	.25	.20	.10
6	Mickey Mantle	2.00	1.50	.80
7	Jimmie Foxx	.25	.20	.10
8	Willie McCovey	.25	.20	.10
9	Ted Williams	.70	.50	.30
10	Ernie Banks	.35	.25	.14
11	Eddie Mathews	.25	.20	.10
12	Mel Ott	.20	.15	.08
13	Reggie Jackson	.40	.30	.15
14	Lou Gehrig	1.00	.70	.40
15	Stan Musial	.60	.45	.25
16	Willie Stargell	.20	.15	.08
17	Carl Yastrzemski	.50	.40	.20
18	Billy Williams	.20	.15	.08
19	Mike Schmidt	.40	.30	.15
20	Duke Snider	.40	.30	.15
21	Al Kaline	.25	.20	.10
22	Johnny Bench	.35	.25	.14
23	Frank Howard	.15	.11	.06
24	Orlando Cepeda	.15	.11	.06
25	Norm Cash	.15	.11	.06
26	Dave Kingman	.15	.11	.06
27	Rocky Colavito	.15	.11	.06
28	Tony Perez	.15	.11	.06
29	Gil Hodges	.20	.15	.08
30	Ralph Kiner	.20	.15	.08
32	Johnny Mize	.20	.15	.08
33	Yogi Berra	.35	.25	.14
34	Lee May	.15	.11	.06

Regional interest may affect the value of a card.

1987 Classic Major League Baseball Game

Pete Rose

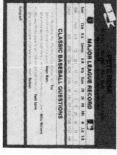

The "Classic Major League Baseball Board Game" set consists of 100 full-color cards which were used to play the game. Game participants were required to answer trivia questions found on the backs of the cards. The attractive cards measure 2 1/2" by 3 1/2" and are printed on glossy card stock. The card backs carry the player's career statistics besides the Classic Baseball Questions. The game was produced by Game Time, Ltd. of Marietta, Ga., and sold for $19.95 in most retail outlets.

		MT	NR MT	EX
Complete Set:		225.00	175.00	90.00
Common Player:		.10	.08	.04
1	Pete Rose	3.00	2.25	1.25
2	Len Dykstra	2.00	1.50	.80
3	Darryl Strawberry	5.00	3.75	2.00
4	Keith Hernandez	.40	.30	.15
5	Gary Carter	.50	.40	.20
6	Wally Joyner	1.00	.70	.40
7	Andres Thomas	.15	.11	.06
8	Pat Dodson	.15	.11	.06
9	Kirk Gibson	.30	.25	.12
10	Don Mattingly	4.00	3.00	1.50
11	Dave Winfield	.50	.40	.20
12	Rickey Henderson	8.00	6.00	3.25
13	Dan Pasqua	.15	.11	.06
14	Don Baylor	.15	.11	.06
15	Bo Jackson	80.00	60.00	30.00
16	Pete Incaviglia	.30	.25	.12
17	Kevin Bass	.10	.08	.04
18	Barry Larkin	1.00	.70	.40
19	Dave Magadan	1.00	.70	.40
20	Steve Sax	.20	.15	.08
21	Eric Davis	1.25	.90	.50
22	Mike Pagliarulo	.15	.11	.06
23	Fred Lynn	.20	.15	.08
24	Reggie Jackson	1.00	.70	.40
25	Larry Parrish	.10	.08	.04
26	Tony Gwynn	2.00	1.50	.80
27	Steve Garvey	.40	.30	.15
28	Glenn Davis	.20	.15	.08
29	Tim Raines	.40	.30	.15
30	Vince Coleman	.20	.15	.08
31	Willie McGee	.15	.11	.06
32	Ozzie Smith	.80	.60	.30
33	Dave Parker	.20	.15	.08
34	Tony Pena	.10	.08	.04
35	Ryne Sandberg	10.00	7.50	4.00
36	Brett Butler	.10	.08	.04
37	Dale Murphy	.50	.40	.20
38	Bob Horner	.15	.11	.06
39	Pedro Guerrero	.25	.20	.10
40	Brook Jacoby	.15	.11	.06
41	Carlton Fisk	.20	.15	.08
42	Harold Baines	.15	.11	.06
43	Rob Deer	.10	.08	.04
44	Robin Yount	5.00	3.75	2.00
45	Paul Molitor	.20	.15	.08
46	Jose Canseco	40.00	30.00	15.00
47	George Brett	1.00	.70	.40
48	Jim Presley	.15	.11	.06
49	Rich Gedman	.10	.08	.04
50	Lance Parrish	.20	.15	.08

		MT	NR MT	EX
51	Eddie Murray	.50	.40	.20
52	Cal Ripken, Jr.	4.00	3.00	1.50
53	Kent Hrbek	.25	.20	.10
54	Gary Gaetti	.20	.15	.08
55	Kirby Puckett	3.00	2.25	1.25
56	George Bell	.40	.30	.15
57	Tony Fernandez	.20	.15	.08
58	Jesse Barfield	.15	.11	.06
59	Jim Rice	.40	.30	.15
60	Wade Boggs	2.00	1.50	.80
61	Marty Barrett	.10	.08	.04
62	Mike Schmidt	5.00	3.75	2.00
63	Von Hayes	.15	.11	.06
64	Jeff Leonard	.10	.08	.04
65	Chris Brown	.15	.11	.06
66	Dave Smith	.10	.08	.04
67	Mike Krukow	.10	.08	.04
68	Ron Guidry	.20	.15	.08
69	Rob Woodward	.15	.11	.06
70	Rob Murphy	.15	.11	.06
71	Andres Galarraga	.25	.20	.10
72	Dwight Gooden	1.25	.90	.50
73	Bob Ojeda	.10	.08	.04
74	Sid Fernandez	.15	.11	.06
75	Jesse Orosco	.10	.08	.04
76	Roger McDowell	.15	.11	.06
77	John Tutor (Tudor)	.15	.11	.06
78	Tom Browning	.15	.11	.06
79	Rick Aguilera	.10	.08	.04
80	Lance McCullers	.15	.11	.06
81	Mike Scott	.20	.15	.08
82	Nolan Ryan	12.00	9.00	4.75
83	Bruce Hurst	.15	.11	.06
84	Roger Clemens	5.00	3.75	2.00
85	Oil Can Boyd	.10	.08	.04
86	Dave Righetti	.20	.15	.08
87	Dennis Rasmussen	.10	.08	.04
88	Bret Saberhagan (Saberhagen)	.35	.25	.14
89	Mark Langston	.35	.25	.14
90	Jack Morris	.15	.11	.06
91	Fernando Valenzuela	.25	.20	.10
92	Orel Hershiser	.35	.25	.14
93	Rick Honeycutt	.10	.08	.04
94	Jeff Reardon	.15	.11	.06
95	John Habyan	.10	.08	.04
96	Goose Gossage	.15	.11	.06
97	Todd Worrell	.20	.15	.08
98	Floyd Youmans	.10	.08	.04
99	Don Aase	.10	.08	.04
100	John Franco	.15	.11	.06

1987 Classic Baseball Travel Edition

B.J. Surhoff

Game Time, Ltd. of Marietta, Ga., issued as an update to their Classic Baseball Board Game a 50-card set entitled "Travel Edition." The cards measure 2-1/2" by 3-1/2" and feature the same outstanding quality characteristic of the first release. Numbered from 101 to 150, the "Travel Edition" is an extension of the original set. Besides updating player trades and showcasing rookies, the set offers several highlights from the 1987 season, including Andre Dawson's beaning. All new trivia questions are contained on the card backs.

	MT	NR MT	EX
Complete Set:	30.00	22.00	12.00
Common Player:	.08	.06	.03

101	Mike Schmidt	2.00	1.50	.80
102	Eric Davis	1.00	.70	.40
103	Pete Rose	1.00	.70	.40
104	Don Mattingly	2.00	1.50	.80
105	Wade Boggs	1.50	1.25	.60
106	Dale Murphy	.40	.30	.15
107	Glenn Davis	.20	.15	.08
108	Wally Joyner	2.00	1.50	.80
109	Bo Jackson	4.00	3.00	1.50
110	Cory Snyder	.20	.15	.08
111	Jim Lindeman	.15	.11	.06
112	Kirby Puckett	2.00	1.50	.80
113	Barry Bonds	5.00	3.75	2.00
114	Roger Clemens	2.00	1.50	.80
115	Oddibe McDowell	.08	.06	.03
116	Bret Saberhagen	.30	.25	.12
117	Joe Magrane	.30	.25	.12
118	Scott Fletcher	.08	.06	.03
119	Mark McLemore	.08	.06	.03
120	Who Me? (Joe Niekro)	.25	.20	.10
121	Mark McGwire	2.00	1.50	.80
122	Darryl Strawberry	1.50	1.25	.60
123	Mike Scott	.20	.15	.08
124	Andre Dawson	.50	.40	.20
125	Jose Canseco	5.00	3.75	2.00
126	Kevin McReynolds	.25	.20	.10
127	Joe Carter	1.00	.70	.40
128	Casey Candaele	.08	.06	.03
129	Matt Nokes	.30	.25	.12
130	Kal Daniels	.50	.40	.20
131	Pete Incaviglia	.50	.40	.20
132	Benito Santiago	1.00	.70	.40
133	Barry Larkin	1.00	.70	.40
134	Gary Pettis	.08	.06	.03
135	B.J. Surhoff	.60	.45	.25
136	Juan Nieves	.15	.11	.06
137	Jim Deshaies	.15	.11	.06
138	Pete O'Brien	.15	.11	.06
139	Kevin Seitzer	.30	.25	.12
140	Devon White	.50	.40	.20
141	Rob Deer	.08	.06	.03
142	Kurt Stillwell	.25	.20	.10
143	Edwin Correa	.08	.06	.03
144	Dion James	.08	.06	.03
145	Danny Tartabull	.60	.45	.25
146	Jerry Browne	.08	.06	.03
147	Ted Higuera	.15	.11	.06
148	Jack Clark	.20	.15	.08
149	Ruben Sierra	2.00	1.50	.80
150	McGwire/Davis (Eric Davis, Mark McGwire)	1.50	1.25	.60

1988 Classic Baseball Travel Edition - Blue

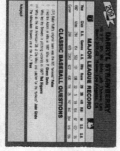

Darryl Strawberry

This 50-card set, numbered 201-250, was produced for use with the travel edition of Game Time's Classic Baseball Board Game. Two cards in the set feature two players: Davis/Murphy and McGwire/Mattingly. A follow-up to the first edition in 1987, the 1988 Blue was designed for use with the 1988 Red Series (151-200). Blue Series card fronts have blue borders, a yellow classic logo in the upper left corner and a black and beige

player name banner beneath the photo. The card backs are printed in blue on white and include the player name, personal info, major league records, a baseball question and space for the player autograph. Classic card series are sold via hobby dealers and retail toy stores nationwide. Game Time Ltd., the set's producer, was purchased by Scoreboard of Cherry Hill, N.J. in 1988.

	MT	NR MT	EX
Complete Set:	20.00	15.00	8.00
Common Player:	.15	.11	.06

201	Davis/Murphy (Eric Davis, Dale Murphy)	.40	.30	.15
202	B.J. Surhoff	.15	.11	.06
203	John Kruk	.20	.15	.08
204	Sam Horn	.15	.11	.06
205	Jack Clark	.25	.20	.10
206	Wally Joyner	.40	.30	.15
207	Matt Nokes	.30	.25	.12
208	Bo Jackson	4.00	3.00	1.50
209	Darryl Strawberry	1.00	.70	.40
210	Ozzie Smith	.25	.20	.10
211	Don Mattingly	1.00	.70	.40
212	Mark McGwire	1.00	.70	.40
213	Eric Davis	.70	.50	.30
214	Wade Boggs	1.50	1.25	.60
215	Dale Murphy	.30	.25	.12
216	Andre Dawson	.30	.25	.12
217	Roger Clemens	1.00	.70	.40
218	Kevin Seitzer	.30	.25	.12
219	Benito Santiago	.30	.25	.12
220	Tony Gwynn	1.00	.70	.40
221	Mike Scott	.20	.15	.08
222	Steve Bedrosian	.15	.11	.06
223	Vince Coleman	.25	.20	.10
224	Rick Sutcliffe	.15	.11	.06
225	Will Clark	7.00	5.25	2.75
226	Pete Rose	1.50	1.25	.60
227	Mike Greenwell	.50	.40	.20
228	Ken Caminiti	.15	.11	.06
229	Ellis Burks	1.00	.70	.40
230	Dave Magadan	.15	.11	.06
231	Alan Trammell	.30	.25	.12
232	Paul Molitor	.25	.20	.10
233	Gary Gaetti	.25	.20	.10
234	Rickey Henderson	1.25	.90	.50
235	Danny Tartabull	1.00	.70	.40
236	Bobby Bonilla	1.25	.90	.50
237	Mike Dunne	.20	.15	.08
238	Al Leiter	.15	.11	.06
239	John Farrell	.15	.11	.06
240	Joe Magrane	.15	.11	.06
241	Mike Henneman	.15	.11	.06
242	George Bell	.40	.30	.15
243	Gregg Jefferies	.60	.45	.25
244	Jay Buhner	.40	.30	.15
245	Todd Benzinger	.30	.25	.12
246	Matt Williams	.80	.60	.30
247	McGwire/Mattingly (Don Mattingly, Mark McGwire) (no card number on back)	1.00	.70	.40
248	George Brett	.60	.45	.25
249	Jimmy Key	.20	.15	.08
250	Mark Langston	.20	.15	.08

NOTE: A card number in parentheses ( ) indicates the set is unnumbered.

1988 Classic Baseball Travel Edition - Red

Kevin Elster

	MT	NR MT	EX
Complete Set:	15.00	11.00	6.00
Common Player:	.08	.06	.03

151	McGwire/Mattingly (Don Mattingly, Mark			
	McGwire)	1.50	1.25	.60
152	Don Mattingly	2.00	1.50	.80
153	Mark McGwire	1.00	.70	.40
154	Eric Davis	1.00	.70	.40
155	Wade Boggs	1.50	1.25	.60
156	Dale Murphy	.70	.50	.30
157	Andre Dawson	.30	.25	.12
158	Roger Clemens	.70	.50	.30
159	Kevin Seitzer	.30	.25	.12
160	Benito Santigo	.30	.25	.12
161	Kal Daniels	.25	.20	.10
162	John Kruk	.15	.11	.06
163	Billy Ripkin (Ripken)	.08	.06	.03
164	Kirby Puckett	.50	.40	.20
165	Jose Canseco	2.50	2.00	1.00
166	Matt Nokes	.20	.15	.08
167	Mike Schmidt	.70	.50	.30
168	Tim Raines	.50	.40	.20
169	Ryne Sandberg	.60	.45	.25
170	Dave Winfield	.40	.30	.15
171	Dwight Gooden	.70	.50	.30
172	Bret Saberhagen	.25	.20	.10
173	Willie McGee	.20	.15	.08
174	Jack Morris	.20	.15	.08
175	Jeff Leonard	.08	.06	.03
176	Cal Ripkin, Jr. (Ripkin)	.60	.45	.25
177	Pete Incaviglia	.20	.15	.08
178	Devon White	.25	.20	.10
179	Nolan Ryan	.50	.40	.20
180	Ruben Sierra	.30	.25	.12
181	Todd Worrell	.20	.15	.08
182	Glenn Davis	.25	.20	.10
183	Frank Viola	.25	.20	.10
184	Cory Snyder	.15	.11	.06
185	Tracy Jones	.20	.15	.08
186	Terry Steinbach	.15	.11	.06
187	Julio Franco	.15	.11	.06
188	Larry Sheets	.08	.06	.03
189	John Marzano	.08	.06	.03
190	Kevin Elster	.20	.15	.08
191	Vince Palacios (Vicente)	.15	.11	.06
192	Kent Hrbek	.30	.25	.12
193	Eric Bell	.08	.06	.03
194	Kelly Downs	.15	.11	.06
195	Jose Lind	.20	.15	.08
196	Dave Stewart	.30	.25	.12
197	McGwire/Canseco (Jose Canseco, Mark			
	McGwire) (no card number on back)	2.00	1.50	.80
198	Phil Niekro (Indians)	.30	.25	.12
199	Phil Niekro (Blue Jays)	.30	.25	.12
200	Phil Niekro (Braves)	.30	.25	.12

1989 Classic Baseball

This 100-card set was released by The Score Board to accompany trivia board games. Cards numbered 1-100 correlate with the 1989 Classic Baseball Game, while cards numbered 101-150 belong to the 1989 Classic Travel Series No. 1. The card fronts display full-color photos with the Classic Baseball logo in the upper left corner. The player's name appears beneath the photo. The flip side includes the card number in the upper left, personal information, and the player's major league record in a boxed area. Another boxed area below the record presents five trivia questions. The lower border of the flip side provides an autograph space. The Classic card series was sold by retail stores and hobby dealers nationwide.

	MT	NR MT	EX
Complete Set:	20.00	15.00	8.00
Common Player:	.08	.06	.03

1	Orel Hershiser	.30	.25	.12
2	Wade Boggs	.60	.45	.25
3	Jose Canseco	1.50	1.25	.60
4	Mark McGwire	.40	.30	.15
5	Don Mattingly	.60	.45	.25
6	Gregg Jefferies	.50	.40	.20
7	Dwight Gooden	.60	.45	.25
8	Darryl Strawberry	.40	.30	.15
9	Eric Davis	.40	.30	.15
10	Joey Meyer	.08	.06	.03
11	Joe Carter	.15	.11	.06
12	Paul Molitor	.15	.11	.06
13	Mark Grace	.60	.45	.25
14	Kurt Stillwell	.08	.06	.03
15	Kirby Puckett	.60	.45	.25
16	Keith Miller	.08	.06	.03
17	Glenn Davis	.15	.11	.06
18	Will Clark	1.75	1.25	.70
19	Cory Snyder	.15	.11	.06
20	Jose Lind	.08	.06	.03
21	Andres Thomas	.08	.06	.03
22	Dave Smith	.08	.06	.03
23	Mike Scott	.15	.11	.06
24	Kevin McReynolds	.20	.15	.08
25	B.J. Surhoff	.20	.15	.08
26	Mackey Sasser	.08	.06	.03
27	Chad Kreuter	.20	.15	.08
28	Hal Morris	1.00	.70	.40
29	Wally Joyner	.20	.15	.08
30	Tony Gwynn	.40	.30	.15
31	Kevin Mitchell	.40	.30	.15
32	Dave Winfield	.25	.20	.10
33	Billy Bean	.08	.06	.03
34	Steve Bedrosian	.08	.06	.03
35	Ron Gant	.70	.50	.30
36	Len Dykstra	.20	.15	.08
37	Andre Dawson	.20	.15	.08
38	Brett Butler	.20	.15	.08
39	Rob Deer	.08	.06	.03
40	Tommy John	.08	.06	.03
41	Gary Gaetti	.20	.15	.08
42	Tim Raines	.20	.15	.08
43	George Bell	.20	.15	.08
44	Dwight Evans	.20	.15	.08
45	Denny Martinez	.08	.06	.03
46	Andres Galarraga	.20	.15	.08
47	George Brett	.40	.30	.15
48	Mike Schmidt	1.25	.90	.50
49	Dave Steib	.20	.15	.08
50	Rickey Henderson	.70	.50	.30
51	Craig Biggio	.80	.60	.30
52	Mark Lemke	.25	.20	.10
53	Chris Sabo	.60	.45	.25
54	Jeff Treadway	.15	.11	.06
55	Kent Hrbek	.15	.11	.06
56	Cal Ripken, Jr.	1.00	.70	.40
57	Tim Belcher	.15	.11	.06
58	Ozzie Smith	.40	.30	.15
59	Keith Hernandez	.20	.15	.08
60	Pedro Guerrero	.20	.15	.08
61	Greg Swindell	.25	.20	.10
62	Bret Saberhagen	.40	.30	.15
63	John Tudor	.08	.06	.03
64	Gary Carter	.15	.11	.06
65	Kevin Seitzer	.20	.15	.08
66	Jesse Barfield	.20	.15	.08
67	Luis Medina	.20	.15	.08
68	Walt Weiss	.35	.25	.14
69	Terry Steinbach	.30	.25	.12
70	Barry Larkin	.30	.25	.12
71	Pete Rose	.80	.60	.30
72	Luis Salazar	.08	.06	.03
73	Benito Santiago	.40	.30	.15
74	Kal Daniels	.20	.15	.08
75	Kevin Elster	.08	.06	.03
76	Rob Dibble	.50	.40	.20
77	Bobby Witt	.50	.40	.20
78	Steve Searcy	.25	.20	.10
79	Sandy Alomar	.30	.25	.12
80	Chili Davis	.20	.15	.08
81	Alvin Davis	.20	.15	.08
82	Charlie Leibrandt	.08	.06	.03

		MT	NR MT	EX
83	Robin Yount	.80	.60	.30
84	Mark Carreon	.25	.20	.10
85	Pascual Perez	.08	.06	.03
86	Dennis Rasmussen	.08	.06	.03
87	Ernie Riles	.08	.06	.03
88	Melido Perez	.20	.15	.08
89	Doug Jones	.08	.06	.03
90	Dennis Eckersley	.15	.11	.06
91	Bob Welch	.15	.11	.06
92	Bob Milacki	.15	.11	.06
93	Jeff Robinson	.15	.11	.06
94	Mike Henneman	.15	.11	.06
95	Randy Johnson	.40	.30	.15
96	Ron Jones	.15	.11	.06
97	Jack Armstrong	.25	.20	.10
98	Willie McGee	.08	.06	.03
99	Ryne Sandberg	.80	.60	.30
100	David Cone/ Danny Jackson	.70	.50	.25
101	Gary Sheffield	1.25	.90	.50
102	Wade Boggs	.60	.45	.25
103	Jose Canseco	1.25	.90	.50
104	Mark McGwire	.80	.60	.30
105	Orel Hershiser	.30	.25	.12
106	Don Mattingly	1.25	.90	.50
107	Dwight Gooden	.70	.50	.30
108	Darryl Strawberry	.40	.30	.15
109	Eric Davis	.40	.30	.15
110	Bam Bam Meulens	.40	.30	.15
111	Andy Van Slyke	.20	.15	.08
112	Al Leiter	.08	.06	.03
113	Matt Nokes	.15	.11	.06
114	Mike Krukow	.08	.06	.03
115	Tony Fernandez	.25	.20	.10
116	Fred McGriff	.30	.25	.12
117	Barry Bonds	.60	.45	.25
118	Gerald Perry	.08	.06	.03
119	Roger Clemens	.60	.45	.25
120	Kirk Gibson	.12	.09	.05
121	Greg Maddux	.30	.25	.12
122	Bo Jackson	1.25	.90	.50
123	Danny Jackson	.08	.06	.03
124	Dale Murphy	.20	.15	.08
125	David Cone	.35	.25	.14
126	Tom Browning	.15	.11	.06
127	Roberto Alomar	1.00	.70	.40
128	Alan Trammell	.15	.11	.06
129	Rickey Jordan	.20	.15	.08
130	Ramon Martinez	1.00	.70	.40
131	Ken Griffey, Jr.	5.00	3.75	2.00
132	Gregg Olson	.50	.40	.20
133	Carlos Quintana	.35	.25	.14
134	Dave West	.30	.25	.12
135	Cameron Drew	.15	.11	.06
136	Ted Higuera	.25	.20	.20
137	Sil Campusano	.20	.15	.08
138	Mark Gubicza	.20	.15	.08
139	Mike Boddicker	.08	.06	.03
140	Paul Gibson	.08	.06	.03
141	Jose Rijo	.30	.25	.12
142	John Costello	.08	.06	.03
143	Cecil Espy	.08	.06	.03
144	Frank Viola	.25	.20	.10
145	Erik Hanson	.30	.25	.12
146	Juan Samuel	.08	.06	.03
147	Harold Reynolds	.15	.11	.06
148	Joe Magrane	.15	.11	.06
149	Mike Greenwell	.30	.25	.12
150	Darryl Strawberry/ Will Clark	1.00	.70	.40

1989 Classic Update

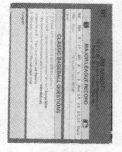

Numbered from 151-200, this 50-card set features

rookies and traded players with their new teams. The cards are purple and gray and were sold as part of a board game with baseball trivia questions.

		MT	NR MT	EX
Complete Set:		10.00	7.50	4.00
Common Player:		.05	.04	.02
151	Jim Abbott	.50	.40	.20
152	Ellis Burks	.30	.25	.12
153	Mike Schmidt	1.00	.70	.30
154	Gregg Jefferies	.50	.40	.20
155	Mark Grace	.30	.25	.12
156	Jerome Walton	.40	.30	.15
157	Bo Jackson	1.00	.70	.40
158	Jack Clark	.05	.04	.02
159	Tom Glavine	.10	.08	.04
160	Eddie Murray	.10	.08	.04
161	John Dopson	.05	.04	.02
162	Ruben Sierra	.40	.30	.15
163	Rafael Palmeiro	.40	.30	.15
164	Nolan Ryan	1.50	1.25	.60
165	Barry Larkin	.20	.15	.08
166	Tommy Herr	.05	.04	.02
167	Roberto Kelly	.25	.20	.10
168	Glenn Davis	.10	.08	.04
169	Glenn Braggs	.05	.04	.02
170	Juan Bell	.20	.15	.08
171	Todd Burns	.05	.04	.02
172	Derek Lilliquist	.10	.08	.04
173	Orel Hershiser	.20	.15	.08
174	John Smoltz	.40	.30	.15
175	Ozzie Guillen/ Ellis Burks	.30	.25	.12
176	Kirby Puckett	1.00	.70	.40
177	Robin Ventura	1.75	1.25	.70
178	Allan Anderson	.05	.04	.02
179	Steve Sax	.05	.04	.02
180	Will Clark	1.00	.70	.40
181	Mike Devereaux	.05	.04	.02
182	Tom Gordon	.40	.30	.15
183	Rob Murphy	.05	.04	.02
184	Pete O'Brien	.05	.04	.02
185	Cris Carpenter	.10	.08	.04
186	Tom Brunansky	.05	.04	.02
187	Bob Boone	.05	.04	.02
188	Lou Whitaker	.05	.04	.02
189	Dwight Gooden	.40	.30	.15
190	Mark McGwire	.40	.30	.15
191	John Smiley	.05	.04	.02
192	Tommy Gregg	.05	.04	.02
193	Ken Griffey, Jr.	4.00	3.00	1.50
194	Bruce Hurst	.05	.04	.02
195	Greg Swindell	.20	.15	.08
196	Nelson Liriano	.05	.04	.02
197	Randy Myers	.05	.04	.02
198	Kevin Mitchell	.40	.30	.15
199	Dante Bichette	.10	.08	.04
200	Deion Sanders	.70	.50	.30

1990 Classic Baseball

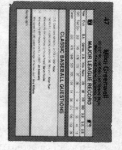

Classic Baseball returned in 1990 with another 150-card set. The cards were again sold as part of a baseball trivia game, and each game included a box designed to store all the cards in the set.

	MT	NR MT	EX
Complete Set:	15.00	11.00	6.00

		MT	NR MT	EX
	Common Player:	.05	.04	.02
1	Nolan Ryan	2.00	1.50	.80
2	Bo Jackson	.50	.40	.20
3	Gregg Olson	.30	.25	.12
4	Tom Gordon	.20	.15	.08
5	Robin Ventura	.80	.60	.30
6	Will Clark	.50	.40	.20
7	Ruben Sierra	.30	.25	.12
8	Mark Grace	.30	.25	.12
9	Luis de los Santos	.05	.04	.02
10	Bernie Williams	.40	.30	.15
11	Eric Davis	.10	.08	.04
12	Carney Lansford	.05	.04	.02
13	John Smoltz	.10	.08	.04
14	Gary Sheffield	.40	.30	.15
15	Kent Merker	.40	.30	.15
16	Don Mattingly	.50	.40	.20
17	Tony Gwynn	.15	.11	.06
18	Ozzie Smith	.05	.04	.02
19	Fred McGriff	.25	.20	.10
20	Ken Griffey, Jr.	2.00	1.50	.80
21a	Deion Sanders ("Prime Time")	4.00	3.00	1.50
21b	Deion Sanders (Deion "Prime Time" Sanders)	.70	.50	.30
22	Jose Canseco	.50	.40	.20
23	Mitch Williams	.20	.15	.08
24	Cal Ripken, Jr.	.10	.08	.04
25	Bob Geren	.20	.15	.08
26	Wade Boggs	.15	.11	.06
27	Ryne Sandberg	.35	.25	.14
28	Kirby Puckett	.45	.35	.20
29	Mike Scott	.05	.04	.02
30	Dwight Smith	.20	.15	.08
31	Craig Worthington	.10	.08	.04
32	Ricky Jordan	.15	.11	.06
33	Darryl Strawberry	.10	.08	.04
34	Jerome Walton	.70	.50	.30
35	John Olerud	.70	.50	.30
36	Tom Glavine	.05	.04	.02
37	Rickey Henderson	.40	.30	.15
38	Rolando Roomes	.10	.08	.04
39	Mickey Tettleton	.10	.08	.04
40	Jim Abbott	.50	.40	.20
41	Dave Righetti	.05	.04	.02
42	Mike LaValliere	.05	.04	.02
43	Rob Dibble	.25	.20	.10
44	Pete Harnisch	.10	.08	.04
45	Jose Offerman	.70	.50	.30
46	Walt Weiss	.05	.04	.02
47	Mike Greenwell	.25	.20	.10
48	Barry Larkin	.10	.08	.04
49	Dave Gallagher	.05	.04	.02
50	Junior Felix	.25	.20	.10
51	Roger Clemens	.20	.15	.08
52	Lonnie Smith	.05	.04	.02
53	Jerry Browne	.05	.04	.02
54	Greg Briley	.25	.20	.10
55	Delino Desheilds	.80	.60	.30
56	Carmelo Martinez	.05	.04	.02
57	Craig Biggio	.20	.15	.08
58	Dwight Gooden	.15	.11	.06
59a	Bo Jackson, Ruben Sierra, Mark McGwire (Bo, Ruben, Mark)	2.00	1.50	.80
59b	Bo Jackson, Ruben Sierra, Mark McGwire (A.L. Fence Busters)	.60	.45	.25
60	Greg Vaughn	.40	.30	.15
61	Roberto Alomar	.10	.08	.04
62	Steve Bedrosian	.05	.04	.02
63	Devon White	.05	.04	.02
64	Kevin Mitchell	.40	.30	.15
65	Marquis Grissom	.70	.50	.30
66	Brian Holman	.05	.04	.02
67	Julio Franco	.10	.08	.04
68	Dave West	.10	.08	.04
69	Harold Baines	.10	.08	.04
70	Eric Anthony	.40	.30	.15
71	Glenn Davis	.05	.04	.02
72	Mark Langston	.15	.11	.06
73	Matt Williams	.25	.20	.10
74	Rafael Palmeiro	.05	.04	.02
75	Pete Rose, Jr.	.20	.15	.08
76	Ramon Martinez	.50	.40	.20
77	Dwight Evans	.10	.08	.04
78	Mackey Sasser	.05	.04	.02
79	Mike Schooler	.05	.04	.02
80	Dennis Cook	.10	.08	.04
81	Orel Hershiser	.20	.15	.08
82	Barry Bonds	.30	.25	.12
83	Geronimo Berroa	.10	.08	.04
84	George Bell	.10	.08	.04
85	Andre Dawson	.10	.08	.04
86	John Franco	.05	.04	.02
87a	Will Clark, Tony Gwynn (Clark/Gwynn)	3.00	2.25	1.25
87b	Will Clark, Tony Gwynn (N.L. Hit Kings)	.40	.30	.15
88	Glenallen Hill	.35	.25	.14
89	Jeff Ballard	.10	.08	.04
90	Todd Zeile	.60	.45	.25
91	Frank Viola	.15	.11	.06
92	Ozzie Guillen	.10	.08	.04
93	Jeff Leonard	.05	.04	.02
94	Dave Smith	.05	.04	.02
95	Dave Parker	.10	.08	.04
96	Jose Gonzalez	.20	.15	.08
97	Dave Steib	.05	.04	.02
98	Charlie Hayes	.15	.11	.06
99	Jesse Barfield	.05	.04	.02
100	Joey Belle	1.00	.70	.40
101	Jeff Reardon	.05	.04	.02
102	Bruce Hurst	.05	.04	.02
103	Luis Medina	.05	.04	.02
104	Mike Moore	.10	.08	.04
105	Vince Coleman	.10	.08	.04
106	Alan Trammell	.10	.08	.04
107	Randy Myers	.05	.04	.02
108	Frank Tanana	.05	.04	.02
109	Craig Lefferts	.05	.04	.02
110	John Wetteland	.20	.15	.08
111	Chris Gwynn	.10	.08	.04
112	Mark Carreon	.10	.08	.04
113	Von Hayes	.05	.04	.02
114	Doug Jones	.05	.04	.02
115	Andres Galarraga	.10	.08	.04
116	Carlton Fisk	.10	.08	.04
117	Paul O'Neill	.05	.04	.02
118	Tim Raines	.10	.08	.04
119	Tom Brunansky	.05	.04	.02
120	Andy Benes	.35	.25	.14
121	Mark Portugal	.05	.04	.02
122	Willie Randolph	.05	.04	.02
123	Jeff Blauser	.05	.04	.02
124	Don August	.05	.04	.02
125	Chuck Cary	.05	.04	.02
126	John Smiley	.05	.04	.02
127	Terry Mullholland	.05	.04	.02
128	Harold Reynolds	.05	.04	.02
129	Hubie Brooks	.05	.04	.02
130	Ben McDonald	.60	.45	.25
131	Kevin Ritz	.20	.15	.08
132	Luis Quinones	.05	.04	.02
133	Bam Bam Meulens	.20	.15	.08
134	Bill Spiers	.20	.15	.08
135	Andy Hawkins	.05	.04	.02
136	Alvin Davis	.10	.08	.04
137	Lee Smith	.05	.04	.02
138	Joe Carter	.10	.08	.04
139	Bret Saberhagen	.10	.08	.04
140	Sammy Sosa	.30	.25	.12
141	Matt Nokes	.05	.04	.02
142	Bert Blyleven	.10	.08	.04
143	Bobby Bonilla	.35	.25	.14
144	Howard Johnson	.10	.08	.04
145	Joe Magrane	.05	.04	.02
146	Pedro Guerrero	.10	.08	.04
147	Robin Yount	.35	.25	.14
148	Dan Gladden	.05	.04	.02
149	Steve Sax	.10	.08	.04
150a	Will Clark, Kevin Mitchell (Clark/Mitchell)	1.00	.70	.40
150b	Will Clark, Kevin Mitchell (Bay Bombers)	.50	.40	.20

1990 Classic Series II

Like in previous years, Classic released a 50-card second series set for use with its baseball trivia game. Unlike the 1989 update set, the 1990 Classic Series II set is numbered 1-50 with a "T" designation accompanying the card number. The cards measure 2-1/2" by 3-1/2" and are designed after the original 1990 Classic cards. Series II cards have pink borders with a blue design, while the cards from the regular issue feature the opposite color combination. The cards are issued in a complete Series II set form.

Derek Parks

Classic's third series of 1990, features the same style as the previous two releases. The only major difference is the border color. Series 3 features yellow borders with blue accent. 100 trivia playing cards are included in series 3. the cards are numbered 1T-100T. No card 51T or '57T exist. Two cards in the set are unnumbered. Like all other Classic issues, the cards are designed for use with the trivia board game.

		MT	NR MT	EX
Complete Set:		10.00	7.50	4.00
Common Player:		.05	.04	.02

		MT	NR MT	EX
Complete Set:		8.00	6.00	3.25
Common Player:		.05	.04	.02

		MT	NR MT	EX
1	Gregg Jefferies	.25	.20	.10
2	Steve Adkins	.30	.25	.12
3	Sandy Alomar, Jr.	.25	.20	.10
4	Steve Avery	1.00	.70	.40
5	Mike Blowers	.20	.15	.08
6	George Brett	.05	.04	.02
7	Tom Browning	.05	.04	.02
8	Ellis Burks	.10	.08	.04
9	Joe Carter	.10	.08	.04
10	Jerald Clark	.10	.08	.04
11	"Hot Corners"	.40	.30	.15
12	Pat Combs	.25	.20	.10
13	Scott Cooper	.25	.20	.10
14	Mark Davis	.05	.04	.02
15	Storm Davis	.05	.04	.02
16	Larry Walker	.10	.08	.04
17	Brian DuBois	.10	.08	.04
18	Len Dykstra	.10	.08	.04
19	John Franco	.10	.08	.04
20	Kirk Gibson	.05	.04	.02
21	Juan Gonzalez	2.00	1.50	.80
22	Tommy Greene	.30	.25	.12
23	Kent Hrbek	.05	.04	.02
24	Mike Huff	.30	.25	.12
25	Bo Jackson	.70	.50	.30
26	Nolan Knows Bo	2.00	1.50	.80
27	Roberto Kelly	.05	.04	.02
28	Mark Langston	.10	.08	.04
29	Ray Lankford	.80	.60	.30
30	Kevin Maas	.40	.30	.15
31	Julio Machado	.15	.11	.06
32	Greg Maddux	.05	.04	.02
33	Mark McGwire	.15	.11	.06
34	Paul Molitor	.05	.04	.02
35	Hal Morris	.60	.45	.25
36	Dale Murphy	.05	.04	.02
37	Eddie Murray	.05	.04	.02
38	Jaime Navarro	.10	.08	.04
39	Dean Palmer	.60	.45	.25
40	Derek Parks	.30	.25	.12
41	Bobby Rose	.20	.15	.08
42	Wally Joyner	.05	.04	.02
43	Chris Sabo	.05	.04	.02
44	Benito Santiago	.05	.04	.02
45	Mike Stanton	.10	.08	.04
46	Terry Steinbach	.05	.04	.02
47	Dave Stewart	.10	.08	.04
48	Greg·Swindell	.05	.04	.02
49	Jose Vizcaino	.15	.11	.06
50	"Royal Flush"	.25	.20	.10

1990 Classic Series III

Jim Leyritz

		MT	NR MT	EX
1	Ken Griffey Jr.	1.50	1.25	.60
2	John Tudor	.05	.04	.02
3	John Kruk	.05	.04	.02
4	Mark Gardner	.15	.11	.06
5	Scott Radinsky	.20	.15	.08
6	John Burkett	.20	.15	.08
7	Will Clark	.40	.30	.15
8	Gary Carter	.05	.04	.02
9	Ted Higuera	.05	.04	.02
10	Dave Parker	.10	.08	.04
11	Dante Bichette	.05	.04	.02
12	Don Mattingly	.35	.25	.14
13	Greg Harris	.05	.04	.02
14	David Hollins	.10	.08	.04
15	Matt Nokes	.05	.04	.02
16	Kevin Tapani	.15	.11	.06
17	Shane Mack	.05	.04	.02
18	Randy Myers	.05	.04	.02
19	Greg Olson	.15	.11	.06
20	Shawn Abner	.05	.04	.02
21	Jim Presley	.05	.04	.02
22	Randy Johnson	.05	.04	.02
23	Edgar Martinez	.05	.04	.02
24	Scott Coolbaugh	.15	.11	.06
25	Jeff Treadway	.05	.04	.02
26	Joe Klink	.05	.04	.02
27	Rickey Henderson	.30	.25	.12
28	Sam Horn	.05	.04	.02
29	Kurt Stillwell	.05	.04	.02
30	Andy Van Slyke	.05	.04	.02
31	Willie Banks	.40	.30	.15
32	Jose Canseco	.40	.30	.15
33	Felix Jose	.10	.08	.04
34	Candy Maldonado	.05	.04	.02
35	Carlos Baerga	.30	.25	.12
36	Keith Hernandez	.05	.04	.02
37	Frank Viola	.05	.04	.02
38	Pete O'Brien	.05	.04	.02
39	Pat Borders	.05	.04	.02
40	Mike Heath	.05	.04	.02
41	Kevin Brown	.10	.08	.04
42	Chris Bosio	.05	.04	.02
43	Shawn Boskie	.25	.20	.10
44	Carlos Quintana	.05	.04	.02
45	Juan Samuel	.05	.04	.02
46	Tim Layana	.15	.11	.06
47	Mike Harkey	.10	.08	.04
48	Gerald Perry	.05	.04	.02
49	Mike Witt	.05	.04	.02
50	Joe Orsulak	.05	.04	.02
52	Willie Blair	.10	.08	.04
53	Gene Larkin	.05	.04	.02
54	Jody Reed	.05	.04	.02
55	Jeff Reardon	.05	.04	.02
56	Kevin McReynolds	.05	.04	.02
58	Eric Yelding	.05	.04	.02
59	Fred Lynn	.05	.04	.02
60	Jim Leyritz	.20	.15	.08
61	John Orton	.05	.04	.02
62	Mike Lieberthal	.50	.40	.20
63	Mike Hartley	.10	.08	.04
64	Kal Daniels	.05	.04	.02
65	Terry Shumpert	.20	.15	.08
66	Sil Campusano	.05	.04	.02
67	Tony Pena	.05	.04	.02
68	Barry Bonds	.35	.25	.14
69	Oddibe McDowell	.05	.04	.02
70	Kelly Gruber	.10	.08	.04
71	Willie Randolph	.05	.04	.02
72	Rick Parker	.15	.11	.06
73	Bobby Bonilla	.20	.15	.08
74	Jack Armstrong	.10	.08	.04
75	Hubie Brooks	.05	.04	.02
76	Sandy Alomar, Jr.	.15	.11	.06
77	Ruben Sierra	.20	.15	.08
78	Erik Hanson	.08	.06	.03
79	Tony Phillips	.05	.04	.02

		MT	NR MT	EX
80	Rondell White	.25	.20	.10
81	Bobby Thigpen	.08	.06	.03
82	Ron Walden	.20	.15	.08
83	Don Peters	.30	.25	.12
84	#6 (Nolan Ryan)	1.00	.70	.40
85	Lance Dickson	.20	.15	.08
86	Ryne Sandberg	.35	.25	.14
87	Eric Christopherson	.20	.15	.08
88	Shane Andrews	.25	.20	.10
89	Marc Newfield	1.25	.90	.50
90	Adam Hyzdu	.25	.20	.10
91	"Texas Heat" (Nolan Ryan, Reid Ryan)	2.00	1.50	.80
92	Chipper Jones	.50	.40	.20
93	Frank Thomas	3.00	2.25	1.25
94	Cecil Fielder	.50	.40	.20
95	Delino DeShields	.30	.25	.12
96	John Olerud	.30	.25	.12
97	Dave Justice	1.00	.70	.40
98	Joe Oliver	.10	.08	.04
99	Alex Fernandez	.40	.30	.15
100	Todd Hundley	.20	.15	.08
----	Mike Marshall (Game Instructions On Back)	.05	.04	.02
----	4 in 1 (Frank Viola)	.30	.25	.12
----	4 in 1 ("Texas Heat")	.30	.25	.12
----	4 in 1 (Chipper Jones)	.30	.25	.12
----	4 in 1 (Don Mattingly)	.30	.25	.12

1990 Classic #1 Draft Picks

Todd Van Poppel and Alex Fernandez head up the 24 1990 first round draft picks featured in this 25-card set. The set is limited with only 150,000 sets released to the hobby. A letter of authenticity accompanies each individually numbered set. Unlike other Classic issues, this set is not designed for use with the trivia board game.

		MT	NR MT	EX
Complete Set:		12.00	9.00	4.75
Common Player:		.20	.15	.08
1	Chipper Jones	1.00	.70	.40
3	Mike Lieberthal	.35	.25	.14
4	Alex Fernandez	.40	.30	.15
5	Kurt Miller	.30	.25	.12
6	Marc Newfield	1.00	.70	.40
7	Dan Wilson	.50	.40	.20
8	Tim Costo	.50	.40	.20
9	Ron Walden	.25	.20	.10
10	Carl Everett	.25	.20	.10
11	Shane Andrews	.20	.15	.08
12	Todd Ritchie	.25	.20	.10
13	Donovan Osborne	1.00	.70	.40
14	Todd Van Poppel	1.00	.70	.40
15	Adam Hyzdu	.20	.15	.08
16	Dan Smith	.20	.15	.08
17	Jeromy Burnitz	1.00	.70	.40
18	Aaron Holbert	.25	.20	.10
19	Eric Christopherson	.20	.15	.08
20	Mike Mussina	2.00	1.50	.80
21	Tom Nevers	.20	.15	.08
23	Lance Dickson	.30	.25	.12
24	Rondell White	.20	.15	.08
25	Robbie Beckett	.20	.15	.08

		MT	NR MT	EX
26	Don Peters	.20	.15	.08
----	Future Stars-Checklist (Chipper Jones/ Rondell White)	.35	.25	.14

1991 Classic

Top rookies and draft picks highlight this 99-card set from Classic. The cards come along with a boardgame and accessories designed for trivia game use. The card fronts feature fading blue borders with a touch of red. A "4-in-1" micro-player piece is included with each game set.

		MT	NR MT	EX
Complete Set:		8.00	6.00	3.25
Common Player:		.08	.06	.03
1	John Olerud	.25	.20	.10
2	Tino Martinez	.30	.25	.12
3	Ken Griffey,Jr.	1.00	.70	.40
4	Jeromy Burnitz	.35	.25	.14
5	Ron Gant	.15	.11	.06
6	Mike Benjamin	.15	.11	.06
7	Steve Decker	.20	.15	.08
8	Matt Williams	.10	.08	.04
9	Rafael Novoa	.20	.15	.08
10	Kevin Mitchell	.10	.08	.04
11	Dave Justice	.35	.25	.14
12	Leo Gomez	.30	.25	.12
13	Chris Hoiles	.20	.15	.08
14	Ben McDonald	.30	.25	.12
15	David Segui	.25	.20	.10
16	Anthony Telford	.25	.20	.10
17	Mike Mussina	.60	.45	.25
18	Roger Clemens	.12	.09	.05
19	Wade Boggs	.10	.08	.04
20	Tim Naehring	.25	.20	.10
21	Joe Carter	.08	.06	.03
22	Phil Plantier	.80	.60	.30
23	Rob Dibble	.08	.06	.03
24	Maurice Vaughn	.50	.40	.20
25	Lee Stevens	.20	.15	.08
26	Chris Sabo	.08	.06	.03
27	Mark Grace	.08	.06	.03
28	Derrick May	.60	.45	.25
29	Ryne Sandberg	.15	.11	.06
30	Matt Stark	.15	.11	.06
31	Bobby Thigpen	.08	.06	.03
32	Frank Thomas	1.50	1.25	.60
33	Don Mattingly	.15	.11	.06
34	Eric Davis	.10	.08	.04
35	Reggie Jefferson	.40	.30	.15
36	Alex Cole	.20	.15	.08
37	Mark Lewis	.20	.15	.08
38	Tim Costo	.40	.30	.15
39	Sandy Alomar,Jr.	.15	.11	.06
40	Travis Fryman	.50	.40	.20
41	Cecil Fielder	.15	.11	.06
42	Milt Cuyler	.15	.11	.06
43	Andujar Cedeno	.50	.40	.20
44	Danny Darwin	.08	.06	.03
45	Randy Henis	.20	.15	.08
46	George Brett	.10	.08	.04
47	Jeff Conine	.20	.15	.08
48	Bo Jackson	.40	.30	.15
49	Brian McRae	.40	.30	.15
50	Brent Mayne	.20	.15	.08
51	Eddie Murray	.08	.06	.03

		MT	NR MT	EX
52	Ramon Martinez	.12	.09	.05
53	Jim Neidlinger	.15	.11	.06
54	Jim Poole	.30	.25	.12
55	Tim McIntosh	.20	.15	.08
56	Randy Veres	.08	.06	.03
57	Kirby Puckett	.10	.08	.04
58	Todd Ritchie	.20	.15	.08
59	Rich Garces	.20	.15	.08
60	Moises Alou	.12	.09	.05
61	Delino DeShields	.15	.11	.06
62	Oscar Azocar	.25	.20	.10
63	Kevin Maas	.25	.20	.10
64	Alan Mills	.15	.11	.06
65	John Franco	.08	.06	.03
66	Chris Jelic	.30	.25	.12
67	Dave Magadan	.08	.06	.03
68	Darryl Strawberry	.12	.09	.05
69	Hensley Muelens	.10	.08	.04
70	Juan Gonzalez	1.25	.90	.50
71	Reggie Harris	.15	.11	.06
72	Rickey Henderson	.20	.15	.08
73	Mark McGwire	.15	.11	.06
74	Willie McGee	.08	.06	.03
75	Todd Van Poppel	1.00	.70	.40
76	Bob Welch	.08	.06	.03
77	"Future Aces"	1.00	.70	.40
78	Lenny Dykstra	.08	.06	.03
79	Mickey Morandini	.20	.15	.08
80	Wes Chamberlain	.40	.30	.15
81	Barry Bonds	.15	.11	.06
82	Doug Drabek	.08	.06	.03
83	Randy Tomlin	.20	.15	.08
84	Scott Chiamparino	.25	.20	.10
85	Rafael Palmeiro	.08	.06	.03
86	Nolan Ryan	.35	.25	.14
87	Bobby Witt	.08	.06	.03
88	Fred McGriff	.08	.06	.03
89	Dave Steib	.08	.06	.03
90	Ed Sprague	.30	.25	.12
91	Vince Coleman	.08	.06	.03
92	Rod Brewer	.12	.09	.05
93	Bernard Gilkey	.35	.25	.14
94	Roberto Alomar	.08	.06	.03
95	Chuck Finley	.08	.06	.03
96	Dale Murphy	.08	.06	.03
97	Jose Rijo	.08	.06	.03
98	Hal Morris	.12	.09	.05
99	Strawberry and Gooden	.10	.08	.04

1991 Classic Series II

Cecil Fielder

Classic released a 100-card second series in 1991 compared to a 50-card second series in 1990. The cards feature the same style as the first Classic series of 1991 with the exception of the border color. The first series featured blue borders, while Series II features maroon borders. The cards are designed for trivia game use. Series II includes several players with new teams and top rookies. Special Four-In-One, 300 Game Winner and Strikout Kings cards are included with each set.

		MT	NR MT	EX
Complete Set:		8.00	6.00	3.25
Common Player:		.08	.06	.03
1	Ken Griffey, Jr.	.80	.60	.30
2	Wilfredo Cordero	.25	.20	.10

		MT	NR MT	EX
3	Cal Ripken, Jr.	.15	.11	.06
4	D.J. Dozier	.15	.11	.06
5	Darrin Fletcher	.08	.06	.03
6	Glenn Davis	.10	.08	.04
7	Alex Fernandez	.20	.15	.08
8	Cory Snyder	.08	.06	.03
9	Tim Raines	.10	.08	.04
10	Greg Swindell	.10	.08	.04
11	Mark Lewis	.25	.20	.10
12	Rico Brogna	.20	.15	.08
13	Gary Sheffield	.10	.08	.04
14	Paul Molitor	.10	.08	.04
15	Kent Hrbek	.08	.04	.02
16	Scott Erickson	.40	.30	.15
17	Steve Sax	.08	.06	.03
18	Dennis Eckersley	.08	.06	.03
19	Jose Canseco	.25	.20	.10
20	Kirk Dressendorfer	.40	.30	.15
21	Ken Griffey,Sr.	.08	.06	.03
22	Erik Hanson	.10	.08	.04
23	Dan Peltier	.15	.11	.06
24	John Olerud	.10	.08	.04
25	Eddie Zosky	.15	.11	.06
26	Steve Avery	.50	.40	.20
27	John Smoltz	.10	.08	.04
28	Frank Thomas	1.00	.70	.40
29	Jerome Walton	.08	.06	.03
30	George Bell	.08	.06	.03
31	Jose Rijo	.08	.06	.03
32	Randy Myers	.08	.06	.03
33	Barry Larkin	.10	.08	.04
34	Eric Anthony	.08	.06	.03
35	Dave Hansen	.08	.06	.03
36	Eric Karros	.50	.40	.20
37	Jose Offerman	.15	.11	.06
38	Marquis Grissom	.10	.08	.04
39	Dwight Gooden	.10	.08	.04
40	Gregg Jefferies	.10	.08	.04
41	Pat Combs	.08	.06	.03
42	Todd Zeile	.10	.08	.04
43	Benito Santiago	.08	.06	.03
44	Dave Staton	.10	.08	.04
45	Tony Fernandez	.08	.06	.03
46	Fred McGriff	.10	.08	.04
47	Jeff Brantley	.08	.06	.03
48	Junior Felix	.08	.06	.03
49	Jack Morris	.10	.08	.04
50	Chris George	.10	.08	.04
51	Henry Rodriguez	.25	.20	.10
52	Paul Marak	.10	.08	.04
53	Ryan Klesko	1.00	.70	.40
54	Darren Lewis	.15	.11	.06
55	Lance Dickson	.15	.11	.06
56	Anthony Young	.25	.20	.10
57	Willie Banks	.10	.08	.04
58	Mike Bordick	.10	.08	.04
59	Roger Salkeld	.20	.15	.08
60	Steve Karsay	.20	.15	.08
61	Bernie Williams	.20	.15	.08
62	Mickey Tettleton	.08	.06	.03
63	Dave Justice	.20	.15	.08
64	Steve Decker	.20	.15	.08
65	Roger Clemens	.15	.11	.06
66	Phil Plantier	.60	.45	.25
67	Ryne Sandberg	.15	.11	.06
68	Sandy Alomar,Jr.	.10	.08	.04
69	Cecil Fielder	.15	.11	.06
70	George Brett	.10	.08	.04
71	Delino DeShields	.10	.08	.04
72	Dave Magadan	.08	.06	.03
73	Darryl Strawberry	.08	.06	.03
74	Juan Gonzalez	.35	.25	.14
75	Rickey Henderson	.10	.08	.04
76	Willie McGee	.08	.06	.03
77	Todd Van Poppel	.70	.50	.30
78	Barry Bonds	.10	.08	.04
79	Doug Drabek	.08	.06	.03
80	Ryan-300 Game Winner	.35	.25	.14
81	Roberto Alomar	.10	.08	.04
82	Ivan Rodriguez	1.00	.70	.40
83	Dan Opperman	.20	.15	.08
84	Jeff Bagwell	1.00	.70	.40
85	Braulio Castillo	.15	.11	.06
86	Doug Simons	.10	.08	.04
87	Wade Taylor	.15	.11	.06
88	Gary Scott	.40	.30	.15
89	Dave Stewart	.08	.06	.03
90	Mike Simms	.15	.11	.06
91	Luis Gonzalez	.50	.40	.20
92	Bobby Bonilla	.10	.08	.04
93	Tony Gwynn	.10	.08	.04

		MT	NR MT	EX
94	Will Clark	.15	.11	.06
95	Rich Rowland	.10	.08	.04
96	Alan Trammell	.08	.06	.03
97	Strikeout Kings	.40	.30	.15
98	Joe Carter	.08	.06	.03
99	Jack Clark	.08	.06	.03
100	Four-In-One	.25	.20	.10

1991 Classic Series III

Wade Boggs

Green borders highlight Classic's third series of cards for 1991. The set includes a gameboard and player cards featuring trivia questions on the back. Statistics, biographical information and card numbers are also found on the card backs.

		MT	NR MT	EX
Complete Set:		8.00	6.00	3.25
Common Player:		.06	.05	.02
1	Jim Abbott	.12	.09	.05
2	Craig Biggio	.10	.08	.04
3	Wade Boggs	.15	.11	.06
4	Bobby Bonilla	.15	.11	.06
5	Ivan Calderon	.08	.06	.03
6	Jose Canseco	.20	.15	.08
7	Andy Benes	.12	.09	.05
8	Wes Chamberlain	.20	.15	.08
9	Will Clark	.15	.11	.06
10	Royce Clayton	.40	.30	.15
11	Gerald Alexander	.08	.06	.03
12	Chili Davis	.08	.06	.03
13	Eric Davis	.12	.09	.05
14	Andre Dawson	.12	.09	.05
15	Rob Dibble	.08	.06	.03
16	Chris Donnels	.20	.15	.08
17	Scott Erickson	.30	.25	.12
18	Monty Fariss	.08	.06	.03
19	Ruben Amaro, Jr.	.25	.20	.10
20	Chuck Finley	.08	.06	.03
21	Carlton Fisk	.12	.09	.05
22	Carlos Baerga	.10	.08	.04
23	Ron Gant	.15	.11	.06
24	Justice/Gant	.30	.25	.12
25	Mike Gardiner	.10	.08	.04
26	Tom Glavine	.10	.08	.04
27	Joe Grahe	.15	.11	.06
28	Derek Bell	.40	.30	.15
29	Mike Greenwell	.08	.06	.03
30	Ken Griffey, Jr.	.50	.40	.20
31	Leo Gomez	.08	.06	.03
32	Tom Goodwin	.30	.25	.12
33	Tony Gwynn	.12	.09	.05
34	Mel Hall	.08	.06	.03
35	Brian Harper	.08	.06	.03
36	Dave Henderson	.06	.05	.02
37	Albert Belle	.20	.15	.08
38	Orel Hershiser	.08	.06	.03
39	Brian Hunter	.40	.30	.15
40	Howard Johnson	.08	.06	.03
41	Felix Jose	.15	.11	.06
42	Wally Joyner	.08	.06	.03
43	Jeff Juden	.15	.11	.06
44	Pat Kelly	.20	.15	.08
45	Jimmy Key	.06	.05	.02
46	Chuck Knoblauch	.30	.25	.12
47	John Kruk	.08	.06	.03
48	Ray Lankford	.20	.15	.08

		MT	NR MT	EX
49	Ced Landrum	.15	.11	.06
50	Scott Livingstone	.25	.20	.10
51	Kevin Maas	.15	.11	.06
52	Greg Maddux	.08	.06	.03
53	Dennis Martinez	.06	.05	.02
54	Edgar Martinez	.06	.05	.02
55	Pedro Martinez	.70	.50	.30
56	Don Mattingly	.15	.11	.06
57	Orlando Merced	.30	.25	.12
58	Keith Mitchell	.10	.08	.04
59	Kevin Mitchell	.10	.08	.04
60	Paul Molitor	.10	.08	.04
61	Jack Morris	.08	.06	.03
62	Hal Morris	.08	.06	.03
63	Kevin Morton	.15	.11	.06
64	Pedro Munoz	.20	.15	.08
65	Eddie Murray	.10	.08	.04
66	Jack McDowell	.10	.08	.04
67	Jeff McNeely	.50	.40	.20
68	Brian McRae	.20	.15	.08
69	Kevin McReynolds	.06	.05	.02
70	Gregg Olson	.08	.06	.03
71	Rafael Palmeiro	.10	.08	.04
72	Dean Palmer	.30	.25	.12
73	Tony Phillips	.06	.05	.02
74	Kirby Puckett	.15	.11	.06
75	Carlos Quintana	.06	.05	.02
76	Pat Rice	.08	.06	.03
77	Cal Ripken, Jr.	.25	.20	.10
78	Ivan Rodriguez	1.00	.70	.40
79	Nolan Ryan	.50	.40	.20
80	Bret Saberhagen	.08	.06	.03
81	Tim Salmon	.30	.25	.12
82	Juan Samuel	.06	.05	.02
83	Ruben Sierra	.15	.11	.06
84	Heathcliff Slocumb	.06	.05	.02
85	Joe Slusarski	.15	.11	.06
86	John Smiley	.06	.05	.02
87	Dave Smith	.06	.05	.02
88	Ed Sprague	.08	.06	.03
89	Todd Stottlemyre	.06	.05	.02
90	Mike Timlin	.15	.11	.06
91	Greg Vaughn	.10	.08	.04
92	Frank Viola	.10	.08	.04
93	John Wehner	.08	.06	.03
94	Devon White	.06	.05	.02
95	Matt Williams	.15	.11	.06
96	Rick Wilkins	.15	.11	.06
97	Bernie Williams	.15	.11	.06
98	Starter & Stopper	.20	.15	.08
99	Gerald Williams	.30	.25	.12
——	4-In-1	.20	.15	.08

1991 Classic Collector's Edition

Jeff Bagwell

The Classic Collector's edition made its debut in 1991. This package includes a board game, trivia baseball cards, a baseball tips booklet and a certificate of authenticity. It is all packaged in an attractive collector's edition box. Each box is individually and sequentially numbered on the outside. This issue was limited with only 100,000 available. The card set features 200 trivia baseball cards. Mickey Morandini's card features a photo of Darren Daulton.

		MT	NR MT	EX
Complete Set:		25.00	18.00	13.00
Common Player:		.08	.06	.03
1	Frank Viola	.10	.08	.04
2	Tim Wallach	.08	.06	.03
3	Lou Whitaker	.08	.06	.03
4	Brett Butler	.10	.08	.04
5	Jim Abbott	.10	.08	.04
6	Jack Armstrong	.08	.06	.03
7	Craig Biggio	.10	.08	.04
8	Brian Barnes	.20	.15	.08
9	Dennis "Oil Can" Boyd	.08	.06	.03
10	Tom Browning	.10	.08	.04
11	Tom Brunansky	.08	.06	.03
12	Ellis Burks	.10	.08	.04
13	Harold Baines	.10	.08	.04
14	Kal Daniels	.10	.08	.04
15	Mark Davis	.08	.06	.03
16	Storm Davis	.08	.06	.03
17	Tom Glavine	.12	.09	.05
18	Mike Greenwell	.10	.08	.04
19	Kelly Gruber	.12	.09	.05
20	Mark Gubicza	.08	.06	.03
21	Pedro Guerrero	.10	.08	.04
22	Mike Harkey	.10	.08	.04
23	Orel Hershiser	.10	.08	.04
24	Ted Higuera	.10	.08	.04
25	Von Hayes	.08	.06	.03
26	Andre Dawson	.15	.11	.06
27	Shawon Dunston	.10	.08	.04
28	Roberto Kelly	.10	.08	.04
29	Joe Magrane	.08	.06	.03
30	Dennis Martinez	.10	.08	.04
31	Kevin McReynolds	.10	.08	.04
32	Matt Nokes	.08	.06	.03
33	Dan Plesac	.08	.06	.03
34	Dave Parker	.10	.08	.04
35	Randy Johnson	.10	.08	.04
36	Bret Saberhagen	.10	.08	.04
37	Mackey Sasser	.08	.06	.03
38	Mike Scott	.08	.06	.03
39	Ozzie Smith	.15	.11	.06
40	Kevin Seitzer	.08	.06	.03
41	Ruben Sierra	.25	.20	.10
42	Kevin Tapani	.10	.08	.04
43	Danny Tartabull	.20	.15	.08
44	Robby Thompson	.08	.06	.03
45	Andy Van Slyke	.12	.09	.05
46	Greg Vaughn	.15	.11	.06
47	Harold Reynolds	.10	.08	.04
48	Will Clark	.40	.30	.15
49	Gary Gaetti	.10	.08	.04
50	Joe Grahe	.15	.11	.06
51	Carlton Fisk	.20	.15	.08
52	Robin Ventura	.30	.25	.12
53	Ozzie Guillen	.12	.09	.05
54	Tom Candiotti	.08	.06	.03
55	Doug Jones	.08	.06	.03
56	Eric King	.08	.06	.03
57	Kirk Gibson	.12	.09	.05
58	Tim Costo	.40	.30	.15
59	Robin Yount	.25	.20	.10
60	Sammy Sosa	.20	.15	.08
61	Jesse Barfield	.10	.08	.04
62	Marc Newfield	1.00	.70	.40
63	Jimmy Key	.10	.08	.04
64	Felix Jose	.30	.25	.12
65	Mark Whiten	.50	.40	.20
66	Tommy Greene	.15	.11	.06
67	Kent Mercker	.10	.08	.04
68	Greg Maddux	.12	.09	.05
69	Danny Jackson	.08	.06	.03
70	Reggie Sanders	1.00	.70	.40
71	Eric Yelding	.08	.06	.03
72	Karl Rhodes	.40	.30	.15
73	Fernando Valenzuela	.10	.08	.04
74	Chris Nabholz	.12	.09	.05
75	Andres Galarraga	.10	.08	.04
76	Howard Johnson	.20	.15	.08
77	Hubie Brooks	.10	.08	.04
78	Terry Mulholland	.10	.08	.04
79	Paul Molitor	.15	.11	.06
80	Roger McDowell	.08	.06	.03
81	Darren Daulton	.08	.06	.03
82	Zane Smith	.08	.06	.03
83	Ray Lankford	.50	.40	.20
84	Bruce Hurst	.10	.08	.04
85	Andy Benes	.25	.20	.10
86	John Burkett	.08	.06	.03
87	Dave Righetti	.15	.11	.06
88	Steve Karsay	.40	.30	.15
89	D.J. Dozier	.40	.30	.15
90	Jeff Bagwell	2.00	1.50	.80
91	Joe Carter	.20	.15	.08
92	Wes Chamberlain	.60	.45	.25
93	Vince Coleman	.15	.11	.06
94	Pat Combs	.10	.08	.04
95	Jerome Walton	.15	.11	.06
96	Jeff Conine	.40	.30	.15
97	Alan Trammell	.15	.11	.06
98	Don Mattingly	.30	.25	.12
99	Ramon Martinez	.40	.30	.15
100	Dave Magadan	.12	.09	.05
101	Greg Swindell	.12	.09	.05
102	Dave Stewart	.15	.11	.06
103	Gary Sheffield	.20	.15	.08
104	George Bell	.15	.11	.06
105	Mark Grace	.25	.20	.10
106	Steve Sax	.10	.08	.04
107	Ryne Sandberg	.50	.40	.20
108	Chris Sabo	.15	.11	.06
109	Jose Rijo	.10	.08	.04
110	Cal Ripken, Jr.	.80	.60	.30
111	Kirby Puckett	.40	.30	.15
112	Eddie Murray	.15	.11	.06
113	Roberto Alomar	.30	.25	.12
114	Randy Myers	.10	.08	.04
115	Rafael Palmeiro	.25	.20	.10
116	John Olerud	.25	.20	.10
117	Gregg Jefferies	.20	.15	.08
118	Kent Hrbek	.10	.08	.04
119	Marquis Grissom	.25	.20	.10
120	Ken Griffey, Jr.	1.50	1.25	.60
121	Dwight Gooden	.35	.25	.14
122	Juan Gonzalez	.80	.60	.30
123	Ron Gant	.20	.15	.08
124	Travis Fryman	.80	.60	.30
125	John Franco	.12	.09	.05
126	Dennis Eckersley	.15	.11	.06
127	Cecil Fielder	.30	.25	.12
128	Phil Plantier	.70	.50	.30
129	Kevin Mitchell	.30	.25	.12
130	Kevin Maas	.40	.30	.15
131	Mark McGwire	.30	.25	.12
132	Ben McDonald	.30	.25	.12
133	Lenny Dykstra	.12	.09	.05
134	Delino DeShields	.20	.15	.08
135	Jose Canseco	.60	.45	.25
136	Eric Davis	.20	.15	.08
137	George Brett	.20	.15	.08
138	Steve Avery	.30	.25	.12
139	Eric Anthony	.10	.08	.04
140	Bobby Thigpen	.12	.09	.05
141	Ken Griffey, Sr.	.10	.08	.04
142	Barry Larkin	.20	.15	.08
143	Jeff Brantley	.08	.06	.03
144	Bobby Bonilla	.30	.25	.12
145	Jose Offerman	.30	.25	.12
146	Mike Mussina	.60	.45	.25
147	Erik Hanson	.15	.11	.06
148	Dale Murphy	.15	.11	.06
149	Roger Clemens	.50	.40	.20
150	Tino Martinez	.50	.40	.20
151	Todd Van Poppel	1.00	.70	.40
152	Maurice Vaughn	1.00	.70	.40
153	Derrick May	.40	.30	.15
154	Jack Clark	.15	.11	.06
155	Dave Hansen	.12	.09	.05
156	Tony Gwynn	.25	.20	.10
157	Brian McRae	.70	.50	.30
158	Matt Williams	.20	.15	.08
159	Kirk Dressendorfer	1.00	.70	.40
160	Scott Erickson	1.50	1.25	.60
161	Tony Fernandez	.12	.09	.05
162	Willie McGee	.12	.09	.05
163	Fred McGriff	.20	.15	.08
164	Leo Gomez	.30	.25	.12
165	Bernard Gilkey	.30	.25	.12
166	Bobby Witt	.10	.08	.04
167	Doug Drabek	.15	.11	.06
168	Rob Dibble	.15	.11	.06
169	Glenn Davis	.15	.11	.06
170	Danny Darwin	.08	.06	.03
171	Eric Karros	.70	.50	.30
172	Eddie Zosky	.30	.25	.12
173	Todd Zeile	.25	.20	.10
174	Tim Raines	.15	.11	.06
175	Benito Santiago	.15	.11	.06
176	Dan Peltier	.35	.25	.14
177	Darryl Strawberry	.40	.30	.15
178	Hal Morris	.30	.25	.12
179	Hensley Meulens	.20	.15	.08

		MT	NR MT	EX
180	John Smoltz	.15	.11	.06
181	Frank Thomas	2.50	2.00	1.00
182	Dave Staton	.35	.25	.12
183	Scott Chiamparino	.12	.09	.05
184	Alex Fernandez	.30	.25	.12
185	Mark Lewis	.50	.40	.20
186	Bo Jackson	1.25	.90	.50
187	Mickey Morandini	.30	.25	.12
188	Cory Snyder	.08	.06	.03
189	Rickey Henderson	.60	.45	.25
190	Junior Felix	.12	.09	.05
191	Milt Cuyler	.25	.20	.10
192	Wade Boggs	.30	.25	.12
193	"Justice Prevails"	1.50	1.25	.60
194	Sandy Alomar, Jr.	.25	.20	.10
195	Barry Bonds	.40	.30	.15
196	Nolan Ryan	1.25	.90	.50
197	Rico Brogna	.35	.25	.14
198	Steve Decker	.30	.25	.12
199	Bob Welch	.10	.08	.04
200	Andujar Cedeno	.50	.40	.20

		MT	NR MT	EX
29	Steve Whitaker	.35	.25	.14
30	Jorge Fabregas	.60	.45	.25
31	Jeff Ware	.35	.25	.12
32	Bobby Jones	.60	.45	.25
33	J.J. Johnson	.40	.30	.15
34	Mike Rossiter	.30	.25	.12
35	Dan Chowlowsky	.30	.25	.12
36	Jimmy Gonzalez	.30	.25	.12
37	Trevor Miller	.30	.25	.12
38	Scott Hatteberg	.30	.25	.12
39	Mike Groppuso	.40	.30	.15
40	Ryan Long	.30	.25	.12
41	Eddie Williams	.30	.25	.14
42	Mike Durant	.30	.25	.14
43	Buck McNabb	.30	.25	.14
44	Jimmy Lewis	.30	.25	.14
45	Eddie Ramos	.30	.25	.14
46	Terry Horn	.30	.25	.14
47	Jon Barnes	.30	.25	.14
48	Shawn Curran	.30	.25	.14
49	Tommy Adams	.50	.40	.20
50	Trevor Mallory	.30	.25	.12
-----	Frankie Rodriguez (Bonus Card)	2.00	1.50	.80

1991 Classic #1
Draft Picks

After releasing a 26-card draft pick set in 1990, Classic returned with a 50-card issue for 1991. Only 330,000 hobby sets were produced. The card fronts feature gray and maroon borders surrounding full-color photos and the Classic logo in the upper left corner. A special bonus card of Frankie Rodriguez is also included with the set. Each set also includes a certificate of authenticity.

		MT	NR MT	EX
Complete Set:		12.00	9.00	4.75
Common Player:		.30	.25	.12
1	Brien Taylor	3.00	2.25	1.25
2	Mike Kelly	2.50	2.00	1.00
3	David McCarty	2.50	2.00	1.00
4	Dmitri Young	1.50	1.25	.60
5	Joe Vitiello	1.50	1.25	.60
6	Mark Smith	.80	.60	.30
7	Tyler Green	1.25	.90	.50
8	Shawn Estes	.50	.40	.20
9	Doug Glanville	.80	.60	.30
10	Manny Ramirez	1.50	1.25	.60
11	Cliff Floyd	.50	.40	.20
12	Tyrone Hill	.80	.60	.30
13	Eduardo Perez	1.50	1.25	.60
14	Al Shirley	.70	.50	.30
15	Benji Gil	.35	.25	.14
16	Calvin Reese	.35	.25	.14
17	Allen Watson	.35	.25	.14
18	Brian Barber	.35	.25	.14
19	Aaron Sele	.50	.40	.20
20	John Farrell	.35	.25	.14
21	Scott Ruffcorn	.40	.30	.15
22	Brent Gates	.40	.30	.15
23	Scott Stahoviak	.50	.40	.20
24	Tom McKinnon	.30	.25	.12
25	Shawn Livsey	.30	.25	.12
26	Jason Pruitt	.30	.25	.12
27	Greg Anthony	.35	.25	.14
28	Justin Thompson	.35	.25	.14

1992 Classic

Classic introduced a new innovative design with the release of its 1992 set. The card fronts feature full-color photos bordered in white, while the flip sides feature statistics, biographical information and trivia questions accented by a fading stadium shot. The cards were released with a gameboard.

		MT	NR MT	EX
Complete Set:		8.00	6.00	3.25
Common Player:		.06	.05	.02
1	Jim Abbott	.15	.11	.06
2	Kyle Abbott	.15	.11	.06
3	Scott Aldred	.10	.08	.04
4	Roberto Alomar	.20	.15	.08
5	Wilson Alvarez	.08	.06	.03
6	Andy Ashby	.10	.08	.04
7	Steve Avery	.20	.15	.08
8	Jeff Bagwell	.50	.40	.20
9	Bret Barberie	.15	.11	.06
10	Kim Batiste	.10	.08	.04
11	Derek Bell	.20	.15	.08
12	Jay Bell	.10	.08	.04
13	Albert Belle	.15	.11	.06
14	Andy Benes	.10	.08	.04
15	Sean Berry	.08	.06	.03
16	Barry Bonds	.10	.08	.04
17	Ryan Bowen	.10	.08	.04
18	Trifecta	.06	.05	.02
19	Scott Brosius	.06	.05	.02
20	Jay Buhner	.06	.05	.02
21	David Burba	.06	.05	.02
22	Jose Canseco	.25	.20	.10
23	Andujar Cedeno	.10	.08	.04
24	Will Clark	.20	.15	.08
25	Royce Clayton	.20	.15	.08
26	Roger Clemens	.20	.15	.08
27	David Cone	.08	.06	.03
28	Scott Cooper	.08	.06	.03
29	Chris Cron	.06	.05	.02
30	Len Dykstra	.06	.05	.02

		MT	NR MT	EX
31	Cal Eldred	.10	.08	.04
32	Hector Fajardo	.20	.15	.08
33	Cecil Fielder	.10	.08	.04
34	Dave Fleming	.25	.20	.10
35	Steve Foster	.06	.05	.02
36	Julio Franco	.08	.06	.03
37	Carlos Garcia	.06	.05	.02
38	Tom Glavine	.10	.08	.04
39	Tom Goodwin	.06	.05	.02
40	Ken Griffey, Jr.	.60	.45	.25
41	Chris Haney	.08	.06	.03
42	Bryan Harvey	.06	.05	.02
43	Rickey Henderson	.25	.20	.10
44	Carlos Hernandez	.06	.05	.02
45	Roberto Hernandez	.06	.05	.02
46	Brook Jacoby	.06	.05	.02
47	Howard Johnson	.08	.06	.03
48	Pat Kelly	.10	.08	.04
49	Darryl Kile	.08	.06	.03
50	Chuck Knoblauch	.20	.15	.08
51	Ray Lankford	.20	.15	.08
52	Mark Leiter	.06	.05	.02
53	Darren Lewis	.10	.08	.04
54	Scott Livingstone	.10	.08	.04
55	Shane Mack	.10	.08	.04
56	Chito Martinez	.20	.15	.08
57	Dennis Martinez	.06	.05	.02
58	Don Mattingly	.15	.11	.06
59	Paul McClellan	.06	.05	.02
60	Chuck McElroy	.06	.05	.02
61	Fred McGriff	.08	.06	.03
62	Orlando Merced	.20	.15	.08
63	Luis Mercedes	.08	.06	.03
64	Kevin Mitchell	.08	.06	.03
65	Hal Morris	.08	.06	.03
66	Jack Morris	.08	.06	.03
67	Mike Mussina	.50	.40	.20
68	Denny Neagle	.20	.15	.08
69	Tom Pagnozzi	.06	.05	.02
70	Terry Pendleton	.08	.06	.03
71	Phil Plantier	.60	.45	.25
72	Kirby Puckett	.15	.11	.06
73	Carlos Quintana	.06	.05	.02
74	Willie Randolph	.06	.05	.02
75	Arthur Rhodes	.08	.06	.03
76	Cal Ripken	.15	.11	.06
77	Ivan Rodriguez	.60	.45	.25
78	Nolan Ryan	.25	.20	.10
79	Ryne Sandberg	.20	.15	.08
80	Deion Sanders	.20	.15	.08
81	Reggie Sanders	.40	.30	.15
82	Mo Sanford	.15	.11	.06
83	Terry Shumpert	.06	.05	.02
84	Tim Spehr	.08	.06	.03
85	Lee Stevens	.06	.05	.02
86	Darryl Strawberry	.15	.11	.06
87	Kevin Tapani	.08	.06	.03
88	Danny Tartabull	.08	.06	.03
89	Frank Thomas	.80	.60	.30
90	Jim Thome	.35	.25	.14
91	Todd Van Poppel	.50	.40	.20
92	Andy Van Slyke	.08	.06	.03
93	John Wehner	.08	.06	.03
94	John Wetteland	.06	.05	.02
95	Devon White	.06	.05	.02
96	Brian Williams	.10	.08	.04
97	Mark Wohlers	.20	.15	.08
98	Robin Yount	.15	.11	.06
99	Eddie Zosky	.06	.05	.02
——	4-in-1	.10	.08	.04

Values for recent cards and sets are listed in Mint (MT), Near Mint (NM) and Excellent (EX), reflecting the fact that many cards from recent years have been preserved in top condition. Recent cards and sets in less than Excellent condition have little collector interest.

Wrong backs, blank backs

Collectors occasionally find recent (1980s) cards which have wrong backs (player on front doesn't match bio/stats on back) or blank backs. Such cards result from mistakes in the printing process. They aren't very popular with collectors, so they have little, if any, premium value. Most collectors feel they are merely damaged cards and value them lower than correctly printed specimens. The only exception seems to be currently hot superstar or rookie cards, for which a few collectors are willing to pay premiums.

Errors/variations

Collectors often wonder about errors found on cards, usually in the statistics or personal data on the card's back.

Such errors add nothing to the value of the card. The only time an error like this is likely to increase a card's value is if the manufacturer corrects the error in a later printing, thus creating two distinct variations. If enough collectors feel the variations are a desirable part of that issue, the value may increase. Whether the error version or the corrected card will have the greater value usually depends on relative scarcity. The more common version will almost always be worth less. So, quite often the error card can be worth less than the corrected version.

Collector-only issues

Collectors may find some recent issues not included in this volume. In most cases these are illegal, unauthorized "collector-only" issues. Such cards often show nothing but the player's photo and his name on the front, and his name and perhaps a line or two of statistics on the back. The sets usually lack a manufacturer's name. They are often sold at shows and in shops, and frequently carry high price tags.

The cards are not legitimate issues. They can be printed and reprinted at will, so they lack any scarcity value.

The values quoted are intended to reflect the market price.

1989 Cleveland Indians Team Set

(49) Tom Candiotti, RHP

The Cleveland Indians released this oversized (2-3/4" by 4-1/2") 28-card set in 1989. The cards feature a full-color player photo on the front with the "Tribe" logo in the upper left corner. Card backs include major and minor league statistics and a facsimile autograph.

		MT	NR MT	EX
Complete Set:		5.00	3.75	2.00
Common Player:		.20	.15	.08
(1)	Doc Edwards	.20	.15	.08
(2)	Joel Skinner	.20	.15	.08
(3)	Andy Allanson	.20	.15	.08
(4)	Tom Candiotti	.20	.15	.08
(5)	Doug Jones	.20	.15	.08
(6)	Keith Atherton	.20	.15	.08
(7)	Rich Yett	.20	.15	.08
(8)	John Farrell	.20	.15	.08
(9)	Rod Nichols	.20	.15	.08
(10)	Joe Skalski	.30	.25	.12
(11)	Pete O'Brien	.30	.25	.12
(12)	Jerry Browne	.30	.25	.12
(13)	Brook Jacoby	.30	.25	.12
(14)	Felix Fermin	.20	.15	.08
(15)	Bud Black	.20	.15	.08
(16)	Brad Havens	.20	.15	.08
(17)	Greg Swindell	.40	.30	.15
(18)	Scott Bailes	.20	.15	.08
(19)	Jesse Orosco	.20	.15	.08
(20)	Oddibe McDowell	.30	.25	.12
(21)	Joe Carter	.50	.40	.20
(22)	Cory Snyder	.25	.20	.10
(23)	Louie Medina	.20	.15	.08
(24)	Dave Clark	.20	.15	.08
(25)	Brad Komminsk	.20	.15	.08
(26)	Luis Aguayo	.20	.15	.08
(27)	Pat Keedy	.20	.15	.08
(28)	Tribe Coaches	.20	.15	.08

1981 Coca-Cola

In 1981, Topps produced for Coca-Cola 12-card sets for 11 various American and National League teams. The sets include 11 player cards and one unnumbered header card. The card fronts, which measure 2-1/2" by 3-1/2", are identical in style to the 1981 Topps regular issue save for the Coca-Cola logo. The backs differ only from the '81 Topps regular set in that they are numbered 1-11 and carry the Coca-Cola trademark and copyright line. The backs of the header cards contain an offer for 132-card uncut sheets of 1981 Topps baseball cards.

		MT	NR MT	EX
Complete Set:		35.00	27.00	15.00
Common Player:		.06	.05	.02
1	Tom Burgmeier	.06	.05	.02
2	Dennis Eckersley	.15	.11	.06
3	Dwight Evans	.60	.45	.25
4	Bob Stanley	.10	.08	.04
5	Glenn Hoffman	.06	.05	.02
6	Carney Lansford	.20	.15	.08
7	Frank Tanana	.10	.08	.04
8	Tony Perez	.20	.15	.08
9	Jim Rice	.80	.60	.30
10	Dave Stapleton	.06	.05	.02
11	Carl Yastrzemski	2.00	1.50	.80
----	Header Card	.03	.02	.01
1	Tim Blackwell	.06	.05	.02
2	Bill Buckner	.15	.11	.06
3	Ivan DeJesus	.06	.05	.02
4	Leon Durham	.15	.11	.06
5	Steve Henderson	.06	.05	.02
6	Mike Krukow	.10	.08	.04
7	Ken Reitz	.06	.05	.02
8	Rick Reuschel	.15	.11	.06
9	Scot Thompson	.06	.05	.02
10	Dick Tidrow	.06	.05	.02
11	Mike Tyson	.06	.05	.02
----	Header Card	.03	.02	.01
1	Britt Burns	.10	.08	.04
2	Todd Cruz	.06	.05	.02
3	Rich Dotson	.20	.15	.08
4	Jim Essian	.06	.05	.02
5	Ed Farmer	.06	.05	.02
6	Lamar Johnson	.06	.05	.02
7	Ron LeFlore	.10	.08	.04
8	Chet Lemon	.10	.08	.04
9	Bob Molinaro	.06	.05	.02
10	Jim Morrison	.06	.05	.02
11	Wayne Nordhagen	.06	.05	.02
----	Header Card	.03	.02	.01
1	Johnny Bench	2.00	1.50	.80
2	Dave Collins	.10	.08	.04
3	Dave Concepcion	.15	.11	.06
4	Dan Driessen	.10	.08	.04
5	George Foster	.25	.20	.10
6	Ken Griffey	.15	.11	.06
7	Tom Hume	.06	.05	.02
8	Ray Knight	.10	.08	.04
9	Ron Oester	.06	.05	.02
10	Tom Seaver	1.25	.90	.50
11	Mario Soto	.10	.08	.04
----	Header Card	.03	.02	.01
1	Champ Summers	.06	.05	.02
2	Al Cowens	.06	.05	.02
3	Rich Hebner	.06	.05	.02
4	Steve Kemp	.10	.08	.04
5	Aurelio Lopez	.06	.05	.02
6	Jack Morris	.35	.25	.14
7	Lance Parrish	.35	.25	.14
8	Johnny Wockenfuss	.06	.05	.02
9	Alan Trammell	1.00	.70	.40
10	Lou Whitaker	1.00	.70	.40
11	Kirk Gibson	1.00	.70	.40
----	Header Card	.03	.02	.01
1	Alan Ashby	.06	.05	.02
2	Cesar Cedeno	.15	.11	.06
3	Jose Cruz	.15	.11	.06
4	Art Howe	.06	.05	.02
5	Rafael Landestoy	.06	.05	.02
6	Joe Niekro	.15	.11	.06
7	Terry Puhl	.06	.05	.02
8	J.R. Richard	.15	.11	.06
9	Nolan Ryan	8.00	6.00	3.25
10	Joe Sambito	.06	.05	.02
11	Don Sutton	.35	.25	.14
----	Header Card	.03	.02	.01
1	Willie Aikens	.06	.05	.02
2	George Brett	1.50	1.25	.60
3	Larry Gura	.06	.05	.02
4	Dennis Leonard	.06	.05	.02

		MT	NR MT	EX
5	Hal McRae	.15	.11	.06
6	Amos Otis	.10	.08	.04
7	Dan Quisenberry	.15	.11	.06
8	U.L. Washington	.06	.05	.02
9	John Wathan	.10	.08	.04
10	Frank White	.10	.08	.04
11	Willie Wilson	.15	.11	.06
----	Header Card	.03	.02	.01
1	Neil Allen	.06	.05	.02
2	Doug Flynn	.06	.05	.02
3	Dave Kingman	.15	.11	.06
4	Randy Jones	.06	.05	.02
5	Pat Zachry	.06	.05	.02
6	Lee Mazzilli	.10	.08	.04
7	Rusty Staub	.15	.11	.06
8	Craig Swan	.06	.05	.02
9	Frank Taveras	.06	.05	.02
10	Alex Trevino	.06	.05	.02
11	Joel Youngblood	.06	.05	.02
----	Header Card	.03	.02	.01
1	Bob Boone	.30	.25	.12
2	Larry Bowa	.15	.11	.06
3	Steve Carlton	1.00	.70	.40
4	Greg Luzinski	.15	.11	.06
5	Garry Maddox	.10	.08	.04
6	Bake McBride	.06	.05	.02
7	Tug McGraw	.15	.11	.06
8	Pete Rose	2.00	1.50	.80
9	Mike Schmidt	2.25	1.75	.90
10	Lonnie Smith	.15	.11	.06
11	Manny Trillo	.06	.05	.02
----	Header Card	.03	.02	.01
1	Jim Bibby	.06	.05	.02
2	John Candelaria	.10	.08	.04
3	Mike Easler	.10	.08	.04
4	Tim Foli	.06	.05	.02
5	Phil Garner	.06	.05	.02
6	Bill Madlock	.15	.11	.06
7	Omar Moreno	.06	.05	.02
8	Ed Ott	.06	.05	.02
9	Dave Parker	.35	.25	.14
10	Willie Stargell	1.00	.70	.40
11	Kent Tekulve	.10	.08	.04
----	Header Card	.03	.02	.01
1	Bob Forsch	.10	.08	.04
2	George Hendrick	.10	.08	.04
3	Keith Hernandez	.50	.40	.20
4	Tom Herr	.15	.11	.06
5	Sixto Lezcano	.06	.05	.02
6	Ken Oberkfell	.06	.05	.02
7	Darrell Porter	.10	.08	.04
8	Tony Scott	.06	.05	.02
9	Lary Sorensen	.06	.05	.02
10	Bruce Sutter	.15	.11	.06
11	Garry Templeton	.10	.08	.04
----	Header Card	.03	.02	.01

including an unnumbered header card.

		MT	NR MT	EX
Complete Set:		8.00	6.00	3.25
Common Player:		.08	.06	.03
1	Gary Allenson	.08	.06	.03
2	Tom Burgmeier	.08	.06	.03
3	Mark Clear	.15	.11	.06
4	Steve Crawford	.08	.06	.03
5	Dennis Eckersley	1.00	.70	.40
6	Dwight Evans	.80	.60	.30
7	Rich Gedman	.30	.25	.12
8	Garry Hancock	.08	.06	.03
9	Glen Hoffman (Glenn)	.08	.06	.03
10	Carney Lansford	.20	.15	.08
11	Rick Miller	.08	.06	.03
12	Reid Nichols	.08	.06	.03
13	Bob Ojeda	.20	.15	.08
14	Tony Perez	.30	.25	.12
15	Chuck Rainey	.08	.06	.03
16	Jerry Remy	.08	.06	.03
17	Jim Rice	.80	.60	.30
18	Bob Stanley	.15	.11	.06
19	Dave Stapleton	.08	.06	.03
20	Mike Torrez	.08	.06	.03
21	John Tudor	.30	.25	.12
22	Carl Yastrzemski	3.00	2.25	1.25
----	Header Card	.05	.04	.02

1982 Coca-Cola Reds

Produced by Topps for Coca-Cola, the set consists of 23 cards featuring the Cincinnati Reds and was distributed in the Cincinnati area. The cards, which are 2-1/2" by 3-1/2" in size, are identical in design to the regular 1982 Topps set but have a Coca-Cola logo on the front and red backs. An unnumbered header card is included in the set.

		MT	NR MT	EX
Complete Set:		9.00	6.75	3.50
Common Player:		.08	.06	.03
1	Johnny Bench	3.00	2.25	1.25
2	Bruce Berenyi	.08	.06	.03
3	Larry Biittner	.08	.06	.03
4	Cesar Cedeno	.15	.11	.06
5	Dave Concepcion	.25	.20	.10
6	Dan Driessen	.15	.11	.06
7	Greg Harris	.08	.06	.03
8	Paul Householder	.08	.06	.03
9	Tom Hume	.08	.06	.03
10	Clint Hurdle	.08	.06	.03
11	Jim Kern	.08	.06	.03
12	Wayne Krenchicki	.08	.06	.03
13	Rafael Landestoy	.08	.06	.03
14	Charlie Leibrandt	.15	.11	.06
15	Mike O'Berry	.08	.06	.03
16	Ron Oester	.08	.06	.03
17	Frank Pastore	.08	.06	.03
18	Joe Price	.08	.06	.03
19	Tom Seaver	3.00	2.25	1.25
20	Mario Soto	.15	.11	.06
21	Alex Trevino	.08	.06	.03
22	Mike Vail	.08	.06	.03
----	Header Card	.04	.03	.02

1982 Coca-Cola Brigham's Red Sox

Coca-Cola, in conjunction with Brigham's Ice Cream stores, issued a 23-card set in the Boston area featuring Red Sox players. The Topps-produced cards, which measure 2-1/2" by 3-1/2", are identical in style to the regular 1982 Topps set but contain the Coca-Cola and Brigham's logos in the corners. The cards were distributed in three-card cello packs,

1985 Coca-Cola White Sox

Featuring past and present White Sox players, the cards in this set were given out on Tuesday night home games. The cards, which measure 2-5/8" by 4-1/8", contain a color photo of a current Sox member. A red box at the bottom of the card carries the team logo, the player's name, uniform number and position, plus a small oval portrait of a past Sox player. The card backs contain the Coca-Cola logo and the lifetime hitting or pitching statistics for the current and past player. The set is numbered in the checklist that follows by the player's uniform number with the last three cards being unnumbered. Complete sets were available through a fan club offer found in White Sox programs.

		MT	NR MT	EX
Complete Set:		14.00	10.50	5.50
Common Player:		.25	.20	.10
	Oscar Gamble (Zeke Bonura)	.25	.20	.10
1	Scott Fletcher (Luke Appling)	.40	.30	.15
3	Harold Baines (Bill Melton)	.80	.60	.30
5	Luis Salazar (Chico Carrasquel)	.25	.20	.10
7	Marc Hill (Sherm Lollar)	.25	.20	.10
8	Daryl Boston (Jim Landis)	.25	.20	.10
10	Tony LaRussa (Al Lopez)	.40	.30	.15
12	Julio Cruz (Nellie Fox)	.40	.30	.15
13	Ozzie Guillen (Luis Aparicio)	1.50	1.25	.60
17	Jerry Hairston (Smoky Burgess)	.25	.20	.10
20	Joe DeSa (Carlos May)	.25	.20	.10
22	Joel Skinner (J.C. Martin)	.25	.20	.10
23	Rudy Law (Bill Skowron)	.25	.20	.10
24	Floyd Bannister (Red Faber)	.35	.25	.14
29	Greg Walker (Dick Allen)	.70	.50	.30
30	Gene Nelson (Early Wynn)	.35	.25	.14
32	Tim Hulett (Pete Ward)	.25	.20	.10
34	Richard Dotson (Ed Walsh)	.35	.25	.14
37	Dan Spillner (Thornton Lee)	.25	.20	.10
40	Britt Burns (Gary Peters)	.25	.20	.10
41	Tom Seaver (Ted Lyons)	1.50	1.25	.60
42	Ron Kittle (Minnie Minoso)	.40	.30	.15
43	Bob James (Hoyt Wilhelm)	.40	.30	.15
44	Tom Paciorek (Eddie Collins)	.35	.25	.14
46	Tim Lollar (Billy Pierce)	.25	.20	.10
50	Juan Agosto (Wilbur Wood)	.25	.20	.10
72	Carlton Fisk (Ray Schalk)	1.50	1.25	.60
----	Comiskey Park	.50	.40	.20
----	Ribbie and Roobarb (mascots)	.25	.20	.10
----	Nancy Faust (organist)	.25	.20	.10

1986 Coca-Cola White Sox

For the second year in a row, Coca-Cola, in conjunction with the Chicago White Sox, issued a 30-card set. As in 1985, cards were given out at the park on Tuesday night games. Full sets were again available through a fan club offer found in the White Sox program. The cards, which measure 2-5/8" by 4-1/8", feature 25 players plus other White Sox personnel. The card fronts feature a color photo (an action shot in most instances) and a white bar at the bottom. A black and white bat with "SOX" shown on the barrel is located within the white bar, along with

the player's name, position and uniform number. The white and grey backs with black print include the Coca-Cola trademark. Lifetime statistics are shown on all player cards, but there is no personal information such as height, weight or age. The non-player cards are blank-backed save for the name and logo at the top. The cards in the checklist that follows are numbered by the players' uniform numbers, with the last five cards of the set being unnumbered.

		MT	NR MT	EX
Complete Set:		15.00	11.00	6.00
Common Player:		.25	.20	.10
1	Wayne Tolleson	.25	.20	.10
3	Harold Baines	.80	.60	.30
7	Marc Hill	.25	.20	.10
8	Daryl Boston	.25	.20	.10
12	Julio Cruz	.25	.20	.10
13	Ozzie Guillen	.80	.60	.30
17	Jerry Hairston	.25	.20	.10
19	Floyd Bannister	.35	.25	.14
20	Reid Nichols	.25	.20	.10
22	Joel Skinner	.25	.20	.10
24	Dave Schmidt	.25	.20	.10
26	Bobby Bonilla	2.50	2.00	1.00
29	Greg Walker	.40	.30	.15
30	Gene Nelson	.25	.20	.10
32	Tim Hulett	.25	.20	.10
33	Neil Allen	.25	.20	.10
34	Richard Dotson	.35	.25	.14
40	Joe Cowley	.25	.20	.10
41	Tom Seaver	1.25	.90	.50
42	Ron Kittle	.35	.25	.14
43	Bob James	.25	.20	.10
44	John Cangelosi	.35	.25	.14
50	Juan Agosto	.25	.20	.10
52	Joel Davis	.25	.20	.10
72	Carlton Fisk	1.25	.90	.50
----	Ribbie & Roobarb (mascots)	.25	.20	.10
----	Nancy Faust (organist)	.25	.20	.10
----	Ken "Hawk" Harrelson	.30	.25	.12
----	Tony LaRussa	.30	.25	.12
----	Minnie Minoso	.30	.25	.12

1987 Coca-Cola Tigers

Coca-Cola and S. Abraham & Sons, Inc. issued a set

of 18 baseball cards featuring members of the Detroit Tigers. The set is comprised of six four-part folding panels. Each panel includes three player cards (each 2-1/2" by 3-1/2") and one team logo card. A bright yellow border surrounds the full-color photo. The backs are designed on a vertical format and contain personal data and career statistics. The set was produced by Mike Schecter and Associates.

		MT	NR MT	EX
Complete Set:		6.00	4.50	2.50
Complete Singles Set:		2.00	1.50	.80
Common Panel:		.60	.45	.25
Common Single Player:		.05	.04	.02
	Panel	1.25	.90	.50
1	Kirk Gibson	.50	.40	.20
2	Larry Herndon	.08	.06	.03
3	Walt Terrell	.10	.08	.04
	Panel	1.25	.90	.50
4	Alan Trammell	.50	.40	.20
5	Frank Tanana	.10	.08	.04
6	Pat Sheridan	.05	.04	.02
	Panel	.90	.70	.35
7	Jack Morris	.30	.25	.12
8	Mike Heath	.05	.04	.02
9	Dave Bergman	.05	.04	.02
	Panel	.60	.45	.25
10	Chet Lemon	.10	.08	.04
11	Dwight Lowry	.08	.06	.03
12	Dan Petry	.10	.08	.04
	Panel	.80	.60	.30
13	Darrell Evans	.20	.15	.08
14	Darnell Coles	.10	.08	.04
15	Willie Hernandez	.10	.08	.04
	Panel	1.00	.70	.40
16	Lou Whitaker	.30	.25	.12
17	Tom Brookens	.05	.04	.02
18	John Grubb	.05	.04	.02

1987 Coca-Cola White Sox

3 Harold Baines, OF

The Chicago White Sox Fan Club, in conjunction with Coca-Cola, offered members a set of 30 trading cards. For the $10 membership fee, fans received the set plus additional fan club gifts and privileges. The cards, which measure 2-5/8" by 4", feature full-color photos inside a blue and red border. The backs include the player's name, position, uniform number and statistics. The Coca-Cola logo is also included on the card backs.

		MT	NR MT	EX
Complete Set:		12.00	9.00	4.75
Common Player:		.25	.20	.10
1	Jerry Royster	.25	.20	.10
3	Harold Baines	.60	.45	.25
5	Ron Karkovice	.30	.25	.12
8	Daryl Boston	.25	.20	.10
10	Fred Manrique	.30	.25	.12
12	Steve Lyons	.25	.20	.10
13	Ozzie Guillen	.60	.45	.25
14	Russ Morman	.30	.25	.12
15	Donnie Hill	.25	.20	.10
16	Jim Fregosi	.30	.25	.12
17	Jerry Hairston	.25	.20	.10

		MT	NR MT	EX
19	Floyd Bannister	.35	.25	.14
21	Gary Redus	.25	.20	.10
22	Ivan Calderon	.60	.45	.25
25	Ron Hassey	.25	.20	.10
26	Jose DeLeon	.30	.25	.12
29	Greg Walker	.30	.25	.14
32	Tim Hulett	.25	.20	.10
33	Neil Allen	.25	.20	.10
34	Rich Dotson	.35	.25	.14
36	Ray Searage	.25	.20	.10
37	Bobby Thigpen	.60	.45	.25
40	Jim Winn	.25	.20	.10
43	Bob James	.25	.20	.10
50	Joel McKeon	.25	.20	.10
52	Joel Davis	.25	.20	.10
72	Carlton Fisk	.80	.60	.30
-----	Ribbie & Roobarb (mascots)	.25	.20	.10
-----	Nancy Faust (organist)	.25	.20	.10
-----	Minnie Minoso	.30	.25	.12

1988 Coca-Cola Padres

A 20-card team set sponsored by Coca-Cola was designed as part of the San Diego Padres Junior Fan Club promotion for 1988. This set was distributed as a nine-card starter sheet, with 11 additional single cards handed out during the team's home games. The standard-size cards feature full-color player photos framed by a black and orange border. The player's name is printed above the photo; uniform number and position appear lower right. A large Padres logo curves upward from the lower left corner. Card backs are brown on white and include the Padres logo upper left opposite the player's name and personal information. Career highlights and 1987 stats appear in the center of the card back above the Coca-Cola and Junior Padres Fan Club logos.

		MT	NR MT	EX
Complete Set:		35.00	25.00	13.00
Common Player:		.50	.40	.20
	Panel			
1	Garry Templeton	.75	.60	.30
5	Randy Ready	.50	.40	.20
10	Larry Bowa	.75	.60	.30
11	Tim Flannery	.50	.40	.20
35	Chris Brown	.75	.60	.30
45	Jimmy Jones	1.00	.70	.40
48	Mark Davis	.50	.40	.20
55	Mark Grant	.50	.40	.20
-----	20th Anniversary Logo Card	.10	.08	.04
	Singles			
7	Keith Moreland	1.00	.70	.40
8	John Kruk	2.25	1.75	.90
9	Benito Santiago	3.25	2.50	1.25
14	Carmelo Martinez	1.00	.70	.40
15	Jack McKeon	1.00	.70	.40
19	Tony Gwynn	10.00	7.50	4.00
22	Stan Jefferson	1.00	.70	.40
27	Mark Parent	2.00	1.50	.80
30	Eric Show	1.50	1.25	.60
31	Ed Whitson	1.00	.70	.40
41	Lance McCullers	1.25	.90	.50
51	Greg Booker	1.00	.70	.40

1988 Coca-Cola White Sox

Part of a fan club membership package, this unnumbered 30-card set features full-color photos of 27 players, the team mascot, team organist and Comiskey Park. Cards have a bright red border, with the team logo in the lower left corner of the photo. A large player name fills the bottom border. Card backs are printed in black on grey and white and include player name, personal info and career summary. The set was included in the $10 membership package, with a portion of the cost going to the ChiSox Kids Charity.

		MT	NR MT	EX
Complete Set:		8.00	6.00	3.25
Common Player:		.20	.15	.08
(1)	Harold Baines	.50	.40	.20
(2)	Daryl Boston	.20	.15	.08
(3)	Ivan Calderon	.40	.30	.15
(4)	John Davis	.20	.15	.08
(5)	Jim Fregosi	.25	.20	.10
(6)	Carlton Fisk	.60	.45	.25
(7)	Ozzie Guillen	.40	.30	.15
(8)	Donnie Hill	.20	.15	.08
(9)	Rick Horton	.20	.15	.08
(10)	Lance Johnson	.30	.25	.12
(11)	Dave LaPoint	.20	.15	.08
(12)	Bill Long	.25	.20	.10
(13)	Steve Lyons	.20	.15	.08
(14)	Jack McDowell	.70	.50	.30
(15)	Fred Manrique	.20	.15	.08
(16)	Minnie Minoso	.25	.20	.10
(17)	Dan Pasqua	.30	.25	.12
(18)	John Pawlowski	.25	.20	.10
(19)	Melido Perez	.40	.30	.15
(20)	Billy Pierce	.25	.20	.10
(21)	Gary Redus	.20	.15	.08
(22)	Jerry Reuss	.25	.20	.10
(23)	Mark Salas	.20	.15	.08
(24)	Jose Segura	.30	.25	.12
(25)	Bobby Thigpen	.35	.25	.14
(26)	Greg Walker	.30	.25	.12
(27)	Kenny Williams	.30	.25	.12
(28)	Nancy Faust (organist)	.20	.15	.08
(29)	Ribbie & Roobarb (mascots)	.20	.15	.08
(30)	Comiskey Park	.40	.30	.15

1989 Coca-Cola Padres

This 20-card set is part of the Junior Padres Fan Club membership package. Members receive a 9-card starter set printed on one large perforated sheet. Additional cards are distributed to kids at specially designated games (free admission for kids). Card fronts feature an orange-and-brown double border, with a bright orange Padres logo printed lower left. Player uniform number and position are printed diagonally across the upper right corner, with the player's name in large block letters along the bottom border.

		MT	NR MT	EX
Complete Set:		30.00	22.00	12.00
Common Player:		.50	.40	.30
	Panel			
1	Garry Templeton	.70	.50	.30
5	Randy Ready	.50	.40	.20
12	Roberto Alomar	1.00	.70	.40
14	Carmelo Martinez	.50	.40	.20
15	Jack McKeon	.50	.40	.20
30	Eric Show	.50	.40	.20
31	Ed Whitson	.50	.40	.20
43	Dennis Rasmussen	.50	.40	.20
-----	Logo Card	.10	.08	.04
	Singles			
6	Luis Salazar	1.00	.70	.40
9	Benito Santiago	3.00	2.25	1.25
10	Leon Roberts	1.00	.70	.40
11	Tim Flannery	1.00	.70	.40
18	Chris James	2.00	1.50	.80
19	Tony Gwynn	8.00	6.00	3.25
25	Jack Clark	3.00	2.25	1.25
27	Mark Parent	2.00	1.50	.80
35	Walt Terrell	1.00	.70	.40
47	Bruce Hurst	2.00	1.50	.80
48	Mark Davis	3.00	2.25	1.25
55	Mark Grant	1.00	.70	.30

1989 Coca-Cola White Sox

For the fifth straight year, Coca-Cola sponsored a set of cards featuring the Chicago White Sox. The 30-card set was distributed to fans attending a special promotional day at Comiskey Park and was also available by mail to members of the ChiSox fan club. The fronts of the cards feature a red, white and blue color scheme and include a pair of crossed bats. "White Sox" appears along the top, while the name and position are in the lower right, and a pennant proclaiming "Chicago's American Pastime" is just below the photo. The horizontal backs include player biographies, other data, special facts about Comiskey Park and the Coca-Cola logo.

		MT	NR MT	EX
Complete Set:		7.00	5.25	2.75
Common Player:		.20	.15	.08
1	New Comiskey Park, 1991	.40	.30	.15
2	Comiskey Park	.40	.30	.15
3	Jeff Torborg	.20	.15	.08
4	Coaching Staff	.20	.15	.08
5	Harold Baines	.50	.40	.20

		MT	NR MT	EX
6	Daryl Boston	.20	.15	.08
7	Ivan Calderon	.30	.25	.12
8	Carlton Fisk	.40	.30	.15
9	Dave Gallagher	.30	.25	.12
10	Ozzie Guillen	.30	.25	.12
11	Shawn Hillegas	.20	.15	.08
12	Barry Jones	.20	.15	.08
13	Ron Karkovice	.20	.15	.08
14	Eric King	.20	.15	.08
15	Ron Kittle	.30	.25	.12
16	Bill Long	.20	.15	.08
17	Steve Lyons	.20	.15	.08
18	Donn Pall	.20	.15	.08
19	Dan Pasqua	.30	.25	.12
20	Ken Patterson	.20	.15	.08
21	Melido Perez	.30	.25	.12
22	Jerry Reuss	.25	.20	.10
23	Billy Jo Robidoux	.20	.15	.08
24	Steve Rosenberg	.20	.15	.08
25	Jeff Schaefer	.25	.20	.10
26	Bobby Thigpen	.35	.25	.14
27	Greg Walker	.25	.20	.10
28	Eddie Williams	.25	.20	.10
29	Nancy Faust, organist	.20	.15	.08
30	Minnie Minoso	.20	.15	.08

1990 Coca-Cola Garry Templeton

Coca-Cola, Vons stores and the San Diego Padres joined forces to release this special pin/baseball card collectible in honor of Garry Templeton becoming the club's all-time leader in games played. The card front features a full-color photo of Templeton and displays "Most Games Played" and "The Captain" in orange at the top of the photo. "Templeton" appears vertically in white along the left border. The Coca-Cola and Padre logos also appear on the card front. The bottom of the card features a perforated edge where the pin is attached as an extension of the card. The card back is printed in black and white and displays biographical information, career highlights and career statistics. The card was created by Imprinted Products Corporation of San Diego.

		MT	NR MT	EX
	Complete Set:	1.50	1.25	.60
(1)	Most Games Played card (Garry Templeton)	.50	.40	.20
(2)	Most Games Played Pin (Garry Templeton)	1.00	.70	.40

A player's name in *italic* indicates a rookie card. An (FC) indicates a player's first card for that particular card company.

1990 Coca-Cola Padres

This set was designed for members of the Junior Padres Club sponsored by Coca-Cola. Each member received an eight-card panel and then received two different single cards at every Junior Padres Club game attended. The card fronts feature full-color photos with the Padres logo in the upper right corner of the card. The backs feature statistics and career highlights. The cards are numbered by the player's uniform number.

		MT	NR MT	EX
	Complete Set:	18.00	13.50	7.25
	Common Player:	.35	.25	.14
	Panel			
10	Bip Roberts	.60	.45	.25
15	Jack McKeon	.35	.25	.14
30	Eric Show	.35	.25	.14
31	Ed Whitson	.35	.25	.14
40	Andy Benes	.80	.60	.30
43	Dennis Rasmussen	.35	.25	.14
55	Mark Grant	.35	.25	.14
----	Logo Card	.35	.25	.14
	Singles			
1	Garry Templeton	1.00	.70	.40
8	Fred Lynn	1.00	.70	.40
9	Benito Santiago	2.00	1.50	.80
11	Craig Lefferts	.80	.60	.30
12	Roberto Alomar	3.00	2.25	1.25
13	Mike Pagliarulo	1.00	.70	.40
17	Joe Carter	2.00	1.50	.80
19	Tony Gwynn	4.00	3.00	1.50
25	Jack Clark	.80	.60	.30
27	Mark Parent	.80	.60	.30
38	Calvin Schiraldi	.80	.60	.30
46	Greg Harris	1.00	.70	.40
47	Bruce Hurst	.80	.60	.30

Values for recent cards and sets are listed in Mint (MT), Near Mint (NM) and Excellent (EX), reflecting the fact that many cards from recent years have been preserved in top condition. Recent cards and sets in less than Excellent condition have little collector interest.

1990 Coca-Cola Tigers

		MT	NR MT	EX
	Complete Set:	6.00	4.50	2.50
	Common Player:	.15	.11	.06
1	Sparky Anderson	.25	.20	.10
2	Dave Bergman	.15	.11	.06
3	Brian DuBois	.20	.15	.08
4	Cecil Fielder	2.00	1.50	.80
5	Paul Gibson	.15	.11	.06
6	Jerry Don Gleaton	.15	.11	.06
7	Mike Heath	.15	.11	.06
8	Mike Henneman	.20	.15	.08
9	Tracy Jones	.15	.11	.06
10	Chet Lemon	.20	.15	.08
11	Urbano Lugo			

1990 Coca-Cola White Sox

An attractive "Comiskey Park 1910-1990" logo is featured on the front of each of the 30 cards in this set. The card fronts feature full-color photos with a thin white inner border. The cards are numbered according to uniform number, with the exception of four special cards including Top Prospect Frank Thomas. The horizontal card backs feature black print on white and gray stock. 1989 statistics and career highlights are provided. The set was made available nationally through hobby dealers. The 1990 set marks the sixth straight year that Coca-Cola sponsored a White Sox set.

		MT	NR MT	EX
Complete Set:		10.00	7.50	4.00
Common Player:		.15	.11	.06
1	Lance Johnson	.20	.15	.08
7	Scott Fletcher	.15	.11	.06
10	Jeff Torborg	.15	.11	.06
12	Steve Lyons	.15	.11	.06
13	Ozzie Guillen	.25	.20	.10
14	Craig Grebeck	.20	.15	.08
17	Dave Gallagher	.15	.11	.06
20	Ron Karkovice	.15	.11	.06
22	Ivan Calderon	.25	.20	.10
23	Robin Ventura	.60	.45	.25
24	Carlos Martinez	.20	.15	.08
25	Sammy Sosa	.30	.25	.12
27	Greg Hibbard	.20	.15	.08
29	Jack McDowell	.35	.25	.14
30	Donn Pall	.15	.11	.06
31	Scott Radinsky	.25	.20	.10
33	Melido Perez	.15	.11	.06
34	Ken Patterson	.15	.11	.06
36	Eric King	.15	.11	.06
37	Bobby Thigpen	.35	.25	.14
42	Ron Kittle	.20	.15	.08
44	Dan Pasqua	.20	.15	.08
45	Wayne Edwards	.15	.11	.06
50	Barry Jones	.15	.11	.06
52	Jerry Kutzler	.15	.11	.06
72	Carlton Fisk	.35	.25	.14
----	Top Prospect (Frank Thomas)	3.00	2.25	1.25
----	Coaches	.15	.11	.06
----	Captains-Guillen, Fisk	.20	.15	.08
----	Rookies	.20	.15	.08

1991 Coca-Cola Tigers

This 27-card set was sponsored by Coca-Cola and Kroger. The oversized cards feature color photos on the front along with the player's name vertically printed on the right border and the Tigers logo in the lower right corner. The backs are printed horizontally and feature statistics. The set is numbered according to uniform number.

		MT	NR MT	EX
Complete Set:		6.00	4.50	2.50
Common Player:		.20	.15	.08
1	Lou Whitaker	.40	.30	.15
3	Alan Trammell	.60	.45	.25

		MT	NR MT	EX
4	Tony Phillips	.25	.20	.10
10	Andy Allanson	.20	.15	.08
11	Sparky Anderson	.30	.25	.12
14	Dave Bergman	.20	.15	.08
15	Lloyd Moseby	.25	.20	.10
19	Jerry Don Gleaton	.20	.15	.08
20	Mickey Tettleton	.35	.25	.14
22	Milt Cuyler	.35	.25	.14
23	Mark Leiter	.20	.15	.08
24	Travis Fryman	.80	.60	.30
25	John Shelby	.20	.15	.08
26	Frank Tanana	.25	.20	.10
27	Mark Salas	.20	.15	.08
29	Pete Incaviglia	.25	.20	.10
31	Kevin Ritz	.25	.20	.10
35	Walt Terrell	.20	.15	.08
36	Bill Gullickson	.25	.20	.10
39	Mike Henneman	.25	.20	.10
44	Rob Deer	.25	.20	.10
45	Cecil Fielder	.70	.50	.30
46	Dan Petry	.20	.15	.08
48	Paul Gibson	.20	.15	.08
49	Steve Searcy	.20	.15	.08
55	John Cerutti	.20	.15	.08
----	Coaches Card	.20	.15	.08

1991-1993 Conlon

This 990-card set was actually released over a three-year period. Cards numbered 1-330 were released in 1991, cards 331-660 in 1992 and cards 661-990 in 1993. The cards feature the photography of Charles Conlon. Megacards worked with The Sporting News to release the set. Several subsetsare featured such as the Hall of Famers, 1927 New York Yankees, MVP's and more. The cards feature black and white photos surrounded by a white frame and black borders. The backs feature statistics and career highlights.

		MT	NR MT	EX
Complete Set:		50.00	37.00	20.00
Common Player:		.10	.08	.04
1	Rogers Hornsby	.20	.15	.08
2	James E. Foxx	.20	.15	.08

		MT	NR MT	EX			MT	NR MT	EX
3	Jay H. Dean	.20	.15	.08	94	John W. Cooney	.10	.08	.04
4	Walter J.V. Maranville	.20	.15	.08	95	Charles J. Grimm	.10	.08	.04
5	Paul G. Waner	.20	.15	.08	96	Robert L. Johnson	.10	.08	.04
6	Lloyd J. Waner	.20	.15	.08	97	John W. Scott	.10	.08	.04
7	Melvin T. Ott	.20	.15	.08	98	Raymond A. Radcliff	.10	.08	.04
8	John P. Wagner	.20	.15	.08	99	Frederick R. Ostermueller	.10	.08	.04
9	Walter P. Johnson	.20	.15	.08	100	Julian V. Wera	.10	.08	.04
10	Carol O. Hubbell	.20	.15	.08	101	Miller J. Huggins	.10	.08	.04
11	Frank F. Frisch	.20	.15	.08	102	Raymond A. Morehart	.10	.08	.04
12	Hazen S. Cuyler	.20	.15	.08	103	Bernard O. Bengough	.10	.08	.04
13	Charles H. Ruffing	.20	.15	.08	104	Walter H. Ruether	.10	.08	.04
14	Henry B. Greenberg	.20	.15	.08	105	Earle B. Combs	.10	.08	.04
15	John J. Evers	.20	.15	.08	106	Myles L. Thomas	.10	.08	.04
16	Hugh A. Jennings	.20	.15	.08	107	Benjamin E. Paschal	.10	.08	.04
17	David J. Bancroft	.20	.15	.08	108	Cedric M. Durst	.10	.08	.04
18	Joseph M. Medwick	.20	.15	.08	109	William W. Moore	.10	.08	.04
19	Theodore A. Lyons	.20	.15	.08	110	George H. Ruth	.50	.40	.20
20	Charles A. Bender	.20	.15	.08	111	Louis H. Gehrig	.50	.40	.20
21	Edward T. Collins	.20	.15	.08	112	Joseph A. Dugan	.10	.08	.04
22	James L. Bottomley	.20	.15	.08	113	Anthony M. Lazzeri	.10	.08	.04
23	Robert M. Grove	.20	.15	.08	114	Urban J. Shocker	.10	.08	.04
24	Max Carey	.20	.15	.08	115	Waite C. Hoyt	.10	.08	.04
25	Burleigh A. Grimes	.20	.15	.08	116	Charles T. O'Leary	.10	.08	.04
26	Ross M. Youngs	.20	.15	.08	117	Arthur Fletcher	.10	.08	.04
27	Ernest N. Lombardi	.20	.15	.08	118	Tharon L. Collins	.10	.08	.04
28	Joseph V. McCarthy	.20	.15	.08	119	Joseph O. Giard	.10	.08	.04
29	Lewis R. Wilson	.20	.15	.08	120	Herbert J. Pennock	.10	.08	.04
30	Charles H. Klein	.20	.15	.08	121	Michael Gazella	.10	.08	.04
31	Howard E. Averill Sr.	.20	.15	.08	122	Robert W. Meusel	.10	.08	.04
32	Grover C. Alexander	.20	.15	.08	123	George W. Pipgras	.10	.08	.04
33	Charles J. Hafey	.20	.15	.08	124	John P. Grabowski	.10	.08	.04
34	William B. Mckechnie	.20	.15	.08	125	Mark A. Koenig	.10	.08	.04
35	Robert W.A. Feller	.20	.15	.08	126	Stanley C. Hack	.10	.08	.04
36	Harold J. Traynor	.20	.15	.08	127	Earl O. Whitehill	.10	.08	.04
37	Charles D. Stengel	.20	.15	.08	128	William C. Lee	.10	.08	.04
38	Joseph F. Vaughan	.20	.15	.08	129	Frank O. Mancuso	.10	.08	.04
39	Eppa Rixey	.20	.15	.08	130	Francis R. Blades	.10	.08	.04
40	Joseph W. Sewell	.20	.15	.08	131	John I. Burns	.10	.08	.04
41	Urban C. Faber	.20	.15	.08	132	Clinton H. Brown	.10	.08	.04
42	Travis C. Jackson	.20	.15	.08	133	William J. Dietrich	.10	.08	.04
43	Jesse J. Haines	.20	.15	.08	134	Darrell E. Blanton	.10	.08	.04
44	Tristram E. Speaker	.20	.15	.08	135	Harry B. Hooper	.10	.08	.04
45	Cornelius Mack	.20	.15	.08	136	Charles H. Shorten	.10	.08	.04
46	Cornelius Mack	.20	.15	.08	137	Clarence W. Walker	.10	.08	.04
47	Cornelius Mack	.20	.15	.08	138	George Foster	.10	.08	.04
48	Raymond W. Schalk	.20	.15	.08	139	John J. Barry	.10	.08	.04
49	Aloysius H. Simmons	.20	.15	.08	140	Samuel P. Jones	.10	.08	.04
50	Joseph E. Cronin	.20	.15	.08	141	Ernest G. Shore	.10	.08	.04
51	Gordon S. Cochrane	.20	.15	.08	142	Hubert B. Leonard	.10	.08	.04
52	Harry E. Heilmann	.20	.15	.08	143	Herbert J. Pennock	.10	.08	.04
53	John R. Mize	.20	.15	.08	144	Harold C. Janvrin	.10	.08	.04
54	Edgar C. Rice	.20	.15	.08	145	George H. Ruth	.40	.30	.15
55	Edd J. Roush	.20	.15	.08	146	George E. Lewis	.10	.08	.04
56	Enos B. Slaughter	.20	.15	.08	147	William L. Gardner	.10	.08	.04
57	Christopher Mathewson	.20	.15	.08	148	Richard C. Hoblitzel	.10	.08	.04
58	Fred C. Lindstrom	.20	.15	.08	149	Lewis E. Scott	.10	.08	.04
59	Charles L. Hartnett	.20	.15	.08	150	Carl W. Mays	.10	.08	.04
60	George L. Kelly	.20	.15	.08	151	John A. Niehoff	.10	.08	.04
61	Stanley R. Harris	.20	.15	.08	152	Burton E. Shotton	.10	.08	.04
62	Leon A. Goslin	.20	.15	.08	153	Leon K. Ames	.10	.08	.04
63	Henry E. Manush	.20	.15	.08	154	Fred Williams	.10	.08	.04
64	William H. Terry	.20	.15	.08	155	William W. Hinchman	.10	.08	.04
65	John J. McGraw	.20	.15	.08	156	James R. Shawkey	.10	.08	.04
66	George H. Sisler	.20	.15	.08	157	Walter C. Pipp	.10	.08	.04
67	Vernon L. Gomez	.20	.15	.08	158	George J. Burns	.10	.08	.04
68	Joseph I. Judge	.20	.15	.08	159	Robert H. Veach	.10	.08	.04
69	Thomas J. Thevenow	.10	.08	.04	160	Harold H. Chase	.10	.08	.04
70	Charles M. Gelbert	.10	.08	.04	161	Thomas L. Hughes	.10	.08	.04
71	Minter C. Hayes	.10	.08	.04	162	Derrill B. Pratt	.10	.08	.04
72	Robert R. Fothergill	.10	.08	.04	163	Henry K. Groh	.10	.08	.04
73	Adam A. Comorosky	.10	.08	.04	164	Zachariah D. Wheat	.10	.08	.04
74	Earl S. Smith	.10	.08	.04	165	Francis J. O'Doul	.10	.08	.04
75	Samuel D. Gray	.10	.08	.04	166	William E. Kamm	.10	.08	.04
76	Peter W. Appleton	.10	.08	.04	167	Paul G. Waner	.10	.08	.04
77	Eugene Moore Jr.	.10	.08	.04	168	Fred C. Snodgrass	.10	.08	.04
78	Arndt L. Jorgens	.10	.08	.04	169	Floyd C. Herman	.10	.08	.04
79	William H. Knickerbocker	.10	.08	.04	170	Albert H. Bridwell	.10	.08	.04
80	Carl N. Reynolds	.10	.08	.04	171	John T. Meyers	.10	.08	.04
81	Oscar D. Melillo	.10	.08	.04	172	John B. Lobert	.10	.08	.04
82	John H. Burnett	.10	.08	.04	173	Raymond B. Bressler	.10	.08	.04
83	Alvin J. Powell	.10	.08	.04	174	Samuel P. Jones	.10	.08	.04
84	John J. Murphy	.10	.08	.04	175	Robert A. O'Farrell	.10	.08	.04
85	Leroy E. Parmelee	.10	.08	.04	176	George Toporcer	.10	.08	.04
86	James A. Ripple	.10	.08	.04	177	George E. McNeely	.10	.08	.04
87	Gerald H. Walker	.10	.08	.04	178	John H. Knott	.10	.08	.04
88	George L. Earnshaw	.10	.08	.04	179	Clarence F. Mueller	.10	.08	.04
89	William H. Southworth	.10	.08	.04	180	Thomas J.D. Bridges	.10	.08	.04
90	Wallace Moses	.10	.08	.04	181	Lloyd A. Brown	.10	.08	.04
91	George E. Walberg	.10	.09	.04	182	Lawrence J. Benton	.10	.08	.04
92	James J. Dykes	.10	.08	.04	183	Max F. Bishop	.10	.08	.04
93	Charles H. Root	.10	.08	.04	184	Morris Berg	.10	.08	.04

#	Name	MT	NR MT	EX
185	Ralph F. Perkins	.10	.08	.04
186	Stephen F. O'Neill	.10	.08	.04
187	Glenn C. Myatt	.10	.08	.04
188	Joseph A. Kuhel	.10	.08	.04
189	Martin J. McManus	.10	.08	.04
190	Charles F. Lucas	.10	.08	.04
191	John P. McInnis	.10	.08	.04
192	Edmund J. Miller	.10	.08	.04
193	James L. Sewell	.10	.08	.04
194	William H. Sherdel	.10	.08	.04
195	Harold J. Rhyne	.10	.08	.04
196	Guy T. Bush	.10	.08	.04
197	Ervin Fox	.10	.08	.04
198	Wesley C. Ferrell	.10	.08	.04
199	Roy C. Johnson	.10	.08	.04
200	William Wambsganss	.10	.08	.04
201	George H. Burns	.10	.08	.04
202	Clarence E. Mitchell	.10	.08	.04
203	Cornelius Ball	.10	.08	.04
204	John H. Neun	.10	.08	.04
205	Homer W. Summa	.10	.08	.04
206	Ernest K. Padgett	.10	.08	.04
207	Walter H. Holke	.10	.08	.04
208	Forrest G. Wright	.10	.08	.04
209	Henry M. Gowdy	.10	.08	.04
210	James W. Taylor	.10	.08	.04
211	Benjamin C. Cantwell	.10	.08	.04
212	Joseph F. Demaree	.10	.08	.04
213	Samuel P. Derringer	.10	.08	.04
214	William A. Hallahan	.10	.08	.04
215	Daniel K. MacFayden	.10	.08	.04
216	Harry F. Rice	.10	.08	.04
217	Robert Eldridge Smith	.10	.08	.04
218	Jackson R. Stephenson	.10	.08	.04
219	Perce L. Malone	.10	.08	.04
220	Henry B. Tate	.10	.08	.04
221	Joseph F. Vosmik	.10	.08	.04
222	George A. Watkins	.10	.08	.04
223	James Wilson	.10	.08	.04
224	George E. Uhle	.10	.08	.04
225	Melvin T. Ott	.10	.08	.04
226	Nicholas Altrock	.10	.08	.04
227	Charles H. Ruffing	.10	.08	.04
228	Joseph V.L. Krakauskas	.10	.08	.04
229	Walter A. Berger	.10	.08	.04
230	Norman L. Newsom	.10	.08	.04
231	Lonnie Warneke	.10	.08	.04
232	Frank E. Snyder	.10	.08	.04
233	Myril O. Hoag	.10	.08	.04
234	Baldomero M. Almada	.10	.08	.04
235	Ivy B. Wingo	.10	.08	.04
236	James P. Austin	.10	.08	.04
237	Henry J. Bonura	.10	.08	.04
238	Russell G. Wrightstone	.10	.08	.04
239	Alfred C. Todd	.10	.08	.04
240	Harold B. Warstler	.10	.08	.04
241	Samuel F. West	.10	.08	.04
242	Arthur C. Reinhart	.10	.08	.04
243	Walter C. Stewart	.10	.08	.04
244	John B. Gooch	.10	.08	.04
245	Eugene F. Hargrave	.10	.08	.04
246	George W. Harper	.10	.08	.04
247	George W. Connally	.10	.08	.04
248	Edgar G. Braxton	.10	.08	.04
249	Walter H. Schang	.10	.08	.04
250	Tyrus R. Cobb	.50	.40	.20
251	Rogers Hornsby	.10	.08	.04
252	Richard W. Marquard	.10	.08	.04
253	Carl O. Hubbell	.10	.08	.04
254	Joe Wood	.10	.08	.04
255	Robert M. Grove	.10	.08	.04
256	Lynwood T. Rowe	.10	.08	.04
257	Alvin F. Crowder	.10	.08	.04
258	Walter P. Johnson	.10	.08	.04
259	Charles J. Hafey	.10	.08	.04
260	Frederick L. Fitzsimmons	.10	.08	.04
261	William E. Webb	.10	.08	.04
262	Earle B. Combs	.10	.08	.04
263	Edward J. Konetchy	.10	.08	.04
264	Taylor L. Douthit	.10	.08	.04
265	Lloyd J. Waner	.10	.08	.04
266	Gordon S. Cochrane	.10	.08	.04
267	John O. Wilson	.10	.08	.04
268	Harold J. Traynor	.10	.08	.04
269	Virgil L. Davis	.10	.08	.04
270	Henry E. Manush	.10	.08	.04
271	Michael F. Higgins	.10	.08	.04
272	Adrian Joss	.10	.08	.04
273	Edward Augustine Walsh	.10	.08	.04
274	Johnny L.R. Martin	.10	.08	.04
275	Joseph W. Sewell	.10	.08	.04
276	Hubert B. Leonard	.10	.08	.04
277	Clifford C. Cravath	.10	.08	.04
278	Oral C. Hildebrand	.10	.08	.04
279	Remy P. Kremer	.10	.08	.04
280	Frank A. Pytlak	.10	.08	.04
281	Samuel D. Byrd	.10	.08	.04
282	Curtis B. Davis	.10	.08	.04
283	Lewis A. Fonseca	.10	.08	.04
284	Herold D. Ruel	.10	.08	.04
285	Julius J. Solters	.10	.08	.04
286	Fred W. Schulte	.10	.08	.04
287	John P. Quinn	.10	.08	.04
288	Arthur C. Whitney	.10	.08	.04
289	Jonathon T. Stone	.10	.08	.04
290	Hugh M. Critz	.10	.08	.04
291	Ira J. Flagstead	.10	.08	.04
292	George F. Grantham	.10	.08	.04
293	Samuel D. Hale	.10	.08	.04
294	James F. Hogan	.10	.08	.04
295	Oswald L. Bluege	.10	.08	.04
296	Debs Garms	.10	.08	.04
297	Augistaf B. Friberg	.10	.08	.04
298	Edward A. Brandt	.10	.08	.04
299	Ralston B. Hemsley	.10	.08	.04
300	Charles H. Klein	.10	.08	.04
301	Morton C. Cooper	.10	.08	.04
302	James L. Bottomley	.10	.08	.04
303	James E. Foxx	.10	.08	.04
304	Frank Schulte	.10	.08	.04
305	Frank F. Frisch	.10	.08	.04
306	Frank A. McCormick	.10	.08	.04
307	Jacob E. Daubert	.10	.08	.04
308	Roger T. Peckinpaugh	.10	.08	.04
309	George H. Burns	.10	.08	.04
310	Louis H. Gehrig	.40	.30	.15
311	Aloysius H. Simmons	.10	.08	.04
312	Edward T. Collins	.10	.08	.04
313	Charles L. Hartnett	.10	.08	.04
314	Joseph E. Cronin	.10	.08	.04
315	Paul G. Waner	.10	.08	.04
316	Robert A. O'Farrell	.10	.08	.04
317	Lawrence J. Doyle	.10	.08	.04
318	Lynford H. Lary	.10	.08	.04
319	Frank S. May	.10	.08	.04
320	Roy H. Spencer	.10	.08	.04
321	Samuel R. Coffman	.10	.08	.04
322	Peter J. Donohue	.10	.08	.04
323	George W. Haas	.10	.08	.04
324	Edward S. Farrell	.10	.08	.04
325	Charles F. Rhem	.10	.08	.04
326	Frederick Marberry	.10	.08	.04
327	Charles Martin Conlon	.10	.08	.04
328	Checklist Cards	.10	.08	.04
329	Checklist Cards	.10	.08	.04
330	Checklist Cards	.10	.08	.04
331	Christopher Mathewson	.20	.15	.08
332	George L. Wiltse	.10	.08	.04
333	George N. Rucker	.10	.08	.04
334	Leon K. Ames	.10	.08	.04
335	Charles A. Bender	.15	.11	.06
336	Joe Wood	.10	.08	.04
337	Edward Augustine Walsh	.10	.08	.04
338	George J. Mullin	.10	.08	.04
339	Earl A. Hamilton	.10	.08	.04
340	Charles M Tesreau	.10	.08	.04
341	James Scott	.10	.08	.04
342	Richard W. Marquard	.10	.08	.04
343	Claude R. Hendrix	.10	.08	.04
344	James S. Lavender	.10	.08	.04
345	Leslie A. Bush	.10	.08	.04
346	Hubert B. Leonard	.10	.08	.04
347	Fred A. Toney	.10	.08	.04
348	James L. Vaughn	.10	.08	.04
349	Ernest G. Koob	.10	.08	.04
350	Robert Groom	.10	.08	.04
351	Ernest G. Shore	.10	.08	.04
352	Horace O. Eller	.10	.08	.04
353	Walter P. Johnson	.20	.15	.08
354	Charles C. Robertson	.10	.08	.04
355	Jesse L. Barnes	.10	.08	.04
356	Samuel P. Jones	.10	.08	.04
357	Howard J. Ehmke	.10	.08	.04
358	Jesse J. Haines	.10	.08	.04
359	Theodore A. Lyons	.10	.08	.04
360	Carl O. Hubbell	.10	.08	.04
361	Wesley C. Ferrell	.10	.08	.04
362	Robert J. Burke	.10	.08	.04
363	Paul D. Dean	.10	.08	.04
364	Norman L. Newsom	.10	.08	.04
365	Lloyd V. Kennedy	.10	.08	.04
366	William J. Dietrich	.10	.08	.04

#	Name	MT	NR MT	EX	#	Name	MT	NR MT	EX
367	John S. Vander Meer	.10	.08	.04	458	Absalom H. Wingo	.10	.08	.04
368	John S. Vander Meer	.10	.08	.04	459	Roger P. Bresnahan	.10	.08	.04
369	Montgomery M. Pearson	.10	.08	.04	460	William J. Klem	.10	.08	.04
370	Robert W.A. Feller	.15	.11	.06	461	Charles L. Gehringer	.15	.11	.06
371	Lonnie Warneke	.10	.08	.04	462	Stanley A. Coveleski	.10	.08	.04
372	James A. Tobin	.10	.08	.04	463	Edward S. Plank	.10	.08	.04
373	Earl A. Moore	.10	.08	.04	464	Clark C.F. Griffith	.10	.08	.04
374	William H. Dineen	.10	.08	.04	465	Herbert J. Pennock	.10	.08	.04
375	Malcolm W. Eason	.10	.08	.04	466	Earle B. Combs	.10	.08	.04
376	George A. Mogridge	.10	.08	.04	467	Robert P. Doerr	.10	.08	.04
377	Clarence A. Vance	.10	.08	.04	468	Waite C. Hoyt	.10	.08	.04
378	James O. Carleton	.10	.08	.04	469	Thomas H. Connolly	.10	.08	.04
379	Clyde M. Shoun	.10	.08	.04	470	Harry B. Hooper	.10	.08	.04
380	Franklin W. Hayes	.10	.08	.04	471	Richard B. Ferrell	.10	.08	.04
381	Benjamin R. Frey	.10	.08	.04	472	William G. Evans	.10	.08	.04
382	Henry W. Johnson	.10	.08	.04	473	William J. Herman	.10	.08	.04
383	Ralph Kress	.10	.08	.04	474	William M. Dickey	.10	.08	.04
384	John T. Allen	.10	.08	.04	475	Lucius B. Appling	.10	.08	.04
385	Harold A. Trosky Sr.	.10	.08	.04	476	Ralph A. Pinelli	.10	.08	.04
386	Eugene E. Robertson	.10	.08	.04	477	Donald E. McNair	.10	.08	.04
387	Lemuel F. Young	.10	.08	.04	478	John F. Blake	.10	.08	.04
388	George A. Selkirk	.10	.08	.04	479	Valentine J. Picinich	.10	.08	.04
389	Edwin L. Wells	.10	.08	.04	480	Fred A. Heimach	.10	.08	.04
390	James D. Weaver	.10	.08	.04	481	John G. Graney	.10	.08	.04
391	George H. McQuinn	.10	.08	.04	482	Ewell A. Russell	.10	.08	.04
392	John B. Lobert	.10	.08	.04	483	Urban C. Faber	.10	.08	.04
393	Ernest E. Swanson	.10	.08	.04	484	Benjamin M. Kauff	.10	.08	.04
394	Ernest A. Nevers	.10	.08	.04	485	Clarence L. Rowland	.10	.08	.04
395	James J. Levey	.10	.08	.04	486	Robert H. Veach	.10	.08	.04
396	Hugo F. Bezdek	.10	.08	.04	487	James C. Bagby	.10	.08	.04
397	Walter E. French	.10	.08	.04	488	William D. Perritt	.10	.08	.04
398	Charles F. Berry	.10	.08	.04	489	Charles L. Herzog	.10	.08	.04
399	Franklin T. Grube	.10	.08	.04	490	Arthur Fletcher	.10	.08	.04
400	Charles W. Dressen	.10	.08	.04	491	Walter H. Holke	.10	.08	.04
401	Alfred E. Neale	.10	.08	.04	492	Arthur N. Nehr	.10	.08	.04
402	Henry A. Vick	.10	.08	.04	493	Lafayette F. Thompson	.10	.08	.04
403	James F. Thorpe	.50	.40	.20	494	James D. Welsh	.10	.08	.04
404	Walter J. Gilbert	.10	.08	.04	495	Oscar J. Vitt	.10	.08	.04
405	John L. Urban	.10	.08	.04	496	Owen T. Carroll	.10	.08	.04
406	Everett V. Purdy	.10	.08	.04	497	James K. O'Dea	.10	.08	.04
407	Albert O. Wright	.10	.08	.04	498	Fredrick M. Frankhouse	.10	.08	.04
408	William M. Urbanski	.10	.08	.04	499	Jewel W. Ens	.10	.08	.04
409	Charles W. Fischer	.10	.08	.04	500	Morris Arnovich	.10	.08	.04
410	John R. Warner	.10	.08	.04	501	Walter Gerber	.10	.08	.04
411	Chalmer W. Cissell	.10	.08	.04	502	George W. Davis	.10	.08	.04
412	Mervin D.J. Shea	.10	.08	.04	503	Charles S. Myer	.10	.08	.04
413	Adolfo Luque	.10	.08	.04	504	Samuel A. Leslie	.10	.08	.04
414	John L. Bassler	.10	.08	.04	505	William C. Bolton	.10	.08	.04
415	Arvel O. Hale	.10	.08	.04	506	Fred Walker	.10	.08	.04
416	Lawrence R. French	.10	.08	.04	507	John W. Smith	.10	.08	.04
417	William C. Walker	.10	.08	.04	508	Irving D. Hadley	.10	.08	.04
418	Allen L. Cooke	.10	.08	.04	509	Clyde E. Crouse	.10	.08	.04
419	Philip J. Todt	.10	.08	.04	510	Joseph C. Glenn	.10	.08	.04
420	Ivy P. Andrews	.10	.08	.04	511	Clyde E. Kimsey	.10	.08	.04
421	William J. Herman	.10	.08	.04	512	Louis K. Finney	.10	.08	.04
422	Tristram E. Speaker	.15	.11	.06	513	Alfred V. Lawson	.10	.08	.04
423	Aloysius H. Simmons	.10	.08	.04	514	Charles P. Fullis	.10	.08	.04
424	Lewis R. Wilson	.10	.08	.04	515	Earl H. Sheely	.10	.08	.04
425	Tyrus R. Cobb	.40	.30	.15	516	George Gibson	.10	.08	.04
426	George H. Ruth	.50	.40	.20	517	John J. Broaca	.10	.08	.04
427	Ernest N. Lombardi	.10	.08	.04	518	Bibb A. Falk	.10	.08	.04
428	Jay H. Dean	.10	.08	.04	519	Frank O. Hurst	.10	.08	.04
429	Lloyd J. Waner	.10	.08	.04	520	Grover A. Hartley	.10	.08	.04
430	Henry B. Greenberg	.10	.08	.04	521	Donald H. Heffner	.10	.08	.04
431	Robert M. Grove	.10	.08	.04	522	Harvey L. Hendrick	.10	.08	.04
432	Gordon S. Cochrane	.10	.08	.04	523	Allen S. Sothoron	.10	.08	.04
433	Burleigh A. Grimes	.10	.08	.04	524	Anthony F. Piet	.10	.08	.04
434	Harold J. Traynor	.10	.08	.04	525	Tyrus R. Cobb	.40	.30	.15
435	John R. Mize	.10	.08	.04	526	James E. Foxx	.10	.08	.04
436	Edgar C. Rice	.10	.08	.04	527	Rogers Hornsby	.10	.08	.04
437	Leon A. Goslin	.10	.08	.04	528	Napoleon LaJoie	.10	.08	.04
438	Charles H. Klein	.10	.08	.04	529	Louis H. Gehrig	.40	.30	.15
439	Cornelius Mack	.10	.08	.04	530	Henry Zimmerman	.10	.08	.04
440	James L. Bottomley	.10	.08	.04	531	Charles H. Klein	.10	.08	.04
441	Jackson R. Stephenson	.10	.08	.04	532	Hugh Duffy	.10	.08	.04
442	Kenneth R. Williams	.10	.08	.04	533	Robert M. Grove	.10	.08	.04
443	Charles B. Adams	.10	.08	.04	534	Grover C. Alexander	.10	.08	.04
444	Joseph J. Jackson	.50	.40	.20	535	Amos W. Rusie	.10	.08	.04
445	Harold Newhouser	.10	.08	.04	536	Vernon L. Gomez	.10	.08	.04
446	Wesley C. Ferrell	.10	.08	.04	537	William H. Walters	.10	.08	.04
447	Francis J. O'Doul	.10	.08	.04	538	Urban J. Hodapp	.10	.08	.04
448	Walter H. Schang	.10	.08	.04	539	Bruce D. Campbell	.10	.08	.04
449	Sherwood R. Magee	.10	.08	.04	540	Horace M. Lisenbee	.10	.08	.04
450	Michael J. Donlin	.10	.08	.04	541	John F. Fournier	.10	.08	.04
451	Roger M. Cramer	.10	.08	.04	542	James R. Tabor	.10	.08	.04
452	Richard W. Bartell	.10	.08	.04	543	John H. Burnett	.10	.08	.04
453	Earle T. Mack	.10	.08	.04	544	Roy A. Hartzell	.10	.08	.04
454	Walter G. Brown	.10	.08	.04	545	Walter P. Gautreau	.10	.08	.04
455	John A. Heving	.10	.08	.04	546	Emil O. Yde	.10	.08	.04
456	Percy L. Jones	.10	.08	.04	547	Robert L. Johnson	.10	.08	.04
457	Theodore Blankenship	.10	.08	.04	548	Joseph J. Hauser	.10	.08	.04

#	Name	MT	NR MT	EX	#	Name	MT	NR MT	EX
549	Edward M. Reulbach	.10	.08	.04	640	Lonnie Warneke	.10	.08	.04
550	Baldomero M. Almada	.10	.08	.04	641	Terry B. Moore	.10	.08	.04
551	Gordon S. Cochrane	.10	.08	.04	642	Enos B. Slaughter	.10	.08	.04
552	Carl O. Hubbell	.10	.08	.04	643	Clarence F. Mueller	.10	.08	.04
553	Charles L. Gehringer	.15	.11	.06	644	George Toporcer	.10	.08	.04
554	Aloysius H. Simmons	.10	.08	.04	645	James L. Bottomely	.10	.08	.04
555	Mordecai P.C. Brown	.10	.08	.04	646	Francis R. Blades	.10	.08	.04
556	Hugh A. Jennings	.10	.08	.04	647	Jesse J. Haines	.10	.08	.04
557	Norman A. Elberfeld	.10	.08	.04	648	Andrew A. High	.10	.08	.04
558	Charles D. Stengel	.15	.11	.06	649	Miller J. Huggins	.10	.08	.04
559	Alexander Schacht	.10	.08	.04	650	Ernesto R. Orsatti	.10	.08	.04
560	James E. Foxx	.10	.08	.04	651	Lester R. Bell	.10	.08	.04
561	George L. Kelly	.10	.08	.04	652	Charles E. Street	.10	.08	.04
562	Lloyd J. Waner	.10	.08	.04	653	Walter H. Roettger	.10	.08	.04
563	Paul G. Waner	.10	.08	.04	654	Sylvester W. Johnson	.10	.08	.04
564	Walter P. Johnson	.15	.11	.06	655	Miguel A. Gonzalez	.10	.08	.04
565	John Franklin Baker	.10	.08	.04	656	James A. Collins	.10	.08	.04
566	Roy J. Hughes	.10	.08	.04	657	Charles J. Hafey	.10	.08	.04
567	Lewis S. Riggs	.10	.08	.04	658	Checklist Cards	.10	.08	.04
568	John H. Whitehead	.10	.08	.04	659	Checklist Cards	.10	.08	.04
569	Elam R. Vangilder	.10	.08	.04	660	Checklist Cards	.10	.08	.04
570	William A. Zitzmann	.10	.08	.04	661	William H. Terry	.10	.08	.04
571	Walter J. Schmidt	.10	.08	.04	662	Vernon L. Gomez	.10	.08	.04
572	John A. Tavener	.10	.08	.04	663	George H. Ruth	.50	.40	.20
573	Joseph E. Genewich	.10	.08	.04	664	Frank F. Frisch	.10	.08	.04
574	John A. Marcum	.10	.08	.04	665	Carl O. Hubbell	.10	.08	.04
575	Fred Hofmann	.10	.08	.04	666	Aloysius H. Simmons	.10	.08	.04
576	Robert A. Rolfe	.10	.08	.04	667	Charles L. Gehringer	.15	.11	.06
577	Victor G. Sorrell	.10	.08	.04	668	Howard E. Averill Sr.	.10	.08	.04
578	Floyd J. Scott	.10	.08	.04	669	Robert M. Grove	.10	.08	.04
579	Alphonse Thomas	.10	.08	.04	670	Harold J. Traynor	.10	.08	.04
580	Alfred J. Smith	.10	.08	.04	671	Charles H. Klein	.10	.08	.04
581	Walter J. Henline	.10	.08	.04	672	Paul G. Waner	.10	.08	.04
582	Edward T. Collins	.10	.08	.04	673	Louis H. Gehrig	.40	.30	.15
583	Earle B. Combs	.10	.08	.04	674	Richard B. Ferrell	.10	.08	.04
584	John J. McGraw	.10	.08	.04	675	Charles L. Hartnett	.10	.08	.04
585	Lewis R. Wilson	.10	.08	.04	676	Joseph E. Cronin	.10	.08	.04
586	Charles L. Hartnett	.10	.08	.04	677	Charles J. Hafey	.10	.08	.04
587	Hazen S. Cuyler	.10	.08	.04	678	James J. Dykes	.10	.08	.04
588	William H. Terry	.10	.08	.04	679	Samuel F. West	.10	.08	.04
589	Joseph V. McCarthy	.10	.08	.04	680	Johnny L.R. Martin	.10	.08	.04
590	Henry B. Greenberg	.10	.08	.04	681	Francis J. O'Doul	.10	.08	.04
591	Tristram E. Speaker	.15	.11	.06	682	Alvin F. Crowder	.10	.08	.04
592	William B. McKechnie	.10	.08	.04	683	James Wilson	.10	.08	.04
593	Stanley R. Harris	.10	.08	.04	684	Richard W. Bartell	.10	.08	.04
594	Herbert J. Pennock	.10	.08	.04	685	William A. Hallahan	.10	.08	.04
595	George H. Sisler	.10	.08	.04	686	Walter A. Berger	.10	.08	.04
596	Fred C. Lindstrom	.10	.08	.04	687	Lonnie Warneke	.10	.08	.04
597	Howard E. Averill Sr.	.10	.08	.04	688	William B. Chapman	.10	.08	.04
598	David J. Bancroft	.10	.08	.04	689	Elwood G. English	.10	.08	.04
599	Cornelius Mack	.10	.08	.04	690	James H. Reese	.10	.08	.04
600	Joseph E. Cronin	.10	.08	.04	691	Roscoe A. Holm	.10	.08	.04
601	Kenneth L. Ash	.10	.08	.04	692	Charles D. Jamieson	.10	.08	.04
602	Alfred R. Spohrer	.10	.08	.04	693	Jonathan T.W. Zachary	.10	.08	.04
603	Lee R. Mahaffey	.10	.08	.04	694	John C. Ryan	.10	.08	.04
604	James F. O'Rourke	.10	.08	.04	695	Earl J. Adams	.10	.08	.04
605	Ulysses S.G. Stoner	.10	.08	.04	696	William E. Hunnefield	.10	.08	.04
606	Frank H. Gabler	.10	.08	.04	697	Henry L. Meadows	.10	.08	.04
607	Thomas F. Padden	.10	.08	.04	698	Thomas F. Carey	.10	.08	.04
608	Charles A. Shires	.10	.08	.04	699	John W. Rawlings	.10	.08	.04
609	Sherrod M. Smith	.10	.08	.04	700	Kenneth E. Holloway	.10	.08	.04
610	Philip Weintraub	.10	.08	.04	701	Lance C. Richbourg	.10	.08	.04
611	Russell Van Atta	.10	.08	.04	702	Raymond L. Fisher	.10	.08	.04
612	Joyner C. White	.10	.08	.04	703	Edward Augustine Walsh	.10	.08	.04
613	Clifford G. Melton	.10	.08	.04	704	Richard Rudolph	.10	.08	.04
614	James J. Ring	.10	.08	.04	705	Raymond B. Caldwell	.10	.08	.04
615	John H. Sand	.10	.08	.04	706	Burleigh A. Grimes	.10	.08	.04
616	David D. Alexander	.10	.08	.04	707	Stanley A. Coveleski	.10	.08	.04
617	Kent Greenfield	.10	.08	.04	708	George A. Hildebrand	.10	.08	.04
618	Edwin H. Dyer	.10	.08	.04	709	John P. Quinn	.10	.08	.04
619	William H. Sherdel	.10	.08	.04	710	Urban C. Faber	.10	.08	.04
620	Hubert M. Lanier	.10	.08	.04	711	Urban J. Shocker	.10	.08	.04
621	Robert A. O'Farrell	.10	.08	.04	712	Hubert B. Leonard	.10	.08	.04
622	Rogers Hornsby	.10	.08	.04	713	Louis L. Koupal	.10	.08	.04
623	William A. Beckman	.10	.08	.04	714	James C. Wasdell	.10	.08	.04
624	Morton C. Cooper	.10	.08	.04	715	John H. Lindell	.10	.08	.04
625	William P. Delancey	.10	.08	.04	716	Don W. Padgett	.10	.08	.04
626	Martin W. Marion	.10	.08	.04	717	Nelson T. Potter	.10	.08	.04
627	William H. Southworth	.10	.08	.04	718	Lynwood T. Rowe	.10	.08	.04
628	John R. Mize	.10	.08	.04	719	David C. Danforth	.10	.08	.04
629	Joseph M. Medwick	.10	.08	.04	720	Claude W. Passeau	.10	.08	.04
630	Grover C. Alexander	.10	.08	.04	721	Harry L. Kelley	.10	.08	.04
631	Paul D. Dean	.10	.08	.04	722	John T. Allen	.10	.08	.04
632	Herman S. Bell	.10	.08	.04	723	Thomas J.D. Bridges	.10	.08	.04
633	William W. Cooper	.10	.08	.04	724	William C. Lee	.10	.08	.04
634	Frank F. Frisch	.10	.08	.04	725	Fredrick M. Frankhouse	.10	.08	.04
635	Jay H. Dean	.10	.08	.04	726	John J. McCarthy	.10	.08	.04
636	Donald J. Gutteridge	.10	.08	.04	727	Glen D. Russell	.10	.08	.04
637	Johnny L.R. Martin	.10	.08	.04	728	Emory E. Rigney	.10	.08	.04
638	Edward J. Konetchy	.10	.08	.04	729	Howard S. Shanks	.10	.08	.04
639	William A. Hallahan	.10	.08	.04	730	Lucius B. Appling	.10	.08	.04

No.	Name	MT	NR MT	EX	No.	Name	MT	NR MT	EX
731	William J. Byron	.10	.08	.04	822	Ted Lyons	.10	.08	.04
732	Earle B. Combs	.10	.08	.04	823	Joe McCarthy	.10	.08	.04
733	Henry B. Greenberg	.15	.11	.06	824	Connie Mack	.10	.08	.04
734	Walter W. Beck	.10	.08	.04	825	George Gibson	.10	.08	.04
735	Hollis J. Thurston	.10	.08	.04	826	Steve O'Neill	.10	.08	.04
736	Lewis R. Wilson	.10	.08	.04	827	Tristram E. Speaker	.15	.11	.06
737	William A. McGowan	.10	.08	.04	828	William F. Carrigan	.10	.08	.04
738	Henry J. Bonura	.10	.08	.04	829	Charles D. Stengel	.10	.08	.04
739	Thomas C. Baker	.10	.08	.04	830	Miller J. Huggins	.10	.08	.04
740	William C. Jacobson	.10	.08	.04	831	William B. McKechnie	.10	.08	.04
741	Hazen S. Cuyler	.10	.08	.04	832	Charles W. Dressen	.10	.08	.04
742	George F. Blaeholder	.10	.08	.04	833	Charles E. Street	.10	.08	.04
743	Wilson D. Miles	.10	.08	.04	834	Melvin T. Ott	.10	.08	.04
744	Lee E. Handley	.10	.08	.04	835	Frank F. Frisch	.10	.08	.04
745	John F. Collins	.10	.08	.04	836	George H. Sisler	.10	.08	.04
746	Wilfred P. Ryan	.10	.08	.04	837	Napoleon LaJoie	.10	.08	.04
747	Aaron L. Ward	.10	.08	.04	838	Tyrus R. Cobb	.40	.30	.15
748	Montgomery M. Pearson	.10	.08	.04	839	William H. Southworth	.10	.08	.04
749	Jacob W. Early	.10	.08	.04	840	Clark C.F. Griffith	.10	.08	.04
750	William F. Atwood	.10	.08	.04	841	William H. Terry	.10	.08	.04
751	Mark A. Koenig	.10	.08	.04	842	Rogers Hornsby	.10	.08	.04
752	John A. Hassett	.10	.08	.04	843	Joseph E. Cronin	.10	.08	.04
753	David J. Jones	.10	.08	.04	844	Alfonso R. Lopez	.10	.08	.04
754	John P. Wagner	.10	.08	.04	845	Stanley R. Harris	.10	.08	.04
755	William M. Dickey	.10	.08	.04	846	Wilbert Robinson	.10	.08	.04
756	Albert M. Butcher	.10	.08	.04	847	Hugh A. Jennings	.10	.08	.04
757	Waite C. Hoyt	.10	.08	.04	848	James J. Dykes	.10	.08	.04
758	Walter P. Johnson	.20	.15	.08	849	Roy J. Cullenbine	.10	.08	.04
759	Howard J. Ehmke	.10	.08	.04	850	Graham E. Moore	.10	.08	.04
760	Norman L. Newsom	.10	.08	.04	851	John H. Rothrock	.10	.08	.04
761	Anthony M. Lazzeri	.10	.08	.04	852	William H. Lamar	.10	.08	.04
762	Anthony M. Lazzeri	.10	.08	.04	853	Monte Weaver	.10	.08	.04
763	Spurgeon F. Chandler	.10	.08	.04	854	Ival R. Goodman	.10	.08	.04
764	Walter K. Higbe	.10	.08	.04	855	Henry L. Severeid	.10	.08	.04
765	Paul R. Richards	.10	.08	.04	856	Fred G. Haney	.10	.08	.04
766	Rogers Hornsby	.10	.08	.04	857	Joseph B. Shaute	.10	.08	.04
767	Joseph F. Vosmik	.10	.08	.04	858	Smead P. Jolley	.10	.08	.04
768	Jesse J. Haines	.10	.08	.04	859	Edwin D. Williams	.10	.08	.04
769	William H. Walters	.10	.08	.04	860	Bernard O. Bengough	.10	.08	.04
770	Thomas D. Henrich	.10	.08	.04	861	Richard B. Ferrell	.10	.08	.04
771	James F. Thorpe	.50	.40	.20	862	Robert A. O'Farrell	.10	.08	.04
772	Euel W. Moore	.50	.40	.20	863	Virgil L. Davis	.10	.08	.04
773	Rudolph P. York	.50	.40	.20	864	Franklin W. Hayes	.10	.08	.04
774	Charles A. Bender	.50	.40	.20	865	Herold D. Ruel	.10	.08	.04
775	John T. Meyers	.50	.40	.20	866	Gordon S. Cochrane	.10	.08	.04
776	Robert L. Johnson	.50	.40	.20	867	John Kling	.10	.08	.04
777	Roy C. Johnson	.50	.40	.20	868	Ivy B. Wingo	.10	.08	.04
778	Richard T. Porter	.50	.40	.20	869	William M. Dickey	.10	.08	.04
779	Ethan N. Allen	.50	.40	.20	870	Frank E. Snyder	.10	.08	.04
780	Harry F. Sallee	.50	.40	.20	871	Roger P. Bresnahan	.10	.08	.04
781	Roy C. Bell	.50	.40	.20	872	Walter H. Schang	.10	.08	.04
782	Arnold J. Statz	.50	.40	.20	873	Alfonso R. Lopez	.10	.08	.04
783	Frank J. Henry	.50	.40	.20	874	James Wilson	.10	.08	.04
784	Charles L. Woodall	.50	.40	.20	875	Valentine J. Picinich	.10	.08	.04
785	Philip E. Collins	.50	.40	.20	876	Stephen F. O'Neill	.10	.08	.04
786	Joseph W. Sewell	.50	.40	.20	877	Ernest N. Lombardi	.10	.08	.04
787	William J. Herman	.50	.40	.20	878	John L. Bassler	.10	.08	.04
788	Rueben H. Oldring	.50	.40	.20	879	Raymond W. Schalk	.10	.08	.04
789	William H. Walker	.50	.40	.20	880	Charles L. Hartnett	.10	.08	.04
790	Joseph C. Schultz	.50	.40	.20	881	Bruce D. Campbell	.10	.08	.04
791	Fred E. Maguire	.50	.40	.20	882	Charles H. Ruffing	.10	.08	.04
792	Claude W. Willoughby	.50	.40	.20	883	Mordecai P.C. Brown	.10	.08	.04
793	James A. Ferguson	.50	.40	.20	884	Peter J. Archer	.10	.08	.04
794	John D. Morrison	.50	.40	.20	885	David E. Keefe	.10	.08	.04
795	Tristram E. Speaker	.15	.11	.06	886	Nathan H. Andrews	.10	.08	.04
796	Tyrus R. Cobb	.40	.30	.15	887	Edgar C. Rice	.10	.08	.04
797	Max Carey	.10	.08	.04	888	George H. Ruth	.50	.40	.20
798	George H. Sisler	.10	.08	.04	889	Charles J. Hafey	.10	.08	.04
799	Charles J. Hollocher	.10	.08	.04	890	Oscar D. Melillo	.10	.08	.04
800	James L. Vaughn	.10	.08	.04	891	Joe Wood	.10	.08	.04
801	Samuel P. Jones	.10	.08	.04	892	John J. Evers	.10	.08	.04
802	Harry B. Hooper	.10	.08	.04	893	George Toporcer	.10	.08	.04
803	Clifford C. Cravath	.10	.08	.04	894	Myril O. Hoag	.10	.08	.04
804	Walter P. Johnson	.15	.11	.06	895	Robert G. Weiland	.10	.08	.04
805	Jacob E. Daubert	.10	.08	.04	896	Joseph A. Marty	.10	.08	.04
806	Jesse C. Milan	.10	.08	.04	897	Sherwood R. Magee	.10	.08	.04
807	Hugh A. McQuillan	.10	.08	.04	898	Daniel T. Taylor	.10	.08	.04
808	George F. Brickell	.10	.08	.04	899	William E. Kamm	.10	.08	.04
809	Joseph V. Stripp	.10	.08	.04	900	Samuel J.T. Sheckard	.10	.08	.04
810	Urban J. Hodapp	.10	.08	.04	901	Sylvester W. Johnson	.10	.08	.04
811	John L. Vergez	.10	.08	.04	902	Stephen R. Sundra	.10	.08	.04
812	Linus R. Frey	.10	.08	.04	903	Roger M. Cramer	.10	.08	.04
813	William W. Regan	.10	.08	.04	904	Hubert S. Pruett	.10	.08	.04
814	Norman R. Young	.10	.08	.04	905	Russell A. Blackburne	.10	.08	.04
815	Charles C. Robertson	.10	.08	.04	906	Eppa Rixey	.10	.08	.04
816	Walter F. Judnich	.10	.08	.04	907	Leon A. Goslin	.10	.08	.04
817	Joseph B. Tinker	.10	.08	.04	908	George L. Kelly	.10	.08	.04
818	John Evers	.10	.08	.04	909	James L. Bottomley	.10	.08	.04
819	Frank L. Chance	.10	.08	.04	910	Christopher Mathewson	.15	.11	.06
820	John J. McGraw	.10	.08	.04	911	Anthony M. Lazzeri	.10	.08	.04
821	Charles J. Grimm	.10	.08	.04	912	John A. Mostil	.10	.08	.04

		MT	NR MT	EX
913	Robert P. Doerr	.10	.08	.04
914	Walter J.V. Maranville	.10	.08	.04
915	Harry E. Heilmann	.10	.08	.04
916	Rodrick J. Wallace	.10	.08	.04
917	James E. Foxx	.10	.08	.04
918	John R. Mize	.10	.08	.04
919	John N. Bentley	.10	.08	.04
920	Alexander Schacht	.10	.08	.04
921	Parke E. Coleman	.10	.08	.04
922	George H. Paskert	.10	.08	.04
923	Horace H. Ford	.10	.08	.04
924	Randolph E. Moore	.10	.08	.04
925	Milburn J. Shoffner	.10	.08	.04
926	Richard W. Siebert	.10	.08	.04
927	Anthony C. Kaufmann	.10	.08	.04
928	Jay H. Dean	.10	.08	.04
929	Clarence A. Vance	.10	.08	.04
930	Robert M. Grove	.10	.08	.04
931	George E. Waddell	.10	.08	.04
932	Grover C. Alexander	.10	.08	.04
933	Robert W.A. Feller	.10	.08	.04
934	Walter P. Johnson	.10	.08	.04
935	Theodore A. Lyons	.10	.08	.04
936	James C. Bagby	.10	.08	.04
937	Joseph Sugden	.10	.08	.04
938	Robert E. Grace	.10	.08	.04
939	John G. Heath	.10	.08	.04
940	Kenneth R. Williams	.10	.08	.04
941	Marvin J. Owen	.10	.08	.04
942	Cyril R. Weatherly	.10	.08	.04
943	Edward C. Morgan	.10	.08	.04
944	John C. Rizzo	.10	.08	.04
945	Archie R. McKain	.10	.08	.04
946	Robert M. Garbark	.10	.08	.04
947	John B. Osborn	.10	.08	.04
948	John S. Podgajny	.10	.08	.04
949	Joseph P. Evans	.10	.08	.04
950	George A. Rensa	.10	.08	.04
951	John H. Humphries	.10	.08	.04
952	Merritt P. Cain	.10	.08	.04
953	Roy E. Hansen	.10	.08	.04
954	John A. Niggeling	.10	.08	.04
955	Harold J. Wiltse	.10	.08	.04
956	Alejandro A.A.E. Carrasquel	.10	.08	.04
957	George A. Grant	.10	.08	.04
958	Philip W. Weinert	.10	.08	.04
959	Ervin B. Brame	.10	.08	.04
960	Raymond J. Harrell	.10	.08	.04
961	Edward K. Linke	.10	.08	.04
962	Samuel B. Gibson	.10	.08	.04
963	John C. Watwood	.10	.08	.04
964	James T. Prothro	.10	.08	.04
965	Julio G. Bonetti	.10	.08	.04
966	Howard R. Mills	.10	.08	.04
967	Clarence E. Galloway	.10	.08	.04
968	Harold J. Kelleher	.10	.08	.04
969	Elon C. Hogsett	.10	.08	.04
970	Edward B. Heusser	.10	.08	.04
971	Edward J. Baecht	.10	.08	.04
972	Otto H. Saltzgaver	.10	.08	.04
973	Leroy G. Herrmann	.10	.08	.04
974	Beveric B. Bean	.10	.08	.04
975	Harry Seibold	.10	.08	.04
976	Howard V. Keen	.10	.08	.04
977	William J. Barrett	.10	.08	.04
978	Patrick H. McNulty	.10	.08	.04
979	George E. Turbeville	.10	.08	.04
980	Edward D. Phillips	.10	.08	.04
981	Garland M. Buckeye	.10	.08	.04
982	Victor P. Frasier	.10	.08	.04
983	John G. Rhodes	.10	.08	.04
984	Emile D. Barnes	.10	.08	.04
985	James C. Edwards	.10	.08	.04
986	Herschel E. Bennett	.10	.08	.04
987	Carmen P. Hill	.10	.08	.04
988	Checklist Cards	.10	.08	.04
989	Checklist Cards	.10	.08	.04
990	Checklist Cards	.10	.08	.04

1993 Color Conlon

The cards in this 23-card set were previously released in black and white in either the 1991 or 1992 regular Conlon sets. The distribution of the color cards is unique. Cards 1-12 were issued as bonus cards in Megacards accessory items. 250,000 of cards 1-12 were produced. Cards 13-20 were randomly inserted in 1993 Conlon counter and blister packs. Only 100,000 of cards 13-20 were produced. Cards 21 and 22 were only available througuhu a send-away offer and card 23 is available exclsively in the SCD Seventh Edition Baseball Card Price Guide. Only 60,000 of card number 23 are available.

		MT	NR MT	EX
	Complete Set:	50.00	37.00	20.00
	Common Player:	1.50	1.25	.60
1	Sunny Jim Bottomley	1.50	1.25	.60
2	Lefty Grove	2.00	1.50	.80
3	Lou Gehrig	3.00	2.25	1.25
4	Babe Ruth	5.00	3.75	2.00
5	Casey Stengel	2.00	1.50	.80
6	Rube Marquard	1.50	1.25	.60
7	Walter Johnson	2.00	1.50	.80
8	Lou Gehrig	3.00	2.25	1.25
9	Christy Mathewson	2.00	1.50	.80
10	Ty Cobb	3.00	2.25	1.25
11	Mel Ott	2.00	1.50	.80
12	Carl Hubbell	2.00	1.50	.80
13	Al Simmons	2.00	1.50	.80
14	Connie Mack	2.00	1.50	.80
15	Grover C. Alexander	2.00	1.50	.80
16	Jimmie Foxx	2.00	1.50	.80
17	Lloyd Waner	2.00	1.50	.80
18	Tris Speaker	3.00	2.25	1.25
19	Dizzy Dean	2.00	1.50	.80
20	Rogers Hornsby	2.00	1.50	.80
21	Shoeless Joe Jackson	4.00	3.00	1.50
22	Jim Thorpe	4.00	3.00	1.50
23	Bob Feller	5.00	3.75	2.00

1992 Megacards Babe Ruth

This 165-card set chronicles the life and times of Babe Ruth. The set was produced by Megacards and is officially entitled "The Babe Ruth Collection". The cards feature classic black and white photos with black borders and captions below the photo. The card backs feature coordinating statistics and information.

		MT	NR MT	EX
	Complete Set:	15.00	11.00	6.00
	Common Player:	.10	.08	.04
1	Career Pitching	.10	.08	.04
2	Career Batting	.10	.08	.04
3	Series Pitching	.10	.08	.04
4	Series Batting	.10	.08	.04
5	Year 1914, Minors	.10	.08	.04
6	Year 1914, Majors	.10	.08	.04
7	Year In Review 1915	.10	.08	.04
8	Year In Review 1916	.10	.08	.04
9	Year In Review 1917	.10	.08	.04
10	Year In Review 1918	.10	.08	.04
11	Year In Review 1919	.10	.08	.04
12	Year In Review 1920	.10	.08	.04
13	Year In Review 1921	.10	.08	.04
14	Year In Review 1922	.10	.08	.04
15	Year In Review 1923	.10	.08	.04
16	Year In Review 1924	.10	.08	.04

		MT	NR MT	EX			MT	NR MT	EX
17	Year In Review 1925	.10	.08	.04	108	SULTN: Hack Wilson	.10	.08	.04
18	Year In Review 1926	.10	.08	.04	109	SULTN: Pitkin	.10	.08	.04
19	Year In Review 1927	.20	.15	.08	110	SULTN: Ball In Orbit	.10	.08	.04
20	Year In Review 1928	.10	.08	.04	111	SULTN: Afraid To Kill	.10	.08	.04
21	Year In Review 1929	.10	.08	.04	112	SULTN: Wonder YRS	.10	.08	.04
22	Year In Review 1930	.10	.08	.04	113	SULTN: Opening Day	.10	.08	.04
23	Year In Review 1931	.10	.08	.04	114	SULTN: Hit/Miss Big	.10	.08	.04
24	Year In Review 1932	.10	.08	.04	115	SULTN: No Equal	.10	.08	.04
25	Year In Review 1933	.10	.08	.04	116	MAN: Childhood	.10	.08	.04
26	Year In Review 1934	.10	.08	.04	117	MAN: ST. MARY'S	.10	.08	.04
27	Year In Review 1935	.10	.08	.04	118	MAN: BR. Mathias	.10	.08	.04
28	Year In Review 1938	.10	.08	.04	119	MAN: Nicknames	.10	.08	.04
29	Babe In Retirement	.10	.08	.04	120	MAN: Wife Helen	.10	.08	.04
30	Series Year, 1915	.10	.08	.04	121	MAN: Wife Claire	.10	.08	.04
31	Series Year, 1916	.10	.08	.04	122	MAN: With Gehrig	.20	.15	.08
32	Series Year, 1918	.10	.08	.04	123	MAN: With Pennock	.10	.08	.04
33	Series Year, 1921	.10	.08	.04	124	MAN: With Huggins	.10	.08	.04
34	Series Year, 1922	.10	.08	.04	125	MAN: With Ty Cobb	.15	.11	.06
35	Series Year, 1923	.10	.08	.04	126	MAN: With Walter J	.15	.11	.06
36	Series Year, 1926	.15	.11	.06	127	MAN: Drawing Card	.10	.08	.04
37	Series Year, 1927	.15	.11	.06	128	MAN: Brainstorming	.10	.08	.04
38	Series Year, 1928	.10	.08	.04	129	MAN: Fines	.10	.08	.04
39	Series Year, 1932	.15	.11	.06	130	MAN: Injuries	.10	.08	.04
40	PIH-CR-WALKS	.10	.08	.04	131	MAN: Highest Paid	.10	.08	.04
41	PIH-CR-STRIKEOUTS	.10	.08	.04	132	MAN: To Be A MGR	.10	.08	.04
42	PIH-CR-MOST RUNS	.15	.11	.06	133	MAN: Golf	.10	.08	.04
43	PIH-CR-TOTAL BASES	.15	.11	.06	134	MAN: Babe In Movies	.10	.08	.04
44	PIH-CR-XTRA BASE HT	.10	.08	.04	135	MAN: War Efforts	.10	.08	.04
45	PIH-CR-HOME RUNS	.10	.08	.04	136	MAN: Negotiator	.10	.08	.04
46	PIH-CR-GRAND SLAMS	.10	.08	.04	137	MAN: Everyone Loved	.10	.08	.04
47	PIH-CR-HOME RUN "	.15	.11	.06	138	MAN: Children	.10	.08	.04
48	PIH-CR-2 HRs/Game	.10	.08	.04	139	MAN: Time For Kids	.10	.08	.04
49	PIH-CR-40 Home Runs	.10	.08	.04	140	MAN: J Sylvester	.10	.08	.04
50	PIH-CR-RBIs	.15	.11	.06	141	MAN: With the Great	.10	.08	.04
51	PIH-CR-Batting AVG.	.15	.11	.06	142	MAN: And America	.10	.08	.04
52	PIH-CR-SLG AVG.	.15	.11	.06	143	REMEM: Bill James-1	.10	.08	.04
53	PIH-SSN- Shutouts	.10	.08	.04	144	REMEM: Bill James-2	.10	.08	.04
54	PIH-SSN- Walks	.10	.08	.04	145	REMEM: Bill James-3	.10	.08	.04
55	PIH-SSN- Most Runs	.20	.15	.08	146	REMEM: Mel Allen-1	.10	.08	.04
56	PIH-SSN- On Base "	.10	.08	.04	147	REMEM: Mel Allen-2	.10	.08	.04
57	PIH-SSN- Total Bases	.15	.11	.06	148	REMEM: Wes Ferrell	.10	.08	.04
58	Xtra Base H	.15	.11	.06	149	REMEM: George Bush	.50	.40	.20
59	Xtra Base H RBI's	.15	.11	.06	150	REMEM: Ethan Allen	.20	.15	.08
60	Xtra Base H Home Runs	.10	.08	.04	151	REMEM: Dorothy	.10	.08	.04
61	Xtra Base H Home Run "	.10	.08	.04	152	REMEM: Julia-1	.10	.08	.04
62	Xtra Base H SLG AVG.	.15	.11	.06	153	REMEM: Julia-2	.10	.08	.04
63	PIH-SRS- Winning "	.10	.08	.04	154	REMEM: Mark Koenig	.10	.08	.04
64	PIH-SRS- ERA	.10	.08	.04	155	REMEM: D Honig	.10	.08	.04
65	PIH-SRS- Most Walks	.10	.08	.04	156	REMEM: Waner/Hoyt	.10	.08	.04
66	PIH-SRS- Most Runs	.10	.08	.04	157	REMEM: Waite Hoyt	.10	.08	.04
67	PIH-SRS- Total Bases	.10	.08	.04	158	REMEM: Bill Dickey	.10	.08	.04
68	PIH-SRS- Home Runs	.10	.08	.04	159	REMEM: Bob Meusel	.10	.08	.04
69	PIH-SRS- RBI's	.10	.08	.04	160	REMEM: Jim Chapman	.10	.08	.04
70	PIH-SRS- SLG AVG.	.20	.15	.08	161	REMEM: C Walsh	.10	.08	.04
71	CH: ML Victory	.10	.08	.04	162	REMEM: Passes Away	.10	.08	.04
72	CH: 1st ML Home Run	.10	.08	.04	163	REMEM: G Rice	.10	.08	.04
73	CH: Walter J Duel	.10	.08	.04	164	Checklist	.10	.08	.04
74	CH: Led AL Fielding	.10	.08	.04	165	Checklist	.10	.08	.04
75	CH: 1st HR Record	.10	.08	.04					
76	CH: Sold To NY	.10	.08	.04					
77	CH: 1st Yankee HR	.10	.08	.04					
78	CH: AL MVP	.10	.08	.04					
79	CH: League Leader	.15	.11	.06					
80	CH: 3 HRs in 1 Series	.10	.08	.04					
81	CH: Babe & Lou's 107	.20	.15	.08					
82	CH: 60th Home Run	.20	.15	.08					
83	CH: 3 HRs/WS Again	.10	.08	.04					
84	CH: Called Shot-1	.10	.08	.04					
85	CH: Called Shot-2	.10	.08	.04					
86	CH: Called Shot-3	.10	.08	.04					
87	CH: Called Shot-4	.10	.08	.04					
88	CH: Called Shot-5	.10	.08	.04					
89	CH: All-Star Games	.15	.11	.06					
90	CH: Pitch Last Game	.10	.08	.04					
91	CH: 700th Home Run	.10	.08	.04					
92	CH: Japan	.10	.08	.04					
93	CH: Hits Last 3 HRs	.10	.08	.04					
94	CH: Hall of Fame	.10	.08	.04					
95	CH: 1942 Exhibition	.10	.08	.04					
96	CH: Babe Ruth Day	.10	.08	.04					
97	CH: Babe's Farewell	.25	.20	.10					
98	CH: Perfect Game	.10	.08	.04					
99	TRIV: Leads in Steals	.10	.08	.04					
100	TRIV: Hub Pruett	.10	.08	.04					
101	TRIV: Out in WS	.10	.08	.04					
102	TRIV: No Triple CRWN	.10	.08	.04					
103	TRIV: 54-ounce bat	.10	.08	.04					
104	TRIV: Right-Handed	.10	.08	.04					
105	SULTN: Greatness	.10	.08	.04					
106	SULTN: Babe's Best	.10	.08	.04					
107	SULTN: Beats Teams	.10	.08	.04					

GRADING GUIDE

Mint (MT): A perfect card. Well-centered with all corners sharp and square. No creases, stains, edge nicks, surface marks, yellowing or fading.

Near Mint (NM): A nearly perfect card. At first glance, a NM card appears to be perfect. May be slightly off-center. No surface marks, creases or loss of gloss.

Excellent (EX): Corners are still fairly sharp with only moderate wear. Borders may be off-center. No creases or stains on fronts or backs, but may show slight loss of surface luster.

Very Good (VG): Shows obvious handling. May have rounded corners, minor creases, major gum or wax stains. No major creases, tape marks, writing, etc.

Good (G): A well-worn card, but exhibits no intentional damage. May have major or multiple creases. Corners may be rounded well beyond card border.

Values quoted in this guide reflect the retail price of a card — the price a collector can expect to pay when buying a card from a dealer. The wholesale price — that which a collector can expect to receive from a dealer when selling cards — will be significantly lower, depending on desirability and condition.

1991 Country Hearth Mariners

This 29-card set was limited and cards were inserted in loaves of bread and also given away at a Mariner home game. The card fronts feature full-color glossy photos, while the flip sides feature statistics.

		MT	NR MT	EX
Complete Set:		15.00	11.00	6.00
Common Player:		.25	.20	.10
1	Jim Lefebvre	.25	.20	.10
2	Jeff Schaefer	.25	.20	.10
3	Harold Reynolds	.35	.25	.14
4	Greg Briley	.25	.20	.10
5	Scott Bradley	.25	.20	.10
6	Dave Valle	.25	.20	.10
7	Edgar Martinez	.50	.40	.20
8	Pete O'Brien	.25	.20	.10
9	Omar Vizquel	.25	.20	.10
10	Tino Martinez	.50	.40	.20
11	Scott Bankhead	.30	.25	.12
12	Bill Swift	.35	.25	.14
13	Jay Buhner	.35	.25	.14
14	Alvin Davis	.30	.25	.12
15	Ken Griffey, Jr.	3.00	2.25	1.25
16	Tracy Jones	.25	.20	.10
17	Brent Knackert	.25	.20	.10
18	Henry Cotto	.25	.20	.10
19	Ken Griffey, Sr.	.50	.40	.20
20	Keith Comstock	.25	.20	.10
21	Brian Holman	.30	.25	.12
22	Russ Swan	.25	.20	.10
23	Mike Jackson	.25	.20	.10
24	Erik Hanson	.40	.30	.15
25	Mike Schooler	.30	.25	.12
26	Randy Johnson	.40	.30	.15
27	Rich DeLucia	.25	.20	.10
28	The Griffey's	1.50	1.25	.60
29	Mascot	.25	.20	.10

1982 Cracker Jack

The Topps-produced 1982 Cracker Jack set was issued to promote the first "Old Timers Baseball Classic," held in Washington, D.C. Sixteen cards comprise the set which was issued in two sheets of eight cards, plus an advertising card located in the center. The individual cards are 2-1/2" by 3-1/2" in size with the complete sheets measuring 7-1/2" by 10-1/2". Card #'s 1-8 feature American League players with #'s 9-16 being former National League stars. The card fronts feature a full-color photo inside a Cracker Jack border. The backs contain the Cracker Jack logo plus a short player biography and his lifetime pitching or batting record. Complete sheets were available through a write-in offer.

		MT	NR MT	EX
Complete Panel Set:		10.00	7.50	4.00
Complete Singles Set:		4.00	3.00	1.50
Common Single Player:		.05	.04	.02
	Panel	5.00	3.75	2.00
1	Larry Doby	.05	.04	.02
2	Bob Feller	.10	.08	.04
3	Whitey Ford	.10	.08	.04
4	Al Kaline	.10	.08	.04
5	Harmon Killebrew	.10	.08	.04
6	Mickey Mantle	2.50	2.00	1.00
7	Tony Oliva	.05	.04	.02
8	Brooks Robinson	.10	.08	.04
	Panel	4.00	3.00	1.50
9	Hank Aaron	1.25	.90	.50
10	Ernie Banks	.10	.08	.04
11	Ralph Kiner	.10	.08	.04
12	Eddie Mathews	.10	.08	.04
13	Willie Mays	1.00	.70	.40
14	Robin Roberts	.10	.08	.04
15	Duke Snider	.10	.08	.04
16	Warren Spahn	.10	.08	.04
----	Advertising Card	.02	.02	.01

1976 Crane Potato Chips

This unnumbered 70-card set of player discs was issued with Crane Potato Chips in 1976. The front of the discs are designed to look like a baseball with the player's portrait in the center and his name, position and team beneath.

		NR MT	EX	VG
Complete Set:		30.00	15.00	9.00
Common Player:		.10	.05	.03
(1)	Henry Aaron	2.25	1.25	.70
(2)	Johnny Bench	1.25	.60	.40
(3)	Vida Blue	.12	.06	.04
(4)	Larry Bowa	.12	.06	.04
(5)	Lou Brock	.60	.30	.20
(6)	Jeff Burroughs	.10	.05	.03
(7)	John Candelaria	.12	.06	.04
(8)	Jose Cardenal	.10	.05	.03
(9)	Rod Carew	1.25	.60	.40
(10)	Steve Carlton	1.25	.60	.40
(11)	Dave Cash	.10	.05	.03
(12)	Cesar Cedeno	.12	.06	.04
(13)	Ron Cey	.12	.06	.04
(14)	Carlton Fisk	.60	.30	.20
(15)	Tito Fuentes	.10	.05	.03
(16)	Steve Garvey	.70	.35	.20
(17)	Ken Griffey	.12	.06	.04
(18)	Don Gullett	.10	.05	.03
(19)	Willie Horton	.10	.05	.03
(20)	Al Hrabosky	.10	.05	.03

		NR MT	EX	VG
(21)	Catfish Hunter	.50	.25	.15
(22)	Reggie Jackson	1.75	.90	.50
(23)	Randy Jones	.10	.05	.03
(24)	Jim Kaat	.15	.08	.05
(25)	Don Kessinger	.10	.05	.03
(26)	Dave Kingman	.15	.08	.05
(27)	Jerry Koosman	.12	.06	.04
(28)	Mickey Lolich	.15	.08	.05
(29)	Greg Luzinski	.15	.08	.05
(30)	Fred Lynn	.20	.10	.06
(31)	Bill Madlock	.15	.08	.05
(32)	Carlos May	.10	.05	.03
(33)	John Mayberry	.10	.05	.03
(34)	Bake McBride	.10	.05	.03
(35)	Doc Medich	.10	.05	.03
(36)	Andy Messersmith	.10	.05	.03
(37)	Rick Monday	.12	.06	.04
(38)	John Montefusco	.10	.05	.03
(39)	Jerry Morales	.10	.05	.03
(40)	Joe Morgan	.60	.30	.20
(41)	Thurman Munson	.60	.30	.20
(42)	Bobby Murcer	.12	.06	.04
(43)	Al Oliver	.15	.08	.05
(44)	Jim Palmer	.60	.30	.20
(45)	Dave Parker	.20	.10	.06
(46)	Tony Perez	.20	.10	.06
(47)	Jerry Reuss	.12	.06	.04
(48)	Brooks Robinson	.70	.35	.20
(49)	Frank Robinson	.70	.35	.20
(50)	Steve Rogers	.10	.05	.03
(51)	Pete Rose	2.25	1.25	.70
(52)	Nolan Ryan	2.25	1.25	.70
(53)	Manny Sanguillen	.10	.05	.03
(54)	Mike Schmidt	1.75	.90	.50
(55)	Tom Seaver	1.75	.90	.50
(56)	Ted Simmons	.15	.08	.05
(57)	Reggie Smith	.12	.06	.04
(58)	Willie Stargell	.60	.30	.20
(59)	Rusty Staub	.15	.08	.05
(60)	Rennie Stennett	.10	.05	.03
(61)	Don Sutton	.20	.10	.06
(62)	Andy Thornton	.12	.06	.04
(63)	Luis Tiant	.15	.08	.05
(64)	Joe Torre	.12	.06	.04
(65)	Mike Tyson	.10	.05	.03
(66)	Bob Watson	.10	.05	.03
(67)	Wilbur Wood	.10	.05	.03
(68)	Jimmy Wynn	.10	.05	.03
(69)	Carl Yastrzemski	1.75	.90	.50
(70)	Richie Zisk	.10	.05	.03

1954 Dan-Dee Potato Chips

AL LOPEZ

Issued in bags of potato chips, the cards in this 29-card set are commonly found with grease stains despite their waxed surface. The unnumbered cards, which measure 2-1/2" by 3-5/8", feature full-color photos. The card backs contain player statistical and biographical information. The set consists mostly of players from the Indians and Pirates. Photos of the Yankees players were also used for the Briggs Meats

and Stahl-Meyer Franks sets. Cooper and Smith are the scarcest cards in the set.

		NR MT	EX	VG
Complete Set		4500.00	2250.00	1350.
Common Player		60.00	30.00	18.00
(1)	Bob Avila	60.00	30.00	18.00
(2)	Hank Bauer	80.00	40.00	24.00
(3)	Walker Cooper	350.00	175.00	105.00
(4)	Larry Doby	90.00	45.00	27.00
(5)	Luke Easter	60.00	30.00	18.00
(6)	Bob Feller	200.00	100.00	60.00
(7)	Bob Friend	60.00	30.00	18.00
(8)	Mike Garcia	60.00	30.00	18.00
(9)	Sid Gordon	60.00	30.00	18.00
(10)	Jim Hegan	60.00	30.00	18.00
(11)	Gil Hodges	150.00	75.00	45.00
(12)	Art Houtteman	60.00	30.00	18.00
(13)	Monte Irvin	100.00	50.00	30.00
(14)	Paul LaPalm (LaPalme)	60.00	30.00	18.00
(15)	Bob Lemon	110.00	55.00	33.00
(16)	Al Lopez	90.00	45.00	27.00
(17)	Mickey Mantle	1500.00	750.00	450.00
(18)	Dale Mitchell	60.00	30.00	18.00
(19)	Phil Rizzuto	125.00	62.00	37.00
(20)	Curtis Roberts	60.00	30.00	18.00
(21)	Al Rosen	80.00	40.00	24.00
(22)	Red Schoendienst	110.00	55.00	33.00
(23)	Paul Smith	450.00	225.00	135.00
(24)	Duke Snider	225.00	112.00	67.00
(25)	George Strickland	60.00	30.00	18.00
(26)	Max Surkont	60.00	30.00	18.00
(27)	Frank Thomas	125.00	62.00	37.00
(28)	Wally Westlake	60.00	30.00	18.00
(29)	Early Wynn	110.00	55.00	33.00

1987 David Berg Hot Dogs Cubs

(17) MARK GRACE, IF

Changing sponsors from Gatorade to David Berg Pure Beef Hot Dogs, the Chicago Cubs handed out a 26-card set of baseball cards to fans attending the July 29th game at Wrigley Field. The cards are printed in full-color on white stock and measure 2-7/8" by 4-1/4" in size. The set is numbered by the players' uniform numbers. The card backs contain player personal and statistical information, plus a full-color picture of a David Berg hot dog in a bun with all the garnishings. The set marked the sixth consecutive year the Cubs held a baseball card giveaway promotion.

		MT	NR MT	EX
Complete Set:		9.00	6.75	3.50
Common Player:		.15	.11	.06
1	Dave Martinez	.50	.40	.20
4	Gene Michael	.15	.11	.06
6	Keith Moreland	.30	.25	.12
7	Jody Davis	.30	.25	.12
8	Andre Dawson	1.00	.70	.40
10	Leon Durham	.30	.25	.12
11	Jim Sundberg	.15	.11	.06
12	Shawon Dunston	.60	.45	.20
19	Manny Trillo	.15	.11	.06

		MT	NR MT	EX
20	Bob Dernier	.15	.11	.06
21	Scott Sanderson	.15	.11	.06
22	Jerry Mumphrey	.15	.11	.06
23	Ryne Sandberg	2.00	1.50	.80
24	Brian Dayett	.15	.11	.06
29	Chico Walker	.15	.11	.06
31	Greg Maddux	.70	.50	.30
33	Frank DiPino	.15	.11	.06
34	Steve Trout	.20	.15	.08
36	Gary Matthews	.20	.15	.08
37	Ed Lynch	.15	.11	.06
39	Ron Davis	.15	.11	.06
40	Rick Sutcliffe	.40	.30	.15
46	Lee Smith	.30	.25	.12
47	Dickie Noles	.15	.11	.06
49	Jamie Moyer	.20	.15	.08
----	The Coaching Staff (Johnny Oates, Jim Snyder, Herm Starrette, John Vukovich, Billy Williams)	.15	.11	.06

1988 David Berg Hot Dogs Cubs

This oversized (2-7/8" by 4-1/2") set of 26 cards was distributed to fans at Wrigley Field on August 24th. The set includes cards for the manager and coaching staff, as well as players. Full-color action photos are framed in red and blue on a white background. The backs feature small black and white player close-ups, colorful team logos, statistics and sponsor logos (David Berg Hot Dogs and Venture Store Restaurants). The numbers in the following checklist refer to players' uniforms.

		MT	NR MT	EX
Complete Set:		10.00	7.50	4.00
Common Player:		.15	.11	.06
2	Vance Law	.15	.11	.06
4	Don Zimmer	.15	.11	.06
7	Jody Davis	.30	.25	.12
8	Andre Dawson	1.00	.70	.40
9	Damon Berryhill	.50	.40	.20
12	Shawon Dunston	.60	.45	.25
17	Mark Grace	2.00	1.50	.80
18	Angel Salazar	.15	.11	.06
19	Manny Trillo	.15	.11	.06
21	Scott Sanderson	.15	.11	.06
22	Jerry Mumphrey	.15	.11	.06
23	Ryne Sandberg	2.00	1.50	.80
24	Gary Varsho	.40	.30	.15
25	Rafael Palmeiro	1.25	.90	.50
28	Mitch Webster	.15	.11	.06
30	Darrin Jackson	.40	.30	.15
31	Greg Maddux	.70	.50	.30
32	Calvin Schiraldi	.20	.15	.08
33	Frank DiPino	.15	.11	.06
37	Pat Perry	.15	.11	.06
40	Rick Sutcliffe	.40	.30	.15
41	Jeff Pico	.25	.20	.10
45	Al Nipper	.15	.11	.06
49	Jamie Moyer	.20	.15	.08
50	Les Lancaster	.15	.11	.06
54	Rich Gossage	.70	.50	.30
----	Joe Altobelli, Chuck Cottier, Larry Cox, Jose Martinez, Dick Pole	.15	.11	.06

Values quoted in this guide reflect the retail price of a card — the price a collector can expect to pay when buying a card from a dealer. The wholesale price — that which a collector can expect to receive from a dealer when selling cards — will be significantly lower, depending on desirability and condition.

1991 Denny's Grand Slam

This 26-card set was produced by Upper Deck and features one player from each Major League team. One hologram card was distributed with the purchase of a Grand Slam meal. The cards are numbered on the front and are 3-D. The card backs describe grand slams hit by the featured player.

		MT	NR MT	EX
Complete Set:		50.00	37.00	20.00
Common Player:		1.50	1.25	.60
1	Ellis Burks	2.00	1.50	.80
2	Cecil Fielder	4.00	3.00	1.50
3	Will Clark	4.00	3.00	1.50
4	Eric Davis	2.00	1.50	.80
5	Dave Parker	1.50	1.25	.60
6	Kelly Gruber	1.50	1.25	.60
7	Kent Hrbek	1.50	1.25	.60
8	Don Mattingly	4.00	3.00	1.50
9	Brook Jacoby	1.50	1.25	.60
10	Mark McGwire	4.00	3.00	1.50
11	Howard Johnson	1.50	1.25	.60
12	Tim Wallach	1.50	1.25	.60
13	Ricky Jordan	1.50	1.25	.60
14	Andre Dawson	3.00	2.25	1.25
15	Eddie Murray	3.00	2.25	1.25
16	Danny Tartabull	2.50	2.00	1.00
17	Bobby Bonilla	3.00	2.25	1.25
18	Benito Santiago	2.00	1.50	.80
19	Alvin Davis	1.50	1.25	.60
20	Cal Ripken	4.00	3.00	1.50
21	Ruben Sierra	3.00	2.25	1.25
22	Pedro Guererro	1.50	1.25	.60
23	Wally Joyner	2.00	1.50	.80
24	Craig Biggio	2.00	1.50	.80
25	Dave Justice	4.00	3.00	1.50
26	Tim Raines	1.50	1.25	.60

1988 Domino's Pizza Tigers

Domino's Pizza produced a 28-card set commemorating the 20th anniversary of the 1968 World Champion Detroit Tigers. The cards were given away at an Old Timers Game at Tiger Stadium in 1988. The cards, which measure 2-1/2" by 3-1/2", feature black and white photos semi-surrounded by a two-stripe band. The stripes on the card's left side are the same color (red and light blue) as the Domino's Pizza logo in the upper corner. The stripes on the card's right side match the colors of the Tigers logo (red and dark blue). The backs of all the cards (except for Ernie Harwell) contain a brief summary of the Tigers' 1968 season. Located at the bottom on the card backs are the players' major league records through 1968 plus their 1968 World Series statistics.

		MT	NR MT	EX
Complete Set:		9.00	6.75	3.50
Common Player:		.20	.15	.08
(1)	Gates Brown	.30	.25	.12
(2)	Norm Cash	.90	.70	.35
(3)	Wayne Comer	.20	.15	.08
(4)	Pat Dobson	.20	.15	.08
(5)	Bill Freehan	.60	.45	.25
(6)	John Hiller	.30	.25	.12
(7)	Ernie Harwell (announcer)	.30	.25	.12
(8)	Willie Horton	.60	.45	.25
(9)	Al Kaline	1.50	1.25	.60
(10)	Fred Lasher	.20	.15	.08
(11)	Mickey Lolich	.90	.70	.35
(12)	Tom Matchick	.20	.15	.08
(13)	Ed Mathews	1.00	.70	.40
(14)	Dick McAuliff (McAuliffe)	.40	.30	.15
(15)	Denny McLain	.80	.60	.30
(16)	Don McMahon	.20	.15	.08
(17)	Jim Northrup	.40	.30	.15
(18)	Ray Oyler	.20	.15	.08
(19)	Daryl Patterson	.20	.15	.08
(20)	Jim Price	.20	.15	.08
(21)	Joe Sparma	.20	.15	.08
(22)	Mickey Stanley	.40	.30	.15
(23)	Dick Tracewski	.20	.15	.08
(24)	Jon Warden	.20	.15	.08
(25)	Don Wert	.20	.15	.08
(26)	Earl Wilson	.20	.15	.08
(27)	Header Card	.20	.15	.08
(28)	Coupon Card	.20	.15	.08

1981 Donruss

ROLLIE FINGERS PITCHER

The Donruss Co. of Memphis, Tenn., produced its premiere baseball card issue in 1981 with a set that consisted of 600 numbered cards and five unnumbered checklists. The cards, which measure 2-1/2" by 3-1/2", are printed on thin stock. The card fronts contain the Donruss logo plus the year of issue. The card backs are designed on a vertical format and have black print on red and white. The set, entitled "First Edition Collector Series," contains nearly 40 variations, those being first-printing errors that were corrected in a subsequent print run. The cards were issued in gum wax packs, with hobby dealer sales being coordinated by TCMA of Amawalk, N.Y. The complete set price does not include the higher priced variations.

	MT	NR MT	EX
Complete Set:	60.00	45.00	25.00

		MT	NR MT	EX
Common Player:		.06	.05	.02
1	Ozzie Smith	3.00	2.25	1.25
2	Rollie Fingers	1.00	.70	.40
3	Rick Wise	.08	.06	.03
4	Gene Richards	.06	.05	.02
5	Alan Trammell	.40	.30	.15
6	Tom Brookens	.08	.06	.03
7a	Duffy Dyer (1980 Avg. .185)	1.00	.70	.40
7b	Duffy Dyer (1980 Avg. 185)	.10	.08	.04
8	Mark Fidrych	.08	.06	.03
9	Dave Rozema	.06	.05	.02
10	Ricky Peters	.06	.05	.02
11	Mike Schmidt	2.50	2.00	1.00
12	Willie Stargell	.80	.60	.30
13	Tim Foli	.06	.05	.02
14	Manny Sanguillen	.06	.05	.02
15	Grant Jackson	.06	.05	.02
16	Eddie Solomon	.06	.05	.02
17	Omar Moreno	.06	.05	.02
18	Joe Morgan	.60	.45	.25
19	Rafael Landestoy	.06	.05	.02
20	Bruce Bochy	.06	.05	.02
21	Joe Sambito	.06	.05	.02
22	Manny Trillo	.08	.06	.03
23a	*Dave Smith* (incomplete box around stats)	1.00	.70	.40
23b	*Dave Smith* (complete box around stats)	.30	.25	.12
24	Terry Puhl	.06	.05	.02
25	Bump Wills	.06	.05	.02
26a	John Ellis (Danny Walton photo - with bat)	1.25	.90	.50
26b	John Ellis (John Ellis photo - with glove)	.10	.08	.04
27	Jim Kern	.06	.05	.02
28	Richie Zisk	.08	.06	.03
29	John Mayberry	.08	.06	.03
30	Bob Davis	.06	.05	.02
31	Jackson Todd	.06	.05	.02
32	Al Woods	.06	.05	.02
33	Steve Carlton	1.00	.70	.40
34	Lee Mazzilli	.08	.06	.03
35	John Stearns	.06	.05	.02
36	Roy Jackson	.06	.05	.02
37	Mike Scott	.70	.50	.30
38	Lamar Johnson	.06	.05	.02
39	Kevin Bell	.06	.05	.02
40	Ed Farmer	.06	.05	.02
41	Ross Baumgarten	.06	.05	.02
42	Leo Sutherland	.06	.05	.02
43	Dan Meyer	.06	.05	.02
44	Ron Reed	.06	.05	.02
45	Mario Mendoza	.06	.05	.02
46	Rick Honeycutt	.06	.05	.02
47	Glenn Abbott	.06	.05	.02
48	Leon Roberts	.06	.05	.02
49	Rod Carew	1.50	1.25	.60
50	Bert Campaneris	.10	.08	.04
51a	Tom Donahue (incorrect spelling)	1.00	.70	.40
51b	Tom Donohue (Donohue on front)	.10	.08	.04
52	Dave Frost	.06	.05	.02
53	Ed Halicki	.06	.05	.02
54	Dan Ford	.06	.05	.02
55	Garry Maddox	.10	.08	.04
56a	Steve Garvey ("Surpassed 25 HR..." on back)	1.75	1.25	.70
56b	Steve Garvey ("Surpassed 21 HR..." on back)	.60	.45	.25
57	Bill Russell	.08	.06	.03
58	Don Sutton	.30	.25	.12
59	Reggie Smith	.10	.08	.04
60	Rick Monday	.10	.08	.04
61	Ray Knight	.10	.08	.04
62	Johnny Bench	1.25	.90	.50
63	Mario Soto	.08	.06	.03
64	Doug Bair	.06	.05	.02
65	George Foster	.20	.15	.08
66	Jeff Burroughs	.08	.06	.03
67	Keith Hernandez	.40	.30	.15
68	Tom Herr	.10	.08	.04
69	Bob Forsch	.08	.06	.03
70	John Fulgham	.06	.05	.02
71a	Bobby Bonds (lifetime HR 986)	1.00	.70	.40
71b	Bobby Bonds (lifetime HR 326)	.15	.11	.06
72a	Rennie Stennett ("...breaking broke leg..." on back)	1.00	.70	.40
72b	Rennie Stennett ("...breaking leg..." on back)	.10	.08	.04
73	Joe Strain	.06	.05	.02
74	Ed Whitson	.06	.05	.02

#	Name	MT	NR MT	EX	#	Name	MT	NR MT	EX
75	Tom Griffin	.06	.05	.02	155	Craig Swan	.06	.05	.02
76	Bill North	.06	.05	.02	156	*Jeff Reardon*	5.00	3.75	2.00
77	Gene Garber	.06	.05	.02	157	Steve Henderson	.06	.05	.02
78	Mike Hargrove	.06	.05	.02	158	Jim Morrison	.06	.05	.02
79	Dave Rosello	.06	.05	.02	159	Glenn Borgmann	.06	.05	.02
80	Ron Hassey	.06	.05	.02	160	*Lamarr Hoyt (LaMarr)*	.10	.08	.04
81	Sid Monge	.06	.05	.02	161	Rich Wortham	.06	.05	.02
82a	*Joe Charboneau* ("For some reason, Phillies..." on back)	1.00	.70	.40	162	Thad Bosley	.06	.05	.02
82b	*Joe Charboneau* ("Phillies..." on back)	.12	.09	.05	163	Julio Cruz	.06	.05	.02
83	Cecil Cooper	.15	.11	.06	164a	Del Unser (no 3B in stat heads)	1.00	.70	.40
84	Sal Bando	.10	.08	.04	164b	Del Unser (3B in stat heads)	.10	.08	.04
85	Moose Haas	.06	.05	.02	165	Jim Anderson	.06	.05	.02
86	Mike Caldwell	.06	.05	.02	166	Jim Beattie	.06	.05	.02
87a	Larry Hisle ("...Twins with 28 RBI." on back)	1.00	.70	.40	167	Shane Rawley	.10	.08	.04
87b	Larry Hisle ("...Twins with 28 HR" on back)	.10	.08	.04	168	Joe Simpson	.06	.05	.02
88	Luis Gomez	.06	.05	.02	169	Rod Carew	1.50	1.25	.60
89	Larry Parrish	.10	.08	.04	170	Fred Patek	.06	.05	.02
90	Gary Carter	.50	.40	.20	171	Frank Tanana	.10	.08	.04
91	*Bill Gullickson*	.15	.11	.06	172	Alfredo Martinez	.06	.05	.02
92	Fred Norman	.06	.05	.02	173	Chris Knapp	.06	.05	.02
93	Tommy Hutton	.06	.05	.02	174	Joe Rudi	.10	.08	.04
94	Carl Yastrzemski	1.00	.70	.40	175	Greg Luzinski	.15	.11	.06
95	Glenn Hoffman	.06	.05	.02	176	Steve Garvey	.50	.40	.20
96	Dennis Eckersley	2.00	1.50	.80	177	Joe Ferguson	.06	.05	.02
97a	Tom Burgmeier (Throws: Right)	1.00	.70	.40	178	Bob Welch	.60	.45	.25
97b	Tom Burgmeier (Throws: Left)	.10	.08	.04	179	Dusty Baker	.10	.08	.04
98	Win Remmerswaal	.06	.05	.02	180	Rudy Law	.06	.05	.02
99	Bob Horner	.12	.09	.05	181	Dave Concepcion	.15	.11	.06
100	George Brett	3.00	2.25	1.25	182	Johnny Bench	1.00	.70	.40
101	Dave Chalk	.06	.05	.02	183	Mike LaCoss	.06	.05	.02
102	Dennis Leonard	.08	.06	.03	184	Ken Griffey	.12	.09	.05
103	Renie Martin	.06	.05	.02	185	Dave Collins	.08	.06	.03
104	Amos Otis	.08	.06	.03	186	Brian Asselstine	.06	.05	.02
105	Graig Nettles	.15	.11	.06	187	Garry Templeton	.10	.08	.04
106	Eric Soderholm	.06	.05	.02	188	Mike Phillips	.06	.05	.02
107	Tommy John	.20	.15	.08	189	Pete Vukovich	.08	.06	.03
108	Tom Underwood	.06	.05	.02	190	John Urrea	.06	.05	.02
109	Lou Piniella	.12	.09	.05	191	Tony Scott	.06	.05	.02
110	Mickey Klutts	.06	.05	.02	192	Darrell Evans	.12	.09	.05
111	Bobby Murcer	.10	.08	.04	193	Milt May	.06	.05	.02
112	Eddie Murray	3.00	2.25	1.25	194	Bob Knepper	.08	.06	.03
113	Rick Dempsey	.08	.06	.03	195	Randy Moffitt	.06	.05	.02
114	Scott McGregor	.08	.06	.03	196	Larry Herndon	.08	.06	.03
115	Ken Singleton	.10	.08	.04	197	Rick Camp	.06	.05	.02
116	Gary Roenicke	.06	.05	.02	198	Andre Thornton	.10	.08	.04
117	Dave Revering	.06	.05	.02	199	Tom Veryzer	.06	.05	.02
118	Mike Norris	.06	.05	.02	200	Gary Alexander	.06	.05	.02
119	Rickey Henderson	18.00	13.50	7.25	201	Rick Waits	.06	.05	.02
120	Mike Heath	.06	.05	.02	202	Rick Manning	.06	.05	.02
121	Dave Cash	.06	.05	.02	203	Paul Molitor	1.25	.90	.50
122	Randy Jones	.08	.06	.03	204	Jim Gantner	.08	.06	.03
123	Eric Rasmussen	.06	.05	.02	205	Paul Mitchell	.06	.05	.02
124	Jerry Mumphrey	.06	.05	.02	206	Reggie Cleveland	.06	.05	.02
125	Richie Hebner	.06	.05	.02	207	Sixto Lezcano	.06	.05	.02
126	Mark Wagner	.06	.05	.02	208	Bruce Benedict	.06	.05	.02
127	Jack Morris	1.50	1.25	.60	209	Rodney Scott	.06	.05	.02
128	Dan Petry	.08	.06	.03	210	John Tamargo	.06	.05	.02
129	Bruce Robbins	.06	.05	.02	211	Bill Lee	.08	.06	.03
130	Champ Summers	.06	.05	.02	212	Andre Dawson	1.75	1.25	.70
131a	Pete Rose ("...see card 251." on back)	2.25	1.75	.90	213	Rowland Office	.06	.05	.02
131b	Pete Rose ("...see card 371." on back)	1.25	.90	.50	214	Carl Yastrzemski	1.25	.90	.50
132	Willie Stargell	.40	.30	.15	215	Jerry Remy	.06	.05	.02
133	Ed Ott	.06	.05	.02	216	Mike Torrez	.08	.06	.03
134	Jim Bibby	.06	.05	.02	217	Skip Lockwood	.06	.05	.02
135	Bert Blyleven	.12	.09	.05	218	Fred Lynn	.20	.15	.08
136	Dave Parker	.30	.25	.12	219	Chris Chambliss	.08	.06	.03
137	Bill Robinson	.06	.05	.02	220	Willie Aikens	.06	.05	.02
138	Enos Cabell	.06	.05	.02	221	John Wathan	.08	.06	.03
139	Dave Bergman	.06	.05	.02	222	Dan Quisenberry	.15	.11	.06
140	J R Richard	.10	.08	.04	223	Willie Wilson	.15	.11	.06
141	Ken Forsch	.06	.05	.02	224	Clint Hurdle	.06	.05	.02
142	Larry Bowa	.15	.11	.06	225	Bob Watson	.08	.06	.03
143	Frank LaCorte (photo actually Randy Niemann)	.06	.05	.02	226	Jim Spencer	.06	.05	.02
144	Dennis Walling	.06	.05	.02	227	Ron Guidry	.25	.20	.10
145	Buddy Bell	.12	.09	.05	228	Reggie Jackson	3.00	2.25	1.25
146	Ferguson Jenkins	.50	.40	.30	229	Oscar Gamble	.08	.06	.03
147	Danny Darwin	.06	.05	.02	230	Jeff Cox	.06	.05	.02
148	John Grubb	.06	.05	.02	231	Luis Tiant	.12	.09	.05
149	Alfredo Griffin	.08	.06	.03	232	Rich Dauer	.06	.05	.02
150	Jerry Garvin	.06	.05	.02	233	Dan Graham	.06	.05	.02
151	*Paul Mirabella*(FC)	.10	.08	.04	234	Mike Flanagan	.10	.08	.04
152	Rick Bosetti	.06	.05	.02	235	John Lowenstein	.06	.05	.02
153	Dick Ruthven	.06	.05	.02	236	Benny Ayala	.06	.05	.02
154	Frank Taveras	.06	.05	.02	237	Wayne Gross	.06	.05	.02
					238	Rick Langford	.06	.05	.02
					239	Tony Armas	.10	.08	.04
					240a	Bob Lacy (incorrect spelling)	1.00	.70	.40
					240b	Bob Lacey (correct spelling)	.10	.08	.04
					241	Gene Tenace	.08	.06	.03
					242	Bob Shirley	.06	.05	.02
					243	Gary Lucas	.08	.06	.03

No.	Player	MT	NR MT	EX
244	Jerry Turner	.06	.05	.02
245	John Wockenfuss	.06	.05	.02
246	Stan Papi	.06	.05	.02
247	Milt Wilcox	.06	.05	.02
248	Dan Schatzeder	.06	.05	.02
249	Steve Kemp	.08	.06	.03
250	Jim Lentine	.06	.05	.02
251	Pete Rose	1.00	.70	.40
252	Bill Madlock	.12	.09	.05
253	Dale Berra	.06	.05	.02
254	Kent Tekulve	.08	.06	.03
255	Enrique Romo	.06	.05	.02
256	Mike Easler	.08	.06	.03
257	Chuck Tanner	.06	.05	.02
258	Art Howe	.06	.05	.02
259	Alan Ashby	.06	.05	.02
260	Nolan Ryan	7.00	5.25	2.75
261a	Vern Ruhle (Ken Forsch photo - head shot)	1.25	.90	.50
261b	Vern Ruhle (Vern Ruhle photo - waist to head shot)	.10	.08	.04
262	Bob Boone	.10	.08	.04
263	Cesar Cedeno	.12	.09	.05
264	Jeff Leonard	.12	.09	.05
265	Pat Putnam	.06	.05	.02
266	Jon Matlack	.08	.06	.03
267	Dave Rajsich	.06	.05	.02
268	Billy Sample	.06	.05	.02
269	Damaso Garcia	.10	.08	.04
270	Tom Buskey	.06	.05	.02
271	Joey McLaughlin	.06	.05	.02
272	Barry Bonnell	.06	.05	.02
273	Tug McGraw	.10	.08	.04
274	Mike Jorgensen	.06	.05	.02
275	Pat Zachry	.06	.05	.02
276	Neil Allen	.08	.06	.03
277	Joel Youngblood	.06	.05	.02
278	Greg Pryor	.06	.05	.02
279	Britt Burns	.10	.08	.04
280	Rich Dotson	.25	.20	.10
281	Chet Lemon	.08	.06	.03
282	Rusty Kuntz	.06	.05	.02
283	Ted Cox	.06	.05	.02
284	Sparky Lyle	.10	.08	.04
285	Larry Cox	.06	.05	.02
286	Floyd Bannister	.10	.08	.04
287	Byron McLaughlin	.06	.05	.02
288	Rodney Craig	.06	.05	.02
289	Bobby Grich	.10	.08	.04
290	Dickie Thon	.08	.06	.03
291	Mark Clear	.06	.05	.02
292	Dave Lemanczyk	.06	.05	.02
293	Jason Thompson	.06	.05	.02
294	Rick Miller	.06	.05	.02
295	Lonnie Smith	.08	.06	.03
296	Ron Cey	.12	.09	.05
297	Steve Yeager	.06	.05	.02
298	Bobby Castillo	.06	.05	.02
299	Manny Mota	.08	.06	.03
300	Jay Johnstone	.08	.06	.03
301	Dan Driessen	.08	.06	.03
302	Joe Nolan	.06	.05	.02
303	Paul Householder	.06	.05	.02
304	Harry Spilman	.06	.05	.02
305	Cesar Geronimo	.06	.05	.02
306a	Gary Mathews (Mathews on front)	1.25	.90	.50
306b	Gary Matthews (Matthews on front)	.10	.08	.04
307	Ken Reitz	.06	.05	.02
308	Ted Simmons	.12	.09	.05
309	John Littlefield	.06	.05	.02
310	George Frazier	.06	.05	.02
311	Dane Iorg	.06	.05	.02
312	Mike Ivie	.06	.05	.02
313	Dennis Littlejohn	.06	.05	.02
314	Gary LaVelle (Lavelle)	.06	.05	.02
315	Jack Clark	.25	.20	.10
316	Jim Wohlford	.06	.05	.02
317	Rick Matula	.06	.05	.02
318	Toby Harrah	.08	.06	.03
319a	Dwane Kuiper (Dwane on front)	1.00	.70	.40
319b	Duane Kuiper (Duane on front)	.10	.08	.04
320	Len Barker	.08	.06	.03
321	Victor Cruz	.06	.05	.02
322	Dell Alston	.06	.05	.02
323	Robin Yount	3.50	2.75	1.50
324	Charlie Moore	.06	.05	.02
325	Lary Sorensen	.06	.05	.02
326a	Gorman Thomas ("...30-HR mark 4th..." on back)	1.25	.90	.50
326b	Gorman Thomas ("...30-HR mark 3rd..." on back)	.10	.08	.04
327	Bob Rodgers	.08	.06	.03
328	Phil Niekro	.30	.25	.12
329	Chris Speier	.06	.05	.02
330a	Steve Rodgers (Rodgers on front)	1.00	.70	.40
330b	Steve Rogers (Rogers on front)	.10	.08	.04
331	Woodie Fryman	.08	.06	.03
332	Warren Cromartie	.06	.05	.02
333	Jerry White	.06	.05	.02
334	Tony Perez	.20	.15	.08
335	Carlton Fisk	1.75	1.25	.70
336	Dick Drago	.06	.05	.02
337	Steve Renko	.06	.05	.02
338	Jim Rice	.50	.40	.20
339	Jerry Royster	.06	.05	.02
340	Frank White	.10	.08	.04
341	Jamie Quirk	.06	.05	.02
342a	Paul Spittorff (Spittorff on front)	1.00	.70	.40
342b	Paul Splittorff (Splittorff on front)	.08	.06	.03
343	Marty Pattin	.06	.05	.02
344	Pete LaCock	.06	.05	.02
345	Willie Randolph	.10	.08	.04
346	Rick Cerone	.06	.05	.02
347	Rich Gossage	.20	.15	.08
348	Reggie Jackson	1.75	1.25	.70
349	Ruppert Jones	.06	.05	.02
350	Dave McKay	.06	.05	.02
351	Yogi Berra	.15	.11	.06
352	Doug Decinces (DeCinces)	.10	.08	.04
353	Jim Palmer	1.00	.70	.40
354	Tippy Martinez	.06	.05	.02
355	Al Bumbry	.08	.06	.03
356	Earl Weaver	.10	.08	.04
357a	Bob Picciolo (Bob on front)	1.00	.70	.40
357b	Rob Picciolo (Rob on front)	.10	.08	.04
358	Matt Keough	.06	.05	.02
359	Dwayne Murphy	.08	.06	.03
360	Brian Kingman	.06	.05	.02
361	Bill Fahey	.06	.05	.02
362	Steve Mura	.06	.05	.02
363	Dennis Kinney	.06	.05	.02
364	Dave Winfield	2.50	2.00	1.00
365	Lou Whitaker	.40	.30	.15
366	Lance Parrish	.35	.25	.14
367	Tim Corcoran	.06	.05	.02
368	Pat Underwood	.06	.05	.02
369	Al Cowens	.06	.05	.02
370	Sparky Anderson	.10	.08	.04
371	Pete Rose	1.00	.70	.40
372	Phil Garner	.08	.06	.03
373	Steve Nicosia	.06	.05	.02
374	John Candelaria	.10	.08	.04
375	Don Robinson	.08	.06	.03
376	Lee Lacy	.06	.05	.02
377	John Milner	.06	.05	.02
378	Craig Reynolds	.06	.05	.02
379a	Luis Pujois (Pujois on front)	1.00	.70	.40
379b	Luis Pujols (Pujols on front)	.10	.08	.04
380	Joe Niekro	.12	.09	.05
381	Joaquin Andujar	.10	.08	.04
382	Keith Moreland	.35	.25	.14
383	Jose Cruz	.12	.09	.05
384	Bill Virdon	.06	.05	.02
385	Jim Sundberg	.08	.06	.03
386	Doc Medich	.06	.05	.02
387	Al Oliver	.15	.11	.06
388	Jim Norris	.06	.05	.02
389	Bob Bailor	.06	.05	.02
390	Ernie Whitt	.08	.06	.03
391	Otto Velez	.06	.05	.02
392	Roy Howell	.06	.05	.02
393	Bob Walk	.35	.25	.14
394	Doug Flynn	.06	.05	.02
395	Pete Falcone	.06	.05	.02
396	Tom Hausman	.06	.05	.02
397	Elliott Maddox	.06	.05	.02
398	Mike Squires	.06	.05	.02
399	Marvis Foley	.06	.05	.02
400	Steve Trout	.06	.05	.02
401	Wayne Nordhagen	.06	.05	.02
402	Tony Larussa (LaRussa)	.08	.06	.03
403	Bruce Bochte	.06	.05	.02
404	Bake McBride	.06	.05	.02
405	Jerry Narron	.06	.05	.02
406	Rob Dressler	.06	.05	.02
407	Dave Heaverlo	.06	.05	.02
408	Tom Paciorek	.06	.05	.02
409	Carney Lansford	.10	.08	.04
410	Brian Downing	.10	.08	.04
411	Don Aase	.06	.05	.02

#	Player	MT	NR MT	EX
412	Jim Barr	.06	.05	.02
413	Don Baylor	.12	.09	.05
414	Jim Fregosi	.08	.06	.03
415	Dallas Green	.08	.06	.03
416	Dave Lopes	.10	.08	.04
417	Jerry Reuss	.10	.08	.04
418	Rick Sutcliffe	.20	.15	.08
419	Derrel Thomas	.06	.05	.02
420	Tommy LaSorda (Lasorda)	.10	.08	.04
421	*Charlie Leibrandt*	.40	.30	.15
422	Tom Seaver	2.00	1.50	.80
423	Ron Oester	.06	.05	.02
424	Junior Kennedy	.06	.05	.02
425	Tom Seaver	2.00	1.50	.80
426	Bobby Cox	.06	.05	.02
427	*Leon Durham*	.20	.15	.08
428	Terry Kennedy	.08	.06	.03
429	Silvio Martinez	.06	.05	.02
430	George Hendrick	.08	.06	.03
431	Red Schoendienst	.08	.06	.03
432	John LeMaster	.06	.05	.02
433	Vida Blue	.12	.09	.05
434	John Montefusco	.08	.06	.03
435	Terry Whitfield	.06	.05	.02
436	Dave Bristol	.06	.05	.02
437	Dale Murphy	.90	.70	.35
438	Jerry Dybzinski	.06	.05	.02
439	Jorge Orta	.06	.05	.02
440	Wayne Garland	.06	.05	.02
441	Miguel Dilone	.06	.05	.02
442	Dave Garcia	.06	.05	.02
443	Don Money	.06	.05	.02
444a	Buck Martinez (photo reversed)	1.00	.70	.40
444b	Buck Martinez (photo correct)	.10	.08	.04
445	Jerry Augustine	.06	.05	.02
446	Ben Oglivie	.08	.06	.03
447	Jim Slaton	.06	.05	.02
448	Doyle Alexander	.10	.08	.04
449	Tony Bernazard	.06	.05	.02
450	Scott Sanderson	.06	.05	.02
451	Dave Palmer	.06	.05	.02
452	Stan Bahnsen	.06	.05	.02
453	Dick Williams	.06	.05	.02
454	Rick Burleson	.08	.06	.03
455	Gary Allenson	.06	.05	.02
456	Bob Stanley	.06	.05	.02
457a	*John Tudor* (lifetime W/L 9.7)	1.50	1.25	.60
457b	*John Tudor* (lifetime W/L 9-7)	1.00	.70	.40
458	Dwight Evans	.15	.11	.06
459	Glenn Hubbard	.08	.06	.03
460	U L Washington	.06	.05	.02
461	Larry Gura	.06	.05	.02
462	Rich Gale	.06	.05	.02
463	Hal McRae	.10	.08	.04
464	Jim Frey	.06	.05	.02
465	Bucky Dent	.10	.08	.04
466	Dennis Werth	.06	.05	.02
467	Ron Davis	.08	.06	.03
468	Reggie Jackson	3.50	2.75	1.50
469	Bobby Brown	.06	.05	.02
470	*Mike Davis*	.20	.15	.08
471	Gaylord Perry	.50	.40	.20
472	Mark Belanger	.08	.06	.03
473	Jim Palmer	.80	.60	.30
474	Sammy Stewart	.06	.05	.02
475	Tim Stoddard	.06	.05	.02
476	Steve Stone	.08	.06	.03
477	Jeff Newman	.06	.05	.02
478	Steve McCatty	.06	.05	.02
479	Billy Martin	.12	.09	.05
480	Mitchell Page	.06	.05	.02
481	Cy Young 1980 (Steve Carlton)	.40	.30	.15
482	Bill Buckner	.12	.09	.05
483a	Ivan DeJesus (lifetime hits 702)	1.00	.70	.40
483b	Ivan DeJesus (lifetime hits 642)	.10	.08	.04
484	Cliff Johnson	.06	.05	.02
485	Lenny Randle	.06	.05	.02
486	Larry Milbourne	.06	.05	.02
487	Roy Smalley	.06	.05	.02
488	John Castino	.06	.05	.02
489	Ron Jackson	.06	.05	.02
490a	Dave Roberts (1980 highlights begins "Showed pop...")	1.00	.70	.40
490b	Dave Roberts (1980 highlights begins "Declared himself...")	.10	.08	.04
491	MVP (George Brett)	1.00	.70	.40
492	Mike Cubbage	.06	.05	.02
493	Rob Wilfong	.06	.05	.02
494	Danny Goodwin	.06	.05	.02
495	Jose Morales	.06	.05	.02
496	Mickey Rivers	.08	.06	.03
497	Mike Edwards	.06	.05	.02
498	Mike Sadek	.06	.05	.02
499	Lenn Sakata	.06	.05	.02
500	Gene Michael	.06	.05	.02
501	Dave Roberts	.06	.05	.02
502	Steve Dillard	.06	.05	.02
503	Jim Essian	.06	.05	.02
504	Rance Mulliniks	.06	.05	.02
505	Darrell Porter	.08	.06	.03
506	Joe Torre	.08	.06	.03
507	Terry Crowley	.06	.05	.02
508	Bill Travers	.06	.05	.02
509	Nelson Norman	.06	.05	.02
510	Bob McClure	.06	.05	.02
511	*Steve Howe*	.10	.08	.04
512	Dave Rader	.06	.05	.02
513	Mick Kelleher	.06	.05	.02
514	Kiko Garcia	.06	.05	.02
515	Larry Biittner	.06	.05	.02
516a	Willie Norwood (1980 highlights begins "Spent most...")	1.00	.70	.40
516b	Willie Norwood (1980 highlights begins "Traded to...")	.10	.08	.04
517	Bo Diaz	.08	.06	.03
518	Juan Beniquez	.06	.05	.02
519	Scot Thompson	.06	.05	.02
520	Jim Tracy	.06	.05	.02
521	Carlos Lezcano	.06	.05	.02
522	Joe Amalfitano	.06	.05	.02
523	Preston Hanna	.06	.05	.02
524a	Ray Burris (1980 highlights begins "Went on...")	1.00	.70	.40
524b	Ray Burris (1980 highlights begins "Drafted by...")	.10	.08	.04
525	Broderick Perkins	.06	.05	.02
526	Mickey Hatcher	.08	.06	.03
527	John Goryl	.06	.05	.02
528	Dick Davis	.06	.05	.02
529	Butch Wynegar	.06	.05	.02
530	Sal Butera	.06	.05	.02
531	Jerry Koosman	.10	.08	.04
532a	Jeff Zahn (Geoff) (1980 highlights begins "Was 2nd in...")	1.00	.70	.40
532b	Jeff Zahn (Geoff) (1980 highlights begins "Signed a 3 year...")	.10	.08	.04
533	Dennis Martinez	.08	.06	.03
534	Gary Thomasson	.06	.05	.02
535	Steve Macko	.06	.05	.02
536	Jim Kaat	.15	.11	.06
537	Best Hitters (George Brett, Rod Carew)	1.50	1.25	.60
538	*Tim Raines*	5.00	3.75	2.00
539	Keith Smith	.06	.05	.02
540	Ken Macha	.06	.05	.02
541	Burt Hooton	.08	.06	.03
542	Butch Hobson	.06	.05	.02
543	Bill Stein	.06	.05	.02
544	Dave Stapleton	.06	.05	.02
545	Bob Pate	.06	.05	.02
546	Doug Corbett	.06	.05	.02
547	Darrell Jackson	.06	.05	.02
548	Pete Redfern	.06	.05	.02
549	Roger Erickson	.06	.05	.02
550	Al Hrabosky	.08	.06	.03
551	Dick Tidrow	.06	.05	.02
552	Dave Ford	.06	.05	.02
553	Dave Kingman	.15	.11	.06
554a	Mike Vail (1980 highlights begins "After...")	1.00	.70	.40
554b	Mike Vail (1980 highlights begins "Traded...")	.10	.08	.04
555a	Jerry Martin (1980 highlights begins "Overcame...")	1.00	.70	.40
555b	Jerry Martin (1980 highlights begins "Traded...")	.10	.08	.04
556a	Jesus Figueroa (1980 highlights begins "Had...")	1.00	.70	.40
556b	Jesus Figueroa (1980 highlights begins "Traded...")	.10	.08	.04
557	Don Stanhouse	.06	.05	.02
558	Barry Foote	.06	.05	.02
559	Tim Blackwell	.06	.05	.02
560	Bruce Sutter	.15	.11	.06
561	Rick Reuschel	.10	.08	.04
562	Lynn McGlothen	.06	.05	.02
563a	Bob Owchinko (1980 highlights begins "Traded...")	1.00	.70	.40
563b	Bob Owchinko (1980 highlights begins "Involved...")	.10	.08	.04
564	John Verhoeven	.06	.05	.02
565	Ken Landreaux	.06	.05	.02

	MT	NR MT	EX
566a Glen Adams (Glen on front)	1.00	.70	.40
566b Glenn Adams (Glenn on front)	.10	.08	.04
567 Hosken Powell	.06	.05	.02
568 Dick Noles	.06	.05	.02
569 *Danny Ainge*	.25	.20	.10
570 Bobby Mattick	.06	.05	.02
571 Joe LeFebvre (Lefebvre)	.06	.05	.02
572 Bobby Clark	.06	.05	.02
573 Dennis Lamp	.06	.05	.02
574 Randy Lerch	.06	.05	.02
575 *Mookie Wilson*	.60	.45	.25
576 Ron LeFlore	.08	.06	.03
577 Jim Dwyer	.06	.05	.02
578 Bill Castro	.06	.05	.02
579 Greg Minton	.06	.05	.02
580 Mark Littell	.06	.05	.02
581 Andy Hassler	.06	.05	.02
582 Dave Stieb	.60	.45	.25
583 Ken Oberkfell	.06	.05	.02
584 Larry Bradford	.06	.05	.02
585 Fred Stanley	.06	.05	.02
586 Bill Caudill	.06	.05	.02
587 Doug Capilla	.06	.05	.02
588 George Riley	.06	.05	.02
589 Willie Hernandez	.10	.08	.04
590 MVP (Mike Schmidt)	1.00	.70	.40
591 Cy Young 1980 (Steve Stone)	.08	.06	.03
592 Rick Sofield	.06	.05	.02
593 Bombo Rivera	.06	.05	.02
594 Gary Ward	.08	.06	.03
595a Dave Edwards (1980 highlights begins "Sidelined...")	1.00	.70	.40
595b Dave Edwards (1980 highlights begins "Traded...")	.10	.08	.04
596 Mike Proly	.06	.05	.02
597 Tommy Boggs	.06	.05	.02
598 Greg Gross	.06	.05	.02
599 Elias Sosa	.06	.05	.02
600 Pat Kelly	.06	.05	.02
---a Checklist 1-120 (51 Tom Donohue)	2.00	1.50	.80
---b Checklist 1-120 (51 Tom Donahue)	.10	.08	.04
---- Checklist 121-240	.06	.05	.02
---a Checklist 241-360 (306 Gary Mathews)	.70	.50	.30
---b Checklist 241-360 (306 Gary Matthews)	.10	.08	.04
---a Checklist 361-480 (379 Luis Pujois)	.70	.50	.30
---b Checklist 361-480 (379 Luis Pujols)	.10	.08	.04
---a Checklist 481-600 (566 Glen Adams)	.70	.50	.30
---b Checklist 481-600 (566 Glenn Adams)	.10	.08	.04

1982 Donruss

Using card stock thicker than the previous year, Donruss issued a 660-card set which includes 653 numbered cards and seven unnumbered checklists. The cards, which measure 2-1/2" by 3-1/2", were sold with puzzle pieces rather than gum as a result of a lawsuit by Topps. The puzzle pieces (three pieces on one card per pack) feature Babe Ruth. The first 26 cards of the set, entitled Diamond Kings, showcase the artwork of Dick Perez of Perez-Steele Galleries. The card fronts display the Donruss logo and the year

of issue. The card backs have black and blue ink on white stock and include the player's career highlights. The complete set price does not include the higher priced variations.

	MT	NR MT	EX
Complete Set:	90.00	67.00	35.00
Common Player:	.06	.05	.02
1 Pete Rose (DK)	1.50	1.25	.60
2 Gary Carter (DK)	.50	.40	.20
3 Steve Garvey (DK)	.50	.40	.20
4 Vida Blue (DK)	.12	.09	.05
5a Alan Trammel (DK) (name incorrect)	1.50	1.25	.60
5b Alan Trammell (DK) (name correct)	.40	.30	.15
6 Len Barker (DK)	.08	.06	.03
7 Dwight Evans (DK)	.15	.11	.06
8 Rod Carew (DK)	.60	.45	.25
9 George Hendrick (DK)	.08	.06	.03
10 Phil Niekro (DK)	.30	.25	.12
11 Richie Zisk (DK)	.08	.06	.03
12 Dave Parker (DK)	.30	.25	.12
13 Nolan Ryan (DK)	3.00	2.25	1.25
14 Ivan DeJesus (DK)	.08	.06	.03
15 George Brett (DK)	1.50	1.25	.60
16 Tom Seaver (DK)	.80	.60	.30
17 Dave Kingman (DK)	.15	.11	.06
18 Dave Winfield (DK)	.80	.60	.30
19 Mike Norris (DK)	.08	.06	.03
20 Carlton Fisk (DK)	.50	.40	.20
21 Ozzie Smith (DK)	.20	.15	.08
22 Roy Smalley (DK)	.08	.06	.03
23 Buddy Bell (DK)	.12	.09	.05
24 Ken Singleton (DK)	.10	.08	.04
25 John Mayberry (DK)	.08	.06	.03
26 Gorman Thomas (DK)	.10	.08	.04
27 Earl Weaver	.10	.08	.04
28 Rollie Fingers	.80	.60	.30
29 Sparky Anderson	.10	.08	.04
30 Dennis Eckersley	1.25	.90	.50
31 Dave Winfield	2.00	1.50	.80
32 Burt Hooton	.08	.06	.03
33 Rick Waits	.06	.05	.02
34 George Brett	2.00	1.50	.80
35 Steve McCatty	.06	.05	.02
36 Steve Rogers	.08	.06	.03
37 Bill Stein	.06	.05	.02
38 Steve Renko	.06	.05	.02
39 Mike Squires	.06	.05	.02
40 George Hendrick	.08	.06	.03
41 Bob Knepper	.08	.06	.03
42 Steve Carlton	1.00	.70	.40
43 Larry Biittner	.06	.05	.02
44 Chris Welsh	.06	.05	.02
45 Steve Nicosia	.06	.05	.02
46 Jack Clark	.25	.20	.10
47 Chris Chambliss	.08	.06	.03
48 Ivan DeJesus	.06	.05	.02
49 Lee Mazzilli	.08	.06	.03
50 Julio Cruz	.06	.05	.02
51 Pete Redfern	.06	.05	.02
52 Dave Stieb	.12	.09	.05
53 Doug Corbett	.06	.05	.02
54 *Jorge Bell* (FC)	7.50	5.65	2.95
55 Joe Simpson	.06	.05	.02
56 Rusty Staub	.10	.08	.04
57 Hector Cruz	.06	.05	.02
58 Claudell Washington (FC)	.10	.08	.04
59 Enrique Romo	.06	.05	.02
60 Gary Lavelle	.06	.05	.02
61 Tim Flannery	.06	.05	.02
62 Joe Nolan	.06	.05	.02
63 Larry Bowa	.15	.11	.06
64 Sixto Lezcano	.06	.05	.02
65 Joe Sambito	.06	.05	.02
66 Bruce Kison	.06	.05	.02
67 Wayne Nordhagen	.06	.05	.02
68 Woodie Fryman	.08	.06	.03
69 Billy Sample	.06	.05	.02
70 Amos Otis	.08	.06	.03
71 Matt Keough	.06	.05	.02
72 Toby Harrah	.08	.06	.03
73 *Dave Righetti* (FC)	1.00	.70	.40
74 Carl Yastrzemski	1.00	.70	.40
75 Bob Welch	.12	.09	.05
76a Alan Trammel (name incorrect)	2.00	1.50	.80
76b Alan Trammell (name correct)	.60	.45	.25
77 Rick Dempsey	.08	.06	.03
78 Paul Molitor	.20	.15	.08

#	Name	MT	NR MT	EX		#	Name	MT	NR MT	EX
79	Dennis Martinez	.08	.06	.03		170	Rick Wise	.08	.06	.03
80	Jim Slaton	.06	.05	.02		171	Jim Bibby	.06	.05	.02
81	Champ Summers	.06	.05	.02		172	Larry Herndon	.08	.06	.03
82	Carney Lansford	.08	.06	.03		173	Bob Horner	.12	.09	.05
83	Barry Foote	.06	.05	.02		174	Steve Dillard	.06	.05	.02
84	Steve Garvey	.50	.40	.20		175	Mookie Wilson	.12	.09	.05
85	Rick Manning	.06	.05	.02		176	Dan Meyer	.06	.05	.02
86	John Wathan	.08	.06	.03		177	Fernando Arroyo	.06	.05	.02
87	Brian Kingman	.06	.05	.02		178	Jackson Todd	.06	.05	.02
88	Andre Dawson	1.50	1.25	.60		179	Darrell Jackson	.06	.05	.02
89	Jim Kern	.06	.05	.02		180	Al Woods	.06	.05	.02
90	Bobby Grich	.10	.08	.04		181	Jim Anderson	.06	.05	.02
91	Bob Forsch	.08	.06	.03		182	Dave Kingman	.15	.11	.06
92	Art Howe	.06	.05	.02		183	Steve Henderson	.06	.05	.02
93	Marty Bystrom	.06	.05	.02		184	Brian Asselstine	.06	.05	.02
94	Ozzie Smith	2.00	1.50	.80		185	Rod Scurry	.06	.05	.02
95	Dave Parker	.30	.25	.12		186	Fred Breining	.06	.05	.02
96	Doyle Alexander	.10	.08	.04		187	Danny Boone	.06	.05	.02
97	Al Hrabosky	.08	.06	.03		188	Junior Kennedy	.06	.05	.02
98	Frank Taveras	.06	.05	.02		189	Sparky Lyle	.10	.08	.04
99	Tim Blackwell	.06	.05	.02		190	Whitey Herzog	.08	.06	.03
100	Floyd Bannister	.10	.08	.04		191	Dave Smith	.10	.08	.04
101	Alfredo Griffin	.08	.06	.03		192	Ed Ott	.06	.05	.02
102	Dave Engle	.06	.05	.02		193	Greg Luzinski	.15	.11	.06
103	Mario Soto	.08	.06	.03		194	Bill Lee	.08	.06	.03
104	Ross Baumgarten	.06	.05	.02		195	Don Zimmer	.06	.05	.02
105	Ken Singleton	.10	.08	.04		196	Hal McRae	.12	.09	.05
106	Ted Simmons	.12	.09	.05		197	Mike Norris	.06	.05	.02
107	Jack Morris	.60	.45	.25		198	Duane Kuiper	.06	.05	.02
108	Bob Watson	.08	.06	.03		199	Rick Cerone	.06	.05	.02
109	Dwight Evans	.15	.11	.06		200	Jim Rice	.40	.30	.15
110	Tom Lasorda	.10	.08	.04		201	Steve Yeager	.06	.05	.02
111	Bert Blyleven	.12	.09	.05		202	Tom Brookens	.06	.05	.02
112	Dan Quisenberry	.15	.11	.06		203	Jose Morales	.06	.05	.02
113	Rickey Henderson	5.00	3.75	2.00		204	Roy Howell	.06	.05	.02
114	Gary Carter	.35	.25	.14		205	Tippy Martinez	.06	.05	.02
115	Brian Downing	.10	.08	.04		206	Moose Haas	.06	.05	.02
116	Al Oliver	.15	.11	.06		207	Al Cowens	.06	.05	.02
117	LaMarr Hoyt	.06	.05	.02		208	Dave Stapleton	.06	.05	.02
118	Cesar Cedeno	.12	.09	.05		209	Bucky Dent	.10	.08	.04
119	Keith Moreland	.10	.08	.04		210	Ron Cey	.12	.09	.05
120	Bob Shirley	.06	.05	.02		211	Jorge Orta	.06	.05	.02
121	Terry Kennedy	.08	.06	.03		212	Jamie Quirk	.06	.05	.02
122	Frank Pastore	.06	.05	.02		213	Jeff Jones	.06	.05	.02
123	Gene Garber	.06	.05	.02		214	Tim Raines	1.00	.70	.40
124	Tony Pena(FC)	.25	.20	.10		215	Jon Matlack	.08	.06	.03
125	Allen Ripley	.06	.05	.02		216	Rod Carew	1.00	.70	.40
126	Randy Martz	.06	.05	.02		217	Jim Kaat	.15	.11	.06
127	Richie Zisk	.08	.06	.03		218	Joe Pittman	.06	.05	.02
128	Mike Scott	.15	.11	.06		219	Larry Christenson	.06	.05	.02
129	Lloyd Moseby(FC)	.20	.15	.08		220	Juan Bonilla	.06	.05	.02
130	Rob Wilfong	.06	.05	.02		221	Mike Easler	.08	.06	.03
131	Tim Stoddard	.06	.05	.02		222	Vida Blue	.12	.09	.05
132	Gorman Thomas	.10	.08	.04		223	Rick Camp	.06	.05	.02
133	Dan Petry	.08	.06	.03		224	Mike Jorgensen	.06	.05	.02
134	Bob Stanley	.06	.05	.02		225	*Jody Davis*(FC)	.30	.25	.12
135	Lou Piniella	.12	.09	.05		226	Mike Parrott	.06	.05	.02
136	Pedro Guerrero(FC)	.70	.50	.30		227	Jim Clancy	.08	.06	.03
137	Len Barker	.08	.06	.03		228	Hosken Powell	.06	.05	.02
138	Richard Gale	.06	.05	.02		229	Tom Hume	.06	.05	.02
139	Wayne Gross	.06	.05	.02		230	Britt Burns	.06	.05	.02
140	*Tim Wallach*(FC)	2.00	1.50	.80		231	Jim Palmer	.70	.50	.30
141	Gene Mauch	.08	.06	.03		232	Bob Rodgers	.08	.06	.03
142	Doc Medich	.06	.05	.02		233	Milt Wilcox	.06	.05	.02
143	Tony Bernazard	.06	.05	.02		234	Dave Revering	.06	.05	.02
144	Bill Virdon	.06	.05	.02		235	Mike Torrez	.08	.06	.03
145	John Littlefield	.06	.05	.02		236	Robert Castillo	.06	.05	.02
146	Dave Bergman	.06	.05	.02		237	*Von Hayes*(FC)	1.00	.70	.40
147	Dick Davis	.06	.05	.02		238	Renie Martin	.06	.05	.02
148	Tom Seaver	1.50	1.25	.60		239	Dwayne Murphy	.08	.06	.03
149	Matt Sinatro	.06	.05	.02		240	Rodney Scott	.06	.05	.02
150	Chuck Tanner	.06	.05	.02		241	Fred Patek	.06	.05	.02
151	Leon Durham	.08	.06	.03		242	Mickey Rivers	.08	.06	.03
152	Gene Tenace	.08	.06	.03		243	Steve Trout	.06	.05	.02
153	Al Bumbry	.08	.06	.03		244	Jose Cruz	.12	.09	.05
154	Mark Brouhard	.06	.05	.02		245	Manny Trillo	.08	.06	.03
155	Rick Peters	.06	.05	.02		246	Lary Sorensen	.06	.05	.02
156	Jerry Remy	.06	.05	.02		247	Dave Edwards	.06	.05	.02
157	Rick Reuschel	.10	.08	.04		248	Dan Driessen	.08	.06	.03
158	Steve Howe	.08	.06	.03		249	Tommy Boggs	.06	.05	.02
159	Alan Bannister	.06	.05	.02		250	Dale Berra	.06	.05	.02
160	U L Washington	.06	.05	.02		251	Ed Whitson	.06	.05	.02
161	Rick Langford	.06	.05	.02		252	*Lee Smith*(FC)	8.00	6.00	3.25
162	Bill Gullickson	.08	.06	.03		253	Tom Paciorek	.06	.05	.02
163	Mark Wagner	.06	.05	.02		254	Pat Zachry	.06	.05	.02
164	Geoff Zahn	.06	.05	.02		255	Luis Leal	.06	.05	.02
165	Ron LeFlore	.08	.06	.03		256	John Castino	.06	.05	.02
166	Dane Iorg	.06	.05	.02		257	Rich Dauer	.06	.05	.02
167	Joe Niekro	.12	.09	.05		258	Cecil Cooper	.15	.11	.06
168	Pete Rose	1.00	.70	.40		259	Dave Rozema	.06	.05	.02
169	Dave Collins	.08	.06	.03		260	John Tudor	.15	.11	.06

		MT	NR MT	EX
261	Jerry Mumphrey	.06	.05	.02
262	Jay Johnstone	.08	.06	.03
263	Bo Diaz	.08	.06	.03
264	Dennis Leonard	.08	.06	.03
265	Jim Spencer	.06	.05	.02
266	John Milner	.06	.05	.02
267	Don Aase	.06	.05	.02
268	Jim Sundberg	.08	.06	.03
269	Lamar Johnson	.06	.05	.02
270	Frank LaCorte	.06	.05	.02
271	Barry Evans	.06	.05	.02
272	Enos Cabell	.06	.05	.02
273	Del Unser	.06	.05	.02
274	George Foster	.20	.15	.08
275	*Brett Butler*(FC)	2.50	2.00	1.00
276	Lee Lacy	.06	.05	.02
277	Ken Reitz	.06	.05	.02
278	Keith Hernandez	.40	.30	.15
279	Doug DeCinces	.10	.08	.04
280	Charlie Moore	.06	.05	.02
281	Lance Parrish	.35	.25	.14
282	Ralph Houk	.08	.06	.03
283	Rich Gossage	.20	.15	.08
284	Jerry Reuss	.10	.08	.04
285	Mike Stanton	.06	.05	.02
286	Frank White	.10	.08	.04
287	Bob Owchinko	.06	.05	.02
288	Scott Sanderson	.06	.05	.02
289	Bump Wills	.06	.05	.02
290	Dave Frost	.06	.05	.02
291	Chet Lemon	.08	.06	.03
292	Tito Landrum	.06	.05	.02
293	Vern Ruhle	.06	.05	.02
294	Mike Schmidt	2.50	2.00	1.00
295	Sam Mejias	.06	.05	.02
296	Gary Lucas	.06	.05	.02
297	John Candelaria	.10	.08	.04
298	Jerry Martin	.06	.05	.02
299	Dale Murphy	.90	.70	.35
300	Mike Lum	.06	.05	.02
301	Tom Hausman	.06	.05	.02
302	Glenn Abbott	.06	.05	.02
303	Roger Erickson	.06	.05	.02
304	Otto Velez	.06	.05	.02
305	Danny Goodwin	.06	.05	.02
306	John Mayberry	.08	.06	.03
307	Lenny Randle	.06	.05	.02
308	Bob Bailor	.06	.05	.02
309	Jerry Morales	.06	.05	.02
310	Rufino Linares	.06	.05	.02
311	Kent Tekulve	.08	.06	.03
312	Joe Morgan	.50	.40	.20
313	John Urrea	.06	.05	.02
314	Paul Householder	.06	.05	.02
315	Garry Maddox	.10	.08	.04
316	Mike Ramsey	.06	.05	.02
317	Alan Ashby	.06	.05	.02
318	Bob Clark	.06	.05	.02
319	Tony LaRussa	.08	.06	.03
320	Charlie Lea	.08	.06	.03
321	Danny Darwin	.06	.05	.02
322	Cesar Geronimo	.06	.05	.02
323	Tom Underwood	.06	.05	.02
324	Andre Thornton	.10	.08	.04
325	Rudy May	.06	.05	.02
326	Frank Tanana	.10	.08	.04
327	Davey Lopes	.10	.08	.04
328	Richie Hebner	.06	.05	.02
329	Mike Flanagan	.10	.08	.04
330	Mike Caldwell	.06	.05	.02
331	Scott McGregor	.08	.06	.03
332	Jerry Augustine	.06	.05	.02
333	Stan Papi	.06	.05	.02
334	Rick Miller	.06	.05	.02
335	Graig Nettles	.15	.11	.06
336	Dusty Baker	.10	.08	.04
337	Dave Garcia	.06	.05	.02
338	Larry Gura	.06	.05	.02
339	Cliff Johnson	.06	.05	.02
340	Warren Cromartie	.06	.05	.02
341	Steve Comer	.06	.05	.02
342	Rick Burleson	.08	.06	.03
343	John Martin	.06	.05	.02
344	Craig Reynolds	.06	.05	.02
345	Mike Proly	.06	.05	.02
346	Ruppert Jones	.06	.05	.02
347	Omar Moreno	.06	.05	.02
348	Greg Minton	.06	.05	.02
349	*Rick Mahler*(FC)	.25	.20	.10
350	Alex Trevino	.06	.05	.02
351	Mike Krukow	.08	.06	.03
352a	Shane Rawley (Jim Anderson photo — shaking hands)	1.25	.90	.50
352b	Shane Rawley (correct photo - kneeling)	.15	.11	.06
353	Garth Iorg	.06	.05	.02
354	Pete Mackanin	.06	.05	.02
355	Paul Moskau	.06	.05	.02
356	Richard Dotson	.10	.08	.04
357	Steve Stone	.08	.06	.03
358	Larry Hisle	.08	.06	.03
359	Aurelio Lopez	.06	.05	.02
360	Oscar Gamble	.08	.06	.03
361	Tom Burgmeier	.06	.05	.02
362	Terry Forster	.08	.06	.03
363	Joe Charboneau	.08	.06	.03
364	Ken Brett	.08	.06	.03
365	Tony Armas	.10	.08	.04
366	Chris Speier	.06	.05	.02
367	Fred Lynn	.20	.15	.08
368	Buddy Bell	.12	.09	.05
369	Jim Essian	.06	.05	.02
370	Terry Puhl	.06	.05	.02
371	Greg Gross	.06	.05	.02
372	Bruce Sutter	.15	.11	.06
373	Joe Lefebvre	.06	.05	.02
374	Ray Knight	.10	.08	.04
375	Bruce Benedict	.06	.05	.02
376	Tim Foli	.06	.05	.02
377	Al Holland	.06	.05	.02
378	Ken Kravec	.06	.05	.02
379	Jeff Burroughs	.08	.06	.03
380	Pete Falcone	.06	.05	.02
381	Ernie Whitt	.08	.06	.03
382	Brad Havens	.06	.05	.02
383	Terry Crowley	.06	.05	.02
384	Don Money	.06	.05	.02
385	Dan Schatzeder	.06	.05	.02
386	Gary Allenson	.06	.05	.02
387	Yogi Berra	.15	.11	.06
388	Ken Landreaux	.06	.05	.02
389	Mike Hargrove	.06	.05	.02
390	Darryl Motley	.06	.05	.02
391	Dave McKay	.06	.05	.02
392	Stan Bahnsen	.06	.05	.02
393	Ken Forsch	.06	.05	.02
394	Mario Mendoza	.06	.05	.02
395	Jim Morrison	.06	.05	.02
396	Mike Ivie	.06	.05	.02
397	Broderick Perkins	.06	.05	.02
398	Darrell Evans	.15	.11	.06
399	Ron Reed	.06	.05	.02
400	Johnny Bench	.60	.45	.25
401	*Steve Bedrosian*(FC)	.80	.60	.30
402	Bill Robinson	.06	.05	.02
403	Bill Buckner	.12	.09	.05
404	Ken Oberkfell	.06	.05	.02
405	*Cal Ripken, Jr.*(FC)	50.00	37.00	20.00
406	Jim Gantner	.08	.06	.03
407	Kirk Gibson(FC)	.90	.70	.35
408	Tony Perez	.20	.15	.08
409	Tommy John	.20	.15	.08
410	*Dave Stewart*(FC)	2.50	2.00	1.00
411	Dan Spillner	.06	.05	.02
412	Willie Aikens	.06	.05	.02
413	Mike Heath	.06	.05	.02
414	Ray Burris	.06	.05	.02
415	Leon Roberts	.06	.05	.02
416	*Mike Witt*(FC)	.35	.25	.14
417	Bobby Molinaro	.06	.05	.02
418	Steve Braun	.06	.05	.02
419	Nolan Ryan	8.00	6.00	3.00
420	Tug McGraw	.12	.09	.05
421	Dave Concepcion	.12	.09	.05
422a	Juan Eichelberger (Gary Lucas photo — white player)	1.25	.90	.50
422b	Juan Eichelberger (correct photo - black player)	.08	.06	.03
423	Rick Rhoden	.10	.08	.04
424	Frank Robinson	.12	.09	.05
425	Eddie Miller	.06	.05	.02
426	Bill Caudill	.06	.05	.02
427	Doug Flynn	.06	.05	.02
428	Larry Anderson (Andersen)	.06	.05	.02
429	Al Williams	.06	.05	.02
430	Jerry Garvin	.06	.05	.02
431	Glenn Adams	.06	.05	.02
432	Barry Bonnell	.06	.05	.02
433	Jerry Narron	.06	.05	.02
434	John Stearns	.06	.05	.02
435	Mike Tyson	.06	.05	.02
436	Glenn Hubbard	.08	.06	.03

#	Player	MT	NR MT	EX
437	Eddie Solomon	.06	.05	.02
438	Jeff Leonard	.10	.08	.04
439	Randy Bass	.06	.05	.02
440	Mike LaCoss	.06	.05	.02
441	Gary Matthews	.10	.08	.04
442	Mark Littell	.06	.05	.02
443	Don Sutton	.30	.25	.12
444	John Harris	.06	.05	.02
445	Vada Pinson	.08	.06	.03
446	Elias Sosa	.06	.05	.02
447	Charlie Hough	.10	.08	.04
448	Willie Wilson	.15	.11	.06
449	Fred Stanley	.06	.05	.02
450	Tom Veryzer	.06	.05	.02
451	Ron Davis	.06	.05	.02
452	Mark Clear	.06	.05	.02
453	Bill Russell	.08	.06	.03
454	Lou Whitaker	.40	.30	.15
455	Dan Graham	.06	.05	.02
456	Reggie Cleveland	.06	.05	.02
457	Sammy Stewart	.06	.05	.02
458	Pete Vuckovich	.08	.06	.03
459	John Wockenfuss	.06	.05	.02
460	Glenn Hoffman	.06	.05	.02
461	Willie Randolph	.10	.08	.04
462	Fernando Valenzuela(FC)	.80	.60	.30
463	Ron Hassey	.06	.05	.02
464	Paul Splittorff	.06	.05	.02
465	Rob Picciolo	.06	.05	.02
466	Larry Parrish	.10	.08	.04
467	Johnny Grubb	.06	.05	.02
468	Dan Ford	.06	.05	.02
469	Silvio Martinez	.06	.05	.02
470	Kiko Garcia	.06	.05	.02
471	Bob Boone	.10	.08	.04
472	Luis Salazar	.08	.06	.03
473	Randy Niemann	.06	.05	.02
474	Tom Griffin	.06	.05	.02
475	Phil Niekro	.30	.25	.12
476	Hubie Brooks(FC)	.25	.20	.10
477	Dick Tidrow	.06	.05	.02
478	Jim Beattie	.06	.05	.02
479	Damaso Garcia	.06	.05	.02
480	Mickey Hatcher	.08	.06	.03
481	Joe Price	.06	.05	.02
482	Ed Farmer	.06	.05	.02
483	Eddie Murray	2.00	1.50	.80
484	Ben Oglivie	.08	.06	.03
485	Kevin Saucier	.06	.05	.02
486	Bobby Murcer	.10	.08	.04
487	Bill Campbell	.06	.05	.02
488	Reggie Smith	.10	.08	.04
489	Wayne Garland	.06	.05	.02
490	Jim Wright	.06	.05	.02
491	Billy Martin	.12	.09	.05
492	Jim Fanning	.06	.05	.02
493	Don Baylor	.12	.09	.05
494	Rick Honeycutt	.06	.05	.02
495	Carlton Fisk	1.50	1.25	.60
496	Denny Walling	.06	.05	.02
497	Bake McBride	.06	.05	.02
498	Darrell Porter	.08	.06	.03
499	Gene Richards	.06	.05	.02
500	Ron Oester	.06	.05	.02
501	Ken Dayley(FC)	.20	.15	.08
502	Jason Thompson	.06	.05	.02
503	Milt May	.06	.05	.02
504	Doug Bird	.06	.05	.02
505	Bruce Bochte	.06	.05	.02
506	Neil Allen	.06	.05	.02
507	Joey McLaughlin	.06	.05	.02
508	Butch Wynegar	.06	.05	.02
509	Gary Roenicke	.06	.05	.02
510	Robin Yount	2.00	1.50	.80
511	Dave Tobik	.06	.05	.02
512	Rich Gedman(FC)	.25	.20	.10
513	Gene Nelson(FC)	.12	.09	.05
514	Rick Monday	.10	.08	.04
515	Miguel Dilone	.06	.05	.02
516	Clint Hurdle	.06	.05	.02
517	Jeff Newman	.06	.05	.02
518	Grant Jackson	.06	.05	.02
519	Andy Hassler	.06	.05	.02
520	Pat Putnam	.06	.05	.02
521	Greg Pryor	.06	.05	.02
522	Tony Scott	.06	.05	.02
523	Steve Mura	.06	.05	.02
524	Johnnie LeMaster	.06	.05	.02
525	Dick Ruthven	.06	.05	.02
526	John McNamara	.06	.05	.02
527	Larry McWilliams	.06	.05	.02
528	Johnny Ray(FC)	.30	.25	.12
529	Pat Tabler(FC)	.40	.30	.15
530	Tom Herr	.10	.08	.04
531a	San Diego Chicken (trademark symbol on front)	1.25	.90	.50
531b	San Diego Chicken (no trademark symbol)	.80	.60	.30
532	Sal Butera	.06	.05	.02
533	Mike Griffin	.06	.05	.02
534	Kelvin Moore	.06	.05	.02
535	Reggie Jackson	2.00	1.50	.80
536	Ed Romero	.06	.05	.02
537	Derrel Thomas	.06	.05	.02
538	Mike O'Berry	.06	.05	.02
539	Jack O'Connor	.06	.05	.02
540	Bob Ojeda(FC)	.50	.40	.20
541	Roy Lee Jackson	.06	.05	.02
542	Lynn Jones	.06	.05	.02
543	Gaylord Perry	.40	.30	.15
544a	Phil Garner (photo reversed)	1.25	.90	.50
544b	Phil Garner (photo correct)	.10	.08	.04
545	Garry Templeton	.10	.08	.04
546	Rafael Ramirez(FC)	.10	.08	.04
547	Jeff Reardon	.20	.15	.08
548	Ron Guidry	.25	.20	.10
549	Tim Laudner(FC)	.25	.20	.10
550	John Henry Johnson	.06	.05	.02
551	Chris Bando	.06	.05	.02
552	Bobby Brown	.06	.05	.02
553	Larry Bradford	.06	.05	.02
554	Scott Fletcher(FC)	.30	.25	.12
555	Jerry Royster	.06	.05	.02
556	Shooty Babbitt	.06	.05	.02
557	Kent Hrbek(FC)	3.00	2.25	1.25
558	Yankee Winners (Ron Guidry, Tommy John)	.15	.11	.06
559	Mark Bomback	.06	.05	.02
560	Julio Valdez	.06	.05	.02
561	Buck Martinez	.06	.05	.02
562	Mike Marshall(FC)	.25	.20	.10
563	Rennie Stennett	.06	.05	.02
564	Steve Crawford	.06	.05	.02
565	Bob Babcock	.06	.05	.02
566	Johnny Podres	.08	.06	.03
567	Paul Serna	.06	.05	.02
568	Harold Baines(FC)	1.25	.90	.50
569	Dave LaRoche	.06	.05	.02
570	Lee May	.08	.06	.03
571	Gary Ward(FC)	.10	.08	.04
572	John Denny	.06	.05	.02
573	Roy Smalley	.06	.05	.02
574	Bob Brenly(FC)	.20	.15	.08
575	Bronx Bombers (Reggie Jackson, Dave Winfield)	1.00	.70	.40
576	Luis Pujols	.06	.05	.02
577	Butch Hobson	.06	.05	.02
578	Harvey Kuenn	.08	.06	.03
579	Cal Ripken, Sr.	.08	.06	.03
580	Juan Berenguer	.08	.06	.03
581	Benny Ayala	.06	.05	.02
582	Vance Law(FC)	.15	.11	.06
583	Rick Leach(FC)	.12	.09	.05
584	George Frazier	.06	.05	.02
585	Phillies Finest (Pete Rose, Mike Schmidt)	.70	.50	.30
586	Joe Rudi	.10	.08	.04
587	Juan Beniquez	.06	.05	.02
588	Luis DeLeon(FC)	.08	.06	.03
589	Craig Swan	.06	.05	.02
590	Dave Chalk	.06	.05	.02
591	Billy Gardner	.06	.05	.02
592	Sal Bando	.08	.06	.03
593	Bert Campaneris	.10	.08	.04
594	Steve Kemp	.08	.06	.03
595a	Randy Lerch (Braves)	1.25	.90	.50
595b	Randy Lerch (Brewers)	.08	.06	.03
596	Bryan Clark	.06	.05	.02
597	Dave Ford	.06	.05	.02
598	Mike Scioscia(FC)	.20	.15	.08
599	John Lowenstein	.06	.05	.02
600	Rene Lachemann (Lachemann)	.06	.05	.02
601	Mick Kelleher	.06	.05	.02
602	Ron Jackson	.06	.05	.02
603	Jerry Koosman	.10	.08	.04
604	Dave Goltz	.08	.06	.03
605	Ellis Valentine	.06	.05	.02
606	Lonnie Smith	.08	.06	.03
607	Joaquin Andujar	.08	.06	.03
608	Garry Hancock	.06	.05	.02
609	Jerry Turner	.06	.05	.02
610	Bob Bonner	.06	.05	.02

		MT	NR MT	EX
611	Jim Dwyer	.06	.05	.02
612	Terry Bulling	.06	.05	.02
613	Joel Youngblood	.06	.05	.02
614	Larry Milbourne	.06	.05	.02
615	Phil Roof (Gene)	.06	.05	.02
616	Keith Drumright	.06	.05	.02
617	Dave Rosello	.06	.05	.02
618	Rickey Keeton	.06	.05	.02
619	Dennis Lamp	.06	.05	.02
620	Sid Monge	.06	.05	.02
621	Jerry White	.06	.05	.02
622	Luis Aguayo(FC)	.10	.08	.04
623	Jamie Easterly	.06	.05	.02
624	Steve Sax(FC)	4.00	3.00	1.50
625	Dave Roberts	.06	.05	.02
626	Rick Bosetti	.06	.05	.02
627	Terry Francona(FC)	.10	.08	.04
628	Pride of the Reds (Johnny Bench, Tom Seaver)	.80	.60	.30
629	Paul Mirabella	.06	.05	.02
630	Rance Mulliniks	.06	.05	.02
631	Kevin Hickey	.06	.05	.02
632	Reid Nichols	.06	.05	.02
633	Dave Geisel	.06	.05	.02
634	Ken Griffey	.12	.09	.05
635	Bob Lemon	.10	.08	.04
636	Orlando Sanchez	.06	.05	.02
637	Bill Almon	.06	.05	.02
638	Danny Ainge	.12	.09	.05
639	Willie Stargell	.40	.30	.15
640	Bob Sykes	.06	.05	.02
641	Ed Lynch	.06	.05	.02
642	John Ellis	.06	.05	.02
643	Fergie Jenkins	.15	.11	.06
644	Lenn Sakata	.06	.05	.02
645	Julio Gonzales	.06	.05	.02
646	Jesse Orosco(FC)	.15	.11	.06
647	Jerry Dybzinski	.06	.05	.02
648	Tommy Davis	.08	.06	.03
649	Ron Gardenhire	.06	.05	.02
650	Felipe Alou	.08	.06	.03
651	Harvey Haddix	.08	.06	.03
652	Willie Upshaw(FC)	.15	.11	.06
653	Bill Madlock	.12	.09	.05
---a	Checklist 1-26 DK (5 Trammel)	.70	.50	.30
---b	Checklist 1-26 DK (5 Trammell)	.08	.06	.03
-----	Checklist 27-130	.06	.05	.02
-----	Checklist 131-234	.06	.05	.02
-----	Checklist 235-338	.06	.05	.02
-----	Checklist 339-442	.06	.05	.02
-----	Checklist 443-544	.06	.05	.02
-----	Checklist 545-653	.06	.05	.02

1983 Donruss

The 1983 Donruss set consists of 653 numbered cards plus seven unnumbered checklists. The cards, which measure 2-1/2" by 3-1/2", were issued with puzzle pieces (three pieces on one card per pack) that feature Ty Cobb. The first 26 cards in the set were once again the Diamond Kings series. The card fronts display the Donruss logo and the year of issue. The card backs have black print on yellow and white and include statistics, career highlights, and the player's contract status. (DK) in the checklist that follows indicates cards which belong to the Diamond Kings series.

		MT	NR MT	EX
	Complete Set:	125.00	90.00	50.00
	Common Player:	.06	.05	.02
1	Fernando Valenzuela (DK)	.40	.30	.15
2	Rollie Fingers (DK)	.20	.15	.08
3	Reggie Jackson (DK)	.60	.45	.25
4	Jim Palmer (DK)	.40	.30	.15
5	Jack Morris (DK)	.30	.25	.12
6	George Foster (DK)	.20	.15	.08
7	Jim Sundberg (DK)	.08	.06	.03
8	Willie Stargell (DK)	.40	.30	.15
9	Dave Stieb (DK)	.12	.09	.05
10	Joe Niekro (DK)	.12	.09	.05
11	Rickey Henderson (DK)	2.00	1.50	.80
12	Dale Murphy (DK)	.50	.40	.20
13	Toby Harrah (DK)	.08	.06	.03
14	Bill Buckner (DK)	.12	.09	.05
15	Willie Wilson (DK)	.15	.11	.06
16	Steve Carlton (DK)	.40	.30	.15
17	Ron Guidry (DK)	.25	.20	.10
18	Steve Rogers (DK)	.08	.06	.03
19	Kent Hrbek (DK)	.40	.30	.15
20	Keith Hernandez (DK)	.40	.30	.15
21	Floyd Bannister (DK)	.10	.08	.04
22	Johnny Bench (DK)	.40	.30	.15
23	Britt Burns (DK)	.08	.06	.03
24	Joe Morgan (DK)	.30	.25	.12
25	Carl Yastrzemski (DK)	.80	.60	.30
26	Terry Kennedy (DK)	.08	.06	.03
27	Gary Roenicke	.06	.05	.02
28	Dwight Bernard	.06	.05	.02
29	Pat Underwood	.06	.05	.02
30	Gary Allenson	.06	.05	.02
31	Ron Guidry	.25	.20	.10
32	Burt Hooton	.08	.06	.03
33	Chris Bando	.06	.05	.02
34	Vida Blue	.12	.09	.05
35	Rickey Henderson	4.00	3.00	1.50
36	Ray Burris	.06	.05	.02
37	John Butcher	.06	.05	.02
38	Don Aase	.06	.05	.02
39	Jerry Koosman	.10	.08	.04
40	Bruce Sutter	.15	.11	.06
41	Jose Cruz	.12	.09	.05
42	Pete Rose	1.00	.70	.40
43	Cesar Cedeno	.12	.09	.05
44	Floyd Chiffer	.06	.05	.02
45	Larry McWilliams	.06	.05	.02
46	Alan Fowlkes	.06	.05	.02
47	Dale Murphy	.70	.50	.30
48	Doug Bird	.06	.05	.02
49	Hubie Brooks	.12	.09	.05
50	Floyd Bannister	.10	.08	.04
51	Jack O'Connor	.06	.05	.02
52	Steve Senteney	.06	.05	.02
53	Gary Gaetti(FC)	.80	.60	.30
54	Damaso Garcia	.06	.05	.02
55	Gene Nelson	.06	.05	.02
56	Mookie Wilson	.10	.08	.04
57	Allen Ripley	.06	.05	.02
58	Bob Horner	.12	.09	.05
59	Tony Pena	.10	.08	.04
60	Gary Lavelle	.06	.05	.02
61	Tim Lollar	.06	.05	.02
62	Frank Pastore	.06	.05	.02
63	Garry Maddox	.10	.08	.04
64	Bob Forsch	.08	.06	.03
65	Harry Spilman	.06	.05	.02
66	Geoff Zahn	.06	.05	.02
67	Salome Barojas	.06	.05	.02
68	David Palmer	.06	.05	.02
69	Charlie Hough	.10	.08	.04
70	Dan Quisenberry	.15	.11	.06
71	Tony Armas	.10	.08	.04
72	Rick Sutcliffe	.12	.09	.05
73	Steve Balboni(FC)	.15	.11	.06
74	Jerry Remy	.06	.05	.02
75	Mike Scioscia	.08	.06	.03
76	John Wockenfuss	.06	.05	.02
77	Jim Palmer	.80	.60	.30
78	Rollie Fingers	.60	.45	.25
79	Joe Nolan	.06	.05	.02
80	Pete Vuckovich	.08	.06	.03
81	Rick Leach	.06	.05	.02
82	Rick Miller	.06	.05	.02
83	Graig Nettles	.15	.11	.06
84	Ron Cey	.12	.09	.05
85	Miguel Dilone	.06	.05	.02
86	John Wathan	.08	.06	.03
87	Kelvin Moore	.06	.05	.02
88a	Byrn Smith (first name incorrect)	.70	.50	.30
88b	Bryn Smith (first name correct)	.08	.06	.03

#	Player	MT	NR MT	EX
89	Dave Hostetler	.06	.05	.02
90	Rod Carew	1.00	.70	.40
91	Lonnie Smith	.08	.06	.03
92	Bob Knepper	.08	.06	.03
93	Marty Bystrom	.06	.05	.02
94	Chris Welsh	.06	.05	.02
95	Jason Thompson	.06	.05	.02
96	Tom O'Malley	.06	.05	.02
97	Phil Niekro	.30	.25	.12
98	Neil Allen	.06	.05	.02
99	Bill Buckner	.12	.09	.05
100	Ed VandeBerg (Vande Berg)(FC)	.10	.08	.04
101	Jim Clancy	.08	.06	.03
102	Robert Castillo	.06	.05	.02
103	Bruce Berenyi	.06	.05	.02
104	Carlton Fisk	1.25	.90	.50
105	Mike Flanagan	.10	.08	.04
106	Cecil Cooper	.15	.11	.06
107	Jack Morris	.80	.60	.30
108	Mike Morgan(FC)	.12	.09	.05
109	Luis Aponte	.06	.05	.02
110	Pedro Guerrero	.25	.20	.10
111	Len Barker	.08	.06	.03
112	Willie Wilson	.15	.11	.06
113	Dave Beard	.06	.05	.02
114	Mike Gates	.06	.05	.02
115	Reggie Jackson	.70	.50	.30
116	George Wright	.06	.05	.02
117	Vance Law	.06	.05	.02
118	Nolan Ryan	6.00	4.50	2.50
119	Mike Krukow	.08	.06	.03
120	Ozzie Smith	1.25	.90	.50
121	Broderick Perkins	.06	.05	.02
122	Tom Seaver	1.50	1.25	.60
123	Chris Chambliss	.08	.06	.03
124	Chuck Tanner	.06	.05	.02
125	Johnnie LeMaster	.06	.05	.02
126	Mel Hall(FC)	1.50	1.25	.60
127	Bruce Bochte	.06	.05	.02
128	Charlie Puleo(FC)	.12	.09	.05
129	Luis Leal	.06	.05	.02
130	John Pacella	.06	.05	.02
131	Glenn Gulliver	.06	.05	.02
132	Don Money	.06	.05	.02
133	Dave Rozema	.06	.05	.02
134	Bruce Hurst(FC)	.25	.20	.10
135	Rudy May	.06	.05	.02
136	Tom LaSorda (Lasorda)	.10	.08	.04
137	Dan Spillner (photo actually Ed Whitson)	.06	.05	.02
138	Jerry Martin	.06	.05	.02
139	Mike Norris	.06	.05	.02
140	Al Oliver	.15	.11	.06
141	Daryl Sconiers	.06	.05	.02
142	Lamar Johnson	.06	.05	.02
143	Harold Baines	.15	.11	.06
144	Alan Ashby	.06	.05	.02
145	Garry Templeton	.10	.08	.04
146	Al Holland	.06	.05	.02
147	Bo Diaz	.08	.06	.03
148	Dave Concepcion	.12	.09	.05
149	Rick Camp	.06	.05	.02
150	Jim Morrison	.06	.05	.02
151	Randy Martz	.06	.05	.02
152	Keith Hernandez	.40	.30	.15
153	John Lowenstein	.06	.05	.02
154	Mike Caldwell	.06	.05	.02
155	Milt Wilcox	.06	.05	.02
156	Rich Gedman	.08	.06	.03
157	Rich Gossage	.20	.15	.08
158	Jerry Reuss	.10	.08	.04
159	Ron Hassey	.06	.05	.02
160	Larry Gura	.06	.05	.02
161	Dwayne Murphy	.08	.06	.03
162	Woodie Fryman	.08	.06	.03
163	Steve Comer	.06	.05	.02
164	Ken Forsch	.06	.05	.02
165	Dennis Lamp	.06	.05	.02
166	David Green	.06	.05	.02
167	Terry Puhl	.06	.05	.02
168	Mike Schmidt	2.00	1.50	.80
169	Eddie Milner(FC)	.10	.08	.04
170	John Curtis	.06	.05	.02
171	Don Robinson	.08	.06	.03
172	Richard Gale	.06	.05	.02
173	Steve Bedrosian	.12	.09	.05
174	Willie Hernandez	.08	.06	.03
175	Ron Gardenhire	.06	.05	.02
176	Jim Beattie	.06	.05	.02
177	Tim Laudner	.08	.06	.03
178	Buck Martinez	.06	.05	.02
179	Kent Hrbek	.80	.60	.30
180	Alfredo Griffin	.08	.06	.03
181	Larry Andersen	.06	.05	.02
182	Pete Falcone	.06	.05	.02
183	Jody Davis	.10	.08	.04
184	Glenn Hubbard	.08	.06	.03
185	Dale Berra	.06	.05	.02
186	Greg Minton	.06	.05	.02
187	Gary Lucas	.06	.05	.02
188	Dave Van Gorder	.06	.05	.02
189	Bob Dernier(FC)	.10	.08	.04
190	Willie McGee(FC)	3.00	2.25	1.25
191	Dickie Thon	.08	.06	.03
192	Bob Boone	.10	.08	.04
193	Britt Burns	.06	.05	.02
194	Jeff Reardon	.80	.60	.30
195	Jon Matlack	.08	.06	.03
196	Don Slaught(FC)	.20	.15	.08
197	Fred Stanley	.06	.05	.02
198	Rick Manning	.06	.05	.02
199	Dave Righetti	.25	.20	.10
200	Dave Stapleton	.06	.05	.02
201	Steve Yeager	.06	.05	.02
202	Enos Cabell	.06	.05	.02
203	Sammy Stewart	.06	.05	.02
204	Moose Haas	.06	.05	.02
205	Lenn Sakata	.06	.05	.02
206	Charlie Moore	.06	.05	.02
207	Alan Trammell	.40	.30	.15
208	Jim Rice	.40	.30	.15
209	Roy Smalley	.06	.05	.02
210	Bill Russell	.08	.06	.03
211	Andre Thornton	.10	.08	.04
212	Willie Aikens	.06	.05	.02
213	Dave McKay	.06	.05	.02
214	Tim Blackwell	.06	.05	.02
215	Buddy Bell	.12	.09	.05
216	Doug DeCinces	.10	.08	.04
217	Tom Herr	.10	.08	.04
218	Frank LaCorte	.06	.05	.02
219	Steve Carlton	1.00	.70	.40
220	Terry Kennedy	.08	.06	.03
221	Mike Easler	.08	.06	.03
222	Jack Clark	.25	.20	.10
223	Gene Garber	.06	.05	.02
224	Scott Holman	.06	.05	.02
225	Mike Proly	.06	.05	.02
226	Terry Bulling	.06	.05	.02
227	Jerry Garvin	.06	.05	.02
228	Ron Davis	.06	.05	.02
229	Tom Hume	.06	.05	.02
230	Marc Hill	.06	.05	.02
231	Dennis Martinez	.08	.06	.03
232	Jim Gantner	.08	.06	.03
233	Larry Pashnick	.06	.05	.02
234	Dave Collins	.08	.06	.03
235	Tom Burgmeier	.06	.05	.02
236	Ken Landreaux	.06	.05	.02
237	John Denny	.06	.05	.02
238	Hal McRae	.12	.09	.05
239	Matt Keough	.06	.05	.02
240	Doug Flynn	.06	.05	.02
241	Fred Lynn	.20	.15	.08
242	Billy Sample	.06	.05	.02
243	Tom Paciorek	.06	.05	.02
244	Joe Sambito	.06	.05	.02
245	Sid Monge	.06	.05	.02
246	Ken Oberkfell	.06	.05	.02
247	Joe Pittman (photo actually Juan Eichelberger)	.06	.05	.02
248	Mario Soto	.08	.06	.03
249	Claudell Washington	.08	.06	.03
250	Rick Rhoden	.10	.08	.04
251	Darrell Evans	.15	.11	.06
252	Steve Henderson	.06	.05	.02
253	Manny Castillo	.06	.05	.02
254	Craig Swan	.06	.05	.02
255	Joey McLaughlin	.06	.05	.02
256	Pete Redfern	.06	.05	.02
257	Ken Singleton	.10	.08	.04
258	Robin Yount	3.00	2.25	1.25
259	Elias Sosa	.06	.05	.02
260	Bob Ojeda	.12	.09	.05
261	Bobby Murcer	.10	.08	.04
262	Candy Maldonado(FC)	.60	.45	.25
263	Rick Waits	.06	.05	.02
264	Greg Pryor	.06	.05	.02
265	Bob Owchinko	.06	.05	.02
266	Chris Speier	.06	.05	.02
267	Bruce Kison	.06	.05	.02

		MT	NR MT	EX
268	Mark Wagner	.06	.05	.02
269	Steve Kemp	.10	.08	.04
270	Phil Garner	.08	.06	.03
271	Gene Richards	.06	.05	.02
272	Renie Martin	.06	.05	.02
273	Dave Roberts	.06	.05	.02
274	Dan Driessen	.08	.06	.03
275	Rufino Linares	.06	.05	.02
276	Lee Lacy	.06	.05	.02
277	*Ryne Sandberg*(FC)	40.00	30.00	15.00
278	Darrell Porter	.08	.06	.03
279	Cal Ripken	15.00	11.00	6.00
280	Jamie Easterly	.06	.05	.02
281	Bill Fahey	.06	.05	.02
282	Glenn Hoffman	.06	.05	.02
283	Willie Randolph	.10	.08	.04
284	Fernando Valenzuela	.30	.25	.12
285	Alan Bannister	.06	.05	.02
286	Paul Splittorff	.06	.05	.02
287	Joe Rudi	.10	.08	.04
288	Bill Gullickson	.06	.05	.02
289	Danny Darwin	.06	.05	.02
290	Andy Hassler	.06	.05	.02
291	Ernesto Escarrega	.06	.05	.02
292	Steve Mura	.06	.05	.02
293	Tony Scott	.06	.05	.02
294	Manny Trillo	.08	.06	.03
295	Greg Harris(FC)	.08	.06	.03
296	Luis DeLeon	.06	.05	.02
297	Kent Tekulve	.08	.06	.03
298	Atlee Hammaker(FC)	.12	.09	.05
299	Bruce Benedict	.06	.05	.02
300	Fergie Jenkins	.15	.11	.06
301	Dave Kingman	.15	.11	.06
302	Bill Caudill	.06	.05	.02
303	John Castino	.06	.05	.02
304	Ernie Whitt	.08	.06	.03
305	Randy Johnson	.06	.05	.02
306	Garth Iorg	.06	.05	.02
307	Gaylord Perry	.40	.30	.15
308	Ed Lynch	.06	.05	.02
309	Keith Moreland	.08	.06	.03
310	Rafael Ramirez	.06	.05	.02
311	Bill Madlock	.12	.09	.05
312	Milt May	.06	.05	.02
313	John Montefusco	.06	.05	.02
314	Wayne Krenchicki	.06	.05	.02
315	George Vukovich	.06	.05	.02
316	Joaquin Andujar	.08	.06	.03
317	Craig Reynolds	.06	.05	.02
318	Rick Burleson	.08	.06	.03
319	Richard Dotson	.10	.08	.04
320	Steve Rogers	.08	.06	.03
321	Dave Schmidt(FC)	.10	.08	.04
322	*Bud Black*(FC)	.20	.15	.08
323	Jeff Burroughs	.08	.06	.03
324	Von Hayes	.15	.11	.06
325	Butch Wynegar	.06	.05	.02
326	Carl Yastrzemski	.80	.60	.30
327	Ron Roenicke	.06	.05	.02
328	*Howard Johnson*(FC)	7.00	5.25	2.75
329	Rick Dempsey	.08	.06	.03
330a	Jim Slaton (one yellow box on back)			
		.70	.50	.30
330b	Jim Slaton (two yellow boxes on back)			
		.08	.06	.03
331	Benny Ayala	.06	.05	.02
332	Ted Simmons	.12	.09	.05
333	Lou Whitaker	.40	.30	.15
334	Chuck Rainey	.06	.05	.02
335	Lou Piniella	.12	.09	.05
336	Steve Sax	.30	.25	.12
337	Toby Harrah	.08	.06	.03
338	George Brett	3.00	2.25	1.25
339	Davey Lopes	.10	.08	.04
340	Gary Carter	.40	.30	.15
341	John Grubb	.06	.05	.02
342	Tim Foli	.06	.05	.02
343	Jim Kaat	.15	.11	.06
344	Mike LaCoss	.06	.05	.02
345	Larry Christenson	.06	.05	.02
346	Juan Bonilla	.06	.05	.02
347	Omar Moreno	.06	.05	.02
348	Charles Davis(FC)	.20	.15	.08
349	Tommy Boggs	.06	.05	.02
350	Rusty Staub	.10	.08	.04
351	Bump Wills	.06	.05	.02
352	Rick Sweet	.06	.05	.02
353	*Jim Gott*(FC)	.20	.15	.08
354	Terry Felton	.06	.05	.02
355	Jim Kern	.06	.05	.02
356	Bill Almon	.06	.05	.02
357	Tippy Martinez	.06	.05	.02
358	Roy Howell	.06	.05	.02
359	Dan Petry	.08	.06	.03
360	Jerry Mumphrey	.06	.05	.02
361	Mark Clear	.06	.05	.02
362	Mike Marshall	.20	.15	.08
363	Lary Sorensen	.06	.05	.02
364	Amos Otis	.08	.06	.03
365	Rick Langford	.06	.05	.02
366	Brad Mills	.06	.05	.02
367	Brian Downing	.10	.08	.04
368	Mike Richardt	.06	.05	.02
369	Aurelio Rodriguez	.08	.06	.03
370	Dave Smith	.08	.06	.03
371	Tug McGraw	.12	.09	.05
372	Doug Bair	.06	.05	.02
373	Ruppert Jones	.06	.05	.02
374	Alex Trevino	.06	.05	.02
375	Ken Dayley	.06	.05	.02
376	Rod Scurry	.06	.05	.02
377	Bob Brenly(FC)	.08	.06	.03
378	Scot Thompson	.06	.05	.02
379	Julio Cruz	.06	.05	.02
380	John Stearns	.06	.05	.02
381	Dale Murray	.06	.05	.02
382	*Frank Viola*(FC)	4.00	3.00	1.50
383	Al Bumbry	.08	.06	.03
384	Ben Oglivie	.08	.06	.03
385	Dave Tobik	.06	.05	.02
386	Bob Stanley	.06	.05	.02
387	Andre Robertson	.06	.05	.02
388	Jorge Orta	.06	.05	.02
389	Ed Whitson	.06	.05	.02
390	Don Hood	.06	.05	.02
391	Tom Underwood	.06	.05	.02
392	Tim Wallach	.20	.15	.08
393	Steve Renko	.06	.05	.02
394	Mickey Rivers	.08	.06	.03
395	Greg Luzinski	.12	.09	.05
396	Art Howe	.06	.05	.02
397	Alan Wiggins	.06	.05	.02
398	Jim Barr	.06	.05	.02
399	Ivan DeJesus	.06	.05	.02
400	*Tom Lawless*(FC)	.08	.06	.03
401	Bob Walk	.08	.06	.03
402	Jimmy Smith	.06	.05	.02
403	Lee Smith	2.00	1.50	.80
404	George Hendrick	.08	.06	.03
405	Eddie Murray	.80	.60	.30
406	Marshall Edwards	.06	.05	.02
407	Lance Parrish	.35	.25	.14
408	Carney Lansford	.08	.06	.03
409	Dave Winfield	2.00	1.50	.80
410	Bob Welch	.12	.09	.05
411	Larry Milbourne	.06	.05	.02
412	Dennis Leonard	.08	.06	.03
413	Dan Meyer	.06	.05	.02
414	Charlie Lea	.06	.05	.02
415	Rick Honeycutt	.06	.05	.02
416	Mike Witt	.15	.11	.06
417	Steve Trout	.06	.05	.02
418	Glenn Brummer	.06	.05	.02
419	Denny Walling	.06	.05	.02
420	Gary Matthews	.10	.08	.04
421	Charlie Liebrandt (Leibrandt)	.08	.06	.03
422	Juan Eichelberger	.06	.05	.02
423	*Matt Guante (Cecilio)*(FC)	.15	.11	.06
424	Bill Laskey	.06	.05	.02
425	Jerry Royster	.06	.05	.02
426	Dickie Noles	.06	.05	.02
427	George Foster	.15	.11	.06
428	*Mike Moore*(FC)	1.00	.70	.40
429	Gary Ward	.08	.06	.03
430	Barry Bonnell	.06	.05	.02
431	Ron Washington	.06	.05	.02
432	Rance Mulliniks	.06	.05	.02
433	Mike Stanton	.06	.05	.02
434	Jesse Orosco	.10	.08	.04
435	Larry Bowa	.12	.09	.05
436	Biff Pocoroba	.06	.05	.02
437	Johnny Ray	.12	.09	.05
438	Joe Morgan	.40	.30	.15
439	*Eric Show*(FC)	.30	.25	.12
440	Larry Biittner	.06	.05	.02
441	Greg Gross	.06	.05	.02
442	Gene Tenace	.08	.06	.03
443	Danny Heep	.06	.05	.02
444	Bobby Clark	.06	.05	.02
445	Kevin Hickey	.06	.05	.02
446	Scott Sanderson	.06	.05	.02

		MT	NR MT	EX
447	Frank Tanana	.10	.08	.04
448	Cesar Geronimo	.06	.05	.02
449	Jimmy Sexton	.06	.05	.02
450	Mike Hargrove	.06	.05	.02
451	Doyle Alexander	.10	.08	.04
452	Dwight Evans	.15	.11	.06
453	Terry Forster	.08	.06	.03
454	Tom Brookens	.06	.05	.02
455	Rich Dauer	.06	.05	.02
456	Rob Picciolo	.06	.05	.02
457	Terry Crowley	.06	.05	.02
458	Ned Yost	.06	.05	.02
459	Kirk Gibson	.40	.30	.15
460	Reid Nichols	.06	.05	.02
461	Oscar Gamble	.08	.06	.03
462	Dusty Baker	.10	.08	.04
463	Jack Perconte	.06	.05	.02
464	Frank White	.10	.08	.04
465	Mickey Klutts	.06	.05	.02
466	Warren Cromartie	.06	.05	.02
467	Larry Parrish	.10	.08	.04
468	Bobby Grich	.10	.08	.04
469	Dane Iorg	.06	.05	.02
470	Joe Niekro	.12	.09	.05
471	Ed Farmer	.06	.05	.02
472	Tim Flannery	.06	.05	.02
473	Dave Parker	.30	.25	.12
474	Jeff Leonard	.10	.08	.04
475	Al Hrabosky	.08	.06	.03
476	Ron Hodges	.06	.05	.02
477	Leon Durham	.08	.06	.03
478	Jim Essian	.06	.05	.02
479	Roy Lee Jackson	.06	.05	.02
480	Brad Havens	.06	.05	.02
481	Joe Price	.06	.05	.02
482	Tony Bernazard	.06	.05	.02
483	Scott McGregor	.08	.06	.03
484	Paul Molitor	.20	.15	.08
485	Mike Ivie	.06	.05	.02
486	Ken Griffey	.12	.09	.05
487	Dennis Eckersley	1.00	.70	.40
488	Steve Garvey	.40	.30	.15
489	Mike Fischlin	.06	.05	.02
490	U.L. Washington	.06	.05	.02
491	Steve McCatty	.06	.05	.02
492	Roy Johnson	.06	.05	.02
493	Don Baylor	.12	.09	.05
494	Bobby Johnson	.06	.05	.02
495	Mike Squires	.06	.05	.02
496	Bert Roberge	.06	.05	.02
497	Dick Ruthven	.06	.05	.02
498	Tito Landrum	.06	.05	.02
499	Sixto Lezcano	.06	.05	.02
500	Johnny Bench	1.00	.70	.40
501	Larry Whisenton	.06	.05	.02
502	Manny Sarmiento	.06	.05	.02
503	Fred Breining	.06	.05	.02
504	Bill Campbell	.06	.05	.02
505	Todd Cruz	.06	.05	.02
506	Bob Bailor	.06	.05	.02
507	Dave Stieb	.12	.09	.05
508	Al Williams	.06	.05	.02
509	Dan Ford	.06	.05	.02
510	Gorman Thomas	.10	.08	.04
511	Chet Lemon	.08	.06	.03
512	Mike Torrez	.08	.06	.03
513	Shane Rawley	.10	.08	.04
514	Mark Belanger	.08	.06	.03
515	Rodney Craig	.06	.05	.02
516	Onix Concepcion	.06	.05	.02
517	Mike Heath	.06	.05	.02
518	Andre Dawson	1.25	.90	.50
519	Luis Sanchez	.06	.05	.02
520	Terry Bogener	.06	.05	.02
521	Rudy Law	.06	.05	.02
522	Ray Knight	.10	.08	.04
523	Joe Lefebvre	.06	.05	.02
524	Jim Wohlford	.06	.05	.02
525	Julio Franco(FC)	11.00	8.25	4.50
526	Ron Oester	.06	.05	.02
527	Rick Mahler	.08	.06	.03
528	Steve Nicosia	.06	.05	.02
529	Junior Kennedy	.06	.05	.02
530a	Whitey Herzog (one yellow box on back)	.70	.50	.30
530b	Whitey Herzog (two yellow boxes on back)	.10	.08	.04
531a	Don Sutton (blue frame around photo)	1.00	.70	.40
531b	Don Sutton (green frame around photo)	.30	.25	.12

		MT	NR MT	EX
532	Mark Brouhard	.06	.05	.02
533a	Sparky Anderson (one yellow box on back)	.70	.50	.30
533b	Sparky Anderson (two yellow boxes on back)	.10	.08	.04
534	Roger LaFrancois	.06	.05	.02
535	George Frazier	.06	.05	.02
536	Tom Niedenfuer	.08	.06	.03
537	Ed Glynn	.06	.05	.02
538	Lee May	.08	.06	.03
539	Bob Kearney	.06	.05	.02
540	Tim Raines	.35	.25	.14
541	Paul Mirabella	.06	.05	.02
542	Luis Tiant	.12	.09	.05
543	Ron LeFlore	.08	.06	.03
544	Dave LaPoint(FC)	.30	.25	.12
545	Randy Moffitt	.06	.05	.02
546	Luis Aguayo	.06	.05	.02
547	Brad Lesley	.06	.05	.02
548	Luis Salazar	.06	.05	.02
549	John Candelaria	.10	.08	.04
550	Dave Bergman	.06	.05	.02
551	Bob Watson	.08	.06	.03
552	Pat Tabler	.10	.08	.04
553	Brent Gaff	.06	.05	.02
554	Al Cowens	.06	.05	.02
555	Tom Brunansky(FC)	.25	.20	.10
556	Lloyd Moseby	.12	.09	.05
557a	Pascual Perez (Twins)(FC)	.90	.70	.35
557b	Pascual Perez (Braves)(FC)	.15	.11	.06
558	Willie Upshaw	.08	.06	.03
559	Richie Zisk	.08	.06	.03
560	Pat Zachry	.06	.05	.02
561	Jay Johnstone	.08	.06	.03
562	Carlos Diaz	.06	.05	.02
563	John Tudor	.10	.08	.04
564	Frank Robinson	.12	.09	.05
565	Dave Edwards	.06	.05	.02
566	Paul Householder	.06	.05	.02
567	Ron Reed	.06	.05	.02
568	Mike Ramsey	.06	.05	.02
569	Kiko Garcia	.06	.05	.02
570	Tommy John	.20	.15	.08
571	Tony LaRussa	.08	.06	.03
572	Joel Youngblood	.06	.05	.02
573	Wayne Tolleson(FC)	.12	.09	.05
574	Keith Creel	.06	.05	.02
575	Billy Martin	.12	.09	.05
576	Jerry Dybzinski	.06	.05	.02
577	Rick Cerone	.06	.05	.02
578	Tony Perez	.20	.15	.08
579	Greg Brock(FC)	.35	.25	.14
580	Glen Wilson (Glenn)(FC)	.35	.25	.14
581	Tim Stoddard	.06	.05	.02
582	Bob McClure	.06	.05	.02
583	Jim Dwyer	.06	.05	.02
584	Ed Romero	.06	.05	.02
585	Larry Herndon	.08	.06	.03
586	Wade Boggs(FC)	25.00	18.00	10.00
587	Jay Howell(FC)	.15	.11	.06
588	Dave Stewart	1.00	.70	.40
589	Bert Blyleven	.12	.09	.05
590	Dick Howser	.06	.05	.02
591	Wayne Gross	.06	.05	.02
592	Terry Francona	.06	.05	.02
593	Don Werner	.06	.05	.02
594	Bill Stein	.06	.05	.02
595	Jesse Barfield(FC)	.70	.50	.30
596	Bobby Molinaro	.06	.05	.02
597	Mike Vail	.06	.05	.02
598	Tony Gwynn(FC)	25.00	18.00	10.00
599	Gary Rajsich	.06	.05	.02
600	Jerry Ujdur	.06	.05	.02
601	Cliff Johnson	.06	.05	.02
602	Jerry White	.06	.05	.02
603	Bryan Clark	.06	.05	.02
604	Joe Ferguson	.06	.05	.02
605	Guy Sularz	.06	.05	.02
606a	Ozzie Virgil (green frame around photo)(FC)	.90	.70	.35
606b	Ozzie Virgil (orange frame around photo)(FC)	.08	.06	.03
607	Terry Harper(FC)	.06	.05	.02
608	Harvey Kuenn	.08	.06	.03
609	Jim Sundberg	.08	.06	.03
610	Willie Stargell	.40	.30	.15
611	Reggie Smith	.10	.08	.04
612	Rob Wilfong	.06	.05	.02
613	Niekro Brothers (Joe Niekro, Phil Niekro)	.15	.11	.06
614	Lee Elia	.06	.05	.02

		MT	NR MT	EX
615	Mickey Hatcher	.08	.06	.03
616	Jerry Hairston	.06	.05	.02
617	John Martin	.06	.05	.02
618	Wally Backman(FC)	.15	.11	.06
619	*Storm Davis*(FC)	.30	.25	.12
620	Alan Knicely	.06	.05	.02
621	John Stuper	.06	.05	.02
622	Matt Sinatro	.06	.05	.02
623	*Gene Petralli*(FC)	.15	.11	.06
624	Duane Walker	.06	.05	.02
625	Dick Williams	.06	.05	.02
626	Pat Corrales	.06	.05	.02
627	Vern Ruhle	.06	.05	.02
628	Joe Torre	.08	.06	.03
629	Anthony Johnson	.06	.05	.02
630	Steve Howe	.08	.06	.03
631	Gary Woods	.06	.05	.02
632	Lamarr Hoyt (LaMarr)	.06	.05	.02
633	Steve Swisher	.06	.05	.02
634	Terry Leach(FC)	.12	.09	.05
635	Jeff Newman	.06	.05	.02
636	Brett Butler	.10	.08	.04
637	Gary Gray	.06	.05	.02
638	Lee Mazzilli	.08	.06	.03
639a	Ron Jackson (A's)	10.00	7.50	4.00
639b	Ron Jackson (Angels - green frame around photo)	.90	.70	.35
639c	Ron Jackson (Angels - red frame around photo)	.20	.15	.08
640	Juan Beniquez	.06	.05	.02
641	Dave Rucker	.06	.05	.02
642	Luis Pujols	.06	.05	.02
643	Rick Monday	.10	.08	.04
644	Hosken Powell	.06	.05	.02
645	San Diego Chicken	.20	.15	.08
646	Dave Engle	.06	.05	.02
647	Dick Davis	.06	.05	.02
648	MVP's (Vida Blue, Joe Morgan, Frank Robinson)	.15	.11	.06
649	Al Chambers	.06	.05	.02
650	Jesus Vega	.06	.05	.02
651	Jeff Jones	.06	.05	.02
652	Marvis Foley	.06	.05	.02
653	Ty Cobb Puzzle	.06	.05	.02
---a	Dick Perez/DK Checklist (no word "Checklist" on back)	.70	.50	.30
---b	Dick Perez/DK Checklist (word "Checklist" on back)	.08	.06	.03
-----	Checklist 27-130	.06	.05	.02
-----	Checklist 131-234	.06	.05	.02
-----	Checklist 235-338	.06	.05	.02
-----	Checklist 339-442	.06	.05	.02
-----	Checklist 443-546	.06	.05	.02
-----	Checklist 547-653	.06	.05	.02

1983 Donruss Action All-Stars

The cards in this 60-card set are designed on a horizontal format and contain a large close-up photo of the player on the left and a smaller action photo on the right. The cards, which measure 3-1/2" by 5", have deep red borders and contain the Donruss logo and the year of issue. The card backs have black print on red and white and contain various statistical and biographical information. The cards were sold with puzzle pieces (three pieces on one card per pack) that feature Mickey Mantle.

		MT	NR MT	EX
	Complete Set:	9.00	6.75	3.50
	Common Player:	.10	.08	.04
1	Eddie Murray	.30	.25	.12
2	Dwight Evans	.15	.11	.06
3a	Reggie Jackson (red covers part of statistics on back)	.60	.45	.25
3b	Reggie Jackson (red does not cover any statistics on back)	.60	.45	.25
4	Greg Luzinski	.12	.09	.05
5	Larry Herndon	.10	.08	.04
6	Al Oliver	.12	.09	.05
7	Bill Buckner	.10	.08	.04
8	Jason Thompson	.10	.08	.04
9	Andre Dawson	.20	.15	.08
10	Greg Minton	.10	.08	.04
11	Terry Kennedy	.10	.08	.04
12	Phil Niekro	.20	.15	.08
13	Willie Wilson	.12	.09	.05
14	Johnny Bench	.60	.45	.25
15	Ron Guidry	.15	.11	.06
16	Hal McRae	.10	.08	.04
17	Damaso Garcia	.10	.08	.04
18	Gary Ward	.10	.08	.04
19	Cecil Cooper	.12	.09	.05
20	Keith Hernandez	.25	.20	.10
21	Ron Cey	.12	.09	.05
22	Rickey Henderson	1.00	.70	.40
23	Nolan Ryan	2.50	2.00	1.00
24	Steve Carlton	.30	.25	.12
25	John Stearns	.10	.08	.04
26	Jim Sundberg	.10	.08	.04
27	Joaquin Andujar	.10	.08	.04
28	Gaylord Perry	.15	.11	.06
29	Jack Clark	.15	.11	.06
30	Bill Madlock	.12	.09	.05
31	Pete Rose	.60	.45	.25
32	Mookie Wilson	.10	.08	.04
33	Rollie Fingers	.15	.11	.06
34	Lonnie Smith	.10	.08	.04
35	Tony Pena	.10	.08	.04
36	Dave Winfield	.30	.25	.12
37	Tim Lollar	.10	.08	.04
38	Rod Carew	.60	.45	.25
39	Toby Harrah	.10	.08	.04
40	Buddy Bell	.10	.08	.04
41	Bruce Sutter	.12	.09	.05
42	George Brett	.70	.50	.30
43	Carlton Fisk	.60	.45	.25
44	Carl Yastrzemski	.70	.50	.30
45	Dale Murphy	.25	.20	.10
46	Bob Horner	.12	.09	.05
47	Dave Concepcion	.12	.09	.05
48	Dave Stieb	.12	.09	.05
49	Kent Hrbek	.20	.15	.08
50	Lance Parrish	.15	.11	.06
51	Joe Niekro	.12	.09	.05
52	Cal Ripken Jr.	.80	.60	.30
53	Fernando Valenzuela	.12	.09	.05
54	Rickie Zisk	.10	.08	.04
55	Leon Durham	.10	.08	.04
56	Robin Yount	.70	.50	.30
57	Mike Schmidt	1.25	.90	.50
58	Gary Carter	.15	.11	.06
59	Fred Lynn	.15	.11	.06
60	Checklist	.10	.08	.04

1983 Donruss Hall Of Fame Heroes

The artwork of Dick Perez is featured in the 44-card Donruss Hall of Fame Heroes set issued in 1983. The standard-size cards (2-1/2" by 3-1/2") were available in wax packs that contained eight cards plus a Mickey Mantle puzzle piece card (three pieces on one card per pack). The backs, which display red and blue print on white stock, contain a short player biographical sketch derived from the Hall of Fame yearbook. The numbered set consists of 44 player cards, a Mantle puzzle card, and a checklist.

		MT	NR MT	EX
	Complete Set:	8.00	6.00	3.25
	Common Player:	.05	.04	.02
1	Ty Cobb	.70	.50	.30
2	Walter Johnson	.15	.11	.06
3	Christy Mathewson	.15	.11	.06
4	Josh Gibson	.10	.08	.04
5	Honus Wagner	.15	.11	.06
6	Jackie Robinson	.50	.40	.20
7	Mickey Mantle	1.00	.70	.40
8	Luke Appling	.05	.04	.02
9	Ted Williams	.70	.50	.30
10	Johnny Mize	.15	.11	.06
11	Satchel Paige	.15	.11	.06
12	Lou Boudreau	.15	.11	.06
13	Jimmie Foxx	.15	.11	.06
14	Duke Snider	.70	.50	.30
15	Monte Irvin	.15	.11	.06
16	Hank Greenberg	.15	.11	.06
17	Roberto Clemente	.50	.40	.20
18	Al Kaline	.50	.40	.20
19	Frank Robinson	.50	.40	.20
20	Joe Cronin	.09	.07	.04
21	Burleigh Grimes	.05	.04	.02
22	The Waner Brothers (Lloyd Waner, Paul Waner)	.09	.07	.04
23	Grover Alexander	.09	.07	.04
24	Yogi Berra	.50	.40	.20
25	James Bell	.05	.04	.02
26	Bill Dickey	.09	.07	.04
27	Cy Young	.15	.11	.06
28	Charlie Gehringer	.09	.07	.04
29	Dizzy Dean	.15	.11	.06
30	Bob Lemon	.15	.11	.06
31	Red Ruffing	.05	.04	.02
32	Stan Musial	.70	.50	.30
33	Carl Hubbell	.15	.11	.06
34	Hank Aaron	.70	.50	.30
35	John McGraw	.09	.07	.04
36	Bob Feller	.50	.40	.20
37	Casey Stengel	.15	.11	.06
38	Ralph Kiner	.15	.11	.06
39	Roy Campanella	.15	.11	.06
40	Mel Ott	.09	.07	.04
41	Robin Roberts	.15	.11	.06
42	Early Wynn	.15	.11	.06
43	Mickey Mantle Puzzle Card	.09	.07	.04
----	Checklist	.09	.07	.04

1984 Donruss

The 1984 Donruss set consists of 651 numbered cards, seven unnumbered checklists and two "Living Legends" cards (designated A and B). The A and B cards were issued only in wax packs and not available to hobby dealers purchasing vending sets. The card

fronts differ in style from the previous years, however the Donruss logo and year of issue are still included. The card backs have black print on green and white and are identical in format to the preceding year. The standard-size cards (2-1/2" by 3-1/2") were issued with a 63-piece puzzle of Duke Snider. A limited print run of the issue by Donruss has caused the set to escalate in price in recent years. The complete set price in the checklist that follows does not include the higher priced variations. Cards marked with (DK) or (RR) in the checklist refer to the Diamond Kings and Rated Rookies subsets.

		MT	NR MT	EX
	Complete Set:	375.00	275.00	125.00
	Common Player:	.12	.09	.05
1a	Robin Yount (DK) (Perez-Steel on back)	1.50	1.25	.60
1b	Robin Yount (DK) (Perez-Steele on back)	4.00	3.00	1.50
2a	Dave Concepcion (DK) (Perez-Steel on back)	.30	.25	.12
2b	Dave Concepcion (DK) (Perez-Steele on back)	.60	.45	.25
3a	Dwayne Murphy (DK) (Perez-Steel on back)	.25	.20	.10
3b	Dwayne Murphy (DK) (Perez-Steele on back)	.60	.45	.25
4a	John Castino (DK) (Perez-Steel on back)	.20	.15	.08
4b	John Castino (DK) (Perez-Steele on back)	.60	.45	.25
5a	Leon Durham (DK) (Perez-Steel on back)	.25	.20	.10
5b	Leon Durham (DK) (Perez-Steele on back)	.60	.45	.25
6a	Rusty Staub (DK) (Perez-Steel on back)	.30	.25	.12
6b	Rusty Staub (DK) (Perez-Steele on back)	.60	.45	.25
7a	Jack Clark (DK) (Perez-Steel on back)	.40	.30	.15
7b	Jack Clark (DK) (Perez-Steele on back)	.80	.60	.30
8a	Dave Dravecky (DK) (Perez-Steel on back)	.25	.20	.10
8b	Dave Dravecky (DK) (Perez-Steele on back)	.60	.45	.25
9a	Al Oliver (DK) (Perez-Steel on back)	.35	.25	.14
9b	Al Oliver (DK) (Perez-Steele on back)	.70	.50	.30
10a	Dave Righetti (DK) (Perez-Steel on back)	.40	.30	.15
10b	Dave Righetti (DK) (Perez-Steele on back)	.80	.60	.30
11a	Hal McRae (DK) (Perez-Steel on back)	.30	.25	.12
11b	Hal McRae (DK) (Perez-Steele on back)	.60	.45	.25
12a	Ray Knight (DK) (Perez-Steel on back)	.25	.20	.10
12b	Ray Knight (DK) (Perez-Steele on back)	.60	.45	.25
13a	Bruce Sutter (DK) (Perez-Steel on back)	.35	.25	.14
13b	Bruce Sutter (DK) (Perez-Steele on back)	.70	.50	.30
14a	Bob Horner (DK) (Perez-Steel on back)	.40	.30	.15
14b	Bob Horner (DK) (Perez-Steele on back)	.80	.60	.30
15a	Lance Parrish (DK) (Perez-Steel on back)	.60	.45	.25
15b	Lance Parrish (DK) (Perez-Steele on back)	1.25	.90	.50
16a	Matt Young (DK) (Perez-Steel on back)	.25	.20	.10
16b	Matt Young (DK) (Perez-Steele on back)	.60	.45	.25
17a	Fred Lynn (DK) (Perez-Steel on back)	.35	.25	.14
17b	Fred Lynn (DK) (Perez-Steele on back)	.70	.50	.30
18a	Ron Kittle (DK) (Perez-Steel on back)(FC)	.35	.25	.14
18b	Ron Kittle (DK) (Perez-Steele on back)(FC)	.70	.50	.30
19a	Jim Clancy (DK) (Perez-Steel on back)	.25	.20	.10

	MT	NR MT	EX
19b Jim Clancy (DK) (Perez-Steele on back)			
	.60	.45	.25
20a Bill Madlock (DK) (Perez-Steele on back)			
	.30	.25	.12
20b Bill Madlock (DK) (Perez-Steele on back)			
	.60	.45	.25
21a Larry Parrish (DK) (Perez-Steel on back)			
	.30	.25	.12
21b Larry Parrish (DK) (Perez-Steele on back)			
	.60	.45	.25
22a Eddie Murray (DK) (Perez-Steele on back)			
	1.25	.90	.50
22b Eddie Murray (DK) (Perez-Steele on back)			
	2.50	2.00	1.00
23a Mike Schmidt (DK) (Perez-Steel on back)			
	1.25	.90	.50
23b Mike Schmidt (DK) (Perez-Steele on back)			
	2.50	2.00	1.00
24a Pedro Guerrero (DK) (Perez-Steel on back)			
	.50	.40	.20
24b Pedro Guerrero (DK) (Perez-Steel on back)			
	1.00	.70	.40
25a Andre Thornton (DK) (Perez-Steel on back)			
	.30	.25	.12
25b Andre Thornton (DK) (Perez-Steele on back)			
	.60	.45	.25
26a Wade Boggs (DK) (Perez-Steel on back)			
	3.00	2.25	1.25
26b Wade Boggs (DK) (Perez-Steel on back)			
	4.00	3.00	1.50
27 *Joel Skinner (RR)(FC)*	.20	.15	.08
28 Tom Dunbar (RR)	.12	.09	.05
29a Mike Stenhouse (RR) (no number on back)			
	.15	.11	.06
29b Mike Stenhouse (RR) (29 on back)			
	4.00	3.00	1.50
30a *Ron Darling* (no number on back)(FC)			
	5.00	3.75	2.00
30b *Ron Darling* (30 on back)(FC)	10.00	7.50	4.00
31 *Dion James (RR)(FC)*	.15	.11	.06
32 *Tony Fernandez (RR)(FC)*	7.00	5.25	2.75
33 Angel Salazar (RR)	.12	.09	.05
34 *Kevin McReynolds (RR)(FC)*	6.00	4.50	2.50
35 *Dick Schofield (RR)(FC)*	.40	.30	.15
36 *Brad Komminsk (RR)(FC)*	.15	.11	.06
37 *Tim Teufel (RR)(FC)*	.30	.25	.12
38 Doug Frobel (RR)	.12	.09	.05
39 *Greg Gagne (RR)(FC)*	.60	.45	.25
40 Mike Fuentes (RR)	.12	.09	.05
41 *Joe Carter (RR)(FC)*	45.00	33.00	16.00
42 Mike Brown (RR)	.12	.09	.05
43 Mike Jeffcoat (RR)	.12	.09	.05
44 *Sid Fernandez (RR)(FC)*	4.00	3.00	1.50
45 Brian Dayett (RR)	.12	.09	.05
46 Chris Smith (RR)	.12	.09	.05
47 Eddie Murray	5.00	3.75	2.00
48 Robin Yount	10.00	7.50	4.00
49 Lance Parrish	.50	.40	.20
50 Jim Rice	.90	.70	.35
51 Dave Winfield	6.00	4.50	2.50
52 Fernando Valenzuela	.50	.40	.20
53 George Brett	10.00	7.50	4.00
54 Rickey Henderson	15.00	11.00	6.00
55 Gary Carter	1.00	.70	.40
56 Buddy Bell	.20	.15	.08
57 Reggie Jackson	5.00	3.75	2.00
58 Harold Baines	.25	.20	.10
59 Ozzie Smith	5.00	3.75	2.00
60 Nolan Ryan	20.00	15.00	8.00
61 Pete Rose	3.00	2.25	1.25
62 Ron Oester	.12	.09	.05
63 Steve Garvey	.90	.70	.35
64 Jason Thompson	.12	.09	.05
65 Jack Clark	.35	.25	.14
66 Dale Murphy	2.00	1.50	.80
67 Leon Durham	.12	.09	.05
68 *Darryl Strawberry*(FC)	45.00	33.00	16.00
69 Richie Zisk	.12	.09	.05
70 Kent Hrbek	.60	.45	.25
71 Dave Stieb	.25	.20	.10
72 Ken Schrom	.12	.09	.05
73 George Bell	2.00	1.50	.80
74 John Moses	.15	.11	.06
75 Ed Lynch	.12	.09	.05
76 Chuck Rainey	.12	.09	.05
77 Biff Pocoroba	.12	.09	.05
78 Cecilio Guante	.12	.09	.05
79 Jim Barr	.12	.09	.05
80 Kurt Bevacqua	.12	.09	.05
81 Tom Foley	.12	.09	.05
82 Joe Lefebvre	.12	.09	.05
83 *Andy Van Slyke*(FC)	12.00	9.00	4.75

	MT	NR MT	EX
84 Bob Lillis	.12	.09	.05
85 Rick Adams	.12	.09	.05
86 Jerry Hairston	.12	.09	.05
87 Bob James	.12	.09	.05
88 Joe Altobelli	.12	.09	.05
89 Ed Romero	.12	.09	.05
90 John Grubb	.12	.09	.05
91 John Henry Johnson	.12	.09	.05
92 Juan Espino	.12	.09	.05
93 Candy Maldonado	.20	.15	.08
94 Andre Thornton	.20	.15	.08
95 Onix Concepcion	.12	.09	.05
96 *Don Hill*(FC)	.20	.15	.08
97 Andre Dawson	5.00	3.75	2.00
98 Frank Tanana	.15	.11	.06
99 *Curt Wilkerson*(FC)	.15	.11	.06
100 Larry Gura	.12	.09	.05
101 Dwayne Murphy	.12	.09	.05
102 Tom Brennan	.12	.09	.05
103 Dave Righetti	.40	.30	.15
104 Steve Sax	.30	.25	.12
105 Dan Petry	.12	.09	.05
106 Cal Ripken	25.00	18.00	10.00
107 Paul Molitor	1.25	.90	.50
108 Fred Lynn	.35	.25	.14
109 Neil Allen	.12	.09	.05
110 Joe Niekro	.20	.15	.08
111 Steve Carlton	3.00	2.25	1.25
112 Terry Kennedy	.15	.11	.06
113 Bill Madlock	.20	.15	.08
114 Chili Davis	.15	.11	.06
115 Jim Gantner	.12	.09	.05
116 Tom Seaver	5.00	3.75	2.00
117 Bill Buckner	.20	.15	.08
118 Bill Caudill	.12	.09	.05
119 Jim Clancy	.15	.11	.06
120 John Castino	.12	.09	.05
121 Dave Concepcion	.20	.15	.08
122 Greg Luzinski	.20	.15	.08
123 Mike Boddicker(FC)	.20	.15	.08
124 Pete Ladd	.12	.09	.05
125 Juan Berenguer	.12	.09	.05
126 John Montefusco	.12	.09	.05
127 Ed Jurak	.12	.09	.05
128 Tom Niedenfuer	.12	.09	.05
129 Bert Blyleven	.30	.25	.12
130 Bud Black	.12	.09	.05
131 Gorman Heimueller	.12	.09	.05
132 Dan Schatzeder	.12	.09	.05
133 Ron Jackson	.12	.09	.05
134 *Tom Henke*(FC)	2.00	1.50	.80
135 Kevin Hickey	.12	.09	.05
136 Mike Scott	.30	.25	.12
137 Bo Diaz	.12	.09	.05
138 Glenn Brummer	.12	.09	.05
139 Sid Monge	.12	.09	.05
140 Rich Gale	.12	.09	.05
141 Brett Butler	.15	.11	.06
142 Brian Harper	.80	.60	.30
143 John Rabb	.12	.09	.05
144 Gary Woods	.12	.09	.05
145 Pat Putnam	.12	.09	.05
146 *Jim Acker*(FC)	.15	.11	.06
147 Mickey Hatcher	.12	.09	.05
148 Todd Cruz	.12	.09	.05
149 Tom Tellmann	.12	.09	.05
150 John Wockenfuss	.12	.09	.05
151 Wade Boggs	18.00	13.50	7.25
152 Don Baylor	.20	.15	.08
153 Bob Welch	.20	.15	.08
154 Alan Bannister	.12	.09	.05
155 Willie Aikens	.12	.09	.05
156 Jeff Burroughs	.12	.09	.05
157 Bryan Little	.12	.09	.05
158 Bob Boone	.15	.11	.06
159 Dave Hostetler	.12	.09	.05
160 Jerry Dybzinski	.12	.09	.05
161 Mike Madden	.12	.09	.05
162 Luis DeLeon	.12	.09	.05
163 Willie Hernandez	.15	.11	.06
164 Frank Pastore	.12	.09	.05
165 Rick Camp	.12	.09	.05
166 Lee Mazzilli	.12	.09	.05
167 Scot Thompson	.12	.09	.05
168 Bob Forsch	.12	.09	.05
169 Mike Flanagan	.15	.11	.06
170 Rick Manning	.12	.09	.05
171 Chet Lemon	.12	.09	.05
172 Jerry Remy	.12	.09	.05
173 Ron Guidry	.35	.25	.14
174 Pedro Guerrero	.50	.40	.20

#	Name	MT	NR MT	EX		#	Name	MT	NR MT	EX
175	Willie Wilson	.25	.20	.10		266	Dickie Noles	.12	.09	.05
176	Carney Lansford	.20	.15	.08		267	Jamie Allen	.12	.09	.05
177	Al Oliver	.30	.25	.12		268	Jim Gott	.15	.11	.06
178	Jim Sundberg	.12	.09	.05		269	Ron Davis	.12	.09	.05
179	Bobby Grich	.20	.15	.08		270	Benny Ayala	.12	.09	.05
180	Richard Dotson	.20	.15	.08		271	Ned Yost	.12	.09	.05
181	Joaquin Andujar	.12	.09	.05		272	Dave Rozema	.12	.09	.05
182	Jose Cruz	.20	.15	.08		273	Dave Stapleton	.12	.09	.05
183	Mike Schmidt	12.00	9.00	4.75		274	Lou Piniella	.20	.15	.08
184	*Gary Redus*(FC)	.30	.25	.12		275	Jose Morales	.12	.09	.05
185	Garry Templeton	.15	.11	.06		276	Brod Perkins	.12	.09	.05
186	Tony Pena	.20	.15	.08		277	Butch Davis	.12	.09	.05
187	Greg Minton	.12	.09	.05		278	*Tony Phillips*(FC)	.20	.15	.08
188	Phil Niekro	.50	.40	.20		279	Jeff Reardon	.25	.20	.10
189	Ferguson Jenkins	.30	.25	.12		280	Ken Forsch	.12	.09	.05
190	Mookie Wilson	.15	.11	.06		281	*Pete O'Brien*(FC)	1.00	.70	.40
191	Jim Beattie	.12	.09	.05		282	Tom Paciorek	.12	.09	.05
192	Gary Ward	.12	.09	.05		283	Frank LaCorte	.12	.09	.05
193	Jesse Barfield	.40	.30	.15		284	Tim Lollar	.12	.09	.05
194	Pete Filson	.12	.09	.05		285	Greg Gross	.12	.09	.05
195	Roy Lee Jackson	.12	.09	.05		286	Alex Trevino	.12	.09	.05
196	Rick Sweet	.12	.09	.05		287	Gene Garber	.12	.09	.05
197	Jesse Orosco	.15	.11	.06		288	Dave Parker	.50	.40	.20
198	*Steve Lake*(FC)	.12	.09	.05		289	Lee Smith	.20	.15	.08
199	Ken Dayley	.12	.09	.05		290	Dave LaPoint	.15	.11	.06
200	Manny Sarmiento	.12	.09	.05		291	*John Shelby*(FC)	.25	.20	.10
201	Mark Davis(FC)	.25	.20	.10		292	Charlie Moore	.12	.09	.05
202	Tim Flannery	.12	.09	.05		293	Alan Trammell	.60	.45	.25
203	Bill Scherrer	.12	.09	.05		294	Tony Armas	.20	.15	.08
204	Al Holland	.12	.09	.05		295	Shane Rawley	.20	.15	.08
205	David Von Ohlen	.12	.09	.05		296	Greg Brock	.15	.11	.06
206	Mike LaCoss	.12	.09	.05		297	Hal McRae	.20	.15	.08
207	Juan Beniquez	.12	.09	.05		298	Mike Davis	.12	.09	.05
208	*Juan Agosto*(FC)	.20	.15	.08		299	Tim Raines	.80	.60	.30
209	Bobby Ramos	.12	.09	.05		300	Bucky Dent	.15	.11	.06
210	Al Bumbry	.12	.09	.05		301	Tommy John	.35	.25	.14
211	Mark Brouhard	.12	.09	.05		302	Carlton Fisk	4.00	3.00	1.50
212	Howard Bailey	.12	.09	.05		303	Darrell Porter	.12	.09	.05
213	Bruce Hurst	.20	.15	.08		304	Dickie Thon	.12	.09	.05
214	Bob Shirley	.12	.09	.05		305	Garry Maddox	.12	.09	.05
215	Pat Zachry	.12	.09	.05		306	Cesar Cedeno	.20	.15	.08
216	Julio Franco	4.50	3.35	1.80		307	Gary Lucas	.12	.09	.05
217	Mike Armstrong	.12	.09	.05		308	Johnny Ray	.20	.15	.08
218	Dave Beard	.12	.09	.05		309	Andy McGaffigan	.12	.09	.05
219	Steve Rogers	.12	.09	.05		310	Claudell Washington	.12	.09	.05
220	John Butcher	.12	.09	.05		311	Ryne Sandberg	25.00	20.00	10.00
221	*Mike Smithson*(FC)	.20	.15	.08		312	George Foster	.30	.25	.12
222	Frank White	.20	.15	.08		313	*Spike Owen*(FC)	.70	.50	.30
223	Mike Heath	.12	.09	.05		314	Gary Gaetti	.40	.30	.15
224	Chris Bando	.12	.09	.05		315	Willie Upshaw	.12	.09	.05
225	Roy Smalley	.12	.09	.05		316	Al Williams	.12	.09	.05
226	Dusty Baker	.20	.15	.08		317	Jorge Orta	.12	.09	.05
227	Lou Whitaker	.60	.45	.25		318	Orlando Mercado	.12	.09	.05
228	John Lowenstein	.12	.09	.05		319	*Junior Ortiz*(FC)	.12	.09	.05
229	Ben Oglivie	.12	.09	.05		320	Mike Proly	.12	.09	.05
230	Doug DeCinces	.15	.11	.06		321	Randy Johnson	.12	.09	.05
231	Lonnie Smith	.12	.09	.05		322	Jim Morrison	.12	.09	.05
232	Ray Knight	.15	.11	.06		323	Max Venable	.12	.09	.05
233	Gary Matthews	.20	.15	.08		324	Tony Gwynn	18.00	13.50	7.25
234	Juan Bonilla	.12	.09	.05		325	Duane Walker	.12	.09	.05
235	Rod Scurry	.12	.09	.05		326	Ozzie Virgil	.12	.09	.05
236	Atlee Hammaker	.12	.09	.05		327	Jeff Lahti	.12	.09	.05
237	Mike Caldwell	.12	.09	.05		328	*Bill Dawley*(FC)	.12	.09	.05
238	Keith Hernandez	.80	.60	.30		329	Rob Wilfong	.12	.09	.05
239	Larry Bowa	.25	.20	.10		330	Marc Hill	.12	.09	.05
240	Tony Bernazard	.12	.09	.05		331	Ray Burris	.12	.09	.05
241	Damaso Garcia	.12	.09	.05		332	Allan Ramirez	.12	.09	.05
242	Tom Brunansky	.35	.25	.14		333	Chuck Porter	.12	.09	.05
243	Dan Driessen	.12	.09	.05		334	Wayne Krenchicki	.12	.09	.05
244	Ron Kittle(FC)	.30	.25	.12		335	Gary Allenson	.12	.09	.05
245	Tim Stoddard	.12	.09	.05		336	*Bob Meacham*(FC)	.20	.15	.08
246	Bob Gibson	.12	.09	.05		337	Joe Beckwith	.12	.09	.05
247	Marty Castillo	.12	.09	.05		338	Rick Sutcliffe	.25	.20	.10
248	*Don Mattingly*(FC)	45.00	33.00	16.00		339	*Mark Huismann*(FC)	.15	.11	.06
249	Jeff Newman	.12	.09	.05		340	*Tim Conroy*(FC)	.15	.11	.06
250	*Alejandro Pena*(FC)	.70	.50	.30		341	Scott Sanderson	.12	.09	.05
251	Toby Harrah	.12	.09	.05		342	Larry Biittner	.12	.09	.05
252	Cesar Geronimo	.12	.09	.05		343	Dave Stewart	2.00	1.50	.80
253	Tom Underwood	.12	.09	.05		344	Darryl Motley	.12	.09	.05
254	Doug Flynn	.12	.09	.05		345	*Chris Codiroli*(FC)	.12	.09	.05
255	Andy Hassler	.12	.09	.05		346	Rick Behenna	.12	.09	.05
256	Odell Jones	.12	.09	.05		347	Andre Robertson	.12	.09	.05
257	Rudy Law	.12	.09	.05		348	Mike Marshall	.25	.20	.10
258	Harry Spilman	.12	.09	.05		349	Larry Herndon	.12	.09	.05
259	Marty Bystrom	.12	.09	.05		350	Rich Dauer	.12	.09	.05
260	Dave Rucker	.12	.09	.05		351	Cecil Cooper	.25	.20	.10
261	Ruppert Jones	.12	.09	.05		352	Rod Carew	4.00	3.00	1.50
262	Jeff Jones	.12	.09	.05		353	Willie McGee	.40	.30	.15
263	*Gerald Perry*(FC)	.50	.40	.20		354	Phil Garner	.12	.09	.05
264	Gene Tenace	.12	.09	.05		355	Joe Morgan	.60	.45	.25
265	Brad Wellman	.12	.09	.05		356	Luis Salazar	.12	.09	.05

		MT	NR MT	EX			MT	NR MT	EX
357	John Candelaria	.20	.15	.08	448	*Charlie Hudson*(FC)	.25	.20	.10
358	Bill Laskey	.12	.09	.05	449	*Danny Cox*(FC)	.70	.50	.30
359	Bob McClure	.12	.09	.05	450	Kevin Bass(FC)	.30	.25	.12
360	Dave Kingman	.30	.25	.12	451	Daryl Sconiers	.12	.09	.05
361	Ron Cey	.20	.15	.08	452	Scott Fletcher	.12	.09	.05
362	*Matt Young*(FC)	.20	.15	.08	453	Bryn Smith	.12	.09	.05
363	Lloyd Moseby	.20	.15	.08	454	Jim Dwyer	.12	.09	.05
364	Frank Viola	2.00	1.50	.80	455	Rob Picciolo	.12	.09	.05
365	Eddie Milner	.12	.09	.05	456	Enos Cabell	.12	.09	.05
366	Floyd Bannister	.20	.15	.08	457	Dennis *"Oil Can" Boyd*(FC)	.70	.50	.30
367	Dan Ford	.12	.09	.05	458	Butch Wynegar	.12	.09	.05
368	Moose Haas	.12	.09	.05	459	Burt Hooton	.12	.09	.05
369	Doug Bair	.12	.09	.05	460	Ron Hassey	.12	.09	.05
370	*Ray Fontenot*(FC)	.12	.09	.05	461	*Danny Jackson*(FC)	1.00	.70	.40
371	Luis Aponte	.12	.09	.05	462	Bob Kearney	.12	.09	.05
372	Jack Fimple	.12	.09	.05	463	Terry Francona	.12	.09	.05
373	*Neal Heaton*(FC)	.20	.15	.08	464	Wayne Tolleson	.12	.09	.05
374	Greg Pryor	.12	.09	.05	465	Mickey Rivers	.12	.09	.05
375	Wayne Gross	.12	.09	.05	466	John Wathan	.12	.09	.05
376	Charlie Lea	.12	.09	.05	467	Bill Almon	.12	.09	.05
377	Steve Lubratich	.12	.09	.05	468	George Vukovich	.12	.09	.05
378	Jon Matlack	.12	.09	.05	469	Steve Kemp	.15	.11	.06
379	Julio Cruz	.12	.09	.05	470	Ken Landreaux	.12	.09	.05
380	John Mizerock	.12	.09	.05	471	Milt Wilcox	.12	.09	.05
381	*Kevin Gross*(FC)	.50	.40	.20	472	Tippy Martinez	.12	.09	.05
382	Mike Ramsey	.12	.09	.05	473	Ted Simmons	.20	.15	.08
383	Doug Gwosdz	.12	.09	.05	474	Tim Foli	.12	.09	.05
384	Kelly Paris	.12	.09	.05	475	George Hendrick	.12	.09	.05
385	Pete Falcone	.12	.09	.05	476	Terry Puhl	.12	.09	.05
386	Milt May	.12	.09	.05	477	Von Hayes	.25	.20	.10
387	Fred Breining	.12	.09	.05	478	Bobby Brown	.12	.09	.05
388	*Craig Lefferts*(FC)	.25	.20	.10	479	Lee Lacy	.12	.09	.05
389	Steve Henderson	.12	.09	.05	480	Joel Youngblood	.12	.09	.05
390	Randy Moffitt	.12	.09	.05	481	Jim Slaton	.12	.09	.05
391	Ron Washington	.12	.09	.05	482	*Mike Fitzgerald*(FC)	.20	.15	.08
392	Gary Roenicke	.12	.09	.05	483	Keith Moreland	.12	.09	.05
393	*Tom Candiotti*(FC)	1.00	.70	.40	484	Ron Roenicke	.12	.09	.05
394	Larry Pashnick	.12	.09	.05	485	Luis Leal	.12	.09	.05
395	Dwight Evans	.30	.25	.12	486	Bryan Oelkers	.12	.09	.05
396	Goose Gossage	.40	.30	.15	487	Bruce Berenyi	.12	.09	.05
397	Derrel Thomas	.12	.09	.05	488	LaMarr Hoyt	.12	.09	.05
398	Juan Eichelberger	.12	.09	.05	489	Joe Nolan	.12	.09	.05
399	Leon Roberts	.12	.09	.05	490	Marshall Edwards	.12	.09	.05
400	Davey Lopes	.15	.11	.06	491	*Mike Laga*(FC)	.12	.09	.05
401	Bill Gullickson	.12	.09	.05	492	Rick Cerone	.12	.09	.05
402	Geoff Zahn	.12	.09	.05	493	Mike Miller (Rick)	.12	.09	.05
403	Billy Sample	.12	.09	.05	494	Rick Honeycutt	.12	.09	.05
404	Mike Squires	.12	.09	.05	495	Mike Hargrove	.12	.09	.05
405	Craig Reynolds	.12	.09	.05	496	Joe Simpson	.12	.09	.05
406	Eric Show	.15	.11	.06	497	*Keith Atherton*(FC)	.25	.20	.10
407	John Denny	.12	.09	.05	498	Chris Welsh	.12	.09	.05
408	Dann Bilardello	.12	.09	.05	499	Bruce Kison	.12	.09	.05
409	Bruce Benedict	.12	.09	.05	500	Bob Johnson	.12	.09	.05
410	Kent Tekulve	.12	.09	.05	501	Jerry Koosman	.15	.11	.06
411	Mel Hall	.20	.15	.08	502	Frank DiPino	.12	.09	.05
412	John Stuper	.12	.09	.05	503	Tony Perez	.40	.30	.15
413	Rick Dempsey	.12	.09	.05	504	Ken Oberkfell	.12	.09	.05
414	Don Sutton	1.00	.70	.40	505	*Mark Thurmond*(FC)	.12	.09	.05
415	Jack Morris	4.00	3.00	1.50	506	Joe Price	.12	.09	.05
416	John Tudor	.20	.15	.08	507	Pascual Perez	.15	.11	.06
417	Willie Randolph	.20	.15	.08	508	*Marvell Wynne*(FC)	.25	.20	.10
418	Jerry Reuss	.15	.11	.06	509	Mike Krukow	.12	.09	.05
419	Don Slaught	.12	.09	.05	510	Dick Ruthven	.12	.09	.05
420	Steve McCatty	.12	.09	.05	511	Al Cowens	.12	.09	.05
421	Tim Wallach	.25	.20	.10	512	Cliff Johnson	.12	.09	.05
422	Larry Parrish	.20	.15	.08	513	*Randy Bush*(FC)	.20	.15	.08
423	Brian Downing	.20	.15	.08	514	Sammy Stewart	.12	.09	.05
424	Britt Burns	.12	.09	.05	515	*Bill Schroeder*(FC)	.25	.20	.10
425	David Green	.12	.09	.05	516	Aurelio Lopez	.12	.09	.05
426	Jerry Mumphrey	.12	.09	.05	517	Mike Brown	.12	.09	.05
427	Ivan DeJesus	.12	.09	.05	518	Graig Nettles	.35	.25	.14
428	Mario Soto	.12	.09	.05	519	Dave Sax	.12	.09	.05
429	Gene Richards	.12	.09	.05	520	Gerry Willard	.12	.09	.05
430	Dale Berra	.12	.09	.05	521	Paul Splittorff	.12	.09	.05
431	Darrell Evans	.25	.20	.10	522	Tom Burgmeier	.12	.09	.05
432	Glenn Hubbard	.12	.09	.05	523	Chris Speier	.12	.09	.05
433	Jody Davis	.15	.11	.06	524	Bobby Clark	.12	.09	.05
434	Danny Heep	.12	.09	.05	525	George Wright	.12	.09	.05
435	*Ed Nunez*(FC)	.20	.15	.08	526	Dennis Lamp	.12	.09	.05
436	Bobby Castillo	.12	.09	.05	527	Tony Scott	.12	.09	.05
437	Ernie Whitt	.12	.09	.05	528	Ed Whitson	.12	.09	.05
438	Scott Ullger	.12	.09	.05	529	Ron Reed	.12	.09	.05
439	Doyle Alexander	.15	.11	.06	530	Charlie Puleo	.12	.09	.05
440	Domingo Ramos	.12	.09	.05	531	Jerry Royster	.12	.09	.05
441	Craig Swan	.12	.09	.05	532	Don Robinson	.12	.09	.05
442	Warren Brusstar	.12	.09	.05	533	Steve Trout	.12	.09	.05
443	Len Barker	.12	.09	.05	534	Bruce Sutter	.30	.25	.12
444	Mike Easler	.12	.09	.05	535	Bob Horner	.20	.15	.08
445	Renie Martin	.12	.09	.05	536	Pat Tabler	.15	.11	.06
446	*Dennis Rasmussen*(FC)	.70	.50	.30	537	Chris Chambliss	.12	.09	.05
447	Ted Power(FC)	.15	.11	.06	538	Bob Ojeda	.15	.11	.06

		MT	NR MT	EX
539	Alan Ashby	.12	.09	.05
540	Jay Johnstone	.12	.09	.05
541	Bob Dernier	.12	.09	.05
542	*Brook Jacoby*(FC)	1.50	1.25	.60
543	U.L. Washington	.12	.09	.05
544	Danny Darwin	.12	.09	.05
545	Kiko Garcia	.12	.09	.05
546	Vance Law	.12	.09	.05
547	Tug McGraw	.20	.15	.08
548	Dave Smith	.12	.09	.05
549	Len Matuszek	.12	.09	.05
550	Tom Hume	.12	.09	.05
551	Dave Dravecky	.15	.11	.06
552	Rick Rhoden	.15	.11	.06
553	Duane Kuiper	.12	.09	.05
554	Rusty Staub	.20	.15	.08
555	Bill Campbell	.12	.09	.05
556	Mike Torrez	.12	.09	.05
557	Dave Henderson(FC)	.25	.20	.10
558	Len Whitehouse	.12	.09	.05
559	Barry Bonnell	.12	.09	.05
560	Rick Lysander	.12	.09	.05
561	Garth Iorg	.12	.09	.05
562	Bryan Clark	.12	.09	.05
563	Brian Giles	.12	.09	.05
564	Vern Ruhle	.12	.09	.05
565	Steve Bedrosian	.20	.15	.08
566	Larry McWilliams	.12	.09	.05
567	Jeff Leonard	.15	.11	.06
568	Alan Wiggins	.12	.09	.05
569	*Jeff Russell*(FC)	.25	.20	.10
570	Salome Barojas	.12	.09	.05
571	Dane Iorg	.12	.09	.05
572	Bob Knepper	.15	.11	.06
573	Gary Lavelle	.12	.09	.05
574	Gorman Thomas	.15	.11	.06
575	Manny Trillo	.12	.09	.05
576	Jim Palmer	4.00	3.00	1.50
577	Dale Murray	.12	.09	.05
578	Tom Brookens	.12	.09	.05
579	Rich Gedman	.15	.11	.06
580	*Bill Doran*(FC)	1.00	.70	.40
581	Steve Yeager	.12	.09	.05
582	Dan Spillner	.12	.09	.05
583	Dan Quisenberry	.15	.11	.06
584	Rance Mulliniks	.12	.09	.05
585	Storm Davis	.15	.11	.06
586	Dave Schmidt	.12	.09	.05
587	Bill Russell	.12	.09	.05
588	*Pat Sheridan*(FC)	.20	.15	.08
589	Rafael Ramirez	.12	.09	.05
590	Bud Anderson	.12	.09	.05
591	George Frazier	.12	.09	.05
592	*Lee Tunnell*(FC)	.12	.09	.05
593	Kirk Gibson	.60	.45	.25
594	Scott McGregor	.12	.09	.05
595	Bob Bailor	.12	.09	.05
596	Tom Herr	.20	.15	.08
597	Luis Sanchez	.12	.09	.05
598	Dave Engle	.12	.09	.05
599	*Craig McMurtry*(FC)	.15	.11	.06
600	Carlos Diaz	.12	.09	.05
601	Tom O'Malley	.12	.09	.05
602	*Nick Esasky*(FC)	.70	.50	.30
603	Ron Hodges	.12	.09	.05
604	Ed Vande Berg	.12	.09	.05
605	Alfredo Griffin	.12	.09	.05
606	Glenn Hoffman	.12	.09	.05
607	Hubie Brooks	.20	.15	.08
608	Richard Barnes (photo actually Neal Heaton)	.12	.09	.05
609	*Greg Walker*(FC)	.40	.30	.15
610	Ken Singleton	.20	.15	.08
611	Mark Clear	.12	.09	.05
612	Buck Martinez	.12	.09	.05
613	Ken Griffey	.15	.11	.06
614	Reid Nichols	.12	.09	.05
615	*Doug Sisk*(FC)	.12	.09	.05
616	Bob Brenly	.12	.09	.05
617	Joey McLaughlin	.12	.09	.05
618	Glenn Wilson	.12	.09	.05
619	Bob Stoddard	.12	.09	.05
620	Len Sakata (Lenn)	.12	.09	.05
621	*Mike Young*(FC)	.25	.20	.10
622	John Stefero	.12	.09	.05
623	*Carmelo Martinez*(FC)	.30	.25	.12
624	Dave Bergman	.12	.09	.05
625	Runnin' Reds (David Green, Willie McGee, Lonnie Smith, Ozzie Smith)	.30	.25	.12
626	Rudy May	.12	.09	.05
627	Matt Keough	.12	.09	.05

		MT	NR MT	EX
628	*Jose DeLeon*(FC)	.50	.40	.20
629	Jim Essian	.12	.09	.05
630	*Darnell Coles*(FC)	.15	.11	.06
631	Mike Warren	.12	.09	.05
632	Del Crandall	.12	.09	.05
633	Dennis Martinez	.12	.09	.05
634	Mike Moore	.12	.09	.05
635	Lary Sorensen	.12	.09	.05
636	Ricky Nelson	.12	.09	.05
637	Omar Moreno	.12	.09	.05
638	Charlie Hough	.15	.11	.06
639	Dennis Eckersley	4.00	3.00	1.50
640	*Walt Terrell*(FC)	.20	.15	.08
641	Denny Walling	.12	.09	.05
642	*Dave Anderson*(FC)	.20	.15	.08
643	*Jose Oquendo*(FC)	.25	.20	.10
644	Bob Stanley	.12	.09	.05
645	Dave Geisel	.12	.09	.05
646	*Scott Garrelts*(FC)	.40	.30	.15
647	*Gary Pettis*(FC)	.40	.30	.15
648	Duke Snider Puzzle Card	.12	.09	.05
649	Johnnie LeMaster	.12	.09	.05
650	Dave Collins	.12	.09	.05
651	San Diego Chicken	.25	.20	.10
---a	Checklist 1-26 DK (Perez-Steel on back)	.12	.09	.05
---b	Checklist 1-26 DK (Perez-Steele on back)	.40	.30	.15
------	Checklist 27-130	.12	.09	.05
------	Checklist 131-234	.12	.09	.05
------	Checklist 235-338	.12	.09	.05
------	Checklist 339-442	.12	.09	.05
------	Checklist 443-546	.12	.09	.05
------	Checklist 547-651	.12	.09	.05
---A	Living Legends (Rollie Fingers, Gaylord Perry)	5.00	3.75	2.00
---B	Living Legends (Johnny Bench, Carl Yastrzemski)	7.00	5.25	2.75

1984 Donruss Action All-Stars

Full-color photos on the card fronts and backs make the 1984 Donruss Action All-Stars set somewhat unusual. The fronts contain a large action photo plus the Donruss logo and year of issue inside a deep red border. The top half of the card backs feature a close-up photo with the bottom portion containing biographical and statistical information. The cards, which measure 3-1/2" by 5", were sold with Ted Williams puzzle pieces.

		MT	NR MT	EX
	Complete Set:	9.00	6.75	3.50
	Common Player:	.09	.07	.04
1	Gary Lavelle	.09	.07	.04
2	Willie McGee	.15	.11	.06
3	Tony Pena	.09	.07	.04
4	Lou Whitaker	.15	.11	.06
5	Robin Yount	.35	.25	.14
6	Doug DeCinces	.09	.07	.04
7	John Castino	.09	.07	.04
8	Terry Kennedy	.09	.07	.04
9	Rickey Henderson	.50	.40	.20
10	Bob Horner	.12	.09	.05

		MT	NR MT	EX
11	Harold Baines	.15	.11	.06
12	Buddy Bell	.09	.07	.04
13	Fernando Valenzuela	.12	.09	.05
14	Nolan Ryan	2.00	1.50	.80
15	Andre Thornton	.09	.07	.04
16	Gary Redus	.09	.07	.04
17	Pedro Guerrero	.15	.11	.06
18	Andre Dawson	.20	.15	.08
19	Dave Stieb	.12	.09	.05
20	Cal Ripken	.60	.45	.25
21	Ken Griffey	.12	.09	.05
22	Wade Boggs	.70	.50	.30
23	Keith Hernandez	.25	.20	.10
24	Steve Carlton	.30	.25	.12
25	Hal McRae	.12	.09	.05
26	John Lowenstein	.09	.07	.04
27	Fred Lynn	.15	.11	.06
28	Bill Buckner	.09	.07	.04
29	Chris Chambliss	.09	.07	.04
30	Richie Zisk	.09	.07	.04
31	Jack Clark	.15	.11	.06
32	George Hendrick	.09	.07	.04
33	Bill Madlock	.12	.09	.05
34	Lance Parrish	.15	.11	.06
35	Paul Molitor	.15	.11	.06
36	Reggie Jackson	.35	.25	.14
37	Kent Hrbek	.20	.15	.08
38	Steve Garvey	.20	.15	.08
39	Carney Lansford	.09	.07	.04
40	Dale Murphy	.30	.25	.12
41	Greg Luzinski	.12	.09	.05
42	Larry Parrish	.09	.07	.04
43	Ryne Sandberg	.60	.45	.25
44	Dickie Thon	.09	.07	.04
45	Bert Blyleven	.12	.09	.05
46	Ron Oester	.09	.07	.04
47	Dusty Baker	.09	.07	.04
48	Steve Rogers	.09	.07	.04
49	Jim Clancy	.09	.07	.04
50	Eddie Murray	.15	.11	.06
51	Ron Guidry	.15	.11	.06
52	Jim Rice	.15	.11	.06
53	Tom Seaver	.30	.25	.12
54	Pete Rose	.30	.25	.12
55	George Brett	.40	.30	.15
56	Dan Quisenberry	.09	.07	.04
57	Mike Schmidt	.60	.45	.25
58	Ted Simmons	.12	.09	.05
59	Dave Righetti	.15	.11	.06
60	Checklist	.09	.07	.04

1984 Donruss Champions

The 60-card Donruss Champions set includes ten Hall of Famers, forty-nine current players and one numbered checklist. The ten Hall of Famers' cards (called Grand Champions) feature the artwork of Dick Perez, while cards of the current players (called Champions) are color photos. The cards measure 3-1/2" by 5". The Grand Champions represent hallmarks of excellence in various statistical categories, while the Champions are the leaders among active players in each category. The ten Grand Champion cards are #'s 1, 8, 14, 20, 26, 31, 37, 43, 50 and 55. The cards were issued with Duke Snider puzzle pieces.

		MT	NR MT	EX
	Complete Set:	7.00	5.25	275.00
	Common Player:	.07	.05	.03
1	Babe Ruth	1.00	.70	.40
2	George Foster	.10	.08	.04
3	Dave Kingman	.10	.08	.04
4	Jim Rice	.10	.08	.04
5	Gorman Thomas	.10	.08	.04
6	Ben Oglivie	.07	.05	.03
7	Jeff Burroughs	.07	.05	.03
8	Hank Aaron	.35	.25	.14
9	Reggie Jackson	.30	.25	.12
10	Carl Yastrzemski	.50	.40	.20
11	Mike Schmidt	.50	.40	.20
12	Graig Nettles	.14	.11	.06
13	Greg Luzinski	.10	.08	.04
14	Ted Williams	1.00	.70	.40
15	George Brett	.35	.25	.14
16	Wade Boggs	.50	.40	.20
17	Hal McRae	.10	.08	.04
18	Bill Buckner	.10	.08	.04
19	Eddie Murray	.10	.08	.04
20	Rogers Hornsby	.14	.11	.06
21	Rod Carew	.20	.15	.08
22	Bill Madlock	.10	.08	.04
23	Lonnie Smith	.07	.05	.03
24	Cecil Cooper	.10	.08	.04
25	Ken Griffey	.10	.08	.04
26	Ty Cobb	.40	.30	.15
27	Pete Rose	.40	.30	.15
28	Rusty Staub	.10	.08	.04
29	Tony Perez	.10	.08	.04
30	Al Oliver	.10	.08	.04
31	Cy Young	.14	.11	.06
32	Gaylord Perry	.14	.11	.06
33	Ferguson Jenkins	.10	.08	.04
34	Phil Niekro	.14	.11	.06
35	Jim Palmer	.30	.25	.12
36	Tommy John	.10	.08	.04
37	Walter Johnson	.20	.15	.08
38	Steve Carlton	.25	.20	.10
39	Nolan Ryan	.50	.40	.20
40	Tom Seaver	.25	.20	.10
41	Don Sutton	.14	.11	.06
42	Bert Blyleven	.10	.08	.04
43	Frank Robinson	.35	.25	.14
44	Joe Morgan	.25	.20	.10
45	Rollie Fingers	.14	.11	.06
46	Keith Hernandez	.10	.08	.04
47	Robin Yount	.50	.40	.20
48	Cal Ripken	.25	.20	.10
49	Dale Murphy	.35	.25	.14
50	Mickey Mantle	1.00	.70	.40
51	Johnny Bench	.50	.40	.20
52	Carlton Fisk	.30	.25	.12
53	Tug McGraw	.10	.08	.04
54	Paul Molitor	.10	.08	.04
55	Carl Hubbell	.14	.11	.06
56	Steve Garvey	.15	.11	.06
57	Dave Parker	.14	.11	.06
58	Gary Carter	.15	.11	.06
59	Fred Lynn	.14	.11	.06
60	Checklist	.10	.08	.04

1985 Donruss

The black-bordered 1985 Donruss set includes 653 numbered cards and seven unnumbered checklists. Displaying the artwork of Dick Perez for the fourth consecutive year, card #'s 1-26 feature the Diamond Kings series. Donruss, realizing the hobby craze over rookie cards, included a Rated Rookies subset (card #'s 27-46). The cards, which are the standard size of 2-1/2" by 3-1/2", were issued with a Lou Gehrig puzzle. The backs of the cards have black print on yellow and white. The complete set price does not include the higher priced variations. (DK) and (RR) refer to the Diamond Kings and Rated Rookies subsets.

		MT	NR MT	EX
	Complete Set:	200.00	150.00	80.00
	Common Player:	.08	.06	.03
1	Ryne Sandberg (DK)	4.00	3.00	1.50
2	Doug DeCinces (DK)	.10	.08	.04
3	Rich Dotson (DK)	.12	.09	.05
4	Bert Blyleven (DK)	.15	.11	.06
5	Lou Whitaker (DK)	.30	.25	.12
6	Dan Quisenberry (DK)	.15	.11	.06
7	Don Mattingly (DK)	2.50	2.00	1.00
8	Carney Lansford (DK)	.10	.08	.04
9	Frank Tanana (DK)	.12	.09	.05
10	Willie Upshaw (DK)	.10	.08	.04
11	Claudell Washington (DK)	.10	.08	.04
12	Mike Marshall (DK)	.20	.15	.08
13	Joaquin Andujar (DK)	.10	.08	.04
14	Cal Ripken, Jr. (DK)	4.00	3.00	1.50
15	Jim Rice (DK)	.50	.40	.20
16	Don Sutton (DK)	.30	.25	.12
17	Frank Viola (DK)	.15	.11	.06
18	Alvin Davis (DK)(FC)	.60	.45	.25
19	Mario Soto (DK)	.10	.08	.04
20	Jose Cruz (DK)	.12	.09	.05
21	Charlie Lea (DK)	.10	.08	.04
22	Jesse Orosco (DK)	.10	.08	.04
23	Juan Samuel (DK)(FC)	.25	.20	.10
24	Tony Pena (DK)	.12	.09	.05
25	Tony Gwynn (DK)	1.00	.70	.40
26	Bob Brenly (DK)	.10	.08	.04
27	Danny Tartabull (RR)(FC)	10.00	7.50	4.00
28	Mike Bielecki (RR)(FC)	.15	.11	.06
29	Steve Lyons (RR)(FC)	.20	.15	.08
30	Jeff Reed (RR)(FC)	.15	.11	.06
31	Tony Brewer (RR)	.08	.06	.03
32	John Morris (RR)(FC)	.15	.11	.06
33	Daryl Boston (RR)(FC)	.25	.20	.10
34	Alfonso Pulido (RR)	.08	.06	.03
35	Steve Kiefer (RR)(FC)	.10	.08	.04
36	Larry Sheets (RR)(FC)	.50	.40	.20
37	Scott Bradley (RR)(FC)	.25	.20	.10
38	Calvin Schiraldi (RR)(FC)	.20	.15	.08
39	Shawon Dunston (RR)(FC)	4.00	3.00	1.50
40	Charlie Mitchell (RR)	.08	.06	.03
41	Billy Hatcher (RR)(FC)	.60	.45	.25
42	Russ Stephans (RR)	.08	.06	.03
43	Alejandro Sanchez (RR)	.08	.06	.03
44	Steve Jeltz (RR)(FC)	.15	.11	.06
45	Jim Traber (RR)(FC)	.30	.25	.12
46	Doug Loman (RR)	.08	.06	.03
47	Eddie Murray	1.50	1.25	.60
48	Robin Yount	4.00	3.00	1.50
49	Lance Parrish	.30	.25	.12
50	Jim Rice	.50	.40	.20
51	Dave Winfield	3.00	2.25	1.25
52	Fernando Valenzuela	.35	.25	.14
53	George Brett	4.00	3.00	1.50
54	Dave Kingman	.15	.11	.06
55	Gary Carter	.40	.30	.15
56	Buddy Bell	.12	.09	.05
57	Reggie Jackson	.60	.45	.25
58	Harold Baines	.20	.15	.08
59	Ozzie Smith	1.50	1.25	.60
60	Nolan Ryan	8.00	6.00	3.25
61	Mike Schmidt	4.00	3.00	1.50
62	Dave Parker	.35	.25	.14
63	Tony Gwynn	5.00	3.75	2.00
64	Tony Pena	.12	.09	.05
65	Jack Clark	.25	.20	.10
66	Dale Murphy	.80	.60	.30
67	Ryne Sandberg	10.00	7.50	4.00
68	Keith Hernandez	.40	.30	.15
69	Alvin Davis(FC)	1.25	.90	.50
70	Kent Hrbek	.30	.25	.12
71	Willie Upshaw	.10	.08	.04
72	Dave Engle	.08	.06	.03
73	Alfredo Griffin	.10	.08	.04
74a	Jack Perconte (last line of highlights begins "Batted .346...")	.10	.08	.04

		MT	NR MT	EX
74b	Jack Perconte (last line of highlights begins "Led the...")	1.25	.90	.50
75	Jesse Orosco	.10	.08	.04
76	Jody Davis	.12	.09	.05
77	Bob Horner	.12	.09	.05
78	Larry McWilliams	.08	.06	.03
79	Joel Youngblood	.08	.06	.03
80	Alan Wiggins	.08	.06	.03
81	Ron Oester	.08	.06	.03
82	Ozzie Virgil	.08	.06	.03
83	Ricky Horton(FC)	.35	.25	.14
84	Bill Doran	.12	.09	.05
85	Rod Carew	1.00	.70	.40
86	LaMarr Hoyt	.08	.06	.03
87	Tim Wallach	.15	.11	.06
88	Mike Flanagan	.12	.09	.05
89	Jim Sundberg	.10	.08	.04
90	Chet Lemon	.10	.08	.04
91	Bob Stanley	.08	.06	.03
92	Willie Randolph	.12	.09	.05
93	Bill Russell	.10	.08	.04
94	Julio Franco	1.50	1.25	.60
95	Dan Quisenberry	.12	.09	.05
96	Bill Caudill	.08	.06	.03
97	Bill Gullickson	.08	.06	.03
98	Danny Darwin	.08	.06	.03
99	Curtis Wilkerson	.08	.06	.03
100	Bud Black	.08	.06	.03
101	Tony Phillips	.08	.06	.03
102	Tony Bernazard	.08	.06	.03
103	Jay Howell	.10	.08	.04
104	Burt Hooton	.10	.08	.04
105	Milt Wilcox	.08	.06	.03
106	Rich Dauer	.08	.06	.03
107	Don Sutton	.35	.25	.14
108	Mike Witt	.15	.11	.06
109	Bruce Sutter	.15	.11	.06
110	Enos Cabell	.08	.06	.03
111	John Denny	.08	.06	.03
112	Dave Dravecky	.10	.08	.04
113	Marvell Wynne	.08	.06	.03
114	Johnnie LeMaster	.08	.06	.03
115	Chuck Porter	.08	.06	.03
116	John Gibbons	.08	.06	.03
117	Keith Moreland	.10	.08	.04
118	Darnell Coles	.12	.09	.05
119	Dennis Lamp	.08	.06	.03
120	Ron Davis	.08	.06	.03
121	Nick Esasky	.10	.08	.04
122	Vance Law	.10	.08	.04
123	Gary Roenicke	.08	.06	.03
124	Bill Schroeder	.08	.06	.03
125	Dave Rozema	.08	.06	.03
126	Bobby Meacham	.08	.06	.03
127	Marty Barrett(FC)	.25	.20	.10
128	R.J. Reynolds(FC)	.30	.25	.12
129	Ernie Camacho	.08	.06	.03
130	Jorge Orta	.08	.06	.03
131	Lary Sorensen	.08	.06	.03
132	Terry Francona	.08	.06	.03
133	Fred Lynn	.25	.20	.10
134	Bobby Jones	.08	.06	.03
135	Jerry Hairston	.08	.06	.03
136	Kevin Bass	.12	.09	.05
137	Garry Maddox	.08	.06	.03
138	Dave LaPoint	.10	.08	.04
139	Kevin McReynolds	1.00	.70	.40
140	Wayne Krenchicki	.08	.06	.03
141	Rafael Ramirez	.08	.06	.03
142	Rod Scurry	.08	.06	.03
143	Greg Minton	.08	.06	.03
144	Tim Stoddard	.08	.06	.03
145	Steve Henderson	.08	.06	.03
146	George Bell	.70	.50	.30
147	Dave Meier	.08	.06	.03
148	Sammy Stewart	.08	.06	.03
149	Mark Brouhard	.08	.06	.03
150	Larry Herndon	.10	.08	.04
151	Oil Can Boyd	.10	.08	.04
152	Brian Dayett	.08	.06	.03
153	Tom Niedenfuer	.10	.08	.04
154	Brook Jacoby	.15	.11	.06
155	Onix Concepcion	.08	.06	.03
156	Tim Conroy	.08	.06	.03
157	Joe Hesketh(FC)	.15	.11	.06
158	Brian Downing	.12	.09	.05
159	Tommy Dunbar	.08	.06	.03
160	Marc Hill	.08	.06	.03
161	Phil Garner	.10	.08	.04
162	Jerry Davis	.08	.06	.03
163	Bill Campbell	.08	.06	.03

#	Player	MT	NR MT	EX
164	*John Franco*(FC)	2.00	1.50	.80
165	Len Barker	.10	.08	.04
166	*Benny Distefano*(FC)	.10	.08	.04
167	George Frazier	.08	.06	.03
168	Tito Landrum	.08	.06	.03
169	Cal Ripken	10.00	7.50	4.00
170	Cecil Cooper	.15	.11	.06
171	Alan Trammell	.40	.30	.15
172	Wade Boggs	5.00	3.75	2.00
173	Don Baylor	.15	.11	.06
174	Pedro Guerrero	.30	.25	.12
175	Frank White	.12	.09	.05
176	Rickey Henderson	5.00	3.75	2.00
177	Charlie Lea	.08	.06	.03
178	Pete O'Brien	.20	.15	.08
179	Doug DeCinces	.12	.09	.05
180	Ron Kittle	.12	.09	.05
181	George Hendrick	.10	.08	.04
182	Joe Niekro	.12	.09	.05
183	Juan Samuel(FC)	.60	.45	.25
184	Mario Soto	.10	.08	.04
185	Goose Gossage	.25	.20	.10
186	Johnny Ray	.15	.11	.06
187	Bob Brenly	.08	.06	.03
188	Craig McMurtry	.08	.06	.03
189	Leon Durham	.10	.08	.04
190	*Dwight Gooden*(FC)	9.00	6.75	3.50
191	Barry Bonnell	.08	.06	.03
192	Tim Teufel	.12	.09	.05
193	Dave Stieb	.15	.11	.06
194	Mickey Hatcher	.08	.06	.03
195	Jesse Barfield	.25	.20	.10
196	Al Cowens	.08	.06	.03
197	Hubie Brooks	.12	.09	.05
198	Steve Trout	.08	.06	.03
199	Glenn Hubbard	.08	.06	.03
200	Bill Madlock	.15	.11	.06
201	*Jeff Robinson*(FC)	.35	.25	.14
202	Eric Show	.10	.08	.04
203	Dave Concepcion	.15	.11	.06
204	Ivan DeJesus	.08	.06	.03
205	Neil Allen	.08	.06	.03
206	Jerry Mumphrey	.08	.06	.03
207	Mike Brown	.08	.06	.03
208	Carlton Fisk	.40	.30	.15
209	Bryn Smith	.08	.06	.03
210	Tippy Martinez	.08	.06	.03
211	Dion James	.10	.08	.04
212	Willie Hernandez	.10	.08	.04
213	Mike Easler	.10	.08	.04
214	Ron Guidry	.30	.25	.12
215	Rick Honeycutt	.08	.06	.03
216	Brett Butler	.12	.09	.05
217	Larry Gura	.08	.06	.03
218	Ray Burris	.08	.06	.03
219	Steve Rogers	.10	.08	.04
220	Frank Tanana	.12	.09	.05
221	Ned Yost	.08	.06	.03
222	*Bret Saberhagen*	8.00	6.00	3.25
223	Mike Davis	.10	.08	.04
224	Bert Blyleven	.15	.11	.06
225	Steve Kemp	.10	.08	.04
226	Jerry Reuss	.10	.08	.04
227	Darrell Evans	.15	.11	.06
228	Wayne Gross	.08	.06	.03
229	Jim Gantner	.10	.08	.04
230	Bob Boone	.10	.08	.04
231	Lonnie Smith	.10	.08	.04
232	Frank DiPino	.08	.06	.03
233	Jerry Koosman	.12	.09	.05
234	Graig Nettles	.20	.15	.08
235	John Tudor	.12	.09	.05
236	John Rabb	.08	.06	.03
237	Rick Manning	.08	.06	.03
238	Mike Fitzgerald	.08	.06	.03
239	Gary Matthews	.12	.09	.05
240	*Jim Presley*(FC)	.50	.40	.20
241	Dave Collins	.10	.08	.04
242	Gary Gaetti	.30	.25	.12
243	Dann Bilardello	.08	.06	.03
244	Rudy Law	.08	.06	.03
245	John Lowenstein	.08	.06	.03
246	Tom Tellmann	.08	.06	.03
247	Howard Johnson	1.75	1.25	.70
248	Ray Fontenot	.08	.06	.03
249	Tony Armas	.12	.09	.05
250	Candy Maldonado	.12	.09	.05
251	*Mike Jeffcoat*(FC)	.10	.08	.04
252	Dane Iorg	.08	.06	.03
253	Bruce Bochte	.08	.06	.03
254	Pete Rose	1.25	.90	.50
255	Don Aase	.08	.06	.03
256	George Wright	.08	.06	.03
257	Britt Burns	.08	.06	.03
258	Mike Scott	.20	.15	.08
259	Len Matuszek	.08	.06	.03
260	Dave Rucker	.08	.06	.03
261	Craig Lefferts	.10	.08	.04
262	*Jay Tibbs*(FC)	.20	.15	.08
263	Bruce Benedict	.08	.06	.03
264	Don Robinson	.10	.08	.04
265	Gary Lavelle	.08	.06	.03
266	Scott Sanderson	.08	.06	.03
267	Matt Young	.08	.06	.03
268	Ernie Whitt	.10	.08	.04
269	Houston Jimenez	.08	.06	.03
270	*Ken Dixon*(FC)	.12	.09	.05
271	Peter Ladd	.08	.06	.03
272	Juan Berenguer	.08	.06	.03
273	*Roger Clemens*(FC)	60.00	45.00	25.00
274	Rick Cerone	.08	.06	.03
275	Dave Anderson	.08	.06	.03
276	George Vukovich	.08	.06	.03
277	Greg Pryor	.08	.06	.03
278	Mike Warren	.08	.06	.03
279	Bob James	.08	.06	.03
280	Bobby Grich	.12	.09	.05
281	*Mike Mason*(FC)	.12	.09	.05
282	Ron Reed	.08	.06	.03
283	Alan Ashby	.08	.06	.03
284	Mark Thurmond	.08	.06	.03
285	Joe Lefebvre	.08	.06	.03
286	Ted Power	.08	.06	.03
287	Chris Chambliss	.10	.08	.04
288	Lee Tunnell	.08	.06	.03
289	Rich Bordi	.08	.06	.03
290	Glenn Brummer	.08	.06	.03
291	Mike Boddicker	.12	.09	.05
292	Rollie Fingers	.25	.20	.10
293	Lou Whitaker	.40	.30	.15
294	Dwight Evans	.15	.11	.06
295	Don Mattingly	8.00	6.00	3.25
296	Mike Marshall	.15	.11	.06
297	Willie Wilson	.15	.11	.06
298	Mike Heath	.08	.06	.03
299	Tim Raines	.50	.40	.20
300	Larry Parrish	.12	.09	.05
301	Geoff Zahn	.08	.06	.03
302	Rich Dotson	.12	.09	.05
303	David Green	.08	.06	.03
304	Jose Cruz	.12	.09	.05
305	Steve Carlton	.80	.60	.30
306	Gary Redus	.10	.08	.04
307	Steve Garvey	.50	.40	.20
308	Jose DeLeon	.10	.08	.04
309	Randy Lerch	.08	.06	.03
310	Claudell Washington	.10	.08	.04
311	Lee Smith	.12	.09	.05
312	Darryl Strawberry	9.00	6.75	3.50
313	Jim Beattie	.08	.06	.03
314	John Butcher	.08	.06	.03
315	Damaso Garcia	.10	.08	.04
316	Mike Smithson	.08	.06	.03
317	Luis Leal	.08	.06	.03
318	Ken Phelps(FC)	.25	.20	.10
319	Wally Backman	.10	.08	.04
320	Ron Cey	.12	.09	.05
321	Brad Komminsk	.08	.06	.03
322	Jason Thompson	.08	.06	.03
323	*Frank Williams*(FC)	.20	.15	.08
324	Tim Lollar	.08	.06	.03
325	*Eric Davis*(FC)	8.00	6.00	3.25
326	Von Hayes	.12	.09	.05
327	Andy Van Slyke	.40	.30	.15
328	Craig Reynolds	.08	.06	.03
329	Dick Schofield	.10	.08	.04
330	Scott Fletcher	.10	.08	.04
331	Jeff Reardon	.15	.11	.06
332	Rick Dempsey	.10	.08	.04
333	Ben Oglivie	.10	.08	.04
334	Dan Petry	.10	.08	.04
335	Jackie Gutierrez	.08	.06	.03
336	Dave Righetti	.25	.20	.10
337	Alejandro Pena	.10	.08	.04
338	Mel Hall	.10	.08	.04
339	Pat Sheridan	.08	.06	.03
340	Keith Atherton	.08	.06	.03
341	David Palmer	.08	.06	.03
342	Gary Ward	.10	.08	.04
343	Dave Stewart	.15	.11	.06
344	*Mark Gubicza*(FC)	1.25	.90	.50
345	Carney Lansford	.12	.09	.05

#	Player	MT	NR MT	EX
346	Jerry Willard	.08	.06	.03
347	Ken Griffey	.12	.09	.05
348	*Franklin Stubbs*(FC)	.60	.45	.25
349	Aurelio Lopez	.08	.06	.03
350	Al Bumbry	.10	.08	.04
351	Charlie Moore	.08	.06	.03
352	Luis Sanchez	.08	.06	.03
353	Darrell Porter	.10	.08	.04
354	Bill Dawley	.08	.06	.03
355	Charlie Hudson	.10	.08	.04
356	Garry Templeton	.10	.08	.04
357	Cecilio Guante	.08	.06	.03
358	Jeff Leonard	.12	.09	.05
359	Paul Molitor	.20	.15	.08
360	Ron Gardenhire	.08	.06	.03
361	Larry Bowa	.12	.09	.05
362	Bob Kearney	.08	.06	.03
363	Garth Iorg	.08	.06	.03
364	Tom Brunansky	.15	.11	.06
365	Brad Gulden	.08	.06	.03
366	Greg Walker	.12	.09	.05
367	Mike Young	.10	.08	.04
368	Rick Waits	.08	.06	.03
369	Doug Bair	.08	.06	.03
370	Bob Shirley	.08	.06	.03
371	Bob Ojeda	.12	.09	.05
372	Bob Welch	.15	.11	.06
373	Neal Heaton	.08	.06	.03
374	Danny Jackson (photo actually Steve Farr)	.80	.60	.30
375	Donnie Hill	.08	.06	.03
376	Mike Stenhouse	.08	.06	.03
377	Bruce Kison	.08	.06	.03
378	Wayne Tolleson	.08	.06	.03
379	Floyd Bannister	.12	.09	.05
380	Vern Ruhle	.08	.06	.03
381	Tim Corcoran	.08	.06	.03
382	Kurt Kepshire	.08	.06	.03
383	Bobby Brown	.08	.06	.03
384	Dave Van Gorder	.08	.06	.03
385	Rick Mahler	.08	.06	.03
386	Lee Mazzilli	.10	.08	.04
387	Bill Laskey	.08	.06	.03
388	Thad Bosley	.08	.06	.03
389	Al Chambers	.08	.06	.03
390	Tony Fernandez	.70	.50	.30
391	Ron Washington	.08	.06	.03
392	Bill Swaggerty	.08	.06	.03
393	Bob Gibson	.08	.06	.03
394	Marty Castillo	.08	.06	.03
395	Steve Crawford	.08	.06	.03
396	Clay Christiansen	.08	.06	.03
397	Bob Bailor	.08	.06	.03
398	Mike Hargrove	.08	.06	.03
399	Charlie Leibrandt	.10	.08	.04
400	Tom Burgmeier	.08	.06	.03
401	Razor Shines	.08	.06	.03
402	Rob Wilfong	.08	.06	.03
403	Tom Henke	.12	.09	.05
404	Al Jones	.08	.06	.03
405	Mike LaCoss	.08	.06	.03
406	Luis DeLeon	.08	.06	.03
407	Greg Gross	.08	.06	.03
408	Tom Hume	.08	.06	.03
409	Rick Camp	.08	.06	.03
410	Milt May	.08	.06	.03
411	*Henry Cotto*(FC)	.20	.15	.08
412	Dave Von Ohlen	.08	.06	.03
413	Scott McGregor	.10	.08	.04
414	Ted Simmons	.15	.11	.06
415	Jack Morris	.30	.25	.12
416	Bill Buckner	.15	.11	.06
417	Butch Wynegar	.08	.06	.03
418	Steve Sax	.25	.20	.10
419	Steve Balboni	.10	.08	.04
420	Dwayne Murphy	.10	.08	.04
421	Andre Dawson	1.25	.90	.50
422	Charlie Hough	.10	.08	.04
423	Tommy John	.25	.20	.10
424a	Tom Seaver (Floyd Bannister photo – throwing left)	3.00	2.25	1.25
424b	Tom Seaver (correct photo - throwing right)	30.00	22.00	12.00
425	Tom Herr	.12	.09	.05
426	Terry Puhl	.08	.06	.03
427	Al Holland	.08	.06	.03
428	Eddie Milner	.08	.06	.03
429	Terry Kennedy	.10	.08	.04
430	John Candelaria	.12	.09	.05
431	Manny Trillo	.10	.08	.04
432	Ken Oberkfell	.08	.06	.03
433	Rick Sutcliffe	.15	.11	.06
434	Ron Darling	.70	.50	.30
435	Spike Owen	.10	.08	.04
436	Frank Viola	.25	.20	.10
437	Lloyd Moseby	.12	.09	.05
438	*Kirby Puckett*(FC)	50.00	37.00	20.00
439	Jim Clancy	.10	.08	.04
440	Mike Moore	.08	.06	.03
441	Doug Sisk	.08	.06	.03
442	Dennis Eckersley	.15	.11	.06
443	Gerald Perry	.25	.20	.10
444	Dale Berra	.08	.06	.03
445	Dusty Baker	.10	.08	.04
446	Ed Whitson	.08	.06	.03
447	Cesar Cedeno	.12	.09	.05
448	*Rick Schu*(FC)	.20	.15	.08
449	Joaquin Andujar	.10	.08	.04
450	*Mark Bailey*(FC)	.12	.09	.05
451	*Ron Romanick*(FC)	.12	.09	.05
452	Julio Cruz	.08	.06	.03
453	Miguel Dilone	.08	.06	.03
454	Storm Davis	.12	.09	.05
455	Jaime Cocanower	.08	.06	.03
456	Barbaro Garbey	.12	.09	.05
457	Rich Gedman	.12	.09	.05
458	Phil Niekro	.30	.25	.12
459	Mike Scioscia	.10	.08	.04
460	Pat Tabler	.10	.08	.04
461	Darryl Motley	.08	.06	.03
462	Chris Codoroli (Codiroli)	.08	.06	.03
463	Doug Flynn	.08	.06	.03
464	Billy Sample	.08	.06	.03
465	Mickey Rivers	.10	.08	.04
466	John Wathan	.10	.08	.04
467	Bill Krueger	.08	.06	.03
468	Andre Thornton	.12	.09	.05
469	Rex Hudler	.12	.09	.05
470	*Sid Bream*(FC)	.80	.60	.30
471	Kirk Gibson	.40	.30	.15
472	John Shelby	.10	.08	.04
473	Moose Haas	.08	.06	.03
474	Doug Corbett	.08	.06	.03
475	Willie McGee	.35	.25	.14
476	Bob Knepper	.10	.08	.04
477	Kevin Gross	.12	.09	.05
478	Carmelo Martinez	.10	.08	.04
479	Kent Tekulve	.10	.08	.04
480	Chili Davis	.12	.09	.05
481	Bobby Clark	.08	.06	.03
482	Mookie Wilson	.12	.09	.05
483	Dave Owen	.08	.06	.03
484	Ed Nunez	.08	.06	.03
485	Rance Mulliniks	.08	.06	.03
486	Ken Schrom	.08	.06	.03
487	Jeff Russell	.08	.06	.03
488	Tom Paciorek	.08	.06	.03
489	Dan Ford	.08	.06	.03
490	Mike Caldwell	.08	.06	.03
491	Scottie Earl	.08	.06	.03
492	*Jose Rijo*(FC)	2.00	1.50	.80
493	Bruce Hurst	.15	.11	.06
494	Ken Landreaux	.08	.06	.03
495	Mike Fischlin	.08	.06	.03
496	Don Slaught	.08	.06	.03
497	Steve McCatty	.08	.06	.03
498	Gary Lucas	.08	.06	.03
499	Gary Pettis	.10	.08	.04
500	Marvis Foley	.08	.06	.03
501	Mike Squires	.08	.06	.03
502	*Jim Pankovitz*(FC)	.15	.11	.06
503	Luis Aguayo	.08	.06	.03
504	Ralph Citarella	.08	.06	.03
505	Bruce Bochy	.08	.06	.03
506	Bob Owchinko	.08	.06	.03
507	Pascual Perez	.10	.08	.04
508	Lee Lacy	.08	.06	.03
509	Atlee Hammaker	.08	.06	.03
510	Bob Dernier	.08	.06	.03
511	Ed Vande Berg	.08	.06	.03
512	Cliff Johnson	.08	.06	.03
513	Len Whitehouse	.08	.06	.03
514	Dennis Martinez	.10	.08	.04
515	Ed Romero	.08	.06	.03
516	Rusty Kuntz	.08	.06	.03
517	Rick Miller	.08	.06	.03
518	Dennis Rasmussen	.15	.11	.06
519	Steve Yeager	.08	.06	.03
520	Chris Bando	.08	.06	.03
521	U.L. Washington	.08	.06	.03
522	*Curt Young*(FC)	.40	.30	.15
523	Angel Salazar	.08	.06	.03

		MT	NR MT	EX
524	Curt Kaufman	.08	.06	.03
525	Odell Jones	.08	.06	.03
526	Juan Agosto	.08	.06	.03
527	Denny Walling	.08	.06	.03
528	Andy Hawkins(FC)	.20	.15	.08
529	Sixto Lezcano	.08	.06	.03
530	Skeeter Barnes	.08	.06	.03
531	Randy Johnson	.08	.06	.03
532	Jim Morrison	.08	.06	.03
533	Warren Brusstar	.08	.06	.03
534a	*Jeff Pendleton* (first name incorrect)(FC)			
		8.00	6.00	3.25
534b	*Terry Pendleton* (first name correct)(FC)			
		15.00	11.00	6.00
535	Vic Rodriguez	.08	.06	.03
536	Bob McClure	.08	.06	.03
537	Dave Bergman	.08	.06	.03
538	Mark Clear	.08	.06	.03
539	*Mike Pagliarulo*(FC)	1.00	.70	.40
540	Terry Whitfield	.08	.06	.03
541	Joe Beckwith	.08	.06	.03
542	Jeff Burroughs	.10	.08	.04
543	Dan Schatzeder	.08	.06	.03
544	Donnie Scott	.08	.06	.03
545	Jim Slaton	.08	.06	.03
546	Greg Luzinski	.12	.09	.05
547	*Mark Salas*(FC)	.15	.11	.06
548	Dave Smith	.10	.08	.04
549	John Wockenfuss	.08	.06	.03
550	Frank Pastore	.08	.06	.03
551	Tim Flannery	.08	.06	.03
552	Rick Rhoden	.12	.09	.05
553	Mark Davis	.08	.06	.03
554	*Jeff Dedmon*(FC)	.15	.11	.06
555	Gary Woods	.08	.06	.03
556	Danny Heep	.08	.06	.03
557	*Mark Langston*(FC)	5.00	3.75	2.00
558	Darrell Brown	.08	.06	.03
559	*Jimmy Key*(FC)	2.00	1.50	.80
560	Rick Lysander	.08	.06	.03
561	Doyle Alexander	.12	.09	.05
562	Mike Stanton	.08	.06	.03
563	Sid Fernandez	.50	.40	.20
564	Richie Hebner	.08	.06	.03
565	Alex Trevino	.08	.06	.03
566	Brian Harper	.08	.06	.03
567	*Dan Gladden*(FC)	.60	.45	.25
568	Luis Salazar	.08	.06	.03
569	Tom Foley	.08	.06	.03
570	Larry Andersen	.08	.06	.03
571	Danny Cox	.12	.09	.05
572	Joe Sambito	.08	.06	.03
573	Juan Beniquez	.08	.06	.03
574	Joel Skinner	.08	.06	.03
575	*Randy St. Claire*(FC)	.15	.11	.06
576	Floyd Rayford	.08	.06	.03
577	Roy Howell	.08	.06	.03
578	John Grubb	.08	.06	.03
579	Ed Jurak	.08	.06	.03
580	John Montefusco	.08	.06	.03
581	*Orel Hershiser*(FC)	3.00	2.25	1.25
582	*Tom Waddell*(FC)	.08	.06	.03
583	Mark Huismann	.08	.06	.03
584	Joe Morgan	.30	.25	.12
585	Jim Wohlford	.08	.06	.03
586	Dave Schmidt	.08	.06	.03
587	*Jeff Kunkel*(FC)	.12	.09	.05
588	Hal McRae	.12	.09	.05
589	Bill Almon	.08	.06	.03
590	Carmen Castillo(FC)	.10	.08	.04
591	Omar Moreno	.08	.06	.03
592	*Ken Howell*(FC)	.20	.15	.08
593	Tom Brookens	.08	.06	.03
594	Joe Nolan	.08	.06	.03
595	Willie Lozado	.08	.06	.03
596	*Tom Nieto*(FC)	.12	.09	.05
597	Walt Terrell	.10	.08	.04
598	Al Oliver	.15	.11	.06
599	Shane Rawley	.12	.09	.05
600	*Denny Gonzalez*(FC)	.10	.08	.04
601	*Mark Grant*(FC)	.15	.11	.06
602	Mike Armstrong	.08	.06	.03
603	George Foster	.15	.11	.06
604	Davey Lopes	.10	.08	.04
605	Salome Barojas	.08	.06	.03
606	Roy Lee Jackson	.08	.06	.03
607	Pete Filson	.08	.06	.03
608	Duane Walker	.08	.06	.03
609	Glenn Wilson	.10	.08	.04
610	*Rafael Santana*(FC)	.20	.15	.08
611	Roy Smith	.08	.06	.03

		MT	NR MT	EX
612	Ruppert Jones	.08	.06	.03
613	Joe Cowley(FC)	.08	.06	.03
614	*Al Nipper* (photo actually Mike Brown)(FC)			
		.20	.15	.08
615	Gene Nelson	.08	.06	.03
616	Joe Carter	8.00	6.00	3.25
617	Ray Knight	.12	.09	.05
618	Chuck Rainey	.08	.06	.03
619	Dan Driessen	.10	.08	.04
620	Daryl Sconiers	.08	.06	.03
621	Bill Stein	.08	.06	.03
622	Roy Smalley	.08	.06	.03
623	Ed Lynch	.08	.06	.03
624	*Jeff Stone*(FC)	.15	.11	.06
625	Bruce Berenyi	.08	.06	.03
626	Kelvin Chapman	.08	.06	.03
627	Joe Price	.08	.06	.03
628	Steve Bedrosian	.12	.09	.05
629	Vic Mata	.08	.06	.03
630	Mike Krukow	.10	.08	.04
631	*Phil Bradley*(FC)	.90	.70	.35
632	Jim Gott	.08	.06	.03
633	Randy Bush	.08	.06	.03
634	*Tom Browning*(FC)	1.50	1.25	.60
635	Lou Gehrig Puzzle Card	.08	.06	.03
636	Reid Nichols	.08	.06	.03
637	*Dan Pasqua*(FC)	.60	.45	.25
638	German Rivera	.08	.06	.03
639	*Don Schulze*(FC)	.10	.08	.04
640a	Mike Jones (last line of highlights begins "Was 11-7...")	.10	.08	.04
640b	Mike Jones (last line of highlights begins "Spent some ...")	1.25	.90	.50
641	Pete Rose	1.25	.90	.50
642	*Wade Rowdon*(FC)	.10	.08	.04
643	Jerry Narron	.08	.06	.03
644	*Darrell Miller*(FC)	.15	.11	.06
645	*Tim Hulett*(FC)	.15	.11	.06
646	Andy McGaffigan	.08	.06	.03
647	Kurt Bevacqua	.08	.06	.03
648	*John Russell*(FC)	.20	.15	.08
649	*Ron Robinson*(FC)	.25	.20	.10
650	Donnie Moore(FC)	.08	.06	.03
651a	Two for the Title (Don Mattingly, Dave Winfield) (player names in yellow)	8.00	6.00	3.25
651b	Two for the Title (Don Mattingly, Dave Winfield) (player names in white)	6.00	4.50	2.50
652	Tim Laudner	.08	.06	.03
653	*Steve Farr*(FC)	.40	.30	.15
-----	Checklist 1-26 DK	.08	.06	.03
-----	Checklist 27-130	.08	.06	.03
-----	Checklist 131-234	.08	.06	.03
-----	Checklist 235-338	.08	.06	.03
-----	Checklist 339-442	.08	.06	.03
-----	Checklist 443-546	.08	.06	.03
-----	Checklist 547-653	.08	.06	.03

1985 Donruss
Action All-Stars

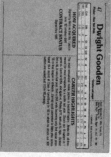

In 1985, Donruss issued an Action All-Stars set for the third consecutive year. The card fronts feature an action photo with an inset head-shot of the player inside a black border with grey boxes through it. The card backs have black print on blue and white and include statistical and biographical information. The cards were issued with a Lou Gehrig puzzle.

		MT	NR MT	EX
	Complete Set:	8.00	6.00	3.25
	Common Player:	.09	.07	.04
1	Tim Raines	.25	.20	.10
2	Jim Gantner	.09	.07	.04
3	Mario Soto	.09	.07	.04
4	Spike Owen	.09	.07	.04
5	Lloyd Moseby	.09	.07	.04
6	Damaso Garcia	.09	.07	.04
7	Cal Ripken	.60	.45	.25
8	Dan Quisenberry	.09	.07	.04
9	Eddie Murray	.12	.09	.05
10	Tony Pena	.09	.07	.04
11	Buddy Bell	.09	.07	.04
12	Dave Winfield	.30	.25	.12
13	Ron Kittle	.12	.09	.05
14	Rich Gossage	.12	.09	.05
15	Dwight Evans	.15	.11	.06
16	Al Davis	.15	.11	.06
17	Mike Schmidt	.40	.30	.15
18	Pascual Perez	.09	.07	.04
19	Tony Gwynn	.30	.25	.12
20	Nolan Ryan	1.25	.90	.50
21	Robin Yount	.50	.40	.20
22	Mike Marshall	.12	.09	.05
23	Brett Butler	.09	.07	.04
24	Ryne Sandberg	.50	.40	.20
25	Dale Murphy	.40	.30	.15
26	George Brett	.40	.30	.15
27	Jim Rice	.15	.11	.06
28	Ozzie Smith	.15	.11	.06
29	Larry Parrish	.09	.07	.04
30	Jack Clark	.15	.11	.06
31	Manny Trillo	.09	.07	.04
32	Dave Kingman	.12	.09	.05
33	Geoff Zahn	.09	.07	.04
34	Pedro Guerrero	.15	.11	.06
35	Dave Parker	.20	.15	.08
36	Rollie Fingers	.15	.11	.06
37	Fernando Valenzuela	.12	.09	.05
38	Wade Boggs	.60	.45	.25
39	Reggie Jackson	.30	.25	.12
40	Kent Hrbek	.20	.15	.08
41	Keith Hernandez	.25	.20	.10
42	Lou Whitaker	.15	.11	.06
43	Tom Herr	.09	.07	.04
44	Alan Trammell	.20	.15	.08
45	Butch Wynegar	.09	.07	.04
46	Leon Durham	.09	.07	.04
47	Dwight Gooden	.80	.60	.30
48	Don Mattingly	1.00	.70	.40
49	Phil Niekro	.20	.15	.08
50	Johnny Ray	.09	.07	.04
51	Doug DeCinces	.09	.07	.04
52	Willie Upshaw	.09	.07	.04
53	Lance Parrish	.15	.11	.06
54	Jody Davis	.09	.07	.04
55	Steve Carlton	.30	.25	.12
56	Juan Samuel	.09	.07	.04
57	Gary Carter	.12	.09	.05
58	Harold Baines	.15	.11	.06
59	Eric Show	.09	.07	.04
60	Checklist	.09	.07	.04

1985 Donruss Box Panels

In 1985, Donruss placed on the bottoms of their wax pack boxes a four-card panel which included three player cards and a Lou Gehrig puzzle card. The player cards, numbered PC 1 through PC 3, have backs identical to the regular 1985 Donruss issue. The card fronts are identical in design to the regular issue, but carry different picture poses.

		MT	NR MT	EX
	Complete Panel Set:	7.00	5.25	2.75
	Complete Singles Set:	5.00	3.75	2.00
	Common Single Player:	.10	.08	.04
	Panel	7.00	5.25	2.75
1	Dwight Gooden	3.00	2.25	1.25
2	Ryne Sanberg	2.00	1.50	.80
3	Ron Kittle	.10	.08	.04
----	Lou Gehrig Puzzle Card	.05	.04	.02

1985 Donruss Diamond Kings Supers

The 1985 Donruss Diamond Kings Supers are enlarged versions of the Diamond Kings card (#'s 1-26) in the regular 1985 Donruss set. The cards measure 4-15/16" by 6-3/4". The Diamond Kings series features the artwork of Dick Perez. Twenty-eight cards make up the set - 26 DK cards, an unnumbered checklist, and an unnumbered Dick Perez card. The back of the Perez card contains a brief history of Dick Perez and the Perez-Steele Galleries. The set could be obtained through a write-in offer found on the wrappers of the regular issue wax packs.

		MT	NR MT	EX
	Complete Set:	15.00	11.00	6.00
	Common Player:	.20	.15	.08
1	Ryne Sandberg	2.00	1.50	.80
2	Doug DeCinces	.20	.15	.08
3	Richard Dotson	.20	.15	.08
4	Bert Blyleven	.25	.20	.10
5	Lou Whitaker	.30	.25	.12
6	Dan Quisenberry	.20	.15	.08
7	Don Mattingly	3.00	2.25	1.25
8	Carney Lansford	.20	.15	.08
9	Frank Tanana	.20	.15	.08
10	Willie Upshaw	.20	.15	.08
11	Claudell Washington	.20	.15	.08
12	Mike Marshall	.25	.20	.10
13	Joaquin Andujar	.20	.15	.08
14	Cal Ripken, Jr.	2.00	1.50	.80
15	Jim Rice	.35	.25	.14
16	Don Sutton	.30	.25	.12
17	Frank Viola	.35	.25	.14
18	Alvin Davis	.30	.25	.12
19	Mario Soto	.20	.15	.08
20	Jose Cruz	.20	.15	.08
21	Charlie Lea	.20	.15	.08
22	Jesse Orosco	.20	.15	.08
23	Juan Samuel	.20	.15	.08
24	Tony Pena	.20	.15	.08
25	Tony Gwynn	.40	.30	.15
26	Bob Brenly	.20	.15	.08
----	Checklist	.12	.09	.05
----	Dick Perez (DK artist)	.12	.09	.05

1985 Donruss Highlights

Designed in the style of the regular 1985 Donruss set, this issue features the Player of the Month in the major leagues plus highlight cards of special baseball events and milestones that occurred during the 1985 season. Fifty-six cards, including an unnumbered checklist, comprise the set which was available only through hobby dealers. The cards measure 2-1/2" by 3-1/2" and have glossy fronts. The last two cards in the set feature Donruss' picks for the A.L. and N.L. Rookies of the Year. The set was issued in a specially designed box.

		MT	NR MT	EX
Complete Set:		30.00	22.00	12.00
Common Player:		.12	.09	.05
1	Sets Opening Day Record (Tom Seaver)			
		.40	.30	.15
2	Establishes A.L. Save Mark (Rollie Fingers)			
		.15	.11	.06
3	A.L. Player of the Month - April (Mike Davis)	.12	.09	.05
4	A.L. Pitcher of the Month - April (Charlie Leibrandt)	.12	.09	.05
5	N.L. Player of the Month - April (Dale Murphy)	.40	.30	.15
6	N.L. Pitcher of the Month - April (Fernando Valenzuela)	.12	.09	.05
7	N.L. Shortstop Record (Larry Bowa)			
		.12	.09	.05
8	Joins Reds 2000 Hit Club (Dave Concepcion)	.12	.09	.05
9	Eldest Grand Slammer (Tony Perez)			
		.15	.11	.06
10	N.L. Career Run Leader (Pete Rose)			
		1.25	.90	.50
11	A.L. Player of the Month - May (George Brett)	.90	.70	.35
12	A.L. Pitcher of the Month - May (Dave Stieb)	.12	.09	.05
13	N.L. Player of the Month - May (Dave Parker)	.20	.15	.08
14	N.L. Pitcher of the Month - May (Andy Hawkins)	.12	.09	.05
15	Records 11th Straight Win (Andy Hawkins)	.12	.09	.05
16	Two Homers In First Inning (Von Hayes)			
		.15	.11	.06
17	A.L. Player of the Month - June (Rickey Henderson)	1.00	.70	.40
18	A.L. Pitcher of the Month - June (Jay Howell)	.12	.09	.05
19	N.L. Player of the Month - June (Pedro Guerrero)	.20	.15	.08
20	N.L. Pitcher of the Month - June (John Tudor)	.12	.09	.05
21	Marathon Game Iron Men (Gary Carter, Keith Hernandez)	.35	.25	.14
22	Records 4000th K (Nolan Ryan)	1.25	.90	.50
23	All-Star Game MVP (LaMarr Hoyt)	.12	.09	.05
24	1st Ranger To Hit For Cycle (Oddibe McDowell)	.40	.30	.15
25	A.L. Player of the Month - July (George Brett)	.90	.70	.35
26	A.L. Pitcher of the Month - July (Bret Saberhagen)	1.50	1.25	.60
27	N.L. Player of the Month - July (Keith Hernandez)	.35	.25	.14
28	N.L. Pitcher of the Month - July (Fernando Valenzuela)	.12	.09	.05

		MT	NR MT	EX
29	Record Setting Base Stealers (Vince Coleman, Willie McGee)	.80	.60	.30
30	Notches 300th Career Win (Tom Seaver)			
		.35	.25	.14
31	Strokes 3000th Hit (Rod Carew)	.40	.30	.15
32	Establishes Met Record (Dwight Gooden)			
		2.25	1.75	.90
33	Achieves Strikeout Milestone (Dwight Gooden)	2.25	1.75	.90
34	Explodes For 9 RBI (Eddie Murray)	.70	.50	.30
35	A.L. Career Hbp Leader (Don Baylor)			
		.15	.11	.06
36	A.L. Player of the Month - August (Don Mattingly)	3.25	2.50	1.25
37	A.L. Pitcher of the Month - August (Dave Righetti)	.20	.15	.08
38	N.L. Player of the Month (Willie McGee)			
		.20	.15	.08
39	N.L. Pitcher of the Month - August (Shane Rawley)	.12	.09	.05
40	Ty-Breaking Hit (Pete Rose)	.90	.70	.35
41	Hits 3 Hrs Drives In 8 Runs (Andre Dawson)	.20	.15	.08
42	Sets Yankee Theft Mark (Rickey Henderson)	1.00	.70	.40
43	20 Wins In Rookie Season (Tom Browning)			
		.35	.25	.14
44	Yankee Milestone For Hits (Don Mattingly)			
		3.25	2.50	1.25
45	A.L. Player of the Month - September (Don Mattingly)	3.25	2.50	1.25
46	A.L. Pitcher of the Month - September (Charlie Leibrandt)	.12	.09	.05
47	N.L. Player of the Month - September (Gary Carter)	.12	.09	.05
48	N.L. Pitcher of the Month - September (Dwight Gooden)	2.25	1.75	.90
49	Major League Record Setter (Wade Boggs)	2.00	1.50	.80
50	Hurls Shutout For 300th Win (Phil Niekro)			
		.30	.25	.12
51	Venerable HR King (Darrell Evans)	.15	.11	.06
52	N.L. Switch-hitting Record (Willie McGee)			
		.20	.15	.08
53	Equals DiMaggio Feat (Dave Winfield)			
		.30	.25	.12
54	Donruss N.L. Rookie of the Year (Vince Coleman)	2.25	1.75	.90
55	Donruss A.L. Rookie of the Year (Ozzie Guillen)	.50	.40	.20
----	Checklist	.20	.15	.08

1985 Donruss Sluggers of the Hall of Fame

In much the same manner as the first Bazooka cards were issued in 1959, this eight-player set from Donruss consists of cards which formed the bottom panel of a box of bubble gum. When cut off the box, cards measure 3-1/2" by 6-1/2", with blank backs. Players are pictured on the cards in paintings done by Dick Perez.

		MT	NR MT	EX
Complete Set:		12.00	9.00	4.75
Common Player:		.60	.45	.25
1	Babe Ruth	2.00	1.50	.80
2	Ted Williams	1.00	.70	.40
3	Lou Gehrig	1.75	1.25	.70
4	Johnny Mize	.60	.45	.25
5	Stan Musial	1.00	.70	.40
6	Mickey Mantle	3.00	2.25	1.25
7	Hank Aaron	2.00	1.50	.80
8	Frank Robinson	.90	.70	.35

1986 Donruss

In 1986, Donruss issued a 660-card set which included 653 numbered cards and seven unnumbered checklists. The cards, which measure 2-1/2" by 3-1/2", have fronts that feature blue borders and backs that have black print on blue and white. For the fifth year in a row, the first 26 cards in the set are Diamond Kings. The Rated Rookies subset (card #'s 27-46) appears once again. The cards were distributed with a Hank Aaron puzzle. The complete set price does not include the higher priced variations. In the checklist that follows, (DK) and (RR) refer to the Diamond Kings and Rated Rookies series.

		MT	NR MT	EX
Complete Set:		175.00	125.00	70.00
Common Player:		.06	.05	.02
1	Kirk Gibson (DK)	.30	.25	.12
2	Goose Gossage (DK)	.20	.15	.08
3	Willie McGee (DK)	.15	.11	.06
4	George Bell (DK)	.30	.25	.12
5	Tony Armas (DK)	.10	.08	.04
6	Chili Davis (DK)	.10	.08	.04
7	Cecil Cooper (DK)	.12	.09	.05
8	Mike Boddicker (DK)	.10	.08	.04
9	Davey Lopes (DK)	.10	.08	.04
10	Bill Doran (DK)	.12	.09	.05
11	Bret Saberhagen (DK)	.25	.20	.10
12	Brett Butler (DK)	.10	.08	.04
13	Harold Baines (DK)	.15	.11	.06
14	Mike Davis (DK)	.10	.08	.04
15	Tony Perez (DK)	.15	.11	.06
16	Willie Randolph (DK)	.12	.09	.05
17	Bob Boone (DK)	.10	.08	.04
18	Orel Hershiser (DK)	.40	.30	.15
19	Johnny Ray (DK)	.12	.09	.05
20	Gary Ward (DK)	.10	.08	.04
21	Rick Mahler (DK)	.08	.06	.03
22	Phil Bradley (DK)	.20	.15	.08
23	Jerry Koosman (DK)	.12	.09	.05
24	Tom Brunansky (DK)	.15	.11	.06
25	Andre Dawson (DK)	.30	.25	.12
26	Dwight Gooden (DK)	1.00	.70	.40
27	Kal Daniels (RR)(FC)	2.00	1.50	.80
28	Fred McGriff (RR)(FC)	26.00	18.70	10.40
29	Cory Snyder (RR)(FC)	1.00	.70	.40
30	Jose Guzman (RR)(FC)	.40	.30	.15
31	Ty Gainey (RR)(FC)	.10	.08	.04
32	Johnny Abrego (RR)(FC)	.08	.06	.03
33a	Andres Galarraga (RR) (no accent mark above "e" in Andres on back)(FC)	1.00	.70	.40
33b	Andres Galarraga (RR) (accent mark above "e" in Andres on back)(FC)	1.50	1.25	.60

		MT	NR MT	EX
34	Dave Shipanoff (RR)(FC)	.08	.06	.03
35	Mark McLemore (RR)(FC)	.20	.15	.08
36	Marty Clary (RR)(FC)	.08	.06	.03
37	Paul O'Neill (RR)(FC)	2.50	2.00	1.00
38	Danny Tartabull (RR)	2.00	1.50	.80
39	Jose Canseco (RR)(FC)	60.00	45.00	25.00
40	Juan Nieves (RR)(FC)	.10	.08	.04
41	Lance McCullers (RR)(FC)	.35	.25	.14
42	Rick Surhoff (RR)(FC)	.08	.06	.03
43	Todd Worrell (RR)(FC)	.40	.30	.15
44	Bob Kipper (RR)(FC)	.20	.15	.08
45	John Habyan (RR)(FC)	.15	.11	.06
46	Mike Woodard (RR)(FC)	.10	.08	.04
47	Mike Boddicker	.10	.08	.04
48	Robin Yount	2.00	1.50	.80
49	Lou Whitaker	.30	.25	.12
50	"Oil Can" Boyd	.08	.06	.03
51	Rickey Henderson	2.50	2.00	1.00
52	Mike Marshall	.15	.11	.06
53	George Brett	2.00	1.50	.80
54	Dave Kingman	.15	.11	.06
55	Hubie Brooks	.10	.08	.04
56	Oddibe McDowell(FC)	.20	.15	.08
57	Doug DeCinces	.10	.08	.04
58	Britt Burns	.06	.05	.02
59	Ozzie Smith	1.00	.70	.40
60	Jose Cruz	.10	.08	.04
61	Mike Schmidt	2.00	1.50	.80
62	Pete Rose	.80	.60	.30
63	Steve Garvey	.40	.30	.15
64	Tony Pena	.10	.08	.04
65	Chili Davis	.10	.08	.04
66	Dale Murphy	.60	.45	.25
67	Ryne Sandberg	4.00	3.00	1.50
68	Gary Carter	.35	.25	.14
69	Alvin Davis	.30	.25	.12
70	Kent Hrbek	.25	.20	.10
71	George Bell	.30	.25	.12
72	Kirby Puckett	9.00	6.75	3.50
73	Lloyd Moseby	.10	.08	.04
74	Bob Kearney	.06	.05	.02
75	Dwight Gooden	2.00	1.50	.80
76	Gary Matthews	.10	.08	.04
77	Rick Mahler	.06	.05	.02
78	Benny Distefano	.06	.05	.02
79	Jeff Leonard	.08	.06	.03
80	Kevin McReynolds	.30	.25	.12
81	Ron Oester	.06	.05	.02
82	John Russell	.06	.05	.02
83	Tommy Herr	.10	.08	.04
84	Jerry Mumphrey	.06	.05	.02
85	Ron Romanick	.06	.05	.02
86	Daryl Boston	.08	.06	.03
87	Andre Dawson	.50	.40	.20
88	Eddie Murray	.50	.40	.20
89	Dion James	.08	.06	.03
90	Chet Lemon	.08	.06	.03
91	Bob Stanley	.06	.05	.02
92	Willie Randolph	.10	.08	.04
93	Mike Scioscia	.08	.06	.03
94	Tom Waddell	.06	.05	.02
95	Danny Jackson	.30	.25	.12
96	Mike Davis	.08	.06	.03
97	Mike Fitzgerald	.06	.05	.02
98	Gary Ward	.08	.06	.03
99	Pete O'Brien	.10	.08	.04
100	Bret Saberhagen	.60	.45	.25
101	Alfredo Griffin	.08	.06	.03
102	Brett Butler	.08	.06	.03
103	Ron Guidry	.20	.15	.08
104	Jerry Reuss	.08	.06	.03
105	Jack Morris	.30	.25	.12
106	Rick Dempsey	.08	.06	.03
107	Ray Burris	.06	.05	.02
108	Brian Downing	.10	.08	.04
109	Willie McGee	.15	.11	.06
110	Bill Doran	.10	.08	.04
111	Kent Tekulve	.08	.06	.03
112	Tony Gwynn	2.00	1.50	.80
113	Marvell Wynne	.06	.05	.02
114	David Green	.06	.05	.02
115	Jim Gantner	.08	.06	.03
116	George Foster	.15	.11	.06
117	Steve Trout	.06	.05	.02
118	Mark Langston	.30	.25	.12
119	Tony Fernandez	.20	.15	.08
120	John Butcher	.06	.05	.02
121	Ron Robinson	.08	.06	.03
122	Dan Spillner	.06	.05	.02
123	Mike Young	.06	.05	.02
124	Paul Molitor	.15	.11	.06

#	Name	MT	NR MT	EX
125	Kirk Gibson	.35	.25	.14
126	Ken Griffey	.12	.09	.05
127	Tony Armas	.08	.06	.03
128	*Mariano Duncan*(FC)	.15	.11	.06
129	Mr. Clutch (Pat Tabler)	.08	.06	.03
130	Frank White	.10	.08	.04
131	Carney Lansford	.10	.08	.04
132	Vance Law	.08	.06	.03
133	Dick Schofield	.06	.05	.02
134	Wayne Tolleson	.06	.05	.02
135	Greg Walker	.10	.08	.04
136	Denny Walling	.06	.05	.02
137	Ozzie Virgil	.06	.05	.02
138	Ricky Horton	.08	.06	.03
139	LaMarr Hoyt	.06	.05	.02
140	Wayne Krenchicki	.06	.05	.02
141	Glenn Hubbard	.06	.05	.02
142	Cecilio Guante	.06	.05	.02
143	Mike Krukow	.08	.06	.03
144	Lee Smith	.10	.08	.04
145	Edwin Nunez	.06	.05	.02
146	Dave Stieb	.12	.09	.05
147	Mike Smithson	.06	.05	.02
148	Ken Dixon	.06	.05	.02
149	Danny Darwin	.06	.05	.02
150	Chris Pittaro	.06	.05	.02
151	Bill Buckner	.12	.09	.05
152	Mike Pagliarulo	.20	.15	.08
153	Bill Russell	.08	.06	.03
154	Brook Jacoby	.10	.08	.04
155	Pat Sheridan	.06	.05	.02
156	*Mike Gallego*(FC)	.15	.11	.06
157	Jim Wohlford	.06	.05	.02
158	Gary Pettis	.06	.05	.02
159	Toby Harrah	.08	.06	.03
160	Richard Dotson	.10	.08	.04
161	Bob Knepper	.08	.06	.03
162	Dave Dravecky	.08	.06	.03
163	Greg Gross	.06	.05	.02
164	Eric Davis	1.50	1.25	.60
165	Gerald Perry	.15	.11	.06
166	Rick Rhoden	.10	.08	.04
167	Keith Moreland	.08	.06	.03
168	Jack Clark	.20	.15	.08
169	Storm Davis	.10	.08	.04
170	Cecil Cooper	.12	.09	.05
171	Alan Trammell	.35	.25	.14
172	Roger Clemens	10.00	7.50	4.00
173	Don Mattingly	4.00	3.00	1.50
174	Pedro Guerrero	.20	.15	.08
175	Willie Wilson	.12	.09	.05
176	Dwayne Murphy	.08	.06	.03
177	Tim Raines	.40	.30	.15
178	Larry Parrish	.10	.08	.04
179	Mike Witt	.10	.08	.04
180	Harold Baines	.15	.11	.06
181	*Vince Coleman*(FC)	2.00	1.50	.80
182	*Jeff Heathcock*(FC)	.10	.08	.04
183	Steve Carlton	.50	.40	.20
184	Mario Soto	.08	.06	.03
185	Goose Gossage	.20	.15	.08
186	Johnny Ray	.12	.09	.05
187	Dan Gladden	.08	.06	.03
188	Bob Horner	.12	.09	.05
189	Rick Sutcliffe	.12	.09	.05
190	Keith Hernandez	.25	.20	.10
191	Phil Bradley	.20	.15	.08
192	Tom Brunansky	.12	.09	.05
193	Jesse Barfield	.20	.15	.08
194	Frank Viola	.20	.15	.08
195	Willie Upshaw	.08	.06	.03
196	Jim Beattie	.06	.05	.02
197	Darryl Strawberry	5.00	3.75	2.00
198	Ron Cey	.10	.08	.04
199	Steve Bedrosian	.12	.09	.05
200	Steve Kemp	.08	.06	.03
201	Manny Trillo	.08	.06	.03
202	Garry Templeton	.08	.06	.03
203	Dave Parker	.25	.20	.10
204	John Denny	.06	.05	.02
205	Terry Pendleton	.15	.11	.06
206	Terry Puhl	.06	.05	.02
207	Bobby Grich	.10	.08	.04
208	*Ozzie Guillen*(FC)	.90	.70	.35
209	Jeff Reardon	.12	.09	.05
210	Cal Ripken Jr.	5.00	3.75	2.00
211	Bill Schroeder	.06	.05	.02
212	Dan Petry	.08	.06	.03
213	Jim Rice	.40	.30	.15
214	Dave Righetti	.20	.15	.08
215	Fernando Valenzuela	.35	.25	.14
216	Julio Franco	.50	.40	.20
217	Darryl Motley	.06	.05	.02
218	Dave Collins	.08	.06	.03
219	Tim Wallach	.12	.09	.05
220	George Wright	.06	.05	.02
221	Tommy Dunbar	.06	.05	.02
222	Steve Balboni	.08	.06	.03
223	Jay Howell	.08	.06	.03
224	Joe Carter	1.25	.90	.50
225	Ed Whitson	.06	.05	.02
226	Orel Hershiser	.80	.60	.30
227	Willie Hernandez	.08	.06	.03
228	Lee Lacy	.06	.05	.02
229	Rollie Fingers	.20	.15	.08
230	Bob Boone	.08	.06	.03
231	Joaquin Andujar	.08	.06	.03
232	Craig Reynolds	.06	.05	.02
233	Shane Rawley	.10	.08	.04
234	Eric Show	.08	.06	.03
235	Jose DeLeon	.08	.06	.03
236	*Jose Uribe*(FC)	.25	.20	.10
237	Moose Haas	.06	.05	.02
238	Wally Backman	.08	.06	.03
239	Dennis Eckersley	.12	.09	.05
240	Mike Moore	.06	.05	.02
241	Damaso Garcia	.06	.05	.02
242	Tim Teufel	.06	.05	.02
243	Dave Concepcion	.12	.09	.05
244	Floyd Bannister	.10	.08	.04
245	Fred Lynn	.20	.15	.08
246	Charlie Moore	.06	.05	.02
247	Walt Terrell	.08	.06	.03
248	Dave Winfield	1.25	.90	.50
249	Dwight Evans	.12	.09	.05
250	*Dennis Powell*(FC)	.10	.08	.04
251	Andre Thornton	.10	.08	.04
252	Onix Concepcion	.06	.05	.02
253	Mike Heath	.06	.05	.02
254a	David Palmer (2B on front)	.06	.05	.02
254b	David Palmer (P on front)	1.00	.70	.40
255	Donnie Moore	.06	.05	.02
256	Curtis Wilkerson	.06	.05	.02
257	Julio Cruz	.06	.05	.02
258	Nolan Ryan	5.00	3.75	2.00
259	Jeff Stone	.06	.05	.02
260a	John Tudor (1981 Games is .18)	.10	.08	.04
260b	John Tudor (1981 Games is 18)	1.00	.70	.40
261	Mark Thurmond	.06	.05	.02
262	Jay Tibbs	.06	.05	.02
263	Rafael Ramirez	.06	.05	.02
264	Larry McWilliams	.06	.05	.02
265	Mark Davis	.06	.05	.02
266	Bob Dernier	.06	.05	.02
267	Matt Young	.06	.05	.02
268	Jim Clancy	.08	.06	.03
269	Mickey Hatcher	.06	.05	.02
270	Sammy Stewart	.06	.05	.02
271	Bob Gibson	.06	.05	.02
272	Nelson Simmons	.06	.05	.02
273	Rich Gedman	.10	.08	.04
274	Butch Wynegar	.06	.05	.02
275	Ken Howell	.06	.05	.02
276	Mel Hall	.08	.06	.03
277	Jim Sundberg	.08	.06	.03
278	Chris Codiroli	.06	.05	.02
279	*Herman Winningham*(FC)	.15	.11	.06
280	Rod Carew	.70	.50	.30
281	Don Slaught	.06	.05	.02
282	Scott Fletcher	.08	.06	.03
283	Bill Dawley	.06	.05	.02
284	Andy Hawkins	.06	.05	.02
285	Glenn Wilson	.08	.06	.03
286	Nick Esasky	.08	.06	.03
287	Claudell Washington	.08	.06	.03
288	Lee Mazzilli	.08	.06	.03
289	Jody Davis	.10	.08	.04
290	Darrell Porter	.08	.06	.03
291	Scott McGregor	.08	.06	.03
292	Ted Simmons	.12	.09	.05
293	Aurelio Lopez	.06	.05	.02
294	Marty Barrett	.10	.08	.04
295	Dale Berra	.06	.05	.02
296	Greg Brock	.08	.06	.03
297	Charlie Leibrandt	.08	.06	.03
298	Bill Krueger	.06	.05	.02
299	Bryn Smith	.06	.05	.02
300	Burt Hooton	.08	.06	.03
301	*Stu Cliburn*(FC)	.12	.09	.05
302	Luis Salazar	.06	.05	.02
303	Ken Dayley	.06	.05	.02
304	Frank DiPino	.06	.05	.02

#	Player	MT	NR MT	EX
305	Von Hayes	.10	.08	.04
306a	Gary Redus (1983 2B is .20)	.08	.06	.03
306b	Gary Redus (1983 2B is 20)	1.00	.70	.40
307	Craig Lefferts	.06	.05	.02
308	Sam Khalifa	.06	.05	.02
309	Scott Garrelts	.06	.05	.02
310	Rick Cerone	.06	.05	.02
311	Shawon Dunston	.20	.15	.08
312	Howard Johnson	.12	.09	.05
313	Jim Presley	.15	.11	.06
314	Gary Gaetti	.25	.20	.10
315	Luis Leal	.06	.05	.02
316	Mark Salas	.06	.05	.02
317	Bill Caudill	.06	.05	.02
318	Dave Henderson	.10	.08	.04
319	Rafael Santana	.06	.05	.02
320	Leon Durham	.08	.06	.03
321	Bruce Sutter	.15	.11	.06
322	Jason Thompson	.06	.05	.02
323	Bob Brenly	.06	.05	.02
324	Carmelo Martinez	.08	.06	.03
325	Eddie Milner	.06	.05	.02
326	Juan Samuel	.15	.11	.06
327	Tom Nieto	.06	.05	.02
328	Dave Smith	.08	.06	.03
329	*Urbano Lugo*(FC)	.08	.06	.03
330	Joel Skinner	.06	.05	.02
331	Bill Gullickson	.06	.05	.02
332	Floyd Rayford	.06	.05	.02
333	Ben Oglivie	.08	.06	.03
334	Lance Parrish	.30	.25	.12
335	Jackie Gutierrez	.06	.05	.02
336	Dennis Rasmussen	.12	.09	.05
337	Terry Whitfield	.06	.05	.02
338	Neal Heaton	.06	.05	.02
339	Jorge Orta	.06	.05	.02
340	Donnie Hill	.06	.05	.02
341	Joe Hesketh	.06	.05	.02
342	Charlie Hough	.10	.08	.04
343	Dave Rozema	.06	.05	.02
344	Greg Pryor	.06	.05	.02
345	*Mickey Tettleton*(FC)	2.00	1.50	.80
346	George Vukovich	.06	.05	.02
347	Don Baylor	.12	.09	.05
348	Carlos Diaz	.06	.05	.02
349	Barbaro Garbey	.06	.05	.02
350	Larry Sheets	.12	.09	.05
351	*Ted Higuera*(FC)	1.00	.70	.40
352	Juan Beniquez	.06	.05	.02
353	Bob Forsch	.08	.06	.03
354	Mark Bailey	.06	.05	.02
355	Larry Andersen	.06	.05	.02
356	Terry Kennedy	.08	.06	.03
357	Don Robinson	.08	.06	.03
358	Jim Gott	.06	.05	.02
359	*Earnest Riles*(FC)	.30	.25	.12
360	*John Christensen*(FC)	.10	.08	.04
361	Ray Fontenot	.06	.05	.02
362	Spike Owen	.06	.05	.02
363	Jim Acker	.06	.05	.02
364a	Ron Davis (last line in highlights ends with "...in May.")	.08	.06	.03
364b	Ron Davis (last line in highlights ends with "...relievers (9).")	1.00	.70	.40
365	Tom Hume	.06	.05	.02
366	Carlton Fisk	.60	.45	.25
367	Nate Snell	.06	.05	.02
368	Rick Manning	.06	.05	.02
369	Darrell Evans	.15	.11	.06
370	Ron Hassey	.06	.05	.02
371	Wade Boggs	2.00	1.50	.80
372	Rick Honeycutt	.06	.05	.02
373	Chris Bando	.06	.05	.02
374	Bud Black	.06	.05	.02
375	Steve Henderson	.06	.05	.02
376	Charlie Lea	.06	.05	.02
377	Reggie Jackson	.40	.30	.15
378	Dave Schmidt	.06	.05	.02
379	Bob James	.06	.05	.02
380	Glenn Davis(FC)	1.25	.90	.50
381	Tim Corcoran	.06	.05	.02
382	Danny Cox	.10	.08	.04
383	Tim Flannery	.06	.05	.02
384	Tom Browning	.20	.15	.08
385	Rick Camp	.06	.05	.02
386	Jim Morrison	.06	.05	.02
387	Dave LaPoint	.08	.06	.03
388	Davey Lopes	.08	.06	.03
389	Al Cowens	.06	.05	.02
390	Doyle Alexander	.10	.08	.04
391	Tim Laudner	.06	.05	.02
392	Don Aase	.06	.05	.02
393	Jaime Cocanower	.06	.05	.02
394	Randy O'Neal(FC)	.08	.06	.03
395	Mike Easler	.08	.06	.03
396	Scott Bradley	.06	.05	.02
397	Tom Niedenfuer	.08	.06	.03
398	Jerry Willard	.06	.05	.02
399	Lonnie Smith	.08	.06	.03
400	Bruce Bochte	.06	.05	.02
401	Terry Francona	.06	.05	.02
402	Jim Slaton	.06	.05	.02
403	Bill Stein	.06	.05	.02
404	Tim Hulett	.06	.05	.02
405	Alan Ashby	.06	.05	.02
406	Tim Stoddard	.06	.05	.02
407	Garry Maddox	.08	.06	.03
408	Ted Power	.06	.05	.02
409	Len Barker	.08	.06	.03
410	Denny Gonzalez	.06	.05	.02
411	George Frazier	.06	.05	.02
412	Andy Van Slyke	.15	.11	.06
413	Jim Dwyer	.06	.05	.02
414	Paul Householder	.06	.05	.02
415	Alejandro Sanchez	.06	.05	.02
416	Steve Crawford	.06	.05	.02
417	Dan Pasqua	.15	.11	.06
418	Enos Cabell	.06	.05	.02
419	Mike Jones	.06	.05	.02
420	Steve Kiefer	.06	.05	.02
421	*Tim Burke*(FC)	.30	.25	.12
422	Mike Mason	.06	.05	.02
423	Ruppert Jones	.06	.05	.02
424	Jerry Hairston	.06	.05	.02
425	Tito Landrum	.06	.05	.02
426	Jeff Calhoun	.06	.05	.02
427	*Don Carman*(FC)	.20	.15	.08
428	Tony Perez	.15	.11	.06
429	Jerry Davis	.06	.05	.02
430	Bob Walk	.06	.05	.02
431	Brad Wellman	.06	.05	.02
432	Terry Forster	.08	.06	.03
433	Billy Hatcher	.10	.08	.04
434	Clint Hurdle	.06	.05	.02
435	*Ivan Calderon*(FC)	2.00	1.50	.80
436	Pete Filson	.06	.05	.02
437	Tom Henke	.08	.06	.03
438	Dave Engle	.06	.05	.02
439	Tom Filer	.06	.05	.02
440	Gorman Thomas	.10	.08	.04
441	*Rick Aguilera*(FC)	.90	.70	.35
442	Scott Sanderson	.06	.05	.02
443	Jeff Dedmon	.06	.05	.02
444	*Joe Orsulak*(FC)	.15	.11	.06
445	Atlee Hammaker	.06	.05	.02
446	Jerry Royster	.06	.05	.02
447	Buddy Bell	.10	.08	.04
448	Dave Rucker	.06	.05	.02
449	Ivan DeJesus	.06	.05	.02
450	Jim Pankovits	.06	.05	.02
451	Jerry Narron	.06	.05	.02
452	Bryan Little	.06	.05	.02
453	Gary Lucas	.06	.05	.02
454	Dennis Martinez	.08	.06	.03
455	Ed Romero	.06	.05	.02
456	*Bob Melvin*(FC)	.12	.09	.05
457	Glenn Hoffman	.06	.05	.02
458	Bob Shirley	.06	.05	.02
459	Bob Welch	.12	.09	.05
460	Carmen Castillo	.06	.05	.02
461	Dave Leeper	.06	.05	.02
462	*Tim Birtsas*(FC)	.12	.09	.05
463	Randy St. Claire	.06	.05	.02
464	Chris Welsh	.06	.05	.02
465	Greg Harris	.06	.05	.02
466	Lynn Jones	.06	.05	.02
467	Dusty Baker	.08	.06	.03
468	Roy Smith	.06	.05	.02
469	Andre Robertson	.06	.05	.02
470	Ken Landreaux	.06	.05	.02
471	Dave Bergman	.06	.05	.02
472	Gary Roenicke	.06	.05	.02
473	Pete Vuckovich	.08	.06	.03
474	*Kirk McCaskill*(FC)	.40	.30	.15
475	Jeff Lahti	.06	.05	.02
476	Mike Scott	.20	.15	.08
477	*Darren Daulton*(FC)	2.25	1.75	.90
478	Graig Nettles	.15	.11	.06
479	Bill Almon	.06	.05	.02
480	Greg Minton	.06	.05	.02
481	Randy Ready(FC)	.10	.08	.04
482	*Lenny Dykstra*(FC)	2.00	1.50	.80

		MT	NR MT	EX			MT	NR MT	EX
483	Thad Bosley	.06	.05	.02	573	Al Holland	.06	.05	.02
484	Harold Reynolds(FC)	1.00	.70	.40	574	Reid Nichols	.06	.05	.02
485	Al Oliver	.12	.09	.05	575	Bert Roberge	.06	.05	.02
486	Roy Smalley	.06	.05	.02	576	Mike Flanagan	.10	.08	.04
487	John Franco	.15	.11	.06	577	Tim Leary(FC)	.35	.25	.14
488	Juan Agosto	.06	.05	.02	578	Mike Laga	.06	.05	.02
489	Al Pardo	.06	.05	.02	579	Steve Lyons	.06	.05	.02
490	Bill Wegman(FC)	.25	.20	.10	580	Phil Niekro	.30	.25	.12
491	Frank Tanana	.10	.08	.04	581	Gilberto Reyes	.06	.05	.02
492	Brian Fisher(FC)	.20	.15	.08	582	Jamie Easterly	.06	.05	.02
493	Mark Clear	.06	.05	.02	583	Mark Gubicza	.12	.09	.05
494	Len Matuszek	.06	.05	.02	584	Stan Javier(FC)	.15	.11	.06
495	Ramon Romero	.06	.05	.02	585	Bill Laskey	.06	.05	.02
496	John Wathan	.08	.06	.03	586	Jeff Russell	.06	.05	.02
497	Rob Picciolo	.06	.05	.02	587	Dickie Noles	.06	.05	.02
498	U.L. Washington	.06	.05	.02	588	Steve Farr	.08	.06	.03
499	John Candelaria	.10	.08	.04	589	Steve Ontiveros(FC)	.15	.11	.06
500	Duane Walker	.06	.05	.02	590	Mike Hargrove	.06	.05	.02
501	Gene Nelson	.06	.05	.02	591	Marty Bystrom	.06	.05	.02
502	John Mizerock	.06	.05	.02	592	Franklin Stubbs	.08	.06	.03
503	Luis Aguayo	.06	.05	.02	593	Larry Herndon	.08	.06	.03
504	Kurt Kepshire	.06	.05	.02	594	Bill Swaggerty	.06	.05	.02
505	Ed Wojna	.06	.05	.02	595	Carlos Ponce	.06	.05	.02
506	Joe Price	.06	.05	.02	596	Pat Perry(FC)	.12	.09	.05
507	Milt Thompson(FC)	.30	.25	.12	597	Ray Knight	.08	.06	.03
508	Junior Ortiz	.06	.05	.02	598	Steve Lombardozzi(FC)	.15	.11	.06
509	Vida Blue	.10	.08	.04	599	Brad Havens	.06	.05	.02
510	Steve Engel	.06	.05	.02	600	Pat Clements(FC)	.12	.09	.05
511	Karl Best	.06	.05	.02	601	Joe Niekro	.12	.09	.05
512	Cecil Fielder(FC)	25.00	18.00	10.00	602	Hank Aaron Puzzle Card	.06	.05	.02
513	Frank Eufemia	.06	.05	.02	603	Dwayne Henry(FC)	.10	.08	.04
514	Tippy Martinez	.06	.05	.02	604	Mookie Wilson	.10	.08	.04
515	Billy Robidoux(FC)	.10	.08	.04	605	Buddy Biancalana	.06	.05	.02
516	Bill Scherrer	.06	.05	.02	606	Rance Mulliniks	.06	.05	.02
517	Bruce Hurst	.12	.09	.05	607	Alan Wiggins	.06	.05	.02
518	Rich Bordi	.06	.05	.02	608	Joe Cowley	.06	.05	.02
519	Steve Yeager	.06	.05	.02	609a	Tom Seaver (green stripes around name)			
520	Tony Bernazard	.06	.05	.02			1.00	.70	.40
521	Hal McRae	.10	.08	.04	609b	Tom Seaver (yellow stripes around name)			
522	Jose Rijo	.10	.08	.04			3.00	2.25	1.25
523	Mitch Webster(FC)	.25	.20	.10	610	Neil Allen	.06	.05	.02
524	Jack Howell(FC)	.35	.25	.14	611	Don Sutton	.30	.25	.12
525	Alan Bannister	.06	.05	.02	612	Fred Toliver(FC)	.15	.11	.06
526	Ron Kittle	.10	.08	.04	613	Jay Baller	.06	.05	.02
527	Phil Garner	.08	.06	.03	614	Marc Sullivan	.06	.05	.02
528	Kurt Bevacqua	.06	.05	.02	615	John Grubb	.06	.05	.02
529	Kevin Gross	.08	.06	.03	616	Bruce Kison	.06	.05	.02
530	Bo Diaz	.08	.06	.03	617	Bill Madlock	.12	.09	.05
531	Ken Oberkfell	.06	.05	.02	618	Chris Chambliss	.08	.06	.03
532	Rick Reuschel	.10	.08	.04	619	Dave Stewart	.12	.09	.05
533	Ron Meridith	.06	.05	.02	620	Tim Lollar	.06	.05	.02
534	Steve Braun	.06	.05	.02	621	Gary Lavelle	.06	.05	.02
535	Wayne Gross	.06	.05	.02	622	Charles Hudson	.06	.05	.02
536	Ray Searage	.06	.05	.02	623	Joel Davis(FC)	.08	.06	.03
537	Tom Brookens	.06	.05	.02	624	Joe Johnson(FC)	.08	.06	.03
538	Al Nipper	.06	.05	.02	625	Sid Fernandez	.12	.09	.05
539	Billy Sample	.06	.05	.02	626	Dennis Lamp	.06	.05	.02
540	Steve Sax	.20	.15	.08	627	Terry Harper	.06	.05	.02
541	Dan Quisenberry	.10	.08	.04	628	Jack Lazorko	.06	.05	.02
542	Tony Phillips	.06	.05	.02	629	Roger McDowell(FC)	.60	.45	.25
543	Floyd Youmans(FC)	.20	.15	.08	630	Mark Funderburk	.06	.05	.02
544	Steve Buechele(FC)	.70	.50	.30	631	Ed Lynch	.06	.05	.02
545	Craig Gerber	.06	.05	.02	632	Rudy Law	.06	.05	.02
546	Joe DeSa	.06	.05	.02	633	Roger Mason(FC)	.08	.06	.03
547	Brian Harper	.06	.05	.02	634	Mike Felder(FC)	.15	.11	.06
548	Kevin Bass	.10	.08	.04	635	Ken Schrom	.06	.05	.02
549	Tom Foley	.06	.05	.02	636	Bob Ojeda	.08	.06	.03
550	Dave Van Gorder	.06	.05	.02	637	Ed Vande Berg	.06	.05	.02
551	Bruce Bochy	.06	.05	.02	638	Bobby Meacham	.06	.05	.02
552	R.J. Reynolds	.08	.06	.03	639	Cliff Johnson	.06	.05	.02
553	Chris Brown(FC)	.20	.15	.08	640	Garth Iorg	.06	.05	.02
554	Bruce Benedict	.06	.05	.02	641	Dan Driessen	.08	.06	.03
555	Warren Brusstar	.06	.05	.02	642	Mike Brown	.06	.05	.02
556	Danny Heep	.06	.05	.02	643	John Shelby	.06	.05	.02
557	Darnell Coles	.08	.06	.03	644	Ty-Breaking Hit (Pete Rose)	.50	.40	.20
558	Greg Gagne	.08	.06	.03	645	Knuckle Brothers (Joe Niekro, Phil			
559	Ernie Whitt	.08	.06	.03		Niekro)	.15	.11	.06
560	Ron Washington	.06	.05	.02	646	Jesse Orosco	.08	.06	.03
561	Jimmy Key	.15	.11	.06	647	Billy Beane(FC)	.06	.05	.02
562	Billy Swift(FC)	.15	.11	.06	648	Cesar Cedeno	.10	.08	.04
563	Ron Darling	.15	.11	.06	649	Bert Blyleven	.15	.11	.06
564	Dick Ruthven	.06	.05	.02	650	Max Venable	.06	.05	.02
565	Zane Smith(FC)	.15	.11	.06	651	Fleet Feet (Vince Coleman, Willie McGee)			
566	Sid Bream	.10	.08	.04			.35	.25	.14
567a	Joel Youngblood (P on front)	.08	.06	.03	652	Calvin Schiraldi	.08	.06	.03
567b	Joel Youngblood (IF on front)	1.00	.70	.40	653	King of Kings (Pete Rose)	.70	.50	.30
568	Mario Ramirez	.06	.05	.02	-----	Checklist 1-26 DK	.06	.05	.02
569	Tom Runnells	.06	.05	.02	---a	Checklist 27-130 (45 is Beane)	.08	.06	.03
570	Rick Schu	.06	.05	.02	---b	Checklist 27-130 (45 is Habyan)	.60	.45	.25
571	Bill Campbell	.06	.05	.02	-----	Checklist 131-234	.06	.05	.02
572	Dickie Thon	.08	.06	.03	-----	Checklist 235-338	.06	.05	.02

		MT	NR MT	EX
----	Checklist 339-442	.06	.05	.02
----	Checklist 443-546	.06	.05	.02
----	Checklist 547-653	.06	.05	.02

1986 Donruss All-Stars

Issued in conjunction with the 1986 Donruss Pop-Ups set, the Donruss All-Stars set consists of 60 cards that measure 3-1/2" by 5". Fifty-nine players involved in the 1985 All-Star game plus an unnumbered checklist comprise the set. The card fronts have the same blue border found on the regular 1986 Donruss issue. Retail packs included one Pop-up card, three All-Star cards and one Hank Aaron puzzle card.

		MT	NR MT	EX
	Complete Set:	8.00	6.00	3.25
	Common Player:	.09	.07	.04
1	Tony Gwynn	.30	.25	.12
2	Tommy Herr	.09	.07	.04
3	Steve Garvey	.30	.25	.12
4	Dale Murphy	.40	.30	.15
5	Darryl Strawberry	.60	.45	.25
6	Graig Nettles	.12	.09	.05
7	Terry Kennedy	.09	.07	.04
8	Ozzie Smith	.15	.11	.06
9	LaMarr Hoyt	.09	.07	.04
10	Rickey Henderson	1.25	.90	.50
11	Lou Whitaker	.15	.11	.06
12	George Brett	.40	.30	.15
13	Eddie Murray	.12	.09	.05
14	Cal Ripken, Jr.	.35	.25	.14
15	Dave Winfield	.25	.20	.10
16	Jim Rice	.12	.09	.05
17	Carlton Fisk	.15	.11	.06
18	Jack Morris	.15	.11	.06
19	Jose Cruz	.09	.07	.04
20	Tim Raines	.25	.20	.10
21	Nolan Ryan	1.25	.90	.50
22	Tony Pena	.09	.07	.04
23	Jack Clark	.15	.11	.06
24	Dave Parker	.15	.11	.06
25	Tim Wallach	.12	.09	.05
26	Ozzie Virgil	.09	.07	.04
27	Fernando Valenzuela	.12	.09	.05
28	Dwight Gooden	.40	.30	.15
29	Glenn Wilson	.09	.07	.04
30	Garry Templeton	.09	.07	.04
31	Goose Gossage	.12	.09	.05
32	Ryne Sandberg	.25	.20	.10
33	Jeff Reardon	.12	.09	.05
34	Pete Rose	.35	.25	.14
35	Scott Garrelts	.09	.07	.04
36	Willie McGee	.12	.09	.05
37	Ron Darling	.12	.09	.05
38	Dick Williams	.09	.07	.04
39	Paul Molitor	.15	.11	.06
40	Damaso Garcia	.09	.07	.04
41	Phil Bradley	.12	.09	.05
42	Dan Petry	.09	.07	.04
43	Willie Hernandez	.09	.07	.04
44	Tom Brunansky	.12	.09	.05
45	Alan Trammell	.20	.15	.08
46	Donnie Moore	.09	.07	.04
47	Wade Boggs	.60	.45	.25
48	Ernie Whitt	.09	.07	.04

		MT	NR MT	EX
49	Harold Baines	.15	.11	.06
50	Don Mattingly	1.50	1.25	.60
51	Gary Ward	.09	.07	.04
52	Bert Blyleven	.12	.09	.05
53	Jimmy Key	.12	.09	.05
54	Cecil Cooper	.12	.09	.05
55	Dave Stieb	.12	.09	.05
56	Rich Gedman	.09	.07	.04
57	Jay Howell	.09	.07	.04
58	Sparky Anderson	.09	.07	.04
59	Minneapolis Metrodome	.09	.07	.04
----	Checklist	.09	.07	.04

1986 Donruss Box Panels

For the second year in a row, Donruss placed baseball cards on the bottom of their wax and cello pack boxes. The cards, which come four to a panel, are the standard 2-1/2" by 3-1/2" in size. With numbering that begins where Donruss left off in 1985, cards PC 4 through PC 6 were found on boxes of regular Donruss issue wax packs. Cards PC 7 through PC 9 were found on boxes of the 1986 All-Star/Pop-up packs. An unnumbered Hank Aaron puzzle card was included on each box.

		MT	NR MT	EX
	Complete Panel Set:	5.00	3.75	2.00
	Complete Singles Set:	3.00	2.25	1.25
	Common Single Player:	.15	.11	.06
	Panel	1.00	.70	.40
4	Kirk Gibson	.35	.25	.14
5	Willie Hernandez	.15	.11	.06
6	Doug DeCinces	.15	.11	.06
----	Aaron Puzzle Card	.04	.03	.02
	Panel	3.00	2.25	1.25
7	Wade Boggs	1.00	.70	.40
8	Lee Smith	.15	.11	.06
9	Cecil Cooper	.20	.15	.08
----	Aaron Puzzle Card	.04	.03	.02

1986 Donruss Diamond Kings Supers

Donruss produced a set of giant-size Diamond

Kings in 1986 for the second year in a row. The cards, which measure 4-11/6" by 6-3/4", are enlarged versions of the 26 Diamond Kings cards found in the regular 1986 Donruss set. Featuring the artwork of Dick Perez, the set consists of 28 cards - 26 DKs, an unnumbered checklist and an unnumbered Pete Rose "King of Kings" card.

		MT	NR MT	EX
	Complete Set:	10.00	7.50	4.00
	Common Player:	.20	.15	.08
1	Kirk Gibson	.50	.40	.20
2	Goose Gossage	.30	.25	.12
3	Willie McGee	.30	.25	.12
4	George Bell	.30	.25	.12
5	Tony Armas	.20	.15	.08
6	Chili Davis	.20	.15	.08
7	Cecil Cooper	.25	.20	.10
8	Mike Boddicker	.20	.15	.08
9	Davey Lopes	.20	.15	.08
10	Bill Doran	.25	.20	.10
11	Bret Saberhagen	.70	.50	.30
12	Brett Butler	.20	.15	.08
13	Harold Baines	.30	.25	.12
14	Mike Davis	.20	.15	.08
15	Tony Perez	.25	.20	.10
16	Willie Randolph	.25	.20	.10
18	Orel Hershiser	.70	.50	.30
19	Johnny Ray	.25	.20	.10
20	Gary Ward	.20	.15	.08
21	Rick Mahler	.20	.15	.08
22	Phil Bradley	.30	.25	.12
23	Jerry Koosman	.20	.15	.08
24	Tom Brunansky	.25	.20	.10
25	Andre Dawson	.35	.25	.14
26	Dwight Gooden	1.00	.70	.40
-----	Checklist	.15	.11	.06
-----	King of Kings (Pete Rose)	1.50	1.25	.60

1986 Donruss Highlights

Donruss, for the second year in a row, issued a 56-card highlights set which featured cards of the A.L. and N.L. Player of the Month plus significant events that took place during the 1986 season. The cards, which measure 2-1/2" by 3-1/2" in size, are similar in design to the regular 1986 Donruss set but have a gold border instead of blue. A "Highlights" logo appears in the lower left corner of each card front. The card backs are designed on a vertical format and feature black print on a yellow background. As in 1985, the set includes Donruss' picks for the Rookies of the Year awards. A new feature was three cards honoring the 1986 Hall of Fame inductees. The set, available only through hobby dealers, was issued in a specially designed box.

		MT	NR MT	EX
	Complete Set:	12.00	9.00	4.75
	Common Player:	.10	.08	.04
1	Homers In First At-Bat (Will Clark)	2.00	1.50	.80
2	Oakland Milestone For Strikeouts (Jose Rijo)	.10	.08	.04
3	Royals' All-Time Hit Man (George Brett)	.20	.15	.08

		MT	NR MT	EX
4	Phillies RBI Leader (Mike Schmidt)	.30	.25	.12
5	KKKKKKKKKKKKKKKKKKKK (Roger Clemens)	.75	.55	.20
6	A.L. Pitcher of the Month-April (Roger Clemens)	.50	.40	.20
7	A.L. Player of the Month-April (Kirby Puckett)	.50	.40	.20
8	N.L. Pitcher of the Month-April (Dwight Gooden)	.50	.40	.20
9	N.L. Player of the Month-April (Johnny Ray)	.10	.08	.04
10	Eclipses Mantle HR Record (Reggie Jackson)	.25	.20	.10
11	First Five Hit Game of Career (Wade Boggs)	.50	.40	.20
12	A.L. Pitcher of the Month-May (Don Aase)	.10	.08	.04
13	A.L. Player of the Month-May (Wade Boggs)	.50	.40	.20
14	N.L. Pitcher of the Month-May (Jeff Reardon)	.15	.11	.06
15	N.L. Player of the Month-May (Hubie Brooks)	.10	.08	.04
16	Notches 300th Career Win (Don Sutton)	.10	.08	.04
17	Starts Season 14-0 (Roger Clemens)	.50	.40	.20
18	A.L. Pitcher of the Month-June (Roger Clemens)	.50	.40	.20
19	A.L. Player of the Month-June (Kent Hrbek)	.10	.08	.04
20	N.L. Pitcher of the Month-June (Rick Rhoden)	.10	.08	.04
21	N.L. Player of the Month-June (Kevin Bass)	.10	.08	.04
22	Blasts 4 HRS in 1 Game (Bob Horner)	.10	.08	.04
23	Starting All Star Rookie (Wally Joyner)	.50	.40	.20
24	Starts 3rd Straight All Star Game (Darryl Strawberry)	.25	.20	.10
25	Ties All Star Game Record (Fernando Valenzuela)	.10	.08	.04
26	All Star Game MVP (Roger Clemens)	.50	.40	.20
27	A.L. Pitcher of the Month-July (Jack Morris)	.10	.08	.04
28	A.L. Player of the Month-July (Scott Fletcher)	.10	.08	.04
29	N.L. Pitcher of the Month-July (Todd Worrell)	.25	.20	.10
30	N.L. PLayer of the Month-July (Eric Davis)	.40	.30	.15
31	Records 3000th Strikeout (Bert Blyleven)	.15	.11	.06
32	1986 Hall of Fame Inductee (Bobby Doerr)	.15	.11	.06
33	1986 Hall of Fame Inductee (Ernie Lombardi)	.15	.11	.06
34	1986 Hall of Fame Inductee (Willie McCovey)	.20	.15	.08
35	Notches 4000th K (Steve Carlton)	.25	.20	.10
36	Surpasses DiMaggio Record (Mike Schmidt)	.40	.30	.15
37	Records 3rd "Quadruple Double" (Juan Samuel)	.10	.08	.04
38	A.L. Pitcher of the Month-August (Mike Witt)	.10	.08	.04
39	A.L. Player of the Month-August (Doug DeCinces)	.10	.08	.04
40	N.L. Pitcher of the Month-August (Bill Gullickson)	.10	.08	.04
41	N.L. Player of the Month-August (Dale Murphy)	.20	.15	.08
42	Sets Tribe Offensive Record (Joe Carter)	.25	.20	.10
43	Longest HR In Royals Stadium (Bo Jackson)	2.00	1.50	.80
44	Majors 1st No-Hitter In 2 Years (Joe Cowley)	.10	.08	.04
45	Sets M.L. Strikeout Record (Jim Deshaies)	.15	.11	.06
46	No Hitter Clinches Division (Mike Scott)	.10	.08	.04
47	A.L. Pitcher of the Month-September (Bruce Hurst)	.10	.08	.04
48	A.L. Player of the Month-September (Don Mattingly)	1.00	.70	.40
49	N.L. Pitcher of the Month-September (Mike Krukow)	.10	.08	.04
50	N.L. Player of the Month-September (Steve Sax)	.10	.08	.04

		MT	NR MT	EX
51	A.L. Record For Steals By A Rookie (John Cangelosi)	.10	.08	.04
52	Shatters M.L. Save Mark (Dave Righetti)	.10	.08	.04
53	Yankee Record For Hits & Doubles (Don Mattingly)	1.00	.70	.40
54	Donruss N.L. Rookie of the Year (Todd Worrell)	.25	.20	.10
55	Donruss A.L. Rookie of the Year (Jose Canseco)	3.00	2.25	1.25
56	Highlight Checklist	.10	.08	.04

1986 Donruss Pop-Ups

Issued in conjunction with the 1986 Donruss All-Stars set, the Donruss Pop-Ups (18 unnumbered cards) feature the 1985 All-Star Game starting lineups. The cards, which measure 2-1/2" by 5", are die-cut and fold out to form a three-dimensional stand-up card. The background for the cards is the Minneapolis Metrodome, site of the 1985 All-Star Game. Retail packs included one Pop-Up card, three All-Star cards and one Hank Aaron puzzle card.

		MT	NR MT	EX
Complete Set:		5.00	3.75	2.00
Common Player:		.20	.15	.08
(1)	George Brett	.60	.45	.25
(2)	Carlton Fisk	.30	.25	.12
(3)	Steve Garvey	.20	.15	.08
(4)	Tony Gwynn	.50	.40	.20
(5)	Rickey Henderson	.70	.50	.30
(6)	Tommy Herr	.20	.15	.08
(7)	LaMarr Hoyt	.20	.15	.08
(8)	Terry Kennedy	.20	.15	.08
(9)	Jack Morris	.20	.15	.08
(10)	Dale Murphy	.30	.25	.12
(11)	Eddie Murray	.30	.25	.12
(12)	Graig Nettles	.20	.15	.08
(13)	Jim Rice	.20	.15	.08
(14)	Cal Ripken Jr.	.50	.40	.20
(15)	Ozzie Smith	.30	.25	.12
(16)	Darryl Strawberry	.70	.50	.30
(17)	Lou Whitaker	.30	.25	.12
(18)	Dave Winfield	.30	.25	.12

1986 Donruss Rookies

Entitled "The Rookies," this 56-card set includes the top 55 rookies of 1986 plus an unnumbered checklist. The cards, which measure 2-1/2" by 3-1/2", are similar to the format used for the 1986 Donruss regular issue, except that the borders are green rather than blue. Several of the rookies who had cards in the regular 1986 Donruss set appear again in "The Rookies" set. The sets, which were only available through hobby dealers, came in a specially designed box.

		MT	NR MT	EX
Complete Set:		60.00	45.00	25.00
Common Player:		.15	.11	.06
1	Wally Joyner(FC)	3.00	2.25	1.25
2	Tracy Jones(FC)	.20	.15	.08
3	Allan Anderson(FC)	.20	.15	.08
4	Ed Correa(FC)	.25	.20	.10
5	Reggie Williams	.20	.15	.08
6	Charlie Kerfeld(FC)	.15	.11	.06
7	Andres Galarraga	.40	.30	.15
8	Bob Tewksbury(FC)	.80	.60	.30
9	Al Newman	.15	.11	.06
10	Andres Thomas(FC)	.20	.15	.08
11	Barry Bonds(FC)	12.00	9.00	4.75
12	Juan Nieves	.15	.11	.06
13	Mark Eichhorn(FC)	.25	.20	.10
14	Dan Plesac(FC)	.25	.20	.10
15	Cory Snyder	.40	.30	.15
16	Kelly Gruber	2.00	1.50	.80
17	Kevin Mitchell(FC)	6.00	4.50	2.50
18	Steve Lombardozzi	.15	.11	.06
19	Mitch Williams	.50	.40	.20
20	John Cerutti(FC)	.25	.20	.10
21	Todd Worrell	.35	.25	.14
22	Jose Canseco	10.00	7.50	4.00
23	Pete Incaviglia(FC)	.70	.50	.30
24	Jose Guzman	.25	.20	.10
25	Scott Bailes(FC)	.25	.20	.10
26	Greg Mathews(FC)	.25	.20	.10
27	Eric King(FC)	.20	.15	.08
28	Paul Assenmacher	.20	.15	.08
29	Jeff Sellers	.25	.20	.10
30	Bobby Bonilla(FC)	7.00	5.25	2.75
31	Doug Drabek(FC)	1.50	1.25	.60
32	Will Clark(FC)	12.00	9.00	4.75
33	Bip Roberts	.90	.70	.35
34	Jim Deshaies(FC)	.25	.20	.10
35	Mike Lavalliere (LaValliere)(FC)	.40	.30	.15
36	Scott Bankhead(FC)	.20	.15	.08
37	Dale Sveum(FC)	.25	.20	.10
38	Bo Jackson(FC)	6.00	4.50	2.50
39	Rob Thompson(FC)	.50	.40	.20
40	Eric Plunk(FC)	.20	.15	.08
41	Bill Bathe	.15	.11	.06
42	John Kruk(FC)	2.00	1.50	.80
43	Andy Allanson(FC)	.20	.15	.08
44	Mark Portugal	.15	.11	.06
45	Danny Tartabull	2.00	1.50	.80
46	Bob Kipper	.15	.11	.06
47	Gene Walter	.15	.11	.06
48	Rey Quinonez	.15	.11	.06
49	Bobby Witt(FC)	.80	.60	.30
50	Bill Mooneyham	.15	.11	.06
51	John Cangelosi(FC)	.20	.15	.08
52	Ruben Sierra(FC)	12.00	9.00	4.75
53	Rob Woodward	.15	.11	.06
54	Ed Hearn	.15	.11	.06
55	Joel McKeon	.15	.11	.06
56	Checklist 1-56	.05	.04	.02

1987 Donruss

The 1987 Donruss set consists of 660 numbered cards, each measuring 2-1/2" by 3-1/2" in size. Full color photos are surrounded by a bold black border separated by two narrow bands of yellow which enclose a brown area filled with baseballs. The player's name, team and team logo appear on the card fronts along with the words "Donruss '87." The

The backs are very similar to those in previous years' sets. Backs of cards issued in wax and rack packs card backs are designed on a horizontal format and contain black print on a yellow and white background. face to the left when turned over, while those issued in vending sets face to the right.

		MT	NR MT	EX
	Complete Set:	60.00	45.00	25.00
	Common Player:	.05	.04	.02
1	Wally Joyner (DK)	.50	.40	.20
2	Roger Clemens (DK)	.70	.50	.30
3	Dale Murphy (DK)	.30	.25	.12
4	Darryl Strawberry (DK)	.40	.30	.15
5	Ozzie Smith (DK)	.12	.09	.05
6	Jose Canseco (DK)	1.25	.90	.50
7	Charlie Hough (DK)	.07	.05	.03
8	Brook Jacoby (DK)	.10	.08	.04
9	Fred Lynn (DK)	.12	.09	.05
10	Rick Rhoden (DK)	.10	.08	.04
11	Chris Brown (DK)	.10	.08	.04
12	Von Hayes (DK)	.10	.08	.04
13	Jack Morris (DK)	.20	.15	.08
14a	Kevin McReynolds (DK) ("Donruss Diamond Kings" in white band on back)	1.25	.90	.50
14b	Kevin McReynolds (DK) ("Donruss Diamond Kings" in yellow band on back)	.20	.15	.08
15	George Brett (DK)	.40	.30	.15
16	Ted Higuera (DK)	.20	.15	.08
17	Hubie Brooks (DK)	.10	.08	.04
18	Mike Scott (DK)	.12	.09	.05
19	Kirby Puckett (DK)	.40	.30	.15
20	Dave Winfield (DK)	.25	.20	.10
21	Lloyd Moseby (DK)	.10	.08	.04
22a	Eric Davis (DK) ("Donruss Diamond Kings" in white band on back)	1.00	.70	.40
22b	Eric Davis (DK) ("Donruss Diamond Kings" in yellow band on back)	.40	.30	.15
23	Jim Presley (DK)	.12	.09	.05
24	Keith Moreland (DK)	.07	.05	.03
25a	Greg Walker (DK) ("Donruss Diamond Kings" in white band on back)	.50	.40	.20
25b	Greg Walker (DK) ("Donruss Diamond Kings" in yellow band on back)	.10	.08	.04
26	Steve Sax (DK)	.12	.09	.05
27	Checklist 1-27	.05	.04	.02
28	B.J. Surhoff (RR)(FC)	.50	.40	.20
29	Randy Myers (RR)(FC)	.30	.25	.12
30	Ken Gerhart (RR)(FC)	.15	.11	.06
31	Benito Santiago (RR)(FC)	1.00	.70	.40
32	Greg Swindell (RR)(FC)	1.00	.70	.40
33	Mike Birkbeck (RR)(FC)	.20	.15	.08
34	Terry Steinbach (RR)(FC)	.50	.40	.20
35	Bo Jackson (RR)	4.00	3.00	1.50
36	Greg Maddux (RR)(FC)	6.00	4.50	2.50
37	Jim Lindeman (RR)(FC)	.15	.11	.06
38	Devon White (RR)(FC)	.80	.60	.30
39	Eric Bell (RR)(FC)	.12	.09	.05
40	Will Fraser (RR)(FC)	.20	.15	.08
41	Jerry Browne (RR)(FC)	.25	.20	.10
42	Chris James (RR)(FC)	.40	.30	.15
43	Rafael Palmeiro (RR)(FC)	6.00	4.50	2.50
44	Pat Dodson (RR)(FC)	.12	.09	.05
45	Duane Ward (RR)(FC)	.30	.25	.12
46	Mark McGwire (RR)(FC)	7.00	5.25	2.75
47	Bruce Fields (RR) (photo actually Darnell Coles)(FC)	.10	.08	.04
48	Eddie Murray	.50	.40	.20
49	Ted Higuera	.20	.15	.08
50	Kirk Gibson	.25	.20	.10
51	Oil Can Boyd	.07	.05	.03
52	Don Mattingly	1.00	.70	.40

		MT	NR MT	EX
53	Pedro Guerrero	.15	.11	.06
54	George Brett	.40	.30	.15
55	Jose Rijo	.07	.05	.03
56	Tim Raines	.30	.25	.12
57	Ed Correa	.15	.11	.06
58	Mike Witt	.10	.08	.04
59	Greg Walker	.10	.08	.04
60	Ozzie Smith	.15	.11	.06
61	Glenn Davis	.35	.25	.14
62	Glenn Wilson	.07	.05	.03
63	Tom Browning	.10	.08	.04
64	Tony Gwynn	.35	.25	.14
65	R.J. Reynolds	.07	.05	.03
66	Will Clark	10.00	7.50	4.00
67	Ozzie Virgil	.05	.04	.02
68	Rick Sutcliffe	.12	.09	.05
69	Gary Carter	.30	.25	.12
70	Mike Moore	.05	.04	.02
71	Bert Blyleven	.12	.09	.05
72	Tony Fernandez	.12	.09	.05
73	Kent Hrbek	.15	.11	.06
74	Lloyd Moseby	.10	.08	.04
75	Alvin Davis	.12	.09	.05
76	Keith Hernandez	.25	.20	.10
77	Ryne Sandberg	2.00	1.50	.80
78	Dale Murphy	.40	.30	.15
79	Sid Bream	.07	.05	.03
80	Chris Brown	.07	.05	.03
81	Steve Garvey	.25	.20	.10
82	Mario Soto	.07	.05	.03
83	Shane Rawley	.07	.05	.03
84	Willie McGee	.12	.09	.05
85	Jose Cruz	.10	.08	.04
86	Brian Downing	.07	.05	.03
87	Ozzie Guillen	.10	.08	.04
88	Hubie Brooks	.10	.08	.04
89	Cal Ripken	2.00	1.50	.80
90	Juan Nieves	.07	.05	.03
91	Lance Parrish	.20	.15	.08
92	Jim Rice	.30	.25	.12
93	Ron Guidry	.15	.11	.06
94	Fernando Valenzuela	.25	.20	.10
95	Andy Allanson	.15	.11	.06
96	Willie Wilson	.12	.09	.05
97	Jose Canseco	6.00	4.50	2.50
98	Jeff Reardon	.10	.08	.04
99	Bobby Witt	.50	.40	.20
100	Checklist 28-133	.05	.04	.02
101	Jose Guzman	.10	.08	.04
102	Steve Balboni	.07	.05	.03
103	Tony Phillips	.05	.04	.02
104	Brook Jacoby	.10	.08	.04
105	Dave Winfield	.30	.25	.12
106	Orel Hershiser	.40	.30	.15
107	Lou Whitaker	.25	.20	.10
108	Fred Lynn	.15	.11	.06
109	Bill Wegman	.07	.05	.03
110	Donnie Moore	.05	.04	.02
111	Jack Clark	.15	.11	.06
112	Bob Knepper	.07	.05	.03
113	Von Hayes	.10	.08	.04
114	Leon "Bip" Roberts	.50	.40	.20
115	Tony Pena	.08	.06	.03
116	Scott Garrelts	.05	.04	.02
117	Paul Molitor	.15	.11	.06
118	Darryl Strawberry	1.00	.70	.40
119	Shawon Dunston	.10	.08	.04
120	Jim Presley	.10	.08	.04
121	Jesse Barfield	.20	.15	.08
122	Gary Gaetti	.15	.11	.06
123	Kurt Stillwell	.40	.30	.15
124	Joel Davis	.05	.04	.02
125	Mike Boddicker	.07	.05	.03
126	Robin Yount	.50	.40	.20
127	Alan Trammell	.25	.20	.10
128	Dave Righetti	.15	.11	.06
129	Dwight Evans	.12	.09	.05
130	Mike Scioscia	.07	.05	.03
131	Julio Franco	.10	.08	.04
132	Bret Saberhagen	.25	.20	.10
133	Mike Davis	.07	.05	.03
134	Joe Hesketh	.05	.04	.02
135	Wally Joyner	1.75	1.25	.70
136	Don Slaught	.05	.04	.02
137	Daryl Boston	.05	.04	.02
138	Nolan Ryan	3.00	2.25	1.25
139	Mike Schmidt	1.00	.70	.40
140	Tommy Herr	.10	.08	.04
141	Garry Templeton	.07	.05	.03
142	Kal Daniels	.80	.60	.30
143	Billy Sample	.05	.04	.02

#	Player	MT	NR MT	EX
144	Johnny Ray	.10	.08	.04
145	*Rob Thompson*	.30	.25	.12
146	Bob Dernier	.05	.04	.02
147	Danny Tartabull	.25	.20	.10
148	Ernie Whitt	.07	.05	.03
149	Kirby Puckett	2.00	1.50	.80
150	Mike Young	.05	.04	.02
151	Ernest Riles	.05	.04	.02
152	Frank Tanana	.07	.05	.03
153	Rich Gedman	.10	.08	.04
154	Willie Randolph	.10	.08	.04
155a	Bill Madlock (name in brown band)	.12	.09	.05
155b	Bill Madlock (name in red band)	.70	.50	.30
156a	Joe Carter (name in brown band)	.15	.11	.06
156b	Joe Carter (name in red band)	.70	.50	.30
157	Danny Jackson	.15	.11	.06
158	Carney Lansford	.10	.08	.04
159	Bryn Smith	.05	.04	.02
160	Gary Pettis	.05	.04	.02
161	Oddibe McDowell	.10	.08	.04
162	*John Cangelosi*	.12	.09	.05
163	Mike Scott	.15	.11	.06
164	Eric Show	.07	.05	.03
165	Juan Samuel	.12	.09	.05
166	Nick Esasky	.07	.05	.03
167	Zane Smith	.07	.05	.03
168	Mike Brown	.05	.04	.02
169	Keith Moreland	.07	.05	.03
170	John Tudor	.10	.08	.04
171	Ken Dixon	.05	.04	.02
172	Jim Gantner	.07	.05	.03
173	Jack Morris	.20	.15	.08
174	Bruce Hurst	.10	.08	.04
175	Dennis Rasmussen	.10	.08	.04
176	Mike Marshall	.12	.09	.05
177	Dan Quisenberry	.07	.05	.03
178	Eric Plunk(FC)	.10	.08	.04
179	Tim Wallach	.12	.09	.05
180	Steve Buechele	.07	.05	.03
181	Don Sutton	.20	.15	.08
182	Dave Schmidt	.05	.04	.02
183	Terry Pendleton	.10	.08	.04
184	*Jim Deshaies*	.35	.25	.14
185	Steve Bedrosian	.12	.09	.05
186	Pete Rose	.60	.45	.25
187	Dave Dravecky	.07	.05	.03
188	Rick Reuschel	.10	.08	.04
189	Dan Gladden	.05	.04	.02
190	Rick Mahler	.05	.04	.02
191	Thad Bosley	.05	.04	.02
192	Ron Darling	.15	.11	.06
193	Matt Young	.05	.04	.02
194	Tom Brunansky	.10	.08	.04
195	Dave Stieb	.12	.09	.05
196	Frank Viola	.15	.11	.06
197	Tom Henke	.07	.05	.03
198	Karl Best	.05	.04	.02
199	Dwight Gooden	.60	.45	.25
200	Checklist 134-239	.05	.04	.02
201	Steve Trout	.05	.04	.02
202	Rafael Ramirez	.05	.04	.02
203	Bob Walk	.05	.04	.02
204	Roger Mason	.05	.04	.02
205	Terry Kennedy	.07	.05	.03
206	Ron Oester	.05	.04	.02
207	John Russell	.05	.04	.02
208	*Greg Mathews*	.20	.15	.08
209	Charlie Kerfeld	.10	.08	.04
210	Reggie Jackson	.35	.25	.14
211	Floyd Bannister	.10	.08	.04
212	Vance Law	.07	.05	.03
213	Rich Bordi	.05	.04	.02
214	*Dan Plesac*	.35	.25	.14
215	Dave Collins	.07	.05	.03
216	Bob Stanley	.05	.04	.02
217	Joe Niekro	.10	.08	.04
218	Tom Niedenfuer	.07	.05	.03
219	Brett Butler	.07	.05	.03
220	Charlie Leibrandt	.07	.05	.03
221	Steve Ontiveros	.05	.04	.02
222	Tim Burke	.05	.04	.02
223	Curtis Wilkerson	.05	.04	.02
224	*Pete Incaviglia*	.40	.20	.15
225	Lonnie Smith	.07	.05	.03
226	Chris Codiroli	.05	.04	.02
227	*Scott Bailes*	.20	.15	.08
228	Rickey Henderson	1.00	.70	.40
229	Ken Howell	.05	.04	.02
230	Darnell Coles	.07	.05	.03
231	Don Aase	.05	.04	.02
232	Tim Leary	.07	.05	.03
233	Bob Boone	.07	.05	.03
234	Ricky Horton	.07	.05	.03
235	Mark Bailey	.05	.04	.02
236	Kevin Gross	.07	.05	.03
237	Lance McCullers	.07	.05	.03
238	Cecilio Guante	.05	.04	.02
239	Bob Melvin	.05	.04	.02
240	Billy Jo Robidoux	.05	.04	.02
241	Roger McDowell	.12	.09	.05
242	Leon Durham	.07	.05	.03
243	Ed Nunez	.05	.04	.02
244	Jimmy Key	.12	.09	.05
245	Mike Smithson	.05	.04	.02
246	Bo Diaz	.07	.05	.03
247	Carlton Fisk	.20	.15	.08
248	Larry Sheets	.08	.06	.03
249	Juan Castillo(FC)	.10	.08	.04
250	*Eric King*	.25	.20	.10
251	*Doug Drabek*	1.50	1.25	.60
252	Wade Boggs	.80	.60	.30
253	Mariano Duncan	.05	.04	.02
254	Pat Tabler	.07	.05	.03
255	Frank White	.10	.08	.04
256	Alfredo Griffin	.07	.05	.03
257	Floyd Youmans	.07	.05	.03
258	Rob Wilfong	.05	.04	.02
259	Pete O'Brien	.10	.08	.04
260	Tim Hulett	.05	.04	.02
261	Dickie Thon	.07	.05	.03
262	Darren Daulton	.05	.04	.02
263	Vince Coleman	.50	.40	.20
264	Andy Hawkins	.05	.04	.02
265	Eric Davis	1.25	.90	.50
266	*Andres Thomas*	.15	.11	.06
267	*Mike Diaz*(FC)	.15	.11	.06
268	Chili Davis	.07	.05	.03
269	Jody Davis	.07	.05	.03
270	Phil Bradley	.12	.09	.05
271	George Bell	.25	.20	.10
272	Keith Atherton	.05	.04	.02
273	Storm Davis	.10	.08	.04
274	Rob Deer(FC)	.20	.15	.08
275	Walt Terrell	.07	.05	.03
276	Roger Clemens	2.00	1.50	.80
277	Mike Easler	.07	.05	.03
278	Steve Sax	.15	.11	.06
279	Andre Thornton	.07	.05	.03
280	Jim Sundberg	.07	.05	.03
281	Bill Bathe	.05	.04	.02
282	Jay Tibbs	.05	.04	.02
283	Dick Schofield	.05	.04	.02
284	Mike Mason	.05	.04	.02
285	Jerry Hairston	.05	.04	.02
286	Bill Doran	.10	.08	.04
287	Tim Flannery	.05	.04	.02
288	Gary Redus	.05	.04	.02
289	John Franco	.10	.08	.04
290	*Paul Assenmacher*	.15	.11	.06
291	Joe Orsulak	.05	.04	.02
292	Lee Smith	.10	.08	.04
293	Mike Laga	.05	.04	.02
294	Rick Dempsey	.07	.05	.03
295	Mike Felder	.05	.04	.02
296	Tom Brookens	.05	.04	.02
297	Al Nipper	.05	.04	.02
298	Mike Pagliarulo	.10	.08	.04
299	Franklin Stubbs	.07	.05	.03
300	Checklist 240-345	.05	.04	.02
301	Steve Farr	.05	.04	.02
302	*Bill Mooneyham*	.10	.08	.04
303	Andres Galarraga	.25	.20	.10
304	Scott Fletcher	.07	.05	.03
305	Jack Howell	.07	.05	.03
306	*Russ Morman*(FC)	.10	.08	.04
307	Todd Worrell	.20	.15	.08
308	Dave Smith	.07	.05	.03
309	Jeff Stone	.05	.04	.02
310	Ron Robinson	.05	.04	.02
311	Bruce Bochy	.05	.04	.02
312	Jim Winn	.05	.04	.02
313	Mark Davis	.05	.04	.02
314	Jeff Dedmon	.05	.04	.02
315	*Jamie Moyer*(FC)	.20	.15	.08
316	Wally Backman	.07	.05	.03
317	Ken Phelps	.07	.05	.03
318	Steve Lombardozzi	.05	.04	.02
319	Rance Mulliniks	.05	.04	.02
320	Tim Laudner	.05	.04	.02
321	*Mark Eichhorn*	.15	.11	.06
322	*Lee Guetterman*	.15	.11	.06
323	Sid Fernandez	.12	.09	.05

#	Player	MT	NR MT	EX
324	Jerry Mumphrey	.05	.04	.02
325	David Palmer	.05	.04	.02
326	Bill Almon	.05	.04	.02
327	Candy Maldonado	.07	.05	.03
328	*John Kruk*	.60	.45	.25
329	John Denny	.05	.04	.02
330	Milt Thompson	.07	.05	.03
331	*Mike LaValliere*	.25	.20	.10
332	Alan Ashby	.05	.04	.02
333	Doug Corbett	.05	.04	.02
334	Ron Karkovice(FC)	.10	.08	.04
335	Mitch Webster	.07	.05	.03
336	Lee Lacy	.05	.04	.02
337	*Glenn Braggs*(FC)	.30	.25	.12
338	Dwight Lowry	.05	.04	.02
339	Don Baylor	.12	.09	.05
340	Brian Fisher	.07	.05	.03
341	*Reggie Williams*	.10	.08	.04
342	Tom Candiotti	.05	.04	.02
343	Rudy Law	.05	.04	.02
344	Curt Young	.07	.05	.03
345	Mike Fitzgerald	.05	.04	.02
346	*Ruben Sierra*	10.00	7.50	4.00
347	*Mitch Williams*	.40	.30	.15
348	Jorge Orta	.05	.04	.02
349	Mickey Tettleton	.10	.08	.04
350	Ernie Camacho	.05	.04	.02
351	Ron Kittle	.10	.08	.04
352	Ken Landreaux	.05	.04	.02
353	Chet Lemon	.07	.05	.03
354	John Shelby	.05	.04	.02
355	Mark Clear	.05	.04	.02
356	Doug DeCinces	.07	.05	.03
357	Ken Dayley	.05	.04	.02
358	Phil Garner	.05	.04	.02
359	Steve Jeltz	.05	.04	.02
360	Ed Whitson	.05	.04	.02
361	*Barry Bonds*	8.00	6.00	3.25
362	Vida Blue	.10	.08	.04
363	Cecil Cooper	.12	.09	.05
364	Bob Ojeda	.07	.05	.03
365	Dennis Eckersley	.12	.09	.05
366	Mike Morgan	.05	.04	.02
367	Willie Upshaw	.07	.05	.03
368	*Allan Anderson*(FC)	.25	.20	.10
369	Bill Gullickson	.07	.05	.03
370	*Bobby Thigpen*(FC)	1.00	.70	.40
371	Juan Beniquez	.05	.04	.02
372	Charlie Moore	.05	.04	.02
373	Dan Petry	.07	.05	.03
374	Rod Scurry	.05	.04	.02
375	Tom Seaver	.40	.30	.15
376	Ed Vande Berg	.05	.04	.02
377	Tony Bernazard	.05	.04	.02
378	Greg Pryor	.05	.04	.02
379	Dwayne Murphy	.07	.05	.03
380	Andy McGaffigan	.05	.04	.02
381	Kirk McCaskill	.07	.05	.03
382	Greg Harris	.05	.04	.02
383	Rich Dotson	.07	.05	.03
384	Craig Reynolds	.05	.04	.02
385	Greg Gross	.05	.04	.02
386	Tito Landrum	.05	.04	.02
387	Craig Lefferts	.05	.04	.02
388	Dave Parker	.20	.15	.08
389	Bob Horner	.10	.08	.04
390	Pat Clements	.05	.04	.02
391	Jeff Leonard	.07	.05	.03
392	Chris Speier	.05	.04	.02
393	John Moses	.05	.04	.02
394	Garth Iorg	.05	.04	.02
395	Greg Gagne	.05	.04	.02
396	Nate Snell	.05	.04	.02
397	*Bryan Clutterbuck*(FC)	.10	.08	.04
398	Darrell Evans	.12	.09	.05
399	Steve Crawford	.05	.04	.02
400	Checklist 346-451	.05	.04	.02
401	*Phil Lombardi*(FC)	.10	.08	.04
402	Rick Honeycutt	.05	.04	.02
403	Ken Schrom	.05	.04	.02
404	Bud Black	.05	.04	.02
405	Donnie Hill	.05	.04	.02
406	Wayne Krenchicki	.05	.04	.02
407	*Chuck Finley*(FC)	1.00	.70	.40
408	Toby Harrah	.07	.05	.03
409	Steve Lyons	.05	.04	.02
410	Kevin Bass	.10	.08	.04
411	Marvell Wynne	.05	.04	.02
412	Ron Roenicke	.05	.04	.02
413	*Tracy Jones*	.25	.20	.10
414	Gene Garber	.05	.04	.02
415	Mike Bielecki	.05	.04	.02
416	Frank DiPino	.05	.04	.02
417	Andy Van Slyke	.12	.09	.05
418	Jim Dwyer	.05	.04	.02
419	Ben Oglivie	.07	.05	.03
420	Dave Bergman	.05	.04	.02
421	Joe Sambito	.05	.04	.02
422	*Bob Tewksbury*	.12	.09	.05
423	Len Matuszek	.05	.04	.02
424	*Mike Kingery*(FC)	.15	.11	.06
425	Dave Kingman	.12	.09	.05
426	Al Newman	.07	.05	.03
427	Gary Ward	.07	.05	.03
428	Ruppert Jones	.05	.04	.02
429	Harold Baines	.15	.11	.06
430	Pat Perry	.05	.04	.02
431	Terry Puhl	.05	.04	.02
432	Don Carman	.07	.05	.03
433	Eddie Milner	.05	.04	.02
434	LaMarr Hoyt	.05	.04	.02
435	Rick Rhoden	.10	.08	.04
436	Jose Uribe	.07	.05	.03
437	Ken Oberkfell	.05	.04	.02
438	Ron Davis	.05	.04	.02
439	Jesse Orosco	.07	.05	.03
440	Scott Bradley	.05	.04	.02
441	Randy Bush	.05	.04	.02
442	*John Cerutti*	.20	.15	.08
443	Roy Smalley	.05	.04	.02
444	Kelly Gruber	2.00	1.50	.80
445	Bob Kearney	.05	.04	.02
446	*Ed Hearn*	.10	.08	.04
447	Scott Sanderson	.05	.04	.02
448	Bruce Benedict	.05	.04	.02
449	Junior Ortiz	.05	.04	.02
450	*Mike Aldrete*	.15	.11	.06
451	Kevin McReynolds	.15	.11	.06
452	*Rob Murphy*(FC)	.20	.15	.08
453	Kent Tekulve	.07	.05	.03
454	Curt Ford(FC)	.07	.05	.03
455	Davey Lopes	.07	.05	.03
456	Bobby Grich	.10	.08	.04
457	Jose DeLeon	.07	.05	.03
458	Andre Dawson	.20	.15	.08
459	Mike Flanagan	.07	.05	.03
460	*Joey Meyer*(FC)	.20	.15	.08
461	*Chuck Cary*(FC)	.10	.08	.04
462	Bill Buckner	.10	.08	.04
463	Bob Shirley	.05	.04	.02
464	*Jeff Hamilton*(FC)	.20	.15	.08
465	Phil Niekro	.20	.15	.08
466	Mark Gubicza	.12	.09	.05
467	Jerry Willard	.05	.04	.02
468	*Bob Sebra*(FC)	.10	.08	.04
469	Larry Parrish	.10	.08	.04
470	Charlie Hough	.07	.05	.03
471	Hal McRae	.10	.08	.04
472	*Dave Leiper*(FC)	.10	.08	.04
473	Mel Hall	.07	.05	.03
474	Dan Pasqua	.10	.08	.04
475	Bob Welch	.10	.08	.04
476	Johnny Grubb	.05	.04	.02
477	Jim Traber	.07	.05	.03
478	*Chris Bosio*(FC)	.40	.30	.15
479	Mark McLemore	.07	.05	.03
480	John Morris	.05	.04	.02
481	Billy Hatcher	.07	.05	.03
482	Dan Schatzeder	.05	.04	.02
483	Rich Gossage	.15	.11	.06
484	Jim Morrison	.05	.04	.02
485	Bob Brenly	.05	.04	.02
486	Bill Schroeder	.05	.04	.02
487	Mookie Wilson	.10	.08	.04
488	*Dave Martinez*(FC)	.25	.20	.10
489	Harold Reynolds	.10	.08	.04
490	Jeff Hearron	.05	.04	.02
491	Mickey Hatcher	.05	.04	.02
492	*Barry Larkin*(FC)	4.00	3.00	1.50
493	Bob James	.05	.04	.02
494	John Habyan	.05	.04	.02
495	*Jim Adduci*(FC)	.07	.05	.03
496	Mike Heath	.05	.04	.02
497	Tim Stoddard	.05	.04	.02
498	Tony Armas	.07	.05	.03
499	Dennis Powell	.05	.04	.02
500	Checklist 452-557	.05	.04	.02
501	Chris Bando	.05	.04	.02
502	*David Cone*(FC)	5.00	3.75	2.00
503	Jay Howell	.07	.05	.03
504	Tom Foley	.05	.04	.02
505	*Ray Chadwick*(FC)	.10	.08	.04

		MT	NR MT	EX
506	*Mike Loynd*(FC)	.15	.11	.06
507	Neil Allen	.05	.04	.02
508	Danny Darwin	.05	.04	.02
509	Rick Schu	.05	.04	.02
510	Jose Oquendo	.05	.04	.02
511	Gene Walter	.07	.05	.03
512	*Terry McGriff*(FC)	.12	.09	.05
513	Ken Griffey	.10	.08	.04
514	Benny Distefano	.05	.04	.02
515	*Terry Mulholland*(FC)	.12	.09	.05
516	Ed Lynch	.05	.04	.02
517	Bill Swift	.05	.04	.02
518	Manny Lee(FC)	.07	.05	.03
519	Andre David	.05	.04	.02
520	Scott McGregor	.07	.05	.03
521	Rick Manning	.05	.04	.02
522	Willie Hernandez	.07	.05	.03
523	Marty Barrett	.10	.08	.04
524	Wayne Tolleson	.05	.04	.02
525	*Jose Gonzalez*(FC)	.15	.11	.06
526	Cory Snyder	.35	.25	.14
527	Buddy Biancalana	.05	.04	.02
528	Moose Haas	.05	.04	.02
529	*Wilfredo Tejada*(FC)	.10	.08	.04
530	Stu Cliburn	.05	.04	.02
531	*Dale Mohorcic*(FC)	.20	.15	.08
532	Ron Hassey	.05	.04	.02
533	Ty Gainey	.05	.04	.02
534	Jerry Royster	.05	.04	.02
535	*Mike Maddux*(FC)	.20	.15	.08
536	Ted Power	.05	.04	.02
537	Ted Simmons	.12	.09	.05
538	*Rafael Belliard*(FC)	.12	.09	.05
539	Chico Walker	.05	.04	.02
540	Bob Forsch	.07	.05	.03
541	John Stefero	.05	.04	.02
542	*Dale Sveum*	.20	.15	.08
543	Mark Thurmond	.05	.04	.02
544	*Jeff Sellers*	.20	.15	.08
545	Joel Skinner	.05	.04	.02
546	Alex Trevino	.05	.04	.02
547	*Randy Kutcher*(FC)	.10	.08	.04
548	Joaquin Andujar	.07	.05	.03
549	*Casey Candaele*(FC)	.15	.11	.06
550	Jeff Russell	.05	.04	.02
551	John Candelaria	.10	.08	.04
552	Joe Cowley	.05	.04	.02
553	Danny Cox	.07	.05	.03
554	Denny Walling	.05	.04	.02
555	*Bruce Ruffin*(FC)	.20	.15	.08
556	Buddy Bell	.10	.08	.04
557	*Jimmy Jones*(FC)	.20	.15	.08
558	*Bobby Bonilla*	4.00	3.00	1.50
559	Jeff Robinson	.07	.05	.03
560	Ed Olwine	.05	.04	.02
561	*Glenallen Hill*(FC)	.50	.40	.20
562	Lee Mazzilli	.07	.05	.03
563	Mike Brown	.05	.04	.02
564	George Frazier	.05	.04	.02
565	*Mike Sharperson*(FC)	.10	.08	.04
566	*Mark Portugal*	.10	.08	.04
567	Rick Leach	.05	.04	.02
568	Mark Langston	.12	.09	.05
569	Rafael Santana	.05	.04	.02
570	Manny Trillo	.07	.05	.03
571	Cliff Speck	.05	.04	.02
572	Bob Kipper	.05	.04	.02
573	*Kelly Downs*(FC)	.30	.25	.12
574	*Randy Asadoor*(FC)	.10	.08	.04
575	*Dave Magadan*(FC)	.40	.30	.15
576	*Marvin Freeman*(FC)	.12	.09	.05
577	Jeff Lahti	.05	.04	.02
578	Jeff Calhoun	.05	.04	.02
579	Gus Polidor(FC)	.07	.05	.03
580	Gene Nelson	.05	.04	.02
581	Tim Teufel	.05	.04	.02
582	Odell Jones	.05	.04	.02
583	Mark Ryal	.05	.04	.02
584	Randy O'Neal	.05	.04	.02
585	*Mike Greenwell*(FC)	1.00	.70	.40
586	Ray Knight	.07	.05	.03
587	*Ralph Bryant*(FC)	.12	.09	.05
588	Carmen Castillo	.05	.04	.02
589	Ed Wojna	.05	.04	.02
590	Stan Javier	.05	.04	.02
591	*Jeff Musselman*(FC)	.20	.15	.08
592	*Mike Stanley*(FC)	.20	.15	.08
593	Darrell Porter	.07	.05	.03
594	*Drew Hall*(FC)	.20	.15	.08
595	*Rob Nelson*(FC)	.10	.08	.04
596	Bryan Oelkers	.05	.04	.02

		MT	NR MT	EX
597	*Scott Nielsen*(FC)	.10	.08	.04
598	*Brian Holton*(FC)	.20	.15	.08
599	*Kevin Mitchell*	2.00	1.50	.80
600	Checklist 558-660	.05	.04	.02
601	Jackie Gutierrez	.05	.04	.02
602	*Barry Jones*(FC)	.12	.09	.05
603	Jerry Narron	.05	.04	.02
604	Steve Lake	.05	.04	.02
605	Jim Pankovits	.05	.04	.02
606	Ed Romero	.05	.04	.02
607	Dave LaPoint	.07	.05	.03
608	Don Robinson	.07	.05	.03
609	Mike Krukow	.07	.05	.03
610	*Dave Valle*(FC)	.12	.09	.05
611	Len Dykstra	.80	.60	.30
612	Roberto Clemente Puzzle Card	.05	.04	.02
613	*Mike Trujillo*(FC)	.05	.04	.02
614	Damaso Garcia	.05	.04	.02
615	Neal Heaton	.05	.04	.02
616	Juan Berenguer	.05	.04	.02
617	Steve Carlton	.25	.20	.10
618	Gary Lucas	.05	.04	.02
619	Geno Petralli	.05	.04	.02
620	Rick Aguilera	.07	.05	.03
621	Fred McGriff	4.00	3.00	1.50
622	Dave Henderson	.10	.08	.04
623	*Dave Clark*(FC)	.20	.15	.08
624	Angel Salazar	.05	.04	.02
625	Randy Hunt	.05	.04	.02
626	John Gibbons	.05	.04	.02
627	*Kevin Brown*(FC)	2.00	1.50	.80
628	Bill Dawley	.05	.04	.02
629	Aurelio Lopez	.05	.04	.02
630	Charlie Hudson	.05	.04	.02
631	Ray Soff	.05	.04	.02
632	*Ray Hayward*(FC)	.12	.09	.05
633	Spike Owen	.05	.04	.02
634	Glenn Hubbard	.05	.04	.02
635	*Kevin Elster*(FC)	.40	.30	.15
636	Mike LaCoss	.05	.04	.02
637	Dwayne Henry	.05	.04	.02
638	*Rey Quinones*	.15	.11	.06
639	Jim Clancy	.07	.05	.03
640	Larry Andersen	.05	.04	.02
641	Calvin Schiraldi	.05	.04	.02
642	*Stan Jefferson*(FC)	.15	.11	.06
643	Marc Sullivan	.05	.04	.02
644	Mark Grant	.05	.04	.02
645	Cliff Johnson	.05	.04	.02
646	Howard Johnson	.25	.20	.10
647	Dave Sax	.05	.04	.02
648	Dave Stewart	.25	.20	.10
649	Danny Heep	.05	.04	.02
650	Joe Johnson	.05	.04	.02
651	*Bob Brower*(FC)	.15	.11	.06
652	Rob Woodward	.07	.05	.03
653	John Mizerock	.05	.04	.02
654	*Tim Pyznarski*(FC)	.10	.08	.04
655	*Luis Aquino*(FC)	.10	.08	.04
656	Mickey Brantley(FC)	.10	.08	.04
657	Doyle Alexander	.07	.05	.03
658	Sammy Stewart	.05	.04	.02
659	Jim Acker	.05	.04	.02
660	Pete Ladd	.05	.04	.02

1987 Donruss All-Stars

Issued in conjunction with the Donruss Pop-Ups set for the second consecutive year, the 1987 Donruss All-Stars set consists of 59 players (plus a checklist)

who were selected to the 1986 All-Star Game. Measuring 3-1/2" by 5" in size, the card fronts feature black borders and American or National League logos. Included on the backs are the player's career highlights and All-Star Game statistics. Retail packs included one pop-Up card, three All-Star cards and one Roberto Clemente puzzle.

		MT	NR MT	EX
	Complete Set:	7.00	5.25	2.75
	Common Player:	.09	.07	.04
1	Wally Joyner	.80	.60	.30
2	Dave Winfield	.25	.20	.10
3	Lou Whitaker	.15	.11	.06
4	Kirby Puckett	.50	.40	.20
5	Cal Ripken, Jr.	.60	.45	.25
6	Rickey Henderson	.50	.40	.20
7	Wade Boggs	.60	.45	.25
8	Roger Clemens	.50	.40	.20
9	Lance Parrish	.09	.07	.04
10	Dick Howser	.09	.07	.04
11	Keith Hernandez	.10	.08	.04
12	Darryl Strawberry	.50	.40	.20
13	Ryne Sandberg	.60	.45	.25
14	Dale Murphy	.40	.30	.15
15	Ozzie Smith	.15	.11	.06
16	Tony Gwynn	.30	.25	.12
17	Mike Schmidt	.40	.30	.15
18	Dwight Gooden	.60	.45	.25
19	Gary Carter	.15	.11	.06
20	Whitey Herzog	.09	.07	.04
21	Jose Canseco	1.50	1.25	.60
22	John Franco	.09	.07	.04
23	Jesse Barfield	.12	.09	.05
24	Rick Rhoden	.09	.07	.04
25	Harold Baines	.15	.11	.06
26	Sid Fernandez	.12	.09	.05
27	George Brett	.40	.30	.15
28	Steve Sax	.15	.11	.06
29	Jim Presley	.12	.09	.05
30	Dave Smith	.09	.07	.04
31	Eddie Murray	.10	.08	.04
32	Mike Scott	.12	.09	.05
33	Don Mattingly	1.00	.70	.40
34	Dave Parker	.15	.11	.06
35	Tony Fernandez	.15	.11	.06
36	Tim Raines	.25	.20	.10
37	Brook Jacoby	.12	.09	.05
38	Chili Davis	.09	.07	.04
39	Rich Gedman	.09	.07	.04
40	Kevin Bass	.09	.07	.04
41	Frank White	.09	.07	.04
42	Glenn Davis	.15	.11	.06
43	Willie Hernandez	.09	.07	.04
44	Chris Brown	.09	.07	.04
45	Jim Rice	.10	.08	.04
46	Tony Pena	.09	.07	.04
47	Don Aase	.09	.07	.04
48	Hubie Brooks	.09	.07	.04
49	Charlie Hough	.09	.07	.04
50	Jody Davis	.09	.07	.04
51	Mike Witt	.09	.07	.04
52	Jeff Reardon	.12	.09	.05
53	Ken Schrom	.09	.07	.04
54	Fernando Valenzuela	.10	.08	.04
55	Dave Righetti	.15	.11	.06
56	Shane Rawley	.09	.07	.04
57	Ted Higuera	.12	.09	.05
58	Mike Krukow	.09	.07	.04
59	Lloyd Moseby	.09	.07	.04
60	Checklist	.09	.07	.04

1987 Donruss Box Panels

Continuing with an idea they initiated in 1985, Donruss once again placed baseball cards on the bottoms of their retail boxes. The cards, which are 2-1/2" by 3-1/2" in size, come four to a panel with each panel containing an unnumbered Roberto Clemente puzzle card. With numbering that begins where Donruss left off in 1986, cards PC 10 through PC 12 were found on boxes of Donruss regular issue wax packs. Cards PC 13 through PC 15 were located on boxes of the 1987 All-Star/Pop-Up packs.

		MT	NR MT	EX
	Complete Panel Set:	5.00	3.75	2.00
	Complete Singles Set:	3.00	2.25	1.25
	Common Single Player:	.15	.11	.06
	Panel	4.00	3.00	1.50
10	Dale Murphy	.35	.25	.14
11	Jeff Reardon	.20	.15	.08
12	Jose Canseco	2.00	1.50	.80
----	Roberto Clemente Puzzle Card	.04	.03	.02
	Panel	2.25	1.75	.90
13	Mike Scott	.20	.15	.08
14	Roger Clemens	1.00	.70	.40
15	Mike Krukow	.15	.11	.06
----	Roberto Clemente Puzzle Card	.04	.03	.02

1987 Donruss Diamond Kings Supers

For a third straight baseball card season, Donruss produced a set of enlarged size Diamond Kings. The cards, which measure 4-11/16" by 6-3/4", are giant versions of the Diamond Kings subset found in the regular 1987 Donruss set. The 28-card set, which features the artwork of Dick Perez, contains 26 player cards, a checklist and a Roberto Clemente puzzle card. The set was available through a mail-in offer for $9.50 plus three wrappers.

		MT	NR MT	EX
	Complete Set:	12.00	9.00	4.75
	Common Player:	.20	.15	.08
1	Wally Joyner	.90	.70	.35
2	Roger Clemens	1.00	.70	.40
3	Dale Murphy	.40	.30	.15
4	Darryl Strawberry	.90	.70	.35
5	Ozzie Smith	.30	.25	.12
6	Jose Canseco	2.00	1.50	.80
7	Charlie Hough	.20	.15	.08
8	Brook Jacoby	.20	.15	.08
9	Fred Lynn	.20	.15	.08
10	Rick Rhoden	.20	.15	.08
11	Chris Brown	.25	.20	.10
12	Von Hayes	.25	.20	.10
13	Jack Morris	.20	.15	.08
14	Kevin McReynolds	.35	.25	.14

		MT	NR MT	EX
15	George Brett	.70	.50	.30
16	Ted Higuera	.20	.15	.08
17	Hubie Brooks	.20	.15	.08
18	Mike Scott	.20	.15	.08
19	Kirby Puckett	.90	.70	.35
20	Dave Winfield	.30	.25	.12
21	Lloyd Moseby	.20	.15	.08
22	Eric Davis	.90	.70	.35
23	Jim Presley	.25	.20	.10
24	Keith Moreland	.20	.15	.08
25	Greg Walker	.20	.15	.08
26	Steve Sax	.30	.25	.12
27	Checklist	.15	.11	.06
----	Roberto Clemente Puzzle Card	.15	.11	.06

1987 Donruss Highlights

For a third consecutive year, Donruss produced a 56-card set which highlighted the special events of the 1987 baseball season. The cards, which measure 2-1/2" by 3-1/2", have a front design similar to the regular 1987 Donruss set. A blue border and the "Highlights" logo are the significant differences. The card backs feature black print on a white background and include the date the event took place plus the particulars about it. As in the past, the set includes Donruss' picks for the A.L. and N.L. Rookies of the Year. The set was issued in a specially designed box and was available only through hobby dealers.

		MT	NR MT	EX
	Complete Set:	8.00	6.00	3.25
	Common Player:	.10	.08	.04
1	First No-Hitter For Brewers (Juan Nieves)	.15	.11	.06
2	Hits 500th Homer (Mike Schmidt)	.40	.30	.15
3	N.L. Player of the Month - April (Eric Davis)	.50	.40	.20
4	N.L. Pitcher of the Month - April (Sid Fernandez)	.10	.08	.04
5	A.L. Player of the Month - April (Brian Downing)	.10	.08	.04
6	A.L. Pitcher of the Month - April (Bret Saberhagen)	.30	.25	.12
7	Free Agent Holdout Returns (Tim Raines)	.25	.20	.10
8	N.L. Player of the Month - May (Eric Davis)	.50	.40	.20
9	N.L. Pitcher of the Month - May (Steve Bedrosian)	.15	.11	.06
10	A.L. Player of the Month - May (Larry Parrish)	.10	.08	.04
11	A.L. Pitcher of the Month - May (Jim Clancy)	.10	.08	.04
12	N.L. Player of the Month - June (Tony Gwynn)	.30	.25	.12
13	N.L. Pitcher of the Month - June (Orel Hershiser)	.25	.20	.10
14	A.L. Player of the Month - June (Wade Boggs)	.80	.60	.30
15	A.L. Pitcher of the Month - June (Steve Ontiveros)	.10	.08	.04
16	All Star Game Hero (Tim Raines)	.25	.20	.10
17	Consecutive Game Homer Streak (Don Mattingly)	1.00	.70	.40
18	1987 Hall of Fame Inductee (Jim "Catfish" Hunter)	.20	.15	.08
19	1987 Hall of Fame Inductee (Ray Dandridge)	.10	.08	.04
20	1987 Hall of Fame Inductee (Billy Williams)	.20	.15	.08
21	N.L. Player of the Month - July (Bo Diaz)	.10	.08	.04
22	N.L. Pitcher of the Month - July (Floyd Youmans)	.10	.08	.04
23	A.L. Player of the Month - July (Don Mattingly)	1.00	.70	.40
24	A.L. Pitcher of the Month - July (Frank Viola)	.20	.15	.08
25	Strikes Out 4 Batters In 1 Inning (Bobby Witt)	.15	.11	.06
26	Ties A.L. 9-Inning Game Hit Mark (Kevin Seitzer)	.50	.40	.20
27	Sets Rookie Home Run Record (Mark McGwire)	1.25	.90	.50
28	Sets Cubs' 1st Year Homer Mark (Andre Dawson)	.20	.15	.08
29	Hits In 39 Straight Games (Paul Molitor)	.15	.11	.06
30	Record Weekend (Kirby Puckett)	.50	.40	.20
31	N.L. Player of the Month - August (Andre Dawson)	.20	.15	.08
32	N.L. Pitcher of the Month - August (Doug Drabek)	.10	.08	.04
33	A.L. Player of the Month - August (Dwight Evans)	.15	.11	.06
34	A.L. Pitcher of the Month - August (Mark Langston)	.25	.20	.10
35	100 RBI In 1st 2 Major League Seasons (Wally Joyner)	.40	.30	.15
36	100 SB In 1st 3 Major League Seasons (Vince Coleman)	.20	.15	.08
37	Orioles' All Time Homer King (Eddie Murray)	.10	.08	.04
38	Ends Consecutive Innings Streak (Cal Ripken)	.30	.25	.12
39	Blue Jays Hit Record 10 Homers In 1 Gamelers. (Rob Ducey, Fred McGriff, Ernie Whitt)	.50	.40	.20
40	Equal A's RBI Marks (Jose Canseco, Mark McGwire)	2.50	2.00	1.00
41	Sets All-Time Catching Record (Bob Boone)	.10	.08	.04
42	Sets Mets' One-Season HR Mark (Darryl Strawberry)	.50	.40	.20
43	N.L.'s All-Time Switch Hit HR King (Howard Johnson)	.15	.11	.06
44	Five Straight 200-Hit Seasons (Wade Boggs)	.80	.60	.30
45	Eclipses Rookie Game Hitting Streak (Benito Santiago)	.40	.30	.15
46	Eclipses Jackson's A's HR Record (Mark McGwire)	1.25	.90	.50
47	13th Rookie To Collect 200 Hits (Kevin Seitzer)	.50	.40	.20
48	Sets Slam Record (Don Mattingly)	1.00	.70	.40
49	N.L. Player of the Month - September (Darryl Strawberry)	.50	.40	.20
50	N.L. Pitcher of the Month - September (Pascual Perez)	.10	.08	.04
51	A.L. Player of the Month - September (Alan Trammell)	.20	.15	.08
52	A.L. Pitcher of the Month - September (Doyle Alexander)	.10	.08	.04
53	Strikeout King - Again (Nolan Ryan)	1.00	.70	.40
54	Donruss A.L. Rookie of the Year (Mark McGwire)	1.25	.90	.50
55	Donruss N.L. Rookie of the Year (Benito Santiago)	.40	.30	.15
56	Highlight Checklist	.10	.08	.04

1987 Donruss Opening Day

The Donruss Opening Day set includes all players in major league baseball's starting lineups on the opening day of the 1987 baseball season. Cards in the 272-piece set measure 2-1/2" by 3-1/2" and have a glossy coating. The card fronts are identical in design to the regular Donruss set, but new photos were utilized and the fronts contain maroon borders as opposed to black. The backs carry black printing on white and yellow and carry a brief player biography plus the player's career statistics. The set was packaged in a sturdy 15" by 5" by 2" box with a clear acetate lid.

		MT	NR MT	EX
	Complete Set:	25.00	18.50	10.00
	Common Player:	.05	.04	.02
1	Doug DeCinces	.07	.05	.03
2	Mike Witt	.12	.09	.05
3	George Hendrick	.07	.05	.03
4	Dick Schofield	.05	.04	.02
5	Devon White	.50	.40	.20
6	Butch Wynegar	.05	.04	.02
7	Wally Joyner	.75	.55	.30
8	Mark McLemore	.05	.04	.02
9	Brian Downing	.07	.05	.03
10	Gary Pettis	.05	.04	.02
11	Bill Doran	.07	.05	.03
12	Phil Garner	.05	.04	.02
13	Jose Cruz	.07	.05	.03
14	Kevin Bass	.07	.05	.03
15	Mike Scott	.12	.09	.05
16	Glenn Davis	.15	.11	.06
17	Alan Ashby	.05	.04	.02
18	Billy Hatcher	.07	.05	.03
19	Craig Reynolds	.05	.04	.02
20	Carney Lansford	.07	.05	.03
21	Mike Davis	.05	.04	.02
22	Reggie Jackson	.30	.25	.12
23	Mickey Tettleton	.07	.05	.03
24	Jose Canseco	2.50	2.00	1.00
25	Rob Nelson	.05	.04	.02
26	Tony Phillips	.05	.04	.02
27	Dwayne Murphy	.05	.04	.02
28	Alfredo Griffin	.07	.05	.03
29	Curt Young	.05	.04	.02
30	Willie Upshaw	.05	.04	.02
31	Mike Sharperson	.05	.04	.02
32	Rance Mulliniks	.05	.04	.02
33	Ernie Whitt	.05	.04	.02
34	Jesse Barfield	.12	.09	.05
35	Tony Fernandez	.12	.09	.05
36	Lloyd Moseby	.07	.05	.03
37	Jimmy Key	.10	.08	.04
38	Fred McGriff	1.50	1.25	.60
39	George Bell	.25	.20	.10
40	Dale Murphy	.40	.30	.15
41	Rick Mahler	.05	.04	.02
42	Ken Griffey	.07	.05	.03
43	Andres Thomas	.10	.08	.04
44	Dion James	.05	.04	.02
45	Ozzie Virgil	.05	.04	.02
46	Ken Oberkfell	.05	.04	.02
47	Gary Roenicke	.05	.04	.02
48	Glenn Hubbard	.05	.04	.02
49	Bill Schroeder	.05	.04	.02
50	Greg Brock	.07	.05	.03
51	Billy Jo Robidoux	.05	.04	.02
52	Glenn Braggs	.12	.09	.05
53	Jim Gantner	.05	.04	.02
54	Paul Molitor	.15	.11	.06
55	Dale Sveum	.15	.11	.06
56	Ted Higuera	.12	.09	.05
57	Rob Deer	.07	.05	.03
58	Robin Yount	.35	.25	.14
59	Jim Lindeman	.10	.08	.04
60	Vince Coleman	.15	.11	.06

		MT	NR MT	EX
61	Tommy Herr	.07	.05	.03
62	Terry Pendleton	.07	.05	.03
63	John Tudor	.10	.08	.04
64	Tony Pena	.07	.05	.03
65	Ozzie Smith	.15	.11	.06
66	Tito Landrum	.05	.04	.02
67	Jack Clark	.15	.11	.06
68	Bob Dernier	.05	.04	.02
69	Rick Sutcliffe	.10	.08	.04
70	Andre Dawson	.20	.15	.08
71	Keith Moreland	.07	.05	.03
72	Jody Davis	.07	.05	.03
73	Brian Dayett	.05	.04	.02
74	Leon Durham	.07	.05	.03
75	Ryne Sandberg	.25	.20	.10
76	Shawon Dunston	.20	.15	.08
77	Mike Marshall	.10	.08	.04
78	Bill Madlock	.07	.05	.03
79	Orel Hershiser	.30	.25	.12
80	Mike Ramsey	.05	.04	.02
81	Ken Landreaux	.05	.04	.02
82	Mike Scioscia	.05	.04	.02
83	Franklin Stubbs	.07	.05	.03
84	Mariano Duncan	.05	.04	.02
85	Steve Sax	.15	.11	.06
86	Mitch Webster	.07	.05	.03
87	Reid Nichols	.05	.04	.02
88	Tim Wallach	.10	.08	.04
89	Floyd Youmans	.07	.05	.03
90	Andres Galarraga	.25	.20	.10
91	Hubie Brooks	.07	.05	.03
92	Jeff Reed	.05	.04	.02
93	Alonzo Powell	.05	.04	.02
94	Vance Law	.05	.04	.02
95	Bob Brenly	.05	.04	.02
96	Will Clark	2.50	2.00	1.00
97	Chili Davis	.07	.05	.03
98	Mike Krukow	.05	.04	.02
99	Jose Uribe	.05	.04	.02
100	Chris Brown	.07	.05	.03
101	Rob Thompson	.10	.08	.04
102	Candy Maldonado	.07	.05	.03
103	Jeff Leonard	.07	.05	.03
104	Tom Candiotti	.05	.04	.02
105	Chris Bando	.05	.04	.02
106	Cory Snyder	.30	.25	.12
107	Pat Tabler	.07	.05	.03
108	Andre Thornton	.07	.05	.03
109	Joe Carter	.25	.20	.10
110	Tony Bernazard	.05	.04	.02
111	Julio Franco	.10	.08	.04
112	Brook Jacoby	.10	.08	.04
113	Brett Butler	.07	.05	.03
114	Donnell Nixon	.05	.04	.02
115	Alvin Davis	.12	.09	.05
116	Mark Langston	.25	.20	.10
117	Harold Reynolds	.07	.05	.03
118	Ken Phelps	.05	.04	.02
119	Mike Kingery	.10	.08	.04
120	Dave Valle	.07	.05	.03
121	Rey Quinones	.07	.05	.03
122	Phil Bradley	.12	.09	.05
123	Jim Presley	.12	.09	.05
124	Keith Hernandez	.12	.09	.05
125	Kevin McReynolds	.12	.09	.05
126	Rafael Santana	.05	.04	.02
127	Bob Ojeda	.07	.05	.03
128	Darryl Strawberry	.60	.45	.25
129	Mookie Wilson	.07	.05	.03
130	Gary Carter	.15	.11	.06
131	Tim Teufel	.05	.04	.02
132	Howard Johnson	.20	.15	.08
133	Cal Ripken	.30	.25	.12
134	Rick Burleson	.05	.04	.02
135	Fred Lynn	.12	.09	.05
136	Eddie Murray	.15	.11	.06
137	Ray Knight	.07	.05	.03
138	Alan Wiggins	.05	.04	.02
139	John Shelby	.05	.04	.02
140	Mike Boddicker	.07	.05	.03
141	Ken Gerhart	.07	.05	.03
142	Terry Kennedy	.07	.05	.03
143	Steve Garvey	.30	.25	.12
144	Marvell Wynne	.05	.04	.02
145	Kevin Mitchell	1.50	1.25	.60
146	Tony Gwynn	.35	.25	.14
147	Joey Cora	.10	.08	.04
148	Benito Santiago	.60	.45	.25
149	Eric Show	.07	.05	.03
150	Garry Templeton	.07	.05	.03
151	Carmelo Martinez	.05	.04	.02

		MT	NR MT	EX
152	Von Hayes	.10	.08	.04
153	Lance Parrish	.10	.08	.04
154	Milt Thompson	.07	.05	.03
155	Mike Easler	.05	.04	.02
156	Juan Samuel	.10	.08	.04
157	Steve Jeltz	.05	.04	.02
158	Glenn Wilson	.05	.04	.02
159	Shane Rawley	.07	.05	.03
160	Mike Schmidt	.40	.30	.15
161	Andy Van Slyke	.10	.08	.04
162	Johnny Ray	.07	.05	.03
163a	Barry Bonds (dark jersey, photo actually Johnny Ray)	125.00	94.00	50.00
163b	Barry Bonds (white jersey, correct photo)	.50	.40	.20
164	Junior Ortiz	.05	.04	.02
165	Rafael Belliard	.05	.04	.02
166	Bob Patterson	.05	.04	.02
167	Bobby Bonilla	.50	.40	.20
168	Sid Bream	.07	.05	.03
169	Jim Morrison	.05	.04	.02
170	Jerry Browne	.10	.08	.04
171	Scott Fletcher	.05	.04	.02
172	Ruben Sierra	1.50	1.25	.60
173	Larry Parrish	.07	.05	.03
174	Pete O'Brien	.07	.05	.03
175	Pete Incaviglia	.35	.25	.14
176	Don Slaught	.05	.04	.02
177	Oddibe McDowell	.10	.08	.04
178	Charlie Hough	.07	.05	.03
179	Steve Buechele	.05	.04	.02
180	Bob Stanley	.05	.04	.02
181	Wade Boggs	1.00	.70	.40
182	Jim Rice	.10	.08	.04
183	Bill Buckner	.07	.05	.03
184	Dwight Evans	.10	.08	.04
185	Spike Owen	.05	.04	.02
186	Don Baylor	.10	.08	.04
187	Marc Sullivan	.05	.04	.02
188	Marty Barrett	.07	.05	.03
189	Dave Henderson	.07	.05	.03
190	Bo Diaz	.05	.04	.02
191	Barry Larkin	.90	.70	.35
192	Kal Daniels	.25	.20	.10
193	Terry Francona	.05	.04	.02
194	Tom Browning	.07	.05	.03
195	Ron Oester	.05	.04	.02
196	Buddy Bell	.07	.05	.03
197	Eric Davis	.60	.45	.25
198	Dave Parker	.15	.11	.06
199	Steve Balboni	.05	.04	.02
200	Danny Tartabull	.30	.25	.12
201	Ed Hearn	.05	.04	.02
202	Buddy Biancalana	.05	.04	.02
203	Danny Jackson	.05	.04	.02
204	Frank White	.08	.06	.03
205	Bo Jackson	2.50	2.00	1.00
206	George Brett	.40	.30	.15
207	Kevin Seitzer	.90	.70	.35
208	Willie Wilson	.10	.08	.04
209	Orlando Mercado	.05	.04	.02
210	Darrell Evans	.07	.05	.03
211	Larry Herndon	.05	.04	.02
212	Jack Morris	.15	.11	.06
213	Chet Lemon	.07	.05	.03
214	Mike Heath	.05	.04	.02
215	Darnell Coles	.07	.05	.03
216	Alan Trammell	.20	.15	.08
217	Terry Harper	.05	.04	.02
218	Lou Whitaker	.15	.11	.06
219	Gary Gaetti	.15	.11	.06
220	Tom Nieto	.05	.04	.02
221	Kirby Puckett	.80	.60	.30
222	Tom Brunansky	.10	.08	.04
223	Greg Gagne	.05	.04	.02
224	Dan Gladden	.07	.05	.03
225	Mark Davidson	.07	.05	.03
226	Bert Blyleven	.10	.08	.04
227	Steve Lombardozzi	.05	.04	.02
228	Kent Hrbek	.15	.11	.06
229	Gary Redus	.05	.04	.02
230	Ivan Calderon	.10	.08	.04
231	Tim Hulett	.05	.04	.02
232	Carlton Fisk	.15	.11	.06
233	Greg Walker	.07	.05	.03
234	Ron Karkovice	.05	.04	.02
235	Ozzie Guillen	.07	.05	.03
236	Harold Baines	.12	.09	.05
237	Donnie Hill	.05	.04	.02
238	Rich Dotson	.07	.05	.03
239	Mike Pagliarulo	.10	.08	.04

		MT	NR MT	EX
240	Joel Skinner	.05	.04	.02
241	Don Mattingly	1.50	1.25	.60
242	Gary Ward	.05	.04	.02
243	Dave Winfield	.20	.15	.08
244	Dan Pasqua	.10	.08	.04
245	Wayne Tolleson	.05	.04	.02
246	Willie Randolph	.07	.05	.03
247	Dennis Rasmussen	.07	.05	.03
248	Rickey Henderson	.50	.40	.20
249	Angels Logo/Checklist	.05	.04	.02
250	Astros Logo/Checklist	.05	.04	.02
251	Athletics Logo/Checklist	.05	.04	.02
252	Blue Jays Logo/Checklist	.05	.04	.02
253	Braves Logo/Checklist	.05	.04	.02
254	Brewers Logo/Checklist	.05	.04	.02
255	Cardinals Logo/Checklist	.05	.04	.02
256	Dodgers Logo/Checklist	.05	.04	.02
257	Expos Logo/Checklist	.05	.04	.02
258	Giants Logo/Checklist	.05	.04	.02
259	Indians Logo/Checklist	.05	.04	.02
260	Mariners Logo/Checklist	.05	.04	.02
261	Orioles Logo/Checklist	.05	.04	.02
262	Padres Logo/Checklist	.05	.04	.02
263	Phillies Logo/Checklist	.05	.04	.02
264	Pirates Logo/Checklist	.05	.04	.02
265	Rangers Logo/Checklist	.05	.04	.02
266	Red Sox Logo/Checklist	.05	.04	.02
267	Reds Logo/Checklist	.05	.04	.02
268	Royals Logo/Checklist	.05	.04	.02
269	Tigers Logo/Checklist	.05	.04	.02
270	Twins Logo/Checklist	.05	.04	.02
271	White Sox-Cubs Logos/Checklist	.05	.04	.02
272	Yankees-Mets Logos/Checklist	.05	.04	.02

1987 Donruss Pop-Ups

For the second straight year, Donruss released in conjunction with its All-Stars issue a set of cards designed to fold out to form a three-dimensional stand-up card. Consisting of 20 cards, as opposed to the previous year's 18, the 1987 Donruss Pop-Ups set contains players selected to the 1986 All-Star Game. Background for the 2-1/2" by 5" cards is the Houston Astrodome, site of the 1986 mid-summer classic. Retail packs included one Pop-Up card, three All-Star cards and one Roberto Clemente puzzle card.

		MT	NR MT	EX
Complete Set:		4.00	3.00	1.50
Common Player:		.20	.15	.08
(1)	Wade Boggs	.70	.50	.30
(2)	Gary Carter	.25	.20	.10
(3)	Roger Clemens	.80	.60	.30
(4)	Dwight Gooden	.80	.60	.30
(5)	Tony Gwynn	.50	.40	.20
(6)	Rickey Henderson	.75	.55	.30
(7)	Keith Hernandez	.25	.20	.10
(8)	Whitey Herzog	.20	.15	.08
(9)	Dick Howser	.20	.15	.08
(10)	Wally Joyner	.40	.30	.15
(11)	Dale Murphy	.40	.30	.15
(12)	Lance Parrish	.20	.15	.08
(13)	Kirby Puckett	.75	.55	.30
(14)	Cal Ripken	.50	.40	.20
(15)	Ryne Sandberg	.80	.60	.30

		MT	NR MT	EX
(16)	Mike Schmidt	.60	.45	.25
(17)	Ozzie Smith	.30	.25	.12
(18)	Darryl Strawberry	.50	.40	.20
(19)	Lou Whitaker	.20	.15	.08
(20)	Dave Winfield	.30	.25	.12

1987 Donruss Rookies

As they did in 1986, Donruss issued a 56-card set highlighting the major league's most promising rookies. The cards are the standard 2-1/2" by 3-1/2" size and are identical in design to the regular Donruss issue. The card fronts have green borders as opposed to the black found in the regular issue and carry the words "The Rookies" in the lower left portion of the card. The set came housed in a specially designed box and was available only through hobby dealers.

		MT	NR MT	EX
	Complete Set:	20.00	15.00	8.00
	Common Player:	.10	.08	.04
1	Mark McGwire	5.00	3.75	2.00
2	Eric Bell	.10	.08	.04
3	Mark Williamson(FC)	.15	.11	.06
4	Mike Greenwell	1.00	.70	.40
5	Ellis Burks(FC)	1.00	.70	.40
6	DeWayne Buice(FC)	.20	.15	.08
7	Mark Mclemore (McLemore)	.10	.08	.04
8	Devon White	.40	.30	.15
9	Willie Fraser	.15	.11	.06
10	Lester Lancaster(FC)	.15	.11	.06
11	Ken Williams(FC)	.20	.15	.08
12	Matt Nokes(FC)	.50	.40	.20
13	Jeff Robinson(FC)	.30	.25	.12
14	Bo Jackson	2.50	2.00	1.00
15	Kevin Seitzer(FC)	.50	.40	.20
16	Billy Ripken(FC)	.25	.20	.10
17	B.J. Surhoff	.20	.15	.08
18	Chuck Crim(FC)	.15	.11	.06
19	Mike Birbeck	.10	.08	.04
20	Chris Bosio	.10	.08	.04
21	Les Straker(FC)	.20	.15	.08
22	Mark Davidson(FC)	.15	.11	.06
23	Gene Larkin(FC)	.35	.25	.14
24	Ken Gerhart	.15	.11	.06
25	Luis Polonia(FC)	.50	.40	.20
26	Terry Steinbach	.25	.20	.10
27	Mickey Brantley	.10	.08	.04
28	Mike Stanley	.20	.15	.08
29	Jerry Browne	.10	.08	.04
30	Todd Benzinger(FC)	.30	.25	.12
31	Fred McGriff	4.00	3.00	1.50
32	Mike Henneman(FC)	.35	.25	.14
33	Casey Candaele	.10	.08	.04
34	Dave Magadan	.50	.40	.20
35	David Cone	3.00	2.25	1.25
36	Mike Jackson(FC)	.20	.15	.08
37	John Mitchell(FC)	.20	.15	.08
38	Mike Dunne(FC)	.15	.11	.06
39	John Smiley(FC)	1.00	.70	.40
40	Joe Magrane(FC)	.60	.45	.25
41	Jim Lindeman	.10	.08	.04
42	Shane Mack(FC)	1.00	.70	.40
43	Stan Jefferson	.10	.08	.04
44	Benito Santiago	.80	.60	.30
45	Matt Williams(FC)	3.00	2.25	1.25

		MT	NR MT	EX
46	Dave Meads(FC)	.20	.15	.08
47	Rafael Palmeiro	3.00	2.25	1.25
48	Bill Long(FC)	.20	.15	.08
49	Bob Brower	.10	.08	.04
50	James Steels(FC)	.15	.11	.06
51	Paul Noce(FC)	.15	.11	.06
52	Greg Maddux	4.00	3.00	1.50
53	Jeff Musselman	.15	.11	.06
54	Brian Holton	.15	.11	.06
55	Chuck Jackson(FC)	.20	.15	.08
56	Checklist 1-56	.10	.08	.04

1988 Donruss

The 1988 Donruss set consists of 660 cards, each measuring 2-1/2" by 3-1/2" in size. The card fronts feature a full-color photo surrounded by a colorful border - alternating stripes of black, red, black, blue, black, blue, black, red and black (in that order), separated by soft-focus edges and airbrushed fades. The player's name and position appear in a red band at the bottom of the card. The Donruss logo is situated in the upper left corner of the card, while the team logo is located in the lower right corner. For the seventh consecutive season, Donruss included a subset of "Diamond Kings" cards (#'s 1-27) in the issue. And for the fifth straight year, Donruss incorporated their highly popular "Rated Rookies" (card #'s 28-47) with the set.

		MT	NR MT	EX
	Complete Set:	15.00	11.00	6.00
	Common Player	.05	.04	.02
1	Mark McGwire (DK)	.25	.20	.10
2	Tim Raines (DK)	.25	.20	.10
3	Benito Santiago (DK)	.30	.25	.12
4	Alan Trammell (DK)	.25	.20	.10
5	Danny Tartabull (DK)	.20	.15	.08
6	Ron Darling (DK)	.12	.09	.05
7	Paul Molitor (DK)	.12	.09	.05
8	Devon White (DK)	.10	.08	.04
9	Andre Dawson (DK)	.20	.15	.08
10	Julio Franco (DK)	.10	.08	.04
11	Scott Fletcher (DK)	.07	.05	.03
12	Tony Fernandez (DK)	.12	.09	.05
13	Shane Rawley (DK)	.07	.05	.03
14	Kal Daniels (DK)	.20	.15	.08
15	Jack Clark (DK)	.15	.11	.06
16	Dwight Evans (DK)	.12	.09	.05
17	Tommy John (DK)	.15	.11	.06
18	Andy Van Slyke (DK)	.15	.11	.06
19	Gary Gaetti (DK)	.12	.09	.05
20	Mark Langston (DK)	.10	.08	.04
21	Will Clark (DK)	.60	.45	.25
22	Glenn Hubbard (DK)	.07	.05	.03
23	Billy Hatcher (DK)	.07	.05	.03
24	Bob Welch (DK)	.10	.08	.04
25	Ivan Calderon (DK)	.10	.08	.04
26	Cal Ripken, Jr. (DK)	.35	.25	.14
27	Checklist 1-27	.05	.04	.02
28	*Mackey Sasser* (RR)(FC)	.20	.15	.08
29	*Jeff Treadway* (RR)(FC)	.25	.20	.10
30	*Mike Campbell* (RR)(FC)	.12	.09	.05
31	*Lance Johnson* (RR)(FC)	.50	.40	.20
32	*Nelson Liriano* (RR)(FC)	.15	.11	.06
33	Shawn Abner (RR)(FC)	.20	.15	.08

#	Player	MT	NR MT	EX
34	*Roberto Alomar* (RR)(FC)	3.50	2.75	1.50
35	*Shawn Hillegas* (RR)(FC)	.25	.20	.10
36	Joey Meyer (RR)	.20	.15	.08
37	Kevin Elster (RR)	.30	.25	.12
38	*Jose Lind* (RR)(FC)	.30	.25	.12
39	*Kirt Manwaring* (RR)(FC)	.20	.15	.08
40	Mark Grace (RR)(FC)	2.00	1.50	.80
41	*Jody Reed* (RR)(FC)	.40	.30	.15
42	*John Farrell* (RR)(FC)	.15	.11	.06
43	*Al Leiter* (RR)(FC)	.12	.09	.05
44	*Gary Thurman* (RR)(FC)	.20	.15	.18
45	*Vicente Palacios* (RR)(FC)	.15	.11	.06
46	*Eddie Williams* (RR)(FC)	.15	.11	.06
47	*Jack McDowell* (RR)(FC)	1.25	.90	.50
48	Ken Dixon	.05	.04	.02
49	Mike Birkbeck	.07	.05	.03
50	Eric King	.07	.05	.03
51	Roger Clemens	.60	.45	.25
52	Pat Clements	.05	.04	.02
53	Fernando Valenzuela	.15	.11	.06
54	Mark Gubicza	.12	.09	.05
55	Jay Howell	.07	.05	.03
56	Floyd Youmans	.05	.04	.02
57	Ed Correa	.05	.04	.02
58	*DeWayne Buice*	.15	.11	.06
59	Jose DeLeon	.07	.05	.03
60	Danny Cox	.07	.05	.03
61	Nolan Ryan	.50	.40	.20
62	Steve Bedrosian	.12	.09	.05
63	Tom Browning	.10	.08	.04
64	Mark Davis	.05	.04	.02
65	R.J. Reynolds	.05	.04	.02
66	Kevin Mitchell	.60	.45	.25
67	Ken Oberkfell	.05	.04	.02
68	Rick Sutcliffe	.10	.08	.04
69	Dwight Gooden	.60	.45	.25
70	Scott Bankhead	.07	.05	.03
71	Bert Blyleven	.12	.09	.05
72	Jimmy Key	.10	.08	.04
73	*Les Straker*	.15	.11	.06
74	Jim Clancy	.07	.05	.03
75	Mike Moore	.05	.04	.02
76	Ron Darling	.12	.09	.05
77	Ed Lynch	.05	.04	.02
78	Dale Murphy	.40	.30	.15
79	Doug Drabek	.07	.05	.03
80	Scott Garrelts	.05	.04	.02
81	Ed Whitson	.05	.04	.02
82	Rob Murphy	.07	.05	.03
83	Shane Rawley	.07	.05	.03
84	Greg Mathews	.07	.05	.03
85	Jim Deshaies	.07	.05	.03
86	Mike Witt	.07	.05	.03
87	Donnie Hill	.05	.04	.02
88	Jeff Reed	.05	.04	.02
89	Mike Boddicker	.07	.05	.03
90	Ted Higuera	.10	.08	.04
91	Walt Terrell	.07	.05	.03
92	Bob Stanley	.05	.04	.02
93	Dave Righetti	.15	.11	.06
94	Orel Hershiser	.25	.20	.10
95	Chris Bando	.05	.04	.02
96	Bret Saberhagen	.15	.11	.06
97	Curt Young	.07	.05	.03
98	Tim Burke	.05	.04	.02
99	Charlie Hough	.07	.05	.03
100a	Checklist 28-137	.05	.04	.02
100b	Checklist 28-133	.10	.08	.04
101	Bobby Witt	.10	.08	.04
102	George Brett	.40	.30	.15
103	Mickey Tettleton	.25	.20	.10
104	Scott Bailes	.07	.05	.03
105	Mike Pagliarulo	.10	.08	.04
106	Mike Scioscia	.07	.05	.03
107	Tom Brookens	.05	.04	.02
108	Ray Knight	.07	.05	.03
109	Dan Plesac	.10	.08	.04
110	Wally Joyner	.30	.25	.12
111	Bob Forsch	.07	.05	.03
112	Mike Scott	.12	.09	.05
113	Kevin Gross	.07	.05	.03
114	Benito Santiago	.35	.25	.14
115	Bob Kipper	.05	.04	.02
116	Mike Krukow	.07	.05	.03
117	Chris Bosio	.07	.05	.03
118	Sid Fernandez	.10	.08	.04
119	Jody Davis	.07	.05	.03
120	Mike Morgan	.05	.04	.02
121	Mark Eichhorn	.07	.05	.03
122	Jeff Reardon	.10	.08	.04
123	John Franco	.10	.08	.04
124	Richard Dotson	.07	.05	.03
125	Eric Bell	.05	.04	.02
126	Juan Nieves	.07	.05	.03
127	Jack Morris	.20	.15	.08
128	Rick Rhoden	.07	.05	.03
129	Rich Gedman	.07	.05	.03
130	Ken Howell	.05	.04	.02
131	Brook Jacoby	.10	.08	.04
132	Danny Jackson	.12	.09	.05
133	Gene Nelson	.05	.04	.02
134	Neal Heaton	.05	.04	.02
135	Willie Fraser	.05	.04	.02
136	Jose Guzman	.07	.05	.03
137	Ozzie Guillen	.07	.05	.03
138	Bob Knepper	.07	.05	.03
139	*Mike Jackson*	.20	.15	.08
140	*Joe Magrane*	.30	.25	.12
141	Jimmy Jones	.07	.05	.03
142	Ted Power	.05	.04	.02
143	Ozzie Virgil	.05	.04	.02
144	*Felix Fermin*(FC)	.15	.11	.06
145	Kelly Downs	.10	.08	.04
146	Shawon Dunston	.10	.08	.04
147	Scott Bradley	.05	.04	.02
148	Dave Stieb	.10	.08	.04
149	Frank Viola	.15	.11	.06
150	Terry Kennedy	.07	.05	.03
151	Bill Wegman	.05	.04	.02
152	*Matt Nokes*	.50	.40	.20
153	Wade Boggs	.60	.45	.25
154	Wayne Tolleson	.05	.04	.02
155	Mariano Duncan	.05	.04	.02
156	Julio Franco	.10	.08	.04
157	Charlie Leibrandt	.07	.05	.03
158	Terry Steinbach	.10	.08	.04
159	Mike Fitzgerald	.05	.04	.02
160	Jack Lazorko	.05	.04	.02
161	Mitch Williams	.07	.05	.03
162	Greg Walker	.07	.05	.03
163	Alan Ashby	.05	.04	.02
164	Tony Gwynn	.35	.25	.14
165	Bruce Ruffin	.07	.05	.03
166	Ron Robinson	.05	.04	.02
167	Zane Smith	.07	.05	.03
168	Junior Ortiz	.05	.04	.02
169	Jamie Moyer	.07	.05	.03
170	Tony Pena	.07	.05	.03
171	Cal Ripken	.35	.25	.14
172	B.J. Surhoff	.12	.09	.05
173	Lou Whitaker	.25	.20	.10
174	*Ellis Burks*	.70	.50	.30
175	Ron Guidry	.15	.11	.06
176	Steve Sax	.15	.11	.06
177	Danny Tartabull	.20	.15	.08
178	Carney Lansford	.10	.08	.04
179	Casey Candaele	.05	.04	.02
180	Scott Fletcher	.07	.05	.03
181	Mark McLemore	.05	.04	.02
182	Ivan Calderon	.10	.08	.04
183	Jack Clark	.15	.11	.06
184	Glenn Davis	.15	.11	.06
185	Luis Aguayo	.05	.04	.02
186	Bo Diaz	.07	.05	.03
187	Stan Jefferson	.07	.05	.03
188	Sid Bream	.07	.05	.03
189	Bob Brenly	.05	.04	.02
190	Dion James	.07	.05	.03
191	Leon Durham	.07	.05	.03
192	Jesse Orosco	.07	.05	.03
193	Alvin Davis	.12	.09	.05
194	Gary Gaetti	.12	.09	.05
195	Fred McGriff	.40	.30	.15
196	Steve Lombardozzi	.05	.04	.02
197	Rance Mulliniks	.05	.04	.02
198	Rey Quinones	.05	.04	.02
199	Gary Carter	.25	.20	.10
200a	Checklist 138-247	.05	.04	.02
200b	Checklist 134-239	.10	.08	.04
201	Keith Moreland	.07	.05	.03
202	Ken Griffey	.07	.05	.03
203	*Tommy Gregg*(FC)	.20	.15	.08
204	Will Clark	1.00	.70	.40
205	John Kruk	.10	.08	.04
206	Buddy Bell	.07	.05	.03
207	Von Hayes	.07	.05	.03
208	Tommy Herr	.07	.05	.03
209	Craig Reynolds	.05	.04	.02
210	Gary Pettis	.05	.04	.02
211	Harold Baines	.12	.09	.05
212	Vance Law	.07	.05	.03
213	Ken Gerhart	.07	.05	.03
214	Jim Gantner	.05	.04	.02

#	Player	MT	NR MT	EX
215	Chet Lemon	.07	.05	.03
216	Dwight Evans	.12	.09	.05
217	Don Mattingly	.80	.60	.30
218	Franklin Stubbs	.07	.05	.03
219	Pat Tabler	.07	.05	.03
220	Bo Jackson	.50	.40	.20
221	Tony Phillips	.05	.04	.02
222	Tim Wallach	.10	.08	.04
223	Ruben Sierra	.60	.45	.25
224	Steve Buechele	.05	.04	.02
225	Frank White	.07	.05	.03
226	Alfredo Griffin	.07	.05	.03
227	Greg Swindell	.20	.15	.08
228	Willie Randolph	.07	.05	.03
229	Mike Marshall	.12	.09	.05
230	Alan Trammell	.25	.20	.10
231	Eddie Murray	.35	.25	.14
232	Dale Sveum	.07	.05	.03
233	Dick Schofield	.05	.04	.02
234	Jose Oquendo	.05	.04	.02
235	Bill Doran	.07	.05	.03
236	Milt Thompson	.05	.04	.02
237	Marvell Wynne	.05	.04	.02
238	Bobby Bonilla	.40	.30	.15
239	Chris Speier	.05	.04	.02
240	Glenn Braggs	.10	.08	.04
241	Wally Backman	.07	.05	.03
242	Ryne Sandberg	.50	.40	.20
243	Phil Bradley	.10	.08	.04
244	Kelly Gruber	.05	.04	.02
245	Tom Brunansky	.10	.08	.04
246	Ron Oester	.05	.04	.02
247	Bobby Thigpen	.10	.08	.04
248	Fred Lynn	.15	.11	.06
249	Paul Molitor	.12	.09	.05
250	Darrell Evans	.10	.08	.04
251	Gary Ward	.07	.05	.03
252	Bruce Hurst	.10	.08	.04
253	Bob Welch	.10	.08	.04
254	Joe Carter	.12	.09	.05
255	Willie Wilson	.10	.08	.04
256	Mark McGwire	.50	.40	.20
257	Mitch Webster	.07	.05	.03
258	Brian Downing	.07	.05	.03
259	Mike Stanley	.10	.08	.04
260	Carlton Fisk	.20	.15	.08
261	Billy Hatcher	.07	.05	.03
262	Glenn Wilson	.07	.05	.03
263	Ozzie Smith	.15	.11	.06
264	Randy Ready	.05	.04	.02
265	Kurt Stillwell	.10	.08	.04
266	David Palmer	.05	.04	.02
267	Mike Diaz	.07	.05	.03
268	Rob Thompson	.07	.05	.03
269	Andre Dawson	.20	.15	.08
270	Lee Guetterman	.05	.04	.02
271	Willie Upshaw	.07	.05	.03
272	Randy Bush	.05	.04	.02
273	Larry Sheets	.07	.05	.03
274	Rob Deer	.07	.05	.03
275	Kirk Gibson	.20	.15	.08
276	Marty Barrett	.07	.05	.03
277	Rickey Henderson	.40	.30	.15
278	Pedro Guerrero	.15	.11	.06
279	Brett Butler	.07	.05	.03
280	Kevin Seitzer	.40	.30	.15
281	Mike Davis	.07	.05	.03
282	Andres Galarraga	.15	.11	.06
283	Devon White	.30	.25	.12
284	Pete O'Brien	.07	.05	.03
285	Jerry Hairston	.05	.04	.02
286	Kevin Bass	.07	.05	.03
287	Carmelo Martinez	.07	.05	.03
288	Juan Samuel	.12	.09	.05
289	Kal Daniels	.20	.15	.08
290	Albert Hall	.05	.04	.02
291	Andy Van Slyke	.12	.09	.05
292	Lee Smith	.10	.08	.04
293	Vince Coleman	.20	.15	.08
294	Tom Niedenfuer	.07	.05	.03
295	Robin Yount	.30	.25	.12
296	*Jeff Robinson*	.15	.11	.06
297	*Todd Benzinger*	.30	.25	.12
298	Dave Winfield	.30	.25	.12
299	Mickey Hatcher	.05	.04	.02
300a	Checklist 248-357	.05	.04	.02
300b	Checklist 240-345	.10	.08	.04
301	Bud Black	.05	.04	.02
302	Jose Canseco	.80	.60	.30
303	Tom Foley	.05	.04	.02
304	Pete Incaviglia	.15	.11	.06
305	Bob Boone	.07	.05	.03
306	*Bill Long*	.20	.15	.08
307	Willie McGee	.12	.09	.05
308	*Ken Caminiti*(FC)	.30	.25	.12
309	Darren Daulton	.05	.04	.02
310	Tracy Jones	.12	.09	.05
311	Greg Booker	.07	.05	.03
312	Mike LaValliere	.07	.05	.03
313	Chili Davis	.07	.05	.03
314	Glenn Hubbard	.05	.04	.02
315	*Paul Noce*	.10	.08	.04
316	Keith Hernandez	.20	.15	.08
317	Mark Langston	.12	.09	.05
318	Keith Atherton	.05	.04	.02
319	Tony Fernandez	.12	.09	.05
320	Kent Hrbek	.15	.11	.06
321	John Cerutti	.07	.05	.03
322	Mike Kingery	.05	.04	.02
323	Dave Magadan	.12	.09	.05
324	Rafael Palmeiro	.40	.30	.15
325	Jeff Dedmon	.05	.04	.02
326	Barry Bonds	.40	.30	.15
327	Jeffrey Leonard	.07	.05	.03
328	Tim Flannery	.05	.04	.02
329	Dave Concepcion	.07	.05	.03
330	Mike Schmidt	.50	.40	.20
331	Bill Dawley	.05	.04	.02
332	Larry Andersen	.05	.04	.02
333	Jack Howell	.07	.05	.03
334	*Ken Williams*	.20	.15	.08
335	Bryn Smith	.05	.04	.02
336	*Billy Ripken*	.25	.20	.10
337	Greg Brock	.07	.05	.03
338	Mike Heath	.05	.04	.02
339	Mike Greenwell	.25	.20	.10
340	Claudell Washington	.07	.05	.03
341	Jose Gonzalez	.05	.04	.02
342	Mel Hall	.07	.05	.03
343	Jim Eisenreich	.07	.05	.03
344	Tony Bernazard	.05	.04	.02
345	Tim Raines	.25	.20	.10
346	Bob Brower	.07	.05	.03
347	Larry Parrish	.07	.05	.03
348	Thad Bosley	.05	.04	.02
349	Dennis Eckersley	.12	.09	.05
350	Cory Snyder	.20	.15	.08
351	Rick Cerone	.05	.04	.02
352	John Shelby	.05	.04	.02
353	Larry Herndon	.05	.04	.02
354	John Habyan	.05	.04	.02
355	*Chuck Crim*	.12	.09	.05
356	Gus Polidor	.05	.04	.02
357	Ken Dayley	.05	.04	.02
358	Danny Darwin	.05	.04	.02
359	Lance Parrish	.15	.11	.06
360	*James Steels*	.12	.09	.05
361	*Al Pedrique*(FC)	.15	.11	.06
362	Mike Aldrete	.07	.05	.03
363	Juan Castillo	.05	.04	.02
364	Len Dykstra	.10	.08	.04
365	Luis Quinones	.05	.04	.02
366	Jim Presley	.10	.08	.04
367	Lloyd Moseby	.07	.05	.03
368	Kirby Puckett	.50	.40	.25
369	Eric Davis	.60	.45	.25
370	Gary Redus	.05	.04	.02
371	Dave Schmidt	.05	.04	.02
372	Mark Clear	.05	.04	.02
373	Dave Bergman	.05	.04	.02
374	Charles Hudson	.05	.04	.02
375	Calvin Schiraldi	.05	.04	.02
376	Alex Trevino	.05	.04	.02
377	Tom Candiotti	.05	.04	.02
378	Steve Farr	.05	.04	.02
379	Mike Gallego	.05	.04	.02
380	Andy McGaffigan	.05	.04	.02
381	Kirk McCaskill	.07	.05	.03
382	Oddibe McDowell	.07	.05	.03
383	Floyd Bannister	.07	.05	.03
384	Denny Walling	.05	.04	.02
385	Don Carman	.07	.05	.03
386	Todd Worrell	.10	.08	.04
387	Eric Show	.07	.05	.03
388	Dave Parker	.20	.15	.08
389	Rick Mahler	.05	.04	.02
390	*Mike Dunne*	.15	.11	.06
391	Candy Maldonado	.07	.05	.03
392	Bob Dernier	.05	.04	.02
393	Dave Valle	.05	.04	.02
394	Ernie Whitt	.07	.05	.03
395	Juan Berenguer	.05	.04	.02

		MT	NR MT	EX			MT	NR MT	EX
396	Mike Young	.05	.04	.02	486	Rick Manning	.05	.04	.02
397	Mike Felder	.05	.04	.02	487	Bill Almon	.05	.04	.02
398	Willie Hernandez	.07	.05	.03	488	Jim Sundberg	.07	.05	.03
399	Jim Rice	.30	.25	.12	489	Ken Phelps	.07	.05	.03
400a	Checklist 358-467	.05	.04	.02	490	Tom Henke	.07	.05	.03
400b	Checklist 346-451	.10	.08	.04	491	Dan Gladden	.05	.04	.02
401	Tommy John	.15	.11	.06	492	Barry Larkin	.40	.30	.15
402	Brian Holton	.07	.05	.03	493	*Fred Manrique*(FC)	.15	.11	.06
403	Carmen Castillo	.05	.04	.02	494	Mike Griffin	.05	.04	.02
404	Jamie Quirk	.05	.04	.02	495	*Mark Knudson*(FC)	.10	.08	.04
405	Dwayne Murphy	.07	.05	.03	496	Bill Madlock	.10	.08	.04
406	*Jeff Parrett*(FC)	.25	.20	.10	497	Tim Stoddard	.05	.04	.02
407	Don Sutton	.20	.15	.08	498	*Sam Horn*(FC)	.30	.25	.12
408	Jerry Browne	.07	.05	.03	499	*Tracy Woodson*(FC)	.15	.11	.06
409	Jim Winn	.05	.04	.02	500a	Checklist 468-577	.05	.04	.02
410	Dave Smith	.07	.05	.03	500b	Checklist 452-557	.10	.08	.04
411	*Shane Mack*	.15	.11	.06	501	Ken Schrom	.05	.04	.02
412	Greg Gross	.05	.04	.02	502	Angel Salazar	.05	.04	.02
413	Nick Esasky	.07	.05	.03	503	Eric Plunk	.05	.04	.02
414	Damaso Garcia	.05	.04	.02	504	Joe Hesketh	.05	.04	.02
415	Brian Fisher	.07	.05	.03	505	Greg Minton	.05	.04	.02
416	Brian Dayett	.05	.04	.02	506	Geno Petralli	.05	.04	.02
417	Curt Ford	.05	.04	.02	507	Bob James	.05	.04	.02
418	*Mark Williamson*	.12	.09	.05	508	*Robbie Wine*(FC)	.12	.09	.05
419	Bill Schroeder	.05	.04	.02	509	Jeff Calhoun	.05	.04	.02
420	*Mike Henneman*	.25	.20	.10	510	Steve Lake	.05	.04	.02
421	*John Marzano*(FC)	.20	.15	.08	511	Mark Grant	.05	.04	.02
422	Ron Kittle	.07	.05	.03	512	Frank Williams	.05	.04	.02
423	Matt Young	.05	.04	.02	513	*Jeff Blauser*(FC)	.30	.25	.12
424	Steve Balboni	.07	.05	.03	514	Bob Walk	.05	.04	.02
425	*Luis Polonia*	.30	.25	.12	515	Craig Lefferts	.05	.04	.02
426	Randy St. Claire	.05	.04	.02	516	Manny Trillo	.07	.05	.03
427	Greg Harris	.05	.04	.02	517	Jerry Reed	.05	.04	.02
428	Johnny Ray	.07	.05	.03	518	Rick Leach	.05	.04	.02
429	Ray Searage	.05	.04	.02	519	*Mark Davidson*	.12	.09	.05
430	Ricky Horton	.07	.05	.03	520	*Jeff Ballard*(FC)	.15	.11	.06
431	*Gerald Young*(FC)	.20	.15	.08	521	*Dave Stapleton*(FC)	.10	.08	.04
432	Rick Schu	.05	.04	.02	522	Pat Sheridan	.05	.04	.02
433	Paul O'Neill	.07	.05	.03	523	Al Nipper	.05	.04	.02
434	Rich Gossage	.15	.11	.06	524	Steve Trout	.05	.04	.02
435	John Cangelosi	.05	.04	.02	525	Jeff Hamilton	.07	.05	.03
436	Mike LaCoss	.05	.04	.02	526	*Tommy Hinzo*(FC)	.15	.11	.06
437	Gerald Perry	.10	.08	.04	527	Lonnie Smith	.07	.05	.03
438	Dave Martinez	.07	.05	.03	528	*Greg Cadaret*(FC)	.20	.15	.08
439	Darryl Strawberry	.35	.25	.14	529	Rob McClure (Bob)	.05	.04	.02
440	John Moses	.05	.04	.02	530	Chuck Finley	.10	.08	.04
441	Greg Gagne	.05	.04	.02	531	Jeff Russell	.05	.04	.02
442	Jesse Barfield	.12	.09	.05	532	Steve Lyons	.05	.04	.02
443	George Frazier	.05	.04	.02	533	Terry Puhl	.05	.04	.02
444	Garth Iorg	.05	.04	.02	534	*Eric Nolte*(FC)	.15	.11	.06
445	Ed Nunez	.05	.04	.02	535	Kent Tekulve	.07	.05	.03
446	Rick Aguilera	.05	.04	.02	536	*Pat Pacillo*(FC)	.15	.11	.06
447	Jerry Mumphrey	.05	.04	.02	537	Charlie Puleo	.05	.04	.02
448	Rafael Ramirez	.05	.04	.02	538	*Tom Prince*(FC)	.15	.11	.06
449	*John Smiley*	.40	.30	.15	539	Greg Maddux	.15	.11	.06
450	Atlee Hammaker	.05	.04	.02	540	Jim Lindeman	.07	.05	.03
451	Lance McCullers	.07	.05	.03	541	*Pete Stanicek*(FC)	.15	.11	.06
452	Guy Hoffman(FC)	.07	.05	.03	542	Steve Kiefer	.05	.04	.02
453	Chris James	.12	.09	.05	543	Jim Morrison	.05	.04	.02
454	Terry Pendleton	.07	.05	.03	544	Spike Owen	.05	.04	.02
455	*Dave Meads*	.15	.11	.06	545	*Jay Buhner*(FC)	.50	.40	.20
456	Bill Buckner	.10	.08	.04	546	*Mike Devereaux*(FC)	.70	.50	.30
457	*John Pawlowski*(FC)	.10	.08	.04	547	Jerry Don Gleaton	.05	.04	.02
458	Bob Sebra	.05	.04	.02	548	Jose Rijo	.07	.05	.03
459	Jim Dwyer	.05	.04	.02	549	Dennis Martinez	.05	.04	.02
460	*Jay Aldrich*(FC)	.12	.09	.05	550	Mike Loynd	.05	.04	.02
461	Frank Tanana	.07	.05	.03	551	Darrell Miller	.05	.04	.02
462	Oil Can Boyd	.07	.05	.03	552	Dave LaPoint	.07	.05	.03
463	Dan Pasqua	.10	.08	.04	553	John Tudor	.10	.08	.04
464	*Tim Crews*(FC)	.15	.11	.06	554	*Rocky Childress*(FC)	.12	.09	.05
465	Andy Allanson	.07	.05	.03	555	*Wally Ritchie*(FC)	.15	.11	.06
466	*Bill Pecota*(FC)	.15	.11	.06	556	Terry McGriff	.05	.04	.02
467	Steve Ontiveros	.05	.04	.02	557	Dave Leiper	.05	.04	.02
468	Hubie Brooks	.10	.08	.04	558	Jeff Robinson	.07	.05	.03
469	*Paul Kilgus*(FC)	.15	.11	.06	559	Jose Uribe	.05	.04	.02
470	Dale Mohorcic	.05	.04	.02	560	Ted Simmons	.10	.08	.04
471	Dan Quisenberry	.07	.05	.03	561	*Lester Lancaster*	.15	.11	.06
472	Dave Stewart	.10	.08	.04	562	*Keith Miller*(FC)	.25	.20	.10
473	Dave Clark	.07	.05	.03	563	Harold Reynolds	.07	.05	.03
474	Joel Skinner	.05	.04	.02	564	*Gene Larkin*	.20	.15	.08
475	Dave Anderson	.05	.04	.02	565	Cecil Fielder	.70	.50	.30
476	Dan Petry	.07	.05	.03	566	Roy Smalley	.05	.04	.02
477	*Carl Nichols*(FC)	.12	.09	.05	567	Duane Ward	.07	.05	.03
478	Ernest Riles	.05	.04	.02	568	*Bill Wilkinson*(FC)	.15	.11	.06
479	George Hendrick	.07	.05	.03	569	Howard Johnson	.10	.08	.04
480	John Morris	.05	.04	.02	570	Frank DiPino	.05	.04	.02
481	*Manny Hernandez*(FC)	.10	.08	.04	571	*Pete Smith*(FC)	.20	.15	.08
482	Jeff Stone	.05	.04	.02	572	Darnell Coles	.07	.05	.03
483	Chris Brown	.07	.05	.03	573	Don Robinson	.07	.05	.03
484	Mike Bielecki	.05	.04	.02	574	Rob Nelson	.05	.04	.02
485	Dave Dravecky	.07	.05	.03	575	Dennis Rasmussen	.10	.08	.04

		MT	NR MT	EX
576	Steve Jeltz (photo actually Juan Samuel)			
		.05	.04	.02
577	*Tom Pagnozzi*(FC)	.30	.25	.12
578	Ty Gainey	.05	.04	.02
579	Gary Lucas	.05	.04	.02
580	Ron Hassey	.05	.04	.02
581	Herm Winningham	.05	.04	.02
582	*Rene Gonzales*(FC)	.15	.11	.06
583	Brad Komminsk	.05	.04	.02
584	Doyle Alexander	.07	.05	.03
585	Jeff Sellers	.07	.05	.03
586	Bill Gullickson	.05	.04	.02
587	Tim Belcher(FC)	.35	.25	.14
588	*Doug Jones*(FC)	.25	.20	.10
589	*Melido Perez*(FC)	.30	.25	.12
590	Rick Honeycutt	.05	.04	.02
591	Pascual Perez	.07	.05	.03
592	Curt Wilkerson	.05	.04	.02
593	Steve Howe	.07	.05	.03
594	*John Davis*(FC)	.15	.11	.06
595	Storm Davis	.10	.08	.04
596	Sammy Stewart	.05	.04	.02
597	Neil Allen	.05	.04	.02
598	Alejandro Pena	.07	.05	.03
599	Mark Thurmond	.05	.04	.02
600a	Checklist 578-BC26	.05	.04	.02
600b	Checklist 558-660	.10	.08	.04
601	*Jose Mesa*(FC)	.20	.15	.08
602	*Don August*(FC)	.15	.11	.06
603	Terry Leach	.10	.08	.04
604	*Tom Newell*(FC)	.15	.11	.06
605	*Randall Byers*(FC)	.15	.11	.06
606	Jim Gott	.05	.04	.02
607	Harry Spilman	.05	.04	.02
608	John Candelaria	.07	.05	.03
609	*Mike Brumley*(FC)	.15	.11	.06
610	Mickey Brantley	.07	.05	.03
611	*Jose Nunez*(FC)	.15	.11	.06
612	Tom Nieto	.05	.04	.02
613	Rick Reuschel	.10	.08	.04
614	Lee Mazzilli	.12	.09	.05
615	*Scott Lusader*(FC)	.15	.11	.06
616	Bobby Meacham	.05	.04	.02
617	Kevin McReynolds	.15	.11	.06
618	Gene Garber	.05	.04	.02
619	*Barry Lyons*(FC)	.15	.11	.06
620	Randy Myers	.10	.08	.04
621	Donnie Moore	.05	.04	.02
622	Domingo Ramos	.05	.04	.02
623	Ed Romero	.05	.04	.02
624	*Greg Myers*(FC)	.25	.20	.10
625	Ripken Baseball Family (Billy Ripken, Cal			
	Ripken, Jr., Cal Ripken, Sr.)	.15	.11	.06
626	Pat Perry	.05	.04	.02
627	Andres Thomas	.10	.08	.04
628	*Matt Williams*	2.00	1.50	.80
629	*Dave Hengel*(FC)	.15	.11	.06
630	Jeff Musselman	.07	.05	.03
631	Tim Laudner	.05	.04	.02
632	Bob Ojeda	.07	.05	.03
633	Rafael Santana	.05	.04	.02
634	*Wes Gardner*(FC)	.15	.11	.06
635	*Roberto Kelly*(FC)	1.25	.90	.50
636	Mike Flanagan	.12	.09	.05
637	*Jay Bell*(FC)	.50	.40	.20
638	Bob Melvin	.05	.04	.02
639	*Damon Berryhill*(FC)	.20	.15	.08
640	*David Wells*(FC)	.25	.20	.10
641	Stan Musial Puzzle Card	.05	.04	.02
642	Doug Sisk	.05	.04	.02
643	*Keith Hughes*(FC)	.20	.15	.08
644	*Tom Glavine*(FC)	2.00	1.50	.80
645	Al Newman	.05	.04	.02
646	Scott Sanderson	.05	.04	.02
647	Scott Terry	.10	.08	.04
648	Tim Teufel	.12	.09	.05
649	Garry Templeton	.12	.09	.05
650	Manny Lee	.05	.04	.02
651	Roger McDowell	.10	.08	.04
652	Mookie Wilson	.15	.11	.06
653	David Cone	.60	.45	.25
654	*Ron Gant*(FC)	2.50	2.00	1.00
655	Joe Price	.12	.09	.05
656	George Bell	.25	.20	.10
657	*Gregg Jefferies*(FC)	1.00	.70	.40
658	*Todd Stottlemyre*(FC)	.50	.40	.20
659	*Geronimo Berroa*(FC)	.25	.20	.10
660	Jerry Royster	.12	.09	.05

1988 Donruss All-Stars

For the third consecutive year, this set of 64 cards featuring major league All-Stars was marketed in conjunction with Donruss Pop-Ups. The 1988 issue included a major change - the cards were reduced in size from 3-1/2" x 5" to a standard 2-1/2" x 3-1/2". The set features players from the 1987 All-Star Game starting lineup. Card fronts feature full-color photos, framed in blue, black and white, with a Donruss logo upper left. Player name and position appear in a red banner below the photo, along with the appropriate National or American League logo. All-Stars card backs include player stats and All-Star Game record. In 1988, All-Stars cards were distributed in individual packages containing three All-Stars, one Pop-Up and three Donruss puzzle pieces.

		MT	NR MT	EX
Complete Set:		7.00	5.25	2.75
Common Player:		.09	.07	.04
1	Don Mattingly	1.25	.90	.50
2	Dave Winfield	.25	.20	.10
3	Willie Randolph	.09	.07	.04
4	Rickey Henderson	.50	.40	.20
5	Cal Ripken, Jr.	.30	.25	.12
6	George Bell	.20	.15	.08
7	Wade Boggs	.80	.60	.30
8	Bret Saberhagen	.15	.11	.06
9	Terry Kennedy	.09	.07	.04
10	John McNamara	.09	.07	.04
11	Jay Howell	.09	.07	.04
12	Harold Baines	.12	.09	.05
13	Harold Reynolds	.09	.07	.04
14	Bruce Hurst	.09	.07	.04
15	Kirby Puckett	.50	.40	.20
16	Matt Nokes	.20	.15	.08
17	Pat Tabler	.09	.07	.04
18	Dan Plesac	.12	.09	.05
19	Mark McGwire	.60	.45	.25
20	Mike Witt	.09	.07	.04
21	Larry Parrish	.09	.07	.04
22	Alan Trammell	.20	.15	.08
23	Dwight Evans	.12	.09	.05
24	Jack Morris	.12	.09	.05
25	Tony Fernandez	.12	.09	.05
26	Mark Langston	.20	.15	.08
27	Kevin Seitzer	.40	.30	.15
28	Tom Henke	.09	.07	.04
29	Dave Righetti	.12	.09	.05
30	Oakland Coliseum	.09	.07	.04
31	Top Vote Getter (Wade Boggs)	.60	.45	.25
32	Checklist 1-32	.09	.07	.04
33	Jack Clark	.15	.11	.06
34	Darryl Strawberry	.40	.30	.15
35	Ryne Sandberg	.20	.15	.08
36	Andre Dawson	.20	.15	.08
37	Ozzie Smith	.15	.11	.06
38	Eric Davis	.50	.40	.20
39	Mike Schmidt	.80	.60	.30
40	Mike Scott	.12	.09	.05
41	Gary Carter	.12	.09	.05
42	Davey Johnson	.09	.07	.04
43	Rick Sutcliffe	.12	.09	.05
44	Willie McGee	.12	.09	.05
45	Hubie Brooks	.09	.07	.04
46	Dale Murphy	.40	.30	.15
47	Bo Diaz	.09	.07	.04

		MT	NR MT	EX
48	Pedro Guerrero	.15	.11	.06
49	Keith Hernandez	.15	.11	.06
50	Ozzie Virgil	.09	.07	.04
51	Tony Gwynn	.25	.20	.10
52	Rick Reuschel	.12	.09	.05
53	John Franco	.12	.09	.05
54	Jeffrey Leonard	.09	.07	.04
55	Juan Samuel	.15	.11	.06
56	Orel Hershiser	.20	.15	.08
57	Tim Raines	.20	.15	.08
58	Sid Fernandez	.12	.09	.05
59	Tim Wallach	.12	.09	.05
60	Lee Smith	.09	.07	.04
61	Steve Bedrosian	.12	.09	.05
62	MVP (Tim Raines)	.20	.15	.08
63	Top Vote Getter (Ozzie Smith)	.15	.11	.06
64	Checklist 33-64	.09	.07	.04

1988 Donruss Baseball's Best

The design of this 336-card set (2-1/2" by 3-1/2") is similar to the regular 1988 Donruss issue with the exception of the borders which are orange, instead of blue. Full-color player photos are framed by the Donruss logo upper left, team logo lower right and a bright red and white player name that spans the bottom margin. The backs are black and white, framed by a yellow border, and include personal information, year-by-year stats and major league totals. This set was packaged in a bright red cardboard box (10" x 11" x 12") that contained six individually shrink-wrapped packs of 56 cards. Donruss marketed the set via retail chain outlets including Walgreens, Venture, Wall-Mart, Ben Franklin, Shopko, Super X, Target, McCrory's, Osco, Woolworth and J.C. Murphy.

		MT	NR MT	EX
Complete Set:		18.00	13.50	7.25
Common Player:		.05	.04	.02
1	Don Mattingly	1.00	.70	.40
2	Ron Gant	.50	.40	.20
3	Bob Boone	.05	.04	.02
4	Mark Grace	1.00	.70	.40
5	Andy Allanson	.05	.04	.02
6	Kal Daniels	.12	.09	.05
7	Floyd Bannister	.07	.05	.03
8	Alan Ashby	.05	.04	.02
9	Marty Barrett	.07	.05	.03
10	Tim Belcher	.10	.08	.04
11	Harold Baines	.12	.09	.05
12	Hubie Brooks	.07	.05	.03
13	Doyle Alexander	.07	.05	.03
14	Gary Carter	.15	.11	.06
15	Glenn Braggs	.07	.05	.03
16	Steve Bedrosian	.07	.05	.03
17	Barry Bonds	.50	.40	.20
18	Bert Blyleven	.10	.08	.04
19	Tom Brunansky	.10	.08	.04
20	John Candelaria	.07	.05	.03
21	Shawn Abner	.15	.11	.06
22	Jose Canseco	1.25	.90	.50
23	Brett Butler	.07	.05	.03

		MT	NR MT	EX
24	Scott Bradley	.05	.04	.02
25	Ivan Calderon	.10	.08	.04
26	Rich Gossage	.10	.08	.04
27	Brian Downing	.07	.05	.03
28	Jim Rice	.10	.08	.04
29	Dion James	.05	.04	.02
30	Terry Kennedy	.07	.05	.03
31	George Bell	.10	.08	.04
32	Scott Fletcher	.05	.04	.02
33	Bobby Bonilla	.50	.40	.20
34	Tim Burke	.05	.04	.02
35	Darrell Evans	.07	.05	.03
36	Mike Davis	.05	.04	.02
37	Shawon Dunston	.15	.11	.06
38	Kevin Bass	.07	.05	.03
39	George Brett	.40	.30	.15
40	David Cone	.25	.20	.10
41	Ron Darling	.10	.08	.04
42	Roberto Alomar	.20	.15	.08
43	Dennis Eckersley	.10	.08	.04
44	Vince Coleman	.15	.11	.06
45	Sid Bream	.07	.05	.03
46	Gary Gaetti	.12	.09	.05
47	Phil Bradley	.12	.09	.05
48	Jim Clancy	.05	.04	.02
49	Jack Clark	.15	.11	.06
50	Mike Krukow	.05	.04	.02
51	Henry Cotto	.05	.04	.02
52	Rich Dotson	.07	.05	.03
53	Jim Gantner	.05	.04	.02
54	John Franco	.07	.05	.03
55	Pete Incaviglia	.12	.09	.05
56	Joe Carter	.20	.15	.08
57	Roger Clemens	.70	.50	.30
58	Gerald Perry	.10	.08	.04
59	Jack Howell	.05	.04	.02
60	Vance Law	.05	.04	.02
61	Jay Bell	.07	.05	.03
62	Eric Davis	.70	.50	.30
63	Gene Garber	.05	.04	.02
64	Glenn Davis	.12	.09	.05
65	Wade Boggs	.80	.60	.30
66	Kirk Gibson	.20	.15	.08
67	Carlton Fisk	.15	.11	.06
68	Casey Candaele	.05	.04	.02
69	Mike Heath	.05	.04	.02
70	Kevin Elster	.15	.11	.06
71	Greg Brock	.07	.05	.03
72	Don Carman	.05	.04	.02
73	Doug Drabek	.12	.09	.05
74	Greg Gagne	.05	.04	.02
75	Danny Cox	.07	.05	.03
76	Rickey Henderson	.60	.45	.25
77	Chris Brown	.07	.05	.03
78	Terry Steinbach	.15	.11	.06
79	Will Clark	.80	.60	.30
80	Mickey Brantley	.05	.04	.02
81	Ozzie Guillen	.12	.09	.05
82	Greg Maddux	.12	.09	.05
83	Kirk McCaskill	.05	.04	.02
84	Dwight Evans	.10	.08	.04
85	Ozzie Virgil	.05	.04	.02
86	Mike Morgan	.05	.04	.02
87	Tony Fernandez	.10	.08	.04
88	Jose Guzman	.05	.04	.02
89	Mike Dunne	.12	.09	.05
90	Andres Galarraga	.15	.11	.06
91	Mike Henneman	.10	.08	.04
92	Alfredo Griffin	.07	.05	.03
93	Rafael Palmeiro	.12	.09	.05
94	Jim Deshaies	.07	.05	.03
95	Mark Gubicza	.07	.05	.03
96	Dwight Gooden	.70	.50	.30
97	Howard Johnson	.25	.20	.10
98	Mark Davis	.05	.04	.02
99	Dave Stewart	.10	.08	.04
100	Joe Magrane	.12	.09	.05
101	Brian Fisher	.07	.05	.03
102	Kent Hrbek	.15	.11	.06
103	Kevin Gross	.05	.04	.02
104	Tom Henke	.07	.05	.03
105	Mike Pagliarulo	.10	.08	.04
106	Kelly Downs	.10	.08	.04
107	Alvin Davis	.12	.09	.05
108	Willie Randolph	.07	.05	.03
109	Rob Deer	.07	.05	.03
110	Bo Diaz	.05	.04	.02
111	Paul Kilgus	.10	.08	.04
112	Tom Candiotti	.05	.04	.02
113	Dale Murphy	.40	.30	.15
114	Rick Mahler	.05	.04	.02

		MT	NR MT	EX			MT	NR MT	EX
115	Wally Joyner	.40	.30	.15	206	Mike Scott	.12	.09	.05
116	Ryne Sandberg	.25	.20	.10	207	Kurt Stillwell	.12	.09	.05
117	John Farrell	.12	.09	.05	208	Mookie Wilson	.07	.05	.03
118	Nick Esasky	.05	.04	.02	209	Lee Mazzilli	.05	.04	.02
119	Bo Jackson	.90	.70	.35	210	Lance McCullers	.07	.05	.03
120	Bill Doran	.07	.05	.03	211	Rick Honeycutt	.05	.04	.02
121	Ellis Burks	.70	.50	.30	212	John Tudor	.10	.08	.04
122	Pedro Guerrero	.12	.09	.05	213	Jim Gott	.05	.04	.02
123	Dave LaPoint	.05	.04	.02	214	Frank Viola	.12	.09	.05
124	Neal Heaton	.05	.04	.02	215	Juan Samuel	.10	.08	.04
125	Willie Hernandez	.05	.04	.02	216	Jesse Barfield	.12	.09	.05
126	Roger McDowell	.07	.05	.03	217	Claudell Washington	.05	.04	.02
127	Ted Higuera	.10	.08	.04	218	Rick Reuschel	.07	.05	.03
128	Von Hayes	.10	.08	.04	219	Jim Presley	.10	.08	.04
129	Mike LaValliere	.07	.05	.03	220	Tommy John	.12	.09	.05
130	Dan Gladden	.07	.05	.03	221	Dan Plesac	.10	.08	.04
131	Willie McGee	.12	.09	.05	222	Barry Larkin	.20	.15	.08
132	Al Lieter	.20	.15	.08	223	Mike Stanley	.07	.05	.03
133	Mark Grant	.05	.04	.02	224	Cory Snyder	.25	.20	.10
134	Bob Welch	.07	.05	.03	225	Andre Dawson	.20	.15	.08
135	Dave Dravecky	.05	.04	.02	226	Ken Oberkfell	.05	.04	.02
136	Mark Langston	.10	.08	.04	227	Devon White	.20	.15	.08
137	Dan Pasqua	.10	.08	.04	228	Jamie Moyer	.05	.04	.02
138	Rick Sutcliffe	.12	.09	.05	229	Brook Jacoby	.10	.08	.04
139	Dan Petry	.05	.04	.02	230	Rob Murphy	.10	.08	.04
140	Rich Gedman	.07	.05	.03	231	Bret Saberhagen	.20	.15	.08
141	Ken Griffey	.07	.05	.03	232	Nolan Ryan	.50	.40	.20
142	Eddie Murray	.10	.08	.04	233	Bruce Hurst	.10	.08	.04
143	Jimmy Key	.10	.08	.04	234	Jesse Orosco	.07	.05	.03
144	Dale Mohoric	.05	.04	.02	235	Bobby Thigpen	.07	.05	.03
145	Jose Lind	.15	.11	.06	236	Pascual Perez	.05	.04	.02
146	Dennis Martinez	.05	.04	.02	237	Matt Nokes	.20	.15	.08
147	Chet Lemon	.07	.05	.03	238	Bob Ojeda	.07	.05	.03
148	Orel Hershiser	.20	.15	.08	239	Joey Meyer	.07	.05	.03
149	Dave Martinez	.07	.05	.03	240	Shane Rawley	.07	.05	.03
150	Billy Hatcher	.07	.05	.03	241	Jeff Robinson	.07	.05	.03
151	Charlie Leibrandt	.07	.05	.03	242	Jeff Reardon	.10	.08	.04
152	Keith Hernandez	.10	.08	.04	243	Ozzie Smith	.15	.11	.06
153	Kevin McReynolds	.12	.09	.05	244	Dave Winfield	.50	.40	.20
154	Tony Gwynn	.50	.40	.20	245	John Kruk	.12	.09	.05
155	Stan Javier	.05	.04	.02	246	Carney Lansford	.07	.05	.03
156	Tony Pena	.07	.05	.03	247	Candy Maldonado	.07	.05	.03
157	Andy Van Slyke	.10	.08	.04	248	Ken Phelps	.05	.04	.02
158	Gene Larkin	.07	.05	.03	249	Ken Williams	.10	.08	.04
159	Chris James	.10	.08	.04	250	Al Nipper	.05	.04	.02
160	Fred McGriff	.50	.40	.20	251	Mark McLemore	.05	.04	.02
161	Rick Rhoden	.07	.05	.03	252	Lee Smith	.07	.05	.03
162	Scott Garrelts	.05	.04	.02	253	Albert Hall	.05	.04	.02
163	Mike Campbell	.12	.09	.05	254	Billy Ripken	.15	.11	.06
164	Dave Righetti	.12	.09	.05	255	Kelly Gruber	.20	.15	.08
165	Paul Molitor	.15	.11	.06	256	Charlie Hough	.07	.05	.03
166	Danny Jackson	.10	.08	.04	257	John Smiley	.07	.05	.03
167	Pete O'Brien	.07	.05	.03	258	Tim Wallach	.10	.08	.04
168	Julio Franco	.10	.08	.04	259	Frank Tanana	.07	.05	.03
169	Mark McGwire	.80	.60	.30	260	Mike Scioscia	.05	.04	.02
170	Zane Smith	.07	.05	.03	261	Damon Berryhill	.10	.08	.04
171	Johnny Ray	.07	.05	.03	262	Dave Smith	.07	.05	.03
172	Lester Lancaster	.07	.05	.03	263	Willie Wilson	.10	.08	.04
173	Mel Hall	.05	.04	.02	264	Len Dykstra	.07	.05	.03
174	Tracy Jones	.12	.09	.05	265	Randy Myers	.10	.08	.04
175	Kevin Seitzer	.35	.25	.14	266	Keith Moreland	.07	.05	.03
176	Bob Knepper	.07	.05	.03	267	Eric Plunk	.05	.04	.02
177	Mike Greenwell	.60	.45	.25	268	Todd Worrell	.10	.08	.04
178	Mike Marshall	.10	.08	.04	269	Bob Walk	.05	.04	.02
179	Melido Perez	.15	.11	.06	270	Keith Atherton	.05	.04	.02
180	Tim Raines	.50	.40	.20	271	Mike Schmidt	.40	.30	.15
181	Jack Morris	.12	.09	.05	272	Mike Flanagan	.07	.05	.03
182	Darryl Strawberry	.60	.45	.25	273	Rafael Santana	.05	.04	.02
183	Robin Yount	.35	.25	.14	274	Rob Thompson	.10	.08	.04
184	Lance Parrish	.15	.11	.06	275	Rey Quinones	.05	.04	.02
185	Darnell Coles	.07	.05	.03	276	Cecilio Guante	.05	.04	.02
186	Kirby Puckett	.40	.30	.15	277	B.J. Surhoff	.15	.11	.06
187	Terry Pendleton	.07	.05	.03	278	Chris Sabo	.80	.60	.30
188	Don Slaught	.05	.04	.02	279	Mitch Williams	.07	.05	.03
189	Jimmy Jones	.07	.05	.03	280	Greg Swindell	.10	.08	.04
190	Dave Parker	.12	.09	.05	281	Alan Trammell	.20	.15	.08
191	Mike Aldrete	.07	.05	.03	282	Storm Davis	.07	.05	.03
192	Mike Moore	.05	.04	.02	283	Chuck Finley	.05	.04	.02
193	Greg Walker	.07	.05	.03	284	Dave Stieb	.10	.08	.04
194	Calvin Schiraldi	.07	.05	.03	285	Scott Bailes	.05	.04	.02
195	Dick Schofield	.05	.04	.02	286	Larry Sheets	.07	.05	.03
196	Jody Reed	.25	.20	.10	287	Danny Tartabull	.20	.15	.08
197	Pete Smith	.10	.08	.04	288	Checklist	.05	.04	.02
198	Cal Ripken	.50	.40	.20	289	Todd Benzinger	.15	.11	.06
199	Lloyd Moseby	.07	.05	.03	290	John Shelby	.05	.04	.02
200	Ruben Sierra	.25	.20	.10	291	Steve Lyons	.05	.04	.02
201	R.J. Reynolds	.07	.05	.03	292	Mitch Webster	.05	.04	.02
202	Bryn Smith	.05	.04	.02	293	Walt Terrell	.05	.04	.02
203	Gary Pettis	.05	.04	.02	294	Pete Stanicek	.12	.09	.05
204	Steve Sax	.12	.09	.05	295	Chris Bosio	.05	.04	.02
205	Frank DiPino	.05	.04	.02	296	Milt Thompson	.07	.05	.03

		MT	NR MT	EX
297	Fred Lynn	.12	.09	.05
298	Juan Berenguer	.05	.04	.02
299	Ken Dayley	.05	.04	.02
300	Joel Skinner	.05	.04	.02
301	Benito Santiago	.50	.40	.20
302	Ron Hassey	.05	.04	.02
303	Jose Uribe	.05	.04	.02
304	Harold Reynolds	.07	.05	.03
305	Dale Sveum	.07	.05	.03
306	Glenn Wilson	.05	.04	.02
307	Mike Witt	.07	.05	.03
308	Ron Robinson	.05	.04	.02
309	Denny Walling	.05	.04	.02
310	Joe Orsulak	.05	.04	.02
311	David Wells	.10	.08	.04
312	Steve Buechele	.05	.04	.02
313	Jose Oquendo	.05	.04	.02
314	Floyd Youmans	.07	.05	.03
315	Lou Whitaker	.12	.09	.05
316	Fernando Valenzuela	.12	.09	.05
317	Mike Boddicker	.07	.05	.03
318	Gerald Young	.15	.11	.06
319	Frank White	.07	.05	.03
320	Bill Wegman	.05	.04	.02
321	Tom Niedenfuer	.05	.04	.02
322	Ed Whitson	.05	.04	.02
323	Curt Young	.05	.04	.02
324	Greg Mathews	.10	.08	.04
325	Doug Jones	.07	.05	.03
326	Tommy Herr	.07	.05	.03
327	Kent Tekulve	.07	.05	.03
328	Rance Mulliniks	.05	.04	.02
329	Checklist	.05	.04	.02
330	Craig Lefferts	.05	.04	.02
331	Franklin Stubbs	.07	.05	.03
332	Rick Cerone	.05	.04	.02
333	Dave Schmidt	.05	.04	.02
334	Larry Parrish	.07	.05	.03
335	Tom Browning	.07	.05	.03
336	Checklist	.05	.04	.02

1988 Donruss Diamond Kings Supers

This 28-card set (including the checklist) marks the fourth edition of Donruss' super-size (5"x7") set. These cards, exact duplicates of the 1988 Diamond Kings that feature player portraits by Dick Perez, have a red, blue and black striped border. A gold Diamond Kings banner curves above the player portrait and a matching oval name banner is printed below. Each card features a large player closeup and a smaller full-figure inset on a split background that is white at the top and striped with multi-colors on the lower portion. Card backs are black and white with a blue border and contain the card number, DK logo, player name, team logo and a paragraph style career summary. A 12-piece Stan Musial puzzle was also included with the purchase of the super-size set which was marketed via a mail-in offer printed on Donruss wrappers.

	MT	NR MT	EX
Complete Set:	10.00	7.50	4.00
Common Player:	.20	.15	.08

		MT	NR MT	EX
1	Mark McGwire	.70	.50	.30
2	Tim Raines	.30	.25	.12
3	Benito Santiago	.30	.25	.12
4	Alan Trammell	.30	.25	.12
5	Danny Tartabull	.35	.25	.14
6	Ron Darling	.30	.25	.12
7	Paul Molitor	.30	.25	.12
8	Devon White	.35	.25	.14
9	Andre Dawson	.30	.25	.12
10	Julio Franco	.25	.20	.10
11	Scott Fletcher	.20	.15	.08
12	Tony Fernandez	.30	.25	.12
13	Shane Rawley	.20	.15	.08
14	Kal Daniels	.30	.25	.12
15	Jack Clark	.30	.25	.12
16	Dwight Evans	.25	.20	.10
17	Tommy John	.25	.20	.10
18	Andy Van Slyke	.25	.20	.10
19	Gary Gaetti	.30	.25	.12
20	Mark Langston	.35	.25	.14
21	Will Clark	1.75	1.25	.70
22	Glenn Hubbard	.20	.15	.08
23	Billy Hatcher	.20	.15	.08
24	Bob Welch	.20	.15	.08
25	Ivan Calderon	.20	.15	.08
26	Cal Ripken, Jr.	.60	.45	.25
27	Checklist	.20	.15	.08
641	Stan Musial Puzzle Card	.20	.15	.08

1988 Donruss MVP

This 26-card set of standard-size player cards replaced the Donruss box-bottom cards in 1988. Instead of box-bottoms, the bonus cards (numbered BC-1 through BC-26) were randomly inserted in Donruss wax or rack packs. Cards feature the company's choice of Most Valuable Player for each major league team and are titled "Donruss MVP." The MVP cards were not included in the factory-collated sets. Card fronts carry the same basic red-blue-black flowing border design as the 1988 Donruss basic 660-card issue (with the exception of the Donruss MVP logo). Card backs are the same as the regular issue, except for the numbering system.

		MT	NR MT	EX
Complete Set:		7.00	5.25	2.75
Common Player:		.15	.11	.06
1	Cal Ripken	.30	.25	.12
2	Eric Davis	.50	.40	.20
3	Paul Molitor	.20	.15	.08
4	Mike Schmidt	.35	.25	.14
5	Ivan Calderon	.15	.11	.06
6	Tony Gwynn	.30	.25	.12
7	Wade Boggs	.75	.55	.30
8	Andy Van Slyke	.15	.11	.06
9	Joe Carter	.25	.20	.10
10	Andre Dawson	.25	.20	.10
11	Alan Trammell	.25	.20	.10
12	Mike Scott	.15	.11	.06
13	Wally Joyner	.25	.20	.10
14	Dale Murphy	.35	.25	.14
15	Kirby Puckett	.50	.40	.30
16	Pedro Guerrero	.20	.15	.08
17	Kevin Seitzer	.50	.40	.30
18	Tim Raines	.25	.20	.10

		MT	NR MT	EX
19	George Bell	.25	.20	.10
20	Darryl Strawberry	.50	.40	.30
21	Don Mattingly	1.00	.70	.40
22	Ozzie Smith	.20	.15	.08
23	Mark McGwire	.70	.50	.30
24	Will Clark	.90	.70	.35
25	Alvin Davis	.15	.11	.06
26	Ruben Sierra	.35	.25	.14

1988 Donruss Pop-Ups

Donruss introduced its Pop-Up cards in 1986. The first two annual issues featured 2-1/2" x 5" cards. In 1988, Donruss reduced the size of the Pop-Ups cards to a standard 2-1/2"x 3-1/2". The 1988 set includes 20 cards that fold out so that the upper portion of the player stands upright, giving a three-dimensional effect. Pop-ups feature players from the All-Star Game starting lineup. Card fronts feature full-color photos, with the player's name, team and position printed in black on a yellow banner near the bottom of the card front. As in previous issues, the card backs contain only the player's name, league and position. Pop-Ups were distributed in individual packages containing one Pop-Up, three puzzle pieces and three All-Star cards.

		MT	NR MT	EX
Complete Set:		4.00	3.00	1.50
Common Player:		.15	.11	.06
(1)	George Bell	.20	.15	.08
(2)	Wade Boggs	.50	.40	.20
(3)	Gary Carter	.20	.15	.08
(4)	Jack Clark	.20	.15	.08
(5)	Eric Davis	.30	.25	.12
(6)	Andre Dawson	.20	.15	.08
(7)	Rickey Henderson	.50	.40	.20
(8)	Davey Johnson	.15	.11	.06
(9)	Don Mattingly	.50	.40	.20
(10)	Terry Kennedy	.15	.11	.06
(11)	John McNamara	.15	.11	.06
(12)	Willie Randolph	.15	.11	.06
(13)	Cal Ripken, Jr.	.60	.45	.25
(14)	Bret Saberhagen	.35	.25	.14
(15)	Ryne Sandberg	.60	.45	.25
(16)	Mike Schmidt	.60	.45	.25
(17)	Mike Scott	.15	.11	.06
(18)	Ozzie Smith	.30	.25	.12
(19)	Darryl Strawberry	.50	.40	.20
(20)	Dave Winfield	.25	.20	.10

1988 Donruss Rookies

For the third consecutive year, Donruss issued this 56-card boxed set highlighting current rookies. The complete set includes a checklist and a 15-piece Stan Musial Diamond Kings puzzle. As in previous years, the set is similar to the company's basic issue, with the exception of the logo and border color. Card fronts feature red, green and black-striped borders, with a red-and-white player name printed in the lower left corner beneath the full-color photo. "The Rookies" logo is printed in red, white and black in the lower right corner. The card backs are printed in black on bright aqua and include personal data, recent performance stats and major league totals, as well as 1984-88 year-by-year minor league stats. The cards are the standard 2-1/2" by 3-1/2" size.

		MT	NR MT	EX
Complete Set:		18.00	13.50	7.25
Common Player:		.10	.08	.04
1	Mark Grace	2.00	1.50	.80
2	Mike Campbell	.10	.08	.04
3	Todd Frowirth(FC)	.20	.15	.08
4	Dave Stapleton	.10	.08	.04
5	Shawn Abner	.15	.11	.06
6	Jose Cecena(FC)	.25	.20	.10
7	Dave Gallagher(FC)	.20	.15	.08
8	Mark Parent(FC)	.20	.15	.08
9	Cecil Espy(FC)	.15	.11	.06
10	Pete Smith	.10	.08	.04
11	Jay Buhner	.20	.15	.08
12	Pat Borders(FC)	.40	.30	.15
13	Doug Jennings(FC)	.15	.11	.06
14	Brady Anderson(FC)	.75	.55	.35
15	Pete Stanicek	.15	.11	.06
16	Roberto Kelly	1.00	.70	.40
17	Jeff Treadway	.15	.11	.06
18	Walt Weiss(FC)	.30	.25	.12
19	Paul Gibson(FC)	.20	.15	.08
20	Tim Crews	.10	.08	.04
21	Melido Perez	.25	.20	.10
22	Steve Peters(FC)	.20	.15	.08
23	Craig Worthington(FC)	.20	.15	.08
24	John Trautwein(FC)	.15	.11	.06
25	DeWayne Vaughn(FC)	.15	.11	.06
26	David Wells	.10	.08	.04
27	Al Leiter	.10	.08	.04
28	Tim Belcher	.20	.15	.08
29	Johnny Paredes(FC)	.20	.15	.08
30	Chris Sabo(FC)	2.00	1.50	.80
31	Damon Berryhill	.25	.20	.10
32	Randy Milligan(FC)	.50	.40	.20
33	Gary Thurman	.20	.15	.08
34	Kevin Elster	.20	.15	.08
35	Roberto Alomar	10.00	5.00	3.00
36	Edgar Martinez(FC)	2.00	1.50	.80
37	Todd Stottlemyre	.25	.20	.10
38	Joey Meyer	.15	.11	.06
39	Carl Nichols	.10	.08	.04
40	Jack McDowell	1.00	.70	.40
41	Jose Bautista(FC)	.20	.15	.08
42	Sil Campusano(FC)	.15	.11	.06
43	John Dopson(FC)	.20	.15	.08
44	Jody Reed	.35	.25	.14
45	Darrin Jackson(FC)	.20	.15	.08
46	Mike Capel(FC)	.20	.15	.08
47	Ron Gant	5.00	3.75	2.00
48	John Davis	.10	.08	.04
49	Kevin Coffman(FC)	.15	.11	.06
50	Cris Carpenter(FC)	.20	.15	.08
51	Mackey Sasser	.10	.08	.04
52	Luis Alicea(FC)	.25	.20	.10
53	Bryan Harvey(FC)	.50	.40	.20
54	Steve Ellsworth(FC)	.15	.11	.06
55	Mike Macfarlane(FC)	.25	.20	.10
56	Checklist 1-56	.10	.08	.04

1989 Donruss

This basic annual issue consists of 660 standard-size (2-1/2" by 3-1/2") cards, including 26 Diamond Kings portrait cards and 20 Rated Rookies cards. Top and bottom borders of the cards are printed in a variety of colors that fade from dark to light (i.e. dark blue to light purple, bright red to pale yellow). A white-lettered player name is printed across the top margin. The team logo appears upper right and the Donruss logo lower left. A black stripe and thin white line make up the vertical side borders. The black outer stripe has a special varnish that gives a faintly visible filmstrip texture to the border. The backs (horizontal format) are printed in orange and black, similar to the 1988 design, with personal info, recent stats and major league totals. Team logo sticker cards (22 total) and Warren Spahn puzzle cards (63 total) are included in individual wax packs of cards.

		MT	NR MT	EX
	Complete Set:	15.00	11.00	6.00
	Common Player:	.04	.03	.02
1	Mike Greenwell (DK)	.20	.15	.08
2	Bobby Bonilla (DK)	.12	.09	.05
3	Pete Incaviglia (DK)	.12	.09	.05
4	Chris Sabo (DK)	.25	.20	.10
5	Robin Yount (DK)	.25	.20	.10
6	Tony Gwynn (DK)	.35	.25	.14
7	Carlton Fisk (DK)	.12	.09	.05
8	Cory Snyder (DK)	.15	.11	.06
9	David Cone (DK)	.20	.15	.08
10	Kevin Seitzer (DK)	.25	.20	.10
11	Rick Reuschel (DK)	.10	.08	.04
12	Johnny Ray (DK)	.10	.08	.04
13	Dave Schmidt (DK)	.08	.06	.03
14	Andres Galarraga (DK)	.15	.11	.06
15	Kirk Gibson (DK)	.20	.15	.08
16	Fred McGriff (DK)	.25	.20	.10
17	Mark Grace (DK)	.20	.15	.08
18	Jeff Robinson (DK)	.12	.09	.05
19	Vince Coleman (DK)	.20	.15	.08
20	Dave Henderson (DK)	.10	.08	.04
21	Harold Reynolds (DK)	.08	.06	.03
22	Gerald Perry (DK)	.10	.08	.04
23	Frank Viola (DK)	.15	.11	.06
24	Steve Bedrosian (DK)	.10	.08	.04
25	Glenn Davis (DK)	.15	.11	.06
26	Don Mattingly (DK)	.50	.40	.20
27	Checklist 1-27	.04	.03	.02
28	Sandy Alomar, Jr. (RR)(FC)	.40	.30	.15
29	Steve Searcy (RR)(FC)	.15	.11	.06
30	Cameron Drew (RR)(FC)	.15	.11	.06
31	Gary Sheffield (RR)(FC)	1.00	.70	.40
32	Erik Hanson (RR)(FC)	.50	.40	.20
33	Ken Griffey, Jr. (RR)(FC)	7.00	5.25	2.75
34	Greg Harris (RR)(FC)	.25	.20	.10
35	Gregg Jefferies (RR)	.40	.30	.15
36	Luis Medina (RR)(FC)	.20	.15	.08
37	Carlos Quintana (RR)	.20	.15	.08
38	Felix Jose (RR)(FC)	1.00	.70	.40
39	Cris Carpenter (RR)(FC)	.20	.15	.08
40	Ron Jones (RR)(FC)	.10	.08	.04
41	Dave West (RR)(FC)	.20	.15	.08
42	Randy Johnson (RR)(FC)	.40	.30	.15
43	Mike Harkey (RR)(FC)	.15	.11	.06
44	Pete Harnisch (RR)(FC)	.25	.20	.10

		MT	NR MT	EX
45	Tom Gordon (RR)(FC)	.20	.15	.08
46	Gregg Olson (RR)(FC)	.35	.25	.14
47	Alex Sanchez (RR)(FC)	.15	.11	.06
48	Ruben Sierra	.35	.25	.14
49	Rafael Palmeiro	.25	.20	.10
50	Ron Gant	.50	.40	.20
51	Cal Ripken, Jr.	.50	.40	.20
52	Wally Joyner	.20	.15	.08
53	Gary Carter	.20	.15	.08
54	Andy Van Slyke	.12	.09	.05
55	Robin Yount	.25	.20	.10
56	Pete Incaviglia	.10	.08	.04
57	Greg Brock	.06	.05	.02
58	Melido Perez	.08	.06	.03
59	Craig Lefferts	.04	.03	.02
60	Gary Pettis	.04	.03	.02
61	Danny Tartabull	.15	.11	.06
62	Guillermo Hernandez	.06	.05	.02
63	Ozzie Smith	.12	.09	.05
64	Gary Gaetti	.12	.09	.05
65	Mark Davis	.04	.03	.02
66	Lee Smith	.08	.06	.03
67	Dennis Eckersley	.10	.08	.04
68	Wade Boggs	.90	.70	.35
69	Mike Scott	.10	.08	.04
70	Fred McGriff	.50	.40	.20
71	Tom Browning	.08	.06	.03
72	Claudell Washington	.06	.05	.02
73	Mel Hall	.06	.05	.02
74	Don Mattingly	.50	.40	.20
75	Steve Bedrosian	.08	.06	.03
76	Juan Samuel	.10	.08	.04
77	Mike Scioscia	.06	.05	.02
78	Dave Righetti	.12	.09	.05
79	Alfredo Griffin	.06	.05	.02
80	Eric Davis	.40	.30	.15
81	Juan Berenguer	.04	.03	.02
82	Todd Worrell	.08	.06	.03
83	Joe Carter	.12	.09	.05
84	Steve Sax	.12	.09	.05
85	Frank White	.06	.05	.02
86	John Kruk	.06	.05	.02
87	Rance Mulliniks	.04	.03	.02
88	Alan Ashby	.04	.03	.02
89	Charlie Leibrandt	.06	.05	.02
90	Frank Tanana	.06	.05	.02
91	Jose Canseco	.50	.40	.20
92	Barry Bonds	.30	.25	.12
93	Harold Reynolds	.06	.05	.02
94	Mark McLemore	.04	.03	.02
95	Mark McGwire	.30	.25	.12
96	Eddie Murray	.25	.20	.10
97	Tim Raines	.25	.20	.10
98	Rob Thompson	.06	.05	.02
99	Kevin McReynolds	.12	.09	.05
100	Checklist 28-137	.04	.03	.02
101	Carlton Fisk	.20	.15	.08
102	Dave Martinez	.06	.05	.02
103	Glenn Braggs	.06	.05	.02
104	Dale Murphy	.30	.25	.12
105	Ryne Sandberg	.40	.30	.15
106	Dennis Martinez	.06	.05	.02
107	Pete O'Brien	.06	.05	.02
108	Dick Schofield	.04	.03	.02
109	Henry Cotto	.04	.03	.02
110	Mike Marshall	.12	.09	.05
111	Keith Moreland	.06	.05	.02
112	Tom Brunansky	.10	.08	.04
113	Kelly Gruber	.04	.03	.02
114	Brook Jacoby	.08	.06	.03
115	Keith Brown(FC)	.15	.11	.06
116	Matt Nokes	.15	.11	.06
117	Keith Hernandez	.20	.15	.08
118	Bob Forsch	.06	.05	.02
119	Bert Blyleven	.10	.08	.04
120	Willie Wilson	.08	.06	.03
121	Tommy Gregg	.08	.06	.03
122	Jim Rice	.25	.20	.10
123	Bob Knepper	.06	.05	.02
124	Danny Jackson	.12	.09	.05
125	Eric Plunk	.04	.03	.02
126	Brian Fisher	.06	.05	.02
127	Mike Pagliarulo	.08	.06	.03
128	Tony Gwynn	.30	.25	.12
129	Lance McCullers	.06	.05	.02
130	Andres Galarraga	.15	.11	.06
131	Jose Uribe	.04	.03	.02
132	Kirk Gibson	.20	.15	.08
133	David Palmer	.04	.03	.02
134	R.J. Reynolds	.04	.03	.02
135	Greg Walker	.06	.05	.02

#	Player	MT	NR MT	EX	#	Player	MT	NR MT	EX
136	Kirk McCaskill	.06	.05	.02	226	Chuck Finley	.08	.06	.03
137	Shawon Dunston	.08	.06	.03	227	Mark Langston	.10	.08	.04
138	Andy Allanson	.04	.03	.02	228	Jesse Orosco	.06	.05	.02
139	Rob Murphy	.04	.03	.02	229	Ed Whitson	.04	.03	.02
140	Mike Aldrete	.06	.05	.02	230	Terry Pendleton	.08	.06	.03
141	Terry Kennedy	.06	.05	.02	231	Lloyd Moseby	.06	.05	.02
142	Scott Fletcher	.06	.05	.02	232	Greg Swindell	.10	.08	.04
143	Steve Balboni	.06	.05	.02	233	John Franco	.08	.06	.03
144	Bret Saberhagen	.12	.09	.05	234	Jack Morris	.15	.11	.06
145	Ozzie Virgil	.04	.03	.02	235	Howard Johnson	.08	.06	.03
146	Dale Sveum	.06	.05	.02	236	Glenn Davis	.12	.09	.05
147	Darryl Strawberry	.40	.30	.15	237	Frank Viola	.12	.09	.05
148	Harold Baines	.10	.08	.04	238	Kevin Seitzer	.25	.20	.10
149	George Bell	.25	.20	.10	239	Gerald Perry	.08	.06	.03
150	Dave Parker	.12	.09	.05	240	Dwight Evans	.10	.08	.04
151	Bobby Bonilla	.25	.20	.10	241	Jim Deshaies	.04	.03	.02
152	Mookie Wilson	.06	.05	.02	242	Bo Diaz	.06	.05	.02
153	Ted Power	.04	.03	.02	243	Carney Lansford	.06	.05	.02
154	Nolan Ryan	.60	.45	.25	244	Mike LaValliere	.06	.05	.02
155	Jeff Reardon	.08	.06	.03	245	Rickey Henderson	.40	.30	.15
156	Tim Wallach	.08	.06	.03	246	Roberto Alomar	.25	.20	.10
157	Jamie Moyer	.04	.03	.02	247	Jimmy Jones	.04	.03	.02
158	Rich Gossage	.10	.08	.04	248	Pascual Perez	.06	.05	.02
159	Dave Winfield	.25	.20	.10	249	Will Clark	.40	.30	.15
160	Von Hayes	.08	.06	.03	250	Fernando Valenzuela	.15	.11	.06
161	Willie McGee	.10	.08	.04	251	Shane Rawley	.06	.05	.02
162	Rich Gedman	.06	.05	.02	252	Sid Bream	.06	.05	.02
163	Tony Pena	.06	.05	.02	253	Steve Lyons	.04	.03	.02
164	Mike Morgan	.04	.03	.02	254	Brian Downing	.06	.05	.02
165	Charlie Hough	.06	.05	.02	255	Mark Grace	.60	.45	.25
166	Mike Stanley	.04	.03	.02	256	Tom Candiotti	.04	.03	.02
167	Andre Dawson	.20	.15	.08	257	Barry Larkin	.30	.25	.12
168	Joe Boever(FC)	.04	.03	.02	258	Mike Krukow	.06	.05	.02
169	Pete Stanicek	.08	.06	.03	259	Billy Ripken	.06	.05	.02
170	Bob Boone	.06	.05	.02	260	Cecilio Guante	.04	.03	.02
171	Ron Darling	.10	.08	.04	261	Scott Bradley	.04	.03	.02
172	Bob Walk	.04	.03	.02	262	Floyd Bannister	.06	.05	.02
173	Rob Deer	.06	.05	.02	263	Pete Smith	.08	.06	.03
174	Steve Buechele	.04	.03	.02	264	Jim Gantner	.04	.03	.02
175	Ted Higuera	.08	.06	.03	265	Roger McDowell	.08	.06	.03
176	Ozzie Guillen	.06	.05	.02	266	Bobby Thigpen	.08	.06	.03
177	Candy Maldonado	.06	.05	.02	267	Jim Clancy	.06	.05	.02
178	Doyle Alexander	.06	.05	.02	268	Terry Steinbach	.08	.06	.03
179	Mark Gubicza	.10	.08	.04	269	Mike Dunne	.08	.06	.03
180	Alan Trammell	.15	.11	.06	270	Dwight Gooden	.50	.40	.20
181	Vince Coleman	.15	.11	.06	271	Mike Heath	.04	.03	.02
182	Kirby Puckett	.30	.25	.12	272	Dave Smith	.06	.05	.02
183	Chris Brown	.06	.05	.02	273	Keith Atherton	.04	.03	.02
184	Marty Barrett	.06	.05	.02	274	Tim Burke	.04	.03	.02
185	Stan Javier	.04	.03	.02	275	Damon Berryhill	.12	.09	.05
186	Mike Greenwell	.30	.25	.12	276	Vance Law	.06	.05	.02
187	Billy Hatcher	.06	.05	.02	277	Rich Dotson	.06	.05	.02
188	Jimmy Key	.08	.06	.03	278	Lance Parrish	.15	.11	.06
189	Nick Esasky	.06	.05	.02	279	Denny Walling	.04	.03	.02
190	Don Slaught	.04	.03	.02	280	Roger Clemens	.40	.30	.15
191	Cory Snyder	.15	.11	.06	281	Greg Mathews	.06	.05	.02
192	John Candelaria	.06	.05	.02	282	Tom Niedenfuer	.06	.05	.02
193	Mike Schmidt	.40	.30	.15	283	Paul Kilgus	.10	.08	.04
194	Kevin Gross	.06	.05	.02	284	Jose Guzman	.08	.06	.03
195	John Tudor	.08	.06	.03	285	Calvin Schiraldi	.04	.03	.02
196	Neil Allen	.04	.03	.02	286	Charlie Puleo	.04	.03	.02
197	Orel Hershiser	.25	.20	.10	287	Joe Orsulak	.04	.03	.02
198	Kal Daniels	.15	.11	.06	288	Jack Howell	.06	.05	.02
199	Kent Hrbek	.15	.11	.06	289	Kevin Elster	.08	.06	.03
200	Checklist 138-247	.04	.03	.02	290	Jose Lind	.10	.08	.04
201	Joe Magrane	.08	.06	.03	291	Paul Molitor	.12	.09	.05
202	Scott Bailes	.04	.03	.02	292	Cecil Espy	.08	.06	.03
203	Tim Belcher	.10	.08	.04	293	Bill Wegman	.04	.03	.02
204	George Brett	.30	.25	.12	294	Dan Pasqua	.08	.06	.03
205	Benito Santiago	.12	.09	.05	295	Scott Garrelts	.04	.03	.02
206	Tony Fernandez	.10	.08	.04	296	Walt Terrell	.06	.05	.02
207	Gerald Young	.10	.08	.04	297	Ed Hearn	.04	.03	.02
208	Bo Jackson	.30	.25	.12	298	Lou Whitaker	.20	.15	.08
209	Chet Lemon	.06	.05	.02	299	Ken Dayley	.04	.03	.02
210	Storm Davis	.08	.06	.03	300	Checklist 248-357	.04	.03	.02
211	Doug Drabek	.06	.05	.02	301	Tommy Herr	.06	.05	.02
212	Mickey Brantley (photo actually Nelson Simmons)	.04	.03	.02	302	Mike Brumley	.06	.05	.02
213	Devon White	.10	.08	.04	303	Ellis Burks	.60	.45	.25
214	Dave Stewart	.08	.06	.03	304	Curt Young	.06	.05	.02
215	Dave Schmidt	.04	.03	.02	305	Jody Reed	.10	.08	.04
216	Bryn Smith	.04	.03	.02	306	Bill Doran	.06	.05	.02
217	Brett Butler	.06	.05	.02	307	David Wells	.06	.05	.02
218	Bob Ojeda	.06	.05	.02	308	Ron Robinson	.04	.03	.02
219	*Steve Rosenberg*(FC)	.15	.11	.06	309	Rafael Santana	.04	.03	.02
220	Hubie Brooks	.08	.06	.03	310	Julio Franco	.10	.08	.04
221	B.J. Surhoff	.08	.06	.03	311	Jack Clark	.15	.11	.06
222	Rick Mahler	.04	.03	.02	312	Chris James	.08	.06	.03
223	Rick Sutcliffe	.08	.06	.03	313	Milt Thompson	.04	.03	.02
224	Neal Heaton	.04	.03	.02	314	John Shelby	.04	.03	.02
225	Mitch Williams	.06	.05	.02	315	Al Leiter	.15	.11	.06
					316	Mike Davis	.06	.05	.02

#	Player	MT	NR MT	EX
317	*Chris Sabo*	.60	.45	.25
318	Greg Gagne	.04	.03	.02
319	Jose Oquendo	.04	.03	.02
320	John Farrell	.10	.08	.04
321	Franklin Stubbs	.04	.03	.02
322	Kurt Stillwell	.06	.05	.02
323	Shawn Abner	.10	.08	.04
324	Mike Flanagan	.06	.05	.02
325	Kevin Bass	.06	.05	.02
326	Pat Tabler	.06	.05	.02
327	Mike Henneman	.08	.06	.03
328	Rick Honeycutt	.04	.03	.02
329	John Smiley	.10	.08	.04
330	Rey Quinones	.04	.03	.02
331	Johnny Ray	.06	.05	.02
332	Bob Welch	.08	.06	.03
333	Larry Sheets	.06	.05	.02
334	Jeff Parrett	.08	.06	.03
335	Rick Reuschel	.08	.06	.03
336	Randy Myers	.10	.08	.04
337	Ken Williams	.06	.05	.02
338	Andy McGaffigan	.04	.03	.02
339	Joey Meyer	.08	.06	.03
340	Dion James	.04	.03	.02
341	Les Lancaster	.06	.05	.02
342	Tom Foley	.04	.03	.02
343	Geno Petralli	.04	.03	.02
344	Dan Petry	.06	.05	.02
345	Alvin Davis	.12	.09	.05
346	Mickey Hatcher	.04	.03	.02
347	Marvell Wynne	.04	.03	.02
348	Danny Cox	.06	.05	.02
349	Dave Stieb	.08	.06	.03
350	Jay Bell	.06	.05	.02
351	Jeff Treadway	.10	.08	.04
352	Luis Salazar	.04	.03	.02
353	Lenny Dykstra	.08	.06	.03
354	Juan Agosto	.04	.03	.02
355	Gene Larkin	.10	.08	.04
356	Steve Farr	.04	.03	.02
357	Paul Assenmacher	.04	.03	.02
358	Todd Benzinger	.12	.09	.05
359	Larry Andersen	.04	.03	.02
360	Paul O'Neill	.04	.03	.02
361	Ron Hassey	.04	.03	.02
362	Jim Gott	.04	.03	.02
363	Ken Phelps	.06	.05	.02
364	Tim Flannery	.04	.03	.02
365	Randy Ready	.04	.03	.02
366	*Nelson Santovenia*(FC)	.15	.11	.06
367	Kelly Downs	.08	.06	.03
368	Danny Heep	.04	.03	.02
369	Phil Bradley	.08	.06	.03
370	Jeff Robinson	.06	.05	.02
371	Ivan Calderon	.06	.05	.02
372	Mike Witt	.06	.05	.02
373	Greg Maddux	.10	.08	.04
374	Carmen Castillo	.04	.03	.02
375	Jose Rijo	.06	.05	.02
376	Joe Price	.04	.03	.02
377	R.C. Gonzalez	.04	.03	.02
378	Oddibe McDowell	.06	.05	.02
379	Jim Presley	.06	.05	.02
380	Brad Wellman	.04	.03	.02
381	Tom Glavine	.10	.08	.04
382	Dan Plesac	.08	.06	.03
383	Wally Backman	.06	.05	.02
384	*Dave Gallagher*	.25	.20	.10
385	Tom Henke	.06	.05	.02
386	Luis Polonia	.06	.05	.02
387	Junior Ortiz	.04	.03	.02
388	David Cone	.35	.25	.14
389	Dave Bergman	.04	.03	.02
390	Danny Darwin	.04	.03	.02
391	Dan Gladden	.04	.03	.02
392	*John Dopson*	.25	.20	.10
393	Frank DiPino	.04	.03	.02
394	Al Nipper	.04	.03	.02
395	Willie Randolph	.06	.05	.02
396	Don Carman	.06	.05	.02
397	Scott Terry	.04	.03	.02
398	Rick Cerone	.04	.03	.02
399	Tom Pagnozzi	.06	.05	.02
400	Checklist 358-467	.04	.03	.02
401	Mickey Tettleton	.08	.06	.03
402	Curtis Wilkerson	.04	.03	.02
403	Jeff Russell	.04	.03	.02
404	Pat Perry	.04	.03	.02
405	*Jose Alvarez*(FC)	.15	.11	.06
406	Rick Schu	.04	.03	.02
407	*Sherman Corbett*(FC)	.15	.11	.06
408	Dave Magadan	.10	.08	.04
409	Bob Kipper	.04	.03	.02
410	Don August	.08	.06	.03
411	Bob Brower	.04	.03	.02
412	Chris Bosio	.04	.03	.02
413	Jerry Reuss	.06	.05	.02
414	Atlee Hammaker	.04	.03	.02
415	Jim Walewander(FC)	.06	.05	.02
416	*Mike Macfarlane*	.25	.20	.10
417	Pat Sheridan	.04	.03	.02
418	Pedro Guerrero	.15	.11	.06
419	Allan Anderson	.06	.05	.02
420	*Mark Parent*	.20	.15	.08
421	Bob Stanley	.04	.03	.02
422	Mike Gallego	.04	.03	.02
423	Bruce Hurst	.08	.06	.03
424	Dave Meads	.04	.03	.02
425	Jesse Barfield	.10	.08	.04
426	*Rob Dibble*(FC)	.50	.40	.20
427	Joel Skinner	.04	.03	.02
428	Ron Kittle	.06	.05	.02
429	Rick Rhoden	.08	.06	.03
430	Bob Dernier	.04	.03	.02
431	Steve Jeltz	.04	.03	.02
432	Rick Dempsey	.06	.05	.02
433	Roberto Kelly	.10	.08	.04
434	Dave Anderson	.04	.03	.02
435	Herm Winningham	.04	.03	.02
436	Al Newman	.04	.03	.02
437	Jose DeLeon	.06	.05	.02
438	Doug Jones	.10	.08	.04
439	Brian Holton	.06	.05	.02
440	Jeff Montgomery(FC)	.06	.05	.02
441	Dickie Thon	.04	.03	.02
442	Cecil Fielder	.35	.25	.14
443	*John Fishel*(FC)	.15	.11	.06
444	Jerry Don Gleaton	.04	.03	.02
445	*Paul Gibson*	.15	.11	.06
446	Walt Weiss	.40	.30	.15
447	Glenn Wilson	.06	.05	.02
448	Mike Moore	.04	.03	.02
449	Chili Davis	.06	.05	.02
450	Dave Henderson	.08	.06	.03
451	*Jose Bautista*	.20	.15	.08
452	Rex Hudler	.04	.03	.02
453	Bob Brenly	.04	.03	.02
454	Mackey Sasser	.06	.05	.02
455	Daryl Boston	.04	.03	.02
456	Mike Fitzgerald	.04	.03	.02
457	Jeffery Leonard	.06	.05	.02
458	Bruce Sutter	.08	.06	.03
459	Mitch Webster	.06	.05	.02
460	Joe Hesketh	.04	.03	.02
461	Bobby Witt	.08	.06	.03
462	Stew Cliburn	.04	.03	.02
463	Scott Bankhead	.04	.03	.02
464	*Ramon Martinez*(FC)	.80	.60	.30
465	Dave Leiper	.04	.03	.02
466	*Luis Alicea*	.20	.15	.08
467	John Cerutti	.06	.05	.02
468	Ron Washington	.04	.03	.02
469	Jeff Reed	.04	.03	.02
470	Jeff Robinson	.12	.09	.05
471	Sid Fernandez	.08	.06	.03
472	Terry Puhl	.04	.03	.02
473	Charlie Lea	.04	.03	.02
474	*Israel Sanchez*(FC)	.15	.11	.06
475	Bruce Benedict	.04	.03	.02
476	Oil Can Boyd	.06	.05	.02
477	Craig Reynolds	.04	.03	.02
478	Frank Williams	.04	.03	.02
479	Greg Cadaret	.10	.08	.04
480	*Randy Kramer*(FC)	.15	.11	.06
481	*Dave Eiland*(FC)	.20	.15	.08
482	Eric Show	.06	.05	.02
483	Garry Templeton	.06	.05	.02
484	Wallace Johnson(FC)	.04	.03	.02
485	Kevin Mitchell	.25	.20	.10
486	Tim Crews	.06	.05	.02
487	Mike Maddux	.04	.03	.02
488	Dave LaPoint	.06	.05	.02
489	Fred Manrique	.06	.05	.02
490	Greg Minton	.04	.03	.02
491	*Doug Dascenzo*(FC)	.25	.20	.10
492	Willie Upshaw	.06	.05	.02
493	*Jack Armstrong*(FC)	.15	.11	.06
494	Kirt Manwaring	.10	.08	.04
495	Jeff Ballard	.06	.05	.02
496	Jeff Kunkel	.04	.03	.02
497	Mike Campbell	.08	.06	.03
498	Gary Thurman	.10	.08	.04

#	Player	MT	NR MT	EX
499	Zane Smith	.06	.05	.02
500	Checklist 468-577	.04	.03	.02
501	Mike Birkbeck	.04	.03	.02
502	Terry Leach	.04	.03	.02
503	Shawn Hillegas	.06	.05	.02
504	Manny Lee	.04	.03	.02
505	*Doug Jennings*	.15	.11	.06
506	Ken Oberkfell	.04	.03	.02
507	Tim Teufel	.04	.03	.02
508	Tom Brookens	.04	.03	.02
509	Rafael Ramirez	.04	.03	.02
510	Fred Toliver	.04	.03	.02
511	*Brian Holman*(FC)	.30	.25	.12
512	Mike Bielecki	.04	.03	.02
513	*Jeff Pico*(FC)	.15	.11	.06
514	Charles Hudson	.04	.03	.02
515	Bruce Ruffin	.04	.03	.02
516	Larry McWilliams	.04	.03	.02
517	Jeff Sellers	.04	.03	.02
518	*John Costello*(FC)	.15	.11	.06
519	*Brady Anderson*	.40	.30	.15
520	Craig McMurtry	.04	.03	.02
521	Ray Hayward	.08	.06	.03
522	Drew Hall	.08	.06	.03
523	*Mark Lemke*(FC)	.20	.15	.08
524	*Oswald Peraza*(FC)	.15	.11	.06
525	*Bryan Harvey*	.30	.25	.12
526	Rick Aguilera	.04	.03	.02
527	Tom Prince	.06	.05	.02
528	Mark Clear	.04	.03	.02
529	Jerry Browne	.04	.03	.02
530	Juan Castillo	.04	.03	.02
531	Jack McDowell	.08	.06	.03
532	Chris Speier	.04	.03	.02
533	Darrell Evans	.08	.06	.03
534	Luis Aquino	.04	.03	.02
535	Eric King	.04	.03	.02
536	*Ken Hill*(FC)	.25	.20	.10
537	Randy Bush	.04	.03	.02
538	Shane Mack	.06	.05	.02
539	Tom Bolton(FC)	.06	.05	.02
540	Gene Nelson	.04	.03	.02
541	Wes Gardner	.06	.05	.02
542	Ken Caminiti	.06	.05	.02
543	Duane Ward	.04	.03	.02
544	*Norm Charlton*(FC)	.30	.25	.12
545	*Hal Morris*(FC)	.80	.60	.30
546	Rich Yett(FC)	.04	.03	.02
547	*Hensley Meulens*(FC)	.25	.20	.10
548	Greg Harris	.04	.03	.02
549	Darren Daulton	.04	.03	.02
550	Jeff Hamilton	.06	.05	.02
551	Luis Aguayo	.04	.03	.02
552	Tim Leary	.06	.05	.02
553	Ron Oester	.04	.03	.02
554	Steve Lombardozzi	.04	.03	.02
555	*Tim Jones*(FC)	.15	.11	.06
556	Bud Black	.04	.03	.02
557	Alejandro Pena	.04	.03	.02
558	*Jose DeJesus*(FC)	.15	.11	.06
559	Dennis Rasmussen	.08	.06	.03
560	*Pat Borders*	.30	.25	.12
561	*Craig Biggio*(FC)	.60	.45	.25
562	*Luis de los Santos*(FC)	.15	.11	.06
563	Fred Lynn	.10	.08	.04
564	*Todd Burns*(FC)	.20	.15	.08
565	Felix Fermin	.06	.05	.02
566	Darnell Coles	.06	.05	.02
567	Willie Fraser	.04	.03	.02
568	Glenn Hubbard	.04	.03	.02
569	*Craig Worthington*	.15	.11	.06
570	*Johnny Paredes*	.15	.11	.06
571	Don Robinson	.04	.03	.02
572	Barry Lyons	.04	.03	.02
573	Bill Long	.06	.05	.02
574	Tracy Jones	.10	.08	.04
575	Juan Nieves	.06	.05	.02
576	Andres Thomas	.06	.05	.02
577	*Rolando Roomes*(FC)	.15	.11	.06
578	Luis Rivera(FC)	.04	.03	.02
579	*Chad Kreuter*(FC)	.15	.11	.06
580	Tony Armas	.06	.05	.02
581	Jay Buhner	.10	.08	.04
582	Ricky Horton	.06	.05	.02
583	Andy Hawkins	.04	.03	.02
584	*Sil Campusano*	.15	.11	.06
585	Dave Clark	.06	.05	.02
586	*Van Snider*(FC)	.15	.11	.06
587	Todd Frohwirth(FC)	.06	.05	.02
588	Warren Spahn Puzzle Card	.04	.03	.02
589	*William Brennan*(FC)	.15	.11	.06
590	*German Gonzalez*(FC)	.15	.11	.06
591	Ernie Whitt	.06	.05	.02
592	Jeff Blauser	.08	.06	.03
593	Spike Owen	.04	.03	.02
594	Matt Williams	.40	.30	.15
595	Lloyd McClendon(FC)	.04	.03	.02
596	Steve Ontiveros	.04	.03	.02
597	*Scott Medvin*(FC)	.15	.11	.06
598	*Hipolito Pena*(FC)	.15	.11	.06
599	*Jerald Clark*(FC)	.30	.25	.12
600a	Checklist 578-BC26 (#635 is Kurt Schilling)	.15	.11	.06
600b	Checklist 578-BC26 (#635 is Curt Schilling)	.06	.05	.02
601	Carmelo Martinez	.04	.03	.02
602	Mike LaCoss	.04	.03	.02
603	Mike Devereaux	.15	.11	.06
604	*Alex Madrid*(FC)	.15	.11	.06
605	Gary Redus	.04	.03	.02
606	Lance Johnson	.06	.05	.02
607	*Terry Clark*(FC)	.15	.11	.06
608	Manny Trillo	.04	.03	.02
609	*Scott Jordan*(FC)	.15	.11	.06
610	Jay Howell	.06	.05	.02
611	*Francisco Melendez*(FC)	.15	.11	.06
612	Mike Boddicker	.06	.05	.02
613	Kevin Brown	.20	.15	.08
614	Dave Valle	.04	.03	.02
615	Tim Laudner	.04	.03	.02
616	*Andy Nezelek*(FC)	.15	.11	.06
617	Chuck Crim	.04	.03	.02
618	Jack Savage(FC)	.10	.08	.04
619	Adam Peterson(FC)	.10	.08	.04
620	Todd Stottlemyre	.10	.08	.04
621	Lance Blankenship(FC)	.25	.20	.10
622	*Miguel Garcia*(FC)	.15	.11	.06
623	Keith Miller	.06	.05	.02
624	*Ricky Jordan*(FC)	.20	.15	.08
625	Ernest Riles	.04	.03	.02
626	John Moses	.04	.03	.02
627	Nelson Liriano	.06	.05	.02
628	Mike Smithson	.04	.03	.02
629	Scott Sanderson	.04	.03	.02
630	Dale Mohorcic	.04	.03	.02
631	Marvin Freeman	.04	.03	.02
632	Mike Young	.04	.03	.02
633	Dennis Lamp	.04	.03	.02
634	*Dante Bichette*(FC)	.25	.20	.10
635	*Curt Schilling*(FC)	.25	.20	.10
636	*Scott May*(FC)	.15	.11	.06
637	*Mike Schooler*(FC)	.25	.20	.10
638	Rick Leach	.04	.03	.02
639	*Tom Lampkin*(FC)	.15	.11	.06
640	*Brian Meyer*(FC)	.15	.11	.06
641	Brian Harper	.04	.03	.02
642	*John Smoltz*(FC)	.80	.60	.30
643	40/40 Club (Jose Canseco)	.35	.25	.14
644	Bill Schroeder	.04	.03	.02
645	*Edgar Martinez*	.60	.45	.25
646	*Dennis Cook*(FC)	.15	.11	.06
647	Barry Jones	.04	.03	.02
648	59 and Counting (Orel Hershiser)	.15	.11	.06
649	*Rod Nichols*(FC)	.15	.11	.06
650	Jody Davis	.06	.05	.02
651	*Bob Milacki*(FC)	.25	.20	.10
652	Mike Jackson	.06	.05	.02
653	*Derek Lilliquist*(FC)	.15	.11	.06
654	Paul Mirabella	.04	.03	.02
655	Mike Diaz	.06	.05	.02
656	Jeff Musselman	.06	.05	.02
657	Jerry Reed	.04	.03	.02
658	*Kevin Blankenship*(FC)	.15	.11	.06
659	Wayne Tolleson	.04	.03	.02
660	*Eric Hetzel*(FC)	.15	.11	.06

1989 Donruss
Grand Slammers

One card from this 12-card set was included in each Donruss cello pack. The featured players all hit grand slams in 1988. The 2-1/2" by 3-1/2" cards feature full color action photos. The card backs feature the story of the player's grand slam. Border variations on the front of the card have been discovered, but the prices are consistent with all forms of the cards.

		MT	NR MT	EX
	Complete Set:	4.00	3.00	1.50
	Common Player:	.12	.09	.05
1	Jose Canseco	1.00	.70	.40
2	Mike Marshall	.12	.09	.05
3	Walt Weiss	.12	.09	.05
4	Kevin McReynolds	.15	.11	.06
5	Mike Greenwell	.25	.20	.10
6	Dave Winfield	.40	.30	.15
7	Mark McGwire	.40	.30	.15
8	Keith Hernandez	.15	.11	.06
9	Franklin Stubbs	.12	.09	.05
10	Danny Tartabull	.30	.25	.12
11	Jesse Barfield	.15	.11	.06
12	Ellis Burks	.30	.25	.12

		MT	NR MT	EX
21	Mike Moore	.08	.06	.03
22	Joel Skinner	.06	.05	.02
23	Steve Sax	.15	.11	.06
24	Rick Mahler	.06	.05	.02
25	Mike Aldrete	.06	.05	.02
26	Jesse Orosco	.08	.06	.03
27	Dave LaPoint	.06	.05	.02
28	Walt Terrell	.08	.06	.03
29	Eddie Williams	.08	.06	.03
30	Mike Devereaux	.10	.08	.04
31	Julio Franco	.15	.11	.06
32	Jim Clancy	.06	.05	.02
33	Felix Fermin	.06	.05	.02
34	Curtis Wilkerson	.06	.05	.02
35	Bert Blyleven	.12	.09	.05
36	Mel Hall	.08	.06	.03
37	Eric King	.06	.05	.02
38	Mitch Williams	.12	.09	.05
39	Jamie Moyer	.06	.05	.02
40	Rick Rhoden	.08	.06	.03
41	Phil Bradley	.08	.06	.03
42	Paul Kilgus	.08	.06	.03
43	Milt Thompson	.06	.05	.02
44	Jerry Browne	.08	.06	.03
45	Bruce Hurst	.08	.06	.03
46	Claudell Washington	.08	.06	.03
47	Todd Benzinger	.12	.09	.05
48	Steve Balboni	.06	.05	.02
49	Oddibe McDowell	.08	.06	.03
50	Charles Hudson	.06	.05	.02
51	Ron Kittle	.08	.06	.03
52	Andy Hawkins	.06	.05	.02
53	Tom Brookens	.06	.05	.02
54	Tom Niedenfuer	.06	.05	.02
55	Jeff Parrett	.08	.06	.03
56	Checklist	.06	.05	.02

1989 Donruss Traded

Donruss issued its first "Traded" set in 1989, releasing a 56-card boxed set designed in the same style as the regular 1989 Donruss set. The set included a Stan Musial puzzle card and a checklist.

		MT	NR MT	EX
	Complete Set:	4.00	3.00	1.50
	Common Player:	.06	.05	.02
1	Jeffrey Leonard	.08	.06	.03
2	Jack Clark	.15	.11	.06
3	Kevin Gross	.06	.05	.02
4	Tommy Herr	.08	.06	.03
5	Bob Boone	.10	.08	.04
6	Rafael Palmeiro	.30	.25	.12
7	John Dopson	.15	.11	.06
8	Willie Randolph	.08	.06	.03
9	Chris Brown	.06	.05	.02
10	Wally Backman	.06	.05	.02
11	Steve Ontiveros	.06	.05	.02
12	Eddie Murray	.30	.25	.12
13	Lance McCullers	.08	.06	.03
14	Spike Owen	.06	.05	.02
15	Rob Murphy	.06	.05	.02
16	Pete O'Brien	.08	.06	.03
17	Ken Williams	.06	.05	.02
18	Nick Esasky	.06	.05	.02
19	Nolan Ryan	1.50	1.25	.60
20	Brian Holton	.06	.05	.02

1989 Donruss Rookies

For the fourth straight year, Donruss issued a 56-card "Rookies" set in 1989. As in previous years, the set is similar in design to the regular Donruss set, except for a new "The Rookies" logo and a green and black border.

		MT	NR MT	EX
	Complete Set:	10.00	7.50	4.00
	Common Player:	.10	.08	.04
1	Gary Sheffield	1.00	.70	.40
2	Gregg Jefferies	.30	.25	.12
3	Ken Griffey, Jr.	5.00	3.75	2.00
4	Tom Gordon	.40	.30	.15
5	Billy Spiers(FC)	.25	.20	.10
6	Deion Sanders(FC)	1.50	1.25	.60
7	Donn Pall(FC)	.20	.15	.08
8	Steve Carter(FC)	.20	.15	.08
9	Francisco Oliveras(FC)	.15	.11	.06
10	Steve Wilson(FC)	.20	.15	.08
11	Bob Geren(FC)	.20	.15	.08
12	Tony Castillo(FC)	.15	.11	.06
13	Kenny Rogers(FC)	.20	.15	.08
14	Carlos Martinez(FC)	.30	.25	.12
15	Edgar Martinez	.50	.35	.20
16	Jim Abbott(FC)	1.00	.70	.40
17	Torey Lovullo(FC)	.20	.15	.08
18	Mark Carreon(FC)	.15	.11	.06
19	Geronimo Berroa	.10	.08	.04

		MT	NR MT	EX
20	Luis Medina	.10	.08	.04
21	Sandy Alomar, Jr.	.30	.25	.12
22	Bob Milacki	.10	.08	.04
23	Joe Girardi(FC)	.30	.25	.12
24	German Gonzalez	.10	.08	.04
25	Craig Worthington	.15	.11	.06
26	Jerome Walton(FC)	.30	.25	.12
27	Gary Wayne(FC)	.20	.15	.08
28	Tim Jones	.10	.08	.04
29	Dante Bichette	.10	.08	.04
30	Alexis Infante(FC)	.15	.11	.06
31	Ken Hill	.10	.08	.04
32	Dwight Smith(FC)	.30	.25	.12
33	Luis de los Santos	.10	.08	.04
34	Eric Yelding(FC)	.40	.30	.15
35	Gregg Olson	.40	.30	.15
36	Phil Stephenson(FC)	.15	.11	.06
37	Ken Patterson(FC)	.15	.11	.06
38	Rick Wrona(FC)	.15	.11	.06
39	Mike Brumley	.10	.08	.04
40	Cris Carpenter	.10	.08	.04
41	Jeff Brantley(FC)	.20	.15	.08
42	Ron Jones	.10	.08	.04
43	Randy Johnson	.10	.08	.04
44	Kevin Brown	.10	.08	.04
45	Ramon Martinez	.70	.50	.30
46	Greg Harris	.10	.08	.04
47	Steve Finley(FC)	.40	.30	.15
48	Randy Kramer	.10	.08	.04
49	Erik Hanson	.70	.50	.30
50	Matt Merullo(FC)	.15	.11	.06
51	Mike Devereaux	.10	.08	.04
52	Clay Parker(FC)	.15	.11	.06
53	Omar Vizquel(FC)	.20	.15	.08
54	Derek Lilliquist	.10	.08	.04
55	Junior Felix(FC)	.30	.25	.12
56	Checklist	.10	.08	.04

		MT	NR MT	EX
(7)	Wade Boggs	.50	.40	.20
(8)	Frank Viola	.25	.20	.10
(9)	Terry Steinbach	.20	.15	.08
(10)	Tom Kelly	.20	.15	.08
(11)	Will Clark	1.00	.70	.40
(12)	Darryl Strawberry	.50	.40	.20
(13)	Ryne Sandberg	.50	.40	.20
(14)	Andre Dawson	.35	.25	.14
(15)	Ozzie Smith	.30	.25	.12
(16)	Vince Coleman	.20	.15	.08
(17)	Bobby Bonilla	.30	.25	.12
(18)	Dwight Gooden	.50	.40	.20
(19)	Gary Carter	.20	.15	.08
(20)	Whitey Herzog	.20	.15	.08

1989 Donruss Pop-Ups

This set features the eighteen starters from the 1988 Major League All-Star game. The cards are designed with a perforated outline so each player can be popped out and made to stand upright. On the front side, each player's name, team, and position is featured in an orange-and-yellow rectangle below the borderless full-color photo. Each Pop-Up includes a unique double card, folded over and glued together on the back. The flip side features a red, white, and blue "Cincinnati Reds All-Star Game" logo at the top, a blue-lettered league designation, and the player's name and position in red. The lower portion of the flip side displays illustrated instructions for creating the base of the Pop-Up. The Pop-Ups were marketed in conjunction with All-Star and Warren Spahn Puzzle Cards.

		MT	NR MT	EX
Complete Set:		5.00	3.75	2.00
Common Player:		.20	.15	.08
(1)	Mark McGwire	.40	.30	.15
(2)	Jose Canseco	.80	.60	.30
(3)	Paul Molitor	.30	.25	.12
(4)	Rickey Henderson	.50	.40	.20
(5)	Cal Ripken, Jr.	.50	.40	.20
(6)	Dave Winfield	.40	.30	.15

1989 Donruss All-Stars

For the fourth consecutive year in conjunction with the Pop-Ups, Donruss featured a 64-card set with players from the 1988 All-Star Game. The card fronts include a red- to-gold fade or gold-to-red fade border and blue vertical side borders. The top border features the player's name and position along with the "Donruss 89" logo. Each full-color player photo is highlighted by a thin white line and includes a league logo in the lower right corner. Card backs reveal an orange-gold border and black and white printing. The player's ID and personal information is displayed with a gold star on both sides. The star in the left corner includes the card number. 1988 All-Star game statistics and run totals follow along with a career highlights feature surrounded by the team, All-Star Game MLB, MLBPA, and Leaf Inc. logos. The All-Stars were distributed in wax packages containing five All-Stars, one Pop-Up, and one three-piece Warren Spahn puzzle card.

		MT	NR MT	EX
Complete Set:		9.00	6.75	3.50
Common Player:		.09	.07	.04
1	Mark McGwire	.50	.40	.20
2	Jose Canseco	1.00	.70	.40
3	Paul Molitor	.12	.09	.05
4	Rickey Henderson	.30	.25	.12
5	Cal Ripken, Jr.	.30	.25	.12
6	Dave Winfield	.20	.15	.08
7	Wade Boggs	.50	.40	.20
8	Frank Viola	.15	.11	.06
9	Terry Steinbach	.09	.07	.04
10	Tom Kelly	.09	.07	.04
11	George Brett	.12	.09	.05
12	Doyle Alexander	.09	.07	.04
13	Gary Gaetti	.12	.09	.05
14	Roger Clemens	.40	.30	.15
15	Mike Greenwell	.25	.20	.10
16	Dennis Eckersley	.12	.09	.05
17	Carney Lansford	.09	.07	.04
18	Mark Gubicza	.09	.07	.04
19	Tim Laudner	.09	.07	.04
20	Doug Jones	.09	.07	.04
21	Don Mattingly	1.00	.70	.40
22	Dan Plesac	.12	.09	.05
23	Kirby Puckett	.30	.25	.12
24	Jeff Reardon	.09	.07	.04
25	Johnny Ray	.09	.07	.04
26	Jeff Russell	.09	.07	.04
27	Harold Reynolds	.09	.07	.04

		MT	NR MT	EX
28	Dave Stieb	.09	.07	.04
29	Kurt Stillwell	.09	.07	.04
30	Jose Canseco	1.00	.70	.40
31	Terry Steinbach	.09	.07	.04
32	AL Checklist	.09	.07	.05
33	Will Clark	1.00	.70	.40
34	Darryl Strawberry	.60	.45	.25
35	Ryne Sandberg	.40	.30	.15
36	Andre Dawson	.20	.15	.08
37	Ozzie Smith	.20	.15	.08
38	Vince Coleman	.15	.11	.06
39	Bobby Bonilla	.15	.11	.06
40	Dwight Gooden	.40	.30	.15
41	Gary Carter	.10	.08	.04
42	Whitey Herzog	.09	.07	.05
43	Shawon Dunston	.09	.07	.05
44	David Cone	.12	.09	.05
45	Andres Galarraga	.09	.07	.04
46	Mark Davis	.09	.07	.04
47	Barry Larkin	.12	.09	.05
48	Kevin Gross	.09	.07	.04
49	Vance Law	.09	.07	.04
50	Orel Hershiser	.20	.15	.08
51	Willie McGee	.09	.07	.04
52	Danny Jackson	.09	.07	.04
53	Rafael Palmeiro	.20	.15	.08
54	Bob Knepper	.09	.07	.04
55	Lance Parrish	.09	.07	.04
56	Greg Maddux	.15	.11	.06
57	Gerald Perry	.09	.07	.04
58	Bob Walk	.09	.07	.04
59	Chris Sabo	.12	.09	.04
60	Todd Worrell	.09	.07	.04
61	Andy Van Slyke	.12	.09	.04
62	Ozzie Smith	.20	.15	.08
63	Riverfront Stadium	.09	.07	.04
64	NL Checklist	.09	.07	.04

		MT	NR MT	EX
10	Andy Van Slyke	.15	.11	.06
11	Dave Winfield	.20	.15	.08
12	Kevin Gross	.15	.11	.06
13	Mike Greenwell	.30	.25	.12
14	Ozzie Smith	.20	.15	.08
15	Cal Ripken	.50	.40	.20
16	Andres Galarraga	.15	.11	.06
17	Alan Trammell	.25	.20	.10
18	Kal Daniels	.20	.15	.08
19	Fred McGriff	.35	.25	.14
20	Tony Gwynn	.30	.25	.12
21	Wally Joyner	.30	.25	.12
22	Will Clark	.75	.55	.30
23	Ozzie Guillen	.15	.11	.06
24	Gerald Perry	.15	.11	.06
25	Alvin Davis	.15	.11	.06
26	Ruben Sierra	.25	.20	.10

1989 Donruss Baseball's Best

For the second consecutive year, Donruss issued a "Baseball's Best" set in 1989 to highlight the game's top players. The special 336-card set was packaged in a special box and was sold at various retail chains nationwide following the conclusion of the 1989 baseball season. The cards are styled after the regular 1989 Donruss set with green borders and a glossy finish. The set included a Warren Spahn puzzle.

1989 Donruss MVP

This 26-card set, numbered BC-1 through BC-26, was randomly packed in Donruss wax packs, but were not included in factory sets or other card packs. Players highlighted in this set are selected by Donruss, one player per team. MVP cards feature a variation of the design in the basic Donruss issue, with multi-color upper and lower borders and black side borders. The player name and Donruss '89 logos appear in the upper margin with the team logo appearing lower right. The "MVP" designation in large, bright letters serves as a backdrop for the full-color player photo. The cards measure 2-1/2" by 3-1/2" in size.

		MT	NR MT	EX
Complete Set:		4.00	3.00	1.50
Common Player:		.15	.11	.06
1	Kirby Puckett	.50	.40	.20
2	Mike Scott	.15	.11	.06
3	Joe Carter	.30	.25	.12
4	Orel Hershiser	.25	.20	.10
5	Jose Canseco	.75	.55	.30
6	Darryl Strawberry	.60	.45	.25
7	George Brett	.35	.25	.14
8	Andre Dawson	.25	.20	.10
9	Paul Molitor	.20	.15	.08

		MT	NR MT	EX
Complete Set:		20.00	15.00	8.00
Common Player:		.05	.04	.02
1	Don Mattingly	1.00	.70	.40
2	Tom Glavine	.15	.11	.06
3	Bert Blyleven	.08	.06	.03
4	Andre Dawson	.10	.08	.04
5	Pete O'Brien	.05	.04	.02
6	Eric Davis	.40	.30	.15
7	George Brett	.10	.08	.04
8	Glenn Davis	.10	.08	.04
9	Ellis Burks	.30	.25	.12
10	Kirk Gibson	.08	.06	.03
11	Carlton Fisk	.08	.06	.03
12	Andres Galarraga	.08	.06	.03
13	Alan Trammell	.06	.05	.02
14	Dwight Gooden	.30	.25	.12
15	Paul Molitor	.10	.08	.04
16	Roger McDowell	.05	.04	.02
17	Doug Drabek	.05	.04	.02
18	Kent Hrbek	.08	.06	.03
19	Vince Coleman	.08	.06	.03
20	Steve Sax	.08	.06	.03
21	Roberto Alomar	.30	.25	.12
22	Carney Lansford	.06	.05	.02
23	Will Clark	1.50	1.25	.60
24	Alvin Davis	.08	.06	.03
25	Bobby Thigpen	.08	.06	.03
26	Ryne Sandberg	.60	.45	.25
27	Devon White	.08	.06	.03
28	Mike Greenwell	.40	.30	.15
29	Dale Murphy	.10	.08	.04
30	Jeff Ballard	.10	.08	.04
31	Kelly Gruber	.08	.06	.03
32	Julio Franco	.15	.11	.06

#	Name	MT	NR MT	EX
33	Bobby Bonilla	.15	.11	.06
34	Tim Wallach	.05	.04	.02
35	Lou Whitaker	.07	.05	.03
36	Jay Howell	.07	.05	.03
37	Greg Maddux	.30	.25	.12
38	Bill Doran	.07	.05	.03
39	Danny Tartabull	.12	.09	.05
40	Darryl Strawberry	.50	.40	.20
41	Ron Darling	.10	.08	.06
42	Tony Gwynn	.30	.25	.12
43	Mark McGwire	.40	.30	.15
44	Ozzie Smith	.15	.11	.06
45	Andy Van Slyke	.12	.09	.05
46	Juan Berenguer	.05	.04	.02
47	Von Hayes	.08	.06	.03
48	Tony Fernandez	.12	.09	.05
49	Eric Plunk	.05	.04	.02
50	Ernest Riles	.05	.04	.02
51	Harold Reynolds	.07	.05	.03
52	Andy Hawkins	.06	.05	.02
53	Robin Yount	.35	.25	.14
54	Danny Jackson	.06	.05	.02
55	Nolan Ryan	1.25	.90	.50
56	Joe Carter	.12	.09	.05
57	Jose Canseco	1.00	.70	.40
58	Jody Davis	.05	.04	.02
59	Lance Parrish	.06	.05	.02
60	Mitch Williams	.15	.11	.06
61	Brook Jacoby	.06	.05	.02
62	Tom Browning	.10	.08	.06
63	Kurt Stillwell	.06	.05	.02
64	Rafael Ramirez	.05	.04	.02
65	Roger Clemens	.50	.40	.20
66	Mike Scioscia	.07	.05	.02
67	Dave Gallagher	.07	.05	.02
68	Mark Langston	.15	.11	.06
69	Chet Lemon	.06	.05	.02
70	Kevin McReynolds	.25	.20	.10
71	Rob Deer	.06	.05	.02
72	Tommy Herr	.07	.05	.03
73	Barry Bonds	.12	.09	.05
74	Frank Viola	.15	.11	.06
75	Pedro Guerrero	.15	.11	.06
76	Dave Righetti	.07	.05	.02
77	Bruce Hurst	.08	.06	.03
78	Rickey Henderson	.40	.30	.15
79	Robby Thompson	.08	.06	.03
80	Randy Johnson	.25	.20	.10
81	Harold Baines	.12	.09	.05
82	Calvin Schiraldi	.05	.04	.02
83	Kirk McCaskill	.05	.04	.02
84	Lee Smith	.07	.05	.03
85	John Smoltz	.25	.20	.10
86	Mickey Tettleton	.20	.15	.08
87	Jimmy Key	.08	.06	.03
88	Rafael Palmeiro	.10	.08	.04
89	Sid Bream	.05	.04	.02
90	Dennis Martinez	.05	.04	.02
91	Frank Tanana	.05	.04	.02
92	Eddie Murray	.15	.11	.06
93	Shawon Dunston	.15	.11	.06
94	Mike Scott	.10	.08	.04
95	Bret Saberhagen	.25	.20	.10
96	David Cone	.20	.15	.08
97	Kevin Elster	.05	.04	.02
98	Jack Clark	.20	.15	.08
99	Dave Stewart	.20	.15	.08
100	Jose Oquendo	.06	.05	.02
101	Jose Lind	.05	.04	.02
102	Gary Gaetti	.12	.09	.05
103	Ricky Jordan	.25	.20	.10
104	Fred McGriff	.50	.40	.20
105	Don Slaught	.05	.04	.02
106	Jose Uribe	.05	.04	.02
107	Jeffrey Leonard	.07	.05	.02
108	Lee Guetterman	.05	.04	.02
109	Chris Bosio	.08	.06	.03
110	Barry Larkin	.15	.11	.06
111	Ruben Sierra	.30	.25	.12
112	Greg Swindell	.12	.09	.05
113	Gary Sheffield	.40	.30	.15
114	Lonnie Smith	.10	.08	.04
115	Chili Davis	.08	.06	.03
116	Damon Berryhill	.08	.06	.03
117	Tom Candiotti	.05	.04	.02
118	Kal Daniels	.10	.08	.04
119	Mark Gubicza	.10	.08	.04
120	Jim Deshaies	.08	.06	.03
121	Dwight Evans	.10	.08	.04
122	Mike Morgan	.05	.04	.02
123	Dan Pasqua	.05	.04	.02

#	Name	MT	NR MT	EX
124	Bryn Smith	.07	.05	.03
125	Doyle Alexander	.07	.05	.03
126	Howard Johnson	.25	.20	.10
127	Chuck Crim	.07	.05	.03
128	Darren Daulton	.05	.04	.02
129	Jeff Robinson	.08	.06	.03
130	Kirby Puckett	.50	.40	.20
131	Joe Magrane	.10	.08	.04
132	Jesse Barfield	.07	.05	.03
133	Mark Davis (Photo actually Dave Leiper)	.25	.20	.10
134	Dennis Eckersley	.10	.08	.04
135	Mike Krukow	.05	.04	.02
136	Jay Buhner	.10	.08	.04
137	Ozzie Guillen	.08	.06	.03
138	Rick Sutcliffe	.12	.09	.05
139	Wally Joyner	.25	.20	.10
140	Wade Boggs	.60	.45	.25
141	Jeff Treadway	.08	.06	.05
142	Cal Ripken	.30	.25	.12
143	Dave Steib	.10	.08	.04
144	Pete Incaviglia	.07	.05	.03
145	Bob Walk	.05	.04	.02
146	Nelson Santovenia	.10	.08	.04
147	Mike Heath	.05	.04	.02
148	Willie Randolph	.08	.06	.03
149	Paul Kilgus	.05	.04	.02
150	Billy Hatcher	.07	.05	.03
151	Steve Farr	.05	.04	.02
152	Gregg Jefferies	.40	.30	.15
153	Randy Myers	.06	.05	.02
154	Garry Templeton	.06	.05	.02
155	Walt Weiss	.10	.08	.04
156	Terry Pendleton	.10	.08	.04
157	John Smiley	.08	.06	.03
158	Greg Gagne	.05	.04	.02
159	Lenny Dykstra	.08	.06	.03
160	Nelson Liriano	.05	.04	.02
161	Alvaro Espinoza	.10	.08	.04
162	Rick Reuschel	.08	.06	.03
163	Omar Vizquel	.15	.11	.06
164	Clay Parker	.15	.11	.06
165	Dan Plesac	.06	.05	.02
166	John Franco	.06	.05	.02
167	Scott Fletcher	.06	.05	.02
168	Cory Snyder	.12	.09	.05
169	Bo Jackson	1.00	.70	.40
170	Tommy Gregg	.08	.06	.03
171	Jim Abbott	.50	.40	.20
172	Jerome Walton	.50	.40	.20
173	Doug Jones	.06	.05	.02
174	Todd Benzinger	.08	.06	.03
175	Frank White	.08	.06	.03
176	Craig Biggio	.20	.15	.08
177	John Dopson	.10	.08	.06
178	Alfredo Griffin	.06	.05	.02
179	Melido Perez	.06	.05	.02
180	Tim Burke	.06	.05	.02
181	Matt Nokes	.10	.08	.04
182	Gary Carter	.10	.08	.04
183	Ted Higuera	.08	.06	.03
184	Ken Howell	.05	.04	.02
185	Rey Quinones	.05	.04	.02
186	Wally Backman	.07	.05	.03
187	Tom Brunansky	.07	.05	.03
188	Steve Balboni	.05	.04	.02
189	Marvell Wynne	.05	.04	.02
190	Dave Henderson	.08	.06	.03
191	Don Robinson	.05	.04	.02
192	Ken Griffey, Jr.	4.00	3.00	1.50
193	Ivan Calderon	.05	.04	.02
194	Mike Bielecki	.07	.05	.03
195	Johnny Ray	.07	.05	.03
196	Rob Murphy	.05	.04	.02
197	Andres Thomas	.05	.04	.02
198	Phil Bradley	.06	.05	.02
199	Junior Felix	.30	.25	.12
200	Jeff Russell	.08	.06	.03
201	Mike LaValliere	.05	.04	.02
202	Kevin Gross	.06	.05	.02
203	Keith Moreland	.06	.05	.02
204	Mike Marshall	.06	.05	.02
205	Dwight Smith	.30	.25	.12
206	Jim Clancy	.05	.04	.02
207	Kevin Seitzer	.10	.08	.04
208	Keith Hernandez	.10	.08	.04
209	Bob Ojeda	.06	.05	.02
210	Ed Whitson	.06	.05	.02
211	Tony Phillips	.06	.05	.02
212	Milt Thompson	.05	.04	.02
213	Randy Kramer	.05	.04	.02

		MT	NR MT	EX
214	Randy Bush	.05	.04	.02
215	Randy Ready	.05	.04	.02
216	Duane Ward	.05	.04	.02
217	Jimmy Jones	.05	.04	.02
218	Scott Garrelts	.08	.06	.03
219	Scott Bankhead	.10	.08	.04
220	Lance McCullers	.06	.05	.02
221	B.J. Surhoff	.06	.05	.02
222	Chris Sabo	.06	.05	.02
223	Steve Buechele	.06	.05	.02
224	Joel Skinner	.05	.04	.02
225	Orel Hershiser	.15	.11	.06
226	Derek Lilliquist	.10	.08	.06
227	Claudell Washington	.08	.06	.05
228	Lloyd McClendon	.10	.08	.04
229	Felix Fermin	.05	.04	.02
230	Paul O'Neill	.08	.06	.03
231	Charlie Leibrandt	.05	.04	.02
232	Dave Smith	.06	.05	.02
233	Bob Stanley	.05	.04	.02
234	Tim Belcher	.15	.11	.06
235	Eric King	.05	.04	.02
236	Spike Owen	.05	.04	.02
237	Mike Henneman	.05	.04	.02
238	Juan Samuel	.06	.05	.02
239	Greg Brock	.06	.05	.02
240	John Kruk	.06	.05	.02
241	Glenn Wilson	.06	.05	.02
242	Jeff Reardon	.06	.05	.02
243	Todd Worrell	.08	.06	.03
244	Dave LaPoint	.05	.04	.02
245	Walt Terrell	.05	.04	.02
246	Mike Moore	.08	.06	.03
247	Kelly Downs	.05	.04	.02
248	Dave Valle	.05	.04	.02
249	Ron Kittle	.06	.05	.04
250	Steve Wilson	.10	.08	.04
251	Dick Schofield	.05	.04	.02
252	Marty Barrett	.06	.05	.02
253	Dion James	.06	.05	.02
254	Bob Milacki	.10	.08	.04
255	Ernie Whitt	.06	.05	.02
256	Kevin Brown	.08	.06	.03
257	R.J. Reynolds	.05	.04	.02
258	Tim Raines	.10	.08	.04
259	Frank Williams	.05	.04	.02
260	Jose Gonzalez	.05	.04	.02
261	Mitch Webster	.05	.04	.02
262	Ken Caminiti	.07	.05	.03
263	Bob Boone	.07	.05	.03
264	Dave Magadan	.07	.05	.03
265	Rick Aguilera	.05	.04	.02
266	Chris James	.05	.04	.02
267	Bob Welch	.07	.05	.03
268	Ken Dayley	.05	.04	.02
269	Junior Ortiz	.05	.04	.02
270	Allan Anderson	.08	.06	.03
271	Steve Jeltz	.05	.04	.02
272	George Bell	.10	.08	.04
273	Roberto Kelly	.10	.08	.04
274	Brett Butler	.07	.05	.03
275	Mike Schooler	.07	.05	.02
276	Ken Phelps	.05	.04	.02
277	Glenn Braggs	.06	.05	.02
278	Jose Rijo	.06	.05	.02
279	Bobby Witt	.06	.05	.02
280	Jerry Browne	.06	.05	.02
281	Kevin Mitchell	.40	.30	.15
282	Craig Worthington	.15	.11	.06
283	Greg Minton	.05	.04	.02
284	Nick Esasky	.07	.05	.03
285	John Farrell	.05	.04	.02
286	Rick Mahler	.05	.04	.02
287	Tom Gordon	.40	.30	.15
288	Gerald Young	.05	.04	.02
289	Jody Reed	.08	.06	.03
290	Jeff Hamilton	.05	.04	.02
291	Gerald Perry	.05	.04	.02
292	Hubie Brooks	.05	.04	.02
293	Bo Diaz	.05	.04	.02
294	Terry Puhl	.05	.04	.02
295	Jim Gantner	.05	.04	.02
296	Jeff Parrett	.05	.04	.02
297	Mike Boddicker	.05	.04	.02
298	Dan Gladden	.05	.04	.02
299	Tony Pena	.07	.05	.03
300	Checklist	.05	.04	.02
301	Tom Henke	.05	.04	.02
302	Pascual Perez	.05	.04	.02
303	Steve Bedrosian	.05	.04	.02
304	Ken Hill	.10	.08	.04

		MT	NR MT	EX
305	Jerry Reuss	.07	.05	.03
306	Jim Eisenreich	.05	.04	.02
307	Jack Howell	.05	.04	.02
308	Rick Cerone	.05	.04	.02
309	Tim Leary	.05	.04	.02
310	Joe Orsulak	.05	.04	.02
311	Jim Dwyer	.05	.04	.02
312	Geno Petralli	.05	.04	.02
313	Rick Honeycutt	.05	.04	.02
314	Tom Foley	.05	.04	.02
315	Kenny Rogers	.10	.08	.04
316	Mike Flanagan	.06	.05	.02
317	Bryan Harvey	.06	.05	.02
318	Billy Ripken	.05	.04	.02
319	Jeff Montgomery	.05	.04	.02
320	Erik Hanson	.12	.09	.05
321	Brian Downing	.06	.05	.02
322	Gregg Olson	.40	.30	.15
323	Terry Steinbach	.12	.09	.05
324	Sammy Sosa	.40	.30	.15
325	Gene Harris	.05	.04	.02
326	Mike Devereaux	.10	.08	.04
327	Dennis Cook	.12	.09	.05
328	David Wells	.08	.06	.03
329	Checklist	.05	.04	.02
330	Kirt Manwaring	.10	.08	.04
331	Jim Presley	.05	.04	.02
332	Checklist	.05	.04	.02
333	Chuck Finley	.05	.04	.02
334	Rob Dibble	.08	.06	.03
335	Cecil Espy	.06	.05	.02
336	Dave Parker	.08	.06	.02

1990 Donruss MVP

This special 26-card set includes one player from each Major League team. Numbered BC-1 (the "BC" stands for "Bonus Card") through BC-26, the cards from this set were randomly packed in 1990 Donruss wax packs and were not available in factory sets or other types of packaging. The red-bordered cards are similar in design to the regular 1990 Donruss set, except the player photos are set against a special background made up of the "MVP" logo.

		MT	NR MT	EX
Complete Set:		4.00	3.00	1.50
Common Player:		.08	.06	.03
1	Bo Jackson	.30	.25	.12
2	Howard Johnson	.10	.08	.04
3	Dave Stewart	.08	.06	.03
4	Tony Gwynn	.15	.11	.06
5	Orel Hershiser	.10	.08	.04
6	Pedro Guerrero	.10	.08	.04
7	Tim Raines	.10	.08	.04
8	Kirby Puckett	.30	.25	.12
9	Alvin Davis	.08	.06	.03
10	Ryne Sandberg	.30	.25	.12
11	Kevin Mitchell	.20	.15	.08
12a	John Smoltz (photo of Tom Glavine)	2.00	1.50	.80
12b	John Smoltz (corrected)	.40	.30	.15
13	George Bell	.10	.08	.04
14	Julio Franco	.15	.11	.06
15	Paul Molitor	.10	.08	.04
16	Bobby Bonilla	.15	.11	.06
17	Mike Greenwell	.15	.11	.06

		MT	NR MT	EX
18	Cal Ripken	.30	.25	.12
19	Carlton Fisk	.12	.09	.05
20	Chili Davis	.08	.06	.03
21	Glenn Davis	.10	.08	.04
22	Steve Sax	.10	.08	.04
23	Eric Davis	.20	.15	.08
24	Greg Swindell	.08	.06	.03
25	Von Hayes	.08	.06	.03
26	Alan Trammell	.10	.08	.04

1990 Donruss

Donruss celebrated its 10th anniversary in the baseball card hobby with a 715-card set in 1990, up from the 660-card sets of previous years. The standard-size cards feature bright red borders with the player's name in script along the top. The 1990 set included 26 "Diamond Kings" and 20 "Rated Rookies," along with a Carl Yastrzemski puzzle.

		MT	NR MT	EX
	Complete Set:	18.00	13.50	7.25
	Common Player:	.04	.03	.02
1	Bo Jackson (DK)	.20	.15	.08
2	Steve Sax (DK)	.12	.09	.05
3a	Ruben Sierra (DK - missing line on top border)	1.00	.70	.40
3b	Ruben Sierra (DK)	.30	.25	.12
4	Ken Griffey, Jr. (DK)	.80	.60	.30
5	Mickey Tettleton (DK)	.12	.09	.05
6	Dave Stewart (DK)	.12	.09	.05
7	Jim Deshaies (DK)	.07	.05	.03
8	John Smoltz (DK)	.25	.20	.10
9	Mike Bielecki (DK)	.07	.05	.03
10a	Brian Downing DK (Reverse Negative)	1.00	.70	.40
10b	Brian Downing DK (Corrected)	.25	.20	.10
11	Kevin Mitchell (DK)	.35	.25	.14
12	Kelly Gruber (DK)	.08	.06	.03
13	Joe Magrane (DK)	.08	.06	.03
14	John Franco (DK)	.08	.06	.03
15	Ozzie Guillen (DK)	.08	.06	.03
16	Lou Whitaker (DK)	.08	.06	.03
17	John Smiley (DK)	.08	.06	.03
18	Howard Johnson (DK)	.30	.25	.12
19	Willie Randolph (DK)	.08	.06	.03
20	Chris Bosio (DK)	.07	.05	.03
21	Tommy Herr (DK)	.07	.05	.03
22	Dan Gladden (DK)	.07	.05	.03
23	Ellis Burks (DK)	.20	.15	.08
24	Pete O'Brien (DK)	.08	.06	.03
25	Bryn Smith (DK)	.07	.05	.03
26	Ed Whitson (DK)	.07	.05	.03
27	Checklist 1-27	.04	.03	.02
28	Robin Ventura (RR)(FC)	.80	.60	.30
29	Todd Zeile (RR)(FC)	.50	.40	.20
30	Sandy Alomar, Jr. (RR)	.35	.25	.14
31	Kent Mercker (RR)(FC)	.30	.25	.12
32	Ben McDonald (RR)(FC)	1.50	1.25	.60
33a	Juan Gonzalez RR (Reverse Negative)(FC)	4.00	3.00	1.50
33b	Juan Gonzalez RR (Corrected)(FC)	2.00	1.50	.80
34	Eric Anthony (RR)(FC)	.50	.40	.20
35	Mike Fetters (RR)(FC)	.20	.15	.08
36	Marquis Grissom (RR)(FC)	.60	.45	.25
37	Greg Vaughn (RR)(FC)	.50	.40	.20

		MT	NR MT	EX
38	Brian Dubois (RR)(FC)	.15	.11	.06
39	Steve Avery (RR)(FC)	.60	.45	.25
40	Mark Gardner (RR)(FC)	.20	.15	.08
41	Andy Benes (RR)(FC)	.40	.30	.15
42	Delino Deshields (RR)(FC)	.80	.60	.30
43	Scott Coolbaugh (RR)(FC)	.15	.11	.06
44	Pat Combs (RR)(FC)	.25	.20	.10
45	Alex Sanchez (RR)	.15	.11	.06
46	Kelly Mann (RR)(FC)	.20	.15	.08
47	Julio Machado (RR)(FC)	.20	.15	.08
48	Pete Incaviglia	.05	.04	.02
49	Shawon Dunston	.07	.05	.03
50	Jeff Treadway	.05	.04	.02
51	Jeff Ballard	.10	.08	.04
52	Claudell Washington	.08	.06	.03
53	Juan Samuel	.10	.08	.04
54	John Smiley	.08	.06	.03
55	Rob Deer	.06	.05	.02
56	Geno Petralli	.04	.03	.02
57	Chris Bosio	.10	.08	.04
58	Carlton Fisk	.12	.09	.05
59	Kirt Manwaring	.10	.08	.04
60	Chet Lemon	.06	.05	.02
61	Bo Jackson	.30	.25	.12
62	Doyle Alexander	.05	.04	.02
63	Pedro Guerrero	.12	.09	.05
64	Allan Anderson	.07	.05	.03
65	Greg Harris	.07	.05	.03
66	Mike Greenwell	.25	.20	.10
67	Walt Weiss	.08	.06	.03
68	Wade Boggs	.30	.25	.12
69	Jim Clancy	.04	.03	.02
70	Junior Felix	.20	.15	.08
71	Barry Larkin	.12	.09	.05
72	Dave LaPoint	.05	.04	.02
73	Joel Skinner	.04	.03	.02
74	Jesse Barfield	.08	.06	.03
75	Tommy Herr	.08	.06	.03
76	Ricky Jordan	.20	.15	.08
77	Eddie Murray	.15	.11	.06
78	Steve Sax	.10	.08	.04
79	Tim Belcher	.10	.08	.04
80	Danny Jackson	.06	.05	.02
81	Kent Hrbek	.10	.08	.04
82	Milt Thompson	.05	.04	.02
83	Brook Jacoby	.07	.05	.03
84	Mike Marshall	.08	.06	.03
85	Kevin Seitzer	.12	.09	.05
86	Tony Gwynn	.15	.11	.06
87	Dave Steib	.08	.06	.03
88	Dave Smith	.06	.05	.02
89	Bret Saberhagen	.15	.11	.06
90	Alan Trammell	.10	.08	.04
91	Tony Phillips	.05	.04	.03
92	Doug Drabek	.05	.04	.03
93	Jeffrey Leonard	.09	.07	.04
94	Wally Joyner	.15	.11	.06
95	Carney Lansford	.09	.07	.04
96	Cal Ripken	.15	.11	.06
97	Andres Galarraga	.15	.11	.06
98	Kevin Mitchell	.30	.25	.12
99	Howard Johnson	.15	.11	.06
100	Checklist	.04	.03	.02
101	Melido Perez	.07	.05	.03
102	Spike Owen	.05	.04	.02
103	Paul Molitor	.10	.08	.04
104	Geronimo Berroa	.06	.05	.02
105	Ryne Sandberg	.25	.20	.10
106	Bryn Smith	.06	.05	.02
107	Steve Buechele	.04	.03	.02
108	Jim Abbott	.30	.25	.12
109	Alvin Davis	.10	.08	.04
110	Lee Smith	.05	.04	.02
111	Roberto Alomar	.15	.11	.06
112	Rick Reuschel	.09	.07	.04
113	Kelly Gruber	.09	.07	.04
114	Joe Carter	.09	.07	.04
115	Jose Rijo	.06	.05	.02
116	Greg Minton	.04	.03	.02
117	Bob Ojeda	.04	.03	.02
118	Glenn Davis	.08	.06	.03
119	Jeff Reardon	.05	.04	.02
120	Kurt Stillwell	.05	.04	.02
121	John Smoltz	.15	.11	.06
122	Dwight Evans	.08	.06	.03
123	Eric Yelding	.08	.06	.03
124	John Franco	.05	.04	.02
125	Jose Canseco	.50	.40	.20
126	Barry Bonds	.25	.20	.10
127	Lee Guetterman	.04	.03	.02
128	Jack Clark	.10	.08	.04

		MT	NR MT	EX			MT	NR MT	EX
129	Dave Valle	.04	.03	.02	220	Tim Wallach	.08	.06	.03
130	Hubie Brooks	.05	.04	.02	221	Chuck Crim	.04	.03	.02
131	Ernest Riles	.04	.03	.02	222	Lonnie Smith	.08	.06	.03
132	Mike Morgan	.04	.03	.02	223	Andre Dawson	.10	.08	.04
133	Steve Jeltz	.04	.03	.02	224	Nelson Santovenia	.07	.05	.03
134	Jeff Robinson	.05	.04	.02	225	Rafael Palmeiro	.07	.05	.03
135	Ozzie Guillen	.05	.04	.02	226	Devon White	.07	.05	.03
136	Chili Davis	.06	.05	.02	227	Harold Reynolds	.07	.05	.03
137	Mitch Webster	.04	.03	.02	228	Ellis Burks	.15	.11	.06
138	Jerry Browne	.06	.05	.02	229	Mark Parent	.04	.03	.02
139	Bo Diaz	.04	.03	.02	230	Will Clark	.40	.30	.15
140	Robby Thompson	.07	.05	.03	231	Jimmy Key	.08	.06	.03
141	Craig Worthington	.09	.07	.04	232	John Farrell	.04	.03	.02
142	Julio Franco	.09	.07	.04	233	Eric Davis	.30	.25	.12
143	Brian Holman	.05	.04	.02	234	Johnny Ray	.05	.04	.02
144	George Brett	.10	.08	.04	235	Darryl Strawberry	.30	.25	.12
145	Tom Glavine	.10	.08	.04	236	Bill Doran	.05	.04	.02
146	Robin Yount	.20	.15	.08	237	Greg Gagne	.05	.04	.02
147	Gary Carter	.06	.05	.02	238	Jim Eisenreich	.04	.03	.02
148	Ron Kittle	.06	.05	.02	239	Tommy Gregg	.06	.05	.02
149	Tony Fernandez	.07	.05	.03	240	Marty Barrett	.05	.04	.02
150	Dave Stewart	.07	.05	.03	241	Rafael Ramirez	.05	.04	.02
151	Gary Gaetti	.07	.05	.03	242	Chris Sabo	.10	.08	.04
152	Kevin Elster	.04	.03	.02	243	Dave Henderson	.07	.05	.03
153	Gerald Perry	.05	.04	.02	244	Andy Van Slyke	.07	.05	.03
154	Jesse Orosco	.05	.04	.02	245	Alvaro Espinoza	.10	.07	.04
155	Wally Backman	.05	.04	.02	246	Garry Templeton	.06	.05	.02
156	Dennis Martinez	.05	.04	.02	247	Gene Harris	.04	.03	.02
157	Rick Sutcliffe	.08	.06	.03	248	Kevin Gross	.05	.04	.02
158	Greg Maddux	.12	.09	.05	249	Brett Butler	.09	.07	.04
159	Andy Hawkins	.05	.04	.02	250	Willie Randolph	.07	.05	.03
160	John Kruk	.05	.04	.02	251	Roger McDowell	.05	.04	.02
161	Jose Oquendo	.05	.04	.02	252	Rafael Belliard	.04	.03	.02
162	John Dopson	.08	.06	.03	253	Steve Rosenberg	.04	.03	.02
163	Joe Magrane	.08	.06	.03	254	Jack Howell	.04	.03	.02
164	Billy Ripken	.04	.03	.02	255	Marvell Wynne	.04	.03	.02
165	Fred Manrique	.04	.03	.02	256	Tom Candiotti	.05	.04	.02
166	Nolan Ryan	.40	.30	.15	257	Todd Benzinger	.05	.04	.02
167	Damon Berryhill	.06	.05	.02	258	Don Robinson	.04	.03	.02
168	Dale Murphy	.09	.07	.04	259	Phil Bradley	.08	.06	.03
169	Mickey Tettleton	.08	.06	.03	260	Cecil Espy	.05	.04	.02
170	Kirk McCaskill	.05	.04	.02	261	Scott Bankhead	.05	.04	.02
171	Dwight Gooden	.15	.11	.06	262	Frank White	.07	.05	.03
172	Jose Lind	.04	.03	.02	263	Andres Thomas	.05	.04	.02
173	B.J. Surhoff	.07	.05	.03	264	Glenn Braggs	.05	.04	.02
174	Ruben Sierra	.15	.11	.06	265	David Cone	.10	.08	.04
175	Dan Plesac	.08	.06	.03	266	Bobby Thigpen	.07	.05	.03
176	Dan Pasqua	.05	.04	.02	267	Nelson Liriano	.04	.03	.02
177	Kelly Downs	.05	.04	.02	268	Terry Steinbach	.09	.07	.04
178	Matt Nokes	.08	.06	.03	269	Kirby Puckett	.30	.25	.12
179	Luis Aquino	.04	.03	.02	270	Gregg Jefferies	.25	.20	.10
180	Frank Tanana	.04	.03	.02	271	Jeff Blauser	.05	.04	.02
181	Tony Pena	.07	.05	.03	272	Cory Snyder	.07	.05	.03
182	Dan Gladden	.05	.04	.02	273	Roy Smith	.05	.04	.02
183	Bruce Hurst	.05	.04	.02	274	Tom Foley	.04	.03	.02
184	Roger Clemens	.20	.15	.08	275	Mitch Williams	.09	.07	.04
185	Mark McGwire	.30	.25	.12	276	Paul Kilgus	.04	.03	.02
186	Rob Murphy	.04	.03	.02	277	Don Slaught	.04	.03	.02
187	Jim Deshaies	.06	.05	.02	278	Von Hayes	.08	.06	.03
188	Fred McGriff	.20	.15	.08	279	Vince Coleman	.10	.08	.04
189	Rob Dibble	.06	.05	.02	280	Mike Boddicker	.05	.04	.02
190	Don Mattingly	.40	.30	.15	281	Ken Dayley	.04	.03	.02
191	Felix Fermin	.04	.03	.02	282	Mike Devereaux	.07	.05	.03
192	Roberto Kelly	.08	.06	.03	283	*Kenny Rogers*	.09	.07	.04
193	Dennis Cook	.08	.06	.03	284	Jeff Russell	.07	.05	.04
194	Darren Daulton	.04	.03	.02	285	*Jerome Walton*	.15	.11	.06
195	Alfredo Griffin	.05	.04	.02	286	Derek Lilliquist	.08	.06	.03
196	Eric Plunk	.05	.04	.02	287	Joe Orsulak	.04	.03	.02
197	Orel Hershiser	.20	.15	.08	288	Dick Schofield	.04	.03	.02
198	Paul O'Neil	.07	.05	.03	289	Ron Darling	.09	.07	.04
199	Randy Bush	.04	.03	.02	290	Bobby Bonilla	.10	.07	.04
200	Checklist	.04	.03	.02	291	Jim Gantner	.05	.04	.02
201	Ozzie Smith	.10	.08	.04	292	Bobby Witt	.05	.04	.02
202	Pete O'Brien	.06	.05	.02	293	Greg Brock	.05	.04	.02
203	Jay Howell	.06	.05	.02	294	Ivan Calderon	.05	.04	.02
204	Mark Gibicza	.08	.06	.03	295	Steve Bedrosian	.06	.05	.02
205	Ed Whitson	.04	.03	.02	296	Mike Henneman	.06	.05	.02
206	George Bell	.09	.07	.04	297	Tom Gordon	.25	.20	.10
207	Mike Scott	.09	.07	.04	298	Lou Whitaker	.08	.06	.03
208	Charlie Leibrandt	.04	.03	.02	299	Terry Pendleton	.07	.05	.03
209	Mike Heath	.04	.03	.02	300	Checklist	.04	.03	.02
210	Dennis Eckersley	.09	.07	.04	301	Juan Berenguer	.04	.03	.02
211	Mike LaValliere	.04	.03	.02	302	Mark Davis	.09	.07	.05
212	Darnell Coles	.04	.03	.02	303	Nick Esasky	.09	.07	.05
213	Lance Parrish	.07	.05	.03	304	Rickey Henderson	.15	.11	.06
214	Mike Moore	.07	.05	.03	305	Rick Cerone	.04	.03	.02
215	*Steve Finley*	.20	.15	.08	306	Craig Biggio	.15	.11	.06
216	Tim Raines	.09	.07	.04	307	Duane Ward	.04	.03	.02
217	Scott Garrelts	.06	.05	.02	308	Tom Browning	.07	.05	.03
218	Kevin McReynolds	.09	.07	.04	309	Walt Terrell	.05	.04	.02
219	Dave Gallagher	.08	.06	.03	310	Greg Swindell	.10	.08	.04

		MT	NR MT	EX			MT	NR MT	EX
311	Dave Righetti	.07	.05	.03	402	Harold Baines	.09	.07	.04
312	Mike Maddux	.04	.03	.02	403	Cecilio Guante	.04	.03	.02
313	Lenny Dykstra	.07	.05	.03	404	Joe Girardi	.15	.11	.06
314	Jose Gonzalez	.08	.06	.03	405	*Sergio Valdez*(FC)	.30	.25	.12
315	Steve Balboni	.04	.03	.02	406	Mark Williamson	.04	.03	.02
316	Mike Scioscia	.07	.05	.02	407	Glenn Hoffman	.04	.03	.02
317	Ron Oester	.04	.03	.02	408	*Jeff Innis*(FC)	.10	.08	.04
318	*Gary Wayne*	.09	.07	.04	409	Randy Kramer	.04	.03	.02
319	Todd Worrell	.06	.05	.02	410	Charlie O'Brien(FC)	.04	.03	.02
320	Doug Jones	.05	.04	.02	411	Charlie Hough	.06	.05	.02
321	Jeff Hamilton	.05	.04	.02	412	Gus Polidor	.04	.03	.02
322	Danny Tartabull	.09	.07	.04	413	Ron Karkovice	.04	.03	.02
323	Chris James	.05	.04	.02	414	Trevor Wilson(FC)	.07	.05	.03
324	Mike Flanagan	.05	.04	.02	415	*Kevin Ritz*(FC)	.20	.15	.08
325	Gerald Young	.05	.04	.02	416	Gary Thurman	.04	.03	.02
326	Bob Boone	.09	.07	.04	417	Jeff Robinson	.04	.03	.02
327	Frank Williams	.04	.03	.02	418	Scott Terry	.05	.04	.02
328	Dave Parker	.09	.07	.04	419	Tim Laudner	.04	.03	.02
329	Sid Bream	.04	.03	.02	420	Dennis Rasmussen	.04	.03	.02
330	Mike Schooler	.06	.05	.02	421	Luis Rivera	.04	.03	.02
331	Bert Blyleven	.08	.06	.03	422	Jim Corsi(FC)	.07	.05	.03
332	Bob Welch	.07	.05	.03	423	Dennis Lamp	.04	.03	.02
333	Bob Milacki	.06	.05	.02	424	Ken Caminiti	.06	.05	.02
334	Tim Burke	.05	.04	.02	425	David Wells	.06	.05	.02
335	Jose Uribe	.05	.04	.02	426	Norm Charlton	.09	.07	.04
336	Randy Myers	.05	.04	.02	427	*Deion Sanders*	.50	.40	.20
337	Eric King	.04	.03	.02	428	Dion James	.05	.04	.02
338	Mark Langston	.12	.09	.05	429	Chuck Cary	.05	.04	.02
339	Ted Higuera	.08	.06	.03	430	Ken Howell	.04	.03	.02
340	Oddibe McDowell	.06	.05	.02	431	Steve Lake	.04	.03	.02
341	Lloyd McClendon	.07	.05	.03	432	Kal Daniels	.09	.07	.04
342	Pascual Perez	.05	.04	.02	433	Lance McCullers	.05	.04	.02
343	Kevin Brown	.08	.06	.03	434	Lenny Harris(FC)	.10	.08	.04
344	Chuck Finley	.05	.04	.02	435	*Scott Scudder*(FC)	.20	.15	.08
345	Erik Hanson	.09	.07	.05	436	Gene Larkin	.04	.03	.02
346	Rich Gedman	.05	.04	.02	437	Dan Quisenberry	.05	.04	.02
347	Bip Roberts	.10	.08	.04	438	*Steve Olin*(FC)	.15	.11	.06
348	Matt Williams	.20	.15	.08	439	Mickey Hatcher	.05	.04	.02
349	Tom Henke	.05	.04	.02	440	Willie Wilson	.05	.04	.02
350	Brad Komminsk	.05	.04	.02	441	Mark Grant	.05	.04	.02
351	Jeff Reed	.04	.03	.02	442	Mookie Wilson	.07	.05	.03
352	Brian Downing	.05	.04	.02	443	Alex Trevino	.04	.03	.02
353	Frank Viola	.09	.07	.04	444	Pat Tabler	.05	.04	.02
354	Terry Puhl	.05	.04	.02	445	Dave Bergman	.04	.03	.02
355	Brian Harper	.05	.04	.02	446	Todd Burns	.04	.03	.02
356	Steve Farr	.05	.04	.02	447	R.J. Reynolds	.04	.03	.02
357	Joe Boever	.05	.04	.02	448	Jay Buhner	.08	.06	.03
358	Danny Heep	.04	.03	.02	449	*Lee Stevens*(FC)	.20	.15	.08
359	Larry Andersen	.04	.03	.02	450	Ron Hassey	.04	.03	.02
360	Rolando Roomes	.10	.08	.04	451	Bob Melvin	.04	.03	.02
361	Mike Gallego	.05	.04	.02	452	Dave Martinez	.05	.04	.02
362	Bob Kipper	.04	.03	.02	453	*Greg Litton*(FC)	.15	.11	.06
363	Clay Parker	.07	.05	.03	454	Mark Carreon	.10	.07	.04
364	Mike Pagliarulo	.05	.04	.02	455	Scott Fletcher	.05	.04	.02
365	Ken Griffey, Jr.	1.00	.70	.40	456	Otis Nixon	.04	.03	.02
366	Rex Hudler	.04	.03	.02	457	*Tony Fossas*(FC)	.10	.08	.04
367	Pat Sheridan	.04	.03	.02	458	John Russell	.04	.03	.02
368	Kirk Gibson	.09	.07	.04	459	Paul Assenmacher	.04	.03	.02
369	Jeff Parrett	.05	.04	.02	460	Zane Smith	.04	.03	.02
370	Bob Walk	.05	.04	.02	461	*Jack Daugherty*	.25	.20	.10
371	Ken Patterson	.04	.03	.02	462	*Rich Monteleone*(FC)	.15	.11	.06
372	Bryan Harvey	.05	.04	.02	463	Greg Briley(FC)	.25	.20	.10
373	Mike Bielecki	.07	.05	.03	464	Mike Smithson	.04	.03	.02
374	*Tom Magrann*(FC)	.12	.09	.05	465	Benito Santiago	.09	.07	.04
375	Rick Mahler	.05	.04	.02	466	*Jeff Brantley*	.10	.08	.04
376	Craig Lefferts	.05	.04	.02	467	Jose Nunez	.07	.05	.03
377	Gregg Olson	.20	.15	.08	468	Scott Bailes	.04	.03	.02
378	Jamie Moyer	.04	.03	.02	469	Ken Griffey	.06	.05	.02
379	Randy Johnson	.09	.07	.04	470	Bob McClure	.04	.03	.02
380	Jeff Montgomery	.06	.05	.02	471	Mackey Sasser	.04	.03	.02
381	Marty Clary	.06	.05	.02	472	Glenn Wilson	.04	.03	.02
382	*Bill Spiers*	.15	.11	.06	473	*Kevin Tapani*(FC)	.30	.25	.15
383	Dave Magadan	.06	.05	.02	474	Bill Buckner	.05	.04	.02
384	*Greg Hibbard*(FC)	.20	.15	.08	475	Ron Gant	.05	.04	.02
385	Ernie Whitt	.05	.04	.02	476	Kevin Romine(FC)	.05	.04	.02
386	Rick Honeycutt	.04	.03	.02	477	Juan Agosto	.04	.03	.02
387	Dave West	.08	.06	.03	478	Herm Winningham	.04	.03	.02
388	Keith Hernandez	.07	.05	.03	479	Storm Davis	.05	.04	.02
389	Jose Alvarez	.04	.03	.02	480	Jeff King(FC)	.09	.07	.04
390	Joey Belle(FC)	.70	.50	.30	481	*Kevin Mmahat*(FC)	.25	.20	.10
391	Rick Aguilera	.05	.04	.02	482	Carmelo Martinez	.05	.04	.02
392	Mike Fitzgerald	.04	.03	.02	483	*Omar Vizquel*	.10	.08	.04
393	*Dwight Smith*	.15	.11	.06	484	Jim Dwyer	.04	.03	.02
394	*Steve Wilson*	.09	.07	.04	485	Bob Knepper	.04	.03	.02
395	Bob Geren	.20	.15	.08	486	Dave Anderson	.04	.03	.02
396	Randy Ready	.04	.03	.02	487	Ron Jones	.09	.07	.04
397	Ken Hill	.07	.05	.03	488	Jay Bell	.05	.04	.02
398	Jody Reed	.05	.04	.02	489	*Sammy Sosa*(FC)	.35	.25	.14
399	Tom Brunansky	.07	.05	.03	490	*Kent Anderson*(FC)	.15	.11	.06
400	Checklist	.04	.03	.02	491	Domingo Ramos	.04	.03	.02
401	Rene Gonzales	.04	.03	.02	492	Dave Clark	.05	.04	.02

		MT	NR MT	EX			MT	NR MT	EX
493	Tim Birtsas	.04	.03	.02	584	Lee Mazzilli	.04	.03	.02
494	Ken Oberkfell	.04	.03	.02	585	Jeff Pico	.04	.03	.02
495	Larry Sheets	.04	.03	.02	586	*Joe Oliver*(FC)	.20	.15	.08
496	Jeff Kunkel	.04	.03	.02	587	Willie Fraser	.04	.03	.02
497	Jim Presley	.04	.03	.02	588	Puzzle Card	.04	.03	.02
498	Mike Macfarlane	.04	.03	.02	589	Kevin Bass	.06	.05	.03
499	Pete Smith	.05	.04	.02	590	John Moses	.04	.03	.02
500	Checklist	.04	.03	.02	591	Tom Pagnozzi	.04	.03	.02
501	Gary Sheffield	.35	.25	.14	592	*Tony Castillo*	.10	.08	.04
502	*Terry Bross*(FC)	.15	.11	.06	593	Jerald Clark	.06	.05	.03
503	*Jerry Kutzler*(FC)	.20	.15	.08	594	Dan Schatzeder	.04	.03	.02
504	Lloyd Moseby	.05	.04	.02	595	Luis Quinones	.04	.03	.02
505	Curt Young	.04	.03	.02	596	Pete Harnisch	.08	.06	.03
506	Al Newman	.04	.03	.02	597	Gary Redus	.04	.03	.02
507	Keith Miller	.04	.03	.02	598	Mel Hall	.05	.04	.02
508	*Mike Stanton*(FC)	.20	.15	.08	599	Rick Schu	.04	.03	.02
509	Rich Yett	.04	.03	.02	600	Checklist	.04	.03	.02
510	*Tim Drummond*(FC)	.20	.15	.08	601	Mike Kingery	.04	.03	.02
511	Joe Hesketh	.04	.03	.02	602	Terry Kennedy	.04	.03	.02
512	*Rick Wrona*	.10	.08	.04	603	Mike Sharperson	.06	.05	.02
513	Luis Salazar	.04	.03	.02	604	Don Carman	.04	.03	.02
514	Hal Morris	.06	.05	.02	605	Jim Gott	.05	.04	.03
515	Terry Mullholland	.07	.05	.03	606	Donn Pall	.05	.04	.03
516	John Morris	.05	.04	.02	607	Rance Mulliniks	.04	.03	.02
517	Carlos Quintana	.08	.06	.03	608	Curt Wilkerson	.04	.03	.02
518	Frank DiPino	.04	.03	.02	609	Mike Felder	.04	.03	.02
519	Randy Milligan	.06	.05	.02	610	Guillermo Hernandez	.04	.03	.02
520	Chad Kreuter	.07	.05	.03	611	Candy Maldonado	.05	.04	.02
521	Mike Jeffcoat	.04	.03	.02	612	Mark Thurmond	.04	.03	.02
522	Mike Harkey	.10	.08	.04	613	Rick Leach	.04	.03	.02
523	Andy Nezelek	.07	.05	.03	614	Jerry Reed	.04	.03	.02
524	Dave Schmidt	.04	.03	.02	615	Franklin Stubbs	.05	.04	.02
525	Tony Armas	.04	.03	.02	616	Billy Hatcher	.05	.04	.02
526	Barry Lyons	.04	.03	.02	617	Don August	.05	.04	.02
527	*Rick Reed*(FC)	.20	.15	.08	618	Tim Teufel	.04	.03	.02
528	Jerry Reuss	.06	.05	.02	619	Shawn Hillegas	.04	.03	.02
529	*Dean Palmer*(FC)	1.00	.70	.40	620	Manny Lee	.04	.03	.02
530	*Jeff Peterek*(FC)	.20	.15	.08	621	Gary Ward	.05	.04	.02
531	*Carlos Martinez*	.20	.15	.08	622	*Mark Guthrie*(FC)	.20	.15	.08
532	Atlee Hammaker	.05	.04	.02	623	Jeff Musselman	.05	.04	.02
533	Mike Brumley	.04	.03	.02	624	Mark Lemke	.07	.05	.03
534	Terry Leach	.04	.03	.02	625	Fernando Valenzuela	.07	.05	.03
535	*Doug Strange*(FC)	.20	.15	.08	626	*Paul Sorrento*(FC)	.25	.20	.10
536	Jose DeLeon	.05	.04	.02	627	Glenallen Hill	.20	.15	.08
537	Shane Rawley	.05	.04	.02	628	Les Lancaster	.05	.04	.03
538	Joey Cora(FC)	.10	.08	.04	629	Vance Law	.04	.03	.02
539	Eric Hetzel	.08	.06	.03	630	Randy Velarde(FC)	.10	.08	.04
540	Gene Nelson	.04	.03	.02	631	Todd Frohwirth	.04	.03	.02
541	Wes Gardner	.04	.03	.02	632	Willie McGee	.06	.05	.02
542	Mark Portugal	.04	.03	.02	633	Oil Can Boyd	.06	.05	.02
543	Al Leiter	.05	.04	.02	634	Cris Carpenter	.09	.07	.04
544	Jack Armstrong	.04	.03	.02	635	Brian Holton	.04	.03	.02
545	Greg Cadaret	.04	.03	.02	636	Tracy Jones	.05	.04	.02
546	Rod Nichols	.04	.03	.02	637	Terry Steinbach (AS)	.09	.07	.04
547	Luis Polonia	.05	.04	.02	638	Brady Anderson	.09	.07	.04
548	Charlie Hayes(FC)	.20	.15	.08	639	Jack Morris	.06	.05	.02
549	Dickie Thon	.04	.03	.02	640	*Jaime Navarro*(FC)	.30	.25	.12
550	Tim Crews	.04	.03	.02	641	Darrin Jackson	.05	.04	.02
551	Dave Winfield	.20	.15	.08	642	*Mike Dyer*(FC)	.20	.15	.08
552	Mike Davis	.04	.03	.02	643	Mike Schmidt	.40	.30	.15
553	Ron Robinson	.04	.03	.02	644	Henry Cotto	.04	.03	.02
554	Carmen Castillo	.04	.03	.02	645	John Cerutti	.05	.04	.02
555	John Costello	.04	.03	.02	646	*Francisco Cabrera*(FC)	.40	.30	.15
556	Bud Black	.04	.03	.02	647	Scott Sanderson	.05	.04	.02
557	Rick Dempsey	.04	.03	.02	648	Brian Meyer	.05	.04	.02
558	Jim Acker	.04	.03	.02	649	Ray Searage	.05	.04	.02
559	Eric Show	.06	.05	.02	650a	Bo Jackson AS (Recent Major League			
560	Pat Borders	.06	.05	.02		Performance on back)	1.50	1.25	.60
561	Danny Darwin	.04	.03	.02	650b	Bo Jackson AS (Corrected)	.50	.40	.20
562	*Rick Luecken*(FC)	.20	.15	.08	651	Steve Lyons	.04	.03	.02
563	Edwin Nunez	.05	.04	.02	652	Mike LaCoss	.04	.03	.02
564	Felix Jose	.09	.07	.04	653	Ted Power	.04	.03	.02
565	John Cangelosi	.04	.03	.02	654	Howard Johnson (AS)	.20	.15	.08
566	Billy Swift	.04	.03	.02	655	*Mauro Gozzo*(FC)	.15	.11	.06
567	Bill Schroeder	.04	.03	.02	656	*Mike Blowers*(FC)	.25	.20	.10
568	Stan Javier	.04	.03	.02	657	Paul Gibson	.05	.04	.02
569	Jim Traber	.04	.03	.02	658	Neal Heaton	.05	.04	.02
570	Wallace Johnson	.04	.03	.02	659a	5000 K (Nolan Ryan) (King card number			
571	Donell Nixon	.04	.03	.02		665 back)	9.00	6.75	3.50
572	Sid Fernandez	.08	.06	.03	659b	5000 K (Nolan Ryan) (Corrected)	1.00	.70	.40
573	Lance Johnson	.09	.07	.04	660a	Harold Baines (AS - recent major league			
574	Andy McGaffigan	.04	.03	.02		performance on back)	5.00	3.75	2.00
575	Mark Knudson	.04	.03	.02	660b	Harold Baines (AS - line through star on			
576	*Tommy Greene*(FC)	.30	.25	.12		front-incorrect back)	7.00	5.25	2.75
577	Mark Grace	.25	.20	.10	660c	Harold Baines (AS - Incorrect front and			
578	*Larry Walker*(FC)	.50	.40	.20		back)	7.00	5.25	2.75
579	Mike Stanley	.04	.03	.02	660d	Harold Baines (AS - Corrected)	.10	.08	.04
580	Mike Witt	.05	.04	.02	661	Gary Pettis	.05	.04	.02
581	Scott Bradley	.04	.03	.02	662	*Clint Zavaras*(FC)	.20	.15	.08
582	Greg Harris	.07	.05	.03	663	Rick Reuschel	.08	.06	.03
583	Kevin Hickey	.04	.03	.02	664	Alejandro Pena	.05	.04	.02

		MT	NR MT	EX
665a	King of Kings (Nolan Ryan) (5000 K card number 659 back)	10.00	7.50	4.00
665b	King of Kings (Nolan Ryan) (Corrected)	1.00	.70	.40
665c	King of Kings (Nolan Ryan) (No card #)	5.00	3.75	2.00
666	Ricky Horton	.04	.03	.02
667	Curt Schilling	.06	.05	.02
668	Bill Landrum(FC)	.05	.04	.02
669	Todd Stottlemyre	.05	.04	.02
670	Tim Leary	.05	.04	.02
671	*John Wetteland*(FC)	.30	.25	.12
672	Calvin Schiraldi	.04	.03	.02
673	Ruben Sierra (AS)	.09	.07	.04
674	Pedro Guerrero (AS)	.09	.07	.04
675	Ken Phelps	.04	.03	.02
676	Cal Ripken (AS)	.09	.07	.04
677	Denny Walling	.04	.03	.02
678	Goose Gossage	.04	.03	.02
679	*Gary Mielke*(FC)	.20	.15	.08
680	Bill Bathe	.04	.03	.02
681	Tom Lawless	.04	.03	.02
682	*Xavier Hernandez*(FC)	.20	.15	.08
683	Kirby Puckett (AS)	.09	.07	.04
684	Mariano Duncan	.05	.04	.02
685	Ramon Martinez	.10	.08	.04
686	Tim Jones	.05	.04	.02
687	Tom Filer	.04	.03	.02
688	Steve Lombardozzi	.04	.03	.02
689	*Bernie Williams*(FC)	.50	.40	.20
690	*Chip Hale*(FC)	.15	.11	.06
691	*Beau Allred*(FC)	.15	.11	.06
692	Ryne Sandberg (AS)	.09	.07	.04
693	*Jeff Huson*(FC)	.25	.20	.10
694	Curt Ford	.04	.03	.02
695	Eric Davis (AS)	.09	.07	.04
696	Scott Lusader	.05	.04	.02
697	Mark McGwire (AS)	.09	.07	.04
698	*Steve Cummings*(FC)	.15	.11	.06
699	*George Canale*(FC)	.15	.11	.06
700	Checklist	.04	.03	.02
701	Julio Franco (AS)	.09	.07	.04
702	*Dave Johnson*(FC)	.10	.08	.04
703	Dave Stewart (AS)	.08	.06	.03
704	*Dave Justice*(FC)	2.50	2.00	1.00
705	Tony Gwynn (AS)	.09	.07	.04
706	Greg Myers	.06	.05	.02
707	Will Clark (AS)	.15	.11	.06
708	Benito Santiago (AS)	.08	.06	.03
709	Larry McWilliams	.04	.03	.02
710	Ozzie Smith (AS)	.08	.06	.03
711	*John Olerud*(FC)	.70	.50	.30
712	Wade Boggs (AS)	.09	.07	.04
713	*Gary Eave*(FC)	.15	.11	.06
714	Bob Tewksbury	.05	.04	.02
715	Kevin Mitchell (AS)	.09	.07	.04
716	A. Bartlett Giamatti	.35	.25	.14

		MT	NR MT	EX
	Complete Set:	12.00	9.00	4.75
	Common Player:	.04	.03	.02
1	Ken Griffey,Jr.	1.50	1.25	.90
2	Bob Milacki	.04	.03	.02
3	Mike Boddicker	.06	.05	.02
4	Bert Blyleven	.08	.06	.03
5	Carlton Fisk	.10	.08	.04
6	Greg Swindell	.06	.05	.02
7	Alan Trammell	.10	.08	.04
8	Mark Davis	.05	.04	.02
9	Chris Bosio	.04	.03	.02
10	Gary Gaetti	.10	.08	.04
11	Matt Nokes	.06	.05	.02
12	Dennis Eckersley	.10	.08	.04
13	Kevin Brown	.08	.06	.03
14	Tom Henke	.06	.05	.02
15	Mickey Tettleton	.08	.06	.03
16	Jody Reed	.08	.06	.03
17	Mark Langston	.08	.06	.03
18	Melido Perez	.06	.05	.02
19	John Farrell	.04	.03	.02
20	Tony Phillips	.04	.03	.02
21	Bret Saberhagen	.10	.08	.04
22	Robin Yount	.10	.08	.04
23	Kirby Puckett	.15	.11	.06
24	Steve Sax	.10	.08	.04
25	Dave Stewart	.10	.08	.04
26	Alvin Davis	.08	.06	.03
27	Geno Petralli	.04	.03	.02
28	Mookie Wilson	.05	.04	.02
29	Jeff Ballard	.04	.03	.02
30	Ellis Burks	.10	.08	.04
31	Wally Joyner	.08	.06	.03
32	Bobby Thigpen	.10	.08	.04
33	Keith Hernandez	.06	.05	.02
34	Jack Morris	.06	.05	.02
35	George Brett	.10	.08	.04
36	Dan Plesac	.08	.06	.03
37	Brian Harper	.05	.04	.02
38	Don Mattingly	.25	.20	.10
39	Dave Henderson	.08	.06	.03
40	Scott Bankhead	.06	.05	.02
41	Rafael Palmeiro	.10	.08	.04
42	Jimmy Key	.06	.05	.02
43	Gregg Olson	.10	.08	.04
44	Tony Pena	.06	.05	.02
45	Jack Howell	.04	.03	.02
46	Eric King	.04	.03	.02
47	Cory Snyder	.06	.05	.02
48	Frank Tanana	.04	.03	.02
49	Nolan Ryan	.60	.45	.25
50	Bob Boone	.06	.05	.02
51	Dave Parker	.10	.08	.04
52	Allan Anderson	.04	.03	.02
53	Tim Leary	.05	.04	.02
54	Mark McGwire	.25	.20	.10
55	Dave Valle	.04	.03	.02
56	Fred McGriff	.25	.20	.10
57	Cal Ripken	.15	.11	.06
58	Roger Clemens	.30	.25	.12
59	Lance Parrish	.08	.06	.03
60	Robin Ventura	.30	.25	.12
61	Doug Jones	.08	.06	.03
62	Lloyd Moseby	.06	.05	.02
63	Bo Jackson	.80	.60	.30
64	Paul Molitor	.08	.06	.03
65	Kent Hrbek	.08	.06	.03
66	Mel Hall	.04	.03	.02
67	Bob Welch	.10	.08	.04
68	Erik Hanson	.10	.08	.04
69	Harold Baines	.08	.06	.03
70	Junior Felix	.10	.08	.04
71	Craig Worthington	.06	.05	.02
72	Jeff Reardon	.08	.06	.03
73	Johnny Ray	.05	.04	.02
74	Ozzie Guillen	.10	.08	.04
75	Brook Jacoby	.08	.06	.03
76	Chet Lemon	.05	.04	.02
77	Mark Gubicza	.08	.06	.03
78	B.J. Surhoff	.08	.06	.03
79	Rick Aguilera	.05	.04	.02
80	Pascual Perez	.04	.03	.02
81	Jose Canseco	.70	.50	.30
82	Mike Schooler	.08	.06	.03
83	Jeff Huson	.12	.09	.05
84	Kelly Gruber	.15	.11	.06
85	Randy Milligan	.08	.06	.03
86	Wade Boggs	.35	.25	.14
87	Dave Winfield	.20	.15	.08

1990 Donruss A.L. Best

This 144-card set features the top players of the American League. The cards measure 2-1/2" by 3-1/2" and feature the same card front design as the regular Donruss set with the exception of having blue borders instead of red. The card backs feature a yellow frame with complete statistics and biographical information provided. 1990 marks the first year that Donruss divided its baseball best issue into two sets designated by league.

		MT	NR MT	EX
88	Scott Fletcher	.04	.03	.02
89	Tom Candiotti	.04	.03	.02
90	Mike Heath	.04	.03	.02
91	Kevin Seitzer	.08	.06	.03
92	Ted Higuera	.08	.06	.03
93	Kevin Tapani	.15	.11	.06
94	Roberto Kelly	.08	.06	.03
95	Walt Weiss	.06	.05	.02
96	Checklist	.04	.03	.02
97	Sandy Alomar	.30	.25	.12
98	Pete O'Brien	.05	.04	.02
99	Jeff Russell	.06	.05	.02
100	John Olerud	.50	.40	.20
101	Pete Harnisch	.05	.04	.02
102	Dwight Evans	.08	.06	.03
103	Chuck Finley	.08	.06	.03
104	Sammy Sosa	.25	.20	.10
105	Mike Henneman	.06	.05	.02
106	Kurt Stillwell	.06	.05	.02
107	Greg Vaughn	.30	.25	.12
108	Dan Gladden	.05	.04	.02
109	Jesse Barfield	.06	.05	.02
110	Willie Randolph	.06	.05	.02
111	Randy Johnson	.08	.06	.03
112	Julio Franco	.08	.06	.03
113	Tony Fernandez	.08	.06	.03
114	Ben McDonald	.50	.40	.20
115	Mike Greenwell	.20	.15	.08
116	Luis Polonia	.04	.03	.02
117	Carney Lansford	.06	.05	.02
118	Bud Black	.05	.04	.02
119	Lou Whitaker	.08	.06	.03
120	Jim Eisenreich	.04	.03	.02
121	Gary Sheffield	.25	.20	.10
122	Shane Mack	.08	.06	.03
123	Alvaro Espinoza	.04	.03	.02
124	Rickey Henderson	.40	.30	.15
125	Jeffrey Leonard	.05	.04	.02
126	Gary Pettis	.04	.03	.02
127	Dave Steib	.08	.06	.03
128	Danny Tartabull	.08	.06	.03
129	Joe Orsulak	.04	.03	.02
130	Tom Brunansky	.06	.05	.02
131	Dick Schofield	.04	.03	.02
132	Candy Maldonado	.06	.05	.02
133	Cecil Fielder	.30	.25	.12
134	Terry Shumpert	.20	.15	.08
135	Greg Gagne	.05	.04	.02
136	Dave Righetti	.08	.06	.03
137	Terry Steinbach	.06	.05	.02
138	Harold Reynolds	.08	.06	.03
139	George Bell	.08	.06	.03
140	Carlos Quintana	.06	.05	.02
141	Ivan Calderon	.08	.06	.03
142	Greg Brock	.04	.03	.02
143	Ruben Sierra	.15	.11	.06
144	Checklist	.04	.03	.02

Definitions for grading conditions are located in the Introduction of this price guide.

1990 Donruss Diamond Kings Supers

Donruss made this set available through a mail-in offer. Three wrappers, $10 and $2 for postage were necessary to obtain this set. The cards are exactly the same design as the regular Donruss Diamond Kings except they measure approximately 5" by 6-3/4" in size. The artwork of Dick Perez is featured.

		MT	NR MT	EX
Complete Set:		10.00	7.50	4.00
Common Player:		.10	.08	.04
1	Bo Jackson	1.25	.90	.50
2	Steve Sax	.15	.11	.06
3	Ruben Sierra	.35	.25	.12
4	Ken Griffey,Jr.	2.00	1.50	.80
5	Mickey Tettleton	.10	.08	.04
6	Dave Stewart	.20	.15	.08
7	Jim Deshaies	.10	.08	.04
8	John Smoltz	.20	.15	.08
9	Mike Bielecki	.10	.08	.04
10	Brian Downing	.10	.08	.04
11	Kevin Mitchell	.20	.15	.08
12	Kelly Gruber	.25	.20	.10
13	Joe Magrane	.15	.11	.06
14	John Franco	.15	.11	.06
15	Ozzie Guillen	.20	.15	.08
16	Lou Whitaker	.15	.11	.06
17	John Smiley	.10	.08	.04
18	Howard Johnson	.25	.20	.10
19	Willie Randolph	.10	.08	.04
20	Chris Bosio	.10	.08	.04
21	Tommy Herr	.10	.08	.04
22	Dan Gladden	.10	.08	.04
23	Ellis Burks	.20	.15	.08
24	Pete O'Brien	.10	.08	.04
25	Bryn Smith	.10	.08	.04
26	Ed Whitson	.10	.08	.04

1990 Donruss Learning Series

Cards from this 55-card set were released as a part of an educational tool. The cards are styled like the 1990 Donruss cards, but feature a special "learning series" logo on the front. The backs are printed horizontally and feature career highlights and statistics. The cards are also numbered on the back. The cards were not released directly to the hobby.

		MT	NR MT	EX
Complete Set:		80.00	60.00	30.00
Common Player:		.40	.30	.15
1	George Brett (DK)	2.50	2.00	1.00
2	Kevin Mitchell	1.50	1.25	.60
3	Andy Van Slyke	.80	.60	.30
4	Benito Santiago	.80	.60	.30
5	Gary Carter	1.25	.90	.50
6	Jose Canseco	8.00	6.00	3.25
7	Rickey Henderson	6.00	4.50	2.50
8	Ken Griffey,Jr.	10.00	7.50	4.00
9	Ozzie Smith	4.00	3.00	1.50
10	Dwight Gooden	3.00	2.25	1.25
11	Ryne Sandberg (DK)	8.00	6.00	3.25
12	Don Mattingly	6.00	4.50	2.50
13	Ozzie Guillen	.50	.40	.20
14	Dave Righetti	.50	.40	.20
15	Rick Dempsey	.40	.30	.15
16	Tom Herr	.40	.30	.15
17	Julio Franco	.80	.60	.30
18	Von Hayes	.40	.30	.15
19	Cal Ripken	10.00	7.50	4.00
20	Alan Trammell	.80	.60	.30
21	Wade Boggs	5.00	3.75	2.00
22	Glenn Davis	.60	.45	.25
23	Will Clark	8.00	6.00	3.25
24	Nolan Ryan	12.00	9.00	4.75
25	George Bell	.60	.45	.25

		MT	NR MT	EX
26	Cecil Fielder	4.00	3.25	2.25
27	Gregg Olson	.60	.45	.25
28	Tim Wallach	.40	.30	.15
29	Ron Darling	.40	.30	.15
30	Kelly Gruber	.50	.40	.20
31	Shawn Boskie	.40	.30	.15
32	Mike Greenwell	.80	.60	.30
33	Dave Parker	.60	.45	.25
34	Joe Magrane	.40	.30	.15
35	Dave Stewart	.60	.45	.25
36	Kent Hrbek	.50	.40	.20
37	Robin Yount	3.00	2.25	1.25
38	Bo Jackson	1.50	1.25	.60
39	Fernando Valenzuela	.50	.40	.20
40	Sandy Alomar, Jr.	.60	.45	.25
41	Lance Parrish	.50	.40	.20
42	Candy Maldonado	.40	.30	.15
43	Mike LaValliere	.40	.30	.15
44	Jim Abbott	1.50	1.25	.60
45	Edgar Martinez	1.00	.70	.40
46	Kirby Puckett	5.00	3.75	2.00
47	Delino DeShields	1.00	.70	.40
48	Tony Gwynn	4.00	3.00	1.50
49	Carlton Fisk	2.00	1.50	.80
50	Mike Scott	.40	.30	.15
51	Barry Larkin	1.50	1.25	.60
52	Andre Dawson	2.00	1.50	.80
53	Tom Glavine	1.25	.90	.50
54	Tom Browning	.40	.30	.15
55	Checklist	.40	.30	.15

1990 Donruss N.L. Best

This 144-card set features the top players in the National League for 1990. The cards measure 2-1/2" by 3-1/2" and feature the same design as the regular Donruss cards. The only difference on the card fronts is the border color. The N.L. Best cards contain blue borders, while the regular cards featured red borders. Traded players are featured with their new teams. This set along with the A.L. Best set was available at select retail stores and within the hobby.

		MT	NR MT	EX
Complete Set:		12.00	9.00	4.75
Common Player:		.04	.03	.02
1	Eric Davis	.20	.15	.08
2	Tom Glavine	.10	.08	.04
3	Mike Bielecki	.05	.04	.02
4	Jim Deshaies	.05	.04	.02
5	Mike Scioscia	.05	.04	.02
6	Spike Owen	.05	.04	.02
7	Dwight Gooden	.20	.15	.08
8	Ricky Jordan	.08	.06	.03
9	Doug Drabek	.10	.08	.04
10	Bryn Smith	.04	.03	.02
11	Tony Gwynn	.10	.08	.04
12	John Burkett	.10	.08	.04
13	Nick Esasky	.06	.05	.02
14	Greg Maddux	.08	.06	.03
15	Joe Oliver	.08	.06	.03
16	Mike Scott	.08	.06	.03
17	Tim Belcher	.08	.06	.03
18	Kevin Gross	.06	.05	.02
19	Howard Johnson	.10	.08	.04

		MT	NR MT	EX
20	Darren Daulton	.06	.05	.02
21	John Smiley	.06	.05	.02
22	Ken Dayley	.05	.04	.02
23	Craig Lefferts	.05	.04	.02
24	Will Clark	.60	.45	.25
25	Greg Olson	.12	.09	.05
26	Ryne Sandberg	.50	.40	.20
27	Tom Browning	.06	.05	.02
28	Eric Anthony	.20	.15	.08
29	Juan Samuel	.06	.05	.02
30	Dennis Martinez	.06	.05	.02
31	Kevin Elster	.05	.04	.02
32	Tom Herr	.06	.05	.02
33	Sid Bream	.06	.05	.02
34	Terry Pendleton	.06	.05	.02
35	Roberto Alomar	.20	.15	.08
36	Kevin Bass	.06	.05	.02
37	Jim Presley	.06	.05	.02
38	Les Lancaster	.04	.03	.02
39	Paul O'Neill	.08	.06	.03
40	Dave Smith	.06	.05	.02
41	Kirk Gibson	.10	.08	.04
42	Tim Burke	.06	.05	.02
43	David Cone	.10	.08	.04
44	Ken Howell	.06	.05	.02
45	Barry Bonds	.20	.15	.08
46	Joe Magrane	.08	.06	.03
47	Andy Benes	.08	.06	.03
48	Gary Carter	.10	.08	.04
49	Pat Combs	.08	.06	.03
50	John Smoltz	.10	.08	.04
51	Mark Grace	.10	.08	.04
52	Barry Larkin	.10	.08	.04
53	Danny Darwin	.08	.06	.03
54	Orel Hershiser	.10	.08	.04
55	Tim Wallach	.08	.06	.03
56	Dave Magadan	.10	.08	.04
57	Roger McDowell	.08	.06	.03
58	Bill Landrum	.06	.05	.02
59	Jose DeLeon	.06	.05	.02
60	Bip Roberts	.06	.05	.02
61	Matt Williams	.10	.08	.04
62	Dale Murphy	.08	.06	.03
63	Dwight Smith	.08	.06	.03
64	Chris Sabo	.10	.08	.04
65	Glenn Davis	.10	.08	.04
66	Jay Howell	.06	.05	.02
67	Andres Galarraga	.08	.06	.03
68	Frank Viola	.10	.08	.04
69	John Kruk	.06	.05	.02
70	Bobby Bonilla	.15	.11	.06
71	Todd Zeile	.60	.45	.25
72	Joe Carter	.10	.08	.04
73	Robby Thompson	.06	.05	.02
74	Jeff Blauser	.04	.03	.02
75	Mitch Williams	.08	.06	.03
76	Rob Dibble	.10	.08	.04
77	Rafael Ramirez	.04	.03	.02
78	Eddie Murray	.10	.08	.04
79	Dave Martinez	.05	.04	.02
80	Darryl Strawberry	.50	.40	.20
81	Dickie Thon	.04	.03	.02
82	Jose Lind	.05	.04	.02
83	Ozzie Smith	.10	.08	.04
84	Bruce Hurst	.06	.05	.02
85	Kevin Mitchell	.20	.15	.08
86	Lonnie Smith	.05	.04	.02
87	Joe Girardi	.08	.06	.03
88	Randy Myers	.10	.08	.04
89	Craig Biggio	.08	.06	.03
90	Fernando Valenzuela	.06	.05	.02
91	Larry Walker	.20	.15	.08
92	John Franco	.10	.08	.04
93	Dennis Cook	.06	.05	.02
94	Bob Walk	.05	.04	.02
95	Pedro Guerrero	.08	.06	.03
96	Checklist	.04	.03	.02
97	Andre Dawson	.10	.08	.04
98	Ed Whitson	.06	.05	.02
99	Steve Bedrosian	.06	.05	.02
100	Oddibe McDowell	.06	.05	.02
101	Todd Benzinger	.06	.05	.02
102	Bill Doran	.08	.06	.03
103	Alfredo Griffin	.04	.03	.02
104	Tim Raines	.10	.08	.04
105	Sid Fernandez	.08	.06	.03
106	Charlie Hayes	.08	.06	.03
107	Mike LaValliere	.05	.04	.02
108	Jose Oquendo	.04	.03	.02
109	Jack Clark	.08	.06	.03
110	Scott Garrelts	.06	.05	.02

		MT	NR MT	EX
111	Ron Gant	.10	.08	.04
112	Shawon Dunston	.10	.08	.04
113	Mariano Duncan	.06	.05	.02
114	Eric Yelding	.10	.08	.04
115	Hubie Brooks	.08	.06	.03
116	Delino DeShields	.25	.20	.10
117	Gregg Jefferies	.20	.15	.08
118	Len Dykstra	.10	.08	.04
119	Andy Van Slyke	.10	.08	.04
120	Lee Smith	.08	.06	.03
121	Benito Santiago	.10	.08	.04
122	Jose Uribe	.04	.03	.02
123	Jeff Treadway	.05	.04	.02
124	Jerome Walton	.10	.08	.04
125	Billy Hatcher	.06	.05	.02
126	Ken Caminiti	.04	.03	.02
127	Kal Daniels	.08	.06	.03
128	Marquis Grissom	.30	.25	.12
129	Kevin McReynolds	.08	.06	.03
130	Wally Backman	.04	.03	.02
131	Willie McGee	.10	.08	.04
132	Terry Kennedy	.04	.03	.02
133	Garry Templeton	.04	.03	.02
134	Lloyd McClendon	.04	.03	.02
135	Daryl Boston	.04	.03	.02
136	Jay Bell	.08	.06	.03
137	Mike Pagliarulo	.06	.05	.02
138	Vince Coleman	.08	.06	.03
139	Brett Butler	.06	.05	.02
140	Von Hayes	.08	.06	.03
141	Ramon Martinez	.20	.15	.08
142	Jack Armstrong	.10	.08	.04
143	Franklin Stubbs	.05	.04	.02
144	Checklist	.04	.03	.02

		MT	NR MT	EX
21	Kevin Appier(FC)	.30	.25	.12
22	Mike Harkey	.20	.15	.08
23	Tim Layana(FC)	.20	.15	.08
24	Glenallen Hill	.20	.15	.08
25	Jerry Kutzler	.10	.08	.04
26	Mike Blowers	.15	.11	.06
27	Scott Ruskin(FC)	.25	.20	.10
28	Dana Kiecker(FC)	.15	.11	.06
29	Willie Blair(FC)	.10	.08	.04
30	Ben McDonald	.60	.45	.25
31	Todd Zeile	.40	.30	.15
32	Scott Coolbaugh	.12	.09	.05
33	Xavier Hernandez	.10	.08	.04
34	Mike Hartley(FC)	.15	.11	.06
35	Kevin Tapani	.30	.25	.12
36	Kevin Wickander(FC)	.10	.08	.04
37	Carlos Hernandez(FC)	.15	.11	.06
38	Brian Traxler(FC)	.20	.15	.08
39	Marty Brown(FC)	.10	.08	.04
40	Scott Radinsky(FC)	.25	.20	.10
41	Julio Machado	.15	.11	.06
42	Steve Avery	.80	.60	.30
43	Mark Lemke	.12	.09	.05
44	Alan Mills(FC)	.25	.20	.10
45	Marquis Grissom	.50	.40	.20
46	Greg Olson(FC)	.15	.11	.06
47	Dave Hollins(FC)	.30	.25	.12
48	Jerald Clark	.10	.08	.04
49	Eric Anthony	.20	.15	.08
50	Tim Drummond	.10	.08	.04
51	John Burkett(FC)	.20	.15	.08
52	Brent Knackert(FC)	.12	.09	.05
53	Jeff Shaw(FC)	.12	.09	.05
54	John Orton(FC)	.10	.08	.04
55	Terry Shumpert(FC)	.15	.11	.06
56	Checklist	.10	.08	.04

1990 Donruss Rookies

For the fifth straight year, Donruss issued a 56-card "Rookies" set in 1990. As in previous years, the set is similar in design to the regular Donruss set, except for a new "The Rookies" logo and green borders instead of red. The set is packaged in a special box and includes a special Carl Yastrzemski puzzle card.

		MT	NR MT	EX
Complete Set:		8.00	6.00	3.25
Common Player:		.10	.08	.04
1	Sandy Alomar	.15	.11	.06
2	John Olerud	.50	.40	.20
3	Pat Combs	.20	.15	.08
4	Brian Dubois	.10	.08	.04
5	Felix Jose	.12	.09	.05
6	Delino DeShields	.50	.40	.20
7	Mike Stanton	.10	.08	.04
8	Mike Munoz(FC)	.10	.08	.04
9	Craig Grebeck(FC)	.15	.11	.06
10	Joe Kraemer(FC)	.10	.08	.04
11	Jeff Huson	.10	.08	.04
12	Bill Sampen(FC)	.30	.25	.12
13	Brian Bohanon(FC)	.12	.09	.05
14	Dave Justice	2.00	1.50	.80
15	Robin Ventura	.80	.60	.30
16	Greg Vaughn	.60	.45	.25
17	Wayne Edwards(FC)	.15	.11	.06
18	Shawn Boskie	.25	.20	.10
19	Carlos Baerga(FC)	1.00	.70	.40
20	Mark Gardner	.20	.15	.08

1990 Donruss Grand Slammers

For the second consecutive year Donruss produced a set in honor of players who hit grand slams in the previous season. The cards are styled after the 1990 Donruss regular issue. The cards were inserted into 1990 Donruss factory sets.

		MT	NR MT	EX
Complete Set:		2.00	1.50	.80
Common Player:		.12	.09	.05
1	Matt Williams	.25	.20	.10
2	Jeffrey Leonard	.12	.09	.05
3	Chris James	.12	.09	.05
4	Mark McGwire	.30	.25	.12
5	Dwight Evans	.15	.11	.06
6	Will Clark	.60	.45	.25
7	Mike Scioscia	.12	.09	.05
8	Todd Benzinger	.12	.09	.05
9	Fred McGriff	.25	.20	.10
10	Kevin Bass	.12	.09	.05
11	Jack Clark	.12	.09	.05
12	Bo Jackson	.60	.45	.25

Regional interest may affect the value of a card.

1991 Donruss

Donruss decided to use a two series format in 1991. The first series was released in December and the second in February. The 1991 design is somewhat reminiscent of the 1986 set. Blue borders are used. Limited edition cards including an autographed Ryne Sandberg card (5,000) were randomly inserted in wax packs. Other features of the set include 40 Rated Rookies, a "Legends Series," Elite Series, and another Diamond King subset. Collectors could also take part in Donruss' Instant Win promotion.

		MT	NR MT	EX
	Complete Set:	18.00	13.50	7.25
	Common Player:	.04	.03	.02
1	Dave Steib (DK)	.04	.03	.02
2	Craig Biggio (DK)	.05	.04	.02
3	Cecil Fielder (DK)	.15	.11	.06
4	Barry Bonds (DK)	.10	.08	.04
5	Barry Larkin (DK)	.06	.05	.02
6	Dave Parker (DK)	.05	.04	.03
7	Len Dykstra (DK)	.06	.05	.02
8	Bobby Thigpen (DK)	.05	.04	.02
9	Roger Clemens (DK)	.10	.08	.04
10	Ron Gant (DK)	.08	.06	.03
11	Delino DeShields (DK)	.08	.06	.03
12	Roberto Alomar (DK)	.08	.06	.03
13	Sandy Alomar (DK)	.12	.09	.05
14	Ryne Sandberg (DK)	.15	.11	.06
15	Ramon Martinez (DK)	.06	.05	.02
16	Edgar Martinez (DK)	.08	.06	.03
17	Dave Magadan (DK)	.04	.03	.02
18	Matt Williams (DK)	.12	.09	.05
19	Rafael Palmeiro (DK)	.05	.04	.02
20	Bob Welch (DK)	.06	.05	.02
21	Dave Righetti (DK)	.04	.03	.02
22	Brian Harper (DK)	.04	.03	.02
23	Gregg Olson (DK)	.05	.04	.02
24	Kurt Stillwell (DK)	.04	.03	.02
25	Pedro Guerrero (DK)	.05	.04	.02
26	Chuck Finley (DK)	.05	.04	.02
27	DK Checklist	.04	.03	.02
28	Tino Martinez (RR)(FC)	.20	.15	.08
29	Mark Lewis (RR)(FC)	.35	.25	.14
30	*Bernard Gilkey* (RR)(FC)	.20	.15	.08
31	Hensley Meulens (RR)	.08	.06	.03
32	*Derek Bell* (RR)(FC)	.40	.30	.15
33	Jose Offerman (RR)(FC)	.25	.20	.10
34	Terry Bross (RR)	.10	.08	.04
35	*Leo Gomez* (RR)(FC)	.40	.30	.15
36	Derrick May (RR)(FC)	.25	.20	.10
37	*Kevin Morton* (RR)(FC)	.25	.20	.10
38	Moises Alou (RR)(FC)	.10	.08	.04
39	*Julio Valera* (RR)(FC)	.15	.11	.06
40	Milt Cuyler (RR)(FC)	.10	.08	.04
41	*Phil Plantier* (RR)(FC)	.80	.60	.30
42	*Scott Chiamparino* (RR)(FC)	.30	.25	.12
43	*Ray Lankford* (RR)(FC)	.40	.30	.15
44	*Mickey Morandini* (RR)(FC)	.20	.15	.08
45	Dave Hansen (RR)(FC)	.10	.08	.04
46	*Kevin Belcher* (RR)(FC)	.15	.11	.06
47	Darrin Fletcher (RR)(FC)	.10	.08	.04
48	Steve Sax (AS)	.05	.04	.02
49	Ken Griffey, Jr. (AS)	.40	.30	.15
50	Jose Canseco (AS)	.25	.20	.10
51	Sandy Alomar (AS)	.10	.08	.04
52	Cal Ripken (AS)	.05	.04	.02
53	Rickey Henderson (AS)	.15	.11	.06
54	Bob Welch (AS)	.05	.04	.02
55	Wade Boggs (AS)	.10	.08	.04
56	Mark McGwire (AS)	.10	.08	.04
57	Jack McDowell	.06	.05	.02
58	Jose Lind	.05	.04	.02
59	*Alex Fernandez*(FC)	.50	.40	.20
60	Pat Combs	.08	.06	.03
61	*Mike Walker*(FC)	.15	.11	.06
62	Juan Samuel	.05	.04	.02
63	Mike Blowers	.05	.04	.02
64	Mark Guthrie	.05	.04	.02
65	Mark Salas	.04	.03	.02
66	Tim Jones	.04	.03	.02
67	Tim Leary	.05	.04	.02
68	Andres Galarraga	.08	.06	.03
69	Bob Milacki	.05	.04	.02
70	Tim Belcher	.08	.06	.03
71	Todd Zeile	.20	.15	.08
72	Jerome Walton	.08	.06	.03
73	Kevin Seitzer	.06	.05	.02
74	Jerald Clark	.06	.05	.02
75	John Smoltz	.08	.06	.03
76	Mike Henneman	.05	.04	.02
77	Ken Griffey, Jr.	.80	.60	.30
78	Jim Abbott	.06	.05	.02
79	Gregg Jefferies	.15	.11	.06
80	Kevin Reimer(FC)	.20	.15	.08
81	Roger Clemens	.15	.11	.06
82	Mike Fitzgerald	.04	.03	.02
83	Bruce Hurst	.06	.05	.02
84	Eric Davis	.15	.11	.06
85	Paul Molitor	.08	.06	.03
86	Will Clark	.25	.20	.10
87	Mike Bielecki	.04	.03	.02
88	Bret Saberhagen	.10	.08	.04
89	Nolan Ryan	.25	.20	.10
90	Bobby Thigpen	.08	.06	.03
91	Dickie Thon	.04	.03	.02
92	Duane Ward	.04	.03	.02
93	Luis Polonia	.04	.03	.02
94	Terry Kennedy	.04	.03	.02
95	Kent Hrbek	.08	.06	.03
96	Danny Jackson	.06	.05	.02
97	Sid Fernandez	.08	.06	.03
98	Jimmy Key	.06	.05	.02
99	Franklin Stubbs	.05	.04	.02
100	Checklist	.04	.03	.02
101	R.J. Reynolds	.04	.03	.02
102	Dave Stewart	.08	.06	.03
103	Dan Pasqua	.05	.04	.02
104	Dan Plesac	.06	.05	.02
105	Mark McGwire	.20	.15	.08
106	John Farrell	.04	.03	.02
107	Don Mattingly	.20	.15	.08
108	Carlton Fisk	.10	.08	.04
109	Ken Oberkfell	.04	.03	.02
110	Darrel Akerfelds	.04	.03	.02
111	Gregg Olson	.08	.06	.03
112	Mike Scioscia	.06	.05	.02
113	Bryn Smith	.04	.03	.02
114	Bob Geren	.05	.04	.02
115	Tom Candiotti	.04	.03	.02
116	Kevin Tapani	.15	.11	.06
117	Jeff Treadway	.05	.04	.02
118	Alan Trammell	.08	.06	.03
119	Pete O'Brien	.04	.03	.02
120	Joel Skinner	.04	.03	.02
121	Mike LaValliere	.05	.04	.02
122	Dwight Evans	.08	.06	.03
123	Jody Reed	.08	.06	.03
124	Lee Guetterman	.04	.03	.02
125	Tim Burke	.05	.04	.02
126	Dave Johnson	.04	.03	.02
127	Fernando Valenzuela	.08	.06	.03
128	Jose DeLeon	.06	.05	.02
129	Andre Dawson	.10	.08	.04
130	Gerald Perry	.05	.04	.02
131	Greg Harris	.04	.03	.02
132	Tom Glavine	.08	.06	.03
133	Lance McCullers	.04	.03	.02
134	Randy Johnson	.08	.06	.03
135	Lance Parrish	.08	.06	.03
136	Mackey Sasser	.08	.06	.03
137	Geno Petralli	.04	.03	.02
138	Dennis Lamp	.04	.03	.02
139	Dennis Martinez	.06	.05	.02
140	Mike Pagliarulo	.05	.04	.02
141	Hal Morris	.10	.08	.04
142	Dave Parker	.10	.08	.04
143	Brett Butler	.06	.05	.02

		MT	NR MT	EX				MT	NR MT	EX
144	Paul Assenmacher	.04	.03	.02		235	Ellis Burks	.10	.08	.04
145	Mark Gubicza	.06	.05	.02		236	Greg Cadaret	.04	.03	.02
146	Charlie Hough	.05	.04	.02		237	Dave Martinez	.05	.04	.02
147	Sammy Sosa	.15	.11	.06		238	Mark Williamson	.04	.03	.02
148	Randy Ready	.04	.03	.02		239	Stan Javier	.05	.04	.02
149	Kelly Gruber	.08	.06	.03		240	Ozzie Smith	.10	.08	.04
150	Devon White	.06	.05	.02		241	*Shawn Boskie*	.15	.11	.06
151	Gary Carter	.08	.06	.03		242	Tom Gordon	.10	.08	.04
152	Gene Larkin	.05	.04	.02		243	Tony Gwynn	.10	.08	.04
153	Chris Sabo	.08	.06	.03		244	Tommy Gregg	.04	.03	.02
154	David Cone	.08	.06	.03		245	Jeff Robinson	.05	.04	.02
155	Todd Stottlemyre	.06	.05	.02		246	Keith Comstock	.04	.03	.02
156	Glenn Wilson	.05	.04	.02		247	Jack Howell	.05	.04	.02
157	Bob Walk	.05	.04	.02		248	Keith Miller	.05	.04	.02
158	Mike Gallego	.04	.03	.02		249	Bobby Witt	.08	.06	.03
159	Greg Hibbard	.06	.05	.02		250	Rob Murphy	.04	.03	.02
160	Chris Bosio	.05	.04	.02		251	Spike Owen	.06	.05	.02
161	Mike Moore	.06	.05	.02		252	Garry Templeton	.06	.05	.02
162	Jerry Browne	.06	.05	.02		253	Glenn Braggs	.06	.05	.02
163	Steve Sax	.08	.06	.03		254	Ron Robinson	.06	.05	.02
164	Melido Perez	.06	.05	.02		255	Kevin Mitchell	.20	.15	.08
165	Danny Darwin	.05	.04	.02		256	Les Lancaster	.04	.03	.02
166	Roger McDowell	.06	.05	.02		257	*Mel Stottlemyre*(FC)	.10	.08	.04
167	Bill Ripken	.04	.03	.02		258	Kenny Rogers	.06	.05	.02
168	Mike Sharperson	.05	.04	.02		259	Lance Johnson	.06	.05	.02
169	Lee Smith	.08	.06	.03		260	John Kruk	.06	.05	.02
170	Matt Nokes	.06	.05	.02		261	Fred McGriff	.15	.11	.06
171	Jesse Orosco	.05	.04	.02		262	Dick Schofield	.04	.03	.02
172	Rick Aguilera	.06	.05	.02		263	Trevor Wilson	.05	.04	.02
173	Jim Presley	.06	.05	.02		264	Scott Scudder, David West	.05	.04	.02
174	Lou Whitaker	.08	.06	.03		266	Dwight Gooden	.20	.15	.08
175	Harold Reynolds	.08	.06	.03		267	*Willie Blair*(FC)	.15	.11	.06
176	Brook Jacoby	.06	.05	.02		268	Mark Portugal	.04	.03	.02
177	Wally Backman	.05	.04	.02		269	Doug Drabek	.10	.08	.04
178	Wade Boggs	.20	.15	.08		270	Dennis Eckersley	.10	.08	.04
179	Chuck Cary	.04	.03	.02		271	Eric King	.05	.04	.02
180	Tom Foley	.04	.03	.02		272	Robin Yount	.10	.08	.04
181	Pete Harnisch	.05	.04	.02		273	Carney Lansford	.08	.06	.02
182	Mike Morgan	.05	.04	.02		274	*Carlos Baerga*	.25	.20	.10
183	Bob Tewksbury	.05	.04	.02		275	Dave Righetti	.08	.06	.03
184	Joe Girardi	.06	.05	.02		276	Scott Fletcher	.04	.03	.02
185	Storm Davis	.05	.04	.02		277	Eric Yelding	.08	.06	.03
186	Ed Whitson	.06	.05	.02		278	Charlie Hayes	.08	.06	.03
187	Steve Avery	.25	.20	.10		279	Jeff Ballard	.05	.04	.02
188	Lloyd Moseby	.06	.05	.02		280	Orel Hershiser	.10	.08	.04
189	Scott Bankhead	.06	.05	.02		281	Jose Oquendo	.04	.03	.02
190	Mark Langston	.08	.06	.03		282	Mike Witt	.05	.04	.02
191	Kevin McReynolds	.06	.05	.02		283	Mitch Webster	.04	.03	.02
192	Julio Franco	.08	.06	.03		284	Greg Gagne	.05	.04	.02
193	John Dopson	.05	.04	.02		285	*Greg Olson*	.10	.08	.04
194	Oil Can Boyd	.05	.04	.02		286	Tony Phillips	.05	.04	.02
195	Bip Roberts	.06	.05	.02		287	Scott Bradley	.04	.03	.02
196	Billy Hatcher	.06	.05	.02		288	Cory Snyder	.08	.06	.03
197	Edgar Diaz(FC)	.08	.06	.03		289	Jay Bell	.06	.05	.02
198	Greg Litton	.05	.04	.02		290	Kevin Romine	.04	.03	.02
199	Mark Grace	.10	.08	.04		291	Jeff Robinson	.05	.04	.02
200	Checklist	.04	.03	.02		292	Steve Frey(FC)	.06	.05	.02
201	George Brett	.10	.08	.04		293	Craig Worthington	.05	.04	.02
202	Jeff Russell	.06	.05	.02		294	Tim Crews	.04	.03	.02
203	Ivan Calderon	.08	.06	.03		295	Joe Magrane	.08	.06	.03
204	Ken Howell	.04	.03	.02		296	*Hector Villanueva*(FC)	.20	.15	.08
205	Tom Henke	.08	.06	.03		297	*Terry Shumpert*	.10	.08	.04
206	Bryan Harvey	.06	.05	.02		298	Joe Carter	.10	.08	.04
207	Steve Bedrosian	.08	.06	.03		299	Kent Mercker	.10	.08	.04
208	Al Newman	.04	.03	.02		300	Checklist	.04	.03	.02
209	Randy Myers	.08	.06	.03		301	Chet Lemon	.05	.04	.02
210	Daryl Boston	.04	.03	.02		302	Mike Schooler	.06	.05	.03
211	Manny Lee	.06	.05	.02		303	Dante Bichette	.06	.05	.02
212	Dave Smith	.06	.05	.02		304	Kevin Elster	.05	.04	.02
213	Don Slaught	.04	.03	.02		305	Jeff Huson	.06	.05	.02
214	Walt Weiss	.06	.05	.02		306	Greg Harris	.05	.04	.02
215	Donn Pall	.04	.03	.02		307	Marquis Grissom	.10	.08	.04
216	Jamie Navarro	.06	.05	.02		308	Calvin Schiraldi	.04	.03	.02
217	Willie Randolph	.06	.05	.02		309	Mariano Duncan	.06	.05	.02
218	Rudy Seanez(FC)	.08	.06	.03		310	Bill Spiers	.06	.05	.02
219	*Jim Leyritz*(FC)	.08	.06	.03		311	Scott Garrelts	.06	.05	.02
220	Ron Karkovice	.05	.04	.02		312	Mitch Williams	.08	.06	.03
221	Ken Caminiti	.05	.04	.02		313	Mike Macfarlane	.05	.04	.02
222	Von Hayes	.08	.06	.03		314	Kevin Brown	.06	.05	.02
223	Cal Ripken	.10	.08	.04		315	Robin Ventura	.10	.08	.04
224	Lenny Harris	.06	.05	.02		316	Darren Daulton	.06	.05	.02
225	Milt Thompson	.05	.04	.02		317	PUuat Borders	.06	.05	.02
226	Alvaro Espinoza	.05	.04	.02		318	Mark Eichhorn	.04	.03	.02
227	Chris James	.06	.05	.02		319	Jeff Brantley	.08	.06	.03
228	Dan Gladden	.06	.05	.02		320	Shane Mack	.05	.04	.02
229	Jeff Blauser	.05	.04	.02		321	Rob Dibble	.10	.08	.04
230	Mike Heath	.04	.03	.02		322	John Franco	.10	.08	.04
231	Omar Vizquel	.05	.04	.02		323	Junior Felix	.08	.06	.03
232	Doug Jones	.08	.06	.03		324	Casey Candaele	.04	.03	.02
233	Jeff King	.06	.05	.02		325	Bobby Bonilla	.10	.08	.04
234	Luis Rivera	.04	.03	.02		326	Dave Henderson	.06	.05	.02

#	Name	MT	NR MT	EX	#	Name	MT	NR MT	EX
327	Wayne Edwards	.06	.05	.02	418	Steve Carter (RR)	.08	.06	.03
328	Mark Knudson	.04	.03	.02	419	*Gerald Alexander* (RR)(FC)	.15	.11	.06
329	Terry Steinbach	.06	.05	.02	420	Rich Garces (RR)(FC)	.20	.15	.08
330	*Colby Ward*(FC)	.20	.15	.08	421	Chuck Knoblauch (RR)(FC)	.60	.45	.25
331	*Oscar Azocar*(FC)	.15	.11	.06	422	*Scott Aldred* (RR)(FC)	.15	.11	.06
332	*Scott Radinsky*	.15	.11	.06	423	*Wes Chamberlain* (RR)(FC)	.40	.30	.15
333	Eric Anthony	.10	.08	.04	424	*Lance Dickson* (RR)(FC)	.25	.20	.10
334	Steve Lake	.04	.03	.02	425	*Greg Colbrunn* (RR)(FC)	.20	.15	.08
335	Bob Melvin	.04	.03	.02	426	Rich Delucia (RR)(FC)	.20	.15	.08
336	Kal Daniels	.08	.06	.03	427	*Jeff Conine* (RR)(FC)	.20	.15	.08
337	Tom Pagnozzi	.05	.04	.02	428	*Steve Decker* (RR)(FC)	.25	.20	.10
338	*Alan Mills*	.15	.11	.06	429	*Turner Ward* (RR)(FC)	.20	.15	.08
339	Steve Olin	.06	.05	.02	430	Mo Vaughn (RR)(FC)	.35	.25	.14
340	Juan Berenguer	.04	.03	.02	431	*Steve Chitren* (RR)(FC)	.20	.15	.08
341	Francisco Cabrera	.06	.05	.02	432	Mike Benjamin (RR)(FC)	.10	.08	.04
342	Dave Bergman	.04	.03	.02	433	Ryne Sandberg (All-Star)	.10	.08	.04
343	Henry Cotto	.04	.03	.02	434	Len Dykstra (All-Star)	.06	.05	.02
344	Sergio Valdez	.08	.06	.03	435	Andre Dawson (All-Star)	.10	.08	.04
345	Bob Patterson	.04	.03	.02	436	Mike Scioscia (All-Star)	.06	.05	.02
346	John Marzano	.05	.04	.02	437	Ozzie Smith (All-Star)	.10	.08	.04
347	*Dana Kiecker*	.08	.06	.03	438	Kevin Mitchell (All-Star)	.10	.08	.04
348	Dion James	.04	.03	.02	439	Jack Armstrong (All-Star)	.06	.05	.02
349	Hubie Brooks	.08	.06	.03	440	Chris Sabo (All-Star)	.08	.06	.03
350	Bill Landrum	.05	.04	.02	441	Will Clark (All-Star)	.15	.11	.06
351	*Bill Sampen*	.20	.15	.08	442	Mel Hall	.05	.04	.02
352	Greg Briley	.05	.04	.02	443	Mark Gardner	.06	.05	.02
353	Paul Gibson	.04	.03	.02	444	Mike Devereaux	.06	.05	.02
354	Dave Eiland	.04	.03	.02	445	Kirk Gibson	.06	.05	.02
355	Steve Finley	.06	.05	.02	446	Terry Pendleton	.08	.06	.03
356	Bob Boone	.06	.05	.02	447	Mike Harkey	.08	.06	.03
357	Steve Buechele	.06	.05	.02	448	Jim Eisenreich	.04	.03	.02
358	*Chris Hoiles*(FC)	.30	.25	.12	449	Benito Santiago	.08	.06	.03
359	Larry Walker	.10	.08	.04	450	Oddibe McDowell	.04	.03	.02
360	Frank DiPino	.04	.03	.02	451	Cecil Fielder	.20	.15	.08
361	Mark Grant	.04	.03	.02	452	Ken Griffey,Sr.	.08	.06	.03
362	Dave Magadan	.08	.06	.03	453	Bert Blyleven	.06	.05	.02
363	Robby Thompson	.06	.05	.02	454	Howard Johnson	.10	.08	.04
364	Lonnie Smith	.05	.04	.02	455	Monty Farris(FC)	.15	.11	.06
365	Steve Farr	.05	.04	.02	456	Tony Pena	.05	.04	.02
366	Dave Valle	.05	.04	.02	457	Tim Raines	.08	.06	.03
367	*Tim Naehring*(FC)	.25	.20	.10	458	Dennis Rasmussen	.04	.03	.02
368	Jim Acker	.04	.03	.02	459	Luis Quinones	.04	.03	.02
369	Jeff Reardon	.08	.06	.04	460	B.J. Surhoff	.06	.05	.02
370	Tim Teufel	.04	.03	.02	461	Ernest Riles	.04	.03	.02
371	Juan Gonzalez	.35	.25	.14	462	Rick Sutcliffe	.06	.05	.02
372	Luis Salazar	.04	.03	.02	463	Danny Tartabull	.10	.08	.04
373	Rick Honeycutt	.04	.03	.02	464	Pete Incaviglia	.06	.05	.02
374	Greg Maddux	.08	.06	.03	465	Carlos Martinez	.05	.04	.02
375	Jose Uribe	.05	.04	.02	466	Ricky Jordan	.06	.05	.02
376	Donnie Hill	.04	.03	.02	467	John Cerutti	.04	.03	.02
377	Don Carman	.04	.03	.02	468	Dave Winfield	.12	.09	.05
378	*Craig Grebeck*	.06	.05	.02	469	Francisco Oliveras	.04	.03	.02
379	Willie Fraser	.05	.04	.02	470	Roy Smith	.04	.03	.02
380	Glenallen Hill	.08	.06	.03	471	Barry Larkin	.12	.09	.05
381	Joe Oliver	.06	.05	.02	472	Ron Darling	.06	.05	.02
382	Randy Bush	.04	.03	.02	473	David Wells	.06	.05	.02
383	Alex Cole(FC)	.30	.25	.12	474	Glenn Davis	.10	.08	.04
384	Norm Charlton	.08	.06	.03	475	Neal Heaton	.04	.03	.02
385	Gene Nelson	.04	.03	.02	476	Ron Hassey	.04	.03	.02
386	Checklist	.04	.03	.02	477	Frank Thomas(FC)	1.25	.90	.50
387	Rickey Henderson (MVP)	.15	.11	.06	478	Greg Vaughn	.15	.11	.06
388	Lance Parrish (MVP)	.05	.04	.02	479	Todd Burns	.04	.03	.02
389	Fred McGriff (MVP)	.10	.08	.04	480	Candy Maldonado	.05	.04	.02
390	Dave Parker (MVP)	.10	.08	.04	481	Dave LaPoint	.04	.03	.02
391	Candy Maldonado (MVP)	.05	.04	.02	482	Alvin Davis	.08	.06	.03
392	Ken Griffey,Jr. (MVP)	.40	.30	.15	483	Mike Scott	.06	.05	.02
393	Gregg Olson (MVP)	.10	.08	.04	484	Dale Murphy	.12	.09	.05
394	Rafael Palmeiro (MVP)	.10	.08	.04	485	Ben McDonald	.35	.25	.14
395	Roger Clemens (MVP)	.15	.11	.06	486	Jay Howell	.06	.05	.02
396	George Brett (MVP)	.10	.08	.04	487	Vince Coleman	.08	.06	.03
397	Cecil Fielder (MVP)	.15	.11	.06	488	Alfredo Griffin	.05	.04	.02
398	Brian Harper (MVP)	.05	.04	.02	489	Sandy Alomar	.15	.11	.06
399	Bobby Thigpen (MVP)	.06	.05	.02	490	Kirby Puckett	.15	.11	.06
400	Roberto Kelly (MVP)	.08	.06	.03	491	Andres Thomas	.04	.03	.02
401	Danny Darwin (MVP)	.05	.04	.02	492	Jack Morris	.08	.06	.03
402	Dave Justice (MVP)	.25	.20	.10	493	Matt Young	.04	.03	.02
403	Lee Smith (MVP)	.05	.04	.02	494	Greg Myers	.04	.03	.02
404	Ryne Sanberg (MVP)	.15	.11	.06	495	Barry Bonds	.15	.11	.06
405	Eddie Murray (MVP)	.10	.08	.04	496	Scott Cooper(FC)	.20	.15	.08
406	Tim Wallach (MVP)	.06	.05	.02	497	Dan Schatzeder	.04	.03	.02
407	Kevin Mitchell (MVP)	.10	.08	.04	498	Jesse Barfield	.06	.05	.02
408	Darryl Strawberry (MVP)	.15	.11	.06	499	Jerry Goff(FC)	.05	.04	.02
409	Joe Carter (MVP)	.06	.05	.02	500	Checklist	.04	.03	.02
410	Len Dykstra (MVP)	.06	.05	.02	501	*Anthony Telford*(FC)	.15	.11	.06
411	Doug Drabek (MVP)	.06	.05	.02	502	Eddie Murray	.12	.09	.05
412	Chris Sabo (MVP)	.08	.06	.03	503	*Omar Olivares*(FC)	.12	.09	.05
413	*Paul Marak* (RR)(FC)	.15	.11	.06	504	Ryne Sandberg	.15	.11	.06
414	Tim MCIntosh (RR)(FC)	.10	.08	.04	505	Jeff Montgomery	.06	.05	.02
415	*Brian Barnes* (RR)(FC)	.20	.15	.08	506	Mark Parent	.04	.03	.02
416	*Eric Gunderson* (RR)(FC)	.15	.11	.06	507	Ron Gant	.15	.11	.06
417	*Mike Gardiner* (RR)(FC)	.20	.15	.08	508	Frank Tanana	.05	.04	.02

		MT	NR MT	EX			MT	NR MT	EX
509	Jay Buhner	.06	.05	.02	600	Checklist	.04	.03	.02
510	Max Venable	.04	.03	.02	601	Jim Gott	.04	.03	.02
511	Wally Whitehurst	.06	.05	.02	602	Jeff Manto(FC)	.12	.09	.05
512	Gary Pettis	.04	.03	.02	603	Nelson Liriano	.04	.03	.02
513	Tom Brunansky	.06	.05	.02	604	Mark Lemke	.06	.05	.02
514	Tim Wallach	.08	.06	.03	605	Clay Parker	.04	.03	.02
515	Craig Lefferts	.05	.04	.02	606	Edgar Martinez	.08	.06	.03
516	*Tim Layana*	.10	.08	.04	607	*Mark Whiten*(FC)	.35	.25	.14
517	Darryl Hamilton	.08	.06	.03	608	Ted Power	.04	.03	.02
518	Rick Reuschel	.05	.04	.02	609	Tom Bolton	.05	.04	.02
519	Steve Wilson	.06	.05	.02	610	Tom Herr	.05	.04	.02
520	Kurt Stillwell	.05	.04	.02	611	Andy Hawkins	.04	.03	.02
521	Rafael Palmeiro	.12	.09	.05	612	Scott Ruskin	.04	.03	.02
522	Ken Patterson	.04	.03	.02	613	Ron Kittle	.05	.04	.02
523	Len Dykstra	.12	.09	.05	614	John Wetteland	.06	.05	.02
524	Tony Fernandez	.06	.05	.02	615	*Mike Perez*(FC)	.12	.09	.05
525	Kent Anderson	.04	.03	.02	616	Dave Clark	.04	.03	.02
526	*Mark Leonard*(FC)	.20	.15	.08	617	Brent Mayne(FC)	.12	.09	.05
527	Allan Anderson	.04	.03	.02	618	Jack Clark	.08	.06	.03
528	Tom Browning	.06	.05	.02	619	Marvin Freeman	.04	.03	.02
529	Frank Viola	.12	.09	.05	620	Edwin Nunez	.04	.03	.02
530	John Olerud	.30	.25	.12	621	Russ Swan(FC)	.08	.06	.03
531	Juan Agosto	.04	.03	.02	622	Johnny Ray	.04	.03	.02
532	Zane Smith	.06	.05	.02	623	Charlie O'Brien	.04	.03	.02
533	Scott Sanderson	.06	.05	.02	624	*Joe Bitker*(FC)	.12	.09	.05
534	Barry Jones	.05	.04	.02	625	Mike Marshall	.04	.03	.02
535	Mike Felder	.04	.03	.02	626	Otis Nixon	.05	.04	.02
536	Jose Canseco	.30	.25	.12	627	Andy Benes	.15	.11	.06
537	Felix Fermin	.04	.03	.02	628	Ron Oester	.04	.03	.02
538	Roberto Kelly	.08	.06	.03	629	Ted Higuera	.06	.05	.02
539	Brian Holman	.05	.04	.02	630	Kevin Bass	.05	.04	.02
540	Mark Davidson	.04	.03	.02	631	Damon Berryhill	.05	.04	.02
541	Terry Mulholland	.06	.05	.02	632	Bo Jackson	.30	.25	.12
542	Randy Milligan	.06	.05	.02	633	Brad Arnsberg	.05	.04	.02
543	Jose Gonzalez	.04	.03	.02	634	Jerry Willard	.04	.03	.02
544	*Craig Wilson*(FC)	.10	.08	.04	635	Tommy Greene	.06	.05	.02
545	Mike Hartley	.04	.03	.02	636	*Bob MacDonald*(FC)	.15	.11	.06
546	Greg Swindell	.06	.05	.02	637	Kirk McCaskill	.05	.04	.02
547	Gary Gaetti	.08	.06	.03	638	John Burkett	.05	.04	.02
548	Dave Justice	.50	.40	.20	639	*Paul Abbott*(FC)	.15	.11	.06
549	Steve Searcy	.04	.03	.02	640	Todd Benzinger	.05	.04	.02
550	Erik Hanson	.12	.09	.05	641	Todd Hundley(FC)	.10	.08	.04
551	Dave Stieb	.08	.06	.03	642	George Bell	.10	.08	.04
552	Andy Van Slyke	.08	.06	.03	643	*Javier Ortiz*(FC)	.12	.09	.05
553	Mike Greenwell	.12	.09	.05	644	Sid Bream	.05	.04	.02
554	Kevin Maas	.30	.25	.12	645	Bob Welch	.06	.05	.02
555	Delino Deshields	.20	.15	.08	646	Phil Bradley	.05	.04	.02
556	Curt Schilling	.05	.04	.02	647	Bill Krueger	.04	.03	.02
557	Ramon Martinez	.20	.15	.08	648	Rickey Henderson	.20	.15	.08
558	Pedro Guerrero	.08	.06	.03	649	Kevin Wickander	.05	.04	.02
559	Dwight Smith	.05	.04	.02	650	Steve Balboni	.04	.03	.02
560	Mark Davis	.04	.03	.02	651	Gene Harris	.05	.04	.02
561	Shawn Abner	.05	.04	.02	652	Jim Deshaies	.04	.03	.02
562	Charlie Leibrandt	.05	.04	.02	653	Jason Grimsley(FC)	.12	.09	.05
563	John Shelby	.04	.03	.02	654	Joe Orsulak	.05	.04	.02
564	Bill Swift	.05	.04	.02	655	*Jimmy Poole*(FC)	.12	.09	.05
565	Mike Fetters	.06	.05	.02	656	Felix Jose	.10	.08	.04
566	Alejandro Pena	.05	.04	.02	657	Dennis Cook	.05	.04	.02
567	Ruben Sierra	.15	.11	.06	658	Tom Brookens	.04	.03	.02
568	Calos Quintana	.08	.06	.03	659	Junior Ortiz	.04	.03	.02
569	Kevin Gross	.05	.04	.02	660	Jeff Parrett	.04	.03	.02
570	Derek Lilliquist	.04	.03	.02	661	Jerry Don Gleaton	.04	.03	.02
571	Jack Armstrong	.06	.05	.02	662	Brent Knackert	.04	.03	.02
572	Greg Brock	.04	.03	.02	663	Rance Mulliniks	.04	.03	.02
573	Mike Kingery	.04	.03	.02	664	John Smiley	.06	.05	.02
574	Greg Smith(FC)	.06	.05	.02	665	Larry Andersen	.04	.03	.02
575	*Brian McRae*(FC)	.40	.30	.15	666	Willie McGee	.08	.06	.03
576	Jack Daugherty	.05	.04	.02	667	*Chris Nabholz*(FC)	.20	.15	.08
577	Ozzie Guillen	.06	.05	.02	668	Brady Anderson	.04	.03	.02
578	Joe Boever	.04	.03	.02	669	*Darren Holmes*(FC)	.12	.09	.05
579	Luis Sojo	.06	.05	.02	670	Ken Hill	.06	.05	.02
580	Chili Davis	.06	.05	.02	671	Gary Varsho	.04	.03	.02
581	Don Robinson	.04	.03	.02	672	Bill Pecota	.05	.04	.02
582	Brian Harper	.06	.05	.02	673	Fred Lynn	.05	.04	.02
583	Paul O'Neill	.06	.05	.02	674	Kevin D. Brown(FC)	.10	.08	.04
584	Bob Ojeda	.05	.04	.02	675	Dan Petry	.04	.03	.02
585	Mookie Wilson	.05	.04	.02	676	Mike Jackson	.05	.04	.02
586	Rafael Ramirez	.04	.03	.02	677	Wally Joyner	.12	.09	.05
587	Gary Redus	.04	.03	.02	678	Danny Jackson	.05	.04	.02
588	Jamie Quirk	.04	.03	.02	679	*Bill Haselman*(FC)	.12	.09	.05
589	Shawn Hilligas	.04	.03	.02	680	Mike Boddicker	.06	.05	.02
590	*Tom Edens*(FC)	.08	.06	.03	681	*Mel Rojas*(FC)	.12	.09	.05
591	Joe Klink(FC)	.05	.04	.02	682	Roberto Alomar	.12	.09	.05
592	Charles Nagy(FC)	.20	.15	.08	683	Dave Justice (R.O.Y.)	.25	.20	.10
593	Eric Plunk	.04	.03	.02	684	Chuck Crim	.04	.03	.02
594	Tracy Jones	.04	.03	.02	685	Matt Williams	.12	.09	.05
595	Craig Biggio	.08	.06	.03	686	Shawon Dunston	.06	.05	.02
596	Jose DeJesus	.06	.05	.02	687	*Jeff Schulz*(FC)	.08	.06	.03
597	Mickey Tettleton	.08	.06	.03	688	*John Barfield*(FC)	.08	.06	.03
598	Chris Gwynn	.05	.04	.02	689	Gerald Young	.04	.03	.02
599	Rex Hudler	.06	.05	.02	690	*Luis Gonzalez*(FC)	.50	.40	.20

		MT	NR MT	EX
691	Frank Wills	.05	.04	.02
692	Chuck Finley	.08	.06	.03
693	Sandy Alomar (R.O.Y.)	.15	.11	.06
694	Tim Drummond	.05	.04	.02
695	Herm Winningham	.04	.03	.02
696	Darryl Strawberry	.25	.20	.10
697	Al Leiter	.04	.03	.02
698	*Karl Rhodes*(FC)	.25	.20	.10
699	Stan Belinda(FC)	.08	.06	.03
700	Checklist	.04	.03	.02
701	Lance Blankenship	.04	.03	.02
702	Willie Stargell (Puzzle Card)	.10	.08	.04
703	Jim Gantner	.05	.04	.02
704	*Reggie Harris*(FC)	.15	.11	.06
705	Rob Ducey	.04	.03	.02
706	Tim Hulett	.04	.03	.02
707	Atlee Hammaker	.04	.03	.02
708	Xavier Hernandez	.04	.03	.02
709	Chuck McElroy(FC)	.08	.06	.03
710	John Mitchell	.04	.03	.02
711	Carlos Hernandez	.05	.04	.02
712	Geronimo Pena(FC)	.10	.08	.04
713	*Jim Neidlinger*(FC)	.15	.11	.06
714	John Orton	.04	.03	.02
715	Terry Leach	.04	.03	.02
716	Mike Stanton	.06	.05	.02
717	Walt Terrell	.04	.03	.02
718	Luis Aquino	.05	.04	.02
719	Bud Black	.05	.04	.02
720	Bob Kipper	.04	.03	.02
721	*Jeff Gray*(FC)	.15	.11	.06
722	Jose Rijo	.08	.06	.03
723	Curt Young	.04	.03	.02
724	Jose Vizcaino(FC)	.08	.06	.03
725	*Randy Tomlin*(FC)	.15	.11	.06
726	Junior Noboa	.05	.04	.02
727	Bob Welch (Award Winner)	.08	.06	.03
728	Gary Ward	.04	.03	.02
729	Rob Deer	.05	.04	.02
730	*David Segui*(FC)	.25	.20	.10
731	Mark Carreon	.04	.03	.02
732	Vicente Palacios	.04	.03	.02
733	Sam Horn	.05	.04	.02
734	*Howard Farmer*(FC)	.15	.11	.06
735	Ken Dayley	.04	.03	.02
736	Kelly Mann	.08	.06	.03
737	*Joe Grahe*(FC)	.12	.09	.05
738	Kelly Downs	.04	.03	.02
739	*Jimmy Kremers*(FC)	.15	.11	.06
740	Kevin Appier	.12	.09	.05
741	Jeff Reed	.04	.03	.02
742	Jose Rijo (World Series)	.08	.06	.03
743	*Dave Rohde*(FC)	.12	.09	.05
744	Dr. Dirt/ Mr. Clean (Len Dykstra, Dale Murphy)	.25	.20	.10
745	Paul Sorrento	.06	.05	.02
746	Thomas Howard(FC)	.10	.08	.04
747	Matt Stark(FC)	.20	.15	.08
748	Harold Baines	.08	.06	.03
749	Doug Dascenzo	.05	.04	.02
750	Doug Drabek (Award Winner)	.08	.06	.03
751	Gary Sheffield	.15	.11	.06
752	*Terry Lee*(FC)	.20	.15	.08
753	*Jim Vatcher*(FC)	.08	.06	.03
754	Lee Stevens	.12	.09	.05
755	Randy Veres(FC)	.08	.06	.03
756	Bill Doran	.06	.05	.02
757	Gary Wayne	.04	.03	.02
758	*Pedro Munoz*(FC)	.35	.25	.14
759	Chris Hammond(FC)	.08	.06	.03
760	Checklist	.04	.03	.02
761	Rickey Henderson (MVP)	.12	.09	.05
762	Barry Bonds (MVP)	.12	.09	.05
763	Billy Hatcher (World Series)	.05	.04	.02
764	Julio Machado	.05	.04	.02
765	Jose Mesa	.05	.04	.02
766	Willie Randolph (World Series)	.05	.04	.02
767	*Scott Erickson*(FC)	.40	.30	.15
768	*Travis Fryman*(FC)	.60	.45	.25
769	Rich Rodriguez(FC)	.12	.09	.05
770	Checklist, Checklist	.04	.03	.02

1991 Donruss Elite

Donruss released a series of special inserts in 1991. 10,000 of each elite card was released, while 7,500 Legend cards and 5,000 Signature cards were also issued. Cards were inserted in wax packs and feature marble borders. The Legend card features a Dick Perez drawing. Each card is designated with a number out of the production number on the card back.

		MT	NR MT	EX
Complete Set:		1500.00	1100.00	600.00
Common Player:		75.00	55.00	30.00
1	Barry Bonds	100.00	75.00	40.00
2	George Brett	100.00	75.00	40.00
3	Jose Canseco	150.00	110.00	60.00
4	Andre Dawson	100.00	75.00	40.00
5	Doug Drabek	75.00	55.00	40.00
6	Cecil Fielder	100.00	75.00	40.00
7	Rickey Henderson	150.00	110.00	60.00
8	Matt Williams	75.00	55.00	30.00
-----	Nolan Ryan (Legend)	350.00	260.00	140.00
-----	Ryne Sandberg (Signature)	350.00	260.00	140.00

Values for recent cards and sets are listed in Mint (MT), Near Mint (NM) and Excellent (EX), reflecting the fact that many cards from recent years have been preserved in top condition. Recent cards and sets in less than Excellent condition have little collector interest.

1991 Donruss Highlights

This 22-card subset features highlights from the 1990 season. The cards feature a "BC" designation along with the number and are styled after the 1991 regular issue Donruss Cards. Cards 1-10 feature blue borders due to their release with Series I cards. Cards 11-22 feature green borders and were released with Series II cards. A highlight logo appears on the front of the card. Each highlight is explained in depth on the card back.

		MT	NR MT	EX
Complete Set:		3.00	2.25	1.25
Common Player:		.10	.08	.04
1	Langston/Witt (No-Hit Mariners)	.15	.11	.06
2	Randy Johnson (No-Hits Tigers)	.15	.11	.06
3	Nolan Ryan (No-Hits A's)	.40	.30	.15
4	Dave Stewart (No-Hits Blue Jays)	.15	.11	.06
5	Cecil Fielder (50 Homer Club)	.25	.20	.10
6	Carlton Fisk (Record Home Run)	.20	.15	.08
7	Ryne Sandberg (Sets Fielding Records)	.20	.15	.08
8	Gary Carter (Breaks Catching Mark)	.15	.11	.06
9	Mark McGwire (Home Run Milestone)	.15	.11	.06
10	Bo Jackson (4 Consecutive HRs)	.25	.20	.10

#	Player	MT	NR MT	EX
11	Fernando Valenzuela (No-Hits Cardinals)			
		.15	.11	.06
12	Andy Hawkins (No-Hits White Sox)	.10	.08	.04
13	Melido Perez (No-Hits Yankees)	.10	.08	.04
14	Terry Mulholland (No-Hits Giants)	.10	.08	.04
15	Nolan Ryan (300th Win)	.40	.30	.15
16	Delino DeShields (4 Hits In Debut)	.15	.11	.06
17	Cal Ripken (Errorless Games)	.20	.15	.08
18	Eddie Murray (Switch Hit Homers)	.15	.11	.06
19	George Brett (3 Decade Champ)	.20	.15	.08
20	Bobby Thigpen (Shatters Save Mark)			
		.15	.11	.06
21	Dave Stieb (No-Hits Indians)	.10	.08	.06
22	Willie McGee (NL Batting Champ)	.10	.08	.04

#	Player	MT	NR MT	EX
41	Carlos Rodriguez(FC)	.10	.08	.04
42	Mark Lewis	.20	.15	.08
43	Brent Mayne	.10	.08	.04
44	Chris Haney(FC)	.15	.11	.06
45	Denis Boucher(FC)	.15	.11	.06
46	Mike Gardiner	.10	.08	.04
47	Jeff Johnson(FC)	.15	.11	.06
48	Dean Palmer	.30	.25	.12
49	Chuck McElroy	.10	.08	.04
50	Chris Jones(FC)	.10	.08	.04
51	Scott Kamieniecki(FC)	.10	.08	.04
52	Al Osuna(FC)	.10	.08	.04
53	Rusty Meacham(FC)	.15	.11	.06
54	Chito Martinez(FC)	.25	.20	.10
55	Reggie Jefferson(FC)	.25	.20	.10
56	Checklist	.05	.04	.02

1991 Donruss Rookies

Red borders highlight the 1991 Donruss Rookies cards. This set marks the sixth year that Donruss has produced such an issue. Like in past years, "The Rookies" logo appears on the card fronts. The set is packaged in a special box and includes a Willie Stargell puzzle card.

		MT	NR MT	EX
	Complete Set:	6.00	4.50	2.50
	Common Player:	.10	.08	.04
1	Pat Kelly(FC)	.20	.15	.08
2	Rich DeLucia	.10	.08	.04
3	Wes Chamberlain	.40	.30	.15
4	Scott Leius(FC)	.10	.08	.04
5	Darryl Kile(FC)	.15	.11	.06
6	Milt Cuyler	.15	.11	.06
7	Todd Van Poppel(FC)	.60	.45	.25
8	Ray Lankford	.20	.15	.08
9	Brian Hunter(FC)	.40	.30	.15
10	Tony Perezchica	.10	.08	.04
11	Ced Landrum(FC)	.10	.08	.04
12	Dave Burba(FC)	.10	.08	.04
13	Ramon Garcia(FC)	.20	.15	.08
14	Ed Sprague(FC)	.15	.11	.06
15	Warren Newson(FC)	.15	.11	.06
16	Paul Faries(FC)	.10	.08	.04
17	Luis Gonzalez	.35	.25	.14
18	Charles Nagy	.15	.11	.06
19	Chris Hammond	.10	.08	.04
20	Frank Castillo(FC)	.25	.20	.10
21	Pedro Munoz	.20	.15	.08
22	Orlando Merced(FC)	.40	.30	.15
23	Jose Melendez(FC)	.10	.08	.04
24	Kirk Dressendorfer(FC)	.30	.25	.12
25	Heathcliff Slocumb(FC)	.10	.08	.04
26	Doug Simons(FC)	.10	.08	.04
27	Mike Timlin(FC)	.20	.15	.08
28	Jeff Fassero(FC)	.10	.08	.04
29	Mark Leiter(FC)	.10	.08	.04
30	Jeff Bagwell(FC)	1.25	.90	.50
31	Brian McRae	.35	.25	.14
32	Mark Whiten	.20	.15	.08
33	Ivan Rodriguez(FC)	1.25	.90	.50
34	Wade Taylor(FC)	.10	.08	.04
35	Darren Lewis(FC)	.35	.25	.12
36	Mo Vaughn	.40	.30	.15
37	Mike Remlinger(FC)	.10	.08	.04
38	Rick Wilkins(FC)	.20	.15	.08
39	Chuck Knoblauch	.40	.30	.15
40	Kevin Morton	.15	.11	.06

1991 Donruss Grand Slammers

This 14-card set features players who hit grand slams in 1990. The cards are styled after the 1991 Donruss regular issue cards. The featured player is showcased with a star in the background. This set is the third Donruss Grand Slammers issue.

		MT	NR MT	EX
	Complete Set:	2.50	2.00	1.00
	Common Player:	.10	.08	.04
1	Joe Carter	.20	.15	.08
2	Bobby Bonilla	.20	.15	.08
3	Kal Daniels	.15	.11	.06
4	Jose Canseco	.30	.25	.12
5	Barry Bonds	.25	.20	.10
6	Jay Buhner	.15	.11	.06
7	Cecil Fielder	.30	.25	.12
8	Matt Williams	.20	.15	.08
9	Andres Galarraga	.10	.08	.04
10	Luis Polonia	.10	.08	.04
11	Mark McGwire	.20	.15	.08
12	Ron Karkovice	.10	.08	.04
13	Darryl Strawberry	.25	.20	.10
14	Mike Greenwell	.20	.15	.06

1991 Donruss Studio

Donruss introduced this 264-card set in 1991. The cards feature marron borders surrounding black and white posed player photos. The card backs are printed in black and white and feature personal data, career highlights, hobbies and interests and the player's hero. The cards were released in foil packs only and feature a special Rod Carew puzzle.

		MT	NR MT	EX
Complete Set:		40.00	30.00	15.00
Common Player:		.12	.09	.05
1	Glenn Davis	.15	.11	.06
2	Dwight Evans	.15	.11	.06
3	Leo Gomez	.50	.40	.20
4	Chris Hoiles	.25	.20	.10
5	Sam Horn	.12	.09	.05
6	Ben McDonald	.50	.40	.20
7	Randy Milligan	.12	.09	.05
8	Gregg Olson	.15	.11	.06
9	Cal Ripken,Jr.	2.00	1.50	.80
10	David Segui	.20	.15	.08
11	Wade Boggs	.60	.45	.25
12	Ellis Burks	.25	.20	.10
13	Jack Clark	.12	.09	.05
14	Roger Clemens	1.00	.70	.40
15	Mike Greenwell	.20	.15	.08
16	Tim Naehring	.15	.11	.06
17	Tony Pena	.12	.09	.05
18	Phil Plantier	2.00	1.50	.80
19	Jeff Reardon	.15	.11	.06
20	Mo Vaughn	1.50	1.25	.60
21	Jimmy Reese	.15	.11	.06
22	Jim Abbott	.30	.25	.12
23	Bert Blyleven	.15	.11	.06
24	Chuck Finley	.20	.15	.08
25	Gary Gaetti	.12	.09	.05
26	Wally Joyner	.30	.25	.12
27	Mark Langston	.25	.20	.10
28	Kirk McCaskill	.12	.09	.05
29	Lance Parrish	.15	.11	.06
30	Dave Winfield	.25	.20	.10
31	Alex Fernandez	.50	.40	.20
32	Carlton Fisk	.35	.25	.14
33	Scott Fletcher	.12	.09	.05
34	Greg Hibbard	.12	.09	.05
35	Charlie Hough	.12	.09	.05
36	Jack McDowell	.25	.20	.10
37	Tim Rock Raines	.25	.20	.10
38	Sammy Sosa	.20	.15	.08
39	Bobby Thigpen	.25	.20	.10
40	Frank Thomas	8.00	6.00	3.00
41	Sandy Alomar	.30	.25	.12
42	John Farrell	.12	.09	.05
43	Glenallen Hill	.15	.11	.06
44	Brook Jacoby	.12	.09	.05
45	Chris James	.12	.09	.05
46	Doug Jones	.12	.09	.05
47	Eric King	.12	.09	.05
48	Mark Lewis	.60	.45	.25
49	Greg Swindell	.15	.11	.06
50	Mark Whiten	.50	.40	.20
51	Milt Cuyler	.30	.25	.12
52	Rob Deer	.12	.09	.05
53	Cecil Fielder	1.00	.70	.40
54	Travis Fryman	3.50	2.25	1.25
55	Bill Gullickson	.12	.09	.05
56	Lloyd Moseby	.12	.09	.05
57	Frank Tanana	.12	.09	.05
58	Mickey Tettleton	.20	.15	.08
59	Alan Trammell	.25	.20	.10
60	Lou Whitaker	.20	.15	.08
61	Mike Boddicker	.12	.09	.05
62	George Brett	.30	.25	.12
63	Jeff Conine	.40	.30	.15
64	Warren Cromartie	.12	.09	.05
65	Storm Davis	.12	.09	.05
66	Kirk Gibson	.20	.15	.08
67	Mark Gubicza	.15	.11	.06
68	Brian McRae	1.00	.70	.40
69	Bret Saberhagen	.15	.11	.06
70	Kurt Stillwell	.12	.09	.05
71	Tim McIntosh	.15	.11	.06
72	Candy Maldonado	.12	.09	.05
73	Paul Molitor	.20	.15	.08
74	Willie Randolph	.12	.09	.05
75	Ron Robinson	.12	.09	.05
76	Gary Sheffield	.25	.20	.10
77	Franklin Stubbs	.12	.09	.05
78	B.J. Surhoff	.12	.09	.05

		MT	NR MT	EX
79	Greg Vaughn	.25	.20	.10
80	Robin Yount	.35	.25	.14
81	Rick Aguilera	.20	.15	.08
82	Steve Bedrosian	.12	.09	.05
83	Scott Erickson	1.50	1.25	.60
84	Greg Gagne	.12	.09	.05
85	Dan Gladden	.12	.09	.05
86	Brian Harper	.15	.11	.06
87	Kent Hrbek	.15	.11	.06
88	Shane Mack	.25	.20	.10
89	Jack Morris	.20	.15	.08
90	Kirby Puckett	.70	.50	.30
91	Jesse Barfield	.12	.09	.05
92	Steve Farr	.12	.09	.05
93	Steve Howe	.12	.09	.05
94	Roberto Kelly	.20	.15	.08
95	Tim Leary	.12	.09	.05
96	Kevin Maas	.50	.40	.20
97	Don Mattingly	.50	.40	.20
98	Hensley Meulens	.20	.15	.08
99	Scott Sanderson	.12	.09	.05
100	Steve Sax	.15	.11	.06
101	Jose Canseco	1.50	1.25	.60
102	Dennis Eckersley	.25	.20	.10
103	Dave Henderson	.15	.11	.06
104	Rickey Henderson	1.00	.70	.40
105	Rick Honeycutt	.12	.09	.05
106	Mark McGwire	.80	.60	.30
107	Dave Stewart	.20	.15	.08
108	Eric Show	.12	.09	.05
109	Todd Van Poppel	2.00	1.50	.80
110	Bob Welch	.15	.11	.06
111	Alvin Davis	.12	.09	.05
112	Ken Griffey,Jr.	3.00	2.25	1.25
113	Ken Griffey,Sr.	.20	.15	.08
114	Erik Hanson	.15	.11	.06
115	Brian Holman	.12	.09	.05
116	Randy Johnson	.15	.11	.06
117	Edgar Martinez	.15	.11	.06
118	Tino Martinez	.35	.25	.14
119	Harold Reynolds	.15	.11	.06
120	David Valle	.12	.09	.05
121	Kevin Belcher	.12	.09	.05
122	Scott Chiamparino	.12	.09	.05
123	Julio Franco	.20	.15	.08
124	Juan Gonzalez	4.00	3.00	1.50
125	Rich Gossage	.15	.11	.06
126	Jeff Kunkel	.12	.09	.05
127	Rafael Palmeiro	.30	.25	.12
128	Nolan Ryan	2.50	2.00	1.00
129	Ruben Sierra	.60	.45	.25
130	Bobby Witt	.15	.11	.06
131	Roberto Alomar	.40	.30	.15
132	Tom Candiotti	.12	.09	.05
133	Joe Carter	.30	.25	.12
134	Ken Dayley	.12	.09	.05
135	Kelly Gruber	.15	.11	.06
136	John Olerud	.40	.30	.15
137	Dave Stieb	.15	.11	.06
138	Turner Ward	.25	.20	.10
139	Devon White	.15	.11	.06
140	Mookie Wilson	.12	.09	.05
141	Steve Avery	2.50	2.00	1.00
142	Sid Bream	.12	.09	.05
143	Nick Esasky	.12	.09	.05
144	Ron Gant	.70	.50	.30
145	Tom Glavine	.20	.15	.08
146	David Justice	3.00	2.25	1.25
147	Kelly Mann	.12	.09	.05
148	Terry Pendleton	.15	.11	.06
149	John Smoltz	.20	.15	.08
150	Jeff Treadway	.12	.09	.05
151	George Bell	.20	.15	.08
152	Shawn Boskie	.12	.09	.05
153	Andre Dawson	.30	.25	.12
154	Lance Dickson	.25	.20	.10
155	Shawon Dunston	.20	.15	.08
156	Joe Girardi	.12	.09	.05
157	Mark Grace	.40	.30	.15
158	Ryne Sandberg	1.25	.90	.50
159	Gary Scott	.25	.20	.10
160	Dave Smith	.12	.09	.05
161	Tom Browning	.15	.11	.06
162	Eric Davis	.30	.25	.12
163	Rob Dibble	.20	.15	.08
164	Mariano Duncan	.12	.09	.05
165	Chris Hammond	.12	.09	.05
166	Billy Hatcher	.12	.09	.05
167	Barry Larkin	.30	.25	.12
168	Hal Morris	.30	.25	.12
169	Paul O'Neill	.15	.11	.06

		MT	NR MT	EX
170	Chris Sabo	.15	.11	.06
171	Eric Anthony	.15	.11	.06
172	Jeff Bagwell	3.00	2.25	1.25
173	Craig Biggio	.20	.15	.08
174	Ken Caminitti	.15	.11	.06
175	Jim Deshaies	.12	.09	.05
176	Steve Finley	.15	.11	.06
177	Pete Harnisch	.15	.11	.06
178	Darryl Kile	.20	.15	.08
179	Curt Schilling	.12	.09	.05
180	Mike Scott	.12	.09	.05
181	Brett Butler	.15	.11	.06
182	Gary Carter	.15	.11	.06
183	Orel Hershiser	.20	.15	.08
184	Ramon Martinez	.60	.45	.25
185	Eddie Murray	.30	.25	.12
186	Jose Offerman	.25	.20	.10
187	Bob Ojeda	.12	.09	.05
188	Juan Samuel	.15	.11	.06
189	Mike Scioscia	.15	.11	.06
190	Darryl Strawberry	.80	.60	.30
191	Moises Alou	.15	.11	.06
192	Brian Barnes	.15	.11	.06
193	Oil Can Boyd	.15	.11	.06
194	Ivan Calderon	.15	.11	.06
195	Delino DeShields	.20	.15	.08
196	Mike Fitzgerald	.12	.09	.05
197	Andres Galarraga	.15	.11	.06
198	Marquis Grissom	.30	.25	.12
199	Bill Sampen	.12	.09	.05
200	Tim Wallach	.12	.09	.05
201	Daryl Boston	.12	.09	.05
202	Vince Coleman	.20	.15	.08
203	John Franco	.15	.11	.06
204	Dwight Gooden	.35	.25	.14
205	Tom Herr	.12	.09	.05
206	Gregg Jefferies	.20	.15	.08
207	Howard Johnson	.20	.15	.08
208	Dave Magadan	.20	.15	.08
209	Kevin McReynolds	.15	.11	.06
210	Frank Viola	.20	.15	.08
211	Wes Chamberlain	.70	.50	.30
212	Darren Daulton	.12	.09	.05
213	Lenny Dykstra	.20	.15	.08
214	Charlie Hayes	.15	.11	.06
215	Ricky Jordan	.15	.11	.06
216	Steve Lake	.12	.09	.05
217	Roger McDowell	.12	.09	.05
218	Mickey Morandini	.15	.11	.06
219	Terry Mulholland	.15	.11	.06
220	Dale Murphy	.20	.15	.08
221	Jay Bell	.15	.11	.06
222	Barry Bonds	.60	.45	.25
223	Bobby Bonilla	.60	.45	.25
224	Doug Drabek	.15	.11	.06
225	Bill Landrum	.12	.09	.05
226	Mike LaValliere	.12	.09	.05
227	Jose Lind	.12	.09	.05
228	Don Slaught	.12	.09	.05
229	John Smiley	.15	.11	.06
230	Andy Van Slyke	.20	.15	.08
231	Bernard Gilkey	.20	.15	.08
232	Pedro Guerrero	.20	.15	.08
233	Rex Hudler	.12	.09	.05
234	Ray Lankford	1.50	1.25	.60
235	Joe Magrane	.12	.09	.05
236	Jose Oquendo	.12	.09	.05
237	Lee Smith	.15	.11	.06
238	Ozzie Smith	.40	.30	.15
239	Milt Thompson	.12	.09	.05
240	Todd Zeile	.30	.25	.12
241	Larry Andersen	.12	.09	.05
242	Andy Benes	.30	.25	.12
243	Paul Faries	.12	.09	.05
244	Tony Fernandez	.12	.09	.05
245	Tony Gwynn	.50	.40	.20
246	Atlee Hammaker	.12	.09	.05
247	Fred McGriff	.35	.25	.14
248	Bip Roberts	.12	.09	.05
249	Benito Santiago	.15	.11	.06
250	Ed Whitson	.12	.09	.05
251	Dave Anderson	.12	.09	.05
252	Mike Benjamin	.15	.11	.06
253	John Burkett	.15	.11	.06
254	Will Clark	1.00	.70	.40
255	Scott Garrelts	.12	.09	.05
256	Willie McGee	.15	.11	.06
257	Kevin Mitchell	.30	.25	.12
258	Dave Righetti	.15	.11	.06
259	Matt Williams	.30	.25	.12
260	Black & Decker	.20	.15	.08

		MT	NR MT	EX
261	Checklist	.10	.08	.04
262	Checklist	.10	.08	.04
263	Checklist	.10	.08	.04
264	Checklist	.10	.08	.04

1992 Donruss

For the second consecutive year, Donruss chose to release its card set in two series. The 1992 cards feature improved stock, an anti-couterfeit feature and include both front and back photos. Once again Rated Rookies and All-Stars are included in the set. Special highlight cards also can be found in the 1992 Donruss set. Production was reduced in 1992 compared to other years.

		MT	NR MT	EX
	Complete Set:	35.00	26.00	14.00
	Common Player:	.05	.04	.02
1	*Mark Wohlers* (RR)(FC)	.15	.11	.06
2	Will Cordero (RR)(FC)	.30	.25	.12
3	Kyle Abbott (RR)(FC)	.30	.25	.12
4	*Dave Nilsson* (RR)(FC)	.50	.40	.20
5	*Kenny Lofton* (RR)(FC)	.60	.45	.25
6	*Luis Mercedes* (RR)(FC)	.20	.15	.08
7	Roger Salkeld (RR)(FC)	.30	.25	.12
8	Eddie Zosky (RR)(FC)	.25	.20	.10
9	Todd Van Poppel (RR)	.30	.25	.12
10	*Frank Seminara* (RR)(FC)	.25	.20	.10
11	*Andy Ashby* (RR)(FC)	.20	.15	.08
12	Reggie Jefferson (RR)(FC)	.35	.25	.14
13	*Ryan Klesko* (RR)(FC)	.50	.40	.20
14	*Carlos Garcia* (RR)(FC)	.25	.20	.10
15	John Ramos (RR)(FC)	.25	.20	.10
16	Eric Karros (RR)(FC)	.70	.50	.30
17	*Pat Lennon* (RR)(FC)	.35	.25	.14
18	*Eddie Taubensee* (RR)(FC)	.40	.30	.15
19	*Roberto Hernandez* (RR)(FC)	.20	.15	.08
20	D.J. Dozier (RR)(FC)	.20	.15	.08
21	Dave Henderson (AS)	.10	.08	.04
22	Cal Ripken (AS)	.20	.15	.08
23	Wade Boggs (AS)	.20	.15	.08
24	Ken Griffey,Jr. (AS)	.60	.45	.25
25	Jack Morris (AS)	.10	.08	.04
26	Danny Tartabull (AS)	.10	.08	.04
27	Cecil Fielder (AS)	.20	.15	.08
28	Roberto Alomar (AS)	.20	.15	.08
29	Sandy Alomar (AS)	.10	.08	.04
30	Rickey Henderson (AS)	.20	.15	.08
31	Ken Hill	.06	.05	.02
32	John Habyan	.05	.04	.02
33	Otis Nixon (Highlight)	.10	.08	.04
34	Tim Wallach	.08	.06	.03
35	Cal Ripken	.25	.20	.10
36	Gary Carter	.08	.06	.03
37	Juan Agosto	.05	.04	.02
38	Doug Dascenzo	.05	.04	.02
39	Kirk Gibson	.08	.06	.03
40	Benito Santiago	.08	.06	.03
41	Otis Nixon	.06	.05	.02
42	Andy Allanson	.05	.04	.02
43	Brian Holman	.06	.05	.02
44	Dick Schofield	.05	.04	.02
45	Dave Magadan	.08	.06	.03
46	Rafael Palmeiro	.10	.08	.04
47	Jody Reed	.06	.03	.02
48	Ivan Calderon	.08	.06	.03
49	Greg Harris	.05	.04	.02

#	Player	MT	NR MT	EX
50	Chris Sabo	.08	.06	.03
51	Paul Molitor	.10	.08	.04
52	Robby Thompson	.06	.05	.02
53	Dave Smith	.05	.04	.02
54	Mark Davis	.05	.04	.02
55	Kevin Brown	.06	.05	.02
56	Donn Pall	.05	.04	.02
57	Lenny Dykstra	.08	.06	.03
58	Roberto Alomar	.15	.11	.06
59	Jeff Robinson	.05	.04	.02
60	Willie McGee	.08	.06	.03
61	Jay Buhner	.08	.06	.03
62	Mike Pagliarulo	.05	.04	.02
63	Paul O'Neill	.08	.06	.03
64	Hubie Brooks	.06	.05	.02
65	Kelly Gruber	.08	.06	.03
66	Ken Caminiti	.06	.05	.02
67	Gary Redus	.05	.04	.02
68	Harold Baines	.08	.06	.03
69	Charlie Hough	.06	.05	.02
70	B.J. Surhoff	.06	.05	.02
71	Walt Weiss	.06	.05	.02
72	Shawn Hillegas	.05	.04	.02
73	Roberto Kelly	.08	.06	.03
74	Jeff Ballard	.05	.04	.02
75	Craig Biggio	.08	.06	.03
76	Pat Combs	.06	.05	.02
77	Jeff Robinson	.05	.04	.02
78	Tim Belcher	.06	.05	.02
79	Cris Carpenter	.06	.05	.02
80	Checklist	.05	.04	.02
81	Steve Avery	.30	.25	.12
82	Chris James	.05	.04	.02
83	Brian Harper	.06	.05	.02
84	Charlie Leibrandt	.06	.05	.02
85	Mickey Tettleton	.08	.06	.03
86	Pete O'Brien	.06	.05	.02
87	Danny Darwin	.05	.04	.02
88	Bob Walk	.05	.04	.02
89	Jeff Reardon	.08	.06	.03
90	Bobby Rose	.08	.06	.03
91	Danny Jackson	.06	.05	.02
92	John Morris	.05	.04	.02
93	Bud Black	.06	.05	.02
94	Tommy Greene (Highlight)	.10	.08	.04
95	Rick Aguilera	.08	.06	.03
96	Gary Gaetti	.08	.06	.03
97	David Cone	.08	.06	.03
98	John Olerud	.20	.15	.08
99	Joel Skinner	.05	.04	.02
100	Jay Bell	.08	.06	.03
101	Bob Milacki	.05	.04	.02
102	Norm Charlton	.06	.05	.02
103	Chuck Crim	.05	.04	.02
104	Terry Steinbach	.06	.05	.02
105	Juan Samuel	.08	.06	.03
106	Steve Howe	.06	.05	.02
107	Rafael Belliard	.05	.04	.02
108	Joey Cora	.05	.04	.02
109	Tommy Greene	.08	.06	.03
110	Gregg Olson	.08	.06	.03
111	Frank Tanana	.06	.05	.02
112	Lee Smith	.08	.06	.03
113	Greg Harris	.05	.04	.02
114	Dwayne Henry	.05	.04	.02
115	Chili Davis	.08	.06	.03
116	Kent Mercker	.08	.06	.03
117	Brian Barnes	.08	.06	.03
118	Rich DeLucia	.06	.05	.02
119	Andre Dawson	.15	.11	.06
120	Carlos Baerga	.08	.06	.03
121	Mike LaValliere	.06	.05	.02
122	Jeff Gray	.06	.05	.02
123	Bruce Hurst	.08	.06	.03
124	Alvin Davis	.08	.06	.03
125	John Candelaria	.06	.05	.02
126	Matt Nokes	.08	.06	.03
127	George Bell	.10	.08	.04
128	Bret Saberhagen	.10	.08	.04
129	Jeff Russell	.08	.06	.03
130	Jim Abbott	.15	.11	.06
131	Bill Gullickson	.06	.05	.02
132	Todd Zeile	.15	.11	.06
133	Dave Winfield	.10	.08	.04
134	Wally Whitehurst	.06	.05	.02
135	Matt Williams	.15	.11	.06
136	Tom Browning	.08	.06	.03
137	Marquis Grissom	.15	.11	.06
138	Erik Hanson	.10	.08	.04
139	Rob Dibble	.08	.06	.03
140	Don August	.05	.04	.02
141	Tom Henke	.08	.06	.03
142	Dan Pasqua	.06	.05	.02
143	George Brett	.15	.11	.06
144	Jerald Clark	.06	.05	.02
145	Robin Ventura	.25	.20	.10
146	Dale Murphy	.10	.08	.04
147	Dennis Eckersley	.10	.08	.04
148	Eric Yelding	.05	.04	.02
149	Mario Diaz	.05	.04	.02
150	Casey Candaele	.05	.04	.02
151	Steve Olin	.06	.05	.02
152	Luis Salazar	.05	.04	.02
153	Kevin Maas	.15	.11	.06
154	Nolan Ryan (Highlight)	.40	.30	.15
155	Barry Jones	.05	.04	.02
156	Chris Hoiles	.15	.11	.06
157	Bobby Ojeda	.06	.05	.02
158	Pedro Guerrero	.08	.06	.03
159	Paul Assenmacher	.05	.04	.02
160	Checklist	.05	.04	.02
161	Mike Macfarlane	.06	.05	.02
162	Craig Lefferts	.06	.05	.02
163	*Brian Hunter*	.20	.15	.08
164	Alan Trammell	.10	.08	.04
165	Ken Griffey, Jr.	.50	.40	.20
166	Lance Parrish	.08	.06	.03
167	Brian Downing	.05	.04	.02
168	John Barfield	.06	.05	.02
169	Jack Clark	.08	.06	.03
170	Chris Nabholz	.06	.05	.02
171	Tim Teufel	.05	.04	.02
172	Chris Hammond	.08	.06	.03
173	Robin Yount	.20	.15	.08
174	Dave Righetti	.08	.04	.02
175	Joe Girardi	.06	.05	.02
176	Mike Boddicker	.06	.05	.02
177	Dean Palmer	.25	.20	.10
178	Greg Hibbard	.06	.05	.02
179	Randy Ready	.05	.04	.02
180	Devon White	.08	.06	.03
181	Mark Eichhorn	.05	.04	.02
182	Mike Felder	.05	.04	.02
183	Joe Klink	.05	.04	.02
184	Steve Bedrosian	.06	.05	.02
185	Barry Larkin	.15	.11	.06
186	John Franco	.08	.06	.03
187	*Ed Sprague*	.15	.11	.06
188	Mark Portugal	.05	.04	.02
189	Jose Lind	.05	.04	.02
190	Bob Welch	.08	.06	.03
191	Alex Fernandez	.25	.20	.10
192	Gary Sheffield	.25	.20	.10
193	Rickey Henderson	.20	.15	.08
194	Rod Nichols	.05	.04	.02
195	*Scott Kamieniecki*	.15	.11	.06
196	Mike Flanagan	.05	.04	.02
197	Steve Finley	.08	.06	.03
198	Darren Daulton	.06	.05	.02
199	Leo Gomez	.15	.11	.06
200	Mike Morgan	.06	.05	.02
201	Bob Tewksbury	.05	.04	.02
202	Sid Bream	.08	.06	.03
203	Sandy Alomar	.15	.11	.06
204	Greg Gagne	.05	.04	.02
205	Juan Berenguer	.05	.04	.02
206	Cecil Fielder	.25	.20	.10
207	Randy Johnson	.08	.06	.03
208	Tony Pena	.06	.05	.02
209	Doug Drabek	.10	.08	.04
210	Wade Boggs	.20	.15	.08
211	Bryan Harvey	.08	.06	.03
212	Jose Vizcaino	.06	.05	.02
213	*Alonzo Powell* (FC)	.15	.11	.06
214	Will Clark	.30	.25	.12
215	Rickey Henderson (Highlight)	.20	.15	.08
216	Jack Morris	.08	.06	.03
217	Junior Felix	.06	.05	.02
218	Vince Coleman	.08	.06	.03
219	Jimmy Key	.08	.06	.03
220	Alex Cole	.08	.06	.03
221	Bill Landrum	.06	.05	.02
222	Randy Milligan	.08	.06	.03
223	Jose Rijo	.08	.06	.03
224	Greg Vaughn	.10	.08	.04
225	Dave Stewart	.08	.06	.03
226	Lenny Harris	.06	.05	.02
227	Scott Sanderson	.06	.05	.02
228	Jeff Blauser	.06	.05	.02
229	Ozzie Guillen	.08	.06	.03
230	John Kruk	.08	.06	.03
231	Bob Melvin	.05	.04	.02

		MT	NR MT	EX				MT	NR MT	EX
232	Milt Cuyler	.15	.11	.06		323	Bryn Smith	.05	.04	.02
233	Felix Jose	.15	.11	.06		324	Jeff Treadway	.06	.05	.02
234	Ellis Burks	.10	.08	.04		325	Mark Whiten	.15	.11	.06
235	Pete Harnisch	.06	.05	.02		326	Kent Hrbek	.08	.06	.03
236	Kevin Tapani	.08	.06	.03		327	David Justice	.35	.25	.14
237	Terry Pendleton	.08	.06	.03		328	Tony Phillips	.06	.05	.02
238	Mark Gardner	.08	.06	.03		329	Rob Murphy	.05	.04	.02
239	Harold Reynolds	.06	.05	.02		330	Kevin Morton	.10	.08	.04
240	Checklist	.05	.04	.02		331	John Smiley	.08	.06	.03
241	Mike Harkey	.06	.05	.02		332	Luis Rivera	.05	.04	.02
242	Felix Fermin	.05	.04	.02		333	Wally Joyner	.15	.11	.06
243	Barry Bonds	.20	.15	.08		334	*Heathcliff Slocumb*	.15	.11	.06
244	Roger Clemens	.25	.20	.10		335	Rick Cerone	.05	.04	.02
245	Dennis Rasmussen	.05	.04	.02		336	*Mike Remlinger*(FC)	.15	.11	.06
246	Jose DeLeon	.06	.05	.02		337	Mike Moore	.06	.05	.02
247	Orel Hershiser	.10	.08	.04		338	Lloyd McClendon	.05	.04	.02
248	Mel Hall	.06	.05	.02		339	Al Newman	.05	.04	.02
249	*Rick Wilkins*	.25	.20	.10		340	Kirk McCaskill	.08	.06	.03
250	Tom Gordon	.08	.06	.03		341	Howard Johnson	.15	.11	.06
251	Kevin Reimer	.06	.05	.02		342	Greg Myers	.05	.04	.02
252	Luis Polonia	.06	.05	.02		343	Kal Daniels	.08	.06	.03
253	Mike Henneman	.06	.05	.02		344	Bernie Williams	.30	.25	.12
254	Tom Pagnozzi	.06	.05	.02		345	Shane Mack	.10	.08	.04
255	Chuck Finley	.10	.08	.04		346	Gary Thurman	.05	.04	.02
256	Mackey Sasser	.05	.04	.02		347	Dante Bichette	.06	.05	.02
257	John Burkett	.06	.05	.02		348	Mark McGwire	.15	.11	.06
258	Hal Morris	.15	.11	.06		349	Travis Fryman	.25	.20	.10
259	Larry Walker	.10	.08	.04		350	Ray Lankford	.20	.15	.08
260	Billy Swift	.06	.05	.02		351	Mike Jeffcoat	.05	.04	.02
261	Joe Oliver	.06	.05	.02		352	Jack McDowell	.10	.08	.04
262	Julio Machado	.05	.04	.02		353	Mitch Williams	.08	.06	.03
263	Todd Stottlemyre	.08	.06	.03		354	Mike Devereaux	.06	.05	.02
264	Matt Merullo	.05	.04	.02		355	Andre Galarraga	.06	.05	.02
265	Brent Mayne	.08	.06	.03		356	Henry Cotto	.05	.04	.02
266	Thomas Howard	.06	.05	.02		357	Scott Bailes	.05	.04	.02
267	Lance Johnson	.06	.05	.02		358	*Jeff Bagwell*	.60	.45	.25
268	Terry Mulholland	.08	.06	.03		359	Scott Leius	.08	.06	.03
269	Rick Honeycutt	.05	.04	.02		360	Zane Smith	.06	.05	.02
270	Luis Gonzalez	.25	.20	.10		361	Bill Pecota	.06	.05	.02
271	Jose Guzman	.06	.05	.02		362	Tony Fernandez	.08	.06	.03
272	Jimmy Jones	.05	.04	.02		363	Glenn Braggs	.06	.05	.02
273	Mark Lewis	.20	.15	.08		364	Bill Spiers	.06	.05	.02
274	Rene Gonzales	.05	.04	.02		365	Vicente Palacios	.05	.04	.02
275	*Jeff Johnson*	.25	.20	.10		366	Tim Burke	.06	.05	.02
276	Dennis Martinez (Highlight)	.10	.08	.04		367	Randy Tomlin	.06	.05	.02
277	Delino DeShields	.08	.06	.03		368	Kenny Rogers	.06	.05	.02
278	Sam Horn	.05	.04	.02		369	Brett Butler	.08	.06	.03
279	Kevin Gross	.06	.05	.02		370	Pat Kelly	.20	.15	.08
280	Jose Oquendo	.05	.04	.02		371	Bip Roberts	.06	.05	.02
281	Mark Grace	.15	.11	.06		372	Gregg Jefferies	.15	.11	.06
282	Mark Gubicza	.08	.06	.03		373	Kevin Bass	.06	.05	.02
283	Fred McGriff	.10	.08	.04		374	Ron Karkovice	.05	.04	.02
284	Ron Gant	.15	.11	.06		375	Paul Gibson	.05	.04	.02
285	Lou Whitaker	.08	.06	.03		376	Bernard Gilkey	.10	.08	.04
286	Edgar Martinez	.08	.06	.03		377	Dave Gallagher	.06	.05	.02
287	Ron Tingley	.05	.04	.02		378	Bill Wegman	.06	.05	.02
288	Kevin McReynolds	.08	.06	.03		379	Pat Borders	.06	.05	.02
289	*Ivan Rodriguez*	.50	.40	.20		380	Ed Whitson	.06	.05	.02
290	Mike Gardiner	.08	.06	.03		381	Gilberto Reyes	.08	.06	.03
291	*Chris Haney*	.20	.15	.08		382	Russ Swan	.08	.06	.03
292	Darrin Jackson	.06	.05	.02		383	Andy Van Slyke	.10	.08	.04
293	Bill Doran	.08	.06	.03		384	Wes Chamberlain	.20	.15	.08
294	Ted Higuera	.08	.06	.03		385	Steve Chitren	.08	.06	.03
295	Jeff Brantley	.08	.06	.03		386	Greg Olson	.06	.05	.02
296	Les Lancaster	.05	.04	.02		387	Brian McRae	.20	.15	.08
297	Jim Eisenreich	.05	.04	.02		388	Rich Rodriguez	.06	.05	.02
298	Ruben Sierra	.20	.15	.08		389	Steve Decker	.15	.11	.06
299	Scott Radinsky	.08	.06	.03		390	Chuck Knoblauch	.20	.15	.08
300	Jose DeJesus	.08	.06	.03		391	Bobby Witt	.06	.05	.02
301	*Mike Timlin*	.20	.15	.08		392	Eddie Murray	.10	.08	.04
302	Luis Sojo	.08	.06	.03		393	Juan Gonzalez	.25	.20	.10
303	Kelly Downs	.05	.04	.02		394	Scott Ruskin	.05	.04	.02
304	Scott Bankhead	.06	.05	.02		395	Jay Howell	.06	.05	.02
305	Pedro Munoz	.20	.15	.08		396	Checklist	.05	.04	.02
306	Scott Scudder	.06	.05	.02		397	Royce Clayton	.30	.25	.12
307	Kevin Elster	.06	.05	.02		398	John Jaha(FC)	.40	.30	.15
308	Duane Ward	.06	.05	.02		399	Dan Wilson (RR)(FC)	.15	.11	.06
309	*Darryl Kile*	.15	.11	.06		400	*Archie Corbin*(FC)	.20	.15	.08
310	Orlando Merced	.35	.25	.14		401	*Barry Manuel*(FC)	.20	.15	.08
311	Dave Henderson	.10	.08	.04		402	Kim Batiste (RR)(FC)	.10	.08	.04
312	Tim Raines	.10	.08	.04		403	*Pat Mahomes*(FC)	.70	.50	.30
313	Mark Lee(FC)	.06	.05	.02		404	Dave Fleming	.40	.30	.15
314	Mike Gallego	.06	.05	.02		405	Jeff Juden	.15	.11	.06
315	Charles Nagy	.10	.08	.04		406	*Jim Thome*(FC)	.50	.40	.20
316	Jesse Barfield	.08	.06	.03		407	Sam Militello (RR)(FC)	.10	.08	.04
317	Todd Frohwirth	.05	.04	.02		408	Jeff Nelson (RR)(FC)	.10	.08	.04
318	Al Osuna	.06	.05	.02		409	Anthony Young (RR)	.15	.11	.06
319	Darrin Fletcher	.06	.05	.02		410	Tino Martinez (RR)	.15	.11	.06
320	Checklist	.05	.04	.02		411	*Jeff Mutis* (RR)(FC)	.15	.11	.06
321	David Segui	.10	.08	.04		412	*Rey Sanchez* (RR)(FC)	.15	.11	.06
322	Stan Javier	.05	.04	.02		413	*Chris Gardner*(FC)	.25	.20	.10

#	Player	MT	NR MT	EX
414	*John Vander Wal*(FC)	.30	.25	.12
415	Reggie Sanders(FC)	.40	.30	.15
416	*Brian Williams*(FC)	.20	.15	.08
417	Mo Sanford (RR)(FC)	.15	.11	.06
418	*David Weathers*(FC)	.15	.11	.06
419	*Hector Fajardo*(FC)	.30	.25	.12
420	*Steve Foster*(FC)	.30	.25	.12
421	Lance Dickson (RR)	.10	.08	.04
422	Andre Dawson (AS)	.08	.06	.03
423	Ozzie Smith (AS)	.08	.06	.03
424	Chris Sabo (AS)	.08	.06	.03
425	Tony Gwynn (AS)	.10	.08	.04
426	Tom Glavine (AS)	.08	.06	.03
427	Bobby Bonilla (AS)	.10	.08	.04
428	Will Clark (AS)	.15	.11	.06
429	Ryne Sandberg (AS)	.15	.11	.06
430	Benito Santiago (AS)	.08	.06	.03
431	Ivan Calderon (AS)	.08	.06	.03
432	Ozzie Smith	.08	.06	.03
433	Tim Leary	.05	.04	.02
434	Bret Saberhagen (HL)	.08	.06	.03
435	Mel Rojas	.06	.05	.02
436	Ben McDonald	.10	.08	.04
437	Tim Crews	.05	.04	.02
438	Rex Hudler	.05	.04	.02
439	Chico Walker	.05	.04	.02
440	Kurt Stillwell	.05	.04	.02
441	Tony Gwynn	.15	.11	.06
442	John Smoltz	.08	.06	.03
443	Lloyd Moseby	.05	.04	.03
444	Mike Schooler	.06	.05	.02
445	Joe Grahe	.06	.05	.02
446	Dwight Gooden	.10	.08	.04
447	Oil Can Boyd	.05	.04	.02
448	John Marzano	.05	.04	.02
449	Bret Barberie	.10	.08	.04
450	Mike Maddux	.05	.04	.02
451	Jeff Reed	.05	.04	.02
452	Dale Sveum	.05	.04	.02
453	Jose Uribe	.05	.04	.02
454	Bob Scanlan	.05	.04	.02
455	Kevin Appier	.08	.06	.03
456	Jeff Huson	.05	.04	.02
457	Ken Patterson	.05	.04	.02
458	Ricky Jordan	.08	.06	.03
459	Tom Candiotti	.06	.05	.02
460	Lee Stevens	.08	.06	.03
461	*Rod Beck*(FC)	.15	.11	.06
462	Dave Valle	.05	.04	.02
463	Scott Erickson	.25	.20	.10
464	Chris Jones	.06	.05	.02
465	Mark Carreon	.05	.04	.02
466	Rob Ducey	.05	.04	.02
467	Jim Corsi	.05	.04	.02
468	Jeff King	.05	.04	.02
469	Curt Young	.05	.04	.02
470	Bo Jackson	.15	.11	.06
471	Chris Bosio	.06	.05	.02
472	Jamie Quirk	.05	.04	.02
473	Jesse Orosco	.05	.04	.02
474	Alvaro Espinoza	.05	.04	.02
475	Joe Orsulak	.05	.04	.02
476	Checklist	.05	.04	.02
477	Gerald Young	.05	.04	.02
478	Wally Backman	.05	.04	.02
479	Juan Bell	.05	.04	.02
480	Mike Scioscia	.06	.05	.02
481	Omar Olivares	.06	.05	.02
482	Francisco Cabrera	.05	.04	.02
483	Greg Swindell	.08	.06	.03
484	Terry Leach	.05	.04	.02
485	Tommy Gregg	.05	.04	.02
486	Scott Aldred	.05	.04	.02
487	Greg Briley	.05	.04	.02
488	Phil Plantier	.30	.25	.14
489	Curtis Wilkerson	.05	.04	.02
490	Tom Brunansky	.06	.05	.02
491	Mike Fetters	.05	.04	.02
492	Frank Castillo	.08	.06	.03
493	Joe Boever	.05	.04	.02
494	Kirt Manwaring	.05	.04	.02
495	Wilson Alvarez (HL)	.06	.05	.02
496	Gene Larkin	.05	.04	.02
497	Gary DiSarcina	.06	.05	.02
498	Frank Viola	.08	.06	.03
499	Manuel Lee	.05	.04	.02
500	Albert Belle	.15	.11	.06
501	Stan Belinda	.05	.04	.02
502	Dwight Evans	.06	.05	.02
503	Eric Davis	.10	.08	.04
504	Darren Holmes	.05	.04	.02

#	Player	MT	NR MT	EX
505	Mike Bordick	.12	.09	.05
506	Dave Hansen	.06	.05	.02
507	Lee Guetterman	.05	.04	.02
508	*Keith Mitchell*(FC)	.15	.11	.06
509	Melido Perez	.05	.04	.02
510	Dickie Thon	.05	.04	.02
511	Mark Williamson	.05	.04	.02
512	Mark Salas	.05	.04	.02
513	Milt Thompson	.05	.04	.02
514	Mo Vaughn	.20	.15	.08
515	Jim Deshaies	.05	.04	.02
516	Rich Garces	.05	.04	.02
517	Lonnie Smith	.05	.04	.02
518	Spike Owen	.06	.05	.02
519	Tracy Jones	.05	.04	.02
520	Greg Maddux	.08	.06	.03
521	Carlos Martinez	.05	.04	.02
522	Neal Heaton	.05	.04	.02
523	Mike Greenwell	.08	.06	.03
524	Andy Benes	.08	.06	.03
525	Jeff Schaefer	.05	.04	.02
526	Mike Sharperson	.06	.05	.02
527	Wade Taylor	.06	.05	.02
528	Jerome Walton	.06	.05	.02
529	Storm Davis	.05	.04	.02
530	*Jose Hernandez*(FC)	.20	.15	.08
531	Mark Langston	.08	.06	.03
532	Rob Deer	.06	.05	.02
533	Geronimo Pena	.06	.05	.02
534	*Juan Guzman*(FC)	.80	.60	.30
535	Pete Schourek	.08	.06	.03
536	Todd Benzinger	.05	.04	.02
537	Billy Hatcher	.05	.04	.02
538	Tom Foley	.05	.04	.02
539	Dave Cochrane	.05	.04	.02
540	Mariano Duncan	.05	.04	.02
541	Edwin Nunez	.05	.04	.02
542	Rance Mulliniks	.05	.04	.02
543	Carlton Fisk	.10	.08	.04
544	Luis Aquino	.05	.04	.02
545	Ricky Bones	.08	.06	.03
546	Craig Grebeck	.05	.04	.02
547	Charlie Hayes	.06	.05	.02
548	Jose Canseco	.20	.15	.08
549	Andujar Cedeno	.10	.08	.04
550	Geno Petralli	.05	.04	.02
551	Javier Ortiz	.05	.04	.02
552	Rudy Seanez	.06	.05	.02
553	Rich Gedman	.05	.04	.02
554	Eric Plunk	.05	.04	.02
555	Nolan Ryan, Rich **Gossage** (HL)	.20	.15	.08
556	Checklist	.05	.04	.02
557	Greg Colbrunn	.06	.05	.02
558	*Chito Martinez*(FC)	.20	.15	.08
559	Darryl Strawberry	.20	.15	.08
560	Luis Alicea	.05	.04	.02
561	Dwight Smith	.06	.05	.02
562	Terry Shumpert	.05	.04	.02
563	Jim Vatcher	.05	.04	.02
564	Deion Sanders	.08	.06	.03
565	Walt Terrell	.05	.04	.02
566	Dave Burba	.05	.04	.02
567	Dave Howard	.05	.04	.02
568	Todd Hundley	.08	.06	.03
569	Jac!: Daugherty	.05	.04	.02
570	Scott Cooper	.10	.08	.04
571	Bill Sampen	.05	.04	.02
572	Jose Melendez	.10	.08	.04
573	Freddie Benavides	.05	.04	.02
574	Jim Gantner	.05	.04	.02
575	Trevor Wilson	.05	.04	.02
576	Ryne Sandberg	.20	.15	.08
577	Kevin Seitzer	.05	.04	.02
578	Gerald Alexander	.05	.04	.02
579	Mike Huff	.05	.04	.02
580	Von Hayes	.06	.05	.02
581	Derek Bell	.30	.25	.12
582	Mike Stanley	.05	.04	.02
583	Kevin Mitchell	.08	.06	.03
584	Mike Jackson	.05	.04	.02
585	Dan Gladden	.05	.04	.02
586	Ted Power	.05	.04	.02
587	Jeff Innis	.05	.04	.02
588	Bob MacDonald	.08	.06	.03
589	*Jose Tolentino*(FC)	.08	.06	.03
590	Bob Patterson	.05	.04	.02
591	*Scott Brosius*(FC)	.10	.08	.04
592	Frank Thomas	.80	.60	.30
593	Darryl Hamilton	.08	.06	.03
594	Kirk Dressendorfer	.08	.06	.03
595	Jeff Shaw	.08	.06	.03

#	Player	MT	NR MT	EX
596	Don Mattingly	.12	.09	.05
597	Glenn Davis	.06	.05	.02
598	Andy Mota	.10	.08	.04
599	Jason Grimsley	.05	.04	.02
600	Jimmy Poole	.06	.05	.02
601	Jim Gott	.05	.04	.02
602	Stan Royer	.08	.06	.03
603	Marvin Freeman	.05	.04	.02
604	Denis Boucher	.08	.06	.03
605	Denny Neagle	.10	.08	.04
606	Mark Lemke	.06	.05	.02
607	Jerry Don Gleaton	.05	.04	.02
608	Brent Knackert	.05	.04	.02
609	Carlos Quintana	.05	.04	.02
610	Bobby Bonilla	.12	.09	.05
611	Joe Hesketh	.05	.04	.02
612	Daryl Boston	.05	.04	.02
613	Shawon Dunston	.08	.06	.03
614	Danny Cox	.05	.04	.02
615	Darren Lewis	.12	.09	.05
616	Alejandro Pena, Kent Mercker, Mark Wohlers (HL)	.10	.08	.04
617	Kirby Puckett	.15	.11	.06
618	Franklin Stubbs	.05	.04	.02
619	Chris Donnels	.10	.08	.04
620	David Wells	.05	.04	.02
621	Mike Aldrete	.05	.04	.02
622	Bob Kipper	.05	.04	.02
623	Anthony Telford	.05	.04	.02
624	Randy Myers	.05	.04	.02
625	Willie Randolph	.05	.04	.02
626	Joe Slusarski	.08	.06	.03
627	John Wetteland	.06	.05	.02
628	Greg Cadaret	.05	.04	.02
629	Tom Glavine	.10	.08	.04
630	Wilson Alvarez	.10	.08	.04
631	Wally Ritchie	.05	.04	.02
632	Mike Mussina(FC)	.50	.40	.20
633	Mark Leiter	.05	.04	.02
634	Gerald Perry	.05	.04	.02
635	Matt Young	.05	.04	.02
636	Checklist	.05	.04	.02
637	Scott Hemond	.05	.04	.02
638	David West	.05	.04	.02
639	Jim Clancy	.05	.04	.02
640	Doug Piatt(FC)	.10	.08	.04
641	Omar Vizquel	.05	.04	.02
642	Rick Sutcliffe	.08	.06	.03
643	Glenallen Hill	.08	.06	.03
644	Gary Varsho	.05	.04	.02
645	Tony Fossas	.05	.04	.02
646	Jack Howell	.05	.04	.02
647	Jim Campanis(FC)	.15	.11	.06
648	Chris Gwynn	.05	.04	.02
649	Jim Leyritz	.05	.04	.02
650	Chuck McElroy	.05	.04	.02
651	Sean Berry(FC)	.08	.06	.03
652	Donald Harris(FC)	.10	.08	.04
653	Don Slaught	.05	.04	.02
654	Rusty Meacham	.10	.08	.04
655	Scott Terry	.05	.04	.02
656	Ramon Martinez	.12	.09	.05
657	Keith Miller	.05	.04	.02
658	Ramon Garcia(FC)	.08	.06	.03
659	Milt Hill(FC)	.10	.08	.04
660	Steve Frey	.05	.04	.02
661	Bob McClure	.05	.04	.02
662	Ced Landrum	.08	.06	.03
663	Doug Henry(FC)	.20	.15	.08
664	Candy Maldonado	.05	.04	.02
665	Carl Willis	.05	.04	.02
666	Jeff Montgomery	.08	.06	.03
667	Craig Shipley(FC)	.10	.08	.04
668	Warren Newson	.08	.06	.03
669	Mickey Morandini	.08	.06	.03
670	Brook Jacoby	.05	.04	.02
671	Ryan Bowen	.10	.08	.04
672	Bill Krueger	.05	.04	.02
673	Rob Mallicoat	.05	.04	.02
674	Doug Jones	.05	.04	.02
675	Scott Livingstone	.10	.08	.04
676	Danny Tartabull	.10	.08	.04
677	Joe Carter (HL)	.08	.06	.03
678	Cecil Espy	.05	.04	.02
679	Randy Velarde	.05	.04	.02
680	Bruce Ruffin	.05	.04	.02
681	Ted Wood(FC)	.25	.20	.10
682	Dan Plesac	.05	.04	.02
683	Eric Bullock	.05	.04	.02
684	Junior Ortiz	.05	.04	.02
685	Dave Hollins	.06	.05	.02
686	Dennis Martinez	.08	.06	.03
687	Larry Andersen	.05	.04	.02
688	Doug Simons	.05	.04	.02
689	Tim Spehr	.08	.06	.03
690	Calvin Jones(FC)	.12	.09	.05
691	Mark Guthrie	.05	.04	.02
692	Alfredo Griffin	.05	.04	.02
693	Joe Carter	.12	.09	.05
694	Terry Mathews(FC)	.08	.06	.03
695	Pascual Perez	.05	.04	.02
696	Gene Nelson	.05	.04	.02
697	Gerald Williams	.15	.11	.06
698	Chris Cron(FC)	.15	.11	.06
699	Steve Buechele	.06	.05	.02
700	Paul McClellan(FC)	.08	.06	.03
701	Jim Lindeman	.05	.04	.02
702	Francisco Oliveras	.05	.04	.02
703	Rob Maurer(FC)	.25	.20	.10
704	Pat Hentgen(FC)	.15	.11	.06
705	Jaime Navarro	.06	.05	.02
706	Mike Magnante(FC)	.10	.08	.04
707	Nolan Ryan	.30	.25	.12
708	Bobby Thigpen	.08	.06	.03
709	John Cerutti	.05	.04	.02
710	Steve Wilson	.05	.04	.02
711	Hensley Meulens	.08	.06	.03
712	Rheal Cormier(FC)	.20	.15	.08
713	Scott Bradley	.05	.04	.02
714	Mitch Webster	.05	.04	.02
715	Roger Mason	.05	.04	.02
716	Checklist	.05	.04	.02
717	Jeff Fassero	.08	.06	.03
718	Cal Eldred(FC)	.35	.25	.12
719	Sid Fernandez	.08	.06	.03
720	Bob Zupcic(FC)	.30	.25	.12
721	Jose Offerman	.08	.06	.03
722	Cliff Brantley(FC)	.20	.15	.08
723	Ron Darling	.06	.05	.02
724	Dave Stieb	.06	.05	.02
725	Hector Villanueva	.06	.05	.02
726	Mike Hartley	.05	.04	.02
727	Arthur Rhodes	.15	.11	.06
728	Randy Bush	.05	.04	.02
729	Steve Sax	.08	.06	.03
730	Dave Otto	.05	.04	.02
731	John Wehner	.10	.08	.04
732	Dave Martinez	.05	.04	.02
733	Ruben Amaro	.10	.08	.04
734	Billy Ripken	.05	.04	.02
735	Steve Farr	.05	.04	.02
736	Shawn Abner	.05	.04	.02
737	Gil Heredia(FC)	.10	.08	.04
738	Ron Jones	.05	.04	.02
739	Tony Castillo	.05	.04	.02
740	Sammy Sosa	.08	.06	.03
741	Julio Franco	.08	.06	.03
742	Tim Naehring	.08	.06	.03
743	Steve Wapnick(FC)	.10	.08	.04
744	Craig Wilson	.08	.06	.03
745	Darrin Chapin(FC)	.15	.11	.06
746	Chris George(FC)	.08	.06	.03
747	Mike Simms	.08	.06	.03
748	Rosario Rodriguez	.08	.06	.03
749	Skeeter Barnes	.05	.04	.02
750	Roger McDowell	.05	.04	.02
751	Dann Howitt	.05	.04	.02
752	Paul Sorrento	.05	.04	.02
753	Braulio Castillo(FC)	.15	.11	.06
754	Yorkis Perez(FC)	.15	.11	.06
755	Willie Fraser	.05	.04	.02
756	Jeremy Hernandez(FC)	.10	.08	.04
757	Curt Schilling	.05	.04	.02
758	Steve Lyons	.05	.04	.02
759	Dave Anderson	.05	.04	.02
760	Willie Banks	.12	.09	.05
761	Mark Leonard	.05	.04	.02
762	Jack Armstrong	.06	.05	.02
763	Scott Servais	.08	.06	.03
764	Ray Stephens	.08	.06	.03
765	Junior Noboa	.05	.04	.02
766	Jim Olander(FC)	.05	.04	.02
767	Joe Magrane	.06	.05	.02
768	Lance Blankenship	.05	.04	.02
769	Mike Humphreys(FC)	.10	.08	.04
770	Jarvis Brown(FC)	.12	.09	.05
771	Damon Berryhill	.05	.04	.02
772	Alejandro Pena	.06	.05	.02
773	Jose Mesa	.05	.04	.02
774	Gary Cooper(FC)	.10	.08	.04
775	Carney Lansford	.06	.05	.02
776	Mike Bielecki	.05	.04	.02

		MT	NR MT	EX
777	Charlie O'Brien	.05	.04	.02
778	Carlos Hernandez	.05	.04	.02
779	Howard Farmer	.05	.04	.02
780	Mike Stanton	.05	.04	.02
781	Reggie Harris	.05	.04	.02
782	Xavier Hernandez	.05	.04	.02
783	*Bryan Hickerson*(FC)	.10	.08	.04
784	Checklist	.05	.04	.02
-----	Cal Ripken (MVP)	.20	.15	.08
-----	Terry Pendleton (MVP)	.08	.06	.03
-----	Roger Clemens (CY Young)	.10	.08	.04
-----	Tom Glavine (CY Young)	.08	.06	.03
-----	Chuck Knoblauch (ROY)	.20	.15	.08
-----	Jeff Bagwell (ROY)	.50	.40	.20
-----	Colorado Rockies	.50	.40	.20
-----	Florida Marlins	.50	.40	.20

1992 Donruss Diamond Kings

Donruss changed its Diamond Kings style and distribution in 1992. The cards still featured the art of Dick Perez, but quality was improved from past years. The cards were randomly inserted in foil packs. One player from each team is featured.

		MT	NR MT	EX
Complete Set:		60.00	45.00	25.00
Common Player:		2.00	1.50	.80
1	Paul Molitor	2.50	2.00	1.00
2	Will Clark	6.00	4.50	2.50
3	Joe Carter	2.50	2.00	1.00
4	Julio Franco	2.50	2.00	1.00
5	Cal Ripken	7.00	5.25	2.75
6	Dave Justice	10.00	7.50	4.00
7	George Bell	2.00	1.50	.80
8	Frank Thomas	18.00	13.50	7.25
9	Wade Boggs	3.00	2.25	1.25
10	Scott Sanderson	2.00	1.50	.80
11	Jeff Bagwell	6.00	4.50	2.50
12	John Kruk	2.50	2.00	1.00
13	Felix Jose	2.50	2.00	1.00
14	Harold Baines	2.00	1.50	.80
15	Dwight Gooden	2.50	2.00	1.00
16	Brian McRae	2.50	2.00	1.00
17	Jay Bell	2.00	1.50	.80
18	Brett Butler	2.00	1.50	.80
19	Hal Morris	2.00	1.50	.80
20	Mark Langston	2.00	1.50	.80
21	Scott Erickson	3.00	2.25	1.25
22	Randy Johnson	2.00	1.50	.80
23	Greg Swindell	2.00	1.50	.80
24	Dennis Martinez	2.00	1.50	.80
25	Tony Phillips	2.00	1.50	.80
26	Fred McGriff	2.50	2.00	1.00
27	Checklist	2.00	1.50	.80

1992 Donruss Elite

Donruss continued its Elite series in 1992 by inserting cards in foil packs. The cards were released at the same scarcity as the 1991 cards. The Elite cards are numbered as a continuation of the 1991 issue. Rickey Henderson and Cal Ripken are the subjects of the Legend card and Signature card respectively.

GRADING GUIDE

Mint (MT): A perfect card. Well-centered with all corners sharp and square. No creases, stains, edge nicks, surface marks, yellowing or fading.

Near Mint (NM): A nearly perfect card. At first glance, a NM card appears to be perfect. May be slightly off-center. No surface marks, creases or loss of gloss.

Excellent (EX): Corners are still fairly sharp with only moderate wear. Borders may be off-center. No creases or stains on fronts or backs, but may show slight loss of surface luster.

Very Good (VG): Shows obvious handling. May have rounded corners, minor creases, major gum or wax stains. No major creases, tape marks, writing, etc.

Good (G): A well-worn card, but exhibits no intentional damage. May have major or multiple creases. Corners may be rounded well beyond card border.

		MT	NR MT	EX
Complete Set:		2000.00	1500.00	800.00
Common Player:		75.00	55.00	30.00
9	Wade Boggs	100.00	75.00	40.00
10	Joe Carter	100.00	75.00	40.00
11	Will Clark	150.00	110.00	60.00
12	Dwight Gooden	75.00	55.00	30.00
13	Ken Griffey, Jr.	200.00	150.00	80.00
14	Tony Gwynn	100.00	75.00	40.00
15	Howard Johnson	75.00	55.00	30.00
16	Terry Pendleton	75.00	55.00	30.00
17	Kirby Puckett	150.00	110.00	60.00
18	Frank Thomas	250.00	190.00	100.00
-----	Rickey Henderson (Legend)	300.00	225.00	125.00
-----	Cal Ripken (Signature)	350.00	260.00	140.00

1992 Donruss Rookies

Donruss increased the size of its Rookies set in 1992 to include 132 cards. In the past the cards were released only in boxed set form, but the 1992 cards were available in packs. Special phenoms insert cards were randomly inserted into Rookies packs. The phenoms cards feature black borders, while the Rookies cards are styled after the regular 1992 Donruss issue. The cards are numbered alphabetically.

		MT	NR MT	EX
Complete Set:		13.00	9.75	5.25
Common Player:		.08	.06	.03
1	Kyle Abbott	.08	.06	.03
2	Troy Afenir	.08	.06	.03
3	Rich Amaral(FC)	.12	.09	.05
4	Ruben Amaro(FC)	.12	.09	.05
5	Billy Ashley(FC)	.30	.25	.12
6	Pedro Astacio(FC)	.25	.20	.10
7	Jim Austin(FC)	.08	.06	.03
8	Robert Ayrault(FC)	.10	.08	.04
9	Kevin Baez(FC)	.10	.08	.04
10	Esteban Beltre	.08	.06	.03
11	Brian Bohanon(FC)	.08	.06	.03
12	Kent Bottenfield(FC)	.12	.09	.05

#	Player	MT	NR MT	EX
13	Jeff Branson(FC)	.20	.15	.08
14	Brad Brink	.08	.06	.03
15	John Briscoe(FC)	.10	.08	.04
16	Doug Brocail(FC)	.10	.08	.04
17	Rico Brogna(FC)	.15	.11	.06
18	J.T. Bruett(FC)	.15	.11	.06
19	Jacob Brumfield	.12	.09	.05
20	Jim Bullinger(FC)	.12	.09	.05
21	Kevin Campbell(FC)	.08	.06	.03
22	Pedro Castellano(FC)	.20	.15	.08
23	Mike Christopher(FC)	.08	.06	.03
24	Archi Cianfrocco(FC)	.40	.30	.15
25	Mark Clark(FC)	.12	.09	.05
26	Craig Colbert(FC)	.08	.06	.03
27	Victor Cole(FC)	.12	.09	.05
28	Steve Cooke(FC)	.12	.09	.05
29	Tim Costo(FC)	.15	.11	.06
30	Chad Curtis(FC)	.25	.20	.10
31	Doug Davis(FC)	.10	.08	.04
32	Gary DiSarcina	.08	.06	.03
33	John Doherty(FC)	.10	.08	.04
34	Mike Draper(FC)	.20	.15	.08
35	Monty Fariss	.08	.06	.03
36	Bien Figueroa(FC)	.10	.08	.04
37	John Flaherty(FC)	.08	.06	.03
38	Tim Fortugno(FC)	.10	.08	.04
39	Eric Fox(FC)	.10	.08	.04
40	Jeff Frye(FC)	.10	.08	.04
41	Ramon Garcia(FC)	.12	.09	.05
42	Brent Gates(FC)	.25	.20	.10
43	Tom Goodwin(FC)	.10	.08	.04
44	Buddy Groom(FC)	.12	.09	.05
45	Jeff Grotewold(FC)	.20	.15	.08
46	Juan Guerrero(FC)	.20	.15	.08
47	Johnny Guzman(FC)	.10	.08	.04
48	Shawn Hare(FC)	.12	.09	.05
49	Ryan Hawblitzel(FC)	.20	.15	.08
50	Bert Heffernan(FC)	.08	.06	.03
51	Butch Henry(FC)	.10	.08	.04
52	Cesar Hernandez(FC)	.10	.08	.04
53	Vince Horsman(FC)	.10	.08	.04
54	Steve Hosey(FC)	.10	.08	.04
55	Pat Howell(FC)	.10	.08	.04
56	Peter Hoy(FC)	.10	.08	.04
57	Jon Hurst(FC)	.10	.08	.04
58	Mark Hutton(FC)	.30	.25	.12
59	Shawn Jeter(FC)	.12	.09	.05
60	Joel Johnston(FC)	.08	.06	.03
61	Jeff Kent(FC)	.30	.25	.12
62	Kurt Knudsen(FC)	.08	.06	.03
63	Kevin Koslofski(FC)	.20	.15	.08
64	Danny Leon(FC)	.10	.08	.04
65	Jesse Levis(FC)	.20	.15	.08
66	Tom Marsh(FC)	.10	.08	.04
67	Ed Martel(FC)	.10	.08	.04
68	Al Martin(FC)	.20	.15	.08
69	Pedro Martinez(FC)	.25	.20	.10
70	Derrick May	.10	.08	.04
71	Matt Maysey	.12	.09	.05
72	Russ McGinnis	.08	.06	.03
73	Tim McIntosh	.08	.06	.03
74	Jim McNamara(FC)	.08	.06	.03
75	Jeff McNeely(FC)	.30	.25	.12
76	Rusty Meacham	.08	.06	.03
77	Tony Melendez(FC)	.10	.08	.04
78	Henry Mercedes(FC)	.10	.08	.04
79	Paul Miller(FC)	.10	.08	.04
80	Joe Millette(FC)	.10	.08	.04
81	Blas Minor(FC)	.10	.08	.04
82	Dennis Moeller(FC)	.10	.08	.04
83	Raul Mondesi(FC)	.25	.20	.10
84	Rob Natal(FC)	.20	.15	.08
85	Troy Neel(FC)	.25	.20	.10
86	David Nied(FC)	.30	.25	.12
87	Jerry Nielsen(FC)	.20	.15	.08
88	Donovan Osborne(FC)	.25	.20	.10
89	John Patterson(FC)	.12	.09	.05
90	Roger Pavlik(FC)	.10	.08	.04
91	Dan Peltier(FC)	.20	.15	.08
92	Jim Pena(FC)	.10	.08	.04
93	William Pennyfeather(FC)	.30	.25	.12
94	Mike Perez	.08	.06	.03
95	Hipolito Pichardo(FC)	.20	.15	.08
96	Greg Pirkl(FC)	.08	.06	.03
97	Harvey Pulliam(FC)	.08	.06	.03
98	Manny Ramirez(FC)	.50	.40	.20
99	Pat Rapp(FC)	.12	.09	.05
100	Jeff Reboulet(FC)	.10	.08	.04
101	Darren Reed(FC)	.10	.08	.04
102	Shane Reynolds(FC)	.10	.08	.04
103	Bill Risley(FC)	.10	.08	.04
104	Ben Rivera(FC)	.10	.08	.04

#	Player	MT	NR MT	EX
105	Henry Rodriguez(FC)	.10	.08	.04
106	Rico Rossy(FC)	.10	.08	.04
107	Johnny Ruffin(FC)	.10	.08	.04
108	Steve Scarsone(FC)	.20	.15	.08
109	Tim Scott(FC)	.08	.06	.03
110	Steve Shifflett(FC)	.10	.08	.04
111	Dave Silvestri(FC)	.20	.15	.08
112	Matt Stairs(FC)	.08	.06	.03
113	William Suero(FC)	.08	.06	.03
114	Jeff Tackett(FC)	.10	.08	.04
115	Eddie Taubensee(FC)	.12	.09	.05
116	Rick Trlicek(FC)	.10	.08	.04
117	Scooter Tucker(FC)	.10	.08	.04
118	Shane Turner(FC)	.10	.08	.04
119	Julio Valera(FC)	.10	.08	.04
120	Paul Wagner(FC)	.10	.08	.04
121	Tim Wakefield(FC)	.50	.40	.20
122	Mike Walker(FC)	.08	.06	.03
123	Bruce Walton(FC)	.08	.06	.03
124	Lenny Webster	.08	.06	.03
125	Bob Wickman(FC)	.40	.30	.15
126	Mike Williams(FC)	.10	.08	.04
127	Kerry Woodson(FC)	.10	.08	.04
128	Eric Young(FC)	.12	.09	.05
129	Kevin Young(FC)	.30	.25	.12
130	Pete Young(FC)	.10	.08	.04
131	Checklist	.08	.06	.03
132	Checklist	.08	.06	.03

1993 Donruss Series I

Rated Rookies and a randomly inserted Diamond Kings subset once again are featured in the 1993 Donruss set. Series I of the set was released first and includes 396 cards. The card fronts feature white borders surrounding a full-color player photo. the player's name and position appear at the bottom of the photo along with a diamond featuring the team logo. The flip sides feature and additional photo, biographical information and career statistics.

#	Player	MT	NR MT	EX
	Complete Set:	15.00	11.00	6.00
	Common Player:	.05	.04	.02
1	Craig Lefferts	.05	.04	.02
2	Kent Mercker	.06	.05	.02
3	Phil Plantier	.10	.08	.04
4	*Alex Arias*(FC)	.15	.11	.06
5	Julio Valera	.08	.06	.03
6	Dan Wilson(FC)	.12	.09	.05
7	Frank Thomas	.30	.25	.12
8	Eric Anthony	.08	.06	.03
9	Derek Lilliquist	.05	.04	.02
10	*Rafael Bournigal*(FC)	.15	.11	.06
11	*Manny Alexander*(FC)	.15	.11	.06
12	Bret Barberie	.08	.06	.03
13	Mickey Tettleton	.08	.06	.03
14	Anthony Young	.08	.06	.03
15	Tim Spehr	.08	.06	.03
16	*Bob Ayrault*	.10	.08	.04
17	Bill Wegman	.06	.05	.02
18	Jay Bell	.08	.06	.03
19	Rick Aguilera	.08	.06	.03
20	Todd Zeile	.08	.06	.03
21	Steve Farr	.06	.05	.02
22	Andy Benes	.08	.06	.03
23	Lance Blankenship	.05	.04	.02

		MT	NR MT	EX			MT	NR MT	EX
24	Ted Wood	.08	.06	.03	116	*Pat Howell*	.12	.09	.05
25	Omar Vizquel	.05	.04	.02	117	Gregg Olson	.08	.06	.03
26	Steve Avery	.08	.06	.03	118	Curt Schilling	.08	.06	.03
27	Brian Bohanon	.08	.06	.03	119	Roger Clemens	.12	.09	.05
28	Rick Wilkins	.08	.06	.03	120	*Victor Cole*	.12	.09	.05
29	Devon White	.08	.06	.03	121	Gary DiSarcina	.05	.04	.02
30	*Bobby Ayala*(FC)	.12	.09	.05	122	Checklist	.05	.04	.02
31	Leo Gomez	.08	.06	.03	123	Steve Sax	.08	.06	.03
32	Mike Simms	.08	.06	.03	124	Chuck Carr(FC)	.08	.06	.03
33	Ellis Burks	.08	.06	.03	125	Mark Lewis	.08	.06	.03
34	Steve Wilson	.05	.04	.02	126	Tony Gwynn	.08	.06	.03
35	Jim Abbott	.08	.06	.03	127	Travis Fryman	.12	.09	.05
36	Tim Wallach	.06	.05	.02	129	Dave Burba	.06	.05	.02
37	Wilson Alvarez	.06	.05	.02	130	John Smoltz	.08	.06	.03
38	Daryl Boston	.05	.04	.02	131	Cal Eldred	.15	.11	.06
39	Sandy Alomar Jr.	.10	.08	.04	132	Checklist	.05	.04	.02
40	Mitch Williams	.08	.06	.03	133	Arthur Rhodes	.10	.08	.04
41	Rico Brogna	.10	.08	.04	134	Jeff Blauser	.06	.05	.02
42	Gary Varsho	.05	.04	.02	135	Scott Cooper	.06	.05	.02
43	Kevin Appier	.08	.06	.03	136	Doug Strange	.06	.05	.02
44	Eric Wedge	.12	.09	.05	137	Luis Sojo	.06	.05	.02
45	Dante Bichette	.05	.04	.02	138	*Jeff Branson*	.15	.11	.06
46	Jose Oquendo	.05	.04	.02	139	Alex Fernandez	.08	.06	.03
47	*Mike Trombley*(FC)	.12	.09	.05	140	Ken Caminiti	.06	.05	.02
48	Dan Walters	.08	.06	.03	141	Charles Nagy	.08	.06	.03
49	Gerald Williams	.08	.06	.03	142	Tom Candiotti	.06	.05	.02
50	Bud Black	.05	.04	.02	143	Willie Green	.10	.08	.04
51	Bobby Witt	.06	.05	.02	144	*Kurt Knudsen*	.10	.08	.04
52	Mark Davis	.05	.04	.02	146	John Franco	.06	.05	.02
53	*Shawn Barton*(FC)	.15	.11	.06	147	*Eddie Pierce*(FC)	.15	.11	.06
54	Paul Assenmacher	.05	.04	.02	148	Kim Batiste	.08	.06	.03
55	Kevin Reimer	.06	.05	.02	149	Darren Holmes	.05	.04	.02
56	*Billy Ashley*(FC)	.20	.15	.08	150	*Steve Cooke*	.15	.11	.06
57	Eddie Zosky	.08	.06	.03	151	Terry Jorgensen	.08	.06	.03
58	Chris Sabo	.08	.06	.03	152	*Mark Clark*	.12	.09	.05
59	Billy Ripken	.05	.04	.02	153	Randy Velarde	.05	.04	.02
60	*Scooter Tucker*	.12	.09	.05	154	Greg Harris	.05	.04	.02
61	*Tim Wakefield*	.30	.25	.12	155	*Kevin Campbell*	.10	.08	.04
62	Mitch Webster	.05	.04	.02	156	John Burkett	.06	.05	.02
63	Jack Clark	.06	.05	.02	157	Kevin Mitchell	.08	.06	.03
64	Mark Gardner	.06	.05	.02	158	Deion Sanders	.10	.08	.04
65	Lee Stevens	.06	.05	.02	159	Jose Canseco	.10	.08	.04
66	Todd Hundley	.08	.06	.03	160	*Jeff Hartsock*(FC)	.15	.11	.06
67	Bobby Thigpen	.08	.06	.03	161	*Tom Quinlan*(FC)	.15	.11	.06
68	Dave Hollins	.10	.08	.04	162	*Tim Pugh*(FC)	.15	.11	.06
69	Jack Armstrong	.06	.05	.02	163	Glenn Davis	.08	.06	.03
70	Alex Cole	.06	.05	.02	164	*Shane Reynolds*	.12	.09	.05
71	Mark Carreon	.05	.04	.02	165	Jody Reed	.06	.05	.02
72	Todd Worrell	.06	.05	.02	166	Mike Sharperson	.06	.05	.02
73	*Steve Shifflett*	.12	.09	.05	167	Scott Lewis	.06	.05	.02
74	Jerald Clark	.06	.05	.02	168	Dennis Martinez	.06	.05	.02
75	Paul Molitor	.08	.06	.03	169	Scott Radinsky	.06	.05	.02
76	*Larry Carter*(FC)	.15	.11	.06	170	Dave Gallagher	.05	.04	.02
77	Rich Rowland(FC)	.10	.08	.04	171	Jime Thome	.08	.06	.03
78	Damon Berryhill	.06	.05	.02	172	Terry Mulholland	.06	.05	.02
79	Willie Banks	.08	.06	.03	173	Milt Cuyler	.06	.05	.02
80	Hector Villanueva	.06	.05	.02	174	Bob Patterson	.05	.04	.02
81	Mike Gallego	.06	.05	.02	175	Jeff Montgomery	.06	.05	.02
82	Tim Belcher	.06	.05	.02	177	Franklin Stubbs	.05	.04	.02
83	Mike Bordick	.08	.06	.03	178	Donovan Osborne	.10	.08	.04
84	Criag Biggio	.08	.06	.03	179	*Jeff Reboulet*	.10	.08	.04
85	Lance Parrish	.06	.05	.02	180	*Jeremy Hernandez*(FC)	.15	.11	.06
86	Brett Butler	.06	.05	.02	181	Charlie Hayes	.06	.05	.02
87	Mike Timlin	.06	.05	.02	182	Matt Williams	.08	.06	.03
88	Brian Barnes	.06	.05	.02	183	Mike Raczka	.15	.11	.06
89	Brady Anderson	.08	.06	.03	184	Francisco Cabrera	.05	.04	.02
90	D.J. Dozier	.08	.06	.03	185	Rich DeLucia	.05	.04	.02
91	Frank Viola	.08	.06	.03	186	Sammy Sosa	.06	.05	.02
92	Darren Daulton	.08	.06	.03	187	Ivan Rodriguez	.10	.08	.04
93	Chad Curtis	.10	.08	.04	188	*Bret Boone*(FC)	.20	.15	.08
94	Zane Smith	.05	.04	.02	189	Juan Guzman	.10	.08	.04
95	George Bell	.08	.06	.03	190	Randy Milligan	.06	.05	.02
96	Rex Hudler	.05	.04	.02	191	Ivan Calderon	.08	.06	.03
97	Mark Whiten	.08	.06	.03	197	Junior Felix	.06	.05	.02
98	Tim Teufel	.05	.04	.02	198	Pete Schourek	.06	.05	.02
99	Kevin Ritz	.05	.04	.02	199	Craig Grebeck	.06	.05	.02
100	Jeff Brantley	.05	.04	.02	200	Juan Bell	.06	.05	.02
101	Jeff Conine	.08	.06	.03	201	Glenallen Hill	.06	.05	.02
102	*Vinny Castilla*(FC)	.15	.11	.06	202	Danny Jackson	.06	.05	.02
103	Greg Vaughn	.08	.06	.03	203	John Kiely			
104	Steve Buechele	.06	.05	.02	204	Bob Tewksbury	.08	.06	.03
106	Darren Reed, Bip Roberts	.08	.06	.03	205	*Kevin Koslofski*(FC)	.15	.11	.06
107	John Habyan	.05	.04	.02	206	Craig Shipley	.08	.06	.03
108	Scott Servais	.05	.04	.02	207	John Jaha(FC)	.20	.15	.08
109	Walt Weiss	.05	.04	.02	208	Royce Clayton	.10	.08	.04
110	*J.T. Snow*(FC)	.15	.11	.06	209	*Mike Piazza*(FC)	.25	.20	.10
111	Jay Buhner	.08	.06	.03	210	Ron Gant	.08	.06	.03
112	Darryl Strawberry	.08	.06	.03	211	Scott Erickson	.08	.06	.03
113	*Roger Pavlik*	.12	.09	.05	212	Doug Dascenzo	.05	.04	.02
114	Chris Nabholz	.06	.05	.02	213	Andy Stankiewicz(FC)	.12	.09	.05
115	Pat Borders	.06	.05	.02	214	Geronimo Berroa	.05	.04	.02

		MT	NR MT	EX
215	Dennis Eckersley	.08	.06	.03
216	Al Osuna	.05	.04	.02
217	Tino Martinez	.08	.06	.03
218	*Henry Rodriguez*	.12	.09	.05
219	Ed Sprague	.08	.06	.03
220	Ken Hill	.08	.06	.03
221	Chito Martinez	.08	.06	.03
222	Bret Saberhagen	.08	.06	.03
223	Mike Greenwell	.08	.06	.03
224	Mickey Morandini	.08	.06	.03
225	Chuck Finley	.08	.06	.03
226	Denny Neagle	.08	.06	.03
227	Kirk McCaskill	.06	.05	.02
228	Rheal Cormier	.08	.06	.03
229	Paul Sorrento	.08	.06	.03
230	Darrin Jackson	.06	.05	.02
231	Rob Deer	.06	.05	.02
232	Bill Swift	.06	.05	.02
233	Kevin McReynolds	.08	.06	.03
234	Terry Pendleton	.08	.06	.03
235	Dave Nilsson	.12	.09	.05
236	Chuck McElroy	.05	.04	.02
237	Derek Parks	.06	.05	.02
238	Norm Charlton	.08	.06	.03
239	Matt Nokes	.06	.05	.02
240	*Juan Guerrero*	.15	.11	.06
241	Jeff Parrett	.05	.04	.02
242	*Ryan Thompson*(FC)	.20	.15	.08
243	Dave Fleming	.10	.08	.04
244	Dave Hansen	.05	.04	.02
245	Monty Fariss	.05	.04	.02
246	*Archi Cianfrocco*	.15	.11	.06
247	*Pat Hentgen*(FC)	.15	.11	.06
248	Bill Pecota	.05	.04	.02
249	Ben McDonald	.08	.06	.03
250	Cliff Brantley	.08	.06	.03
251	*John Valentin*(FC)	.15	.11	.06
252	Jeff King	.06	.05	.02
253	*Reggie Williams*(FC)	.15	.11	.06
254	Checklist	.05	.04	.02
255	Ozzie Guillen	.08	.06	.03
256	Mike Perez	.06	.05	.02
257	Thomas Howard	.06	.05	.02
258	Kurt Stillwell	.05	.04	.02
259	Mike Henneman	.06	.05	.02
260	Steve Decker	.06	.05	.02
261	Brent Mayne	.06	.05	.02
262	Otis Nixon	.08	.06	.03
263	*Mark Keifer*(FC)	.15	.11	.06
264	Checklist	.05	.04	.02
265	*Richie Lewis*(FC)	.15	.11	.06
266	*Pat Gomez*(FC)	.15	.11	.06
267	*Scott Taylor*(FC)	.15	.11	.06
268	Shawon Dunston	.06	.05	.02
269	Greg Myers	.05	.04	.02
270	Tim Costo	.10	.08	.04
271	Greg Hibbard	.06	.05	.02
272	Pete Harnisch	.06	.05	.02
273	*Dave Mlicki*(FC)	.12	.09	.05
274	Orel Hershiser	.08	.06	.03
275	Sean Berry	.08	.06	.03
276	Doug Simons	.08	.06	.03
277	*John Doherty*	.10	.08	.04
278	Eddie Murray	.08	.06	.03
279	Chris Haney	.08	.06	.03
280	Stan Javier	.05	.04	.02
281	Jaime Navarro	.08	.06	.03
282	Orlando Merced	.08	.06	.03
283	Kent Hrbek	.08	.06	.03
284	Bernard Gilkey	.08	.06	.03
285	Russ Springer	.06	.05	.02
286	Mike Maddux	.05	.04	.02
287	*Eric Fox*	.12	.09	.05
288	Mark Leonard	.05	.04	.02
289	Tim Leary	.05	.04	.02
290	Brian Hunter	.08	.06	.03
291	Donald Harris	.08	.06	.03
292	Bob Scanlan	.05	.04	.02
293	Turner Ward	.08	.06	.03
294	Hal Morris	.08	.06	.03
295	Jimmy Poole	.08	.06	.03
296	Doug Jones	.06	.05	.02
297	Tony Pena	.06	.05	.02
298	Ramon Martinez	.08	.06	.03
299	*Tim Fortugno*	.12	.09	.05
300	Marquis Grissom	.10	.08	.04
301	Lance Johnson	.06	.05	.02
302	*Jeff Kent*	.15	.11	.06
303	Reggie Jefferson	.08	.06	.03
304	Wes Chamberlain	.08	.06	.03
305	*Shawn Hare*	.12	.09	.05

		MT	NR MT	EX
306	Mike LaValliere	.05	.04	.02
307	Gregg Jefferies	.08	.06	.03
308	*Troy Neel*	.20	.15	.08
309	*Pat Listach*(FC)	.30	.25	.12
310	Geronimo Pena	.06	.05	.02
311	Pedro Munoz	.08	.06	.03
312	*Guillermo Pena*(FC)	.15	.11	.06
313	Roberto Kelly	.08	.06	.03
314	Mike Jackson	.05	.04	.02
315	Rickey Henderson	.12	.09	.05
316	Mark Lemke	.06	.05	.02
317	Erik Hanson	.08	.06	.03
318	Derrick May	.08	.06	.03
319	Geno Petralli	.05	.04	.02
320	*Melvin Nieves*(FC)	.20	.15	.08
321	*Doug Linton*(FC)	.15	.11	.06
322	Rob Dibble	.08	.06	.03
323	Chris Hoiles	.10	.08	.04
324	Jimmy Jones	.05	.04	.02
325	Dave Staton	.06	.05	.02
326	Pedro Martinez	.15	.11	.06
327	*Paul Quantrill*(FC)	.15	.11	.06
328	Greg Colbrunn	.05	.04	.02
329	*Hilly Hathaway*(FC)	.20	.15	.08
330	Jeff Innis	.06	.05	.02
331	Ron Karkovice	.06	.05	.02
332	*Keith Shepherd*(FC)	.15	.11	.06
333	*Alan Embree*(FC)	.15	.11	.06
334	Paul Wagner	.15	.11	.06
335	*Dave Haas*(FC)	.15	.11	.06
336	Ozzie Canseco	.10	.08	.04
337	Bill Sampen	.05	.04	.02
338	Rich Rodriguez	.05	.04	.02
339	Dean Palmer	.08	.06	.03
340	Greg Litton	.05	.04	.02
341	*Jim Tatum*(FC)	.20	.15	.08
342	*Todd Haney*(FC)	.20	.15	.08
343	Larry Casian	.06	.05	.02
344	Ryne Sandberg	.12	.09	.05
345	*Sterling Hitchcock*(FC)	.15	.11	.06
346	Chris Hammond	.06	.05	.02
347	*Vince Horseman*	.12	.09	.05
348	*Butch Henry*	.12	.09	.05
349	Dann Howitt	.05	.04	.02
350	Roger McDowell	.05	.04	.02
351	Jack Morris	.08	.06	.03
352	Bill Krueger	.05	.04	.02
353	*Cris Colon*(FC)	.15	.11	.06
354	*Joe Vitko*(FC)	.15	.11	.06
355	Willie McGee	.08	.06	.03
356	Jay Baller	.06	.05	.02
357	Pat Mahomes	.20	.15	.08
358	Roger Mason	.05	.04	.02
359	Jerry Nielsen	.15	.11	.06
360	Tom Pagnozzi	.06	.05	.02
361	Kevin Baez	.15	.11	.06
362	*Tim Scott*	.15	.11	.06
363	*Domingo Martinez*(FC)	.20	.15	.08
364	Kirt Manwaring	.05	.04	.02
365	Rafael Palmeiro	.08	.06	.03
366	Ray Lankford	.12	.09	.05
367	Tim McIntosh	.08	.06	.03
368	*Jessie Hollins*(FC)	.15	.11	.06
369	Scott Leius	.06	.05	.02
370	Bill Doran	.05	.04	.02
371	*Sam Militello*(FC)	.20	.15	.08
372	Ryan Bowen	.08	.06	.03
373	Dave Henderson	.08	.06	.03
374	Dan Smith(FC)	.12	.09	.05
375	*Steve Reed*(FC)	.12	.09	.05
376	Jose Offerman	.08	.06	.03
377	Kevin Brown	.08	.06	.03
378	Darrin Fletcher	.05	.04	.02
379	Duane Ward	.06	.05	.02
380	Wayne Kirby(FC)	.12	.09	.05
381	*Steve Scarsone*	.15	.11	.06
382	Mariano Duncan	.06	.05	.02
383	*Ken Ryan*(FC)	.15	.11	.06
384	Lloyd McClendon	.05	.04	.02
385	Brian Holman	.05	.04	.02
386	Braulio Castillo	.08	.06	.03
387	*Danny Leon*	.12	.09	.05
388	Omar Olivares	.05	.04	.02
389	Kevin Wickander	.05	.04	.02
390	Fred McGriff	.10	.08	.04
391	Phil Clark(FC)	.12	.09	.05
392	Darren Lewis	.06	.05	.02
393	*Phil Hiatt*(FC)	.15	.11	.06
394	Mike Morgan	.06	.05	.02
395	Shane Mack	.08	.06	.03
396	Checklist	.05	.04	.02

1993 DONRUSS SERIES 2 CHECKLIST

The checklist for Donruss Series 2 arrived in time to be included in this catalog, but because the cards were not available in the hobby market no prices were available at press time.

397. David Segui
398. Rafael Belliard
399. Tim Naehring
400. Frank Castillo
401. Joe Grahe
402. Reggie Sanders
403. Roberto Henandez
404. Luis Gonzalez
405. Carlos Baerga
406. Carlos Hernandez
407. Pedro Astacio
408. Mel Rojas
409. Scott Livingstone
410. Chico Walker
411. Brian McRae
412. Ben Rivera
413. Ricky Bones
414. Andy Van Slyke
415. Chuck Knoblauch
416. Luis Alicea
417. Bob Wickman
418. Doug Brocail
419. Scott Brosius
420. Rod Beck
421. Edgar Martinez
422. Ryan Klesko
423. Nolan Ryan
424. Rey Sanchez
425. Roberto Alomar
426. Barry Larkin
427. Mike Mussina
428. Jeff Bagwell
429. Mo Vaughn
430. Eric Karros
431. John Orton
432. Wil Cordero
433. Jack McDowell
434. Howard Johnson
435. Albert Belle
436. John Kruk
437. Skeeter Barnes
438. Don Slaught
439. Rusty Meacham
440. Tim Laker
441. Robin Yount
442. Brian Jordan
443. Kevin Tapani
444. Gary Sheffield
445. Rich Monteleone
446. Will Clark
447. Jerry Browne
448. Jeff Treadway
449. Mike Schooler
450. Mike Harkey
451. Julio Franco
452. Kevin Young
453. Kelly Gruber
454. Jose Rijo
455. Mike Devereaux
456. Andujar Cedeno
457. Damion Easley
458. Kevin Gross
459. Matt Young
460. Matt Stairs
461. Luis Polonia
462. Dwight Gooden
463. Warren Newson
464. Jose DeLeon

465. Jose Mesa
466. Danny Cox
467. Dan Gladden
468. Gerald Perry
469. Mike Boddicker
470. Jeff Gardner
471. Doug Henry
472. Mike Benjamin
473. Dan Peltier
474. Mike Stanton
475. John Smiley
476. Dwight Smith
477. Jim Leyritz
478. Dwayne Henry
479. Mark McGwire
480. Pete Incaviglia
481. Dave Cochrane
482. Eric Davis
483. John Olerud
484. Kent Bottenfield
485. Mark McLemore
486. Dave Magadan
487. John Marzano
488. Ruben Amaro
489. Rob Ducey
490. Stan Belinda
491. Dan Pasqua
492. Joe Magrane
493. Brook Jacoby
494. Gene Harris
495. Mark Leiter
496. Bryan Hickerson
497. Tom Gordon
498. Pete Smith
499. Chris Bosio
500. Shawn Boskie
501. Dave West
502. Milt Hill
503. Pat Kelly
504. Joe Boever
505. Terry Steinbach
506. Butch Huskey
507. David Valle
508. Mike Scioscia
509. Kenny Rogers
510. Moises Alou
511. David Wells
512. Mackey Sasser
513. Todd Frohwirth
514. Ricky Jordan
515. Mike Gardiner
516. Gary Redus
517. Gary Gaetti
518. Checklist
519. Carlton Fisk
520. Ozzie Smith
521. Rod Nichols
522. Benito Santiago
523. Bill Gullickson
524. Robby Thompson
525. Mike Macfarlane
526. Sid Bream
527. Darryl Hamilton
528. Checklist
529. Jeff Tackett
530. Greg Olson
531. Bob Zupcic
532. Mark Grace

	MT	NR MT	EX
533. Steve Frey			
534. Dave Martinez			
535. Robin Ventura			
536. Casey Candaele			
537. Kenny Lofton			
538. Jay Howell			
539. Fernando Ramsey			
540. Larry Walker			
541. Cecil Fielder			
542. Lee Guetterman			
543. Keith Miller			
544. Lenny Dykstra			
545. B.J. Surhoff			
546. Bob Walk			
547. Brian Harper			
548. Lee Smith			
549. Danny Tartabull			
550. Frank Seminara			
551. Henry Mercedes			
552. Dave Righetti			
553. Ken Griffey, Jr.			
554. Tom Glavine			
555. Juan Gonzalez			
556. Jim Bullinger			
557. Derek Bell			
558. Cesar Hernandez			
559. Cal Ripken, Jr.			
560. Eddie Taubensee			
561. John Flaherty			
562. Todd Benzinger			
563. Hubie Brooks			
564. Delino DeShields			
565. Tim Raines			
566. Sid Fernandez			
567. Steve Olin			
568. Tommy Greene			
569. Buddy Groom			
570. Randy Tomlin			
571. Hipolito Pichardo			
572. Rene Arocha			
573. Mike Fetters			
574. Felix Jose			
575. Gene Larkin			
576. Bruce Hurst			
577. Bernie Williams			
578. Trevor Wilson			
579. Bob Welch			
580. David Justice			
581. Randy Johnson			
582. Jose Vizcaino			
583. Jeff Huson			
584. Rob Maurer			
585. Todd Stottlemyre			
586. Joe Oliver			
587. Bob Milacki			
588. Rob Murphy			
589. Greg Pirkl			
590. Lenny Harris			
591. Luis Rivera			
592. John Wetteland			
593. Mark Langston			
594. Bobby Bonilla			
595. Este Beltre			
596. Mike Hartley			
597. Felix Fermin			
598. Carlos Garcia			
599. Frank Tanana			
600. Pedro Guerrero			
601. Terry Shumpert			
602. Wally Whitehurst			
603. Kevin Seitzer			
604. Chris James			
605. Greg Gohr			

	MT	NR MT	EX
606. Mark Wohlers			
607. Kirby Puckett			
608. Greg Maddux			
609. Don Mattingly			
610. Greg Cadaret			
611. Dave Stewart			
612. Mark Portugal			
613. Pete O'Brien			
614. Bobb Ojeda			
615. Joe Carter			
616. Pete Young			
617. Sam Horn			
618. Vince Coleman			
619. Wade Boggs			
620. Todd Pratt			
621. Ron Tingley			
622. Doug Drabek			
623. Scott Hemond			
624. Tim Jones			
625. Dennis Cook			
626. Jose Melendez			
627. Mike Munoz			
628. Jim Pena			
629. Gary Thurman			
630. Charlie Leibrandt			
631. Scott Fletcher			
632. Andre Dawson			
633. Greg Gagne			
634. Greg Swindell			
635. Kevin Maas			
636. Xavier Hernandez			
637. Ruben Sierra			
638. Dmitri Young			
639. Harold Reynolds			
640. Tom Goodwin			
641. Todd Burns			
642. Jeff Fassero			
643. Dave Winfield			
644. Willie Randolph			
645. Luis Mercedes			
646. Dale Murphy			
647. Danny Darwin			
648. Dennis Moeller			
649. Chuck Crim			
650. Checklist			
651. Shawn Abner			
652. Tracy Woodson			
653. Scott Scudder			
654. Tom Lampkin			
655. Alan Trammell			
656. Cory Snyder			
657. Chris Gwynn			
658. Lonnie Smith			
659. Jim Austin			
660. Checklist			
661. Tim Hulett			
662. Marvin Freeman			
663. Greg Harris			
664. Heathcliff Slocumb			
665. Mike Butcher			
666. Steve Foster			
667. Donn Pall			
668. Darryl Kile			
669. Jesse Levis			
670. Jim Gott			
671. Mark Hutton			
672. Brian Drahman			
673. Chad Kreuter			
674. Tony Fernandez			
675. Jose Lind			
676. Kyle Abbott			
677. Dan Plesac			
678. Barry Bonds			

	MT	NR MT	EX
679. Chili Davis			
680. Stan Royer			
681. Scott Kamieniecki			
682. Carlos Martinez			
683. Mike Moore			
684. Candy Maldanado			
685. Jeff Nelson			
686. Lou Whitaker			
687. Jose Guzman			
688. Manuel Lee			
689. Bob MacDonald			
690. Scott Bankhead			
691. Alan Mills			
692. Brian Williams			
693. Tom Brunansky			
694. Lenny Webster			
695. Greg Briley			
696. Paul O'Neill			
697. Joey Cora			
698. Charlie O'Brien			
699. Junior Ortiz			
700. Ron Darling			
701. Tony Phillips			
702. William Pennyfeather			
703. Mark Gubicza			
704. Steve Hosey			
705. Henry Cotto			
706. David Hulse			
707. Mike Pagliarulo			
708. Dave Stieb			
709. Melido Perez			
710. Jimmy Key			
711. Jeff Russell			
712. David Cone			
713. Russ Swan			
714. Mark Guthrie			
715. Checklist			
716. Al Martin			
717. Randy Knorr			
718. Mike Stanley			
719. Rick Sutcliffe			
720. Terry Leach			
721. Chipper Jones			
722. Jim Eisenreich			
723. Tom Henke			
724. Jeff Frye			
725. Harold Baines			
726. Scott Sanderson			
727. Tom Foley			
728. Bryan Harvey			
729. Tom Edens			
730. Eric Young			
731. Dave Weathers			
732. Spike Owen			
733. Scott Aldred			
734. Cris Carpenter			
735. Dion James			
736. Joe Girardi			
737. Nigel Wilson			
738. Scott Chiamparino			
739. Jeff Reardon			
740. Willie Blair			
741. Jim Corsi			
742. Ken Patterson			
743. Andy Ashby			
744. Rob Natal			
745. Kevin Bass			
746. Freddie Benavides			
747. Chris Donnels			
748. Kerry Woodson			
749. Calvin Jones			
750. Gary Scott			
751. Joe Orsulak			

	MT	NR MT	EX
752. Armando Reynoso			
753. Monty Fariss			
754. Billy Hatcher			
755. Denis Boucher			
756. Walt Weiss			
757. Mike Fitzgerald			
758. Rudy Seanez			
759. Bret Barberie			
760. Mo Sanford			
761. Pedro Castellano			
762. Chuck Carr			
763. Steve Howe			
764. Andres Galarraga			
765. Jeff Conine			
766. Ted Power			
767. Butch Henry			
768. Steve Decker			
769. Storm Davis			
770. Vinny Castilla			
771. Junior Felix			
772. Walt Terrell			
773. Brad Ausmus			
774. Jamie McAndrew			
775. Milt Thompson			
776. Charlie Hayes			
777. Jack Armstrong			
778. Dennis Rasmussen			
779. Darren Homes			
780. Alex Arias			
781. Randy Bush			
782. Javy Lopez			
783. Dante Bichette			
784. John Johnstone			
785. Rene Gonzales			
786. Alex Cole			
787. Jeromy Burnitz			
788. Michael Huff			
789. Anthony Telford			
790. Jerald Clark			
791. Joel Johnston			
792. David Nied			

Card company addresses

Collectors frequently want to know the addresses of the major baseball card manufacturers. They are:

Donruss-Leaf
2355 Waukegan Road
Bannockburn, Ill. 60015

Fleer Corp.
Executive Plaza
Suite 300
1120 Route 73
Mt.Laurel, N.J. 08054

Score
c/o Major League Marketing
25 Ford Road
Westport, Conn. 06880

Topps Gum Co.
254 36th St.
Brooklyn, N.Y. 11232

Upper Deck Co.
5909 Sea Otter Place
Carlsbad, Calif. 92008-6621

1986 Dorman's Cheese

Found in specially-marked packages of Dorman's American Cheese Singles, the Dorman's set consists of ten two-card panels of baseball superstars. Labeled as a "Super Star Limited Edition" set, the panels measure 1-1/2" by 2" each and have a perforation line in the center. The fronts contain a color photo along with the Dorman's logo and the player's name, team and position. Due to a lack of proper licensing, all team insignias have been airbrushed from the players' caps. The backs of the cards contain brief player statistics.

		MT	NR MT	EX
	Complete Panel Set:	35.00	26.00	14.00
	Complete Singles Set:	20.00	15.00	8.00
	Common Panel:	1.25	.90	.50
	Common Single Player:	.20	.15	.08
()	Panel	2.00	1.50	.80
(1)	George Brett	.50	.40	.20
(2)	Jack Morris	.20	.15	.08
()	Panel	2.00	1.50	.80
(3)	Gary Carter	.30	.25	.12
(4)	Cal Ripken	.40	.30	.15
()	Panel	2.00	1.50	.80
(5)	Dwight Gooden	.60	.45	.25
(6)	Kent Hrbek	.20	.15	.08
()	Panel	3.00	1.50	.90
(7)	Rickey Henderson	.60	.45	.25
(8)	Mike Schmidt	.80	.60	.30
()	Panel	2.00	1.50	.80
(9)	Keith Hernandez	.30	.25	.12
(10)	Dale Murphy	.30	.25	.12
()	Panel	2.00	1.50	.80
(11)	Reggie Jackson	.40	.30	.15
(12)	Eddie Murray	.40	.30	.15
()	Panel	4.00	3.00	1.50
(13)	Don Mattingly	1.00	.70	.40
(14)	Ryne Sandberg	.60	.45	.25
()	Panel	1.25	.90	.50
(15)	Willie McGee	.20	.15	.08
(16)	Robin Yount	.30	.25	.12
()	Panel	2.25	1.75	.90
(17)	Rick Sutcliffe (Sutcliffe)	.20	.15	.08
(18)	Wade Boggs	.80	.60	.30
()	Panel	1.50	1.25	.60
(19)	Dave Winfield	.40	.30	.15
(20)	Jim Rice	.20	.15	.10

NOTE: A card number in parentheses ( ) indicates the set is unnumbered.

1950 Drake's

Entitled "TV Baseball Series", the 1950 Drake's Bakeries set pictures 36 different players on a television screen format. The cards, which measure 2-1/2" by 2-1/2", contain black and white photos surrounded by a black border. The card backs carry a player biography plus an advertisement advising collectors to look for the cards in packages of Oatmeal or Jumble cookies. The ACC designation for the set is D358.

		NR MT	EX	VG
	Complete Set:	5000.00	3000.00	1500.
	Common Player:	50.00	25.00	15.00
1	Elwin "Preacher" Roe	100.00	50.00	30.00
2	Clint Hartung	50.00	25.00	15.00
3	Earl Torgeson	50.00	25.00	15.00
4	Leland "Lou" Brissie	50.00	25.00	15.00
5	Edwin "Duke" Snider	350.00	175.00	100.00
6	Roy Campanella	400.00	200.00	125.00
7	Sheldon "Available" Jones	50.00	25.00	15.00
8	Carroll "Whitey" Lockman	50.00	25.00	15.00
9	Bobby Thomson	80.00	40.00	25.00
10	Dick Sisler	50.00	25.00	15.00
11	Gil Hodges	200.00	100.00	60.00
12	Eddie Waitkus	50.00	25.00	15.00
13	Bobby Doerr	150.00	75.00	45.00
14	Warren Spahn	250.00	125.00	75.00
15	John "Buddy" Kerr	50.00	25.00	15.00
16	Sid Gordon	50.00	25.00	15.00
17	Willard Marshall	50.00	25.00	15.00
18	Carl Furillo	90.00	45.00	25.00
19	Harold "Pee Wee" Reese	300.00	150.00	90.00
20	Alvin Dark	70.00	35.00	20.00
21	Del Ennis	50.00	25.00	15.00
22	Ed Stanky	70.00	35.00	20.00
23	Tommy "Old Reliable" Henrich	90.00	45.00	25.00
24	Larry "Yogi" Berra	400.00	200.00	125.00
25	Phil "Scooter" Rizzuto	275.00	150.00	100.00
26	Jerry Coleman	70.00	35.00	20.00
27	Joe Page	70.00	35.00	20.00
28	Allie Reynolds	90.00	45.00	25.00
29	Ray Scarborough	50.00	25.00	15.00
30	George "Birdie" Tebbetts	50.00	25.00	15.00
31	Maurice "Lefty" McDermott	50.00	25.00	15.00
32	Johnny Pesky	70.00	35.00	20.00
33	Dom "Little Professor" DiMaggio	80.00	40.00	25.00
34	Vern "Junior" Stephens	50.00	25.00	15.00
35	Bob Elliott	50.00	25.00	15.00
36	Enos "Country" Slaughter	250.00	125.00	75.00

1981 Drake's

Producing their first baseball card set since 1950, Drake Bakeries, in conjunction with Topps, issued a 33-card set entitled "Big Hitters." The cards, which are the standard 2-1/2" by 3-1/2" in size, feature 19 American League and 14 National League sluggers. Full-color photos, containing a facsimile autograph, are positioned in red frames for A.L. players and blue frames for N.L. hitters. The player's name, team, position, and the Drake's logo are also included on the card fronts. The card backs, which are similar to the regular 1981 Topps issue, contain the card number (1-33), statistical and biographical information, and the Drake's logo.

		MT	NR MT	EX
Complete Set:		8.00	6.00	3.25
Common Player:		.12	.09	.05
1	Carl Yastrzemski	.70	.50	.30
2	Rod Carew	.60	.45	.25
3	Pete Rose	1.00	.70	.40
4	Dave Parker	.25	.20	.10
5	George Brett	.70	.50	.30
6	Eddie Murray	.60	.45	.25
7	Mike Schmidt	1.00	.70	.40
8	Jim Rice	.45	.35	.20
9	Fred Lynn	.25	.20	.10
10	Reggie Jackson	.60	.45	.25
11	Steve Garvey	.45	.35	.20
12	Ken Singleton	.12	.09	.05
13	Bill Buckner	.12	.09	.05
14	Dave Winfield	.60	.45	.25
15	Jack Clark	.30	.25	.12
16	Cecil Cooper	.20	.15	.08
17	Bob Horner	.20	.15	.08
18	George Foster	.20	.15	.08
19	Dave Kingman	.20	.15	.08
20	Cesar Cedeno	.12	.09	.05
21	Joe Charboneau	.12	.09	.05
22	George Hendrick	.12	.09	.05
23	Gary Carter	.45	.35	.20
24	Al Oliver	.20	.15	.08
25	Bruce Bochte	.12	.09	.05
26	Jerry Mumphrey	.12	.09	.05
27	Steve Kemp	.12	.09	.05
28	Bob Watson	.12	.09	.05
29	John Castino	.12	.09	.05
30	Tony Armas	.12	.09	.05
31	John Mayberry	.12	.09	.05
32	Carlton Fisk	.30	.25	.12
33	Lee Mazzilli	.12	.09	.05

1982 Drake's

Drake Bakeries produced, in conjunction with Topps, a "2nd Annual Collectors' Edition" in 1982. Thirty-three standard-size cards (2-1/2" by 3-1/2") make up the set. Like the previous year, the set is entitled "Big Hitters" and is comprised of 19 American League players and 14 from the National League. The card fronts have a mounted photo appearance and contain a facsimile autograph. The player's name, team, position, and the Drake's logo also are located on the fronts. The card backs, other than being numbered 1-33 and containing a Drake's copyright line, are identical to the regular 1982 Topps issue.

		MT	NR MT	EX
Complete Set:		9.00	6.75	3.50
Common Player:		.12	.09	.05
1	Tony Armas	.12	.09	.05
2	Buddy Bell	.20	.15	.08

		MT	NR MT	EX
3	Johnny Bench	.50	.40	.20
4	George Brett	.70	.50	.30
5	Bill Buckner	.12	.09	.05
6	Rod Carew	.50	.40	.20
7	Gary Carter	.45	.35	.20
8	Jack Clark	.30	.25	.12
9	Cecil Cooper	.20	.15	.08
10	Jose Cruz	.12	.09	.05
11	Dwight Evans	.20	.15	.08
12	Carlton Fisk	.30	.25	.12
13	George Foster	.20	.15	.08
14	Steve Garvey	.45	.35	.20
15	Kirk Gibson	.40	.30	.15
16	Mike Hargrove	.12	.09	.05
17	George Hendrick	.12	.09	.05
18	Bob Horner	.20	.15	.08
19	Reggie Jackson	.80	.60	.30
20	Terry Kennedy	.12	.09	.05
21	Dave Kingman	.20	.15	.08
22	Greg Luzinski	.20	.15	.08
23	Bill Madlock	.20	.15	.08
24	John Mayberry	.12	.09	.05
25	Eddie Murray	.50	.40	.20
26	Graig Nettles	.20	.15	.08
27	Jim Rice	.45	.35	.20
28	Pete Rose	1.00	.70	.40
29	Mike Schmidt	1.00	.70	.40
30	Ken Singleton	.12	.09	.05
31	Dave Winfield	.50	.40	.20
32	Butch Wynegar	.12	.09	.05
33	Richie Zisk	.12	.09	.05

1983 Drake's

Seventeen American League and 16 National League "Big Hitters" make up the 33-card "3rd Annual Collectors' Edition" set issued by Drake Bakeries in 1983. The Topps-produced set contains 33 cards which measure 2-1/2" by 3-1/2" in size. The card fronts are somewhat similar in design to the previous year's set. The backs are identical to the 1983 Topps regular issue except for being numbered 1-33 and containing a Drake's logo and copyright line.

		MT	NR MT	EX
Complete Set:		7.00	5.25	2.75
Common Player:		.12	.09	.05
1	Don Baylor	.20	.15	.08
2	Bill Buckner	.12	.09	.05
3	Rod Carew	.50	.40	.20
4	Gary Carter	.45	.35	.20
5	Jack Clark	.25	.20	.10
6	Cecil Cooper	.20	.15	.08
7	Dwight Evans	.20	.15	.08
8	George Foster	.20	.15	.08
9	Pedro Guerrero	.25	.20	.10
10	George Hendrick	.12	.09	.05
11	Bob Horner	.20	.15	.08
12	Reggie Jackson	.60	.45	.25
13	Steve Kemp	.12	.09	.05
14	Dave Kingman	.20	.15	.08
15	Bill Madlock	.20	.15	.08
16	Gary Matthews	.12	.09	.05
17	Hal McRae	.12	.09	.05
18	Dale Murphy	.40	.30	.15

		MT	NR MT	EX
19	Eddie Murray	.50	.40	.20
20	Ben Oglivie	.12	.09	.05
21	Al Oliver	.20	.15	.08
22	Jim Rice	.45	.35	.20
23	Cal Ripken	.60	.45	.25
24	Pete Rose	1.00	.70	.40
25	Mike Schmidt	1.00	.70	.40
26	Ken Singleton	.12	.09	.05
27	Gorman Thomas	.12	.09	.05
28	Jason Thompson	.12	.09	.05
29	Mookie Wilson	.10	.08	.04
30	Willie Wilson	.20	.15	.08
31	Dave Winfield	.50	.40	.20
32	Carl Yastrzemski	.40	.30	.15
33	Robin Yount	.40	.30	.15

1984 Drake's

For the fourth year in a row, Drake Bakeries issued a 33-card "Big Hitters" set. The 1984 edition, produced again by Topps, includes 17 National League players and 16 from the American League. As in all previous years, the card fronts feature the player in a batting pose. The backs are identical to the 1984 Topps regular issue except for being numbered 1-33 and carrying the Drake's logo and copyright line. The cards are the standard size 2-1/2" by 3-1/2".

		MT	NR MT	EX
	Complete Set:	9.00	6.75	3.50
	Complete Set:	.12	.09	.05
1	Don Baylor	.20	.15	.08
2	Wade Boggs	1.25	.90	.50
3	George Brett	.70	.50	.30
4	Bill Buckner	.12	.09	.05
5	Rod Carew	.60	.45	.25
6	Gary Carter	.45	.35	.20
7	Ron Cey	.12	.09	.05
8	Cecil Cooper	.20	.15	.08
9	Andre Dawson	.35	.25	.14
10	Steve Garvey	.45	.35	.20
11	Pedro Guerrero	.25	.20	.10
12	George Hendrick	.12	.09	.05
13	Keith Hernandez	.40	.30	.15
14	Bob Horner	.20	.15	.08
15	Reggie Jackson	.60	.45	.25
16	Steve Kemp	.12	.09	.05
17	Ron Kittle	.20	.15	.08
18	Greg Luzinski	.20	.15	.08
19	Fred Lynn	.20	.15	.08
20	Bill Madlock	.20	.15	.08
21	Gary Matthews	.12	.09	.05
22	Dale Murphy	.70	.50	.30
23	Eddie Murray	.60	.45	.25
24	Al Oliver	.20	.15	.08
25	Jim Rice	.45	.35	.20
26	Cal Ripken	.60	.45	.25
27	Pete Rose	1.00	.70	.40
28	Mike Schmidt	1.00	.70	.40
29	Darryl Strawberry	1.25	.90	.50
30	Alan Trammell	.30	.25	.12
31	Mookie Wilson	.12	.09	.05
32	Dave Winfield	.60	.45	.25
33	Robin Yount	.40	.30	.15

1985 Drake's

The "5th Annual Collectors' Edition" set produced by Topps for Drake Bakeries consists of 33 "Big Hitters" and 11 "Super Pitchers." The new "Super Pitchers" feature increased the set's size from the usual 33 cards to 44. The cards, which measure 2-1/2" by 3-1/2", show the player in either a batting or pitching pose. The backs differ only from the regular 1985 Topps issue in that they are numbered 1-44 and carry the Drake's logo.

		MT	NR MT	EX
	Complete Set:	12.00	9.00	4.75
	Commmon Player:	.12	.09	.05
1	Tony Armas	.12	.09	.05
2	Harold Baines	.20	.15	.08
3	Don Baylor	.20	.15	.08
4	George Brett	.70	.50	.30
5	Gary Carter	.45	.35	.20
6	Ron Cey	.12	.09	.05
7	Jose Cruz	.12	.09	.05
8	Alvin Davis	.25	.20	.10
9	Chili Davis	.12	.09	.05
10	Dwight Evans	.20	.15	.08
11	Steve Garvey	.45	.35	.20
12	Kirk Gibson	.35	.25	.14
13	Pedro Guerrero	.25	.20	.10
14	Tony Gwynn	.60	.45	.25
15	Keith Hernandez	.40	.30	.15
16	Kent Hrbek	.35	.25	.14
17	Reggie Jackson	.60	.45	.25
18	Gary Matthews	.12	.09	.05
19	Don Mattingly	1.50	1.25	.60
20	Dale Murphy	.70	.50	.30
21	Eddie Murray	.45	.35	.20
22	Dave Parker	.20	.15	.08
23	Lance Parrish	.25	.20	.10
24	Tim Raines	.45	.35	.20
25	Jim Rice	.45	.35	.20
26	Cal Ripken	.60	.45	.25
27	Juan Samuel	.25	.20	.10
28	Ryne Sandberg	.40	.30	.15
29	Mike Schmidt	1.00	.70	.40
30	Darryl Strawberry	.90	.70	.35
31	Alan Trammell	.30	.25	.12
32	Dave Winfield	.50	.40	.20
33	Robin Yount	.40	.30	.15
34	Mike Boddicker	.12	.09	.05
35	Steve Carlton	.40	.30	.15
36	Dwight Gooden	1.00	.70	.40
37	Willie Hernandez	.12	.09	.05
38	Mark Langston	.20	.15	.08
39	Dan Quisenberry	.12	.09	.05
40	Dave Righetti	.20	.15	.08
41	Tom Seaver	.40	.30	.15
42	Bob Stanley	.12	.09	.05
43	Rick Sutcliffe	.20	.15	.08
44	Bruce Sutter	.20	.15	.08

The values quoted are intended to reflect the market price.

1986 Drake's

For the sixth year in a row, Drake Bakeries issued a baseball card set. Produced for Drake's by Topps in the past, the 1986 set was not and was available only by buying the actual products the cards were printed on. The cards, which measure 2-1/2" by 3-1/2", were issued in either two-, three-, or four-card panels. Fourteen panels, consisting of 37 different players, comprise the set. The players who make up the set are tabbed as either "Big Hitters" or "Super Pitchers." Logos of various Drake's products can be found on the panel backs. The value of the set is higher when collected in either panel or complete box form.

		MT	NR MT	EX
Complete Panel Set:		45.00	34.00	18.00
Complete Singles Set:		35.00	26.00	14.00
Common Panel:		1.75	1.25	.70
Common Single Player:		.20	.15	.08
	Panel	1.75	1.25	.70
1	Gary Carter	.50	.40	.20
2	Dwight Evans	.25	.20	.10
	Panel	2.00	1.50	.80
3	Reggie Jackson	.60	.45	.25
4	Dave Parker	.25	.20	.10
	Panel	2.00	1.50	.80
5	Rickey Henderson	1.00	.70	.40
6	Pedro Guerrero	.30	.25	.12
	Panel	5.00	3.75	2.00
7	Don Mattingly	2.00	1.50	.80
8	Mike Marshall	.25	.20	.10
9	Keith Moreland	.20	.15	.08
	Panel	2.00	1.50	.80
10	Keith Hernandez	.40	.30	.15
11	Cal Ripken	.60	.45	.25
	Panel	2.25	1.75	.90
12	Dale Murphy	.60	.45	.25
13	Jim Rice	.40	.30	.15
	Panel	2.25	1.75	.90
14	George Brett	.60	.45	.25
15	Tim Raines	.50	.40	.20
	Panel	2.00	1.50	.80
16	Darryl Strawberry	.80	.60	.30
17	Bill Buckner	.20	.15	.08
	Panel	2.75	2.00	1.00
18	Dave Winfield	.50	.40	.20
19	Ryne Sandberg	.40	.30	.15
20	Steve Balboni	.20	.15	.08
21	Tom Herr	.25	.20	.10
	Panel	3.75	2.75	1.50
22	Pete Rose	.90	.70	.35
23	Willie McGee	.25	.20	.10
24	Harold Baines	.25	.20	.10
25	Eddie Murray	.50	.40	.20
	Panel	4.00	3.00	1.50
26	Mike Schmidt	1.00	.70	.40
27	Wade Boggs	1.25	.90	.50
28	Kirk Gibson	.35	.25	.14
	Panel	2.00	1.50	.80
29	Bret Saberhagen	.35	.25	.14
30	John Tudor	.20	.15	.08
31	Orel Hershiser	.40	.30	.15
	Panel	2.00	1.50	.80
32	Ron Guidry	.25	.20	.10
33	Nolan Ryan	1.00	.70	.40
34	Dave Stieb	.25	.20	.10

		MT	NR MT	EX
	Panel	2.75	2.00	1.00
35	Dwight Gooden	.80	.60	.30
36	Fernando Valenzuela	.35	.25	.14
37	Tom Browning	.25	.20	.10

1987 Drake's

For the seventh consecutive season, Drake Bakeries produced a baseball card set. The cards, which measure 2-1/2" by 3-1/2", were included in either two-, three-, or four-card panels on boxes of various Drake's products distributed in the eastern United States. The set is comprised of 33 cards, with 25 players branded as "Big Hitters" and 8 as "Super Pitchers". The card fronts carry a full-color photo and the Drake's logo surrounded by a brown and yellow border. The backs contain the player's complete major league record.

		MT	NR MT	EX
Complete Panel Set:		45.00	34.00	18.00
Complete Singles Set:		30.00	22.00	12.00
Common Panel:		1.75	1.25	.70
Common Single Player:		.20	.15	.08
	Panel	4.00	3.00	1.50
1	Darryl Strawberry	.80	.60	.30
2	Wally Joyner	1.25	.90	.50
	Panel	3.75	2.75	1.50
3	Von Hayes	.25	.20	.10
4	Jose Canseco	1.75	1.25	.70
	Panel	2.00	1.50	.80
5	Dave Winfield	.50	.40	.20
6	Cal Ripken	.60	.45	.25
	Panel	4.50	3.50	1.75
7	Keith Moreland	.20	.15	.08
8	Don Mattingly	2.00	1.50	.80
9	Willie McGee	.25	.20	.10
	Panel	2.00	1.50	.80
10	Keith Hernandez	.40	.30	.15
11	Tony Gwynn	.60	.45	.25
	Panel	4.25	3.25	1.75
12	Rickey Henderson	1.00	.70	.40
13	Dale Murphy	.60	.45	.25
14	George Brett	.60	.45	.25
15	Jim Rice	.40	.30	.15
	Panel	4.00	3.00	1.50
16	Wade Boggs	1.25	.90	.50
17	Kevin Bass	.20	.15	.08
18	Dave Parker	.25	.20	.10
19	Kirby Puckett	.50	.40	.20
	Panel	2.00	1.50	.80
20	Gary Carter	.50	.40	.20
21	Ryne Sandberg	.40	.30	.15
22	Harold Baines	.25	.20	.10
	Panel	2.75	2.00	1.00
23	Mike Schmidt	1.00	.70	.40
24	Eddie Murray	.50	.40	.20
25	Steve Sax	.25	.20	.10
	Panel	1.75	1.25	.70
26	Dwight Gooden	.80	.60	.30
27	Jack Morris	.25	.20	.10
	Panel	1.75	1.25	.70
28	Ron Darling	.25	.20	.10
29	Fernando Valenzuela	.35	.25	.14
30	John Tudor	.20	.15	.10
	Panel	2.50	2.00	1.00

		MT	NR MT	EX
31	Roger Clemens	.80	.60	.30
32	Nolan Ryan	1.00	.70	.40
33	Mike Scott	.25	.20	.10

		MT	NR MT	EX
31	Rick Sutcliffe	.20	.15	.08
32	Jack Morris	.25	.20	.10
33	John Tudor	.20	.15	.08

1988 Drake's

The 8th annual edition of this set includes 33 glossy full-color cards printed on cut-out panels of 2, 3 or 4 cards on Drake's dessert snack boxes. Card fronts have white borders with a large red and blue "Super Pitchers" (6 cards) or "Big Hitters" (27 cards) caption upper left, beside the "8th Annual Collector's Edition label. The Drake logo, player name and team logo are printed in black and include the card number, personal data, batting/pitching record and sponsor logos. Sets were available exclusively on 12 different Drake's packages. To complete the set, collectors had to purchase all 12 products.

		MT	NR MT	EX
	Complete Panel Set:	45.00	34.00	18.00
	Complete Singles Set:	30.00	22.00	12.00
	Common Panel:	1.75	1.25	.70
	Common Single Player:	.20	.15	.08
	Panel	4.25	3.25	1.75
1	Don Mattingly	2.00	1.50	.80
2	Tim Raines	.50	.40	.20
	Panel	3.75	2.75	1.50
3	Darryl Strawberry	.80	.60	.30
4	Wade Boggs	1.25	.90	.50
	Panel	3.25	2.50	1.25
5	Keith Hernandez	.40	.30	.15
6	Mark McGwire	1.25	.90	.50
	Panel	2.75	2.00	1.00
7	Rickey Henderson	1.00	.70	.40
8	Mike Schmidt	.60	.45	.25
9	Dwight Evans	.25	.20	.10
	Panel	1.75	1.25	.70
10	Gary Carter	.50	.40	.20
11	Paul Molitor	.30	.25	.12
	Panel	2.75	2.00	1.00
12	Dave Winfield	.50	.40	.20
13	Alan Trammell	.35	.25	.14
14	Tony Gwynn	.50	.40	.20
	Panel	2.50	2.00	1.00
15	Dale Murphy	.60	.45	.25
16	Andre Dawson	.30	.25	.12
17	Von Hayes	.20	.15	.08
18	Willie Randolph	.20	.15	.08
	Panel	2.00	1.50	.80
19	Kirby Puckett	.50	.40	.20
20	Juan Samuel	.25	.20	.10
21	Eddie Murray	.40	.30	.15
	Panel	3.00	2.25	1.25
22	George Bell	.35	.25	.14
23	Larry Sheets	.20	.15	.08
24	Eric Davis	.70	.50	.30
	Panel	2.25	1.75	.90
25	Cal Ripken	.60	.45	.25
26	Pedro Guerrero	.25	.20	.10
27	Will Clark	1.75	1.25	.70
	Panel	2.00	1.50	.80
28	Dwight Gooden	.80	.60	.30
29	Frank Viola	.25	.20	.10
	Panel	3.00	2.25	1.25
30	Roger Clemens	.80	.60	.30

1966 East Hills Pirates

Stores in the East Hills Shopping Center, a large mall located in suburban Pittsburgh, distributed cards from this 25-card full-color set in 1966. The cards, which measure 3-1/4" by 4-1/4", are blank-backed and are numbered by the players' uniform numbers. The numbers appear in the lower right corners of the cards.

		NR MT	EX	VG
	Complete Set:	40.00	20.00	12.00
	Common Player:	.50	.25	.15
3	Harry Walker	.70	.35	.20
7	Bob Bailey	.50	.25	.15
8	Willie Stargell	8.00	4.00	2.50
9	Bill Mazeroski	3.00	1.50	.90
10	Jim Pagliaroni	.50	.25	.15
11	Jose Pagan	.50	.25	.15
12	Jerry May	.50	.25	.15
14	Gene Alley	.60	.30	.20
15	Manny Mota	.80	.40	.25
16	Andy Rodgers	.50	.25	.15
17	Donn Clendenon	.60	.30	.20
18	Matty Alou	.80	.40	.25
19	Pete Mikkelsen	.50	.25	.15
20	Jesse Gonder	.50	.25	.15
21	Bob Clemente	20.00	10.00	6.00
22	Woody Fryman	.60	.30	.20
24	Jerry Lynch	.50	.25	.15
25	Tommie Sisk	.50	.25	.15
26	Roy Face	1.25	.60	.40
28	Steve Blass	.60	.30	.20
32	Vernon Law	1.25	.60	.40
34	Al McBean	.50	.25	.15
39	Bob Veale	.60	.30	.20
43	Don Cardwell	.50	.25	.15
45	Gene Michael	.60	.30	.20

Exhibits - 1947-1966

Called "Exhibits" as they were produced by the Exhibit Supply Co. of Chicago, Ill., this group covers a span of twenty years. Each unnumbered, black and white card, printed on heavy stock, measures 3-3/8" by 5-3/8" and is blank-backed. The Exhibit Supply Co. issued new sets each year, with many players being repeated year after year. Other players appeared in only one or two years, thereby creating levels of scarcity. Many variations of the same basic pose are found in the group. Those cards are listed in the checklist that follows with an "a", "b", etc. following the assigned card number. The complete set includes all variations

		NR MT	EX	VG
Complete Set:		5000.00	2500.00	1500.
Common Player:		4.00	2.00	1.25
(1)	Hank Aaron	30.00	15.00	9.00
(2a)	Joe Adcock (script signature)	4.00	2.00	1.25
(2b)	Joe Adcock (plain signature)	5.00	2.50	1.50
(3)	Max Alvis	25.00	12.50	7.50
(4)	Johnny Antonelli (Braves)	4.00	2.00	1.25
(5)	Johnny Antonelli (Giants)	5.00	2.50	1.50
(6)	Luis Aparicio (portrait)	7.00	3.50	2.00
(7)	Luis Aparicio (batting)	25.00	12.50	7.50
(8)	Luke Appling	7.00	3.50	2.00
(9a)	Ritchie Ashburn (Phillies, first name incorrect)	5.00	2.50	1.50
(9b)	Richie Ashburn (Phillies, first name correct)	7.00	3.50	2.00
(10)	Richie Ashburn (Cubs)	13.00	6.50	4.00
(11)	Bob Aspromonte	4.00	2.00	1.25
(12)	Toby Atwell	4.00	2.00	1.25
(13)	Ed Bailey (with cap)	5.00	2.50	1.50
(14)	Ed Bailey (no cap)	4.00	2.00	1.25
(15)	Gene Baker	4.00	2.00	1.25
(16a)	Ernie Banks (bat on shoulder, script signature)	25.00	12.50	7.50
(16b)	Ernie Banks (bat on shoulder, plain signature)	10.00	5.00	3.00
(17)	Ernie Banks (portrait)	25.00	12.50	7.50
(18)	Steve Barber	4.00	2.00	1.25
(19)	Earl Battey	5.00	2.50	1.50
(20)	Matt Batts	4.00	2.00	1.25
(21a)	Hank Bauer (N.Y. cap)	5.00	2.50	1.50
(21b)	Hank Bauer (plain cap)	7.00	3.50	2.00
(22)	Frank Baumholtz	4.00	2.00	1.25
(23)	Gene Bearden	4.00	2.00	1.25
(24)	Joe Beggs	12.00	6.00	3.50
(25)	Larry "Yogi" Berra	30.00	15.00	9.00
(26)	Yogi Berra	10.00	5.00	3.00
(27)	Steve Bilko	5.00	2.50	1.50
(28)	Ewell Blackwell (pitching)	7.00	3.50	2.00
(29)	Ewell Blackwell (portrait)	4.00	2.00	1.25
(30a)	Don Blasingame (St. Louis cap)	4.00	2.00	1.25
(30b)	Don Blasingame (plain cap)	6.00	3.00	1.75
(31)	Ken Boyer	7.00	3.50	2.00
(32)	Ralph Branca	7.00	3.50	2.00
(33)	Jackie Brandt	50.00	25.00	15.00
(34)	Harry Brecheen	4.00	2.00	1.25
(35)	Tom Brewer	12.00	6.00	3.50
(36)	Lou Brissie	5.00	2.50	1.50
(37)	Bill Bruton	4.00	2.00	1.25
(38)	Lew Burdette (pitching, side view)	4.00	2.00	1.25
(39)	Lew Burdette (pitching, front view)	6.00	3.00	1.75
(40)	Johnny Callison	7.00	3.50	2.00
(41)	Roy Campanella	13.00	6.50	4.00
(42)	Chico Carrasquel (portrait)	13.00	6.50	4.00
(43)	Chico Carrasquel (leaping)	4.00	2.00	1.25
(44)	George Case	12.00	6.00	3.50
(45)	Hugh Casey	5.00	2.50	1.50
(46)	Norm Cash	7.00	3.50	2.00
(47)	Orlando Cepeda (portrait)	7.00	3.50	2.00
(48)	Orlando Cepeda (batting)	7.00	3.50	2.00
(49a)	Bob Cerv (A's cap)	7.00	3.50	2.00
(49b)	Bob Cerv (plain cap)	16.00	8.00	4.75
(50)	Dean Chance	4.00	2.00	1.25
(51)	Spud Chandler	12.00	6.00	3.50

		NR MT	EX	VG
(52)	Tom Cheney	4.00	2.00	1.25
(53)	Bubba Church	5.00	2.50	1.50
(54)	Roberto Clemente	30.00	15.00	9.00
(55)	Rocky Colavito (portrait)	30.00	15.00	9.00
(56)	Rocky Colavito (batting)	7.00	3.50	2.00
(57)	Choo Choo Coleman	13.00	6.50	4.00
(58)	Gordy Coleman	25.00	12.50	7.50
(59)	Jerry Coleman	5.00	2.50	1.50
(60)	Mort Cooper	12.00	6.00	3.50
(61)	Walker Cooper	4.00	2.00	1.25
(62)	Roger Craig	12.00	6.00	3.50
(63)	Delmar Crandall	4.00	2.00	1.25
(64)	Joe Cunningham (batting)	30.00	15.00	9.00
(65)	Joe Cunningham (portrait)	7.00	3.50	2.00
(66)	Guy Curtwright (Curtright)	5.00	2.50	1.50
(67)	Bud Daley	35.00	17.50	10.50
(68a)	Alvin Dark (Braves)	7.00	3.50	2.00
(68b)	Alvin Dark (Giants)	5.00	2.50	1.50
(69)	Alvin Dark (Cubs)	7.00	3.50	2.00
(70)	Murray Dickson (Murry)	5.00	2.50	1.50
(71)	Bob Dillinger	7.00	3.50	2.00
(72)	Dom DiMaggio	18.00	9.00	5.50
(73)	Joe Dobson	7.00	3.50	2.00
(74)	Larry Doby	4.00	2.00	1.25
(75)	Bobby Doerr	12.00	6.00	3.50
(76)	Dick Donovan (plain cap)	7.00	3.50	2.00
(77)	Dick Donovan (Sox cap)	4.00	2.00	1.25
(78)	Walter Dropo	4.00	2.00	1.25
(79)	Don Drysdale (glove at waist)	30.00	15.00	9.00
(80)	Don Drysdale (portrait)	30.00	15.00	9.00
(81)	Luke Easter	5.00	2.50	1.50
(82)	Bruce Edwards	5.00	2.50	1.50
(83)	Del Ennis	4.00	2.00	1.25
(84)	Al Evans	4.50	2.25	1.25
(85)	Walter Evers	4.00	2.00	1.25
(86)	Ferris Fain (fielding)	7.00	3.50	2.00
(87)	Ferris Fain (portrait)	4.00	2.00	1.25
(88)	Dick Farrell	4.00	2.00	1.25
(89)	Ed "Whitey" Ford	15.00	7.50	4.50
(90)	Whitey Ford (pitching)	10.00	5.00	3.00
(91)	Whitey Ford (portrait)	60.00	30.00	17.50
(92)	Dick Fowler	7.00	3.50	2.00
(93)	Nelson Fox	5.00	2.50	1.50
(94)	Tito Francona	4.00	2.00	1.25
(95)	Bob Friend	4.00	2.00	1.25
(96)	Carl Furillo	7.00	3.50	2.00
(97)	Augie Galan	7.00	3.50	2.00
(98)	Jim Gentile	4.00	2.00	1.25
(99)	Tony Gonzalez	4.00	2.00	1.25
(100)	Billy Goodman (leaping)	4.00	2.00	1.25
(101)	Billy Goodman (batting)	7.00	3.50	2.00
(102)	Ted Greengrass (Jim)	4.00	2.00	1.25
(103)	Dick Groat	7.00	3.50	2.00
(104)	Steve Gromek	4.00	2.00	1.25
(105)	Johnny Groth	4.00	2.00	1.25
(106)	Orval Grove	13.00	6.50	4.00
(107a)	Frank Gustine (Pirates uniform)	5.00	2.50	1.50
(107b)	Frank Gustine (plain uniform)	5.00	2.50	1.50
(108)	Berthold Haas	13.00	6.50	4.00
(109)	Grady Hatton	5.00	2.50	1.50
(110)	Jim Hegan	4.00	2.00	1.25
(111)	Tom Henrich	7.00	3.50	2.00
(112)	Ray Herbert	25.00	12.50	7.50
(113)	Gene Hermanski	4.50	2.25	1.25
(114)	Whitey Herzog	7.00	3.50	2.00
(115)	Kirby Higbe	13.00	6.50	4.00
(116)	Chuck Hinton	4.00	2.00	1.25
(117)	Don Hoak	13.00	6.50	4.00
(118a)	Gil Hodges ("B" on cap)	9.00	4.50	2.75
(118b)	Gil Hodges ("LA" on cap)	9.00	4.50	2.75
(119)	Johnny Hopp	12.00	6.00	3.50
(120)	Elston Howard	4.00	2.00	1.25
(121)	Frank Howard	7.00	3.50	2.00
(122)	Ken Hubbs	35.00	17.50	10.50
(123)	Tex Hughson	12.00	6.00	3.50
(124)	Fred Hutchinson	4.50	2.25	1.25
(125)	Monty Irvin	7.00	3.50	2.00
(126)	Joey Jay	4.00	2.00	1.25
(127)	Jackie Jensen	30.00	15.00	9.00
(128)	Sam Jethroe	5.00	2.50	1.50
(129)	Bill Johnson	5.00	2.50	1.50
(130)	Walter Judnich	12.00	6.00	3.50
(131)	Al Kaline (kneeling)	30.00	15.00	9.00
(132)	Al Kaline (portrait)	30.00	15.00	9.00
(133)	George Kell	7.00	3.50	2.00
(134)	Charley Keller	4.50	2.25	1.25
(135)	Alex Kellner	4.00	2.00	1.25
(136)	Kenn Keltner (Ken)	5.00	2.50	1.50
(137)	Harmon Killebrew (batting)	30.00	15.00	9.00
(138)	Harmon Killebrew (throwing)	30.00	15.00	9.00
(139)	Harmon Killibrew (Killebrew) (portrait)	30.00	15.00	9.00

	NR MT	EX	VG
(140) Ellis Kinder	4.00	2.00	1.25
(141) Ralph Kiner	6.00	3.00	1.75
(142) Billy Klaus	25.00	12.50	7.50
(143) Ted Kluzewski (Kluszewski) (batting)	5.00	2.50	1.50
(144a)Ted Kluzewski (Kluszewski) (Pirates uniform)	5.00	2.50	1.50
(144b)Ted Kluzewski (Kluszewski) (plain uniform)	13.00	6.50	4.00
(145) Don Kolloway	7.00	3.50	2.00
(146) Jim Konstanty	5.00	2.50	1.50
(147) Sandy Koufax	25.00	12.50	7.50
(148) Ed Kranepool	50.00	25.00	15.00
(149a)Tony Kubek (light background)	7.00	3.50	2.00
(149b)Tony Kubek (dark background)	5.00	2.50	1.50
(150a)Harvey Kuenn ("D" on cap)	12.00	6.00	3.50
(150b)Harvey Kuenn (plain cap)	13.00	6.50	4.00
(151) Harvey Kuenn ("SF" on cap)	7.00	3.50	2.00
(152) Kurowski (Whitey)	4.50	2.25	1.25
(153) Eddie Lake	5.00	2.50	1.50
(154) Jim Landis	4.00	2.00	1.25
(155) Don Larsen	4.00	2.00	1.25
(156) Bob Lemon (glove not visible)	7.00	3.50	2.00
(157) Bob Lemon (glove partially visible)	30.00	15.00	9.00
(158) Buddy Lewis	12.00	6.00	3.50
(159) Johnny Lindell	25.00	12.50	7.50
(160) Phil Linz	25.00	12.50	7.50
(161) Don Lock	25.00	12.50	7.50
(162) Whitey Lockman	4.00	2.00	1.25
(163) Johnny Logan	4.00	2.00	1.25
(164) Dale Long ("P" on cap)	4.00	2.00	1.25
(165) Dale Long ("C" on cap)	7.00	3.50	2.00
(166) Ed Lopat	5.00	2.50	1.50
(167a)Harry Lowery (name misspelled)	5.00	2.50	1.50
(167b)Harry Lowrey (name correct)	5.00	2.50	1.50
(168) Sal Maglie	4.00	2.00	1.25
(169) Art Mahaffey	5.00	2.50	1.50
(170) Hank Majeski	4.00	2.00	1.25
(171) Frank Malzone	4.00	2.00	1.25
(172) Mickey Mantle (batting, pinstriped uniform)	100.00	50.00	30.00
(173a)Mickey Mantle (batting, no pinstripes, first name outlined in white)	75.00	38.00	23.00
173b Mickey Mantle (batting, no pinstripes, first name not outlined in white)	75.00	38.00	23.00
(174) Mickey Mantle (portrait)	400.00	200.00	120.00
(175) Martin Marion	7.00	3.50	2.00
(176) Roger Maris	25.00	12.50	7.50
(177) Willard Marshall	5.00	2.50	1.50
(178a)Eddie Matthews (name incorrect)	12.00	6.00	3.50
(178b)Eddie Mathews (name correct)	13.00	6.50	4.00
(179) Ed Mayo	5.00	2.50	1.50
(180) Willie Mays (batting)	18.00	9.00	5.50
(181) Willie Mays (portrait)	25.00	12.50	7.50
(182) Bill Mazeroski (portrait)	7.00	3.50	2.00
(183) Bill Mazeroski (batting)	7.00	3.50	2.00
(184) Ken McBride	4.00	2.00	1.25
(185a)Barney McCaskey (McCosky)	13.00	6.50	4.00
(185b)Barney McCoskey (McCosky)	90.00	45.00	27.00
(186) Lindy McDaniel	4.00	2.00	1.25
(187) Gil McDougald	4.00	2.00	1.25
(188) Albert Mele	13.00	6.50	4.00
(189) Sam Mele	5.00	2.50	1.50
(190) Orestes Minoso ("C" on cap)	7.00	3.50	2.00
(191) Orestes Minoso (Sox on cap)	4.00	2.00	1.25
(192) Dale Mitchell	4.00	2.00	1.25
(193) Wally Moon	7.00	3.50	2.00
(194) Don Mueller	5.00	2.50	1.50
(195) Stan Musial (kneeling)	15.00	7.50	4.50
(196) Stan Musial (batting)	35.00	17.50	10.50
(197) Charley Neal	18.00	9.00	5.50
(198) Don Newcombe (shaking hands)	7.00	3.50	2.00
(199a)Don Newcombe (Dodgers on jacket)	5.00	2.50	1.50
(199b)Don Newcombe (plain jacket)	5.00	2.50	1.50
(200) Hal Newhouser	4.00	2.00	1.25
(201) Ron Northey	12.00	6.00	3.50
(202) Bill O'Dell	4.00	2.00	1.25
(203) Joe Page	12.00	6.00	3.50
(204) Satchel Paige	35.00	17.50	10.50
(205) Milt Pappas	4.00	2.00	1.25
(206) Camilo Pascual	4.00	2.00	1.25
(207) Albie Pearson	25.00	12.50	7.50
(208) Johnny Pesky	4.00	2.00	1.25
(209) Gary Peters	25.00	12.50	7.50
(210) Dave Philley	4.00	2.00	1.25
(211) Billy Pierce	4.00	2.00	1.25
(212) Jimmy Piersall	16.00	8.00	4.75
(213) Vada Pinson	7.00	3.50	2.00

	NR MT	EX	VG
(214) Bob Porterfield	4.00	2.00	1.25
(215) John "Boog" Powell	35.00	17.50	10.50
(216) Vic Raschi	4.50	2.25	1.25
(217a)Harold "Peewee" Reese (fielding, ball partially visible)	10.00	5.00	3.00
(217b)Harold "Peewee" Reese (fielding, ball not visible)	10.00	5.00	3.00
(218) Del Rice	4.00	2.00	1.25
(219) Bobby Richardson	55.00	28.00	16.50
(220) Phil Rizzuto	6.00	3.00	1.75
(221a)Robin Roberts (script signature)	12.00	6.00	3.50
(221b)Robin Roberts (plain signature)	6.00	3.00	1.75
(222) Brooks Robinson	30.00	15.00	9.00
(223) Eddie Robinson	4.00	2.00	1.25
(224) Floyd Robinson	25.00	12.50	7.50
(225) Frankie Robinson	18.00	9.00	5.50
(226) Jackie Robinson	30.00	15.00	9.00
(227) Preacher Roe	4.50	2.25	1.25
(228) Bob Rogers (Rodgers)	25.00	12.50	7.50
(229) Richard Rollins	25.00	12.50	7.50
(230) Pete Runnels	12.00	6.00	3.50
(231) John Sain	5.00	2.50	1.50
(232) Ron Santo	6.00	3.00	1.75
(233) Henry Sauer	5.00	2.50	1.50
(234a)Carl Sawatski ("M" on cap)	4.00	2.00	1.25
(234b)Carl Sawatski ("P" on cap)	4.00	2.00	1.25
(234c)Carl Sawatski (plain cap)	13.00	6.50	4.00
(235) Johnny Schmitz	5.00	2.50	1.50
(236a)Red Schoendeinst (Schoendienst) (fielding, name in white)	5.00	2.50	1.50
(236b)Red Schoendeinst (Schoendienst) (fielding, name in red-brown)	7.00	3.50	2.00
(237) Red Schoendinst (Schoendienst) (batting)	4.00	2.00	1.25
(238a)Herb Score ("C" on cap)	5.00	2.50	1.50
(238b)Herb Score (plain cap)	12.00	6.00	3.50
(239) Andy Seminick	4.00	2.00	1.25
(240) Rip Sewell	7.00	3.50	2.00
(241) Norm Siebern	4.00	2.00	1.25
(242) Roy Sievers (batting)	5.00	2.50	1.50
(243a)Roy Sievers (portrait, "W" on cap, light background)	7.00	3.50	2.00
(243b)Roy Sievers (portrait, "W" on cap, dark background)	5.00	2.50	1.50
(243c)Roy Sievers (portrait, plain cap)	4.50	2.25	1.25
(244) Curt Simmons	5.00	2.50	1.50
(245) Dick Sisler	5.00	2.50	1.50
(246) Bill Skowron	5.00	2.50	1.50
(247) Bill "Moose" Skowron	55.00	28.00	16.50
(248) Enos Slaughter	7.00	3.50	2.00
(249a)Duke Snider ("B" on cap)	8.50	4.25	2.50
(249b)Duke Snider ("LA" on cap)	18.00	9.00	5.50
(250a)Warren Spahn ("B" on cap)	10.00	5.00	3.00
(250b)Warren Spahn ("M" on cap)	12.00	6.00	3.50
(251) Stanley Spence	13.00	6.50	4.00
(252) Ed Stanky (plain uniform)	5.00	2.50	1.50
(253) Ed Stanky (Giants uniform)	5.00	2.50	1.50
(254) Vern Stephens (batting)	5.00	2.50	1.50
(255) Vern Stephens (portrait)	5.00	2.50	1.50
(256) Ed Stewart	5.00	2.50	1.50
(257) Snuffy Stirnweiss	13.00	6.50	4.00
(258) George "Birdie" Tebbetts	12.00	6.00	3.50
(259) Frankie Thomas (photo actually Bob Skinner)	30.00	15.00	9.00
(260) Frank Thomas (portrait)	13.00	6.50	4.00
(261) Lee Thomas	4.00	2.00	1.25
(262) Bobby Thomson	7.00	3.50	2.00
(263a)Earl Torgeson (Braves uniform)	4.00	2.00	1.25
(263b)Earl Torgeson (plain uniform)	5.00	2.50	1.50
(264) Gus Triandos	7.00	3.50	2.00
(265) Virgil Trucks	4.00	2.00	1.25
(266) Johnny Vandermeer (VanderMeer)	13.00	6.50	4.00
(267) Emil Verban	7.00	3.50	2.00
(268) Mickey Vernon (throwing)	4.00	2.00	1.25
(269) Mickey Vernon (batting)	4.00	2.00	1.25
(270) Bill Voiselle	7.00	3.50	2.00
(271) Leon Wagner	4.00	2.00	1.25
(272a)Eddie Waitkus (throwing, Chicago uniform)	7.00	3.50	2.00
(272b)Eddie Waitkus (throwing, plain uniform)	5.00	2.50	1.50
(273) Eddie Waitkus (portrait)	13.00	6.50	4.00
(274) Dick Wakefield	5.00	2.50	1.50
(275) Harry Walker	7.00	3.50	2.00
(276) Bucky Walters	4.50	2.25	1.25
(277) Pete Ward	30.00	15.00	9.00
(278) Herman Wehmeier	5.00	2.50	1.50
(279) Vic Wertz (batting)	4.00	2.00	1.25
(280) Vic Wertz (portrait)	4.00	2.00	1.25
(281) Wally Westlake	5.00	2.50	1.50

		NR MT	EX	VG
(282)	Wes Westrum	13.00	6.50	4.00
(283)	Billy Williams	13.00	6.50	4.00
(284)	Maurice Wills	12.00	6.00	3.50
(285a)	Gene Woodling (script signature)	4.00	2.00	1.25
(285b)	Gene Woodling (plain signature)	7.00	3.50	2.00
(286)	Taffy Wright	5.00	2.50	1.50
(287)	Carl Yastrazemski (Yastrzemski)			
		175.00	90.00	50.00
(288)	Al Zarilla	5.00	2.50	1.50
(289a)	Gus Zernial (script signature)	4.00	2.00	1.25
(289b)	Gus Zernial (plain signature)	7.00	3.50	2.00
(290)	Braves Team - 1948	18.00	9.00	5.50
(291)	Dodgers Team - 1949	25.00	12.50	7.50
(292)	Dodgers Team - 1952	25.00	12.50	7.50
(293)	Dodgers Team - 1955	25.00	12.50	7.50
(294)	Dodgers Team - 1956	25.00	12.50	7.50
(295)	Giants Team - 1951	18.00	9.00	5.50
(296)	Giants Team - 1954	18.00	9.00	5.50
(297)	Indians Team - 1948	18.00	9.00	5.50
(298)	Indians Team - 1954	18.00	9.00	5.50
(299)	Phillies Team - 1950	18.00	9.00	5.50
(300)	Yankees Team - 1949	30.00	15.00	9.00
(301)	Yankees Team - 1950	30.00	15.00	9.00
(302)	Yankees Team - 1951	30.00	15.00	9.00
(303)	Yankees Team - 1952	30.00	15.00	9.00
(304)	Yankees Team - 1955	30.00	15.00	9.00
(305)	Yankees Team - 1956	30.00	15.00	9.00

1962 Exhibit Supply Co.
Statistic Backs

In 1962, the Exhibit Supply Co. added career statistics to the yearly set they produced. The black and white, unnumbered cards measure 3-3/8" by 5-3/8". The statistics found on the back are printed in black or red. The red backs are three times greater in value. The set is comprised of 32 cards.

		NR MT	EX	VG
Complete Set:		425.00	212.00	127.00
Common Player:		3.00	1.50	.90
(1)	Hank Aaron	35.00	17.50	10.50
(2)	Luis Aparicio	4.00	2.00	1.25
(3)	Ernie Banks	7.00	3.50	2.00
(4)	Larry "Yogi" Berra	10.00	5.00	3.00
(5)	Ken Boyer	4.00	2.00	1.25
(6)	Lew Burdette	3.50	1.75	1.00
(7)	Norm Cash	3.50	1.75	1.00
(8)	Orlando Cepeda	3.00	1.50	.90
(9)	Roberto Clemente	35.00	17.50	10.50
(10)	Rocky Colavito	4.00	2.00	1.25
(11)	Ed "Whitey" Ford	7.00	3.50	2.00
(12)	Nelson Fox	3.00	1.50	.90
(13)	Tito Francona	3.00	1.50	.90
(14)	Jim Gentile	3.00	1.50	.90
(15)	Dick Groat	3.50	1.75	1.00
(16)	Don Hoak	3.50	1.75	1.00
(17)	Al Kaline	10.00	5.00	3.00
(18)	Harmon Killebrew	10.00	5.00	3.00
(19)	Sandy Koufax	25.00	12.50	7.50
(20)	Jim Landis	3.00	1.50	.90
(21)	Art Mahaffey	3.00	1.50	.90
(22)	Frank Malzone	3.00	1.50	.90
(23)	Mickey Mantle	90.00	45.00	27.00
(24)	Roger Maris	10.00	5.00	3.00
(25)	Eddie Mathews	5.00	2.50	1.50

		NR MT	EX	VG
(26)	Willie Mays	35.00	17.50	10.50
(27)	Wally Moon	3.50	1.75	1.00
(28)	Stan Musial	35.00	17.50	10.50
(29)	Milt Pappas	3.50	1.75	1.00
(30)	Vada Pinson	4.00	2.00	1.25
(31)	Norm Siebern	3.00	1.50	.90
(32)	Warren Spahn	10.00	5.00	3.00

1963 Exhibit Supply Co.
Statistic Backs

The Exhibit Supply Co. issued a 64-card set with career statistics on the backs of the cards in 1963. The unnumbered, black and white cards are printed on thick cardboard and measure 3-3/8" by 5-3/8" in size. The statistics on the back are printed in black.

		NR MT	EX	VG
Complete Set:		525.00	262.00	157.00
Common Player:		3.00	1.50	.90
(1)	Hank Aaron	35.00	17.50	10.50
(2)	Luis Aparicio	4.00	2.00	1.25
(3)	Bob Aspromonte	3.00	1.50	.90
(4)	Ernie Banks	20.00	10.00	6.00
(5)	Steve Barber	3.00	1.50	.90
(6)	Earl Battey	3.00	1.50	.90
(7)	Larry "Yogi" Berra	12.00	6.00	3.50
(8)	Ken Boyer	4.00	2.00	1.25
(9)	Lew Burdette	3.50	1.75	1.00
(10)	Johnny Callison	3.50	1.75	1.00
(11)	Norm Cash	3.50	1.75	1.00
(12)	Orlando Cepeda	3.00	1.50	.90
(13)	Dean Chance	3.00	1.50	.90
(14)	Tom Cheney	3.00	1.50	.90
(15)	Roberto Clemente	35.00	17.50	10.50
(16)	Rocky Colavito	4.00	2.00	1.25
(17)	Choo Choo Coleman	3.00	1.50	.90
(18)	Roger Craig	3.50	1.75	1.00
(19)	Joe Cunningham	3.00	1.50	.90
(20)	Don Drysdale	7.00	3.50	2.00
(21)	Dick Farrell	3.00	1.50	.90
(22)	Ed "Whitey" Ford	15.00	7.50	4.50
(23)	Nelson Fox	3.00	1.50	.90
(24)	Tito Francona	3.00	1.50	.90
(25)	Jim Gentile	3.00	1.50	.90
(26)	Tony Gonzalez	3.00	1.50	.90
(27)	Dick Groat	3.50	1.75	1.00
(28)	Ray Herbert	3.00	1.50	.90
(29)	Chuck Hinton	3.00	1.50	.90
(30)	Don Hoak	3.50	1.75	1.00
(31)	Frank Howard	4.00	2.00	1.25
(32)	Ken Hubbs	3.50	1.75	1.00
(33)	Joey Jay	3.00	1.50	.90
(34)	Al Kaline	15.00	7.50	4.50
(35)	Harmon Killebrew	15.00	7.50	4.50
(36)	Sandy Koufax	20.00	10.00	6.00
(37)	Harvey Kuenn	4.00	2.00	1.25
(38)	Jim Landis	3.00	1.50	.90
(39)	Art Mahaffey	3.00	1.50	.90
(40)	Frank Malzone	3.00	1.50	.90
(41)	Mickey Mantle	150.00	75.00	45.00
(42)	Roger Maris	15.00	7.50	4.50
(43)	Eddie Mathews	5.00	2.50	1.50
(44)	Willie Mays	35.00	17.50	10.50
(45)	Bill Mazeroski	4.00	2.00	1.25
(46)	Ken McBride	3.00	1.50	.90

		NR MT	EX	VG
(47)	Wally Moon	3.50	1.75	1.00
(48)	Stan Musial	35.00	17.50	10.50
(49)	Charlie Neal	3.00	1.50	.90
(50)	Bill O'Dell	3.00	1.50	.90
(51)	Milt Pappas	3.50	1.75	1.00
(52)	Camilo Pascual	3.50	1.75	1.00
(53)	Jimmy Piersall	4.00	2.00	1.25
(54)	Vada Pinson	4.00	2.00	1.25
(55)	Brooks Robinson	15.00	7.50	4.50
(56)	Frankie Robinson	15.00	7.50	4.50
(57)	Pete Runnels	3.50	1.75	1.00
(58)	Ron Santo	4.00	2.00	1.25
(59)	Norm Siebern	3.00	1.50	.90
(60)	Warren Spahn	12.00	6.00	3.50
(61)	Lee Thomas	3.00	1.50	.90
(62)	Leon Wagner	3.00	1.50	.90
(63)	Billy Williams	4.00	2.00	1.25
(64)	Maurice Wills	3.00	1.50	.90

F

1988 Fantastic Sam's

This set of 20 full-color player discs (2-1/2" diameter) was distributed during a Superstar Sweepstakes sponsored by Fantastic Sam's Family Haircutters' 1,800 stores nationwide. Each sweepstakes card consists of two connected discs (bright orange fronts, white backs) perforated for easy separation. One disc features the baseball player photo, the other carries the sweepstakes logo and a list of prizes. Player discs carry a Fantastic Sam's Baseball Superstars header curved above the photo, with his name, team and position printed in black. The disc backs are black and white and include personal info, card number and 1987 player stats. Sweepstakes discs list contest prizes (Grand Prize was 4 tickets to a 1988 Championship game) on the front and an entry form on the flipside. Below the prize list is a silver scratch-off rectangle which may reveal an instant prize.

		MT	NR MT	EX
Complete Set:		7.00	5.25	2.75
Common Player:		.20	.15	.08
1	Kirby Puckett	.75	.60	.30
2	George Brett	1.00	.70	.40
3	Mark McGwire	1.25	.90	.50
4	Wally Joyner	1.25	.90	.50
5	Paul Molitor	.20	.15	.08
6	Alan Trammell	.40	.30	.15
7	George Bell	.50	.40	.20
8	Wade Boggs	1.25	.90	.50
9	Don Mattingly	2.00	1.50	.80
10	Julio Franco	.20	.15	.08
11	Ozzie Smith	.20	.15	.08
12	Will Clark	.75	.60	.30
13	Dale Murphy	1.00	.70	.40
14	Eric Davis	1.50	1.25	.60
15	Andre Dawson	.50	.40	.20

		MT	NR MT	EX
16	Tim Raines	.60	.45	.25
17	Darryl Strawberry	1.25	.90	.50
18	Tony Gwynn	.75	.60	.30
19	Mike Schmidt	1.50	1.25	.60
20	Pedro Guerrero	.20	.15	.08

1987 Farmland Dairies Mets

The New York Mets and Farmland Dairies produced a nine-card panel of baseball cards for members of the Junior Mets Club. Members of the club, kids 14 years of age and younger, received the perforated panel as part of a package featuring gifts and special privileges. The cards are the standard 2-1/2" by 3-1/2" with fronts containing a full-color photo encompassed by a blue border. The backs are designed on a vertical format and have player statistics and career highlights. The Farmland Dairies and Junior Mets Club logos are also carried on the card backs.

		MT	NR MT	EX
Complete Panel Set:		15.00	11.00	6.00
Complete Singles Set:		6.00	4.50	2.50
Common Single Player:		.25	.20	.10
	Panel	12.00	9.00	4.75
1	Mookie Wilson	.25	.20	.10
4	Len Dykstra	.60	.45	.25
8	Gary Carter	.70	.50	.30
12	Ron Darling	.40	.30	.15
18	Darryl Strawberry	1.50	1.25	.60
19	Bob Ojeda	.25	.20	.10
22	Kevin McReynolds	.40	.30	.15
42	Roger McDowell	.35	.25	.14
——	Team Card	.25	.20	.10

1988 Farmland Dairies Mets

Part of the Junior Mets Fan Club membership package, this set of 9 standard size cards was printed on a single panel. Card fronts feature full-color action shots framed in orange and blue. A white player name runs across the top border, with a large team logo, uniform number and position printed below the photo. Card backs are blue on brown and include personal data, stats and 1987 season highlights. The set was offered to fans 14 years and younger for a $6 fan club membership fee, with a $1 discount for those who sent in two proofs of purchase from Farmland Dairies milk cartons.

		MT	NR MT	EX
	Complete Panel Set:	15.00	11.00	6.00
	Complete Singles Set:	6.00	4.50	2.50
	Common Single Player:	.25	.20	.10
	Panel	12.00	9.00	4.75
8	Gary Carter	.70	.50	.30
16	Dwight Gooden	1.25	.90	.50
17	Keith Hernandez	.40	.30	.15
18	Darryl Strawberry	1.25	.90	.50
20	Howard Johnson	.70	.50	.30
21	Kevin Elster	.35	.25	.14
42	Roger McDowell	.25	.20	.10
48	Randy Myers	.35	.25	.14

1959 Fleer Ted Williams

1938 – First Spring Training

This 80-card 1959 Fleer set tells of the life of baseball great Ted Williams, from his childhood years up to 1958. The full-color cards measure 2-1/2" by 3-1/2" in size and make use of both horizontal and vertical formats. The card backs, all designed horizontally, contain a continuing biography of Williams. Card #68 was withdrawn from the set early in production and is scarce. Counterfeit cards of #68 have been produced and can be distinguished by a cross-hatch pattern which appears over the photo on the card fronts.

		NR MT	EX	VG
	Complete Set:	1000.00	500.00	300.00
	Common Player:	5.00	2.50	1.50
1	The Early Years	25.00	12.50	7.50
2	Ted's Idol - Babe Ruth	25.00	12.50	7.50
3	Practice Makes Perfect	5.00	2.50	1.50
4	1934 - Ted Learns The Fine Points	5.00	2.50	1.50
5	Ted's Fame Spreads - 1935-36	5.00	2.50	1.50
6	Ted Turns Professional	5.00	2.50	1.50
7	1936 - From Mound To Plate	5.00	2.50	1.50
8	1937 - First Full Season	5.00	2.50	1.50
9	1937 - First Step To The Majors	5.00	2.50	1.50
10	1938 - Gunning As A Pastime	5.00	2.50	1.50
11	1938 - First Spring Training	4.00	2.00	1.25
12	1939 - Burning Up The Minors	5.00	2.50	1.50
13	1939 - Ted Shows He Will Stay	5.00	2.50	1.50
14	Outstanding Rookie of 1939	5.00	2.50	1.50
15	1940 - Williams Licks Sophomore Jinx	5.00	2.50	1.50
16	1941 - Williams' Greatest Year	5.00	2.50	1.50
17	1941 - How Ted Hit .400	5.00	2.50	1.50
18	1941 - All-Star Hero	5.00	2.50	1.50
19	1942 - Ted Wins Triple Crown	5.00	2.50	1.50
20	1942 - On To Naval Training	5.00	2.50	1.50
21	1943 - Honors For Williams	5.00	2.50	1.50
22	1944 - Ted Solos	5.00	2.50	1.50
23	1944 - Williams Wins His Wings	5.00	2.50	1.50
24	1945 - Sharpshooter	5.00	2.50	1.50
25	1945 - Ted Is Discharged	5.00	2.50	1.50
26	1946 - Off To A Flying Start	5.00	2.50	1.50
27	July 9, 1946 - One Man Show	5.00	2.50	1.50
28	July 14, 1946 - The Williams Shift	5.00	2.50	1.50
29	July 21, 1946, Ted Hits For The Cycle	5.00	2.50	1.50
30	1946 - Beating The Williams Shift	5.00	2.50	1.50
31	Oct. 1946 - Sox Lose The Series	5.00	2.50	1.50
32	1946 - Most Valuable Player	5.00	2.50	1.50
33	1947 - Another Triple Crown For Ted	5.00	2.50	1.50
34	1947 - Ted Sets Runs-Scored Record	5.00	2.50	1.50
35	1948 - The Sox Miss The Pennant	5.00	2.50	1.50
36	1948 - Banner Year For Ted	5.00	2.50	1.50
37	1949 - Sox Miss Out Again	5.00	2.50	1.50
38	1949 - Power Rampage	5.00	2.50	1.50
39	1950 - Great Start	4.50	2.25	1.25
40	July 11, 1950 - Ted Crashes Into Wall	5.00	2.50	1.50
41	1950 - Ted Recovers	5.00	2.50	1.50
42	1951 - Williams Slowed By Injury	5.00	2.50	1.50
43	1951 - Leads Outfielders In Double Plays	5.00	2.50	1.50
44	1952 - Back To The Marines	5.00	2.50	1.50
45	1952 - Farewell To Baseball?	5.00	2.50	1.50
46	1952 - Ready For Combat	5.00	2.50	1.50
47	1953 - Ted Crash Lands Jet	5.00	2.50	1.50
48	July 14, 1953 - Ted Returns	5.00	2.50	1.50
49	1953 - Smash Return	5.00	2.50	1.50
50	March 1954 - Spring Injury	5.00	2.50	1.50
51	May 16, 1954 - Ted Is Patched Up	5.00	2.50	1.50
52	1954 - Ted's Comeback	5.00	2.50	1.50
53	1954 - Ted's Comeback Is A Sucess	5.00	2.50	1.50
54	Dec. 1954, Fisherman Ted Hooks a Big One	5.00	2.50	1.50
55	1955 - Ted Decides Retirement Is "No Go"	5.00	2.50	1.50
56	1956 - Ted Reaches 400th Homer,	5.00	2.50	1.50
58	1957 - Williams Hits .388	5.00	2.50	1.50
59	1957 - Hot September For Ted	5.00	2.50	1.50
60	1957 - More Records For Ted	5.00	2.50	1.50
61	1957 - Outfielder Ted	5.00	2.50	1.50
62	1958 - 6th Batting Title For Ted	5.00	2.50	1.50
63	Ted's All-Star Record	5.00	2.50	1.50
64	1958 - Daughter And Famous Daddy	5.00	2.50	1.50
65	August 30, 1958	5.00	2.50	1.50
66	1958 - Powerhouse	5.00	2.50	1.50
67	Two Famous Fisherman	4.50	2.25	1.25
68	Jan. 23, 1959 - Ted Signs For 1959	525.00	262.00	157.00
69	A Future Ted Williams?	5.00	2.50	1.50
70	Ted Williams & Jim Thorpe	4.50	2.25	1.25
71	Ted's Hitting Fundamentals #1	5.00	2.50	1.50
72	Ted's Hitting Fundamentals #2	5.00	2.50	1.50
73	Ted's Hitting Fundamentals #3	5.00	2.50	1.50
74	Here's How!	5.00	2.50	1.50
75	Williams' Value To Red Sox	12.00	6.00	3.50
76	Ted's Remarkable "On Base" Record	5.00	2.50	1.50
77	Ted Relaxes	5.00	2.50	1.50
78	Honors For Williams	5.00	2.50	1.50
79	Where Ted Stands	5.00	2.50	1.50
80	Ted's Goals For 1959	12.00	6.00	3.50

1960 Fleer

RABBIT MARANVILLE

The 1960 Fleer Baseball Greats set consists of 79

cards of the game's top players from the past. (The set does include a card of Ted Williams, who was in his final major league season). The cards are standard size (2-1/2" by 3-1/2") and feature color photos inside blue, green, red or yellow borders. The card backs carry a short player biography plus career hitting or pitching statistics. Cards with a Pepper Martin back (#80), but with another player pictured on the front are in existence.

		NR MT	EX	VG
Complete Set:		400.00	200.00	120.00
Common Player:		2.00	1.00	.60
1	Nap Lajoie	8.00	4.00	2.50
2	Christy Mathewson	8.00	4.00	2.50
3	Babe Ruth	70.00	35.00	21.00
4	Carl Hubbell	2.50	1.25	.70
5	Grover Cleveland Alexander	4.00	2.00	1.25
6	Walter Johnson	8.00	4.00	2.50
7	Chief Bender	2.00	1.00	.60
8	Roger Bresnahan	2.00	1.00	.60
9	Mordecai Brown	2.00	1.00	.60
10	Tris Speaker	2.50	1.25	.70
11	Arky Vaughan	2.00	1.00	.60
12	Zack Wheat	2.00	1.00	.60
13	George Sisler	2.50	1.25	.70
14	Connie Mack	4.00	2.00	1.25
15	Clark Griffith	2.00	1.00	.60
16	Lou Boudreau	2.00	1.00	.60
17	Ernie Lombardi	2.00	1.00	.60
18	Heinie Manush	2.00	1.00	.60
19	Marty Marion	2.00	1.00	.60
20	Eddie Collins	2.50	1.25	.70
21	Rabbit Maranville	2.00	1.00	.60
22	Joe Medwick	2.00	1.00	.60
23	Ed Barrow	2.00	1.00	.60
24	Mickey Cochrane	2.50	1.25	.70
25	Jimmy Collins	2.00	1.00	.60
26	Bob Feller	7.00	3.50	2.00
27	Luke Appling	2.00	1.00	.60
28	Lou Gehrig	35.00	17.50	10.50
29	Gabby Hartnett	2.00	1.00	.60
30	Chuck Klein	2.00	1.00	.60
31	Tony Lazzeri	2.00	1.00	.60
32	Al Simmons	2.00	1.00	.60
33	Wilbert Robinson	2.00	1.00	.60
34	Sam Rice	2.00	1.00	.60
35	Herb Pennock	2.00	1.00	.60
36	Mel Ott	2.50	1.25	.70
37	Lefty O'Doul	2.00	1.00	.60
38	Johnny Mize	2.50	1.25	.70
39	Bing Miller	2.00	1.00	.60
40	Joe Tinker	2.00	1.00	.60
41	Frank Baker	2.00	1.00	.60
42	Ty Cobb	35.00	17.50	10.50
43	Paul Derringer	2.00	1.00	.60
44	Cap Anson	2.50	1.25	.70
45	Jim Bottomley	2.00	1.00	.60
46	Eddie Plank	2.00	1.00	.60
47	Cy Young	5.00	2.50	1.50
48	Hack Wilson	2.00	1.00	.60
49	Ed Walsh	2.00	1.00	.60
50	Frank Chance	2.00	1.00	.60
51	Dazzy Vance	2.00	1.00	.60
52	Bill Terry	2.50	1.25	.70
53	Jimmy Foxx	4.00	2.00	1.25
54	Lefty Gomez	2.50	1.25	.70
55	Branch Rickey	2.00	1.00	.60
56	Ray Schalk	2.00	1.00	.60
57	Johnny Evers	2.00	1.00	.60
58	Charlie Gehringer	2.50	1.25	.70
59	Burleigh Grimes	2.00	1.00	.60
60	Lefty Grove	2.50	1.25	.70
61	Rube Waddell	2.00	1.00	.60
62	Honus Wagner	8.00	4.00	2.50
63	Red Ruffing	2.00	1.00	.60
64	Judge Landis	2.00	1.00	.60
65	Harry Heilmann	2.00	1.00	.60
66	John McGraw	2.50	1.25	.70
67	Hughie Jennings	2.00	1.00	.60
68	Hal Newhouser	2.00	1.00	.60
69	Waite Hoyt	2.00	1.00	.60
70	Bobo Newsom	2.00	1.00	.60
71	Earl Averill	2.00	1.00	.60
72	Ted Williams	55.00	27.00	16.50
73	Warren Giles	2.00	1.00	.60
74	Ford Frick	2.00	1.00	.60
75	Ki Ki Cuyler	2.00	1.00	.60
76	Paul Waner	2.00	1.00	.60

		NR MT	EX	VG
77	Pie Traynor	2.00	1.00	.60
78	Lloyd Waner	2.00	1.00	.60
79	Ralph Kiner	8.00	4.00	2.50

1961 Fleer

Over a two-year period, Fleer issued another set utilizing the Baseball Greats theme. The 154-card set was issued in two series and features a color player portrait against a color background. The player's name is located in a pennant set at the bottom of the card. The card backs feature orange and black on white stock and contain player biographical and statistical information. The cards measure 2-1/2" by 3-1/2" in size. The second series cards (#'s 89-154) were issued in 1962.

		NR MT	EX	VG
Complete Set:		800.00	400.00	240.00
Common Player: 1-88		2.00	1.00	.60
Common Player: 89-154		4.00	2.00	1.25
1	Baker, Cobb, Wheat/Checklist	35.00	17.50	10.50
2	G.C. Alexander	4.00	2.00	1.25
3	Nick Altrock	2.00	1.00	.60
4	Cap Anson	2.50	1.25	.70
5	Earl Averill	2.00	1.00	.60
6	Home Run Baker	2.00	1.00	.60
7	Dave Bancroft	2.00	1.00	.60
8	Chief Bender	2.00	1.00	.60
9	Jim Bottomley	2.00	1.00	.60
10	Roger Bresnahan	2.00	1.00	.60
11	Mordecai Brown	2.00	1.00	.60
12	Max Carey	2.00	1.00	.60
13	Jack Chesbro	2.00	1.00	.60
14	Ty Cobb	35.00	17.50	10.50
15	Mickey Cochrane	2.50	1.25	.70
16	Eddie Collins	2.50	1.25	.70
17	Earle Combs	2.00	1.00	.60
18	Charles Comiskey	2.00	1.00	.60
19	Ki Ki Cuyler	2.00	1.00	.60
20	Paul Derringer	2.00	1.00	.60
21	Howard Ehmke	2.00	1.00	.60
22	Billy Evans	2.00	1.00	.60
23	Johnny Evers	2.00	1.00	.60
24	Red Faber	2.00	1.00	.60
25	Bob Feller	6.00	3.00	1.75
26	Wes Ferrell	2.00	1.00	.60
27	Lew Fonseca	2.00	1.00	.60
28	Jimmy Foxx	4.00	2.00	1.25
29	Ford Frick	2.00	1.00	.60
30	Frankie Frisch	2.50	1.25	.70
31	Lou Gehrig	35.00	17.50	10.50
32	Charlie Gehringer	2.50	1.25	.70
33	Warren Giles	2.00	1.00	.60
34	Lefty Gomez	2.50	1.25	.70
35	Goose Goslin	2.00	1.00	.60
36	Clark Griffith	2.00	1.00	.60
37	Burleigh Grimes	2.00	1.00	.60
38	Lefty Grove	1.50	.70	.45
39	Chick Hafey	2.00	1.00	.60
40	Jesse Haines	2.00	1.00	.60
41	Gabby Hartnett	2.00	1.00	.60
42	Harry Heilmann	2.00	1.00	.60
43	Rogers Hornsby	4.00	2.00	1.25
44	Waite Hoyt	2.00	1.00	.60
45	Carl Hubbell	1.50	.70	.45

		NR MT	EX	VG
46	Miller Huggins	2.00	1.00	.60
47	Hughie Jennings	2.00	1.00	.60
48	Ban Johnson	2.00	1.00	.60
49	Walter Johnson	4.00	2.00	1.25
50	Ralph Kiner	2.50	1.25	.70
51	Chuck Klein	2.00	1.00	.60
52	Johnny Kling	2.00	1.00	.60
53	Judge Landis	2.00	1.00	.60
54	Tony Lazzeri	2.00	1.00	.60
55	Ernie Lombardi	2.00	1.00	.60
56	Dolf Luque	2.00	1.00	.60
57	Heinie Manush	2.00	1.00	.60
58	Marty Marion	2.00	1.00	.60
59	Christy Mathewson	2.50	1.25	.70
60	John McGraw	2.50	1.25	.70
61	Joe Medwick	2.00	1.00	.60
62	Bing Miller	2.00	1.00	.60
63	Johnny Mize	2.50	1.25	.70
64	Johnny Mostil	2.00	1.00	.60
65	Art Nehf	2.00	1.00	.60
66	Hal Newhouser	2.00	1.00	.60
67	Bobo Newsom	2.00	1.00	.60
68	Mel Ott	1.50	.70	.45
69	Allie Reynolds	2.00	1.00	.60
70	Sam Rice	2.00	1.00	.60
71	Eppa Rixey	2.00	1.00	.60
72	Edd Roush	2.00	1.00	.60
73	Schoolboy Rowe	2.00	1.00	.60
74	Red Ruffing	2.00	1.00	.60
75	Babe Ruth	65.00	32.00	19.50
76	Joe Sewell	2.00	1.00	.60
77	Al Simmons	2.00	1.00	.60
78	George Sisler	2.50	1.25	.70
79	Tris Speaker	1.50	.70	.45
80	Fred Toney	2.00	1.00	.60
81	Dazzy Vance	2.00	1.00	.60
82	Jim Vaughn	2.00	1.00	.60
83	Big Ed Walsh	2.00	1.00	.60
84	Lloyd Waner	2.00	1.00	.60
85	Paul Waner	2.00	1.00	.60
86	Zach Wheat	2.00	1.00	.60
87	Hack Wilson	2.00	1.00	.60
88	Jimmy Wilson	2.00	1.00	.60
89	Sisler & Traynor/Checklist	35.00	17.50	10.50
90	Babe Adams	4.00	2.00	1.25
91	Dale Alexander	4.00	2.00	1.25
92	Jim Bagby	4.00	2.00	1.25
93	Ossie Bluege	4.00	2.00	1.25
94	Lou Boudreau	6.00	3.00	1.75
95	Tommy Bridges	4.00	2.00	1.25
96	Donnie Bush (Donie)	4.00	2.00	1.25
97	Dolph Camilli	4.00	2.00	1.25
98	Frank Chance	6.00	3.00	1.75
99	Jimmy Collins	4.00	2.00	1.25
100	Stanley Coveleskie (Coveleski)	4.00	2.00	1.25
101	Hughie Critz	4.00	2.00	1.25
102	General Crowder	4.00	2.00	1.25
103	Joe Dugan	4.00	2.00	1.25
104	Bibb Falk	4.00	2.00	1.25
105	Rick Ferrell	4.00	2.00	1.25
106	Art Fletcher	4.00	2.00	1.25
107	Dennis Galehouse	4.00	2.00	1.25
108	Chick Galloway	4.00	2.00	1.25
109	Mule Haas	4.00	2.00	1.25
110	Stan Hack	4.00	2.00	1.25
111	Bump Hadley	4.00	2.00	1.25
112	Billy Hamilton	4.00	2.00	1.25
113	Joe Hauser	4.00	2.00	1.25
114	Babe Herman	4.00	2.00	1.25
115	Travis Jackson	4.00	2.00	1.25
116	Eddie Joost	4.00	2.00	1.25
117	Addie Joss	4.00	2.00	1.25
118	Joe Judge	4.00	2.00	1.25
119	Joe Kuhel	4.00	2.00	1.25
120	Nap Lajoie	8.00	4.00	2.50
121	Dutch Leonard	4.00	2.00	1.25
122	Ted Lyons	4.00	2.00	1.25
123	Connie Mack	8.00	4.00	2.50
124	Rabbit Maranville	4.00	2.00	1.25
125	Fred Marberry	4.00	2.00	1.25
126	Iron Man McGinnity	4.00	2.00	1.25
127	Oscar Melillo	4.00	2.00	1.25
128	Ray Mueller	4.00	2.00	1.25
129	Kid Nichols	4.00	2.00	1.25
130	Lefty O'Doul	4.00	2.00	1.25
131	Bob O'Farrell	4.00	2.00	1.25
132	Roger Peckinpaugh	4.00	2.00	1.25
133	Herb Pennock	4.00	2.00	1.25
134	George Pipgras	4.00	2.00	1.25
135	Eddie Plank	4.00	2.00	1.25
136	Ray Schalk	4.00	2.00	1.25

		NR MT	EX	VG
137	Hal Schumacher	4.00	2.00	1.25
138	Luke Sewell	4.00	2.00	1.25
139	Bob Shawkey	4.00	2.00	1.25
140	Riggs Stephenson	4.00	2.00	1.25
141	Billy Sullivan	4.00	2.00	1.25
142	Bill Terry	7.00	3.50	2.00
143	Joe Tinker	2.75	1.50	.80
144	Pie Traynor	6.00	3.00	1.75
145	George Uhle	4.00	2.00	1.25
146	Hal Troskey (Trosky)	4.00	2.00	1.25
147	Arky Vaughan	4.00	2.00	1.25
148	Johnny Vander Meer	4.00	2.00	1.25
149	Rube Waddell	4.00	2.00	1.25
150	Honus Wagner	35.00	17.50	10.50
151	Dixie Walker	4.00	2.00	1.25
152	Ted Williams	65.00	32.00	19.50
153	Cy Young	10.00	5.00	3.00
154	Ross Young (Youngs)	8.00	4.00	2.50

1963 Fleer

FRANK BOLLING
Milwaukee Braves—2nd Base

A lawsuit by Topps stopped Fleer's 1963 set at one series of 66 cards. Issued with a cookie rather than gum, the set features color photos of current players. The card backs include statistical information for 1962 and career plus a brief player biography. The cards, which measure 2-1/2" by 3-1/2", are numbered 1-66. An unnumbered checklist was issued with the set and is included in the complete set price in the checklist that follows. The checklist and #46 Adcock are scarce.

		NR MT	EX	VG
Complete Set:		1100.00	550.00	330.00
Common Player:		6.00	3.00	1.75
1	Steve Barber	10.00	2.00	1.25
2	Ron Hansen	6.00	3.00	1.75
3	Milt Pappas	2.25	1.25	.70
4	Brooks Robinson	40.00	20.00	12.00
5	Willie Mays	110.00	55.00	33.00
6	Lou Clinton	6.00	3.00	1.75
7	Bill Monbouquette	6.00	3.00	1.75
8	Carl Yastrzemski	90.00	45.00	27.00
9	Ray Herbert	6.00	3.00	1.75
10	Jim Landis	6.00	3.00	1.75
11	Dick Donovan	6.00	3.00	1.75
12	Tito Francona	6.00	3.00	1.75
13	Jerry Kindall	6.00	3.00	1.75
14	Frank Lary	2.25	1.25	.70
15	Dick Howser	8.00	4.00	2.50
16	Jerry Lumpe	6.00	3.00	1.75
17	Norm Siebern	6.00	3.00	1.75
18	Don Lee	6.00	3.00	1.75
19	Albie Pearson	6.00	3.00	1.75
20	Bob Rodgers	2.25	1.25	.70
21	Leon Wagner	6.00	3.00	1.75
22	Jim Kaat	7.00	3.50	2.00
23	Vic Power	6.00	3.00	1.75
24	Rich Rollins	6.00	3.00	1.75
25	Bobby Richardson	7.00	3.50	2.00
26	Ralph Terry	10.00	5.00	3.00
27	Tom Cheney	2.25	1.25	.70
28	Chuck Cottier	6.00	3.00	1.75
29	Jimmy Piersall	10.00	5.00	3.00
30	Dave Stenhouse	6.00	3.00	1.75
31	Glen Hobbie	6.00	3.00	1.75

		NR MT	EX	VG
32	Ron Santo	12.00	6.00	3.50
33	Gene Freese	6.00	3.00	1.75
34	Vada Pinson	10.00	5.00	3.00
35	Bob Purkey	6.00	3.00	1.75
36	Joe Amalfitano	6.00	3.00	1.75
37	Bob Aspromonte	6.00	3.00	1.75
38	Dick Farrell	6.00	3.00	1.75
39	Al Spangler	6.00	3.00	1.75
40	Tommy Davis	10.00	5.00	3.00
41	Don Drysdale	30.00	15.00	9.00
42	Sandy Koufax	130.00	65.00	37.00
43	Maury Wills	50.00	25.00	15.00
44	Frank Bolling	6.00	3.00	1.75
45	Warren Spahn	40.00	20.00	12.00
46	Joe Adcock	150.00	75.00	45.00
47	Roger Craig	12.00	6.00	3.50
48	Al Jackson	2.25	1.25	.70
49	Rod Kanehl	2.25	1.25	.70
50	Ruben Amaro	6.00	3.00	1.75
51	John Callison	2.25	1.25	.70
52	Clay Dalrymple	6.00	3.00	1.75
53	Don Demeter	6.00	3.00	1.75
54	Art Mahaffey	6.00	3.00	1.75
55	"Smoky" Burgess	2.25	1.25	.70
56	Roberto Clemente	125.00	67.00	37.00
57	Elroy Face	2.25	1.25	.70
58	Vernon Law	2.25	1.25	.70
59	Bill Mazeroski	10.00	5.00	3.00
60	Ken Boyer	10.00	5.00	3.00
61	Bob Gibson	40.00	20.00	12.00
62	Gene Oliver	6.00	3.00	1.75
63	Bill White	12.00	6.00	3.50
64	Orlando Cepeda	15.00	7.50	4.50
65	Jimmy Davenport	6.00	3.00	1.75
66	Billy O'Dell	8.00	4.00	2.50
——	Checklist 1-66	375.00	150.00	90.00

1981 Fleer

For the first time in 18 years, Fleer issued a baseball card set featuring current players. Fleer's 660-card effort included numerous errors in the first printing run which were subsequently corrected in additional runs. The cards, which measure 2-1/2" by 3-1/2", are numbered alphabetically by team. The card fronts feature a full-color photo inside a border which is color-coded by team. The card backs have black, grey and yellow ink on white stock and carry player statistical information. The player's batting average or earned run average is located in a circle in the upper right corner of the card. The complete set price in the checklist that follows does not include the higher priced variations.

		MT	NR MT	EX
Complete Set:		60.00	45.00	25.00
Common Player:		.06	.05	.02
1	Pete Rose	1.75	1.25	.70
2	Larry Bowa	.15	.11	.06
3	Manny Trillo	.08	.06	.03
4	Bob Boone	.10	.08	.04
5a	Mike Schmidt (portrait)	2.00	1.50	.80
5b	Mike Schmidt (batting)	2.00	1.50	.80
6a	Steve Carlton ("Lefty" on front)	1.00	.70	.40
6b	Steve Carlton (Pitcher of the Year on front, date 1066 on back)	2.00	1.50	.80

		MT	NR MT	EX
6c	Steve Carlton (Pitcher of the Year on front, date 1966 on back)	3.00	2.25	1.25
7a	Tug McGraw (Game Saver on front)	.50	.40	.20
7b	Tug McGraw (Pitcher on front)	.12	.09	.05
8	Larry Christenson	.06	.05	.02
9	Bake McBride	.06	.05	.02
10	Greg Luzinski	.15	.11	.06
11	Ron Reed	.06	.05	.02
12	Dickie Noles	.06	.05	.02
13	Keith Moreland	.20	.15	.08
14	Bob Walk	.25	.20	.10
15	Lonnie Smith	.08	.06	.03
16	Dick Ruthven	.06	.05	.02
17	Sparky Lyle	.10	.08	.04
18	Greg Gross	.06	.05	.02
19	Garry Maddox	.10	.08	.04
20	Nino Espinosa	.06	.05	.02
21	George Vukovich	.06	.05	.02
22	John Vukovich	.06	.05	.02
23	Ramon Aviles	.06	.05	.02
24a	Kevin Saucier (Ken Saucier on back)	.15	.11	.06
24b	Kevin Saucier (Kevin Saucier on back)	.70	.50	.30
25	Randy Lerch	.06	.05	.02
26	Del Unser	.06	.05	.02
27	Tim McCarver	.15	.11	.06
28a	George Brett (batting)	3.00	2.25	1.25
28b	George Brett (portrait)	1.00	.70	.40
29a	Willie Wilson (portrait)	.60	.45	.25
29b	Willie Wilson (batting)	.15	.11	.06
30	Paul Splittorff	.06	.05	.02
31	Dan Quisenberry	.15	.11	.06
32a	Amos Otis (batting)	.50	.40	.20
32b	Amos Otis (portrait)	.10	.08	.04
33	Steve Busby	.08	.06	.03
34	U.L. Washington	.06	.05	.02
35	Dave Chalk	.06	.05	.02
36	Darrell Porter	.08	.06	.03
37	Marty Pattin	.06	.05	.02
38	Larry Gura	.06	.05	.02
39	Renie Martin	.06	.05	.02
40	Rich Gale	.06	.05	.02
41a	Hal McRae (dark blue "Royals" on front)	.40	.30	.15
41b	Hal McRae (light blue "Royals" on front)	.10	.08	.04
42	Dennis Leonard	.08	.06	.03
43	Willie Aikens	.06	.05	.02
44	Frank White	.10	.08	.04
45	Clint Hurdle	.06	.05	.02
46	John Wathan	.08	.06	.03
47	Pete LaCock	.06	.05	.02
48	Rance Mulliniks	.06	.05	.02
49	Jeff Twitty	.06	.05	.02
50	Jamie Quirk	.06	.05	.02
51	Art Howe	.06	.05	.02
52	Ken Forsch	.06	.05	.02
53	Vern Ruhle	.06	.05	.02
54	Joe Niekro	.12	.09	.05
55	Frank LaCorte	.06	.05	.02
56	J.R. Richard	.10	.08	.04
57	Nolan Ryan	7.00	5.25	2.75
58	Enos Cabell	.06	.05	.02
59	Cesar Cedeno	.12	.09	.05
60	Jose Cruz	.12	.09	.05
61	Bill Virdon	.06	.05	.02
62	Terry Puhl	.06	.05	.02
63	Joaquin Andujar	.10	.08	.04
64	Alan Ashby	.06	.05	.02
65	Joe Sambito	.06	.05	.02
66	Denny Walling	.06	.05	.02
67	Jeff Leonard	.12	.09	.05
68	Luis Pujols	.06	.05	.02
69	Bruce Bochy	.06	.05	.02
70	Rafael Landestoy	.06	.05	.02
71	Dave Smith	.30	.25	.12
72	Danny Heep	.10	.08	.04
73	Julio Gonzalez	.06	.05	.02
74	Craig Reynolds	.06	.05	.02
75	Gary Woods	.06	.05	.02
76	Dave Bergman	.06	.05	.02
77	Randy Niemann	.06	.05	.02
78	Joe Morgan	.70	.50	.30
79a	Reggie Jackson (portrait)	3.00	2.25	1.25
79b	Reggie Jackson (batting)	1.00	.70	.40
80	Bucky Dent	.10	.08	.04
81	Tommy John	.20	.15	.08
82	Luis Tiant	.12	.09	.05
83	Rick Cerone	.06	.05	.02

		MT	NR MT	EX
84	Dick Howser	.06	.05	.02
85	Lou Piniella	.12	.09	.05
86	Ron Davis	.08	.06	.03
87a	Graig Nettles (Craig on back)	12.00	9.00	4.75
87b	Graig Nettles (Graig on back)	.30	.25	.12
88	Ron Guidry	.25	.20	.10
89	Rich Gossage	.20	.15	.08
90	Rudy May	.06	.05	.02
91	Gaylord Perry	.60	.45	.25
92	Eric Soderholm	.06	.05	.02
93	Bob Watson	.08	.06	.03
94	Bobby Murcer	.10	.08	.04
95	Bobby Brown	.06	.05	.02
96	Jim Spencer	.06	.05	.02
97	Tom Underwood	.06	.05	.02
98	Oscar Gamble	.08	.06	.03
99	Johnny Oates	.06	.05	.02
100	Fred Stanley	.06	.05	.02
101	Ruppert Jones	.06	.05	.02
102	Dennis Werth	.06	.05	.02
103	Joe Lefebvre	.06	.05	.02
104	Brian Doyle	.06	.05	.02
105	Aurelio Rodriguez	.08	.06	.03
106	Doug Bird	.06	.05	.02
107	Mike Griffin	.06	.05	.02
108	Tim Lollar	.06	.05	.02
109	Willie Randolph	.10	.08	.04
110	Steve Garvey	.70	.50	.30
111	Reggie Smith	.10	.08	.04
112	Don Sutton	.30	.25	.12
113	Burt Hooton	.08	.06	.03
114a	Davy Lopes (Davey) (no finger on back)	.10	.08	.04
114b	Davy Lopes (Davey) (small finger on back)	1.00	.70	.40
115	Dusty Baker	.10	.08	.04
116	Tom Lasorda	.10	.08	.04
117	Bill Russell	.08	.06	.03
118	Jerry Reuss	.10	.08	.04
119	Terry Forster	.08	.06	.03
120a	Robert Welch (Bob Welch on back)	.60	.45	.25
120b	Robert Welch (Robert Welch on back)	1.00	.70	.40
121	Don Stanhouse	.06	.05	.02
122	Rick Monday	.10	.08	.04
123	Derrel Thomas	.06	.05	.02
124	Joe Ferguson	.06	.05	.02
125	Rick Sutcliffe	.20	.15	.08
126a	Ron Cey (no finger on back)	.12	.09	.05
126b	Ron Cey (small finger on back)	1.00	.70	.40
127	Dave Goltz	.08	.06	.03
128	Jay Johnstone	.08	.06	.03
129	Steve Yeager	.06	.05	.02
130	Gary Weiss	.06	.05	.02
131	*Mike Scioscia*	1.00	.70	.40
132	Vic Davalillo	.08	.06	.03
133	Doug Rau	.06	.05	.02
134	Pepe Frias	.06	.05	.02
135	Mickey Hatcher	.08	.06	.03
136	*Steve Howe*	.10	.08	.04
137	Robert Castillo	.06	.05	.02
138	Gary Thomasson	.06	.05	.02
139	Rudy Law	.06	.05	.02
140	*Fernand Valenzuela (Fernando)*	3.00	2.25	1.25
141	Manny Mota	.08	.06	.03
142	Gary Carter	.70	.50	.30
143	Steve Rogers	.08	.06	.03
144	Warren Cromartie	.06	.05	.02
145	Andre Dawson	2.00	1.50	.80
146	Larry Parrish	.10	.08	.04
147	Rowland Office	.06	.05	.02
148	Ellis Valentine	.06	.05	.02
149	Dick Williams	.06	.05	.02
150	*Bill Gullickson*	.15	.11	.06
151	Elias Sosa	.06	.05	.02
152	John Tamargo	.06	.05	.02
153	Chris Speier	.06	.05	.02
154	Ron LeFlore	.08	.06	.03
155	Rodney Scott	.06	.05	.02
156	Stan Bahnsen	.06	.05	.02
157	Bill Lee	.08	.06	.03
158	Fred Norman	.06	.05	.02
159	Woodie Fryman	.08	.06	.03
160	Dave Palmer	.06	.05	.02
161	Jerry White	.06	.05	.02
162	Roberto Ramos	.06	.05	.02
163	John D'Acquisto	.06	.05	.02
164	Tommy Hutton	.06	.05	.02
165	*Charlie Lea*	.12	.09	.05
166	Scott Sanderson	.06	.05	.02
167	Ken Macha	.06	.05	.02

		MT	NR MT	EX
168	Tony Bernazard	.06	.05	.02
169	Jim Palmer	1.00	.70	.40
170	Steve Stone	.08	.06	.03
171	Mike Flanagan	.10	.08	.04
172	Al Bumbry	.08	.06	.03
173	Doug DeCinces	.10	.08	.04
174	Scott McGregor	.08	.06	.03
175	Mark Belanger	.08	.06	.03
176	Tim Stoddard	.06	.05	.02
177a	Rick Dempsey (no finger on front)	.10	.08	.04
177b	Rick Dempsey (small finger on front)	1.00	.70	.40
178	Earl Weaver	.10	.08	.04
179	Tippy Martinez	.06	.05	.02
180	Dennis Martinez	.08	.06	.03
181	Sammy Stewart	.06	.05	.02
182	Rich Dauer	.06	.05	.02
183	Lee May	.08	.06	.03
184	Eddie Murray	3.00	2.25	1.25
185	Benny Ayala	.06	.05	.02
186	John Lowenstein	.06	.05	.02
187	Gary Roenicke	.06	.05	.02
188	Ken Singleton	.10	.08	.04
189	Dan Graham	.06	.05	.02
190	Terry Crowley	.06	.05	.02
191	Kiko Garcia	.06	.05	.02
192	Dave Ford	.06	.05	.02
193	Mark Corey	.06	.05	.02
194	Lenn Sakata	.06	.05	.02
195	Doug DeCinces	.10	.08	.04
196	Johnny Bench	1.00	.70	.40
197	Dave Concepcion	.15	.11	.06
198	Ray Knight	.10	.08	.04
199	Ken Griffey	.12	.09	.05
200	Tom Seaver	2.00	1.50	.80
201	Dave Collins	.08	.06	.03
202	George Foster	.20	.15	.08
203	Junior Kennedy	.06	.05	.02
204	Frank Pastore	.06	.05	.02
205	Dan Driessen	.08	.06	.03
206	Hector Cruz	.06	.05	.02
207	Paul Moskau	.06	.05	.02
208	*Charlie Leibrandt*	.40	.30	.15
209	Harry Spilman	.06	.05	.02
210	*Joe Price*	.12	.09	.05
211	Tom Hume	.06	.05	.02
212	Joe Nolan	.06	.05	.02
213	Doug Bair	.06	.05	.02
214	Mario Soto	.08	.06	.03
215a	Bill Bonham (no finger on back)	.08	.06	.03
215b	Bill Bonham (small finger on back)	1.00	.70	.40
216a	George Foster (Slugger on front)	.25	.20	.10
216b	George Foster (Outfield on front)	.20	.15	.08
217	Paul Householder	.06	.05	.02
218	Ron Oester	.06	.05	.02
219	Sam Mejias	.06	.05	.02
220	Sheldon Burnside	.06	.05	.02
221	Carl Yastrzemski	1.25	.90	.50
222	Jim Rice	.50	.40	.20
223	Fred Lynn	.20	.15	.08
224	Carlton Fisk	2.00	1.50	.80
225	Rick Burleson	.08	.06	.03
226	Dennis Eckersley	1.50	1.25	.60
227	Butch Hobson	.06	.05	.02
228	Tom Burgmeier	.06	.05	.02
229	Garry Hancock	.06	.05	.02
230	Don Zimmer	.06	.05	.02
231	Steve Renko	.06	.05	.02
232	Dwight Evans	.15	.11	.06
233	Mike Torrez	.08	.06	.03
234	Bob Stanley	.06	.05	.02
235	Jim Dwyer	.06	.05	.02
236	Dave Stapleton	.06	.05	.02
237	Glenn Hoffman	.06	.05	.02
238	Jerry Remy	.06	.05	.02
239	Dick Drago	.06	.05	.02
240	Bill Campbell	.06	.05	.02
241	Tony Perez	.20	.15	.08
242	Phil Niekro	.30	.25	.12
243	Dale Murphy	.90	.70	.35
244	Bob Horner	.12	.09	.05
245	Jeff Burroughs	.08	.06	.03
246	Rick Camp	.06	.05	.02
247	Bob Cox	.06	.05	.02
248	Bruce Benedict	.06	.05	.02
249	Gene Garber	.06	.05	.02
250	Jerry Royster	.06	.05	.02
251a	Gary Matthews (no finger on back)	.12	.09	.05
251b	Gary Matthews (small finger on back)	1.00	.70	.40

		MT	NR MT	EX			MT	NR MT	EX
252	Chris Chambliss	.08	.06	.03	342b	Britt Burns (small finger on front)	1.00	.70	.40
253	Luis Gomez	.06	.05	.02	343	Kevin Bell	.06	.05	.02
254	Bill Nahorodny	.06	.05	.02	344	Tony LaRussa	.08	.06	.03
255	Doyle Alexander	.10	.08	.04	345	Steve Trout	.06	.05	.02
256	Brian Asselstine	.06	.05	.02	346	Harold Baines	5.00	3.75	2.00
257	Biff Pocoroba	.06	.05	.02	347	Richard Wortham	.06	.05	.02
258	Mike Lum	.06	.05	.02	348	Wayne Nordhagen	.06	.05	.02
259	Charlie Spikes	.06	.05	.02	349	Mike Squires	.06	.05	.02
260	Glenn Hubbard	.08	.06	.03	350	Lamar Johnson	.06	.05	.02
261	Tommy Boggs	.06	.05	.02	351	Rickey Henderson	8.00	6.00	3.25
262	Al Hrabosky	.08	.06	.03	352	Francisco Barrios	.06	.05	.02
263	Rick Matula	.06	.05	.02	353	Thad Bosley	.06	.05	.02
264	Preston Hanna	.06	.05	.02	354	Chet Lemon	.08	.06	.03
265	Larry Bradford	.06	.05	.02	355	Bruce Kimm	.06	.05	.02
266	Rafael Ramirez	.20	.15	.08	356	Richard Dotson	.25	.20	.10
267	Larry McWilliams	.06	.05	.02	357	Jim Morrison	.06	.05	.02
268	Rod Carew	1.50	1.25	.60	358	Mike Proly	.06	.05	.02
269	Bobby Grich	.10	.08	.04	359	Greg Pryor	.06	.05	.02
270	Carney Lansford	.10	.08	.04	360	Dave Parker	.30	.25	.12
271	Don Baylor	.12	.09	.05	361	Omar Moreno	.06	.05	.02
272	Joe Rudi	.10	.08	.04	362a	Kent Tekulve (1071 Waterbury on back)			
273	Dan Ford	.06	.05	.02			.15	.11	.06
274	Jim Fregosi	.08	.06	.03	362b	Kent Tekulve (1971 Waterbury on back)			
275	Dave Frost	.06	.05	.02			.70	.50	.30
276	Frank Tanana	.10	.08	.04	363	Willie Stargell	.40	.30	.15
277	Dickie Thon	.08	.06	.03	364	Phil Garner	.08	.06	.03
278	Jason Thompson	.06	.05	.02	365	Ed Ott	.06	.05	.02
279	Rick Miller	.06	.05	.02	366	Don Robinson	.08	.06	.03
280	Bert Campaneris	.10	.08	.04	367	Chuck Tanner	.06	.05	.02
281	Tom Donohue	.06	.05	.02	368	Jim Rooker	.06	.05	.02
282	Brian Downing	.10	.08	.04	369	Dale Berra	.06	.05	.02
283	Fred Patek	.06	.05	.02	370	Jim Bibby	.06	.05	.02
284	Bruce Kison	.06	.05	.02	371	Steve Nicosia	.06	.05	.02
285	Dave LaRoche	.06	.05	.02	372	Mike Easler	.08	.06	.03
286	Don Aase	.06	.05	.02	373	Bill Robinson	.06	.05	.02
287	Jim Barr	.06	.05	.02	374	Lee Lacy	.06	.05	.02
288	Alfredo Martinez	.06	.05	.02	375	John Candelaria	.10	.08	.04
289	Larry Harlow	.06	.05	.02	376	Manny Sanguillen	.06	.05	.02
290	Andy Hassler	.06	.05	.02	377	Rick Rhoden	.10	.08	.04
291	Dave Kingman	.15	.11	.06	378	Grant Jackson	.06	.05	.02
292	Bill Buckner	.12	.09	.05	379	Tim Foli	.06	.05	.02
293	Rick Reuschel	.10	.08	.04	380	Rod Scurry	.08	.06	.03
294	Bruce Sutter	.15	.11	.06	381	Bill Madlock	.12	.09	.05
295	Jerry Martin	.06	.05	.02	382a	Kurt Bevacqua (photo reversed,			
296	Scot Thompson	.06	.05	.02		backwards "P" on cap)	.15	.11	.06
297	Ivan DeJesus	.06	.05	.02	382b	Kurt Bevacqua (correct photo)	.70	.50	.30
298	Steve Dillard	.06	.05	.02	383	Bert Blyleven	.12	.09	.05
299	Dick Tidrow	.06	.05	.02	384	Eddie Solomon	.06	.05	.02
300	Randy Martz	.06	.05	.02	385	Enrique Romo	.06	.05	.02
301	Lenny Randle	.06	.05	.02	386	John Milner	.06	.05	.02
302	Lynn McGlothen	.06	.05	.02	387	Mike Hargrove	.06	.05	.02
303	Cliff Johnson	.06	.05	.02	388	Jorge Orta	.06	.05	.02
304	Tim Blackwell	.06	.05	.02	389	Toby Harrah	.08	.06	.03
305	Dennis Lamp	.06	.05	.02	390	Tom Veryzer	.06	.05	.02
306	Bill Caudill	.06	.05	.02	391	Miguel Dilone	.06	.05	.02
307	Carlos Lezcano	.06	.05	.02	392	Dan Spillner	.06	.05	.02
308	Jim Tracy	.06	.05	.02	393	Jack Brohamer	.06	.05	.02
309	Doug Capilla	.06	.05	.02	394	Wayne Garland	.06	.05	.02
310	Willie Hernandez	.10	.08	.04	395	Sid Monge	.06	.05	.02
311	Mike Vail	.06	.05	.02	396	Rick Waits	.06	.05	.02
312	Mike Krukow	.08	.06	.03	397	Joe Charboneau	.10	.08	.04
313	Barry Foote	.06	.05	.02	398	Gary Alexander	.06	.05	.02
314	Larry Biittner	.06	.05	.02	399	Jerry Dybzinski	.06	.05	.02
315	Mike Tyson	.06	.05	.02	400	Mike Stanton	.06	.05	.02
316	Lee Mazzilli	.08	.06	.03	401	Mike Paxton	.06	.05	.02
317	John Stearns	.06	.05	.02	402	Gary Gray	.06	.05	.02
318	Alex Trevino	.06	.05	.02	403	Rick Manning	.06	.05	.02
319	Craig Swan	.06	.05	.02	404	Bo Diaz	.08	.06	.03
320	Frank Taveras	.06	.05	.02	405	Ron Hassey	.06	.05	.02
321	Steve Henderson	.06	.05	.02	406	Ross Grimsley	.06	.05	.02
322	Neil Allen	.08	.06	.03	407	Victor Cruz	.06	.05	.02
323	Mark Bomback	.06	.05	.02	408	Len Barker	.08	.06	.03
324	Mike Jorgensen	.06	.05	.02	409	Bob Bailor	.06	.05	.02
325	Joe Torre	.08	.06	.03	410	Otto Velez	.06	.05	.02
326	Elliott Maddox	.06	.05	.02	411	Ernie Whitt	.08	.06	.03
327	Pete Falcone	.06	.05	.02	412	Jim Clancy	.08	.06	.03
328	Ray Burris	.06	.05	.02	413	Barry Bonnell	.06	.05	.02
329	Claudell Washington	.08	.06	.03	414	Dave Stieb	.60	.45	.25
330	Doug Flynn	.06	.05	.02	415	Damaso Garcia	.10	.08	.04
331	Joel Youngblood	.06	.05	.02	416	John Mayberry	.08	.06	.03
332	Bill Almon	.06	.05	.02	417	Roy Howell	.06	.05	.02
333	Tom Hausman	.06	.05	.02	418	Dan Ainge	1.25	.90	.50
334	Pat Zachry	.06	.05	.02	419a	Jesse Jefferson (Pirates on back)	.10	.08	.04
335	Jeff Reardon	5.00	3.75	2.00	419b	Jesse Jefferson (Blue Jays on back)			
336	Wally Backman	.35	.25	.14			.50	.40	.20
337	Dan Norman	.06	.05	.02	420	Joey McLaughlin	.06	.05	.02
338	Jerry Morales	.06	.05	.02	421	Lloyd Moseby	.40	.30	.15
339	Ed Farmer	.06	.05	.02	422	Al Woods	.06	.05	.02
340	Bob Molinaro	.06	.05	.02	423	Garth Iorg	.06	.05	.02
341	Todd Cruz	.06	.05	.02	424	Doug Ault	.06	.05	.02
342a	Britt Burns (no finger on front)	.20	.15	.08	425	Ken Schrom	.06	.05	.02

		MT	NR MT	EX
426	Mike Willis	.06	.05	.02
427	Steve Braun	.06	.05	.02
428	Bob Davis	.06	.05	.02
429	Jerry Garvin	.06	.05	.02
430	Alfredo Griffin	.08	.06	.03
431	Bob Mattick	.06	.05	.02
432	Vida Blue	.12	.09	.05
433	Jack Clark	.25	.20	.10
434	Willie McCovey	.40	.30	.15
435	Mike Ivie	.06	.05	.02
436a	Darrel Evans (Darrel on front)	.15	.11	.06
436b	Darrell Evans (Darrell on front)	.70	.50	.30
437	Terry Whitfield	.06	.05	.02
438	Rennie Stennett	.06	.05	.02
439	John Montefusco	.08	.06	.03
440	Jim Wohlford	.06	.05	.02
441	Bill North	.06	.05	.02
442	Milt May	.06	.05	.02
443	Max Venable	.06	.05	.02
444	Ed Whitson	.06	.05	.02
445	*Al Holland*	.08	.06	.03
446	Randy Moffitt	.06	.05	.02
447	Bob Knepper	.08	.06	.03
448	Gary Lavelle	.06	.05	.02
449	Greg Minton	.06	.05	.02
450	Johnnie LeMaster	.06	.05	.02
451	Larry Herndon	.08	.06	.03
452	Rich Murray	.06	.05	.02
453	Joe Pettini	.06	.05	.02
454	Allen Ripley	.06	.05	.02
455	Dennis Littlejohn	.06	.05	.02
456	Tom Griffin	.06	.05	.02
457	Alan Hargesheimer	.06	.05	.02
458	Joe Strain	.06	.05	.02
459	Steve Kemp	.08	.06	.03
460	Sparky Anderson	.10	.08	.04
461	Alan Trammell	.40	.30	.15
462	Mark Fidrych	.08	.06	.03
463	Lou Whitaker	.40	.30	.15
464	Dave Rozema	.06	.05	.02
465	Milt Wilcox	.06	.05	.02
466	Champ Summers	.06	.05	.02
467	Lance Parrish	.35	.25	.14
468	Dan Petry	.08	.06	.03
469	Pat Underwood	.06	.05	.02
470	Rick Peters	.06	.05	.02
471	Al Cowens	.06	.05	.02
472	John Wockenfuss	.06	.05	.02
473	Tom Brookens	.08	.06	.03
474	Richie Hebner	.06	.05	.02
475	Jack Morris	2.00	1.50	.80
476	Jim Lentine	.06	.05	.02
477	Bruce Robbins	.06	.05	.02
478	Mark Wagner	.06	.05	.02
479	Tim Corcoran	.06	.05	.02
480a	Stan Papi (Pitcher on front)	.15	.11	.06
480b	Stan Papi (Shortstop on front)	.70	.50	.30
481	*Kirk Gibson*	2.50	2.00	1.00
482	Dan Schatzeder	.06	.05	.02
483	Amos Otis	.70	.50	.30
484	Dave Winfield	1.50	1.25	.60
485	Rollie Fingers	1.00	.70	.40
486	Gene Richards	.06	.05	.02
487	Randy Jones	.08	.06	.03
488	Ozzie Smith	2.00	1.50	.80
489	Gene Tenace	.08	.06	.03
490	Bill Fahey	.06	.05	.02
491	John Curtis	.06	.05	.02
492	Dave Cash	.06	.05	.02
493a	Tim Flannery (photo reversed, batting righty)	.15	.11	.06
493b	Tim Flannery (photo correct, batting lefty)	.70	.50	.30
494	Jerry Mumphrey	.06	.05	.02
495	Bob Shirley	.06	.05	.02
496	Steve Mura	.06	.05	.02
497	Eric Rasmussen	.06	.05	.02
498	Broderick Perkins	.06	.05	.02
499	Barry Evans	.06	.05	.02
500	Chuck Baker	.06	.05	.02
501	*Luis Salazar*	.15	.11	.06
502	Gary Lucas	.08	.06	.03
503	Mike Armstrong	.06	.05	.02
504	Jerry Turner	.06	.05	.02
505	Dennis Kinney	.06	.05	.02
506	Willy Montanez (Willie)	.06	.05	.02
507	Gorman Thomas	.10	.08	.04
508	Ben Oglivie	.08	.06	.03
509	Larry Hisle	.08	.06	.03
510	Sal Bando	.10	.08	.04
511	Robin Yount	3.00	2.25	1.25
512	Mike Caldwell	.06	.05	.02
513	Sixto Lezcano	.06	.05	.02
514a	Jerry Augustine (Billy Travers photo)	.15	.11	.06
514b	Billy Travers (correct name with photo)	.70	.50	.30
515	Paul Molitor	.20	.15	.08
516	Moose Haas	.06	.05	.02
517	Bill Castro	.06	.05	.02
518	Jim Slaton	.06	.05	.02
519	Lary Sorensen	.06	.05	.02
520	Bob McClure	.06	.05	.02
521	Charlie Moore	.06	.05	.02
522	Jim Gantner	.08	.06	.03
523	Reggie Cleveland	.06	.05	.02
524	Don Money	.06	.05	.02
525	Billy Travers	.06	.05	.02
526	Buck Martinez	.06	.05	.02
527	Dick Davis	.06	.05	.02
528	Ted Simmons	.12	.09	.05
529	Garry Templeton	.10	.08	.04
530	Ken Reitz	.06	.05	.02
531	Tony Scott	.06	.05	.02
532	Ken Oberkfell	.06	.05	.02
533	Bob Sykes	.06	.05	.02
534	Keith Smith	.06	.05	.02
535	John Littlefield	.06	.05	.02
536	Jim Kaat	.15	.11	.06
537	Bob Forsch	.08	.06	.03
538	Mike Phillips	.06	.05	.02
539	*Terry Landrum*	.10	.08	.04
540	*Leon Durham*	.20	.15	.08
541	Terry Kennedy	.08	.06	.03
542	George Hendrick	.08	.06	.03
543	Dane Iorg	.06	.05	.02
544	Mark Littell (photo actually Jeff Little)	.06	.05	.02
545	Keith Hernandez	.40	.30	.15
546	Silvio Martinez	.06	.05	.02
547a	Pete Vuckovich (photo actually Don Hood)	.15	.11	.06
547b	Don Hood (correct name with photo)	.70	.50	.30
548	Bobby Bonds	.10	.08	.04
549	Mike Ramsey	.06	.05	.02
550	Tom Herr	.10	.08	.04
551	Roy Smalley	.06	.05	.02
552	Jerry Koosman	.10	.08	.04
553	Ken Landreaux	.06	.05	.02
554	John Castino	.06	.05	.02
555	Doug Corbett	.06	.05	.02
556	Bombo Rivera	.06	.05	.02
557	Ron Jackson	.06	.05	.02
558	Butch Wynegar	.06	.05	.02
559	Hosken Powell	.06	.05	.02
560	Pete Redfern	.06	.05	.02
561	Roger Erickson	.06	.05	.02
562	Glenn Adams	.06	.05	.02
563	Rick Sofield	.06	.05	.02
564	Geoff Zahn	.06	.05	.02
565	Pete Mackanin	.06	.05	.02
566	Mike Cubbage	.06	.05	.02
567	Darrell Jackson	.06	.05	.02
568	Dave Edwards	.06	.05	.02
569	Rob Wilfong	.06	.05	.02
570	Sal Butera	.06	.05	.02
571	Jose Morales	.06	.05	.02
572	Rick Langford	.06	.05	.02
573	Mike Norris	.06	.05	.02
574	Rickey Henderson	12.00	9.00	4.75
575	Tony Armas	.10	.08	.04
576	Dave Revering	.06	.05	.02
577	Jeff Newman	.06	.05	.02
578	Bob Lacey	.06	.05	.02
579	Brian Kingman (photo actually Alan Wirth)	.06	.05	.02
580	Mitchell Page	.06	.05	.02
581	Billy Martin	.12	.09	.05
582	Rob Picciolo	.06	.05	.02
583	Mike Heath	.06	.05	.02
584	Mickey Klutts	.06	.05	.02
585	Orlando Gonzalez	.06	.05	.02
586	*Mike Davis*	.25	.20	.10
587	Wayne Gross	.06	.05	.02
588	Matt Keough	.06	.05	.02
589	Steve McCatty	.06	.05	.02
590	Dwayne Murphy	.08	.06	.03
591	Mario Guerrero	.06	.05	.02
592	Dave McKay	.06	.05	.02
593	Jim Essian	.06	.05	.02
594	Dave Heaverlo	.06	.05	.02

		MT	NR MT	EX
595	Maury Wills	.10	.08	.04
596	Juan Beniquez	.06	.05	.02
597	Rodney Craig	.06	.05	.02
598	Jim Anderson	.06	.05	.02
599	Floyd Bannister	.10	.08	.04
600	Bruce Bochte	.06	.05	.02
601	Julio Cruz	.06	.05	.02
602	Ted Cox	.06	.05	.02
603	Dan Meyer	.06	.05	.02
604	Larry Cox	.06	.05	.02
605	Bill Stein	.06	.05	.02
606	Steve Garvey	.50	.40	.20
607	Dave Roberts	.06	.05	.02
608	Leon Roberts	.06	.05	.02
609	Reggie Walton	.06	.05	.02
610	Dave Edler	.06	.05	.02
611	Larry Milbourne	.06	.05	.02
612	Kim Allen	.06	.05	.02
613	Mario Mendoza	.06	.05	.02
614	Tom Paciorek	.06	.05	.02
615	Glenn Abbott	.06	.05	.02
616	Joe Simpson	.06	.05	.02
617	Mickey Rivers	.08	.06	.03
618	Jim Kern	.06	.05	.02
619	Jim Sundberg	.08	.06	.03
620	Richie Zisk	.08	.06	.03
621	Jon Matlack	.08	.06	.03
622	Ferguson Jenkins	.50	.40	.20
623	Pat Corrales	.06	.05	.02
624	Ed Figueroa	.06	.05	.02
625	Buddy Bell	.12	.09	.05
626	Al Oliver	.15	.11	.06
627	Doc Medich	.06	.05	.02
628	Bump Wills	.06	.05	.02
629	Rusty Staub	.10	.08	.04
630	Pat Putnam	.06	.05	.02
631	John Grubb	.06	.05	.02
632	Danny Darwin	.06	.05	.02
633	Ken Clay	.06	.05	.02
634	Jim Norris	.06	.05	.02
635	John Butcher	.06	.05	.02
636	Dave Roberts	.06	.05	.02
637	Billy Sample	.06	.05	.02
638	Carl Yastrzemski	1.00	.70	.40
639	Cecil Cooper	.15	.11	.06
640	Mike Schmidt	2.00	1.50	.80
641a	Checklist 1-50 (41 Hal McRae)	.10	.08	.04
641b	Checklist 1-50 (41 Hal McRae Double Threat)	.40	.30	.15
642	Checklist 51-109	.06	.05	.02
643	Checklist 110-168	.06	.05	.02
644a	Checklist 169-220 (202 George Foster)	.10	.08	.04
644b	Checklist 169-220 (202 George Foster "Slugger")	.40	.30	.15
645a	Triple Threat (Larry Bowa, Pete Rose, Mike Schmidt) (no number on back)	1.00	.70	.40
645b	Triple Threat (Larry Bowa, Pete Rose, Mike Schmidt) (645 on back)	2.00	1.50	.80
646	Checklist 221-267	.06	.05	.02
647	Checklist 268-315	.06	.05	.02
648	Checklist 316-359	.06	.05	.02
649	Checklist 360-408	.06	.05	.02
650	Reggie Jackson	3.25	2.50	1.25
651	Checklist 409-458	.06	.05	.02
652a	Checklist 459-509 (483 Aurelio Lopez)	.10	.08	.04
652b	Checklist 459-506 (no 483)	.40	.30	.15
653	Willie Wilson	1.00	.70	.40
654a	Checklist 507-550 (514 Jerry Augustine)	.10	.08	.04
654b	Checklist 507-550 (514 Billy Travers)	.40	.30	.15
655	George Brett	2.00	1.50	.80
656	Checklist 551-593	.06	.05	.02
657	Tug McGraw	1.00	.70	.40
658	Checklist 594-637	.06	.05	.02
659a	Checklist 640-660 (last number on front is 551)	.10	.08	.04
659b	Checklist 640-660 (last number on front is 483)	.40	.30	.15
660a	Steve Carlton (date 1066 on back)	1.00	.70	.40
660b	Steve Carlton (date 1966 on back)	2.00	1.50	.80

Regional interest may affect the value of a card.

1981 Fleer Star Stickers

The 128-card 1981 Fleer Star Sticker set was designed for the card fronts to be peeled away from the cardboard backs. The card obverses feature color photos with blue and yellow trim. The card backs are identical in design to the regular 1981 Fleer set except for color and numbering. The set contains three unnumbered checklist cards whose fronts depict Reggie Jackson (#'s 1-42), George Brett (#'s 43-83) and Mike Schmidt (#'s 84-125). The cards, which are the standard 2-1/2" by 3-1/2", were issued in gum wax packs.

		MT	NR MT	EX
	Complete Set	65.00	49.00	26.00
	Common Player	.10	.08	.04
1	Steve Garvey	1.00	.70	.40
2	Ron LeFlore	.10	.08	.04
3	Ron Cey	.25	.20	.10
4	Dave Revering	.10	.08	.04
5	Tony Armas	.15	.11	.06
6	Mike Norris	.10	.08	.04
7	Steve Kemp	.15	.11	.06
8	Bruce Bochte	.10	.08	.04
9	Mike Schmidt	4.00	3.00	1.50
10	Scott McGregor	.10	.08	.04
11	Buddy Bell	.20	.15	.08
12	Carney Lansford	.20	.15	.08
13	Carl Yastrzemski	4.00	3.00	1.50
14	Ben Oglivie	.10	.08	.04
15	Willie Stargell	4.00	3.00	1.50
16	Cecil Cooper	.15	.11	.06
17	Gene Richards	.10	.08	.04
18	Jim Kern	.10	.08	.04
19	Jerry Koosman	.15	.11	.06
20	Larry Bowa	.20	.15	.08
21	Kent Tekulve	.15	.11	.06
22	Dan Driessen	.10	.08	.04
23	Phil Niekro	1.00	.70	.40
24	Dan Quisenberry	.30	.25	.12
25	Dave Winfield	1.00	.70	.40
26	Dave Parker	1.00	.70	.40
27	Rick Langford	.10	.08	.04
28	Amos Otis	.15	.11	.06
29	Bill Buckner	.15	.11	.06
30	Al Bumbry	.10	.08	.04
31	Bake McBride	.10	.08	.04
32	Mickey Rivers	.10	.08	.04
33	Rick Burleson	.10	.08	.04
34	Dennis Eckersley	.60	.45	.25
35	Cesar Cedeno	.20	.15	.08
36	Enos Cabell	.10	.08	.04
37	Johnny Bench	4.00	3.00	1.50
38	Robin Yount	4.00	3.00	1.50
39	Mark Belanger	.10	.08	.04
40	Rod Carew	1.00	.70	.40
41	George Foster	.40	.30	.15
42	Lee Mazzilli	.15	.11	.06
43	Triple Threat (Larry Bowa, Pete Rose, Mike Schmidt)	2.00	1.50	.80
44	J.R. Richard	.15	.11	.06
45	Lou Piniella	.30	.25	.12
46	Ken Landreaux	.10	.08	.04
47	Rollie Fingers	1.00	.70	.40
48	Joaquin Andujar	.10	.08	.04
49	Tom Seaver	4.00	3.00	1.50
50	Bobby Grich	.20	.15	.08

		MT	NR MT	EX
51	Jon Matlack	.10	.08	.04
52	Jack Clark	.25	.20	.10
53	Jim Rice	.25	.20	.10
54	Rickey Henderson	4.00	3.00	1.50
55	Roy Smalley	.10	.08	.04
56	Mike Flanagan	.15	.11	.06
57	Steve Rogers	.10	.08	.04
58	Carlton Fisk	.60	.45	.25
59	Don Sutton	1.00	.70	.40
60	Ken Griffey	.20	.15	.08
61	Burt Hooton	.10	.08	.04
62	Dusty Baker	.20	.15	.08
63	Vida Blue	.25	.20	.10
64	Al Oliver	.30	.25	.12
65	Jim Bibby	.10	.08	.04
66	Tony Perez	1.00	.70	.40
67	Davy Lopes (Davey)	.15	.11	.06
68	Bill Russell	.15	.11	.06
69	Larry Parrish	.20	.15	.08
70	Garry Maddox	.15	.11	.06
71	Phil Garner	.15	.11	.06
72	Graig Nettles	.35	.25	.14
73	Gary Carter	1.00	.70	.40
74	Pete Rose	4.00	3.00	1.50
75	Greg Luzinski	.30	.25	.12
76	Ron Guidry	.25	.20	.10
77	Gorman Thomas	.15	.11	.06
78	Jose Cruz	.20	.15	.08
79	Bob Boone	.15	.11	.06
80	Bruce Sutter	.35	.25	.14
81	Chris Chambliss	.15	.11	.06
82	Paul Molitor	.60	.45	.25
83	Tug McGraw	.25	.20	.10
84	Ferguson Jenkins	.40	.30	.15
85	Steve Carlton	5.00	3.75	2.00
86	Miguel Dilone	.10	.08	.04
87	Reggie Smith	.20	.15	.08
88	Rick Cerone	.10	.08	.04
89	Alan Trammell	1.00	.70	.40
90	Doug DeCinces	.20	.15	.08
91	Sparky Lyle	.15	.11	.06
92	Warren Cromartie	.10	.08	.04
93	Rick Reuschel	.25	.20	.10
94	Larry Hisle	.10	.08	.04
95	Paul Splittorff	.10	.08	.04
96	Manny Trillo	.10	.08	.04
97	Frank White	.20	.15	.08
98	Fred Lynn	.25	.20	.10
99	Bob Horner	.15	.11	.06
100	Omar Moreno	.10	.08	.04
101	Dave Concepcion	.20	.15	.08
102	Larry Gura	.10	.08	.04
103	Ken Singleton	.20	.15	.08
104	Steve Stone	.15	.11	.06
105	Richie Zisk	.10	.08	.04
106	Willie Wilson	.40	.30	.15
107	Willie Randolph	.20	.15	.08
108	Nolan Ryan	6.00	4.50	2.50
109	Joe Morgan	1.00	.70	.40
110	Bucky Dent	.20	.15	.08
111	Dave Kingman	.40	.30	.15
112	John Castino	.10	.08	.04
113	Joe Rudi	.20	.15	.08
114	Ed Farmer	.10	.08	.04
115	Reggie Jackson	4.00	3.00	1.50
116	George Brett	1.00	.70	.40
117	Eddie Murray	.25	.20	.10
118	Rich Gossage	.25	.20	.10
119	Dale Murphy	1.00	.70	.40
120	Ted Simmons	.15	.11	.06
121	Tommy John	.25	.20	.10
122	Don Baylor	.30	.25	.12
123	Andre Dawson	1.00	.70	.40
124	Jim Palmer	4.00	3.00	1.50
125	Garry Templeton	.20	.15	.08
-----	Reggie Jackson/Checklist 1-42	4.00	3.00	1.50
-----	George Brett/Checklist 43-83	4.00	3.00	1.50
-----	Mike Schmidt/Checklist 84-125	4.00	3.00	1.50

1982 Fleer

Fleer's 1982 set did not match the quality of the previous year's effort. Many of the photos in the set are blurred and have muddied backgrounds. The cards, which measure 2-1/2" by 3-1/2", feature color photos surrounded by a border frame which is color-coded by team. The card backs are blue, white,

and yellow and contain the player's team logo plus the logos of Major League Baseball and the Major League Baseball Players Association. Due to a lawsuit by Topps, Fleer was forced to issue the set with team logo stickers rather than gum. The complete set price does not include the higher priced variations.

		MT	NR MT	EX
Complete Set:		80.00	60.00	33.00
Common Player:		.06	.05	.02
1	Dusty Baker	.10	.08	.04
2	Robert Castillo	.06	.05	.02
3	Ron Cey	.12	.09	.05
4	Terry Forster	.08	.06	.03
5	Steve Garvey	.50	.40	.20
6	Dave Goltz	.08	.06	.03
7	Pedro Guerrero(FC)	.35	.25	.15
8	Burt Hooton	.08	.06	.03
9	Steve Howe	.08	.06	.03
10	Jay Johnstone	.08	.06	.03
11	Ken Landreaux	.06	.05	.02
12	Davey Lopes	.10	.08	.04
13	*Mike Marshall*(FC)	.25	.20	.10
14	Bobby Mitchell	.06	.05	.02
15	Rick Monday	.10	.08	.04
16	*Tom Niedenfuer*(FC)	.20	.15	.08
17	*Ted Power*(FC)	.20	.15	.08
18	Jerry Reuss	.10	.08	.04
19	Ron Roenicke	.06	.05	.02
20	Bill Russell	.08	.06	.03
21	*Steve Sax*(FC)	4.00	3.00	1.50
22	Mike Scioscia	.08	.06	.03
23	Reggie Smith	.10	.08	.04
24	*Dave Stewart*(FC)	3.00	2.25	1.25
25	Rick Sutcliffe	.15	.11	.06
26	Derrel Thomas	.06	.05	.02
27	Fernando Valenzuela	.60	.45	.25
28	Bob Welch	.12	.09	.05
29	Steve Yeager	.06	.05	.02
30	Bobby Brown	.06	.05	.02
31	Rick Cerone	.06	.05	.02
32	Ron Davis	.06	.05	.02
33	Bucky Dent	.10	.08	.04
34	Barry Foote	.06	.05	.02
35	George Frazier	.06	.05	.02
36	Oscar Gamble	.08	.06	.03
37	Rich Gossage	.20	.15	.08
38	Ron Guidry	.25	.20	.10
39	Reggie Jackson	2.00	1.50	.80
40	Tommy John	.20	.15	.08
41	Rudy May	.06	.05	.02
42	Larry Milbourne	.06	.05	.02
43	Jerry Mumphrey	.06	.05	.02
44	Bobby Murcer	.10	.08	.04
45	*Gene Nelson*	.12	.09	.05
46	Graig Nettles	.15	.11	.06
47	Johnny Oates	.06	.05	.02
48	Lou Piniella	.12	.09	.05
49	Willie Randolph	.10	.08	.04
50	Rick Reuschel	.10	.08	.04
51	Dave Revering	.06	.05	.02
52	*Dave Righetti*(FC)	1.00	.70	.40
53	Aurelio Rodriguez	.08	.06	.03
54	Bob Watson	.08	.06	.03
55	Dennis Werth	.06	.05	.02
56	Dave Winfield	2.00	1.50	.80
57	Johnny Bench	.80	.60	.30
58	Bruce Berenyi	.06	.05	.02
59	Larry Biittner	.06	.05	.02

		MT	NR MT	EX				MT	NR MT	EX
60	Scott Brown	.06	.05	.02		151	Ben Oglivie	.08	.06	.03
61	Dave Collins	.08	.06	.03		152	Ted Simmons	.12	.09	.05
62	Geoff Combe	.06	.05	.02		153	Jim Slaton	.06	.05	.02
63	Dave Concepcion	.12	.09	.05		154	Gorman Thomas	.10	.08	.04
64	Dan Driessen	.08	.06	.03		155	Robin Yount	2.00	1.50	.80
65	Joe Edelen	.06	.05	.02		156	Pete Vukovich	.08	.06	.03
66	George Foster	.20	.15	.08		157	Benny Ayala	.06	.05	.02
67	Ken Griffey	.12	.09	.05		158	Mark Belanger	.08	.06	.03
68	Paul Householder	.06	.05	.02		159	Al Bumbry	.08	.06	.03
69	Tom Hume	.06	.05	.02		160	Terry Crowley	.06	.05	.02
70	Junior Kennedy	.06	.05	.02		161	Rich Dauer	.06	.05	.02
71	Ray Knight	.10	.08	.04		162	Doug DeCinces	.10	.08	.04
72	Mike LaCoss	.06	.05	.02		163	Rick Dempsey	.08	.06	.03
73	Rafael Landestoy	.06	.05	.02		164	Jim Dwyer	.06	.05	.02
74	Charlie Leibrandt	.10	.08	.04		165	Mike Flanagan	.10	.08	.04
75	Sam Mejias	.06	.05	.02		166	Dave Ford	.06	.05	.02
76	Paul Moskau	.06	.05	.02		167	Dan Graham	.06	.05	.02
77	Joe Nolan	.06	.05	.02		168	Wayne Krenchicki	.06	.05	.02
78	Mike O'Berry	.06	.05	.02		169	John Lowenstein	.06	.05	.02
79	Ron Oester	.06	.05	.02		170	Dennis Martinez	.08	.06	.03
80	Frank Pastore	.06	.05	.02		171	Tippy Martinez	.06	.05	.02
81	Joe Price	.06	.05	.02		172	Scott McGregor	.08	.06	.03
82	Tom Seaver	1.50	1.25	.60		173	Jose Morales	.06	.05	.02
83	Mario Soto	.08	.06	.03		174	Eddie Murray	.80	.60	.30
84	Mike Vail	.06	.05	.02		175	Jim Palmer	.60	.45	.25
85	Tony Armas	.10	.08	.04		176	Cal Ripken, Jr.(FC)	50.00	37.00	20.00
86	Shooty Babitt	.06	.05	.02		177	Gary Roenicke	.06	.05	.02
87	Dave Beard	.06	.05	.02		178	Lenn Sakata	.06	.05	.02
88	Rick Bosetti	.06	.05	.02		179	Ken Singleton	.10	.08	.04
89	Keith Drumright	.06	.05	.02		180	Sammy Stewart	.06	.05	.02
90	Wayne Gross	.06	.05	.02		181	Tim Stoddard	.06	.05	.02
91	Mike Heath	.06	.05	.02		182	Steve Stone	.08	.06	.03
92	Rickey Henderson	6.00	4.50	2.50		183	Stan Bahnsen	.06	.05	.02
93	Cliff Johnson	.06	.05	.02		184	Ray Burris	.06	.05	.02
94	Jeff Jones	.06	.05	.02		185	Gary Carter	.35	.25	.14
95	Matt Keough	.06	.05	.02		186	Warren Cromartie	.06	.05	.02
96	Brian Kingman	.06	.05	.02		187	Andre Dawson	2.00	1.50	.80
97	Mickey Klutts	.06	.05	.02		188	Terry Francona(FC)	.10	.08	.04
98	Rick Langford	.06	.05	.02		189	Woodie Fryman	.08	.06	.03
99	Steve McCatty	.06	.05	.02		190	Bill Gullickson	.08	.06	.03
100	Dave McKay	.06	.05	.02		191	Grant Jackson	.06	.05	.02
101	Dwayne Murphy	.08	.06	.03		192	Wallace Johnson	.06	.05	.02
102	Jeff Newman	.06	.05	.02		193	Charlie Lea	.06	.05	.02
103	Mike Norris	.06	.05	.02		194	Bill Lee	.08	.06	.03
104	Bob Owchinko	.06	.05	.02		195	Jerry Manuel	.06	.05	.02
105	Mitchell Page	.06	.05	.02		196	Brad Mills	.06	.05	.02
106	Rob Picciolo	.06	.05	.02		197	John Milner	.06	.05	.02
107	Jim Spencer	.06	.05	.02		198	Rowland Office	.06	.05	.02
108	Fred Stanley	.06	.05	.02		199	David Palmer	.06	.05	.02
109	Tom Underwood	.06	.05	.02		200	Larry Parrish	.10	.08	.04
110	Joaquin Andujar	.08	.06	.03		201	Mike Phillips	.06	.05	.02
111	Steve Braun	.06	.05	.02		202	Tim Raines	1.50	1.25	.60
112	Bob Forsch	.08	.06	.03		203	Bobby Ramos	.06	.05	.02
113	George Hendrick	.08	.06	.03		204	Jeff Reardon	1.00	.70	.40
114	Keith Hernandez	.40	.30	.15		205	Steve Rogers	.08	.06	.03
115	Tom Herr	.10	.08	.04		206	Scott Sanderson	.06	.05	.02
116	Dane Iorg	.06	.05	.02		207	Rodney Scott (photo actually Tim Raines)			
117	Jim Kaat	.15	.11	.06				.10	.08	.04
118	Tito Landrum	.06	.05	.02		208	Elias Sosa	.06	.05	.02
119	Sixto Lezcano	.06	.05	.02		209	Chris Speier	.06	.05	.02
120	Mark Littell	.06	.05	.02		210	Tim Wallach(FC)	2.00	1.50	.80
121	John Martin	.06	.05	.02		211	Jerry White	.06	.05	.02
122	Silvio Martinez	.06	.05	.02		212	Alan Ashby	.06	.05	.02
123	Ken Oberkfell	.06	.05	.02		213	Cesar Cedeno	.12	.09	.05
124	Darrell Porter	.08	.06	.03		214	Jose Cruz	.12	.09	.05
125	Mike Ramsey	.06	.05	.02		215	Kiko Garcia	.06	.05	.02
126	Orlando Sanchez	.06	.05	.02		216	Phil Garner	.08	.06	.03
127	Bob Shirley	.06	.05	.02		217	Danny Heep	.06	.05	.02
128	Lary Sorensen	.06	.05	.02		218	Art Howe	.06	.05	.02
129	Bruce Sutter	.15	.11	.06		219	Bob Knepper	.08	.06	.03
130	Bob Sykes	.06	.05	.02		220	Frank LaCorte	.06	.05	.02
131	Garry Templeton	.10	.08	.04		221	Joe Niekro	.12	.09	.05
132	Gene Tenace	.08	.06	.03		222	Joe Pittman	.06	.05	.02
133	Jerry Augustine	.06	.05	.02		223	Terry Puhl	.06	.05	.02
134	Sal Bando	.08	.06	.03		224	Luis Pujols	.06	.05	.02
135	Mark Brouhard	.06	.05	.02		225	Craig Reynolds	.06	.05	.02
136	Mike Caldwell	.06	.05	.02		226	J.R. Richard	.10	.08	.04
137	Reggie Cleveland	.06	.05	.02		227	Dave Roberts	.06	.05	.02
138	Cecil Cooper	.15	.11	.06		228	Vern Ruhle	.06	.05	.02
139	Jamie Easterly	.06	.05	.02		229	Nolan Ryan	8.00	6.00	3.25
140	Marshall Edwards	.06	.05	.02		230	Joe Sambito	.06	.05	.02
141	Rollie Fingers	.50	.40	.20		231	Tony Scott	.06	.05	.02
142	Jim Gantner	.08	.06	.03		232	Dave Smith	.10	.08	.04
143	Moose Haas	.06	.05	.02		233	Harry Spilman	.06	.05	.02
144	Larry Hisle	.08	.06	.03		234	Don Sutton	.30	.25	.12
145	Roy Howell	.06	.05	.02		235	Dickie Thon	.08	.06	.03
146	Rickey Keeton	.06	.05	.02		236	Denny Walling	.06	.05	.02
147	Randy Lerch	.06	.05	.02		237	Gary Woods	.06	.05	.02
148	Paul Molitor	.20	.15	.08		238	Luis Aguayo(FC)	.10	.08	.04
149	Don Money	.06	.05	.02		239	Ramon Aviles	.06	.05	.02
150	Charlie Moore	.06	.05	.02		240	Bob Boone	.10	.08	.04

	MT	NR MT	EX			MT	NR MT	EX
241 Larry Bowa	.15	.11	.06	332 Jim Sundberg	.08	.06	.03
242 Warren Brusstar	.06	.05	.02	333 Mark Wagner	.06	.05	.02
243 Steve Carlton	1.00	.70	.40	334 Bump Wills	.06	.05	.02
244 Larry Christenson	.06	.05	.02	335 Bill Almon	.06	.05	.02
245 Dick Davis	.06	.05	.02	336 Harold Baines	.30	.25	.12
246 Greg Gross	.06	.05	.02	337 Ross Baumgarten	.06	.05	.02
247 Sparky Lyle	.10	.08	.04	338 Tony Bernazard	.06	.05	.02
248 Garry Maddox	.10	.08	.04	339 Britt Burns	.06	.05	.02
249 Gary Matthews	.10	.08	.04	340 Richard Dotson	.10	.08	.04
250 Bake McBride	.06	.05	.02	341 Jim Essian	.06	.05	.02
251 Tug McGraw	.12	.09	.05	342 Ed Farmer	.06	.05	.02
252 Keith Moreland	.10	.08	.04	343 Carlton Fisk	1.50	1.25	.60
253 Dickie Noles	.06	.05	.02	344 Kevin Hickey	.06	.05	.02
254 Mike Proly	.06	.05	.02	345 Lamarr Hoyt (LaMarr)	.06	.05	.02
255 Ron Reed	.06	.05	.02	346 Lamar Johnson	.06	.05	.02
256 Pete Rose	1.00	.70	.40	347 Jerry Koosman	.10	.08	.04
257 Dick Ruthven	.06	.05	.02	348 Rusty Kuntz	.06	.05	.02
258 Mike Schmidt	2.00	1.50	.80	349 Dennis Lamp	.06	.05	.02
259 Lonnie Smith	.08	.06	.03	350 Ron LeFlore	.08	.06	.03
260 Manny Trillo	.08	.06	.03	351 Chet Lemon	.08	.06	.03
261 Del Unser	.06	.05	.02	352 Greg Luzinski	.15	.11	.06
262 George Vukovich	.06	.05	.02	353 Bob Molinaro	.06	.05	.02
263 Tom Brookens	.06	.05	.02	354 Jim Morrison	.06	.05	.02
264 George Cappuzzello	.06	.05	.02	355 Wayne Nordhagen	.06	.05	.02
265 Marty Castillo	.06	.05	.02	356 Greg Pryor	.06	.05	.02
266 Al Cowens	.06	.05	.02	357 Mike Squires	.06	.05	.02
267 Kirk Gibson	.70	.50	.30	358 Steve Trout	.06	.05	.02
268 Richie Hebner	.06	.05	.02	359 Alan Bannister	.06	.05	.02
269 Ron Jackson	.06	.05	.02	360 Len Barker	.08	.06	.03
270 Lynn Jones	.06	.05	.02	361 Bert Blyleven	.12	.09	.05
271 Steve Kemp	.08	.06	.03	362 Joe Charboneau	.08	.06	.03
272 Rick Leach(FC)	.12	.09	.05	363 John Denny	.06	.05	.02
273 Aurelio Lopez	.06	.05	.02	364 Bo Diaz	.08	.06	.03
274 Jack Morris	.30	.25	.12	365 Miguel Dilone	.06	.05	.02
275 Kevin Saucier	.06	.05	.02	366 Jerry Dybzinski	.06	.05	.02
276 Lance Parrish	.35	.25	.14	367 Wayne Garland	.06	.05	.02
277 Rick Peters	.06	.05	.02	368 Mike Hargrove	.06	.05	.02
278 Dan Petry	.08	.06	.03	369 Toby Harrah	.08	.06	.03
279 David Rozema	.06	.05	.02	370 Ron Hassey	.06	.05	.02
280 Stan Papi	.06	.05	.02	371 Von Hayes(FC)	1.00	.70	.40
281 Dan Schatzeder	.06	.05	.02	372 Pat Kelly	.06	.05	.02
282 Champ Summers	.06	.05	.02	373 Duane Kuiper	.06	.05	.02
283 Alan Trammell	.40	.30	.15	374 Rick Manning	.06	.05	.02
284 Lou Whitaker	.40	.30	.15	375 Sid Monge	.06	.05	.02
285 Milt Wilcox	.06	.05	.02	376 Jorge Orta	.06	.05	.02
286 John Wockenfuss	.06	.05	.02	377 Dave Rosello	.06	.05	.02
287 Gary Allenson	.06	.05	.02	378 Dan Spillner	.06	.05	.02
288 Tom Burgmeier	.06	.05	.02	379 Mike Stanton	.06	.05	.02
289 Bill Campbell	.06	.05	.02	380 Andre Thornton	.10	.08	.04
290 Mark Clear	.06	.05	.02	381 Tom Veryzer	.06	.05	.02
291 Steve Crawford	.06	.05	.02	382 Rick Waits	.06	.05	.02
292 Dennis Eckersley	1.50	1.25	.60	383 Doyle Alexander	.10	.08	.04
293 Dwight Evans	.15	.11	.06	384 Vida Blue	.12	.09	.05
294 Rich Gedman(FC)	.25	.20	.10	385 Fred Breining	.06	.05	.02
295 Garry Hancock	.06	.05	.02	386 Enos Cabell	.06	.05	.02
296 Glenn Hoffman	.06	.05	.02	387 Jack Clark	.25	.20	.10
297 Bruce Hurst(FC)	.30	.25	.12	388 Darrell Evans	.15	.11	.06
298 Carney Lansford	.08	.06	.03	389 Tom Griffin	.06	.05	.02
299 Rick Miller	.06	.05	.02	390 Larry Herndon	.08	.06	.03
300 Reid Nichols	.06	.05	.02	391 Al Holland	.06	.05	.02
301 Bob Ojeda(FC)	.50	.40	.20	392 Gary Lavelle	.06	.05	.02
302 Tony Perez	.20	.15	.08	393 Johnnie LeMaster	.06	.05	.02
303 Chuck Rainey	.06	.05	.02	394 Jerry Martin	.06	.05	.02
304 Jerry Remy	.06	.05	.02	395 Milt May	.06	.05	.02
305 Jim Rice	.40	.30	.15	396 Greg Minton	.06	.05	.02
306 Joe Rudi	.10	.08	.04	397 Joe Morgan	.50	.40	.20
307 Bob Stanley	.06	.05	.02	398 Joe Pettini	.06	.05	.02
308 Dave Stapleton	.06	.05	.02	399 Alan Ripley	.06	.05	.02
309 Frank Tanana	.10	.08	.04	400 Billy Smith	.06	.05	.02
310 Mike Torrez	.08	.06	.03	401 Rennie Stennett	.06	.05	.02
311 John Tudor(FC)	.25	.20	.10	402 Ed Whitson	.06	.05	.02
312 Carl Yastrzemski	1.00	.70	.40	403 Jim Wohlford	.06	.05	.02
313 Buddy Bell	.12	.09	.05	404 Willie Aikens	.06	.05	.02
314 Steve Comer	.06	.05	.02	405 George Brett	2.00	1.50	.80
315 Danny Darwin	.06	.05	.02	406 Ken Brett	.08	.06	.03
316 John Ellis	.06	.05	.02	407 Dave Chalk	.06	.05	.02
317 John Grubb	.06	.05	.02	408 Rich Gale	.06	.05	.02
318 Rick Honeycutt	.06	.05	.02	409 Cesar Geronimo	.06	.05	.02
319 Charlie Hough	.10	.08	.04	410 Larry Gura	.06	.05	.02
320 Ferguson Jenkins	.15	.11	.06	411 Clint Hurdle	.06	.05	.02
321 John Henry Johnson	.06	.05	.02	412 Mike Jones	.06	.05	.02
322 Jim Kern	.06	.05	.02	413 Dennis Leonard	.08	.06	.03
323 Jon Matlack	.08	.06	.03	414 Renie Martin	.06	.05	.02
324 Doc Medich	.06	.05	.02	415 Lee May	.08	.06	.03
325 Mario Mendoza	.06	.05	.02	416 Hal McRae	.12	.09	.05
326 Al Oliver	.15	.11	.06	417 Darryl Motley	.06	.05	.02
327 Pat Putnam	.06	.05	.02	418 Rance Mulliniks	.06	.05	.02
328 Mickey Rivers	.08	.06	.03	419 Amos Otis	.08	.06	.03
329 Leon Roberts	.06	.05	.02	420 Ken Phelps(FC)	.10	.08	.04
330 Billy Sample	.06	.05	.02	421 Jamie Quirk	.06	.05	.02
331 Bill Stein	.06	.05	.02	422 Dan Quisenberry	.15	.11	.06

		MT	NR MT	EX
423	Paul Splittorff	.06	.05	.02
424	U.L. Washington	.06	.05	.02
425	John Wathan	.08	.06	.03
426	Frank White	.10	.08	.04
427	Willie Wilson	.15	.11	.06
428	Brian Asselstine	.06	.05	.02
429	Bruce Benedict	.06	.05	.02
430	Tom Boggs	.06	.05	.02
431	Larry Bradford	.06	.05	.02
432	Rick Camp	.06	.05	.02
433	Chris Chambliss	.08	.06	.03
434	Gene Garber	.06	.05	.02
435	Preston Hanna	.06	.05	.02
436	Bob Horner	.12	.09	.05
437	Glenn Hubbard	.08	.06	.03
438a	Al Hrabosky (All Hrabosky, 5'1" on back)	20.00	15.00	8.00
438b	Al Hrabosky (Al Hrabosky, 5'1" on back)	1.25	.90	.50
438c	Al Hrabosky (Al Hrabosky, 5'10" on back)	.35	.25	.14
439	Rufino Linares	.06	.05	.02
440	*Rick Mahler*(FC)	.25	.20	.10
441	Ed Miller	.06	.05	.02
442	John Montefusco	.08	.06	.03
443	Dale Murphy	.90	.70	.35
444	Phil Niekro	.30	.25	.12
445	Gaylord Perry	.40	.30	.15
446	Biff Pocoroba	.06	.05	.02
447	Rafael Ramirez	.08	.06	.03
448	Jerry Royster	.06	.05	.02
449	Claudell Washington	.08	.06	.03
450	Don Aase	.06	.05	.02
451	Don Baylor	.12	.09	.05
452	Juan Beniquez	.06	.05	.02
453	Rick Burleson	.08	.06	.03
454	Bert Campaneris	.10	.08	.04
455	Rod Carew	1.00	.70	.40
456	Bob Clark	.06	.05	.02
457	Brian Downing	.10	.08	.04
458	Dan Ford	.06	.05	.02
459	Ken Forsch	.06	.05	.02
460	Dave Frost	.06	.05	.02
461	Bobby Grich	.10	.08	.04
462	Larry Harlow	.06	.05	.02
463	John Harris	.06	.05	.02
464	Andy Hassler	.06	.05	.02
465	Butch Hobson	.06	.05	.02
466	Jesse Jefferson	.06	.05	.02
467	Bruce Kison	.06	.05	.02
468	Fred Lynn	.20	.15	.08
469	Angel Moreno	.06	.05	.02
470	Ed Ott	.06	.05	.02
471	Fred Patek	.06	.05	.02
472	Steve Renko	.06	.05	.02
473	*Mike Witt*(FC)	.35	.25	.12
474	Geoff Zahn	.06	.05	.02
475	Gary Alexander	.06	.05	.02
476	Dale Berra	.06	.05	.02
477	Kurt Bevacqua	.06	.05	.02
478	Jim Bibby	.06	.05	.02
479	John Candelaria	.10	.08	.04
480	Victor Cruz	.06	.05	.02
481	Mike Easler	.08	.06	.03
482	Tim Foli	.06	.05	.02
483	Lee Lacy	.06	.05	.02
484	Vance Law(FC)	.12	.09	.05
485	Bill Madlock	.12	.09	.05
486	Willie Montanez	.06	.05	.02
487	Omar Moreno	.06	.05	.02
488	Steve Nicosia	.06	.05	.02
489	Dave Parker	.30	.25	.12
490	Tony Pena(FC)	.25	.20	.10
491	Pascual Perez(FC)	.15	.11	.06
492	*Johnny Ray*(FC)	.30	.25	.12
493	Rick Rhoden	.10	.08	.04
494	Bill Robinson	.06	.05	.02
495	Don Robinson	.08	.06	.03
496	Enrique Romo	.06	.05	.02
497	Rod Scurry	.06	.05	.02
498	Eddie Solomon	.06	.05	.02
499	Willie Stargell	.40	.30	.15
500	Kent Tekulve	.08	.06	.03
501	Jason Thompson	.06	.05	.02
502	Glenn Abbott	.06	.05	.02
503	Jim Anderson	.06	.05	.02
504	Floyd Bannister	.10	.08	.04
505	Bruce Bochte	.06	.05	.02
506	Jeff Burroughs	.08	.06	.03
507	Bryan Clark	.06	.05	.02
508	Ken Clay	.06	.05	.02

		MT	NR MT	EX
509	Julio Cruz	.06	.05	.02
510	Dick Drago	.06	.05	.02
511	Gary Gray	.06	.05	.02
512	Dan Meyer	.06	.05	.02
513	Jerry Narron	.06	.05	.02
514	Tom Paciorek	.06	.05	.02
515	Casey Parsons	.06	.05	.02
516	Lenny Randle	.06	.05	.02
517	Shane Rawley	.10	.08	.04
518	Joe Simpson	.06	.05	.02
519	Richie Zisk	.08	.06	.03
520	Neil Allen	.06	.05	.02
521	Bob Bailor	.06	.05	.02
522	Hubie Brooks(FC)	.50	.40	.20
523	Mike Cubbage	.06	.05	.02
524	Pete Falcone	.06	.05	.02
525	Doug Flynn	.06	.05	.02
526	Tom Hausman	.06	.05	.02
527	Ron Hodges	.06	.05	.02
528	Randy Jones	.08	.06	.03
529	Mike Jorgensen	.06	.05	.02
530	Dave Kingman	.15	.11	.06
531	Ed Lynch	.06	.05	.02
532	Mike Marshall	.10	.08	.04
533	Lee Mazzilli	.08	.06	.03
534	Dyar Miller	.06	.05	.02
535	Mike Scott(FC)	.20	.15	.08
536	Rusty Staub	.10	.08	.04
537	John Stearns	.06	.05	.02
538	Craig Swan	.06	.05	.02
539	Frank Taveras	.06	.05	.02
540	Alex Trevino	.06	.05	.02
541	Ellis Valentine	.06	.05	.02
542	Mookie Wilson(FC)	.15	.11	.06
543	Joel Youngblood	.06	.05	.02
544	Pat Zachry	.06	.05	.02
545	Glenn Adams	.06	.05	.02
546	Fernando Arroyo	.06	.05	.02
547	John Verhoeven	.06	.05	.02
548	Sal Butera	.06	.05	.02
549	John Castino	.06	.05	.02
550	Don Cooper	.06	.05	.02
551	Doug Corbett	.06	.05	.02
552	Dave Engle	.06	.05	.02
553	Roger Erickson	.06	.05	.02
554	Danny Goodwin	.06	.05	.02
555a	Darrell Jackson (black cap)	1.00	.70	.40
555b	Darrell Jackson (red cap with emblem)	.10	.08	.04
555c	Darrell Jackson (red cap, no emblem)	.25	.20	.10
556	Pete Mackanin	.06	.05	.02
557	Jack O'Connor	.06	.05	.02
558	Hosken Powell	.06	.05	.02
559	Pete Redfern	.06	.05	.02
560	Roy Smalley	.06	.05	.02
561	Chuck Baker	.06	.05	.02
562	Gary Ward	.08	.06	.03
563	Rob Wilfong	.06	.05	.02
564	Al Williams	.06	.05	.02
565	Butch Wynegar	.06	.05	.02
566	Randy Bass	.06	.05	.02
567	Juan Bonilla	.06	.05	.02
568	Danny Boone	.06	.05	.02
569	John Curtis	.06	.05	.02
570	Juan Eichelberger	.06	.05	.02
571	Barry Evans	.06	.05	.02
572	Tim Flannery	.06	.05	.02
573	Ruppert Jones	.06	.05	.02
574	Terry Kennedy	.08	.06	.03
575	Joe Lefebvre	.06	.05	.02
576a	John Littlefield (pitching lefty)	200.00	150.00	80.00
576b	John Littlefield (pitching righty)	.08	.06	.03
577	Gary Lucas	.06	.05	.02
578	Steve Mura	.06	.05	.02
579	Broderick Perkins	.06	.05	.02
580	Gene Richards	.06	.05	.02
581	Luis Salazar	.06	.05	.02
582	Ozzie Smith	1.00	.70	.40
583	John Urrea	.06	.05	.02
584	Chris Welsh	.06	.05	.02
585	Rick Wise	.08	.06	.03
586	Doug Bird	.06	.05	.02
587	Tim Blackwell	.06	.05	.02
588	Bobby Bonds	.10	.08	.04
589	Bill Buckner	.12	.09	.05
590	Bill Caudill	.06	.05	.02
591	Hector Cruz	.06	.05	.02
592	*Jody Davis*(FC)	.10	.08	.04
593	Ivan DeJesus	.06	.05	.02
594	Steve Dillard	.06	.05	.02

		MT	NR MT	EX
595	Leon Durham	.08	.06	.03
596	Rawly Eastwick	.06	.05	.02
597	Steve Henderson	.06	.05	.02
598	Mike Krukow	.08	.06	.03
599	Mike Lum	.06	.05	.02
600	Randy Martz	.06	.05	.02
601	Jerry Morales	.06	.05	.02
602	Ken Reitz	.06	.05	.02
603a	*Lee Smith* (Cubs logo reversed on back)(FC)	8.00	6.00	3.25
603b	*Lee Smith* (Cubs logo correct)(FC)	5.00	3.75	2.00
604	Dick Tidrow	.06	.05	.02
605	Jim Tracy	.06	.05	.02
606	Mike Tyson	.06	.05	.02
607	Ty Waller	.06	.05	.02
608	Danny Ainge	.25	.20	.10
609	*Jorge Bell*(FC)	7.50	5.65	3.00
610	Mark Bomback	.06	.05	.02
611	Barry Bonnell	.06	.05	.02
612	Jim Clancy	.08	.06	.03
613	Damaso Garcia	.06	.05	.02
614	Jerry Garvin	.06	.05	.02
615	Alfredo Griffin	.08	.06	.03
616	Garth Iorg	.06	.05	.02
617	Luis Leal	.06	.05	.02
618	Ken Macha	.06	.05	.02
619	John Mayberry	.08	.06	.03
620	Joey McLaughlin	.06	.05	.02
621	Lloyd Moseby	.12	.09	.05
622	Dave Stieb	.12	.09	.05
623	Jackson Todd	.06	.05	.02
624	Willie Upshaw(FC)	.15	.11	.06
625	Otto Velez	.06	.05	.02
626	Ernie Whitt	.08	.06	.03
627	Al Woods	.06	.05	.02
628	1981 All-Star Game	.08	.06	.03
629	All-Star Infielders (Bucky Dent, Frank White)	.10	.08	.04
630	Big Red Machine (Dave Concepcion, Dan Driessen, George Foster)	.15	.11	.06
631	Top N.L. Relief Pitcher (Bruce Sutter)	.15	.11	.06
632	Steve & Carlton (Steve Carlton, Carlton Fisk)	.25	.20	.10
633	3000th Game, May 25, 1981 (Carl Yastrzemski)	.35	.25	.14
634	Dynamic Duo (Johnny Bench, Tom Seaver)	.30	.25	.12
635	West Meets East (Gary Carter, Fernando Valenzuela)	.30	.25	.12
636a	N.L. Strikeout King (Fernando Valenzuela) ("...led he National League...")	1.00	.70	.40
636b	N.L. Strikeout King (Fernando Valenzuela) ("...led the National League...")	.50	.40	.20
637	1981 Home Run King (Mike Schmidt)	.40	.30	.15
638	N.L. All-Stars (Gary Carter, Dave Parker)	.25	.20	.10
639	Perfect Game! (Len Barker, Bo Diaz)	.08	.06	.03
640	Pete & Re-Pete (Pete Rose, Pete Rose, Jr.)	2.50	2.00	1.00
641	Phillies' Finest (Steve Carlton, Mike Schmidt, Lonnie Smith)	.50	.40	.20
642	Red Sox Reunion (Dwight Evans, Fred Lynn)	.15	.11	.06
643	1981 Most Hits, Most Runs (Rickey Henderson)	3.00	2.25	1.25
644	Most Saves 1981 A.L. (Rollie Fingers)	.15	.11	.06
645	Most 1981 Wins (Tom Seaver)	.25	.20	.10
646a	Yankee Powerhouse (Reggie Jackson, Dave Winfield) (comma after "outfielder" on back)	1.25	.90	.50
646b	Yankee Powerhouse (Reggie Jackson, Dave Winfield) (no comma after "oufielder")	.60	.45	.25
647	Checklist 1-56	.06	.05	.02
648	Checklist 57-109	.06	.05	.02
649	Checklist 110-156	.06	.05	.02
650	Checklist 157-211	.06	.05	.02
651	Checklist 212-262	.06	.05	.02
652	Checklist 263-312	.06	.05	.02
653	Checklist 313-358	.06	.05	.02
654	Checklist 359-403	.06	.05	.02
655	Checklist 404-449	.06	.05	.02
656	Checklist 450-501	.06	.05	.02
657	Checklist 502-544	.06	.05	.02
658	Checklist 545-585	.06	.05	.02
659	Checklist 586-627	.06	.05	.02

		MT	NR MT	EX
660	Checklist 628-646	.06	.05	.02

1983 Fleer

Ron Guidry PITCHER

The 1983 Fleer set features color photos set inside a light brown border. The cards are the standard size of 2-1/2" by 3-1/2". A team logo is located at the card bottom and the word "Fleer" is found at the top. The card backs are designed on a vertical format and include a small black and white photo of the player along with biographical and statistical information. The reverses are done in two shades of brown on white stock. The set was issued with team logo stickers.

		MT	NR MT	EX
Complete Set:		125.00	90.00	50.00
Common Player:		.06	.05	.02
1	Joaquin Andujar	.08	.06	.03
2	Doug Bair	.06	.05	.02
3	Steve Braun	.06	.05	.02
4	Glenn Brummer	.06	.05	.02
5	Bob Forsch	.08	.06	.03
6	David Green	.06	.05	.02
7	George Hendrick	.08	.06	.03
8	Keith Hernandez	.40	.30	.15
9	Tom Herr	.10	.08	.04
10	Dane Iorg	.06	.05	.02
11	Jim Kaat	.15	.11	.06
12	Jeff Lahti	.06	.05	.02
13	Tito Landrum	.06	.05	.02
14	*Dave LaPoint*(FC)	.30	.25	.12
15	*Willie McGee*(FC)	3.00	2.25	1.25
16	Steve Mura	.06	.05	.02
17	Ken Oberkfell	.06	.05	.02
18	Darrell Porter	.08	.06	.03
19	Mike Ramsey	.06	.05	.02
20	Gene Roof	.06	.05	.02
21	Lonnie Smith	.08	.06	.03
22	Ozzie Smith	1.25	.90	.50
23	John Stuper	.06	.05	.02
24	Bruce Sutter	.15	.11	.06
25	Gene Tenace	.08	.06	.03
26	Jerry Augustine	.06	.05	.02
27	Dwight Bernard	.06	.05	.02
28	Mark Brouhard	.06	.05	.02
29	Mike Caldwell	.06	.05	.02
30	Cecil Cooper	.15	.11	.06
31	Jamie Easterly	.06	.05	.02
32	Marshall Edwards	.06	.05	.02
33	Rollie Fingers	.60	.45	.25
34	Jim Gantner	.08	.06	.03
35	Moose Haas	.06	.05	.02
36	Roy Howell	.06	.05	.02
37	Peter Ladd	.06	.05	.02
38	Bob McClure	.06	.05	.02
39	Doc Medich	.06	.05	.02
40	Paul Molitor	.20	.15	.08
41	Don Money	.06	.05	.02
42	Charlie Moore	.06	.05	.02
43	Ben Oglivie	.08	.06	.03
44	Ed Romero	.06	.05	.02
45	Ted Simmons	.12	.09	.05
46	Jim Slaton	.06	.05	.02
47	Don Sutton	.30	.25	.12
48	Gorman Thomas	.10	.08	.04

#	Player	MT	NR MT	EX
49	Pete Vuckovich	.08	.06	.03
50	Ned Yost	.06	.05	.02
51	Robin Yount	3.00	2.25	1.25
52	Benny Ayala	.06	.05	.02
53	Bob Bonner	.06	.05	.02
54	Al Bumbry	.08	.06	.03
55	Terry Crowley	.06	.05	.02
56	Storm Davis(FC)	.30	.25	.12
57	Rich Dauer	.06	.05	.02
58	Rick Dempsey	.08	.06	.03
59	Jim Dwyer	.06	.05	.02
60	Mike Flanagan	.10	.08	.04
61	Dan Ford	.06	.05	.02
62	Glenn Gulliver	.06	.05	.02
63	John Lowenstein	.06	.05	.02
64	Dennis Martinez	.08	.06	.03
65	Tippy Martinez	.06	.05	.02
66	Scott McGregor	.08	.06	.03
67	Eddie Murray	1.00	.70	.40
68	Joe Nolan	.06	.05	.02
69	Jim Palmer	.50	.40	.20
70	Cal Ripken, Jr.	18.00	13.50	7.25
71	Gary Roenicke	.06	.05	.02
72	Lenn Sakata	.06	.05	.02
73	Ken Singleton	.10	.08	.04
74	Sammy Stewart	.06	.05	.02
75	Tim Stoddard	.06	.05	.02
76	Don Aase	.06	.05	.02
77	Don Baylor	.12	.09	.05
78	Juan Beniquez	.06	.05	.02
79	Bob Boone	.10	.08	.04
80	Rick Burleson	.08	.06	.03
81	Rod Carew	1.00	.70	.40
82	Bobby Clark	.06	.05	.02
83	Doug Corbett	.06	.05	.02
84	John Curtis	.06	.05	.02
85	Doug DeCinces	.10	.08	.04
86	Brian Downing	.10	.08	.04
87	Joe Ferguson	.06	.05	.02
88	Tim Foli	.06	.05	.02
89	Ken Forsch	.06	.05	.02
90	Dave Goltz	.08	.06	.03
91	Bobby Grich	.10	.08	.04
92	Andy Hassler	.06	.05	.02
93	Reggie Jackson	.50	.40	.20
94	Ron Jackson	.06	.05	.02
95	Tommy John	.20	.15	.08
96	Bruce Kison	.06	.05	.02
97	Fred Lynn	.20	.15	.08
98	Ed Ott	.06	.05	.02
99	Steve Renko	.06	.05	.02
100	Luis Sanchez	.06	.05	.02
101	Rob Wilfong	.06	.05	.02
102	Mike Witt	.15	.11	.06
103	Geoff Zahn	.06	.05	.02
104	Willie Aikens	.06	.05	.02
105	Mike Armstrong	.06	.05	.02
106	Vida Blue	.12	.09	.05
107	Bud Black(FC)	.50	.40	.20
108	George Brett	3.00	2.25	1.25
109	Bill Castro	.06	.05	.02
110	Onix Concepcion	.06	.05	.02
111	Dave Frost	.06	.05	.02
112	Cesar Geronimo	.06	.05	.02
113	Larry Gura	.06	.05	.02
114	Steve Hammond	.06	.05	.02
115	Don Hood	.06	.05	.02
116	Dennis Leonard	.08	.06	.03
117	Jerry Martin	.06	.05	.02
118	Lee May	.08	.06	.03
119	Hal McRae	.12	.09	.05
120	Amos Otis	.08	.06	.03
121	Greg Pryor	.06	.05	.02
122	Dan Quisenberry	.15	.11	.06
123	Don Slaught(FC)	.20	.15	.08
124	Paul Splittorff	.06	.05	.02
125	U.L. Washington	.06	.05	.02
126	John Wathan	.08	.06	.03
127	Frank White	.10	.08	.04
128	Willie Wilson	.15	.11	.06
129	Steve Bedrosian(FC)	.25	.20	.10
130	Bruce Benedict	.06	.05	.02
131	Tommy Boggs	.06	.05	.02
132	Brett Butler(FC)	.15	.11	.06
133	Rick Camp	.06	.05	.02
134	Chris Chambliss	.08	.06	.03
135	Ken Dayley(FC)	.10	.08	.04
136	Gene Garber	.06	.05	.02
137	Terry Harper	.06	.05	.02
138	Bob Horner	.12	.09	.05
139	Glenn Hubbard	.08	.06	.03
140	Rufino Linares	.06	.05	.02
141	Rick Mahler	.08	.06	.03
142	Dale Murphy	.90	.70	.35
143	Phil Niekro	.30	.25	.12
144	Pascual Perez	.08	.06	.03
145	Biff Pocoroba	.06	.05	.02
146	Rafael Ramirez	.06	.05	.02
147	Jerry Royster	.06	.05	.02
148	Ken Smith	.06	.05	.02
149	Bob Walk	.08	.06	.03
150	Claudell Washington	.08	.06	.03
151	Bob Watson	.08	.06	.03
152	Larry Whisenton	.06	.05	.02
153	Porfirio Altamirano	.06	.05	.02
154	Marty Bystrom	.06	.05	.02
155	Steve Carlton	.50	.40	.20
156	Larry Christenson	.06	.05	.02
157	Ivan DeJesus	.06	.05	.02
158	John Denny	.06	.05	.02
159	Bob Dernier(FC)	.10	.08	.04
160	Bo Diaz	.08	.06	.03
161	Ed Farmer	.06	.05	.02
162	Greg Gross	.06	.05	.02
163	Mike Krukow	.08	.06	.03
164	Garry Maddox	.10	.08	.04
165	Gary Matthews	.10	.08	.04
166	Tug McGraw	.12	.09	.05
167	Bob Molinaro	.06	.05	.02
168	Sid Monge	.06	.05	.02
169	Ron Reed	.06	.05	.02
170	Bill Robinson	.06	.05	.02
171	Pete Rose	1.00	.70	.40
172	Dick Ruthven	.06	.05	.02
173	Mike Schmidt	1.50	1.25	.60
174	Manny Trillo	.08	.06	.03
175	Ozzie Virgil(FC)	.10	.08	.04
176	George Vukovich	.06	.05	.02
177	Gary Allenson	.06	.05	.02
178	Luis Aponte	.06	.05	.02
179	Wade Boggs(FC)	25.00	18.00	10.00
180	Tom Burgmeier	.06	.05	.02
181	Mark Clear	.06	.05	.02
182	Dennis Eckersley	.12	.09	.05
183	Dwight Evans	.15	.11	.06
184	Rich Gedman	.08	.06	.03
185	Glenn Hoffman	.06	.05	.02
186	Bruce Hurst	.10	.08	.04
187	Carney Lansford	.08	.06	.03
188	Rick Miller	.06	.05	.02
189	Reid Nichols	.06	.05	.02
190	Bob Ojeda	.12	.09	.05
191	Tony Perez	.20	.15	.08
192	Chuck Rainey	.06	.05	.02
193	Jerry Remy	.06	.05	.02
194	Jim Rice	.40	.30	.15
195	Bob Stanley	.06	.05	.02
196	Dave Stapleton	.06	.05	.02
197	Mike Torrez	.08	.06	.03
198	John Tudor	.10	.08	.04
199	Julio Valdez	.06	.05	.02
200	Carl Yastrzemski	1.00	.70	.40
201	Dusty Baker	.10	.08	.04
202	Joe Beckwith	.06	.05	.02
203	Greg Brock(FC)	.35	.25	.14
204	Ron Cey	.12	.09	.05
205	Terry Forster	.08	.06	.03
206	Steve Garvey	.40	.30	.15
207	Pedro Guerrero	.25	.20	.10
208	Burt Hooton	.08	.06	.03
209	Steve Howe	.08	.06	.03
210	Ken Landreaux	.06	.05	.02
211	Mike Marshall	.20	.15	.08
212	Candy Maldonado(FC)	.80	.60	.30
213	Rick Monday	.10	.08	.04
214	Tom Niedenfuer	.10	.08	.04
215	Jorge Orta	.06	.05	.02
216	Jerry Reuss	.10	.08	.04
217	Ron Roenicke	.06	.05	.02
218	Vicente Romo	.06	.05	.02
219	Bill Russell	.08	.06	.03
220	Steve Sax	.30	.25	.12
221	Mike Scioscia	.08	.06	.03
222	Dave Stewart	.70	.50	.30
223	Derrel Thomas	.06	.05	.02
224	Fernando Valenzuela	.30	.25	.12
225	Bob Welch	.12	.09	.05
226	Ricky Wright	.06	.05	.02
227	Steve Yeager	.06	.05	.02
228	Bill Almon	.06	.05	.02
229	Harold Baines	.15	.11	.06
230	Salome Barojas	.06	.05	.02

		MT	NR MT	EX
231	Tony Bernazard	.06	.05	.02
232	Britt Burns	.06	.05	.02
233	Richard Dotson	.10	.08	.04
234	Ernesto Escarrega	.06	.05	.02
235	Carlton Fisk	1.00	.70	.40
236	Jerry Hairston	.06	.05	.02
237	Kevin Hickey	.06	.05	.02
238	LaMarr Hoyt	.06	.05	.02
239	Steve Kemp	.10	.08	.04
240	Jim Kern	.06	.05	.02
241	Ron Kittle(FC)	.30	.25	.12
242	Jerry Koosman	.10	.08	.04
243	Dennis Lamp	.06	.05	.02
244	Rudy Law	.06	.05	.02
245	Vance Law	.08	.06	.03
246	Ron LeFlore	.08	.06	.03
247	Greg Luzinski	.12	.09	.05
248	Tom Paciorek	.06	.05	.02
249	Aurelio Rodriguez	.08	.06	.03
250	Mike Squires	.06	.05	.02
251	Steve Trout	.06	.05	.02
252	Jim Barr	.06	.05	.02
253	Dave Bergman	.06	.05	.02
254	Fred Breining	.06	.05	.02
255	Bob Brenly(FC)	.08	.06	.03
256	Jack Clark	.25	.20	.10
257	Chili Davis(FC)	.20	.15	.08
258	Darrell Evans	.15	.11	.06
259	Alan Fowlkes	.06	.05	.02
260	Rich Gale	.06	.05	.02
261	Atlee Hammaker(FC)	.12	.09	.05
262	Al Holland	.06	.05	.02
263	Duane Kuiper	.06	.05	.02
264	Bill Laskey	.06	.05	.02
265	Gary Lavelle	.06	.05	.02
266	Johnnie LeMaster	.06	.05	.02
267	Renie Martin	.06	.05	.02
268	Milt May	.06	.05	.02
269	Greg Minton	.06	.05	.02
270	Joe Morgan	.50	.40	.20
271	Tom O'Malley	.06	.05	.02
272	Reggie Smith	.10	.08	.04
273	Guy Sularz	.06	.05	.02
274	Champ Summers	.06	.05	.02
275	Max Venable	.06	.05	.02
276	Jim Wohlford	.06	.05	.02
277	Ray Burris	.06	.05	.02
278	Gary Carter	.35	.25	.14
279	Warren Cromartie	.06	.05	.02
280	Andre Dawson	1.25	.90	.50
281	Terry Francona	.06	.05	.02
282	Doug Flynn	.06	.05	.02
283	Woody Fryman	.08	.06	.03
284	Bill Gullickson	.06	.05	.02
285	Wallace Johnson	.06	.05	.02
286	Charlie Lea	.06	.05	.02
287	Randy Lerch	.06	.05	.02
288	Brad Mills	.06	.05	.02
289	Dan Norman	.06	.05	.02
290	Al Oliver	.15	.11	.06
291	David Palmer	.06	.05	.02
292	Tim Raines	.35	.25	.14
293	Jeff Reardon	.80	.60	.30
294	Steve Rogers	.08	.06	.03
295	Scott Sanderson	.06	.05	.02
296	Dan Schatzeder	.06	.05	.02
297	Bryn Smith	.08	.06	.03
298	Chris Speier	.06	.05	.02
299	Tim Wallach	.20	.15	.08
300	Jerry White	.06	.05	.02
301	Joel Youngblood	.06	.05	.02
302	Ross Baumgarten	.06	.05	.02
303	Dale Berra	.06	.05	.02
304	John Candelaria	.10	.08	.04
305	Dick Davis	.06	.05	.02
306	Mike Easler	.08	.06	.03
307	Richie Hebner	.06	.05	.02
308	Lee Lacy	.06	.05	.02
309	Bill Madlock	.12	.09	.05
310	Larry McWilliams	.06	.05	.02
311	John Milner	.06	.05	.02
312	Omar Moreno	.06	.05	.02
313	Jim Morrison	.06	.05	.02
314	Steve Nicosia	.06	.05	.02
315	Dave Parker	.30	.25	.12
316	Tony Pena	.10	.08	.04
317	Johnny Ray	.12	.09	.05
318	Rick Rhoden	.10	.08	.04
319	Don Robinson	.08	.06	.03
320	Enrique Romo	.06	.05	.02
321	Manny Sarmiento	.06	.05	.02

		MT	NR MT	EX
322	Rod Scurry	.06	.05	.02
323	Jim Smith	.06	.05	.02
324	Willie Stargell	.40	.30	.15
325	Jason Thompson	.06	.05	.02
326	Kent Tekulve	.08	.06	.03
327a	Tom Brookens (narrow (1/4") brown box at bottom on back)	.30	.25	.12
327b	Tom Brookens (wide (1 1/4") brown box at bottom on back)	.08	.06	.03
328	Enos Cabell	.06	.05	.02
329	Kirk Gibson	.40	.30	.15
330	Larry Herndon	.08	.06	.03
331	Mike Ivie	.06	.05	.02
332	Howard Johnson(FC)	7.00	5.25	2.75
333	Lynn Jones	.06	.05	.02
334	Rick Leach	.06	.05	.02
335	Chet Lemon	.08	.06	.03
336	Jack Morris	.80	.60	.30
337	Lance Parrish	.35	.25	.14
338	Larry Pashnick	.06	.05	.02
339	Dan Petry	.08	.06	.03
340	Dave Rozema	.06	.05	.02
341	Dave Rucker	.06	.05	.02
342	Elias Sosa	.06	.05	.02
343	Dave Tobik	.06	.05	.02
344	Alan Trammell	.40	.30	.15
345	Jerry Turner	.06	.05	.02
346	Jerry Ujdur	.06	.05	.02
347	Pat Underwood	.06	.05	.02
348	Lou Whitaker	.40	.30	.15
349	Milt Wilcox	.06	.05	.02
350	Glenn Wilson(FC)	.35	.25	.14
351	John Wockenfuss	.06	.05	.02
352	Kurt Bevacqua	.06	.05	.02
353	Juan Bonilla	.06	.05	.02
354	Floyd Chiffer	.06	.05	.02
355	Luis DeLeon	.06	.05	.02
356	Dave Dravecky(FC)	.60	.45	.25
357	Dave Edwards	.06	.05	.02
358	Juan Eichelberger	.06	.05	.02
359	Tim Flannery	.06	.05	.02
360	Tony Gwynn(FC)	25.00	18.00	10.00
361	Ruppert Jones	.06	.05	.02
362	Terry Kennedy	.08	.06	.03
363	Joe Lefebvre	.06	.05	.02
364	Sixto Lezcano	.06	.05	.02
365	Tim Lollar	.06	.05	.02
366	Gary Lucas	.06	.05	.02
367	John Montefusco	.06	.05	.02
368	Broderick Perkins	.06	.05	.02
369	Joe Pittman	.06	.05	.02
370	Gene Richards	.06	.05	.02
371	Luis Salazar	.06	.05	.02
372	Eric Show(FC)	.30	.25	.12
373	Garry Templeton	.10	.08	.04
374	Chris Welsh	.06	.05	.02
375	Alan Wiggins	.06	.05	.02
376	Rick Cerone	.06	.05	.02
377	Dave Collins	.08	.06	.03
378	Roger Erickson	.06	.05	.02
379	George Frazier	.06	.05	.02
380	Oscar Gamble	.08	.06	.03
381	Goose Gossage	.20	.15	.08
382	Ken Griffey	.12	.09	.05
383	Ron Guidry	.25	.20	.10
384	Dave LaRoche	.06	.05	.02
385	Rudy May	.06	.05	.02
386	John Mayberry	.08	.06	.03
387	Lee Mazzilli	.08	.06	.03
388	Mike Morgan(FC)	.12	.09	.05
389	Jerry Mumphrey	.06	.05	.02
390	Bobby Murcer	.10	.08	.04
391	Graig Nettles	.15	.11	.06
392	Lou Piniella	.12	.09	.05
393	Willie Randolph	.10	.08	.04
394	Shane Rawley	.10	.08	.04
395	Dave Righetti	.25	.20	.10
396	Andre Robertson	.06	.05	.02
397	Roy Smalley	.06	.05	.02
398	Dave Winfield	2.00	1.50	.80
399	Butch Wynegar	.06	.05	.02
400	Chris Bando	.06	.05	.02
401	Alan Bannister	.06	.05	.02
402	Len Barker	.08	.06	.03
403	Tom Brennan	.06	.05	.02
404	Carmelo Castillo(FC)	.12	.09	.05
405	Miguel Dilone	.06	.05	.02
406	Jerry Dybzinski	.06	.05	.02
407	Mike Fischlin	.06	.05	.02
408	Ed Glynn (photo actually Bud Anderson)	.06	.05	.02

		MT	NR MT	EX			MT	NR MT	EX
409	Mike Hargrove	.06	.05	.02	500	Junior Kennedy	.06	.05	.02
410	Toby Harrah	.08	.06	.03	501	Randy Martz	.06	.05	.02
411	Ron Hassey	.06	.05	.02	502	Jerry Morales	.06	.05	.02
412	Von Hayes	.15	.11	.06	503	Keith Moreland	.08	.06	.03
413	Rick Manning	.06	.05	.02	504	Dickie Noles	.06	.05	.02
414	Bake McBride	.06	.05	.02	505	Mike Proly	.06	.05	.02
415	Larry Milbourne	.06	.05	.02	506	Allen Ripley	.06	.05	.02
416	Bill Nahorodny	.06	.05	.02	507	*Ryne Sandberg*(FC)	35.00	27.00	15.00
417	Jack Perconte	.06	.05	.02	508	Lee Smith	2.00	1.50	.80
418	Lary Sorensen	.06	.05	.02	509	Pat Tabler(FC)	.15	.11	.06
419	Dan Spillner	.06	.05	.02	510	Dick Tidrow	.06	.05	.02
420	Rick Sutcliffe	.12	.09	.05	511	Bump Wills	.06	.05	.02
421	Andre Thornton	.10	.08	.04	512	Gary Woods	.06	.05	.02
422	Rick Waits	.06	.05	.02	513	Tony Armas	.10	.08	.04
423	Eddie Whitson	.06	.05	.02	514	Dave Beard	.06	.05	.02
424	Jesse Barfield(FC)	.60	.45	.25	515	Jeff Burroughs	.08	.06	.03
425	Barry Bonnell	.06	.05	.02	516	John D'Acquisto	.06	.05	.02
426	Jim Clancy	.08	.06	.03	517	Wayne Gross	.06	.05	.02
427	Damaso Garcia	.06	.05	.02	518	Mike Heath	.06	.05	.02
428	Jerry Garvin	.06	.05	.02	519	Rickey Henderson	4.00	3.00	1.50
429	Alfredo Griffin	.08	.06	.03	520	Cliff Johnson	.06	.05	.02
430	Garth Iorg	.06	.05	.02	521	Matt Keough	.06	.05	.02
431	Roy Lee Jackson	.06	.05	.02	522	Brian Kingman	.06	.05	.02
432	Luis Leal	.06	.05	.02	523	Rick Langford	.06	.05	.02
433	Buck Martinez	.06	.05	.02	524	Davey Lopes	.10	.08	.04
434	Joey McLaughlin	.06	.05	.02	525	Steve McCatty	.06	.05	.02
435	Lloyd Moseby	.12	.09	.05	526	Dave McKay	.06	.05	.02
436	Rance Mulliniks	.06	.05	.02	527	Dan Meyer	.06	.05	.02
437	Dale Murray	.06	.05	.02	528	Dwayne Murphy	.08	.06	.03
438	Wayne Nordhagen	.06	.05	.02	529	Jeff Newman	.06	.05	.02
439	*Gene Petralli*(FC)	.15	.11	.06	530	Mike Norris	.06	.05	.02
440	Hosken Powell	.06	.05	.02	531	Bob Owchinko	.06	.05	.02
441	Dave Stieb	.12	.09	.05	532	Joe Rudi	.10	.08	.04
442	Willie Upshaw	.08	.06	.03	533	Jimmy Sexton	.06	.05	.02
443	Ernie Whitt	.08	.06	.03	534	Fred Stanley	.06	.05	.02
444	Al Woods	.06	.05	.02	535	Tom Underwood	.06	.05	.02
445	Alan Ashby	.06	.05	.02	536	Neil Allen	.06	.05	.02
446	Jose Cruz	.12	.09	.05	537	Wally Backman	.08	.06	.03
447	Kiko Garcia	.06	.05	.02	538	Bob Bailor	.06	.05	.02
448	Phil Garner	.08	.06	.03	539	Hubie Brooks	.12	.09	.05
449	Danny Heep	.06	.05	.02	540	Carlos Diaz	.06	.05	.02
450	Art Howe	.06	.05	.02	541	Pete Falcone	.06	.05	.02
451	Bob Knepper	.08	.06	.03	542	George Foster	.15	.11	.06
452	Alan Knicely	.06	.05	.02	543	Ron Gardenhire	.06	.05	.02
453	Ray Knight	.10	.08	.04	544	Brian Giles	.06	.05	.02
454	Frank LaCorte	.06	.05	.02	545	Ron Hodges	.06	.05	.02
455	Mike LaCoss	.06	.05	.02	546	Randy Jones	.08	.06	.03
456	Randy Moffitt	.06	.05	.02	547	Mike Jorgensen	.06	.05	.02
457	Joe Niekro	.12	.09	.05	548	Dave Kingman	.15	.11	.06
458	Terry Puhl	.06	.05	.02	549	Ed Lynch	.06	.05	.02
459	Luis Pujols	.06	.05	.02	550	Jesse Orosco(FC)	.15	.11	.06
460	Craig Reynolds	.06	.05	.02	551	Rick Ownbey	.06	.05	.02
461	Bert Roberge	.06	.05	.02	552	*Charlie Puleo*(FC)	.12	.09	.05
462	Vern Ruhle	.06	.05	.02	553	Gary Rajsich	.06	.05	.02
463	Nolan Ryan	6.00	4.50	2.50	554	Mike Scott	.15	.11	.06
464	Joe Sambito	.06	.05	.02	555	Rusty Staub	.10	.08	.04
465	Tony Scott	.06	.05	.02	556	John Stearns	.06	.05	.02
466	Dave Smith	.08	.06	.03	557	Craig Swan	.06	.05	.02
467	Harry Spilman	.06	.05	.02	558	Ellis Valentine	.06	.05	.02
468	Dickie Thon	.08	.06	.03	559	Tom Veryzer	.06	.05	.02
469	Denny Walling	.06	.05	.02	560	Mookie Wilson	.10	.08	.04
470	Larry Andersen	.06	.05	.02	561	Pat Zachry	.06	.05	.02
471	Floyd Bannister	.10	.08	.04	562	Buddy Bell	.12	.09	.05
472	Jim Beattie	.06	.05	.02	563	John Butcher	.06	.05	.02
473	Bruce Bochte	.06	.05	.02	564	Steve Comer	.06	.05	.02
474	Manny Castillo	.06	.05	.02	565	Danny Darwin	.06	.05	.02
475	Bill Caudill	.06	.05	.02	566	Bucky Dent	.10	.08	.04
476	Bryan Clark	.06	.05	.02	567	John Grubb	.06	.05	.02
477	Al Cowens	.06	.05	.02	568	Rick Honeycutt	.06	.05	.02
478	Julio Cruz	.06	.05	.02	569	Dave Hostetler	.06	.05	.02
479	Todd Cruz	.06	.05	.02	570	Charlie Hough	.10	.08	.04
480	Gary Gray	.06	.05	.02	571	Lamar Johnson	.06	.05	.02
481	Dave Henderson(FC)	.20	.15	.08	572	Jon Matlack	.08	.06	.03
482	*Mike Moore*(FC)	1.00	.70	.40	573	Paul Mirabella	.06	.05	.02
483	Gaylord Perry	.40	.30	.15	574	Larry Parrish	.10	.08	.04
484	Dave Revering	.06	.05	.02	575	Mike Richardt	.06	.05	.02
485	Joe Simpson	.06	.05	.02	576	Mickey Rivers	.08	.06	.03
486	Mike Stanton	.06	.05	.02	577	Billy Sample	.06	.05	.02
487	Rick Sweet	.06	.05	.02	578	*Dave Schmidt*(FC)	.10	.08	.04
488	*Ed Vande Berg*(FC)	.10	.08	.04	579	Bill Stein	.06	.05	.02
489	Richie Zisk	.08	.06	.03	580	Jim Sundberg	.08	.06	.03
490	Doug Bird	.06	.05	.02	581	Frank Tanana	.10	.08	.04
491	Larry Bowa	.12	.09	.05	582	Mark Wagner	.06	.05	.02
492	Bill Buckner	.12	.09	.05	583	George Wright	.06	.05	.02
493	Bill Campbell	.06	.05	.02	584	Johnny Bench	1.00	.70	.40
494	Jody Davis	.10	.08	.04	585	Bruce Berenyi	.06	.05	.02
495	Leon Durham	.08	.06	.03	586	Larry Biittner	.06	.05	.02
496	Steve Henderson	.06	.05	.02	587	Cesar Cedeno	.12	.09	.05
497	Willie Hernandez	.08	.06	.03	588	Dave Concepcion	.12	.09	.05
498	Ferguson Jenkins	.15	.11	.06	589	Dan Driessen	.08	.06	.03
499	Jay Johnstone	.08	.06	.03	590	Greg Harris(FC)	.08	.06	.03

		MT	NR MT	EX
591	Ben Hayes	.06	.05	.02
592	Paul Householder	.06	.05	.02
593	Tom Hume	.06	.05	.02
594	Wayne Krenchicki	.06	.05	.02
595	Rafael Landestoy	.06	.05	.02
596	Charlie Leibrandt	.08	.06	.03
597	*Eddie Milner*(FC)	.10	.08	.04
598	Ron Oester	.06	.05	.02
599	Frank Pastore	.06	.05	.02
600	Joe Price	.06	.05	.02
601	Tom Seaver	1.00	.70	.40
602	Bob Shirley	.06	.05	.02
603	Mario Soto	.08	.06	.03
604	Alex Trevino	.06	.05	.02
605	Mike Vail	.06	.05	.02
606	Duane Walker	.06	.05	.02
607	Tom Brunansky(FC)	.25	.20	.10
608	Bobby Castillo	.06	.05	.02
609	John Castino	.06	.05	.02
610	Ron Davis	.06	.05	.02
611	Lenny Faedo	.06	.05	.02
612	Terry Felton	.06	.05	.02
613	*Gary Gaetti*(FC)	.80	.60	.30
614	Mickey Hatcher	.08	.06	.03
615	Brad Havens	.06	.05	.02
616	Kent Hrbek(FC)	1.00	.70	.40
617	Randy Johnson	.06	.05	.02
618	Tim Laudner(FC)	.12	.09	.05
619	Jeff Little	.06	.05	.02
620	Bob Mitchell	.06	.05	.02
621	Jack O'Connor	.06	.05	.02
622	John Pacella	.06	.05	.02
623	Pete Redfern	.06	.05	.02
624	Jesus Vega	.06	.05	.02
625	*Frank Viola*(FC)	4.00	3.00	1.50
626	Ron Washington	.06	.05	.02
627	Gary Ward	.08	.06	.03
628	Al Williams	.06	.05	.02
629	Red Sox All-Stars (Mark Clear, Dennis Eckersley, Carl Yastrzemski) .25			.20	.10
630	300 Career Wins (Terry Bulling, Gaylord Perry) .15			.11	.06
631	Pride of Venezuela (Dave Concepcion, Manny Trillo) .10			.08	.04
632	All-Star Infielders (Buddy Bell, Robin Yount) .15			.11	.06
633	Mr. Vet & Mr. Rookie (Kent Hrbek, Dave Winfield) .25			.20	.10
634	Fountain of Youth (Pete Rose, Willie Stargell) .40			.30	.15
635	Big Chiefs (Toby Harrah, Andre Thornton) .08			.06	.03
636	"Smith Bros." (Lonnie Smith, Ozzie Smith) .10			.08	.04
637	Base Stealers' Threat (Gary Carter, Bo Diaz) .15			.11	.06
638	All-Star Catchers (Gary Carter, Carlton Fisk) .20			.15	.08
639	The Silver Shoe (Rickey Henderson) 2.00			1.50	.80
640	Home Run Threats (Reggie Jackson, Ben Oglivie) .25			.20	.10
641	Two Teams - Same Day (Joel Youngblood) .08			.06	.03
642	Last Perfect Game (Len Barker, Ron Hassey) .08			.06	.03
643	Blue (Vida Blue)	.10	.08	.04
644	Black & (Bud Black)	.10	.08	.04
645	Power (Reggie Jackson)	.30	.25	.12
646	Speed & (Rickey Henderson)	.30	.25	.12
647	Checklist 1-51	.06	.05	.02
648	Checklist 52-103	.06	.05	.02
649	Checklist 104-152	.06	.05	.02
650	Checklist 153-200	.06	.05	.02
651	Checklist 201-251	.06	.05	.02
652	Checklist 252-301	.06	.05	.02
653	Checklist 302-351	.06	.05	.02
654	Checklist 352-399	.06	.05	.02
655	Checklist 400-444	.06	.05	.02
656	Checklist 445-489	.06	.05	.02
657	Checklist 490-535	.06	.05	.02
658	Checklist 536-583	.06	.05	.02
659	Checklist 584-628	.06	.05	.02
660	Checklist 629-646	.06	.05	.02

**The values quoted are intended
to reflect the market price.**

1984 Fleer

The 1984 Fleer set contained 660 cards for the fourth consecutive year. The cards, which measure 2-1/2" by 3-1/2", feature a color photo surrounded by four white borders and two blue stripes. The top stripe contains the word "Fleer" with the lower carrying the player's name. The card backs contain a small black and white photo of the player and are done in blue ink on white stock. The set was issued with team logo stickers.

		MT	NR MT	EX
Complete Set:		200.00	150.00	80.00
Common Player:		.08	.06	.03
1	Mike Boddicker(FC)	.20	.15	.08
2	Al Bumbry	.10	.08	.04
3	Todd Cruz	.08	.06	.03
4	Rich Dauer	.08	.06	.03
5	Storm Davis	.12	.09	.05
6	Rick Dempsey	.10	.08	.04
7	Jim Dwyer	.08	.06	.03
8	Mike Flanagan	.12	.09	.05
9	Dan Ford	.08	.06	.03
10	John Lowenstein	.08	.06	.03
11	Dennis Martinez	.10	.08	.04
12	Tippy Martinez	.08	.06	.03
13	Scott McGregor	.10	.08	.04
14	Eddie Murray	2.00	1.50	.80
15	Joe Nolan	.08	.06	.03
16	Jim Palmer	1.25	.90	.50
17	Cal Ripken, Jr.	18.00	13.50	7.25
18	Gary Roenicke	.08	.06	.03
19	Lenn Sakata	.08	.06	.03
20	*John Shelby*(FC)	.25	.20	.10
21	Ken Singleton	.12	.09	.05
22	Sammy Stewart	.08	.06	.03
23	Tim Stoddard	.08	.06	.03
24	Marty Bystrom	.08	.06	.03
25	Steve Carlton	2.00	1.50	.80
26	Ivan DeJesus	.08	.06	.03
27	John Denny	.08	.06	.03
28	Bob Dernier	.08	.06	.03
29	Bo Diaz	.10	.08	.04
30	Kiko Garcia	.08	.06	.03
31	Greg Gross	.08	.06	.03
32	*Kevin Gross*(FC)	.35	.25	.14
33	Von Hayes	.15	.11	.06
34	Willie Hernandez	.12	.09	.05
35	Al Holland	.08	.06	.03
36	*Charles Hudson*(FC)	.20	.15	.08
37	Joe Lefebvre	.08	.06	.03
38	Sixto Lezcano	.08	.06	.03
39	Garry Maddox	.10	.08	.04
40	Gary Matthews	.12	.09	.05
41	Len Matuszek	.08	.06	.03
42	Tug McGraw	.12	.09	.05
43	Joe Morgan	.40	.30	.15
44	Tony Perez	.20	.15	.08
45	Ron Reed	.08	.06	.03
46	Pete Rose	2.00	1.50	.80
47	*Juan Samuel*(FC)	2.50	2.00	1.00
48	Mike Schmidt	8.00	6.00	3.25
49	Ozzie Virgil	.08	.06	.03
50	*Juan Agosto*(FC)	.15	.11	.06
51	Harold Baines	.25	.20	.10
52	Floyd Bannister	.12	.09	.05
53	Salome Barojas	.08	.06	.03

#	Player	MT	NR MT	EX
54	Britt Burns	.08	.06	.03
55	Julio Cruz	.08	.06	.03
56	Richard Dotson	.12	.09	.05
57	Jerry Dybzinski	.08	.06	.03
58	Carlton Fisk	2.50	2.00	1.00
59	Scott Fletcher(FC)	.15	.11	.06
60	Jerry Hairston	.08	.06	.03
61	Kevin Hickey	.08	.06	.03
62	Marc Hill	.08	.06	.03
63	LaMarr Hoyt	.08	.06	.03
64	Ron Kittle	.15	.11	.06
65	Jerry Koosman	.12	.09	.05
66	Dennis Lamp	.08	.06	.03
67	Rudy Law	.08	.06	.03
68	Vance Law	.10	.08	.04
69	Greg Luzinski	.12	.09	.05
70	Tom Paciorek	.08	.06	.03
71	Mike Squires	.08	.06	.03
72	Dick Tidrow	.08	.06	.03
73	*Greg Walker*(FC)	.45	.35	.20
74	Glenn Abbott	.08	.06	.03
75	Howard Bailey	.08	.06	.03
76	Doug Bair	.08	.06	.03
77	Juan Berenguer	.08	.06	.03
78	Tom Brookens	.08	.06	.03
79	Enos Cabell	.08	.06	.03
80	Kirk Gibson	.40	.30	.15
81	John Grubb	.08	.06	.03
82	Larry Herndon	.10	.08	.04
83	Wayne Krenchicki	.08	.06	.03
84	Rick Leach	.08	.06	.03
85	Chet Lemon	.10	.08	.04
86	Aurelio Lopez	.08	.06	.03
87	Jack Morris	2.00	1.50	.80
88	Lance Parrish	.35	.25	.14
89	Dan Petry	.10	.08	.04
90	Dave Rozema	.08	.06	.03
91	Alan Trammell	.40	.30	.15
92	Lou Whitaker	.40	.30	.15
93	Milt Wilcox	.08	.06	.03
94	Glenn Wilson	.10	.08	.04
95	John Wockenfuss	.08	.06	.03
96	Dusty Baker	.12	.09	.05
97	Joe Beckwith	.08	.06	.03
98	Greg Brock	.12	.09	.05
99	Jack Fimple	.08	.06	.03
100	Pedro Guerrero	.35	.25	.14
101	Rick Honeycutt	.08	.06	.03
102	Burt Hooton	.10	.08	.04
103	Steve Howe	.12	.09	.05
104	Ken Landreaux	.08	.06	.03
105	Mike Marshall	.15	.11	.06
106	Rick Monday	.10	.08	.04
107	Jose Morales	.08	.06	.03
108	Tom Niedenfuer	.10	.08	.04
109	*Alejandro Pena*(FC)	.30	.25	.12
110	Jerry Reuss	.12	.09	.05
111	Bill Russell	.10	.08	.04
112	Steve Sax	.20	.15	.08
113	Mike Scioscia	.10	.08	.04
114	Derrel Thomas	.08	.06	.03
115	Fernando Valenzuela	.40	.30	.15
116	Bob Welch	.15	.11	.06
117	Steve Yeager	.08	.06	.03
118	Pat Zachry	.08	.06	.03
119	Don Baylor	.15	.11	.06
120	Bert Campaneris	.12	.09	.05
121	Rick Cerone	.08	.06	.03
122	*Ray Fontenot*(FC)	.10	.08	.04
123	George Frazier	.08	.06	.03
124	Oscar Gamble	.10	.08	.04
125	Goose Gossage	.25	.20	.10
126	Ken Griffey	.12	.09	.05
127	Ron Guidry	.30	.25	.12
128	Jay Howell(FC)	.15	.11	.06
129	Steve Kemp	.10	.08	.04
130	Matt Keough	.08	.06	.03
131	*Don Mattingly*(FC)	30.00	22.00	12.00
132	John Montefusco	.08	.06	.03
133	Omar Moreno	.08	.06	.03
134	Dale Murray	.08	.06	.03
135	Graig Nettles	.20	.15	.08
136	Lou Piniella	.15	.11	.06
137	Willie Randolph	.12	.09	.05
138	Shane Rawley	.12	.09	.05
139	Dave Righetti	.25	.20	.10
140	Andre Robertson	.08	.06	.03
141	Bob Shirley	.08	.06	.03
142	Roy Smalley	.08	.06	.03
143	Dave Winfield	4.00	3.00	1.50
144	Butch Wynegar	.08	.06	.03
145	*Jim Acker*(FC)	.12	.09	.05
146	Doyle Alexander	.12	.09	.05
147	Jesse Barfield	.25	.20	.10
148	Jorge Bell	2.00	1.50	.80
149	Barry Bonnell	.08	.06	.03
150	Jim Clancy	.10	.08	.04
151	Dave Collins	.10	.08	.04
152	*Tony Fernandez*(FC)	4.00	3.00	1.50
153	Damaso Garcia	.08	.06	.03
154	Dave Geisel	.08	.06	.03
155	Jim Gott(FC)	.10	.08	.04
156	Alfredo Griffin	.10	.08	.04
157	Garth Iorg	.08	.06	.03
158	Roy Lee Jackson	.08	.06	.03
159	Cliff Johnson	.08	.06	.03
160	Luis Leal	.08	.06	.03
161	Buck Martinez	.08	.06	.03
162	Joey McLaughlin	.08	.06	.03
163	Randy Moffitt	.08	.06	.03
164	Lloyd Moseby	.12	.09	.05
165	Rance Mulliniks	.08	.06	.03
166	Jorge Orta	.08	.06	.03
167	Dave Stieb	.15	.11	.06
168	Willie Upshaw	.10	.08	.04
169	Ernie Whitt	.10	.08	.04
170	Len Barker	.10	.08	.04
171	Steve Bedrosian	.12	.09	.05
172	Bruce Benedict	.08	.06	.03
173	Brett Butler	.10	.08	.04
174	Rick Camp	.08	.06	.03
175	Chris Chambliss	.10	.08	.04
176	Ken Dayley	.08	.06	.03
177	Pete Falcone	.08	.06	.03
178	Terry Forster	.10	.08	.04
179	Gene Garber	.08	.06	.03
180	Terry Harper	.08	.06	.03
181	Bob Horner	.12	.09	.05
182	Glenn Hubbard	.10	.08	.04
183	Randy Johnson	.08	.06	.03
184	*Craig McMurtry*(FC)	.12	.09	.05
185	Donnie Moore(FC)	.10	.08	.04
186	Dale Murphy	1.00	.70	.40
187	Phil Niekro	.30	.25	.12
188	Pascual Perez	.10	.08	.04
189	Biff Pocoroba	.08	.06	.03
190	Rafael Ramirez	.08	.06	.03
191	Jerry Royster	.08	.06	.03
192	Claudell Washington	.10	.08	.04
193	Bob Watson	.10	.08	.04
194	Jerry Augustine	.08	.06	.03
195	Mark Brouhard	.08	.06	.03
196	Mike Caldwell	.08	.06	.03
197	*Tom Candiotti*(FC)	1.00	.70	.40
198	Cecil Cooper	.15	.11	.06
199	Rollie Fingers	.25	.20	.10
200	Jim Gantner	.10	.08	.04
201	Bob Gibson	.08	.06	.03
202	Moose Haas	.08	.06	.03
203	Roy Howell	.08	.06	.03
204	Pete Ladd	.08	.06	.03
205	Rick Manning	.08	.06	.03
206	Bob McClure	.08	.06	.03
207	Paul Molitor	.20	.15	.08
208	Don Money	.08	.06	.03
209	Charlie Moore	.08	.06	.03
210	Ben Oglivie	.10	.08	.04
211	Chuck Porter	.08	.06	.03
212	Ed Romero	.08	.06	.03
213	Ted Simmons	.15	.11	.06
214	Jim Slaton	.08	.06	.03
215	Don Sutton	.30	.25	.12
216	Tom Tellmann	.08	.06	.03
217	Pete Vuckovich	.10	.08	.04
218	Ned Yost	.08	.06	.03
219	Robin Yount	5.00	3.75	2.00
220	Alan Ashby	.08	.06	.03
221	Kevin Bass(FC)	.20	.15	.08
222	Jose Cruz	.12	.09	.05
223	*Bill Dawley*(FC)	.10	.08	.04
224	Frank DiPino	.08	.06	.03
225	*Bill Doran*(FC)	1.00	.70	.50
226	Phil Garner	.10	.08	.04
227	Art Howe	.08	.06	.03
228	Bob Knepper	.10	.08	.04
229	Ray Knight	.12	.09	.05
230	Frank LaCorte	.08	.06	.03
231	Mike LaCoss	.08	.06	.03
232	Mike Madden	.08	.06	.03
233	Jerry Mumphrey	.08	.06	.03
235	Terry Puhl	.08	.06	.03
236	Luis Pujols	.08	.06	.03

		MT	NR MT	EX			MT	NR MT	EX
237	Craig Reynolds	.08	.06	.03	328	Dave LaPoint	.10	.08	.04
238	Vern Ruhle	.08	.06	.03	329	Willie McGee	.35	.25	.14
239	Nolan Ryan	15.00	11.00	6.00	330	Ken Oberkfell	.08	.06	.03
240	Mike Scott	.20	.15	.08	331	Darrell Porter	.10	.08	.04
241	Tony Scott	.08	.06	.03	332	Jamie Quirk	.08	.06	.03
242	Dave Smith	.10	.08	.04	333	Mike Ramsey	.08	.06	.03
243	Dickie Thon	.10	.08	.04	334	Floyd Rayford	.08	.06	.03
244	Denny Walling	.08	.06	.03	335	Lonnie Smith	.10	.08	.04
245	Dale Berra	.08	.06	.03	336	Ozzie Smith	1.50	1.25	.60
246	Jim Bibby	.08	.06	.03	337	John Stuper	.08	.06	.03
247	John Candelaria	.12	.09	.05	338	Bruce Sutter	.20	.15	.08
248	*Jose DeLeon*(FC)	.50	.40	.20	339	*Andy Van Slyke*(FC)	6.00	4.50	2.50
249	Mike Easler	.10	.08	.04	340	Dave Von Ohlen	.08	.06	.03
250	Cecilio Guante(FC)	.10	.08	.04	341	Willie Aikens	.08	.06	.03
251	Richie Hebner	.08	.06	.03	342	Mike Armstrong	.08	.06	.03
252	Lee Lacy	.08	.06	.03	343	Bud Black	.10	.08	.04
253	Bill Madlock	.12	.09	.05	344	George Brett	5.00	3.75	2.00
254	Milt May	.08	.06	.03	345	Onix Concepcion	.08	.06	.03
255	Lee Mazzilli	.10	.08	.04	346	Keith Creel	.08	.06	.03
256	Larry McWilliams	.08	.06	.03	347	Larry Gura	.08	.06	.03
257	Jim Morrison	.08	.06	.03	348	Don Hood	.08	.06	.03
258	Dave Parker	.30	.25	.12	349	Dennis Leonard	.10	.08	.04
259	Tony Pena	.12	.09	.05	350	Hal McRae	.12	.09	.05
260	Johnny Ray	.12	.09	.05	351	Amos Otis	.12	.09	.05
261	Rick Rhoden	.12	.09	.05	352	Gaylord Perry	.60	.45	.25
262	Don Robinson	.10	.08	.04	353	Greg Pryor	.08	.06	.03
263	Manny Sarmiento	.08	.06	.03	354	Dan Quisenberry	.12	.09	.05
264	Rod Scurry	.08	.06	.03	355	Steve Renko	.08	.06	.03
265	Kent Tekulve	.10	.08	.04	356	Leon Roberts	.08	.06	.03
266	Gene Tenace	.10	.08	.04	357	*Pat Sheridan*(FC)	.15	.11	.06
267	Jason Thompson	.08	.06	.03	358	Joe Simpson	.08	.06	.03
268	*Lee Tunnell*(FC)	.10	.08	.04	359	Don Slaught	.08	.06	.03
269	*Marvell Wynne*(FC)	.20	.15	.08	360	Paul Splittorff	.08	.06	.03
270	Ray Burris	.08	.06	.03	361	U.L. Washington	.08	.06	.03
271	Gary Carter	.40	.30	.15	362	John Wathan	.10	.08	.04
272	Warren Cromartie	.08	.06	.03	363	Frank White	.12	.09	.05
273	Andre Dawson	3.00	2.25	1.25	364	Willie Wilson	.15	.11	.06
274	Doug Flynn	.08	.06	.03	365	Jim Barr	.08	.06	.03
275	Terry Francona	.08	.06	.03	366	Dave Bergman	.08	.06	.03
276	Bill Gullickson	.08	.06	.03	367	Fred Breining	.08	.06	.03
277	Bob James	.08	.06	.03	368	Bob Brenly	.08	.06	.03
278	Charlie Lea	.08	.06	.03	369	Jack Clark	.25	.20	.10
279	Bryan Little	.08	.06	.03	370	Chili Davis	.12	.09	.05
280	Al Oliver	.20	.15	.08	371	Mark Davis(FC)	.20	.15	.08
281	Tim Raines	.70	.50	.30	372	Darrell Evans	.15	.11	.06
282	Bobby Ramos	.08	.06	.03	373	Atlee Hammaker	.08	.06	.03
283	Jeff Reardon	.15	.11	.06	374	Mike Krukow	.10	.08	.04
284	Steve Rogers	.10	.08	.04	375	Duane Kuiper	.08	.06	.03
285	Scott Sanderson	.08	.06	.03	376	Bill Laskey	.08	.06	.03
286	Dan Schatzeder	.08	.06	.03	377	Gary Lavelle	.08	.06	.03
287	Bryn Smith	.08	.06	.03	378	Johnnie LeMaster	.08	.06	.03
288	Chris Speier	.08	.06	.03	379	Jeff Leonard	.12	.09	.05
289	Manny Trillo	.10	.08	.04	380	Randy Lerch	.08	.06	.03
290	Mike Vail	.08	.06	.03	381	Renie Martin	.08	.06	.03
291	Tim Wallach	.15	.11	.06	382	Andy McGaffigan	.08	.06	.03
292	Chris Welsh	.08	.06	.03	383	Greg Minton	.08	.06	.03
293	Jim Wohlford	.08	.06	.03	384	Tom O'Malley	.08	.06	.03
294	Kurt Bevacqua	.08	.06	.03	385	Max Venable	.08	.06	.03
295	Juan Bonilla	.08	.06	.03	386	Brad Wellman	.08	.06	.03
296	Bobby Brown	.08	.06	.03	387	Joel Youngblood	.08	.06	.03
297	Luis DeLeon	.08	.06	.03	388	Gary Allenson	.08	.06	.03
298	Dave Dravecky	.10	.08	.04	389	Luis Aponte	.08	.06	.03
299	Tim Flannery	.08	.06	.03	390	Tony Armas	.12	.09	.05
300	Steve Garvey	.50	.40	.20	391	Doug Bird	.08	.06	.03
301	Tony Gwynn	12.00	9.00	4.75	392	Wade Boggs	12.00	9.00	4.75
302	*Andy Hawkins*(FC)	.20	.15	.08	393	*Dennis Boyd*(FC)	.70	.50	.30
303	Ruppert Jones	.08	.06	.03	394	Mike Brown	.08	.06	.03
304	Terry Kennedy	.10	.08	.04	395	Mark Clear	.08	.06	.03
305	Tim Lollar	.08	.06	.03	396	Dennis Eckersley	.15	.11	.06
306	Gary Lucas	.08	.06	.03	397	Dwight Evans	.20	.15	.08
307	*Kevin McReynolds*(FC)	3.00	2.25	1.25	398	Rich Gedman	.10	.08	.04
308	Sid Monge	.08	.06	.03	399	Glenn Hoffman	.08	.06	.03
309	Mario Ramirez	.08	.06	.03	400	Bruce Hurst	.15	.11	.06
310	Gene Richards	.08	.06	.03	401	John Henry Johnson	.08	.06	.03
311	Luis Salazar	.08	.06	.03	402	Ed Jurak	.08	.06	.03
312	Eric Show	.12	.09	.05	403	Rick Miller	.08	.06	.03
313	Elias Sosa	.08	.06	.03	404	Jeff Newman	.08	.06	.03
314	Garry Templeton	.12	.09	.05	405	Reid Nichols	.08	.06	.03
315	*Mark Thurmond*(FC)	.10	.08	.04	406	Bob Ojeda	.12	.09	.05
316	Ed Whitson	.08	.06	.03	407	Jerry Remy	.08	.06	.03
317	Alan Wiggins	.08	.06	.03	408	Jim Rice	.40	.30	.15
318	Neil Allen	.08	.06	.03	409	Bob Stanley	.08	.06	.03
319	Joaquin Andujar	.10	.08	.04	410	Dave Stapleton	.08	.06	.03
320	Steve Braun	.08	.06	.03	411	John Tudor	.12	.09	.05
321	Glenn Brummer	.08	.06	.03	412	Carl Yastrzemski	.80	.60	.30
322	Bob Forsch	.10	.08	.04	413	Buddy Bell	.12	.09	.05
323	David Green	.08	.06	.03	414	Larry Biittner	.08	.06	.03
324	George Hendrick	.10	.08	.04	415	John Butcher	.08	.06	.03
325	Tom Herr	.12	.09	.05	416	Danny Darwin	.08	.06	.03
326	Dane Iorg	.08	.06	.03	417	Bucky Dent	.12	.09	.05
327	Jeff Lahti	.08	.06	.03	418	Dave Hostetler	.08	.06	.03

#	Name	MT	NR MT	EX	#	Name	MT	NR MT	EX
419	Charlie Hough	.12	.09	.05	510	Rick Burleson	.10	.08	.04
420	Bobby Johnson	.08	.06	.03	511	Rod Carew	1.25	.90	.50
421	Odell Jones	.08	.06	.03	512	Bobby Clark	.08	.06	.03
422	Jon Matlack	.10	.08	.04	513	John Curtis	.08	.06	.03
423	*Pete O'Brien*(FC)	.80	.60	.30	514	Doug DeCinces	.12	.09	.05
424	Larry Parrish	.12	.09	.05	515	Brian Downing	.12	.09	.05
425	Mickey Rivers	.10	.08	.04	516	Tim Foli	.08	.06	.03
426	Billy Sample	.08	.06	.03	517	Ken Forsch	.08	.06	.03
427	Dave Schmidt	.08	.06	.03	518	Bobby Grich	.12	.09	.05
428	*Mike Smithson*(FC)	.15	.11	.06	519	Andy Hassler	.08	.06	.03
429	Bill Stein	.08	.06	.03	520	Reggie Jackson	1.50	1.25	.60
430	Dave Stewart	.15	.11	.06	521	Ron Jackson	.08	.06	.03
431	Jim Sundberg	.10	.08	.04	522	Tommy John	.25	.20	.10
432	Frank Tanana	.12	.09	.05	523	Bruce Kison	.08	.06	.03
433	Dave Tobik	.08	.06	.03	524	Steve Lubratich	.08	.06	.03
434	Wayne Tolleson(FC)	.10	.08	.04	525	Fred Lynn	.25	.20	.10
435	George Wright	.08	.06	.03	526	*Gary Pettis*(FC)	.25	.20	.10
436	Bill Almon	.08	.06	.03	527	Luis Sanchez	.08	.06	.03
437	*Keith Atherton*(FC)	.20	.15	.08	528	Daryl Sconiers	.08	.06	.03
438	Dave Beard	.08	.06	.03	529	Ellis Valentine	.08	.06	.03
439	Tom Burgmeier	.08	.06	.03	530	Rob Wilfong	.08	.06	.03
440	Jeff Burroughs	.10	.08	.04	531	Mike Witt	.15	.11	.06
441	*Chris Codiroli*(FC)	.10	.08	.04	532	Geoff Zahn	.08	.06	.03
442	*Tim Conroy*(FC)	.12	.09	.05	533	Bud Anderson	.08	.06	.03
443	Mike Davis	.10	.08	.04	534	Chris Bando	.08	.06	.03
444	Wayne Gross	.08	.06	.03	535	Alan Bannister	.08	.06	.03
445	Garry Hancock	.08	.06	.03	536	Bert Blyleven	.20	.15	.08
446	Mike Heath	.08	.06	.03	537	Tom Brennan	.08	.06	.03
447	Rickey Henderson	10.00	7.50	4.00	538	Jamie Easterly	.08	.06	.03
448	*Don Hill*(FC)	.15	.11	.06	539	Juan Eichelberger	.08	.06	.03
449	Bob Kearney	.08	.06	.03	540	Jim Essian	.08	.06	.03
450	Bill Krueger	.08	.06	.03	541	Mike Fischlin	.08	.06	.03
451	Rick Langford	.08	.06	.03	542	Julio Franco(FC)	4.50	3.50	1.75
452	Carney Lansford	.12	.09	.05	543	Mike Hargrove	.08	.06	.03
453	Davey Lopes	.10	.08	.04	544	Toby Harrah	.10	.08	.04
454	Steve McCatty	.08	.06	.03	545	Ron Hassey	.08	.06	.03
455	Dan Meyer	.08	.06	.03	546	*Neal Heaton*(FC)	.15	.11	.06
456	Dwayne Murphy	.10	.08	.04	547	Bake McBride	.08	.06	.03
457	Mike Norris	.08	.06	.03	548	Broderick Perkins	.08	.06	.03
458	Ricky Peters	.08	.06	.03	549	Lary Sorensen	.08	.06	.03
459	*Tony Phillips*(FC)	.15	.11	.06	550	Dan Spillner	.08	.06	.03
460	Tom Underwood	.08	.06	.03	551	Rick Sutcliffe	.15	.11	.06
461	Mike Warren	.08	.06	.03	552	Pat Tabler	.10	.08	.04
462	Johnny Bench	.80	.60	.30	553	Gorman Thomas	.10	.08	.04
463	Bruce Berenyi	.08	.06	.03	554	Andre Thornton	.12	.09	.05
464	Dann Bilardello	.08	.06	.03	555	George Vukovich	.08	.06	.03
465	Cesar Cedeno	.12	.09	.05	556	Darrell Brown	.08	.06	.03
466	Dave Concepcion	.15	.11	.06	557	Tom Brunansky	.20	.15	.08
467	Dan Driessen	.10	.08	.04	558	*Randy Bush*(FC)	.15	.11	.06
468	*Nick Esasky*(FC)	.70	.50	.30	559	Bobby Castillo	.08	.06	.03
469	Rich Gale	.08	.06	.03	560	John Castino	.08	.06	.03
470	Ben Hayes	.08	.06	.03	561	Ron Davis	.08	.06	.03
471	Paul Householder	.08	.06	.03	562	Dave Engle	.08	.06	.03
472	Tom Hume	.08	.06	.03	563	Lenny Faedo	.08	.06	.03
473	Alan Knicely	.08	.06	.03	564	Pete Filson	.08	.06	.03
474	Eddie Milner	.08	.06	.03	565	Gary Gaetti	.60	.45	.25
475	Ron Oester	.08	.06	.03	566	Mickey Hatcher	.10	.08	.04
476	Kelly Paris	.08	.06	.03	567	Kent Hrbek	.40	.30	.15
477	Frank Pastore	.08	.06	.03	568	Rusty Kuntz	.08	.06	.03
478	Ted Power	.10	.08	.04	569	Tim Laudner	.08	.06	.03
479	Joe Price	.08	.06	.03	570	Rick Lysander	.08	.06	.03
480	Charlie Puleo	.08	.06	.03	571	Bobby Mitchell	.08	.06	.03
481	*Gary Redus*(FC)	.25	.20	.10	572	Ken Schrom	.08	.06	.03
482	Bill Scherrer	.08	.06	.03	573	Ray Smith	.08	.06	.03
483	Mario Soto	.10	.08	.04	574	*Tim Teufel*(FC)	.30	.25	.12
484	Alex Trevino	.08	.06	.03	575	Frank Viola	1.50	1.25	.60
485	Duane Walker	.08	.06	.03	576	Gary Ward	.10	.08	.04
486	Larry Bowa	.15	.11	.06	577	Ron Washington	.08	.06	.03
487	Warren Brusstar	.08	.06	.03	578	Len Whitehouse	.08	.06	.03
488	Bill Buckner	.15	.11	.06	579	Al Williams	.08	.06	.03
489	Bill Campbell	.08	.06	.03	580	Bob Bailor	.08	.06	.03
490	Ron Cey	.12	.09	.05	581	Mark Bradley	.08	.06	.03
491	Jody Davis	.10	.08	.04	582	Hubie Brooks	.15	.11	.06
492	Leon Durham	.10	.08	.04	583	Carlos Diaz	.08	.06	.03
493	Mel Hall(FC)	.20	.15	.08	584	George Foster	.20	.15	.08
494	Ferguson Jenkins	.20	.15	.08	585	Brian Giles	.08	.06	.03
495	Jay Johnstone	.10	.08	.04	586	Danny Heep	.08	.06	.03
496	*Craig Lefferts*(FC)	.20	.15	.08	587	Keith Hernandez	.40	.30	.15
497	*Carmelo Martinez*(FC)	.15	.11	.06	588	Ron Hodges	.08	.06	.03
498	Jerry Morales	.08	.06	.03	589	Scott Holman	.08	.06	.03
499	Keith Moreland	.10	.08	.04	590	Dave Kingman	.15	.11	.06
500	Dickie Noles	.08	.06	.03	591	Ed Lynch	.08	.06	.03
501	Mike Proly	.08	.06	.03	592	*Jose Oquendo*(FC)	.15	.11	.06
502	Chuck Rainey	.08	.06	.03	593	Jesse Orosco	.10	.08	.04
503	Dick Ruthven	.08	.06	.03	594	*Junior Ortiz*(FC)	.10	.08	.04
504	Ryne Sandberg	20.00	15.00	8.00	595	Tom Seaver	4.00	3.00	1.50
505	Lee Smith	.15	.11	.06	596	*Doug Sisk*(FC)	.10	.08	.04
506	Steve Trout	.08	.06	.03	597	Rusty Staub	.12	.09	.05
507	Gary Woods	.08	.06	.03	598	John Stearns	.08	.06	.03
508	Juan Beniquez	.08	.06	.03	599	*Darryl Strawberry*(FC)	30.00	22.00	12.00
509	Bob Boone	.10	.08	.04	600	Craig Swan	.08	.06	.03

		MT	NR MT	EX
601	*Walt Terrell*(FC)	.25	.20	.10
602	Mike Torrez	.10	.08	.04
603	Mookie Wilson	.12	.09	.05
604	Jamie Allen	.08	.06	.03
605	Jim Beattie	.08	.06	.03
606	Tony Bernazard	.08	.06	.03
607	Manny Castillo	.08	.06	.03
608	Bill Caudill	.08	.06	.03
609	Bryan Clark	.08	.06	.03
610	Al Cowens	.08	.06	.03
611	Dave Henderson	.12	.09	.05
612	Steve Henderson	.08	.06	.03
613	Orlando Mercado	.08	.06	.03
614	Mike Moore	.10	.08	.04
615	Ricky Nelson	.08	.06	.03
616	*Spike Owen*(FC)	.20	.15	.08
617	Pat Putnam	.08	.06	.03
618	Ron Roenicke	.08	.06	.03
619	Mike Stanton	.08	.06	.03
620	Bob Stoddard	.08	.06	.03
621	Rick Sweet	.08	.06	.03
622	Roy Thomas	.08	.06	.03
623	Ed Vande Berg	.08	.06	.03
624	*Matt Young*(FC)	.15	.11	.06
625	Richie Zisk	.10	.08	.04
626	'83 All-Star Game Record Breaker (Fred Lynn)	.12	.09	.05
627	'83 All-Star Game Record Breaker (Manny Trillo)	.10	.08	.04
628	N.L. Iron Man (Steve Garvey)	.20	.15	.08
629	A.L. Batting Runner-Up (Rod Carew)	.25	.20	.10
630	A.L. Batting Champion (Wade Boggs)	1.00	.70	.40
631	Letting Go Of The Raines (Tim Raines)	.20	.15	.08
632	Double Trouble (Al Oliver)	.10	.08	.04
633	All-Star Second Base (Steve Sax)	.15	.11	.06
634	All-Star Shortstop (Dickie Thon)	.10	.08	.04
635	Ace Firemen (Tippy Martinez, Dan Quisenberry)	.10	.08	.04
636	Reds Reunited (Joe Morgan, Tony Perez, Pete Rose)	.50	.40	.20
637	Backstop Stars (Bob Boone, Lance Parrish)	.15	.11	.06
638	The Pine Tar Incident, 7/24/83 (George Brett, Gaylord Perry)	.30	.25	.12
639	1983 No-Hitters (Bob Forsch, Dave Righetti, Mike Warren)	.10	.08	.04
640	Retiring Superstars (Johnny Bench, Carl Yastrzemski)	2.00	1.50	.80
641	Going Out In Style (Gaylord Perry)	.15	.11	.06
642	300 Club & Strikeout Record (Steve Carlton)	.20	.15	.08
643	The Managers (Joe Altobelli, Paul Owens)	.10	.08	.04
644	The MVP (Rick Dempsey)	.10	.08	.04
645	The Rookie Winner (Mike Boddicker)(FC)	.12	.09	.05
646	The Clincher (Scott McGregor)	.10	.08	.04
647	Checklist: Orioles/Royals (Joe Altobelli)	.08	.06	.03
648	Checklist: Phillies/Giants (Paul Owens)	.08	.06	.03
649	Checklist: White Sox/Red Sox (Tony LaRussa)	.08	.06	.03
650	Checklist: Tigers/Rangers (Sparky Anderson)	.08	.06	.03
651	Checklist: Dodgers/A's (Tom Lasorda)	.08	.06	.03
652	Checklist: Yankees/Reds (Billy Martin)	.08	.06	.03
653	Checklist: Blue Jays/Cubs (Bobby Cox)	.08	.06	.03
654	Checklist: Braves/Angels (Joe Torre)	.08	.06	.03
655	Checklist: Brewers/Indians (Rene Lachemann)	.08	.06	.03
656	Checklist: Astros/Twins (Bob Lillis)	.08	.06	.03
657	Checklist: Pirates/Mets (Chuck Tanner)	.08	.06	.03
658	Checklist: Expos/Mariners (Bill Virdon)	.08	.06	.03
659	Checklist: Padres/Specials (Dick Williams)	.08	.06	.03
660	Checklist: Cardinals/Specials (Whitey Herzog)	.08	.06	.03

Definitions for grading conditions are located in the Introduction of this price guide.

1984 Fleer Update

Following the lead of Topps, Fleer issued near the end of the baseball season a 132-card set to update player trades and include rookies not depicted in the regular issue. The cards, which measure 2-1/2" by 3-1/2", are identical in design to the regular issue but are numbered U-1 through U-132. Available to the collecting public only through hobby dealers, the set was printed in limited quantities and has escalated in price quite rapidly the past several years. The set was issued with team logo stickers in a specially designed box.

		MT	NR MT	EX
	Complete Set:	900.00	675.00	350.00
	Common Player:	.15	.11	.06
1	Willie Aikens	.15	.11	.06
2	Luis Aponte	.15	.11	.06
3	Mark Bailey(FC)	.20	.15	.08
4	Bob Bailor	.15	.11	.06
5	Dusty Baker	.30	.25	.12
6	Steve Balboni(FC)	.40	.30	.15
7	Alan Bannister	.15	.11	.06
8	Marty Barrett(FC)	.50	.40	.20
9	Dave Beard	.15	.11	.06
10	Joe Beckwith	.15	.11	.06
11	Dave Bergman	.15	.11	.06
12	Tony Bernazard	.15	.11	.06
13	Bruce Bochte	.15	.11	.06
14	Barry Bonnell	.15	.11	.06
15	Phil Bradley(FC)	.80	.60	.30
16	Fred Breining	.15	.11	.06
17	Mike Brown	.15	.11	.06
18	Bill Buckner	.50	.40	.20
19	Ray Burris	.15	.11	.06
20	John Butcher	.15	.11	.06
21	Brett Butler	2.00	1.50	.80
22	Enos Cabell	.15	.11	.06
23	Bill Campbell	.15	.11	.06
24	Bill Caudill	.15	.11	.06
25	Bobby Clark	.15	.11	.06
26	Bryan Clark	.15	.11	.06
27	Roger Clemens(FC)	400.00	300.00	150.00
28	Jaime Cocanower	.15	.11	.06
29	Ron Darling(FC)	7.00	5.25	2.75
30	Alvin Davis(FC)	5.00	3.75	2.50
31	Bob Dernier	.15	.11	.06
32	Carlos Diaz	.15	.11	.06
33	Mike Easler	.20	.15	.08
34	Dennis Eckersley	12.00	9.00	4.75
35	Jim Essian	.15	.11	.06
36	Darrell Evans	.60	.45	.25
37	Mike Fitzgerald(FC)	.20	.15	.08
38	Tim Foli	.15	.11	.06
39	John Franco(FC)	10.00	7.50	4.00
40	George Frazier	.15	.11	.06
41	Rich Gale	.15	.11	.06
42	Barbaro Garbey	.20	.15	.08
43	Dwight Gooden(FC)	100.00	75.00	40.00
44	Goose Gossage	1.00	.70	.40
45	Wayne Gross	.15	.11	.06
46	Mark Gubicza(FC)	4.00	3.00	1.50
47	Jackie Gutierrez	.15	.11	.06
48	Toby Harrah	.20	.15	.08
49	Ron Hassey	.15	.11	.06
50	Richie Hebner	.15	.11	.06
51	Willie Hernandez	.40	.30	.15

		MT	NR MT	EX
52	Ed Hodge	.15	.11	.06
53	Ricky Horton(FC)	.50	.40	.20
54	Art Howe	.15	.11	.06
55	Dane Iorg	.15	.11	.06
56	Brook Jacoby(FC)	4.00	3.00	1.50
57	Dion James(FC)	.30	.25	.12
58	Mike Jeffcoat(FC)	.20	.15	.08
59	Ruppert Jones	.15	.11	.06
60	Bob Kearney	.15	.11	.06
61	Jimmy Key(FC)	10.00	7.50	4.00
62	Dave Kingman	.70	.50	.30
63	Brad Komminsk(FC)	.20	.15	.08
64	Jerry Koosman	.50	.40	.20
65	Wayne Krenchicki	.15	.11	.06
66	Rusty Kuntz	.15	.11	.06
67	Frank LaCorte	.15	.11	.06
68	Dennis Lamp	.15	.11	.06
69	Tito Landrum	.15	.11	.06
70	Mark Langston(FC)	20.00	15.00	8.00
71	Rick Leach	.15	.11	.06
72	Craig Lefferts(FC)	.30	.25	.12
73	Gary Lucas	.15	.11	.06
74	Jerry Martin	.15	.11	.06
75	Carmelo Martinez	.30	.25	.12
76	Mike Mason(FC)	.20	.15	.08
77	Gary Matthews	.30	.25	.12
78	Andy McGaffigan	.15	.11	.06
79	Joey McLaughlin	.15	.11	.06
80	Joe Morgan	6.00	4.50	2.50
81	Darryl Motley	.15	.11	.06
82	Graig Nettles	1.00	.70	.40
83	Phil Niekro	4.00	3.00	1.50
84	Ken Oberkfell	.15	.11	.06
85	Al Oliver	.80	.60	.30
86	Jorge Orta	.15	.11	.06
87	Amos Otis	.30	.25	.12
88	Bob Owchinko	.15	.11	.06
89	Dave Parker	4.00	3.00	1.50
90	Jack Perconte	.15	.11	.06
91	Tony Perez	6.00	4.50	2.50
92	Gerald Perry(FC)	1.00	.70	.40
93	Kirby Puckett(FC)	350.00	250.00	150.00
94	Shane Rawley	.35	.30	.14
95	Floyd Rayford	.15	.11	.06
96	Ron Reed	.20	.15	.08
97	R.J. Reynolds(FC)	.90	.70	.35
98	Gene Richards	.15	.11	.06
99	Jose Rijo(FC)	18.00	13.50	7.25
100	Jeff Robinson(FC)	.50	.40	.20
101	Ron Romanick(FC)	.20	.15	.08
102	Pete Rose	15.00	11.00	6.00
103	Bret Saberhagen(FC)	38.00	28.50	14.30
104	Scott Sanderson	.15	.11	.06
105	Dick Schofield(FC)	.40	.30	.15
106	Tom Seaver	25.00	18.00	10.00
107	Jim Slaton	.15	.11	.06
108	Mike Smithson	.20	.15	.08
109	Lary Sorensen	.15	.11	.06
110	Tim Stoddard	.15	.11	.06
111	Jeff Stone(FC)	.30	.25	.12
112	Champ Summers	.15	.11	.06
113	Jim Sundberg	.20	.15	.08
114	Rick Sutcliffe	.80	.60	.30
115	Craig Swan	.15	.11	.06
116	Derrel Thomas	.15	.11	.06
117	Gorman Thomas	.35	.30	.14
118	Alex Trevino	.15	.11	.06
119	Manny Trillo	.20	.15	.08
120	John Tudor	.60	.45	.25
121	Tom Underwood	.15	.11	.06
122	Mike Vail	.15	.11	.06
123	Tom Waddell(FC)	.15	.11	.06
124	Gary Ward	.20	.15	.08
125	Terry Whitfield	.15	.11	.06
126	Curtis Wilkerson	.15	.11	.06
127	Frank Williams(FC)	.35	.25	.14
128	Glenn Wilson	.25	.20	.10
129	John Wockenfuss	.15	.11	.06
130	Ned Yost	.15	.11	.06
131	Mike Young(FC)	.35	.25	.14
132	Checklist 1-132	.15	.11	.06

1985 Fleer

The 1985 Fleer set consists of 660 cards, each measuring 2-1/2" by 3-1/2" in size. The card fronts feature a color photo plus the player's team logo and the word "Fleer." The photos have a color-coded

frame which corresponds to the player's team. A grey border surrounds the color-coded frame. The card backs are similar in design to the previous two years, but have two shades of red and black ink on white stock. For the fourth consecutive year, Fleer included special cards and team checklists in the set. Also incorporated in a set for the first time were ten "Major League Prospect" cards, each featuring two rookie hopefuls. The set was issued with team logo stickers.

		MT	NR MT	EX
	Complete Set:	200.00	150.00	80.00
	Common Player:	.06	.05	.02
1	Doug Bair	.06	.05	.02
2	Juan Berenguer	.06	.05	.02
3	Dave Bergman	.06	.05	.02
4	Tom Brookens	.06	.05	.02
5	Marty Castillo	.06	.05	.02
6	Darrell Evans	.12	.09	.05
7	Barbaro Garbey	.12	.09	.05
8	Kirk Gibson	.35	.25	.14
9	John Grubb	.06	.05	.02
10	Willie Hernandez	.08	.06	.03
11	Larry Herndon	.08	.06	.03
12	Howard Johnson	3.00	2.25	1.25
13	Ruppert Jones	.06	.05	.02
14	Rusty Kuntz	.06	.05	.02
15	Chet Lemon	.08	.06	.03
16	Aurelio Lopez	.06	.05	.02
17	Sid Monge	.06	.05	.02
18	Jack Morris	.25	.20	.10
19	Lance Parrish	.30	.25	.12
20	Dan Petry	.08	.06	.03
21	Dave Rozema	.06	.05	.02
22	Bill Scherrer	.06	.05	.02
23	Alan Trammell	.35	.25	.14
24	Lou Whitaker	.35	.25	.14
25	Milt Wilcox	.06	.05	.02
26	Kurt Bevacqua	.06	.05	.02
27	Greg Booker(FC)	.15	.11	.06
28	Bobby Brown	.06	.05	.02
29	Luis DeLeon	.06	.05	.02
30	Dave Dravecky	.08	.06	.03
31	Tim Flannery	.06	.05	.02
32	Steve Garvey	.40	.30	.15
33	Goose Gossage	.20	.15	.08
34	Tony Gwynn	5.00	3.75	2.00
35	Greg Harris	.06	.05	.02
36	Andy Hawkins	.08	.06	.03
37	Terry Kennedy	.08	.06	.03
38	Craig Lefferts	.08	.06	.03
39	Tim Lollar	.06	.05	.02
40	Carmelo Martinez	.08	.06	.03
41	Kevin McReynolds	1.00	.70	.40
42	Graig Nettles	.15	.11	.06
43	Luis Salazar	.06	.05	.02
44	Eric Show	.08	.06	.03
45	Garry Templeton	.08	.06	.03
46	Mark Thurmond	.06	.05	.02
47	Ed Whitson	.06	.05	.02
48	Alan Wiggins	.06	.05	.02
49	Rich Bordi	.06	.05	.02
50	Larry Bowa	.12	.09	.05
51	Warren Brusstar	.06	.05	.02
52	Ron Cey	.10	.08	.04
53	Henry Cotto(FC)	.15	.11	.06
54	Jody Davis	.10	.08	.04
55	Bob Dernier	.06	.05	.02

#	Name	MT	NR MT	EX
56	Leon Durham	.08	.06	.03
57	Dennis Eckersley	1.25	.90	.50
58	George Frazier	.06	.05	.02
59	Richie Hebner	.06	.05	.02
60	Dave Lopes	.08	.06	.03
61	Gary Matthews	.10	.08	.04
62	Keith Moreland	.08	.06	.03
63	Rick Reuschel	.10	.08	.04
64	Dick Ruthven	.06	.05	.02
65	Ryne Sandberg	8.00	6.00	3.00
66	Scott Sanderson	.06	.05	.02
67	Lee Smith	.10	.08	.04
68	Tim Stoddard	.06	.05	.02
69	Rick Sutcliffe	.12	.09	.05
70	Steve Trout	.06	.05	.02
71	Gary Woods	.06	.05	.02
72	Wally Backman	.08	.06	.03
73	Bruce Berenyi	.06	.05	.02
74	Hubie Brooks	.10	.08	.04
75	Kelvin Chapman	.06	.05	.02
76	Ron Darling	.80	.60	.30
77	Sid Fernandez(FC)	1.00	.70	.40
78	Mike Fitzgerald	.08	.06	.03
79	George Foster	.15	.11	.06
80	Brent Gaff	.06	.05	.02
81	Ron Gardenhire	.06	.05	.02
82	*Dwight Gooden*	9.00	6.75	3.50
83	Tom Gorman	.06	.05	.02
84	Danny Heep	.06	.05	.02
85	Keith Hernandez	.30	.25	.12
86	Ray Knight	.10	.08	.04
87	Ed Lynch	.06	.05	.02
88	Jose Oquendo	.08	.06	.03
89	Jesse Orosco	.08	.06	.03
90	*Rafael Santana*(FC)	.20	.15	.08
91	Doug Sisk	.06	.05	.02
92	Rusty Staub	.12	.09	.05
93	Darryl Strawberry	10.00	7.50	4.00
94	Walt Terrell	.08	.06	.03
95	Mookie Wilson	.10	.08	.04
96	Jim Acker	.06	.05	.02
97	Willie Aikens	.06	.05	.02
98	Doyle Alexander	.10	.08	.04
99	Jesse Barfield	.25	.20	.10
100	George Bell	.50	.40	.20
101	Jim Clancy	.08	.06	.03
102	Dave Collins	.08	.06	.03
103	Tony Fernandez	.35	.25	.14
104	Damaso Garcia	.06	.05	.02
105	Jim Gott	.06	.05	.02
106	Alfredo Griffin	.08	.06	.03
107	Garth Iorg	.06	.05	.02
108	Roy Lee Jackson	.06	.05	.02
109	Cliff Johnson	.06	.05	.02
110	*Jimmy Key*	2.00	1.50	.80
111	Dennis Lamp	.06	.05	.02
112	Rick Leach	.06	.05	.02
113	Luis Leal	.06	.05	.02
114	Buck Martinez	.06	.05	.02
115	Lloyd Moseby	.10	.08	.04
116	Rance Mulliniks	.06	.05	.02
117	Dave Stieb	.12	.09	.05
118	Willie Upshaw	.08	.06	.03
119	Ernie Whitt	.08	.06	.03
120	Mike Armstrong	.06	.05	.02
121	Don Baylor	.12	.09	.05
122	Marty Bystrom	.06	.05	.02
123	Rick Cerone	.06	.05	.02
124	Joe Cowley(FC)	.06	.05	.02
125	Brian Dayett(FC)	.06	.05	.02
126	Tim Foli	.06	.05	.02
127	Ray Fontenot	.06	.05	.02
128	Ken Griffey	.10	.08	.04
129	Ron Guidry	.25	.20	.10
130	Toby Harrah	.08	.06	.03
131	Jay Howell	.08	.06	.03
132	Steve Kemp	.08	.06	.03
133	Don Mattingly	8.00	6.00	3.25
134	Bobby Meacham	.06	.05	.02
135	John Montefusco	.06	.05	.02
136	Omar Moreno	.06	.05	.02
137	Dale Murray	.06	.05	.02
138	Phil Niekro	.25	.20	.10
139	*Mike Pagliarulo*(FC)	.70	.50	.30
140	Willie Randolph	.10	.08	.04
141	Dennis Rasmussen(FC)	.30	.25	.12
142	Dave Righetti	.20	.15	.08
143	*Jose Rijo*	3.00	2.25	1.25
144	Andre Robertson	.06	.05	.02
145	Bob Shirley	.06	.05	.02
146	Dave Winfield	3.00	2.25	1.25
147	Butch Wynegar	.06	.05	.02

#	Name	MT	NR MT	EX
148	Gary Allenson	.06	.05	.02
149	Tony Armas	.10	.08	.04
150	Marty Barrett	.20	.15	.08
151	Wade Boggs	4.00	3.00	1.50
152	Dennis Boyd	.10	.08	.04
153	Bill Buckner	.12	.09	.05
154	Mark Clear	.06	.05	.02
155	*Roger Clemens*	60.00	45.00	25.00
156	Steve Crawford	.06	.05	.02
157	Mike Easler	.08	.06	.03
158	Dwight Evans	.12	.09	.05
159	Rich Gedman	.10	.08	.04
160	Jackie Gutierrez	.06	.05	.02
161	Bruce Hurst	.12	.09	.05
162	John Henry Johnson	.06	.05	.02
163	Rick Miller	.06	.05	.02
164	Reid Nichols	.06	.05	.02
165	*Al Nipper*(FC)	.15	.11	.06
166	Bob Ojeda	.10	.08	.04
167	Jerry Remy	.06	.05	.02
168	Jim Rice	.35	.25	.14
169	Bob Stanley	.06	.05	.02
170	Mike Boddicker	.10	.08	.04
171	Al Bumbry	.08	.06	.03
172	Todd Cruz	.06	.05	.02
173	Rich Dauer	.06	.05	.02
174	Storm Davis	.10.	.08	.04
175	Rick Dempsey	.08	.06	.03
176	Jim Dwyer	.06	.05	.02
177	Mike Flanagan	.10	.08	.04
178	Dan Ford	.06	.05	.02
179	Wayne Gross	.06	.05	.02
180	John Lowenstein	.06	.05	.02
181	Dennis Martinez	.08	.06	.03
182	Tippy Martinez	.06	.05	.02
183	Scott McGregor	.08	.06	.03
184	Eddie Murray	.50	.40	.20
185	Joe Nolan	.06	.05	.02
186	Floyd Rayford	.06	.05	.02
187	Cal Ripken, Jr.	10.00	7.50	4.00
188	Gary Roenicke	.06	.05	.02
189	Lenn Sakata	.06	.05	.02
190	John Shelby	.08	.06	.03
191	Ken Singleton	.08	.06	.03
192	Sammy Stewart	.06	.05	.02
193	Bill Swaggerty	.06	.05	.02
194	Tom Underwood	.06	.05	.02
195	Mike Young	.12	.09	.05
196	Steve Balboni	.08	.06	.03
197	Joe Beckwith	.06	.05	.02
198	Bud Black	.06	.05	.02
199	George Brett	4.00	3.00	1.50
200	Onix Concepcion	.06	.05	.02
201	*Mark Gubicza*	1.25	.90	.50
202	Larry Gura	.06	.05	.02
203	Mark Huismann(FC)	.06	.05	.02
204	Dane Iorg	.06	.05	.02
205	Danny Jackson(FC)	1.00	.70	.40
206	Charlie Leibrandt	.08	.06	.03
207	Hal McRae	.10	.08	.04
208	Darryl Motley	.06	.05	.02
209	Jorge Orta	.06	.05	.02
210	Greg Pryor	.06	.05	.02
211	Dan Quisenberry	.10	.08	.04
212	*Bret Saberhagen*	6.00	4.50	2.50
213	Pat Sheridan	.06	.05	.02
214	Don Slaught	.06	.05	.02
215	U.L. Washington	.06	.05	.02
216	John Wathan	.08	.06	.03
217	Frank White	.10	.08	.04
218	Willie Wilson	.12	.09	.05
219	Neil Allen	.06	.05	.02
220	Joaquin Andujar	.08	.06	.03
221	Steve Braun	.06	.05	.02
222	Danny Cox(FC)	.20	.20	.10
223	Bob Forsch	.08	.06	.03
224	David Green	.06	.05	.02
225	George Hendrick	.08	.06	.03
226	Tom Herr	.10	.08	.04
227	*Ricky Horton*	.30	.25	.12
228	Art Howe	.06	.05	.02
229	Mike Jorgensen	.06	.05	.02
230	Kurt Kepshire	.06	.05	.02
231	Jeff Lahti	.06	.05	.02
232	Tito Landrum	.06	.05	.02
233	Dave LaPoint	.08	.06	.03
234	Willie McGee	.30	.25	.12
235	*Tom Nieto*(FC)	.10	.08	.04
236	Terry Pendleton(FC)	8.00	6.00	3.25
237	Darrell Porter	.08	.06	.03
238	Dave Rucker	.06	.05	.02

#	Player	MT	NR MT	EX
239	Lonnie Smith	.08	.06	.03
240	Ozzie Smith	.15	.11	.06
241	Bruce Sutter	.12	.09	.05
242	Andy Van Slyke	.35	.25	.14
243	Dave Von Ohlen	.06	.05	.02
244	Larry Andersen	.06	.05	.02
245	Bill Campbell	.06	.05	.02
246	Steve Carlton	.40	.30	.15
247	Tim Corcoran	.06	.05	.02
248	Ivan DeJesus	.06	.05	.02
249	John Denny	.06	.05	.02
250	Bo Diaz	.08	.06	.03
251	Greg Gross	.06	.05	.02
252	Kevin Gross	.10	.08	.04
253	Von Hayes	.12	.09	.05
254	Al Holland	.06	.05	.02
255	Charles Hudson	.08	.06	.03
256	Jerry Koosman	.10	.08	.04
257	Joe Lefebvre	.06	.05	.02
258	Sixto Lezcano	.06	.05	.02
259	Garry Maddox	.10	.08	.04
260	Len Matuszek	.06	.05	.02
261	Tug McGraw	.10	.08	.04
262	Al Oliver	.12	.09	.05
263	Shane Rawley	.10	.08	.04
264	Juan Samuel	.20	.15	.08
265	Mike Schmidt	2.00	1.50	.80
266	*Jeff Stone*	.12	.09	.05
267	Ozzie Virgil	.06	.05	.02
268	Glenn Wilson	.08	.06	.03
269	John Wockenfuss	.06	.05	.02
270	Darrell Brown	.06	.05	.02
271	Tom Brunansky	.12	.09	.05
272	Randy Bush	.06	.05	.02
273	John Butcher	.06	.05	.02
274	Bobby Castillo	.06	.05	.02
275	Ron Davis	.06	.05	.02
276	Dave Engle	.06	.05	.02
277	Pete Filson	.06	.05	.02
278	Gary Gaetti	.25	.20	.10
279	Mickey Hatcher	.06	.05	.02
280	Ed Hodge	.06	.05	.02
281	Kent Hrbek	.25	.20	.10
282	Houston Jimenez	.06	.05	.02
283	Tim Laudner	.06	.05	.02
284	Rick Lysander	.06	.05	.02
285	Dave Meier	.06	.05	.02
286	*Kirby Puckett*	50.00	37.00	20.00
287	Pat Putnam	.06	.05	.02
288	Ken Schrom	.06	.05	.02
289	Mike Smithson	.06	.05	.02
290	Tim Teufel	.08	.06	.03
291	Frank Viola	.20	.15	.08
292	Ron Washington	.06	.05	.02
293	Don Aase	.06	.05	.02
294	Juan Beniquez	.06	.05	.02
295	Bob Boone	.08	.06	.03
296	Mike Brown	.06	.05	.02
297	Rod Carew	.40	.30	.15
298	Doug Corbett	.06	.05	.02
299	Doug DeCinces	.10	.08	.04
300	Brian Downing	.10	.08	.04
301	Ken Forsch	.06	.05	.02
302	Bobby Grich	.10	.08	.04
303	Reggie Jackson	.40	.30	.15
304	Tommy John	.20	.15	.08
305	Curt Kaufman	.06	.05	.02
306	Bruce Kison	.06	.05	.02
307	Fred Lynn	.20	.15	.08
308	Gary Pettis	.08	.06	.03
309	*Ron Romanick*	.10	.08	.04
310	Luis Sanchez	.06	.05	.02
311	Dick Schofield	.12	.09	.05
312	Daryl Sconiers	.06	.05	.02
313	Jim Slaton	.06	.05	.02
314	Derrel Thomas	.06	.05	.02
315	Rob Wilfong	.06	.05	.02
316	Mike Witt	.12	.09	.05
317	Geoff Zahn	.06	.05	.02
318	Len Barker	.08	.06	.03
319	Steve Bedrosian	.12	.09	.05
320	Bruce Benedict	.06	.05	.02
321	Rick Camp	.06	.05	.02
322	Chris Chambliss	.08	.06	.03
323	*Jeff Dedmon*(FC)	.12	.09	.05
324	Terry Forster	.08	.06	.03
325	Gene Garber	.06	.05	.02
326	*Albert Hall*(FC)	.15	.11	.06
327	Terry Harper	.06	.05	.02
328	Bob Horner	.12	.09	.05
329	Glenn Hubbard	.06	.05	.02
330	Randy Johnson	.06	.05	.02
331	Brad Komminsk	.06	.05	.02
332	Rick Mahler	.06	.05	.02
333	Craig McMurtry	.06	.05	.02
334	Donnie Moore	.06	.05	.02
335	Dale Murphy	.60	.45	.25
336	Ken Oberkfell	.06	.05	.02
337	Pascual Perez	.08	.06	.03
338	Gerald Perry	.35	.25	.14
339	Rafael Ramirez	.06	.05	.02
340	Jerry Royster	.06	.05	.02
341	Alex Trevino	.06	.05	.02
342	Claudell Washington	.08	.06	.03
343	Alan Ashby	.06	.05	.02
344	*Mark Bailey*	.10	.08	.04
345	Kevin Bass	.10	.08	.04
346	Enos Cabell	.06	.05	.02
347	Jose Cruz	.10	.08	.04
348	Bill Dawley	.06	.05	.02
349	Frank DiPino	.06	.05	.02
350	Bill Doran	.12	.09	.05
351	Phil Garner	.08	.06	.03
352	Bob Knepper	.08	.06	.03
353	Mike LaCoss	.06	.05	.02
354	Jerry Mumphrey	.06	.05	.02
355	Joe Niekro	.10	.08	.04
356	Terry Puhl	.06	.05	.02
357	Craig Reynolds	.06	.05	.02
358	Vern Ruhle	.06	.05	.02
359	Nolan Ryan	8.00	6.00	3.25
360	Joe Sambito	.06	.05	.02
361	Mike Scott	.15	.11	.06
362	Dave Smith	.08	.06	.03
363	*Julio Solano*(FC)	.08	.06	.03
364	Dickie Thon	.08	.06	.03
365	Denny Walling	.06	.05	.02
366	Dave Anderson	.06	.05	.02
367	Bob Bailor	.06	.05	.02
368	Greg Brock	.08	.06	.03
369	Carlos Diaz	.06	.05	.02
370	Pedro Guerrero	.25	.20	.10
371	*Orel Hershiser*(FC)	5.00	3.75	2.00
372	Rick Honeycutt	.06	.05	.02
373	Burt Hooton	.08	.06	.03
374	*Ken Howell*(FC)	.15	.11	.06
375	Ken Landreaux	.08	.06	.03
376	Candy Maldonado	.10	.08	.04
377	Mike Marshall	.15	.11	.06
378	Tom Niedenfuer	.08	.06	.03
379	Alejandro Pena	.08	.06	.03
380	Jerry Reuss	.08	.06	.03
381	*R.J. Reynolds*	.25	.20	.10
382	German Rivera	.06	.05	.02
383	Bill Russell	.08	.06	.03
384	Steve Sax	.20	.15	.08
385	Mike Scioscia	.08	.06	.03
386	*Franklin Stubbs*(FC)	.60	.45	.25
387	Fernando Valenzuela	.35	.25	.14
388	Bob Welch	.12	.09	.05
389	Terry Whitfield	.06	.05	.02
390	Steve Yeager	.06	.05	.02
391	Pat Zachry	.06	.05	.02
392	Fred Breining	.06	.05	.02
393	Gary Carter	.35	.25	.14
394	Andre Dawson	.60	.45	.25
395	Miguel Dilone	.06	.05	.02
396	Dan Driessen	.08	.06	.03
397	Doug Flynn	.06	.05	.02
398	Terry Francona	.06	.05	.02
399	Bill Gullickson	.06	.05	.02
400	Bob James	.06	.05	.02
401	Charlie Lea	.06	.05	.02
402	Bryan Little	.06	.05	.02
403	Gary Lucas	.06	.05	.02
404	David Palmer	.06	.05	.02
405	Tim Raines	.35	.25	.14
406	Mike Ramsey	.06	.05	.02
407	Jeff Reardon	.12	.09	.05
408	Steve Rogers	.08	.06	.03
409	Dan Schatzeder	.06	.05	.02
410	Bryn Smith	.06	.05	.02
411	Mike Stenhouse	.06	.05	.02
412	Tim Wallach	.12	.09	.05
413	Jim Wohlford	.06	.05	.02
414	Bill Almon	.06	.05	.02
415	Keith Atherton	.06	.05	.02
416	Bruce Bochte	.06	.05	.02
417	Tom Burgmeier	.06	.05	.02
418	Ray Burris	.06	.05	.02
419	Bill Caudill	.06	.05	.02
420	Chris Codiroli	.06	.05	.02

		MT	NR MT	EX				MT	NR MT	EX
421	Tim Conroy	.06	.05	.02	512	Jerry Dybzinski	.06	.05	.02
422	Mike Davis	.08	.06	.03	513	Carlton Fisk	.40	.30	.15
423	Jim Essian	.06	.05	.02	514	Scott Fletcher	.08	.06	.03
424	Mike Heath	.06	.05	.02	515	Jerry Hairston	.06	.05	.02
425	Rickey Henderson	4.00	3.00	1.50	516	Marc Hill	.06	.05	.02
426	Donnie Hill	.06	.05	.02	517	LaMarr Hoyt	.06	.05	.02
427	Dave Kingman	.15	.11	.06	518	Ron Kittle	.10	.08	.04
428	Bill Krueger	.06	.05	.02	519	Rudy Law	.06	.05	.02
429	Carney Lansford	.10	.08	.04	520	Vance Law	.08	.06	.03
430	Steve McCatty	.06	.05	.02	521	Greg Luzinski	.10	.08	.04
431	Joe Morgan	.30	.25	.12	522	Gene Nelson	.06	.05	.02
432	Dwayne Murphy	.08	.06	.03	523	Tom Paciorek	.06	.05	.02
433	Tony Phillips	.06	.05	.02	524	Ron Reed	.06	.05	.02
434	Lary Sorensen	.06	.05	.02	525	Bert Roberge	.06	.05	.02
435	Mike Warren	.06	.05	.02	526	Tom Seaver	.40	.30	.15
436	Curt Young(FC)	.35	.25	.14	527	Roy Smalley	.06	.05	.02
437	Luis Aponte	.06	.05	.02	528	Dan Spillner	.06	.05	.02
438	Chris Bando	.06	.05	.02	529	Mike Squires	.06	.05	.02
439	Tony Bernazard	.06	.05	.02	530	Greg Walker	.12	.09	.05
440	Bert Blyleven	.15	.11	.06	531	Cesar Cedeno	.10	.08	.04
441	Brett Butler	.10	.08	.04	532	Dave Concepcion	.12	.09	.05
442	Ernie Camacho	.06	.05	.02	533	Eric Davis(FC)	8.00	6.00	3.25
443	Joe Carter(FC)	9.00	6.75	3.50	534	Nick Esasky	.08	.06	.03
444	Carmelo Castillo	.06	.05	.02	535	Tom Foley	.06	.05	.02
445	Jamie Easterly	.06	.05	.02	536	John Franco	2.00	1.50	.80
446	Steve Farr(FC)	.40	.30	.15	537	Brad Gulden	.06	.05	.02
447	Mike Fischlin	.06	.05	.02	538	Tom Hume	.06	.05	.02
448	Julio Franco	.12	.09	.05	539	Wayne Krenchicki	.06	.05	.02
449	Mel Hall	.08	.06	.03	540	Andy McGaffigan	.06	.05	.02
450	Mike Hargrove	.06	.05	.02	541	Eddie Milner	.06	.05	.02
451	Neal Heaton	.06	.05	.02	542	Ron Oester	.06	.05	.02
452	Brook Jacoby	.30	.25	.12	543	Bob Owchinko	.06	.05	.02
453	Mike Jeffcoat	.08	.06	.03	544	Dave Parker	.25	.20	.10
454	Don Schulze(FC)	.08	.06	.03	545	Frank Pastore	.06	.05	.02
455	Roy Smith	.06	.05	.02	546	Tony Perez	.15	.11	.06
456	Pat Tabler	.08	.06	.03	547	Ted Power	.06	.05	.02
457	Andre Thornton	.10	.08	.04	548	Joe Price	.06	.05	.02
458	George Vukovich	.06	.05	.02	549	Gary Redus	.08	.06	.03
459	Tom Waddell	.06	.05	.02	550	Pete Rose	1.00	.70	.40
460	Jerry Willard	.06	.05	.02	551	Jeff Russell(FC)	.10	.08	.04
461	Dale Berra	.06	.05	.02	552	Mario Soto	.08	.06	.03
462	John Candelaria	.10	.08	.04	553	Jay Tibbs(FC)	.15	.11	.06
463	Jose DeLeon	.08	.06	.03	554	Duane Walker	.06	.05	.02
464	Doug Frobel	.06	.05	.02	555	Alan Bannister	.06	.05	.02
465	Cecilio Guante	.06	.05	.02	556	Buddy Bell	.12	.09	.05
466	Brian Harper	.06	.05	.02	557	Danny Darwin	.06	.05	.02
467	Lee Lacy	.06	.05	.02	558	Charlie Hough	.08	.06	.03
468	Bill Madlock	.12	.09	.05	559	Bobby Jones	.06	.05	.02
469	Lee Mazzilli	.08	.06	.03	560	Odell Jones	.06	.05	.02
470	Larry McWilliams	.06	.05	.02	561	Jeff Kunkel(FC)	.10	.08	.04
471	Jim Morrison	.06	.05	.02	562	Mike Mason	.10	.08	.04
472	Tony Pena	.10	.08	.04	563	Pete O'Brien	.12	.09	.05
473	Johnny Ray	.12	.09	.05	564	Larry Parrish	.10	.08	.04
474	Rick Rhoden	.10	.08	.04	565	Mickey Rivers	.08	.06	.03
475	Don Robinson	.08	.06	.03	566	Billy Sample	.06	.05	.02
476	Rod Scurry	.06	.05	.02	567	Dave Schmidt	.06	.05	.02
477	Kent Tekulve	.08	.06	.03	568	Donnie Scott	.06	.05	.02
478	Jason Thompson	.06	.05	.02	569	Dave Stewart	.12	.09	.05
479	John Tudor	.10	.08	.04	570	Frank Tanana	.10	.08	.04
480	Lee Tunnell	.06	.05	.02	571	Wayne Tolleson	.06	.05	.02
481	Marvell Wynne	.06	.05	.02	572	Gary Ward	.08	.06	.03
482	Salome Barojas	.06	.05	.02	573	Curtis Wilkerson	.08	.06	.03
483	Dave Beard	.06	.05	.02	574	George Wright	.06	.05	.02
484	Jim Beattie	.06	.05	.02	575	Ned Yost	.06	.05	.02
485	Barry Bonnell	.06	.05	.02	576	Mark Brouhard	.06	.05	.02
486	Phil Bradley	.90	.70	.35	577	Mike Caldwell	.06	.05	.02
487	Al Cowens	.06	.05	.02	578	Bobby Clark	.06	.05	.02
488	Alvin Davis	1.00	.70	.40	579	Jaime Cocanower	.06	.05	.02
489	Dave Henderson	.10	.08	.04	580	Cecil Cooper	.15	.11	.06
490	Steve Henderson	.06	.05	.02	581	Rollie Fingers	.20	.15	.08
491	Bob Kearney	.06	.05	.02	582	Jim Gantner	.08	.06	.03
492	Mark Langston	5.00	3.75	2.00	583	Moose Haas	.06	.05	.02
493	Larry Milbourne	.06	.05	.02	584	Dion James	.12	.09	.05
494	Paul Mirabella	.06	.05	.02	585	Pete Ladd	.06	.05	.02
495	Mike Moore	.06	.05	.02	586	Rick Manning	.06	.05	.02
496	Edwin Nunez(FC)	.08	.06	.03	587	Bob McClure	.06	.05	.02
497	Spike Owen	.08	.06	.03	588	Paul Molitor	.15	.11	.06
498	Jack Perconte	.06	.05	.02	589	Charlie Moore	.06	.05	.02
499	Ken Phelps	.10	.08	.04	590	Ben Oglivie	.08	.06	.03
500	Jim Presley(FC)	.50	.40	.20	591	Chuck Porter	.06	.05	.02
501	Mike Stanton	.06	.05	.02	592	Randy Ready(FC)	.20	.15	.08
502	Bob Stoddard	.06	.05	.02	593	Ed Romero	.06	.05	.02
503	Gorman Thomas	.10	.08	.04	594	Bill Schroeder(FC)	.10	.08	.04
504	Ed Vande Berg	.06	.05	.02	595	Ray Searage	.06	.05	.02
505	Matt Young	.06	.05	.02	596	Ted Simmons	.12	.09	.05
506	Juan Agosto	.06	.05	.02	597	Jim Sundberg	.08	.06	.03
507	Harold Baines	.15	.11	.06	598	Don Sutton	.30	.25	.12
508	Floyd Bannister	.10	.08	.04	599	Tom Tellmann	.06	.05	.02
509	Britt Burns	.06	.05	.02	600	Rick Waits	.06	.05	.02
510	Julio Cruz	.06	.05	.02	601	Robin Yount	4.00	3.00	1.50
511	Richard Dotson	.10	.08	.04	602	Dusty Baker	.08	.06	.03

		MT	NR MT	EX
603	Bob Brenly	.06	.05	.02
604	Jack Clark	.20	.15	.08
605	Chili Davis	.10	.08	.04
606	Mark Davis	.06	.05	.02
607	*Dan Gladden*(FC)	.50	.40	.20
608	Atlee Hammaker	.06	.05	.02
609	Mike Krukow	.08	.06	.03
610	Duane Kuiper	.06	.05	.02
611	Bob Lacey	.06	.05	.02
612	Bill Laskey	.06	.05	.02
613	Gary Lavelle	.06	.05	.02
614	Johnnie LeMaster	.06	.05	.02
615	Jeff Leonard	.10	.08	.04
616	Randy Lerch	.06	.05	.02
617	Greg Minton	.06	.05	.02
618	Steve Nicosia	.06	.05	.02
619	Gene Richards	.06	.05	.02
620	*Jeff Robinson*	.30	.25	.12
621	Scot Thompson	.06	.05	.02
622	Manny Trillo	.08	.06	.03
623	Brad Wellman	.06	.05	.02
624	*Frank Williams*	.15	.11	.06
625	Joel Youngblood	.06	.05	.02
626	Ripken-In-Action (Cal Ripken)	2.50	2.00	1.00
627	Schmidt-In-Action (Mike Schmidt)	1.00	.70	.40
628	Giving the Signs (Sparky Anderson)	.08	.06	.03
629	A.L. Pitcher's Nightmare (Rickey Henderson, Dave Winfield)	.30	.25	.12
630	N.L. Pitcher's Nightmare (Ryne Sandberg, Mike Schmidt)	.30	.25	.12
631	N.L. All-Stars (Gary Carter, Steve Garvey, Ozzie Smith, Darryl Strawberry)	.30	.25	.12
632	All-Star Game Winning Battery (Gary Carter, Charlie Lea)	.15	.11	.06
633	N.L. Pennant Clinchers (Steve Garvey, Goose Gossage)	.20	.15	.08
634	N.L. Rookie Phenoms (Dwight Gooden, Juan Samuel)	1.00	.70	.40
635	Toronto's Big Guns (Willie Upshaw)	.08	.06	.03
636	Toronto's Big Guns (Lloyd Moseby)	.08	.06	.03
637	Holland (Al Holland)	.08	.06	.03
638	Tunnell (Lee Tunnell)	.08	.06	.03
639	500th Homer (Reggie Jackson)	.30	.25	.12
640	4,000th Hit (Pete Rose)	.50	.40	.20
641	Father & Son (Cal Ripken, Jr., Cal Ripken, Sr.)	.30	.25	.12
642	Cubs Team	.08	.06	.03
643	1984's Two Perfect Games & One No Hitter (Jack Morris, David Palmer, Mike Witt)	.15	.11	.06
644	Major League Prospect (Willie Lozado, Vic Mata)	.06	.05	.02
645	Major League Prospect (*Kelly Gruber, Randy O'Neal*)(FC)	6.00	4.50	2.50
646	Major League Prospect (*Jose Roman, Joel Skinner*)(FC)	.12	.09	.05
647	Major League Prospect (*Steve Kiefer, Danny Tartabull*)(FC)	10.00	7.50	4.00
648	Major League Prospect (*Rob Deer, Alejandro Sanchez*)(FC)	1.75	1.25	.70
649	Major League Prospect (*Shawon Dunston, Bill Hatcher*)(FC)	3.00	2.25	1.25
650	Major League Prospect (*Mike Bielecki, Ron Robinson*)(FC)	.30	.25	.12
651	Major League Prospect (*Zane Smith, Paul Zuvella*)(FC)	1.25	.90	.50
652	Major League Prospect (*Glenn Davis, Joe Hesketh*)(FC)	4.00	3.00	1.50
653	Major League Prospect (*Steve Jeltz, John Russell*)(FC)	.20	.15	.08
654	Checklist 1-95	.06	.05	.02
655	Checklist 96-195	.06	.05	.02
656	Checklist 196-292	.06	.05	.02
657	Checklist 293-391	.06	.05	.02
658	Checklist 392-481	.06	.05	.02
659	Checklist 482-575	.06	.05	.02
660	Checklist 576-660	.06	.05	.02

1985 Fleer Limited Edition

The 1985 Fleer Limited Edition 44-card set was distributed through McCrory's, J.J. Newbury, McClellan, Kress, YDC, and Green stores. The cards, which are the standard 2-1/2" by 3-1/2" size, have full-color photos inside a red and yellow frame. The card backs are set in black type against two different

shades of yellow and contain the player's personal and statistical information. The set was issued in a specially designed box which carried the complete checklist for the set on the back. Six team logo stickers were also included with the set.

		MT	NR MT	EX
Complete Set:		6.00	4.50	2.50
Common Player:		.05	.04	.02
1	Buddy Bell	.07	.05	.03
2	Bert Blyleven	.10	.08	.04
3	Wade Boggs	.70	.50	.30
4	George Brett	.30	.25	.12
5	Rod Carew	.30	.25	.12
6	Steve Carlton	.25	.20	.10
7	Alvin Davis	.20	.15	.08
8	Andre Dawson	.15	.11	.06
9	Steve Garvey	.25	.20	.10
10	Goose Gossage	.12	.09	.05
11	Tony Gwynn	.40	.30	.15
12	Keith Hernandez	.20	.15	.08
13	Kent Hrbek	.15	.11	.06
14	Reggie Jackson	.30	.25	.12
15	Dave Kingman	.10	.08	.04
16	Ron Kittle	.07	.05	.03
17	Mark Langston	.25	.20	.10
18	Jeff Leonard	.05	.04	.02
19	Bill Madlock	.07	.05	.03
20	Don Mattingly	.70	.50	.30
21	Jack Morris	.15	.11	.06
22	Dale Murphy	.30	.25	.12
23	Eddie Murray	.25	.20	.10
24	Tony Pena	.07	.05	.03
25	Dan Quisenberry	.07	.05	.03
26	Tim Raines	.25	.20	.10
27	Jim Rice	.25	.20	.10
28	Cal Ripken, Jr.	.60	.45	.25
29	Pete Rose	.60	.45	.25
30	Nolan Ryan	1.25	.90	.50
31	Ryne Sandberg	.70	.50	.30
32	Steve Sax	.15	.11	.06
33	Mike Schmidt	.50	.40	.20
34	Tom Seaver	.50	.40	.20
35	Ozzie Smith	.12	.09	.05
36	Mario Soto	.05	.04	.02
37	Dave Stieb	.10	.08	.04
38	Darryl Strawberry	.60	.45	.25
39	Rick Sutcliffe	.10	.08	.04
40	Alan Trammell	.20	.15	.08
41	Willie Upshaw	.05	.04	.02
42	Fernando Valenzuela	.20	.15	.08
43	Dave Winfield	.25	.20	.10
44	Robin Yount	.50	.40	.20

1985 Fleer Update

For the second straight year, Fleer issued a 132-card update set. The cards, which measure 2-1/2" by 3-1/2", portray players on their new teams and also includes rookies not depicted in the regular issue. The cards are identical in design to the 1985 Fleer set but are numbered U-1 through U-132. The set was issued with team logo stickers in a specially designed box and was available only through hobby dealers.

	MT	NR MT	EX
Complete Set:	30.00	22.00	12.00
Common Player:	.10	.08	.04

		MT	NR MT	EX
1	Don Aase	.15	.11	.06
2	Bill Almon	.10	.08	.04
3	Dusty Baker	.15	.11	.06
4	Dale Berra	.10	.08	.04
5	Karl Best(FC)	.10	.08	.04
6	Tim Birtsas(FC)	.20	.15	.08
7	Vida Blue	.20	.15	.08
8	Rich Bordi	.10	.08	.04
9	Daryl Boston(FC)	.20	.15	.08
10	Hubie Brooks	.20	.15	.08
11	Chris Brown(FC)	.25	.20	.10
12	Tom Browning(FC)	1.50	1.25	.60
13	Al Bumbry	.10	.08	.04
14	Tim Burke(FC)	.40	.30	.15
15	Ray Burris	.10	.08	.04
16	Jeff Burroughs	.15	.11	.06
17	Ivan Calderon(FC)	3.00	2.25	1.25
18	Jeff Calhoun	.10	.08	.04
19	Bill Campbell	.10	.08	.04
20	Don Carman(FC)	.15	.11	.06
21	Gary Carter	1.00	.70	.40
22	Bobby Castillo	.10	.08	.04
23	Bill Caudill	.10	.08	.04
24	Rick Cerone	.10	.08	.04
25	Jack Clark	.35	.25	.14
26	Pat Clements(FC)	.20	.15	.08
27	Stewart Cliburn(FC)	.15	.11	.06
28	Vince Coleman(FC)	4.00	3.00	1.50
29	Dave Collins	.15	.11	.06
30	Fritz Connally	.10	.08	.04
31	Henry Cotto(FC)	.20	.15	.08
32	Danny Darwin	.15	.11	.06
33	Darren Daulton(FC)	4.00	3.00	1.50
34	Jerry Davis	.10	.08	.04
35	Brian Dayett	.10	.08	.04
36	Ken Dixon(FC)	.10	.08	.04
37	Tommy Dunbar	.10	.08	.04
38	Mariano Duncan(FC)	.80	.60	.30
39	Bob Fallon	.10	.08	.04
40	Brian Fisher(FC)	.15	.11	.06
41	Mike Fitzgerald	.10	.08	.04
42	Ray Fontenot	.10	.08	.04
43	Greg Gagne(FC)	.35	.25	.14
44	Oscar Gamble	.15	.11	.06
45	Jim Gott	.10	.08	.04
46	David Green	.10	.08	.04
47	Alfredo Griffin	.15	.11	.06
48	Ozzie Guillen(FC)	1.25	.90	.50
49	Toby Harrah	.15	.11	.06
50	Ron Hassey	.10	.08	.04
51	Rickey Henderson	5.00	3.75	2.00
52	Steve Henderson	.10	.08	.04
53	George Hendrick	.15	.11	.06
54	Teddy Higuera(FC)	.50	.40	.20
55	Al Holland	.10	.08	.04
56	Burt Hooton	.15	.11	.06
57	Jay Howell	.15	.11	.06
58	LaMarr Hoyt	.10	.08	.04
59	Tim Hulett(FC)	.20	.15	.08
60	Bob James	.10	.08	.04
61	Cliff Johnson	.10	.08	.04
62	Howard Johnson	3.00	2.25	1.25
63	Ruppert Jones	.10	.08	.04
64	Steve Kemp	.15	.11	.06
65	Bruce Kison	.10	.08	.04
66	Mike LaCoss	.15	.11	.06
67	Lee Lacy	.15	.11	.06
68	Dave LaPoint	.20	.15	.08

		MT	NR MT	EX
69	Gary Lavelle	.10	.08	.04
70	Vance Law	.15	.11	.06
71	Manny Lee(FC)	.20	.15	.08
72	Sixto Lezcano	.10	.08	.04
73	Tim Lollar	.10	.08	.04
74	Urbano Lugo(FC)	.15	.11	.06
75	Fred Lynn	.30	.25	.12
76	Steve Lyons(FC)	.15	.11	.06
77	Mickey Mahler	.10	.08	.04
78	Ron Mathis(FC)	.10	.08	.04
79	Len Matuszek	.10	.08	.04
80	Oddibe McDowell(FC)	.15	.11	.06
81	Roger McDowell(FC)	.50	.40	.20
82	Donnie Moore	.10	.08	.04
83	Ron Musselman	.10	.08	.04
84	Al Oliver	.25	.20	.10
85	Joe Orsulak(FC)	.20	.15	.08
86	Dan Pasqua(FC)	.60	.45	.25
87	Chris Pittaro(FC)	.10	.08	.04
88	Rick Reuschel	.20	.15	.08
89	Earnie Riles(FC)	.20	.15	.08
90	Jerry Royster	.10	.08	.04
91	Dave Rozema	.10	.08	.04
92	Dave Rucker	.10	.08	.04
93	Vern Ruhle	.10	.08	.04
94	Mark Salas(FC)	.20	.15	.08
95	Luis Salazar	.10	.08	.04
96	Joe Sambito	.10	.08	.04
97	Billy Sample	.10	.08	.04
98	Alex Sanchez	.10	.08	.04
99	Calvin Schiraldi(FC)	.25	.20	.10
100	Rick Schu(FC)	.20	.15	.08
101	Larry Sheets(FC)	.50	.40	.20
102	Ron Shepherd	.10	.08	.04
103	Nelson Simmons(FC)	.10	.08	.04
104	Don Slaught	.10	.08	.04
105	Roy Smalley	.15	.11	.06
106	Lonnie Smith	.15	.11	.06
107	Nate Snell(FC)	.10	.08	.04
108	Lary Sorensen	.10	.08	.04
109	Chris Speier	.10	.08	.04
110	Mike Stenhouse	.10	.08	.04
111	Tim Stoddard	.10	.08	.04
112	John Stuper	.10	.08	.04
113	Jim Sundberg	.15	.11	.06
114	Bruce Sutter	.25	.20	.10
115	Don Sutton	.60	.45	.25
116	Bruce Tanner(FC)	.10	.08	.04
117	Kent Tekulve	.15	.11	.06
118	Walt Terrell	.15	.11	.06
119	Mickey Tettleton(FC)	5.00	3.75	2.00
120	Rich Thompson	.10	.08	.04
121	Louis Thornton(FC)	.10	.08	.04
122	Alex Trevino	.10	.08	.04
123	John Tudor	.30	.25	.12
124	Jose Uribe(FC)	.25	.20	.10
125	Dave Valle(FC)	.20	.15	.08
126	Dave Von Ohlen	.10	.08	.04
127	Curt Wardle	.10	.08	.04
128	U.L. Washington	.10	.08	.04
129	Ed Whitson	.10	.08	.04
130	Herm Winningham(FC)	.20	.15	.08
131	Rich Yett(FC)	.15	.11	.06
132	Checklist	.10	.08	.04

1986 Fleer

The 1986 Fleer set contains 660 color photos, with each card measuring 2-1/2" by 3-1/2" in size. The card fronts include the word "Fleer," the player's team logo, and a player picture enclosed by a dark blue border. The card reverses are minus the black and white photo that was included in past Fleer efforts. Player biographical and statistical information appear in black and yellow ink on white stock. As in 1985, Fleer devoted ten cards, entitled "Major League Prospects," to twenty promising rookie players. The 1986 set, as in the previous four years, was issued with team logo stickers.

	MT	NR MT	EX
Complete Set:	125.00	90.00	50.00
Common Player:	.06	.05	.02

#	Player	MT	NR MT	EX
1	Steve Balboni	.08	.06	.03
2	Joe Beckwith	.06	.05	.02
3	Buddy Biancalana	.06	.05	.02
4	Bud Black	.06	.05	.02
5	George Brett	2.00	1.50	.80
6	Onix Concepcion	.06	.05	.02
7	Steve Farr	.08	.06	.03
8	Mark Gubicza	.12	.09	.05
9	Dane Iorg	.06	.05	.02
10	Danny Jackson	.20	.15	.08
11	Lynn Jones	.06	.05	.02
12	Mike Jones	.06	.05	.02
13	Charlie Leibrandt	.08	.06	.03
14	Hal McRae	.10	.08	.04
15	Omar Moreno	.06	.05	.02
16	Darryl Motley	.06	.05	.02
17	Jorge Orta	.06	.05	.02
18	Dan Quisenberry	.08	.06	.03
19	Bret Saberhagen	1.00	.70	.40
20	Pat Sheridan	.06	.05	.02
21	Lonnie Smith	.08	.06	.03
22	Jim Sundberg	.08	.06	.03
23	John Wathan	.08	.06	.03
24	Frank White	.10	.08	.04
25	Willie Wilson	.12	.09	.05
26	Joaquin Andujar	.08	.06	.03
27	Steve Braun	.06	.05	.02
28	Bill Campbell	.06	.05	.02
29	Cesar Cedeno	.10	.08	.04
30	Jack Clark	.20	.15	.08
31	*Vince Coleman*	2.00	1.50	.80
32	Danny Cox	.10	.08	.04
33	Ken Dayley	.06	.05	.02
34	Ivan DeJesus	.06	.05	.02
35	Bob Forsch	.08	.06	.03
36	Brian Harper	.06	.05	.02
37	Tom Herr	.10	.08	.04
38	Ricky Horton	.08	.06	.03
39	Kurt Kepshire	.06	.05	.02
40	Jeff Lahti	.06	.05	.02
41	Tito Landrum	.06	.05	.02
42	Willie McGee	.15	.11	.06
43	Tom Nieto	.06	.05	.02
44	Terry Pendleton	.80	.60	.30
45	Darrell Porter	.08	.06	.03
46	Ozzie Smith	1.00	.70	.40
47	John Tudor	.10	.08	.04
48	Andy Van Slyke	.15	.11	.06
49	*Todd Worrell*(FC)	.40	.30	.15
50	Jim Acker	.06	.05	.02
51	Doyle Alexander	.10	.08	.04
52	Jesse Barfield	.20	.15	.08
53	George Bell	.30	.25	.12
54	Jeff Burroughs	.08	.06	.03
55	Bill Caudill	.06	.05	.02
56	Jim Clancy	.08	.06	.03
57	Tony Fernandez	.20	.15	.08
58	Tom Filer	.06	.05	.02
59	Damaso Garcia	.06	.05	.02
60	Tom Henke(FC)	.15	.11	.06
61	Garth Iorg	.06	.05	.02
62	Cliff Johnson	.06	.05	.02
63	Jimmy Key	.15	.11	.06
64	Dennis Lamp	.06	.05	.02
65	Gary Lavelle	.06	.05	.02
66	Buck Martinez	.06	.05	.02
67	Lloyd Moseby	.10	.08	.04
68	Rance Mulliniks	.06	.05	.02
69	Al Oliver	.10	.08	.04
70	Dave Stieb	.12	.09	.05
71	Louis Thornton	.06	.05	.02
72	Willie Upshaw	.08	.06	.03
73	Ernie Whitt	.08	.06	.03
74	*Rick Aguilera*(FC)	1.00	.70	.40
75	Wally Backman	.08	.06	.03
76	Gary Carter	.25	.20	.10
77	Ron Darling	.15	.11	.06
78	*Len Dykstra*(FC)	2.00	1.50	.80
79	Sid Fernandez	.12	.09	.05
80	George Foster	.15	.11	.06
81	Dwight Gooden	2.00	1.50	.80
82	Tom Gorman	.06	.05	.02
83	Danny Heep	.06	.05	.02
84	Keith Hernandez	.30	.25	.12
85	Howard Johnson	.50	.40	.20
86	Ray Knight	.08	.06	.03
87	Terry Leach	.08	.06	.03
88	Ed Lynch	.06	.05	.02
89	*Roger McDowell*(FC)	.40	.30	.15
90	Jesse Orosco	.08	.06	.03
91	Tom Paciorek	.06	.05	.02
92	Ronn Reynolds	.06	.05	.02
93	Rafael Santana	.06	.05	.02
94	Doug Sisk	.06	.05	.02
95	Rusty Staub	.10	.08	.04
96	Darryl Strawberry	3.00	2.25	1.25
97	Mookie Wilson	.10	.08	.04
98	Neil Allen	.06	.05	.02
99	Don Baylor	.12	.09	.05
100	Dale Berra	.06	.05	.02
101	Rich Bordi	.06	.05	.02
102	Marty Bystrom	.06	.05	.02
103	Joe Cowley	.06	.05	.02
104	*Brian Fisher*	.15	.11	.06
105	Ken Griffey	.10	.08	.04
106	Ron Guidry	.20	.15	.08
107	Ron Hassey	.06	.05	.02
108	Rickey Henderson	2.00	1.50	.80
109	Don Mattingly	2.50	2.00	1.00
110	Bobby Meacham	.06	.05	.02
111	John Montefusco	.06	.05	.02
112	Phil Niekro	.25	.20	.10
113	Mike Pagliarulo	.20	.15	.08
114	Dan Pasqua	.20	.15	.08
115	Willie Randolph	.10	.08	.04
116	Dave Righetti	.20	.15	.08
117	Andre Robertson	.06	.05	.02
118	Billy Sample	.06	.05	.02
119	Bob Shirley	.06	.05	.02
120	Ed Whitson	.06	.05	.02
121	Dave Winfield	1.00	.70	.40
122	Butch Wynegar	.06	.05	.02
123	Dave Anderson	.06	.05	.02
124	Bob Bailor	.06	.05	.02
125	Greg Brock	.08	.06	.03
126	Enos Cabell	.06	.05	.02
127	Bobby Castillo	.06	.05	.02
128	Carlos Diaz	.06	.05	.02
129	*Mariano Duncan*	.15	.11	.06
130	Pedro Guerrero	.20	.15	.08
131	Orel Hershiser	.70	.50	.30
132	Rick Honeycutt	.06	.05	.02
133	Ken Howell	.06	.05	.02
134	Ken Landreaux	.06	.05	.02
135	Bill Madlock	.12	.09	.05
136	Candy Maldonado	.10	.08	.04
137	Mike Marshall	.15	.11	.06
138	Len Matuszek	.06	.05	.02
139	Tom Niedenfuer	.08	.06	.03
140	Alejandro Pena	.08	.06	.03
141	Jerry Reuss	.08	.06	.03
142	Bill Russell	.08	.06	.03
143	Steve Sax	.20	.15	.08
144	Mike Scioscia	.08	.06	.03
145	Fernando Valenzuela	.30	.25	.12
146	Bob Welch	.12	.09	.05
147	Terry Whitfield	.06	.05	.02
148	Juan Beniquez	.06	.05	.02
149	Bob Boone	.08	.06	.03
150	John Candelaria	.10	.08	.04
151	Rod Carew	.70	.50	.30
152	*Stewart Cliburn*(FC)	.12	.09	.05
153	Doug DeCinces	.10	.08	.04
154	Brian Downing	.08	.06	.03
155	Ken Forsch	.06	.05	.02
156	Craig Gerber	.06	.05	.02
157	Bobby Grich	.10	.08	.04
158	George Hendrick	.08	.06	.03
159	Al Holland	.06	.05	.02
160	Reggie Jackson	.50	.40	.20
161	Ruppert Jones	.06	.05	.02
162	*Urbano Lugo*	.08	.06	.03
163	*Kirk McCaskill*(FC)	.35	.25	.14
164	Donnie Moore	.06	.05	.02
165	Gary Pettis	.06	.05	.02
166	Ron Romanick	.06	.05	.02
167	Dick Schofield	.06	.05	.02

#	Name	MT	NR MT	EX		#	Name	MT	NR MT	EX
168	Daryl Sconiers	.06	.05	.02		259	Dan Schatzeder	.06	.05	.02
169	Jim Slaton	.06	.05	.02		260	Bryn Smith	.06	.05	.02
170	Don Sutton	.25	.20	.10		261	Randy St. Claire(FC)	.08	.06	.03
171	Mike Witt	.10	.08	.04		262	Scot Thompson	.06	.05	.02
172	Buddy Bell	.10	.08	.04		263	Tim Wallach	.12	.09	.05
173	Tom Browning	.30	.25	.12		264	U.L. Washington	.06	.05	.02
174	Dave Concepcion	.12	.09	.05		265	Mitch Webster(FC)	.25	.20	.10
175	Eric Davis	1.00	.70	.40		266	Herm Winningham	.15	.11	.06
176	Bo Diaz	.08	.06	.03		267	Floyd Youmans(FC)	.15	.11	.06
177	Nick Esasky	.08	.06	.03		268	Don Aase	.06	.05	.02
178	John Franco	.12	.09	.05		269	Mike Boddicker	.08	.06	.03
179	Tom Hume	.06	.05	.02		270	Rich Dauer	.06	.05	.02
180	Wayne Krenchicki	.06	.05	.02		271	Storm Davis	.10	.08	.04
181	Andy McGaffigan	.06	.05	.02		272	Rick Dempsey	.08	.06	.03
182	Eddie Milner	.06	.05	.02		273	Ken Dixon	.06	.05	.02
183	Ron Oester	.06	.05	.02		274	Jim Dwyer	.06	.05	.02
184	Dave Parker	.20	.15	.08		275	Mike Flanagan	.10	.08	.04
185	Frank Pastore	.06	.05	.02		276	Wayne Gross	.06	.05	.02
186	Tony Perez	.15	.11	.06		277	Lee Lacy	.06	.05	.02
187	Ted Power	.08	.06	.03		278	Fred Lynn	.20	.15	.08
188	Joe Price	.06	.05	.02		279	Tippy Martinez	.06	.05	.02
189	Gary Redus	.06	.05	.02		280	Dennis Martinez	.08	.06	.03
190	Ron Robinson	.08	.06	.03		281	Scott McGregor	.08	.06	.03
191	Pete Rose	.70	.50	.30		282	Eddie Murray	.40	.30	.15
192	Mario Soto	.08	.06	.03		283	Floyd Rayford	.06	.05	.02
193	John Stuper	.06	.05	.02		284	Cal Ripken, Jr.	5.00	3.75	2.00
194	Jay Tibbs	.06	.05	.02		285	Gary Roenicke	.06	.05	.02
195	Dave Van Gorder	.06	.05	.02		286	Larry Sheets	.20	.15	.08
196	Max Venable	.06	.05	.02		287	John Shelby	.06	.05	.02
197	Juan Agosto	.06	.05	.02		288	Nate Snell	.06	.05	.02
198	Harold Baines	.15	.11	.06		289	Sammy Stewart	.06	.05	.02
199	Floyd Bannister	.10	.08	.04		290	Alan Wiggins	.06	.05	.02
200	Britt Burns	.06	.05	.02		291	Mike Young	.06	.05	.02
201	Julio Cruz	.06	.05	.02		292	Alan Ashby	.06	.05	.02
202	Joel Davis(FC)	.08	.06	.03		293	Mark Bailey	.06	.05	.02
203	Richard Dotson	.10	.08	.04		294	Kevin Bass	.10	.08	.04
204	Carlton Fisk	.50	.40	.20		295	Jeff Calhoun	.06	.05	.02
205	Scott Fletcher	.08	.06	.03		296	Jose Cruz	.10	.08	.04
206	Ozzie Guillen	1.00	.70	.40		297	Glenn Davis	1.50	1.25	.60
207	Jerry Hairston	.06	.05	.02		298	Bill Dawley	.06	.05	.02
208	Tim Hulett	.08	.06	.03		299	Frank DiPino	.06	.05	.02
209	Bob James	.06	.05	.02		300	Bill Doran	.10	.08	.04
210	Ron Kittle	.10	.08	.04		301	Phil Garner	.08	.06	.03
211	Rudy Law	.06	.05	.02		302	Jeff Heathcock(FC)	.10	.08	.04
212	Bryan Little	.06	.05	.02		303	Charlie Kerfeld(FC)	.15	.11	.06
213	Gene Nelson	.06	.05	.02		304	Bob Knepper	.08	.06	.03
214	Reid Nichols	.06	.05	.02		305	Ron Mathis	.06	.05	.02
215	Luis Salazar	.06	.05	.02		306	Jerry Mumphrey	.06	.05	.02
216	Tom Seaver	1.00	.70	.40		307	Jim Pankovits	.06	.05	.02
217	Dan Spillner	.06	.05	.02		308	Terry Puhl	.06	.05	.02
218	Bruce Tanner	.06	.05	.02		309	Craig Reynolds	.06	.05	.02
219	Greg Walker	.10	.08	.04		310	Nolan Ryan	6.00	4.50	2.50
220	Dave Wehrmeister	.06	.05	.02		311	Mike Scott	.15	.11	.06
221	Juan Berenguer	.06	.05	.02		312	Dave Smith	.08	.06	.03
222	Dave Bergman	.06	.05	.02		313	Dickie Thon	.08	.06	.03
223	Tom Brookens	.06	.05	.02		314	Denny Walling	.06	.05	.02
224	Darrell Evans	.12	.09	.05		315	Kurt Bevacqua	.06	.05	.02
225	Barbaro Garbey	.06	.05	.02		316	Al Bumbry	.06	.05	.02
226	Kirk Gibson	.30	.25	.12		317	Jerry Davis	.06	.05	.02
227	John Grubb	.06	.05	.02		318	Luis DeLeon	.06	.05	.02
228	Willie Hernandez	.08	.06	.03		319	Dave Dravecky	.08	.06	.03
229	Larry Herndon	.08	.06	.03		320	Tim Flannery	.06	.05	.02
230	Chet Lemon	.08	.06	.03		321	Steve Garvey	.30	.25	.12
231	Aurelio Lopez	.06	.05	.02		322	Goose Gossage	.20	.15	.08
232	Jack Morris	.20	.15	.08		323	Tony Gwynn	.70	.50	.30
233	Randy O'Neal	.06	.05	.02		324	Andy Hawkins	.06	.05	.02
234	Lance Parrish	.20	.15	.08		325	LaMarr Hoyt	.06	.05	.02
235	Dan Petry	.08	.06	.03		326	Roy Lee Jackson	.06	.05	.02
236	Alex Sanchez	.06	.05	.02		327	Terry Kennedy	.08	.06	.03
237	Bill Scherrer	.06	.05	.02		328	Craig Lefferts	.06	.05	.02
238	Nelson Simmons	.06	.05	.02		329	Carmelo Martinez	.08	.06	.03
239	Frank Tanana	.10	.08	.04		330	Lance McCullers(FC)	.25	.20	.10
240	Walt Terrell	.08	.06	.03		331	Kevin McReynolds	.30	.25	.12
241	Alan Trammell	.30	.25	.12		332	Graig Nettles	.15	.11	.06
242	Lou Whitaker	.30	.25	.12		333	Jerry Royster	.06	.05	.02
243	Milt Wilcox	.06	.05	.02		334	Eric Show	.08	.06	.03
244	Hubie Brooks	.10	.08	.04		335	Tim Stoddard	.06	.05	.02
245	Tim Burke(FC)	.30	.25	.12		336	Garry Templeton	.08	.06	.03
246	Andre Dawson	.30	.25	.12		337	Mark Thurmond	.06	.05	.02
247	Mike Fitzgerald	.06	.05	.02		338	Ed Wojna	.06	.05	.02
248	Terry Francona	.06	.05	.02		339	Tony Armas	.08	.06	.03
249	Bill Gullickson	.06	.05	.02		340	Marty Barrett	.10	.08	.04
250	Joe Hesketh	.06	.05	.02		341	Wade Boggs	2.25	1.75	.90
251	Bill Laskey	.06	.05	.02		342	Dennis Boyd	.08	.06	.03
252	Vance Law	.08	.06	.03		343	Bill Buckner	.12	.09	.05
253	Charlie Lea	.06	.05	.02		344	Mark Clear	.06	.05	.02
254	Gary Lucas	.06	.05	.02		345	Roger Clemens	10.00	7.50	4.00
255	David Palmer	.06	.05	.02		346	Steve Crawford	.06	.05	.02
256	Tim Raines	.30	.25	.12		347	Mike Easler	.08	.06	.03
257	Jeff Reardon	.12	.09	.05		348	Dwight Evans	.12	.09	.05
258	Bert Roberge	.06	.05	.02		349	Rich Gedman	.10	.08	.04

#	Name	MT	NR MT	EX
350	Jackie Gutierrez	.06	.05	.02
351	Glenn Hoffman	.06	.05	.02
352	Bruce Hurst	.12	.09	.05
353	Bruce Kison	.06	.05	.02
354	Tim Lollar	.06	.05	.02
355	Steve Lyons	.08	.06	.03
356	Al Nipper	.08	.06	.03
357	Bob Ojeda	.08	.06	.03
358	Jim Rice	.30	.25	.12
359	Bob Stanley	.06	.05	.02
360	Mike Trujillo	.06	.05	.02
361	Thad Bosley	.06	.05	.02
362	Warren Brusstar	.06	.05	.02
363	Ron Cey	.10	.08	.04
364	Jody Davis	.10	.08	.04
365	Bob Dernier	.06	.05	.02
366	Shawon Dunston	.70	.50	.30
367	Leon Durham	.08	.06	.03
368	Dennis Eckersley	.12	.09	.05
369	Ray Fontenot	.06	.05	.02
370	George Frazier	.06	.05	.02
371	Bill Hatcher	.10	.08	.04
372	Dave Lopes	.08	.06	.03
373	Gary Matthews	.10	.08	.04
374	Ron Meredith	.06	.05	.02
375	Keith Moreland	.08	.06	.03
376	Reggie Patterson	.06	.05	.02
377	Dick Ruthven	.06	.05	.02
378	Ryne Sandberg	4.00	3.00	1.50
379	Scott Sanderson	.06	.05	.02
380	Lee Smith	.10	.08	.04
381	Lary Sorensen	.06	.05	.02
382	Chris Speier	.06	.05	.02
383	Rick Sutcliffe	.12	.09	.05
384	Steve Trout	.06	.05	.02
385	Gary Woods	.06	.05	.02
386	Bert Blyleven	.15	.11	.06
387	Tom Brunansky	.12	.09	.05
388	Randy Bush	.06	.05	.02
389	John Butcher	.06	.05	.02
390	Ron Davis	.06	.05	.02
391	Dave Engle	.06	.05	.02
392	Frank Eufemia	.06	.05	.02
393	Pete Filson	.06	.05	.02
394	Gary Gaetti	.20	.15	.08
395	Greg Gagne	.10	.08	.04
396	Mickey Hatcher	.06	.05	.02
397	Kent Hrbek	.20	.15	.08
398	Tim Laudner	.06	.05	.02
399	Rick Lysander	.06	.05	.02
400	Dave Meier	.06	.05	.02
401	Kirby Puckett	7.00	5.25	2.75
402	Mark Salas	.08	.06	.03
403	Ken Schrom	.06	.05	.02
404	Roy Smalley	.06	.05	.02
405	Mike Smithson	.06	.05	.02
406	Mike Stenhouse	.06	.05	.02
407	Tim Teufel	.06	.05	.02
408	Frank Viola	.15	.11	.06
409	Ron Washington	.06	.05	.02
410	Keith Atherton	.06	.05	.02
411	Dusty Baker	.08	.06	.03
412	Tim Birtsas	.12	.09	.05
413	Bruce Bochte	.06	.05	.02
414	Chris Codiroli	.06	.05	.02
415	Dave Collins	.08	.06	.03
416	Mike Davis	.08	.06	.03
417	Alfredo Griffin	.08	.06	.03
418	Mike Heath	.06	.05	.02
419	Steve Henderson	.06	.05	.02
420	Donnie Hill	.06	.05	.02
421	Jay Howell	.08	.06	.03
422	Tommy John	.20	.15	.08
423	Dave Kingman	.15	.11	.06
424	Bill Krueger	.06	.05	.02
425	Rick Langford	.06	.05	.02
426	Carney Lansford	.10	.08	.04
427	Steve McCatty	.06	.05	.02
428	Dwayne Murphy	.08	.06	.03
429	Steve Ontiveros(FC)	.12	.09	.05
430	Tony Phillips	.06	.05	.02
431	Jose Rijo	.10	.08	.04
432	Mickey Tettleton	2.00	1.50	.80
433	Luis Aguayo	.06	.05	.02
434	Larry Andersen	.06	.05	.02
435	Steve Carlton	.30	.25	.12
436	Don Carman	.30	.25	.12
437	Tim Corcoran	.06	.05	.02
438	Darren Daulton	2.25	1.75	.90
439	John Denny	.06	.05	.02
440	Tom Foley	.06	.05	.02
441	Greg Gross	.06	.05	.02
442	Kevin Gross	.08	.06	.03
443	Von Hayes	.10	.08	.04
444	Charles Hudson	.06	.05	.02
445	Garry Maddox	.08	.06	.03
446	Shane Rawley	.10	.08	.04
447	Dave Rucker	.06	.05	.02
448	John Russell	.06	.05	.02
449	Juan Samuel	.12	.09	.05
450	Mike Schmidt	2.00	1.50	.80
451	Rick Schu	.08	.06	.03
452	Dave Shipanoff	.06	.05	.02
453	Dave Stewart	.12	.09	.05
454	Jeff Stone	.06	.05	.02
455	Kent Tekulve	.08	.06	.03
456	Ozzie Virgil	.06	.05	.02
457	Glenn Wilson	.08	.06	.03
458	Jim Beattie	.06	.05	.02
459	Karl Best	.06	.05	.02
460	Barry Bonnell	.06	.05	.02
461	Phil Bradley	.20	.15	.08
462	Ivan Calderon	2.00	1.50	.80
463	Al Cowens	.06	.05	.02
464	Alvin Davis	.30	.25	.12
465	Dave Henderson	.10	.08	.04
466	Bob Kearney	.06	.05	.02
467	Mark Langston	.30	.25	.12
468	Bob Long	.06	.05	.02
469	Mike Moore	.06	.05	.02
470	Edwin Nunez	.06	.05	.02
471	Spike Owen	.06	.05	.02
472	Jack Perconte	.06	.05	.02
473	Jim Presley	.15	.11	.06
474	Donnie Scott	.06	.05	.02
475	Bill Swift(FC)	.12	.09	.05
476	Danny Tartabull	2.00	1.50	.80
477	Gorman Thomas	.10	.08	.04
478	Roy Thomas	.06	.05	.02
479	Ed Vande Berg	.06	.05	.02
480	Frank Wills	.06	.05	.02
481	Matt Young	.06	.05	.02
482	Ray Burris	.06	.05	.02
483	Jaime Cocanower	.06	.05	.02
484	Cecil Cooper	.12	.09	.05
485	Danny Darwin	.06	.05	.02
486	Rollie Fingers	.20	.15	.08
487	Jim Gantner	.08	.06	.03
488	Bob Gibson	.06	.05	.02
489	Moose Haas	.06	.05	.02
490	Teddy Higuera	.60	.45	.25
491	Paul Householder	.06	.05	.02
492	Pete Ladd	.06	.05	.02
493	Rick Manning	.06	.05	.02
494	Bob McClure	.06	.05	.02
495	Paul Molitor	.15	.11	.06
496	Charlie Moore	.06	.05	.02
497	Ben Oglivie	.08	.06	.03
498	Randy Ready	.06	.05	.02
499	Earnie Riles	.20	.15	.08
500	Ed Romero	.06	.05	.02
501	Bill Schroeder	.06	.05	.02
502	Ray Searage	.06	.05	.02
503	Ted Simmons	.12	.09	.05
504	Pete Vuckovich	.08	.06	.03
505	Rick Waits	.06	.05	.02
506	Robin Yount	2.00	1.50	.80
507	Len Barker	.08	.06	.03
508	Steve Bedrosian	.12	.09	.05
509	Bruce Benedict	.06	.05	.02
510	Rick Camp	.06	.05	.02
511	Rick Cerone	.06	.05	.02
512	Chris Chambliss	.08	.06	.03
513	Jeff Dedmon	.06	.05	.02
514	Terry Forster	.08	.06	.03
515	Gene Garber	.06	.05	.02
516	Terry Harper	.06	.05	.02
517	Bob Horner	.12	.09	.05
518	Glenn Hubbard	.06	.05	.02
519	Joe Johnson(FC)	.08	.06	.03
520	Brad Komminsk	.06	.05	.02
521	Rick Mahler	.06	.05	.02
522	Dale Murphy	.50	.40	.20
523	Ken Oberkfell	.06	.05	.02
524	Pascual Perez	.08	.06	.03
525	Gerald Perry	.12	.09	.05
526	Rafael Ramirez	.06	.05	.02
527	Steve Shields(FC)	.12	.09	.05
528	Zane Smith	.10	.08	.04
529	Bruce Sutter	.12	.09	.05
530	Milt Thompson(FC)	.15	.11	.06
531	Claudell Washington	.08	.06	.03

#	Player	MT	NR MT	EX
532	Paul Zuvella	.06	.05	.02
533	Vida Blue	.10	.08	.04
534	Bob Brenly	.06	.05	.02
535	*Chris Brown*	.20	.15	.08
536	Chili Davis	.10	.08	.04
537	Mark Davis	.06	.05	.02
538	Rob Deer	.12	.09	.05
539	Dan Driessen	.08	.06	.03
540	Scott Garrelts	.08	.06	.03
541	Dan Gladden	.08	.06	.03
542	Jim Gott	.06	.05	.02
543	David Green	.06	.05	.02
544	Atlee Hammaker	.06	.05	.02
545	Mike Jeffcoat	.06	.05	.02
546	Mike Krukow	.08	.06	.03
547	Dave LaPoint	.08	.06	.03
548	Jeff Leonard	.08	.06	.03
549	Greg Minton	.06	.05	.02
550	Alex Trevino	.06	.05	.02
551	Manny Trillo	.08	.06	.03
552	*Jose Uribe*	.20	.15	.08
553	Brad Wellman	.06	.05	.02
554	Frank Williams	.06	.05	.02
555	Joel Youngblood	.06	.05	.02
556	Alan Bannister	.06	.05	.02
557	Glenn Brummer	.06	.05	.02
558	*Steve Buechele*(FC)	.20	.15	.08
559	*Jose Guzman*(FC)	.20	.15	.08
560	Toby Harrah	.08	.06	.03
561	Greg Harris	.06	.05	.02
562	*Dwayne Henry*(FC)	.10	.08	.04
563	Burt Hooton	.08	.06	.03
564	Charlie Hough	.08	.06	.03
565	Mike Mason	.06	.05	.02
566	*Oddibe McDowell*	.20	.15	.08
567	Dickie Noles	.06	.05	.02
568	Pete O'Brien	.10	.08	.04
569	Larry Parrish	.10	.08	.04
570	Dave Rozema	.06	.05	.02
571	Dave Schmidt	.06	.05	.02
572	Don Slaught	.06	.05	.02
573	Wayne Tolleson	.06	.05	.02
574	Duane Walker	.06	.05	.02
575	Gary Ward	.08	.06	.03
576	Chris Welsh	.06	.05	.02
577	Curtis Wilkerson	.06	.05	.02
578	George Wright	.06	.05	.02
579	Chris Bando	.06	.05	.02
580	Tony Bernazard	.06	.05	.02
581	Brett Butler	.08	.06	.03
582	Ernie Camacho	.06	.05	.02
583	Joe Carter	.20	.15	.08
584	Carmello Castillo **(Carmelo)**	.06	.05	.02
585	Jamie Easterly	.06	.05	.02
586	Julio Franco	.10	.08	.04
587	Mel Hail	.08	.06	.03
588	Mike Hargrove	.06	.05	.02
589	Neal Heaton	.06	.05	.02
590	Brook Jacoby	.10	.08	.04
591	*Otis Nixon*(FC)	.12	.09	.05
592	Jerry Reed	.06	.05	.02
593	Vern Ruhle	.06	.05	.02
594	Pat Tabler	.08	.06	.03
595	Rich Thompson	.06	.05	.02
596	Andre Thornton	.08	.06	.03
597	Dave Von Ohlen	.06	.05	.02
598	George Vukovich	.06	.05	.02
599	Tom Waddell	.06	.05	.02
600	Curt Wardle	.06	.05	.02
601	Jerry Willard	.06	.05	.02
602	Bill Almon	.06	.05	.02
603	Mike Bielecki	.08	.06	.03
604	Sid Bream	.10	.08	.04
605	Mike Brown	.06	.05	.02
606	*Pat Clements*	.12	.09	.05
607	Jose DeLeon	.08	.06	.03
608	Denny Gonzalez	.06	.05	.02
609	Cecilio Guante	.06	.05	.02
610	Steve Kemp	.08	.06	.03
611	Sam Khalifa	.06	.05	.02
612	Lee Mazzilli	.08	.06	.03
613	Larry McWilliams	.06	.05	.02
614	Jim Morrison	.06	.05	.02
615	*Joe Orsulak*	.15	.11	.06
616	Tony Pena	.10	.08	.04
617	Johnny Ray	.10	.08	.04
618	Rick Reuschel	.10	.08	.04
619	R.J. Reynolds	.08	.06	.03
620	Rick Rhoden	.10	.08	.04
621	Don Robinson	.08	.06	.03
622	Jason Thompson	.06	.05	.02
623	Lee Tunnell	.06	.05	.02
624	Jim Winn	.06	.05	.02
625	Marvell Wynne	.06	.05	.02
626	Gooden In Action (Dwight Gooden)	.50	.40	.20
627	Mattingly In Action (Don Mattingly)	1.25	.90	.50
628	4,192! (Pete Rose)	.50	.40	.20
629	3,000 Career Hits (Rod Carew)	.50	.40	.20
630	300 Career Wins (Phil Niekro, Tom Seaver)	.20	.15	.08
631	Ouch! (Don Baylor)	.08	.06	.03
632	Instant Offense (Tim Raines, Darryl Strawberry)	.30	.25	.12
633	Shortstops Supreme (Cal Ripken, Jr., Alan Trammell)	.30	.25	.12
634	Boggs & "Hero" (Wade Boggs, George Brett)	.60	.45	.25
635	Braves Dynamic Duo (Bob Horner, Dale Murphy)	.30	.25	.12
636	Cardinal Ignitors (Vince Coleman, Willie McGee)	.35	.25	.14
637	Terror on the Basepaths (Vince Coleman)	.50	.40	.20
638	Charlie Hustle & Dr. K (Dwight Gooden, Pete Rose)	.70	.50	.30
639	1984 and 1985 A.L. Batting Champs (Wade Boggs, Don Mattingly)	1.00	.70	.40
640	N.L. West Sluggers (Steve Garvey, Dale Murphy, Dave Parker)	.30	.25	.12
641	Staff Aces (Dwight Gooden, Fernando Valenzuela)	.40	.30	.15
642	Blue Jay Stoppers (Jimmy Key, Dave Stieb)	.10	.08	.04
643	A.L. All-Star Backstops (Carlton Fisk, Rich Gedman)	.10	.08	.04
644	Major League Prospect (*Benito Santiago, Gene Walter*)(FC)	4.00	3.00	1.50
645	Major League Prospect (*Colin Ward, Mike Woodard*)(FC)	.10	.08	.04
646	Major League Prospect (*Kal Daniels, Paul O'Neill*)(FC)	4.50	3.40	1.75
647	Major League Prospect (*Andres Galarraga, Fred Toliver*)(FC)	.80	.60	.30
648	Major League Prospect (*Curt Ford, Bob Kipper*)(FC)	.25	.20	.10
649	Major League Prospect (*Jose Canseco, Eric Plunk*)(FC)	40.00	30.00	15.00
650	Major League Prospect (*Mark McLemore, Gus Polidor*)(FC)	.15	.11	.06
651	Major League Prospect (*Mickey Brantley, Rob Woodward*)(FC)	.15	.11	.06
652	Major League Prospect (*Mark Funderburk, Billy Joe Robidoux*)(FC)	.10	.08	.04
653	Major League Prospect (*Cecil Fielder, Cory Snyder*)(FC)	20.00	15.00	8.00
654	Checklist 1-97	.06	.05	.02
655	Checklist 98-196	.06	.05	.02
656	Checklist 197-291	.06	.05	.02
657	Checklist 292-385	.06	.05	.02
658	Checklist 386-482	.06	.05	.02
659	Checklist 483-578	.06	.05	.02
660	Checklist 579-660	.06	.05	.02

1986 Fleer
All Star Team

Fleer's choices for a major league All-Star team make up this 12-card set. The cards, which measure

2-1/2" by 3-1/2", were randomly inserted in 35¢ wax packs and 59¢ cello packs. The card fronts have a color photo set against a bright red background for A.L. players or a bright blue background for N.L. players. The card backs feature the player's career highlights set in white type against a red and blue background.

		MT	NR MT	EX
Complete Set:		16.00	12.00	6.50
Common Player:		.60	.45	.25
1	Don Mattingly	4.00	3.00	1.50
2	Tom Herr	.60	.45	.25
3	George Brett	2.00	1.50	.80
4	Gary Carter	1.00	.70	.40
5	Cal Ripken, Jr.	2.50	2.00	1.00
6	Dave Parker	.75	.60	.30
7	Rickey Henderson	3.00	2.25	1.25
8	Pedro Guerrero	.75	.60	.30
9	Dan Quisenberry	.60	.45	.25
10	Dwight Gooden	3.00	2.25	1.25
11	Gorman Thomas	.60	.45	.25
12	John Tudor	.60	.45	.25

1986 Fleer Baseball's Best

The 1986 Fleer Baseball's Best set consists of 44 cards and was produced for the McCrory's store chain and their affiliated stores. Subtitled "Sluggers vs. Pitchers," the set contains 22 each of the game's best hitters and pitchers. The cards, which measure 2-1/2" by 3-1/2", have color photos depicting an action pose. The backs are done in blue and red ink on white stock and carry the player's personal and statistical information. The sets were issued in a specially designed box with six team logo stickers.

		MT	NR MT	EX
Complete Set:		7.00	5.25	2.75
Common Player:		.05	.04	.02
1	Bert Blyleven	.10	.08	.04
2	Wade Boggs	.70	.50	.30
3	George Brett	.30	.25	.12
4	Tom Browning	.15	.11	.06
5	Jose Canseco	2.50	2.00	1.00
6	Will Clark	1.50	1.25	.60
7	Roger Clemens	.70	.50	.30
8	Alvin Davis	.10	.08	.04
9	Julio Franco	.10	.08	.04
10	Kirk Gibson	.20	.15	.08
11	Dwight Gooden	.70	.50	.30
12	Goose Gossage	.12	.09	.05
13	Pedro Guerrero	.15	.11	.06
14	Ron Guidry	.12	.09	.05
15	Tony Gwynn	.25	.20	.10
16	Orel Hershiser	.20	.15	.08
17	Kent Hrbek	.15	.11	.06
18	Reggie Jackson	.25	.20	.10
19	Wally Joyner	.50	.40	.20
20	Charlie Leibrandt	.05	.04	.02
21	Don Mattingly	1.00	.70	.40
22	Willie McGee	.12	.09	.05

		MT	NR MT	EX
23	Jack Morris	.15	.11	.06
24	Dale Murphy	.30	.25	.12
25	Eddie Murray	.25	.20	.10
26	Jeff Reardon	.07	.05	.03
27	Rick Reuschel	.07	.05	.03
28	Cal Ripken, Jr	.80	.60	.30
29	Pete Rose	.60	.45	.25
30	Nolan Ryan	1.75	1.25	.70
31	Bret Saberhagen	.15	.11	.06
32	Ryne Sandberg	.60	.45	.25
33	Mike Schmidt	.30	.25	.12
34	Tom Seaver	.25	.20	.10
35	Bryn Smith	.05	.04	.02
36	Mario Soto	.05	.04	.02
37	Dave Stieb	.10	.08	.04
38	Darryl Strawberry	.40	.30	.15
39	Rick Sutcliffe	.10	.08	.04
40	John Tudor	.10	.08	.04
41	Fernando Valenzuela	.20	.15	.08
42	Bobby Witt	.15	.11	.06
43	Mike Witt	.07	.05	.03
44	Robin Yount	.35	.25	.14

1986 Fleer Box Panels

Picking up on a Donruss idea, Fleer issued eight cards in panels of four on the bottoms of the wax and cello pack boxes. The cards are numbered C-1 through C-8 and are 2-1/2" by 3-1/2", with a complete panel measuring 5" by 7-1/8" in size. Included in the eight cards are six player cards and two team logo/checklist cards.

		MT	NR MT	EX
Complete Panel Set:		3.50	2.75	1.50
Complete Singles Set:		1.75	1.25	.70
Common Single Player:		.20	.15	.08
	Panel	2.00	1.50	.80
1	Royals Logo/Checklist.	.05	.04	.02
2	George Brett	.60	.45	.25
3	Ozzie Guillen	.40	.30	.15
4	Dale Murphy	.40	.30	.15
	Panel	1.50	1.25	.60
5	Cardinals Logo/Checklist	.05	.04	.02
6	Tom Browning	.20	.15	.08
7	Gary Carter	.35	.25	.14
8	Carlton Fisk	.20	.15	.08

1986 Fleer Future Hall Of Famers

The 1986 Fleer Future Hall of Famers set is comprised of six players Fleer felt would gain eventual entrance into the Baseball Hall of Fame. The cards are the standard 2-1/2" by 3-1/2" in size and were randomly inserted in three-pack cello packs. The card fronts feature a player photo set against a blue background with horizontal light blue stripes. The card backs are printed in black on a blue background and feature player highlights in paragraph form.

		MT	NR MT	EX
	Complete Set:	12.00	9.00	4.75
	Common Player:	1.75	1.25	.70
1	Pete Rose	1.75	1.25	.70
2	Steve Carlton	1.75	1.25	.70
3	Tom Seaver	1.75	1.25	.70
4	Rod Carew	1.75	1.25	.70
5	Nolan Ryan	3.00	2.25	1.25
6	Reggie Jackson	1.75	1.25	.70

		MT	NR MT	EX
16	Dwight Gooden	.60	.45	.25
17	Ozzie Guillen	.10	.08	.04
18	Willie Hernandez	.05	.04	.02
19	Bob Horner	.07	.05	.03
20	Kent Hrbek	.15	.11	.06
21	Charlie Leibrandt	.05	.04	.02
22	Don Mattingly	.80	.60	.30
23	Oddibe McDowell	.12	.09	.05
24	Willie McGee	.10	.08	.04
25	Keith Moreland	.05	.04	.02
26	Lloyd Moseby	.07	.05	.03
27	Dale Murphy	.30	.25	.12
28	Phil Niekro	.15	.11	.06
29	Joe Orsulak	.05	.04	.02
30	Dave Parker	.12	.09	.05
31	Lance Parrish	.15	.11	.06
32	Kirby Puckett	.70	.50	.30
33	Tim Raines	.25	.20	.10
34	Earnie Riles	.07	.05	.03
35	Cal Ripken, Jr.	.80	.60	.30
36	Pete Rose	.60	.45	.25
37	Bret Saberhagen	.15	.11	.06
38	Juan Samuel	.10	.08	.04
39	Ryne Sandberg	.60	.45	.25
40	Tom Seaver	.25	.20	.10
41	Lee Smith	.07	.05	.03
42	Ozzie Smith	.12	.09	.05
43	Dave Stieb	.10	.08	.04
44	Robin Yount	.35	.25	.12

1986 Fleer
League Leaders

Fleer's 1986 "League Leaders" set features 44 of the game's top players and was issued through the Walgreens drug store chain. The card fronts contain a color photo and feature the player's name, team and postition in a blue band near the bottom of the card. The words "League Leaders" appear in a red band at the top of the card. The background for the card fronts is alternating blue and white stripes. The card backs are printed in blue, red and white and carry the player's statistical information and team logo. The cards are the standard 2-1/2" by 3-1/2" size. The set was issued in a special cardboard box, along with six team logo stickers.

		MT	NR MT	EX
	Complete Set:	7.00	5.25	2.75
	Common Player:	.05	.04	.02
1	Wade Boggs	.60	.45	.25
2	George Brett	.30	.25	.12
3	Jose Canseco	2.50	2.00	1.00
4	Rod Carew	.30	.25	.12
5	Gary Carter	.25	.20	.10
6	Jack Clark	.12	.09	.05
7	Vince Coleman	.30	.25	.12
8	Jose Cruz	.05	.04	.02
9	Alvin Davis	.10	.08	.04
10	Mariano Duncan	.05	.04	.02
11	Leon Durham	.05	.04	.02
12	Carlton Fisk	.15	.11	.06
13	Julio Franco	.10	.08	.04
14	Scott Garrelts	.05	.04	.02
15	Steve Garvey	.25	.20	.10

1986 Fleer
Limited Edition

Produced for the McCrory's store chain and their affiliates for the second year in a row, the 1986 Fleer Limited Edition set contains 44 cards. The cards, which are the standard 2-1/2" by 3-1/2" size, have color photos enclosed by green, red and yellow trim. The card backs carry black print on two shades of red. The set was issued in a special cardboard box, along with six team logo stickers.

		MT	NR MT	EX
	Complete Set:	6.00	4.50	2.50
	Common Player:	.05	.04	.02
1	Doyle Alexander	.05	.04	.02
2	Joaquin Andujar	.05	.04	.02
3	Harold Baines	.12	.09	.05
4	Wade Boggs	.70	.50	.30
5	Phil Bradley	.12	.09	.05
6	George Brett	.30	.25	.12
7	Hubie Brooks	.07	.05	.03
8	Chris Brown	.12	.09	.05
9	Tom Brunansky	.10	.08	.04
10	Gary Carter	.25	.20	.10
11	Vince Coleman	.60	.45	.25
12	Cecil Cooper	.07	.05	.03
13	Jose Cruz	.05	.04	.02
14	Mike Davis	.05	.04	.02
15	Carlton Fisk	.15	.11	.06
16	Julio Franco	.10	.08	.04
17	Damaso Garcia	.05	.04	.02
18	Rich Gedman	.05	.04	.02
19	Kirk Gibson	.20	.15	.08
20	Dwight Gooden	.70	.50	.30
21	Pedro Guerrero	.15	.11	.06

		MT	NR MT	EX
22	Tony Gwynn	.25	.20	.10
23	Rickey Henderson	.50	.40	.20
24	Orel Hershiser	.20	.15	.08
25	LaMarr Hoyt	.05	.04	.02
26	Reggie Jackson	.30	.25	.12
27	Don Mattingly	.90	.70	.35
28	Oddibe McDowell	.12	.09	.05
29	Willie McGee	.10	.08	.04
30	Paul Molitor	.12	.09	.05
31	Dale Murphy	.30	.25	.12
32	Eddie Murray	.25	.20	.10
33	Dave Parker	.12	.09	.05
34	Tony Pena	.07	.05	.03
35	Jeff Reardon	.07	.05	.03
36	Cal Ripken, Jr.	.60	.45	.25
37	Pete Rose	.60	.45	.25
38	Bret Saberhagen	.15	.11	.06
39	Juan Samuel	.10	.08	.04
40	Ryne Sandberg	.60	.45	.25
41	Mike Schmidt	.30	.25	.12
42	Lee Smith	.07	.05	.03
43	Don Sutton	.12	.09	.05
44	Lou Whitaker	.15	.11	.06

1986 Fleer Mini

Fleer's 1986 "Classic Miniatures" set contains 120 cards that measure 1-13/16" by 2-9/16" in size. The design of the high-gloss cards is identical to the regular 1986 Fleer set but the player photos are entirely different. The set, which was issued in a specially designed box along with 18 team logo stickers, was available to the collecting public only through hobby dealers.

		MT	NR MT	EX
Complete Set:		15.00	11.00	6.00
Common Player:		.05	.04	.02
1	George Brett	.30	.25	.12
2	Dan Quisenberry	.07	.05	.03
3	Bret Saberhagen	.15	.11	.06
4	Lonnie Smith	.05	.04	.02
5	Willie Wilson	.10	.08	.04
6	Jack Clark	.12	.09	.05
7	Vince Coleman	.50	.40	.20
8	Tom Herr	.07	.05	.03
9	Willie McGee	.10	.08	.04
10	Ozzie Smith	.12	.09	.05
11	John Tudor	.07	.05	.03
12	Jesse Barfield	.12	.09	.05
13	George Bell	.20	.15	.08
14	Tony Fernandez	.10	.08	.04
15	Damaso Garcia	.05	.04	.02
16	Dave Stieb	.07	.05	.03
17	Gary Carter	.20	.15	.08
18	Ron Darling	.10	.08	.04
19	Dwight Gooden	.60	.45	.25
20	Keith Hernandez	.20	.15	.08
21	Darryl Strawberry	.50	.40	.20
22	Ron Guidry	.15	.11	.06
23	Rickey Henderson	1.00	.70	.40
24	Don Mattingly	1.25	.90	.50
25	Dave Righetti	.12	.09	.05
26	Dave Winfield	.20	.15	.08
27	Mariano Duncan	.07	.05	.03
28	Pedro Guerrero	.12	.09	.05
29	Bill Madlock	.10	.08	.04

		MT	NR MT	EX
30	Mike Marshall	.10	.08	.04
31	Fernando Valenzuela	.10	.08	.04
32	Reggie Jackson	.30	.25	.12
33	Gary Pettis	.05	.04	.02
34	Ron Romanick	.05	.04	.02
35	Don Sutton	.12	.09	.05
36	Mike Witt	.07	.05	.03
37	Buddy Bell	.07	.05	.03
38	Tom Browning	.10	.08	.04
39	Dave Parker	.12	.09	.05
40	Pete Rose	.60	.45	.25
41	Mario Soto	.05	.04	.02
42	Harold Baines	.12	.09	.05
43	Carlton Fisk	.15	.11	.06
44	Ozzie Guillen	.12	.09	.05
45	Ron Kittle	.07	.05	.03
46	Tom Seaver	.20	.15	.08
47	Kirk Gibson	.20	.15	.08
48	Jack Morris	.15	.11	.06
49	Lance Parrish	.15	.11	.06
50	Alan Trammell	.20	.15	.08
51	Lou Whitaker	.15	.11	.06
52	Hubie Brooks	.07	.05	.03
53	Andre Dawson	.15	.11	.06
54	Tim Raines	.20	.15	.08
55	Bryn Smith	.05	.04	.02
56	Tim Wallach	.10	.08	.04
57	Mike Boddicker	.05	.04	.02
58	Eddie Murray	.25	.20	.10
59	Cal Ripken	1.00	.70	.40
60	John Shelby	.05	.04	.02
61	Mike Young	.05	.04	.02
62	Jose Cruz	.07	.05	.03
63	Glenn Davis	.15	.11	.06
64	Phil Garner	.05	.04	.02
65	Nolan Ryan	2.00	1.50	.80
66	Mike Scott	.12	.09	.05
67	Steve Garvey	.20	.15	.08
68	Goose Gossage	.12	.09	.05
69	Tony Gwynn	.25	.20	.10
70	Andy Hawkins	.05	.04	.02
71	Garry Templeton	.05	.04	.02
72	Wade Boggs	.80	.60	.30
73	Roger Clemens	.80	.60	.30
74	Dwight Evans	.12	.09	.05
75	Rich Gedman	.05	.04	.02
76	Jim Rice	.20	.15	.08
77	Shawon Dunston	.10	.08	.04
78	Leon Durham	.05	.04	.02
79	Keith Moreland	.05	.04	.02
80	Ryne Sandberg	.20	.15	.08
81	Rick Sutcliffe	.10	.08	.04
82	Bert Blyleven	.12	.09	.05
83	Tom Brunansky	.10	.08	.04
84	Kent Hrbek	.15	.11	.06
85	Kirby Puckett	.70	.50	.30
86	Bruce Bochte	.05	.04	.02
87	Jose Canseco	3.00	2.25	1.25
88	Mike Davis	.05	.04	.02
89	Jay Howell	.07	.05	.03
90	Dwayne Murphy	.05	.04	.02
91	Steve Carlton	.20	.15	.08
92	Von Hayes	.10	.08	.04
93	Juan Samuel	.12	.09	.05
94	Mike Schmidt	.30	.25	.12
95	Glenn Wilson	.05	.04	.02
96	Phil Bradley	.10	.08	.04
97	Alvin Davis	.10	.08	.04
98	Jim Presley	.10	.08	.04
99	Danny Tartabull	.15	.11	.06
100	Cecil Cooper	.10	.08	.04
101	Paul Molitor	.12	.09	.05
102	Earnie Riles	.07	.05	.03
103	Robin Yount	.30	.25	.12
104	Bob Horner	.10	.08	.04
105	Dale Murphy	.30	.25	.12
106	Bruce Sutter	.10	.08	.04
107	Claudell Washington	.05	.04	.02
108	Chris Brown	.12	.09	.05
109	Chili Davis	.05	.04	.02
110	Scott Garrelts	.05	.04	.02
111	Oddibe McDowell	.12	.09	.05
112	Pete O'Brien	.07	.05	.03
113	Gary Ward	.05	.04	.02
114	Brett Butler	.05	.04	.02
115	Julio Franco	.10	.08	.04
116	Brook Jacoby	.10	.08	.04
117	Mike Brown	.05	.04	.02
118	Joe Orsulak	.05	.04	.02
119	Tony Pena	.07	.05	.03
120	R.J. Reynolds	.05	.04	.02

1986 Fleer Star Stickers

After a five-year layoff, Fleer once again produced a Star Sticker set. The cards, which measure 2-1/2" by 3-1/2", have color photos inside dark maroon borders. The card backs are identical to the 1986 regular issue except for the 1-132 numbering system and blue ink instead of yellow. The words "Bend and Peel" are found in the upper right corner of the card backs. Card #132 is a multi-player card featuring Dwight Gooden and Dale Murphy on the front and a complete checklist for the set on the reverse. The cards were sold in wax packs with team logo stickers.

		MT	NR MT	EX
	Complete Set	30.00	22.00	12.00
	Common Player	.05	.04	.02
1	Harold Baines	.20	.15	.08
2	Jesse Barfield	.20	.15	.08
3	Don Baylor	.12	.09	.05
4	Juan Beniquez	.05	.04	.02
5	Tim Birtsas	.08	.06	.03
6	Bert Blyleven	.15	.11	.06
7	Bruce Bochte	.05	.04	.02
8	Wade Boggs	1.00	.70	.40
9	Dennis Boyd	.12	.09	.05
10	Phil Bradley	.20	.15	.08
11	George Brett	.50	.40	.20
12	Hubie Brooks	.12	.09	.05
13	Chris Brown	.45	.35	.20
14	Tom Browning	.15	.11	.06
15	Tom Brunansky	.15	.11	.06
16	Bill Buckner	.10	.08	.04
17	Britt Burns	.05	.04	.02
18	Brett Butler	.08	.06	.03
19	Jose Canseco	3.00	2.25	1.25
20	Rod Carew	.40	.30	.15
21	Steve Carlton	.40	.30	.15
22	Don Carman	.20	.15	.08
23	Gary Carter	.40	.30	.15
24	Jack Clark	.20	.15	.08
25	Vince Coleman	.70	.50	.30
26	Cecil Cooper	.15	.11	.06
27	Jose Cruz	.10	.08	.04
28	Ron Darling	.20	.15	.08
29	Alvin Davis	.20	.15	.08
30	Jody Davis	.08	.06	.03
31	Mike Davis	.05	.04	.02
32	Andre Dawson	.25	.20	.10
33	Mariano Duncan	.10	.08	.04
34	Shawon Dunston	.15	.11	.06
35	Leon Durham	.08	.06	.03
36	Darrell Evans	.12	.09	.05
37	Tony Fernandez.	.15	.11	.06
38	Carlton Fisk	.20	.15	.08
39	John Franco	.10	.08	.04
40	Julio Franco	.12	.09	.05
41	Damaso Garcia	.05	.04	.02
42	Scott Garrelts	.05	.04	.02
43	Steve Garvey	.25	.20	.10
44	Rich Gedman	.10	.08	.04
45	Kirk Gibson	.30	.25	.12
46	Dwight Gooden	.90	.70	.35
47	Pedro Guerrero	.20	.15	.08
48	Ron Guidry	.20	.15	.08
49	Ozzie Guillen	.30	.25	.12

		MT	NR MT	EX
50	Tony Gwynn	.40	.30	.15
51	Andy Hawkins	.08	.06	.03
52	Von Hayes	.12	.09	.05
53	Rickey Henderson	1.00	.70	.40
54	Tom Henke	.12	.09	.05
55	Keith Hernandez	.35	.25	.14
56	Willie Hernandez	.05	.04	.02
57	Tom Herr	.10	.08	.04
58	Orel Hershiser	.30	.25	.12
59	Teddy Higuera	.60	.45	.25
60	Bob Horner	.12	.09	.05
61	Charlie Hough	.08	.06	.03
62	Jay Howell	.08	.06	.03
63	LaMarr Hoyt	.05	.04	.02
64	Kent Hrbek	.30	.25	.12
65	Reggie Jackson	.50	.40	.20
66	Bob James	.05	.04	.02
67	Dave Kingman	.12	.09	.05
68	Ron Kittle	.12	.09	.05
69	Charlie Leibrandt	.08	.06	.03
70	Fred Lynn	.25	.20	.10
71	Mike Marshall	.20	.15	.08
72	Don Mattingly	1.75	1.25	.70
73	Oddibe McDowell	.25	.20	.10
74	Willie McGee	.20	.15	.08
75	Scott McGregor	.05	.04	.02
76	Paul Molitor	.20	.15	.08
77	Donnie Moore	.05	.04	.02
78	Keith Moreland	.08	.06	.03
79	Jack Morris	.25	.20	.10
80	Dale Murphy	.40	.30	.15
81	Eddie Murray	.50	.40	.20
82	Phil Niekro	.25	.20	.10
83	Joe Orsulak	.10	.08	.04
84	Dave Parker	.25	.20	.10
85	Lance Parrish	.25	.20	.10
86	Larry Parrish	.08	.06	.03
87	Tony Pena	.10	.08	.04
88	Gary Pettis	.05	.04	.02
89	Jim Presley	.15	.11	.06
90	Kirby Puckett	1.00	.70	.40
91	Dan Quisenberry	.12	.09	.05
92	Tim Raines	.35	.25	.14
93	Johnny Ray	.10	.08	.04
94	Jeff Reardon	.10	.08	.04
95	Rick Reuschel	.10	.08	.04
96	Jim Rice	.15	.11	.06
97	Dave Righetti	.20	.15	.08
98	Earnie Riles	.12	.09	.05
99	Cal Ripken, Jr.	1.00	.70	.40
100	Ron Romanick	.05	.04	.02
101	Pete Rose	1.00	.70	.40
102	Nolan Ryan	2.00	1.50	.80
103	Bret Saberhagen	.25	.20	.10
104	Mark Salas	.05	.04	.02
105	Juan Samuel	.15	.11	.06
106	Ryne Sandberg	.70	.50	.30
107	Mike Schmidt	1.00	.70	.40
108	Mike Scott	.15	.11	.06
109	Tom Seaver	.30	.25	.12
110	Bryn Smith	.05	.04	.02
111	Dave Smith	.05	.04	.02
112	Lee Smith	.10	.08	.04
113	Ozzie Smith	.20	.15	.08
114	Mario Soto	.05	.04	.02
115	Dave Stieb	.12	.09	.05
116	Darryl Strawberry	1.00	.70	.40
117	Bruce Sutter	.10	.08	.04
118	Garry Templeton	.08	.06	.03
119	Gorman Thomas	.08	.06	.03
120	Andre Thornton	.10	.08	.04
121	Allan Trammell	.20	.15	.08
122	John Tudor	.12	.09	.05
123	Fernando Valenzuela	.30	.25	.12
124	Frank Viola	.20	.15	.08
125	Gary Ward	.05	.04	.02
126	Lou Whitaker	.25	.20	.10
127	Frank White	.10	.08	.04
128	Glenn Wilson	.08	.06	.03
129	Willie Wilson	.15	.11	.06
130	Dave Winfield	.40	.30	.15
131	Robin Yount	.35	.25	.14
132	Dwight Gooden, Dale Murphy/Checklist			
		1.25	.90	.50

The values quoted are intended to reflect the market price.

1986 Fleer
Star Stickers Box Panels

Four cards, numbered S-1 through S-4, were placed on the bottoms of 1986 Fleer Star Stickers wax pack boxes. The cards are nearly identical in format to the regular issue sticker cards. Individual cards measure 2-1/2" by 3-1/2" in size, while a complete panel of four measures 5" by 7-1/8".

		MT	NR MT	EX
Complete Panel Set:		2.00	1.50	.80
Complete Singles Set:		1.00	.70	.40
Common Single Player:		.30	.25	.12
	Panel	2.00	1.50	.80
1	Dodgers Logo	.05	.04	.02
2	Wade Boggs	1.00	.70	.40
3	Steve Garvey	.30	.25	.12
4	Dave Winfield	.30	.25	.12

1986 Fleer Update

Issued near the end of the baseball season, the 1986 Fleer Update set consists of 132 cards numbered U-1 through U-132. The cards, which measure 2-1/2" by 3-1/2" in size, are identical in design to the regular 1986 Fleer set. The purpose of the set is to update player trades and include new players not depicted in the regular issue. The set was issued with team logo stickers in a specially designed box and was available only through hobby dealers.

		MT	NR MT	EX
Complete Set:		30.00	22.00	12.00
Common Player:		.08	.06	.03
1	Mike Aldrete(FC)	.15	.11	.06
2	Andy Allanson(FC)	.20	.15	.08
3	Neil Allen	.08	.06	.03
4	Joaquin Andujar	.10	.08	.04
5	Paul Assenmacher(FC)	.20	.15	.08
6	Scott Bailes(FC)	.15	.11	.06
7	Jay Baller(FC)	.15	.11	.06
8	Scott Bankhead(FC)	.20	.15	.08

		MT	NR MT	EX
9	Bill Bathe(FC)	.08	.06	.03
10	Don Baylor	.15	.11	.06
11	Billy Beane(FC)	.08	.06	.03
12	Steve Bedrosian	.15	.11	.06
13	Juan Beniquez	.08	.06	.03
14	Barry Bonds(FC)	9.00	6.75	3.50
15	Bobby Bonilla(FC)	7.00	5.25	2.75
16	Rich Bordi	.08	.06	.03
17	Bill Campbell	.08	.06	.03
18	Tom Candiotti	.08	.06	.03
19	John Cangelosi(FC)	.20	.15	.08
20	Jose Canseco	10.00	7.50	4.00
21	Chuck Cary(FC)	.15	.11	.06
22	Juan Castillo(FC)	.10	.08	.04
23	Rick Cerone	.08	.06	.03
24	John Cerutti(FC)	.15	.11	.06
25	Will Clark(FC)	12.00	9.00	4.75
26	Mark Clear	.08	.06	.03
27	Darnell Coles(FC)	.15	.11	.06
28	Dave Collins	.10	.08	.04
29	Tim Conroy	.08	.06	.03
30	Ed Correa(FC)	.20	.15	.08
31	Joe Cowley	.08	.06	.03
32	Bill Dawley	.08	.06	.03
33	Rob Deer	.15	.11	.06
34	John Denny	.08	.06	.03
35	Jim DeShaies (Deshaies)(FC)	.25	.20	.10
36	Doug Drabek(FC)	1.25	.90	.50
37	Mike Easler	.12	.09	.05
38	Mark Eichhorn(FC)	.20	.15	.08
39	Dave Engle	.08	.06	.03
40	Mike Fischlin	.08	.06	.03
41	Scott Fletcher	.15	.11	.06
42	Terry Forster	.12	.09	.05
43	Terry Francona	.08	.06	.03
44	Andres Galarraga	.40	.30	.15
45	Lee Guetterman(FC)	.20	.15	.08
46	Bill Gullickson	.08	.06	.03
47	Jackie Gutierrez	.08	.06	.03
48	Moose Haas	.08	.06	.03
49	Billy Hatcher	.15	.11	.06
50	Mike Heath	.08	.06	.03
51	Guy Hoffman(FC)	.10	.08	.04
52	Tom Hume	.08	.06	.03
53	Pete Incaviglia(FC)	.40	.30	.15
54	Dane Iorg	.08	.06	.03
55	Chris James(FC)	.50	.40	.20
56	Stan Javier(FC)	.25	.20	.10
57	Tommy John	.20	.15	.08
58	Tracy Jones(FC)	.20	.15	.08
59	Wally Joyner(FC)	2.00	1.50	.80
60	Wayne Krenchicki	.08	.06	.03
61	John Kruk(FC)	1.50	1.25	.60
62	Mike LaCoss	.08	.06	.03
63	Pete Ladd	.08	.06	.03
64	Dave LaPoint	.15	.11	.06
65	Mike LaValliere(FC)	.40	.30	.15
66	Rudy Law	.08	.06	.03
67	Dennis Leonard	.10	.08	.04
68	Steve Lombardozzi(FC)	.20	.15	.08
69	Aurelio Lopez	.08	.06	.03
70	Mickey Mahler	.08	.06	.03
71	Candy Maldonado	.15	.11	.06
72	Roger Mason(FC)	.10	.08	.04
73	Greg Mathews(FC)	.25	.20	.10
74	Andy McGaffigan	.08	.06	.03
75	Joel McKeon(FC)	.12	.09	.05
76	Kevin Mitchell(FC)	3.00	2.25	1.25
77	Bill Mooneyham(FC)	.12	.09	.05
78	Omar Moreno	.08	.06	.03
79	Jerry Mumphrey	.08	.06	.03
80	Al Newman(FC)	.12	.09	.05
81	Phil Niekro	.40	.30	.15
82	Randy Niemann	.08	.06	.03
83	Juan Nieves(FC)	.20	.15	.08
84	Bob Ojeda	.12	.09	.05
85	Rick Ownbey	.08	.06	.03
86	Tom Paciorek	.08	.06	.03
87	David Palmer	.08	.06	.03
88	Jeff Parrett(FC)	.25	.20	.10
89	Pat Perry(FC)	.15	.11	.06
90	Dan Plesac(FC)	.25	.20	.10
91	Darrell Porter	.12	.09	.05
92	Luis Quinones(FC)	.12	.09	.05
93	Rey Quinonez(FC)	.20	.15	.08
94	Gary Redus	.10	.08	.04
95	Jeff Reed(FC)	.12	.09	.05
96	Bip Roberts(FC)	.08	.06	.03
97	Billy Joe Robidoux	.12	.09	.05
98	Gary Roenicke	.08	.06	.03
99	Ron Roenicke	.08	.06	.03
100	Angel Salazar	.08	.06	.03

		MT	NR MT	EX
101	Joe Sambito	.08	.06	.03
102	Billy Sample	.08	.06	.03
103	Dave Schmidt	.08	.06	.03
104	Ken Schrom	.08	.06	.03
105	Ruben Sierra(FC)	7.00	5.25	2.75
106	Ted Simmons	.20	.15	.08
107	Sammy Stewart	.08	.06	.03
108	Kurt Stillwell(FC)	.30	.25	.12
109	Dale Sveum(FC)	.25	.20	.10
110	Tim Teufel	.08	.06	.03
111	Bob Tewksbury(FC)	.12	.09	.05
112	Andres Thomas(FC)	.15	.11	.06
113	Jason Thompson	.08	.06	.03
114	Milt Thompson	.12	.09	.05
115	Rob Thompson(FC)	.40	.30	.15
116	Jay Tibbs	.08	.06	.03
117	Fred Toliver	.12	.09	.05
118	Wayne Tolleson	.08	.06	.03
119	Alex Trevino	.08	.06	.03
120	Manny Trillo	.10	.08	.04
121	Ed Vande Berg	.08	.06	.03
122	Ozzie Virgil	.08	.06	.03
123	Tony Walker(FC)	.08	.06	.03
124	Gene Walter	.12	.09	.05
125	Duane Ward(FC)	.30	.25	.12
126	Jerry Willard	.08	.06	.03
127	Mitch Williams(FC)	.40	.30	.15
128	Reggie Williams(FC)	.20	.15	.08
129	Bobby Witt(FC)	.50	.40	.20
130	Marvell Wynne	.08	.06	.03
131	Steve Yeager	.08	.06	.03
132	Checklist	.08	.06	.03

1987 Fleer

The 1987 Fleer set consists of 660 cards, each measuring 2-1/2" by 3-1/2". The card fronts feature an attractive blue and white border. The player's name and position appears in the upper left corner of the card. The player's team logo is located in the lower right corner. The card backs are done in blue, red and white and contain an innovative "Pro Scouts Report" feature which lists the hitter's or pitcher's batting and pitching strengths. For the third year in a row, Fleer included its "Major League Prospects" subset. Fleer produced a glossy-finish Collectors Edition set which came housed in a specially-designed tin box. It was speculated that 100,000 of the glossy sets were produced. After experiencing a dramatic drop in price during 1987, the glossy set now sells for only a few dollars more than the regular issue.

		MT	NR MT	EX
Complete Set:		90.00	67.00	35.00
Common Player:		.06	.05	.02
1	Rick Aguilera	.08	.06	.03
2	Richard Anderson	.06	.05	.02
3	Wally Backman	.08	.06	.03
4	Gary Carter	.25	.20	.10
5	Ron Darling	.15	.11	.06
6	Len Dykstra	.70	.50	.30
7	*Kevin Elster*(FC)	.50	.40	.20
8	Sid Fernandez	.12	.09	.05
9	Dwight Gooden	1.00	.70	.40
10	*Ed Hearn*(FC)	.10	.08	.04
11	Danny Heep	.06	.05	.02

		MT	NR MT	EX
12	Keith Hernandez	.25	.20	.10
13	Howard Johnson	.10	.08	.04
14	Ray Knight	.08	.06	.03
15	Lee Mazzilli	.08	.06	.03
16	Roger McDowell	.12	.09	.05
17	*Kevin Mitchell*	4.00	3.00	1.50
18	Randy Niemann	.06	.05	.02
19	Bob Ojeda	.08	.06	.03
20	Jesse Orosco	.08	.06	.03
21	Rafael Santana	.06	.05	.02
22	Doug Sisk	.06	.05	.02
23	Darryl Strawberry	3.00	2.25	1.25
24	Tim Teufel	.06	.05	.02
25	Mookie Wilson	.10	.08	.04
26	Tony Armas	.08	.06	.03
27	Marty Barrett	.10	.08	.04
28	Don Baylor	.12	.09	.05
29	Wade Boggs	1.50	1.25	.60
30	Oil Can Boyd	.08	.06	.03
31	Bill Buckner	.10	.08	.04
32	Roger Clemens	4.00	3.00	1.50
33	Steve Crawford	.06	.05	.02
34	Dwight Evans	.12	.09	.05
35	Rich Gedman	.10	.08	.04
36	Dave Henderson	.10	.08	.04
37	Bruce Hurst	.10	.08	.04
38	Tim Lollar	.06	.05	.02
39	Al Nipper	.06	.05	.02
40	Spike Owen	.06	.05	.02
41	Jim Rice	.20	.15	.08
42	Ed Romero	.06	.05	.02
43	Joe Sambito	.06	.05	.02
44	Calvin Schiraldi	.10	.08	.04
45	Tom Seaver	1.00	.70	.40
46	*Jeff Sellers*(FC)	.20	.15	.08
47	Bob Stanley	.06	.05	.02
48	Sammy Stewart	.06	.05	.02
49	Larry Andersen	.06	.05	.02
50	Alan Ashby	.06	.05	.02
51	Kevin Bass	.10	.08	.04
52	Jeff Calhoun	.06	.05	.02
53	Jose Cruz	.10	.08	.04
54	Danny Darwin	.06	.05	.02
55	Glenn Davis	.40	.30	.15
56	*Jim Deshaies*	.25	.20	.10
57	Bill Doran	.10	.08	.04
58	Phil Garner	.06	.05	.02
59	Billy Hatcher	.08	.06	.03
60	Charlie Kerfeld	.06	.05	.02
61	Bob Knepper	.08	.06	.03
62	Dave Lopes	.08	.06	.03
63	Aurelio Lopez	.06	.05	.02
64	Jim Pankovits	.06	.05	.02
65	Terry Puhl	.06	.05	.02
66	Craig Reynolds	.06	.05	.02
67	Nolan Ryan	4.00	3.00	1.50
68	Mike Scott	.15	.11	.06
69	Dave Smith	.08	.06	.03
70	Dickie Thon	.08	.06	.03
71	Tony Walker	.06	.05	.02
72	Denny Walling	.06	.05	.02
73	Bob Boone	.08	.06	.03
74	Rick Burleson	.08	.06	.03
75	John Candelaria	.10	.08	.04
76	Doug Corbett	.06	.05	.02
77	Doug DeCinces	.08	.06	.03
78	Brian Downing	.08	.06	.03
79	*Chuck Finley*(FC)	3.00	2.25	1.25
80	Terry Forster	.08	.06	.03
81	Bobby Grich	.10	.08	.04
82	George Hendrick	.08	.06	.03
83	Jack Howell(FC)	.10	.08	.04
84	Reggie Jackson	.35	.25	.14
85	Ruppert Jones	.06	.05	.02
86	*Wally Joyner*	4.00	3.00	1.50
87	Gary Lucas	.06	.05	.02
88	Kirk McCaskill	.08	.06	.03
89	Donnie Moore	.06	.05	.02
90	Gary Pettis	.06	.05	.02
91	Vern Ruhle	.06	.05	.02
92	Dick Schofield	.06	.05	.02
93	Don Sutton	.20	.15	.08
94	Rob Wilfong	.06	.05	.02
95	Mike Witt	.10	.08	.04
96	*Doug Drabek*	3.00	2.25	1.25
97	Mike Easler	.08	.06	.03
98	Mike Fischlin	.06	.05	.02
99	Brian Fisher	.08	.06	.03
100	Ron Guidry	.15	.11	.06
101	Rickey Henderson	2.00	1.50	.80
102	Tommy John	.20	.15	.08
103	Ron Kittle	.10	.08	.04

#	Player	MT	NR MT	EX		#	Player	MT	NR MT	EX
104	Don Mattingly	2.00	1.50	.80		195	Sal Butera	.06	.05	.02
105	Bobby Meacham	.06	.05	.02		196	Dave Concepcion	.12	.09	.05
106	Joe Niekro	.10	.08	.04		197	Kal Daniels	.80	.60	.30
107	Mike Pagliarulo	.10	.08	.04		198	Eric Davis	1.50	1.25	.60
108	Dan Pasqua	.10	.08	.04		199	John Denny	.06	.05	.02
109	Willie Randolph	.10	.08	.04		200	Bo Diaz	.08	.06	.03
110	Dennis Rasmussen	.10	.08	.04		201	Nick Esasky	.08	.06	.03
111	Dave Righetti	.15	.11	.06		202	John Franco	.10	.08	.04
112	Gary Roenicke	.06	.05	.02		203	Bill Gullickson	.06	.05	.02
113	Rod Scurry	.06	.05	.02		204	Barry Larkin(FC)	7.00	5.25	2.75
114	Bob Shirley	.06	.05	.02		205	Eddie Milner	.06	.05	.02
115	Joel Skinner	.06	.05	.02		206	Rob Murphy(FC)	.20	.15	.08
116	Tim Stoddard	.06	.05	.02		207	Ron Oester	.06	.05	.02
117	Bob Tewksbury	.80	.60	.30		208	Dave Parker	.20	.15	.08
118	Wayne Tolleson	.06	.05	.02		209	Tony Perez	.15	.11	.06
119	Claudell Washington	.08	.06	.03		210	Ted Power	.06	.05	.02
120	Dave Winfield	.30	.25	.12		211	Joe Price	.06	.05	.02
121	Steve Buechele	.08	.06	.03		212	Ron Robinson	.06	.05	.02
122	Ed Correa	.15	.11	.06		213	Pete Rose	.60	.45	.25
123	Scott Fletcher	.08	.06	.03		214	Mario Soto	.08	.06	.03
124	Jose Guzman	.10	.08	.04		215	Kurt Stillwell	.60	.45	.25
125	Toby Harrah	.08	.06	.03		216	Max Venable	.06	.05	.02
126	Greg Harris	.06	.05	.02		217	Chris Welsh	.06	.05	.02
127	Charlie Hough	.08	.06	.03		218	Carl Willis(FC)	.10	.08	.04
128	Pete Incaviglia	.60	.45	.25		219	Jesse Barfield	.15	.11	.06
129	Mike Mason	.06	.05	.02		220	George Bell	.25	.20	.10
130	Oddibe McDowell	.10	.08	.04		221	Bill Caudill	.06	.05	.02
131	Dale Mohorcic(FC)	.20	.15	.08		222	John Cerutti	.20	.15	.08
132	Pete O'Brien	.10	.08	.04		223	Jim Clancy	.08	.06	.03
133	Tom Paciorek	.06	.05	.02		224	Mark Eichhorn	.15	.11	.06
134	Larry Parrish	.08	.06	.03		225	Tony Fernandez	.12	.09	.05
135	Geno Petralli	.06	.05	.02		226	Damaso Garcia	.06	.05	.02
136	Darrell Porter	.08	.06	.03		227	Kelly Gruber	1.00	.70	.40
137	Jeff Russell	.06	.05	.02		228	Tom Henke	.08	.06	.03
138	Ruben Sierra	10.00	7.50	4.00		229	Garth Iorg	.06	.05	.02
139	Don Slaught	.06	.05	.02		230	Cliff Johnson	.06	.05	.02
140	Gary Ward	.08	.06	.03		231	Joe Johnson	.06	.05	.02
141	Curtis Wilkerson	.06	.05	.02		232	Jimmy Key	.12	.09	.05
142	Mitch Williams	.60	.45	.25		233	Dennis Lamp	.06	.05	.02
143	Bobby Witt	1.00	.70	.40		234	Rick Leach	.06	.05	.02
144	Dave Bergman	.06	.05	.02		235	Buck Martinez	.06	.05	.02
145	Tom Brookens	.06	.05	.02		236	Lloyd Moseby	.10	.08	.04
146	Bill Campbell	.06	.05	.02		237	Rance Mulliniks	.06	.05	.02
147	Chuck Cary	.10	.08	.04		238	Dave Stieb	.12	.09	.05
148	Darnell Coles	.08	.06	.03		239	Willie Upshaw	.08	.06	.03
149	Dave Collins	.08	.06	.03		240	Ernie Whitt	.08	.06	.03
150	Darrell Evans	.12	.09	.05		241	Andy Allanson	.15	.11	.06
151	Kirk Gibson	.25	.20	.10		242	Scott Bailes	.20	.15	.08
152	John Grubb	.06	.05	.02		243	Chris Bando	.06	.05	.02
153	Willie Hernandez	.08	.06	.03		244	Tony Bernazard	.06	.05	.02
154	Larry Herndon	.08	.06	.03		245	John Butcher	.06	.05	.02
155	Eric King	.25	.20	.10		246	Brett Butler	.08	.06	.03
156	Chet Lemon	.08	.06	.03		247	Ernie Camacho	.06	.05	.02
157	Dwight Lowry	.06	.05	.02		248	Tom Candiotti	.06	.05	.02
158	Jack Morris	.20	.15	.08		249	Joe Carter	.80	.60	.30
159	Randy O'Neal	.06	.05	.02		250	Carmen Castillo	.06	.05	.02
160	Lance Parrish	.20	.15	.08		251	Julio Franco	.10	.08	.04
161	Dan Petry	.08	.06	.03		252	Mel Hall	.08	.06	.03
162	Pat Sheridan	.06	.05	.02		253	Brook Jacoby	.10	.08	.04
163	Jim Slaton	.06	.05	.02		254	Phil Niekro	.20	.15	.08
164	Frank Tanana	.08	.06	.03		255	Otis Nixon	.06	.05	.02
165	Walt Terrell	.08	.06	.03		256	Dickie Noles	.06	.05	.02
166	Mark Thurmond	.06	.05	.02		257	Bryan Oelkers	.06	.05	.02
167	Alan Trammell	.25	.20	.10		258	Ken Schrom	.06	.05	.02
168	Lou Whitaker	.25	.20	.10		259	Don Schulze	.06	.05	.02
169	Luis Aguayo	.06	.05	.02		260	Cory Snyder	.50	.40	.20
170	Steve Bedrosian	.12	.09	.05		261	Pat Tabler	.08	.06	.03
171	Don Carman	.10	.08	.04		262	Andre Thornton	.08	.06	.03
172	Darren Daulton	.06	.05	.02		263	Rich Yett(FC)	.12	.09	.05
173	Greg Gross	.06	.05	.02		264	Mike Aldrete	.25	.20	.10
174	Kevin Gross	.08	.06	.03		265	Juan Berenguer	.06	.05	.02
175	Von Hayes	.10	.08	.04		266	Vida Blue	.10	.08	.04
176	Charles Hudson	.06	.05	.02		267	Bob Brenly	.06	.05	.02
177	Tom Hume	.06	.05	.02		268	Chris Brown	.08	.06	.03
178	Steve Jeltz	.06	.05	.02		269	Will Clark	25.00	18.00	10.00
179	Mike Maddux(FC)	.20	.15	.08		270	Chili Davis	.08	.06	.03
180	Shane Rawley	.08	.06	.03		271	Mark Davis	.06	.05	.02
181	Gary Redus	.06	.05	.02		272	Kelly Downs(FC)	.30	.25	.12
182	Ron Roenicke	.06	.05	.02		273	Scott Garrelts	.06	.05	.02
183	Bruce Ruffin(FC)	.20	.15	.08		274	Dan Gladden	.06	.05	.02
184	John Russell	.06	.05	.02		275	Mike Krukow	.08	.06	.03
185	Juan Samuel	.12	.09	.05		276	Randy Kutcher(FC)	.10	.08	.04
186	Dan Schatzeder	.06	.05	.02		277	Mike LaCoss	.06	.05	.02
187	Mike Schmidt	1.50	1.25	.60		278	Jeff Leonard	.08	.06	.03
188	Rick Schu	.06	.05	.02		279	Candy Maldonado	.08	.06	.03
189	Jeff Stone	.06	.05	.02		280	Roger Mason	.06	.05	.02
190	Kent Tekulve	.08	.06	.03		281	Bob Melvin(FC)	.08	.06	.03
191	Milt Thompson	.08	.06	.03		282	Greg Minton	.06	.05	.02
192	Glenn Wilson	.08	.06	.03		283	Jeff Robinson	.08	.06	.03
193	Buddy Bell	.10	.08	.04		284	Harry Spilman	.06	.05	.02
194	Tom Browning	.10	.08	.04		285	Rob Thompson	.35	.25	.14

#	Player	MT	NR MT	EX
286	Jose Uribe	.08	.06	.03
287	Frank Williams	.06	.05	.02
288	Joel Youngblood	.06	.05	.02
289	Jack Clark	.15	.11	.06
290	Vince Coleman	.70	.50	.30
291	Tim Conroy	.06	.05	.02
292	Danny Cox	.08	.06	.03
293	Ken Dayley	.06	.05	.02
294	Curt Ford	.06	.05	.02
295	Bob Forsch	.08	.06	.03
296	Tom Herr	.10	.08	.04
297	Ricky Horton	.08	.06	.03
298	Clint Hurdle	.06	.05	.02
299	Jeff Lahti	.06	.05	.02
300	Steve Lake	.06	.05	.02
301	Tito Landrum	.06	.05	.02
302	*Mike LaValliere*	.25	.20	.10
303	*Greg Mathews*(FC)	.20	.15	.08
304	Willie McGee	.12	.09	.05
305	Jose Oquendo	.06	.05	.02
306	Terry Pendleton	.10	.08	.04
307	Pat Perry	.08	.06	.03
308	Ozzie Smith	.80	.60	.30
309	Ray Soff	.06	.05	.02
310	John Tudor	.10	.08	.04
311	Andy Van Slyke	.12	.09	.05
312	Todd Worrell	.20	.15	.08
313	Dann Bilardello	.06	.05	.02
314	Hubie Brooks	.10	.08	.04
315	Tim Burke	.06	.05	.02
316	Andre Dawson	.20	.15	.08
317	Mike Fitzgerald	.06	.05	.02
318	Tom Foley	.06	.05	.02
319	Andres Galarraga	.40	.30	.15
320	Joe Hesketh	.06	.05	.02
321	Wallace Johnson	.06	.05	.02
322	Wayne Krenchicki	.06	.05	.02
323	Vance Law	.08	.06	.03
324	Dennis Martinez	.08	.06	.03
325	Bob McClure	.06	.05	.02
326	Andy McGaffigan	.06	.05	.02
327	*Al Newman*	.08	.06	.03
328	Tim Raines	.30	.25	.12
329	Jeff Reardon	.10	.08	.04
330	*Luis Rivera*(FC)	.10	.08	.04
331	*Bob Sebra*(FC)	.10	.08	.04
332	Bryn Smith	.06	.05	.02
333	Jay Tibbs	.06	.05	.02
334	Tim Wallach	.12	.09	.05
335	Mitch Webster	.08	.06	.03
336	Jim Wohlford	.06	.05	.02
337	Floyd Youmans	.08	.06	.03
338	*Chris Bosio*(FC)	.40	.30	.15
339	*Glenn Braggs*(FC)	.40	.30	.15
340	Rick Cerone	.06	.05	.02
341	Mark Clear	.06	.05	.02
342	*Bryan Clutterbuck*(FC)	.10	.08	.04
343	Cecil Cooper	.12	.09	.05
344	Rob Deer	.10	.08	.04
345	Jim Gantner	.08	.06	.03
346	Ted Higuera	.20	.15	.08
347	John Henry Johnson	.06	.05	.02
348	Tim Leary(FC)	.30	.25	.12
349	Rick Manning	.06	.05	.02
350	Paul Molitor	.15	.11	.06
351	Charlie Moore	.06	.05	.02
352	Juan Nieves	.10	.08	.04
353	Ben Oglivie	.08	.06	.03
354	*Dan Plesac*	.35	.25	.14
355	Ernest Riles	.06	.05	.02
356	Billy Joe Robidoux	.06	.05	.02
357	Bill Schroeder	.06	.05	.02
358	*Dale Sveum*	.20	.15	.08
359	Gorman Thomas	.10	.08	.04
360	Bill Wegman(FC)	.10	.08	.04
361	Robin Yount	.50	.40	.20
362	Steve Balboni	.08	.06	.03
363	*Scott Bankhead*	.30	.25	.12
364	Buddy Biancalana	.06	.05	.02
365	Bud Black	.06	.05	.02
366	George Brett	.50	.40	.20
367	Steve Farr	.06	.05	.02
368	Mark Gubicza	.12	.09	.05
369	Bo Jackson	6.00	4.50	2.50
370	Danny Jackson	.15	.11	.06
371	*Mike Kingery*	.15	.11	.06
372	Rudy Law	.06	.05	.02
373	Charlie Leibrandt	.08	.06	.03
374	Dennis Leonard	.08	.06	.03
375	Hal McRae	.10	.08	.04
376	Jorge Orta	.06	.05	.02
377	Jamie Quirk	.06	.05	.02
378	Dan Quisenberry	.08	.06	.03
379	Bret Saberhagen	.30	.25	.12
380	Angel Salazar	.06	.05	.02
381	Lonnie Smith	.08	.06	.03
382	Jim Sundberg	.08	.06	.03
383	Frank White	.10	.08	.04
384	Willie Wilson	.12	.09	.05
385	Joaquin Andujar	.08	.06	.03
386	Doug Bair	.06	.05	.02
387	Dusty Baker	.08	.06	.03
388	Bruce Bochte	.06	.05	.02
389	Jose Canseco	10.00	7.50	4.00
390	Chris Codiroli	.06	.05	.02
391	Mike Davis	.08	.06	.03
392	Alfredo Griffin	.08	.06	.03
393	Moose Haas	.06	.05	.02
394	Donnie Hill	.06	.05	.02
395	Jay Howell	.08	.06	.03
396	Dave Kingman	.12	.09	.05
397	Carney Lansford	.10	.08	.04
398	*David Leiper*(FC)	.12	.09	.05
399	*Bill Mooneyham*	.10	.08	.04
400	Dwayne Murphy	.08	.06	.03
401	Steve Ontiveros	.06	.05	.02
402	Tony Phillips	.06	.05	.02
403	Eric Plunk	.08	.06	.03
404	Jose Rijo	.08	.06	.03
405	*Terry Steinbach*(FC)	.90	.70	.35
406	Dave Stewart	.12	.09	.05
407	Mickey Tettleton	.06	.05	.02
408	Dave Von Ohlen	.06	.05	.02
409	Jerry Willard	.06	.05	.02
410	Curt Young	.08	.06	.03
411	Bruce Bochy	.06	.05	.02
412	Dave Dravecky	.08	.06	.03
413	Tim Flannery	.06	.05	.02
414	Steve Garvey	.25	.20	.10
415	Goose Gossage	.15	.11	.06
416	Tony Gwynn	1.00	.70	.40
417	Andy Hawkins	.06	.05	.02
418	LaMarr Hoyt	.06	.05	.02
419	Terry Kennedy	.08	.06	.03
420	*John Kruk*	1.50	1.25	.60
421	Dave LaPoint	.08	.06	.03
422	Craig Lefferts	.06	.05	.02
423	Carmelo Martinez	.08	.06	.03
424	Lance McCullers	.08	.06	.03
425	Kevin McReynolds	.15	.11	.06
426	Graig Nettles	.12	.09	.05
427	*Bip Roberts*	.80	.60	.30
428	Jerry Royster	.06	.05	.02
429	Benito Santiago	.70	.50	.30
430	Eric Show	.08	.06	.03
431	Bob Stoddard	.06	.05	.02
432	Garry Templeton	.08	.06	.03
433	Gene Walter	.06	.05	.02
434	Ed Whitson	.06	.05	.02
435	Marvell Wynne	.06	.05	.02
436	Dave Anderson	.06	.05	.02
437	Greg Brock	.08	.06	.03
438	Enos Cabell	.06	.05	.02
439	Mariano Duncan	.06	.05	.02
440	Pedro Guerrero	.15	.11	.06
441	Orel Hershiser	.40	.30	.15
442	Rick Honeycutt	.06	.05	.02
443	Ken Howell	.06	.05	.02
444	Ken Landreaux	.06	.05	.02
445	Bill Madlock	.12	.09	.05
446	Mike Marshall	.12	.09	.05
447	Len Matuszek	.06	.05	.02
448	Tom Niedenfuer	.08	.06	.03
449	Alejandro Pena	.08	.06	.03
450	Dennis Powell(FC)	.08	.06	.03
451	Jerry Reuss	.08	.06	.03
452	Bill Russell	.08	.06	.03
453	Steve Sax	.15	.11	.06
454	Mike Scioscia	.08	.06	.03
455	Franklin Stubbs	.08	.06	.03
456	Alex Trevino	.06	.05	.02
457	Fernando Valenzuela	.25	.20	.10
458	Ed Vande Berg	.06	.05	.02
459	Bob Welch	.10	.08	.04
460	*Reggie Williams*	.10	.08	.04
461	Don Aase	.06	.05	.02
462	Juan Beniquez	.06	.05	.02
463	Mike Boddicker	.08	.06	.03
464	Juan Bonilla	.06	.05	.02
465	Rich Bordi	.06	.05	.02
466	Storm Davis	.10	.08	.04
467	Rick Dempsey	.08	.06	.03

		MT	NR MT	EX
468	Ken Dixon	.06	.05	.02
469	Jim Dwyer	.06	.05	.02
470	Mike Flanagan	.08	.06	.03
471	Jackie Gutierrez	.06	.05	.02
472	Brad Havens	.06	.05	.02
473	Lee Lacy	.06	.05	.02
474	Fred Lynn	.15	.11	.06
475	Scott McGregor	.08	.06	.03
476	Eddie Murray	.35	.25	.14
477	Tom O'Malley	.06	.05	.02
478	Cal Ripken, Jr.	4.00	3.00	1.50
479	Larry Sheets	.08	.06	.03
480	John Shelby	.06	.05	.02
481	Nate Snell	.06	.05	.02
482	Jim Traber(FC)	.10	.08	.04
483	Mike Young	.06	.05	.02
484	Neil Allen	.06	.05	.02
485	Harold Baines	.15	.11	.06
486	Floyd Bannister	.10	.08	.04
487	Daryl Boston	.08	.06	.03
488	Ivan Calderon	.50	.40	.20
489	*John Cangelosi*	.12	.09	.05
490	Steve Carlton	.25	.20	.10
491	Joe Cowley	.06	.05	.02
492	Julio Cruz	.06	.05	.02
493	Bill Dawley	.06	.05	.02
494	Jose DeLeon	.08	.06	.03
495	Richard Dotson	.08	.06	.03
496	Carlton Fisk	.30	.25	.12
497	Ozzie Guillen	.10	.08	.04
498	Jerry Hairston	.06	.05	.02
499	Ron Hassey	.06	.05	.02
500	Tim Hulett	.06	.05	.02
501	Bob James	.06	.05	.02
502	Steve Lyons	.06	.05	.02
503	*Joel McKeon*	.10	.08	.04
504	Gene Nelson	.06	.05	.02
505	Dave Schmidt	.06	.05	.02
506	Ray Searage	.06	.05	.02
507	*Bobby Thigpen*(FC)	2.00	1.50	.80
508	Greg Walker	.10	.08	.04
509	Jim Acker	.06	.05	.02
510	Doyle Alexander	.08	.06	.03
511	*Paul Assenmacher*	.15	.11	.06
512	Bruce Benedict	.06	.05	.02
513	Chris Chambliss	.08	.06	.03
514	Jeff Dedmon	.06	.05	.02
515	Gene Garber	.06	.05	.02
516	Ken Griffey	.10	.08	.04
517	Terry Harper	.06	.05	.02
518	Bob Horner	.10	.08	.04
519	Glenn Hubbard	.06	.05	.02
520	Rick Mahler	.06	.05	.02
521	Omar Moreno	.06	.05	.02
522	Dale Murphy	.40	.30	.15
523	Ken Oberkfell	.06	.05	.02
524	Ed Olwine	.06	.05	.02
525	David Palmer	.06	.05	.02
526	Rafael Ramirez	.06	.05	.02
527	Billy Sample	.06	.05	.02
528	Ted Simmons	.12	.09	.05
529	Zane Smith	.08	.06	.03
530	Bruce Sutter	.12	.09	.05
531	*Andres Thomas*	.15	.11	.06
532	Ozzie Virgil	.06	.05	.02
533	Allan Anderson(FC)	.25	.20	.10
534	Keith Atherton	.06	.05	.02
535	Billy Beane	.06	.05	.02
536	Bert Blyleven	.12	.09	.05
537	Tom Brunansky	.10	.08	.04
538	Randy Bush	.06	.05	.02
539	George Frazier	.06	.05	.02
540	Gary Gaetti	.15	.11	.06
541	Greg Gagne	.06	.05	.02
542	Mickey Hatcher	.06	.05	.02
543	Neal Heaton	.06	.05	.02
544	Kent Hrbek	.15	.11	.06
545	Roy Lee Jackson	.06	.05	.02
546	Tim Laudner	.06	.05	.02
547	Steve Lombardozzi	.10	.08	.04
548	*Mark Portugal*(FC)	.10	.08	.04
549	Kirby Puckett	3.00	2.25	1.25
550	Jeff Reed	.08	.06	.03
551	Mark Salas	.06	.05	.02
552	Roy Smalley	.06	.05	.02
553	Mike Smithson	.06	.05	.02
554	Frank Viola	.15	.11	.06
555	Thad Bosley	.06	.05	.02
556	Ron Cey	.10	.08	.04
557	Jody Davis	.08	.06	.03
558	Ron Davis	.06	.05	.02
559	Bob Dernier	.06	.05	.02
560	Frank DiPino	.06	.05	.02
561	Shawon Dunston	.35	.25	.14
562	Leon Durham	.08	.06	.03
563	Dennis Eckersley	.12	.09	.05
564	Terry Francona	.06	.05	.02
565	Dave Gumpert	.06	.05	.02
566	Guy Hoffman	.08	.06	.03
567	Ed Lynch	.06	.05	.02
568	Gary Matthews	.10	.08	.04
569	Keith Moreland	.08	.06	.03
570	*Jamie Moyer*(FC)	.20	.15	.08
571	Jerry Mumphrey	.06	.05	.02
572	Ryne Sandberg	2.50	2.00	1.00
573	Scott Sanderson	.06	.05	.02
574	Lee Smith	.10	.08	.04
575	Chris Speier	.06	.05	.02
576	Rick Sutcliffe	.12	.09	.05
577	Manny Trillo	.08	.06	.03
578	Steve Trout	.06	.05	.02
579	Karl Best	.06	.05	.02
580	Scott Bradley(FC)	.08	.06	.03
581	Phil Bradley	.12	.09	.05
582	Mickey Brantley	.08	.06	.03
583	Mike Brown	.06	.05	.02
584	Alvin Davis	.12	.09	.05
585	*Lee Guetterman*(FC)	.15	.11	.06
586	Mark Huismann	.06	.05	.02
587	Bob Kearney	.06	.05	.02
588	Pete Ladd	.06	.05	.02
589	Mark Langston	.12	.09	.05
590	Mike Moore	.06	.05	.02
591	Mike Morgan	.06	.05	.02
592	John Moses	.06	.05	.02
593	Ken Phelps	.08	.06	.03
594	Jim Presley	.10	.08	.04
595	*Rey Quinonez (Quinones)*	.15	.11	.06
596	Harold Reynolds	.15	.11	.06
597	Billy Swift	.06	.05	.02
598	Danny Tartabull	.50	.40	.20
599	Steve Yeager	.06	.05	.02
600	Matt Young	.06	.05	.02
601	Bill Almon	.06	.05	.02
602	*Rafael Belliard*(FC)	.12	.09	.05
603	Mike Bielecki	.06	.05	.02
604	*Barry Bonds*	18.00	13.50	7.25
605	*Bobby Bonilla*	8.00	6.00	3.25
606	Sid Bream	.08	.06	.03
607	Mike Brown	.06	.05	.02
608	Pat Clements	.06	.05	.02
609	*Mike Diaz*(FC)	.15	.11	.06
610	Cecillo Guante	.06	.05	.02
611	*Barry Jones*(FC)	.12	.09	.05
612	Bob Kipper	.06	.05	.02
613	Larry McWilliams	.06	.05	.02
614	Jim Morrison	.06	.05	.02
615	Joe Orsulak	.06	.05	.02
616	Junior Ortiz	.06	.05	.02
617	Tony Pena	.08	.06	.03
618	Johnny Ray	.10	.08	.04
619	Rick Reuschel	.10	.08	.04
620	R.J. Reynolds	.06	.05	.02
621	Rick Rhoden	.10	.08	.04
622	Don Robinson	.08	.06	.03
623	Bob Walk	.06	.05	.02
624	Jim Winn	.06	.05	.02
625	Youthful Power (Jose Canseco, Pete Incaviglia)	.70	.50	.30
626	300 Game Winners (Phil Niekro, Don Sutton)	.12	.09	.05
627	A.L. Firemen (Don Aase, Dave Righetti)	.08	.06	.03
628	Rookie All-Stars (Jose Canseco, Wally Joyner)	1.50	1.25	.60
629	Magic Mets (Gary Carter, Sid Fernandez, Dwight Gooden, Keith Hernandez, Darryl Strawberry)	.60	.45	.25
630	N.L. Best Righties (Mike Krukow, Mike Scott)	.08	.06	.03
631	Sensational Southpaws (John Franco, Fernando Valenzuela)	.10	.08	.04
632	Count 'Em (Bob Horner)	.08	.06	.03
633	A.L. Pitcher's Nightmare (Jose Canseco, Kirby Puckett, Jim Rice)	.70	.50	.30
634	All Star Battery (Gary Carter, Roger Clemens)	.25	.20	.10
635	4,000 Strikeouts (Steve Carlton)	.12	.09	.05
636	Big Bats At First Sack (Glenn Davis, Eddie Murray)	.20	.15	.08
637	On Base (Wade Boggs, Keith Hernandez)	.35	.25	.14

		MT	NR MT	EX
638	Sluggers From Left Side (Don Mattingly, Darryl Strawberry) .90		.70	.35
639	Former MVP's (Dave Parker, Ryne Sandberg) .12		.09	.05
640	Dr. K. & Super K (Roger Clemens, Dwight Gooden) .50		.40	.20
641	A.L. West Stoppers (Charlie Hough, Mike Witt) .08		.06	.03
642	Doubles & Triples (Tim Raines, Juan Samuel) .12		.09	.05
643	Outfielders With Punch (Harold Baines, Jesse Barfield) .10		.08	.04
644	Major League Prospects (Dave Clark, Greg Swindell)(FC) 2.00		1.50	.80
645	Major League Prospects (Ron Karkovice, Russ Morman)(FC) .12		.09	.05
646	Major League Prospects (Willie Fraser, Devon White)(FC) 1.50		1.25	.60
647	Major League Prospects (Jerry Browne, Mike Stanley)(FC) .40		.30	.15
648	Major League Prospects (Phil Lombardi, Dave Magadan)(FC) .50		.40	.20
649	Major League Prospects (Ralph Bryant, Jose Gonzalez)(FC) .20		.15	.08
650	Major League Prospects (Randy Asadoor, Jimmy Jones)(FC) .20		.15	.08
651	Major League Prospects (Marvin Freeman, Tracy Jones) .25		.20	.10
652	Major League Prospects (Kevin Seitzer, John Stefero)(FC) .60		.45	.25
653	Major League Prospects (Steve Fireovid, Rob Nelson)(FC) .10		.08	.04
654	Checklist 1-95 .06		.05	.02
655	Checklist 96-192 .06		.05	.02
656	Checklist 193-288 .06		.05	.02
657	Checklist 289-384 .06		.05	.02
658	Checklist 385-483 .06		.05	.02
659	Checklist 484-578 .06		.05	.02
660	Checklist 579-660 .06		.05	.02

1987 Fleer All Star Team

As in 1986, Fleer All Star Team cards were randomly inserted in Fleer wax and cello packs. Twelve cards, each measuring the standard 2-1/2" by 3-1/2", comprise the set. The card fronts feature a full-color player photo set against a gray background for American League players and a black background for National Leaguers. Card backs are printed in black, red and white and feature a lengthy player biography. Fleer's choices for a major league All-Star team is once again the theme for the set.

		MT	NR MT	EX
Complete Set:		18.00	13.50	7.25
Common Player:		.60	.45	.25
1	Don Mattingly	4.00	3.00	1.50
2	Gary Carter	1.00	.70	.40
3	Tony Fernandez	.75	.60	.30
4	Steve Sax	.75	.60	.30
5	Kirby Puckett	3.00	2.25	1.25
6	Mike Schmidt	2.00	1.50	.80
7	Mike Easler	.60	.45	.25
8	Todd Worrell	.75	.60	.30

		MT	NR MT	EX
9	George Bell	1.00	.70	.40
10	Fernando Valenzuela	1.00	.70	.40
11	Roger Clemens	2.25	1.75	.90
12	Tim Raines	1.25	.90	.50

1987 Fleer Baseball's Award Winners

The 1987 Fleer Award Winners boxed set was prepared by Fleer for distribution by 7-Eleven stores. The cards, which measure 2-1/2" by 3-1/2", feature players who have won various major league awards during their careers. The card fronts contain full-color photos surrounded by a yellow border. The name of the award won is printed at the bottom of the card in an oval-shaped band designed to resemble a metal nameplate on a trophy. Card backs, printed in black, yellow and white, include lifetime major and minor league statistics along with typical personal information. Each boxed set contained six team logo stickers.

		MT	NR MT	EX
Complete Set:		6.00	4.50	2.50
Common Player:		.05	.04	.02
1	Marty Barrett	.07	.05	.03
2	George Bell	.20	.15	.08
3	Bert Blyleven	.10	.08	.04
4	Bob Boone	.05	.04	.02
5	John Candelaria	.05	.04	.02
6	Jose Canseco	1.00	.70	.40
7	Gary Carter	.25	.20	.10
8	Joe Carter	.25	.20	.10
9	Roger Clemens	.50	.40	.20
10	Cecil Cooper	.10	.08	.04
11	Eric Davis	.60	.45	.25
12	Tony Fernandez	.10	.08	.04
13	Scott Fletcher	.05	.04	.02
14	Bob Forsch	.05	.04	.02
15	Dwight Gooden	.50	.40	.20
16	Ron Guidry	.12	.09	.05
17	Ozzie Guillen	.07	.05	.03
18	Bill Gullickson	.05	.04	.02
19	Tony Gwynn	.25	.20	.10
20	Bob Knepper	.05	.04	.02
21	Ray Knight	.05	.04	.02
22	Mark Langston	.20	.15	.08
23	Candy Maldonado	.05	.04	.02
24	Don Mattingly	1.00	.70	.40
25	Roger McDowell	.07	.05	.03
26	Dale Murphy	.30	.25	.12
27	Dave Parker	.12	.09	.05
28	Lance Parrish	.15	.11	.06
29	Gary Pettis	.05	.04	.02
30	Kirby Puckett	.70	.50	.40
31	Johnny Ray	.07	.05	.03
32	Dave Righetti	.12	.09	.05
33	Cal Ripken, Jr.	.60	.45	.25
34	Bret Saberhagen	.15	.11	.06
35	Ryne Sandberg	.20	.15	.08
36	Mike Schmidt	.30	.25	.12
37	Mike Scott	.12	.09	.05
38	Ozzie Smith	.12	.09	.05
39	Robbie Thompson	.10	.08	.04
40	Fernando Valenzuela	.20	.15	.08

		MT	NR MT	EX
41	Mitch Webster	.05	.04	.02
42	Frank White	.07	.05	.03
43	Mike Witt	.07	.05	.03
44	Todd Worrell	.15	.11	.06

1987 Fleer Baseball All Stars

Produced by Fleer for exclusive distribution through Ben Franklin stores, the "Baseball All Stars" set is comprised of 44 cards which are the standard 2-1/2" by 3-1/2" size. The cards have full-color photos surrounded by a bright red border with white pinstripes at the top and bottom. The card backs are printed in blue, white and dark red and include complete major and minor league statistics. The set was issued in a special cardboard box.

		MT	NR MT	EX
	Complete Set:	6.00	4.50	2.50
	Common Player:	.05	.04	.02
1	Harold Baines	.10	.08	.04
2	Jesse Barfield	.12	.09	.05
3	Wade Boggs	.60	.45	.25
4	Dennis "Oil Can" Boyd	.05	.04	.02
5	Scott Bradley	.05	.04	.02
6	Jose Canseco	1.00	.70	.40
7	Gary Carter	.25	.20	.10
8	Joe Carter	.25	.20	.10
9	Mark Clear	.05	.04	.02
10	Roger Clemens	.50	.40	.20
11	Jose Cruz	.05	.04	.02
12	Chili Davis	.07	.05	.03
13	Jody Davis	.05	.04	.02
14	Rob Deer	.05	.04	.02
15	Brian Downing	.05	.04	.02
16	Sid Fernandez	.07	.05	.03
17	John Franco	.07	.05	.03
18	Andres Galarraga	.15	.11	.06
19	Dwight Gooden	.50	.40	.20
20	Tony Gwynn	.25	.20	.10
21	Charlie Hough	.05	.04	.02
22	Bruce Hurst	.10	.08	.04
23	Wally Joyner	.70	.50	.30
24	Carney Lansford	.05	.04	.02
25	Fred Lynn	.12	.09	.05
26	Don Mattingly	1.50	1.25	.60
27	Willie McGee	.10	.08	.04
28	Jack Morris	.15	.11	.06
29	Dale Murphy	.30	.25	.12
30	Bob Ojeda	.07	.05	.03
31	Tony Pena	.07	.05	.03
32	Kirby Puckett	.70	.50	.30
33	Dan Quisenberry	.07	.05	.03
34	Tim Raines	.25	.20	.10
35	Willie Randolph	.07	.05	.03
36	Cal Ripken, Jr.	.50	.40	.20
37	Pete Rose	.50	.40	.20
38	Nolan Ryan	1.00	.70	.40
39	Juan Samuel	.10	.08	.04
40	Mike Schmidt	.30	.25	.12
41	Ozzie Smith	.12	.09	.05
42	Andres Thomas	.10	.08	.04
43	Fernando Valenzuela	.20	.15	.08
44	Mike Witt	.07	.05	.03

1987 Fleer Baseball's Best

For a second straight baseball card season, Fleer produced for McCrory's stores and their affiliates a 44-card "Baseball's Best" set. Subtitled "Sluggers vs. Pitchers," 28 everyday players and 16 pitchers are featured. The card design is nearly identical to the previous year's effort. The cards, which measure 2-1/2" by 3-1/2", were housed in a specially designed box along with six team logo stickers.

		MT	NR MT	EX
	Complete Set:	6.00	4.50	2.50
	Common Player:	.05	.04	.02
1	Kevin Bass	.07	.05	.03
2	Jesse Barfield	.12	.09	.05
3	George Bell	.20	.15	.08
4	Wade Boggs	.60	.45	.25
5	Sid Bream	.05	.04	.02
6	George Brett	.30	.25	.12
7	Ivan Calderon	.10	.08	.04
8	Jose Canseco	1.00	.70	.40
9	Jack Clark	.12	.09	.05
10	Roger Clemens	.50	.40	.20
11	Eric Davis	.50	.40	.20
12	Andre Dawson	.15	.11	.06
13	Sid Fernandez	.07	.05	.03
14	John Franco	.07	.05	.03
15	Dwight Gooden	.50	.40	.20
16	Pedro Guerrero	.15	.11	.06
17	Tony Gwynn	.25	.20	.10
18	Rickey Henderson	.30	.25	.12
19	Tom Henke	.05	.04	.02
20	Ted Higuera	.10	.08	.04
21	Pete Incaviglia	.30	.25	.12
22	Wally Joyner	.50	.40	.20
23	Jeff Leonard	.05	.04	.02
24	Joe Magrane	.15	.11	.06
25	Don Mattingly	1.00	.70	.40
26	Mark McGwire	.60	.45	.25
27	Jack Morris	.15	.11	.06
28	Dale Murphy	.30	.25	.12
29	Dave Parker	.12	.09	.05
30	Ken Phelps	.05	.04	.02
31	Kirby Puckett	.70	.50	.30
32	Tim Raines	.25	.20	.10
33	Jeff Reardon	.10	.08	.04
34	Dave Righetti	.12	.09	.05
35	Cal Ripken, Jr.	.60	.45	.25
36	Bret Saberhagen	.15	.11	.06
37	Mike Schmidt	.30	.25	.12
38	Mike Scott	.12	.09	.05
39	Kevin Seitzer	.50	.40	.20
40	Darryl Strawberry	.40	.30	.15
41	Rick Sutcliffe	.10	.08	.04
42	Pat Tabler	.05	.04	.02
43	Fernando Valenzuela	.10	.08	.04
44	Mike Witt	.07	.05	.03

A player's name in italic type indicates a rookie card. An (FC) indicates a player's first card for that particular card company.

1987 Fleer Baseball's Game Winners

1987 Fleer Baseball's Hottest Stars

The 1987 Fleer "Baseball's Game Winners" boxed set of 44 cards was produced for distribution through Bi-Mart Discount Drug, Pay'n-Save, Mott's 5 & 10, M.E. Moses, and Winn's stores. The cards, which measure 2-1/2" by 3-1/2", have a light blue border with the player's name and game winning RBI or games won statistics in a yellow oval band at the top of the card. Below the full-color player photo is the name of the set in blue, yellow and red. Included with the boxed set were six team logo stickers.

The "Baseball's Hottest Stars" 44-card set was produced by Fleer for the Revco Drug Store chain. Measuring the standard 2-1/2" by 3-1/2", the cards feature full-color photos surrounded by a red, white and blue border. The player's name, position and team appear in a blue band at the bottom of the card. Card backs are printed in red, white and black and contain the player's lifetime professional statistics. The set was housed in a special cardboard box with six team logo stickers.

		MT	NR MT	EX
Complete Set:		6.00	4.50	2.50
Common Player:		.05	.04	.02
1	Harold Baines	.10	.08	.04
2	Don Baylor	.10	.08	.04
3	George Bell	.20	.15	.08
4	Tony Bernazard	.05	.04	.02
5	Wade Boggs	.60	.45	.25
6	George Brett	.40	.30	.15
7	Hubie Brooks	.07	.05	.03
8	Jose Canseco	1.00	.70	.40
9	Gary Carter	.20	.15	.08
10	Roger Clemens	.40	.30	.15
11	Eric Davis	.50	.40	.20
12	Glenn Davis	.15	.11	.06
13	Shawon Dunston	.07	.05	.03
14	Mark Eichhorn	.10	.08	.04
15	Gary Gaetti	.12	.09	.05
16	Steve Garvey	.25	.20	.10
17	Kirk Gibson	.20	.15	.08
18	Dwight Gooden	.50	.40	.20
19	Von Hayes	.07	.05	.03
20	Willie Hernandez	.07	.05	.03
21	Ted Higuera	.10	.08	.04
22	Wally Joyner	.80	.60	.30
23	Bob Knepper	.05	.04	.02
24	Mike Krukow	.05	.04	.02
25	Jeff Leonard	.05	.04	.02
26	Don Mattingly	1.00	.70	.40
27	Kirk McCaskill	.07	.05	.03
28	Kevin McReynolds	.12	.09	.05
29	Jim Morrison	.05	.04	.02
30	Dale Murphy	.30	.25	.12
31	Pete O'Brien	.07	.05	.03
32	Bob Ojeda	.07	.05	.03
33	Larry Parrish	.05	.04	.02
34	Ken Phelps	.05	.04	.02
35	Dennis Rasmussen	.07	.05	.03
36	Ernest Riles	.07	.05	.03
37	Cal Ripken, Jr.	.60	.45	.25
38	Ron Robinson	.05	.04	.02
39	Steve Sax	.15	.11	.06
40	Mike Schmidt	.30	.25	.12
41	John Tudor	.07	.05	.03
42	Fernando Valenzuela	.20	.15	.08
43	Mike Witt	.07	.05	.03
44	Curt Young	.05	.04	.02

		MT	NR MT	EX
Complete Set:		6.00	4.50	2.50
Common Player:		.05	.04	.02
1	Joaquin Andujar	.05	.04	.02
2	Harold Baines	.10	.08	.04
3	Kevin Bass	.07	.05	.03
4	Don Baylor	.10	.08	.04
5	Barry Bonds	.20	.15	.08
6	George Brett	.30	.25	.12
7	Tom Brunansky	.10	.08	.04
8	Brett Butler	.05	.04	.02
9	Jose Canseco	1.00	.70	.40
10	Roger Clemens	.50	.40	.20
11	Ron Darling	.10	.08	.04
12	Eric Davis	.50	.40	.20
13	Andre Dawson	.15	.11	.06
14	Doug DeCinces	.05	.04	.02
15	Leon Durham	.07	.05	.03
16	Mark Eichhorn	.10	.08	.04
17	Scott Garrelts	.05	.04	.02
18	Dwight Gooden	.50	.40	.20
19	Dave Henderson	.05	.04	.02
20	Rickey Henderson	.50	.40	.20
21	Keith Hernandez	.15	.11	.06
22	Ted Higuera	.10	.08	.04
23	Bob Horner	.07	.05	.03
24	Pete Incaviglia	.30	.25	.15
25	Wally Joyner	.50	.40	.20
26	Mark Langston	.07	.05	.03
27	Don Mattingly	1.00	.70	.40
28	Dale Murphy	.30	.25	.12
29	Kirk McCaskill	.07	.05	.03
30	Willie McGee	.10	.08	.04
31	Dave Righetti	.12	.09	.05
32	Pete Rose	.40	.30	.15
33	Bruce Ruffin	.15	.11	.06
34	Steve Sax	.15	.11	.06
35	Mike Schmidt	.30	.25	.12
36	Larry Sheets	.10	.08	.04
37	Eric Show	.07	.05	.03
38	Dave Smith	.05	.04	.02
39	Cory Snyder	.07	.05	.03
40	Frank Tanana	.05	.04	.02
41	Alan Trammell	.20	.15	.08
42	Reggie Williams	.07	.05	.03
43	Mookie Wilson	.07	.05	.03
44	Todd Worrell	.15	.11	.06

1987 Fleer Box Panels

For the second straight year, Fleer produced a special set of cards designed to stimulate sales of their wax and cello pack boxes. In 1987, Fleer issued 16 cards in panels of four on the bottoms of retail boxes. The cards are numbered C-1 through C-16 and are 2-1/2" by 3-1/2" in size. The cards have the same design as the regular issue set with the player photos and card numbers being different.

		MT	NR MT	EX
Complete Panel Set:		8.00	6.00	3.25
Complete Singles Set:		3.50	2.75	1.50
Common Panel:		2.25	1.75	.90
Common Single Player:		.20	.15	.08
	Panel	2.50	2.00	1.00
1	Mets Logo	.05	.04	.02
6	Keith Hernandez	.30	.25	.12
8	Dale Murphy	.60	.45	.25
14	Ryne Sandberg	.30	.25	.12
	Panel	2.25	1.75	.90
2	Jesse Barfield	.20	.15	.08
3	George Brett	.60	.45	.25
5	Red Sox Logo	.05	.04	.02
11	Kirby Puckett	.30	.25	.12
	Panel	2.75	2.00	1.00
4	Dwight Gooden	.80	.60	.30
9	Astros Logo	.05	.04	.02
10	Dave Parker	.25	.20	.10
15	Mike Schmidt	.60	.45	.25
	Panel	2.75	2.00	1.00
7	Wally Joyner	1.00	.70	.40
12	Dave Righetti	.20	.15	.08
13	Angels Logo	.05	.04	.02
16	Robin Yount	.25	.20	.10

1987 Fleer 1986 World Series

 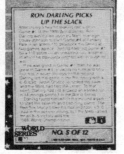

Fleer issued a set of 12 cards highlighting the 1986 World Series between the Boston Red Sox and New York Mets. The sets were available only with Fleer factory-packaged sets of 660 regular issue cards. The cards, which are the standard 2-1/2" by 3-1/2"

size, have either horizontal or vertical formats. The fronts are bordered in red, white and blue stars and stripes with a thin gold frame around the photo. The backs are printed in red and blue ink on white stock and include information regarding the photo on the card fronts.

		MT	NR MT	EX
Complete Set:		4.00	3.00	1.50
Common Player:		.50	.40	.20
1	Left-Hand Finesse Beats Mets (Bruce Hurst)	.50	.40	.20
2	Hernandez And Boggs (Wade Boggs, Keith Hernandez)	.70	.50	.30
3	Roger Clemens	.70	.50	.30
4	Clutch Hitting (Gary Carter)	.50	.40	.20
5	Darling Picks Up The Slack (Ron Darling)	.50	.40	.20
6	.433 Series Batting Average (Marty Barrett)	.50	.40	.20
7	Dwight Gooden	.70	.50	.30
8	Strategy At Work	.50	.40	.20
9	Dewey! (Dwight Evans)	.50	.40	.20
10	One Strike From Boston Victory (Dave Henderson, Spike Owen)	.50	.40	.20
11	Series Home Run Duo (Ray Knight, Darryl Strawberry)	.50	.40	.20
12	Series M.V.P. (Ray Knight)	.50	.40	.20

1987 Fleer Headliners

A continuation of the 1986 Future Hall of Famers idea, Fleer encountered legal problems with using the Hall of Fame name and abated them by entitling the set "Headliners." The cards, which are the standard 2-1/2" by 3-1/2" size, were randomly inserted in three-pack cello packs. Card fronts feature a player photo set against a beige background with bright red stripes. The card backs are printed in black, red and gray and offer a brief biography with an emphasis on the player's performance during the 1986 season.

		MT	NR MT	EX
Complete Set:		10.00	7.50	4.00
Common Player:		1.00	.70	.40
1	Wade Boggs	2.25	1.75	.90
2	Jose Canseco	3.00	2.25	1.25
3	Dwight Gooden	1.50	1.25	.60
4	Rickey Henderson	3.00	2.25	1.25
5	Keith Hernandez	1.00	.70	.40
6	Jim Rice	1.00	.70	.40

Regional interest may affect the value of a card.

1987 Fleer
League Leaders

1987 Fleer
Limited Edition

For the second year in a row, Fleer produced a 44-card "League Leaders" set for Walgreens. The card fronts feature a border style which is identical to that used in 1986. However, an elliptical shaped full-color player photo is placed diagonally on the front. "1987 Fleer League Leaders" appears in the upper left corner of the front although nowhere on the card does it state in which pitching, hitting or fielding department was the player a league leader. The card backs are printed in red and blue on white stock. The cards in the boxed set are the standard 2-1/2" by 3-1/2" size.

For the third straight year, Fleer produced a Limited Edition set for the McCrory's store chain and their affiliates. The cards are the standard 2-1/2" by 3-1/2" size and feature light blue borders at the top and bottom and a diagonal red and white border running along both sides. The set was issued in a specially prepared cardboard box, along with six team logo stickers.

		MT	NR MT	EX
Complete Set:		5.00	3.75	2.00
Common Player:		.05	.04	.02
1	Floyd Bannister	.05	.04	.02
2	Marty Barrett	.07	.05	.03
3	Steve Bedrosian	.10	.08	.04
4	George Bell	.20	.15	.08
5	George Brett	.30	.25	.12
6	Jose Canseco	1.00	.70	.40
7	Joe Carter	.12	.09	.05
8	Will Clark	1.00	.70	.40
9	Roger Clemens	.40	.30	.15
10	Vince Coleman	.15	.11	.06
11	Glenn Davis	.15	.11	.06
12	Mike Davis	.05	.04	.02
13	Len Dykstra	.07	.05	.03
14	John Franco	.07	.05	.03
15	Julio Franco	.10	.08	.04
16	Steve Garvey	.25	.20	.10
17	Kirk Gibson	.20	.15	.08
18	Dwight Gooden	.40	.30	.15
19	Tony Gwynn	.25	.20	.10
20	Keith Hernandez	.20	.15	.08
21	Teddy Higuera	.10	.08	.04
22	Kent Hrbek	.15	.11	.06
23	Wally Joyner	.50	.40	.20
24	Mike Krukow	.05	.04	.02
25	Mike Marshall	.10	.08	.04
26	Don Mattingly	1.00	.70	.40
27	Oddibe McDowell	.10	.08	.04
28	Jack Morris	.15	.11	.06
29	Lloyd Moseby	.07	.05	.03
30	Dale Murphy	.30	.25	.12
31	Eddie Murray	.25	.20	.10
32	Tony Pena	.07	.05	.03
33	Jim Presley	.10	.08	.04
34	Jeff Reardon	.10	.08	.04
35	Jim Rice	.20	.15	.08
36	Pete Rose	.40	.30	.15
37	Mike Schmidt	.30	.25	.12
38	Mike Scott	.12	.09	.05
39	Lee Smith	.07	.05	.03
40	Lonnie Smith	.05	.04	.02
41	Gary Ward	.05	.04	.02
42	Dave Winfield	.25	.20	.10
43	Todd Worrell	.12	.09	.05
44	Robin Yount	.20	.15	.08

		MT	NR MT	EX
Complete Set:		5.00	3.75	2.00
Common Player:		.05	.04	.02
1	Jesse Barfield	.12	.09	.05
2	Mike Boddicker	.07	.05	.03
3	Wade Boggs	.60	.45	.25
4	Phil Bradley	.10	.08	.04
5	George Brett	.30	.25	.12
6	Hubie Brooks	.07	.05	.03
7	Chris Brown	.07	.05	.03
8	Jose Canseco	.70	.50	.30
9	Joe Carter	.12	.09	.05
10	Roger Clemens	.40	.30	.15
11	Vince Coleman	.15	.11	.06
12	Joe Cowley	.05	.04	.02
13	Kal Daniels	.20	.15	.08
14	Glenn Davis	.15	.11	.06
15	Jody Davis	.07	.05	.03
16	Darrell Evans	.07	.05	.03
17	Dwight Evans	.10	.08	.04
18	John Franco	.07	.05	.03
19	Julio Franco	.10	.08	.04
20	Dwight Gooden	.40	.30	.15
21	Goose Gossage	.12	.09	.05
22	Tom Herr	.07	.05	.03
23	Ted Higuera	.10	.08	.04
24	Bob Horner	.07	.05	.03
25	Pete Incaviglia	.40	.30	.15
26	Wally Joyner	.40	.30	.15
27	Dave Kingman	.10	.08	.04
28	Don Mattingly	1.00	.70	.40
29	Willie McGee	.10	.08	.04
30	Donnie Moore	.05	.04	.02
31	Keith Moreland	.05	.04	.02
32	Eddie Murray	.25	.20	.10
33	Mike Pagliarulo	.10	.08	.04
34	Larry Parrish	.05	.04	.02
35	Tony Pena	.07	.05	.03
36	Kirby Puckett	.50	.40	.20
37	Pete Rose	.50	.40	.20
38	Juan Samuel	.12	.09	.05
39	Ryne Sandberg	.20	.15	.08
40	Mike Schmidt	.30	.25	.12
41	Darryl Strawberry	.40	.30	.15
42	Greg Walker	.07	.05	.03
43	Bob Welch	.07	.05	.03
44	Todd Worrell	.12	.09	.05

Definitions for grading conditions are located in the Introduction of this price guide.

1987 Fleer Mini

Continuing with an idea originated the previous year, the Fleer "Classic Miniatures" set consists of 120 cards that measure 1-13/16" by 2-9/16" in size. The cards are identical in design to the regular issue set produced by Fleer, but use completely different photos. The set was issued in a specially prepared collectors box along with 18 team logo stickers. The Fleer Mini set was available only through hobby dealers.

		MT	NR MT	EX
	Complete Set:	9.00	6.75	3.50
	Common Player:	.05	.04	.02
1	Don Aase	.05	.04	.02
2	Joaquin Andujar	.05	.04	.02
3	Harold Baines	.12	.09	.05
4	Jesse Barfield	.12	.09	.05
5	Kevin Bass	.05	.04	.02
6	Don Baylor	.10	.08	.04
7	George Bell	.20	.15	.08
8	Tony Bernazard	.05	.04	.02
9	Bert Blyleven	.12	.09	.05
10	Wade Boggs	.60	.45	.25
11	Phil Bradley	.10	.08	.04
12	Sid Bream	.05	.04	.02
13	George Brett	.30	.25	.12
14	Hubie Brooks	.07	.05	.03
15	Chris Brown	.07	.05	.03
16	Tom Candiotti	.05	.04	.02
17	Jose Canseco	1.00	.70	.40
18	Gary Carter	.20	.15	.08
19	Joe Carter	.12	.09	.05
20	Roger Clemens	.60	.45	.25
21	Vince Coleman	.15	.11	.06
22	Cecil Cooper	.10	.08	.04
23	Ron Darling	.10	.08	.04
24	Alvin Davis	.10	.08	.04
25	Chili Davis	.05	.04	.02
26	Eric Davis	.60	.45	.25
27	Glenn Davis	.15	.11	.06
28	Mike Davis	.05	.04	.02
29	Doug DeCinces	.05	.04	.02
30	Rob Deer	.07	.05	.03
31	Jim Deshaies	.10	.08	.04
32	Bo Diaz	.05	.04	.02
33	Richard Dotson	.07	.05	.03
34	Brian Downing	.05	.04	.02
35	Shawon Dunston	.07	.05	.03
36	Mark Eichhorn	.10	.08	.04
37	Dwight Evans	.12	.09	.05
38	Tony Fernandez	.10	.08	.04
39	Julio Franco	.10	.08	.04
40	Gary Gaetti	.12	.09	.05
41	Andres Galarraga	.15	.11	.06
42	Scott Garrelts	.05	.04	.02
43	Steve Garvey	.20	.15	.08
44	Kirk Gibson	.20	.15	.08
45	Dwight Gooden	.60	.45	.25
46	Ken Griffey	.07	.05	.03
47	Mark Gubicza	.10	.08	.04
48	Ozzie Guillen	.07	.05	.03
49	Bill Gullickson	.05	.04	.02
50	Tony Gwynn	.25	.20	.10
51	Von Hayes	.10	.08	.04
52	Rickey Henderson	.80	.60	.30
53	Keith Hernandez	.15	.11	.06

		MT	NR MT	EX
54	Willie Hernandez	.05	.04	.02
55	Ted Higuera	.10	.08	.04
56	Charlie Hough	.05	.04	.02
57	Kent Hrbek	.15	.11	.06
58	Pete Incaviglia	.40	.30	.15
59	Wally Joyner	.80	.60	.30
60	Bob Knepper	.07	.05	.03
61	Mike Krukow	.05	.04	.02
62	Mark Langston	.10	.08	.04
63	Carney Lansford	.07	.05	.03
64	Jim Lindeman	.12	.09	.05
65	Bill Madlock	.10	.08	.04
66	Don Mattingly	.80	.60	.30
67	Kirk McCaskill	.05	.04	.02
68	Lance McCullers	.10	.08	.04
69	Keith Moreland	.05	.04	.02
70	Jack Morris	.15	.11	.06
71	Jim Morrison	.05	.04	.02
72	Lloyd Moseby	.07	.05	.03
73	Jerry Mumphrey	.05	.04	.02
74	Dale Murphy	.30	.25	.12
75	Eddie Murray	.25	.20	.10
76	Pete O'Brien	.07	.05	.03
77	Bob Ojeda	.07	.05	.03
78	Jesse Orosco	.05	.04	.02
79	Dan Pasqua	.10	.08	.04
80	Dave Parker	.12	.09	.05
81	Larry Parrish	.05	.04	.02
82	Jim Presley	.10	.08	.04
83	Kirby Puckett	.50	.40	.20
84	Dan Quisenberry	.07	.05	.03
85	Tim Raines	.20	.15	.08
86	Dennis Rasmussen	.07	.05	.03
87	Johnny Ray	.07	.05	.03
88	Jeff Reardon	.07	.05	.03
89	Jim Rice	.20	.15	.08
90	Dave Righetti	.12	.09	.05
91	Earnest Riles	.05	.04	.02
92	Cal Ripken, Jr.	.60	.45	.25
93	Ron Robinson	.05	.04	.02
94	Juan Samuel	.12	.09	.05
95	Ryne Sandberg	.20	.15	.08
96	Steve Sax	.15	.11	.06
97	Mike Schmidt	.30	.25	.12
98	Ken Schrom	.05	.04	.02
99	Mike Scott	.12	.09	.05
100	Ruben Sierra	1.50	1.25	.60
101	Lee Smith	.07	.05	.03
102	Ozzie Smith	.12	.09	.05
103	Cory Snyder	.20	.15	.08
104	Kent Tekulve	.05	.04	.02
105	Andres Thomas	.10	.08	.04
106	Rob Thompson	.10	.08	.04
107	Alan Trammell	.20	.15	.08
108	John Tudor	.07	.05	.03
109	Fernando Valenzuela	.20	.15	.08
110	Greg Walker	.07	.05	.03
111	Mitch Webster	.05	.04	.02
112	Lou Whitaker	.15	.11	.06
113	Frank White	.07	.05	.03
114	Reggie Williams	.10	.08	.04
115	Glenn Wilson	.05	.04	.02
116	Willie Wilson	.10	.08	.04
117	Dave Winfield	.20	.15	.08
118	Mike Witt	.07	.05	.03
119	Todd Worrell	.12	.09	.05
120	Floyd Youmans	.05	.04	.02

1987 Fleer Baseball Record Setters

Produced by Fleer for the Eckerd Drug chain, the

1987 Fleer Record Setters set contains 44 cards that measure the standard 2-1/2" by 3-1/2" size. Although the set is titled "Record Setters," the actual records the players have set is not specified anywhere on the cards. Given that several players included in the set were young prospects, a better title for those cards might have been "Possible Record Setters." The set came housed in a special cardboard box with six team logo stickers.

		MT	NR MT	EX
	Complete Set:	5.00	3.75	2.00
	Common Player:	.05	.04	.02
1	George Brett	.30	.25	.12
2	Chris Brown	.07	.05	.03
3	Jose Canseco	1.00	.70	.40
4	Roger Clemens	.40	.30	.15
5	Alvin Davis	.10	.08	.04
6	Shawon Dunston	.07	.05	.03
7	Tony Fernandez	.10	.08	.04
8	Carlton Fisk	.12	.09	.05
9	Gary Gaetti	.10	.08	.04
10	Gene Garber	.05	.04	.02
11	Rich Gedman	.05	.04	.02
12	Dwight Gooden	.40	.30	.15
13	Ozzie Guillen	.07	.05	.03
14	Bill Gullickson	.05	.04	.02
15	Billy Hatcher	.07	.05	.03
16	Orel Hershiser	.20	.15	.08
17	Wally Joyner	.70	.50	.30
18	Ray Knight	.05	.04	.02
19	Craig Lefferts	.05	.04	.02
20	Don Mattingly	1.00	.70	.40
21	Kevin Mitchell	.70	.50	.30
22	Lloyd Moseby	.07	.05	.03
23	Dale Murphy	.30	.25	.12
24	Eddie Murray	.25	.20	.10
25	Phil Niekro	.15	.11	.06
26	Ben Oglivie	.05	.04	.02
27	Jesse Orosco	.05	.04	.02
28	Joe Orsulak	.05	.04	.02
29	Larry Parrish	.05	.04	.02
30	Tim Raines	.25	.20	.10
31	Shane Rawley	.07	.05	.03
32	Dave Righetti	.12	.09	.05
33	Pete Rose	.40	.30	.15
34	Steve Sax	.15	.11	.06
35	Mike Schmidt	.30	.25	.12
36	Mike Scott	.12	.09	.05
37	Don Sutton	.12	.09	.05
38	Alan Trammell	.20	.15	.08
39	John Tudor	.10	.08	.04
40	Gary Ward	.05	.04	.02
41	Lou Whitaker	.15	.11	.06
42	Willie Wilson	.10	.08	.04
43	Todd Worrell	.15	.11	.06
44	Floyd Youmans	.10	.08	.04

1987 Fleer Star Stickers

The 1987 Fleer Star Stickers set contains 132 cards which become stickers if the back is bent and peeled off. As in the previous year, the card backs are identical, save the numbering system, to the regular issue cards. The cards measure 2-1/2" by 3-1/2" and were sold in wax packs with team logo stickers. The fronts have a green border with a red and white banner wrapped across the upper left corner and the sides. The backs are printed in green and yellow.

		MT	NR MT	EX
	Complete Set:	20.00	15.00	8.00
	Common Player:	.05	.04	.02
1	Don Aase	.05	.04	.02
2	Harold Baines	.20	.15	.08
3	Floyd Bannister	.08	.06	.03
4	Jesse Barfield	.20	.15	.08
5	Marty Barrett	.10	.08	.04
6	Kevin Bass	.10	.08	.04
7	Don Baylor	.12	.09	.05
8	Steve Bedrosian	.15	.11	.06
9	George Bell	.35	.25	.14
10	Bert Blyleven	.15	.11	.06
11	Mike Boddicker	.08	.06	.03
12	Wade Boggs	1.00	.70	.40
13	Phil Bradley	.15	.11	.06
14	Sid Bream	.08	.06	.03
15	George Brett	.70	.50	.30
16	Hubie Brooks	.10	.08	.04
17	Tom Brunansky	.15	.11	.06
18	Tom Candiotti	.05	.04	.02
19	Jose Canseco	1.00	.70	.40
20	Gary Carter	.40	.30	.15
21	Joe Carter	.20	.15	.08
22	Will Clark	1.00	.70	.40
23	Mark Clear	.05	.04	.02
24	Roger Clemens	.90	.70	.35
25	Vince Coleman	.25	.20	.10
26	Jose Cruz	.10	.08	.04
27	Ron Darling	.20	.15	.08
28	Alvin Davis	.20	.15	.08
29	Chili Davis	.10	.08	.04
30	Eric Davis	.60	.45	.25
31	Glenn Davis	.20	.15	.08
32	Mike Davis	.05	.04	.02
33	Andre Dawson	.25	.20	.10
34	Doug DeCinces	.08	.06	.03
35	Brian Downing	.08	.06	.03
36	Shawon Dunston	.12	.09	.05
37	Mark Eichhorn	.12	.09	.05
38	Dwight Evans	.15	.11	.06
39	Tony Fernandez	.15	.11	.06
40	Bob Forsch	.05	.04	.02
41	John Franco	.10	.08	.04
42	Julio Franco	.12	.09	.05
43	Gary Gaetti	.20	.15	.08
44	Gene Garber	.05	.04	.02
45	Scott Garrelts	.05	.04	.02
46	Steve Garvey	.40	.30	.15
47	Kirk Gibson	.30	.25	.12
48	Dwight Gooden	.90	.70	.35
49	Ken Griffey	.10	.08	.04
50	Ozzie Guillen	.10	.08	.04
51	Bill Gullickson	.05	.04	.02
52	Tony Gwynn	.40	.30	.15
53	Mel Hall	.08	.06	.03
54	Greg Harris	.05	.04	.02
55	Von Hayes	.12	.09	.05
56	Rickey Henderson	1.00	.70	.40
57	Tom Henke	.10	.08	.04
58	Keith Hernandez	.35	.25	.14
59	Willie Hernandez	.05	.04	.02
60	Ted Higuera	.20	.15	.08
61	Bob Horner	.12	.09	.05
62	Charlie Hough	.08	.06	.03
63	Jay Howell	.08	.06	.03
64	Kent Hrbek	.30	.25	.12
65	Bruce Hurst	.12	.09	.05
66	Pete Incaviglia	.60	.45	.25
67	Bob James	.05	.04	.02
68	Wally Joyner	.50	.40	.20
69	Mike Krukow	.05	.04	.02
70	Mark Langston	.15	.11	.06
71	Carney Lansford	.08	.06	.03
72	Fred Lynn	.25	.20	.10
73	Bill Madlock	.12	.09	.05
74	Don Mattingly	1.00	.70	.40
75	Kirk McCaskill	.05	.04	.02
76	Lance McCullers	.12	.09	.05
77	Oddibe McDowell	.15	.11	.06
78	Paul Molitor	.20	.15	.08
79	Keith Moreland	.08	.06	.03
80	Jack Morris	.25	.20	.10
81	Jim Morrison	.05	.04	.02
82	Jerry Mumphrey	.05	.04	.02
83	Dale Murphy	.70	.50	.30
84	Eddie Murray	.50	.40	.20

		MT	NR MT	EX
85	Ben Oglivie	.05	.04	.02
86	Bob Ojeda	.10	.08	.04
87	Jesse Orosco	.08	.06	.03
88	Dave Parker	.25	.20	.10
89	Larry Parrish	.08	.06	.03
90	Tony Pena	.10	.08	.04
91	Jim Presley	.15	.11	.06
92	Kirby Puckett	.70	.50	.30
93	Dan Quisenberry	.12	.09	.05
94	Tim Raines	.35	.25	.14
95	Dennis Rasmussen	.10	.08	.04
96	Shane Rawley	.08	.06	.03
97	Johnny Ray	.10	.08	.04
98	Jeff Reardon	.10	.08	.04
99	Jim Rice	.35	.25	.14
100	Dave Righetti	.20	.15	.08
101	Cal Ripken, Jr.	1.00	.70	.40
102	Pete Rose	1.00	.70	.40
103	Nolan Ryan	2.00	1.50	.80
104	Juan Samuel	.15	.11	.06
105	Ryne Sandberg	.60	.45	.25
106	Steve Sax	.20	.15	.08
107	Mike Schmidt	1.25	.90	.50
108	Mike Scott	.15	.11	.06
109	Dave Smith	.05	.04	.02
110	Lee Smith	.10	.08	.04
111	Lonnie Smith	.05	.04	.02
112	Ozzie Smith	.20	.15	.08
113	Cory Snyder	.50	.40	.20
114	Darryl Strawberry	.70	.50	.30
115	Don Sutton	.25	.20	.10
116	Kent Tekulve	.08	.06	.03
117	Gorman Thomas	.08	.06	.03
118	Alan Trammell	.30	.25	.12
119	John Tudor	.12	.09	.05
120	Fernando Valenzuela	.12	.09	.05
121	Bob Welch	.12	.09	.05
122	Lou Whitaker	.25	.20	.10
123	Frank White	.10	.08	.04
124	Reggie Williams	.12	.09	.05
125	Willie Wilson	.15	.11	.06
126	Dave Winfield	.40	.30	.15
127	Mike Witt	.10	.08	.04
128	Todd Worrell	.25	.20	.10
129	Curt Young	.08	.06	.03
130	Robin Yount	.30	.25	.12
131	Jose Canseco, Don Mattingly/Checklist	2.50	2.00	1.00
132	Eric Davis, Bo Jackson/Checklist	1.25	.90	.50

1987 Fleer Star Sticker Box Panels

Fleer issued on the bottoms of their Fleer Star Stickers wax pack boxes six player cards plus two team logo/checklist cards. The cards, which measure 2-1/2" by 3-1/2", are numbered S-1 through S-8. The cards are identical in design to the Star Stickers.

		MT	NR MT	EX
	Complete Panel Set:	6.00	4.50	2.50
	Complete Singles Set:	3.25	2.50	1.25
	Common Single Player:	.15	.11	.06
	Panel	5.00	3.75	2.00
2	Wade Boggs	.60	.45	.25

		MT	NR MT	EX
3	Bert Blyleven	.20	.15	.08
6	Phillies Logo	.05	.04	.02
8	Don Mattingly	1.50	1.25	.60
	Panel	1.00	.70	.40
1	Tigers Logo	.05	.04	.02
4	Jose Cruz	.15	.11	.06
5	Glenn Davis	.20	.15	.08
7	Bob Horner	.15	.11	.06

1987 Fleer Update

Fleer followed suit on a Topps idea in 1984 and began producing "Update" sets. The 1987 edition brings the regular Fleer set to date by including traded players and hot rookies. The cards measure 2-1/2" by 3-1/2" and are housed in a specially designed box with 25 team logo stickers. As a companion to the glossy-coated Fleer Collectors Edition set, Fleer produced a special edition Update set in its own tin box. Values of the glossy-coated cards are only a few dollars more than the regular Update cards.

		MT	NR MT	EX
	Complete Set:	15.00	11.00	6.00
	Common Player:	.06	.05	.02
1	Scott Bankhead	.08	.06	.03
2	Eric Bell(FC)	.15	.11	.06
3	Juan Beniquez	.06	.05	.02
4	Juan Berenguer	.06	.05	.02
5	Mike Birkbeck(FC)	.20	.15	.08
6	Randy Bockus(FC)	.15	.11	.06
7	Rod Booker(FC)	.15	.11	.06
8	Thad Bosley	.06	.05	.02
9	Greg Brock	.10	.08	.04
10	Bob Brower(FC)	.15	.11	.06
11	Chris Brown	.12	.09	.05
12	Jerry Browne	.15	.11	.06
13	Ralph Bryant	.10	.08	.04
14	DeWayne Buice(FC)	.20	.15	.08
15	Ellis Burks(FC)	1.00	.70	.40
16	Casey Candaele(FC)	.15	.11	.06
17	Steve Carlton	.40	.30	.15
18	Juan Castillo	.08	.06	.03
19	Chuck Crim(FC)	.15	.11	.06
20	Mark Davidson(FC)	.20	.15	.08
21	Mark Davis	.06	.05	.02
22	Storm Davis	.12	.09	.05
23	Bill Dawley	.06	.05	.02
24	Andre Dawson	.40	.30	.15
25	Brian Dayett	.06	.05	.02
26	Rick Dempsey	.08	.06	.03
27	Ken Dowell(FC)	.15	.11	.06
28	Dave Dravecky	.10	.08	.04
29	Mike Dunne(FC)	.20	.15	.08
30	Dennis Eckersley	.30	.25	.12
31	Cecil Fielder	2.00	1.50	.80
32	Brian Fisher	.10	.08	.04
33	Willie Fraser	.10	.08	.04
34	Ken Gerhart(FC)	.15	.11	.06
35	Jim Gott	.06	.05	.02
36	Dan Gladden	.06	.05	.02
37	Mike Greenwell(FC)	1.00	.70	.40
38	Cecilio Guante	.06	.05	.02
39	Albert Hall	.06	.05	.02
40	Atlee Hammaker	.06	.05	.02

		MT	NR MT	EX
41	Mickey Hatcher	.06	.05	.02
42	Mike Heath	.06	.05	.02
43	Neal Heaton	.06	.05	.02
44	Mike Henneman(FC)	.30	.25	.12
45	Guy Hoffman	.06	.05	.02
46	Charles Hudson	.06	.05	.02
47	Chuck Jackson(FC)	.20	.15	.08
48	Mike Jackson(FC)	.20	.15	.08
49	Reggie Jackson	.60	.45	.25
50	Chris James	.35	.25	.14
51	Dion James	.12	.09	.05
52	Stan Javier	.06	.05	.02
53	Stan Jefferson(FC)	.20	.15	.08
54	Jimmy Jones	.10	.08	.04
55	Tracy Jones	.20	.15	.08
56	Terry Kennedy	.08	.06	.03
57	Mike Kingery	.08	.06	.03
58	Ray Knight	.10	.08	.04
59	Gene Larkin(FC)	.30	.25	.12
60	Mike LaValliere	.12	.09	.05
61	Jack Lazorko(FC)	.06	.05	.02
62	Terry Leach	.06	.05	.02
63	Rick Leach	.06	.05	.02
64	Craig Lefferts	.06	.05	.02
65	Jim Lindeman(FC)	.15	.11	.06
66	Bill Long(FC)	.20	.15	.08
67	Mike Loynd(FC)	.15	.11	.06
68	Greg Maddux(FC)	4.00	3.00	1.50
69	Bill Madlock	.15	.11	.06
70	Dave Magadan	.80	.60	.30
71	Joe Magrane(FC)	.60	.45	.25
72	Fred Manrique(FC)	.20	.15	.08
73	Mike Mason	.06	.05	.02
74	Lloyd McClendon(FC)	.15	.11	.06
75	Fred McGriff(FC)	4.00	3.00	1.50
76	Mark McGwire(FC)	6.00	4.50	2.50
77	Mark McLemore	.06	.05	.02
78	Kevin McReynolds	.30	.25	.12
79	Dave Meads(FC)	.15	.11	.06
80	Greg Minton	.06	.05	.02
81	John Mitchell(FC)	.15	.11	.06
82	Kevin Mitchell	1.00	.70	.40
83	John Morris	.06	.05	.02
84	Jeff Musselman(FC)	.15	.11	.06
85	Randy Myers(FC)	.25	.20	.10
86	Gene Nelson	.06	.05	.02
87	Joe Niekro	.10	.08	.04
88	Tom Nieto	.06	.05	.02
89	Reid Nichols	.06	.05	.02
90	Matt Nokes(FC)	.40	.30	.15
91	Dickie Noles	.06	.05	.02
92	Edwin Nunez	.06	.05	.02
93	Jose Nunez(FC)	.12	.09	.05
94	Paul O'Neill	.50	.40	.20
95	Jim Paciorek(FC)	.06	.05	.02
96	Lance Parrish	.20	.15	.08
97	Bill Pecota(FC)	.20	.15	.08
98	Tony Pena	.12	.09	.05
99	Luis Polonia(FC)	.40	.30	.15
100	Randy Ready	.06	.05	.02
101	Jeff Reardon	.15	.11	.06
102	Gary Redus	.08	.06	.03
103	Rick Rhoden	.10	.08	.04
104	Wally Ritchie(FC)	.15	.11	.06
105	Jeff Robinson(FC)	.30	.25	.12
106	Mark Salas	.06	.05	.02
107	Dave Schmidt	.06	.05	.02
108	Kevin Seitzer	.40	.30	.15
109	John Shelby	.06	.05	.02
110	John Smiley(FC)	.90	.70	.35
111	Lary Sorenson	.06	.05	.02
112	Chris Speier	.06	.05	.02
113	Randy St. Claire	.06	.05	.02
114	Jim Sundberg	.08	.06	.03
115	B.J. Surhoff(FC)	.35	.25	.14
116	Greg Swindell	.50	.40	.20
117	Danny Tartabull	.40	.30	.15
118	Dorn Taylor(FC)	.12	.09	.05
119	Lee Tunnell	.06	.05	.02
120	Ed Vande Berg	.06	.05	.02
121	Andy Van Slyke	.20	.15	.08
122	Gary Ward	.06	.05	.02
123	Devon White	.40	.30	.15
124	Alan Wiggins	.06	.05	.02
125	Bill Wilkinson(FC)	.15	.11	.06
126	Jim Winn	.06	.05	.02
127	Frank Williams	.06	.05	.02
128	Ken Williams(FC)	.20	.15	.08
129	Matt Williams(FC)	2.00	1.50	.80
130	Herm Winningham	.06	.05	.02
131	Matt Young	.06	.05	.02

		MT	NR MT	EX
132	Checklist 1-132	.06	.05	.02

1987 Fleer Baseball's Exciting Stars

Another entry into the Fleer lineup of individual boxed sets, the "Baseball's Exciting Stars" set was produced by Fleer for Cumberland Farms stores. The card fronts feature a red, white and blue border with the words "Exciting Stars" printed in yellow at the top. The backs are printed in red and blue and carry complete major and minor league statistics. Included with the boxed set of 44 cards were six team logo stickers.

		MT	NR MT	EX
	Complete Set:	6.00	4.50	2.50
	Common Player:	.05	.04	.02
1	Don Aase	.05	.04	.02
2	Rick Aguilera	.07	.05	.03
3	Jesse Barfield	.12	.09	.05
4	Wade Boggs	.60	.45	.25
5	Dennis "Oil Can" Boyd	.05	.04	.02
6	Sid Bream	.07	.05	.03
7	Jose Canseco	1.00	.70	.40
8	Steve Carlton	.25	.20	.10
9	Gary Carter	.25	.20	.10
10	Will Clark	1.00	.70	.40
11	Roger Clemens	.40	.30	.15
12	Danny Cox	.07	.05	.03
13	Alvin Davis	.10	.08	.04
14	Eric Davis	.50	.40	.20
15	Rob Deer	.07	.05	.03
16	Brian Downing	.05	.04	.02
17	Gene Garber	.05	.04	.02
18	Steve Garvey	.25	.20	.10
19	Dwight Gooden	.50	.40	.20
20	Mark Gubicza	.10	.08	.04
21	Mel Hall	.05	.04	.02
22	Terry Harper	.05	.04	.02
23	Von Hayes	.10	.08	.04
24	Rickey Henderson	.60	.45	.25
25	Tom Henke	.05	.04	.02
26	Willie Hernandez	.05	.04	.02
27	Ted Higuera	.10	.08	.04
28	Rick Honeycutt	.05	.04	.02
29	Kent Hrbek	.15	.11	.06
30	Wally Joyner	.60	.45	.25
31	Charlie Kerfeld	.05	.04	.02
32	Fred Lynn	.12	.09	.05
33	Don Mattingly	1.50	1.25	.60
34	Tim Raines	.25	.20	.10
35	Dennis Rasmussen	.07	.05	.03
36	Johnny Ray	.07	.05	.03
37	Jim Rice	.20	.15	.08
38	Pete Rose	.50	.40	.20
39	Lee Smith	.07	.05	.03
40	Cory Snyder	.25	.20	.10
41	Darryl Strawberry	.40	.30	.15
42	Kent Tekulve	.05	.04	.02
43	Willie Wilson	.10	.08	.04
44	Bobby Witt	.12	.09	.05

1988 Fleer

A clean, uncluttered look was the trademark of the 660-card 1988 Fleer set. The cards, which are the standard 2-1/2" by 3-1/2", feature blue and red diagonal lines set inside a white border. The player name and position are located on a slant in the upper left corner of the card. The player's team logo appears in the upper right corner. Below the player photo a blue and red band with the word "Fleer" appears. The backs of the cards include the card number, player personal information, and career statistics, plus a new feature called "At Their Best." This feature graphically shows a player's pitching or hitting statistics for home and road games and how he fared during day games as opposed to night contests. The set includes 19 special cards (#'s 622-640) and 12 "Major League Prospects" cards (#'s 641-653).

		MT	NR MT	EX
	Complete Set:	35.00	27.00	13.50
	Common Player:	.06	.05	.02
1	Keith Atherton	.06	.05	.02
2	Don Baylor	.10	.08	.04
3	Juan Berenguer	.06	.05	.02
4	Bert Blyleven	.12	.09	.05
5	Tom Brunansky	.10	.08	.04
6	Randy Bush	.06	.05	.02
7	Steve Carlton	.30	.25	.12
8	*Mark Davidson*(FC)	.12	.09	.05
9	George Frazier	.06	.05	.02
10	Gary Gaetti	.15	.11	.06
11	Greg Gagne	.06	.05	.02
12	Dan Gladden	.06	.05	.02
13	Kent Hrbek	.15	.11	.06
14	*Gene Larkin*	.20	.15	.08
15	Tim Laudner	.06	.05	.02
16	Steve Lombardozzi	.06	.05	.02
17	Al Newman	.06	.05	.02
18	Joe Niekro	.08	.06	.03
19	Kirby Puckett	.60	.45	.25
20	Jeff Reardon	.10	.08	.04
21a	Dan Schatzader (incorrect spelling)	.20	.15	.08
21b	Dan Schatzader (correct spelling)	.06	.05	.02
22	Roy Smalley	.06	.05	.02
23	Mike Smithson	.06	.05	.02
24	*Les Straker*(FC)	.15	.11	.06
25	Frank Viola	.15	.11	.06
26	Jack Clark	.15	.11	.06
27	Vince Coleman	.20	.15	.08
28	Danny Cox	.08	.06	.03
29	Bill Dawley	.06	.05	.02
30	Ken Dayley	.06	.05	.02
31	Doug DeCinces	.08	.06	.03
32	Curt Ford	.06	.05	.02
33	Bob Forsch	.08	.06	.03
34	David Green	.06	.05	.02
35	Tom Herr	.08	.06	.03
36	Ricky Horton	.08	.06	.03
37	*Lance Johnson*(FC)	.75	.55	.35
38	Steve Lake	.06	.05	.02
39	Jim Lindeman	.10	.08	.04
40	*Joe Magrane*	.30	.25	.12
41	Greg Mathews	.08	.06	.03
42	Willie McGee	.12	.09	.05
43	John Morris	.06	.05	.02

		MT	NR MT	EX
44	Jose Oquendo	.06	.05	.02
45	Tony Pena	.08	.06	.03
46	Terry Pendleton	.08	.06	.03
47	Ozzie Smith	.15	.11	.06
48	John Tudor	.10	.08	.04
49	Lee Tunnell	.06	.05	.02
50	Todd Worrell	.10	.08	.04
51	Doyle Alexander	.08	.06	.03
52	Dave Bergman	.06	.05	.02
53	Tom Brookens	.06	.05	.02
54	Darrell Evans	.10	.08	.04
55	Kirk Gibson	.20	.15	.08
56	Mike Heath	.06	.05	.02
57	*Mike Henneman*	.25	.20	.10
58	Willie Hernandez	.08	.06	.03
59	Larry Herndon	.06	.05	.02
60	Eric King	.08	.06	.03
61	Chet Lemon	.08	.06	.03
62	*Scott Lusader*(FC)	.15	.11	.06
63	Bill Madlock	.10	.08	.04
64	Jack Morris	.20	.15	.08
65	Jim Morrison	.06	.05	.02
66	*Matt Nokes*	.50	.40	.20
67	Dan Petry	.08	.06	.03
68a	*Jeff Robinson* (Born 12-13-60 on back)	.30	.25	.12
68b	*Jeff Robinson* (Born 12/14/61 on back)	.15	.11	.06
69	Pat Sheridan	.06	.05	.02
70	Nate Snell	.06	.05	.02
71	Frank Tanana	.08	.06	.03
72	Walt Terrell	.08	.06	.03
73	Mark Thurmond	.06	.05	.02
74	Alan Trammell	.25	.20	.10
75	Lou Whitaker	.25	.20	.10
76	Mike Aldrete	.08	.06	.03
77	Bob Brenly	.06	.05	.02
78	Will Clark	2.00	1.50	.80
79	Chili Davis	.08	.06	.03
80	Kelly Downs	.10	.08	.04
81	Dave Dravecky	.08	.06	.03
82	Scott Garrelts	.06	.05	.02
83	Atlee Hammaker	.06	.05	.02
84	Dave Henderson	.10	.08	.04
85	Mike Krukow	.08	.06	.03
86	Mike LaCoss	.06	.05	.02
87	Craig Lefferts	.06	.05	.02
88	Jeff Leonard	.08	.06	.03
89	Candy Maldonado	.08	.06	.03
90	Ed Milner	.06	.05	.02
91	Bob Melvin	.06	.05	.02
92	Kevin Mitchell	.70	.50	.30
93	*Jon Perlman*(FC)	.12	.09	.05
94	Rick Reuschel	.10	.08	.04
95	Don Robinson	.08	.06	.03
96	Chris Speier	.06	.05	.02
97	Harry Spilman	.06	.05	.02
98	Robbie Thompson	.08	.06	.03
99	Jose Uribe	.06	.05	.02
100	*Mark Wasinger*(FC)	.15	.11	.06
101	*Matt Williams*	4.00	3.00	1.50
102	Jesse Barfield	.15	.11	.06
103	George Bell	.25	.20	.10
104	Juan Beniquez	.06	.05	.02
105	John Cerutti	.08	.06	.03
106	Jim Clancy	.08	.06	.03
107	*Rob Ducey*(FC)	.15	.11	.06
108	Mark Eichhorn	.08	.06	.03
109	Tony Fernandez	.12	.09	.05
110	Cecil Fielder	1.50	1.25	.60
111	Kelly Gruber	.50	.40	.20
112	Tom Henke	.08	.06	.03
113	Garth Iorq (Iorg)	.06	.05	.02
114	Jimmy Key	.10	.08	.04
115	Rick Leach	.06	.05	.02
116	Manny Lee	.08	.06	.03
117	*Nelson Liriano*(FC)	.15	.11	.06
118	*Fred McGriff*	1.75	1.25	.70
119	Lloyd Moseby	.08	.06	.03
120	Rance Mulliniks	.06	.05	.02
121	Jeff Musselman	.10	.08	.04
122	*Jose Nunez*	.15	.11	.06
123	Dave Stieb	.10	.08	.04
124	Willie Upshaw	.08	.06	.03
125	Duane Ward(FC)	.08	.06	.03
126	Ernie Whitt	.08	.06	.03
127	Rick Aguilera	.06	.05	.02
128	Wally Backman	.08	.06	.03
129	*Mark Carreon*(FC)	.12	.09	.05
130	Gary Carter	.25	.20	.10
131	David Cone(FC)	1.00	.70	.40

#	Player	MT	NR MT	EX		#	Player	MT	NR MT	EX
132	Ron Darling	.12	.09	.05		223	Wayne Tolleson	.06	.05	.02
133	Len Dykstra	.10	.08	.04		224	Gary Ward	.08	.06	.03
134	Sid Fernandez	.10	.08	.04		225	Claudell Washington	.08	.06	.03
135	Dwight Gooden	.60	.45	.25		226	Dave Winfield	.30	.25	.12
136	Keith Hernandez	.20	.15	.08		227	Buddy Bell	.08	.06	.03
137	*Gregg Jefferies*(FC)	1.25	.90	.50		228	Tom Browning	.10	.08	.04
138	Howard Johnson	.10	.08	.04		229	Dave Concepcion	.08	.06	.03
139	Terry Leach	.06	.05	.02		230	Kal Daniels	.20	.15	.08
140	*Barry Lyons*(FC)	.15	.11	.06		231	Eric Davis	.80	.60	.30
141	Dave Magadan	.30	.25	.12		232	Bo Diaz	.08	.06	.03
142	Roger McDowell	.10	.08	.04		233	Nick Esasky	.08	.06	.03
143	Kevin McReynolds	.15	.11	.06		234	John Franco	.10	.08	.04
144	*Keith Miller*(FC)	.15	.11	.06		235	Guy Hoffman	.06	.05	.02
145	*John Mitchell*(FC)	.20	.15	.08		236	Tom Hume	.06	.05	.02
146	Randy Myers	.15	.11	.06		237	Tracy Jones	.12	.09	.05
147	Bob Ojeda	.08	.06	.03		238	*Bill Landrum*(FC)	.10	.08	.04
148	Jesse Orosco	.08	.06	.03		239	Barry Larkin	1.00	.70	.40
149	Rafael Santana	.06	.05	.02		240	Terry McGriff(FC)	.06	.05	.02
150	Doug Sisk	.06	.05	.02		241	Rob Murphy	.08	.06	.03
151	Darryl Strawberry	.60	.45	.25		242	Ron Oester	.06	.05	.02
152	Tim Teufel	.06	.05	.02		243	Dave Parker	.20	.15	.08
153	Gene Walter	.06	.05	.02		244	Pat Perry	.06	.05	.02
154	Mookie Wilson	.08	.06	.03		245	Ted Power	.06	.05	.02
155	*Jay Aldrich*(FC)	.12	.09	.05		246	Dennis Rasmussen	.10	.08	.04
156	Chris Bosio	.08	.06	.03		247	Ron Robinson	.06	.05	.02
157	Glenn Braggs	.10	.08	.04		248	Kurt Stillwell	.10	.08	.04
158	Greg Brock	.08	.06	.03		249	*Jeff Treadway*(FC)	.40	.30	.15
159	Juan Castillo	.06	.05	.02		250	Frank Williams	.06	.05	.02
160	Mark Clear	.06	.05	.02		251	Steve Balboni	.08	.06	.03
161	Cecil Cooper	.10	.08	.04		252	Bud Black	.06	.05	.02
162	*Chuck Crim*	.12	.09	.05		253	Thad Bosley	.06	.05	.02
163	Rob Deer	.08	.06	.03		254	George Brett	.40	.30	.15
164	Mike Felder	.06	.05	.02		255	*John Davis*(FC)	.15	.11	.06
165	Jim Gantner	.06	.05	.02		256	Steve Farr	.06	.05	.02
166	Ted Higuera	.10	.08	.04		257	Gene Garber	.06	.05	.02
167	Steve Kiefer	.06	.05	.02		258	Jerry Gleaton	.06	.05	.02
168	Rick Manning	.06	.05	.02		259	Mark Gubicza	.12	.09	.05
169	Paul Molitor	.12	.09	.05		260	Bo Jackson	2.00	1.50	.80
170	Juan Nieves	.08	.06	.03		261	Danny Jackson	.12	.09	.05
171	Dan Plesac	.10	.08	.04		262	*Ross Jones*(FC)	.12	.09	.05
172	Earnest Riles	.06	.05	.02		263	Charlie Leibrandt	.08	.06	.03
173	Bill Schroeder	.06	.05	.02		264	*Bill Pecota*	.15	.11	.06
174	*Steve Stanicek*(FC)	.15	.11	.06		265	*Melido Perez*(FC)	.30	.25	.12
175	B.J. Surhoff	.15	.11	.06		266	Jamie Quirk	.06	.05	.02
176	Dale Sveum	.08	.06	.03		267	Dan Quisenberry	.08	.06	.03
177	Bill Wegman	.06	.05	.02		268	Bret Saberhagen	.15	.11	.06
178	Robin Yount	.30	.25	.12		269	Angel Salazar	.06	.05	.02
179	Hubie Brooks	.10	.08	.04		270	Kevin Seitzer	.50	.40	.20
180	Tim Burke	.06	.05	.02		271	Danny Tartabull	.30	.25	.12
181	Casey Candaele	.06	.05	.02		272	*Gary Thurman*(FC)	.20	.15	.08
182	Mike Fitzgerald	.06	.05	.02		273	Frank White	.08	.06	.03
183	Tom Foley	.06	.05	.02		274	Willie Wilson	.10	.08	.04
184	Andres Galarraga	.15	.11	.06		275	Tony Bernazard	.06	.05	.02
185	Neal Heaton	.06	.05	.02		276	Jose Canseco	2.00	1.50	.80
186	Wallace Johnson	.06	.05	.02		277	Mike Davis	.08	.06	.03
187	Vance Law	.08	.06	.03		278	Storm Davis	.10	.08	.04
188	Dennis Martinez	.08	.06	.03		279	Dennis Eckersley	.12	.09	.05
189	Bob McClure	.06	.05	.02		280	Alfredo Griffin	.08	.06	.03
190	Andy McGaffigan	.06	.05	.02		281	Rick Honeycutt	.06	.05	.02
191	Reid Nichols	.06	.05	.02		282	Jay Howell	.08	.06	.03
192	Pascual Perez	.08	.06	.03		283	Reggie Jackson	.50	.40	.20
193	Tim Raines	.25	.20	.10		284	Dennis Lamp	.06	.05	.02
194	Jeff Reed	.06	.05	.02		285	Carney Lansford	.10	.08	.04
195	Bob Sebra	.06	.05	.02		286	Mark McGwire	2.00	1.50	.80
196	Bryn Smith	.06	.05	.02		287	Dwayne Murphy	.08	.06	.03
197	Randy St. Claire	.06	.05	.02		288	Gene Nelson	.06	.05	.02
198	Tim Wallach	.10	.08	.04		289	Steve Ontiveros	.06	.05	.02
199	Mitch Webster	.08	.06	.03		290	Tony Phillips	.06	.05	.02
200	Herm Winningham	.06	.05	.02		291	Eric Plunk	.06	.05	.02
201	Floyd Youmans	.06	.05	.02		292	*Luis Polonia*	.40	.30	.15
202	*Brad Arnsberg*(FC)	.20	.15	.08		293	*Rick Rodriguez*(FC)	.12	.09	.05
203	Rick Cerone	.06	.05	.02		294	Terry Steinbach	.10	.08	.04
204	Pat Clements	.06	.05	.02		295	Dave Stewart	.10	.08	.04
205	Henry Cotto	.06	.05	.02		296	Curt Young	.08	.06	.03
206	Mike Easler	.08	.06	.03		297	Luis Aguayo	.06	.05	.02
207	Ron Guidry	.15	.11	.06		298	Steve Bedrosian	.12	.09	.05
208	Bill Gullickson	.06	.05	.02		299	Jeff Calhoun	.06	.05	.02
209	Rickey Henderson	.60	.45	.25		300	Don Carman	.08	.06	.03
210	Charles Hudson	.06	.05	.02		301	*Todd Frohwirth*(FC)	.20	.15	.08
211	Tommy John	.15	.11	.06		302	Greg Gross	.06	.05	.02
212	*Roberto Kelly*(FC)	2.00	1.50	.80		303	Kevin Gross	.08	.06	.03
213	Ron Kittle	.08	.06	.03		304	Von Hayes	.08	.06	.03
214	Don Mattingly	.60	.45	.25		305	*Keith Hughes*(FC)	.15	.11	.06
215	Bobby Meacham	.06	.05	.02		306	*Mike Jackson*	.20	.15	.08
216	Mike Pagliarulo	.10	.08	.04		307	Chris James	.20	.15	.08
217	Dan Pasqua	.10	.08	.04		308	Steve Jeltz	.06	.05	.02
218	Willie Randolph	.08	.06	.03		309	Mike Maddux	.07	.05	.03
219	Rick Rhoden	.08	.06	.03		310	Lance Parrish	.15	.11	.06
220	Dave Righetti	.15	.11	.06		311	Shane Rawley	.08	.06	.03
221	Jerry Royster	.06	.05	.02		312	*Wally Ritchie*	.15	.11	.06
222	Tim Stoddard	.06	.05	.02		313	Bruce Ruffin	.08	.06	.03

		MT	NR MT	EX
314	Juan Samuel	.12	.09	.05
315	Mike Schmidt	.50	.40	.20
316	Rick Schu	.06	.05	.02
317	Jeff Stone	.06	.05	.02
318	Kent Tekulve	.08	.06	.03
319	Milt Thompson	.06	.05	.02
320	Glenn Wilson	.08	.06	.03
321	Rafael Belliard	.06	.05	.02
322	Barry Bonds	1.75	1.25	.70
323	Bobby Bonilla	1.25	.90	.50
324	Sid Bream	.08	.06	.03
325	John Cangelosi	.06	.05	.02
326	Mike Diaz	.08	.06	.03
327	Doug Drabek	.08	.06	.03
328	*Mike Dunne*	.15	.11	.06
329	Brian Fisher	.08	.06	.03
330	*Brett Gideon*(FC)	.12	.09	.05
331	Terry Harper	.06	.05	.02
332	Bob Kipper	.06	.05	.02
333	Mike LaValliere	.08	.06	.03
334	*Jose Lind*(FC)	.30	.25	.12
335	Junior Ortiz	.06	.05	.02
336	*Vicente Palacios*(FC)	.30	.25	.12
337	*Bob Patterson*(FC)	.12	.09	.05
338	*Al Pedrique*(FC)	.15	.11	.06
339	R.J. Reynolds	.06	.05	.02
340	*John Smiley*	1.00	.70	.40
341	Andy Van Slyke	.12	.09	.05
342	Bob Walk	.06	.05	.02
343	Marty Barrett	.08	.06	.03
344	*Todd Benzinger*(FC)	.30	.25	.12
345	Wade Boggs	.70	.50	.30
346	*Tom Bolton*(FC)	.15	.11	.06
347	Oil Can Boyd	.08	.06	.03
348	*Ellis Burks*	1.50	1.25	.60
349	Roger Clemens	1.00	.70	.40
350	Steve Crawford	.06	.05	.02
351	Dwight Evans	.12	.09	.05
352	*Wes Gardner*(FC)	.25	.20	.10
353	Rich Gedman	.08	.06	.03
354	Mike Greenwell	.70	.50	.30
355	*Sam Horn*(FC)	.30	.25	.12
356	Bruce Hurst	.10	.08	.04
357	*John Marzano*(FC)	.20	.15	.08
358	Al Nipper	.06	.05	.02
359	Spike Owen	.06	.05	.02
360	*Jody Reed*(FC)	.60	.45	.25
361	Jim Rice	.30	.25	.12
362	Ed Romero	.06	.05	.02
363	Kevin Romine(FC)	.08	.06	.03
364	Joe Sambito	.06	.05	.02
365	Calvin Schiraldi	.06	.05	.02
366	Jeff Sellers	.08	.06	.03
367	Bob Stanley	.06	.05	.02
368	Scott Bankhead	.06	.05	.02
369	Phil Bradley	.10	.08	.04
370	Scott Bradley	.06	.05	.02
371	Mickey Brantley	.06	.05	.02
372	*Mike Campbell*(FC)	.15	.11	.06
373	Alvin Davis	.12	.09	.05
374	Lee Guetterman	.06	.05	.02
375	*Dave Hengel*(FC)	.20	.15	.08
376	Mike Kingery	.06	.05	.02
377	Mark Langston	.12	.09	.05
378	*Edgar Martinez*(FC)	1.50	1.25	.60
379	Mike Moore	.06	.05	.02
380	Mike Morgan	.06	.05	.02
381	John Moses	.06	.05	.02
382	*Donnell Nixon*(FC)	.20	.15	.08
383	Edwin Nunez	.06	.05	.02
384	Ken Phelps	.08	.06	.03
385	Jim Presley	.10	.08	.04
386	Rey Quinones	.06	.05	.02
387	Jerry Reed	.06	.05	.02
388	Harold Reynolds	.08	.06	.03
389	Dave Valle	.08	.06	.03
390	*Bill Wilkinson*	.15	.11	.06
391	Harold Baines	.12	.09	.05
392	Floyd Bannister	.08	.06	.03
393	Daryl Boston	.06	.05	.02
394	Ivan Calderon	.30	.25	.12
395	Jose DeLeon	.08	.06	.03
396	Richard Dotson	.08	.06	.03
397	Carlton Fisk	.20	.15	.08
398	Ozzie Guillen	.08	.06	.03
399	Ron Hassey	.06	.05	.02
400	Donnie Hill	.06	.05	.02
401	Bob James	.06	.05	.02
402	Dave LaPoint	.08	.06	.03
403	*Bill Lindsey*(FC)	.12	.09	.05
404	*Bill Long*(FC)	.15	.11	.06

		MT	NR MT	EX
405	Steve Lyons	.06	.05	.02
406	*Fred Manrique*	.15	.11	.06
407	*Jack McDowell*(FC)	2.00	1.50	.80
408	Gary Redus	.06	.05	.02
409	Ray Searage	.06	.05	.02
410	Bobby Thigpen	.20	.15	.08
411	Greg Walker	.08	.06	.03
412	*Kenny Williams*	.20	.15	.08
413	Jim Winn	.06	.05	.02
414	Jody Davis	.08	.06	.03
415	Andre Dawson	.20	.15	.08
416	Brian Dayett	.06	.05	.02
417	Bob Dernier	.06	.05	.02
418	Frank DiPino	.06	.05	.02
419	Shawon Dunston	.10	.08	.04
420	Leon Durham	.08	.06	.03
421	*Les Lancaster*(FC)	.20	.15	.08
422	Ed Lynch	.06	.05	.02
423	Greg Maddux	1.50	1.25	.60
424	Dave Martinez(FC)	.07	.05	.03
425a	Keith Moreland (bunting, photo actually Jody Davis)	3.00	2.25	1.25
425b	Keith Moreland (standing upright, correct photo)	.08	.06	.03
426	Jamie Moyer	.08	.06	.03
427	Jerry Mumphrey	.06	.05	.02
428	Paul Noce(FC)	.10	.08	.04
429	Rafael Palmeiro(FC)	1.75	1.25	.70
430	Wade Rowdon(FC)	.08	.06	.03
431	Ryne Sandberg	1.00	.70	.40
432	Scott Sanderson	.06	.05	.02
433	Lee Smith	.10	.08	.04
434	Jim Sundberg	.08	.06	.03
435	Rick Sutcliffe	.10	.08	.04
436	Manny Trillo	.08	.06	.03
437	Juan Agosto	.06	.05	.02
438	Larry Andersen	.06	.05	.02
439	Alan Ashby	.06	.05	.02
440	Kevin Bass	.08	.06	.03
441	*Ken Caminiti*(FC)	.35	.25	.14
442	*Rocky Childress*(FC)	.12	.09	.05
443	Jose Cruz	.08	.06	.03
444	Danny Darwin	.06	.05	.02
445	Glenn Davis	.15	.11	.06
446	Jim Deshaies	.08	.06	.03
447	Bill Doran	.08	.06	.03
448	Ty Gainey	.06	.05	.02
449	Billy Hatcher	.08	.06	.03
450	Jeff Heathcock	.06	.05	.02
451	Bob Knepper	.08	.06	.03
452	*Rob Mallicoat*(FC)	.12	.09	.05
453	*Dave Meads*	.15	.11	.06
454	Craig Reynolds	.06	.05	.02
455	Nolan Ryan	1.25	.90	.50
456	Mike Scott	.12	.09	.05
457	Dave Smith	.08	.06	.03
458	Denny Walling	.06	.05	.02
459	*Robbie Wine*(FC)	.12	.09	.05
460	*Gerald Young*(FC)	.15	.11	.06
461	Bob Brower	.08	.06	.03
462a	Jerry Browne (white player, photo actually Bob Brower)	3.50	2.75	1.50
462b	Jerry Browne (black player, correct photo)	.08	.06	.03
463	Steve Buechele	.06	.05	.02
464	Edwin Correa	.06	.05	.02
465	*Cecil Espy*(FC)	.15	.11	.06
466	Scott Fletcher	.08	.06	.03
467	Jose Guzman	.08	.06	.03
468	Greg Harris	.06	.05	.02
469	Charlie Hough	.08	.06	.03
470	Pete Incaviglia	.15	.11	.06
471	*Paul Kilgus*(FC)	.15	.11	.06
472	Mike Loynd	.08	.06	.03
473	Oddibe McDowell	.08	.06	.03
474	Dale Mohorcic	.08	.06	.03
475	Pete O'Brien	.08	.06	.03
476	Larry Parrish	.08	.06	.03
477	Geno Petralli	.06	.05	.02
478	Jeff Russell	.06	.05	.02
479	Ruben Sierra	2.00	1.50	.80
480	Mike Stanley	.08	.06	.03
481	Curtis Wilkerson	.06	.05	.02
482	Mitch Williams	.08	.06	.03
483	Bobby Witt	.10	.08	.04
484	Tony Armas	.08	.06	.03
485	Bob Boone	.08	.06	.03
486	Bill Buckner	.10	.08	.04
487	*DeWayne Buice*	.15	.11	.06
488	Brian Downing	.08	.06	.03
489	Chuck Finley	.06	.05	.02

		MT	NR MT	EX
490	Willie Fraser	.06	.05	.02
491	Jack Howell	.08	.06	.03
492	Ruppert Jones	.06	.05	.02
493	Wally Joyner	.40	.30	.15
494	Jack Lazorko	.06	.05	.02
495	Gary Lucas	.06	.05	.02
496	Kirk McCaskill	.08	.06	.03
497	Mark McLemore	.06	.05	.02
498	Darrell Miller	.06	.05	.02
499	Greg Minton	.06	.05	.02
500	Donnie Moore	.06	.05	.02
501	Gus Polidor	.06	.05	.02
502	Johnny Ray	.08	.06	.03
503	Mark Ryal(FC)	.06	.05	.02
504	Dick Schofield	.06	.05	.02
505	Don Sutton	.20	.15	.08
506	Devon White	.25	.20	.10
507	Mike Witt	.08	.06	.03
508	Dave Anderson	.06	.05	.02
509	Tim Belcher(FC)	.60	.45	.25
510	Ralph Bryant	.06	.05	.02
511	Tim Crews(FC)	.15	.11	.06
512	Mike Devereaux(FC)	2.00	1.50	.80
513	Mariano Duncan	.06	.05	.02
514	Pedro Guerrero	.15	.11	.06
515	Jeff Hamilton(FC)	.12	.09	.05
516	Mickey Hatcher	.06	.05	.02
517	Brad Havens	.06	.05	.02
518	Orel Hershiser	.25	.20	.10
519	Shawn Hillegas(FC)	.20	.15	.08
520	Ken Howell	.06	.05	.02
521	Tim Leary	.08	.06	.03
522	Mike Marshall	.12	.09	.05
523	Steve Sax	.15	.11	.06
524	Mike Scioscia	.08	.06	.03
525	Mike Sharperson(FC)	.06	.05	.02
526	John Shelby	.06	.05	.02
527	Franklin Stubbs	.08	.06	.03
528	Fernando Valenzuela	.20	.15	.08
529	Bob Welch	.10	.08	.04
530	Matt Young	.06	.05	.02
531	Jim Acker	.06	.05	.02
532	Paul Assenmacher	.06	.05	.02
533	Jeff Blauser(FC)	.25	.20	.10
534	Joe Boever(FC)	.25	.20	.10
535	Martin Clary(FC)	.06	.05	.02
536	Kevin Coffman(FC)	.12	.09	.05
537	Jeff Dedmon	.06	.05	.02
538	Ron Gant(FC)	6.00	4.50	2.50
539	Tom Glavine(FC)	8.00	6.00	3.25
540	Ken Griffey	.08	.06	.03
541	Al Hall	.06	.05	.02
542	Glenn Hubbard	.06	.05	.02
543	Dion James	.08	.06	.03
544	Dale Murphy	.40	.30	.15
545	Ken Oberkfell	.06	.05	.02
546	David Palmer	.06	.05	.02
547	Gerald Perry	.10	.08	.04
548	Charlie Puleo	.06	.05	.02
549	Ted Simmons	.10	.08	.04
550	Zane Smith	.08	.06	.03
551	Andres Thomas	.08	.06	.03
552	Ozzie Virgil	.06	.05	.02
553	Don Aase	.06	.05	.02
554	Jeff Ballard(FC)	.35	.25	.14
555	Eric Bell	.08	.06	.03
556	Mike Boddicker	.08	.06	.03
557	Ken Dixon	.06	.05	.02
558	Jim Dwyer	.06	.05	.02
559	Ken Gerhart	.08	.06	.03
560	Rene Gonzales(FC)	.15	.11	.06
561	Mike Griffin	.06	.05	.02
562	John Hayban (Habyan)	.06	.05	.02
563	Terry Kennedy	.08	.06	.03
564	Ray Knight	.08	.06	.03
565	Lee Lacy	.06	.05	.02
566	Fred Lynn	.15	.11	.06
567	Eddie Murray	.35	.25	.14
568	Tom Niedenfuer	.08	.06	.03
569	Bill Ripken(FC)	.25	.20	.10
570	Cal Ripken, Jr.	.60	.45	.25
571	Dave Schmidt	.06	.05	.02
572	Larry Sheets	.08	.06	.03
573	Pete Stanicek(FC)	.15	.11	.06
574	Mark Williamson(FC)	.12	.09	.05
575	Mike Young	.06	.05	.02
576	Shawn Abner(FC)	.20	.15	.08
577	Greg Booker	.06	.05	.02
578	Chris Brown	.08	.06	.03
579	Keith Comstock(FC)	.12	.09	.05
580	Joey Cora(FC)	.12	.09	.05

		MT	NR MT	EX
581	Mark Davis	.06	.05	.02
582	Tim Flannery	.06	.05	.02
583	Goose Gossage	.15	.11	.06
584	Mark Grant	.06	.05	.02
585	Tony Gwynn	.35	.25	.14
586	Andy Hawkins	.06	.05	.02
587	Stan Jefferson	.10	.08	.04
588	Jimmy Jones	.08	.06	.03
589	John Kruk	.10	.08	.04
590	Shane Mack(FC)	.50	.40	.20
591	Carmelo Martinez	.08	.06	.03
592	Lance McCullers	.08	.06	.03
593	Eric Nolte(FC)	.15	.11	.06
594	Randy Ready	.06	.05	.02
595	Luis Salazar	.06	.05	.02
596	Benito Santiago	.35	.25	.14
597	Eric Show	.08	.06	.03
598	Garry Templeton	.08	.06	.03
599	Ed Whitson	.06	.05	.02
600	Scott Bailes	.08	.06	.03
601	Chris Bando	.06	.05	.02
602	Jay Bell(FC)	.60	.45	.25
603	Brett Butler	.08	.06	.03
604	Tom Candiotti	.06	.05	.02
605	Joe Carter	.12	.09	.05
606	Carmen Castillo	.06	.05	.02
607	Brian Dorsett(FC)	.15	.11	.06
608	John Farrell(FC)	.20	.15	.08
609	Julio Franco	.10	.08	.04
610	Mel Hall	.08	.06	.03
611	Tommy Hinzo(FC)	.15	.11	.06
612	Brook Jacoby	.10	.08	.04
613	Doug Jones(FC)	.40	.30	.15
614	Ken Schrom	.06	.05	.02
615	Cory Snyder	.20	.15	.08
616	Sammy Stewart	.06	.05	.02
617	Greg Swindell	.25	.20	.10
618	Pat Tabler	.08	.06	.03
619	Ed Vande Berg	.06	.05	.02
620	Eddie Williams(FC)	.15	.11	.06
621	Rich Yett	.06	.05	.02
622	Slugging Sophomores (Wally Joyner, Cory Snyder)	.35	.25	.14
623	Dominican Dynamite (George Bell, Pedro Guerrero)	.12	.09	.05
624	Oakland's Power Team (Jose Canseco, Mark McGwire)	.50	.40	.20
625	Classic Relief (Dan Plesac, Dave Righetti)	.08	.06	.03
626	All Star Righties (Jack Morris, Bret Saberhagen, Mike Witt)	.10	.08	.04
627	Game Closers (Steve Bedrosian, John Franco)	.08	.06	.03
628	Masters of the Double Play (Ryne Sandberg, Ozzie Smith)	.12	.09	.05
629	Rookie Record Setter (Mark McGwire)	1.00	.70	.40
630	Changing the Guard in Boston (Todd Benzinger, Ellis Burks, Mike Greenwell)	1.00	.70	.40
631	N.L. Batting Champs (Tony Gwynn, Tim Raines)	.15	.11	.06
632	Pitching Magic (Orel Hershiser, Mike Scott)	.12	.09	.05
633	Big Bats At First (Mark McGwire, Pat Tabler)	.60	.45	.25
634	Hitting King and the Thief (Vince Coleman, Tony Gwynn)	.12	.09	.05
635	A.L. Slugging Shortstops (Tony Fernandez, Cal Ripken, Jr., Alan Trammell)	.15	.11	.06
636	Tried and True Sluggers (Gary Carter, Mike Schmidt)	.20	.15	.08
637	Crunch Time (Eric Davis, Darryl Strawberry)	.70	.50	.30
638	A.L. All Stars (Matt Nokes, Kirby Puckett)	.20	.15	.08
639	N.L. All Stars (Keith Hernandez, Dale Murphy)	.20	.15	.08
640	The "O's" Brothers (Bill Ripken, Cal Ripken, Jr.)	.12	.09	.05
641	Major League Prospects (Mark Grace, Darrin Jackson)(FC)	4.00	3.00	1.50
642	Major League Prospects (Damon Berryhill, Jeff Montgomery)(FC)	.80	.60	.30
643	Major League Prospects (Felix Fermin, Jessie Reid)(FC)	.20	.15	.08
644	Major League Prospects (Greg Myers, Greg Tabor)(FC)	.20	.15	.08
645	Major League Prospects (Jim Eppard, Joey Meyer)(FC)	.20	.15	.08

		MT	NR MT	EX
646	Major League Prospects (Adam Peterson, Randy Velarde)(FC)	.20	.15	.08
647	Major League Prospects (Chris Gwynn, Peter Smith)(FC)	.25	.20	.10
648	Major League Prospects (Greg Jelks, Tom Newell)(FC)	.25	.20	.10
649	Major League Prospects (Mario Diaz, Clay Parker)(FC)	.25	.20	.10
650	Major League Prospects (Jack Savage, Todd Simmons)(FC)	.25	.20	.10
651	Major League Prospects (John Burkett, Kirt Manwaring)(FC)	.35	.25	.14
652	Major League Prospects (Dave Otto, Walt Weiss)(FC)	.40	.30	.15
653	Major League Prospects (Randell Byers (Randall), Jeff King)(FC)	.40	.30	.15
654a	Checklist 1-101 (21 is Schatzader)	.10	.08	.04
654b	Checklist 1-101 (21 is Schatzeder)	.06	.05	.02
655	Checklist 102-201	.06	.05	.02
656	Checklist 202-296	.06	.05	.02
657	Checklist 297-390	.06	.05	.02
658	Checklist 391-483	.06	.05	.02
659	Checklist 484-575	.06	.05	.02
660	Checklist 576-660	.06	.05	.02

1988 Fleer
All Star Team

For the third consecutive year, Fleer randomly inserted All Star Team cards in their wax and cello packs. Twelve cards make up the set, each card measuring 2-1/2" by 3-1/2" in size. Players chosen for the set are Fleer's choices for a major league All-Star team.

		MT	NR MT	EX
	Complete Set:	15.00	11.00	6.00
	Common Player:	.60	.45	.25
1	Matt Nokes	.75	.60	.30
2	Tom Henke	.60	.45	.25
3	Ted Higuera	.60	.45	.25
4	Roger Clemens	2.25	1.75	.90
5	George Bell	1.00	.70	.40
6	Andre Dawson	1.00	.70	.40
7	Eric Davis	2.25	1.75	.90
8	Wade Boggs	2.50	2.00	1.00
9	Alan Trammell	1.00	.70	.40
10	Juan Samuel	.75	.60	.30
11	Jack Clark	.75	.60	.30
12	Paul Molitor	.75	.60	.30

Values quoted in this guide reflect the retail price of a card — the price a collector can expect to pay when buying a card from a dealer. The wholesale price — that which a collector can expect to receive from a dealer when selling cards — will be significantly lower, depending on desirability and condition.

1988 Fleer Baseball's
Hottest Stars

This boxed set of 44 standard-size player cards and six team logo sticker cards was produced by Fleer for exclusive distribution at Revco drug stores nationwide. Card fronts feature full-color photos of players representing every major league team. Photos are framed in red, orange and yellow, with a blue and white player name printed across the bottom of the card front. A flaming baseball logo bearing the words "Hottest Stars" appears in the lower left corner of the player photo. Card backs are red, white and blue. The player's name, position, card number and team logo are printed across the top section, followed by a stats box, personal data, batting and throwing preferences. The set also includes six team logo sticker cards with flipside stadium photos in black and white.

		MT	NR MT	EX
	Complete Set:	6.00	4.50	2.50
	Common Player:	.05	.04	.02
1	George Bell	.20	.15	.08
2	Wade Boggs	.80	.60	.30
3	Bobby Bonilla	.12	.09	.05
4	George Brett	.30	.25	.12
5	Jose Canseco	.80	.60	.30
6	Will Clark	.80	.60	.30
7	Roger Clemens	.40	.30	.15
8	Eric Davis	.50	.40	.20
9	Andre Dawson	.15	.11	.06
10	Tony Fernandez	.10	.08	.04
11	Julio Franco	.07	.05	.03
12	Gary Gaetti	.10	.08	.04
13	Dwight Gooden	.40	.30	.15
14	Mike Greenwell	.40	.30	.15
15	Tony Gwynn	.25	.20	.10
16	Rickey Henderson	.50	.40	.20
17	Keith Hernandez	.15	.11	.06
18	Tom Herr	.07	.05	.03
19	Orel Hershiser	.20	.15	.08
20	Ted Higuera	.10	.08	.04
21	Wally Joyner	.30	.25	.12
22	Jimmy Key	.07	.05	.03
23	Mark Langston	.10	.08	.04
24	Don Mattingly	.80	.60	.30
25	Jack McDowell	.20	.15	.08
26	Mark McGwire	.80	.60	.30
27	Kevin Mitchell	.50	.40	.20
28	Jack Morris	.12	.09	.05
29	Dale Murphy	.30	.25	.12
30	Kirby Puckett	.50	.40	.20
31	Tim Raines	.25	.20	.10
32	Shane Rawley	.05	.04	.02
33	Benito Santiago	.25	.20	.10
34	Mike Schmidt	.30	.25	.12
35	Mike Scott	.10	.08	.04
36	Kevin Seitzer	.60	.45	.25
37	Larry Sheets	.07	.05	.03
38	Ruben Sierra	.50	.40	.20
39	Dave Smith	.05	.04	.02
41	Darryl Strawberry	.40	.30	.15
42	Rick Sutcliffe	.10	.08	.04
43	Pat Tabler	.05	.04	.02
44	Alan Trammell	.15	.11	.06

1988 Fleer Box Panels

Fleer's third annual box-bottom issue once again included 16 full-color trading cards printed on the bottoms of four different wax and cello pack retail display boxes. Each box contains three player cards and one team logo card. Player cards follow the same design as the basic 1988 Fleer issue - full-color player photo, name upper left, team logo upper right, Fleer logo lower right. Card fronts feature a blue and red striped border, with a thin white line framing the photo. Card backs are printed in blue and red and include personal information and statistics. Standard-size, the cards are numbered C-1 through C-16.

		MT	NR MT	EX
	Complete Panel Set:	6.25	4.75	2.50
	Complete Singles Set:	2.50	2.00	1.00
	Common Panel:	1.25	.90	.50
	Common Single Player:	.15	.11	.06
	Panel	2.00	1.50	.80
1	Cardinals Logo	.05	.04	.02
11	Mike Schmidt	.60	.45	.25
14	Dave Stewart	.15	.11	.06
15	Tim Wallach	.20	.15	.08
	Panel	1.25	.90	.50
2	Dwight Evans	.15	.11	.06
8	Shane Rawley	.15	.11	.06
10	Ryne Sandberg	.30	.25	.12
13	Tigers Logo	.05	.04	.02
	Panel	2.75	2.00	1.00
3	Andres Galarraga	.25	.20	.10
6	Dale Murphy	.60	.45	.25
9	Giants Logo	.05	.04	.02
12	Kevin Seitzer	.80	.60	.30
	Panel	2.25	1.75	.90
4	Wally Joyner	.60	.45	.25
5	Twins Logo	.05	.04	.02
7	Kirby Puckett	.40	.30	.15
16	Todd Worrell	.20	.15	.08

1988 Fleer '87 World Series

Highlights of the 1987 Series are captured in this full-color insert set found only in Fleer's regular 660-card factory sealed sets. This second World Series edition by Fleer features cards framed in red, with a blue and white starred bunting draped over the upper edges of the photo and a brief photo caption printed on a yellow band across the lower border. Numbered card backs are red, white and blue and include a description of the action pictured on the front, with stats for the Series.

		MT	NR MT	EX
	Complete Set:	3.00	2.25	1.25
	Common Player:	.30	.25	.12
1	"Grand" Hero In Game 1 (Dan Gladden)	.30	.25	.12
2	The Cardinals "Bush" Whacked (Randy Bush, Tony Pena)	.30	.25	.12
3	Masterful Performance Turns Momentum (John Tudor)	.30	.25	.12
4	The Wizard (Ozzie Smith)	.35	.25	.14
5	Throw Smoke! (Tony Pena, Todd Worrell)	.35	.25	.14
6	Cardinal Attack - Disruptive Speed (Vince Coleman)	.40	.30	.15
7	Herr's Wallop (Dan Driessen, Tom Herr)	.30	.25	.12
8	Kirby's Bat Comes Alive in Game 6 (Kirby Puckett)	1.00	.70	.40
9	Hrbek's Slam Forces Game 7 (Kent Hrbek)	.30	.25	.12
10	Herr, Out At First? (Rich Hacker (coach), Tom Herr, Lee Weyer (umpire))	.30	.25	.12
11	Game 7's Play At The Plate (Don Baylor, Dave Phillips (umpire))	.30	.25	.12
12	Series MVP with 16 K's (Frank Viola)	.35	.25	.14

1988 Fleer Headliners

This six-card special set was inserted in Fleer three-packs, sold by retail outlets and hobby dealers nationwide. The card fronts feature crisp full-color player cut-outs printed on a grey and white USA Today-style sports page. "Fleer Headliners 1988" is printed in black and red on a white banner across the top of the card, both front and back. A similar white banner across the card bottom bears the black and white National or American League logo and a red player/team name. Card backs are black on grey with red accents and include the card number and a three-paragraph career summary.

		MT	NR MT	EX
	Complete Set:	8.00	6.00	3.25
	Common Player:	1.00	.70	.40
1	Don Mattingly	2.00	1.50	.80
2	Mark McGwire	1.50	1.25	.60
3	Jack Morris	1.00	.70	.40
4	Darryl Strawberry	1.50	1.25	.60
5	Dwight Gooden	1.50	1.25	.60
6	Tim Raines	1.25	.90	.50

1988 Fleer Award Winners

1988 Fleer Baseball All Stars

This limited edition 44-card boxed set of 1987 award-winning player cards also includes six team logo sticker cards. Red, white, blue and yellow bands border the sharp, full-color player photos printed below a "Fleer Award Winners 1988" banner. The player's name and award are printed beneath the photo. Flip sides are red, white and blue and list personal information, career data, team logo and card number. This set was sold exclusively at 7-11 stores nationwide.

		MT	NR MT	EX
Complete Set:		5.00	3.75	2.00
Common Player:		.05	.04	.02
1	Steve Bedrosian	.10	.08	.04
2	George Bell	.20	.15	.08
3	Wade Boggs	.70	.50	.30
4	Jose Canseco	.70	.50	.30
5	Will Clark	.50	.40	.20
6	Roger Clemens	.40	.30	.15
7	Kal Daniels	.20	.15	.08
8	Eric Davis	.50	.40	.20
9	Andre Dawson	.15	.11	.06
10	Mike Dunne	.10	.08	.04
11	Dwight Evans	.10	.08	.04
12	Carlton Fisk	.15	.11	.06
13	Julio Franco	.07	.05	.03
14	Dwight Gooden	.40	.30	.15
15	Pedro Guerrero	.15	.11	.06
16	Tony Gwynn	.25	.20	.10
17	Orel Hershiser	.20	.15	.08
18	Tom Henke	.05	.04	.02
19	Ted Higuera	.10	.08	.04
20	Charlie Hough	.05	.04	.02
21	Wally Joyner	.30	.25	.12
22	Jimmy Key	.07	.05	.03
23	Don Mattingly	.70	.50	.30
24	Mark McGwire	.70	.50	.30
25	Paul Molitor	.12	.09	.05
26	Jack Morris	.12	.09	.05
27	Dale Murphy	.30	.25	.12
28	Terry Pendleton	.05	.04	.02
29	Kirby Puckett	.70	.50	.30
30	Tim Raines	.25	.20	.10
31	Jeff Reardon	.07	.05	.03
32	Harold Reynolds	.05	.04	.02
33	Dave Righetti	.12	.09	.05
34	Benito Santiago	.25	.20	.10
35	Mike Schmidt	.30	.25	.12
36	Mike Scott	.10	.08	.04
37	Kevin Seitzer	.60	.45	.25
38	Larry Sheets	.07	.05	.03
39	Ozzie Smith	.15	.11	.06
40	Darryl Strawberry	.40	.30	.15
41	Rick Sutcliffe	.10	.08	.04
42	Danny Tartabull	.12	.09	.05
43	Alan Trammell	.15	.11	.06
44	Tim Wallach	.10	.08	.04

The values quoted are intended to reflect the market price.

This limited edition 44-card boxed set features excellent photography of major league All-Stars. The standard-size cards feature a sporty bright blue- and yellow-striped background. The player name is printed in white across the upper left front corner. "Fleer Baseball 88 All Stars" appears on a yellow band beneath the photo. Card backs feature a blue- and white-striped design with a yellow highlighted section at the top that contains the player name, card number, team, position and personal data, followed by lifetime career stats. Fleer All Stars are cello-wrapped in blue and yellow striped boxes with checklist backs. The set includes six team logo sticker cards that feature black and white aerial shots of major league ballparks. The set was marketed exclusively by Ben Franklin stores.

		MT	NR MT	EX
Complete Set:		6.00	4.50	2.50
Common Player:		.05	.04	.02
1	George Bell	.20	.15	.08
2	Wade Boggs	.70	.50	.30
3	Bobby Bonilla	.12	.09	.05
4	George Brett	.30	.25	.12
5	Jose Canseco	.70	.50	.30
6	Jack Clark	.15	.11	.06
7	Will Clark	.70	.50	.30
8	Roger Clemens	.40	.30	.15
9	Eric Davis	.50	.40	.20
10	Andre Dawson	.15	.11	.06
11	Julio Franco	.07	.05	.03
12	Dwight Gooden	.40	.30	.15
13	Tony Gwynn	.25	.20	.10
14	Orel Hershiser	.20	.15	.08
15	Teddy Higuera	.10	.08	.04
16	Charlie Hough	.05	.04	.02
17	Kent Hrbek	.15	.11	.06
18	Bruce Hurst	.10	.08	.04
19	Wally Joyner	.30	.25	.12
20	Mark Langston	.10	.08	.04
21	Dave LaPoint	.05	.04	.02
22	Candy Maldonado	.05	.04	.02
23	Don Mattingly	.70	.50	.30
24	Roger McDowell	.07	.05	.03
25	Mark McGwire	.70	.50	.30
26	Jack Morris	.12	.09	.05
27	Dale Murphy	.30	.25	.12
28	Eddie Murray	.20	.15	.08
29	Matt Nokes	.30	.25	.12
30	Kirby Puckett	.70	.50	.30
31	Tim Raines	.25	.20	.10
32	Willie Randolph	.07	.05	.03
33	Jeff Reardon	.07	.05	.03
34	Nolan Ryan	1.50	1.25	.60
35	Juan Samuel	.10	.08	.04
36	Mike Schmidt	.30	.25	.12
37	Mike Scott	.10	.08	.04
38	Kevin Seitzer	.60	.45	.25
39	Ozzie Smith	.15	.11	.06
40	Darryl Strawberry	.40	.30	.15
41	Rick Sutcliffe	.10	.08	.04
42	Alan Trammell	.15	.11	.06
43	Tim Wallach	.10	.08	.04

		MT	NR MT	EX
44	Dave Winfield	.20	.15	.08

		MT	NR MT	EX
43	Dave Winfield	.20	.15	.08
44	Robin Yount	.25	.20	.10

1988 Fleer Baseball MVP

This boxed set of 44 standard-size cards and six team logo stickers was produced by Fleer for exclusive distribution at Toys "R" Us stores. This premiere edition features full-color player photos framed by a yellow and blue border. The player's name is printed in red below and to the left of the photo; team and position are printed in black in the lower right corner. The "Fleer Baseball MVP" logo appears bottom center. Card backs are yellow and blue on a white background. The player's team, position and personal data are followed by stats, logo and a blue banner bearing the player's name, team logo and card number. The six sticker cards feature black and white stadium photos on the backs.

		MT	NR MT	EX
	Complete Set:	6.00	4.50	2.50
	Common Player:	.05	.04	.02
1	George Bell	.20	.15	.08
2	Wade Boggs	.80	.60	.30
3	Jose Canseco	.80	.60	.30
4	Ivan Calderon	.07	.05	.03
5	Will Clark	.80	.60	.30
6	Roger Clemens	.40	.30	.15
7	Vince Coleman	.15	.11	.06
8	Eric Davis	.50	.40	.20
9	Andre Dawson	.15	.11	.06
10	Dave Dravecky	.05	.04	.02
11	Mike Dunne	.10	.08	.04
12	Dwight Evans	.10	.08	.04
13	Sid Fernandez	.07	.05	.03
14	Tony Fernandez	.10	.08	.04
15	Julio Franco	.07	.05	.03
16	Dwight Gooden	.40	.30	.15
17	Tony Gwynn	.25	.20	.10
18	Ted Higuera	.10	.08	.04
19	Charlie Hough	.05	.04	.02
20	Wally Joyner	.30	.25	.12
21	Mark Langston	.10	.08	.04
22	Don Mattingly	.80	.60	.30
23	Mark McGwire	.80	.60	.30
24	Jack Morris	.12	.09	.05
25	Dale Murphy	.30	.25	.12
26	Kirby Puckett	.50	.40	.20
27	Tim Raines	.25	.20	.10
28	Willie Randolph	.07	.05	.03
29	Ryne Sandberg	.20	.15	.08
30	Benito Santiago	.25	.20	.10
31	Mike Schmidt	.30	.25	.12
32	Mike Scott	.10	.08	.04
33	Kevin Seitzer	.60	.45	.25
34	Larry Sheets	.07	.05	.03
35	Ozzie Smith	.15	.11	.06
36	Dave Stewart	.10	.08	.04
37	Darryl Strawberry	.40	.30	.15
38	Rick Sutcliffe	.10	.08	.04
39	Alan Trammell	.15	.11	.06
40	Fernando Valenzuela	.20	.15	.08
41	Frank Viola	.12	.09	.05
42	Tim Wallach	.10	.08	.04

1988 Fleer Baseball's Best

This boxed set of 44 standard-size cards (2-1/2" by 3-1/2") and six team logo stickers is the third annual issue from Fleer highlighting the best major league sluggers and pitchers. Five additional player cards were printed on retail display box bottoms, along with a checklist logo card (numbered C-1 through C-6). Full-color player photos are framed by a green border that fades to yellow. A red (slugger) or blue (pitcher) player name is printed beneath the photo. The card backs are printed in green on a white background with yellow highlights. Card number, player name and personal info appear in a green vertical box on the left-hand side of the card back with a yellow cartoon-style team logo overprinted across a stats chart on the right. This set was produced by Fleer for exclusive distribution by McCrory's stores (McCrory, McClellan, J.J. Newberry, H.L. Green, TG&Y).

		MT	NR MT	EX
	Complete Set:	6.00	4.50	2.50
	Common Player:	.05	.04	.02
1	George Bell	.20	.15	.08
2	Wade Boggs	.80	.60	.30
3	Bobby Bonilla	.12	.09	.05
4	Tom Brunansky	.10	.08	.04
5	Ellis Burks	.80	.60	.30
6	Jose Canseco	.80	.60	.30
7	Joe Carter	.12	.09	.05
8	Will Clark	.80	.60	.30
9	Roger Clemens	.40	.30	.15
10	Eric Davis	.50	.40	.20
11	Glenn Davis	.12	.09	.05
12	Andre Dawson	.15	.11	.06
13	Dennis Eckersley	.07	.05	.03
14	Andres Galarraga	.15	.11	.06
15	Dwight Gooden	.40	.30	.15
16	Pedro Guerrero	.15	.11	.06
17	Tony Gwynn	.25	.20	.10
18	Orel Hershiser	.20	.15	.08
19	Ted Higuera	.10	.08	.04
20	Pete Incaviglia	.12	.09	.05
21	Danny Jackson	.10	.08	.04
22	Doug Jennings	.07	.05	.03
23	Mark Langston	.10	.08	.04
24	Dave LaPoint	.05	.04	.02
25	Mike LaValliere	.07	.05	.03
26	Don Mattingly	.80	.60	.30
27	Mark McGwire	.80	.60	.30
28	Dale Murphy	.30	.25	.12
29	Ken Phelps	.05	.04	.02
30	Kirby Puckett	.50	.40	.20
31	Johnny Ray	.05	.04	.02
32	Jeff Reardon	.07	.05	.03
33	Dave Righetti	.12	.09	.05
34	Cal Ripkin, Jr. (Ripken)	.60	.45	.25
35	Chris Sabo	.90	.70	.35
36	Mike Schmidt	.30	.25	.12
37	Mike Scott	.10	.08	.04

		MT	NR MT	EX
38	Kevin Seitzer	.60	.45	.25
39	Dave Stewart	.10	.08	.04
40	Darryl Strawberry	.40	.30	.15
41	Greg Swindell	.10	.08	.04
42	Frank Tanana	.05	.04	.02
43	Dave Winfield	.20	.15	.08
44	Todd Worrell	.10	.08	.04

1988 Fleer Baseball's Best Box Panel

Six cards were placed on the bottoms of retail boxes of the Fleer 44-card Baseball's Best boxed sets in 1988. The cards, which measure 2-1/2" by 3-1/2", are identical in design to cards found in the 44-card set. The cards are numbered C-1 through C-6 and were produced by Fleer for distribution by McCrory stores and its affiliates.

		MT	NR MT	EX
Complete Panel Set:		1.50	1.25	.60
Complete Singles Set:		.90	.70	.35
Common Single Player:		.15	.11	.06
	Panel	1.50	1.25	.60
1	Ron Darling	.20	.15	.08
2	Rickey Henderson	.60	.45	.25
3	Carney Lansford	.15	.11	.06
4	Rafael Palmeiro	.20	.15	.08
5	Frank Viola	.20	.15	.08
6	Twins Logo	.05	.04	.02

1988 Fleer Baseball's Exciting Stars

This 44-card limited-edition boxed set showcases star major leaguers. Player photos are slanted upwards to the right, framed by a blue border with a red and white bar stripe across the middle. The player's name is printed in white above the photo. "Baseball's Exciting Stars" is printed in red and yellow across the bottom margin, following the upward slant of the photo. Fleer's logo appears lower right

intersecting a white baseball bearing the number "88." Card backs are numbered and printed in red, white and blue. The set was packaged in a checklist box, with six team logo sticker cards featuring black and white stadium photos on the flip sides. Exciting Stars was distributed via Cumberland Farm stores throughout the northeastern U.S. and Florida.

		MT	NR MT	EX
Complete Set:		5.00	3.75	2.00
Common Player:		.05	.04	.02
1	Harold Baines	.10	.08	.04
2	Kevin Bass	.07	.05	.03
3	George Bell	.20	.15	.08
4	Wade Boggs	.80	.60	.30
5	Mickey Brantley	.05	.04	.02
6	Sid Bream	.05	.04	.02
7	Jose Canseco	.80	.60	.30
8	Jack Clark	.15	.11	.06
9	Will Clark	.80	.60	.30
10	Roger Clemens	.40	.30	.15
11	Vince Coleman	.15	.11	.06
12	Eric Davis	.50	.40	.20
13	Andre Dawson	.15	.11	.06
14	Julio Franco	.07	.05	.03
15	Dwight Gooden	.40	.30	.15
16	Mike Greenwell	.40	.30	.15
17	Tony Gwynn	.25	.20	.10
18	Von Hayes	.07	.05	.03
19	Tom Henke	.05	.04	.02
20	Orel Hershiser	.20	.15	.08
21	Teddy Higuera	.10	.08	.04
22	Brook Jacoby	.07	.05	.03
23	Wally Joyner	.30	.25	.12
24	Jimmy Key	.07	.05	.03
25	Don Mattingly	.80	.60	.30
26	Mark McGwire	.80	.60	.30
27	Jack Morris	.12	.09	.05
28	Dale Murphy	.30	.25	.12
29	Matt Nokes	.30	.25	.12
30	Kirby Puckett	.50	.40	.20
31	Tim Raines	.25	.20	.10
32	Ryne Sandberg	.20	.15	.08
33	Benito Santiago	.25	.20	.10
34	Mike Schmidt	.30	.25	.12
35	Mike Scott	.10	.08	.04
36	Kevin Seitzer	.60	.45	.25
37	Larry Sheets	.07	.05	.03
38	Ruben Sierra	.12	.09	.05
39	Darryl Strawberry	.40	.30	.15
40	Ozzie Smith	.15	.11	.06
41	Danny Tartabull	.10	.08	.04
42	Alan Trammell	.15	.11	.06
43	Fernando Valenzuela	.20	.15	.08
44	Devon White	.20	.15	.08

Errors/variations

Collectors often wonder about errors found on cards, usually in the statistics or personal data on the card's back.

Such errors add nothing to the value of the card. The only time an error like this is likely to increase a card's value is if the manufacturer corrects the error in a later printing, thus creating two distinct variations. If enough collectors feel the variations are a desirable part of that issue, the value may increase. Whether the error version or the corrected card will have the greater value usually depends on relative scarcity. The more common version will almost always be worth less. So, quite often the error card can be worth less than the corrected version.

1988 Fleer League Leaders

This 44-card boxed set is the third annual limited edition set from Fleer highlighting leading players. The 1988 edition contains the same type of information, front and back, as the previous sets, with a new color scheme and design. Card fronts have bright blue borders, solid on the lower portion, striped on the upper, with a gold bar separating the two sections. "Fleer's Baseball's League Leaders '88" headlines the card face. The full-color player photo is centered above a yellow player name banner. The numbered card backs are blue, pink and white, and contain player stats and personal notes. Six team logo sticker cards, with flipside black and white photos of ballparks, accompany this set which was marketed exclusively by Walgreen drug stores.

		MT	NR MT	EX
Complete Set:		6.00	4.50	2.50
Common Player:		.05	.04	.02
1	George Bell	.20	.15	.08
2	Wade Boggs	.80	.60	.30
3	Ivan Calderon	.07	.05	.03
4	Jose Canseco	.80	.60	.30
5	Will Clark	.80	.60	.30
6	Roger Clemens	.40	.30	.15
7	Vince Coleman	.15	.11	.06
8	Eric Davis	.50	.40	.20
9	Andre Dawson	.15	.11	.06
10	Bill Doran	.07	.05	.03
11	Dwight Evans	.10	.08	.04
12	Julio Franco	.07	.05	.03
13	Gary Gaetti	.10	.08	.04
14	Andres Galarraga	.15	.11	.06
15	Dwight Gooden	.40	.30	.15
16	Tony Gwynn	.25	.20	.10
17	Tom Henke	.05	.04	.02
18	Keith Hernandez	.20	.15	.08
19	Orel Hershiser	.20	.15	.08
20	Ted Higuera	.10	.08	.04
21	Kent Hrbek	.15	.11	.06
22	Wally Joyner	.30	.25	.12
23	Jimmy Key	.07	.05	.03
24	Mark Langston	.10	.08	.04
25	Don Mattingly	.80	.60	.30
26	Mark McGwire	.80	.60	.30
27	Paul Molitor	.12	.09	.05
28	Jack Morris	.12	.09	.05
29	Dale Murphy	.30	.25	.12
30	Kirby Puckett	.50	.40	.20
31	Tim Raines	.25	.20	.10
32	Rick Rueschel	.07	.05	.03
33	Bret Saberhagen	.15	.11	.06
34	Benito Santiago	.25	.20	.10
35	Mike Schmidt	.30	.25	.12
36	Mike Scott	.10	.08	.04
37	Kevin Seitzer	.60	.45	.25
38	Larry Sheets	.07	.05	.03
39	Ruben Sierra	.50	.40	.20
40	Darryl Strawberry	.40	.30	.15
41	Rick Sutcliffe	.10	.08	.04
42	Alan Trammell	.15	.11	.06
43	Andy Van Slyke	.10	.08	.04
44	Todd Worrell	.10	.08	.04

1988 Fleer Mini

This third annual issue of miniatures (1-7/8" by 2-5/8") includes 120 high-gloss cards featuring new photos, not copies from the regular issue, although the card designs are identical. Card fronts have white borders, with red and blue striping and a bright color band beneath the photo leading to a blue Fleet logo lower right. The player name is printed upper left; the full-color team logo appears upper right. Card backs are red, white and blue and include personal data, yearly career stats and a stats breakdown of batting average, slugging percentage and on-base average, listed for day, night, home and road games. Card backs are numbered in alphabetical order by teams which are also listed alphabetically. The set includes 18 team logo stickers with black and white aerial stadium photos on the flip sides.

		MT	NR MT	EX
Complete Set:		12.00	9.00	4.75
Common Player:		.05	.04	.02
1	Eddie Murray	.25	.20	.10
2	Dave Schmidt	.05	.04	.02
3	Larry Sheets	.07	.05	.03
4	Wade Boggs	.70	.50	.30
5	Roger Clemens	.80	.60	.30
6	Dwight Evans	.12	.09	.05
7	Mike Greenwell	.40	.30	.15
8	Sam Horn	.20	.15	.08
9	Lee Smith	.07	.05	.03
10	Brian Downing	.05	.04	.02
11	Wally Joyner	.30	.25	.12
12	Devon White	.10	.08	.04
13	Mike Witt	.07	.05	.03
14	Ivan Calderon	.15	.11	.06
15	Ozzie Guillen	.07	.05	.03
16	Jack McDowell	.50	.40	.20
17	Kenny Williams	.12	.09	.05
18	Joe Carter	.20	.15	.08
19	Julio Franco	.20	.15	.08
20	Pat Tabler	.05	.04	.02
21	Doyle Alexander	.05	.04	.02
22	Jack Morris	.15	.11	.06
23	Matt Nokes	.30	.25	.12
24	Walt Terrell	.05	.04	.02
25	Alan Trammell	.20	.15	.08
26	Bret Saberhagen	.15	.11	.06
27	Kevin Seitzer	.20	.15	.08
28	Danny Tartabull	.15	.11	.06
29	Gary Thurman	.20	.15	.08
30	Ted Higuera	.10	.08	.04
31	Paul Molitor	.12	.09	.05
32	Dan Plesac	.10	.08	.04
33	Robin Yount	.25	.20	.10
34	Gary Gaetti	.12	.09	.05
35	Kent Hrbek	.15	.11	.06
36	Kirby Puckett	.50	.40	.20
37	Jeff Reardon	.07	.05	.03
38	Frank Viola	.12	.09	.05
39	Jack Clark	.12	.09	.05
40	Rickey Henderson	.80	.60	.30
41	Don Mattingly	.80	.60	.30
42	Willie Randolph	.05	.04	.02
43	Dave Righetti	.12	.09	.05
44	Dave Winfield	.20	.15	.08
45	Jose Canseco	.80	.60	.30

		MT	NR MT	EX
46	Mark McGwire	.60	.45	.25
47	Dave Parker	.12	.09	.05
48	Dave Stewart	.07	.05	.03
49	Walt Weiss	.60	.45	.25
50	Bob Welch	.07	.05	.03
51	Mickey Brantley	.05	.04	.02
52	Mark Langston	.10	.08	.04
53	Harold Reynolds	.07	.05	.03
54	Scott Fletcher	.05	.04	.02
55	Charlie Hough	.05	.04	.02
56	Pete Incaviglia	.12	.09	.05
57	Larry Parrish	.05	.04	.02
58	Ruben Sierra	.35	.25	.14
59	George Bell	.20	.15	.08
60	Mark Eichhorn	.05	.04	.02
61	Tony Fernandez	.10	.08	.04
62	Tom Henke	.05	.04	.02
63	Jimmy Key	.07	.05	.03
64	Dion James	.05	.04	.02
65	Dale Murphy	.30	.25	.12
66	Zane Smith	.05	.04	.02
67	Andre Dawson	.15	.11	.06
68	Mark Grace	1.00	.70	.40
69	Jerry Mumphrey	.05	.04	.02
70	Ryne Sandberg	.40	.30	.15
71	Rick Sutcliffe	.10	.08	.04
72	Kal Daniels	.12	.09	.05
73	Eric Davis	.40	.30	.15
74	John Franco	.07	.05	.03
75	Ron Robinson	.05	.04	.02
76	Jeff Treadway	.20	.15	.08
77	Kevin Bass	.07	.05	.03
78	Glenn Davis	.15	.11	.06
79	Nolan Ryan	1.00	.70	.40
80	Mike Scott	.12	.09	.05
81	Dave Smith	.05	.04	.02
82	Kirk Gibson	.20	.15	.08
83	Pedro Guerrero	.12	.09	.05
84	Orel Hershiser	.20	.15	.08
85	Steve Sax	.15	.11	.06
86	Fernando Valenzuela	.15	.11	.06
87	Tim Burke	.05	.04	.02
88	Andres Galarraga	.15	.11	.06
89	Neal Heaton	.05	.04	.02
90	Tim Raines	.20	.15	.08
91	Tim Wallach	.10	.08	.04
92	Dwight Gooden	.40	.30	.15
93	Keith Hernandez	.15	.11	.06
94	Gregg Jefferies	.70	.50	.30
95	Howard Johnson	.10	.08	.04
96	Roger McDowell	.05	.04	.02
97	Darryl Strawberry	.50	.40	.20
98	Steve Bedrosian	.10	.08	.04
99	Von Hayes	.10	.08	.04
100	Shane Rawley	.05	.04	.02
101	Juan Samuel	.12	.09	.05
102	Mike Schmidt	.30	.25	.12
103	Bobby Bonilla	.30	.25	.12
104	Mike Dunne	.07	.05	.03
105	Andy Van Slyke	.10	.08	.04
106	Vince Coleman	.15	.11	.06
107	Bob Horner	.07	.05	.03
108	Willie McGee	.10	.08	.04
109	Ozzie Smith	.12	.09	.05
110	John Tudor	.07	.05	.03
111	Todd Worrell	.10	.08	.04
112	Tony Gwynn	.25	.20	.10
113	John Kruk	.12	.09	.05
114	Lance McCullers	.05	.04	.02
115	Benito Santiago	.15	.11	.06
116	Will Clark	.40	.30	.15
117	Jeff Leonard	.05	.04	.02
118	Candy Maldonado	.05	.04	.02
119	Rick Rueschel	.07	.05	.03
120	Don Robinson	.05	.04	.02

1988 Fleer
Record Setters

For the second consecutive year, Fleer Corp. issued this special limited-edition 44-card set for exclusive distribution by Eckerd Drug stores. Cards are standard-size with red and blue borders framing the full-color player photos. A "1988 Fleer Record Setters" headline is printed on a yellow strip above the player's photo. The player's name, team and position appear beneath the pose. Card backs list personal information and career stats in red and blue ink on a white background. Each 44-card set comes cello-wrapped in a checklist box that contains six additional cards with peel-off team logo stickers. The sticker cards feature black and white aerial photos of major league ballparks, along with stadium statistics such as field size, seating capacity and date of the first game played.

		MT	NR MT	EX
Complete Set:		5.00	3.75	2.00
Common Player:		.05	.04	.02
1	Jesse Barfield	.10	.08	.04
2	George Bell	.20	.15	.08
3	Wade Boggs	.80	.60	.30
4	Jose Canseco	.80	.60	.30
5	Jack Clark	.15	.11	.06
6	Will Clark	.80	.60	.30
7	Roger Clemens	.40	.30	.15
8	Alvin Davis	.10	.08	.04
9	Eric Davis	.50	.40	.20
10	Andre Dawson	.15	.11	.06
11	Mike Dunne	.10	.08	.04
12	John Franco	.07	.05	.03
13	Julio Franco	.07	.05	.03
14	Dwight Gooden	.40	.30	.15
15	Mark Gubicza	.07	.05	.03
16	Ozzie Guillen	.07	.05	.03
17	Tony Gwynn	.25	.20	.10
18	Orel Hershiser	.20	.15	.08
19	Teddy Higuera	.10	.08	.04
20	Howard Johnson	.07	.05	.03
21	Wally Joyner	.30	.25	.12
22	Jimmy Key	.07	.05	.03
23	Jeff Leonard	.05	.04	.02
24	Don Mattingly	.80	.60	.30
25	Mark McGwire	.80	.60	.30
26	Jack Morris	.12	.09	.05
27	Dale Murphy	.30	.25	.12
28	Larry Parrish	.05	.04	.02
29	Kirby Puckett	.50	.40	.20
30	Tim Raines	.25	.20	.10
31	Harold Reynolds	.07	.05	.03
32	Dave Righetti	.12	.09	.05
33	Cal Ripken, Jr.	.60	.45	.25
34	Benito Santiago	.25	.20	.10
35	Mike Schmidt	.30	.25	.12
36	Mike Scott	.10	.08	.04
37	Kevin Seitzer	.60	.45	.25
38	Ozzie Smith	.12	.09	.05
39	Darryl Strawberry	.40	.30	.15
40	Rick Sutcliffe	.10	.08	.04
41	Alan Trammell	.15	.11	.06
42	Frank Viola	.12	.09	.05
43	Mitch Williams	.05	.04	.02
44	Todd Worrell	.10	.08	.04

1988 Fleer Star Stickers

This set of 132 standard-size sticker cards (including a checklist card) features exclusive player photos, different from those in the Fleer regular issue. Card fronts have light gray borders sprinkled with multi-colored stars. The "Fleer Star Stickers" logo appears upper left, player names are printed beneath the photos. Card backs are printed in red, gray and black on white and include personal data and a breakdown of pitching and batting stats into day, night, home and road categories. Cards were marketed in two different display boxes that feature six players and two team logos from Fleer's 1988 Limited Edition box-bottom set.

		MT	NR MT	EX
	Complete Set:	20.00	15.00	8.00
	Common Player:	.05	.04	.02
1	Mike Boddicker	.08	.06	.03
2	Eddie Murray	.50	.40	.20
3	Cal Ripken, Jr.	.60	.45	.25
4	Larry Sheets	.15	.11	.06
5	Wade Boggs	.80	.60	.30
6	Ellis Burks	.60	.45	.25
7	Roger Clemens	.90	.70	.35
8	Dwight Evans	.15	.11	.06
9	Mike Greenwell	.40	.30	.15
10	Bruce Hurst	.12	.09	.05
11	Brian Downing	.08	.06	.03
12	Wally Joyner	.40	.30	.15
13	Mike Witt	.10	.08	.04
14	Ivan Calderon	.12	.09	.05
15	Jose DeLeon	.05	.04	.02
16	Ozzie Guillen	.15	.11	.06
17	Bobby Thigpen	.10	.08	.04
18	Joe Carter	.20	.15	.08
19	Julio Franco	.12	.09	.05
20	Brook Jacoby	.12	.09	.05
21	Cory Snyder	.05	.04	.02
22	Pat Tabler	.10	.08	.04
23	Doyle Alexander	.08	.06	.03
24	Kirk Gibson	.30	.25	.12
25	Mike Henneman	.20	.15	.08
26	Jack Morris	.25	.20	.10
27	Matt Nokes	.30	.25	.12
28	Walt Terrell	.05	.04	.02
29	Alan Trammell	.30	.25	.12
30	George Brett	.70	.50	.30
31	Charlie Leibrandt	.05	.04	.02
32	Bret Saberhagen	.25	.20	.10
33	Kevin Seitzer	.15	.11	.06
34	Danny Tartabull	.25	.20	.10
35	Frank White	.10	.08	.04
36	Rob Deer	.10	.08	.04
37	Ted Higuera	.15	.11	.06
38	Paul Molitor	.20	.15	.08
39	Dan Plesac	.12	.09	.05
40	Robin Yount	.30	.25	.12
41	Bert Blyleven	.15	.11	.06
42	Tom Brunansky	.15	.11	.06
43	Gary Gaetti	.20	.15	.08
44	Kent Hrbek	.30	.25	.12
45	Kirby Puckett	.50	.40	.20
46	Jeff Reardon	.10	.08	.04
47	Frank Viola	.15	.11	.06
48	Don Mattingly	1.00	.70	.40
49	Mike Pagliarulo	.12	.09	.05
50	Willie Randolph	.08	.06	.03
51	Rick Rhoden	.08	.06	.03
52	Dave Righetti	.20	.15	.08
53	Dave Winfield	.40	.30	.15
54	Jose Canseco	1.00	.70	.40
55	Carney Lansford	.08	.06	.03
56	Mark McGwire	.60	.45	.25
57	Dave Stewart	.12	.09	.05

		MT	NR MT	EX
58	Curt Young	.08	.06	.03
59	Alvin Davis	.15	.11	.06
60	Mark Langston	.15	.11	.06
61	Ken Phelps	.05	.04	.02
62	Harold Reynolds	.10	.08	.04
63	Scott Fletcher	.05	.04	.02
64	Charlie Hough	.08	.06	.03
65	Pete Incaviglia	.25	.20	.10
66	Oddibe McDowell	.10	.08	.04
67	Pete O'Brien	.10	.08	.04
68	Larry Parrish	.08	.06	.03
69	Ruben Sierra	.25	.20	.10
70	Jesse Barfield	.12	.09	.05
71	George Bell	.25	.20	.10
72	Tony Fernandez	.12	.09	.05
73	Tom Henke	.10	.08	.04
74	Jimmy Key	.12	.09	.05
75	Lloyd Moseby	.10	.08	.04
76	Dion James	.05	.04	.02
77	Dale Murphy	.35	.25	.12
78	Zane Smith	.08	.06	.03
79	Andre Dawson	.25	.20	.10
80	Ryne Sandberg	.35	.25	.14
81	Rick Sutcliffe	.15	.11	.06
82	Kal Daniels	.25	.20	.10
83	Eric Davis	.30	.25	.12
84	John Franco	.10	.08	.04
85	Kevin Bass	.10	.08	.04
86	Glenn Davis	.20	.15	.08
87	Bill Doran	.10	.08	.04
88	Nolan Ryan	1.00	.70	.40
89	Mike Scott	.15	.11	.06
90	Dave Smith	.05	.04	.02
91	Pedro Guerrero	.20	.15	.08
92	Orel Hershiser	.35	.25	.14
93	Steve Sax	.20	.15	.08
94	Fernando Valenzuela	.25	.20	.10
95	Tim Burke	.05	.04	.02
96	Andres Galarraga	.20	.15	.08
97	Tim Raines	.25	.20	.10
98	Tim Wallach	.12	.09	.05
99	Mitch Webster	.05	.04	.02
100	Ron Darling	.20	.15	.08
101	Sid Fernandez	.10	.08	.04
102	Dwight Gooden	.90	.70	.35
103	Keith Hernandez	.30	.25	.12
104	Howard Johnson	.12	.09	.05
105	Roger McDowell	.10	.08	.04
106	Darryl Strawberry	.70	.50	.30
107	Steve Bedrosian	.12	.09	.05
108	Von Hayes	.12	.09	.05
109	Shane Rawley	.08	.06	.03
110	Juan Samuel	.15	.11	.06
111	Mike Schmidt	.70	.50	.30
112	Milt Thompson	.05	.04	.02
113	Sid Bream	.08	.06	.03
114	Bobby Bonilla	.35	.25	.14
115	Mike Dunne	.15	.11	.06
116	Andy Van Slyke	.12	.09	.05
117	Vince Coleman	.25	.20	.10
118	Willie McGee	.15	.11	.06
119	Terry Pendleton	.10	.08	.04
120	Ozzie Smith	.20	.15	.08
121	John Tudor	.12	.09	.05
122	Todd Worrell	.20	.15	.08
123	Tony Gwynn	.40	.30	.15
124	John Kruk	.20	.15	.08
125	Benito Santiago	.30	.25	.12
126	Will Clark	1.00	.70	.40
127	Dave Dravecky	.05	.04	.02
128	Jeff Leonard	.05	.04	.02
129	Candy Maldonado	.05	.04	.02
130	Rick Rueschel	.10	.08	.04
131	Don Robinson	.05	.04	.02
132	Checklist	.05	.04	.02

1988 Fleer Star Stickers Box Panels

This set of eight box-bottom cards was printed on two different retail display boxes. Six players and two team logo sticker cards are included in the set, three player photos and one team photo per box. The full-color player photos are exclusively limited to the Fleer Star Sticker set. The cards, which measure 2-1/2" by 3-1/2", have a light gray border sprinkled

RON GUIDRY

with multi-color stars. The backs are printed in navy blue and red.

	MT	NR MT	EX
Complete Panel Set:	3.50	2.75	1.50
Complete Singles Set:	1.75	1.25	.70
Common Singles Player:	.15	.11	.06
	Panel	2.50	2.00	1.00

		MT	NR MT	EX
	Panel	2.50	2.00	1.00
1	Eric Davis, Mark McGwire	.70	.50	.30
3	Kevin Mitchell	.50	.40	.20
5	Rickey Henderson	.50	.40	.20
7	Tigers Logo	.05	.04	.02
	Panel	1.25	.90	.50
2	Gary Carter	.35	.25	.14
4	Ron Guidry	.20	.15	.08
6	Don Baylor	.15	.11	.06
8	Giants Logo	.05	.04	.02

		MT	NR MT	EX
6	Joe Carter	.12	.09	.05
7	Jack Clark	.15	.11	.06
8	Will Clark	.80	.60	.30
9	Roger Clemens	.40	.30	.15
10	Alvin Davis	.10	.08	.04
11	Eric Davis	.50	.40	.20
12	Glenn Davis	.12	.09	.05
13	Andre Dawson	.15	.11	.06
14	Dwight Gooden	.40	.30	.15
15	Orel Hershiser	.20	.15	.08
16	Teddy Higuera	.10	.08	.04
17	Kent Hrbek	.15	.11	.06
18	Wally Joyner	.30	.25	.12
19	Jimmy Key	.07	.05	.03
20	John Kruk	.10	.08	.04
21	Jeff Leonard	.05	.04	.02
22	Don Mattingly	.80	.60	.30
23	Mark McGwire	.80	.60	.30
24	Kevin McReynolds	.12	.09	.05
25	Dale Murphy	.30	.25	.12
26	Matt Nokes	.30	.25	.12
27	Terry Pendleton	.05	.04	.02
28	Kirby Puckett	.50	.40	.20
29	Tim Raines	.25	.20	.10
30	Rick Rhoden	.07	.05	.03
31	Cal Ripken, Jr.	.60	.45	.25
32	Benito Santiago	.25	.20	.10
33	Mike Schmidt	.30	.25	.12
34	Mike Scott	.10	.08	.04
35	Kevin Seitzer	.60	.45	.25
36	Ruben Sierra	.25	.20	.10
37	Cory Snyder	.12	.09	.05
38	Darryl Strawberry	.40	.30	.15
39	Rick Sutcliffe	.10	.08	.04
40	Danny Tartabull	.12	.09	.05
41	Alan Trammell	.15	.11	.06
42	Ken Williams	.07	.05	.03
43	Mike Witt	.07	.05	.03
44	Robin Yount	.15	.11	.06

1988 Fleer Superstars

OREL HERSHISER

FLEER SUPERSTARS
OREL HERSHISER

No. 15 of 44

This is the fourth edition of Fleer's 44-card boxed set produced for distribution by McCrory's (1985-87 issues were simply titled "Fleer Limited Edition"). The Superstars standard-size card set features full-color player photos framed by red, white and blue striped top and bottom borders. "Fleer 1988" is printed in an elongated yellow oval banner above the photo. A pale yellow rectangle below the photo carries the player's name and team logo. Card fronts have a semi-glossy slightly textured finish. Card backs are red and blue on white and include card numbers, personal data and statistics. Six team logo sticker cards are also included in this set which was marketed in red, white and blue boxes with checklist backs. Boxed sets were sold exclusively at McCrory's stores and its affiliates.

		MT	NR MT	EX
Complete Set:		6.00	4.50	2.50
Common Player:		.05	.04	.02
1	Steve Bedrosian	.10	.08	.04
2	George Bell	.20	.15	.08
3	Wade Boggs	.80	.60	.30
4	Barry Bonds	.12	.09	.05
5	Jose Canseco	.80	.60	.30

1988 Fleer Update

Rob Dibble

ROB DIBBLE

This 132-card update set (numbered U-1 through U-132 and 2-1/2" by 3-1/2") features traded veterans and rookies in a mixture of full-color action shots and close-ups, framed by white borders with red and blue stripes. Player name and position appear upper left, printed on an upward slant leading into the team logo, upper right. A bright stripe in a variety of colors (blue, red, green, yellow) edges the bottom of the photo and leads into the Fleer logo at lower right. The backs are red, white and blue-grey and include personal info, along with yearly and "At Their Best" (day, night, home, road) stats charts. The set was packaged in white cardboard boxes with red and blue stripes. A glossy-coated edition of the update set was issued in its own tin box and is valued at two times greater than the regular issue.

		MT	NR MT	EX
Complete Set:		13.00	9.75	5.25
Common Player:		.06	.05	.02
1	Jose Bautista(FC)	.20	.15	.08
2	Joe Orsulak	.06	.05	.02
3	Doug Sisk	.06	.05	.02
4	Craig Worthington(FC)	.20	.15	.08

		MT	NR MT	EX
5	Mike Boddicker	.08	.06	.03
6	Rick Cerone	.06	.05	.02
7	Larry Parrish	.08	.06	.03
8	Lee Smith	.10	.08	.04
9	Mike Smithson	.06	.05	.02
10	John Trautwein(FC)	.15	.11	.06
11	Sherman Corbett(FC)	.15	.11	.06
12	Chili Davis	.10	.08	.04
13	Jim Eppard	.08	.06	.03
14	Bryan Harvey(FC)	.50	.40	.20
15	John Davis	.08	.06	.03
16	Dave Gallagher(FC)	.20	.15	.08
17	Ricky Horton	.08	.06	.03
18	Dan Pasqua	.10	.08	.04
19	Melido Perez	.12	.09	.05
20	Jose Segura(FC)	.15	.11	.06
21	Andy Allanson	.08	.06	.03
22	Jon Perlman	.06	.05	.02
23	Domingo Ramos	.06	.05	.02
24	Rick Rodriguez	.08	.06	.03
25	Willie Upshaw	.10	.08	.04
26	Paul Gibson(FC)	.15	.11	.06
27	Don Heinkel(FC)	.15	.11	.06
28	Ray Knight	.08	.06	.03
29	Gary Pettis	.08	.06	.03
30	Luis Salazar	.06	.05	.02
31	Mike MacFarlane (Macfarlane)(FC)	.25	.20	.10
32	Jeff Montgomery	.08	.06	.03
33	Ted Power	.06	.05	.02
34	Israel Sanchez(FC)	.15	.11	.06
35	Kurt Stillwell	.10	.08	.04
36	Pat Tabler	.08	.06	.03
37	Don August(FC)	.15	.11	.06
38	Darryl Hamilton(FC)	.40	.30	.15
39	Jeff Leonard	.08	.06	.03
40	Joey Meyer	.15	.11	.06
41	Allan Anderson	.10	.08	.04
42	Brian Harper	.06	.05	.02
43	Tom Herr	.10	.08	.04
44	Charlie Lea	.06	.05	.02
45	John Moses	.06	.05	.02
46	John Candelaria	.10	.08	.04
47	Jack Clark	.15	.11	.06
48	Richard Dotson	.10	.08	.04
49	Al Leiter(FC)	.15	.11	.06
50	Rafael Santana	.06	.05	.02
51	Don Slaught	.06	.05	.02
52	Todd Burns(FC)	.25	.20	.10
53	Dave Henderson	.10	.08	.04
54	Doug Jennings(FC)	.20	.15	.08
55	Dave Parker	.12	.09	.05
56	Walt Weiss	.20	.15	.08
57	Bob Welch	.10	.08	.04
58	Henry Cotto	.06	.05	.02
59	Marion Diaz (Mario)	.08	.06	.03
60	Mike Jackson	.06	.05	.02
61	Bill Swift	.06	.05	.02
62	Jose Cecena(FC)	.15	.11	.06
63	Ray Hayward(FC)	.08	.06	.03
64	Jim Steels(FC)	.08	.06	.03
65	Pat Borders(FC)	.60	.45	.25
66	Sil Campusano(FC)	.20	.15	.08
67	Mike Flanagan	.10	.08	.04
68	Todd Stottlemyre(FC)	.70	.50	.30
69	David Wells(FC)	.08	.06	.03
70	Jose Alvarez(FC)	.15	.11	.06
71	Paul Runge	.06	.05	.02
72	Cesar Jimenez (German)(FC)	.15	.11	.06
73	Pete Smith	.08	.06	.03
74	John Smoltz(FC)	5.00	3.75	2.00
75	Damon Berryhill	.10	.08	.04
76	Goose Gossage	.15	.11	.06
77	Mark Grace	2.00	1.50	.80
78	Darrin Jackson	.08	.06	.03
79	Vance Law	.08	.06	.03
80	Jeff Pico(FC)	.20	.15	.08
81	Gary Varsho(FC)	.20	.15	.08
82	Tim Birtsas	.06	.05	.02
83	Rob Dibble(FC)	.80	.60	.30
84	Danny Jackson	.15	.11	.06
85	Paul O'Neill	.15	.11	.06
86	Jose Rijo	.08	.06	.03
87	Chris Sabo(FC)	1.00	.70	.40
88	Jim Fishel(FC)	.15	.11	.06
89	Craig Biggio(FC)	1.50	1.25	.60
90	Terry Puhl	.06	.05	.02
91	Rafael Ramirez	.06	.05	.02
92	Louie Meadows(FC)	.15	.11	.06
93	Kirk Gibson(FC)	.20	.15	.08
94	Alfredo Griffin	.08	.06	.03
95	Jay Howell	.08	.06	.03

		MT	NR MT	EX
96	Jesse Orosco	.08	.06	.03
97	Alejandro Pena	.08	.06	.03
98	Tracy Woodson(FC)	.10	.08	.04
99	John Dopson(FC)	.25	.20	.10
100	Brian Holman(FC)	.40	.30	.15
101	Rex Hudler(FC)	.08	.06	.03
102	Jeff Parrett(FC)	.10	.08	.04
103	Nelson Santovenia(FC)	.15	.11	.06
104	Kevin Elster	.12	.09	.05
105	Jeff Innis(FC)	.20	.15	.08
106	Mackey Sasser(FC)	.10	.08	.04
107	Phil Bradley	.10	.08	.04
108	Danny Clay(FC)	.15	.11	.06
109	Greg Harris	.06	.05	.02
110	Ricky Jordan(FC)	.30	.25	.12
111	David Palmer	.06	.05	.02
112	Jim Gott	.06	.05	.02
113	Tommy Gregg (photo actually Randy Milligan)(FC)	.10	.08	.04
114	Barry Jones	.06	.05	.02
115	Randy Milligan(FC)	.60	.45	.25
116	Luis Alicea(FC)	.15	.11	.06
117	Tom Brunansky	.12	.09	.05
118	John Costello(FC)	.15	.11	.06
119	Jose DeLeon	.08	.06	.03
120	Bob Horner	.10	.08	.04
121	Scott Terry(FC)	.08	.06	.04
122	Roberto Alomar(FC)	8.00	6.00	3.25
123	Dave Leiper	.06	.05	.02
124	Keith Moreland	.08	.06	.03
125	Mark Parent(FC)	.20	.15	.08
126	Dennis Rasmussen	.10	.08	.04
127	Randy Bockus	.06	.05	.02
128	Brett Butler	.08	.06	.03
129	Donell Nixon	.06	.05	.02
130	Earnest Riles	.06	.05	.02
131	Roger Samuels(FC)	.15	.11	.06
132	Checklist	.06	.05	.02

1989 Fleer

This set includes 660 standard-size cards and was issued with 45 team logo stickers. Individual card fronts feature a grey and white striped background with full-color player photos framed by a bright line of color that slants upward to the right. The set also includes two subsets: 15 Major League Prospects and 12 SuperStar Specials. A special bonus set of 12 All-Star Team cards was randomly inserted in individual wax packs of 15 cards. The last seven cards in the set are checklists, with players listed alphabetically by teams.

		MT	NR MT	EX
Complete Set:		15.00	11.00	6.00
Common Player:		.05	.04	.02
1	Don Baylor	.10	.08	.04
2	Lance Blankenship(FC)	.15	.11	.06
3	Todd Burns	.15	.11	.06
4	Greg Cadaret(FC)	.07	.05	.03
5	Jose Canseco	.80	.60	.30
6	Storm Davis	.10	.08	.04
7	Dennis Eckersley	.12	.09	.05
8	Mike Gallego(FC)	.05	.04	.02
9	Ron Hassey	.05	.04	.02
10	Dave Henderson	.10	.08	.04

		MT	NR MT	EX
11	Rick Honeycutt	.05	.04	.02
12	Glenn Hubbard	.05	.04	.02
13	Stan Javier	.05	.04	.02
14	*Doug Jennings*	.15	.11	.06
15	*Felix Jose*(FC)	1.00	.70	.40
16	Carney Lansford	.07	.05	.03
17	Mark McGwire	.40	.30	.15
18	Gene Nelson	.05	.04	.02
19	Dave Parker	.12	.09	.05
20	Eric Plunk	.05	.04	.02
21	Luis Polonia	.07	.05	.03
22	Terry Steinbach	.10	.08	.04
23	Dave Stewart	.10	.08	.04
24	Walt Weiss	.20	.15	.08
25	Bob Welch	.10	.08	.04
26	Curt Young	.07	.05	.03
27	Rick Aguilera	.05	.04	.02
28	Wally Backman	.07	.05	.03
29	Mark Carreon	.07	.05	.03
30	Gary Carter	.20	.15	.08
31	David Cone	.25	.20	.10
32	Ron Darling	.12	.09	.05
33	Len Dykstra	.10	.08	.04
34	Kevin Elster	.10	.08	.04
35	Sid Fernandez	.10	.08	.04
36	Dwight Gooden	.20	.15	.08
37	Keith Hernandez	.25	.20	.10
38	Gregg Jefferies	.30	.25	.12
39	Howard Johnson	.10	.08	.04
40	Terry Leach	.05	.04	.02
41	Dave Magadan	.10	.08	.04
42	Bob McClure	.05	.04	.02
43	Roger McDowell	.10	.08	.04
44	Kevin McReynolds	.15	.11	.06
45	Keith Miller	.10	.08	.04
46	Randy Myers	.10	.08	.04
47	Bob Ojeda	.07	.05	.03
48	Mackey Sasser	.07	.05	.03
49	Darryl Strawberry	.40	.30	.15
50	Tim Teufel	.05	.04	.02
51	*Dave West*(FC)	.20	.15	.08
52	Mookie Wilson	.07	.05	.03
53	Dave Anderson	.05	.04	.02
54	Tim Belcher	.10	.08	.04
55	Mike Davis	.07	.05	.03
56	Mike Devereaux	.15	.11	.06
57	Kirk Gibson	.20	.15	.08
58	Alfredo Griffin	.07	.05	.03
59	Chris Gwynn	.12	.09	.05
60	Jeff Hamilton	.07	.05	.03
61a	Danny Heep (Home: San Antonio, TX)	.70	.50	.30
61b	Danny Heep (Home: Lake Hills, TX)	.05	.04	.02
62	Orel Hershiser	.25	.20	.10
63	Brian Holton(FC)	.07	.05	.03
64	Jay Howell	.07	.05	.03
65	Tim Leary	.07	.05	.03
66	Mike Marshall	.12	.09	.05
67	*Ramon Martinez*(FC)	1.00	.70	.40
68	Jesse Orosco	.07	.05	.03
69	Alejandro Pena	.07	.05	.03
70	Steve Sax	.15	.11	.06
71	Mike Scioscia	.07	.05	.03
72	Mike Sharperson	.05	.04	.02
73	John Shelby	.05	.04	.02
74	Franklin Stubbs	.05	.04	.02
75	John Tudor	.10	.08	.04
76	Fernando Valenzuela	.20	.15	.08
77	Tracy Woodson	.10	.08	.04
78	Marty Barrett	.07	.05	.03
79	Todd Benzinger	.12	.09	.05
80	Mike Boddicker	.07	.05	.03
81	Wade Boggs	.50	.40	.20
82	"Oil Can" Boyd	.07	.05	.03
83	Ellis Burks	.40	.30	.15
84	Rick Cerone	.05	.04	.02
85	Roger Clemens	.50	.40	.20
86	*Steve Curry*(FC)	.20	.15	.08
87	Dwight Evans	.10	.08	.04
88	Wes Gardner	.07	.05	.03
89	Rich Gedman	.07	.05	.03
90	Mike Greenwell	.40	.30	.15
91	Bruce Hurst	.10	.08	.04
92	Dennis Lamp	.05	.04	.02
93	Spike Owen	.05	.04	.02
94	Larry Parrish	.07	.05	.03
95	*Carlos Quintana*(FC)	.20	.15	.08
96	Jody Reed	.12	.09	.05
97	Jim Rice	.25	.20	.10
98a	Kevin Romine (batting follow-thru, photo actually Randy Kutcher)	.50	.40	.20
98b	Kevin Romine (arms crossed on chest, correct photo)	.60	.45	.25
99	Lee Smith	.10	.08	.04
100	Mike Smithson	.05	.04	.02
101	Bob Stanley	.05	.04	.02
102	Allan Anderson	.07	.05	.03
103	Keith Atherton	.05	.04	.02
104	Juan Berenguer	.05	.04	.02
105	Bert Blyleven	.12	.09	.05
106	*Eric Bullock*(FC)	.15	.11	.06
107	Randy Bush	.05	.04	.02
108	John Christensen(FC)	.05	.04	.02
109	Mark Davidson	.07	.05	.03
110	Gary Gaetti	.15	.11	.06
111	Greg Gagne	.05	.04	.02
112	Dan Gladden	.05	.04	.02
113	*German Gonzalez*(FC)	.20	.15	.08
114	Brian Harper	.05	.04	.02
115	Tom Herr	.07	.05	.03
116	Kent Hrbek	.20	.15	.08
117	Gene Larkin	.10	.08	.04
118	Tim Laudner	.05	.04	.02
119	Charlie Lea	.05	.04	.02
120	Steve Lombardozzi	.05	.04	.02
121a	John Moses (Home: Phoenix, AZ)	1.00	.70	.40
121b	John Moses (Home: Tempe, AZ)	.05	.04	.02
122	Al Newman	.05	.04	.02
123	Mark Portugal	.05	.04	.02
124	Kirby Puckett	.35	.25	.14
125	Jeff Reardon	.10	.08	.04
126	Fred Toliver	.05	.04	.02
127	Frank Viola	.15	.11	.06
128	Doyle Alexander	.07	.05	.03
129	Dave Bergman	.05	.04	.02
130a	Tom Brookens (Mike Heath stats on back)	2.25	1.75	.90
130b	Tom Brookens (correct stats on back)	.30	.25	.12
131	*Paul Gibson*	.15	.11	.06
132a	Mike Heath (Tom Brookens stats on back)	2.25	1.75	.90
132b	Mike Heath (correct stats on back)	.30	.25	.12
133	*Don Heinkel*	.15	.11	.06
134	Mike Henneman	.10	.08	.04
135	Guillermo Hernandez	.07	.05	.03
136	Eric King	.05	.04	.02
137	Chet Lemon	.07	.05	.03
138	Fred Lynn	.10	.08	.04
139	Jack Morris	.15	.11	.06
140	Matt Nokes	.20	.15	.08
141	Gary Pettis	.05	.04	.02
142	Ted Power	.05	.04	.02
143	Jeff Robinson	.12	.09	.05
144	Luis Salazar	.05	.04	.02
145	*Steve Searcy*(FC)	.20	.15	.08
146	Pat Sheridan	.05	.04	.02
147	Frank Tanana	.07	.05	.03
148	Alan Trammell	.20	.15	.08
149	Walt Terrell	.07	.05	.03
150	Jim Walewander(FC)	.07	.05	.03
151	Lou Whitaker	.20	.15	.08
152	Tim Birtsas	.05	.04	.02
153	Tom Browning	.10	.08	.04
154	*Keith Brown*(FC)	.15	.11	.06
155	*Norm Charlton*(FC)	.30	.25	.12
156	Dave Concepcion	.10	.08	.04
157	Kal Daniels	.15	.11	.06
158	Eric Davis	.30	.25	.12
159	Bo Diaz	.07	.05	.03
160	*Rob Dibble*	.30	.25	.12
161	Nick Esasky	.07	.05	.03
162	John Franco	.10	.08	.04
163	Danny Jackson	.15	.11	.06
164	Barry Larkin	.25	.20	.10
165	Rob Murphy	.05	.04	.02
166	Paul O'Neill	.05	.04	.02
167	Jeff Reed	.05	.04	.02
168	Jose Rijo	.07	.05	.03
169	Ron Robinson	.05	.04	.02
170	*Chris Sabo*	.40	.30	.15
171	*Candy Sierra*(FC)	.15	.11	.06
172	*Van Snider*(FC)	.15	.11	.06
173	Jeff Treadway	.12	.09	.05
174	Frank Williams	.05	.04	.02
175	Herm Winningham	.05	.04	.02
176	Jim Adduci(FC)	.05	.04	.02
177	Don August	.10	.08	.04
178	Mike Birkbeck	.05	.04	.02
179	Chris Bosio	.05	.04	.02
180	Glenn Braggs	.07	.05	.03
181	Greg Brock	.07	.05	.03

		MT	NR MT	EX
182	Mark Clear	.05	.04	.02
183	Chuck Crim	.05	.04	.02
184	Rob Deer	.07	.05	.03
185	Tom Filer	.05	.04	.02
186	Jim Gantner	.05	.04	.02
187	*Darryl Hamilton*	.30	.25	.12
188	Ted Higuera	.10	.08	.04
189	Odell Jones	.05	.04	.02
190	Jeffrey Leonard	.07	.05	.03
191	Joey Meyer	.10	.08	.04
192	Paul Mirabella	.05	.04	.02
193	Paul Molitor	.15	.11	.06
194	Charlie O'Brien(FC)	.07	.05	.03
195	Dan Plesac	.10	.08	.04
196	*Gary Sheffield*(FC)	1.00	.70	.40
197	B.J. Surhoff	.10	.08	.04
198	Dale Sveum	.07	.05	.03
199	Bill Wegman	.05	.04	.02
200	Robin Yount	.25	.20	.10
201	Rafael Belliard	.05	.04	.02
202	Barry Bonds	.40	.30	.15
203	Bobby Bonilla	.30	.25	.12
204	Sid Bream	.07	.05	.03
205	Benny Distefano(FC)	.05	.04	.02
206	Doug Drabek	.07	.05	.03
207	Mike Dunne	.10	.08	.04
208	Felix Fermin	.07	.05	.03
209	Brian Fisher	.07	.05	.03
210	Jim Gott	.05	.04	.02
211	Bob Kipper	.05	.04	.02
212	Dave LaPoint	.07	.05	.03
213	Mike LaValliere	.07	.05	.03
214	Jose Lind	.10	.08	.04
215	Junior Ortiz	.05	.04	.02
216	Vicente Palacios	.07	.05	.03
217	Tom Prince(FC)	.10	.08	.04
218	Gary Redus	.05	.04	.02
219	R.J. Reynolds	.05	.04	.02
220	Jeff Robinson	.07	.05	.03
221	John Smiley	.12	.09	.05
222	Andy Van Slyke	.12	.09	.05
223	Bob Walk	.05	.04	.02
224	Glenn Wilson	.07	.05	.03
225	Jesse Barfield	.10	.08	.04
226	George Bell	.25	.20	.10
227	*Pat Borders*	.30	.25	.12
228	John Cerutti	.07	.05	.03
229	Jim Clancy	.07	.05	.03
230	Mark Eichhorn	.07	.05	.03
231	Tony Fernandez	.12	.09	.05
232	Cecil Fielder	.25	.20	.10
233	Mike Flanagan	.07	.05	.03
234	Kelly Gruber	.05	.04	.02
235	Tom Henke	.07	.05	.03
236	Jimmy Key	.10	.08	.04
237	Rick Leach	.05	.04	.02
238	Manny Lee	.05	.04	.02
239	Nelson Liriano	.07	.05	.03
240	Fred McGriff	.50	.40	.20
241	Lloyd Moseby	.07	.05	.03
242	Rance Mulliniks	.05	.04	.02
243	Jeff Musselman	.07	.05	.03
244	Dave Stieb	.10	.08	.04
245	Todd Stottlemyre	.10	.08	.04
246	Duane Ward	.05	.04	.02
247	David Wells	.10	.08	.04
248	Ernie Whitt	.07	.05	.03
249	Luis Aguayo	.05	.04	.02
250a	Neil Allen (Home: Sarasota, FL)	1.50	1.25	.60
250b	Neil Allen (Home: Syosset, NY)	.05	.04	.02
251	John Candelaria	.07	.05	.03
252	Jack Clark	.15	.11	.06
253	Richard Dotson	.07	.05	.03
254	Rickey Henderson	.35	.25	.14
255	Tommy John	.12	.09	.05
256	Roberto Kelly	.20	.15	.08
257	Al Leiter	.15	.11	.06
258	Don Mattingly	.80	.60	.30
259	Dale Mohorcic	.05	.04	.02
260	*Hal Morris*(FC)	1.25	.90	.50
261	Scott Nielsen(FC)	.10	.08	.04
262	Mike Pagliarulo	.10	.08	.04
263	*Hipolito Pena*(FC)	.15	.11	.06
264	Ken Phelps	.07	.05	.03
265	Willie Randolph	.07	.05	.03
266	Rick Rhoden	.07	.05	.03
267	Dave Righetti	.12	.09	.05
268	Rafael Santana	.05	.04	.02
269	Steve Shields(FC)	.07	.05	.03
270	Joel Skinner	.05	.04	.02
271	Don Slaught	.05	.04	.02

		MT	NR MT	EX
272	Claudell Washington	.07	.05	.03
273	Gary Ward	.07	.05	.03
274	Dave Winfield	.30	.25	.12
275	Luis Aquino(FC)	.05	.04	.02
276	Floyd Bannister	.07	.05	.03
277	George Brett	.35	.25	.14
278	Bill Buckner	.10	.08	.04
279	*Nick Capra*(FC)	.15	.11	.06
280	*Jose DeJesus*(FC)	.15	.11	.06
281	Steve Farr	.05	.04	.02
282	Jerry Gleaton	.05	.04	.02
283	Mark Gubicza	.10	.08	.04
284	*Tom Gordon*(FC)	.40	.30	.15
285	Bo Jackson	.80	.60	.30
286	Charlie Leibrandt	.07	.05	.03
287	*Mike Macfarlane*	.20	.15	.08
288	Jeff Montgomery	.07	.05	.03
289	Bill Pecota	.07	.05	.03
290	Jamie Quirk	.05	.04	.02
291	Bret Saberhagen	.15	.11	.06
292	Kevin Seitzer	.30	.25	.12
293	Kurt Stillwell	.07	.05	.03
294	Pat Tabler	.07	.05	.03
295	Danny Tartabull	.20	.15	.08
296	Gary Thurman	.12	.09	.05
297	Frank White	.07	.05	.03
298	Willie Wilson	.10	.08	.04
299	Roberto Alomar	1.00	.70	.40
300	*Sandy Alomar, Jr.*(FC)	.60	.45	.25
301	Chris Brown	.07	.05	.03
302	Mike Brumley(FC)	.07	.05	.03
303	Mark Davis	.05	.04	.02
304	Mark Grant	.05	.04	.02
305	Tony Gwynn	.35	.25	.14
306	*Greg Harris*(FC)	.20	.15	.08
307	Andy Hawkins	.05	.04	.02
308	Jimmy Jones	.05	.04	.02
309	John Kruk	.07	.05	.03
310	Dave Leiper	.05	.04	.02
311	Carmelo Martinez	.05	.04	.02
312	Lance McCullers	.07	.05	.03
313	Keith Moreland	.07	.05	.03
314	Dennis Rasmussen	.10	.08	.04
315	Randy Ready	.05	.04	.02
316	Benito Santiago	.15	.11	.06
317	Eric Show	.07	.05	.03
318	Todd Simmons	.10	.08	.04
319	Garry Templeton	.07	.05	.03
320	Dickie Thon	.05	.04	.02
321	Ed Whitson	.05	.04	.02
322	Marvell Wynne	.05	.04	.02
323	Mike Aldrete	.07	.05	.03
324	Brett Butler	.07	.05	.03
325	Will Clark	.80	.60	.30
326	Kelly Downs	.10	.08	.04
327	Dave Dravecky	.07	.05	.03
328	Scott Garrelts	.05	.04	.02
329	Atlee Hammaker	.05	.04	.02
330	*Charlie Hayes*(FC)	.30	.25	.12
331	Mike Krukow	.07	.05	.03
332	Craig Lefferts	.05	.04	.02
333	Candy Maldonado	.07	.05	.03
334	Kirt Manwaring	.10	.08	.04
335	Bob Melvin	.05	.04	.02
336	Kevin Mitchell	.60	.45	.25
337	Donell Nixon	.05	.04	.02
338	*Tony Perezchica*(FC)	.15	.11	.06
339	Joe Price	.05	.04	.02
340	Rick Reuschel	.10	.08	.04
341	Earnest Riles	.05	.04	.02
342	Don Robinson	.05	.04	.02
343	Chris Speier	.05	.04	.02
344	Robby Thompson	.07	.05	.03
345	Jose Uribe	.05	.04	.02
346	Matt Williams	.12	.09	.05
347	*Trevor Wilson*(FC)	.15	.11	.06
348	Juan Agosto	.05	.04	.02
349	Larry Andersen	.05	.04	.02
350	Alan Ashby	.05	.04	.02
351	Kevin Bass	.07	.05	.03
352	Buddy Bell	.07	.05	.03
353	*Craig Biggio*	.60	.45	.25
354	Danny Darwin	.05	.04	.02
355	Glenn Davis	.25	.20	.10
356	Jim Deshaies	.05	.04	.02
357	Bill Doran	.07	.05	.03
358	*John Fishel*	.20	.15	.08
359	Billy Hatcher	.07	.05	.03
360	Bob Knepper	.07	.05	.03
361	*Louie Meadows*	.15	.11	.06
362	Dave Meads	.05	.04	.02

#	Name	MT	NR MT	EX	#	Name	MT	NR MT	EX
363	Jim Pankovits	.05	.04	.02	454	Steve Lake	.05	.04	.02
364	Terry Puhl	.05	.04	.02	455	Joe Magrane	.10	.08	.04
365	Rafael Ramirez	.05	.04	.02	456	Greg Mathews	.07	.05	.03
366	Craig Reynolds	.05	.04	.02	457	Willie McGee	.12	.09	.05
367	Mike Scott	.12	.09	.05	458	Larry McWilliams	.05	.04	.02
368	Nolan Ryan	.50	.40	.20	459	Jose Oquendo	.05	.04	.02
369	Dave Smith	.07	.05	.03	460	Tony Pena	.07	.05	.03
370	Gerald Young	.12	.09	.05	461	Terry Pendleton	.10	.08	.04
371	Hubie Brooks	.10	.08	.04	462	*Steve Peters*(FC)	.15	.11	.06
372	Tim Burke	.05	.04	.02	463	Ozzie Smith	.15	.11	.06
373	*John Dopson*	.25	.20	.10	464	Scott Terry	.08	.06	.03
374	Mike Fitzgerald	.05	.04	.02	465	Denny Walling	.05	.04	.02
375	Tom Foley	.05	.04	.02	466	Todd Worrell	.10	.08	.04
376	Andres Galarraga	.15	.11	.06	467	Tony Armas	.07	.05	.03
377	Neal Heaton	.05	.04	.02	468	*Dante Bichette*(FC)	.30	.25	.12
378	Joe Hesketh	.05	.04	.02	469	Bob Boone	.07	.05	.03
379	*Brian Holman*	.35	.25	.14	470	*Terry Clark*(FC)	.15	.11	.06
380	Rex Hudler	.05	.04	.02	471	Stew Cliburn(FC)	.05	.04	.02
381	*Randy Johnson*(FC)	.50	.40	.20	472	*Mike Cook*(FC)	.15	.11	.06
382	Wallace Johnson	.05	.04	.02	473	*Sherman Corbett*	.15	.11	.06
383	Tracy Jones	.10	.08	.04	474	Chili Davis	.07	.05	.03
384	Dave Martinez	.07	.05	.03	475	Brian Downing	.07	.05	.03
385	Dennis Martinez	.07	.05	.03	476	Jim Eppard	.07	.05	.03
386	Andy McGaffigan	.05	.04	.02	477	Chuck Finley	.05	.04	.02
387	Otis Nixon	.05	.04	.02	478	Willie Fraser	.05	.04	.02
388	*Johnny Paredes*(FC)	.12	.09	.05	479	*Bryan Harvey*	.30	.25	.12
389	Jeff Parrett	.10	.08	.04	480	Jack Howell	.07	.05	.03
390	Pascual Perez	.07	.05	.03	481	Wally Joyner	.25	.20	.10
391	Tim Raines	.25	.20	.10	482	Jack Lazorko	.05	.04	.02
392	Luis Rivera	.05	.04	.02	483	Kirk McCaskill	.07	.05	.03
393	*Nelson Santovenia*	.15	.11	.06	484	Mark McLemore	.05	.04	.02
394	Bryn Smith	.05	.04	.02	485	Greg Minton	.05	.04	.02
395	Tim Wallach	.10	.08	.04	486	Dan Petry	.07	.05	.03
396	Andy Allanson	.05	.04	.02	487	Johnny Ray	.07	.05	.03
397	*Rod Allen*	.15	.11	.06	488	Dick Schofield	.05	.04	.02
398	Scott Bailes	.05	.04	.02	489	Devon White	.12	.09	.05
399	Tom Candiotti	.05	.04	.02	490	Mike Witt	.07	.05	.03
400	Joe Carter	.12	.09	.05	491	Harold Baines	.12	.09	.05
401	Carmen Castillo	.05	.04	.02	492	Daryl Boston	.05	.04	.02
402	Dave Clark	.07	.05	.03	493	Ivan Calderon	.07	.05	.03
403	John Farrell	.10	.08	.04	494	Mike Diaz	.07	.05	.03
404	Julio Franco	.10	.08	.04	495	Carlton Fisk	.20	.15	.08
405	Don Gordon	.05	.04	.02	496	*Dave Gallagher*	.15	.11	.06
406	Mel Hall	.07	.05	.03	497	Ozzie Guillen	.07	.05	.03
407	Brad Havens	.05	.04	.02	498	Shawn Hillegas	.07	.05	.03
408	Brook Jacoby	.10	.08	.04	499	Lance Johnson	.07	.05	.03
409	Doug Jones	.12	.09	.05	500	Barry Jones	.05	.04	.02
410	*Jeff Kaiser*(FC)	.15	.11	.06	501	Bill Long	.07	.05	.03
411	*Luis Medina*(FC)	.20	.15	.08	502	Steve Lyons	.05	.04	.02
412	Cory Snyder	.15	.11	.06	503	Fred Manrique	.07	.05	.03
413	Greg Swindell	.12	.09	.05	504	Jack McDowell	.10	.08	.04
414	*Ron Tingley*(FC)	.15	.11	.06	505	*Donn Pall*	.15	.11	.06
415	Willie Upshaw	.07	.05	.03	506	Kelly Paris	.05	.04	.02
416	Ron Washington	.05	.04	.02	507	Dan Pasqua	.10	.08	.04
417	Rich Yett	.05	.04	.02	508	*Ken Patterson*	.15	.11	.06
418	Damon Berryhill	.12	.09	.05	509	Melido Perez	.10	.08	.04
419	Mike Bielecki	.05	.04	.02	510	Jerry Reuss	.07	.05	.03
420	*Doug Dascenzo*(FC)	.20	.15	.08	511	Mark Salas	.05	.04	.02
421	Jody Davis	.07	.05	.03	512	Bobby Thigpen	.10	.08	.04
422	Andre Dawson	.20	.15	.08	513	Mike Woodard	.05	.04	.02
423	Frank DiPino	.05	.04	.02	514	Bob Brower	.05	.04	.02
424	Shawon Dunston	.10	.08	.04	515	Steve Buechele	.05	.04	.02
425	"Goose" Gossage	.12	.09	.05	516	*Jose Cecena*	.15	.11	.06
426	Mark Grace	.40	.30	.15	517	Cecil Espy	.07	.05	.03
427	*Mike Harkey*(FC)	.35	.25	.14	518	Scott Fletcher	.07	.05	.03
428	Darrin Jackson	.07	.05	.03	519	Cecilio Guante	.05	.04	.02
429	Les Lancaster	.07	.05	.03	520	Jose Guzman	.10	.08	.04
430	Vance Law	.07	.05	.03	521	Ray Hayward	.05	.04	.02
431	Greg Maddux	.12	.09	.05	522	Charlie Hough	.07	.05	.03
432	Jamie Moyer	.05	.04	.02	523	Pete Incaviglia	.12	.09	.05
433	Al Nipper	.05	.04	.02	524	Mike Jeffcoat	.05	.04	.02
434	Rafael Palmeiro	.20	.15	.08	525	Paul Kilgus	.10	.08	.04
435	Pat Perry	.05	.04	.02	526	*Chad Kreuter*(FC)	.15	.11	.06
436	*Jeff Pico*	.12	.09	.05	527	Jeff Kunkel	.05	.04	.02
437	Ryne Sandberg	.40	.30	.15	528	Oddibe McDowell	.07	.05	.03
438	Calvin Schiraldi	.05	.04	.02	529	Pete O'Brien	.07	.05	.03
439	Rick Sutcliffe	.10	.08	.04	530	Geno Petralli	.05	.04	.02
440	Manny Trillo	.05	.04	.02	531	Jeff Russell	.05	.04	.02
441	*Gary Varsho*	.20	.15	.08	532	Ruben Sierra	.35	.25	.12
442	Mitch Webster	.07	.05	.03	533	Mike Stanley	.05	.04	.02
443	*Luis Alicea*	.15	.11	.06	534	Ed Vande Berg	.05	.04	.02
444	Tom Brunansky	.12	.09	.05	535	Curtis Wilkerson	.05	.04	.02
445	Vince Coleman	.15	.11	.06	536	Mitch Williams	.07	.05	.03
446	*John Costello*	.15	.11	.06	537	Bobby Witt	.10	.08	.04
447	Danny Cox	.07	.05	.03	538	Steve Balboni	.07	.05	.03
448	Ken Dayley	.05	.04	.02	539	Scott Bankhead	.05	.04	.02
449	Jose DeLeon	.07	.05	.03	540	Scott Bradley	.05	.04	.02
450	Curt Ford	.05	.04	.02	541	Mickey Brantley	.05	.04	.02
451	Pedro Guerrero	.15	.11	.06	542	Jay Buhner(FC)	.10	.08	.04
452	Bob Horner	.10	.08	.04	543	Mike Campbell	.10	.08	.04
453	*Tim Jones*(FC)	.15	.11	.06	544	Darnell Coles	.07	.05	.03

		MT	NR MT	EX
545	Henry Cotto	.05	.04	.02
546	Alvin Davis	.12	.09	.05
547	Mario Diaz	.07	.05	.03
548	*Ken Griffey, Jr.*(FC)	6.00	4.50	2.50
549	Erik Hanson(FC)	.50	.40	.20
550	Mike Jackson	.07	.05	.03
551	Mark Langston	.10	.08	.04
552	Edgar Martinez	.30	.20	.12
553	*Bill McGuire*(FC)	.15	.11	.06
554	Mike Moore	.05	.04	.02
555	Jim Presley	.07	.05	.03
556	Rey Quinones	.05	.04	.02
557	Jerry Reed	.05	.04	.02
558	Harold Reynolds	.07	.05	.03
559	*Mike Schooler*(FC)	.35	.25	.14
560	Bill Swift	.05	.04	.02
561	Dave Valle	.05	.04	.02
562	Steve Bedrosian	.10	.08	.04
563	Phil Bradley	.10	.08	.04
564	Don Carman	.07	.05	.03
565	Bob Dernier	.05	.04	.02
566	Marvin Freeman	.05	.04	.02
567	Todd Frohwirth	.07	.05	.03
568	Greg Gross	.05	.04	.02
569	Kevin Gross	.07	.05	.03
570	Greg Harris	.05	.04	.02
571	Von Hayes	.10	.08	.04
572	Chris James	.10	.08	.04
573	Steve Jeltz	.05	.04	.02
574	Ron Jones(FC)	.15	.11	.06
575	*Ricky Jordan*	.50	.40	.20
576	Mike Maddux	.05	.04	.02
577	David Palmer	.05	.04	.02
578	Lance Parrish	.15	.11	.06
579	Shane Rawley	.07	.05	.03
580	Bruce Ruffin	.05	.04	.02
581	Juan Samuel	.12	.09	.05
582	Mike Schmidt	.50	.40	.20
583	Kent Tekulve	.07	.05	.03
584	Milt Thompson	.05	.04	.02
585	*Jose Alvarez*	.15	.11	.06
586	Paul Assenmacher	.05	.04	.02
587	Bruce Benedict	.05	.04	.02
588	Jeff Blauser	.10	.08	.04
589	*Terry Blocker*(FC)	.15	.11	.06
590	Ron Gant	.12	.09	.05
591	Tom Glavine	.10	.08	.04
592	Tommy Gregg	.10	.08	.04
593	Albert Hall	.05	.04	.02
594	Dion James	.05	.04	.02
595	Rick Mahler	.05	.04	.02
596	Dale Murphy	.40	.30	.15
597	Gerald Perry	.10	.08	.04
598	Charlie Puleo	.05	.04	.02
599	Ted Simmons	.10	.08	.04
600	Pete Smith	.10	.08	.04
601	Zane Smith	.07	.05	.03
602	*John Smoltz*	.80	.60	.30
603	Bruce Sutter	.10	.08	.04
604	Andres Thomas	.07	.05	.03
605	Ozzie Virgil	.05	.04	.02
606	*Brady Anderson*(FC)	.70	.50	.30
607	Jeff Ballard	.07	.05	.03
608	*Jose Bautista*	.20	.15	.08
609	Ken Gerhart	.07	.05	.03
610	Terry Kennedy	.07	.05	.03
611	Eddie Murray	.30	.25	.12
612	Carl Nichols(FC)	.10	.08	.04
613	Tom Niedenfuer	.07	.05	.03
614	Joe Orsulak	.05	.04	.02
615	*Oswaldo Peraza (Oswald)*(FC)	.15	.11	.06
616a	Bill Ripken (obscenity on bat)	15.00	11.00	6.00
616b	Bill Ripken (obscenity on bat scrawled out in black)	15.00	11.00	6.00
616c	Bill Ripken (obscenity on bat blocked out in black)	.60	.45	.25
616d	Bill Ripken (obscenity on bat whiteout)	30.00	22.00	12.5C
617	Cal Ripken, Jr.	.40	.30	.15
618	Dave Schmidt	.05	.04	.02
619	Rick Schu	.05	.04	.02
620	Larry Sheets	.07	.05	.03
621	Doug Sisk	.05	.04	.02
622	Pete Stanicek	.10	.08	.04
623	Mickey Tettleton	.05	.04	.02
624	Jay Tibbs	.05	.04	.02
625	Jim Traber	.07	.05	.03
626	Mark Williamson	.07	.05	.03
627	*Craig Worthington*	.20	.15	.08
628	Speed and Power (Jose Canseco)	.60	.45	.25
629	Pitcher Perfect (Tom Browning)	.10	.08	.04

		MT	NR MT	EX
630	Like Father - Like Sons (Roberto Alomar, Sandy Alomar, Jr.)	.50	.40	.20
631	N.L. All-Stars (Will Clark, Rafael Palmeiro)	.40	.30	.15
632	Homeruns Coast to Coast (Will Clark, Darryl Strawberry)	.30	.25	.12
633	Hot Corner's - Hot Hitters (Wade Boggs, Carney Lansford)	.40	.30	.15
634	Triple A's (Jose Canseco, Mark McGwire, Terry Steinbach)	.30	.25	.12
635	Dual Heat (Mark Davis, Dwight Gooden)	.20	.15	.08
636	N.L. Pitching Power (David Cone, Danny Jackson)	.15	.11	.06
637	Cannon Arms (Bobby Bonilla, Chris Sabo)	.20	.15	.08
638	Double Trouble (Andres Galarraga, Gerald Perry)	.10	.08	.04
639	Power Center (Eric Davis, Kirby Puckett)	.15	.11	.06
640	Major League Prospects (*Cameron Drew, Steve Wilson*)(FC)	.15	.11	.06
641	Major League Prospects (Kevin Brown, *Kevin Reimer*)(FC)	.80	.60	.30
642	Major League Prospects (*Jerald Clark, Brad Pounders*)(FC)	.40	.30	.15
643	Major League Prospects (*Mike Capel, Drew Hall*)(FC)	.15	.11	.06
644	Major League Prospects (*Joe Girardi, Rolando Roomes*)(FC)	.30	.25	.12
645	Major League Prospects (*Marty Brown, Lenny Harris*)(FC)	.40	.30	.15
646	Major League Prospects (*Luis de los Santos, Jim Campbell*)(FC)	.20	.15	.08
647	Major League Prospects (*Miguel Garcia, Randy Kramer*)(FC)	.15	.11	.06
648	Major League Prospects (*Torey Lovullo, Robert Palacios*)(FC)	.15	.11	.06
649	Major League Prospects (*Jim Corsi, Bob Milacki*)(FC)	.25	.20	.10
650	Major League Prospects (*Grady Hall, Mike Rochford*)(FC)	.15	.11	.06
651	Major League Prospects (*Vance Lovelace, Terry Taylor*)(FC)	.15	.11	.06
652	Major League Prospects (*Dennis Cook, Ken Hill*)(FC)	.35	.25	.14
653	Major League Prospects (*Scott Service, Shane Turner*)(FC)	.15	.11	.06
654	Checklist 1-101	.05	.04	.02
655	Checklist 102-200	.05	.04	.02
656	Checklist 201-298	.05	.04	.02
657	Checklist 299-395	.05	.04	.02
658	Checklist 396-490	.05	.04	.02
659	Checklist 491-584	.05	.04	.02
660	Checklist 585-660	.05	.04	.02

1989 Fleer
All Star Team

This special 12-card set represents Fleer's choices for its 1989 Major League All-Star Team. For the fourth consecutive year, Fleer inserted the special cards randomly inside their regular 1989 wax and cello packs. The cards feature two player photos set against a green background with the "1989 Fleer All Star Team" logo bannered across the top, and the player's name, position and team in the lower left corner. The backs contain a several-paragraph player profile.

		MT	NR MT	EX
Complete Set:		15.00	11.00	6.00
Common Player:		.50	.40	.20
1	Bobby Bonilla	1.25	.90	.50
2	Jose Canseco	2.00	1.50	.80
3	Will Clark	2.50	2.00	1.00
4	Dennis Eckersley	.80	.60	.30
5	Julio Franco	.80	.60	.30
6	Mike Greenwell	.50	.40	.20
7	Orel Hershiser	.70	.50	.30
8	Paul Molitor	.70	.50	.30
9	Mike Scioscia	.50	.40	.20
10	Darryl Strawberry	1.25	.90	.50
11	Alan Trammell	.70	.50	.30
12	Frank Viola	.80	.60	.30

1989 Fleer Baseball All Stars

This specially-boxed set was produced by Fleer for the Ben Franklin store chain. The full-color player photos are surrounded by a border of pink and yellow vertical bands. "Fleer Baseball All-Stars" appears along the top in red, white and blue. The set was sold in a box with a checklist on the back.

		MT	NR MT	EX
Complete Set:		4.00	3.00	1.50
Common Player:		.05	.04	.02
1	Doyle Alexander	.05	.04	.02
2	George Bell	.12	.09	.05
3	Wade Boggs	.40	.30	.15
4	Bobby Bonilla	.08	.06	.04
5	Jose Canseco	.50	.40	.20
6	Will Clark	.90	.70	.35
7	Roger Clemens	.30	.25	.12
8	Vince Coleman	.15	.11	.06
9	David Cone	.15	.11	.06
10	Mark Davis	.08	.06	.03
11	Andre Dawson	.10	.08	.04
12	Dennis Eckersley	.08	.06	.03
13	Andres Galarraga	.12	.09	.05
14	Kirk Gibson	.12	.09	.05
15	Dwight Gooden	.30	.25	.12
16	Mike Greenwell	.40	.30	.15
17	Mark Gubicza	.08	.06	.03
18	Ozzie Guillen	.05	.04	.02
19	Tony Gwynn	.20	.15	.08
20	Rickey Henderson	.15	.08	.04
21	Orel Hershiser	.20	.15	.08
22	Danny Jackson	.05	.04	.02
23	Doug Jones	.05	.04	.02
24	Ricky Jordan	.25	.20	.10
25	Bob Knepper	.05	.04	.02
26	Barry Larkin	.20	.15	.08
27	Vance Law	.05	.04	.02
28	Don Mattingly	.80	.60	.30
29	Mark McGwire	.50	.40	.20
30	Paul Molitor	.08	.06	.02
31	Gerald Perry	.05	.04	.02
32	Kirby Puckett	.35	.25	.12
33	Johnny Ray	.05	.04	.02
34	Harold Reynolds	.08	.06	.03

		MT	NR MT	EX
35	Cal Ripken, Jr.	.30	.25	.12
36	Don Robinson	.05	.04	.02
37	Ruben Sierra	.30	.25	.12
38	Dave Smith	.05	.04	.02
39	Darryl Strawberry	.35	.25	.14
40	Dave Steib	.08	.06	.03
41	Alan Trammell	.15	.11	.06
42	Andy Van Slyke	.10	.08	.04
43	Frank Viola	.15	.11	.06
44	Dave Winfield	.15	.11	.06

1989 Fleer Update

Fleer produced its sixth consecutive "Update" set in 1989 to supplement the company's regular set. As in the past, the set consisted of 132 cards (numbered U-1 through U-132) that were sold by hobby dealers in special collector's boxes.

		MT	NR MT	EX
Complete Set:		12.00	9.00	4.75
Common Player:		.06	.05	.02
1	Phil Bradley	.06	.05	.02
2	Mike Devereaux	.10	.08	.04
3	Steve Finley(FC)	.40	.30	.15
4	Kevin Hickey	.06	.05	.02
5	Brian Holton	.06	.05	.02
6	Bob Milacki	.20	.15	.08
7	Randy Milligan	.10	.08	.04
8	John Dopson	.15	.11	.06
9	Nick Esasky	.10	.08	.04
10	Rob Murphy	.06	.05	.02
11	Jim Abbott(FC)	1.00	.70	.40
12	Bert Blyleven	.06	.05	.02
13	Jeff Manto(FC)	.30	.25	.12
14	Bob McClure	.06	.05	.02
15	Lance Parrish	.06	.05	.02
16	Lee Stevens(FC)	.60	.45	.25
17	Claudell Washington	.06	.05	.02
18	Mark Davis	.06	.05	.02
19	Eric King	.06	.05	.02
20	Ron Kittle	.06	.05	.02
21	Matt Merullo(FC)	.15	.11	.06
22	Steve Rosenberg(FC)	.08	.06	.03
23	Robin Ventura(FC)	3.00	2.25	1.25
24	Keith Atherton	.06	.05	.02
25	Joey Belle(FC)	2.00	1.50	.80
26	Jerry Browne	.06	.05	.02
27	Felix Fermin	.06	.05	.02
28	Brad Komminsk	.06	.05	.02
29	Pete O'Brien	.06	.05	.02
30	Mike Brumley	.06	.05	.02
31	Tracy Jones	.06	.05	.02
32	Mike Schwabe(FC)	.30	.25	.12
33	Gary Ward	.06	.05	.02
34	Frank Williams	.06	.05	.02
35	Kevin Appier(FC)	.50	.40	.20
36	Bob Boone	.06	.05	.02
37	Luis de los Santos	.10	.08	.04
38	Jim Eisenreich(FC)	.06	.05	.02
39	Jaime Navarro(FC)	.50	.40	.20
40	Bill Spiers(FC)	.40	.30	.15
41	Greg Vaughn(FC)	1.25	.90	.50
42	Randy Veres(FC)	.15	.11	.06
43	Wally Backman	.06	.05	.02
44	Shane Rawley	.06	.05	.02
45	Steve Balboni	.06	.05	.02

		MT	NR MT	EX
46	Jesse Barfield	.06	.05	.02
47	Alvaro Espinoza(FC)	.25	.20	.10
48	Bob Geren(FC)	.40	.30	.15
49	Mel Hall	.06	.05	.02
50	Andy Hawkins	.06	.05	.02
51	Hensley Meulens(FC)	.50	.40	.20
52	Steve Sax	.15	.11	.06
53	Deion Sanders(FC)	2.00	1.50	.80
54	Rickey Henderson	.50	.40	.20
55	Mike Moore	.10	.08	.04
56	Tony Phillips	.06	.05	.02
57	Greg Briley(FC)	.35	.25	.14
58	Gene Harris	.10	.08	.04
59	Randy Johnson	.08	.06	.03
60	Jeffrey Leonard	.06	.05	.02
61	Dennis Powell	.06	.05	.02
62	Omar Vizquel(FC)	.20	.15	.08
63	Kevin Brown	.08	.06	.03
64	Julio Franco	.25	.20	.10
65	Jamie Moyer	.06	.05	.02
66	Rafael Palmeiro	.15	.11	.06
67	Nolan Ryan	1.75	1.25	.70
68	Francisco Cabrera(FC)	.20	.15	.08
69	Junior Felix(FC)	.40	.30	.15
70	Al Leiter	.06	.05	.02
71	Alex Sanchez(FC)	.12	.09	.05
72	Geronimo Berroa(FC)	.08	.06	.03
73	Derek Lilliquist(FC)	.15	.11	.06
74	Lonnie Smith	.10	.08	.04
75	Jeff Treadway	.06	.05	.02
76	Paul Kilgus	.06	.05	.02
77	Lloyd McClendon	.15	.11	.06
78	Scott Sanderson	.06	.05	.02
79	Dwight Smith(FC)	.15	.11	.06
80	Jerome Walton(FC)	.15	.11	.06
81	Mitch Williams	.15	.11	.06
82	Steve Wilson	.25	.20	.10
83	Todd Benzinger	.06	.05	.02
84	Ken Griffey	.20	.15	.08
85	Rick Mahler	.06	.05	.02
86	Rolando Roomes	.15	.11	.06
87	Scott Scudder(FC)	.20	.15	.08
88	Jim Clancy	.06	.05	.02
89	Rick Rhoden	.06	.05	.02
90	Dan Schatzeder	.06	.05	.02
91	Mike Morgan	.06	.05	.02
92	Eddie Murray	.20	.15	.08
93	Willie Randolph	.06	.05	.02
94	Ray Searage	.06	.05	.02
95	Mike Aldrete	.06	.05	.02
96	Kevin Gross	.06	.05	.02
97	Mark Langston	.15	.11	.06
98	Spike Owen	.06	.05	.02
99	Zane Smith	.06	.05	.02
100	Don Aase	.06	.05	.02
101	Barry Lyons	.06	.05	.02
102	Juan Samuel	.06	.05	.02
103	Wally Whitehurst(FC)	.20	.15	.08
104	Dennis Cook	.15	.11	.06
105	Lenny Dykstra	.06	.05	.02
106	Charlie Hayes(FC)	.10	.08	.04
107	Tommy Herr	.06	.05	.02
108	Ken Howell	.06	.05	.02
109	John Kruk	.06	.05	.02
110	Roger McDowell	.06	.05	.02
111	Terry Mulholland(FC)	.06	.05	.02
112	Jeff Parrett	.06	.05	.02
113	Neal Heaton	.06	.05	.02
114	Jeff King	.10	.08	.04
115	Randy Kramer	.06	.05	.02
116	Bill Landrum	.06	.05	.02
117	Cris Carpenter(FC)	.15	.11	.06
118	Frank DiPino	.06	.05	.02
119	Ken Hill	.15	.11	.06
120	Dan Quisenberry	.06	.05	.02
121	Milt Thompson	.06	.05	.02
122	Todd Zeile(FC)	.80	.60	.30
123	Jack Clark	.10	.08	.04
124	Bruce Hurst	.06	.05	.02
125	Mark Parent	.06	.05	.02
126	Bip Roberts	.06	.05	.02
127	Jeff Brantley(FC)	.25	.20	.10
128	Terry Kennedy	.06	.05	.02
129	Mike LaCoss	.06	.05	.02
130	Greg Litton(FC)	.25	.20	.10
131	Mike Schmidt	.60	.45	.25
132	Checklist	.06	.05	.02

1989 Fleer Baseball MVP

Filled with superstars, this 44-card boxed set was produced by Fleer in 1989 for the Toys 'R' Us chain. The fronts of the cards are designed in a yellow and green color scheme and include a "Fleer Baseball MVP" logo above the color player photo. The backs are printed in shades of green and yellow and include biographical notes and stats. The set was issued in a special box with a checklist on the back.

		MT	NR MT	EX
Complete Set:		3.75	2.75	1.50
Common Player:		.05	.04	.02
1	Steve Bedrosian	.05	.04	.02
2	George Bell	.12	.09	.05
3	Wade Boggs	.70	.50	.30
4	George Brett	.15	.11	.06
5	Hubie Brooks	.05	.04	.02
6	Jose Canseco	.90	.70	.35
7	Will Clark	.90	.70	.35
8	Roger Clemens	.30	.25	.12
9	Eric Davis	.20	.15	.08
10	Glenn Davis	.12	.09	.05
11	Andre Dawson	.12	.09	.05
12	Andres Galarraga	.12	.09	.05
13	Kirk Gibson	.15	.11	.06
14	Dwight Gooden	.30	.25	.12
15	Mark Grace	.25	.20	.10
16	Mike Greenwell	.50	.40	.20
17	Tony Gwynn	.20	.15	.08
18	Bryan Harvey	.05	.04	.02
19	Orel Hershiser	.25	.20	.10
20	Ted Higuera	.07	.05	.03
21	Danny Jackson	.05	.04	.02
22	Mike Jackson	.05	.04	.02
23	Doug Jones	.05	.04	.02
24	Greg Maddux	.07	.05	.03
25	Mike Marshall	.05	.04	.02
26	Don Mattingly	.80	.60	.30
27	Fred McGriff	.30	.25	.12
28	Mark McGwire	.80	.60	.30
29	Kevin McReynolds	.15	.11	.06
30	Jack Morris	.05	.04	.02
31	Gerald Perry	.05	.04	.02
32	Kirby Puckett	.35	.25	.12
33	Chris Sabo	.20	.15	.08
34	Mike Scott	.12	.09	.05
35	Ruben Sierra	.25	.20	.10
36	Darryl Strawberry	.35	.25	.12
37	Danny Tartabull	.09	.07	.04
38	Bobby Thigpen	.09	.07	.04
39	Alan Trammell	.15	.11	.06
40	Andy Van Slyke	.12	.09	.05
41	Frank Viola	.12	.09	.05
42	Walt Weiss	.20	.15	.08
43	Dave Winfield	.15	.11	.06
44	Todd Worrell	.07	.05	.03

A player's name in italic indicates a rookie card. An (FC) indicates a player's first card for that particular card company.

The values quoted are intended
to reflect the market price.

1989 Fleer Baseball's Exciting Stars

Sold exclusively in Cumberland Farm stores, this 44-card boxed set pictures the game's top stars. The card fronts feature a color player photo surrounded by a blue border with "Baseball's Exciting Stars" along the top. The cards were were numbered alphabetically and packed in a special box with a complete checklist on the back.

		MT	NR MT	EX
Complete Set:		3.50	2.75	1.50
Common Player:		.05	.04	.02
1	Harold Baines	.07	.05	.03
2	Wade Boggs	.70	.50	.30
3	Jose Canseco	.90	.70	.35
4	Joe Carter	.12	.09	.05
5	Will Clark	.90	.70	.35
6	Roger Clemens	.30	.25	.12
7	Vince Coleman	.15	.11	.06
8	David Cone	.15	.11	.06
9	Eric Davis	.20	.15	.08
10	Glenn Davis	.15	.11	.06
11	Andre Dawson	.12	.09	.05
12	Dwight Evans	.09	.07	.04
13	Andres Galarraga	.12	.09	.05
14	Kirk Gibson	.12	.09	.05
15	Dwight Gooden	.30	.25	.12
16	Jim Gott	.05	.04	.02
17	Mark Grace	.30	.25	.12
18	Mike Greenwell	.40	.30	.15
19	Mark Gibicza	.07	.05	.03
20	Tony Gwynn	.20	.15	.08
21	Rickey Henderson	.40	.30	.15
22	Tom Henke	.05	.04	.02
23	Mike Henneman	.05	.04	.02
24	Orel Hershiser	.25	.20	.10
25	Danny Jackson	.05	.04	.02
26	Gregg Jefferies	.40	.30	.15
27	Ricky Jordan	.30	.25	.12
28	Wally Joyner	.15	.11	.06
29	Mark Langston	.15	.11	.06
30	Tim Leary	.05	.04	.02
31	Don Mattingly	.70	.50	.30
32	Mark McGwire	.80	.60	.30
33	Dale Murphy	.15	.11	.06
34	Kirby Puckett	.35	.25	.14
35	Chris Sabo	.30	.25	.12
36	Kevin Seitzer	.15	.11	.06
37	Ruben Sierra	.30	.25	.12
38	Ozzie Smith	.15	.11	.06
39	Dave Stewart	.07	.05	.03
40	Darryl Strawberry	.35	.25	.14
41	Alan Trammell	.15	.11	.06
42	Frank Viola	.15	.11	.06
43	Dave Winfield	.15	.11	.06
44	Robin Yount	.15	.11	.06

1989 Fleer Heroes of Baseball

This 44-card boxed set was produced by Fleer for the Woolworth store chain. The fronts of the cards are designed in a red and blue color scheme and feature full-color photos that fade into a soft focus on all edges. "Fleer Heroes of Baseball" appears just above the player's name, team and position at the bottom of the card. The set is numbered alphabetically and was packaged in a special box with a checklist on the back.

		MT	NR MT	EX
Complete Set:		3.50	2.75	1.50
Common Player:		.05	.04	.02
1	George Bell	.12	.09	.05
2	Wade Boggs	.70	.50	.30
3	Barry Bonds	.12	.09	.05
4	Tom Brunansky	.08	.06	.03
5	Jose Canseco	.90	.70	.35
6	Joe Carter	.12	.09	.05
7	Will Clark	.90	.70	.35
8	Roger Clemens	.30	.25	.12
9	David Cone	.15	.11	.06
10	Eric Davis	.40	.30	.15
11	Glenn Davis	.12	.09	.05
12	Andre Dawson	.12	.09	.05
13	Dennis Eckersley	.07	.05	.03
14	John Franco	.05	.04	.02
15	Gary Gaetti	.12	.09	.05
16	Andres Galarraga	.15	.11	.06
17	Kirk Gibson	.12	.09	.05
18	Dwight Gooden	.30	.25	.12
19	Mike Greenwell	.50	.40	.20
20	Tony Gwynn	.25	.20	.10
21	Bryan Harvey	.05	.04	.02
22	Orel Hershiser	.20	.15	.08
23	Ted Higuera	.07	.05	.03
24	Danny Jackson	.05	.04	.02
25	Ricky Jordan	.40	.30	.15
26	Don Mattingly	.70	.50	.30
27	Fred McGriff	.30	.25	.12
28	Mark McGwire	.60	.45	.25
29	Kevin McReynolds	.15	.11	.06
30	Gerald Perry	.05	.04	.02
31	Kirby Puckett	.30	.25	.12
32	Johnny Ray	.05	.04	.02
33	Harold Reynolds	.05	.04	.02
34	Cal Ripken, Jr.	.15	.11	.06
35	Ryne Sandberg	.15	.11	.06
36	Kevin Seitzer	.15	.11	.06
37	Ruben Sierra	.30	.25	.12
38	Darryl Strawberry	.30	.25	.12
39	Bobby Thigpen	.05	.04	.02
40	Alan Trammell	.12	.09	.05
41	Andy Van Slyke	.10	.08	.04
42	Frank Viola	.15	.11	.06
43	Dave Winfield	.15	.11	.06
44	Robin Yount	.20	.15	.08

Regional interest may affect the value of a card.

1989 Fleer
League Leaders

Eric Davis

Another of the various small, boxed sets issued by Fleer, the 44-card "League Leaders" set was produced for Walgreen stores. The standard-size cards feature color photos on the front surrounded by a red border with "Fleer League Leaders" across the top. The player's name, team and position appear in a yellow band at the bottom. The backs include player stats and data and the team logo. The cards are numbered alphabetically and packaged in a special box that includes the full checklist on the back.

		MT	NR MT	EX
Complete Set:		4.00	3.00	1.50
Common Player:		.05	.04	.02
1	Allan Anderson	.05	.04	.02
2	Wade Boggs	.70	.50	.30
3	Jose Canseco	.90	.70	.35
4	Will Clark	.90	.70	.35
5	Roger Clemens	.40	.30	.15
6	Vince Coleman	.15	.11	.06
7	David Cone	.15	.11	.06
8	Kal Daniels	.12	.09	.05
9	Chili Davis	.05	.04	.02
10	Eric Davis	.20	.15	.08
11	Glenn Davis	.15	.11	.06
12	Andre Dawson	.12	.09	.05
13	John Franco	.05	.04	.02
14	Andres Galarraga	.12	.09	.05
15	Kirk Gibson	.12	.09	.05
16	Dwight Gooden	.30	.25	.12
17	Mark Grace	.30	.25	.12
18	Mike Greenwell	.60	.45	.25
19	Tony Gwynn	.20	.15	.08
20	Orel Hershiser	.25	.20	.10
21	Pete Incaviglia	.05	.04	.02
22	Danny Jackson	.05	.04	.02
23	Gregg Jefferies	.90	.70	.35
24	Joe Magrane	.09	.07	.05
25	Don Mattingly	.70	.50	.30
26	Fred McGriff	.30	.25	.12
27	Mark McGwire	.80	.60	.30
28	Dale Murphy	.15	.11	.06
29	Dan Plesac	.07	.05	.03
30	Kirby Puckett	.40	.30	.15
31	Harold Reynolds	.12	.09	.05
32	Cal Ripken, Jr.	.15	.11	.06
33	Jeff Robinson	.05	.04	.02
34	Mike Scott	.12	.09	.05
35	Ozzie Smith	.15	.09	.05
36	Dave Stewart	.07	.05	.03
37	Darryl Strawberry	.30	.25	.12
38	Greg Swindell	.15	.11	.06
39	Bobby Thigpen	.08	.06	.03
40	Alan Trammell	.12	.09	.05
41	Andy Van Slyke	.12	.09	.05
42	Frank Viola	.12	.09	.05
43	Dave Winfield	.12	.09	.05
44	Robin Yount	.20	.15	.08

1989 Fleer Superstars

This 44-card boxed set was produced by Fleer for the McCrory store chain. The cards are the standard 2-1/2" by 3-1/2" and the full-color player photos are outlined in red with a tan-and-white striped border. The player's name, position and team logo appear at the bottom of the card. The backs carry yellow and white stripes and include the Fleer "SuperStars" logo, player stats and biographical information. The cards are numbered alphabetically and packaged in a special box that includes a checklist on the back.

		MT	NR MT	EX
Complete Set:		4.00	3.00	1.50
Common Player:		.05	.04	.02
1	Roberto Alomar	.20	.15	.08
2	Harold Baines	.12	.09	.05
3	Tim Belcher	.12	.09	.05
4	Wade Boggs	.70	.50	.30
5	George Brett	.15	.11	.06
6	Jose Canseco	.90	.70	.35
7	Gary Carter	.05	.04	.02
8	Will Clark	.90	.70	.35
9	Roger Clemens	.30	.25	.12
10	Kal Daniels	.15	.11	.06
11	Eric Davis	.20	.15	.08
12	Andre Dawson	.12	.09	.05
13	Tony Fernandez	.12	.09	.05
14	Scott Fletcher	.05	.04	.02
15	Andres Galarraga	.15	.11	.06
16	Kirk Gibson	.15	.11	.06
17	Dwight Gooden	.30	.25	.12
18	Jim Gott	.05	.04	.02
19	Mark Grace	.30	.25	.12
20	Mike Greenwell	.50	.40	.20
21	Tony Gwynn	.20	.15	.08
22	Rickey Henderson	.20	.15	.08
23	Orel Hershiser	.20	.15	.08
24	Ted Higuera	.07	.05	.02
25	Gregg Jefferies	.90	.70	.35
26	Wally Joyner	.15	.11	.06
27	Mark Langston	.15	.11	.06
28	Greg Maddux	.15	.11	.06
29	Don Mattingly	.70	.50	.30
30	Fred McGriff	.30	.25	.12
31	Mark McGwire	.80	.60	.30
32	Dan Plesac	.09	.07	.04
33	Kirby Puckett	.30	.25	.12
34	Jeff Reardon	.05	.04	.02
35	Chris Sabo	.12	.09	.05
36	Mike Schmidt	.25	.20	.10
37	Mike Scott	.10	.08	.04
38	Cory Snyder	.10	.08	.04
39	Darryl Strawberry	.30	.25	.12
40	Alan Trammell	.12	.09	.05
41	Frank Viola	.12	.09	.05
42	Walt Weiss	.12	.09	.05
43	Dave Winfield	.12	.09	.05
44	Todd Worrell	.05	.04	.02

A player's name in italic type indicates a rookie card. An (FC) indicates a player's first card for that particular card company.

1989 Fleer Box Panels

For the fourth consecutive year, Fleer issued a series of cards on the bottom panels of its regular 1989 wax pack boxes. The 28-card set includes 20 players and eight team logo cards, all designed in the identical style of the regular 1989 Fleer set. The box-bottom cards were randomly printed, four cards (three player cards and one team logo) on each bottom panel. The cards were numbered from C-1 to C-28.

		MT	NR MT	EX
Complete Panel Set:		6.00	4.50	2.50
Complete Singles Set:		3.00	2.25	1.25
Common Single Player:		.15	.11	.06
1	Mets Logo	.05	.04	.02
2	Wade Boggs	.40	.30	.15
3	George Brett	.25	.20	.10
4	Jose Canseco	.50	.40	.20
5	A's Logo	.05	.04	.02
6	Will Clark	.50	.40	.20
7	David Cone	.25	.20	.10
8	Andres Galarraga	.25	.20	.10
9	Dodgers Logo	.05	.04	.02
10	Kirk Gibson	.15	.11	.06
11	Mike Greenwell	.25	.20	.10
12	Tony Gwynn	.25	.20	.10
13	Tigers Logo	.05	.04	.02
14	Orel Hershiser	.20	.15	.08
15	Danny Jackson	.15	.11	.06
16	Wally Joyner	.50	.40	.20
17	Red Sox Logo	.05	.04	.02
18	Yankees Logo	.05	.04	.02
19	Fred McGriff	.60	.45	.25
20	Kirby Puckett	.30	.25	.12
21	Chris Sabo	.15	.11	.06
22	Kevin Seitzer	.30	.25	.12
23	Pirates Logo	.05	.04	.02
24	Astros Logo	.05	.04	.02
25	Darryl Strawberry	.40	.30	.15
26	Alan Trammell	.20	.15	.08
27	Andy Van Slyke	.25	.20	.10
28	Frank Viola	.20	.15	.08

1989 Fleer For The Record

Fleer's "For the Record" set features six players and their achievements from 1988. Fronts of the standard 2-1/2" by 3-1/2" cards feature a full color photo of the player set against a red background. The words "For the Record" appear in blue script at the top of the card and the players name on the bottom, printed in white type. Card backs are grey and describe individual accomplishments. The cards were distributed randomly in rack packs.

		MT	NR MT	EX
Complete Set:		4.00	3.00	1.50
Common Player:		.80	.60	.30
1	Wade Boggs	1.00	.70	.40
2	Roger Clemens	1.25	.90	.50
3	Andres Galarraga	.80	.60	.30
4	Kirk Gibson	.80	.60	.30
5	Greg Maddux	.80	.60	.30
6	Don Mattingly	1.00	.70	.40

1989 Fleer '88 World Series

This 12-card set, which depicts highlights of the 1988 World Series, was included as a special sub-set with the regular factory-collated Fleer set. It was not available as individual cards in wax packs, cello packs or any other form.

		MT	NR MT	EX
Complete Set:		3.00	2.25	1.25
Common Player:		.25	.20	.10
1	Dodgers' Secret Weapon (Mickey Hatcher)	.25	.20	.10
2	Rookie Starts Series (Tim Belcher)	.35	.25	.14
3	Canseco Slams L.A. (Jose Canseco)	.40	.30	.20
4	Dramatic Comeback (Mike Scioscia)	.25	.20	.10
5	Gibson Steals The Show (Kirk Gibson)	.40	.30	.15
6	"Bulldog" (Orel Hershiser)	.30	.25	.12
7	One Swing, Three RBI's (Mike Marshall)	.25	.20	.10
8	Game-Winning Home Run (Mark McGwire)	.40	.30	.15
9	Sax's Speed Wins Game 4 (Steve Sax)	.25	.20	.10
10	Series Caps Award-Winning Year (Walt Weiss)	.25	.20	.10
11	The M.V.P. And His Shutout Magic (Orel Hershiser)	.35	.25	.14
12	Dodger Blue, World Champs	.25	.20	.10

1990 Fleer

Fleer's 1990 set, its 10th consecutive baseball card offering, again consisted of 660 cards numbered by team. The front of the cards feature mostly action photos surrounded by one of several different color bands and a white border. The "Fleer '90" logo appears in the upper left corner, while the team logo is the upper right. The player's name and position are printed in a flowing banner below the photo. The set includes various special cards, including a series of "Major League Prospects," Players of the Decade, team checklist cards and a series of multi-player cards. The backs include complete career stats, player data, and a special "Vital Signs" section showing on-base percentage, slugging percentage, etc. for batters; and strikeout and walk ratios, opposing batting averages, etc. for pitchers.

		MT	NR MT	EX
	Complete Set:	18.00	13.50	7.25
	Common Player:	.05	.04	.02
1	Lance Blankenship	.07	.05	.03
2	Todd Burns	.06	.05	.02
3	Jose Canseco	.50	.40	.20
4	Jim Corsi	.09	.07	.04
5	Storm Davis	.06	.05	.02
6	Dennis Eckersley	.12	.09	.05
7	Mike Gallego	.06	.05	.02
8	Ron Hassey	.05	.04	.02
9	Dave Henderson	.10	.08	.06
10	Rickey Henderson	.30	.25	.12
11	Rick Honeycutt	.05	.04	.02
12	Stan Javier	.05	.04	.02
13	Felix Jose	.20	.15	.08
14	Carney Lansford	.07	.05	.03
15	Mark McGwire	.25	.20	.10
16	Mike Moore	.10	.08	.04
17	Gene Nelson	.05	.04	.02
18	Dave Parker	.12	.09	.05
19	Tony Phillips	.05	.04	.02
20	Terry Steinbach	.10	.08	.06
21	Dave Stewart	.10	.08	.06
22	Walt Weiss	.10	.08	.06
23	Bob Welch	.06	.05	.03
24	Curt Young	.05	.04	.02
25	Paul Assenmacher	.05	.04	.02
26	Damon Berryhill	.10	.08	.04
27	Mike Bielecki	.10	.08	.04
28	Kevin Blankenship	.07	.05	.03
29	Andre Dawson	.12	.09	.05
30	Shawon Dunston	.09	.07	.04
31	Joe Girardi	.12	.09	.05
32	Mark Grace	.25	.20	.10
33	Mike Harkey	.12	.09	.05
34	Paul Kilgus	.05	.04	.02
35	Les Lancaster	.06	.05	.02
36	Vance Law	.05	.04	.02
37	Greg Maddux	.10	.08	.04
38	Lloyd McClendon	.10	.08	.04
39	Jeff Pico	.05	.04	.02
40	Ryne Sandberg	.35	.25	.14
41	Scott Sanderson	.05	.04	.02
42	Dwight Smith	.25	.20	.10
43	Rick Sutcliffe	.08	.06	.03
44	*Jerome Walton*	.30	.25	.12
45	Mitch Webster	.05	.04	.02
46	Curt Wilkerson	.05	.04	.02
47	*Dean Wilkins*(FC)	.15	.11	.06
48	Mitch Williams	.08	.06	.03
49	Steve Wilson	.15	.11	.06
50	Steve Bedrosian	.06	.05	.02
51	*Mike Benjamin*(FC)	.25	.20	.10
52	*Jeff Brantley*	.25	.20	.10

		MT	NR MT	EX
53	Brett Butler	.07	.05	.03
54	Will Clark	.40	.30	.15
55	Kelly Downs	.05	.04	.02
56	Scott Garrelts	.09	.07	.04
57	Atlee Hammaker	.05	.04	.02
58	Terry Kennedy	.05	.04	.02
59	Mike LaCoss	.05	.04	.02
60	Craig Lefferts	.06	.05	.02
61	*Greg Litton*	.25	.20	.10
62	Candy Maldonado	.06	.05	.02
63	Kirt Manwaring	.09	.07	.04
64	*Randy McCament*(FC)	.20	.15	.08
65	Kevin Mitchell	.30	.25	.12
66	Donell Nixon	.05	.04	.02
67	Ken Oberkfell	.05	.04	.02
68	Rick Reuschel	.09	.07	.04
69	Ernest Riles	.05	.04	.02
70	Don Robinson	.05	.04	.02
71	Pat Sheridan	.05	.04	.02
72	Chris Speier	.05	.04	.02
73	Robby Thompson	.07	.05	.03
74	Jose Uribe	.06	.05	.02
75	Matt Williams	.20	.15	.08
76	George Bell	.10	.08	.04
77	Pat Borders	.07	.05	.03
78	John Cerutti	.05	.04	.02
79	*Junior Felix*	.20	.15	.08
80	Tony Fernandez	.09	.07	.04
81	Mike Flanagan	.05	.04	.02
82	*Mauro Gozzo*(FC)	.15	.11	.06
83	Kelly Gruber	.07	.05	.03
84	Tom Henke	.05	.04	.02
85	Jimmy Key	.07	.05	.03
86	Manny Lee	.05	.04	.02
87	Nelson Liriano	.05	.04	.02
88	Lee Mazzilli	.05	.04	.02
89	Fred McGriff	.25	.20	.10
90	Lloyd Moseby	.06	.05	.02
91	Rance Mulliniks	.05	.04	.02
92	Alex Sanchez	.15	.11	.06
93	Dave Steib	.09	.07	.05
94	Todd Stottlemyre	.09	.07	.05
95	Duane Ward	.05	.04	.02
96	David Wells	.05	.04	.02
97	Ernie Whitt	.06	.05	.02
98	Frank Wills	.05	.04	.02
99	Mookie Wilson	.09	.07	.04
100	*Kevin Appier*(FC)	.25	.20	.10
101	Luis Aquino	.05	.04	.02
102	Bob Boone	.07	.05	.03
103	George Brett	.15	.11	.06
104	Jose DeJesus	.08	.06	.03
105	Luis de los Santos	.08	.06	.03
106	Jim Eisenreich	.05	.04	.02
107	Steve Farr	.05	.04	.02
108	Tom Gordon	.25	.20	.10
109	Mark Gubicza	.09	.07	.04
110	Bo Jackson	.35	.25	.14
111	Terry Leach	.05	.04	.02
112	Charlie Leibrandt	.05	.04	.02
113	*Rick Luecken*(FC)	.20	.15	.08
114	Mike Macfarlane	.05	.04	.02
115	Jeff Montgomery	.06	.05	.03
116	Bret Saberhagen	.10	.08	.04
117	Kevin Seitzer	.10	.08	.04
118	Kurt Stillwell	.06	.05	.02
119	Pat Tabler	.05	.04	.02
121	Gary Thurman	.05	.04	.02
122	Frank White	.07	.05	.03
123	Willie Wilson	.06	.05	.03
124	*Matt Winters*(FC)	.20	.15	.08
125	Jim Abbott	.35	.25	.14
126	Tony Armas	.05	.04	.02
127	Dante Bichette	.09	.07	.04
128	Bert Blyleven	.09	.07	.04
129	Chili Davis	.06	.05	.02
130	Brian Downing	.06	.05	.02
131	*Mike Fetters*(FC)	.20	.15	.08
132	Chuck Finley	.06	.05	.02
133	Willie Fraser	.05	.04	.02
134	Bryan Harvey	.05	.04	.02
135	Jack Howell	.05	.04	.02
136	Wally Joyner	.10	.08	.04
137	*Jeff Manto*	.20	.15	.08
138	Kirk McCaskill	.06	.05	.02
139	Bob McClure	.05	.04	.02
140	Greg Minton	.05	.04	.02
141	Lance Parrish	.07	.05	.02
142	Dan Petry	.05	.04	.02
143	Johnny Ray	.05	.04	.02
144	Dick Schofield	.06	.05	.02
145	*Lee Stevens*	.20	.15	.08

#	Player	MT	NR MT	EX
146	Claudell Washington	.06	.05	.02
147	Devon White	.08	.06	.03
148	Mike Witt	.06	.05	.02
149	Roberto Alomar	.30	.25	.12
150	Sandy Alomar, Jr.	.25	.20	.10
151	Andy Benes(FC)	.30	.25	.12
152	Jack Clark	.06	.05	.02
153	Pat Clements	.05	.04	.02
154	Joey Cora	.15	.11	.06
155	Mark Davis	.09	.07	.04
156	Mark Grant	.05	.04	.02
157	Tony Gwynn	.25	.20	.10
158	Greg Harris	.10	.08	.04
159	Bruce Hurst	.06	.05	.02
160	Darrin Jackson	.05	.04	.02
161	Chris James	.06	.05	.02
162	Carmelo Martinez	.06	.05	.02
163	Mike Pagliarulo	.06	.05	.02
164	Mark Parent	.05	.04	.02
165	Dennis Rasmussen	.05	.04	.02
166	Bip Roberts	.08	.06	.03
167	Benito Santiago	.12	.09	.05
168	Calvin Schiraldi	.05	.04	.02
169	Eric Show	.06	.05	.02
170	Garry Templeton	.06	.05	.02
171	Ed Whitson	.06	.05	.02
172	Brady Anderson	.07	.05	.03
173	Jeff Ballard	.07	.05	.03
174	Phil Bradley	.07	.05	.03
175	Mike Devereaux	.07	.05	.03
176	*Steve Finley*	.20	.15	.08
177	Pete Harnisch(FC)	.10	.08	.04
178	Kevin Hickey	.10	.08	.04
179	Brian Holton	.05	.04	.02
180	*Ben McDonald*(FC)	.80	.60	.30
181	Bob Melvin	.05	.04	.02
182	Bob Milacki	.07	.05	.03
183	Randy Milligan	.06	.05	.02
184	Gregg Olson(FC)	.30	.25	.12
185	Joe Orsulak	.05	.04	.02
186	Bill Ripken	.05	.04	.02
187	Cal Ripken, Jr.	.30	.25	.12
188	Dave Schmidt	.05	.04	.02
189	Larry Sheets	.05	.04	.02
190	Mickey Tettleton	.08	.06	.03
191	Mark Thurmond	.05	.04	.02
192	Jay Tibbs	.05	.04	.02
193	Jim Traber	.05	.04	.02
194	Mark Williamson	.05	.04	.02
195	Craig Worthington	.15	.11	.06
196	Don Aase	.05	.04	.02
197	*Blaine Beatty*(FC)	.25	.20	.10
198	Mark Carreon	.10	.08	.04
199	Gary Carter	.06	.05	.02
200	David Cone	.10	.08	.04
201	Ron Darling	.07	.05	.03
202	Kevin Elster	.05	.04	.02
203	Sid Fernandez	.09	.07	.04
204	Dwight Gooden	.20	.15	.08
205	Keith Hernandez	.06	.05	.02
206	*Jeff Innis*	.15	.11	.06
207	Gregg Jefferies	.20	.15	.08
208	Howard Johnson	.15	.11	.06
209	Barry Lyons	.05	.04	.02
210	Dave Magadan	.06	.05	.02
211	Kevin McReynolds	.07	.05	.03
212	Jeff Musselman	.05	.04	.02
213	Randy Myers	.06	.05	.02
214	Bob Ojeda	.06	.05	.02
215	Juan Samuel	.06	.05	.02
216	Mackey Sasser	.05	.04	.02
217	Darryl Strawberry	.25	.20	.10
218	Tim Teufel	.05	.04	.02
219	Frank Viola	.10	.08	.04
220	Juan Agosto	.05	.04	.02
221	Larry Anderson	.05	.04	.02
222	*Eric Anthony*(FC)	.50	.40	.20
223	Kevin Bass	.08	.06	.03
224	Craig Biggio	.10	.08	.04
225	Ken Caminiti	.06	.05	.02
226	Jim Clancy	.05	.04	.02
227	Danny Darwin	.05	.04	.02
228	Glenn Davis	.09	.07	.04
229	Jim Deshaies	.07	.05	.03
230	Bill Doran	.06	.05	.02
231	Bob Forsch	.05	.04	.02
233	Terry Puhl	.05	.04	.02
234	Rafael Ramirez	.05	.04	.02
235	Rick Rhoden	.05	.04	.02
236	Dan Schatzeder	.05	.04	.02
237	Mike Scott	.08	.06	.03
238	Dave Smith	.06	.05	.02
239	Alex Trevino	.05	.04	.02
240	Glenn Wilson	.05	.04	.02
241	Gerald Young	.05	.04	.02
242	Tom Brunansky	.07	.05	.03
243	Cris Carpenter	.10	.08	.04
244	*Alex Cole*(FC)	.20	.15	.08
245	Vince Coleman	.10	.08	.04
246	John Costello	.05	.04	.02
247	Ken Dayley	.05	.04	.02
248	Jose DeLeon	.06	.05	.02
249	Frank DiPino	.05	.04	.02
250	Pedro Guerrero	.09	.07	.04
251	Ken Hill	.09	.07	.04
252	Joe Magrane	.09	.07	.04
253	Willie McGee	.06	.05	.02
254	John Morris	.05	.04	.02
255	Jose Oquendo	.06	.05	.02
256	Tony Pena	.06	.05	.02
257	Terry Pendleton	.06	.05	.02
258	Ted Power	.05	.04	.02
259	Dan Quisenberry	.05	.04	.02
260	Ozzie Smith	.09	.07	.04
261	Scott Terry	.06	.05	.02
262	Milt Thompson	.05	.04	.02
263	Denny Walling	.05	.04	.02
264	Todd Worrell	.06	.05	.02
265	*Todd Zeile*	.50	.40	.20
266	Marty Barrett	.05	.04	.02
267	Mike Boddicker	.05	.04	.02
268	Wade Boggs	.40	.30	.15
269	Ellis Burks	.35	.25	.12
270	Rick Cerone	.05	.04	.02
271	Roger Clemens	.25	.20	.10
272	John Dopson	.06	.05	.02
273	Nick Esasky	.07	.05	.03
274	Dwight Evans	.09	.07	.05
275	Wes Gardner	.05	.04	.02
276	Rich Gedman	.05	.04	.02
277	Mike Greenwell	.50	.40	.20
278	Danny Heep	.05	.04	.02
279	Eric Hetzel	.10	.08	.04
280	Dennis Lamp	.05	.04	.02
281	Rob Murphy	.05	.04	.02
282	Joe Price	.05	.04	.02
283	Carlos Quintana	.10	.07	.04
284	Jody Reed	.06	.05	.02
285	Luis Rivera	.05	.04	.02
286	Kevin Romine	.05	.04	.02
287	Lee Smith	.05	.04	.02
288	Mike Smithson	.05	.04	.02
289	Bob Stanley	.05	.04	.02
290	Harold Baines	.09	.07	.04
291	Kevin Brown	.09	.07	.04
292	Steve Buechele	.05	.04	.02
293	*Scott Coolbaugh*(FC)	.25	.20	.10
294	*Jack Daugherty*(FC)	.25	.20	.10
295	Cecil Espy	.06	.05	.02
296	Julio Franco	.07	.05	.03
297	*Juan Gonzalez*(FC)	2.00	1.50	.80
298	Cecilio Guante	.05	.04	.02
299	Drew Hall	.05	.04	.02
300	Charlie Hough	.06	.05	.02
301	Pete Incaviglia	.08	.06	.03
302	Mike Jeffcoat	.05	.04	.02
303	Chad Kreuter	.08	.06	.03
304	Jeff Kunkel	.05	.04	.02
305	Rick Leach	.05	.04	.02
306	Fred Manrique	.05	.04	.02
307	Jamie Moyer	.06	.05	.02
308	Rafael Palmeiro	.07	.05	.02
309	Geno Petralli	.05	.04	.02
310	Kevin Reimer	.10	.08	.06
311	*Kenny Rogers*(FC)	.20	.15	.08
312	Jeff Russell	.06	.05	.02
313	Nolan Ryan	.50	.40	.20
314	Ruben Sierra	.15	.11	.06
315	Bobby Witt	.05	.04	.02
316	Chris Bosio	.07	.05	.03
317	Glenn Braggs	.07	.05	.03
318	Greg Brock	.05	.04	.02
319	Chuck Crim	.05	.04	.02
320	Rob Deer	.06	.05	.02
321	Mike Felder	.05	.04	.02
322	Tom Filer	.05	.04	.02
323	*Tony Fossas*(FC)	.10	.08	.04
324	Jim Gantner	.06	.05	.02
325	Darryl Hamilton	.08	.06	.03
326	Ted Higuera	.08	.06	.03
327	Mark Knudson(FC)	.10	.08	.04
328	Bill Krueger	.05	.04	.02

#	Player	MT	NR MT	EX
329	Tim McIntosh(FC)	.20	.15	.08
330	Paul Molitor	.08	.06	.03
331	Jaime Navarro	.25	.20	.10
332	Charlie O'Brien	.05	.04	.02
333	Jeff Peterek(FC)	.15	.11	.06
334	Dan Plesac	.07	.05	.03
335	Jerry Reuss	.06	.05	.02
336	Gary Sheffield	.30	.25	.12
337	Bill Spiers	.35	.25	.12
338	B.J. Surhoff	.07	.05	.02
339	Greg Vaughn	.60	.45	.25
340	Robin Yount	.20	.15	.08
341	Hubie Brooks	.06	.05	.02
342	Tim Burke	.06	.05	.02
343	Mike Fitzgerald	.05	.04	.02
344	Tom Foley	.05	.04	.02
345	Andres Galarraga	.15	.11	.06
346	Damaso Garcia	.05	.04	.02
347	Marquis Grissom(FC)	.50	.40	.20
348	Kevin Gross	.06	.05	.02
349	Joe Hesketh	.05	.04	.02
350	Jeff Huson(FC)	.25	.20	.10
351	Wallace Johnson	.05	.04	.02
352	Mark Langston	.15	.11	.06
353	Dave Martinez	.06	.05	.02
354	Dennis Martinez	.06	.05	.02
355	Andy McGaffigan	.05	.04	.02
356	Otis Nixon	.05	.04	.02
357	Spike Owen	.05	.04	.02
358	Pascual Perez	.06	.05	.02
359	Tim Raines	.10	.08	.04
360	Nelson Santovenia	.10	.08	.04
361	Bryn Smith	.06	.05	.02
362	Zane Smith	.05	.04	.02
363	Larry Walker(FC)	.60	.45	.25
364	Tim Wallach	.06	.05	.02
365	Rick Aguilera	.05	.04	.02
366	Allan Anderson	.06	.05	.02
367	Wally Backman	.06	.05	.02
368	Doug Baker(FC)	.08	.06	.03
369	Juan Berenguer	.05	.04	.02
370	Randy Bush	.05	.04	.02
371	Carmen Castillo	.05	.04	.02
372	Mike Dyer(FC)	.15	.11	.06
373	Gary Gaetti	.07	.05	.03
374	Greg Gagne	.05	.04	.02
375	Dan Gladden	.05	.04	.02
376	German Gonzalez	.05	.04	.02
377	Brian Harper	.06	.05	.02
378	Kent Hrbek	.10	.08	.04
379	Gene Larkin	.05	.04	.02
380	Tim Laudner	.05	.04	.02
381	John Moses	.05	.04	.02
382	Al Newman	.05	.04	.02
383	Kirby Puckett	.40	.30	.15
384	Shane Rawley	.06	.05	.02
385	Jeff Reardon	.06	.05	.02
386	Roy Smith	.05	.04	.02
387	Gary Wayne(FC)	.15	.11	.06
388	Dave West	.25	.20	.10
389	Tim Belcher	.12	.09	.05
390	Tim Crews	.05	.04	.02
391	Mike Davis	.05	.04	.02
392	Rick Dempsey	.05	.04	.02
393	Kirk Gibson	.09	.07	.04
394	Jose Gonzalez	.05	.04	.02
395	Alfredo Griffin	.06	.05	.02
396	Jeff Hamilton	.06	.05	.02
397	Lenny Harris	.10	.08	.06
398	Mickey Hatcher	.05	.04	.02
399	Orel Hershiser	.12	.09	.05
400	Jay Howell	.06	.05	.02
401	Mike Marshall	.06	.05	.02
402	Ramon Martinez	.25	.20	.10
403	Mike Morgan	.05	.04	.02
404	Eddie Murray	.10	.08	.04
405	Alejandro Pena	.05	.04	.02
406	Willie Randolph	.08	.06	.03
407	Mike Scioscia	.06	.05	.02
408	Ray Searage	.05	.04	.02
409	Fernando Valenzuela	.07	.05	.03
410	Jose Vizcaino(FC)	.20	.15	.08
411	John Wetteland(FC)	.15	.11	.06
412	Jack Armstrong	.05	.04	.02
413	Todd Benzinger	.07	.05	.03
414	Tim Birtsas	.05	.04	.02
415	Tom Browning	.07	.05	.03
416	Norm Charlton	.08	.06	.03
417	Eric Davis	.20	.15	.08
418	Rob Dibble	.15	.11	.06
419	John Franco	.07	.05	.03
420	Ken Griffey, Sr.	.07	.05	.03
421	Chris Hammond(FC)	.25	.20	.10
422	Danny Jackson	.06	.05	.02
423	Barry Larkin	.15	.11	.06
424	Tim Leary	.06	.05	.02
425	Rick Mahler	.05	.04	.02
426	Joe Oliver(FC)	.30	.25	.12
427	Paul O'Neill	.07	.05	.03
428	Luis Quinones	.05	.04	.02
429	Jeff Reed	.05	.04	.02
430	Jose Rijo	.07	.05	.03
431	Ron Robinson	.05	.04	.02
432	Rolando Roomes	.10	.08	.04
433	Chris Sabo	.15	.11	.06
434	Scott Scudder	.30	.25	.12
435	Herm Winningham	.05	.04	.02
436	Steve Balboni	.05	.04	.02
437	Jesse Barfield	.08	.06	.03
438	Mike Blowers(FC)	.20	.15	.08
439	Tom Brookens	.05	.04	.02
440	Greg Cadaret	.05	.04	.02
441	Alvaro Espinoza	.25	.20	.10
442	Bob Geren	.15	.11	.06
443	Lee Guetterman	.05	.04	.02
444	Mel Hall	.06	.05	.02
445	Andy Hawkins	.06	.05	.02
446	Roberto Kelly	.15	.11	.06
447	Don Mattingly	.35	.25	.14
448	Lance McCullers	.05	.04	.02
449	Hensley Meulens	.35	.25	.14
450	Dale Mohorcic	.05	.04	.02
451	Clay Parker	.10	.07	.04
452	Eric Plunk	.05	.04	.02
453	Dave Righetti	.07	.05	.03
454	Deion Sanders	.30	.25	.12
455	Steve Sax	.07	.05	.03
456	Don Slaught	.05	.04	.02
457	Walt Terrell	.05	.04	.02
458	Dave Winfield	.15	.11	.06
459	Jay Bell	.05	.04	.02
460	Rafael Belliard	.05	.04	.02
461	Barry Bonds	.10	.08	.04
462	Bobby Bonilla	.10	.08	.04
463	Sid Bream	.05	.04	.02
464	Benny Distefano	.06	.05	.02
465	Doug Drabek	.06	.05	.02
466	Jim Gott	.06	.05	.02
467	Billy Hatcher	.06	.05	.02
468	Neal Heaton	.06	.05	.02
469	Jeff King	.20	.15	.08
470	Bob Kipper	.05	.04	.02
471	Randy Kramer	.05	.04	.02
472	Bill Landrum	.06	.05	.02
473	Mike LaValliere	.06	.05	.02
474	Jose Lind	.06	.05	.02
475	Junior Ortiz	.05	.04	.02
476	Gary Redus	.05	.04	.02
477	Rick Reed(FC)	.15	.11	.06
478	R.J. Reynolds	.05	.04	.02
479	Jeff Robinson	.05	.04	.02
480	John Smiley	.07	.05	.03
481	Andy Van Slyke	.09	.07	.04
482	Bob Walk	.06	.05	.04
483	Andy Allanson	.05	.04	.02
484	Scott Bailes	.05	.04	.02
485	Joey Belle	.80	.60	.30
486	Bud Black	.05	.04	.02
487	Jerry Browne	.07	.05	.03
488	Tom Candiotti	.05	.04	.02
489	Joe Carter	.08	.06	.03
490	David Clark	.06	.05	.02
491	John Farrell	.06	.05	.02
492	Felix Fermin	.05	.04	.02
493	Brook Jacoby	.06	.05	.02
494	Dion James	.06	.05	.02
495	Doug Jones	.06	.05	.02
496	Brad Komminsk	.05	.04	.02
497	Rod Nichols	.05	.04	.02
498	Pete O'Brien	.07	.05	.03
499	Steve Olin(FC)	.35	.25	.12
500	Jesse Orosco	.05	.04	.02
501	Joel Skinner	.05	.04	.02
502	Cory Snyder	.09	.07	.04
503	Greg Swindell	.10	.08	.04
504	Rich Yett	.05	.04	.02
505	Scott Bankhead	.07	.05	.03
506	Scott Bradley	.05	.04	.02
507	Greg Briley	.15	.11	.06
508	Jay Buhner	.07	.05	.03
509	Darnell Coles	.05	.04	.02
510	Keith Comstock	.05	.04	.02

#	Player	MT	NR MT	EX
511	Henry Cotto	.05	.04	.02
512	Alvin Davis	.12	.09	.05
513	Ken Griffey, Jr.	1.00	.70	.40
514	Erik Hanson	.20	.15	.08
515	Gene Harris	.15	.11	.06
516	Brian Holman	.07	.05	.03
517	Mike Jackson	.05	.04	.02
518	Randy Johnson	.15	.11	.06
519	Jeffrey Leonard	.08	.06	.03
520	Edgar Martinez	.10	.08	.04
521	Dennis Powell	.05	.04	.02
522	Jim Presley	.06	.05	.02
523	Jerry Reed	.05	.04	.02
524	Harold Reynolds	.07	.05	.03
525	Mike Schooler	.06	.05	.04
526	Bill Swift	.05	.04	.02
527	David Valle	.05	.04	.02
528	*Omar Vizquel*	.20	.15	.08
529	Ivan Calderon	.06	.05	.02
530	Carlton Fisk	.10	.08	.04
531	Scott Fletcher	.06	.05	.02
532	Dave Gallagher	.09	.07	.04
533	Ozzie Guillen	.07	.05	.03
534	*Greg Hibbard*(FC)	.20	.15	.08
535	Shawn Hillegas	.05	.04	.02
536	Lance Johnson	.07	.05	.03
537	Eric King	.05	.04	.02
538	Ron Kittle	.07	.05	.02
539	Steve Lyons	.05	.04	.02
540	Carlos Martinez	.15	.11	.06
541	*Tom McCarthy*(FC)	.10	.07	.04
542	*Matt Merullo*	.25	.20	.10
543	Donn Pall	.05	.04	.02
544	Dan Pasqua	.06	.05	.02
545	Ken Patterson	.06	.05	.02
546	Melido Perez	.07	.05	.03
547	Steve Rosenberg	.07	.05	.03
548	*Sammy Sosa*(FC)	.40	.30	.15
549	Bobby Thigpen	.07	.05	.03
550	Robin Ventura	.60	.45	.25
551	Greg Walker	.06	.05	.02
552	Don Carman	.05	.04	.02
553	*Pat Combs*(FC)	.25	.20	.10
554	Dennis Cook	.20	.15	.08
555	Darren Daulton	.05	.04	.02
556	Lenny Dykstra	.07	.05	.03
557	Curt Ford	.05	.04	.02
558	Charlie Hayes	.10	.08	.04
559	Von Hayes	.07	.05	.03
560	Tom Herr	.06	.05	.02
561	Ken Howell	.05	.04	.02
562	Steve Jeltz	.05	.04	.02
563	Ron Jones	.15	.11	.06
564	Ricky Jordan	.35	.25	.14
565	John Kruk	.07	.05	.03
566	Steve Lake	.05	.04	.02
567	Roger McDowell	.06	.05	.02
568	Terry Mulholland	.05	.04	.02
569	Dwayne Murphy	.05	.04	.02
570	Jeff Parrett	.06	.05	.02
571	Randy Ready	.05	.04	.02
572	Bruce Ruffin	.05	.04	.02
573	Dickie Thon	.05	.04	.02
574	Jose Alvarez	.05	.04	.02
575	Geronimo Berroa	.06	.05	.03
576	Jeff Blauser	.05	.04	.02
577	Joe Boever	.07	.05	.03
578	Marty Clary	.05	.04	.02
579	Jody Davis	.05	.04	.02
580	Mark Eichhorn	.05	.04	.02
581	Darrell Evans	.06	.05	.02
582	Ron Gant	.06	.05	.02
583	Tom Glavine	.09	.07	.04
584	*Tommy Greene*(FC)	.35	.25	.14
585	Tommy Gregg	.10	.07	.04
586	*David Justice*(FC)	2.00	1.50	.80
587	Mark Lemke(FC)	.10	.08	.04
588	Derek Lilliquist	.10	.08	.04
589	Oddibe McDowell	.07	.05	.03
590	*Kent Mercker*(FC)	.30	.25	.12
591	Dale Murphy	.15	.11	.06
592	Gerald Perry	.06	.05	.02
593	Lonnie Smith	.06	.05	.02
594	Pete Smith	.07	.05	.03
595	John Smoltz	.15	.11	.06
596	*Mike Stanton*(FC)	.25	.20	.10
597	Andres Thomas	.06	.05	.02
598	Jeff Treadway	.06	.05	.02
599	Doyle Alexander	.06	.05	.02
600	Dave Bergman	.05	.04	.02
601	*Brian Dubois*(FC)	.15	.11	.06

#	Player	MT	NR MT	EX
602	Paul Gibson	.06	.05	.02
603	Mike Heath	.05	.04	.02
604	Mike Henneman	.07	.05	.03
605	Guillermo Hernandez	.05	.04	.02
606	*Shawn Holman*(FC)	.20	.15	.08
607	Tracy Jones	.09	.07	.04
608	Chet Lemon	.06	.05	.02
609	Fred Lynn	.06	.05	.02
610	Jack Morris	.07	.05	.02
611	Matt Nokes	.10	.08	.04
612	Gary Pettis	.05	.04	.02
613	*Kevin Ritz*(FC)	.15	.11	.06
614	Jeff Robinson	.07	.05	.03
615	Steve Searcy	.10	.08	.04
616	Frank Tanana	.06	.05	.02
617	Alan Trammell	.09	.07	.04
618	Gary Ward	.05	.04	.02
619	Lou Whitaker	.09	.07	.04
620	Frank Williams	.05	.04	.02
621a	Players Of The Decade - 1980 (George Brett) (10 .390 hitting seasons)	2.25	1.75	.90
621b	Players Of The Decade - 1980 (George Brett) (10 .300 hitting seasons)	.50	.40	.20
622	Players Of The Decade - 1981 (Fernando Valenzuela)	.20	.15	.08
623	Players Of The Decade - 1982 (Dale Murphy)	.25	.20	.10
624a	Players Of The Decade - 1983 (Cal Ripkin, Jr.)	3.00	2.25	1.25
624b	Players Of The Decade - 1983 (Cal Ripken, Jr.)	.25	.20	.10
625	Players Of The Decade - 1984 (Ryne Sandberg)	.25	.20	.10
626	Players Of The Decade - 1985 (Don Mattingly)	.50	.40	.20
627	Players Of The Decade - 1986 (Roger Clemens)	.25	.20	.10
628	Players Of The Decade - 1987 (George Bell)	.20	.15	.08
629	Players Of The Decade - (Jose Canseco)	.60	.45	.25
630a	Players Of The Decade - 1989 (Will Clark) (total bases (32))	1.50	1.25	.60
630b	Players Of The Decade - 1989 (Will Clark) (total bases (321))	.60	.45	.25
631	Game Savers	.10	.08	.04
632	Boston Igniters	.10	.08	.04
633	The Starter & Stopper	.10	.08	.04
634	League's Best Shortstops	.10	.08	.04
635	Human Dynamos	.10	.08	.04
636	300 Strikeout Club	.10	.08	.04
637	The Dynamic Duo	.10	.08	.04
638	A.L. All Stars	.10	.08	.04
639	N.L. East Rivals	.10	.08	.04
640	*Rudy Seanez, Colin Charland*(FC)	.15	.11	.06
641	*George Canale, Kevin Maas*(FC)	.50	.40	.20
642	*Kelly Mann, Dave Hansen*(FC)	.30	.25	.12
643	*Greg Smith, Stu Tate*(FC)	.15	.11	.06
644	*Tom Drees, Dan Howitt*(FC)	.15	.11	.06
645	*Mike Roesler, Derrick May*(FC)	.50	.40	.20
646	*Scott Hemond, Mark Gardner*(FC)	.35	.25	.14
647	*John Orton, Scott Leuis*(FC)	.25	.20	.10
648	*Rich Monteleone, Dana Williams*(FC)	.15	.11	.06
649	*Mike Huff, Steve Frey*(FC)	.25	.20	.10
650	*Chuck McElroy, Moises Alou*(FC)	.25	.20	.10
651	*Bobby Rose, Mike Hartley*(FC)	.15	.11	.06
652	*Matt Kinzer, Wayne Edwards*(FC)	.20	.15	.08
653	*Delino DeShields, Jason Grimsley*(FC)	.80	.60	.30
654	Athletics, Cubs, Giants & Blue Jays (Checklist)	.05	.04	.03
655	Royals, Angels, Padres & Orioles (Checklist)	.05	.04	.03
656	Mets, Astros, Cardinals & Red Sox (Checklist)	.05	.04	.03
657	Rangers, Brewers, Expos & Twins (Checklist)	.05	.04	.03
658	Dodgers, Reds, Yankees & Pirates (Checklist)	.05	.04	.03
659	Indians, Mariners, White Sox & Phillies (Checklist)	.05	.04	.03
660	Braves, Tigers & Special Cards (Checklist)	.05	.04	.03

A player's name in italic type indicates a rookie card. An (FC) indicates a player's first card for that particular card company.

1990 Fleer All-Star Team

The top players at each position, as selected by Fleer, are featured in this 12-card set. The cards were inserted in cello packs and some wax packs. The cards measure 2-1/2" by 3-1/2" and feature a unique two-photo format on the card fronts.

		MT	NR MT	EX
Complete Set:		10.00	7.50	4.00
Common Player:		.20	.15	.08
1	Harold Baines	.25	.20	.10
2	Will Clark	2.00	1.50	.80
3	Mark Davis	.20	.15	.08
4	Howard Johnson	.40	.30	.15
5	Joe Magrane	.25	.20	.10
6	Kevin Mitchell	.40	.30	.15
7	Kirby Puckett	.60	.45	.25
8	Cal Ripken	1.00	.70	.40
9	Ryne Sandberg	2.00	1.50	.80
10	Mike Scott	.20	.15	.08
11	Ruben Sierra	1.00	.70	.40
12	Mickey Tettleton	.20	.15	.08

1990 Fleer Award Winners

Hill's Department Stores and 7-Eleven Outlets are exclusively carrying the 1990 Fleer "Award Winners." This 44-card boxed set includes baseball's statistical leaders of 1989, six special cards that feature peel-off team logo stickers and a baseball trivia quiz. The card fronts feature a full-color player photo framed by a winner's cup design and a blue border. The card backs showcase player statistics in blue on a yellow and white background. The cards measure 2-1/2" by 3-1/2" in size. A complete checklist is provided on the back of each box. The checklist incorrectly lists Bob Boone's team as the Angels.

		MT	NR MT	EX
Complete Set:		3.50	2.75	1.50
Common Player:		.05	.04	.02
1	Jeff Ballard	.05	.04	.02
2	Tim Belcher	.08	.06	.03

		MT	NR MT	EX
3	Bert Blyleven	.08	.06	.03
4	Wade Boggs	.35	.25	.14
5	Bob Boone	.05	.04	.02
6	Jose Canseco	.60	.45	.25
7	Will Clark	.50	.40	.20
8	Jack Clark	.05	.04	.02
9	Vince Coleman	.05	.04	.02
10	Ron Darling	.05	.04	.02
11	Eric Davis	.40	.30	.15
12	Jose DeLeon	.05	.04	.02
13	Tony Fernandez	.05	.04	.02
14	Carlton Fisk	.10	.08	.04
15	Scott Garrelts	.05	.04	.02
16	Tom Gordon	.15	.11	.06
17	Ken Griffey, Jr.	1.75	1.25	.60
18	Von Hayes	.05	.04	.02
19	Rickey Henderson	.35	.25	.14
20	Bo Jackson	.80	.60	.30
21	Howard Johnson	.15	.11	.06
22	Don Mattingly	.40	.30	.15
23	Fred McGriff	.25	.20	.10
24	Kevin Mitchell	.30	.25	.12
25	Gregg Olson	.15	.11	.06
26	Gary Pettis	.05	.04	.02
27	Kirby Puckett	.30	.25	.12
28	Harold Reynolds	.05	.04	.02
29	Jeff Russell	.05	.04	.02
30	Nolan Ryan	.70	.50	.30
31	Bret Saberhagen	.10	.08	.04
32	Ryne Sandberg	.25	.20	.10
33	Benito Santiago	.10	.08	.04
34	Mike Scott	.05	.04	.02
35	Ruben Sierra	.25	.20	.10
36	Lonnie Smith	.05	.04	.02
37	Ozzie Smith	.10	.08	.04
38	Dave Stewart	.10	.08	.04
39	Greg Swindell	.05	.04	.02
40	Andy Van Slyke	.08	.06	.03
41	Tim Wallach	.05	.04	.02
42	Jerome Walton	.20	.15	.08
43	Mitch Williams	.08	.06	.03
44	Robin Yount	.15	.11	.06

1990 Fleer Baseball All Stars

Sold exclusively in Ben Franklin stores, this 44-card boxed set showcases the game's top players. The card fronts feature a full color player photo surrounded by a tan border. The flip side contains individual player statistics and data printed in red and black. The cards measure 2-1/2" by 3-1/2" in size and are packed in a special box with a complete checklist on the back. Like other Fleer boxed sets, the cards are numbered alphabetically.

		MT	NR MT	EX
Complete Set:		4.00	3.00	1.50
Common Player:		.05	.04	.02
1	Wade Boggs	.35	.25	.14
2	Bobby Bonilla	.20	.15	.08
3	Tim Burke	.05	.04	.02
4	Jose Canseco	.60	.45	.25
5	Will Clark	.50	.40	.20
6	Eric Davis	.40	.30	.15
7	Glenn Davis	.20	.15	.08
8	Julio Franco	.10	.08	.04
9	Tony Fernandez	.10	.08	.04

		MT	NR MT	EX
10	Gary Gaetti	.10	.08	.04
11	Scott Garrelts	.05	.04	.02
12	Mark Grace	.20	.15	.08
13	Mike Greenwell	.20	.15	.08
14	Ken Griffey,Jr.	1.75	1.25	.70
15	Mark Gubicza	.05	.04	.02
16	Pedro Guerrero	.10	.08	.04
17	Von Hayes	.05	.04	.02
18	Orel Hershiser	.10	.08	.04
19	Bruce Hurst	.05	.04	.02
20	Bo Jackson	.80	.60	.30
21	Howard Johnson	.20	.15	.08
22	Doug Jones	.05	.04	.02
23	Barry Larkin	.30	.25	.12
24	Don Mattingly	.60	.45	.25
25	Mark McGwire	.50	.40	.20
26	Kevin McReynolds	.05	.04	.02
27	Kevin Mitchell	.40	.30	.15
28	Dan Plesac	.05	.04	.02
29	Kirby Puckett	.40	.30	.15
30	Cal Ripken,Jr.	.35	.25	.14
31	Bret Saberhagen	.10	.08	.04
32	Ryne Sandberg	.35	.25	.14
33	Steve Sax	.10	.08	.04
34	Ruben Sierra	.35	.25	.14
35	Ozzie Smith	.10	.08	.04
36	John Smoltz	.10	.08	.04
37	Darryl Strawberry	.30	.25	.12
38	Terry Steinbach	.05	.04	.02
39	Dave Stewart	.10	.08	.04
40	Bobby Thigpen	.10	.08	.04
41	Alan Trammell	.10	.08	.04
42	Devon White	.05	.04	.02
43	Mitch Williams	.05	.04	.02
44	Robin Yount	.15	.11	.06

		MT	NR MT	EX
15	Pedro Guerrero	.08	.06	.03
16	Tony Gwynn	.15	.11	.06
17	Rickey Henderson	.40	.30	.15
18	Tom Herr	.05	.04	.02
19	Orel Hershiser	.10	.08	.04
20	Kent Hrbek	.05	.04	.02
21	Bo Jackson	.80	.60	.30
22	Howard Johnson	.25	.20	.10
23	Don Mattingly	.50	.40	.20
24	Fred McGriff	.25	.20	.10
25	Mark McGwire	.50	.40	.20
26	Kevin Mitchell	.35	.25	.14
27	Paul Molitor	.10	.08	.04
28	Dale Murphy	.10	.08	.04
29	Kirby Puckett	.40	.30	.15
30	Tim Raines	.10	.08	.04
31	Cal Ripken,Jr.	.30	.25	.12
32	Bret Saberhagen	.10	.08	.04
33	Ryne Sandberg	.20	.15	.08
34	Ruben Sierra	.30	.25	.12
35	Dwight Smith	.08	.06	.03
36	Ozzie Smith	.10	.08	.04
37	Darryl Strawberry	.35	.25	.14
38	Dave Stewart	.10	.08	.04
39	Greg Swindell	.05	.04	.02
40	Bobby Thigpen	.08	.06	.03
41	Alan Trammell	.10	.08	.04
42	Jerome Walton	.25	.20	.10
43	Mitch Williams	.08	.06	.03
44	Robin Yount	.20	.15	.08

1990 Fleer Baseball MVP

This 44-card boxed set was produced by Fleer for the Toys "R" Us chain. Card fronts are designed with graduating black-to-white borders, surrounding a color photo of each player. Card backs contain individual player data and career statistics. The back of each box carries a checklist of all the players in the set. Six peel-off team logo stickers featuring a baseball trivia quiz on the back are also included with each set. The cards are 2-1/2" by 3-1/2" in size and are numbered alphabetically.

		MT	NR MT	EX
	Complete Set:	4.00	3.00	1.50
	Common Player:	.05	.04	.02
1	George Bell	.10	.08	.04
2	Bert Blyleven	.10	.08	.04
3	Wade Boggs	.40	.30	.15
4	Bobby Bonilla	.15	.11	.06
5	George Brett	.15	.11	.06
6	Jose Canseco	.70	.50	.30
7	Will Clark	.60	.45	.25
8	Roger Clemens	.30	.25	.12
9	Eric Davis	.60	.45	.25
10	Glenn Davis	.15	.11	.06
11	Tony Fernandez	.08	.06	.03
12	Dwight Gooden	.25	.20	.10
13	Mike Greenwell	.20	.15	.08
14	Ken Griffey,Jr.	2.00	1.50	.80

Values for recent cards and sets are listed in Mint (MT), Near Mint (NM) and Excellent (EX), reflecting the fact that many cards from recent years have been preserved in top condition. Recent cards and sets in less than Excellent condition have little collector interest.

1990 Fleer Box Panels

For the fifth consecutive year, Fleer issued a series of cards on the bottom panels of its regular 1990 wax pack boxes. This 28-card set features both players and team logo cards. The cards were numbered C-1 to C-28.

		MT	NR MT	EX
	Complete Set:	5.00	3.75	2.00
	Common Player:	.05	.04	.02
1	Giants Logo	.05	.04	.02
2	Tim Belcher	.06	.05	.02
3	Roger Clemens	.35	.25	.14
4	Eric Davis	.35	.25	.14
5	Glenn Davis	.10	.08	.04
6	Cubs Logo	.05	.04	.02
7	Jon Franco	.06	.05	.02
8	Mike Greenwell	.30	.25	.12
9	Athletics Logo	.05	.04	.02
10	Ken Griffey, Jr.	1.50	1.25	.60
11	Pedro Guerrero	.05	.04	.02
12	Tony Gwynn	.20	.15	.08
13	Blue Jays Logo	.05	.04	.02
14	Orel Hershiser	.20	.15	.08
15	Bo Jackson	.70	.50	.30
16	Howard Johnson	.15	.11	.06
17	Mets Logo	.05	.04	.02
18	Cardinals Logo	.05	.04	.02
19	Don Mattingly	.60	.45	.25
20	Mark McGwire	.40	.30	.15
21	Kevin Mitchell	.25	.20	.10
22	Kirby Puckett	.35	.25	.14
23	Royals Logo	.05	.04	.02
24	Orioles Logo	.05	.04	.02
25	Ruben Sierra	.30	.25	.12

		MT	NR MT	EX
26	Dave Stewart	.20	.15	.08
27	Jerome Walton	.50	.40	.20
28	Robin Yount	.25	.20	.10

1990 Fleer '89 World Series

This 12-card set, which depicts highlights of the 1989 World Series, was included as a special sub-set with the regular factory-collated Fleer set. Ironically, single World Series cards were discovered in cello and three-packs. This was not intended to happen. Fronts of the 2-1/2" by 3-1/2" cards feature full-color photos set against a white background with a red and blue "'89 World Series" banner. The card backs are pink and white and describe the events of the 1989 Fall Classic.

		MT	NR MT	EX
Complete Set:		3.00	2.25	1.25
Common Player:		.20	.15	.08
1	The Final Piece To The Puzzle (Mike Moore)	.20	.15	.08
2	The National League M.V.P. (Kevin Mitchell)	.30	.25	.12
3	Game Two's Crushing Blow	.20	.15	.08
4	Clark Pwers The Giants Into The Series (Will Clark)	.35	.25	.14
5	Canseco Crushed World Series Slump (Jose Canseco)	.40	.30	.15
6	Great leather In The Field	.20	.15	.08
7	Game One And A's Break Out On Top	.20	.15	.08
8	Oakland's M.V.P. (Dave Stewart)	.25	.20	.10
9	Parker's Bat Produces Power (Dave Parker)	.20	.15	.08
10	World Series Record Book Game 3	.20	.15	.08
11	Swipes Championship Series Records (Rickey Henderson)	.35	.25	.14
12	Oakland A's - Baseball's Best In '89	.25	.20	.10

1990 Fleer League Leaders

For the fifth consecutive year Fleer released a "League Leaders" trading card set. The set includes 44 top Major League players and features six special cards containing peel-off team logos and a baseball

trivia quiz. Card number 42 (Jerome Walton) pictures a player other than Walton. The cards measure 2-1/2" by 3-1/2" in size. The card fronts display a full-color photo bordered by a blue frame. The card backs feature complete statistics. The cards are numbered alphabetically and a complete checklist is displayed on the back of the card box. The set is available at Walgreen Drug Stores.

		MT	NR MT	EX
Complete Set:		4.00	3.00	1.50
Common Player:		.05	.04	.02
1	Roberto Alomar	.35	.25	.14
2	Tim Belcher	.08	.06	.03
3	George Bell	.10	.08	.04
4	Wade Boggs	.35	.25	.14
5	Jose Canseco	.60	.45	.25
6	Will Clark	.50	.40	.20
7	David Cone	.08	.06	.03
8	Eric Davis	.40	.30	.15
9	Glenn Davis	.20	.15	.08
10	Nick Esasky	.10	.08	.04
11	Dennis Eckersley	.10	.08	.04
12	Mark Grace	.15	.11	.06
13	Mike Greenwell	.20	.15	.08
14	Ken Griffey,Jr.	1.75	1.25	.70
15	Mark Gubicza	.05	.04	.02
16	Pedro Guerrero	.05	.04	.02
17	Tony Gwynn	.15	.11	.06
18	Rickey Henderson	.40	.30	.15
19	Bo Jackson	.80	.60	.30
20	Doug Jones	.05	.04	.02
21	Ricky Jordan	.08	.06	.03
22	Barry Larkin	.25	.20	.10
23	Don Mattingly	.40	.30	.15
24	Fred McGriff	.25	.20	.10
25	Mark McGwire	.40	.30	.15
26	Kevin Mitchell	.40	.30	.15
27	Jack Morris	.05	.04	.02
28	Gregg Olson	.15	.11	.06
29	Dan Plesac	.05	.04	.02
30	Kirby Puckett	.30	.25	.12
31	Nolan Ryan	.50	.40	.20
32	Bret Saberhagen	.10	.08	.04
33	Ryne Sandberg	.20	.15	.08
34	Steve Sax	.10	.08	.04
35	Mike Scott	.05	.04	.02
36	Ruben Sierra	.30	.25	.12
37	Lonnie Smith	.05	.04	.02
38	Darryl Strawberry	.30	.25	.12
39	Bobby Thigpen	.08	.06	.03
40	Andy Van Slyke	.10	.08	.04
41	Tim Wallach	.05	.04	.02
42	Jerome Walton	.20	.15	.08
43	Devon White	.05	.04	.02
44	Robin Yount	.15	.11	.06

1990 Fleer League Standouts

 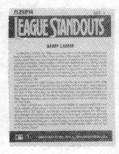

Fleer's "League Standouts" set features six of baseball's top players. The cards were distributed randomly in Fleer three-packs. The card fronts feature full color photos with a six dimensional effect. An attractive black and gold frame borders the photo. The card backs are yellow and describe the player's individual accomplishments. The cards measure 2-1/2" by 3-1/2" in size.

	MT	NR MT	EX
Complete Set:	4.00	3.00	1.50
Common Player:	.50	.40	.20
1 Barry Larkin	.50	.40	.20
2 Mark Grace	.50	.40	.20
3 Don Mattingly	.80	.60	.30
4 Darryl Strawberry	.60	.45	.25
5 Jose Canseco	1.00	.70	.40
6 Wade Boggs	.60	.45	.25

1990 Fleer Soaring Stars

Cards from this 12-card set could be found in 1990 Fleer jumbo cello packs. The cards are styled with a cartoon flavor, featuring astronomical graphics surrounding the player. The card backs feature information about the promising young player.

	MT	NR MT	EX
Complete Set:	8.00	6.00	3.25
Common Player:	.20	.15	.08
1 Todd Zeile	.60	.45	.25
2 Mike Stanton	.20	.15	.08
3 Larry Walker	.80	.60	.30
4 Robin Ventura	1.25	.90	.50
5 Scott Coolbaugh	.20	.15	.08
6 Ken Griffey,Jr.	4.00	3.00	1.50
7 Tom Gordon	.25	.20	.10
8 Jerome Walton	.25	.20	.10
9 Junior Felix	.35	.25	.14
10 Jim Abbott	1.00	.70	.40
11 Ricky Jordan	.30	.25	.12
12 Dwight Smith	.20	.15	.08

1990 Fleer Update

Fleer produced its seventh consecutive "Update" set in 1990 to supplement the company's regular set. As in the past, the set consists of 132 cards (numbered U-1 through U-132) that were sold by hobby dealers in special collectors boxes. The cards are designed in the exact same style as the regular issue. A special Nolan Ryan commemorative card is included in the 1990 Fleer Update set.

	MT	NR MT	EX
Complete Set:	10.00	7.50	4.00
Common Player:	.06	.05	.02
1 Steve Avery(FC)	1.00	.70	.40
2 Francisco Cabrera	.20	.15	.08
3 Nick Esasky	.06	.05	.02
4 Jim Kremers(FC)	.15	.11	.06
5 Greg Olson(FC)	.12	.09	.05
6 Jim Presley	.06	.05	.02
7 Shawn Boskie(FC)	.25	.20	.10
8 Joe Kraemer(FC)	.08	.06	.03
9 Luis Salazar	.06	.05	.02
10 Hector Villanueva(FC)	.30	.25	.12
11 Glenn Braggs	.06	.05	.02
12 Mariano Duncan	.06	.05	.02
13 Billy Hatcher	.06	.05	.02
14 Tim Layana(FC)	.20	.15	.08
15 Hal Morris	.40	.30	.15
16 Javier Ortiz(FC)	.20	.15	.08
17 Dave Rohde(FC)	.15	.11	.06
18 Eric Yelding(FC)	.20	.15	.08
19 Hubie Brooks	.08	.06	.03
20 Kal Daniels	.08	.06	.03
21 Dave Hansen	.15	.11	.06
22 Mike Hartley	.15	.11	.06
23 Stan Javier	.06	.05	.02
24 Jose Offerman(FC)	.30	.25	.12
25 Juan Samuel	.06	.05	.02
26 Dennis Boyd	.06	.05	.02
27 Delino DeShields	.70	.50	.30
28 Steve Frey	.12	.09	.05
29 Mark Gardner	.15	.11	.06
30 Chris Nabholz(FC)	.40	.30	.15
31 Bill Sampen(FC)	.25	.20	.10
32 Dave Schmidt	.06	.05	.02
33 Daryl Boston	.06	.05	.02
34 Chuck Carr(FC)	.20	.15	.08
35 John Franco	.08	.06	.03
36 Todd Hundley(FC)	.25	.20	.10
37 Julio Machado(FC)	.15	.11	.06
38 Alejandro Pena	.06	.05	.02
39 Darren Reed(FC)	.25	.20	.10
40 Kelvin Torve(FC)	.12	.09	.05
41 Darrel Akerfelds(FC)	.12	.09	.05
42 Jose DeJesus	.20	.15	.08
43 Dave Hollins(FC)	.40	.30	.15
44 Carmelo Martinez	.06	.05	.02
45 Brad Moore(FC)	.15	.11	.06
46 Dale Murphy	.10	.08	.04
47 Wally Backman	.06	.05	.02
48 Stan Belinda(FC)	.20	.15	.08
49 Bob Patterson	.06	.05	.02
50 Ted Power	.06	.05	.02
51 Don Slaught	.06	.05	.02
52 Geronimo Pena(FC)	.25	.20	.10
53 Lee Smith	.08	.06	.03
54 John Tudor	.06	.05	.02
55 Joe Carter	.10	.08	.04
56 Tom Howard(FC)	.20	.15	.08
57 Craig Lefferts	.06	.05	.02
58 Rafael Valdez(FC)	.20	.15	.08
59 Dave Anderson	.06	.05	.02
60 Kevin Bass	.06	.05	.02
61 John Burkett	.25	.20	.10
62 Gary Carter	.10	.08	.04
63 Rick Parker(FC)	.10	.08	.04
64 Trevor Wilson	.10	.08	.04
65 Chris Hoiles(FC)	.25	.20	.10
66 Tim Hulett	.06	.05	.02
67 Dave Johnson(FC)	.10	.08	.04
68 Curt Schilling(FC)	.10	.08	.04
69 David Segui(FC)	.35	.25	.12
70 Tom Brunansky	.08	.06	.03
71 Greg Harris	.06	.05	.02
72 Dana Kiecker(FC)	.12	.09	.05
73 Tim Naehring(FC)	.40	.30	.15
74 Tony Pena	.06	.05	.02
75 Jeff Reardon	.08	.06	.03
76 Jerry Reed	.06	.05	.02
77 Mark Eichhorn	.06	.05	.02
78 Mark Langston	.08	.06	.03
79 John Orton	.12	.09	.05
80 Luis Polonia	.06	.05	.02
81 Dave Winfield	.12	.09	.05
82 Cliff Young(FC)	.20	.15	.08
83 Wayne Edwards	.10	.08	.04
84 Alex Fernandez(FC)	.50	.40	.20
85 Craig Grebeck(FC)	.15	.11	.06
86 Scott Radinsky(FC)	.25	.20	.10
87 Frank Thomas(FC)	5.00	3.75	2.00

		MT	NR MT	EX
88	Beau Allred(FC)	.20	.15	.08
89	Sandy Alomar,Jr.	.35	.25	.14
90	Carlos Baerga(FC)	1.00	.70	.40
91	Kevin Bearse(FC)	.25	.20	.10
92	Chris James	.06	.05	.02
93	Candy Maldonado	.06	.05	.02
94	Jeff Manto	.12	.09	.05
95	Cecil Fielder	.40	.30	.15
96	Travis Fryman(FC)	1.50	1.25	.60
97	Lloyd Moseby	.06	.05	.02
98	Edwin Nunez	.06	.05	.02
99	Tony Phillips	.06	.05	.02
100	Larry Sheets	.06	.05	.02
101	Mark Davis	.06	.05	.02
102	Storm Davis	.06	.05	.02
103	Gerald Perry	.06	.05	.02
104	Terry Shumpert(FC)	.15	.11	.06
105	Edgar Diaz(FC)	.15	.11	.06
106	Dave Parker	.10	.08	.04
107	Tim Drummond(FC)	.15	.11	.06
108	Junior Ortiz	.06	.05	.02
109	Park Pittman(FC)	.15	.11	.06
110	Kevin Tapani(FC)	.25	.20	.10
111	Oscar Azocar(FC)	.15	.11	.06
112	Jim Leyritz(FC)	.15	.11	.06
113	Kevin Maas	.30	.25	.12
114	Alan Mills(FC)	.25	.20	.10
115	Matt Nokes	.06	.05	.02
116	Pascual Perez	.06	.05	.02
117	Ozzie Canseco(FC)	.20	.15	.08
118	Scott Sanderson	.06	.05	.02
119	Tino Martinez(FC)	.60	.45	.25
120	Jeff Schaefer(FC)	.15	.11	.06
121	Matt Young	.06	.05	.02
122	Brian Bohanon(FC)	.20	.15	.08
123	Jeff Huson	.15	.11	.06
124	Ramon Manon(FC)	.20	.15	.08
125	Gary Mielke(FC)	.15	.11	.06
126	Willie Blair(FC)	.15	.11	.06
127	Glenallen Hill(FC)	.15	.11	.06
128	John Olerud(FC)	.50	.40	.20
129	Luis Sojo(FC)	.15	.11	.06
130	Mark Whiten(FC)	.70	.50	.30
131	Three Decades Of No Hitters (Nolan Ryan)	.70	.50	.30
132	Checklist	.06	.05	.02

1991 Fleer

Fleer expanded its 1991 set to include 720 cards. The cards feature yellow boders surrounding full-color action photos. The player's name appears above the photo, while the team and position in displayed below. The "Fleer 91" logo appears in the lower right corner of the photo. The card backs feature a player photo in a circle design, biographical information, complete statistics, and career high-lights. Five special Super Star cards are among the cards in the regular set. Once again the cards are numbered according to team.

		MT	NR MT	EX
Complete Set:		20.00	15.00	8.00
Common Player:		.05	.04	.02
1	Troy Afenir(FC)	.10	.08	.04
2	Harold Baines	.08	.06	.03
3	Lance Blankenship	.06	.05	.02
4	Todd Burns	.05	.04	.02
5	Jose Canseco	.30	.25	.12
6	Dennis Eckersley	.10	.08	.04
7	Mike Gallego	.05	.04	.02
8	Ron Hassey	.05	.04	.02
9	Dave Henderson	.08	.06	.03
10	Rickey Henderson	.20	.15	.08
11	Rick Honeycutt	.05	.04	.02
12	Doug Jennings	.06	.05	.02
13	Joe Klink(FC)	.10	.08	.04
14	Carney Lansford	.08	.06	.03
15	Darren Lewis(FC)	.20	.15	.08
16	Willie McGee	.08	.06	.03
17	Mark McGwire	.20	.15	.08
18	Mike Moore	.06	.05	.02
19	Gene Nelson	.05	.04	.02
20	Dave Otto	.05	.04	.02
21	Jamie Quirk	.05	.04	.02
22	Willie Randolph	.06	.05	.02
23	Scott Sanderson	.06	.05	.02
24	Terry Steinbach	.06	.05	.02
25	Dave Stewart	.10	.08	.04
26	Walt Weiss	.06	.05	.02
27	Bob Welch	.08	.06	.03
28	Curt Young	.05	.04	.02
29	Wally Backman	.05	.04	.02
30	Stan Belinda	.10	.08	.04
31	Jay Bell	.06	.05	.02
32	Rafael Belliard	.05	.04	.02
33	Barry Bonds	.20	.15	.08
34	Bobby Bonilla	.15	.11	.06
35	Sid Bream	.06	.05	.02
36	Doug Drabek	.10	.08	.04
37	Carlos Garcia(FC)	.15	.11	.06
38	Neal Heaton	.06	.05	.02
39	Jeff King	.08	.06	.03
40	Bob Kipper	.05	.04	.02
41	Bill Landrum	.06	.05	.02
42	Mike LaValliere	.06	.05	.02
43	Jose Lind	.06	.05	.02
44	Carmelo Martinez	.05	.04	.02
45	Bob Patterson	.05	.04	.02
46	Ted Power	.05	.04	.02
47	Gary Redus	.05	.04	.02
48	R.J. Reynolds	.05	.04	.02
49	Don Slaught	.05	.04	.02
50	John Smiley	.05	.04	.02
51	Zane Smith	.06	.05	.02
52	Randy Tomlin(FC)	.20	.15	.08
53	Andy Van Slyke	.08	.06	.03
54	Bob Walk	.05	.04	.02
55	Jack Armstrong	.08	.06	.03
56	Todd Benzinger	.06	.05	.02
57	Glenn Braggs	.06	.05	.02
58	Keith Brown	.06	.05	.02
59	Tom Browning	.06	.05	.02
60	Norm Charlton	.08	.06	.03
61	Eric Davis	.20	.15	.08
62	Rob Dibble	.10	.08	.04
63	Bill Doran	.08	.06	.03
64	Mariano Duncan	.06	.05	.02
65	Chris Hammond	.06	.05	.02
66	Billy Hatcher	.06	.05	.02
67	Danny Jackson	.06	.05	.02
68	Barry Larkin	.15	.11	.06
69	Tim Layana	.10	.08	.04
70	Terry Lee(FC)	.15	.11	.06
71	Rick Mahler	.05	.04	.02
72	Hal Morris	.15	.11	.06
73	Randy Myers	.08	.06	.03
74	Ron Oester	.05	.04	.02
75	Joe Oliver	.08	.06	.03
76	Paul O'Neill	.06	.05	.02
77	Luis Quinones	.05	.04	.02
78	Jeff Reed	.05	.04	.02
79	Jose Rijo	.08	.06	.03
80	Chris Sabo	.08	.06	.03
81	Scott Scudder	.06	.05	.02
82	Herm Winningham	.05	.04	.02
83	Larry Andersen	.05	.04	.02
84	Marty Barrett	.05	.04	.02
85	Mike Boddicker	.06	.05	.02
86	Wade Boggs	.20	.15	.08
87	Tom Bolton	.05	.04	.02
88	Tom Brunansky	.06	.05	.02
89	Ellis Burks	.15	.11	.06
90	Roger Clemens	.20	.15	.08
91	Scott Cooper(FC)	.15	.11	.06
92	John Dopson	.05	.04	.02
93	Dwight Evans	.06	.05	.02
94	Wes Gardner	.05	.04	.02

#	Player	MT	NR MT	EX
95	Jeff Gray(FC)	.15	.11	.06
96	Mike Greenwell	.10	.08	.04
97	Greg Harris	.05	.04	.02
98	Daryl Irvine(FC)	.20	.15	.08
99	Dana Kiecker	.10	.08	.04
100	Randy Kutcher	.05	.04	.02
101	Dennis Lamp	.05	.04	.02
102	Mike Marshall	.05	.04	.02
103	John Marzano	.05	.04	.02
104	Rob Murphy	.05	.04	.02
105	Tim Naehring	.20	.15	.08
106	Tony Pena	.06	.05	.02
107	Phil Plantier(FC)	1.00	.70	.40
108	Carlos Quintana	.06	.05	.02
109	Jeff Reardon	.06	.05	.02
110	Jerry Reed	.05	.04	.02
111	Jody Reed	.06	.05	.02
112	Luis Rivera	.05	.04	.02
113	Kevin Romine	.05	.04	.02
114	Phil Bradley	.06	.05	.02
115	Ivan Calderon	.06	.05	.02
116	Wayne Edwards	.05	.04	.02
117	Alex Fernandez	.25	.20	.10
118	Carlton Fisk	.10	.08	.04
119	Scott Fletcher	.05	.04	.02
120	Craig Grebeck	.15	.11	.06
121	Ozzie Guillen	.08	.06	.03
122	Greg Hibbard	.06	.05	.02
123	Lance Johnson	.06	.05	.02
124	Barry Jones	.05	.04	.02
125	Ron Karkovice	.05	.04	.02
126	Eric King	.05	.04	.02
127	Steve Lyons	.05	.04	.02
128	Carlos Martinez	.06	.05	.02
129	Jack McDowell	.06	.05	.02
130	Donn Pall	.05	.04	.02
131	Dan Pasqua	.05	.04	.02
132	Ken Patterson	.05	.04	.02
133	Melido Perez	.06	.05	.02
134	Adam Peterson	.05	.04	.02
135	Scott Radinsky	.15	.11	.06
136	Sammy Sosa	.15	.11	.06
137	Bobby Thigpen	.08	.06	.03
138	Frank Thomas	1.25	.90	.50
139	Robin Ventura	.25	.20	.10
140	Daryl Boston	.05	.04	.02
141	Chuck Carr	.10	.08	.04
142	Mark Carreon	.05	.04	.02
143	David Cone	.06	.05	.02
144	Ron Darling	.06	.05	.02
145	Kevin Elster	.05	.04	.02
146	Sid Fernandez	.06	.05	.02
147	John Franco	.08	.06	.03
148	Dwight Gooden	.20	.15	.08
149	Tom Herr	.06	.05	.02
150	Todd Hundley	.20	.15	.08
151	Gregg Jefferies	.15	.11	.06
152	Howard Johnson	.08	.06	.03
153	Dave Magadan	.08	.06	.03
154	Kevin McReynolds	.08	.06	.03
155	Keith Miller	.06	.05	.02
156	Bob Ojeda	.05	.04	.02
157	Tom O'Malley	.05	.04	.02
158	Alejandro Pena	.05	.04	.02
159	Darren Reed	.20	.15	.08
160	Mackey Sasser	.06	.05	.02
161	Darryl Strawberry	.25	.20	.10
162	Tim Teufel	.05	.04	.02
163	Kelvin Torve	.08	.06	.03
164	Julio Valera	.25	.20	.10
165	Frank Viola	.12	.09	.05
166	Wally Whitehurst	.05	.04	.02
167	Jim Acker	.05	.04	.02
168	Derek Bell(FC)	.35	.25	.14
169	George Bell	.08	.06	.03
170	Willie Blair	.15	.11	.06
171	Pat Borders	.06	.05	.02
172	John Cerutti	.05	.04	.02
173	Juunior Felix	.12	.09	.05
174	Tony Fernandez	.08	.06	.03
175	Kelly Gruber	.12	.09	.05
176	Tom Henke	.06	.05	.02
177	Glenallen Hill	.08	.06	.03
178	Jimmy Key	.06	.05	.02
179	Manny Lee	.05	.04	.02
180	Fred McGriff	.15	.11	.06
181	Rance Mulliniks	.05	.04	.02
182	Greg Myers	.05	.04	.02
183	John Olerud	.50	.40	.20
184	Luis Sojo	.15	.11	.06
185	Dave Steib	.08	.06	.03
186	Todd Stottlemyre	.06	.05	.02
187	Duane Ward	.05	.04	.02
188	David Wells	.05	.04	.02
189	Mark Whiten	.40	.30	.15
190	Ken Williams	.05	.04	.02
191	Frank Wills	.05	.04	.02
192	Mookie Wilson	.05	.04	.02
193	Don Aase	.05	.04	.02
194	Tim Belcher	.08	.06	.03
195	Hubie Brooks	.08	.06	.03
196	Dennis Cook	.06	.05	.02
197	Tim Crews	.05	.04	.02
198	Kal Daniels	.06	.05	.02
199	Kirk Gibson	.08	.06	.03
200	Jim Gott	.05	.04	.02
201	Alfredo Griffin	.05	.04	.02
202	Chris Gwynn	.06	.05	.02
203	Dave Hansen	.20	.15	.08
204	Lenny Harris	.06	.05	.02
205	Mike Hartley	.10	.08	.04
206	Mickey Hatcher	.05	.04	.02
207	Carlos Hernandez(FC)	.20	.15	.08
208	Orel Hershiser	.10	.08	.04
209	Jay Howell	.06	.05	.02
210	Mike Huff	.10	.08	.04
211	Stan Javier	.05	.04	.02
212	Ramon Martinez	.20	.15	.08
213	Mike Morgan	.05	.04	.02
214	Eddie Murray	.08	.06	.03
215	Jim Neidlinger(FC)	.20	.15	.08
216	Jose Offerman	.30	.25	.12
217	Jim Poole(FC)	.20	.15	.08
218	Juan Samuel	.06	.05	.02
219	Mike Scioscia	.06	.05	.02
220	Ray Searage	.05	.04	.02
221	Mike Sharperson	.06	.05	.02
222	Fernando Valenzuela	.06	.05	.02
223	Jose Vizcaino	.10	.08	.04
224	Mike Aldrete	.05	.04	.02
225	Scott Anderson(FC)	.20	.15	.08
226	Dennis Boyd	.06	.05	.02
227	Tim Burke	.06	.05	.02
228	Delino DeShields	.30	.25	.12
229	Mike Fitzgerald	.05	.04	.02
230	Tom Foley	.05	.04	.02
231	Steve Frey	.05	.04	.02
232	Andres Galarraga	.08	.06	.03
233	Mark Gardner	.10	.08	.04
234	Marquis Grissom(FC)	.20	.15	.08
235	Kevin Gross	.06	.05	.02
236	Drew Hall	.05	.04	.02
237	Dave Martinez	.06	.05	.02
238	Dennis Martinez	.06	.05	.02
239	Dale Mohorcic	.05	.04	.02
240	Chris Nabholz	.25	.20	.10
241	Otis Nixon	.05	.04	.02
242	Junior Noboa(FC)	.08	.06	.03
243	Spike Owen	.06	.05	.02
244	Tim Raines	.08	.06	.03
245	Mel Rojas(FC)	.12	.09	.05
246	Scott Ruskin(FC)	.15	.11	.06
247	Bill Sampen	.25	.20	.10
248	Nelson Santovenia	.05	.04	.02
249	Dave Schmidt	.05	.04	.02
250	Larry Walker	.15	.11	.06
251	Tim Wallach	.08	.06	.03
252	Dave Anderson	.05	.04	.02
253	Kevin Bass	.06	.05	.02
254	Steve Bedrosian	.06	.05	.02
255	Jeff Brantley	.08	.06	.03
256	John Burkett	.12	.09	.05
257	Brett Butler	.06	.05	.02
258	Gary Carter	.08	.06	.03
259	Will Clark	.25	.20	.10
260	Steve Decker(FC)	.20	.15	.08
261	Kelly Downs	.05	.04	.02
262	Scott Garrelts	.06	.05	.02
263	Terry Kennedy	.05	.04	.02
264	Mike LaCoss	.05	.04	.02
265	Mark Leonard(FC)	.20	.15	.08
266	Greg Litton	.06	.05	.02
267	Kevin Mitchell	.20	.15	.08
268	Randy O'Neal(FC)	.05	.04	.02
269	Rick Parker	.15	.11	.06
270	Rick Reuschel	.06	.05	.02
271	Ernest Riles	.05	.04	.02
272	Don Robinson	.05	.04	.02
273	Robby Thompson	.06	.05	.02
274	Mark Thurmond	.05	.04	.02
275	Jose Uribe	.05	.04	.02
276	Matt Williams	.15	.11	.06

		MT	NR MT	EX			MT	NR MT	EX
277	Trevor Wilson	.06	.05	.02	368	Keith Hernandez	.08	.06	.03
278	Gerald Alexander(FC)	.15	.11	.06	369	Brook Jacoby	.08	.06	.03
279	Brad Arnsberg	.06	.05	.02	370	Chris James	.06	.05	.02
280	Kevin Belcher(FC)	.15	.11	.06	371	Dion James	.05	.04	.02
281	Joe Bitker(FC)	.15	.11	.06	372	Doug Jones	.08	.06	.03
282	Kevin Brown	.06	.05	.02	373	Candy Maldonado	.08	.06	.03
283	Steve Buechele	.05	.04	.02	374	Steve Olin	.06	.05	.02
284	Jack Daugherty	.06	.05	.02	375	Jesse Orosco	.05	.04	.02
285	Julio Franco	.10	.08	.04	376	Rudy Seanez	.06	.05	.02
286	Juan Gonzalez	.30	.25	.12	377	Joel Skinner	.05	.04	.02
287	Bill Haselman(FC)	.15	.11	.06	378	Cory Snyder	.08	.06	.03
288	Charlie Hough	.05	.04	.02	379	Greg Swindell	.06	.05	.02
289	Jeff Huson	.06	.05	.02	380	Sergio Valdez(FC)	.08	.06	.03
290	Pete Incaviglia	.06	.05	.02	381	Mike Walker(FC)	.15	.11	.06
291	Mike Jeffcoat	.05	.04	.02	382	Colby Ward(FC)	.20	.15	.08
292	Jeff Kunkel	.05	.04	.02	383	Turner Ward(FC)	.20	.15	.08
293	Gary Mielke	.08	.06	.03	384	Mitch Webster	.05	.04	.02
294	Jamie Moyer	.05	.04	.02	385	Kevin Wickander(FC)	.15	.11	.06
295	Rafael Palmeiro	.08	.06	.03	386	Darrel Akerfelds	.06	.05	.02
296	Geno Petralli	.05	.04	.02	387	Joe Boever	.05	.04	.02
297	Gary Pettis	.06	.05	.02	388	Rod Booker	.05	.04	.02
298	Kevin Reimer	.10	.08	.04	389	Sil Campusano	.05	.04	.02
299	Kenny Rogers	.06	.05	.02	390	Don Carman	.05	.04	.02
300	Jeff Russell	.06	.05	.02	391	Wes Chamberlain(FC)	.50	.40	.20
301	John Russell	.05	.04	.02	392	Pat Combs	.06	.05	.02
302	Nolan Ryan	.25	.20	.10	393	Darren Daulton	.06	.05	.02
303	Ruben Sierra	.12	.09	.05	394	Jose DeJesus	.06	.05	.02
304	Bobby Witt	.08	.06	.03	395	Len Dykstra	.08	.06	.03
305	Jim Abbott	.08	.06	.03	396	Jason Grimsley	.06	.05	.02
306	Kent Anderson(FC)	.06	.05	.02	397	Charlie Hayes	.06	.05	.02
307	Dante Bichette	.06	.05	.02	398	Von Hayes	.08	.06	.03
308	Bert Blyleven	.08	.06	.03	399	David Hollins	.30	.25	.12
309	Chili Davis	.06	.05	.02	400	Ken Howell	.06	.05	.02
310	Brian Downing	.05	.04	.02	401	Ricky Jordan	.10	.08	.04
311	Mark Eichhorn	.05	.04	.02	402	John Kruk	.06	.05	.02
312	Mike Fetters	.08	.06	.03	403	Steve Lake	.05	.04	.02
313	Chuck Finley	.08	.06	.03	404	Chuck Malone(FC)	.15	.11	.06
314	Willie Fraser	.05	.04	.02	405	Roger McDowell	.08	.06	.03
315	Bryan Harvey	.06	.05	.02	406	Chuck McElroy	.15	.11	.06
316	Donnie Hill	.05	.04	.02	407	Mickey Morandini(FC)	.15	.11	.06
317	Wally Joyner	.10	.08	.04	408	Terry Mulholland	.06	.05	.02
318	Mark Langston	.10	.08	.04	409	Dale Murphy	.10	.08	.04
319	Kirk McCaskill	.06	.05	.02	410	Randy Ready	.05	.04	.02
320	John Orton	.06	.05	.02	411	Bruce Ruffin	.05	.04	.02
321	Lance Parrish	.08	.06	.03	412	Dickie Thon	.05	.04	.02
322	Luis Polonia	.05	.04	.02	413	Paul Assenmacher	.05	.04	.02
323	Johnny Ray	.05	.04	.02	414	Damon Berryhill	.06	.05	.02
324	Bobby Rose	.06	.05	.02	415	Mike Bielecki	.06	.05	.02
325	Dick Schofield	.05	.04	.02	416	Shawn Boskie	.15	.11	.06
326	Rick Schu	.05	.04	.02	417	Dave Clark	.05	.04	.02
327	Lee Stevens	.10	.08	.04	418	Doug Dascenzo	.05	.04	.02
328	Devon White	.06	.05	.02	419	Andre Dawson	.10	.08	.04
329	Dave Winfield	.12	.09	.05	420	Shawon Dunston	.10	.08	.04
330	Cliff Young	.15	.11	.06	421	Joe Girardi	.06	.05	.02
331	Dave Bergman	.05	.04	.02	422	Mark Grace	.15	.11	.06
332	Phil Clark(FC)	.25	.20	.10	423	Mike Harkey	.08	.06	.03
333	Darnell Coles	.05	.04	.02	424	Les Lancaster	.05	.04	.02
334	Milt Cuyler(FC)	.20	.15	.08	425	Bill Long	.05	.04	.02
335	Cecil Fielder	.30	.25	.12	426	Greg Maddux	.08	.06	.03
336	Travis Fryman	.60	.45	.25	427	Derrick May	.25	.20	.10
337	Paul Gibson	.05	.04	.02	428	Jeff Pico	.05	.04	.02
338	Jerry Don Gleaton	.05	.04	.02	429	Domingo Ramos	.05	.04	.02
339	Mike Heath	.05	.04	.02	430	Luis Salazar	.05	.04	.02
340	Mike Henneman	.06	.05	.02	431	Ryne Sandberg	.20	.15	.08
341	Chet Lemon	.06	.05	.02	432	Dwight Smith	.06	.05	.02
342	Lance McCullers	.05	.04	.02	433	Greg Smith	.08	.06	.03
343	Jack Morris	.08	.06	.03	434	Rick Sutcliffe	.08	.06	.03
344	lloyd Moseby	.06	.05	.02	435	Gary Varsho	.05	.04	.02
345	Edwin Nunez	.05	.04	.02	436	Hector Villanueva	.15	.11	.06
346	Clay Parker	.05	.04	.02	437	Jerome Walton	.08	.06	.03
347	Dan Petry	.05	.04	.02	438	Curtis Wilkerson	.05	.04	.02
348	Tony Phillips	.06	.05	.02	439	Mitch Williams	.08	.06	.03
349	Jeff Robinson	.06	.05	.02	440	Steve Wilson	.06	.05	.02
350	Mark Salas	.05	.04	.02	441	Marvell Wynne	.05	.04	.02
351	Mike Schwabe	.15	.11	.06	442	Scott Bankhead	.06	.05	.02
352	Larry Sheets	.05	.04	.02	443	Scott Bradley	.05	.04	.02
353	John Shelby	.05	.04	.02	444	Greg Briley	.06	.05	.02
354	Frank Tanana	.06	.05	.02	445	Mike Brumley	.05	.04	.02
355	Alan Trammell	.08	.06	.03	446	Jay Buhner	.06	.05	.02
356	Gary Ward	.05	.04	.02	447	Dave Burba(FC)	.15	.11	.06
357	Lou Whitaker	.08	.06	.03	448	Henry Cotto	.05	.04	.02
358	Beau Allred	.15	.11	.06	449	Alvin Davis	.08	.06	.03
359	Sandy Alomar,Jr.	.20	.15	.08	450	Ken Griffey,Jr.	1.00	.70	.40
360	Carlos Baerga	.25	.20	.10	451	Erik Hanson	.12	.09	.05
361	Kevin Bearse	.12	.09	.05	452	Gene Harris	.05	.04	.02
362	Tom Brookens	.05	.04	.02	453	Brian Holman	.06	.05	.02
363	Jerry Browne	.06	.05	.02	454	Mike Jackson	.06	.05	.02
364	Tom Candiotti	.05	.04	.02	455	Randy Johnson	.10	.08	.04
365	Alex Cole	.25	.20	.10	456	Jeffrey Leonard	.06	.05	.02
366	John Farrell	.05	.04	.02	457	Edgar Martinez	.06	.05	.02
367	Felix Fermin	.05	.04	.02	458	Tino Martinez	.35	.25	.14

#	Player	MT	NR MT	EX
459	Pete O'Brien	.05	.04	.02
460	Harold Reynolds	.08	.06	.03
461	Mike Schooler	.08	.06	.03
462	Bill Swift	.06	.05	.02
463	David Valle	.05	.04	.02
464	Omar Vizquel	.06	.05	.02
465	Matt Young	.06	.05	.02
466	Brady Anderson	.05	.04	.02
467	Jeff Ballard	.06	.05	.02
468	Juan Bell(FC)	.20	.15	.08
469	Mike Devereaux	.06	.05	.02
470	Steve Finley	.06	.05	.02
471	Dave Gallagher	.05	.04	.02
472	*Leo Gomez*(FC)	.30	.25	.14
473	Rene Gonzales	.05	.04	.02
474	Pete Harnisch	.06	.05	.02
475	Kevin Hickey	.05	.04	.02
476	*Chris Hoiles*	.20	.15	.08
477	Sam Horn	.06	.05	.02
478	Tim Hulett	.05	.04	.02
479	Dave Johnson	.05	.04	.02
480	Ron Kittle	.08	.06	.03
481	Ben McDonald	.40	.30	.15
482	Bob Melvin	.05	.04	.02
483	Bob Milacki	.06	.05	.02
484	Randy Milligan	.06	.05	.02
485	John Mitchell(FC)	.15	.11	.06
486	Gregg Olson	.08	.06	.03
487	Joe Orsulak	.05	.04	.02
488	Joe Price	.05	.04	.02
489	Bill Ripken	.05	.04	.02
490	Cal Ripken,Jr.	.20	.15	.08
491	Curt Schilling	.06	.05	.02
492	*David Segui*	.30	.25	.12
493	*Anthony Telford*(FC)	.20	.15	.08
494	Mickey Tettleton	.06	.05	.02
495	Mark Williamson	.05	.04	.02
496	Craig Worthington	.06	.05	.02
497	Juan Agosto	.05	.04	.02
498	Eric Anthony	.15	.11	.06
499	Craig Biggio	.08	.06	.03
500	Ken Caminiti	.06	.05	.02
501	Casey Candaele	.05	.04	.02
502	*Andujar Cedeno*(FC)	.25	.20	.10
503	Danny Darwin	.06	.05	.02
504	Mark Davidson	.05	.04	.02
505	Glenn Davis	.15	.11	.06
506	Jim Deshaies	.06	.05	.02
507	*Luis Gonzalez*(FC)	.50	.40	.20
508	Bill Gullickson	.05	.04	.02
509	Xavier Hernandez(FC)	.08	.06	.03
510	Brian Meyer	.06	.05	.02
511	Ken Oberkfell	.05	.04	.02
512	Mark Portugal	.05	.04	.02
513	Rafael Ramirez	.05	.04	.02
514	*Karl Rhodes*(FC)	.25	.20	.10
515	Mike Scott	.08	.06	.03
516	*Mike Simms*(FC)	.25	.20	.10
517	Dave Smith	.06	.05	.02
518	Franklin Stubbs	.06	.05	.02
519	Glenn Wilson	.06	.05	.02
520	Eric Yelding	.10	.08	.04
521	Gerald Young	.05	.04	.02
522	Shawn Abner	.05	.04	.02
523	Roberto Alomar	.10	.08	.04
524	Andy Benes	.15	.11	.06
525	Joe Carter	.10	.08	.04
526	Jack Clark	.08	.06	.03
527	Joey Cora	.06	.05	.02
528	*Paul Faries*(FC)	.20	.15	.08
529	Tony Gwynn	.15	.11	.06
530	Atlee Hammaker	.05	.04	.02
531	Greg Harris	.06	.05	.02
532	*Thomas Howard*	.20	.15	.08
533	Bruce Hurst	.06	.05	.02
534	Craig Lefferts	.06	.05	.02
535	Derek Lilliquist	.06	.05	.02
536	Fred Lynn	.06	.05	.02
537	Mike Pagliarulo	.06	.05	.02
538	Mark Parent	.05	.04	.02
539	Dennis Rasmussen	.05	.04	.02
540	Bip Roberts	.08	.06	.03
541	*Richard Rodriguez*(FC)	.20	.15	.08
542	Benito Santiago	.10	.08	.04
543	Calvin Schiraldi	.05	.04	.02
544	Eric Show	.06	.05	.02
545	Phil Stephenson	.05	.04	.02
546	Garry Templeton	.06	.05	.02
547	Ed Whitson	.06	.05	.02
548	Eddie Williams	.05	.04	.02
549	Kevin Appier	.10	.08	.04
550	Luis Aquino	.05	.04	.02
551	Bob Boone	.08	.06	.03
552	George Brett	.12	.09	.05
553	*Jeff Conine*(FC)	.20	.15	.08
554	Steve Crawford	.05	.04	.02
555	Mark Davis	.06	.05	.02
556	Storm Davis	.06	.05	.02
557	Jim Eisenreich	.06	.05	.02
558	Steve Farr	.05	.04	.02
559	Tom Gordon	.10	.08	.04
560	Mark Gubicza	.08	.06	.03
561	Bo Jackson	.30	.25	.12
562	Mike Macfarlane	.05	.04	.02
563	*Brian McRae*(FC)	.40	.30	.15
564	Jeff Montgomery	.06	.05	.02
565	Bill Pecota	.05	.04	.02
566	Gerald Perry	.06	.05	.02
567	Bret Saberhagen	.10	.08	.04
568	*Jeff Schulz*(FC)	.15	.11	.06
569	Kevin Seitzer	.08	.06	.03
570	*Terry Shumpert*	.15	.11	.06
571	Kurt Stillwell	.06	.05	.02
572	Danny Tartabull	.08	.06	.03
573	Gary Thurman	.05	.04	.02
574	Frank White	.06	.05	.02
575	Willie Wilson	.06	.05	.02
576	Chris Bosio	.06	.05	.02
577	Greg Brock	.06	.05	.02
578	George Canale	.06	.05	.02
579	Chuck Crim	.05	.04	.02
580	Rob Deer	.06	.05	.02
581	*Edgar Diaz*	.06	.05	.02
582	*Tom Edens*(FC)	.08	.06	.03
583	Mike Felder	.05	.04	.02
584	Jim Gantner	.06	.05	.02
585	Darryl Hamilton	.06	.05	.02
586	Ted Higuera	.08	.06	.03
587	Mark Knudson	.05	.04	.02
588	Bill Krueger	.05	.04	.02
589	Tim McIntosh	.08	.06	.03
590	Paul Mirabella	.05	.04	.02
591	Paul Molitor	.10	.08	.04
592	Jaime Navarro	.08	.06	.03
593	Dave Parker	.12	.09	.05
594	Dan Plesac	.06	.05	.02
595	Ron Robinson	.06	.05	.02
596	Gary Sheffield	.15	.11	.06
597	Bill Spiers	.06	.05	.02
598	B.J. Surhoff	.06	.05	.02
599	Greg Vaughn	.15	.11	.06
600	Randy Veres	.05	.04	.02
601	Robin Yount	.15	.11	.06
602	Rick Aguilera	.06	.05	.02
603	Allan Anderson	.05	.04	.02
604	Juan Berenguer	.05	.04	.02
605	Randy Bush	.05	.04	.02
606	Carmen Castillo	.05	.04	.02
607	Tim Drummond	.06	.05	.02
608	*Scott Erickson*(FC)	.30	.25	.12
609	Gary Gaetti	.08	.06	.03
610	Greg Gagne	.06	.05	.02
611	Dan Gladden	.06	.05	.02
612	Mark Guthrie(FC)	.06	.05	.02
613	Brian Harper	.06	.05	.02
614	Kent Hrbek	.08	.06	.03
615	Gene Larkin	.06	.05	.02
616	Terry Leach	.05	.04	.02
617	Nelson Liriano	.05	.04	.02
618	Shane Mack	.06	.05	.02
619	John Moses	.05	.04	.02
620	*Pedro Munoz*(FC)	.35	.25	.14
621	Al Newman	.05	.04	.02
622	Junior Ortiz	.05	.04	.02
623	Kirby Puckett	.15	.11	.06
624	Roy Smith	.05	.04	.02
625	Kevin Tapani	.10	.08	.04
626	Gary Wayne	.05	.04	.02
627	David West	.06	.05	.02
628	Cris Carpenter	.06	.05	.02
629	Vince Coleman	.08	.06	.03
630	Ken Dayley	.06	.05	.02
631	Jose DeLeon	.06	.05	.02
632	Frank DiPino	.05	.04	.02
633	*Bernard Gilkey*(FC)	.25	.20	.10
634	Pedro Guerrero	.08	.06	.03
635	Ken Hill	.06	.05	.02
636	Felix Jose	.08	.06	.03
637	*Ray Lankford*(FC)	.50	.40	.20
638	Joe Magrane	.08	.06	.03
639	Tom Niedenfuer	.05	.04	.02
640	Jose Oquendo	.05	.04	.02

		MT	NR MT	EX
641	Tom Pagnozzi	.05	.04	.02
642	Terry Pendleton	.06	.05	.02
643	*Mike Perez*(FC)	.20	.15	.08
644	Bryn Smith	.05	.04	.02
645	Lee Smith	.08	.06	.03
646	Ozzie Smith	.10	.08	.04
647	Scott Terry	.05	.04	.02
648	Bob Tewksbury	.05	.04	.02
649	Milt Thompson	.05	.04	.02
650	John Tudor	.06	.05	.02
651	Denny Walling	.05	.04	.02
652	*Craig Wilson*(FC)	.15	.11	.06
653	Todd Worrell	.06	.05	.02
654	Todd Zeile	.20	.15	.08
655	*Oscar Azocar*	.20	.15	.08
656	Steve Balboni	.05	.04	.02
657	Jesse Barfield	.08	.06	.03
658	Greg Cadaret	.05	.04	.02
659	Chuck Cary	.05	.04	.02
660	Rick Cerone	.05	.04	.02
661	Dave Eiland(FC)	.06	.05	.02
662	Alvaro Espinoza	.06	.05	.02
663	Bob Geren	.06	.05	.02
664	Lee Guetterman	.05	.04	.02
665	Mel Hall	.06	.05	.02
666	Andy Hawkins	.06	.05	.02
667	Jimmy Jones	.05	.04	.02
668	Roberto Kelly	.10	.08	.04
669	Dave LaPoint	.05	.04	.02
670	Tim Leary	.06	.05	.02
671	*Jim Leyritz*	.15	.11	.06
672	Kevin Maas	.20	.15	.08
673	Don Mattingly	.20	.15	.08
674	Matt Nokes	.06	.05	.02
675	Pascual Perez	.06	.05	.02
676	Eric Plunk	.05	.04	.02
677	Dave Righetti	.08	.06	.03
678	Jeff Robinson	.05	.04	.02
679	Steve Sax	.10	.08	.04
680	Mike Witt	.06	.05	.02
681	Steve Avery	.30	.25	.12
682	Mike Bell	.15	.11	.06
683	Jeff Blauser	.06	.05	.02
684	Francisco Cabrera	.10	.08	.04
685	Tony Castillo(FC)	.08	.06	.03
686	Marty Clary	.05	.04	.02
687	Nick Esasky	.08	.06	.03
688	Ron Gant	.10	.08	.04
689	Tom Glavine	.06	.05	.02
690	Mark Grant	.05	.04	.02
691	Tommy Gregg	.06	.05	.02
692	Dwayne Henry	.05	.04	.02
693	Dave Justice	.50	.40	.20
694	*Jimmy Kremers*	.15	.11	.06
695	Charlie Leibrandt	.06	.05	.02
696	Mark Lemke	.06	.05	.02
697	Oddibe McDowell	.06	.05	.02
698	*Greg Olson*	.08	.06	.03
699	Jeff Parrett	.06	.05	.02
700	Jim Presley	.06	.05	.02
701	*Victor Rosario*(FC)	.20	.15	.08
702	Lonnie Smith	.06	.05	.02
703	Pete Smith	.06	.05	.02
704	John Smoltz	.08	.06	.03
705	Mike Stanton	.08	.06	.03
706	Andres Thomas	.05	.04	.02
707	Jeff Treadway	.06	.05	.02
708	*Jim Vatcher*(FC)	.15	.11	.06
709	Home Run Kings (Ryne Sandberg, Cecil Fielder)	.25	.20	.10
710	Second Generation Stars (Barry Bonds, Ken Griffey,Jr.)	.30	.25	.12
711	NLCS Team Leaders (Bobby Bonilla, Barry Larkin)	.15	.11	.06
712	Top Game Savers (Bobby Thigpen, John Franco)	.10	.08	.04
713	Chicago's 100 Club (Andre Dawson, Ryne Sandberg)	.15	.11	.06
714	Checklists (Athletics, Pirates, Reds, Red Sox)	.05	.04	.02
715	Checklists (White Sox, Mets Blue Jays, Dodgers)	.05	.04	.02
716	Checklists (Expos, Giants, Rangers, Angels)	.05	.04	.02
717	Checklists (Tigers, Indians, Phillies, Cubs)	.05	.04	.02
718	Checklists (Mariners, Orioles, Astros, Padres)	.05	.04	.02
719	Checklists (Royals, Brewers, Twins, Cardinals)	.05	.04	.02
720	Checklists (Yankees, Braves, Super Stars)	.05	.04	.02

1991 Fleer All Stars

Three player photos are featured on each card in this special insert set. An action shot and facial close-up are featured on the front, while a full-figure pose is showcased on the back. The cards are horizontal and were inseted into 1991 Fleer cello packs.

		MT	NR MT	EX
Complete Set:		18.00	13.50	7.25
Common Player:		.60	.45	.25
1	Ryne Sandberg	2.50	2.00	1.00
2	Barry Larkin	1.00	.70	.40
3	Matt Williams	1.00	.70	.40
4	Cecil Fielder	2.00	1.50	.80
5	Barry Bonds	2.00	1.50	.80
6	Rickey Henderson	2.00	1.50	.80
7	Ken Griffey,Jr.	5.00	3.75	2.00
8	Jose Canseco	2.50	2.00	1.00
9	Benito Santiago	.60	.45	.25
10	Roger Clemens	2.00	1.50	.80

Definitions for grading conditions are located in the Introduction of this price guide.

1991 Fleer '90 World Series

Once again Fleer released a set in honor of the World Series from the previous season. The 1991 issue features only eight cards compared to twelve in 1990. The cards feature white borders surrounding full-color action shots from the 1990 Fall Classic. The card backs feature an overview of the World Series action.

		MT	NR MT	EX
Complete Set:		2.50	2.00	1.00
Common Player:		.20	.15	.08
1	Eric Davis	.25	.20	.10
2	Billy Hatcher	.20	.15	.08
3	Jose Canseco	.35	.25	.14
4	Rickey Henderson	.35	.25	.14
5	Sabo/Lansford	.20	.15	.08
6	Dave Stewart	.25	.20	.10
7	Jose Rijo	.25	.20	.10
8	Reds Celebrate	.20	.15	.08

1991 Fleer Pro Visions

The illustrations of artist Terry Smith are showcased in this special set. Twelve fantasy portraits were produced for cards inserted into rack packs. Four other pro vision cards were inserted into factory sets. The rack pack cards feature black borders, while the factory set cards have white borders. Information on the card backs supports the manner in which Smith painted each player.

		MT	NR MT	EX
Complete Set:		4.00	3.00	1.50
Common Player:		.25	.20	.10
Complete Factory Set:		3.00	2.25	1.25
Common Player:		.40	.30	.15
1	Kirby Puckett	.40	.30	.15
2	Will Clark	.60	.45	.25
3	Ruben Sierra	.40	.30	.15
4	Mark McGwire	.40	.30	.15
5	Bo Jackson	.60	.45	.25
6	Jose Canseco	.60	.45	.25
7	Dwight Gooden	.25	.20	.10
8	Mike Greenwell	.25	.20	.10
9	Roger Clemens	.40	.30	.15
10	Eric Davis	.25	.20	.10
11	Don Mattingly	.40	.30	.15
12	Darryl Strawberry	.40	.30	.15
----	Barry Bonds (1 of 4)	.70	.50	.30
----	Rickey Henderson (2 of 4)	1.00	.70	.40
----	Ryne Sandberg (3 of 4)	1.00	.70	.40
----	Dave Stewart (4 of 4)	.40	.30	.15

1991 Fleer Update

Fleer produced its eight consecutive "Update" set in 1991 to supplement the company's regular set. As in the past, the set consists of 132 cards that were sold by hobby dealers in special collectors boxes. The cards are designed in the same style as the regular Fleer issue.

		MT	NR MT	EX
Complete Set:		6.00	4.50	2.50
Common Player:		.06	.05	.02
1	Glenn Davis	.12	.09	.05

		MT	NR MT	EX
2	Dwight Evans	.08	.06	.03
3	Jose Mesa(FC)	.08	.06	.03
4	Jack Clark	.12	.09	.05
5	Danny Darwin	.06	.05	.02
6	Steve Lyons	.06	.05	.02
7	Mo Vaughn(FC)	.25	.20	.10
8	Floyd Bannister	.06	.05	.02
9	Gary Gaetti	.08	.06	.03
10	Dave Parker	.10	.08	.04
11	Joey Cora	.06	.05	.02
12	Charlie Hough	.06	.05	.02
13	Matt Merullo	.08	.06	.03
14	Warren Newson(FC)	.30	.25	.12
15	Tim Raines	.15	.11	.06
16	Albert Belle	.30	.25	.12
17	Glenallen Hill	.15	.11	.06
18	Shawn Hillegas	.06	.05	.02
19	Mark Lewis(FC)	.30	.25	.12
20	Charles Nagy(FC)	.25	.20	.10
21	Mark Whiten	.20	.15	.08
22	John Cerutti	.06	.05	.02
23	Rob Deer	.06	.05	.02
24	Mickey Tettleton	.08	.06	.03
25	Warren Cromartie	.06	.05	.02
26	Kirk Gibson	.08	.06	.03
27	David Howard(FC)	.25	.20	.10
28	Brent Mayne(FC)	.15	.11	.06
29	Dante Bichette	.06	.05	.02
30	Mark Lee(FC)	.08	.06	.03
31	Julio Machado	.06	.05	.02
32	Edwin Nunez	.06	.05	.02
33	Willie Randolph	.08	.06	.03
34	Franklin Stubbs	.06	.05	.02
35	Bill Wegman	.06	.05	.02
36	Chili Davis	.08	.06	.03
37	Chuck Knoblauch(FC)	.50	.40	.20
38	Scott Leius	.15	.11	.06
39	Jack Morris	.10	.08	.04
40	Mike Pagliarulo	.06	.05	.02
41	Lenny Webster(FC)	.12	.09	.05
42	John Habyan(FC)	.12	.09	.05
43	Steve Howe	.08	.06	.03
44	Jeff Johnson(FC)	.20	.15	.08
45	Scott Kamieniecki(FC)	.25	.20	.10
46	Pat Kelly(FC)	.25	.20	.10
47	Hensley Meulens	.12	.09	.05
48	Wade Taylor(FC)	.20	.15	.08
49	Bernie Williams(FC)	.35	.25	.14
50	Kirk Dressendorfer(FC)	.35	.25	.14
51	Ernest Riles	.06	.05	.02
52	Rich DeLucia(FC)	.15	.11	.06
53	Tracy Jones	.06	.05	.02
54	Bill Krueger	.06	.05	.02
55	Alonzo Powell(FC)	.15	.11	.06
56	Jeff Schaefer	.06	.05	.02
57	Russ Swan(FC)	.08	.06	.03
58	John Barfield(FC)	.15	.11	.06
59	Rich Gossage	.08	.06	.03
60	Jose Guzman	.06	.05	.02
61	Dean Palmer(FC)	.40	.30	.15
62	Ivan Rodriguez(FC)	1.25	.90	.50
63	Roberto Alomar	.25	.20	.10
64	Tom Candiotti	.06	.05	.02
65	Joe Carter	.15	.11	.06
66	Ed Sprague(FC)	.20	.15	.08
67	Pat Tabler	.06	.05	.02
68	Mike Timlin(FC)	.20	.15	.08
69	Devon White	.08	.06	.03
70	Rafael Belliard	.06	.05	.02
71	Juan Berenguer	.06	.05	.02
72	Sid Bream	.08	.06	.03
73	Marvin Freeman	.06	.05	.02
74	Kent Mercker	.08	.06	.03
75	Otis Nixon	.06	.05	.02
76	Terry Pendleton	.08	.06	.03
77	George Bell	.10	.08	.04
78	Danny Jackson	.06	.05	.02
79	Chuck McElroy	.06	.05	.02
80	Gary Scott(FC)	.30	.25	.12
81	Heathcliff Slocumb(FC)	.15	.11	.06
82	Dave Smith	.06	.05	.02
83	Rick Wilkins(FC)	.30	.25	.12
84	Freddie Benavides(FC)	.20	.15	.08
85	Ted Power	.06	.05	.02
86	Mo Sanford(FC)	.30	.25	.12
87	Jeff Bagwell(FC)	1.25	.90	.50
88	Steve Finley	.08	.06	.03
89	Pete Harnisch	.08	.06	.03
90	Darryl Kile(FC)	.20	.15	.08
91	Brett Butler	.08	.06	.03
92	John Candelaria	.06	.05	.02
93	Gary Carter	.08	.06	.03

		MT	NR MT	EX
94	Kevin Gross	.06	.05	.02
95	Bob Ojeda	.06	.05	.02
96	Darryl Strawberry	.30	.25	.12
97	Ivan Calderon	.08	.06	.03
98	Ron Hassey	.06	.05	.02
99	Gilberto Reyes	.08	.06	.03
100	Hubie Brooks	.08	.06	.03
101	Rick Cerone	.06	.05	.02
102	Vince Coleman	.08	.06	.03
103	Jeff Innis	.08	.06	.03
104	Pete Schourek(FC)	.20	.15	.08
105	Andy Ashby(FC)	.12	.09	.05
106	Wally Backman	.06	.05	.02
107	Darrin Fletcher(FC)	.12	.09	.05
108	Tommy Greene	.08	.06	.03
109	John Morris	.06	.05	.02
110	Mitch Williams	.08	.06	.03
111	Lloyd McClendon	.06	.05	.02
112	Orlando Merced(FC)	.40	.30	.15
113	Vicente Palacios	.06	.05	.02
114	Gary Varsho	.06	.05	.02
115	John Wehner(FC)	.25	.20	.10
116	Rex Hudler	.06	.05	.02
117	Tim Jones	.06	.05	.02
118	Geronimo Pena(FC)	.15	.11	.06
119	Gerald Perry	.06	.05	.02
120	Larry Andersen	.06	.05	.02
121	Jerald Clark	.06	.05	.02
122	Scott Coolbaugh	.08	.06	.03
123	Tony Fernandez	.08	.06	.03
124	Darrin Jackson	.06	.05	.02
125	Fred McGriff	.15	.11	.06
126	Jose Mota(FC)	.25	.20	.10
127	Tim Teufel	.06	.05	.02
128	Bud Black	.06	.05	.02
129	Mike Felder	.06	.05	.02
130	Willie McGee	.08	.06	.03
131	Dave Righetti	.08	.06	.03
132	Checklist	.06	.05	.02

1991 Fleer Ultra

This 400-card set was originally going to be called the Elite set, but Fleer chose to use the Ultra label. The card fronts feature gray borders surrounding full-color action photos. The backs feature three player photos and statistics. Hot Prospects and Great Performers are among the special cards featured within the set. This set is the premier release for Fleer Ultra.

		MT	NR MT	EX
Complete Set:		30.00	22.00	12.00
Common Player:		.06	.05	.02
1	Steve Avery	1.00	.70	.40
2	Jeff Blauser	.06	.05	.02
3	Francisco Cabrera	.08	.06	.03
4	Ron Gant	.35	.25	.14
5	Tom Glavine	.15	.11	.06
6	Tommy Gregg	.06	.05	.02
7	Dave Justice	1.25	.90	.50
8	Oddibe McDowell	.06	.05	.02
9	Greg Olson	.08	.06	.03
10	Terry Pendleton	.15	.11	.06
11	Lonnie Smith	.06	.05	.02
12	John Smoltz	.15	.11	.06
13	Jeff Treadway	.06	.05	.02
14	Glenn Davis	.10	.08	.04

		MT	NR MT	EX
15	Mike Devereaux	.08	.06	.03
16	Leo Gomez	.40	.30	.15
17	Chris Hoiles	.50	.40	.20
18	Dave Johnson	.06	.05	.02
19	Ben McDonald	.20	.15	.08
20	Randy Milligan	.08	.06	.03
21	Gregg Olson	.10	.08	.04
22	Joe Orsulak	.06	.05	.02
23	Bill Ripken	.06	.05	.02
24	Cal Ripken,Jr.	.50	.40	.20
25	David Segui	.15	.11	.06
26	Craig Worthington	.08	.06	.03
27	Wade Boggs	.25	.20	.10
28	Tom Bolton	.06	.05	.02
29	Tom Brunansky	.08	.06	.03
30	Ellis Burks	.12	.09	.05
31	Roger Clemens	.50	.40	.20
32	Mike Greenwell	.15	.11	.06
33	Greg Harris	.06	.05	.02
34	Daryl Irvine	.15	.11	.06
35	Mike Marshall	.06	.05	.02
36	Tim Naehring	.15	.11	.06
37	Tony Pena	.06	.05	.02
38	Phil Plantier	2.00	1.50	.80
39	Carlos Quintana	.08	.06	.03
40	Jeff Reardon	.08	.06	.03
41	Jody Reed	.06	.05	.02
42	Luis Rivera	.06	.05	.02
43	Jim Abbott	.20	.15	.08
44	Chuck Finley	.15	.11	.06
45	Bryan Harvey	.08	.06	.03
46	Donnie Hill	.06	.05	.02
47	Jack Howell	.06	.05	.02
48	Wally Joyner	.15	.11	.06
49	Mark Langston	.12	.09	.05
50	Kirk McCaskill	.06	.05	.02
51	Lance Parrish	.08	.06	.03
52	Dick Schofield	.06	.05	.02
53	Lee Stevens	.15	.11	.06
54	Dave Winfield	.15	.11	.06
55	George Bell	.12	.09	.05
56	Damon Berryhill	.06	.05	.02
57	Mike Bielecki	.06	.05	.02
58	Andre Dawson	.20	.15	.08
59	Shawon Dunston	.10	.08	.04
60	Joe Girardi	.06	.05	.02
61	Mark Grace	.15	.11	.06
62	Mike Harkey	.08	.06	.03
63	Les Lancaster	.06	.05	.02
64	Greg Maddux	.08	.06	.03
65	Derrick May	.20	.15	.08
66	Ryne Sandberg	.50	.40	.20
67	Luis Salazar	.06	.05	.02
68	Dwight Smith	.06	.05	.02
69	Hector Villanueva	.08	.06	.03
70	Jerome Walton	.12	.09	.05
71	Mitch Williams	.08	.06	.03
72	Carlton Fisk	.20	.15	.08
73	Scott Fletcher	.06	.05	.02
74	Ozzie Guillen	.10	.08	.04
75	Greg Hibbard	.08	.06	.03
76	Lance Johnson	.06	.05	.02
77	Steve Lyons	.06	.05	.02
78	Jack McDowell	.12	.09	.05
79	Dan Pasqua	.06	.05	.02
80	Melido Perez	.06	.05	.02
81	Tim Raines	.10	.08	.04
82	Sammy Sosa	.10	.08	.04
83	Cory Snyder	.06	.05	.02
84	Bobby Thigpen	.08	.06	.03
85	Frank Thomas	6.00	4.50	2.50
86	Robin Ventura	1.00	.70	.40
87	Todd Benzinger	.06	.05	.02
88	Glenn Braggs	.06	.05	.02
89	Tom Browning	.08	.06	.03
90	Norm Charlton	.08	.06	.03
91	Eric Davis	.15	.11	.06
92	Rob Dibble	.10	.08	.04
93	Bill Doran	.08	.06	.03
94	Mariano Duncan	.06	.05	.02
95	Billy Hatcher	.06	.05	.02
96	Barry Larkin	.15	.11	.06
97	Randy Myers	.08	.06	.03
98	Hal Morris	.20	.15	.08
99	Joe Oliver	.06	.05	.02
100	Paul O'Neill	.08	.06	.03
101	Jeff Reed	.06	.05	.02
102	Jose Rijo	.08	.06	.03
103	Chris Sabo	.10	.08	.04
104	Beau Allred	.06	.05	.02
105	Sandy Alomar,Jr.	.10	.08	.04

		MT	NR MT	EX			MT	NR MT	EX
106	Carlos Baerga	.15	.11	.06	197	Dennis Boyd	.06	.05	.02
107	Albert Belle	.50	.40	.20	198	Tim Burke	.06	.05	.02
108	Jerry Browne	.06	.05	.02	199	Ivan Calderon	.08	.06	.03
109	Tom Candiotti	.06	.05	.02	200	Delino DeShields	.10	.08	.04
110	Alex Cole	.06	.05	.02	201	Mike Fitzgerald	.06	.05	.02
111	John Farrell	.06	.05	.02	202	Steve Frey	.06	.05	.02
112	Felix Fermin	.06	.05	.02	203	Andres Galarraga	.08	.06	.03
113	Brook Jacoby	.06	.05	.02	204	Marquis Grissom	.20	.15	.08
114	Chris James	.06	.05	.02	205	Dave Martinez	.06	.05	.02
115	Doug Jones	.06	.05	.02	206	Dennis Martinez	.08	.06	.03
116	Steve Olin	.06	.05	.03	207	Junior Noboa	.06	.05	.02
117	Greg Swindell	.08	.06	.03	208	Spike Owen	.06	.05	.02
118	Turner Ward	.20	.15	.08	209	Scott Ruskin	.06	.05	.02
119	Mitch Webster	.06	.05	.02	210	Tim Wallach	.08	.06	.03
120	Dave Bergman	.06	.05	.02	211	Daryl Boston	.06	.05	.02
121	Cecil Fielder	.40	.30	.15	212	Vince Coleman	.10	.08	.04
122	Travis Fryman	2.00	1.50	.80	213	David Cone	.10	.08	.04
123	Mike Henneman	.08	.06	.03	214	Ron Darling	.08	.06	.03
124	Lloyd Moseby	.06	.05	.02	215	Kevin Elster	.06	.05	.02
125	Dan Petry	.06	.05	.02	216	Sid Fernandez	.08	.06	.03
126	Tony Phillips	.06	.05	.02	217	John Franco	.08	.06	.03
127	Mark Salas	.06	.05	.02	218	Dwight Gooden	.20	.15	.08
128	Frank Tanana	.06	.05	.02	219	Tom Herr	.06	.05	.02
129	Alan Trammell	.15	.11	.06	220	Todd Hundley	.15	.11	.06
130	Lou Whitaker	.08	.06	.03	221	Gregg Jefferies	.15	.11	.06
131	Eric Anthony	.10	.08	.04	222	Howard Johnson	.15	.11	.06
132	Craig Biggio	.15	.11	.06	223	Dave Magadan	.10	.08	.04
133	Ken Caminiti	.08	.06	.03	224	Kevin McReynolds	.10	.08	.04
134	Casey Candaele	.06	.05	.02	225	Keith Miller	.06	.05	.02
135	Andujar Cedeno	.60	.45	.25	226	Mackey Sasser	.06	.05	.02
136	Mark Davidson	.06	.05	.02	227	Frank Viola	.10	.08	.04
137	Jim Deshaies	.06	.05	.02	228	Jesse Barfield	.08	.06	.03
138	Mark Portugal	.06	.05	.02	229	Greg Cadaret	.06	.05	.02
139	Rafael Ramirez	.06	.05	.02	230	Alvaro Espinoza	.06	.05	.02
140	Mike Scott	.08	.06	.03	231	Bob Geren	.06	.05	.02
141	Eric Yelding	.06	.05	.02	232	Lee Guetterman	.06	.05	.02
142	Gerald Young	.06	.05	.02	233	Mel Hall	.08	.06	.03
143	Kevin Appier	.10	.08	.04	234	Andy Hawkins	.06	.05	.02
144	George Brett	.25	.20	.10	235	Roberto Kelly	.10	.08	.04
145	Jeff Conine	.20	.15	.08	236	Tim Leary	.06	.05	.02
146	Jim Eisenreich	.06	.05	.02	237	Jim Leyritz	.06	.05	.02
147	Tom Gordon	.10	.08	.04	238	Kevin Maas	.25	.20	.10
148	Mark Gubicza	.08	.06	.03	239	Don Mattingly	.30	.25	.12
149	Bo Jackson	.60	.45	.25	240	Hensley Meulens	.10	.08	.04
150	Brent Mayne	.15	.11	.06	241	Eric Plunk	.06	.05	.02
151	Mike Macfarlane	.06	.05	.02	242	Steve Sax	.08	.06	.03
152	Brian McRae	.60	.45	.25	243	Todd Burns	.06	.05	.02
153	Jeff Montgomery	.08	.06	.03	244	Jose Canseco	.60	.45	.25
154	Bret Saberhagen	.10	.08	.04	245	Dennis Eckersley	.10	.08	.04
155	Kevin Seitzer	.06	.05	.02	246	Mike Gallego	.06	.05	.02
156	Terry Shumpert	.06	.05	.02	247	Dave Henderson	.10	.08	.04
157	Kurt Stillwell	.06	.05	.02	248	Rickey Henderson	.50	.40	.20
158	Danny Tartabull	.15	.11	.06	249	Rick Honeycutt	.06	.05	.02
159	Tim Belcher	.08	.06	.03	250	Carney Lansford	.08	.06	.03
160	Kal Daniels	.10	.08	.04	251	Mark McGwire	.15	.11	.06
161	Alfredo Griffin	.06	.05	.02	252	Mike Moore	.06	.05	.02
162	Lenny Harris	.06	.05	.02	253	Terry Steinbach	.06	.05	.02
163	Jay Howell	.06	.05	.02	254	Dave Stewart	.10	.08	.04
164	Ramon Martinez	.40	.30	.15	255	Walt Weiss	.06	.05	.02
165	Mike Morgan	.06	.05	.02	256	Bob Welch	.08	.06	.03
166	Eddie Murray	.20	.15	.08	257	Curt Young	.06	.05	.02
167	Jose Offerman	.15	.11	.06	258	Wes Chamberlain	.60	.45	.25
168	Juan Samuel	.08	.06	.03	259	Pat Combs	.08	.06	.03
169	Mike Scioscia	.08	.06	.03	260	Darren Daulton	.06	.05	.02
170	Mike Sharperson	.06	.05	.02	261	Jose DeJesus	.06	.05	.02
171	Darryl Strawberry	.40	.30	.15	262	Len Dykstra	.10	.08	.04
172	Greg Brock	.06	.05	.02	263	Charlie Hayes	.08	.06	.03
173	Chuck Crim	.06	.05	.02	264	Von Hayes	.08	.06	.03
174	Jim Gantner	.08	.06	.03	265	Ken Howell	.06	.05	.02
175	Ted Higuera	.08	.06	.03	266	John Kruk	.08	.06	.03
176	Mark Knudson	.06	.05	.02	267	Roger McDowell	.08	.06	.03
177	Tim McIntosh	.08	.06	.03	268	Mickey Morandini	.15	.11	.06
178	Paul Molitor	.15	.11	.06	269	Terry Mulholland	.08	.06	.03
179	Dan Plesac	.06	.05	.02	270	Dale Murphy	.10	.08	.04
180	Gary Sheffield	.12	.09	.05	271	Randy Ready	.06	.05	.02
181	Bill Spiers	.06	.05	.02	272	Dickie Thon	.06	.05	.02
182	B.J. Surhoff	.06	.05	.02	273	Stan Belinda	.06	.05	.02
183	Greg Vaughn	.20	.15	.08	274	Jay Bell	.08	.06	.03
184	Robin Yount	.20	.15	.08	275	Barry Bonds	.25	.20	.10
185	Rick Aguilera	.08	.06	.03	276	Bobby Bonilla	.25	.20	.10
186	Greg Gagne	.06	.05	.02	277	Doug Drabek	.10	.08	.04
187	Dan Gladden	.06	.05	.02	278	Carlos Garcia	.20	.15	.08
188	Brian Harper	.06	.05	.02	279	Neal Heaton	.06	.05	.02
189	Kent Hrbek	.08	.06	.03	280	Jeff King	.08	.06	.03
190	Gene Larkin	.06	.05	.04	281	Bill Landrum	.06	.05	.02
191	Shane Mack	.08	.06	.03	282	Mike LaValliere	.06	.05	.02
192	Pedro Munoz	.80	.60	.30	283	Jose Lind	.06	.05	.02
193	Al Newman	.06	.05	.02	284	Orlando Merced	.70	.50	.30
194	Junior Ortiz	.06	.05	.02	285	Gary Redus	.06	.05	.02
195	Kirby Puckett	.25	.20	.10	286	Don Slaught	.06	.05	.02
196	Kevin Tapani	.08	.06	.03	287	Andy Van Slyke	.10	.08	.04

		MT	NR MT	EX
288	Jose DeLeon	.06	.05	.02
289	Pedro Guerrero	.10	.08	.04
290	Ray Lankford	1.00	.70	.40
291	Joe Magrane	.08	.06	.03
292	Jose Oquendo	.06	.05	.02
293	Tom Pagnozzi	.06	.05	.02
294	Bryn Smith	.06	.05	.02
295	Lee Smith	.08	.06	.03
296	Ozzie Smith	.20	.15	.08
297	Milt Thompson	.06	.05	.02
298	Craig Wilson	.12	.09	.05
299	Todd Zeile	.20	.15	.08
300	Shawn Abner	.06	.05	.02
301	Andy Benes	.15	.11	.06
302	Paul Faries	.15	.11	.06
303	Tony Gwynn	.20	.15	.08
304	Greg Harris	.06	.05	.02
305	Thomas Howard	.10	.08	.04
306	Bruce Hurst	.08	.06	.03
307	Craig Lefferts	.06	.05	.02
308	Fred McGriff	.15	.11	.06
309	Dennis Rasmussen	.06	.05	.02
310	Bip Roberts	.08	.06	.03
311	Benito Santiago	.10	.08	.04
312	Garry Templeton	.06	.05	.02
313	Ed Whitson	.06	.05	.02
314	Dave Anderson	.06	.05	.02
315	Kevin Bass	.06	.05	.02
316	Jeff Brantley	.06	.05	.02
317	John Burkett	.08	.06	.03
318	Will Clark	.50	.40	.20
319	Steve Decker	.30	.25	.12
320	Scott Garrelts	.06	.05	.02
321	Terry Kennedy	.06	.05	.02
322	Mark Leonard	.20	.15	.08
323	Darren Lewis	.50	.40	.20
324	Greg Litton	.06	.05	.02
325	Willie McGee	.10	.08	.04
326	Kevin Mitchell	.15	.11	.06
327	Don Robinson	.06	.05	.02
328	Andres Santana	.25	.20	.10
329	Robby Thompson	.06	.05	.02
330	Jose Uribe	.06	.05	.02
331	Matt Williams	.15	.11	.06
332	Scott Bradley	.06	.05	.02
334	Alvin Davis	.08	.06	.03
335	Ken Griffey,Sr.	.08	.06	.03
336	Ken Griffey,Jr.	2.00	1.50	.80
337	Erik Hanson	.10	.08	.04
338	Brian Holman	.06	.05	.02
339	Randy Johnson	.08	.06	.03
340	Edgar Martinez	.08	.06	.03
341	Tino Martinez	.20	.15	.08
342	Pete O'Brien	.06	.05	.02
343	Harold Reynolds	.08	.06	.03
344	David Valle	.06	.05	.02
345	Omar Vizquel	.06	.05	.02
346	Brad Arnsberg	.06	.05	.02
347	Kevin Brown	.06	.05	.02
348	Julio Franco	.10	.08	.04
349	Jeff Huson	.06	.05	.02
350	Rafael Palmeiro	.20	.15	.08
351	Geno Petralli	.06	.05	.02
352	Gary Pettis	.06	.05	.02
353	Kenny Rogers	.06	.05	.02
354	Jeff Russell	.06	.05	.02
355	Nolan Ryan	1.00	.70	.40
356	Ruben Sierra	.25	.20	.10
357	Bobby Witt	.08	.06	.03
358	Roberto Alomar	.70	.50	.30
359	Pat Borders	.06	.05	.02
360	Joe Carter	.15	.11	.06
361	Kelly Gruber	.08	.06	.03
362	Tom Henke	.08	.06	.03
363	Glenallen Hill	.08	.06	.03
364	Jimmy Key	.08	.06	.03
365	Manny Lee	.06	.05	.02
366	Rance Mulliniks	.06	.05	.02
367	John Olerud	.20	.15	.08
368	Dave Stieb	.08	.06	.03
369	Duane Ward	.06	.05	.02
370	David Wells	.06	.05	.02
371	Mark Whiten	.30	.25	.12
372	Mookie Wilson	.06	.05	.02
373	Willie Banks	.30	.25	.12
374	Steve Carter	.06	.05	.02
375	Scott Chiamparino	.10	.08	.04
376	Steve Chitren	.10	.08	.04
377	Darrin Fletcher	.10	.08	.04
378	Rich Garces	.10	.08	.04
379	Reggie Jefferson	.60	.45	.25

		MT	NR MT	EX
380	Eric Karros	.70	.50	.30
381	Pat Kelly	.70	.50	.30
382	Chuck Knoblauch	2.00	1.50	.80
383	Denny Neagle	.50	.40	.20
384	Dan Opperman	.20	.15	.08
385	John Ramos	.20	.15	.08
386	Henry Rodriguez	.30	.25	.12
387	Maurice Vaughn	.40	.30	.15
388	Gerald Williams	.40	.30	.15
389	Mike York	.20	.15	.08
390	Eddie Zosky	.20	.15	.08
391	Barry Bonds (Great Performer)	.20	.15	.08
392	Cecil Fielder (Great Performer)	.20	.15	.08
393	Rickey Henderson (Great Performer)	.20	.15	.08
394	Dave Justice (Great Performer)	.60	.45	.25
395	Nolan Ryan (Great Performer)	.40	.30	.15
396	Bobby Thigpen (Great Performer)	.10	.08	.04
397	Checklist	.06	.05	.02
398	Checklist	.06	.05	.02
399	Checklist	.06	.05	.02
400	Checklist	.06	.05	.02

GRADING GUIDE

Mint (MT): A perfect card. Well-centered with all corners sharp and square. No creases, stains, edge nicks, surface marks, yellowing or fading.

Near Mint (NM): A nearly perfect card. At first glance, a NM card appears to be perfect. May be slightly off-center. No surface marks, creases or loss of gloss.

Excellent (EX): Corners are still fairly sharp with only moderate wear. Borders may be off-center. No creases or stains on fronts or backs, but may show slight loss of surface luster.

Very Good (VG): Shows obvious handling. May have rounded corners, minor creases, major gum or wax stains. No major creases, tape marks, writing, etc.

Good (G): A well-worn card, but exhibits no intentional damage. May have major or multiple creases. Corners may be rounded well beyond card border.

1991 Fleer Ultra Gold

A three dimensional effect is presented on the front of the Fleer Ultra Gold cards. The flip sides feature career information. The cards are numbered on the back. The Puckett and Sandberg cards feature incorrect historical information on the backs.

		MT	NR MT	EX
Complete Set:		10.00	7.50	4.00
Common Player:		.40	.30	.15
1	Barry Bonds	1.25	.90	.50
2	Will Clark	1.25	.90	.50
3	Doug Drabek	.40	.30	.15
4	Ken Griffey, Jr.	3.00	2.25	1.25
5	Rickey Henderson	1.25	.90	.50
6	Bo Jackson	1.25	.90	.50
7	Ramon Martinez	.40	.30	.15
8	Kirby Puckett	1.25	.90	.50
9	Chris Sabo	.40	.30	.15
10	Ryne Sandberg	1.50	1.25	.60

Values quoted in this guide reflect the retail price of a card — the price a collector can expect to pay when buying a card from a dealer. The wholesale price — that which a collector can expect to receive from a dealer when selling cards — will be significantly lower, depending on desirability and condition.

1991 Fleer Ultra Update

This 120-card set was produced as a supplement to the premier Fleer Ultra set. The cards feature the same style as the regular Fleer Ultra cards. The 4-photo Ultra look is featured on each card. The cards were sold in full color, overwrapped boxes.

		MT	NR MT	EX
Complete Set:		30.00	22.00	12.00
Common Player:		.06	.05	.02
1	Dwight Evans	.08	.06	.03
2	Chito Martinez	1.25	.90	.50
3	Bob Melvin	.06	.05	.02
4	Mike Mussina	5.00	3.75	2.00
5	Jack Clark	.08	.06	.03
6	Dana Kiecker	.06	.05	.02
7	Steve Lyons	.06	.05	.02
8	Gary Gaetti	.08	.06	.03
9	Dave Gallagher	.06	.05	.02
10	Dave Parker	.08	.06	.03
11	Luis Polonia	.06	.05	.02
12	Luis Sojo	.08	.06	.03
13	Wilson Alvarez	.20	.15	.08
14	Alex Fernandez	.40	.30	.15
15	Craig Grebeck	.06	.05	.02
16	Ron Karkovice	.06	.05	.02
17	Warren Newson	.40	.30	.15
18	Scott Radinsky	.08	.06	.03
19	Glenallen Hill	.12	.09	.05
20	Charles Nagy	.15	.11	.06
21	Mark Whiten	.30	.25	.12
22	Milt Cuyler	.35	.25	.14
23	Paul Gibson	.06	.05	.02
24	Mickey Tettleton	.08	.06	.03
25	Todd Benzinger	.08	.06	.03
26	Storm Davis	.06	.05	.02
27	Kirk Gibson	.08	.06	.03
28	Bill Pecota	.06	.05	.02
29	Gary Thurman	.06	.05	.02
30	Darryl Hamilton	.08	.06	.03
31	Jaime Navarro	.08	.06	.03
32	Willie Randolph	.08	.06	.03
33	Bill Wegman	.06	.05	.02
34	Randy Bush	.06	.05	.02
35	Chili Davis	.08	.06	.03
36	Scott Erickson	1.50	1.25	.60
37	Chuck Knoblauch	2.00	1.50	.80
38	Scott Leius	.15	.11	.06
39	Jack Morris	.12	.09	.05
40	John Habyan	.08	.06	.03
41	Pat Kelly	.60	.45	.25
42	Matt Nokes	.08	.06	.03
43	Scott Sanderson	.08	.06	.03
44	Bernie Williams	.70	.50	.30
45	Harold Baines	.10	.08	.04
46	Brook Jacoby	.08	.06	.03
47	Ernest Riles	.06	.05	.02
48	Willie Wilson	.06	.05	.02
49	Jay Buhner	.08	.06	.03
50	Rich DeLucia	.20	.15	.08
51	Mike Jackson	.06	.05	.02
52	Bill Krueger	.06	.05	.02
53	Bill Swift	.06	.05	.02
54	Brian Downing	.06	.05	.02
55	Juan Gonzalez	3.00	2.25	1.25
56	Dean Palmer	2.00	1.50	.80
57	Kevin Reimer	.20	.15	.08
58	Ivan Rodriguez	4.00	3.00	1.50
59	Tom Candiotti	.06	.05	.02
60	Juan Guzman	5.00	3.75	2.00
61	Bob MacDonald	.20	.15	.08
62	Greg Myers	.06	.05	.02
63	Ed Sprague	.20	.15	.08
64	Devon White	.08	.06	.03
65	Rafael Belliard	.06	.05	.02
66	Juan Berenguer	.06	.05	.02
67	Brian Hunter	1.00	.70	.40
68	Kent Mercker	.08	.06	.03
69	Otis Nixon	.06	.05	.02
70	Danny Jackson	.06	.05	.04
71	Chuck McElroy	.06	.05	.04
72	Gary Scott	.35	.25	.14
73	Heathcliff Slocumb	.15	.11	.06
74	Chico Walker	.10	.08	.04
75	Rick Wilkins	.35	.25	.14
76	Chris Hammond	.15	.11	.06
77	Luis Quinones	.06	.05	.02
78	Herm Winningham	.06	.05	.02
79	Jeff Bagwell	5.00	3.75	2.00
80	Jim Corsi	.06	.05	.02
81	Steve Finley	.08	.06	.03

		MT	NR MT	EX
82	Luis Gonzalez	1.25	.90	.50
83	Pete Harnisch	.08	.06	.03
84	Darryl Kile	.25	.20	.10
85	Brett Butler	.08	.06	.03
86	Gary Carter	.15	.11	.06
87	Tim Crews	.06	.05	.02
88	Orel Hershiser	.15	.11	.06
89	Bob Ojeda	.06	.05	.02
90	Bret Barberie	.40	.30	.15
91	Barry Jones	.06	.05	.02
92	Gilberto Reyes	.08	.06	.03
93	Larry Walker	.15	.11	.06
94	Hubie Brooks	.08	.06	.03
95	Tim Burke	.06	.05	.02
96	Rick Cerone	.06	.05	.02
97	Jeff Innis	.08	.06	.03
98	Wally Backman	.06	.05	.02
99	Tommy Greene	.15	.11	.06
100	Ricky Jordan	.10	.08	.04
101	Mitch Williams	.08	.06	.03
102	John Smiley	.08	.06	.03
103	Randy Tomlin	.40	.30	.15
104	Gary Varsho	.06	.05	.02
105	Cris Carpenter	.06	.05	.02
106	Ken Hill	.08	.06	.03
107	Felix Jose	.25	.20	.10
108	Omar Oliveras	.25	.20	.10
109	Gerald Perry	.06	.05	.02
110	Jerald Clark	.08	.06	.03
111	Tony Fernandez	.08	.06	.03
112	Darrin Jackson	.08	.06	.03
113	Mike Maddux	.06	.05	.02
114	Tim Teufel	.06	.05	.02
115	Bud Black	.06	.05	.02
116	Kelly Downs	.06	.05	.02
117	Mike Felder	.06	.05	.02
118	Willie McGee	.12	.09	.05
119	Trevor Wilson	.12	.09	.05
120	Checklist	.06	.05	.02

1992 Fleer

For the second consecutive year, Fleer produced a 720-card set. The standard card fronts feature full-color action photos bordered in blue with the player's name, position and team logo on the right border. The backs feature another full-color action photo, biographical information and statistics. A special twelve card Roger Clemens subset is also included in the 1992 Fleer set. Three more Clemens cards are available through a mail-in offer, and 2,000 Roger Clemens autographed cards were inserted in 1992 packs. Once again the cards are numbered according to team.

		MT	NR MT	EX
Complete Set:		25.00	18.00	10.00
Common Player:		.04	.03	.02
1	Brady Anderson	.04	.03	.02
2	Jose Bautista	.04	.03	.02
3	Juan Bell	.06	.05	.02
4	Glenn Davis	.08	.06	.03
5	Mike Devereaux	.05	.04	.02
6	Dwight Evans	.08	.06	.03
7	Mike Flanagan	.04	.03	.02
8	Leo Gomez	.15	.11	.06
9	Chris Hoiles	.10	.08	.04
10	Sam Horn	.05	.04	.02

		MT	NR MT	EX			MT	NR MT	EX
11	Tim Hulett	.04	.03	.02	102	Mike Aldrete	.04	.03	.02
12	Dave Johnson	.04	.03	.02	103	Sandy Alomar, Jr.	.10	.08	.04
13	Chito Martinez(FC)	.20	.15	.08	104	Carlos Baerga	.10	.08	.04
14	Ben McDonald	.10	.08	.04	105	Albert Belle	.15	.11	.06
15	Bob Melvin	.04	.03	.02	106	Willie Blair	.05	.04	.02
16	Luis Mercedes(FC)	.15	.11	.06	107	Jerry Browne	.04	.03	.02
17	Jose Mesa	.05	.04	.02	108	Alex Cole	.06	.05	.02
18	Bob Milacki	.05	.04	.02	109	Felix Fermin	.04	.03	.02
19	Randy Milligan	.06	.05	.02	110	Glenallen Hill	.06	.05	.02
20	Mike Mussina	.50	.40	.20	111	Shawn Hillegas	.04	.03	.02
21	Gregg Olson	.08	.06	.03	112	Chris James	.05	.04	.02
22	Joe Orsulak	.04	.03	.02	113	Reggie Jefferson(FC)	.20	.15	.08
23	Jim Poole	.05	.04	.02	114	Doug Jones	.05	.04	.02
24	Arthur Rhodes(FC)	.40	.30	.15	115	Eric King	.04	.03	.02
25	Billy Ripken	.04	.03	.02	116	Mark Lewis	.15	.11	.06
26	Cal Ripken, Jr.	.20	.15	.08	117	Carlos Martinez	.05	.04	.02
27	David Segui	.08	.06	.03	118	Charles Nagy	.08	.06	.03
28	Roy Smith	.04	.03	.02	119	Rod Nichols	.04	.03	.02
29	Anthony Telford	.04	.03	.02	120	Steve Olin	.04	.03	.02
30	Mark Williamson	.04	.03	.02	121	Jesse Orosco	.04	.03	.02
31	Craig Worthington	.06	.05	.02	122	Rudy Seanez	.04	.03	.02
32	Wade Boggs	.15	.11	.06	123	Joel Skinner	.04	.03	.02
33	Tom Bolton	.04	.03	.02	124	Greg Swindell	.08	.06	.03
34	Tom Brunansky	.05	.04	.02	125	Jim Thome(FC)	.50	.40	.20
35	Ellis Burks	.08	.06	.03	126	Mark Whiten	.10	.08	.04
36	Jack Clark	.08	.06	.03	127	Scott Aldred	.10	.08	.04
37	Roger Clemens	.15	.11	.06	128	Andy Allanson	.04	.03	.02
38	Danny Darwin	.04	.03	.02	129	John Cerutti	.04	.03	.02
39	Mike Greenwell	.08	.06	.03	130	Milt Cuyler	.10	.08	.04
40	Joe Hesketh	.04	.03	.02	131	Mike Dalton(FC)	.15	.11	.06
41	Daryl Irvine	.05	.04	.02	132	Rob Deer	.05	.04	.02
42	Dennis Lamp	.04	.03	.02	133	Cecil Fielder	.15	.11	.06
43	Tony Pena	.05	.04	.02	134	Travis Fryman	.25	.20	.10
44	Phil Plantier	.25	.20	.10	135	Dan Gakeler(FC)	.15	.11	.06
45	Carlos Quintana	.06	.05	.02	136	Paul Gibson	.04	.03	.02
46	Jeff Reardon	.08	.06	.03	137	Bill Gullickson	.05	.04	.02
47	Jody Reed	.05	.04	.02	138	Mike Henneman	.05	.04	.02
48	Luis Rivera	.04	.03	.02	139	Pete Incaviglia	.05	.04	.02
49	Mo Vaughn	.30	.25	.12	140	Mark Leiter(FC)	.12	.09	.05
50	Jim Abbott	.10	.08	.04	141	Scott Livingstone(FC)	.20	.15	.08
51	Kyle Abbott	.08	.06	.03	142	Lloyd Moseby	.04	.03	.02
52	Ruben Amaro, Jr.(FC)	.15	.11	.06	143	Tony Phillips	.05	.04	.02
53	Scott Bailes	.04	.03	.02	144	Mark Salas	.04	.03	.02
54	Chris Beasley(FC)	.12	.09	.05	145	Frank Tanana	.05	.04	.02
55	Mark Eichhorn	.04	.03	.02	146	Walt Terrell	.04	.03	.02
56	Mike Fetters	.04	.03	.02	147	Mickey Tettleton	.06	.05	.02
57	Chuck Finley	.08	.06	.03	148	Alan Trammell	.10	.08	.04
58	Gary Gaetti	.08	.06	.03	149	Lou Whitaker	.08	.06	.03
59	Dave Gallagher	.05	.04	.02	150	Kevin Appier	.06	.05	.02
60	Donnie Hill	.04	.03	.02	151	Luis Aquino	.04	.03	.02
61	Bryan Harvey	.06	.05	.02	152	Todd Benzinger	.05	.04	.02
62	Wally Joyner	.10	.08	.04	153	Mike Boddicker	.05	.04	.02
63	Mark Langston	.10	.08	.04	154	George Brett	.15	.11	.06
64	Kirk McCaskill	.05	.04	.02	155	Storm Davis	.05	.04	.02
65	John Orton	.04	.03	.02	156	Jim Eisenreich	.04	.03	.02
66	Lance Parrish	.06	.05	.02	157	Kirk Gibson	.08	.06	.03
67	Luis Polonia	.05	.04	.02	158	Tom Gordon	.06	.05	.02
68	Bobby Rose	.05	.04	.02	159	Mark Gubicza	.06	.05	.02
69	Dick Schofield	.04	.03	.02	160	David Howard(FC)	.20	.15	.08
70	Luis Sojo	.05	.04	.02	161	Mike Macfarlane	.05	.04	.02
71	Lee Stevens	.08	.06	.03	162	Brent Mayne	.05	.04	.02
72	Dave Winfield	.12	.09	.05	163	Brian McRae	.25	.20	.10
73	Cliff Young	.06	.05	.02	164	Jeff Montgomery	.05	.04	.02
74	Wilson Alvarez	.08	.06	.03	165	Bill Pecota	.04	.03	.02
75	Esteban Beltre(FC)	.20	.15	.08	166	Harvey Pulliam(FC)	.15	.11	.06
76	Joey Cora	.04	.03	.02	167	Bret Saberhagen	.08	.06	.03
77	Brian Drahman(FC)	.15	.11	.06	168	Kevin Seitzer	.05	.04	.02
78	Alex Fernandez	.15	.11	.06	169	Terry Shumpert	.05	.04	.02
79	Carlton Fisk	.10	.08	.04	170	Kurt Stillwell	.05	.04	.02
80	Scott Fletcher	.04	.03	.02	171	Danny Tartabull	.08	.06	.03
81	Craig Grebeck	.04	.03	.02	172	Gary Thurman	.04	.03	.02
82	Ozzie Guillen	.06	.05	.02	173	Dante Bichette	.05	.04	.02
83	Greg Hibbard	.06	.05	.02	174	Kevin Brown	.04	.03	.02
84	Charlie Hough	.05	.04	.02	175	Chuck Crim	.04	.03	.02
85	Mike Huff	.05	.04	.02	176	Jim Gantner	.05	.04	.02
86	Bo Jackson	.40	.30	.15	177	Darryl Hamilton	.05	.04	.02
87	Lance Johnson	.04	.03	.02	178	Ted Higuera	.06	.05	.02
88	Ron Karkovice	.04	.03	.02	179	Darren Holmes	.04	.03	.02
89	Jack McDowell	.08	.06	.03	180	Mark Lee	.04	.03	.02
90	Matt Merullo	.04	.03	.02	181	Julio Machado	.04	.03	.02
91	Warren Newson	.15	.11	.06	182	Paul Molitor	.10	.08	.04
92	Donn Pall	.04	.03	.02	183	Jaime Navarro	.06	.05	.02
93	Dan Pasqua	.05	.04	.02	184	Edwin Nunez	.04	.03	.02
94	Ken Patterson	.04	.03	.02	185	Dan Plesac	.05	.04	.02
95	Melido Perez	.05	.04	.02	186	Willie Randolph	.05	.04	.02
96	Scott Radinsky	.04	.03	.02	187	Ron Robinson	.04	.03	.02
97	Tim Raines	.10	.08	.04	188	Gary Sheffield	.25	.20	.10
98	Sammy Sosa	.08	.06	.03	189	Bill Spiers	.05	.04	.02
99	Bobby Thigpen	.08	.06	.03	190	B.J. Surhoff	.05	.04	.02
100	Frank Thomas	1.00	.70	.40	191	Dale Sveum	.04	.03	.02
101	Robin Ventura	.20	.15	.08	192	Greg Vaughn	.10	.08	.04

#	Player	MT	NR MT	EX
193	Bill Wegman	.05	.04	.02
194	Robin Yount	.15	.11	.06
195	Rick Aguilera	.05	.04	.02
196	Allan Anderson	.04	.03	.02
197	Steve Bedrosian	.04	.03	.02
198	Randy Bush	.04	.03	.02
199	Larry Casian(FC)	.05	.04	.02
200	Chili Davis	.06	.05	.02
201	Scott Erickson	.20	.15	.08
202	Greg Gagne	.04	.03	.02
203	Dan Gladden	.04	.03	.02
204	Brian Harper	.05	.04	.02
205	Kent Hrbek	.06	.05	.02
206	Chuck Knoblauch	.20	.15	.08
207	Gene Larkin	.04	.03	.02
208	Terry Leach	.04	.03	.02
209	Scott Leius	.10	.08	.04
210	Shane Mack	.08	.06	.03
211	Jack Morris	.08	.06	.03
212	Pedro Munoz(FC)	.20	.15	.08
213	*Denny Neagle*(FC)	.20	.15	.08
214	Al Newman	.04	.03	.02
215	Junior Ortiz	.04	.03	.02
216	Mike Pagliarulo	.04	.03	.02
217	Kirby Puckett	.15	.11	.06
218	Paul Sorrento	.06	.05	.02
219	Kevin Tapani	.08	.06	.03
220	Lenny Webster	.06	.05	.02
221	Jesse Barfield	.06	.05	.02
222	Greg Cadaret	.04	.03	.02
223	Dave Eiland	.04	.03	.02
224	Alvaro Espinoza	.04	.03	.02
225	Steve Farr	.05	.04	.02
226	Bob Geren	.04	.03	.02
227	Lee Guetterman	.04	.03	.02
228	John Habyan	.04	.03	.02
229	Mel Hall	.06	.05	.02
230	Steve Howe	.06	.05	.02
231	*Mike Humphreys*(FC)	.20	.15	.08
232	*Scott Kamieniecki*	.15	.11	.06
233	Pat Kelly	.15	.11	.06
234	Roberto Kelly	.08	.06	.03
235	Tim Leary	.04	.03	.02
236	Kevin Maas	.15	.11	.06
237	Don Mattingly	.25	.20	.10
238	Hensley Meulens	.08	.06	.03
239	Matt Nokes	.06	.05	.02
240	Pascual Perez	.05	.04	.02
241	Eric Plunk	.04	.03	.02
242	*John Ramos*(FC)	.15	.11	.06
243	Scott Sanderson	.05	.04	.02
244	Steve Sax	.06	.05	.02
245	*Wade Taylor*	.15	.11	.06
246	Randy Velarde	.04	.03	.02
247	Bernie Williams	.20	.15	.08
248	Troy Afenir	.05	.04	.02
249	Harold Baines	.08	.06	.03
250	Lance Blankenship	.04	.03	.02
251	*Mike Bordick*(FC)	.10	.08	.04
252	Jose Canseco	.25	.20	.10
253	Steve Chitren	.06	.05	.02
254	Ron Darling	.06	.05	.02
255	Dennis Eckersley	.08	.06	.03
256	Mike Gallego	.04	.03	.02
257	Dave Henderson	.08	.06	.03
258	Rickey Henderson	.20	.15	.08
259	Rick Honeycutt	.04	.03	.02
260	Brook Jacoby	.06	.05	.02
261	Carney Lansford	.06	.05	.02
262	Mark McGwire	.15	.11	.06
263	Mike Moore	.05	.04	.02
264	Gene Nelson	.04	.03	.02
265	Jamie Quirk	.04	.03	.02
266	*Joe Slusarski*(FC)	.15	.11	.06
267	Terry Steinbach	.06	.05	.02
268	Dave Stewart	.08	.06	.03
269	Todd Van Poppel(FC)	.70	.50	.30
270	Walt Weiss	.06	.05	.02
271	Bob Welch	.06	.05	.02
272	Curt Young	.04	.03	.02
273	Scott Bradley	.04	.03	.02
274	Greg Briley	.04	.03	.02
275	Jay Buhner	.06	.05	.02
276	Henry Cotto	.04	.03	.02
277	Alvin Davis	.06	.05	.02
278	Rich DeLucia	.06	.05	.02
279	Ken Griffey, Jr.	.70	.50	.30
280	Erik Hanson	.08	.06	.03
281	Brian Holman	.05	.04	.02
282	Mike Jackson	.04	.03	.02
283	Randy Johnson	.08	.06	.03
284	Tracy Jones	.04	.03	.02
285	Bill Krueger	.04	.03	.02
286	Edgar Martinez	.06	.05	.02
287	Tino Martinez	.10	.08	.04
288	Rob Murphy	.04	.03	.02
289	Pete O'Brien	.04	.03	.02
290	Alonzo Powell	.06	.05	.02
291	Harold Reynolds	.06	.05	.02
292	Mike Schooler	.05	.04	.02
293	Russ Swan	.04	.03	.02
294	Bill Swift	.04	.03	.02
295	Dave Valle	.04	.03	.02
296	Omar Vizquel	.04	.03	.02
297	Gerald Alexander	.05	.04	.02
298	Brad Arnsberg	.05	.04	.02
299	Kevin Brown	.05	.04	.02
300	Jack Daugherty	.04	.03	.02
301	Mario Diaz	.04	.03	.02
302	Brian Downing	.05	.04	.02
303	Julio Franco	.08	.06	.03
304	Juan Gonzalez	.25	.20	.10
305	Rich Gossage	.05	.04	.02
306	Jose Guzman	.05	.04	.02
307	*Jose Hernandez*(FC)	.20	.15	.08
308	Jeff Huson	.05	.04	.02
309	Mike Jeffcoat	.04	.03	.02
310	*Terry Mathews*(FC)	.20	.15	.08
311	Rafael Palmeiro	.10	.08	.04
312	Dean Palmer	.20	.15	.08
313	Geno Petralli	.04	.03	.02
314	Gary Pettis	.04	.03	.02
315	Kevin Reimer	.05	.04	.02
316	*Ivan Rodriguez*	.80	.60	.30
317	Kenny Rogers	.05	.04	.02
318	*Wayne Rosenthal*(FC)	.10	.08	.04
319	Jeff Russell	.05	.04	.02
320	Nolan Ryan	.25	.20	.10
321	Ruben Sierra	.15	.11	.06
322	Jim Acker	.04	.03	.02
323	Roberto Alomar	.10	.08	.04
324	Derek Bell	.35	.25	.14
325	Pat Borders	.05	.04	.02
326	Tom Candiotti	.05	.04	.02
327	Joe Carter	.08	.06	.03
328	Rob Ducey	.05	.04	.02
329	Kelly Gruber	.08	.06	.03
330	*Juan Guzman*(FC)	.80	.60	.30
331	Tom Henke	.06	.05	.02
332	Jimmy Key	.05	.04	.02
333	Manny Lee	.05	.04	.02
334	Al Leiter	.04	.03	.02
335	*Bob MacDonald*(FC)	.10	.08	.04
336	Candy Maldonado	.05	.04	.02
337	Rance Mulliniks	.04	.03	.02
338	Greg Myers	.05	.04	.02
339	John Olerud	.15	.11	.06
340	*Ed Sprague*	.10	.08	.04
341	Dave Stieb	.08	.06	.03
342	Todd Stottlemyre	.05	.04	.02
343	*Mike Timlin*	.15	.11	.06
344	Duane Ward	.05	.04	.02
345	David Wells	.05	.04	.02
346	Devon White	.08	.06	.03
347	Mookie Wilson	.04	.03	.02
348	Eddie Zosky	.08	.06	.03
349	Steve Avery	.20	.15	.08
350	Mike Bell(FC)	.08	.06	.03
351	Rafael Belliard	.04	.03	.02
352	Juan Berenguer	.04	.03	.02
353	Jeff Blauser	.05	.04	.02
354	Sid Bream	.05	.04	.02
355	Francisco Cabrera	.05	.04	.02
356	Marvin Freeman	.04	.03	.02
357	Ron Gant	.15	.11	.06
358	Tom Glavine	.10	.08	.04
359	*Brian Hunter*(FC)	.25	.20	.10
360	Dave Justice	.20	.15	.08
361	Charlie Leibrandt	.04	.03	.02
362	Mark Lemke	.05	.04	.02
363	Kent Mercker	.05	.04	.02
364	*Keith Mitchell*(FC)	.20	.15	.08
365	Greg Olson	.05	.04	.02
366	Terry Pendleton	.08	.06	.03
367	*Armando Reynoso*(FC)	.15	.11	.06
368	Deion Sanders	.15	.11	.06
369	Lonnie Smith	.04	.03	.02
370	Pete Smith	.04	.03	.02
371	John Smoltz	.10	.08	.04
372	Mike Stanton	.05	.04	.02
373	Jeff Treadway	.05	.04	.02
374	*Mark Wohlers*(FC)	.25	.20	.10

#	Player	MT	NR MT	EX
375	Paul Assenmacher	.04	.03	.02
376	George Bell	.08	.06	.03
377	Shawn Boskie	.06	.05	.02
378	*Frank Castillo*(FC)	.25	.20	.10
379	Andre Dawson	.12	.09	.05
380	Shawon Dunston	.08	.06	.03
381	Mark Grace	.08	.06	.03
382	Mike Harkey	.05	.04	.02
383	Danny Jackson	.05	.04	.02
384	Les Lancaster	.04	.03	.02
385	*Cedric Landrum*(FC)	.15	.11	.06
386	Greg Maddux	.06	.05	.02
387	Derrick May	.15	.11	.06
388	Chuck McElroy	.04	.03	.02
389	Ryne Sandberg	.20	.15	.08
390	*Heathcliff Slocumb*	.10	.08	.04
391	Dave Smith	.05	.04	.02
392	Dwight Smith	.05	.04	.02
393	Rick Sutcliffe	.05	.04	.02
394	Hector Villanueva	.06	.05	.02
395	*Chico Walker*(FC)	.10	.08	.04
396	Jerome Walton	.06	.05	.02
397	*Rick Wilkins*	.15	.11	.06
398	Jack Armstrong	.06	.05	.02
399	*Freddie Benavides*	.10	.08	.04
400	Glenn Braggs	.05	.04	.02
401	Tom Browning	.06	.05	.02
402	Norm Charlton	.06	.05	.02
403	Eric Davis	.12	.09	.05
404	Rob Dibble	.08	.06	.03
405	Bill Doran	.05	.04	.02
406	Mariano Duncan	.05	.04	.02
407	*Kip Gross*(FC)	.10	.08	.04
408	Chris Hammond	.06	.05	.02
409	Billy Hatcher	.04	.03	.02
410	*Chris Jones*(FC)	.15	.11	.06
411	Barry Larkin	.10	.08	.04
412	Hal Morris	.10	.08	.04
413	Randy Myers	.05	.04	.02
414	Joe Oliver	.05	.04	.02
415	Paul O'Neill	.06	.05	.02
416	Ted Power	.04	.03	.02
417	Luis Quinones	.04	.03	.02
418	Jeff Reed	.04	.03	.02
419	Jose Rijo	.08	.06	.03
420	Chris Sabo	.08	.06	.03
421	Reggie Sanders(FC)	.40	.30	.15
422	Scott Scudder	.05	.04	.02
423	Glenn Sutko	.05	.04	.02
424	Eric Anthony	.08	.06	.03
425	*Jeff Bagwell*	.80	.60	.30
426	Craig Biggio	.08	.06	.03
427	Ken Caminiti	.05	.04	.02
428	Casey Candaele	.04	.03	.02
429	Mike Capel	.04	.03	.02
430	Andujar Cedeno	.15	.11	.06
431	Jim Corsi	.04	.03	.02
432	Mark Davidson	.04	.03	.02
433	Steve Finley	.06	.05	.02
434	Luis Gonzalez	.20	.15	.08
435	Pete Harnisch	.06	.05	.02
436	Dwayne Henry	.04	.03	.02
437	Xavier Hernandez	.04	.03	.02
438	Jimmy Jones	.04	.03	.02
439	*Darryl Kile*	.10	.08	.04
440	*Rob Mallicoat*(FC)	.15	.11	.06
441	*Andy Mota*(FC)	.15	.11	.06
442	Al Osuna	.05	.04	.02
443	Mark Portugal	.04	.03	.02
444	*Scott Servais*(FC)	.10	.08	.04
445	Mike Simms	.10	.08	.04
446	Gerald Young	.04	.03	.02
447	Tim Belcher	.06	.05	.02
448	Brett Butler	.08	.06	.03
449	John Candelaria	.04	.03	.02
450	Gary Carter	.08	.06	.03
451	Dennis Cook	.04	.03	.02
452	Tim Crews	.04	.03	.02
453	Kal Daniels	.08	.06	.03
454	Jim Gott	.04	.03	.02
455	Alfredo Griffin	.04	.03	.02
456	Kevin Gross	.04	.03	.02
457	Chris Gwynn	.04	.03	.02
458	Lenny Harris	.05	.04	.02
459	Orel Hershiser	.08	.06	.03
460	Jay Howell	.05	.04	.02
461	Stan Javier	.04	.03	.02
462	Eric Karros(FC)	.50	.40	.20
463	Ramon Martinez	.12	.09	.05
464	Roger McDowell	.05	.04	.02
465	Mike Morgan	.05	.04	.02
466	Eddie Murray	.12	.09	.05
467	Jose Offerman	.12	.09	.05
468	Bob Ojeda	.05	.04	.02
469	Juan Samuel	.06	.05	.02
470	Mike Scioscia	.06	.05	.02
471	Darryl Strawberry	.15	.11	.06
472	*Bret Barberie*(FC)	.15	.11	.06
473	Brian Barnes	.06	.05	.02
474	Eric Bullock	.04	.03	.02
475	Ivan Calderon	.08	.06	.03
476	Delino DeShields	.08	.06	.03
477	*Jeff Fassero*(FC)	.10	.08	.04
478	Mike Fitzgerald	.04	.03	.02
479	Steve Frey	.04	.03	.02
480	Andres Galarraga	.06	.05	.02
481	Mark Gardner	.06	.05	.02
482	Marquis Grissom	.12	.09	.05
483	*Chris Haney*(FC)	.20	.15	.08
484	Barry Jones	.04	.03	.02
485	Dave Martinez	.05	.04	.02
486	Dennis Martinez	.08	.06	.03
487	Chris Nabholz	.06	.05	.02
488	Spike Owen	.04	.03	.02
489	Gilberto Reyes	.05	.04	.02
490	Mel Rojas	.05	.04	.02
491	Scott Ruskin	.05	.04	.02
492	Bill Sampen	.05	.04	.02
493	Larry Walker	.10	.08	.04
494	Tim Wallach	.08	.06	.03
495	Daryl Boston	.04	.03	.02
496	Hubie Brooks	.06	.05	.02
497	Tim Burke	.05	.04	.02
498	Mark Carreon	.04	.03	.02
499	Tony Castillo	.04	.03	.02
500	Vince Coleman	.08	.06	.03
501	David Cone	.08	.06	.03
502	Kevin Elster	.04	.03	.02
503	Sid Fernandez	.06	.05	.02
504	John Franco	.06	.05	.02
505	Dwight Gooden	.12	.09	.05
506	Todd Hundley	.12	.09	.05
507	Jeff Innis	.04	.03	.02
508	Gregg Jefferies	.12	.09	.05
509	Howard Johnson	.12	.09	.05
510	Dave Magadan	.06	.05	.02
511	*Terry McDaniel*(FC)	.20	.15	.08
512	Kevin McReynolds	.08	.06	.03
513	Keith Miller	.04	.03	.02
514	Charlie O'Brien	.04	.03	.02
515	Mackey Sasser	.04	.03	.02
516	*Pete Schourek*	.10	.08	.04
517	Julio Valera	.06	.05	.02
518	Frank Viola	.10	.08	.04
519	Wally Whitehurst	.05	.04	.02
520	*Anthony Young*(FC)	.20	.15	.08
521	*Andy Ashby*	.10	.08	.04
522	*Kim Batiste*(FC)	.10	.08	.04
523	Joe Boever	.04	.03	.02
524	Wes Chamberlain	.20	.15	.08
525	Pat Combs	.05	.04	.02
526	Danny Cox	.04	.03	.02
527	Darren Daulton	.05	.04	.02
528	Jose DeJesus	.05	.04	.02
529	Lenny Dykstra	.08	.06	.03
530	Darrin Fletcher	.05	.04	.02
531	Tommy Greene	.06	.05	.02
532	Jason Grimsley	.05	.04	.02
533	Charlie Hayes	.05	.04	.02
534	Von Hayes	.06	.05	.02
535	Dave Hollins	.08	.06	.03
536	Ricky Jordan	.08	.06	.03
537	John Kruk	.06	.05	.02
538	Jim Lindeman	.04	.03	.02
539	Mickey Morandini	.08	.06	.03
540	Terry Mulholland	.06	.05	.02
541	Dale Murphy	.12	.09	.05
542	Randy Ready	.04	.03	.02
543	Wally Ritchie	.04	.03	.02
544	Bruce Ruffin	.04	.03	.02
545	Steve Searcy	.04	.03	.02
546	Dickie Thon	.04	.03	.02
547	Mitch Williams	.08	.06	.03
548	Stan Belinda	.04	.03	.02
549	Jay Bell	.06	.05	.02
550	Barry Bonds	.15	.11	.06
551	Bobby Bonilla	.12	.09	.05
552	Steve Buechele	.05	.04	.02
553	Doug Drabek	.08	.06	.03
554	Neal Heaton	.04	.03	.02
555	Jeff King	.05	.04	.02
556	Bob Kipper	.04	.03	.02

		MT	NR MT	EX
557	Bill Landrum	.04	.03	.02
558	Mike LaValliere	.05	.04	.02
559	Jose Lind	.04	.03	.02
560	Lloyd McClendon	.04	.03	.02
561	Orlando Merced	.25	.20	.10
562	Bob Patterson	.04	.03	.02
563	*Joe Redfield*(FC)	.10	.08	.04
564	Gary Redus	.04	.03	.02
565	Rosario Rodriguez	.04	.03	.02
566	Don Slaught	.04	.03	.02
567	John Smiley	.06	.05	.02
568	Zane Smith	.05	.04	.02
569	Randy Tomlin	.08	.06	.03
570	Andy Van Slyke	.08	.06	.03
571	Gary Varsho	.04	.03	.02
572	Bob Walk	.04	.03	.02
573	*John Wehner*(FC)	.25	.20	.10
574	Juan Agosto	.04	.03	.02
575	Cris Carpenter	.05	.04	.02
576	Jose DeLeon	.05	.04	.02
577	Rich Gedman	.04	.03	.02
578	Bernard Gilkey	.10	.08	.04
579	Pedro Guerrero	.08	.06	.03
580	Ken Hill	.05	.04	.02
581	Rex Hudler	.04	.03	.02
582	Felix Jose	.10	.08	.04
583	Ray Lankford	.15	.11	.06
584	Omar Olivares	.06	.05	.02
585	Jose Oquendo	.04	.03	.02
586	Tom Pagnozzi	.05	.04	.02
587	Geronimo Pena	.05	.04	.02
588	Mike Perez	.05	.04	.02
589	Gerald Perry	.04	.03	.02
590	Bryn Smith	.04	.03	.02
591	Lee Smith	.06	.05	.02
592	Ozzie Smith	.12	.09	.05
593	Scott Terry	.04	.03	.02
594	Bob Tewksbury	.04	.03	.02
595	Milt Thompson	.04	.03	.02
596	Todd Zeile	.12	.09	.05
597	Larry Andersen	.04	.03	.02
598	Oscar Azocar	.04	.03	.02
599	Andy Benes	.10	.08	.04
600	*Ricky Bones*(FC)	.10	.08	.04
601	Jerald Clark	.05	.04	.02
602	Pat Clements	.04	.03	.02
603	Paul Faries	.06	.05	.02
604	Tony Fernandez	.06	.05	.02
605	Tony Gwynn	.12	.09	.05
606	Greg Harris	.05	.04	.02
607	Thomas Howard	.05	.04	.02
608	Bruce Hurst	.06	.05	.02
609	Darrin Jackson	.04	.03	.02
610	Tom Lampkin	.04	.03	.02
611	Craig Lefferts	.04	.03	.02
612	*Jim Lewis*(FC)	.20	.15	.08
613	Mike Maddux	.04	.03	.02
614	Fred McGriff	.10	.08	.04
615	*Jose Melendez*(FC)	.20	.15	.08
616	*Jose Mota*	.15	.11	.06
617	Dennis Rasmussen	.04	.03	.02
618	Bip Roberts	.06	.05	.02
619	Rich Rodriguez	.04	.03	.02
620	Benito Santiago	.08	.06	.03
621	*Craig Shipley*(FC)	.10	.08	.04
622	Tim Teufel	.04	.03	.02
623	*Kevin Ward*(FC)	.15	.11	.06
624	Ed Whitson	.05	.04	.02
625	Dave Anderson	.04	.03	.02
626	Kevin Bass	.05	.04	.02
627	*Rod Beck*(FC)	.10	.08	.04
628	Bud Black	.05	.04	.02
629	Jeff Brantley	.05	.04	.02
630	John Burkett	.05	.04	.02
631	Will Clark	.25	.20	.10
632	*Royce Clayton*(FC)	.20	.15	.08
633	Steve Decker	.10	.08	.04
634	Kelly Downs	.04	.03	.02
635	Mike Felder	.04	.03	.02
636	Scott Garrelts	.04	.03	.02
637	Eric Gunderson	.08	.06	.03
638	*Bryan Hickerson*(FC)	.20	.15	.08
639	Darren Lewis	.15	.11	.06
640	Greg Litton	.04	.03	.02
641	Kirt Manwaring	.06	.05	.02
642	*Paul McClellan*(FC)	.10	.08	.04
643	Willie McGee	.08	.06	.03
644	Kevin Mitchell	.12	.09	.05
645	Francisco Olivares	.04	.03	.02
646	*Mike Remlinger*(FC)	.10	.08	.04
647	Dave Righetti	.06	.05	.02

		MT	NR MT	EX
648	Robby Thompson	.05	.04	.02
649	Jose Uribe	.04	.03	.02
650	Matt Williams	.12	.09	.05
651	Trevor Wilson	.06	.05	.02
652	Tom Goodwin(FC)	.25	.20	.10
653	Terry Bross(FC)	.08	.06	.03
654	*Mike Christopher*(FC)	.20	.15	.08
655	*Kenny Lofton*(FC)	.50	.40	.20
656	*Chris Cron*(FC)	.20	.15	.08
657	Willie Banks(FC)	.25	.20	.10
658	*Pat Rice*(FC)	.25	.20	.10
659a	*Rob Mauer*(FC)	1.25	.90	.50
659b	*Rob Maurer*(FC)	.25	.20	.10
660	Don Harris(FC)	.20	.15	.08
661	Henry Rodriguez(FC)	.10	.08	.04
662	*Cliff Brantley*(FC)	.20	.15	.08
663	*Mike Linskey*(FC)	.20	.15	.08
664	Gary Disarcina(FC)	.08	.06	.03
665	Gil Heredia(FC)	.20	.15	.08
666	*Vinny Castilla*(FC)	.25	.20	.10
667	Paul Abbott(FC)	.08	.06	.03
668	Monty Fariss(FC)	.08	.06	.03
669	*Jarvis Brown*(FC)	.10	.08	.04
670	*Wayne Kirby*(FC)	.20	.15	.08
671	*Scott Brosius*(FC)	.15	.11	.06
672	Bob Hamelin(FC)	.10	.08	.04
673	*Joel Johnston*(FC)	.20	.15	.08
674	*Tim Spehr*(FC)	.15	.11	.06
675	*Jeff Gardner*(FC)	.15	.11	.06
676	*Rico Rossy*(FC)	.20	.15	.08
677	Roberto Hernandez(FC)	.20	.15	.08
678	*Ted Wood*(FC)	.25	.20	.10
679	Cal Eldred(FC)	.40	.30	.15
680	Sean Berry(FC)	.08	.06	.03
681	Rickey Henderson (RS)	.15	.11	.06
682	Nolan Ryan (RS)	.20	.15	.08
683	Dennis Martinez (RS)	.05	.04	.02
684	Wilson Alvarez (RS)	.05	.04	.02
685	Joe Carter (RS)	.06	.05	.02
686	Dave Winfield (RS)	.10	.08	.04
687	David Cone (RS)	.06	.05	.02
688	Jose Canseco (LL)	.15	.11	.06
689	Howard Johnson (LL)	.08	.06	.03
690	Julio Franco (LL)	.08	.06	.03
691	Terry Pendleton (LL)	.08	.06	.03
692	Cecil Fielder (LL)	.10	.08	.04
693	Scott Erickson (LL)	.10	.08	.04
694	Tom Glavine (LL)	.08	.06	.03
695	Dennis Martinez (LL)	.05	.04	.02
696	Bryan Harvey (LL)	.05	.04	.02
697	Lee Smith (LL)	.05	.04	.02
698	Super Siblings (Roberto & Sandy Alomar)			
		.08	.06	.03
699	The Indispensables (Bonilla & Clark)			
		.10	.08	.04
700	Teamwork (Wohlers, Mercker & Pena)			
		.06	.05	.02
701	Tiger Tandems (Jones. Jackson, Olson & Thomas)	.20	.15	.08
702	The Ignitors (Molitor & Butler)	.06	.05	.02
703	The Indespensables II (Ripken, Jr. & Carter)	.15	.11	.06
704	Power Packs (Larkin & Puckett)	.10	.08	.04
705	Today & Tomorrow (Vaughn & Fielder)			
		.15	.11	.06
706	Teenage Sensations (Martinez & Guillen)			
		.08	.06	.03
707	Designated Hitters (Baines & Boggs)			
		.08	.06	.03
708	Robin Yount (PV)	.40	.30	.15
709	Ken Griffey, Jr. (PV)	.80	.60	.30
710	Nolan Ryan (PV)	.80	.60	.30
711	Cal Ripken, Jr. (PV)	.70	.50	.30
712	Frank Thomas (PV)	1.00	.70	.40
713	Dave Justice (PV)	.70	.50	.30
714	Checklist	.04	.03	.02
715	Checklist	.04	.03	.02
716	Checklist	.04	.03	.02
717	Checklist	.04	.03	.02
718	Checklist	.04	.03	.02
719	Checklist	.04	.03	.02
720	Checklist	.04	.03	.02

A player's name in italic type indicates a rookie card. An (FC) indicates a player's first card for that particular card company.

1992 Fleer All-Stars

Black borders with gold highlights are featured on these special insert cards. The fronts feature glossy action photos with a portrait photo inset. The card backs feature career highlights and are numbered.

		MT	NR MT	EX
Complete Set:		30.00	22.00	12.00
Common Player:		.40	.30	.15
1	Felix Jose	.70	.50	.30
2	Tony Gwynn	1.50	1.25	.60
3	Barry Bonds	1.50	1.25	.60
4	Bobby Bonilla	1.25	.90	.50
5	Mike LaValliere	.40	.30	.15
6	Tom Glavine	.80	.60	.30
7	Ramon Martinez	.60	.45	.25
8	Lee Smith	.40	.30	.15
9	Mickey Tettleton	.50	.40	.20
10	Scott Erickson	1.00	.70	.40
11	Frank Thomas	8.00	6.00	3.25
12	Danny Tartabull	.80	.60	.30
13	Will Clark	2.00	1.50	.80
14	Ryne Sandberg	2.50	2.00	1.00
15	Terry Pendleton	.60	.45	.25
16	Barry Larkin	.80	.60	.30
17	Rafael Palmeiro	.80	.60	.30
18	Julio Franco	.80	.60	.30
19	Robin Ventura	2.00	1.50	.80
20	Cal Ripken	3.00	2.25	1.25
21	Joe Carter	1.00	.70	.40
22	Kirby Puckett	2.00	1.50	.80
23	Ken Griffey, Jr.	4.00	3.00	1.50
24	Jose Canseco	3.00	2.25	1.25

1992 Fleer Roger Clemens

This 15-card set honors the career highlights of Roger Clemens. The initial 12 cards from the set were inserted in 1992 Fleer wax packs. A limited number of autographed cards were inserted as well. The additional three cards from the set were available through a mail-in offer. The card fronts feature black borders with metallic gold type. The flip side is yellow with black borders. Various career highlights are featured on the backs of the different cards.

	MT	NR MT	EX
Complete Set:	30.00	22.00	12.00
Common Player: (1-12)	2.00	1.50	.80
Common Player: (13-15)	3.00	2.25	1.25

1992 Fleer Lumber Co.

Baseball's top power hitters at each position are featured in this nine-card set. The card fronts feature full-color action photos bordered in black. "The Lumber Co." appears along the right border in the shape of a baseball bat. The card backs feature posed player photos and career highlights.

		MT	NR MT	EX
Complete Set:		18.00	13.50	7.25
Common Player:		1.25	.90	.50
1	Cecil Fielder	2.50	2.00	1.00
2	Mickey Tettleton	1.25	.90	.50
3	Darryl Strawberry	2.00	1.50	.80
4	Ryne Sandberg	4.00	3.00	1.50
5	Jose Canseco	4.00	3.00	1.50
6	Matt Williams	1.25	.90	.50
7	Cal Ripken	4.00	3.00	1.50
8	Barry Bonds	2.50	2.00	1.00
9	Ron Gant	2.00	1.50	.80

1992 Fleer Rookie Sensations

This 20-card set features the top rookies of 1991 and rookie prospects from 1992. The card fronts feature blue borders with "Rookie Sensations" in gold along the top border. A name plate is featured below the photo and also includes the team. The flip sides feature background information on the player. The cards were randomly inserted in 1992 Fleer cello packs.

		MT	NR MT	EX
Complete Set:		175.00	125.00	70.00
Common Player:		4.00	3.00	1.50
1	Frank Thomas	50.00	37.00	20.00
2	Todd Van Poppel	10.00	7.50	4.00
3	Orlando Merced	8.00	6.00	3.00
4	Jeff Bagwell	25.00	18.00	10.00
5	Jeff Fassero	4.00	3.00	1.50
6	Darren Lewis	7.00	5.25	2.75
7	Milt Cuyler	5.00	3.75	2.00

		MT	NR MT	EX
8	Mike Timlin	4.00	3.00	1.50
9	Brian McRae	6.00	4.50	2.50
10	Chuck Knoblauch	12.00	9.00	5.00
11	Rich DeLucia	4.00	3.00	1.50
12	Ivan Rodriguez	15.00	11.00	6.00
13	Juan Guzman	8.00	6.00	3.00
14	Steve Chitren	4.00	3.00	1.50
15	Mark Wohlers	6.00	4.50	2.50
16	Wes Chamberlain	6.00	4.50	2.50
17	Ray Lankford	10.00	7.50	4.00
18	Chito Martinez	6.00	4.50	2.50
19	Phil Plantier	20.00	15.00	8.00
20	Scott Leius	4.00	3.00	1.50

A player's name in italic indicates a rookie card. An (FC) indicates a player's first card for that particular card company.

1992 Fleer Team Leaders

White and green borders highlight this insert set from Fleer. The card fronts also feature a special "team leaders" logo within the full-color player photo. The card backs feature player information. The cards were randomly inserted in 1992 Fleer rack packs.

		MT	NR MT	EX
Complete Set:		28.00	21.00	11.00
Common Player:		.50	.40	.20
1	Don Mattingly	1.50	1.25	.60
2	Howard Johnson	.70	.50	.30
3	Chris Sabo	.50	.40	.20
4	Carlton Fisk	1.00	.70	.40
5	Kirby Puckett	2.00	1.50	.80
6	Cecil Fielder	1.75	1.25	.70
7	Tony Gwynn	2.00	1.50	.80
8	Will Clark	2.00	1.50	.80
9	Bobby Bonilla	1.25	.90	.50
10	Len Dykstra	.50	.40	.20
11	Tom Glavine	.70	.50	.30
12	Rafael Palmeiro	.80	.60	.30
13	Wade Boggs	1.50	1.25	.60
14	Joe Carter	1.00	.70	.40
15	Ken Griffey, Jr.	4.00	3.00	1.50
16	Darryl Strawberry	1.75	1.25	.70
17	Cal Ripken	2.50	2.00	1.00
18	Danny Tartabull	.80	.60	.30
19	Jose Canseco	2.50	2.00	1.00
20	Andre Dawson	1.00	.70	.40

1992 Fleer Ultra

Fleer released its second consecutive Ultra set in 1992. The card fronts feature full-color action photos with a marble accent at the card bottom. The flip sides are horizontal with two additional player photos. Many subsets including rookies, award winners and others were inserted in the set. A two-card Tony Gwynn send-away set was also available through an offer from Fleer. For $1 and 10 Ultra wrappers, collectors could receive the Gwynn cards. The cards are numbered in order by team.

		MT	NR MT	EX
Complete Set:		70.00	52.00	27.00
Common Player:		.12	.09	.05

		MT	NR MT	EX
1	Glenn Davis	.12	.09	.05
2	Mike Devereaux	.15	.11	.06
3	Dwight Evans	.12	.09	.05
4	Leo Gomez	.30	.25	.12
5	Chris Hoiles	.30	.25	.12
6	Sam Horn	.12	.09	.05
7	Chito Martinez	.15	.11	.06
8	Randy Milligan	.12	.09	.05
9	Mike Mussina	3.50	2.75	1.50
10	Billy Ripken	.12	.09	.05
11	Cal Ripken	2.50	2.00	1.00
12	Tom Brunansky	.12	.09	.05
13	Ellis Burks	.15	.11	.06
14	Jack Clark	.12	.09	.05
15	Roger Clemens	1.50	1.25	.60
16	Mike Greenwell	.12	.09	.05
17	Joe Hesketh	.12	.09	.05
18	Tony Pena	.12	.09	.05
19	Carlos Quintana	.12	.09	.05
20	Jeff Reardon	.12	.09	.05
21	Jody Reed	.12	.09	.05
22	Luis Rivera	.12	.09	.05
23	Mo Vaughn	.40	.30	.15
24	Gary DiSarcina	.12	.09	.05
25	Chuck Finley	.15	.11	.06
26	Gary Gaetti	.12	.09	.05
27	Bryan Harvey	.15	.11	.06
28	Lance Parrish	.12	.09	.05
29	Luis Polonia	.12	.09	.05
30	Dick Schofield	.12	.09	.05
31	Luis Polonia	.12	.09	.05
32	Wilson Alvarez	.12	.09	.05
33	Carlton Fisk	.30	.25	.12
34	Craig Grebeck	.12	.09	.05
35	Ozzie Guillen	.12	.09	.05
36	Greg Hibbard	.12	.09	.05
37	Charlie Hough	.12	.09	.05
38	Lance Johnson	.12	.09	.05
39	Ron Karkovice	.12	.09	.05
40	Jack McDowell	.15	.11	.06
41	Donn Pall	.12	.09	.05
42	Melido Perez	.12	.09	.05
43	Tim Raines	.15	.11	.06
44	Frank Thomas	5.00	3.75	2.00
45	Sandy Alomar, Jr.	.15	.11	.06
46	Carlos Baerga	.15	.11	.06
47	Albert Belle	.60	.45	.25
48	Jerry Browne	.12	.09	.05
49	Felix Fermin	.12	.09	.05
50	Reggie Jefferson	.15	.11	.06
51	Mark Lewis	.40	.30	.15
52	Carlos Martinez	.12	.09	.05
53	Steve Olin	.12	.09	.05
54	Jim Thome	1.50	1.25	.60
55	Mark Whiten	.15	.11	.06
56	Dave Bergman	.12	.09	.05
57	Milt Cuyler	.12	.09	.05
58	Rob Deer	.12	.09	.05
59	Cecil Fielder	1.50	1.25	.60
60	Travis Fryman	1.75	1.25	.70
61	Scott Livingstone	.15	.11	.06
62	Tony Phillips	.15	.11	.06
63	Mickey Tettleton	.15	.11	.06
64	Alan Trammell	.15	.11	.06
65	Lou Whitaker	.15	.11	.06
66	Kevin Appier	.15	.11	.06
67	Mike Boddicker	.12	.09	.05
68	George Brett	.40	.30	.15
69	Jim Eisenreich	.12	.09	.05
70	Mark Gubicza	.12	.09	.05
71	David Howard	.12	.09	.05
72	Joel Johnston	.12	.09	.05

		MT	NR MT	EX			MT	NR MT	EX
73	Mike Macfarlane	.12	.09	.05	166	Greg Olson	.12	.09	.05
74	Brent Mayne	.12	.09	.05	167	Terry Pendleton	.15	.11	.06
75	Brian McRae	.30	.25	.12	168	Lonnie Smith	.12	.09	.05
76	Jeff Montgomery	.12	.09	.05	169	John Smoltz	.15	.11	.06
77	Danny Tartabull	.15	.11	.06	170	Mike Stanton	.12	.09	.05
78	Danny Tartabull	.30	.25	.12	171	Jeff Treadway	.12	.09	.05
79	Dante Bichette	.12	.09	.05	172	Paul Assenmacher	.12	.09	.05
80	Ted Higuera	.12	.09	.05	173	George Bell	.15	.11	.06
81	Paul Molitor	.15	.11	.06	174	Shawon Dunston	.12	.09	.05
82	Jamie Navarro	.15	.11	.06	175	Mark Grace	.30	.25	.12
83	Gary Sheffield	1.50	1.25	.60	176	Danny Jackson	.12	.09	.05
84	Bill Spiers	.12	.09	.05	177	Les Lancaster	.12	.09	.05
85	B.J. Surhoff	.12	.09	.05	178	Greg Maddux	.15	.11	.06
86	Greg Vaughn	.30	.25	.12	179	Luis Salazar	.12	.09	.05
87	Robin Yount	.40	.30	.15	180	Rey Sanchez	.15	.11	.06
88	Rick Aguilera	.12	.09	.05	181	Ryne Sandberg	1.50	1.25	.60
89	Chili Davis	.12	.09	.05	182	Jose Vizcaino	.12	.09	.05
90	Scott Erickson	.40	.30	.15	183	Chico Walker	.12	.09	.05
91	Brian Harper	.12	.09	.05	184	Jerome Walton	.12	.09	.05
92	Kent Hrbek	.12	.09	.05	185	Glenn Braggs	.12	.09	.05
93	Chuck Knoblauch	1.00	.70	.40	186	Tom Browning	.12	.09	.05
94	Scott Leius	.12	.09	.05	187	Rob Dibble	.15	.11	.06
95	Shane Mack	.15	.11	.06	188	Bill Doran	.12	.09	.05
96	Mike Pagliarulo	.12	.09	.05	189	Chris Hammond	.15	.11	.06
97	Kirby Puckett	1.50	1.25	.60	190	Billy Hatcher	.12	.09	.05
98	Kevin Tapani	.12	.09	.05	191	Barry Larkin	.40	.30	.15
99	Jesse Barfield	.12	.09	.05	192	Hal Morris	.15	.11	.06
100	Alvaro Espinoza	.12	.09	.05	193	Joe Oliver	.12	.09	.05
101	Mel Hall	.12	.09	.05	194	Paul O'Neill	.12	.09	.05
102	Pat Kelly	.12	.09	.05	195	Jeff Reed	.12	.09	.05
103	Roberto Kelly	.30	.25	.12	196	Jose Rijo	.12	.09	.05
104	Kevin Maas	.12	.09	.05	197	Chris Sabo	.15	.11	.06
105	Don Mattingly	.50	.40	.20	198	Jeff Bagwell	2.00	1.50	.80
106	Hensley Meulens	.12	.09	.05	199	Craig Biggio	.15	.11	.06
107	Matt Nokes	.12	.09	.05	200	Ken Caminiti	.12	.09	.05
108	Steve Sax	.15	.11	.06	201	Andujar Cedeno	.15	.11	.06
109	Harold Baines	.15	.11	.06	202	Steve Finley	.15	.11	.06
110	Jose Canseco	2.00	1.50	.80	203	Luis Gonzalez	.15	.11	.06
111	Ron Darling	.12	.09	.05	204	Pete Harnisch	.15	.11	.06
112	Mike Gallego	.12	.09	.05	205	Xavier Hernandez	.12	.09	.05
113	Dave Henderson	.12	.09	.05	206	Darryl Kile	.12	.09	.05
114	Rickey Henderson	1.00	.70	.40	207	Al Osuna	.12	.09	.05
115	Mark McGwire	1.00	.70	.40	208	Curt Schilling	.12	.09	.05
116	Terry Steinbach	.12	.09	.05	209	Brett Butler	.12	.09	.05
117	Dave Stewart	.15	.11	.06	210	Kal Daniels	.12	.09	.05
118	Todd Van Poppel	1.00	.70	.40	211	Lenny Harris	.12	.09	.05
119	Bob Welch	.12	.09	.05	212	Stan Javier	.12	.09	.05
120	Greg Briley	.12	.09	.05	213	Ramon Martinez	.15	.11	.06
121	Jay Buhner	.12	.09	.05	214	Roger McDowell	.12	.09	.05
122	Rich DeLucia	.12	.09	.05	215	Jose Offerman	.12	.09	.05
123	Ken Griffey, Jr.	4.00	3.00	1.50	216	Juan Samuel	.12	.09	.05
124	Erik Hanson	.12	.09	.05	217	Mike Scioscia	.12	.09	.05
125	Randy Johnson	.12	.09	.05	218	Mike Sharperson	.12	.09	.05
126	Edgar Martinez	.15	.11	.06	219	Darryl Strawberry	1.00	.70	.40
127	Tino Martinez	.15	.11	.06	220	Delino DeShields	.15	.11	.06
128	Pete O'Brien	.12	.09	.05	221	Tom Foley	.12	.09	.05
129	Harold Reynolds	.12	.09	.05	222	Steve Frey	.12	.09	.05
130	Dave Valle	.12	.09	.05	223	Dennis Martinez	.12	.09	.05
131	Julio Franco	.15	.11	.06	224	Spike Owen	.12	.09	.05
132	Juan Gonzalez	2.00	1.50	.80	225	Gilberto Reyes	.12	.09	.05
133	Jeff Huson	.12	.09	.05	226	Tim Wallach	.12	.09	.05
134	Mike Jeffcoat	.12	.09	.05	227	Daryl Boston	.12	.09	.05
135	Terry Mathews	.12	.09	.05	228	Tim Burke	.12	.09	.05
136	Rafael Palmeiro	.30	.25	.12	229	Vince Coleman	.12	.09	.05
137	Dean Palmer	1.00	.70	.40	230	David Cone	.15	.11	.06
138	Geno Petralli	.12	.09	.05	231	Kevin Elster	.12	.09	.05
139	Ivan Rodriguez	2.00	1.50	.80	232	Dwight Gooden	.40	.30	.15
140	Jeff Russell	.12	.09	.05	233	Todd Hundley	.15	.11	.06
141	Nolan Ryan	3.00	2.25	1.25	234	Jeff Innis	.12	.09	.05
142	Ruben Sierra	1.00	.70	.40	235	Howard Johnson	.15	.11	.06
143	Roberto Alomar	1.00	.70	.40	236	Dave Magadan	.12	.09	.05
144	Pat Borders	.12	.09	.05	237	Mackey Sasser	.12	.09	.05
145	Joe Carter	.30	.25	.12	238	Anthony Young	.40	.30	.15
146	Kelly Gruber	.12	.09	.05	239	Wes Chamberlain, Wes Chamberlain			
147	Jimmy Key	.12	.09	.05	240	Darren Daulton	.15	.11	.06
148	Manny Lee	.12	.09	.05	241	Lenny Dykstra	.15	.11	.06
149	Rance Mulliniks	.12	.09	.05	242	Tommy Greene	.12	.09	.05
150	Greg Myers	.12	.09	.05	243	Charlie Hayes	.12	.09	.05
151	John Olerud	.30	.25	.12	244	Dave Hollins	.15	.11	.06
152	Dave Stieb	.12	.09	.05	245	Ricky Jordan	.12	.09	.05
153	Todd Stottlemyre	.12	.09	.05	246	John Kruk	.15	.11	.06
154	Duane Ward	.12	.09	.05	247	Mickey Morandini	.15	.11	.06
155	Devon White	.12	.09	.05	248	Terry Mulholland	.12	.09	.05
156	Eddie Zosky	.15	.11	.06	249	Dale Murphy	.15	.11	.06
157	Steve Avery	1.00	.70	.40	250	Jay Bell	.15	.11	.06
158	Rafael Belliard	.12	.09	.05	251	Barry Bonds	1.00	.70	.40
159	Jeff Blauser	.12	.09	.05	252	Steve Buechele	.12	.09	.05
160	Mark Lemke	.12	.09	.05	253	Doug Drabek	.15	.11	.06
161	Ron Gant	.60	.45	.25	254	Mike LaValliere	.12	.09	.05
162	Tom Glavine	.50	.40	.20	255	Jose Lind	.12	.09	.05
163	Brian Hunter	.30	.25	.12	256	Lloyd McClendon	.12	.09	.05
164	Dave Justice	2.00	1.50	.80	257	Orlando Merced	.30	.25	.12

#	Player	MT	NR MT	EX
258	Don Slaught	.12	.09	.05
259	John Smiley	.12	.09	.05
260	Zane Smith	.12	.09	.05
261	Randy Tomlin	.30	.25	.12
262	Andy Van Slyke	.15	.11	.06
263	Pedro Guerrero	.15	.11	.06
264	Felix Jose	.30	.25	.12
265	Ray Lankford	.80	.60	.30
266	Omar Olivares	.12	.09	.05
267	Jose Oquendo	.12	.09	.05
268	Tom Pagnozzi	.12	.09	.05
269	Bryn Smith	.12	.09	.05
270	Lee Smith	.12	.09	.05
271	Ozzie Smith	.50	.40	.20
272	Milt Thompson	.12	.09	.05
273	Todd Zeile	.12	.09	.05
274	Andy Benes	.40	.30	.15
275	Jerald Clark	.12	.09	.05
276	Tony Fernandez	.12	.09	.05
277	Tony Gwynn	1.00	.70	.40
278	Greg Harris	.12	.09	.05
279	Thomas Howard	.12	.09	.05
280	Bruce Hurst	.12	.09	.05
281	Mike Maddux	.12	.09	.05
282	Fred McGriff	.35	.25	.14
283	Benito Santiago	.15	.11	.06
284	Kevin Bass	.12	.09	.05
285	Jeff Brantley	.12	.09	.05
286	John Burkett	.12	.09	.05
287	Will Clark	2.00	1.50	.80
288	Royce Clayton	.60	.45	.25
289	Steve Decker	.12	.09	.05
290	Kelly Downs	.12	.09	.05
291	Mike Felder	.12	.09	.05
292	Darren Lewis	.40	.30	.15
293	Kirt Manwaring	.12	.09	.05
294	Willie McGee	.12	.09	.05
295	Robby Thompson	.12	.09	.05
296	Matt Williams	.40	.30	.15
297	Trevor Wilson	.12	.09	.05
298	Checklist	.10	.08	.04
299	Checklist	.10	.08	.04
300	Checklist	.10	.08	.04
301	Brady Anderson	.20	.15	.08
302	Todd Frohwirth	.12	.09	.05
303	Ben McDonald	.30	.25	.12
304	Mark McLemore	.12	.09	.05
305	Jose Mesa	.12	.09	.05
306	Bob Milacki	.12	.09	.05
307	Gregg Olson	.20	.15	.08
308	David Segui	.12	.09	.05
309	Rick Sutcliffe	.20	.15	.08
310	Jeff Tackett	.20	.15	.08
311	Wade Boggs	.50	.40	.20
312	Scott Cooper	.20	.15	.08
313	John Flaherty	.25	.20	.10
314	Wayne Housie	.20	.15	.08
315	Peter Hoy	.20	.15	.08
316	John Marzano	.12	.09	.05
317	Tim Naehring	.20	.15	.08
318	Phil Plantier	.60	.45	.25
319	Frank Viola	.40	.30	.15
320	Matt Young	.12	.09	.05
321	Jim Abbott	.40	.30	.15
322	Hubie Brooks	.12	.09	.05
323	Chad Curtis	.35	.25	.14
324	Alvin Davis	.12	.09	.05
325	Junior Felix	.20	.15	.08
326	Von Hayes	.12	.09	.05
327	Mark Langston	.30	.25	.12
328	Scott Lewis	.12	.09	.05
329	Don Robinson	.12	.09	.05
330	Bobby Rose	.12	.09	.05
331	Lee Stevens	.12	.09	.05
332	George Bell	.30	.25	.12
333	Esteban Beltre	.12	.09	.05
334	Joey Cora	.12	.09	.05
335	Alex Fernandez	.40	.30	.15
336	Roberto Hernandez	.15	.11	.06
337	Mike Huff	.12	.09	.05
338	Kirk McCaskill	.12	.09	.05
339	Dan Pasqua	.12	.09	.05
340	Scott Radinsky	.12	.09	.05
341	Steve Sax	.20	.15	.08
342	Bobby Thigpen	.30	.25	.12
343	Robin Ventura	1.00	.70	.40
344	Jack Armstrong	.12	.09	.05
345	Alex Cole	.12	.09	.05
346	Dennis Cook	.12	.09	.05
347	Glenallen Hill	.12	.09	.05
348	Thomas Howard	.12	.09	.05
349	Brook Jacoby	.12	.09	.05
350	Kenny Lofton	2.00	1.50	.80
351	Charles Nagy	.50	.40	.20
352	Rod Nichols	.12	.09	.05
353	Junior Ortiz	.12	.09	.05
354	Dave Otto	.12	.09	.05
355	Tony Perezchica	.12	.09	.05
356	Scott Scudder	.12	.09	.05
357	Paul Sorrento	.12	.09	.05
358	Skeeter Barnes	.12	.09	.05
359	Mark Carreon	.12	.09	.05
360	John Doherty	.12	.09	.05
361	Dan Gladden	.12	.09	.05
362	Bill Gullickson	.20	.15	.08
363	Shawn Hare	.15	.11	.06
364	Mike Henneman	.20	.15	.08
365	Chad Kreuter	.12	.09	.05
366	Mark Leiter	.12	.09	.05
367	Mike Munoz	.12	.09	.05
368	Kevin Ritz	.12	.09	.05
369	Mark Davis	.12	.09	.05
370	Tom Gordon	.12	.09	.05
371	Tony Gwynn	.12	.09	.05
372	Gregg Jefferies	.25	.20	.10
373	Wally Joyner	.40	.30	.15
374	Kevin McReynolds	.20	.15	.08
375	Keith Miller	.12	.09	.05
376	Rico Rossy	.25	.20	.10
377	Curtis Wilkerson	.12	.09	.05
378	Ricky Bones	.12	.09	.05
379	Chris Bosio	.12	.09	.05
380	Cal Eldred	2.00	1.50	.80
381	Scott Fletcher	.12	.09	.05
382	Jim Gantner	.12	.09	.05
383	Darryl Hamilton	.12	.09	.05
384	Doug Henry	.25	.20	.10
385	Pat Listach	4.00	3.00	1.50
386	Tim McIntosh	.12	.09	.05
387	Edwin Nunez	.12	.09	.05
388	Dan Plesac	.12	.09	.05
389	Kevin Seitzer	.12	.09	.05
390	Franklin Stubbs	.12	.09	.05
391	William Suero	.25	.20	.10
392	Bill Wegman	.12	.09	.05
393	Willie Banks	.12	.09	.05
394	Jarvis Brown	.20	.15	.08
395	Greg Gagne	.12	.09	.05
396	Mark Guthrie	.12	.09	.05
397	Bill Krueger	.12	.09	.05
398	Pat Mahomes	.50	.40	.20
399	Pedro Munoz	.50	.40	.20
400	John Smiley	.12	.09	.05
401	Gary Wayne	.12	.09	.05
402	Lenny Webster	.12	.09	.05
403	Carl Willis	.12	.09	.05
404	Greg Cadaret	.12	.09	.05
405	Steve Farr	.12	.09	.05
406	Mike Gallego	.12	.09	.05
407	Charlie Hayes	.12	.09	.05
408	Steve Howe	.12	.09	.05
409	Dion James	.12	.09	.05
410	Jeff Johnson	.12	.09	.05
411	Tim Leary	.12	.09	.05
412	Jim Leyritz	.12	.09	.05
413	Melido Perez	.12	.09	.05
414	Scott Sanderson	.12	.09	.05
415	Andy Stankiewicz	.35	.25	.14
416	Mike Stanley	.12	.09	.05
417	Danny Tartabull	.40	.30	.15
418	Lance Blankenship	.12	.09	.05
419	Mike Bordick	.20	.15	.08
420	Scott Brosius	.12	.09	.05
421	Dennis Eckersley	.35	.25	.14
422	Scott Hemond	.12	.09	.05
423	Carney Lansford	.12	.09	.05
424	Henry Mercedes	.25	.20	.10
425	Mike Moore	.12	.09	.05
426	Gene Nelson	.12	.09	.05
427	Randy Ready	.12	.09	.05
428	Bruce Wilson	.20	.15	.08
429	Willie Wilson	.12	.09	.05
430	Rich Amaral	.20	.15	.08
431	Dave Cochrane	.12	.09	.05
432	Henry Cotto	.12	.09	.05
433	Calvin Jones	.20	.15	.08
434	Kevin Mitchell	.25	.20	.10
435	Clay Parker	.12	.09	.05
436	Omar Vizquel	.12	.09	.05
437	Floyd Bannister	.12	.09	.05
438	Kevin Brown	.12	.09	.05
439	John Cangelosi	.12	.09	.05

		MT	NR MT	EX
440	Brian Downing	.12	.09	.05
441	Monty Fariss	.12	.09	.05
443	Donald Harris	.25	.20	.10
444	Kevin Reimer	.12	.09	.05
445	Kenny Rogers	.12	.09	.05
446	Wayne Rosenthal	.12	.09	.05
447	Dickie Thon	.12	.09	.05
448	Derek Bell	.50	.40	.20
449	Juan Guzman	4.00	3.00	1.50
450	Tom Henke	.12	.09	.05
451	Candy Maldonado	.12	.09	.05
452	Jack Morris	.30	.25	.12
453	David Wells	.12	.09	.05
454	Dave Winfield	.50	.40	.20
455	Juan Berenguer	.12	.09	.05
456	Damon Berryhill	.12	.09	.05
457	Mike Bielecki	.12	.09	.05
458	Marvin Freeman	.12	.09	.05
459	Charlie Leibrandt	.12	.09	.05
460	Kent Mercker	.12	.09	.05
461	Otis Nixon	.15	.11	.06
462	Alejandro Pena	.12	.09	.05
463	Ben Rivera	.15	.11	.06
464	Deion Sanders	.50	.40	.20
465	Mark Wohlers	.30	.25	.12
466	Shawn Boskie	.12	.09	.05
467	Frank Castillo	.12	.09	.05
468	Andre Dawson	.40	.30	.15
469	Joe Girardi	.12	.09	.05
470	Chuck McElroy	.12	.09	.05
471	Mike Morgan	.12	.09	.05
472	Ken Patterson	.12	.09	.05
473	Bob Scanlan	.12	.09	.05
474	Gary Scott	.25	.20	.10
475	Dave Smith	.12	.09	.05
476	Sammy Sosa	.20	.15	.08
477	Hector Villanueva	.12	.09	.05
478	Scott Bankhead	.12	.09	.05
479	Tim Belcher	.12	.09	.05
480	Freddie Benavides	.15	.11	.06
481	Jacob Brumfield	.25	.20	.10
482	Norm Charlton	.15	.11	.06
483	Dwayne Henry	.12	.09	.05
484	Dave Martinez	.12	.09	.05
485	Bip Roberts	.15	.11	.06
486	Reggie Sanders	1.50	1.25	.60
487	Greg Swindell	.15	.11	.06
488	Ryan Bowen	.25	.20	.10
489	Casey Candaele	.12	.09	.05
490	Juan Guerrero	.25	.20	.10
491	Pete Incaviglia	.12	.09	.05
492	Jeff Juden	.20	.15	.08
493	Rob Murphy	.12	.09	.05
494	Mark Portugal	.12	.09	.05
495	Rafael Ramirez	.12	.09	.05
496	Scott Servais	.12	.09	.05
497	Ed Taubensee	.35	.25	.14
498	Brian Williams	.30	.25	.12
499	Todd Benzinger	.12	.09	.05
500	John Candelaria	.12	.09	.05
501	Tom Candiotti	.12	.09	.05
502	Tim Crews	.12	.09	.05
503	Eric Davis	.50	.40	.20
504	Jim Gott	.12	.09	.05
505	Dave Hansen	.12	.09	.05
506	Carlos Hernandez	.12	.09	.05
507	Orel Hershiser	.30	.25	.12
508	Eric Karros	3.00	1.50	.80
509	Bob Ojeda	.12	.09	.05
510	Steve Wilson	.12	.09	.05
511	Moises Alou	.15	.11	.06
512	Bret Barberie	.20	.15	.08
513	Ivan Calderon	.25	.20	.10
514	Gary Carter	.25	.20	.10
515	Archi Cianfrocco	.60	.45	.25
516	Jeff Fassero	.12	.09	.05
517	Darrin Fletcher	.12	.09	.05
518	Marquis Grissom	.30	.25	.12
519	Chris Haney	.20	.15	.08
520	Ken Hill	.15	.11	.06
521	Chris Nabholz	.12	.09	.05
522	Bill Sampen	.12	.09	.05
523	John VanderWal	.30	.25	.12
524	David Wainhouse	.25	.20	.10
525	Larry Walker	.25	.20	.10
526	John Wetteland	.15	.11	.06
527	Bobby Bonilla	.80	.60	.30
528	Sid Fernandez	.15	.11	.06
529	John Franco	.12	.09	.05
530	Dave Gallagher	.12	.09	.05
531	Paul Gibson	.12	.09	.05
532	Eddie Murray	.50	.40	.20
533	Junior Noboa	.12	.09	.05
534	Charlie O'Brien	.12	.09	.05
535	Bill Pecota	.12	.09	.05
536	Willie Randolph	.12	.09	.05
537	Bret Saberhagen	.25	.20	.10
538	Dick Schofield	.12	.09	.05
539	Pete Schourek	.12	.09	.05
540	Ruben Amaro	.20	.15	.08
541	Andy Ashby	.12	.09	.05
542	Kim Batiste	.25	.20	.10
543	Cliff Brantley	.20	.15	.08
544	Mariano Duncan	.12	.09	.05
545	Jeff Grotewold	.20	.15	.08
546	Barry Jones	.12	.09	.05
547	Julio Peguero	.20	.15	.08
548	Curt Schilling	.12	.09	.05
549	Mitch Williams	.20	.15	.08
550	Stan Belinda	.12	.09	.05
551	Scott Bullett	.20	.15	.08
552	Cecil Espy	.12	.09	.05
553	Jeff King	.12	.09	.05
554	Roger Mason	.12	.09	.05
555	Paul Miller	.20	.15	.08
556	Denny Neagle	.20	.15	.08
557	Vocente Palacios	.12	.09	.05
558	Bob Patterson	.12	.09	.05
559	Tom Prince	.12	.09	.05
560	Gary Redus	.12	.09	.05
561	Gary Varsho	.12	.09	.05
562	Juan Agosto	.12	.09	.05
563	Cris Carpenter	.12	.09	.05
564	Mark Clark	.20	.15	.08
565	Jose DeLeon	.12	.09	.05
566	Rich Gedman	.12	.09	.05
567	Bernard Gilkey	.15	.11	.06
568	Rex Hudler	.12	.09	.05
569	Tim Jones	.12	.09	.05
570	Donovan Osborne	.60	.45	.25
571	Mike Perez	.12	.09	.05
572	Gerald Perry	.12	.09	.05
573	Bob Tewksbury	.15	.11	.06
574	Todd Worrell	.12	.09	.05
575	Dave Eiland	.12	.09	.05
576	Jeremy Hernandez	.20	.15	.08
577	Craig Lefferts	.12	.09	.05
578	Jose Melendez, Jose Melendez	.12	.09	.05
579	Randy Myers	.12	.09	.05
580	Gary Pettis	.12	.09	.05
581	Rich Rodriguez	.12	.09	.05
582	Gary Sheffield	1.00	.70	.40
583	Craig Shipley	.12	.09	.05
584	Kurt Stillwell	.12	.09	.05
585	Tim Teufel	.12	.09	.05
586	Rod Beck	.20	.15	.08
587	Dave Burba	.12	.09	.05
588	Craig Colbert	.20	.15	.08
589	Bryan Hickerson	.12	.09	.05
590	Mike Jackson	.12	.09	.05
591	Mark Leonard	.12	.09	.05
592	Jim McNamara	.25	.20	.10
593	John Patterson	.20	.15	.08
594	Dave Righetti	.12	.09	.05
595	Cory Snyder	.12	.09	.05
596	Bill Swift	.20	.15	.08
597	Ted Wood	.15	.11	.06
598	Checklist	.10	.08	.04
599	Checklist	.10	.08	.04
600	Checklist	.10	.08	.04

Values quoted in this guide reflect the retail price of a card — the price a collector can expect to pay when buying a card from a dealer. The wholesale price — that which a collector can expect to receive from a dealer when selling cards — will be significantly lower, depending on desirability and condition.

1992 Fleer Update

This 132-card set was released in boxed set form and features traded players, free agents and top rookies from 1992. The cards are styled after the regular 1992 Fleer and are numbered alphabetically according to team. This set marks the ninth year that Fleer has released an update set.

	MT	NR MT	EX
Complete Set:	9.00	6.75	3.50
Common Player:	.05	.04	.02

		MT	NR MT	EX
1	Todd Frohwirth	.05	.04	.02
2	Alan Mills	.05	.04	.02
3	Rick Sutcliffe	.08	.06	.03
4	John Valentin(FC)	.15	.11	.06
5	Frank Viola	.08	.06	.03
6	Bob Zupcic(FC)	.15	.11	.06
7	Mike Butcher(FC)	.15	.11	.06
8	Chad Curtis(FC)	.15	.11	.06
9	Damion Easley(FC)	.15	.11	.06
10	Tim Salmon(FC)	.70	.50	.30
11	Julio Valera	.08	.06	.03
12	George Bell	.08	.06	.03
13	Roberto Hernandez(FC)	.12	.09	.05
14	Shawn Jeter(FC)	.12	.09	.05
15	Thomas Howard	.05	.04	.02
16	Jesse Levis(FC)	.15	.11	.06
17	Kenny Lofton	.25	.20	.10
18	Paul Sorrento	.06	.05	.02
19	Rico Brogna(FC)	.12	.09	.05
20	John Doherty(FC)	.12	.09	.05
21	Dan Gladden	.05	.04	.02
22	Buddy Groom(FC)	.15	.11	.06
23	Shawn Hare(FC)	.12	.09	.05
24	John Kiely(FC)	.12	.09	.05
25	Kurt Knudsen(FC)	.12	.09	.05
26	Gregg Jefferies	.12	.09	.05
27	Wally Joyner	.12	.09	.05
28	Kevin Koslofski(FC)	.20	.15	.08
29	Kevin McReynolds	.08	.06	.03
30	Rusty Meacham	.08	.06	.03
31	Keith Miller	.06	.05	.02
32	Hipolito Pichardo(FC)	.10	.08	.04
33	James Austin(FC)	.10	.08	.04
34	Scott Fletcher	.05	.04	.02
35	John Jaha(FC)	.15	.11	.06
36	Pat Listach(FC)	1.00	.70	.40
37	Dave Nilsson(FC)	.20	.15	.08
38	Kevin Seitzer	.05	.04	.02
39	Tom Edens	.05	.04	.02
40	Pat Mahomes(FC)	.40	.30	.15
41	John Smiley	.08	.06	.03
42	Charlie Hayes	.06	.05	.02
43	Sam Militello(FC)	.50	.40	.20
44	Andy Stankiewicz(FC)	.35	.25	.14
45	Danny Tartabull	.10	.08	.04
46	Bob Wickman(FC)	.40	.30	.15
47	Jerry Browne	.05	.04	.02
48	Kevin Campbell(FC)	.10	.08	.04
49	Vince Horsman(FC)	.10	.08	.04
50	Troy Neel(FC)	.25	.20	.10
51	Ruben Sierra	.12	.09	.05
52	Bruce Walton(FC)	.10	.08	.04
53	Willie Wilson	.08	.06	.03
54	Bret Boone(FC)	.50	.40	.20
55	Dave Fleming(FC)	.50	.40	.20
56	Kevin Mitchell	.08	.06	.03
57	Jeff Nelson(FC)	.08	.06	.03
58	Shane Turner(FC)	.12	.09	.05
59	Jose Canseco	.25	.20	.10
60	Jeff Frye(FC)	.12	.09	.05
61	Damilo Leon(FC)	.12	.09	.05
62	Roger Pavlik(FC)	.12	.09	.05
63	David Cone	.10	.08	.04
64	Pat Hentgen(FC)	.10	.08	.04
65	Randy Knorr(FC)	.10	.08	.04
66	Jack Morris	.08	.06	.03
67	Dave Winfield	.10	.08	.04
68	David Nied(FC)	.30	.25	.12
69	Otis Nixon	.08	.06	.03
70	Alejandro Pena	.06	.05	.02
71	Jeff Reardon	.08	.06	.03
72	Alex Arias(FC)	.12	.09	.05
73	Jim Bullinger(FC)	.12	.09	.05
74	Mike Morgan	.06	.05	.02
75	Rey Sanchez(FC)	.10	.08	.04
76	Bob Scanlan	.05	.04	.02
77	Sammy Sosa	.08	.06	.03
78	Scott Bankhead	.05	.04	.02
79	Tim Belcher	.08	.06	.03
80	Steve Foster(FC)	.12	.09	.05
81	Willie Greene(FC)	.20	.15	.08
82	Bip Roberts	.08	.06	.03
83	Scott Ruskin	.05	.04	.02
84	Greg Swindell	.08	.06	.03
85	Juan Guerrero(FC)	.20	.15	.08
86	Butch Henry(FC)	.12	.09	.05
87	Doug Jones	.08	.06	.03
88	Brian Williams(FC)	.12	.09	.05
89	Tom Candiotti	.06	.05	.02
90	Eric Davis	.08	.06	.03
91	Carlos Hernandez(FC)	.10	.08	.04
92	Mike Piazza(FC)	.20	.15	.08
93	Mike Sharperson	.06	.05	.02
94	Eric Young(FC)	.20	.15	.08
95	Moises Alou	.20	.15	.08
96	Greg Colbrunn	.06	.05	.02
97	Wil Cordero(FC)	.30	.25	.12
98	Ken Hill	.08	.06	.03
99	John Vander Wal(FC)	.15	.11	.06
100	John Wetteland	.08	.06	.03
101	Bobby Bonilla	.10	.08	.04
102	Eric Hilman(FC)	.20	.15	.08
103	Pat Howell(FC)	.12	.09	.05
104	Jeff Kent(FC)	.15	.11	.06
105	Dick Schofield	.05	.04	.02
106	Ryan Thompson(FC)	.35	.25	.12
107	Chico Walker	.05	.04	.02
108	Juan Bell	.05	.04	.02
109	Mariano Duncan	.05	.04	.02
110	Jeff Gretewold(FC)	.20	.15	.08
111	Ben Rivera(FC)	.10	.08	.04
112	Curt Schilling	.08	.06	.03
113	Victor Cole(FC)	.12	.09	.05
114	Albert Martin(FC)	.12	.09	.05
115	Roger Mason	.06	.05	.02
116	Blas Minor(FC)	.12	.09	.05
117	Tim Wakefield(FC)	.40	.30	.15
118	Mark Clark(FC)	.15	.11	.06
119	Rheal Cormier(FC)	.15	.11	.06
120	Donovan Osborne(FC)	.25	.20	.10
121	Todd Worrell	.06	.05	.02
122	Jeremy Hernandez(FC)	.12	.09	.05
123	Randy Myers	.06	.05	.02
124	Frank Seminara(FC)	.12	.09	.05
125	Gary Sheffield	.15	.11	.06
126	Dan Walters(FC)	.12	.09	.05
127	Steve Hosey(FC)	.20	.15	.08
128	Mike Jackson	.05	.04	.02
129	Jim Pena(FC)	.12	.09	.05
130	Cory Snyder	.08	.04	.02
131	Bill Swift	.08	.04	.02
132	Checklist	.05	.04	.02

1993 Fleer Series I

Fleer introduced a two series format in 1993. Series one featured cards 1-343. The card fronts feature silver borders with the player's name, team and position in a banner along the left side of the card. The Fleer logo appears in the lower right corner. The backs feature an action photo of the player with his name in bold behind him. A box featuring biographical, information, statistics and player information is located to the right of the action photo. The cards are numbered alphabetically by team.

		MT	NR MT	EX
Complete Set:		15.00	11.00	6.00
Common Player:		.04	.03	.02
1	Steve Avery	.10	.08	.04
2	Sid Bream	.04	.03	.02
3	Ron Gant	.08	.06	.03
4	Tom Glavine	.10	.08	.04
5	Brian Hunter	.08	.06	.03
6	Ryan Klesko(FC)	.15	.11	.06
7	Charlie Leibrandt	.04	.03	.02
8	Kent Mercker	.04	.03	.02
9	David Nied(FC)	.25	.20	.10
10	Otis Nixon	.06	.05	.02
11	Greg Olson	.04	.03	.02
12	Terry Pendleton	.08	.06	.03
13	Deion Sanders	.15	.11	.06
14	John Smoltz	.08	.06	.03
15	Mike Stanton	.04	.03	.02
16	Mark Wohlers	.08	.06	.03
17	Paul Assenmacher	.04	.03	.02
18	Steve Buechele	.04	.03	.02
19	Shawon Dunston	.06	.05	.02
20	Mark Grace	.08	.06	.03
21	Derrick May	.10	.08	.04
22	Chuck McElroy	.04	.03	.02
23	Mike Morgan	.06	.05	.02
24	Rey Sanchez	.10	.08	.04
25	Ryne Sandberg	.12	.09	.05
26	Bob Scanlan	.04	.03	.02
27	Sammy Sosa	.06	.05	.02
28	Rick Wilkins	.06	.05	.02
29	Bobby Ayala(FC)	.15	.11	.06
30	Tim Belcher	.06	.05	.02
31	Jeff Branson(FC)	.12	.09	.05
32	Norm Charlton	.08	.06	.03
33	Steve Foster(FC)	.12	.09	.05
34	Willie Greene(FC)	.12	.09	.05
35	Chris Hammond	.06	.05	.02
36	Milt Hill(FC)	.10	.08	.04
37	Hal Morris	.06	.05	.02
38	Joe Oliver	.06	.05	.02
39	Paul O'Neill	.06	.05	.02
40	Tim Pugh(FC)	.12	.09	.05
41	Jose Rijo	.08	.06	.03
42	Bip Roberts	.08	.06	.03
43	Chris Sabo	.08	.06	.03
44	Reggie Sanders	.15	.11	.06
45	Eric Anthony	.08	.06	.03
46	Jeff Bagwell	.12	.09	.05
47	Craig Biggio	.08	.06	.03
48	Joe Boever	.04	.03	.02
49	Casey Candaele	.04	.03	.02
50	Steve Finley	.06	.05	.02
51	Luis Gonzalez	.08	.06	.03
52	Pete Harnisch	.08	.06	.03
53	Xavier Hernandez	.04	.03	.02
54	Doug Jones	.05	.04	.02
55	Eddie Taubensee	.08	.06	.03
56	Brian Williams	.08	.06	.03
57	Pedro Astacio(FC)	.20	.15	.08
58	Todd Benzinger	.04	.03	.02
59	Brett Butler	.06	.05	.02
60	Tom Candiotti	.06	.05	.02
61	Lenny Harris	.04	.03	.02
62	Carlos Hernandez	.08	.06	.03
63	Orel Hershiser	.08	.06	.03
64	Eric Karros	.15	.11	.06
65	Ramon Martinez	.08	.06	.03
66	Jose Offerman	.06	.05	.02
67	Mike Scioscia	.04	.03	.02
68	Mike Sharperson	.04	.03	.02
69	Eric Young(FC)	.15	.11	.06
70	Moises Alou	.08	.06	.03
71	Ivan Calderon	.08	.06	.03
72	Archi Cianfrocco	.15	.11	.06
73	Wil Cordero	.10	.08	.04
74	Delino DeShields	.08	.06	.03
75	Mark Gardner	.05	.04	.02
76	Ken Hill	.08	.06	.03
77	Tim Laker(FC)	.15	.11	.06
78	Chris Nabholz	.06	.05	.02
79	Mel Rojas	.04	.03	.02
80	John Vander Wal	.12	.09	.05
81	Larry Walker	.10	.08	.04
82	Tim Wallach	.06	.05	.02

		MT	NR MT	EX
83	John Wetteland	.08	.06	.03
84	Bobby Bonilla	.12	.09	.05
85	Daryl Boston	.04	.03	.02
86	Sid Fernandez	.08	.06	.03
87	Eric Hillman(FC)	.12	.09	.05
88	Todd Hundley	.08	.06	.03
89	Howard Johnson	.08	.06	.03
90	Jeff Kent	.15	.11	.06
91	Eddie Murray	.10	.08	.04
92	Bill Pecota	.04	.03	.02
93	Bret Saberhagen	.08	.06	.03
94	Dick Schofield	.04	.03	.02
95	Pete Schourek	.04	.03	.02
96	Anthony Young	.06	.05	.02
97	Ruben Amaro Jr.	.06	.05	.02
98	Juan Bell	.06	.05	.02
99	Wes Chamberlain	.06	.05	.02
100	Darren Daulton	.08	.06	.03
101	Mariano Duncan	.04	.03	.02
102	Mike Hartley	.04	.03	.02
103	Ricky Jordan	.06	.05	.02
104	John Kruk	.08	.06	.03
105	Mickey Morandini	.08	.06	.03
106	Terry Mulholland	.06	.05	.02
107	Ben Rivera(FC)	.12	.09	.05
108	Curt Schilling	.08	.06	.03
109	Keith Shepherd(FC)	.12	.09	.05
110	Stan Belinda	.05	.04	.02
111	Jay Bell	.06	.05	.02
112	Barry Bonds	.12	.09	.05
113	Jeff King	.05	.04	.02
114	Mike LaValliere	.04	.03	.02
115	Jose Lind	.04	.03	.02
116	Roger Mason	.04	.03	.02
117	Orlando Merced	.06	.05	.02
118	Bob Patterson	.04	.03	.02
119	Don Slaught	.04	.03	.02
120	Zane Smith	.05	.04	.02
121	Randy Tomlin	.06	.05	.02
122	Andy Van Slyke	.08	.06	.03
123	Tim Wakefield	.15	.11	.06
124	Rheal Cormier	.08	.06	.03
125	Bernard Gilkey	.08	.06	.03
126	Felix Jose	.08	.06	.03
127	Ray Lankford	.12	.09	.05
128	Bob McClure	.04	.03	.02
129	Donovan Osborne	.10	.08	.04
130	Tom Pagnozzi	.06	.05	.02
131	Geronimo Pena	.06	.05	.02
132	Mike Perez	.06	.05	.02
133	Lee Smith	.06	.05	.02
134	Bob Tewksbury	.06	.05	.02
135	Todd Worrell	.06	.05	.02
136	Todd Zeile	.08	.06	.03
137	Jerald Clark	.05	.04	.02
138	Tony Gwynn	.12	.09	.05
139	Greg Harris	.05	.04	.02
140	Jeremy Hernandez	.05	.04	.02
141	Darrin Jackson	.05	.04	.02
142	Mike Maddux	.04	.03	.02
143	Fred McGriff	.10	.08	.04
144	Jose Melendez	.08	.06	.03
145	Rich Rodriguez	.04	.03	.02
146	Frank Seminara	.08	.06	.03
147	Gary Sheffield	.12	.09	.05
148	Kurt Stillwell	.05	.04	.02
149	Dan Walters	.10	.08	.04
150	Rod Beck	.06	.05	.02
151	Bud Black	.04	.03	.02
152	Jeff Brantley	.05	.04	.02
153	John Burkett	.05	.04	.02
154	Will Clark	.15	.11	.06
155	Royce Clayton	.08	.06	.03
156	Mike Jackson	.04	.03	.02
157	Darren Lewis	.08	.06	.03
158	Kirt Manwaring	.05	.04	.02
159	Willie McGee	.06	.05	.02
160	Cory Snyder	.06	.05	.02
161	Bill Swift	.06	.05	.02
162	Trevor Wilson	.05	.04	.02
163	Brady Anderson	.10	.08	.04
164	Glenn Davis	.06	.05	.02
165	Mike Devereaux	.08	.06	.03
166	Todd Frohwirth	.04	.03	.02
167	Leo Gomez	.06	.05	.02
168	Chris Hoiles	.08	.06	.03
169	Ben McDonald	.08	.06	.03
170	Randy Milligan	.04	.03	.02
171	Alan Mills	.04	.03	.02
172	Mike Mussina	.12	.09	.05
173	Gregg Olson	.08	.06	.03

		MT	NR MT	EX			MT	NR MT	EX
174	Arthur Rhodes	.10	.08	.04	265	Mark Guthrie	.04	.03	.02
175	David Segui	.05	.04	.02	266	Brian Harper	.08	.06	.03
176	Ellis Burks	.08	.06	.03	267	Kent Hrbek	.08	.06	.03
177	Roger Clemens	.15	.11	.06	268	Terry Jorgensen	.08	.06	.03
178	Scott Cooper	.08	.06	.03	269	Gene Larkin	.04	.03	.02
179	Danny Darwin	.04	.03	.02	270	Scott Leius	.06	.05	.02
180	Tony Fossas	.04	.03	.02	271	Pat Mahomes	.15	.11	.06
181	Paul Quantrill(FC)	.12	.09	.05	272	Pedro Munoz	.10	.08	.04
182	Jody Reed	.05	.04	.02	273	Kirby Puckett	.15	.11	.06
183	John Valentin	.12	.09	.05	274	Kevin Tapani	.08	.06	.03
184	Mo Vaughn	.08	.06	.03	275	Carl Willis	.04	.03	.02
185	Frank Viola	.08	.06	.03	276	Steve Farr	.05	.04	.02
186	Bob Zupcic	.08	.06	.03	277	John Habyan	.04	.03	.02
187	Jim Abbott	.08	.06	.03	278	Mel Hall	.06	.05	.02
188	Gary DiSarcina	.04	.03	.02	279	Charlie Hayes	.06	.05	.02
189	Damion Easley	.15	.11	.06	280	Pat Kelly	.06	.05	.02
190	Junior Felix	.06	.05	.02	281	Don Mattingly	.12	.09	.05
191	Chuck Finley	.06	.05	.02	282	Sam Militello	.12	.09	.05
192	Joe Grahe	.06	.05	.02	283	Matt Nokes	.06	.05	.02
193	Bryan Harvey	.06	.05	.02	284	Melido Perez	.06	.05	.02
194	Mark Langston	.08	.06	.03	285	Andy Stankiewicz	.10	.08	.04
195	John Orton	.04	.03	.02	286	Danny Tartabull	.10	.08	.04
196	Luis Polonia	.05	.04	.02	287	Randy Velarde	.04	.03	.02
197	Tim Salmon	.20	.15	.08	288	Bob Wickman	.15	.11	.06
198	Luis Sojo	.05	.04	.02	289	Bernie Williams	.10	.08	.04
199	Wilson Alvarez	.05	.04	.02	290	Lance Blankenship	.05	.04	.02
200	George Bell	.08	.04	.02	291	Mike Bordick	.08	.06	.03
201	Alex Fernandez	.08	.04	.02	292	Jerry Browne	.04	.03	.02
202	Craig Grebeck	.04	.03	.02	293	Dennis Eckersley	.10	.08	.04
203	Ozzie Guillen	.06	.05	.02	294	Rickey Henderson	.15	.11	.06
204	Lance Johnson	.06	.05	.02	295	Vince Horsman	.12	.09	.05
205	Ron Karkovice	.04	.03	.02	296	Mark McGwire	.20	.15	.08
206	Kirk McCaskill	.05	.04	.02	297	Jeff Parrett	.04	.03	.02
207	Jack McDowell	.10	.08	.04	298	Ruben Sierra	.15	.11	.06
208	Scott Radinsky	.04	.03	.02	299	Terry Steinbach	.06	.05	.04
209	Tim Raines	.08	.06	.03	300	Walt Weiss	.05	.04	.02
210	Frank Thomas	.40	.30	.15	301	Bob Welch	.06	.05	.04
211	Robin Ventura	.12	.09	.05	302	Willie Wilson	.06	.05	.04
212	Sandy Alomar Jr.	.10	.08	.04	303	Bobby Witt	.06	.05	.04
213	Carlos Baerga	.12	.09	.05	304	Bret Boone	.20	.15	.08
214	Dennis Cook	.04	.03	.02	305	Jay Buhner	.06	.05	.02
215	Thomas Howard	.06	.05	.02	306	Dave Fleming	.12	.09	.05
216	Mark Lewis	.08	.06	.03	307	Ken Griffey Jr.	.40	.30	.15
217	Derek Lilliquist	.04	.03	.02	308	Erik Hanson	.06	.05	.02
218	Kenny Lofton	.15	.11	.06	309	Edgar Martinez	.12	.09	.05
219	Charles Nagy	.15	.11	.06	310	Tino Martinez	.08	.06	.03
220	Steve Olin	.06	.05	.02	311	Jeff Nelson	.12	.09	.05
221	Paul Sorrento	.06	.05	.02	312	Dennis Powell	.04	.03	.02
222	Jim Thome	.10	.08	.04	313	Mike Schooler	.05	.04	.02
223	Mark Whiten	.10	.08	.04	314	Russ Swan	.04	.03	.02
224	Milt Cuyler	.06	.05	.02	315	Dave Valle	.04	.03	.02
225	Rob Deer	.06	.05	.02	316	Omar Vizquel	.04	.03	.02
226	John Doherty	.12	.09	.05	317	Kevin Brown	.08	.06	.03
227	Cecil Fielder	.12	.09	.05	318	Todd Burns	.04	.03	.02
228	Travis Fryman	.15	.11	.06	319	Jose Canseco	.20	.15	.08
229	Mike Henneman	.06	.05	.02	320	Julio Franco	.08	.06	.03
230	John Kiely	.12	.09	.05	321	Jeff Frye(FC)	.12	.09	.05
231	Kurt Knudsen	.12	.09	.05	322	Juan Gonzalez	.25	.20	.10
232	Scott Livingstone	.10	.08	.04	323	Jose Guzman	.06	.05	.02
233	Tony Phillips	.08	.06	.03	324	Jeff Huson	.05	.04	.02
234	Mickey Tettleton	.08	.06	.03	325	Dean Palmer	.08	.06	.03
235	Kevin Appier	.08	.06	.03	326	Kevin Reimer	.06	.05	.02
236	George Brett	.12	.09	.05	327	Ivan Rodriguez	.15	.11	.06
237	Tom Gordon	.05	.04	.02	328	Kenny Rogers	.04	.03	.02
238	Gregg Jefferies	.10	.08	.04	329	Dan Smith(FC)	.08	.06	.03
239	Wally Joyner	.10	.08	.04	330	Roberto Alomar	.20	.15	.08
240	Kevin Koslofski	.12	.09	.05	331	Derek Bell	.12	.09	.05
241	Mike Macfarlane	.05	.04	.02	332	Pat Borders	.06	.05	.02
242	Brian McRae	.08	.06	.03	333	Joe Carter	.12	.09	.05
243	Rusty Meacham	.08	.06	.03	334	Kelly Gruber	.08	.06	.03
244	Keith Miller	.06	.05	.02	335	Tom Henke	.08	.06	.03
245	Jeff Montgomery	.06	.05	.02	336	Jimmy Key	.08	.06	.03
246	Hipolito Pichardo	.10	.08	.04	337	Manuel Lee	.05	.04	.02
247	Ricky Bones	.08	.06	.03	338	Candy Maldonado	.06	.05	.02
248	Cal Eldred	.15	.11	.06	339	John Olerud	.15	.11	.06
249	Mike Fetters	.05	.04	.02	340	Todd Stottlemyre	.05	.04	.02
250	Darryl Hamilton	.08	.06	.03	341	Duane Ward	.05	.04	.02
251	Doug Henry	.06	.05	.02	342	Devon White	.08	.06	.03
252	John Jaha(FC)	.15	.11	.06	343	Dave Winfield	.15	.11	.06
253	Pat Listach	.20	.15	.08					
254	Paul Molitor	.12	.09	.05					
255	Jaime Navarro	.08	.06	.03					
256	Kevin Seitzer	.06	.05	.02					
257	B.J. Surhoff	.06	.05	.02					
258	Greg Vaughn	.06	.05	.02					
259	Bill Wegman	.06	.05	.02					
260	Robin Yount	.15	.11	.06					
261	Rick Aguilera	.08	.06	.03					
262	Chili Davis	.06	.05	.02					
263	Scott Erickson	.06	.05	.02					
264	Greg Gagne	.05	.04	.02					

Definitions for grading conditions are located in the Introduction section at the front of this book.

Fleer 1993 Series II Baseball Checklist

The Checklist for 1993 Fleer Series II arrived in time to be included in this catalog, but because the cards were not available in the hobby market, no prices were available at press time.

361. Rafael Belliard
362. Damon Berryhill
363. Mike Bielecki
364. Jeff Blauser
365. Francisco Cabrera
366. Marvin Freeman
367. David Justice
368. Mark Lemke
369. Alejandro Pena
370. Jeff Reardon
371. Lonnie Smith
372. Pete Smith
373. Shawn Boskie
374. Jim Bullinger
375. Frank Castillo
376. Doug Dascenzo
377. Andre Dawson
378. Mike Harkey
379. Greg Hibbard
380. Greg Maddux
381. Ken Patterson
382. Jeff Robinson
383. Luis Salazar
384. Dwight Smith
385. Jose Vizcaino
386. Scott Bankhead
387. Tom Browning
388. Darnell ColesB
389. Rob Dibble
390. Bill Doran
391. Dwayne Henry
392. Cesar Hernandez
393. Roberto Kelly
394. Barry Larkin
395. Dave Martinez
396. Kevin Mitchell
397. Jeff Reed
398. Scott Ruskin
399. Greg Swindell
400. Dan Wilson
401. Andy Ashby
402. Freddie Benavides
403. Dante Bichette
404. Willie Blair
405. Denis Boucher
406. Vinny Castilla
407. Braulio Castillo
408. Alex Cole
409. Andres Galarraga
410. Joe Giardi
411. Butch HenryP
412. Darren Holmes
413. Calvin Jones
414. Steve Reed
415. Kevin Ritz
416. Jim Tatum
417. Jack Armstrong
418. Bret Barberie
419. Ryan Bowen
420. Cris Carpenter
421. Chuck Carr
422. Scott Chiamparino
423. Jeff Conine
424. Jim Corsi
425. Steve Decker
426. Chris Donnels
427. Monty Fariss
428. Bob Natal
429. Pat Rapp
430. Dave Weathers
431. Nigel Wilson
432. Ken Caminiti
433. Andujar Cedeno
434. Tom Edens
435. Juan Guerrero
436. Pete Incaviglia
437. Jimmy Jones
438. Darryl Kile
439. Rob Murphy
440. Al Osuna
441. Mark Portugal
442. Scott Servais
443. John Candelaria
444. Tim Crews
445. Eric Davis
446. Tom Goodwin
447. Jim Gott
448. Kevin Gross
449. Dave Hansen
450. Jay Howell
451. Roger McDowell
452. Bob Ojeda
453. Henry Rodriguez
454. Darryl Strawberry
455. Mitch Webster
456. Steve Wilson
457. Brian Barnes
458. Sean Berry
459. Jeff Fassero
460. Darrin Fletcher
461. Marquis Grissom
462. Dennis Martinez
463. Spike Owen
464. Matt Stairs
465. Sergio Valdez
466. Kevin Bass
467. Vince Coleman
468. Mark Dewey
469. Kevin Elster
470. Tony Fernandez
471. John Franco
472. Dave Gallagher
473. Paul Gibson
474. Dwight Gooden
475. Lee Guetterman
476. Jeff Innis
477. Dave Magadan
478. Charlie O'Brien
479. Willie Randolph
480. Mackey Sasser
481. Ryan Thompson
482. Chico Walker
483. Kyle Abbott
484. Bob Ayrault
485. Kim Batiste
486. Cliff Brantley
487. Jose DeLeon
488. Lenny Dykstra
489. Tommy Greene
490. Jeff Grotewold
491. Dave Hollins
492. Danny Jackson
493. Stan Javier
494. Tom Marsh
495. Greg Mathews
496. Dale Murphy
497. Todd Pratt
498. Mitch Williams
499. Danny Cox
500. Doug Drabek
501. Carlos Garcia
502. Lloyd McClendon
503. Denny Neagle
504. Gary Redus
505. Bob Walk
506. John Wehner
507. Luis Alicea
508. Mark Clark
509. Pedro Guerrero
510. Rex Hudler
511. Brian Jordan
512. Omar Olivares
513. Jose Oquendo
514. Gerald Perry
515. Bryn Smith
516. Craig Wilson
517. Tracy Woodson
518. Larry Andersen
519. Andy Benes
520. Jim Deshaies
521. Bruce Hurst
522. Randy Myers
523. Benito Santiago
524. Tim Scott
525. Tim Teufel
526. Mike Benjamin
527. Dave Burba
528. Craig Colbert
529. Mike Felder
530. Bryan Hickerson
531. Chris James
532. Mark Leonard
533. Greg Litton
534. Francisco Oliveras
535. John Patterson
536. Jim Pena
537. Dave Righetti
538. Robby Thompson
539. Jose Uribe
540. Matt Williams
541. Storm Davis
542. Sam Horn
543. Tim Hulett
544. Craig Lefferts
545. Chito Martinez
546. Mark McLemore
547. Luis Mercedes
548. Bob Milacki
549. Joe Orsulak
550. Billy Ripken
551. Cal Ripken, Jr
552. Rick Sutcliffe
553. Jeff Tackett
554. Wade Boggs
555. Tom Brunansky
556. Jack Clark
557. John Dopson
558. Mike Gardiner
559. Mike Greenwell
560. Greg Harris
561. Billy Hatcher
562. Joe Hesketh
563. Tony Pena
564. Phil Plantier
565. Luis Riveria
566. Herm Winningham
567. Matt Young

568. Bert Blyleven
569. Mike Butcher
570. Chuck Crim
571. Chad Curtis
572. Tim Fortugno
573. Steve Frey
574. Gary Gaetti
575. Scott Lewis
576. Lee Stevens
577. Ron Tingley
578. Julio Valera
579. Shawn Abner
580. Joey Cora
581. Chris Cron
582. Carlton Fisk
583. Roberto Hernandez
584. Charlie Hough
585. Terry Leach
586. Donn Pall
587. Dan Pasqua
588. Steve Sax
589. Bobby Thigpen
590. Albert Belle
591. Felix Fermin
592. Glenallen Hill
593. Brook Jacoby
594. Reggie Jefferson
595. Carlos Martinez
596. Jose Mesa
597. Rod Nichols
598. Junior Ortiz
599. Eric Plunk
600. Ted Power
601. Scott Scudder
602. Kevin Wickander
603. Skeeter Barnes
604. Mark Carreon
605. Dan Gladden
606. Bill Gullickson
607. Chad Kreuter
608. Mark Leiter
609. Mike Munoz
610. Rich Rowland
611. Frank Tanana
612. Walt Terrell
613. Alan Trammell
614. Lou Whitaker
615. Luis Aquino
616. Mike Boddicker
617. Jim Eisenreich
618. Mark Gubicza
619. David Howard
620. Mike Magnante
621. Brent Mayne
622. Kevin McReynolds
623. Ed Pierce
624. Bill Sampen
625. Steve Shifflett
626. Gary Thurman
627. Curtis Wilkerson
628. Chris Bosio
629. Scott Fletcher
630. Jim Gantner
631. Dave Nilsson
632. Jesse Orosco
633. Dan Plesac
634. Ron Robinson
635. Bill Spiers
636. Franklin Stubbs
637. Willie Banks
638. Randy Bush
639. Chuck Knoblauch
640. Shane Mack
641. Mike Pagliarulo

642. Jeff Reboulet
643. John Smiley
644. Mike Trombley
645. Gary Wayne
646. Lenny Webster
647. Tim Burke
648. Mike Gallego
649. Dion James
650. Jeff Johnson
651. Scott Kamieniecki
652. Kevin Maas
653. Rich Monteleone
654. Jerry Nielsen
655. Scott Sanderson
656. Mike Stanley
657. Gerald Williams
658. Curt YoungP
659. Harold Baines
660. Kevin Campbell
661. Ron Darling
662. Kelly Downs
663. Eric Fox
664. Dave Henderson
665. Rick Honeycutt
666. Mike Moore
667. Jamie Quirk
668. Jeff Russell
669. Dave Stewart
670. Greg Briley
671. Dave Cochrane
672. Henry Cotto
673. Rich DeLucia
674. Brian Fisher
675. Mark Grant
676. Randy Johnson
677. Tim Leary
678. Pete O'Brien
679. Lance Parrish
680. Harold Reynolds
681. Shane Turner
682. Jack Daugherty
683. David Hulse
684. Terry Mathews
685. Al Newman
686. Edwin Nunez
687. Rafael Palmeiro
688. Roger Pavlik
689. Geno Petralli
690. Nolan Ryan
691. David Cone
692. Alfredo Griffin
693. Juan Guzman
694. Pat Hentgen
695. Randy Knorr
696. Bob MacDonald
697. Jack Morris
698. Ed Sprague
699. Dave Stieb
700. Pat Tabler
701. Mike Timlin
702. David Wells
703. Eddie Zosky
704. Gary Sheffield
705. Darren Daulton
706. Marquis Grissom
707. Greg Maddux
708. Bill Swift
709. Juan Gonzales
710. Mark McGwire
711. Cecil Fielder
712. Albert Belle
713. Joe Carter
714. Power Brokers (Cecil Fielder
     and Frank Thomas)

715. Unsung Heroes (Larry Walker
     and Darren Daulton)
716. Hot Corner Hammers (Edgar
     Martinez and Robin Ventura)
717. Start to Finish (Roger Clemens
     and Dennis Eckersley)
718. Checklist
719. Checklist
720. Checklist

Golden Moments
1 of 3 Dennis Eckersley Consecutive
     Saves Record
2 of 3 Bip Roberts ties NL Consecutifve
     Hits Record
3 of 3 Juan Gonzales/Frank Thomas
     100 + RBI Season in first
     Two Years

American League All-Stars
1 of 12 Frank Thomas, 1B White Sox
2 of 12 Roberto Alomar, 2B Blue Jays
3 of 12 Edgar Martinez, 3B Mariners
4 of 12 Pat Listach, SS Brewers
5 of 12 Cecil Fielder, DH Tigers
6 of 12 Juan Gonzales, OF Rangers
7 of 12 Ken Griffey, Jr, OF Mariners
8 of 12 Joe Carter, OF Blue Jays
9 of 12 Kirby Puckett, OF Twins
10 of 12 Brian Harper, C Twins
11 of 12 Dave Fleming, LHP Mariners
12 of 12 Jack McDowell RHP White Sox

Major League Prospects
1 of 18 Scooter Tucker, C Astros
2 of 18 Kerry Woodson, P Mariners
3 of 18 Greg Colbrunn, 1B Expos
4 of 18 Pedro Martinez, P Dodgers
5 of 18 Dave Silvestri, SS Yankees
6 of 18 Ken Bottenfield, P Expos
7 of 18 Rafael Bournigal, SS Dodgers
8 of 18 J.T. Bruett, OF Twins
9 of 18 Dave Mlicki, PIndians
10 of 18 Paul Wagner, P Pirates
11 of 18 Mike Williams, P Phillies
12 of 18 Henry Mercedes, C Athletics
13 of 18 Scott Taylor, P Red Sox
14 of 18 Dennis Moeller, P Royals
15 of 18 Javier Lopez, C Braves
16 of 18 Steve Cooke, P Pirates
17 of 18 Peter Young, P Expos
18 of 18 Ken Ryan, P Red Sox

Tom Glavine Career Highlights
Tom Glavine12 cards

Pro-Visions
1 of 3 Andy Van Slyke
2 of 3 Tom Glavine
3 of 3 Cecil Fielder

1963 French Bauer Milk Caps

This regional set of cardboard milk bottle caps was issued in the Cincinnati area in 1963 and features 30 members of the Cincinnati Reds. The unnumbered, blank-backed cards are approximately 1-1/4" in diameter and feature rather crude drawings of the players with their names in script alongside the artwork and the words "Visit Beautiful Crosley Field/See The Reds in Action" along the outside. An album was issued to house the set.

	NR MT	EX	VG
Complete Set:	550.00	275.00	165.00
Common Player:	5.00	2.50	1.50
Album:	100.00	50.00	10.00
(1) Don Blasingame	5.00	2.50	1.50
(2) Leo Cardenas	5.00	2.50	1.50
(3) Gordon Coleman	5.00	2.50	1.50
(4) Wm. O. DeWitt	5.00	2.50	1.50
(5) John Edwards	5.00	2.50	1.50
(6) Jesse Gonder	5.00	2.50	1.50
(7) Tommy Harper	5.00	2.50	1.50
(8) Bill Henry	5.00	2.50	1.50
(9) Fred Hutchinson	8.00	4.00	2.50
(10) Joey Jay	5.00	2.50	1.50
(11) Eddie Kasko	5.00	2.50	1.50
(12) Marty Keough	5.00	2.50	1.50
(13) Jim Maloney	8.00	4.00	2.50
(14) Joe Nuxhall	8.00	4.00	2.50
(15) Reggie Otero	5.00	2.50	1.50
(16) Jim O'Toole	5.00	2.50	1.50
(17) Jim Owens	5.00	2.50	1.50
(18) Vada Pinson	18.00	9.00	5.50
(19) Bob Purkey	5.00	2.50	1.50
(20) Frank Robinson	80.00	40.00	24.00
(21) Dr. Richard Rohde	5.00	2.50	1.50
(22) Pete Rose	200.00	100.00	60.00
(23) Ray Shore	5.00	2.50	1.50
(24) Dick Sisler	5.00	2.50	1.50
(25) Bob Skinner	5.00	2.50	1.50
(26) John Tsitorius	5.00	2.50	1.50
(27) Jim Turner	5.00	2.50	1.50
(28) Ken Walters	5.00	2.50	1.50
(29) Al Worthington	5.00	2.50	1.50
(30) Dom Zanni	5.00	2.50	1.50

1987 French/Bray Orioles

8 CAL RIPKEN, IF
Compliments of
FRENCH/BRAY, INC.

The Baltimore Orioles and French Bray, Inc. issued a baseball card set to be handed out to fans in attendance at Memorial Stadium on July 26th. Thirty perforated, detachable cards were printed within a three-panel fold-out piece measuring 9-1/2" by 11-1/4". The card fronts feature full-color player photos surrounded by an orange border. The French/Bray logo appears on the card front. The backs are of simple design, containing only the player's name, uniform number, position and professional record.

	MT	NR MT	EX
Complete Set:	10.00	7.50	4.00
Common Player:	.15	.11	.06
2 Alan Wiggins	.15	.11	.06
3 Bill Ripken	.80	.60	.30
6 Floyd Rayford	.15	.11	.06
7 Cal Ripken, Sr.	.15	.11	.06
8 Cal Ripken	3.00	2.25	1.25
9 Jim Dwyer	.15	.11	.06
10 Terry Crowley	.15	.11	.06
15 Terry Kennedy	.20	.15	.08
16 Scott McGregor	.20	.15	.08
18 Larry Sheets	.50	.40	.20
19 Fred Lynn	.50	.40	.20
20 Frank Robinson	.40	.30	.15
24 Dave Schmidt	.15	.11	.06
25 Ray Knight	.20	.15	.08
27 Lee Lacy	.15	.11	.06
31 Mark Wiley	.15	.11	.06
32 Mark Williamson	.30	.25	.12
33 Eddie Murray	1.50	1.25	.60
38 Ken Gerhart	.50	.40	.20
39 Ken Dixon	.15	.11	.06
40 Jimmy Williams	.15	.11	.06
42 Mike Griffin	.15	.11	.06
43 Mike Young	.20	.15	.08
44 Elrod Hendricks	.15	.11	.06
45 Eric Bell	.30	.25	.12
46 Mike Flanagan	.25	.20	.10
49 Tom Niedenfuer	.20	.15	.08
52 Mike Boddicker	.25	.20	.10
54 John Habyan	.15	.11	.06
57 Tony Arnold	.15	.11	.06

1988 French/Bray Orioles

48 JOSE BAUTISTA, RHS
Compliments of
FRENCH-BRAY, INC.

French-Bray sponsored a full-color brochure that was distributed to fans during an in-stadium promotion. A blue and orange front cover features inset photos of the Orioles in action on the upper left in a filmstrip motif. To the right is the Orioles logo and their 1988 slogan, "You Gotta Be There" above a baseball glove and ball. The 3-panel foldout measures approximately 9-1/2" by 11-1/4" and includes a team photo on the inside cover, with two perforated pages of individual cards featuring players, coaches and the team manager. Individual cards measure 2-1/4" by 3-1/8", with close-ups framed in white with an orange accent line. The player name and sponsor logo are printed beneath the photo. The black and white backs are numbered by player uniform and provide career stats. Additional copies of the brochure were made available from the Orioles Baseball Store following the free giveaway.

	MT	NR MT	EX
Complete Set:	8.00	6.00	3.25
Common Player:	.15	.11	.06
2 Don Buford	.15	.11	.06
6 Joe Orsulak	.15	.11	.06
7 Bill Ripken	.40	.30	.15
8 Cal Ripken	2.50	2.00	1.00
9 Jim Dwyer	.15	.11	.06

		MT	NR MT	EX
10	Terry Crowley	.15	.11	.06
12	Mike Morgan	.15	.11	.06
14	Mickey Tettleton	.50	.40	.20
15	Terry Kennedy	.20	.15	.08
17	Pete Stanicek	.60	.45	.25
18	Larry Sheets	.40	.30	.15
19	Fred Lynn	.50	.40	.20
20	Frank Robinson	.40	.30	.15
23	Ozzie Peraza	.40	.30	.15
24	Dave Schmidt	.15	.11	.06
25	Rich Schu	.15	.11	.06
28	Jim Traber	.25	.20	.10
31	Herm Starrette	.15	.11	.06
33	Eddie Murray	1.50	1.25	.60
34	Jeff Ballard	.30	.25	.12
38	Ken Gerhart	.30	.25	.12
40	Minnie Mendoza	.15	.11	.06
41	Don Aase	.20	.15	.08
44	Elrod Hendricks	.15	.11	.06
47	John Hart	.15	.11	.06
48	Jose Bautista	.30	.25	.12
49	Tom Niedenfuer	.20	.15	.08
52	Mike Boddicker	.25	.20	.10
53	Jay Tibbs	.15	.11	.06
88	Rene Gonzales	.30	.25	.12

1989 French/Bray Orioles

This 32-card Baltimore Orioles team set was co-sponsored by French-Bray and the Wilcox Walter Furlong Paper Co., and was distributed as an in-stadium promotion to fans attending the May 12, 1989, Orioles game. Smaller than standard size, the cards measure 2-1/4" by 3" and feature a full-color player photo with number, name and position below. The backs, done in black and white, include brief player data and complete major and minor league stats.

		MT	NR MT	EX
	Complete Set:	8.00	6.00	3.25
	Common Player:	.15	.11	.06
3	Bill Ripken	.30	.25	.12
6	Joe Orsulak	.15	.11	.06
7	Cal Ripken, Sr.	.15	.11	.06
8	Cal Ripken, Jr.	2.50	2.00	1.00
9	Brady Anderson	.50	.40	.20
10	Steve Finley	.80	.60	.30
11	Craig Worthington	.50	.40	.20
12	Mike Devereaux	.20	.15	.08
14	Mickey Tettleton	.20	.15	.08
15	Randy Milligan	.15	.11	.06
16	Phil Bradley	.20	.15	.08
18	Bob Milacki	.20	.15	.08
19	Larry Sheets	.15	.11	.06
20	Frank Robinson	.40	.30	.15
21	Mark Thurmond	.15	.11	.06
23	Kevin Hickey	.15	.11	.06
24	Dave Schmidt	.15	.11	.06
28	Jim Traber	.20	.15	.08
29	Jeff Ballard	.30	.25	.12
30	Gregg Olson	1.00	.70	.40
31	Al Jackson	.15	.11	.06
32	Mark Williamson	.15	.11	.06
36	Bob Melvin	.15	.11	.06
37	Brian Holton	.15	.11	.06
40	Tom McCraw	.15	.11	.06
42	Pete Harnisch	.35	.25	.14
43	Fransisco Melendez	.20	.15	.08
44	Elrod Hendricks	.15	.11	.06
46	Johnny Oates	.15	.11	.06
48	Jose Bautista	.20	.15	.08
88	Rene Gonzales	.25	.20	.10

1991 Front Row Draft Picks

Only 240,000 of these sets were produced. The bonus card in the set must be sent in to Front Row in exchange for a special Frankie Rodriguez card. The first 120,000 collectors returning bonus cards also received Front Row's mini-update set. The cards feature full-color photos on both sides. Each set includes an official certificate of authenticity. 1991 marks the premier issue of Front Row baseball draft picks.

		MT	NR MT	EX
	Complete Set:	8.00	6.00	3.25
	Common Player:	.20	.15	.08
1	Frankie Rodriguez	1.25	.90	.50
2	Aaron Sele	.25	.20	.10
3	Chad Schoenvogel	.20	.15	.08
4	Scott Ruffcorn	.20	.15	.08
5	Dan Chowlowski	.20	.15	.08
6	Gene Schall	.20	.15	.08
7	Trever Miller	.25	.20	.10
8	Chris Durkin	.20	.15	.08
9	Mike Neill	.20	.15	.08
10	Kevin Stocker	.20	.15	.08
11	Bobby Jones	.50	.40	.20
12	John Farrell	.20	.15	.08
13	Ronnie Allen	.20	.15	.08
14	Mike Rossiter	.20	.15	.08
15	Scott Hatteberg	.25	.20	.10
16	Rodney Pedraza	.20	.15	.08
17	Mike Durant	.20	.15	.08
18	Ryan Long	.20	.15	.08
19	Greg Anthony	.20	.15	.08
20	Jon Barnes	.20	.15	.08
21	Brian Barber	.20	.15	.08
22	Brent Gates	.35	.25	.14
23	Calvin Reese	.30	.25	.14
24	Terry Horn	.20	.15	.08
25	Scott Stahoviak	.35	.25	.14
26	Jason Pruitt	.30	.25	.12
27	Shawn Curran	.20	.15	.08
28	Jimmy Lewis	.25	.20	.10
29	Alex Ochoa	.20	.15	.08
30	Joe Deberry	.20	.15	.08
31	Justin Thompson	.30	.25	.12
32	Jimmy Gonzalez	.30	.25	.12
33	Eddie Ramos	.20	.15	.08
34	Tyler Green	.80	.60	.30
35	Toby Rumfield	.20	.15	.08
36	Dave Doorneweerd	.20	.15	.08
37	Jeff Hostetler	.20	.15	.08
38	Shawn Livsey	.25	.20	.10
39	Mike Groppuso	.40	.30	.15
40	Steve Whitaker	.30	.25	.12
41	Tom McKinnon	.30	.25	.12
42	Buck McNabb	.25	.20	.10
43	Al Shirley	.50	.40	.20
44	Allan Watson	.25	.20	.10
45	Bill Bliss	.20	.15	.08
46	Todd Hollandsworth	.20	.15	.08
47	Manny Ramirez	1.50	1.25	.60
48	J.J. Johnson	.25	.20	.10
49	Cliff Floyd	.50	.40	.20
50	Bonus Card	.25	.20	.10

1985 Fun Food Buttons

Fun Foods of Little Silver, N.J. issued a set of 133 full-color metal pins in 1985. The buttons, which are 1-1/4" in diameter and have a "safety pin" back, have bright borders which correspond to the player's team colors. The button backs are numbered and contain the player's 1984 batting or earned run average. The buttons were available as complete sets through hobby dealers and were also distributed in packs (three buttons per pack) through retail stores.

		MT	NR MT	EX
Complete Set:		25.00	20.00	10.00
Common Player:		.10	.08	.04
1	Dave Winfield	.40	.30	.15
2	Lance Parrish	.25	.20	.10
3	Gary Carter	.35	.25	.14
4	Pete Rose	.80	.60	.30
5	Jim Rice	.35	.25	.14
6	George Brett	.60	.45	.25
7	Fernando Valenzuela	.30	.25	.12
8	Darryl Strawberry	.70	.50	.30
9	Steve Garvey	.35	.25	.14
10	Rollie Fingers	.20	.15	.08
11	Mike Schmidt	1.25	.90	.50
12	Kent Tekulve	.10	.08	.04
13	Ryne Sandberg	.40	.30	.15
14	Bruce Sutter	.15	.11	.06
15	Tom Seaver	.30	.25	.12
16	Reggie Jackson	.70	.50	.30
17	Rickey Henderson	.70	.50	.30
18	Mark Langston	.35	.25	.14
19	Jack Clark	.20	.15	.08
20	Willie Randolph	.15	.11	.06
21	Kirk Gibson	.30	.25	.12
22	Andre Dawson	.30	.25	.12
23	Dave Concepcion	.15	.11	.06
24	Tony Armas	.10	.08	.04
25	Dan Quisenberry	.10	.08	.04
26	Pedro Guerrero	.25	.20	.10
27	Dwight Gooden	1.00	.70	.40
28	Tony Gwynn	.40	.30	.15
29	Robin Yount	.70	.50	.30
30	Steve Carlton	1.00	.70	.40
31	Bill Madlock	.15	.11	.06
32	Rick Sutcliffe	.15	.11	.06
33	Willie McGee	.20	.15	.08
34	Greg Luzinski	.15	.11	.06
35	Rod Carew	.40	.30	.15
36	Dave Kingman	.15	.11	.06
37	Alvin Davis	.40	.30	.15
38	Chili Davis	.15	.11	.06
39	Don Baylor	.15	.11	.06
40	Alan Trammell	.30	.25	.12
41	Tim Raines	.35	.25	.14
42	Cesar Cedeno	.15	.11	.06
43	Wade Boggs	1.00	.70	.40
44	Frank White	.15	.11	.06
45	Steve Sax	.25	.20	.10
46	George Foster	.15	.11	.06
47	Terry Kennedy	.10	.08	.04
48	Cecil Cooper	.15	.11	.06
49	John Denny	.10	.08	.04
50	John Candelaria	.10	.08	.04
51	Jody Davis	.10	.08	.04
52	George Hendrick	.10	.08	.04
53	Ron Kittle	.15	.11	.06
54	Fred Lynn	.20	.15	.08
55	Carney Lansford	.10	.08	.04
56	Gorman Thomas	.10	.08	.04
57	Manny Trillo	.10	.08	.04
58	Steve Kemp	.10	.08	.04
59	Jack Morris	.20	.15	.08
60	Dan Petry	.10	.08	.04
61	Mario Soto	.10	.08	.04
62	Dwight Evans	.20	.15	.08
63	Hal McRae	.10	.08	.04
64	Mike Marshall	.15	.11	.06

		MT	NR MT	EX
65	Mookie Wilson	.15	.11	.06
66	Graig Nettles	.15	.11	.06
67	Ben Oglivie	.10	.08	.04
68	Juan Samuel	.20	.15	.08
69	Johnny Ray	.15	.11	.06
70	Gary Matthews	.15	.11	.06
71	Ozzie Smith	.20	.15	.08
72	Carlton Fisk	.40	.30	.15
73	Doug DeCinces	.10	.08	.04
74	Joe Morgan	.60	.45	.25
75	Dave Stieb	.15	.11	.06
76	Buddy Bell	.15	.11	.06
77	Don Mattingly	1.75	1.25	.70
78	Lou Whitaker	.25	.20	.10
79	Willie Hernandez	.10	.08	.04
80	Dave Parker	.20	.15	.08
81	Bob Stanley	.10	.08	.04
82	Willie Wilson	.15	.11	.06
83	Orel Hershiser	.30	.25	.12
84	Rusty Staub	.15	.11	.06
85	Goose Gossage	.20	.15	.08
86	Don Sutton	.25	.20	.10
87	Al Holland	.10	.08	.04
88	Tony Pena	.15	.11	.06
89	Ron Cey	.15	.11	.06
90	Joaquin Andujar	.10	.08	.04
91	LaMarr Hoyt	.10	.08	.04
92	Tommy John	.20	.15	.08
93	Dwayne Murphy	.10	.08	.04
94	Willie Upshaw	.10	.08	.04
95	Gary Ward	.10	.08	.04
96	Ron Guidry	.20	.15	.08
97	Chet Lemon	.10	.08	.04
98	Aurelio Lopez	.10	.08	.04
99	Tony Perez	.20	.15	.08
100	Bill Buckner	.15	.11	.06
101	Mike Hargrove	.10	.08	.04
102	Scott McGregor	.10	.08	.04
103	Dale Murphy	.60	.45	.25
104	Keith Hernandez	.35	.25	.14
105	Paul Molitor	.20	.15	.08
106	Bert Blyleven	.15	.11	.06
107	Leon Durham	.10	.08	.04
108	Lee Smith	.15	.11	.06
109	Nolan Ryan	2.00	1.50	.80
110	Harold Baines	.15	.11	.06
111	Kent Hrbek	.25	.20	.10
112	Ron Davis	.10	.08	.04
113	George Bell	.30	.25	.12
114	Charlie Hough	.10	.08	.04
115	Phil Niekro	.25	.20	.10
116	Dave Righetti	.20	.15	.08
117	Darrell Evans	.15	.11	.06
118	Cal Ripken, Jr.	1.75	1.25	.60
119	Eddie Murray	.45	.35	.20
120	Storm Davis	.10	.08	.04
121	Mike Boddicker	.10	.08	.04
122	Bob Horner	.15	.11	.06
123	Chris Chambliss	.10	.08	.04
124	Ted Simmons	.15	.11	.06
125	Andre Thornton	.15	.11	.06
126	Larry Bowa	.15	.11	.06
127	Bob Dernier	.10	.08	.04
128	Joe Niekro	.15	.11	.06
129	Jose Cruz	.15	.11	.06
130	Tom Brunansky	.20	.15	.08
131	Gary Gaetti	.25	.20	.10
132	Lloyd Moseby	.15	.11	.06
133	Frank Tanana	.10	.08	.04

1983 Gardner's Brewers

Topps produced in 1983 for Gardner's Bakery of Madison, Wisconsin, a 22-card set featuring the American League champion Milwaukee Brewers. The cards, which measure 2-1/2" by 3-1/2", have colorful fronts which contain the player's name, team and position plus the Brewers and Gardner's logos. The card backs are identical to the regular Topps issue but are numbered 1-22. The cards were inserted in specially marked packages of Gardner's bread products and were susceptible to grease stains.

		MT	NR MT	EX
	Complete Set	25.00	18.50	10.00
	Common Player	.50	.40	.20
1	Harvey Kuenn	.70	.50	.30
2	Dwight Bernard	.50	.40	.20
3	Mark Brouhard	.50	.40	.20
4	Mike Caldwell	.50	.40	.20
5	Cecil Cooper	1.25	.90	.50
6	Marshall Edwards	.50	.40	.20
7	Rollie Fingers	4.00	3.00	1.50
8	Jim Gantner	.70	.50	.30
9	Moose Haas	.50	.40	.20
10	Bob McClure	.50	.40	.20
11	Paul Molitor	4.00	3.00	1.50
12	Don Money	.50	.40	.20
13	Charlie Moore	.50	.40	.20
14	Ben Oglivie	.60	.45	.25
15	Ed Romero	.50	.40	.20
16	Ted Simmons	.90	.70	.35
17	Jim Slaton	.50	.40	.20
18	Don Sutton	2.00	1.50	.80
19	Gorman Thomas	.70	.50	.30
20	Pete Vuckovich	.70	.50	.30
21	Ned Yost	.50	.40	.20
22	Robin Yount	7.00	5.25	2.75

**Definitions for grading conditions are located
in the Introduction of this price guide.**

1984 Gardner's Brewers

For the second straight year, Gardner's Bakery inserted baseball cards featuring the Milwaukee Brewers with their bread products. The 22-card set, entitled "1984 Series II," have multi-colored fronts that include the Brewers and Gardner's logos. The card backs are identical to the regular 1984 Topps issue except for the 1-22 numbering system. The Topps-produced cards are the standard 2-1/2" by 3-1/2" size. The cards are sometimes found with grease stains, resulting from contact with the bread.

		MT	NR MT	EX
	Complete Set:	20.00	15.00	8.00
	Common Player:	.50	.40	.20
1	Rene Lachemann	.50	.40	.20

		MT	NR MT	EX
2	Mark Brouhard	.50	.40	.20
3	Mike Caldwell	.50	.40	.20
4	Bobby Clark	.50	.40	.20
5	Cecil Cooper	1.00	.70	.40
6	Rollie Fingers	2.00	1.50	.80
7	Jim Gantner	.70	.50	.30
8	Moose Haas	.50	.40	.20
9	Roy Howell	.50	.40	.20
10	Pete Ladd	.50	.40	.20
11	Rick Manning	.50	.40	.20
12	Bob McClure	.50	.40	.20
13	Paul Molitor	2.00	1.50	.80
14	Charlie Moore	.50	.40	.20
15	Ben Oglivie	.60	.45	.25
16	Ed Romero	.50	.40	.20
17	Ted Simmons	.80	.60	.30
18	Jim Sundberg	.50	.40	.20
19	Don Sutton	1.25	.90	.50
20	Tom Tellmann	.50	.40	.20
21	Pete Vuckovich	.60	.45	.25
22	Robin Yount	5.00	3.75	2.00

1985 Gardner's Brewers

Gardner's Bakery issued a 22-card set featuring the Milwaukee Brewers for the third consecutive year in 1985. The set was produced by Topps and is designed in a horizontal format. The card fronts feature color photos inside blue, red and yellow frames. The player's name and position are placed in orange boxes to the right of the photo and are accompanied by the Brewers and Gardner's logos. The card backs are identical in design to the regular 1985 Topps set but are blue rather than green and are numbered 1-22. The cards, which were inserted in specially marked bread products, are often found with grease stains.

		MT	NR MT	EX
	Complete Set:	15.00	11.00	6.00
	Common Player:	.35	.25	.14
1	George Bamberger	.35	.25	.14
2	Mark Brouhard	.35	.25	.14
3	Bob Clark	.35	.25	.14
4	Jaime Cocanower	.35	.25	.14
5	Cecil Cooper	.90	.70	.35
6	Rollie Fingers	1.25	.90	.50
7	Jim Gantner	.50	.40	.20
8	Moose Haas	.35	.25	.14
9	Dion James	.70	.50	.30
10	Pete Ladd	.35	.25	.14
11	Rick Manning	.35	.25	.14
12	Bob McClure	.35	.25	.14
13	Paul Molitor	1.50	1.25	.60
14	Charlie Moore	.35	.25	.14
15	Ben Oglivie	.50	.40	.20
16	Chuck Porter	.35	.25	.14
17	Ed Romero	.35	.25	.14
18	Bill Schroeder	.35	.25	.14
19	Ted Simmons	.70	.50	.30
20	Tom Tellmann	.35	.25	.14
21	Pete Vuckovich	.50	.40	.20
22	Robin Yount	4.00	3.00	1.50

1989 Gardners Brewers

Returning after a three-year hiatus, Gardner's Bread of Madison, Wis., issued a 15-card Milwaukee Brewers set in 1989. The blue and white-bordered cards are the standard size and feature posed portrait photos with all Brewer logos airbrushed from the players' caps. The Gardner's logo appears at the top of the card, while the player's name is below the photo. The set, which was produced in conjunction with Mike Schechter Associates, was issued with loaves of bread or packages of buns, one card per package.

		MT	NR MT	EX
Complete Set:		5.00	3.75	2.00
Common Player:		.10	.08	.04
1	Paul Molitor	1.00	.70	.40
2	Robin Yount	1.25	.90	.50
3	Jim Gantner	.25	.20	.10
4	Rob Deer	.25	.20	.10
5	B.J. Surhoff	.25	.20	.10
6	Dale Sveum	.20	.15	.08
7	Ted Higuera	.25	.20	.10
8	Dan Plesac	.25	.20	.10
9	Bill Wegman	.15	.11	.06
10	Juan Nieves	.15	.11	.06
11	Greg Brock	.20	.15	.08
12	Glenn Braggs	.25	.20	.10
13	Joey Meyer	.15	.11	.06
14	Ernest Riles	.10	.08	.04
15	Don August	.15	.11	.06

1953 Glendale Hot Dogs Tigers

Glendale Meats issued these unnumbered, full-color cards (2-5/8" by 3-3/4") in packages of hot dogs. Featuring Detroit Tigers players, the card fronts contain a player picture plus the player's name, a facsimile autograph, and the Tigers logo. The card reverses carry player statistical and biographical information plus an offer for a trip for two to the World Series. Collectors were advised to mail all the cards they had saved to Glendale Meats. The World Series trip plus 150 other prizes were to be given to

the individuals sending in the most cards. As with most cards issued with food products, quality-condition cards are tough to find because of the cards' susceptibilty to stains. The Houtteman card is extremely scarce.

		NR MT	EX	VG
Complete Set:		6000.00	3000.00	1800.00
Common Player:		125.00	62.00	37.00
(1)	Matt Batts	125.00	62.00	37.00
(2)	Johnny Bucha	125.00	62.00	37.00
(3)	Frank Carswell	125.00	62.00	37.00
(4)	Jim Delsing	125.00	62.00	37.00
(5)	Walt Dropo	125.00	62.00	37.00
(6)	Hal Erickson	125.00	62.00	37.00
(7)	Paul Foytack	125.00	62.00	37.00
(8)	Owen Friend	150.00	75.00	45.00
(9)	Ned Garver	125.00	62.00	37.00
(10)	Joe Ginsberg	350.00	175.00	105.00
(11)	Ted Gray	125.00	62.00	37.00
(12)	Fred Hatfield	125.00	62.00	37.00
(13)	Ray Herbert	150.00	75.00	45.00
(14)	Bill Hitchcock	125.00	62.00	37.00
(15)	Bill Hoeft	275.00	137.00	82.00
(16)	Art Houtteman	2200.00	1100.00	660.00
(17)	Milt Jordan	200.00	100.00	60.00
(18)	Harvey Kuenn	325.00	162.00	97.00
(19)	Don Lund	125.00	62.00	37.00
(20)	Dave Madison	125.00	62.00	37.00
(21)	Dick Marlowe	125.00	62.00	37.00
(22)	Pat Mullin	125.00	62.00	37.00
(23)	Bob Neiman	125.00	62.00	37.00
(24)	Johnny Pesky	150.00	75.00	45.00
(25)	Jerry Priddy	125.00	62.00	37.00
(26)	Steve Souchock	125.00	62.00	37.00
(27)	Russ Sullivan	125.00	62.00	37.00
(28)	Bill Wight	200.00	100.00	60.00

1961 Golden Press

The 1961 Golden Press set features 33 players, all enshrined in the Baseball Hall of Fame. The full color cards measure 2-1/2" by 3-1/2" and came in a booklet with perforations so that they could be easily removed. Full books with the cards intact would command 50 percent over the set price in the checklist that follows. Card numbers 1-3 and 28-33 are slightly higher in price as they were located on the book's front and back covers, making them more susceptible to scuffing and wear.

		NR MT	EX	VG
Complete Set:		80.00	40.00	24.00
Common Player:		.75	.40	.25
1	Mel Ott	1.75	.90	.50
2	Grover Cleveland Alexander	1.75	.90	.50
3	Babe Ruth	25.00	12.50	7.50
4	Hank Greenberg	1.50	.70	.45
5	Bill Terry	.90	.45	.25
6	Carl Hubbell	.90	.45	.25
7	Rogers Hornsby	2.00	1.00	.60
8	Dizzy Dean	5.00	2.50	1.50
9	Joe DiMaggio	16.00	8.00	4.75
10	Charlie Gehringer	.90	.45	.25
11	Gabby Hartnett	.75	.40	.25

		NR MT	EX	VG
12	Mickey Cochrane	.90	.45	.25
13	George Sisler	.90	.45	.25
14	Joe Cronin	.90	.45	.25
15	Pie Traynor	.75	.40	.25
16	Lou Gehrig	16.00	8.00	4.75
17	Lefty Grove	1.25	.60	.40
18	Chief Bender	.75	.40	.25
19	Frankie Frisch	.90	.45	.25
20	Al Simmons	.75	.40	.25
21	Home Run Baker	.75	.40	.25
22	Jimmy Foxx	2.00	1.00	.60
23	John McGraw	1.25	.60	.40
24	Christy Mathewson	4.00	2.00	1.25
25	Ty Cobb	16.00	8.00	4.75
26	Dazzy Vance	.75	.40	.25
27	Bill Dickey	1.25	.60	.40
28	Eddie Collins	.90	.45	.25
29	Walter Johnson	4.00	2.00	1.25
30	Tris Speaker	1.75	.90	.50
31	Nap Lajoie	1.75	.90	.50
32	Honus Wagner	4.00	2.00	1.25
33	Cy Young	4.00	2.00	1.25

1933 Goudey

Goudey Gum Co.'s first baseball card issue was their 240-card effort in 1933. The cards are color art reproductions of either portrait or action photos. The numbered cards measure 2-3/8" by 2-7/8" in size and carry a short player biography on the reverses. Card #106 (Napoleon Lajoie) is listed in the set though it was not actually issued until 1934. The card is very scarce and is unique in that it carries a 1934 design obverse and a 1933 reverse. The ACC designation for the set is R319.

	NR MT	EX	VG
Complete Set:	85000.00	40000.00	25000.
Common Player: 1-40	150.00	75.00	45.00
Common Player: 41-44	75.00	37.00	22.00
Common Player: 45-52	150.00	75.00	45.00
Common Player: 53-240	75.00	37.00	22.00

		NR MT	EX	VG
1	Benny Bengough	12000.00	2000.00	1050.
2	Arthur (Dazzy) Vance	500.00	200.00	75.00
3	Hugh Critz	150.00	75.00	45.00
4	Henry "Heinie" Schuble	150.00	75.00	45.00
5	Floyd (Babe) Herman	200.00	80.00	35.00
6a	Jimmy Dykes (age is 26 in bio)	200.00	80.00	35.00
6b	Jimmy Dykes (age is 36 in bio)	200.00	80.00	35.00
7	Ted Lyons	275.00	125.00	50.00
8	Roy Johnson	150.00	75.00	45.00
9	Dave Harris	150.00	75.00	45.00
10	Glenn Myatt	150.00	75.00	45.00
11	Billy Rogell	150.00	75.00	45.00
12	George Pipgras	150.00	75.00	45.00
13	Lafayette Thompson	150.00	75.00	25.00
14	Henry Johnson	150.00	75.00	45.00
15	Victor Sorrell	150.00	75.00	45.00
16	George Blaeholder	150.00	75.00	45.00
17	Watson Clark	150.00	75.00	45.00
18	Herold (Muddy) Ruel	150.00	75.00	45.00
19	Bill Dickey	550.00	275.00	100.00
20	Bill Terry	425.00	200.00	75.00
21	Phil Collins	150.00	75.00	45.00
22	Harold (Pie) Traynor	400.00	200.00	90.00
23	Hazen (Ki-Ki) Cuyler	350.00	175.00	105.00

		NR MT	EX	VG
24	Horace Ford	150.00	75.00	45.00
25	Paul Waner	350.00	175.00	105.00
26	Chalmer Cissell	150.00	75.00	45.00
27	George Connally	150.00	75.00	45.00
28	Dick Bartell	150.00	75.00	45.00
29	Jimmy Foxx	700.00	350.00	150.00
30	Frank Hogan	150.00	75.00	45.00
31	Tony Lazzeri	400.00	200.00	80.00
32	John (Bud) Clancy	150.00	75.00	45.00
33	Ralph Kress	150.00	75.00	45.00
34	Bob O'Farrell	150.00	75.00	45.00
35	Al Simmons	500.00	225.00	90.00
36	Tommy Thevenow	150.00	75.00	45.00
37	Jimmy Wilson	150.00	75.00	45.00
38	Fred Brickell	150.00	75.00	45.00
39	Mark Koenig	150.00	75.00	45.00
40	Taylor Douthit	150.00	75.00	45.00
41	Gus Mancuso	75.00	37.00	22.00
42	Eddie Collins	225.00	100.00	50.00
43	Lew Fonseca	85.00	40.00	20.00
44	Jim Bottomley	225.00	100.00	50.00
45	Larry Benton	150.00	75.00	45.00
46	Ethan Allen	150.00	75.00	45.00
47	Henry "Heinie" Manush	350.00	150.00	50.00
48	Marty McManus	150.00	75.00	45.00
49	Frank Frisch	400.00	200.00	90.00
50	Ed Brandt	150.00	75.00	45.00
51	Charlie Grimm	200.00	100.00	30.00
52	Andy Cohen	150.00	75.00	45.00
53	George Herman (Babe) Ruth	6000.00	3000.00	1800.
54	Ray Kremer	75.00	37.00	22.00
55	Perce (Pat) Malone	75.00	37.00	22.00
56	Charlie Ruffing	250.00	100.00	45.00
57	Earl Clark	75.00	37.00	22.00
58	Frank (Lefty) O'Doul	100.00	50.00	22.00
59	Edmund (Bing) Miller	75.00	37.00	22.00
60	Waite Hoyt	200.00	100.00	45.00
61	Max Bishop	75.00	37.00	22.00
62	"Pepper" Martin	125.00	60.00	22.00
63	Joe Cronin	275.00	125.00	50.00
64	Burleigh Grimes	225.00	100.00	50.00
65	Milton Gaston	75.00	37.00	22.00
66	George Grantham	75.00	37.00	22.00
67	Guy Bush	75.00	37.00	22.00
68	Horace Lisenbee	75.00	37.00	22.00
69	Randy Moore	75.00	37.00	22.00
70	Floyd (Pete) Scott	75.00	37.00	22.00
71	Robert J. Burke	75.00	37.00	22.00
72	Owen Carroll	75.00	37.00	22.00
73	Jesse Haines	200.00	100.00	45.00
74	Eppa Rixey	200.00	100.00	45.00
75	Willie Kamm	75.00	37.00	22.00
76	Gordon (Mickey) Cochrane	250.00	100.00	50.00
77	Adam Comorosky	75.00	37.00	22.00
78	Jack Quinn	75.00	37.00	22.00
79	Urban (Red) Faber	200.00	100.00	45.00
80	Clyde Manion	75.00	37.00	22.00
81	Sam Jones	85.00	40.00	25.00
82	Dibrell Williams	75.00	37.00	22.00
83	Pete Jablonowski	150.00	75.00	45.00
84	Glenn Spencer	75.00	37.00	22.00
85	John Henry "Heinie" Sand	75.00	37.00	22.00
86	Phil Todt	75.00	37.00	22.00
87	Frank O'Rourke	75.00	37.00	22.00
88	Russell Rollings	75.00	37.00	22.00
89	Tris Speaker	450.00	200.00	70.00
90	Jess Petty	75.00	37.00	22.00
91	Tom Zachary	75.00	37.00	22.00
92	Lou Gehrig	4000.00	2000.00	1200.
93	John Welch	75.00	37.00	22.00
94	Bill Walker	75.00	37.00	22.00
95	Alvin Crowder	75.00	37.00	22.00
96	Willis Hudlin	75.00	37.00	22.00
97	Joe Morrissey	75.00	37.00	22.00
98	Walter Berger	75.00	37.00	22.00
99	Tony Cuccinello	75.00	37.00	22.00
100	George Uhle	90.00	45.00	22.00
101	Richard Coffman	75.00	37.00	22.00
102	Travis C. Jackson	200.00	100.00	45.00
103	Earl Combs (Earle)	200.00	100.00	45.00
104	Fred Marberry	75.00	37.00	22.00
105	Bernie Friberg	75.00	37.00	22.00
106	Napoleon (Larry) Lajoie	30000.00	13500.00	7500.
107	Henry (Heinie) Manush	200.00	100.00	45.00
108	Joe Kuhel	75.00	37.00	22.00
109	Joe Cronin	200.00	100.00	45.00
110	Leon "Goose" Goslin	200.00	100.00	45.00
111	Monte Weaver	75.00	37.00	22.00
112	Fred Schulte	75.00	37.00	22.00
113	Oswald Bluege	75.00	37.00	22.00
114	Luke Sewell	75.00	37.00	22.00

		NR MT	EX	VG
115	Cliff Heathcote	75.00	37.00	22.00
116	Eddie Morgan	75.00	37.00	22.00
117	Walter (Rabbit) Maranville	200.00	100.00	45.00
118	Valentine J. (Val) Picinich	75.00	37.00	22.00
119	Rogers Hornsby	500.00	250.00	100.00
120	Carl Reynolds	75.00	37.00	22.00
121	Walter Stewart	75.00	37.00	22.00
122	Alvin Crowder	75.00	37.00	22.00
123	Jack Russell	75.00	37.00	22.00
124	Earl Whitehill	75.00	37.00	22.00
125	Bill Terry	300.00	135.00	60.00
126	Joe Moore	75.00	37.00	22.00
127	Melvin Ott	350.00	150.00	60.00
128	Charles (Chuck) Klein	225.00	100.00	50.00
129	Harold Schumacher	90.00	40.00	20.00
130	Fred Fitzsimmons	75.00	37.00	22.00
131	Fred Frankhouse	75.00	37.00	22.00
132	Jim Elliott	75.00	37.00	22.00
133	Fred Lindstrom	200.00	100.00	45.00
134	Edgar (Sam) Rice	200.00	100.00	45.00
135	Elwood (Woody) English	75.00	37.00	22.00
136	Flint Rhem	75.00	37.00	22.00
137	Fred (Red) Lucas	75.00	37.00	22.00
138	Herb Pennock	200.00	100.00	45.00
139	Ben Cantwell	75.00	37.00	22.00
140	Irving (Bump) Hadley	75.00	37.00	22.00
141	Ray Benge	75.00	37.00	22.00
142	Paul Richards	125.00	60.00	25.00
143	Glenn Wright	85.00	40.00	22.00
144	George Herman (Babe) Ruth	4500.00	1750.00	1050.
145	George Walberg	75.00	37.00	22.00
146	Walter Stewart	75.00	37.00	22.00
147	Leo Durocher	225.00	100.00	45.00
148	Eddie Farrell	75.00	37.00	22.00
149	George Herman (Babe) Ruth	5500.00	2750.00	1650.
150	Ray Kolp	75.00	37.00	22.00
151	D'Arcy (Jake) Flowers	75.00	37.00	22.00
152	James (Zack) Taylor	75.00	37.00	22.00
153	Charles (Buddy) Myer	75.00	37.00	22.00
154	Jimmy Foxx	450.00	225.00	75.00
155	Joe Judge	75.00	37.00	22.00
156	Danny Macfayden (MacFayden)	100.00	50.00	27.00
157	Sam Byrd	100.00	50.00	27.00
158	Morris (Moe) Berg	150.00	70.00	30.00
159	Oswald Bluege	75.00	37.00	22.00
160	Lou Gehrig	4000.00	2000.00	1200.
161	Al Spohrer	75.00	37.00	22.00
162	Leo Mangum	75.00	37.00	22.00
163	Luke Sewell	75.00	37.00	22.00
164	Lloyd Waner	200.00	100.00	45.00
165	Joe Sewell	200.00	100.00	45.00
166	Sam West	75.00	37.00	22.00
167	Jack Russell	75.00	37.00	22.00
168	Leon (Goose) Goslin	200.00	100.00	45.00
169	Al Thomas	75.00	37.00	22.00
170	Harry McCurdy	75.00	37.00	22.00
171	Charley Jamieson	75.00	37.00	22.00
172	Billy Hargrave	75.00	37.00	22.00
173	Roscoe Holm	75.00	37.00	22.00
174	Warren (Curley) Ogden	75.00	37.00	22.00
175	Dan Howley	75.00	37.00	22.00
176	John Ogden	75.00	37.00	22.00
177	Walter French	75.00	37.00	22.00
178	Jackie Warner	75.00	37.00	22.00
179	Fred Leach	75.00	37.00	22.00
180	Eddie Moore	75.00	37.00	22.00
181	George Herman (Babe) Ruth	5500.00	2750.00	1650.
182	Andy High	75.00	37.00	22.00
183	George Walberg	75.00	37.00	22.00
184	Charley Berry	75.00	37.00	22.00
185	Bob Smith	75.00	37.00	22.00
186	John Schulte	75.00	37.00	22.00
187	Henry (Heinie) Manush	200.00	100.00	45.00
188	Rogers Hornsby	500.00	200.00	105.00
189	Joe Cronin	200.00	100.00	45.00
190	Fred Schulte	75.00	37.00	22.00
191	Ben Chapman	125.00	60.00	27.00
192	Walter Brown	125.00	60.00	27.00
193	Lynford Lary	100.00	50.00	27.00
194	Earl Averill	200.00	100.00	45.00
195	Evar Swanson	75.00	37.00	22.00
196	Leroy Mahaffey	75.00	37.00	22.00
197	Richard (Rick) Ferrell	200.00	100.00	45.00
198	Irving (Jack) Burns	75.00	37.00	22.00
199	Tom Bridges	80.00	40.00	22.00
200	Bill Hallahan	75.00	37.00	22.00
201	Ernie Orsatti	75.00	37.00	22.00
202	Charles Leo (Gabby) Hartnett	200.00	100.00	45.00
203	Lonnie Warneke	75.00	37.00	22.00
204	Jackson Riggs Stephenson	125.00	60.00	27.00

		NR MT	EX	VG
205	Henry (Heinie) Meine	75.00	37.00	22.00
206	Gus Suhr	75.00	37.00	22.00
207	Melvin Ott	400.00	200.00	45.00
208	Byrne (Bernie) James	75.00	37.00	22.00
209	Adolfo Luque	75.00	37.00	22.00
210	Virgil Davis	75.00	37.00	22.00
211	Lewis (Hack) Wilson	350.00	175.00	45.00
212	Billy Urbanski	75.00	37.00	22.00
213	Earl Adams	75.00	37.00	22.00
214	John Kerr	75.00	37.00	22.00
215	Russell Van Atta	90.00	45.00	27.00
216	Vernon Gomez	400.00	175.00	45.00
217	Frank Crosetti	200.00	100.00	45.00
218	Wesley Ferrell	100.00	50.00	22.00
219	George (Mule) Haas	75.00	37.00	22.00
220	Robert (Lefty) Grove	500.00	250.00	100.00
221	Dale Alexander	75.00	37.00	22.00
222	Charley Gehringer	350.00	175.00	67.00
223	Jerome (Dizzy) Dean	800.00	400.00	200.00
224	Frank Demaree	75.00	37.00	22.00
225	Bill Jurges	75.00	37.00	22.00
226	Charley Root	90.00	45.00	22.00
227	Bill Herman	200.00	100.00	45.00
228	Tony Piet	75.00	37.00	22.00
229	Floyd Vaughan	200.00	100.00	45.00
230	Carl Hubbell	300.00	150.00	60.00
231	Joe Moore	75.00	37.00	22.00
232	Frank (Lefty) O'Doul	90.00	45.00	22.00
233	Johnny Vergez	75.00	37.00	22.00
234	Carl Hubbell	300.00	150.00	60.00
235	Fred Fitzsimmons	75.00	37.00	22.00
236	George Davis	75.00	37.00	22.00
237	Gus Mancuso	75.00	37.00	22.00
238	Hugh Critz	75.00	37.00	22.00
239	Leroy Parmelee	100.00	50.00	27.00
240	Harold Schumacher	350.00	125.00	15.00

1934 Goudey

The 1934 Goudey set contains 96 cards (2-3/8" by 2-7/8") that feature color art reproductions of actual photographs. The card fronts have two different designs; one featuring a small head-shot photo of Lou Gehrig with the words "Lou Gehrig says..." inside a blue band, while the other design carries a "Chuck Klein says..." and also has his photo. The card backs contain a short player biography that appears to have been written by Gehrig or Klein. The ACC designation for the set is R320.

		NR MT	EX	VG
Complete Set:		25000.00	12500.00	7500.
Common Player:		75.00	37.00	22.00
Common Player: 49-72		90.00	45.00	27.00
Common Player: 73-96		275.00	137.00	82.00
1	Jimmy Foxx	1000.00	250.00	125.00
2	Gordon (Mickey) Cochrane	250.00	125.00	75.00
3	Charlie Grimm	70.00	35.00	21.00
4	Elwood (Woody) English	75.00	37.00	22.00
5	Ed Brandt	75.00	37.00	22.00
6	Jerome (Dizzy) Dean	600.00	300.00	185.00
7	Leo Durocher	200.00	100.00	60.00
8	Tony Piet	75.00	37.00	22.00
9	Ben Chapman	90.00	45.00	27.00
10	Charles (Chuck) Klein	200.00	100.00	60.00
11	Paul Waner	200.00	100.00	60.00

		NR MT	EX	VG
12	Carl Hubbell	250.00	125.00	75.00
13	Frank Frisch	200.00	100.00	60.00
14	Willie Kamm	75.00	37.00	22.00
15	Alvin Crowder	75.00	37.00	22.00
16	Joe Kuhel	75.00	37.00	22.00
17	Hugh Critz	75.00	37.00	22.00
18	Henry (Heinie) Manush	200.00	100.00	60.00
19	Robert (Lefty) Grove	350.00	175.00	105.00
20	Frank Hogan	75.00	37.00	22.00
21	Bill Terry	250.00	125.00	75.00
22	Floyd Vaughan	200.00	100.00	60.00
23	Charley Gehringer	110.00	55.00	33.00
24	Ray Benge	75.00	37.00	22.00
25	Roger Cramer	75.00	37.00	22.00
26	Gerald Walker	75.00	37.00	22.00
27	Luke Appling	200.00	100.00	60.00
28	Ed. Coleman	75.00	37.00	22.00
29	Larry French	75.00	37.00	22.00
30	Julius Solters	75.00	37.00	22.00
31	Baxter Jordan	75.00	37.00	22.00
32	John (Blondy) Ryan	75.00	37.00	22.00
33	Frank (Don) Hurst	75.00	37.00	22.00
34	Charles (Chick) Hafey	200.00	100.00	60.00
35	Ernie Lombardi	200.00	100.00	60.00
36	Walter (Huck) Betts	75.00	37.00	22.00
37	Lou Gehrig	3500.00	1750.00	1050.
38	Oral Hildebrand	75.00	37.00	22.00
39	Fred Walker	75.00	37.00	22.00
40	John Stone	75.00	37.00	22.00
41	George Earnshaw	75.00	37.00	22.00
42	John Allen	90.00	45.00	27.00
43	Dick Porter	75.00	37.00	22.00
44	Tom Bridges	55.00	27.00	16.50
45	Oscar Melillo	75.00	37.00	22.00
46	Joe Stripp	75.00	37.00	22.00
47	John Frederick	75.00	37.00	22.00
48	James (Tex) Carleton	75.00	37.00	22.00
49	Sam Leslie	90.00	45.00	27.00
50	Walter Beck	90.00	45.00	27.00
51	Jim (Rip) Collins	90.00	45.00	27.00
52	Herman Bell	90.00	45.00	27.00
53	George Watkins	90.00	45.00	27.00
54	Wesley Schulmerich	90.00	45.00	27.00
55	Ed Holley	90.00	45.00	27.00
56	Mark Koenig	90.00	45.00	27.00
57	Bill Swift	90.00	45.00	27.00
58	Earl Grace	90.00	45.00	27.00
59	Joe Mowry	90.00	45.00	27.00
60	Lynn Nelson	90.00	45.00	27.00
61	Lou Gehrig	3700.00	1850.00	1150.
62	Henry Greenberg	350.00	175.00	105.00
63	Minter Hayes	90.00	45.00	27.00
64	Frank Grube	90.00	45.00	27.00
65	Cliff Bolton	90.00	45.00	27.00
66	Mel Harder	90.00	45.00	27.00
67	Bob Weiland	90.00	45.00	27.00
68	Bob Johnson	90.00	45.00	27.00
69	John Marcum	90.00	45.00	27.00
70	Ervin (Pete) Fox	90.00	45.00	27.00
71	Lyle Tinning	90.00	45.00	27.00
72	Arndt Jorgens	45.00	22.00	13.50
73	Ed Wells	275.00	137.00	82.00
74	Bob Boken	275.00	137.00	82.00
75	Bill Werber	275.00	137.00	82.00
76	Hal Trosky	275.00	137.00	82.00
77	Joe Vosmik	275.00	137.00	82.00
78	Frank (Pinkey) Higgins	275.00	137.00	82.00
79	Eddie Durham	275.00	137.00	82.00
80	Marty McManus	275.00	137.00	82.00
81	Bob Brown	275.00	137.00	82.00
82	Bill Hallahan	275.00	137.00	82.00
83	Jim Mooney	275.00	137.00	82.00
84	Paul Derringer	300.00	150.00	90.00
85	Adam Comorosky	275.00	137.00	82.00
86	Lloyd Johnson	275.00	137.00	82.00
87	George Darrow	275.00	137.00	82.00
88	Homer Peel	275.00	137.00	82.00
89	Linus Frey	275.00	137.00	82.00
90	Hazen (Ki-Ki) Cuyler	500.00	250.00	150.00
91	Dolph Camilli	275.00	137.00	82.00
92	Steve Larkin	275.00	137.00	82.00
93	Fred Ostermueller	275.00	137.00	82.00
94	Robert A. (Red) Rolfe	350.00	175.00	105.00
95	Myril Hoag	300.00	150.00	90.00
96	Jim DeShong	400.00	100.00	60.00

H

1989 Hills Team MVP's

This high-gloss, 33-card boxed set of superstars was produced by Topps for the Hills department store chain. The words "Hills Team MVP's" appear above the player photos, while the player's name and team are printed below. The front of the card carries a red, white and blue color scheme with yellow and gold accents. The horizontal backs include player data set against a green playing field background.

		MT	NR MT	EX
	Complete Set:	3.00	2.25	1.25
	Common Player:	.05	.04	.02
1	Harold Baines	.05	.04	.02
2	Wade Boggs	.30	.25	.12
3	George Brett	.09	.07	.04
4	Tom Brunansky	.05	.04	.02
5	Jose Canseco	.35	.25	.14
6	Joe Carter	.09	.07	.04
7	Will Clark	.35	.25	.12
8	Roger Clemens	.15	.11	.06
9	Dave Cone	.05	.04	.02
10	Glenn Davis	.05	.04	.02
11	Andre Dawson	.09	.07	.04
12	Dennis Eckersley	.09	.07	.04
13	Andres Galarraga	.05	.04	.02
14	Kirk Gibson	.06	.05	.02
15	Mike Greenwell	.10	.08	.04
16	Tony Gwynn	.15	.11	.06
17	Orel Hershiser	.09	.07	.03
18	Danny Jackson	.05	.04	.02
19	Mark Langston	.09	.07	.04
20	Fred McGriff	.10	.08	.04
21	Dale Murphy	.06	.05	.04
22	Eddie Murray	.06	.05	.04
23	Kirby Puckett	.20	.15	.08
24	Johnny Ray	.05	.04	.02
25	Juan Samuel	.05	.04	.02
26	Ruben Sierra	.15	.11	.06
27	Dave Stewart	.05	.04	.02
28	Darryl Strawberry	.20	.15	.08
29	Allan Trammell	.06	.05	.02
30	Andy Van Slyke	.05	.04	.02
31	Frank Viola	.06	.05	.02
32	Dave Winfield	.06	.05	.02
33	Robin Yount	.09	.07	.03

1990 Hills Hit Men

The 33 slugging percentage leaders are featured in this high-gloss set. The cards were produced by Topps for the Hills department store chain. The card fronts feature "Hit Men" in a bat design above the photo. The player's name appears on a band below the photo. The horizontal backs feature a breakdown of the player's slugging percentage and also display career statistics.

		MT	NR MT	EX
	Complete Set:	3.00	2.25	1.25
	Common Player:	.05	.04	.02

which it was given away. Values quoted here are for cards with tabs. Cards without tabs would be valued approximately 50 per cent lower.

	NR MT	EX	VG
Complete Set:	1550.00	775.00	465.00
Common Player:	130.00	65.00	39.00
(1) Johnny Antonelli	150.00	75.00	45.00
(2) Jim Busby	130.00	65.00	39.00
(3) Chico Fernandez	130.00	65.00	39.00
(4) Bob Friend	150.00	75.00	45.00
(5) Vern Law	150.00	75.00	45.00
(6) Stan Lopata	130.00	65.00	39.00
(7) Willie Mays	550.00	280.00	165.00
(8) Al Pilarcik	130.00	65.00	39.00

		MT	NR MT	EX
1	Eric Davis	.10	.08	.04
2	Will Clark	.25	.20	.10
3	Don Mattingly	.20	.15	.08
4	Darryl Strawberry	.20	.15	.08
5	Kevin Mitchell	.10	.08	.04
6	Pedro Guerrero	.05	.04	.02
7	Jose Canseco	.30	.25	.12
8	Jim Rice	.05	.04	.02
9	Danny Tartabull	.09	.07	.03
10	George Brett	.09	.07	.04
11	Kent Hrbek	.05	.04	.02
12	George Bell	.09	.07	.03
13	Eddie Murray	.08	.06	.03
14	Fred Lynn	.05	.04	.02
15	Andre Dawson	.09	.07	.04
16	Dale Murphy	.09	.07	.04
17	Dave Winfield	.09	.07	.04
18	Jack Clark	.05	.04	.02
19	Wade Boggs	.25	.20	.10
20	Ruben Sierra	.15	.11	.06
21	Dave Parker	.10	.08	.04
22	Glenn Davis	.05	.04	.02
23	Dwight Evans	.05	.04	.02
24	Jesse Barfield	.05	.04	.02
25	Kirk Gibson	.06	.05	.02
26	Alvin Davis	.05	.04	.02
27	Kirby Puckett	.20	.15	.08
28	Joe Carter	.09	.07	.03
29	Carlton Fisk	.10	.08	.04
30	Harold Baines	.05	.04	.02
31	Andres Galarraga	.05	.04	.02
32	Cal Ripken	.15	.11	.06
33	Howard Johnson	.08	.06	.03

1958 Hires Root Beer

TED KLUSZEWSKI
INFIELD—PITTSBURGH PIRATES

Like most baseball cards issued with a tab in the 1950s, the Hires cards are extremely scarce today in their original form. The basic card was attached to a wedge-shaped tab that served the dual purpose of offering a fan club membership and of holding the card into the cardboard carton of soda bottles with which it was distributed. The card itself measures 2-5/16" by 3-1/2". The tab extends for another 3-1/2". Numbering of the Hires set begins at 10 and goes through 76, with card #69 never issued, making a set complete at 66 cards. Values given below are for cards with tabs. Cards without tabs would be valued approximately 50 per cent lower.

		NR MT	EX	VG
Complete Set:		2400.00	1200.00	720.00
Common Player:		25.00	12.50	7.50
10	Richie Ashburn	100.00	50.00	30.00
11	Chico Carrasquel	25.00	12.50	7.50
12	Dave Philley	25.00	12.50	7.50
13	Don Newcombe	28.00	14.00	8.50
14	Wally Post	25.00	12.50	7.50
15	Rip Repulski	25.00	12.50	7.50
16	Chico Fernandez	25.00	12.50	7.50
17	Larry Doby	28.00	14.00	8.50
18	Hector Brown	25.00	12.50	7.50
19	Danny O'Connell	25.00	12.50	7.50
20	Granny Hamner	25.00	12.50	7.50
21	Dick Groat	30.00	15.00	9.00
22	Ray Narleski	25.00	12.50	7.50
23	Pee Wee Reese	100.00	50.00	30.00
24	Bob Friend	30.00	15.00	9.00
25	Willie Mays	275.00	150.00	80.00
26	Bob Nieman	25.00	12.50	7.50
27	Frank Thomas	25.00	12.50	7.50
28	Curt Simmons	30.00	15.00	9.00
29	Stan Lopata	25.00	12.50	7.50
30	Bob Skinner	25.00	12.50	7.50
31	Ron Kline	25.00	12.50	7.50
32	Willie Miranda	25.00	12.50	7.50
33	Bob Avila	25.00	12.50	7.50
34	Clem Labine	30.00	15.00	9.00
35	Ray Jablonski	25.00	12.50	7.50
36	Bill Mazeroski	28.00	14.00	8.50
37	Billy Gardner	25.00	12.50	7.50
38	Pete Runnels	30.00	15.00	9.00
39	Jack Sanford	25.00	12.50	7.50

1958 Hires Root Beer Test Set

Johnny Antonelli

PITCHER—SAN FRANCISCO GIANTS

Among the scarcest of the regional issues of the late 1950s is the eight-card test issue which preceded the Hires Root Beer set of 66 cards. Probably issued in a very limited area in the Northeast, the test cards differ from the regular issue in that they have sepia-toned, rather than color pictures, which are set against plain yellow or orange backgrounds (much like the 1958 Topps), instead of viewed through a knothole. Like the regular Hires cards, the 2-5/16" by 3-1/2" cards were issued with an attached wedge-shaped tab of like size. The tab offered membership in Hires baseball fan club, and served to hold the card into the carton of bottled root beer with

		NR MT	EX	VG
40	Dave Sisler	25.00	12.50	7.50
41	Don Zimmer	30.00	15.00	9.00
42	Johnny Podres	28.00	14.00	8.50
43	Dick Farrell	25.00	12.50	7.50
44	Hank Aaron	275.00	150.00	80.00
45	Bill Virdon	30.00	15.00	9.00
46	Bobby Thomson	30.00	15.00	9.00
47	Willard Nixon	25.00	12.50	7.50
48	Billy Loes	25.00	12.50	7.50
49	Hank Sauer	25.00	12.50	7.50
50	Johnny Antonelli	30.00	15.00	9.00
51	Daryl Spencer	25.00	12.50	7.50
52	Ken Lehman	25.00	12.50	7.50
53	Sammy White	25.00	12.50	7.50
54	Charley Neal	25.00	12.50	7.50
55	Don Drysdale	80.00	40.00	24.00
56	Jack Jensen	28.00	14.00	8.50
57	Ray Katt	25.00	12.50	7.50
58	Franklin Sullivan	25.00	12.50	7.50
59	Roy Face	30.00	15.00	9.00
60	Willie Jones	25.00	12.50	7.50
61	Duke Snider	125.00	62.00	37.00
62	Whitey Lockman	25.00	12.50	7.50
63	Gino Cimoli	30.00	15.00	9.00
64	Marv Grissom	25.00	12.50	7.50
65	Gene Baker	25.00	12.50	7.50
66	George Zuverink	25.00	12.50	7.50
67	Ted Kluszewski	28.00	14.00	8.50
68	Jim Busby	25.00	12.50	7.50
69	Not Issued			
70	Curt Barclay	25.00	12.50	7.50
71	Hank Foiles	25.00	12.50	7.50
72	Gene Stephens	25.00	12.50	7.50
73	Al Worthington	25.00	12.50	7.50
74	Al Walker	25.00	12.50	7.50
75	Bob Boyd	25.00	12.50	7.50
76	Al Pilarcik	30.00	9.00	5.50

1992 Holoprisms

The Holoprism set actually consists of two 4-card hologram sets of Rookies of the Year, Jeff Bagwell and Chuck Knoblauch. Each player set was packaged in a special plastic case. The production was limited to 250,000 of each set. Each set is numbered and contains a letter of authenticity.

	MT	NR MT	EX
Complete Bagwell Set:	8.00	6.00	3.25
Complete Knoblauch Set:	10.00	7.50	4.00
Jeff Bagwell (1-4)	2.00	1.50	.80
Chuck Knoblauch (1-4)	2.50	2.00	1.00

1959 Home Run Derby

This 20-card unnumbered set was produced by American Motors to publicize the Home Run Derby television program. The cards measure approximately 3-1/4" by 5-1/4" and feature black and white player photos on black-backed white stock. The player name and team are printed beneath the photo. This set was reprinted (and marked as such) in 1988 by Card Collectors' Company of New York.

HANK AARON
MILWAUKEE BRAVES

		NR MT	EX	VG
Complete Set:		4000.00	2000.00	1200.
Common Player:		100.00	50.00	30.00
(1)	Hank Aaron	450.00	225.00	135.00
(2)	Bob Allison	100.00	50.00	30.00
(3)	Ernie Banks	300.00	150.00	90.00
(4)	Ken Boyer	175.00	87.00	52.00
(5)	Bob Cerv	100.00	50.00	30.00
(6)	Rocky Colavito	175.00	87.00	52.00
(7)	Gil Hodges	225.00	112.00	67.00
(8)	Jackie Jensen	175.00	87.00	52.00
(9)	Al Kaline	300.00	150.00	90.00
(10)	Harmon Killebrew	225.00	112.00	67.00
(11)	Jim Lemon	100.00	50.00	30.00
(12)	Mickey Mantle	1200.00	600.00	400.00
(13)	Ed Mathews	275.00	137.00	82.00
(14)	Willie Mays	450.00	225.00	135.00
(15)	Wally Post	100.00	50.00	30.00
(16)	Frank Robinson	275.00	137.00	82.00
(17)	Mark Scott (host)	175.00	87.00	52.00
(18)	Duke Snider	450.00	225.00	135.00
(19)	Dick Stuart	100.00	50.00	30.00
(20)	Gus Triandos	100.00	50.00	30.00

1991 Homers Cookies

LOU GEHRIG

One card was inserted in each box of Homers Cookies. The cards measure 2 1/2" by 3 1/2" and feature sepia-toned photos. The card backs feature lifetime statistics and career highlights. The cards are also numbered on the back and a checklist is featured on the back of each card.

		MT	NR MT	EX
Complete Set:		8.00	6.00	3.25
Complete Set:		1.00	.70	.40
1	Babe Ruth	1.75	1.25	.70
2	Satchel Paige	1.00	.70	.40
3	Lefty Gomez	1.00	.70	.40
4	Ty Cobb	1.25	.90	.50
5	Cy Young	1.00	.70	.40
6	Bob Feller	1.00	.70	.40
7	Roberto Clemente	1.25	.90	.50
8	Dizzy Dean	1.00	.70	.40
9	Lou Gehrig	1.25	.90	.50

1975 Hostess

The first of what would become five annual issues, the 1975 Hostess set consists of 50 three-card panels which formed the bottom of boxes of family-size snack cake products. Unlike many similar issues, the Hostess cards do not share common borders, so it was possible to cut them neatly and evenly from the box. Well-cut single cards measure 2-1/4" by 3-1/4", while a three-card panel measures 7-1/4" by 3-1/4". Because some of the panels were issued on packages of less popular snack cakes, they are somewhat scarcer today. Since the hobby was quite well-developed when the Hostess cards were first issued, there is no lack of complete panels. Even unused complete boxes are available today. Some of the photos in this issue also appear on Topps cards of the era.

		NR MT	EX	VG
	Complete Panel Set:	400.00	200.00	120.00
	Complete Singles Set:	200.00	100.00	60.00
	Common Panel:	2.50	1.25	.70
	Common Single Player:	.40	.20	.12
	Panel 1	2.50	1.25	.70
1	Bobby Tolan	.40	.20	.12
2	Cookie Rojas	.40	.20	.12
3	Darrell Evans	.70	.35	.20
	Panel 2	5.50	2.75	1.75
4	Sal Bando	.50	.25	.15
5	Joe Morgan	2.00	1.00	.60
6	Mickey Lolich	.60	.30	.20
	Panel 3	4.00	2.00	1.25
7	Don Sutton	1.50	.70	.45
8	Bill Melton	.40	.20	.12
9	Tim Foli	.40	.20	.12
	Panel 4	5.00	2.50	1.50
10	Joe Lahoud	.40	.20	.12
11a	Bert Hooten (incorrect spelling)	1.50	.70	.45
11b	Burt Hooton (correct spelling)	1.50	.70	.45
12	Paul Blair	.40	.20	.12
	Panel 5	2.50	1.25	.70
13	Jim Barr	.40	.20	.12
14	Toby Harrah	.50	.25	.15
15	John Milner	.40	.20	.12
	Panel 6	3.50	1.75	1.00
16	Ken Holtzman	.50	.25	.15
17	Cesar Cedeno	.50	.25	.15
18	Dwight Evans	.90	.45	.25
	Panel 7	7.50	3.75	2.25
19	Willie McCovey	3.00	1.50	.90
20	Tony Oliva	.70	.35	.20
21	Manny Sanguillen	.40	.20	.12
	Panel 8	8.00	4.00	2.50
22	Mickey Rivers	.50	.25	.15
23	Lou Brock	3.00	1.50	.90
24	Craig Nettles	.90	.45	.25
	Panel 9	3.00	1.50	.90
25	Jimmy Wynn	.50	.25	.15
26	George Scott	.50	.25	.15
27	Greg Luzinski	.50	.25	.15
	Panel 10	20.00	10.00	6.00
28	Bert Campaneris	.50	.25	.15
29	Pete Rose	8.00	4.00	2.50
30	Buddy Bell	.50	.25	.15
	Panel 11	2.50	1.25	.70
31	Gary Matthews	.50	.25	.15
32	Fred Patek	.40	.20	.12
33	Mike Lum	.40	.20	.12

		NR MT	EX	VG
	Panel 12	2.50	1.25	.70
34	Ellie Rodriguez	.40	.20	.12
35	Milt May	.40	.20	.12
36	Willie Horton	.50	.25	.15
	Panel 13	10.00	5.00	3.00
37	Dave Winfield	4.50	2.25	1.25
38	Tom Grieve	.40	.20	.12
39	Barry Foote	.40	.20	.12
	Panel 14	2.50	1.25	.70
40	Joe Rudi	.50	.25	.15
41	Bake McBride	.40	.20	.12
42	Mike Cuellar	.50	.25	.15
	Panel 15	2.50	1.25	.70
43	Garry Maddox	.50	.25	.15
44	Carlos May	.40	.20	.12
45	Bud Harrelson	.40	.20	.12
	Panel 16	15.00	7.50	4.50
46	Dave Chalk	.40	.20	.12
47	Dave Concepcion	.50	.25	.15
48	Carl Yastrzemski	6.50	3.25	2.00
	Panel 17	9.00	4.50	2.75
49	Steve Garvey	4.00	2.00	1.25
50	Amos Otis	.50	.25	.15
51	Rickey Reuschel	.50	.25	.15
	Panel 18	3.75	2.00	1.25
52	Rollie Fingers	1.25	.60	.40
53	Bob Watson	.40	.20	.12
54	John Ellis	.40	.20	.12
	Panel 19	9.50	4.75	2.75
55	Bob Bailey	.40	.20	.12
56	Rod Carew	4.00	2.00	1.25
57	Richie Hebner	.40	.20	.12
	Panel 20	15.00	7.50	4.50
58	Nolan Ryan	10.00	5.00	3.00
59	Reggie Smith	.50	.25	.15
60	Joe Coleman	.40	.20	.12
	Panel 21	10.00	5.00	3.00
61	Ron Cey	.50	.25	.15
62	Darrell Porter	.50	.25	.15
63	Steve Carlton	4.00	2.00	1.25
	Panel 22	2.50	1.25	.70
64	Gene Tenace	.40	.20	.12
65	Jose Cardenal	.40	.20	.12
66	Bill Lee	.40	.20	.12
	Panel 23	2.50	1.25	.70
67	Dave Lopes	.50	.25	.15
68	Wilbur Wood	.50	.25	.15
69	Steve Renko	.40	.20	.12
	Panel 24	3.00	1.50	.90
70	Joe Torre	.50	.25	.15
71	Ted Sizemore	.40	.20	.12
72	Bobby Grich	.50	.25	.15
	Panel 25	11.00	5.50	3.25
73	Chris Speier	.40	.20	.12
74	Bert Blyleven	.70	.35	.20
75	Tom Seaver	4.50	2.25	1.25
	Panel 26	2.50	1.25	.70
76	Nate Colbert	.40	.20	.12
77	Don Kessinger	.40	.20	.12
78	George Medich	.40	.20	.12
	Panel 27	30.00	15.00	9.00
79	Andy Messersmith	.70	.35	.20
80	Robin Yount	20.00	10.00	6.00
81	Al Oliver	1.50	.70	.45
	Panel 28	18.00	9.00	5.50
82	Bill Singer	.50	.25	.15
83	Johnny Bench	6.00	3.00	1.75
84	Gaylord Perry	3.00	1.50	.90
	Panel 29	5.00	2.50	1.50
85	Dave Kingman	1.25	.60	.40
86	Ed Herrmann	.50	.25	.15
87	Ralph Garr	.60	.30	.20
	Panel 30	23.00	11.50	7.00
88	Reggie Jackson	9.00	4.50	2.75
89a	Doug Radar (incorrect spelling)	2.00	1.00	.60
89b	Doug Rader (correct spelling)	2.00	1.00	.60
90	Elliott Maddox	.50	.25	.15
	Panel 31	3.50	1.75	1.00
91	Bill Russell	.60	.30	.20
92	John Mayberry	.50	.25	.15
93	Dave Cash	.50	.25	.15
	Panel 32	5.00	2.50	1.50
94	Jeff Burroughs	.60	.30	.20
95	Ted Simmons	1.25	.60	.40
96	Joe Decker	.50	.25	.15
	Panel 33	10.00	5.00	3.00
97	Bill Buckner	1.00	.50	.30
98	Bobby Darwin	.50	.25	.15
99	Phil Niekro	3.50	1.75	1.00
	Panel 34	3.00	1.50	.90
100	Mike Sundberg (Jim)	.50	.25	.15
101	Greg Gross	.40	.20	.12

#	Player	NR MT	EX	VG
102	Luis Tiant	.70	.35	.20
	Panel 35	2.50	1.25	.70
103	Glenn Beckert	.40	.20	.12
104	Hal McRae	.50	.25	.15
105	Mike Jorgensen	.40	.20	.12
	Panel 36	2.50	1.25	.70
106	Mike Hargrove	.40	.20	.12
107	Don Gullett	.40	.20	.12
108	Tito Fuentes	.40	.20	.12
	Panel 37	3.50	1.75	1.00
109	John Grubb	.40	.20	.12
110	Jim Kaat	.90	.45	.25
111	Felix Millan	.40	.20	.12
	Panel 38	2.50	1.25	.70
112	Don Money	.40	.20	.12
113	Rick Monday	.50	.25	.15
114	Dick Bosman	.40	.20	.12
	Panel 39	3.50	1.75	1.00
115	Roger Metzger	.40	.20	.12
116	Fergie Jenkins	.90	.45	.25
117	Dusky Baker	.50	.25	.15
	Panel 40	10.00	5.00	3.00
118	Billy Champion	.50	.25	.15
119	Bob Gibson	3.50	1.75	1.00
120	Bill Freehan	.80	.40	.25
	Panel 41	2.50	1.25	.70
121	Cesar Geronimo	.40	.20	.12
122	Jorge Orta	.40	.20	.12
123	Cleon Jones	.40	.20	.12
	Panel 42	10.50	5.25	3.25
124	Steve Busby	.40	.20	.12
125a	Bill Madlock (Pitcher)	2.00	1.00	.60
125b	Bill Madlock (Third Base)	2.00	1.00	.60
126	Jim Palmer	2.75	1.50	.80
	Panel 43	4.25	2.25	1.25
127	Tony Perez	1.00	.50	.30
128	Larry Hisle	.40	.20	.12
129	Rusty Staub	.70	.35	.20
	Panel 44	20.00	10.00	6.00
130	Hank Aaron	9.00	4.50	2.75
131	Rennie Stennett	.50	.25	.15
132	Rico Petrocelli	.70	.35	.20
	Panel 45	16.00	8.00	4.75
133	Mike Schmidt	6.00	3.00	1.75
134	Sparky Lyle	.50	.25	.15
135	Willie Stargell	3.00	1.50	.90
	Panel 46	7.00	3.50	2.00
136	Ken Henderson	.40	.20	.12
137	Willie Montanez	.40	.20	.12
138	Thurman Munson	2.50	1.25	.70
	Panel 47	2.50	1.25	.70
139	Richie Zisk	.40	.20	.12
140	Geo. Hendricks (Hendrick)	.50	.25	.15
141	Bobby Murcer	.50	.25	.15
	Panel 48	10.00	5.00	3.00
142	Lee May	.50	.25	.15
143	Carlton Fisk	1.00	.50	.30
144	Brooks Robinson	3.50	1.75	1.00
	Panel 49	2.50	1.25	.70
145	Bobby Bonds	.50	.25	.15
146	Gary Sutherland	.40	.20	.12
147	Oscar Gamble	.40	.20	.12
	Panel 50	6.00	3.00	1.75
148	Jim Hunter	2.50	1.25	.70
149	Tug McGraw	.50	.25	.15
150	Dave McNally	.50	.25	.15

1975 Hostess Twinkies

HANK AARON
DESIGNATED HITTER
Milwaukee BREWERS

Believed to have been issued only in the Western

states, and on a limited basis at that, the 1975 Hostess Twinkie set features 60 of the cards from the "regular" Hostess set of that year. The cards were issued one per pack with the popular snack cake. Card #'s 1-36 are a direct pick-up from the Hostess set, while the remaining 24 cards in the set were selected from the more popular names in the remainder of the Hostess issue - with an emphasis on West Coast players. Thus, after card #36, the '75 Twinkie cards are skip-numbered from 40-136. In identical 2-1/4" by 3-1/4" size, the Twinkie cards differ from the Hostess issue only in the presence of small black bars at top and bottom center of the back of the card. Values quoted are for full bottom panels.

#	Player	NR MT	EX	VG
	Complete Set:	200.00	100.00	60.00
	Common Player:	.90	.45	.25
1	Bobby Tolan	.90	.45	.25
2	Cookie Rojas	.90	.45	.25
3	Darrell Evans	2.00	1.00	.60
4	Sal Bando	1.25	.60	.40
5	Joe Morgan	5.00	2.50	1.50
6	Mickey Lolich	2.00	1.00	.60
7	Don Sutton	4.50	2.25	1.25
8	Bill Melton	.90	.45	.25
9	Tim Foli	.90	.45	.25
10	Joe Lahoud	.90	.45	.25
11	Bert Hooten (Burt Hooton)	1.25	.60	.40
12	Paul Blair	.90	.45	.25
13	Jim Barr	.90	.45	.25
14	Toby Harrah	.90	.45	.25
15	John Milner	.90	.45	.25
16	Ken Holtzman	1.00	.50	.30
17	Cesar Cedeno	1.25	.60	.40
18	Dwight Evans	3.00	1.50	.90
19	Willie McCovey	7.00	3.50	2.00
20	Tony Oliva	2.00	1.00	.60
21	Manny Sanguillen	.90	.45	.25
22	Mickey Rivers	.90	.45	.25
23	Lou Brock	6.50	3.25	2.00
24	Graig Nettles	3.00	1.50	.90
25	Jim Wynn	.90	.45	.25
26	George Scott	.90	.45	.25
27	Greg Luzinski	1.25	.60	.40
28	Bert Campaneris	1.25	.60	.40
29	Pete Rose	20.00	10.00	6.00
30	Buddy Bell	1.75	.90	.50
31	Gary Matthews	1.25	.60	.40
32	Fred Patek	.90	.45	.25
33	Mike Lum	.90	.45	.25
34	Ellie Rodriguez	.90	.45	.25
35	Milt May (photo actually Lee May)	1.25	.60	.40
36	Willie Horton	.90	.45	.25
40	Joe Rudi	1.25	.60	.40
43	Garry Maddox	.90	.45	.25
46	Dave Chalk	.90	.45	.25
49	Steve Garvey	10.00	5.00	3.00
52	Rollie Fingers	4.00	2.00	1.25
58	Nolan Ryan	12.00	6.00	3.50
61	Ron Cey	1.50	.70	.45
64	Gene Tenace	.90	.45	.25
65	Jose Cardenal	.90	.45	.25
67	Dave Lopes	1.25	.60	.40
68	Wilbur Wood	.90	.45	.25
73	Chris Speier	.90	.45	.25
77	Don Kessinger	.90	.45	.25
79	Andy Messersmith	.90	.45	.25
80	Robin Yount	20.00	10.00	6.00
82	Bill Singer	.90	.45	.25
103	Glenn Beckert	.90	.45	.25
110	Jim Kaat	2.50	1.25	.70
112	Don Money	.90	.45	.25
113	Rick Monday	1.25	.60	.40
122	Jorge Orta	.90	.45	.25
125	Bill Madlock	2.25	1.25	.70
130	Hank Aaron	15.00	7.50	4.50
136	Ken Henderson	.90	.45	.25

A player's name in italic indicates a rookie card. An (FC) indicates a player's first card for that particular card company.

1976 Hostess

The second of five annual Hostess issues, the 1976 cards carried a "Bicentennial" color theme, with red, white and blue stripes at the bottom of the 2-1/4" by 3-1/4" cards. Like other Hostess issues, the cards were printed in panels of three as the bottom of family-size boxes of snack cake products. This leads to a degree of scarcity for some of the 150 cards in the set; those which were found on less-popular brands. A well-trimmed three-card panel measures 7-1/4" by 3-1/4" size. Some of the photos used in the 1976 Hostess set can also be found on Topps issues of the era.

		NR MT	EX	VG
	Complete Panel Set:	400.00	200.00	120.00
	Complete Singles Set:	225.00	112.00	67.00
	Common Panel:	2.50	1.25	.70
	Common Single Player:	.40	.20	.12
	Panel 1	11.75	6.00	3.50
1	Fred Lynn	1.25	.60	.40
2	Joe Morgan	2.00	1.00	.60
3	Phil Niekro	2.25	1.25	.70
	Panel 2	4.50	2.25	1.25
4	Gaylord Perry	1.75	.90	.50
5	Bob Watson	.40	.20	.12
6	Bill Freehan	.50	.25	.15
	Panel 3	6.50	3.25	2.00
7	Lou Brock	3.00	1.50	.90
8	Al Fitzmorris	.40	.20	.12
9	Rennie Stennett	.40	.20	.12
	Panel 4	9.00	4.50	2.75
10	Tony Oliva	.70	.35	.20
11	Robin Yount	10.00	5.00	3.00
12	Rick Manning	.40	.20	.12
	Panel 5	3.50	1.75	1.00
13	Bobby Grich	.50	.25	.15
14	Terry Forster	.40	.20	.12
15	Dave Kingman	.70	.35	.20
	Panel 6	7.00	3.50	2.00
16	Thurman Munson	2.50	1.25	.70
17	Rick Reuschel	.50	.25	.15
18	Bobby Bonds	.50	.25	.15
	Panel 7	9.50	4.75	2.75
19	Steve Garvey	4.00	2.00	1.25
20	Vida Blue	.50	.25	.15
21	Dave Rader	.40	.20	.12
	Panel 8	9.00	4.50	2.75
22	Johnny Bench	4.00	2.00	1.25
23	Luis Tiant	.50	.25	.15
24	Darrell Evans	.70	.35	.20
	Panel 9	2.50	1.25	.70
25	Larry Dierker	.40	.20	.12
26	Willie Horton	.50	.25	.15
27	John Ellis	.40	.20	.12
	Panel 10	3.00	1.50	.90
28	Al Cowens	.40	.20	.12
29	Jerry Reuss	.50	.25	.15
30	Reggie Smith	.50	.25	.15
	Panel 11	13.00	6.50	4.00
31	Bobby Darwin	.50	.25	.15
32	Fritz Peterson	.50	.25	.15
33	Rod Carew	6.00	3.00	1.75
	Panel 12	21.00	10.50	6.25
34	Carlos May	.50	.25	.15
35	Tom Seaver	6.00	3.00	1.75
36	Brooks Robinson	5.00	2.50	1.50

		NR MT	EX	VG
	Panel 13	2.50	1.25	.70
37	Jose Cardenal	.40	.20	.12
38	Ron Blomberg	.40	.20	.12
39	Lee Stanton	.40	.20	.12
	Panel 14	2.50	1.25	.70
40	Dave Cash	.40	.20	.12
41	John Montefusco	.40	.20	.12
42	Bob Tolan	.40	.20	.12
	Panel 15	2.50	1.25	.70
43	Carl Morton	.40	.20	.12
44	Rick Burleson	.50	.25	.15
45	Don Gullett	.40	.20	.12
	Panel 16	2.50	1.25	.70
46	Vern Ruhle	.40	.20	.12
47	Cesar Cedeno	.50	.25	.15
48	Toby Harrah	.50	.25	.15
	Panel 17	6.00	3.00	1.75
49	Willie Stargell	3.00	1.50	.90
50	Al Hrabosky	.40	.20	.12
51	Amos Otis	.50	.25	.15
	Panel 18	2.50	1.25	.70
52	Bud Harrelson	.50	.25	.15
53	Jim Hughes	.40	.20	.12
54	George Scott	.50	.25	.15
	Panel 19	9.50	4.75	2.75
55	Mike Vail	.50	.25	.15
56	Jim Palmer	4.00	2.00	1.25
57	Jorge Orta	.80	.40	.25
	Panel 20	3.50	1.75	1.00
58	Chris Chambliss	.80	.40	.25
59	Dave Chalk	.50	.25	.15
60	Ray Burris	.50	.25	.15
	Panel 21	14.00	7.00	4.25
61	Bert Campaneris	.80	.40	.25
62	Gary Carter	6.00	3.00	1.75
63	Ron Cey	.90	.45	.25
	Panel 22	28.00	14.00	8.50
64	Carlton Fisk	2.00	1.00	.60
65	Marty Perez	.50	.25	.15
66	Pete Rose	10.00	5.00	3.00
	Panel 23	3.50	1.75	1.00
67	Roger Metzger	.50	.25	.15
68	Jim Sundberg	.60	.30	.20
69	Ron LeFlore	.60	.30	.20
	Panel 24	3.50	1.75	1.00
70	Ted Sizemore	.50	.25	.15
71	Steve Busby	.50	.25	.15
72	Manny Sanguillen	.50	.25	.15
	Panel 25	5.00	2.50	1.50
73	Larry Hisle	.60	.30	.20
74	Pete Broberg	.50	.25	.15
75	Boog Powell	1.25	.60	.40
	Panel 26	6.50	3.25	2.00
76	Ken Singleton	.80	.40	.25
77	Rich Gossage	2.00	1.00	.60
78	Jerry Grote	.50	.25	.15
	Panel 27	16.00	8.00	4.75
79	Nolan Ryan	12.00	6.00	3.50
80	Rick Monday	.70	.35	.20
81	Graig Nettles	1.25	.60	.40
	Panel 28	18.00	9.00	5.50
82	Chris Speier	.40	.20	.12
83	Dave Winfield	4.00	2.00	1.25
84	Mike Schmidt	6.00	3.00	1.75
	Panel 29	4.00	2.00	1.25
85	Buzz Capra	.40	.20	.12
86	Tony Perez	1.00	.50	.30
87	Dwight Evans	.90	.45	.25
	Panel 30	2.50	1.25	.70
88	Mike Hargrove	.40	.20	.12
89	Joe Coleman	.40	.20	.12
90	Greg Gross	.40	.20	.12
	Panel 31	2.50	1.25	.70
91	John Mayberry	.40	.20	.12
92	John Candelaria	.50	.25	.15
93	Bake McBride	.40	.20	.12
	Panel 32	15.00	7.50	4.50
94	Hank Aaron	7.00	3.50	2.00
95	Buddy Bell	.50	.25	.15
96	Steve Braun	.40	.20	.12
	Panel 33	2.50	1.25	.70
97	Jon Matlack	.40	.20	.12
98	Lee May	.50	.25	.15
99	Wilbur Wood	.50	.25	.15
	Panel 34	4.00	2.00	1.25
100	Bill Madlock	.90	.45	.25
101	Frank Tanana	.50	.25	.15
102	Mickey Rivers	.50	.25	.15
	Panel 35	3.75	2.00	1.25
103	Mike Ivie	.40	.20	.12
104	Rollie Fingers	1.25	.60	.40

		NR MT	EX	VG
105	Dave Lopes	.50	.25	.15
	Panel 36	3.50	1.75	1.00
106	George Foster	.90	.45	.25
107	Denny Doyle	.40	.20	.12
108	Earl Williams	.40	.20	.12
	Panel 37	2.50	1.25	.70
109	Tom Veryzer	.40	.20	.12
110	J.R. Richard	.50	.25	.15
111	Jeff Burroughs	.40	.20	.12
	Panel 38	14.00	7.00	4.25
112	Al Oliver	.90	.45	.25
113	Ted Simmons	.80	.40	.25
114	George Brett	5.00	2.50	1.50
	Panel 39	3.00	1.50	.90
115	Frank Duffy	.40	.20	.12
116	Bert Blyleven	.80	.40	.25
117	Darrell Porter	.50	.25	.15
	Panel 40	2.50	1.25	.70
118	Don Baylor	.70	.35	.20
119	Bucky Dent	.50	.25	.15
120	Felix Millan	.40	.20	.12
	Panel 41	2.50	1.25	.70
121	Mike Cuellar	.50	.25	.15
122	Gene Tenace	.40	.20	.12
123	Bobby Murcer	.50	.25	.15
	Panel 42	7.00	3.50	2.00
124	Willie McCovey	3.00	1.50	.90
125	Greg Luzinski	.50	.25	.15
126	Larry Parrish	.50	.25	.15
	Panel 43	10.00	5.00	3.00
127	Jim Rice	4.00	2.00	1.25
128	Dave Concepcion	.50	.25	.15
129	Jim Wynn	.50	.25	.15
	Panel 44	2.50	1.25	.70
130	Tom Grieve	.40	.20	.12
131	Mike Cosgrove	.40	.20	.12
132	Dan Meyer	.40	.20	.12
	Panel 45	5.00	2.50	1.50
133	Dave Parker	1.50	.70	.45
134	Don Kessinger	.40	.20	.12
135	Hal McRae	.50	.25	.15
	Panel 46	4.00	2.00	1.25
136	Don Money	.70	.35	.20
137	Dennis Eckersley	.90	.45	.25
138	Fergie Jenkins	.80	.40	.25
	Panel 47	4.00	2.00	1.25
139	Mike Torrez	.40	.20	.12
140	Jerry Morales	.40	.20	.12
141	Jim Hunter	1.25	.60	.40
	Panel 48	2.50	1.25	.70
142	Gary Matthews	.50	.25	.15
143	Randy Jones	.40	.20	.12
144	Mike Jorgensen	.40	.20	.12
	Panel 49	13.00	6.50	4.00
145	Larry Bowa	.60	.30	.20
146	Reggie Jackson	5.00	2.50	1.50
147	Steve Yeager	.40	.20	.12
	Panel 50	15.00	7.50	4.50
148	Dave May	.40	.20	.12
149	Carl Yastrzemski	6.50	3.25	2.00
150	Cesar Geronimo	.40	.20	.12

1976 Hostess Twinkies

The 60 cards in this regionally-issued (West Coast only) set closely parallel the first 60 cards in the numerical sequence of the "regular" 1976 Hostess issue. The singular difference is the appearance on the back of a black band toward the center of the card at top and bottom. Also unlike the three-card

panels of the regular Hostess issue, the 2-1/4" by 3-1/4" Twinkie cards were issued singly, as the cardboard stiffener for the cellophane-wrapped snack cakes. Values quoted are for complete bottom panels.

		NR MT	EX	VG
	Complete Set:	200.00	100.00	60.00
	Common Player:	.90	.45	.25
1	Fred Lynn	3.00	1.50	.90
2	Joe Morgan	5.00	2.50	1.50
3	Phil Niekro	4.50	2.25	1.25
4	Gaylord Perry	5.00	2.50	1.50
5	Bob Watson	.90	.45	.25
6	Bill Freehan	1.25	.60	.40
7	Lou Brock	7.00	3.50	2.00
8	Al Fitzmorris	.90	.45	.25
9	Rennie Stennett	.90	.45	.25
10	Tony Oliva	2.00	1.00	.60
11	Robin Yount	12.00	6.00	3.50
12	Rick Manning	.90	.45	.25
13	Bobby Grich	1.25	.60	.40
14	Terry Forster	.90	.45	.25
15	Dave Kingman	2.00	1.00	.60
16	Thurman Munson	6.50	3.25	2.00
17	Rick Reuschel	1.25	.60	.40
18	Bobby Bonds	1.25	.60	.40
19	Steve Garvey	10.00	5.00	3.00
20	Vida Blue	1.75	.90	.50
21	Dave Rader	.90	.45	.25
22	Johnny Bench	10.00	5.00	3.00
23	Luis Tiant	1.50	.70	.45
24	Darrell Evans	2.00	1.00	.60
25	Larry Dierker	.90	.45	.25
26	Willie Horton	.90	.45	.25
27	John Ellis	.90	.45	.25
28	Al Cowens	.90	.45	.25
29	Jerry Reuss	1.25	.60	.40
30	Reggie Smith	1.25	.60	.40
31	Bobby Darwin	.90	.45	.25
32	Fritz Peterson	.90	.45	.25
33	Rod Carew	10.00	5.00	3.00
34	Carlos May	.90	.45	.25
35	Tom Seaver	10.00	5.00	3.00
36	Brooks Robinson	9.00	4.50	2.75
37	Jose Cardenal	.90	.45	.25
38	Ron Blomberg	.90	.45	.25
39	Lee Stanton	.90	.45	.25
40	Dave Cash	.90	.45	.25
41	John Montefusco	.90	.45	.25
42	Bob Tolan	.90	.45	.25
43	Carl Morton	.90	.45	.25
44	Rick Burleson	.90	.45	.25
45	Don Gullett	.90	.45	.25
46	Vern Ruhle	.90	.45	.25
47	Cesar Cedeno	1.25	.60	.40
48	Toby Harrah	.90	.45	.25
49	Willie Stargell	7.00	3.50	2.00
50	Al Hrabosky	.90	.45	.25
51	Amos Otis	.90	.45	.25
52	Bud Harrelson	.90	.45	.25
53	Jim Hughes	.90	.45	.25
54	George Scott	.90	.45	.25
55	Mike Vail	.90	.45	.25
56	Jim Palmer	7.00	3.50	2.00
57	Jorge Orta	.90	.45	.25
58	Chris Chambliss	1.25	.60	.40
59	Dave Chalk	.90	.45	.25
60	Ray Burris	.90	.45	.25

1977 Hostess

The third of five consecutive annual issues, the 1977 Hostess cards retained the same card size 2-1/4" by 3-1/4", set size - 150 cards, and mode of issue - three cards on a 7-1/4" by 3-1/4" panel, as the previous two efforts. Because they were issued as the bottom panel of snack cake boxes, and because some brands of Hostess products were more popular than others, certain cards in the set are scarcer than others.

	NR MT	EX	VG
Complete Panel Set:	350.00	175.00	105.00
Complete Singles Set:	225.00	112.00	70.00
Common Panel:	2.50	1.25	.70
Common Single Player:	.40	.20	.12

PETE ROSE
Cincinnati REDS
THIRD BASE

Peter Edward Rose

#	Name	NR MT	EX	VG
	Panel 1	20.00	10.00	6.00
1	Jim Palmer	3.00	1.50	.80
2	Joe Morgan	3.00	1.50	.80
3	Reggie Jackson	5.00	2.50	1.50
	Panel 2	23.00	11.50	7.00
4	Carl Yastrzemski	6.00	3.00	1.75
5	Thurman Munson	2.50	1.25	.70
6	Johnny Bench	4.00	2.00	1.25
	Panel 3	32.00	16.00	9.50
7	Tom Seaver	3.00	1.50	.90
8	Pete Rose	8.00	4.00	2.50
9	Rod Carew	4.00	2.00	1.25
	Panel 4	2.50	1.25	.70
10	Luis Tiant	.60	.30	.20
11	Phil Garner	.50	.25	.15
12	Sixto Lezcano	.40	.20	.12
	Panel 5	2.50	1.25	.70
13	Mike Torrez	.40	.20	.12
14	Dave Lopes	.50	.25	.15
15	Doug DeCinces	.50	.25	.15
	Panel 6	2.50	1.25	.70
16	Jim Spencer	.40	.20	.12
17	Hal McRae	.50	.25	.15
18	Mike Hargrove	.40	.20	.12
	Panel 7	4.50	2.25	1.25
19	Willie Montanez	.50	.25	.15
20	Roger Metzger	.50	.25	.15
21	Dwight Evans	1.50	.70	.45
	Panel 8	10.00	5.00	3.00
22	Steve Rogers	.50	.25	.15
23	Jim Rice	4.00	2.00	1.25
24	Pete Falcone	.50	.25	.15
	Panel 9	9.00	4.50	2.75
25	Greg Luzinski	.90	.45	.25
26	Randy Jones	.50	.25	.15
27	Willie Stargell	3.00	1.50	.90
	Panel 10	3.50	1.75	1.00
28	John Hiller	.50	.25	.15
29	Bobby Murcer	.70	.35	.20
30	Rick Monday	.70	.35	.20
	Panel 11	9.00	4.50	2.75
31	John Montefusco	.50	.25	.15
32	Lou Brock	4.00	2.00	1.25
33	Bill North	.50	.25	.15
	Panel 12	32.00	16.00	9.50
34	Robin Yount	8.00	4.00	2.50
35	Steve Garvey	5.00	2.50	1.50
36	George Brett	8.00	4.00	2.50
	Panel 13	3.50	1.75	1.00
37	Toby Harrah	.70	.35	.20
38	Jerry Royster	.50	.25	.15
39	Bob Watson	.60	.30	.20
	Panel 14	9.50	4.75	2.75
40	George Foster	.90	.45	.25
41	Gary Carter	3.50	1.75	1.00
42	John Denny	.40	.20	.12
	Panel 15	18.00	9.00	5.50
43	Mike Schmidt	5.00	2.50	1.50
44	Dave Winfield	3.75	2.00	1.25
45	Al Oliver	.90	.45	.25
	Panel 16	3.00	1.50	.90
46	Mark Fidrych	.60	.30	.20
47	Larry Herndon	.50	.25	.15
48	Dave Goltz	.40	.20	.12
	Panel 17	3.50	1.75	1.00
49	Jerry Morales	.40	.20	.12
50	Ron LeFlore	.50	.25	.15
51	Fred Lynn	.90	.45	.25
	Panel 18	3.50	1.75	1.00
52	Vida Blue	.50	.25	.15
53	Rick Manning	.40	.20	.12
54	Bill Buckner	.70	.35	.20
	Panel 19	2.50	1.25	.70
55	Lee May	.50	.25	.15
56	John Mayberry	.40	.20	.12
57	Darrel Chaney	.40	.20	.12
	Panel 20	3.50	1.75	1.00
58	Cesar Cedeno	.50	.25	.15
59	Ken Griffey	.50	.25	.15
60	Dave Kingman	.80	.40	.25
	Panel 21	3.50	1.75	1.00
61	Ted Simmons	.80	.40	.25
62	Larry Bowa	.50	.25	.15
63	Frank Tanana	.50	.25	.15
	Panel 22	2.50	1.25	.70
64	Jason Thompson	.40	.20	.12
65	Ken Brett	.40	.20	.12
66	Roy Smalley	.40	.20	.12
	Panel 23	2.50	1.25	.70
67	Ray Burris	.40	.20	.12
68	Rick Burleson	.40	.20	.12
69	Buddy Bell	.50	.25	.15
	Panel 24	5.00	2.50	1.50
70	Don Sutton	2.00	1.00	.60
71	Mark Belanger	.40	.20	.12
72	Dennis Leonard	.40	.20	.12
	Panel 25	5.00	2.50	1.50
73	Gaylord Perry	1.50	.70	.45
74	Dick Ruthven	.40	.20	.12
75	Jose Cruz	.50	.25	.15
	Panel 26	4.25	2.25	1.25
76	Cesar Geronimo	.40	.20	.12
77	Jerry Koosman	.50	.25	.15
78	Garry Templeton	.80	.40	.25
	Panel 27	15.00	7.50	4.50
79	Jim Hunter	1.25	.60	.40
80	John Candelaria	.50	.25	.15
81	Nolan Ryan	10.00	5.00	3.00
	Panel 28	2.50	1.25	.70
82	Rusty Staub	.50	.25	.15
83	Jim Barr	.40	.20	.12
84	Butch Wynegar	.50	.25	.15
	Panel 29	2.50	1.25	.70
85	Jose Cardenal	.40	.20	.12
86	Claudell Washington	.50	.25	.15
87	Bill Travers	.40	.20	.12
	Panel 30	2.50	1.25	.70
88	Rick Waits	.40	.20	.12
89	Ron Cey	.50	.25	.15
90	Al Bumbry	.40	.20	.12
	Panel 31	2.50	1.25	.70
91	Bucky Dent	.50	.25	.15
92	Amos Otis	.50	.25	.15
93	Tom Grieve	.40	.20	.12
	Panel 32	2.50	1.25	.70
94	Enos Cabell	.40	.20	.12
95	Dave Concepcion	.50	.25	.15
96	Felix Millan	.40	.20	.12
	Panel 33	2.50	1.25	.70
97	Bake McBride	.40	.20	.12
98	Chris Chambliss	.50	.25	.15
99	Butch Metzger	.40	.20	.12
	Panel 34	2.50	1.25	.70
100	Rennie Stennett	.40	.20	.12
101	Dave Roberts	.40	.20	.12
102	Lyman Bostock	.50	.25	.15
	Panel 35	3.50	1.75	1.00
103	Rick Reuschel	.50	.25	.15
104	Carlton Fisk	1.00	.50	.30
105	Jim Slaton	.40	.20	.12
	Panel 36	2.50	1.25	.70
106	Dennis Eckersley	.60	.30	.20
107	Ken Singleton	.50	.25	.15
108	Ralph Garr	.40	.20	.12
	Panel 37	8.00	4.00	2.50
109	Freddie Patek	.50	.25	.15
110	Jim Sundberg	.60	.30	.20
111	Phil Niekro	3.25	1.75	1.00
	Panel 38	3.50	1.75	1.00
112	J.R. Richard	.70	.35	.20
113	Gary Nolan	.50	.25	.15
114	Jon Matlack	.60	.30	.20
	Panel 39	20.00	10.00	6.00
115	Keith Hernandez	4.00	2.00	1.25
116	Graig Nettles	.70	.35	.20
117	Steve Carlton	4.50	2.25	1.25
	Panel 40	6.50	3.25	2.00
118	Bill Madlock	1.50	.70	.45
119	Jerry Reuss	.80	.40	.25
120	Aurelio Rodriguez	.50	.25	.15
	Panel 41	3.50	1.75	1.00
121	Dan Ford	.50	.25	.15
122	Ray Fosse	.50	.25	.15
123	George Hendrick	.70	.35	.20
	Panel 42	2.50	1.25	.70

	NR MT	EX	VG
124 Alan Ashby	.40	.20	.12
125 Joe Lis	.40	.20	.12
126 Sal Bando	.50	.25	.15
Panel 43	4.00	2.00	1.25
127 Richie Zisk	.50	.25	.15
128 Rich Gossage	.90	.45	.25
129 Don Baylor	.60	.30	.20
Panel 44	2.50	1.25	.70
130 Dave McKay	.40	.20	.12
131 Bob Grich	.50	.25	.15
132 Dave Pagan	.40	.20	.12
Panel 45	2.50	1.25	.70
133 Dave Cash	.40	.20	.12
134 Steve Braun	.40	.20	.12
135 Dan Meyer	.40	.20	.12
Panel 46	4.25	2.25	1.25
136 Bill Stein	.40	.20	.12
137 Rollie Fingers	1.50	.70	.45
138 Brian Downing	.50	.25	.15
Panel 47	2.50	1.25	.70
139 Bill Singer	.40	.20	.12
140 Doyle Alexander	.50	.25	.15
141 Gene Tenace	.40	.20	.12
Panel 48	2.50	1.25	.70
142 Gary Matthews	.50	.25	.15
143 Don Gullett	.40	.20	.12
144 Wayne Garland	.40	.20	.12
Panel 49	2.50	1.25	.70
145 Pete Broberg	.40	.20	.12
146 Joe Rudi	.50	.25	.15
147 Glenn Abbott	.40	.20	.12
Panel 50	2.50	1.25	.70
148 George Scott	.50	.25	.15
149 Bert Campaneris	.50	.25	.15
150 Andy Messersmith	.50	.25	.15

1977 Hostess Twinkies

The 1977 Hostess Twinkie issue, at 150 different cards, is the largest of the single-panel Twinkie sets. It is also the most obscure. The cards, which measure 2-1/4" by 3-1/4", but are part of a larger panel, were found not only with Twinkies, but with Hostess Cupcakes as well. Card #'s 1-30 and 111-150 are Twinkies panels and #'s 31-135 are Cupcakes panels. Complete Cupcakes panels are approximately 2-1/4" by 4-1/2" in size, while complete Twinkies panels measure 3-1/8" by 4-1/4". The photos used in the set are identical to those in the 1977 Hostess three-card panel set. The main difference is the appearance of a black band at the center of the card back. The values quoted in the checklist that follows are for complete bottom panels.

	NR MT	EX	VG
Complete Set:	300.00	150.00	90.00
Common Player:	.80	.40	.25
1 Jim Palmer	6.00	3.00	1.75
2 Joe Morgan	4.00	2.00	1.25
3 Reggie Jackson	10.00	5.00	3.00
4 Carl Yastrzemski	12.00	6.00	3.50
5 Thurman Munson	5.00	2.50	1.50
6 Johnny Bench	8.00	4.00	2.50
7 Tom Seaver	7.00	3.50	2.00
8 Pete Rose	15.00	7.50	4.50
9 Rod Carew	8.00	4.00	2.50

	NR MT	EX	VG
10 Luis Tiant	1.00	.50	.30
11 Phil Garner	.80	.40	.25
12 Sixto Lezcano	.80	.40	.25
13 Mike Torrez	.80	.40	.25
14 Dave Lopes	1.00	.50	.30
15 Doug DeCinces	1.00	.50	.30
16 Jim Spencer	.80	.40	.25
17 Hal McRae	1.00	.50	.30
18 Mike Hargrove	.80	.40	.25
19 Willie Montanez	.80	.40	.25
20 Roger Metzger	.80	.40	.25
21 Dwight Evans	2.00	1.00	.60
22 Steve Rogers	.80	.40	.25
23 Jim Rice	6.00	3.00	1.75
24 Pete Falcone	.80	.40	.25
25 Greg Luzinski	1.50	.70	.45
26 Randy Jones	.80	.40	.25
27 Willie Stargell	6.00	3.00	1.75
28 John Hiller	.80	.40	.25
29 Bobby Murcer	1.25	.60	.40
30 Rick Monday	1.00	.50	.30
31 John Montefusco	.80	.40	.25
32 Lou Brock	6.00	3.00	1.75
33 Bill North	.80	.40	.25
34 Robin Yount	8.00	4.00	2.50
35 Steve Garvey	7.00	3.50	2.00
36 George Brett	10.00	5.00	3.00
37 Toby Harrah	.80	.40	.25
38 Jerry Royster	.80	.40	.25
39 Bob Watson	1.00	.50	.30
40 George Foster	1.75	.90	.50
41 Gary Carter	7.00	3.50	2.00
42 John Denny	.80	.40	.25
43 Mike Schmidt	9.00	4.50	2.75
44 Dave Winfield	7.00	3.50	2.00
45 Al Oliver	1.75	.90	.50
46 Mark Fidrych	1.50	.70	.45
47 Larry Herndon	1.00	.50	.30
48 Dave Goltz	.80	.40	.25
49 Jerry Morales	.80	.40	.25
50 Ron LeFlore	1.00	.50	.30
51 Fred Lynn	1.75	.90	.50
52 Vida Blue	1.00	.50	.30
53 Rick Manning	.80	.40	.25
54 Bill Buckner	1.50	.70	.45
55 Lee May	1.00	.50	.30
56 John Mayberry	.80	.40	.25
57 Darrel Chaney	.80	.40	.25
58 Cesar Cedeno	1.25	.60	.40
59 Ken Griffey	1.25	.60	.40
60 Dave Kingman	1.75	.90	.50
61 Ted Simmons	1.50	.70	.45
62 Larry Bowa	1.25	.60	.40
63 Frank Tanana	1.00	.50	.30
64 Jason Thompson	.80	.40	.25
65 Ken Brett	.80	.40	.25
66 Roy Smalley	.80	.40	.25
67 Ray Burris	.80	.40	.25
68 Rick Burleson	.80	.40	.25
69 Buddy Bell	1.25	.60	.40
70 Don Sutton	3.50	1.75	1.00
71 Mark Belanger	.80	.40	.25
72 Dennis Leonard	.80	.40	.25
73 Gaylord Perry	4.00	2.00	1.25
74 Dick Ruthven	.80	.40	.25
75 Jose Cruz	1.25	.60	.40
76 Cesar Geronimo	.80	.40	.25
77 Jerry Koosman	1.25	.60	.40
78 Garry Templeton	2.50	1.25	.70
79 Jim Hunter	4.00	2.00	1.25
80 John Candelaria	1.00	.50	.30
81 Nolan Ryan	10.00	5.00	3.00
82 Rusty Staub	1.50	.70	.45
83 Jim Barr	.80	.40	.25
84 Butch Wynegar	1.00	.50	.30
85 Jose Cardenal	.80	.40	.25
86 Claudell Washington	1.00	.50	.30
87 Bill Travers	.80	.40	.25
88 Rick Waits	.80	.40	.25
89 Ron Cey	1.25	.60	.40
90 Al Bumbry	.80	.40	.25
91 Bucky Dent	1.00	.50	.30
92 Amos Otis	1.00	.50	.30
93 Tom Grieve	.80	.40	.25
94 Enos Cabell	.80	.40	.25
95 Dave Concepcion	1.25	.60	.40
96 Felix Millan	.80	.40	.25
97 Bake McBride	.80	.40	.25
98 Chris Chambliss	1.00	.50	.30
99 Butch Metzger	.80	.40	.25
100 Rennie Stennett	.80	.40	.25
101 Dave Roberts	.80	.40	.25

		NR MT	EX	VG
102	Lyman Bostock	1.00	.50	.30
103	Rick Reuschel	1.00	.50	.30
104	Carlton Fisk	2.25	1.25	.70
105	Jim Slaton	.80	.40	.25
106	Dennis Eckersley	1.25	.60	.40
107	Ken Singleton	1.00	.50	.30
108	Ralph Garr	.80	.40	.25
109	Freddie Patek	.80	.40	.25
110	Jim Sundberg	.80	.40	.25
111	Phil Niekro	3.50	1.75	1.00
112	J. R. Richard	1.00	.50	.30
113	Gary Nolan	.80	.40	.25
114	Jon Matlack	.80	.40	.25
115	Keith Hernandez	5.00	2.50	1.50
116	Graig Nettles	2.00	1.00	.60
117	Steve Carlton	7.00	3.50	2.00
118	Bill Madlock	1.50	.70	.45
119	Jerry Reuss	1.00	.50	.30
120	Aurelio Rodriguez	.80	.40	.25
121	Dan Ford	.80	.40	.25
122	Ray Fosse	.80	.40	.25
123	George Hendrick	1.00	.50	.30
124	Alan Ashby	.80	.40	.25
125	Joe Lis	.80	.40	.25
126	Sal Bando	1.00	.50	.30
127	Richie Zisk	1.00	.50	.30
128	Rich Gossage	1.75	.90	.50
129	Don Baylor	1.50	.70	.45
130	Dave McKay	.80	.40	.25
131	Bob Grich	1.00	.50	.30
132	Dave Pagan	.80	.40	.25
133	Dave Cash	.80	.40	.25
134	Steve Braun	.80	.40	.25
135	Dan Meyer	.80	.40	.25
136	Bill Stein	.80	.40	.25
137	Rollie Fingers	3.00	1.50	.90
138	Brian Downing	1.00	.50	.30
139	Bill Singer	.80	.40	.25
140	Doyle Alexander	1.00	.50	.30
141	Gene Tenace	1.00	.50	.30
142	Gary Matthews	1.00	.50	.30
143	Don Gullett	.80	.40	.25
144	Wayne Garland	.80	.40	.25
145	Pete Broberg	.80	.40	.25
146	Joe Rudi	1.00	.50	.30
147	Glenn Abbott	.80	.40	.25
148	George Scott	1.00	.50	.30
149	Bert Campaneris	1.25	.60	.40
150	Andy Messersmith	1.00	.50	.30

1978 Hostess

MICKEY RIVERS
NEW YORK YANKEES

Other than the design on the front of the card, there was little different about the 1978 Hostess cards from the three years' issues which had preceded it, or the one which followed. The 2-1/4" by 3-1/4" cards were printed in panels of three (7-1/4" by 3-1/4") as the bottom of family-sized boxes of snake cakes. The 1978 set was again complete at 150 cards. Like other years of Hostess issues, there are scarcities within the 1978 set that are the result of those panels having been issued with less-popular brands of snack cakes.

	NR MT	EX	VG
Complete Panel:	325.00	162.00	97.00
Complete Singles Set:	225.00	112.00	70.00

		NR MT	EX	VG
	Common Panel:	2.50	1.25	.70
	Common Single Player:	.40	.20	.12
	Panel 1	4.00	2.00	1.25
1	Butch Hobson	.40	.20	.12
2	George Foster	.90	.45	.25
3	Bob Forsch	.50	.25	.15
	Panel 2	5.00	2.50	1.50
4	Tony Perez	1.00	.50	.30
5	Bruce Sutter	.90	.45	.25
6	Hal McRae	.50	.25	.15
	Panel 3	6.00	3.00	1.75
7	Tommy John	1.50	.70	.45
8	Greg Luzinski	.50	.25	.15
9	Enos Cabell	.40	.20	.12
	Panel 4	7.00	3.50	2.00
10	Doug DeCinces	.50	.25	.15
11	Willie Stargell	3.00	1.50	.90
12	Ed Halicki	.40	.20	.12
	Panel 5	2.50	1.25	.70
13	Larry Hisle	.40	.20	.12
14	Jim Slaton	.40	.20	.12
15	Buddy Bell	.50	.25	.15
	Panel 6	2.50	1.25	.70
16	Earl Williams	.40	.20	.12
17	Glenn Abbott	.40	.20	.12
18	Dan Ford	.40	.20	.12
	Panel 7	2.50	1.25	.70
19	Gary Mathews	.50	.25	.15
20	Eric Soderholm	.40	.20	.12
21	Bump Wills	.40	.20	.12
	Panel 8	7.00	3.50	2.00
22	Keith Hernandez	2.50	1.25	.70
23	Dave Cash	.40	.20	.12
24	George Scott	.50	.25	.15
	Panel 9	15.00	7.50	4.50
25	Ron Guidry	1.50	.70	.45
26	Dave Kingman	.80	.40	.25
27	George Brett	7.00	3.50	2.00
	Panel 10	3.50	1.75	1.00
28	Bob Watson	.50	.25	.15
29	Bob Boone	.70	.35	.20
30	Reggie Smith	.70	.35	.20
	Panel 11	20.00	10.00	6.00
31	Eddie Murray	10.00	5.00	3.00
32	Gary Lavelle	.50	.25	.15
33	Rennie Stennett	.50	.25	.15
	Panel 12	3.50	1.75	1.00
34	Duane Kuiper	.50	.25	.15
35	Sixto Lezcano	.50	.25	.15
36	Dave Rozema	.50	.25	.15
	Panel 13	3.50	1.75	1.00
37	Butch Wynegar	.50	.25	.15
38	Mitchell Page	.50	.25	.15
39	Bill Stein	.50	.25	.15
	Panel 14	2.50	1.25	.70
40	Elliott Maddox	.40	.20	.12
41	Mike Hargrove	.40	.20	.12
42	Bobby Bonds	.50	.25	.15
	Panel 15	15.00	7.50	4.50
43	Garry Templeton	.80	.40	.25
44	Johnny Bench	4.00	2.00	1.25
45	Jim Rice	4.00	2.00	1.25
	Panel 16	13.00	6.50	4.00
46	Bill Buckner	.80	.40	.25
47	Reggie Jackson	5.00	2.50	1.50
48	Freddie Patek	.40	.20	.12
	Panel 17	8.50	4.25	2.50
49	Steve Carlton	3.50	1.75	1.00
50	Cesar Cedeno	.50	.25	.15
51	Steve Yeager	.40	.20	.12
	Panel 18	3.50	1.75	1.00
52	Phil Garner	.50	.25	.15
53	Lee May	.50	.25	.15
54	Darrell Evans	.70	.35	.20
	Panel 19	2.50	1.25	.70
55	Steve Kemp	.50	.25	.15
56	Dusty Baker	.50	.25	.15
57	Ray Fosse	.40	.20	.12
	Panel 20	2.50	1.25	.70
58	Manny Sanguillen	.40	.20	.12
59	Tom Johnson	.40	.20	.12
60	Lee Stanton	.40	.20	.12
	Panel 21	10.00	5.00	3.00
61	Jeff Burroughs	.40	.20	.12
62	Bobby Grich	.50	.25	.15
63	Dave Winfield	4.00	2.00	1.25
	Panel 22	3.50	1.75	1.00
64	Dan Driessen	.50	.25	.15
65	Ted Simmons	.80	.40	.25
66	Jerry Remy	.40	.20	.12

		NR MT	EX	VG
	Panel 23	2.50	1.25	.70
67	Al Cowens	.40	.20	.12
68	Sparky Lyle	.50	.25	.15
69	Manny Trillo	.50	.25	.15
	Panel 24	5.00	2.50	1.50
70	Don Sutton	1.50	.70	.45
71	Larry Bowa	.50	.25	.15
72	Jose Cruz	.50	.25	.15
	Panel 25	8.00	4.00	2.50
73	Willie McCovey	3.00	1.50	.90
74	Bert Blyleven	.70	.35	.20
75	Ken Singleton	.50	.25	.15
	Panel 26	2.50	1.25	.70
76	Bill North	.40	.20	.12
77	Jason Thompson	.40	.20	.12
78	Dennis Eckersley	.50	.25	.15
	Panel 27	2.50	1.25	.70
79	Jim Sundberg	.50	.25	.15
80	Jerry Koosman	.50	.25	.15
81	Bruce Bochte	.40	.20	.12
	Panel 28	15.00	7.50	4.50
82	George Hendrick	.50	.25	.15
83	Nolan Ryan	10.00	5.00	3.00
84	Roy Howell	.40	.20	.12
	Panel 29	5.50	2.75	1.75
85	Butch Metzger	.40	.20	.12
86	George Medich	.40	.20	.12
87	Joe Morgan	2.00	1.00	.60
	Panel 30	3.00	1.50	.90
88	Dennis Leonard	.50	.25	.15
89	Willie Randolph	.50	.25	.15
90	Bobby Murcer	.50	.25	.15
	Panel 31	3.00	1.50	.90
91	Rick Manning	.40	.20	.12
92	J.R. Richard	.50	.25	.15
93	Ron Cey	.60	.30	.20
	Panel 32	2.50	1.25	.70
94	Sal Bando	.50	.25	.15
95	Ron LeFlore	.50	.25	.15
96	Dave Goltz	.40	.20	.12
	Panel 33	2.50	1.25	.70
97	Dan Meyer	.40	.20	.12
98	Chris Chambliss	.50	.25	.15
99	Biff Pocoroba	.40	.20	.12
	Panel 34	2.50	1.25	.70
100	Oscar Gamble	.40	.20	.12
101	Frank Tanana	.50	.25	.15
102	Lenny Randle	.40	.20	.12
	Panel 35	2.50	1.25	.70
103	Tommy Hutton	.40	.20	.12
104	John Candelaria	.50	.25	.15
105	Jorge Orta	.40	.20	.12
	Panel 36	3.00	1.50	.90
106	Ken Reitz	.40	.20	.12
107	Bill Campbell	.40	.20	.12
108	Dave Concepcion	.70	.35	.20
	Panel 37	2.50	1.25	.70
109	Joe Ferguson	.40	.20	.12
110	Mickey Rivers	.50	.25	.15
111	Paul Splittorff	.40	.20	.12
	Panel 38	12.00	6.00	3.50
112	Davey Lopes	.50	.25	.15
113	Mike Schmidt	7.00	3.50	2.00
114	Joe Rudi	.50	.25	.15
	Panel 39	7.00	3.50	2.00
115	Milt May	.40	.20	.12
116	Jim Palmer	3.00	1.50	.90
117	Bill Madlock	.70	.35	.20
	Panel 40	2.50	1.25	.70
118	Roy Smalley	.40	.20	.12
119	Cecil Cooper	.50	.25	.15
120	Rick Langford	.40	.20	.12
	Panel 41	5.75	3.00	1.75
121	Ruppert Jones	.40	.20	.12
122	Phil Niekro	2.25	1.25	.70
123	Toby Harrah	.50	.25	.15
	Panel 42	2.50	1.25	.70
124	Chet Lemon	.50	.25	.15
125	Gene Tenace	.40	.20	.12
126	Steve Henderson	.40	.20	.12
	Panel 43	20.00	10.00	6.00
127	Mike Torrez	.40	.20	.12
128	Pete Rose	8.00	4.00	2.50
129	John Denny	.50	.25	.15
	Panel 44	4.00	2.00	1.25
130	Darrell Porter	.50	.25	.15
131	Rick Reuschel	.50	.25	.15
132	Graig Nettles	.90	.45	.25
	Panel 45	4.50	2.25	1.25
133	Garry Maddox	.50	.25	.15
134	Mike Flanagan	.50	.25	.15

		NR MT	EX	VG
135	Dave Parker	1.25	.60	.40
	Panel 46	12.00	6.00	3.50
136	Terry Whitfield	.40	.20	.12
137	Wayne Garland	.40	.20	.12
138	Robin Yount	8.00	4.00	2.50
	Panel 47	12.00	6.00	3.50
139	Gaylord Perry	2.50	1.25	.70
140	Rod Carew	4.00	2.00	1.25
141	Wayne Gross	.40	.20	.12
	Panel 48	5.00	2.50	1.50
142	Barry Bonnell	.40	.20	.12
143	Willie Montanez	.40	.20	.12
144	Rollie Fingers	1.75	.90	.50
	Panel 49	12.00	6.00	3.50
145	Bob Bailor	.40	.20	.12
146	Tom Seaver	3.50	1.75	1.00
147	Thurman Munson	2.50	1.25	.70
	Panel 50	8.00	4.00	2.50
148	Lyman Bostock	.50	.25	.15
149	Gary Carter	3.50	1.75	1.00
150	Ron Blomberg	.40	.20	.12

1979 Hostess

The last of five consecutive annual issues, the 1979 Hostess set retained the 150-card set size, 2-1/4" by 3-1/4" single-card size and 7-1/4" by 3-1/4" three-card panel format from the previous years. The cards were printed as the bottom panel on family-size boxes of Hostess snack cakes. Some panels, which were printed on less-popular brands, are somewhat scarcer today than the rest of the set. Like all Hostess issues, because the hobby was in a well-developed state at the time of issue, the 1979s survive today in complete panels and complete unused boxes, for collectors who like original packaging.

		NR MT	EX	VG
Complete Panel Set:		350.00	175.00	105.00
Complete Singles Set:		200.00	100.00	60.00
Common Panel:		2.50	1.25	.70
Common Single Player:		.40	.20	.12
	Panel 1	9.50	4.75	2.75
1	John Denny	.40	.20	.12
2	Jim Rice	4.00	2.00	1.25
3	Doug Bair	.40	.20	.12
	Panel 2	2.50	1.25	.70
4	Darrell Porter	.50	.25	.15
5	Ross Grimsley	.40	.20	.12
6	Bobby Murcer	.50	.25	.15
	Panel 3	18.00	9.00	5.50
7	Lee Mazzilli	.50	.25	.15
8	Steve Garvey	4.00	2.00	1.25
9	Mike Schmidt	5.00	2.50	1.50
	Panel 4	6.50	3.25	2.00
10	Terry Whitfield	.40	.20	.12
11	Jim Palmer	3.00	1.50	.90
12	Omar Moreno	.40	.20	.12
	Panel 5	2.50	1.25	.70
13	Duane Kuiper	.40	.20	.12
14	Mike Caldwell	.40	.20	.12
15	Steve Kemp	.50	.25	.15
	Panel 6	2.50	1.25	.70
16	Dave Goltz	.40	.20	.12
17	Mitchell Page	.40	.20	.12

#	Player	NR MT	EX	VG
18	Bill Stein	.40	.20	.12
	Panel 7	2.50	1.25	.70
19	Gene Tenace	.40	.20	.12
20	Jeff Burroughs	.40	.20	.12
21	Francisco Barrios	.40	.20	.12
	Panel 8	8.00	4.00	2.50
22	Mike Torrez	.40	.20	.12
23	Ken Reitz	.40	.20	.12
24	Gary Carter	3.50	1.75	1.00
	Panel 9	8.00	4.00	2.50
25	Al Hrabosky	.50	.25	.15
26	Thurman Munson	2.50	1.25	.70
27	Bill Buckner	.80	.40	.25
	Panel 10	5.00	2.50	1.50
28	Ron Cey	.90	.45	.25
29	J.R. Richard	.70	.35	.20
30	Greg Luzinski	.90	.45	.25
	Panel 11	5.00	2.50	1.50
31	Ed Ott	.50	.25	.15
32	Denny Martinez	.50	.25	.15
33	Darrell Evans	1.25	.60	.40
	Panel 12	2.50	1.25	.70
34	Ron LeFlore	.50	.25	.15
35	Rick Waits	.40	.20	.12
36	Cecil Cooper	.50	.25	.15
	Panel 13	9.50	4.75	2.75
37	Leon Roberts	.40	.20	.12
38	Rod Carew	4.00	2.00	1.25
39	John Henry Johnson	.40	.20	.12
	Panel 14	2.50	1.25	.70
40	Chet Lemon	.50	.25	.15
41	Craig Swan	.40	.20	.12
42	Gary Matthews	.50	.25	.15
	Panel 15	3.50	1.75	1.00
43	Lamar Johnson	.40	.20	.12
44	Ted Simmons	.80	.40	.25
45	Ken Griffey	.50	.25	.15
	Panel 16	4.00	2.00	1.25
46	Freddie Patek	.40	.20	.12
47	Frank Tanana	.50	.25	.15
48	Rich Gossage	1.25	.60	.40
	Panel 17	2.50	1.25	.70
49	Burt Hooton	.40	.20	.12
50	Ellis Valentine	.40	.20	.12
51	Ken Forsch	.40	.20	.12
	Panel 18	5.00	2.50	1.50
52	Bob Knepper	.50	.25	.15
53	Dave Parker	1.50	.70	.45
54	Doug DeCinces	.50	.25	.15
	Panel 19	12.00	6.00	3.50
55	Robin Yount	6.00	3.00	1.75
56	Rusty Staub	.80	.40	.25
57	Gary Alexander	.40	.20	.12
	Panel 20	2.50	1.25	.70
58	Julio Cruz	.40	.20	.12
59	Matt Keough	.40	.20	.12
60	Roy Smalley	.40	.20	.12
	Panel 21	10.00	5.00	3.00
61	Joe Morgan	2.50	1.25	.70
62	Phil Niekro	2.50	1.25	.70
63	Don Baylor	.80	.40	.25
	Panel 22	10.00	5.00	3.00
64	Dwight Evans	.90	.45	.25
65	Tom Seaver	4.00	2.00	1.25
66	George Hendrick	.50	.25	.15
	Panel 23	14.00	7.00	4.25
67	Rick Reuschel	.50	.25	.15
68	Geroge Brett	6.00	3.00	1.75
69	Lou Piniella	.80	.40	.25
	Panel 24	8.50	4.25	2.50
70	Enos Cabell	.40	.20	.12
71	Steve Carlton	3.50	1.75	1.00
72	Reggie Smith	.50	.25	.15
	Panel 25	4.00	2.00	1.25
73	Rick Dempsey	.50	.25	.15
74	Vida Blue	.80	.40	.25
75	Phil Garner	.70	.35	.20
	Panel 26	3.50	1.75	1.00
76	Rick Manning	.50	.25	.15
77	Mark Fidrych	.80	.40	.25
78	Mario Guerrero	.50	.25	.15
	Panel 27	5.00	2.50	1.50
79	Bob Stinson	.50	.25	.15
80	Al Oliver	1.25	.60	.40
81	Doug Flynn	.50	.25	.15
	Panel 28	6.00	3.00	1.75
82	John Mayberry	.40	.20	.12
83	Gaylord Perry	2.50	1.25	.70
84	Joe Rudi	.50	.25	.15
	Panel 29	3.50	1.75	1.00
85	Dave Concepcion	.70	.35	.20

#	Player	NR MT	EX	VG
86	John Candelaria	.50	.25	.15
87	Pete Vuckovich	.50	.25	.15
	Panel 30	5.00	2.50	1.50
88	Ivan DeJesus	.40	.20	.12
89	Ron Guidry	1.50	.70	.45
90	Hal McRae	.50	.25	.15
	Panel 31	5.50	2.75	1.75
91	Cesar Cedeno	.50	.25	.15
92	Don Sutton	2.00	1.00	.60
93	Andre Thornton	.50	.25	.15
	Panel 32	2.50	1.25	.70
94	Roger Erickson	.40	.20	.12
95	Larry Hisle	.40	.20	.12
96	Jason Thompson	.40	.20	.12
	Panel 33	7.50	3.75	2.25
97	Jim Sundberg	.50	.25	.15
98	Bob Horner	3.00	1.50	.90
99	Ruppert Jones	.40	.20	.12
	Panel 34	20.00	10.00	6.00
100	Willie Montanez	.40	.20	. -.12
101	Nolan Ryan	8.00	4.00	2.50
102	Ozzie Smith	12.00	6.00	3.50
	Panel 35	7.50	3.75	2.25
103	Eric Soderholm	.40	.20	.12
104	Willie Stargell	3.00	1.50	.90
105	Bob Bailor	.40	.20	.12
	Panel 36	9.00	4.50	2.75
106	Carlton Fisk	1.25	.60	.40
107	George Foster	.90	.45	.25
108	Keith Hernandez	2.50	1.25	.70
	Panel 37	4.00	2.00	1.25
109	Dennis Leonard	.50	.25	.15
110	Graig Nettles	.90	.45	.25
111	Jose Cruz	.50	.25	.15
	Panel 38	3.50	1.75	1.00
112	Bobby Grich	.50	.25	.15
113	Bob Boone	.50	.25	.15
114	Dave Lopes	.50	.25	.15
	Panel 39	15.00	7.50	4.50
115	Eddie Murray	4.50	2.25	1.25
116	Jack Clark	.90	.45	.25
117	Lou Whitaker	.50	.25	.15
	Panel 40	10.00	5.00	3.00
118	Miguel Dilone	.40	.20	.12
119	Sal Bando	.50	.25	.15
120	Reggie Jackson	4.50	2.25	1.25
	Panel 41	14.00	7.00	4.25
121	Dale Murphy	7.00	3.50	2.00
122	Jon Matlack	.40	.20	.12
123	Bruce Bochte	.40	.20	.12
	Panel 42	9.00	4.50	2.75
124	John Stearns	.40	.20	.12
125	Dave Winfield	3.50	1.75	1.00
126	Jorge Orta	.40	.20	.12
	Panel 43	9.00	4.50	2.75
127	Garry Templeton	.70	.35	.20
128	Johnny Bench	4.00	2.00	1.25
129	Butch Hobson	.40	.20	.12
	Panel 44	4.50	2.25	1.25
130	Bruce Sutter	1.25	.60	.40
131	Bucky Dent	.50	.25	.15
132	Amos Otis	.50	.25	.15
	Panel 45	3.50	1.75	1.00
133	Bert Blyleven	.70	.35	.20
134	Larry Bowa	.50	.25	.15
135	Ken Singleton	.50	.25	.15
	Panel 46	3.50	1.75	1.00
136	Sixto Lezcano	.40	.20	.12
137	Roy Howell	.40	.20	.12
138	Bill Madlock	.80	.40	.25
	Panel 47	2.50	1.25	.70
139	Dave Revering	.40	.20	.12
140	Richie Zisk	.50	.25	.15
141	Butch Wynegar	.50	.25	.15
	Panel 48	18.00	9.00	5.50
142	Alan Ashby	.40	.20	.12
143	Sparky Lyle	.50	.25	.15
144	Pete Rose	8.00	4.00	2.50
	Panel 49	4.00	2.00	1.25
145	Dennis Eckersley	.60	.30	.20
146	Dave Kingman	.80	.40	.25
147	Buddy Bell	.60	.30	.20
	Panel 50	2.50	1.25	.70
148	Mike Hargrove	.40	.20	.12
149	Jerry Koosman	.50	.25	.15
150	Toby Harrah	.50	.25	.15

**The values quoted are intended
to reflect the market price.**

1985 Hostess Braves

After a five-year hiatus, Hostess returned to the production of baseball cards in 1985 with an Atlanta Braves team set. The 22 cards in the set were printed by Topps and inserted into packages of snack cake products, three cello-wrapped player cards and a header card per box. The 2-1/2" by 3-1/2" cards share a common back design with the regular-issue Topps cards of 1985.

		MT	NR MT	EX
Complete Set:		7.00	5.25	2.75
Common Player:		.35	.25	.14
1	Eddie Haas	.35	.25	.14
2	Len Barker	.35	.25	.14
3	Steve Bedrosian	.50	.40	.20
4	Bruce Benedict	.35	.25	.14
5	Rick Camp	.35	.25	.14
6	Rick Cerone	.35	.25	.14
7	Chris Chambliss	.40	.30	.15
8	Terry Forster	.35	.25	.14
9	Gene Garber	.35	.25	.14
10	Albert Hall	.35	.25	.14
11	Bob Horner	.50	.40	.20
12	Glenn Hubbard	.35	.25	.14
13	Brad Komminsk	.35	.25	.14
14	Rick Mahler	.40	.30	.15
15	Craig McMurtry	.35	.25	.14
16	Dale Murphy	2.00	1.50	.80
17	Ken Oberkfell	.40	.30	.15
18	Pascual Perez	.40	.30	.15
19	Gerald Perry	.50	.40	.20
20	Rafael Ramirez	.35	.25	.14
21	Bruce Sutter	.70	.50	.30
22	Claudell Washington	.40	.30	.15
———	Header Card	.10	.08	.04

1987 Hostess Stickers

Hostess of Canada issued a 30-card set of stickers in specially marked bags of potato chips. One sticker, measuring 1-3/4" by 1-3/8" in size, was found in each bag. The stickers have full-color fronts with the player's name appearing in black type in a white band. The Hostess logo and the sticker number are also included on the fronts. The backs are written in both English and French and contain the player's name, position and team.

		MT	NR MT	EX
Complete Set:		25.00	18.50	10.00
Common Player:		.15	.11	.06
1	Jesse Barfield	.25	.20	.10
2	Ernie Whitt	.15	.11	.06
3	George Bell	1.00	.70	.40
4	Hubie Brooks	.15	.11	.06
5	Tim Wallach	.25	.20	.10
6	Floyd Youmans	.15	.11	.06
7	Dale Murphy	1.50	1.25	.60
8	Ryne Sandberg	1.00	.70	.40
9	Eric Davis	2.00	1.50	.80
10	Mike Scott	.25	.20	.10
11	Fernando Valenzuela	.75	.60	.30
12	Gary Carter	1.00	.70	.40
13	Mike Schmidt	1.50	1.25	.60
14	Tony Pena	.15	.11	.06
15	Ozzie Smith	.60	.45	.25
16	Tony Gwynn	1.25	.90	.50
17	Mike Krukow	.15	.11	.06
18	Eddie Murray	1.25	.90	.50
19	Wade Boggs	1.75	1.25	.70
20	Wally Joyner	2.00	1.50	.80
21	Harold Baines	.25	.20	.10
22	Brook Jacoby	.25	.20	.10
23	Lou Whitaker	.50	.40	.20
24	George Brett	1.50	1.25	.60
25	Robin Yount	.75	.60	.30
26	Kirby Puckett	1.25	.90	.50
27	Don Mattingly	2.50	2.00	1.00
28	Jose Canseco	3.00	2.25	1.25
29	Phil Bradley	.25	.20	.10
30	Pete O'Brien	.15	.11	.06

Definitions for grading conditions are located in the Introduction of this price guide.

1988 Hostess Potato Chips Expos

The Expos and Blue Jays are showcased in this set of 24 discs (1-1/2" diameter). Full-color head shots are framed in white, surrounded by red stars. A yellow-banner "1988 Collectors Edition" label is printed (English and French) beneath the photo, followed by the player's name in black. Numbered disc backs are bilingual, blue and white, and include player name and stats. This set was distributed inside Hostess potato chip packages sold in Canada.

		MT	NR MT	EX
Complete Panel Set:		15.00	11.00	6.00
Complete Singles Set:		9.00	6.75	3.50
Common Panel:		.75	.60	.30
Common Single Player:		.25	.20	.10
	Panel	.90	.70	.35
1	Mitch Webster	.25	.20	.10
20	Lloyd Moseby	.40	.30	.15
	Panel	.90	.70	.35
2	Tim Burke	.25	.20	.10
23	Tom Henke	.40	.30	.15
	Panel	.80	.60	.30
3	Tom Foley	.25	.20	.10

		MT	NR MT	EX
13	Jim Clancy	.30	.25	.12
	Panel	.75	.60	.30
4	Herm Winningham	.25	.20	.10
14	Rance Mulliniks	.25	.20	.10
	Panel	1.25	.90	.50
5	Hubie Brooks	.40	.30	.15
24	Jimmy Key	.60	.45	.25
	Panel	1.50	1.25	.60
6	Mike Fitzgerald	.25	.20	.10
17	Dave Stieb	.60	.45	.25
	Panel	2.25	1.75	.90
7	Tim Wallach	.70	.50	.30
15	Fred McGriff	1.50	1.25	.60
	Panel	2.25	1.75	.90
8	Andres Galarraga	1.50	1.25	.60
21	Tony Fernandez	.70	.50	.30
	Panel	.80	.60	.30
9	Floyd Youmans	.30	.25	.12
18	Mark Eichhorn	.30	.25	.12
	Panel	1.50	1.25	.60
10	Neal Heaton	.25	.20	.10
19	Jesse Barfield	.70	.50	.30
	Panel	2.00	1.50	.80
11	Tim Raines	1.25	.90	.50
16	Ernie Whitt	.25	.20	.10
	Panel	1.75	1.25	.70
12	Casey Candaele	.25	.20	.10
22	George Bell	1.50	1.25	.60

1953 Hunter
Wieners Cardinals

From the great era of the regionally issued hot dog cards in the mid-1950s, the 1953 Hunter wieners set of St. Louis Cardinals is certainly among the rarest today. Originally issued in two-card panels, the cards are most often found as 2-1/4" by 3-1/4" singles today when they can be found at all. The cards feature a light blue facsimile autograph printed over the stat box at the bottom. They are blank-backed.

		NR MT	EX	VG
Complete Set:		2500.00	1250.00	750.00
Common Player:		60.00	30.00	18.00
(1)	Steve Bilko	60.00	30.00	18.00
(2)	Alpha Brazle	60.00	30.00	18.00
(3)	Cloyd Boyer	60.00	30.00	18.00
(4)	Cliff Chambers	60.00	30.00	18.00
(5)	Michael Clark	60.00	30.00	18.00
(6)	Jack Crimian	60.00	30.00	18.00
(7)	Lester Fusselman	60.00	30.00	18.00
(8)	Harvey Haddix	65.00	33.00	20.00
(9)	Solly Hemus	60.00	30.00	18.00
(10)	Ray Jablonski	60.00	30.00	18.00
(11)	William Johnson	60.00	30.00	18.00
(12)	Harry Lowrey	60.00	30.00	18.00
(13)	Lawrence Miggins	60.00	30.00	18.00
(14)	Stuart Miller	60.00	30.00	18.00
(15)	Wilmer Mizell	60.00	30.00	18.00
(16)	Stanley Musial	600.00	300.00	175.00
(17)	Joseph Presko	60.00	30.00	18.00
(18)	Delbert Rice	60.00	30.00	18.00
(19)	Harold Rice	60.00	30.00	18.00
(20)	Willard Schmidt	60.00	30.00	18.00
(21)	Albert Schoendienst	100.00	50.00	30.00

		NR MT	EX	VG
(22)	Richard Sisler	60.00	30.00	18.00
(23)	Enos Slaughter	150.00	75.00	45.00
(24)	Gerald Staley	60.00	30.00	18.00
(25)	Edward Stanky	70.00	35.00	21.00
(26)	John Yuhas	60.00	30.00	18.00

1954 Hunter
Wieners Cardinals

A nearly impossible set to complete today by virtue of the method of its issue, the 1954 Hunter hot dog set essentially features what would traditionally be the front and back of a normal baseball card on two different cards. The "front," containing a color photo of one of 30 St. Louis Cardinals has a box at bottom challenging the collector to name him and quote his stats. The "back" features cartoon Cardinals in action, and contains the answers. However, because both parts were printed on a single panel, and because most of the back (non-picture) panels were thrown away years ago, it is an impossible challenge to complete a '54 Hunter set today. There is no back printing on the 2-1/4" by 3-1/2" cards.

		NR MT	EX	VG
Complete Set:		4000.00	2000.00	1200.
Common Player:		60.00	30.00	18.00
(1)	Tom Alston	60.00	30.00	18.00
(2)	Steve Bilko	60.00	30.00	18.00
(3)	Al Brazle	60.00	30.00	18.00
(4)	Tom Burgess	60.00	30.00	18.00
(5)	Cot Deal	60.00	30.00	18.00
(6)	Alex Grammas	60.00	30.00	18.00
(7)	Harvey Haddix	60.00	30.00	18.00
(8)	Solly Hemus	60.00	30.00	18.00
(9)	Ray Jablonski	60.00	30.00	18.00
(10)	Royce Lint	60.00	30.00	18.00
(11)	Peanuts Lowrey	60.00	30.00	18.00
(12)	Memo Luna	60.00	30.00	18.00
(13)	Stu Miller	60.00	30.00	18.00
(14)	Stan Musial	600.00	300.00	180.00
(15)	Tom Poholsky	60.00	30.00	18.00
(16)	Bill Posedel	60.00	30.00	18.00
(17)	Joe Presko	60.00	30.00	18.00
(18)	Vic Raschi	60.00	30.00	18.00
(19)	Dick Rand	60.00	30.00	18.00
(20)	Rip Repulski	60.00	30.00	18.00
(21)	Del Rice	60.00	30.00	18.00
(22)	John Riddle	60.00	30.00	18.00
(23)	Mike Ryba	60.00	30.00	18.00
(24)	Red Schoendienst	100.00	50.00	30.00
(25)	Dick Schofield	100.00	50.00	30.00
(26)	Eddie Stanky	110.00	55.00	33.00
(27)	Enos Slaughter	150.00	75.00	45.00
(28)	Gerry Staley	60.00	30.00	18.00
(29)	Ed Yuhas	60.00	30.00	18.00
(30)	Sal Yvars	60.00	30.00	18.00

Regional interest may affect
the value of a card.

1955 Hunter
Wieners Cardinals

The 1955 team set of St. Louis Cardinals, included with packages of Hunter hot dogs, features the third format change in three years of issue. For 1955, the cards were printed in a tall, narrow 2" by 4-3/4" format, two to a panel. The cards featured both a posed action photo and a portrait photo, along with a facsimile autograph and brief biographical data on the front. There is no back printing, as the cards were part of the wrapping for packages of hot dogs.

		NR MT	EX	VG
Complete Set:		3500.00	1750.00	1050.
Common Player:		75.00	37.00	22.00
(1)	Thomas Edison Alston	75.00	37.00	22.00
(2)	Kenton Lloyd Boyer	225.00	112.00	67.00
(3)	Harry Lewis Elliott	75.00	37.00	22.00
(4)	John Edward Faszholz	75.00	37.00	22.00
(5)	Joseph Filmore Frazier	75.00	37.00	22.00
(6)	Alexander Pete Grammas	75.00	37.00	22.00
(7)	Harvey Haddix	125.00	62.00	37.00
(8)	Solly Joseph Hemus	75.00	37.00	22.00
(9)	Lawrence Curtis Jackson	75.00	37.00	22.00
(10)	Tony R. Jacobs	75.00	37.00	22.00
(11)	Gordon Bassett Jones	75.00	37.00	22.00
(12)	Paul Edmore LaPalme	75.00	37.00	22.00
(13)	Brooks Ulysses Lawrence	75.00	37.00	22.00
(14)	Wallace Wade Moon	125.00	62.00	37.00
(15)	Stanley Frank Musial	1000.00	500.00	300.00
(16)	Thomas George Poholsky	75.00	37.00	22.00
(17)	William John Posedel	75.00	37.00	22.00
(18)	Victor Angelo John Raschi	75.00	37.00	22.00
(19)	Eldon John Repulski	75.00	37.00	22.00
(20)	Delbert Rice	75.00	37.00	22.00
(21)	John Ludy Riddle	75.00	37.00	22.00
(22)	William F. Sarni	75.00	37.00	22.00
(23)	Albert Fred Schoendienst	175.00	87.00	52.00
(24)	Richard John Schofield (actually John Richard)	75.00	37.00	22.00
(25)	Frank Thomas Smith	75.00	37.00	22.00
(26)	Edward R. Stanky	125.00	62.00	37.00
(27)	Bobby Gene Tiefenauer	75.00	37.00	22.00
(28)	William Charles Virdon	175.00	87.00	52.00
(29)	Frederick E. Walker	75.00	37.00	22.00
(30)	Floyd Lewis Woolridge	75.00	37.00	22.00

1962 Jell-O

Virtually identical in content to the 1962 Post cereal cards, the '62 Jell-O set of 197 was only issued

in the Midwest. Players and card numbers are identical in the two sets, except Brooks Robinson (#29), Ted Kluszewski (#82) and Smoky Burgess (#176) were not issued in the Jell-O version. The Jell-O cards are easy to distinguish from the Post of that year by the absence of the red oval Post logo and red or blue border around the stat box. Cards which have been neatly trimmed from the box which they were printed will measure 3-1/2" by 2-1/2".

		NR MT	EX	VG
Complete Set:		4500.00	2250.00	1350.
Common Player:		5.00	2.50	1.50
1	Bill Skowron	20.00	10.00	6.00
2	Bobby Richardson	20.00	10.00	6.00
3	Cletis Boyer	10.00	5.00	3.00
4	Tony Kubek	15.00	7.50	4.50
5	Mickey Mantle	700.00	350.00	210.00
6	Roger Maris	125.00	62.00	37.00
7	Yogi Berra	60.00	30.00	18.00
8	Elston Howard	15.00	7.50	4.50
9	Whitey Ford	40.00	20.00	12.00
10	Ralph Terry	10.00	5.00	3.00
11	John Blanchard	6.00	3.00	1.75
12	Luis Arroyo	6.00	3.00	1.75
13	Bill Stafford	20.00	10.00	6.00
14	Norm Cash	10.00	5.00	3.00
15	Jake Wood	5.00	2.50	1.50
16	Steve Boros	5.00	2.50	1.50
17	Chico Fernandez	5.00	2.50	1.50
18	Billy Bruton	5.00	2.50	1.50
19	Ken Aspromonte	5.00	2.50	1.50
20	Al Kaline	40.00	20.00	12.00
21	Dick Brown	5.00	2.50	1.50
22	Frank Lary	6.00	3.00	1.75
23	Don Mossi	6.00	3.00	1.75
24	Phil Regan	5.00	2.50	1.50
25	Charley Maxwell	5.00	2.50	1.50
26	Jim Bunning	15.00	7.50	4.50
27	Jim Gentile	6.00	3.00	1.75
28	Marv Breeding	5.00	2.50	1.50
29	Not Issued			
30	Ron Hansen	5.00	2.50	1.50
31	Jackie Brandt	20.00	10.00	6.00
32	Dick Williams	6.00	3.00	1.75
33	Gus Triandos	6.00	3.00	1.75
34	Milt Pappas	6.00	3.00	1.75
35	Hoyt Wilhelm	25.00	12.50	7.50
36	Chuck Estrada	5.00	2.50	1.50
37	Vic Power	5.00	2.50	1.50
38	Johnny Temple	5.00	2.50	1.50
39	Bubba Phillips	20.00	10.00	6.00
40	Tito Francona	6.00	3.00	1.75
41	Willie Kirkland	5.00	2.50	1.50
42	John Romano	5.00	2.50	1.50
43	Jim Perry	10.00	5.00	3.00
44	Woodie Held	5.00	2.50	1.50
45	Chuck Essegian	5.00	2.50	1.50
46	Roy Sievers	6.00	3.00	1.75
47	Nellie Fox	15.00	7.50	4.50
48	Al Smith	5.00	2.50	1.50
49	Luis Aparicio	25.00	12.50	7.50
50	Jim Landis	5.00	2.50	1.50
51	Minnie Minoso	10.00	5.00	3.00
52	Andy Carey	20.00	10.00	6.00
53	Sherman Lollar	6.00	3.00	1.75
54	Bill Pierce	6.00	3.00	1.75
55	Early Wynn	25.00	12.50	7.50
56	Chuck Schilling	20.00	10.00	6.00
57	Pete Runnels	6.00	3.00	1.75
58	Frank Malzone	6.00	3.00	1.75
59	Don Buddin	10.00	5.00	3.00
60	Gary Geiger	5.00	2.50	1.50
61	Carl Yastrzemski	200.00	100.00	60.00

		NR MT	EX	VG
62	Jackie Jensen	20.00	10.00	6.00
63	Jim Pagliaroni	20.00	10.00	6.00
64	Don Schwall	5.00	2.50	1.50
65	Dale Long	6.00	3.00	1.75
66	Chuck Cottier	10.00	5.00	3.00
67	Billy Klaus	20.00	10.00	6.00
68	Coot Veal	5.00	2.50	1.50
69	Marty Keough	40.00	20.00	12.00
70	Willie Tasby	40.00	20.00	12.00
71	Gene Woodling	6.00	3.00	1.75
72	Gene Green	40.00	20.00	12.00
73	Dick Donovan	10.00	5.00	3.00
74	Steve Bilko	10.00	5.00	3.00
75	Rocky Bridges	20.00	10.00	6.00
76	Eddie Yost	10.00	5.00	3.00
77	Leon Wagner	10.00	5.00	3.00
78	Albie Pearson	10.00	5.00	3.00
79	Ken Hunt	10.00	5.00	3.00
80	Earl Averill	40.00	20.00	12.00
81	Ryne Duren	10.00	5.00	3.00
82	Not Issued			
83	Bob Allison	6.00	3.00	1.75
84	Billy Martin	15.00	7.50	4.50
85	Harmon Killebrew	40.00	20.00	12.00
86	Zorro Versalles	6.00	3.00	1.75
87	Lennie Green	20.00	10.00	6.00
88	Bill Tuttle	5.00	2.50	1.50
89	Jim Lemon	6.00	3.00	1.75
90	Earl Battey	20.00	10.00	6.00
91	Camilo Pascual	6.00	3.00	1.75
92	Norm Siebern	10.00	5.00	3.00
93	Jerry Lumpe	10.00	5.00	3.00
94	Dick Howser	10.00	5.00	3.00
95	Gene Stephens	40.00	20.00	12.00
96	Leo Posada	10.00	5.00	3.00
97	Joe Pignatano	10.00	5.00	3.00
98	Jim Archer	10.00	5.00	3.00
99	Haywood Sullivan	20.00	10.00	6.00
100	Art Ditmar	10.00	5.00	3.00
101	Gil Hodges	40.00	20.00	12.00
102	Charlie Neal	10.00	5.00	3.00
103	Daryl Spencer	10.00	5.00	3.00
104	Maury Wills	20.00	10.00	6.00
105	Tommy Davis	10.00	5.00	3.00
106	Willie Davis	10.00	5.00	3.00
107	John Roseboro	40.00	20.00	12.00
108	John Podres	10.00	5.00	3.00
109	Sandy Koufax	80.00	40.00	24.00
110	Don Drysdale	50.00	25.00	15.00
111	Larry Sherry	20.00	10.00	6.00
112	Jim Gilliam	20.00	10.00	6.00
113	Norm Larker	40.00	20.00	12.00
114	Duke Snider	70.00	35.00	21.00
115	Stan Williams	20.00	10.00	6.00
116	Gordon Coleman	70.00	35.00	21.00
117	Don Blasingame	20.00	10.00	6.00
118	Gene Freese	40.00	20.00	12.00
119	Ed Kasko	40.00	20.00	12.00
120	Gus Bell	20.00	10.00	6.00
121	Vada Pinson	10.00	5.00	3.00
122	Frank Robinson	40.00	20.00	12.00
123	Bob Purkey	10.00	5.00	3.00
124	Joey Jay	10.00	5.00	3.00
125	Jim Brosnan	10.00	5.00	3.00
126	Jim O'Toole	10.00	5.00	3.00
127	Jerry Lynch	10.00	5.00	3.00
128	Wally Post	10.00	5.00	3.00
129	Ken Hunt	10.00	5.00	3.00
130	Jerry Zimmerman	10.00	5.00	3.00
131	Willie McCovey	40.00	20.00	12.00
132	Jose Pagan	20.00	10.00	6.00
133	Felipe Alou	10.00	5.00	3.00
134	Jim Davenport	10.00	5.00	3.00
135	Harvey Kuenn	10.00	5.00	3.00
136	Orlando Cepeda	15.00	7.50	4.50
137	Ed Bailey	10.00	5.00	3.00
138	Sam Jones	10.00	5.00	3.00
139	Mike McCormick	10.00	5.00	3.00
140	Juan Marichal	40.00	20.00	12.00
141	Jack Sanford	10.00	5.00	3.00
142	Willie Mays	150.00	75.00	45.00
143	Stu Miller	70.00	35.00	21.00
144	Joe Amalfitano	10.00	5.00	3.00
145	Joe Adcock	10.00	5.00	3.00
146	Frank Bolling	5.00	2.50	1.50
147	Ed Mathews	40.00	20.00	12.00
148	Roy McMillan	6.00	3.00	1.75
149	Hank Aaron	150.00	75.00	45.00
150	Gino Cimoli	20.00	10.00	6.00
151	Frank Thomas	6.00	3.00	1.75
152	Joe Torre	10.00	5.00	3.00

		NR MT	EX	VG
153	Lou Burdette	10.00	5.00	3.00
154	Bob Buhl	6.00	3.00	1.75
155	Carlton Willey	5.00	2.50	1.50
156	Lee Maye	18.00	9.00	5.50
157	Al Spangler	40.00	20.00	12.00
158	Bill White	40.00	20.00	12.00
159	Ken Boyer	15.00	7.50	4.50
160	Joe Cunningham	10.00	5.00	3.00
161	Carl Warwick	10.00	5.00	3.00
162	Carl Sawatski	5.00	2.50	1.50
163	Lindy McDaniel	5.00	2.50	1.50
164	Ernie Broglio	10.00	5.00	3.00
165	Larry Jackson	5.00	2.50	1.50
166	Curt Flood	15.00	7.50	4.50
167	Curt Simmons	40.00	20.00	12.00
168	Alex Grammas	20.00	10.00	6.00
169	Dick Stuart	6.00	3.00	1.75
170	Bill Mazeroski	20.00	10.00	6.00
171	Don Hoak	10.00	5.00	3.00
172	Dick Groat	10.00	5.00	3.00
173	Roberto Clemente	150.00	75.00	45.00
174	Bob Skinner	20.00	10.00	6.00
175	Bill Virdon	40.00	20.00	12.00
176	Not Issued			
177	Elroy Face	10.00	5.00	3.00
178	Bob Friend	6.00	3.00	1.75
179	Vernon Law	20.00	10.00	6.00
180	Harvey Haddix	40.00	20.00	12.00
181	Hal Smith	20.00	10.00	6.00
182	Ed Bouchee	20.00	10.00	6.00
183	Don Zimmer	6.00	3.00	1.75
184	Ron Santo	10.00	5.00	3.00
185	Andre Rodgers	5.00	2.50	1.50
186	Richie Ashburn	15.00	7.50	4.50
187	George Altman	5.00	2.50	1.50
188	Ernie Banks	40.00	20.00	12.00
189	Sam Taylor	5.00	2.50	1.50
190	Don Elston	5.00	2.50	1.50
191	Jerry Kindall	20.00	10.00	6.00
192	Pancho Herrera	5.00	2.50	1.50
193	Tony Taylor	5.00	2.50	1.50
194	Ruben Amaro	20.00	10.00	6.00
195	Don Demeter	5.00	2.50	1.50
196	Bobby Gene Smith	5.00	2.50	1.50
197	Clay Dalrymple	5.00	2.50	1.50
198	Robin Roberts	25.00	12.50	7.50
199	Art Mahaffey	5.00	2.50	1.50
200	John Buzhardt	5.00	2.50	1.50

1963 Jell-O

Like the other Post and Jell-O issues of the era, the '63 Jell-O set includes many scarce cards; primarily those which were printed as the backs of less popular brands and sizes of the gelatin dessert. Slightly smaller than the virtually identical Post cereal cards of the same year, the 200 cards in the Jell-O issue measure 3-3/8" by 2-1/2". The easiest way to distinguish 1963 Jell-O cards from Post cards is by the red line that separates the 1962 stats from the lifetime stats. On Post cards, the line extends almost all the way to the side borders, on the Jell-O cards, the line begins and ends much closer to the stats.

	NR MT	EX	VG
Complete Set:	3000.00	1500.00	900.00
Common Player:	2.00	1.00	.60

#	Name	NR MT	EX	VG
1	Vic Power	2.50	1.25	.70
2	Bernie Allen	20.00	10.00	6.00
3	Zoilo Versalles	20.00	10.00	6.00
4	Rich Rollins	2.00	1.00	.60
5	Harmon Killebrew	8.00	4.00	2.50
6	Lenny Green	20.00	10.00	6.00
7	Bob Allison	3.00	1.50	.90
8	Earl Battey	15.00	7.50	4.50
9	Camilo Pascual	2.50	1.25	.70
10	Jim Kaat	35.00	17.50	10.50
11	Jack Kralick	2.00	1.00	.60
12	Bill Skowron	20.00	10.00	6.00
13	Bobby Richardson	5.00	2.50	1.50
14	Cletis Boyer	2.50	1.25	.70
15	Mickey Mantle	250.00	125.00	75.00
16	Roger Maris	20.00	10.00	6.00
17	Yogi Berra	20.00	10.00	6.00
18	Elston Howard	20.00	10.00	6.00
19	Whitey Ford	10.00	5.00	3.00
20	Ralph Terry	2.00	1.00	.60
21	John Blanchard	15.00	7.50	4.50
22	Bill Stafford	20.00	10.00	6.00
23	Tom Tresh	2.50	1.25	.70
24	Steve Bilko	2.00	1.00	.60
25	Bill Moran	2.00	1.00	.60
26	Joe Koppe	2.00	1.00	.60
27	Felix Torres	2.00	1.00	.60
28	Leon Wagner	2.50	1.25	.70
29	Albie Pearson	2.00	1.00	.60
30	Lee Thomas	2.00	1.00	.60
31	Bob Rodgers	20.00	10.00	6.00
32	Dean Chance	1.50	.70	.45
33	Ken McBride	20.00	10.00	6.00
34	George Thomas	20.00	10.00	6.00
35	Joe Cunningham	20.00	10.00	6.00
36	Nelson Fox	5.00	2.50	1.50
37	Luis Aparicio	6.00	3.00	1.75
38	Al Smith	2.00	1.00	.60
39	Floyd Robinson	2.00	1.00	.60
40	Jim Landis	2.00	1.00	.60
41	Charlie Maxwell	2.00	1.00	.60
42	Sherman Lollar	2.00	1.00	.60
43	Early Wynn	6.00	3.00	1.75
44	Juan Pizarro	20.00	10.00	6.00
45	Ray Herbert	20.00	10.00	6.00
46	Norm Cash	3.50	1.75	1.00
47	Steve Boros	20.00	10.00	6.00
48	Dick McAuliffe	2.00	1.00	.60
49	Bill Bruton	2.00	1.00	.60
50	Rocky Colavito	5.00	2.50	1.50
51	Al Kaline	12.00	6.00	3.50
52	Dick Brown	20.00	10.00	6.00
53	Jim Bunning	5.00	2.50	1.50
54	Hank Aguirre	2.00	1.00	.60
55	Frank Lary	20.00	10.00	6.00
56	Don Mossi	20.00	10.00	6.00
57	Jim Gentile	2.00	1.00	.60
58	Jackie Brandt	2.00	1.00	.60
59	Brooks Robinson	15.00	7.50	4.50
60	Ron Hansen	2.00	1.00	.60
61	Jerry Adair	55.00	27.00	16.50
62	John Powell	3.50	1.75	1.00
63	Russ Snyder	20.00	10.00	6.00
64	Steve Barber	2.00	1.00	.60
65	Milt Pappas	20.00	10.00	6.00
66	Robin Roberts	6.00	3.00	1.75
67	Tito Francona	2.00	1.00	.60
68	Jerry Kindall	20.00	10.00	6.00
69	Woodie Held	2.00	1.00	.60
70	Bubba Phillips	2.00	1.00	.60
71	Chuck Essegian	2.00	1.00	.60
72	Willie Kirkland	20.00	10.00	6.00
73	Al Luplow	2.00	1.00	.60
74	Ty Cline	20.00	10.00	6.00
75	Dick Donovan	2.00	1.00	.60
76	John Romano	2.00	1.00	.60
77	Pete Runnels	2.00	1.00	.60
78	Ed Bressoud	20.00	10.00	6.00
79	Frank Malzone	2.00	1.00	.60
80	Carl Yastrzemski	70.00	35.00	21.00
81	Gary Geiger	2.00	1.00	.60
82	Lou Clinton	20.00	10.00	6.00
83	Earl Wilson	2.50	1.25	.70
84	Bill Monbouquette	2.50	1.25	.70
85	Norm Siebern	2.50	1.25	.70
86	Jerry Lumpe	2.50	1.25	.70
87	Manny Jimenez	2.00	1.00	.60
88	Gino Cimoli	2.00	1.00	.60
89	Ed Charles	55.00	27.00	16.50
90	Ed Rakow	2.00	1.00	.60
91	Bob Del Greco	20.00	10.00	6.00
92	Haywood Sullivan	20.00	10.00	6.00
93	Chuck Hinton	2.00	1.00	.60
94	Ken Retzer	20.00	10.00	6.00
95	Harry Bright	20.00	10.00	6.00
96	Bob Johnson	2.00	1.00	.60
97	Dave Stenhouse	20.00	10.00	6.00
98	Chuck Cottier	2.00	1.00	.60
99	Tom Cheney	2.00	1.00	.60
100	Claude Osteen	20.00	10.00	6.00
101	Orlando Cepeda	5.00	2.50	1.50
102	Charley Hiller	20.00	10.00	6.00
103	Jose Pagan	20.00	10.00	6.00
104	Jim Davenport	2.00	1.00	.60
105	Harvey Kuenn	3.50	1.75	1.00
106	Willie Mays	75.00	37.00	22.00
107	Felipe Alou	3.00	1.50	.90
108	Tom Haller	2.00	1.00	.60
109	Juan Marichal	6.00	3.00	1.75
110	Jack Sanford	2.00	1.00	.60
111	Bill O'Dell	2.00	1.00	.60
112	Willie McCovey	90.00	45.00	27.00
113	Lee Walls	20.00	10.00	6.00
114	Jim Gilliam	20.00	10.00	6.00
115	Maury Wills	5.00	2.50	1.50
116	Ron Fairly	2.00	1.00	.60
117	Tommy Davis	3.00	1.50	.90
118	Duke Snider	9.00	4.50	2.75
119	Willie Davis	3.00	1.50	.90
120	John Roseboro	2.00	1.00	.60
121	Sandy Koufax	20.00	10.00	6.00
122	Stan Williams	20.00	10.00	6.00
123	Don Drysdale	9.00	4.50	2.75
124	Daryl Spencer	2.00	1.00	.60
125	Gordy Coleman	2.00	1.00	.60
126	Don Blasingame	20.00	10.00	6.00
127	Leo Cardenas	2.00	1.00	.60
128	Eddie Kasko	20.00	10.00	6.00
129	Jerry Lynch	2.00	1.00	.60
130	Vada Pinson	4.00	2.00	1.25
131	Frank Robinson	9.00	4.50	2.75
132	John Edwards	20.00	10.00	6.00
133	Joey Jay	2.00	1.00	.60
134	Bob Purkey	2.00	1.00	.60
135	Marty Keough	55.00	27.00	16.50
136	Jim O'Toole	20.00	10.00	6.00
137	Dick Stuart	2.00	1.00	.60
138	Bill Mazeroski	3.50	1.75	1.00
139	Dick Groat	3.00	1.50	.90
140	Don Hoak	2.00	1.00	.60
141	Bob Skinner	2.00	1.00	.60
142	Bill Virdon	3.00	1.50	.90
143	Roberto Clemente	75.00	37.00	22.00
144	Smoky Burgess	3.00	1.50	.90
145	Bob Friend	2.00	1.00	.60
146	Al McBean	20.00	10.00	6.00
147	ElRoy Face	3.00	1.50	.90
148	Joe Adcock	3.50	1.75	1.00
149	Frank Bolling	2.00	1.00	.60
150	Roy McMillan	2.00	1.00	.60
151	Eddie Mathews	8.00	4.00	2.50
152	Hank Aaron	75.00	37.00	22.00
153	Del Crandall	20.00	10.00	6.00
154	Bob Shaw	2.00	1.00	.60
155	Lew Burdette	3.50	1.75	1.00
156	Joe Torre	20.00	10.00	6.00
157	Tony Cloninger	35.00	17.50	10.50
158	Bill White	2.50	1.25	.70
159	Julian Javier	20.00	10.00	6.00
160	Ken Boyer	4.00	2.00	1.25
161	Julio Gotay	20.00	10.00	6.00
162	Curt Flood	3.00	1.50	.90
163	Charlie James	35.00	17.50	10.50
164	Gene Oliver	20.00	10.00	6.00
165	Ernie Broglio	2.00	1.00	.60
166	Bob Gibson	75.00	37.00	22.00
167	Lindy McDaniel	20.00	10.00	6.00
168	Ray Washburn	2.00	1.00	.60
169	Ernie Banks	12.00	6.00	3.50
170	Ron Santo	3.50	1.75	1.00
171	George Altman	2.00	1.00	.60
172	Billy Williams	75.00	37.00	22.00
173	Andre Rodgers	20.00	10.00	6.00
174	Ken Hubbs	3.00	1.50	.90
175	Don Landrum	20.00	10.00	6.00
176	Dick Bertell	20.00	10.00	6.00
177	Roy Sievers	2.50	1.25	.70
178	Tony Taylor	20.00	10.00	6.00
179	John Callison	2.50	1.25	.70
180	Don Demeter	2.00	1.00	.60
181	Tony Gonzalez	20.00	10.00	6.00
182	Wes Covington	20.00	10.00	6.00

		NR MT	EX	VG
183	Art Mahaffey	2.00	1.00	.60
184	Clay Dalrymple	2.00	1.00	.60
185	Al Spangler	2.00	1.00	.60
186	Roman Mejias	2.00	1.00	.60
187	Bob Aspromonte	50.00	25.00	15.00
188	Norm Larker	2.00	1.00	.60
189	Johnny Temple	2.00	1.00	.60
190	Carl Warwick	20.00	10.00	6.00
191	Bob Lillis	20.00	10.00	6.00
192	Dick Farrell	50.00	25.00	15.00
193	Gil Hodges	8.00	4.00	2.50
194	Marv Throneberry	3.00	1.50	.90
195	Charlie Neal	20.00	10.00	6.00
196	Frank Thomas	2.00	1.00	.60
197	Richie Ashburn	5.00	2.50	1.50
198	Felix Mantilla	20.00	10.00	6.00
199	Rod Kanehl	20.00	10.00	6.00
200	Roger Craig	20.00	10.00	6.00

1986 Jiffy Pop

One of the scarcer of the 1986 "regionals," the 20-card Jiffy Pop issue was inserted in packages of heat-and-eat popcorn. A production of Mike Schecter Associates, the 2-7/8" round discs feature 20 popular stars, many in the same pictures found in other '86 regionals. Like other MSA issues, caps have had the team logos erased, allowing Jiffy Pop to avoid having to pay a licensing fee to the teams.

		MT	NR MT	EX
Complete Set:		30.00	22.00	12.00
Common Player:		1.00	.70	.40
1	Jim Rice	2.50	2.00	1.00
2	Wade Boggs	2.00	1.50	.80
3	Lance Parrish	1.00	.70	.40
4	George Brett	2.50	2.00	1.00
5	Robin Yount	2.50	2.00	1.00
6	Don Mattingly	3.50	2.75	1.50
7	Dave Winfield	2.00	1.50	.80
8	Reggie Jackson	2.50	2.00	1.00
9	Cal Ripken	2.50	2.00	1.00
10	Eddie Murray	2.00	1.50	.80
11	Pete Rose	2.00	1.50	.80
12	Ryne Sandberg	2.50	2.00	1.00
13	Nolan Ryan	4.00	3.00	1.50
14	Fernando Valenzuela	1.25	.90	.50
15	Willie McGee	1.00	.70	.40
16	Dale Murphy	2.50	2.00	1.00
17	Mike Schmidt	2.50	2.00	1.00
18	Steve Garvey	2.00	1.50	.80
19	Gary Carter	2.00	1.50	.80
20	Dwight Gooden	2.00	1.50	.80

1987 Jiffy Pop

For the second year in a row, Jiffy Pop inserted baseball discs in their packages of popcorn. The full-color discs measure 2-7/8" in diameter and were produced by Mike Schecter Associates of Cos Cob, Conn. Titled "2nd Annual Collectors' Edition," the card fronts feature player photos with all team insignias airbrushed away. Information on the backs

of the discs are printed in bright red on white stock. Die-cut press sheets containing all 20 discs were available via a mail-in offer.

		MT	NR MT	EX
Complete Set:		25.00	18.50	10.00
Common Player:		1.00	.70	.40
1	Ryne Sandberg	2.50	2.00	1.00
2	Dale Murphy	2.50	2.00	1.00
3	Jack Morris	1.00	.70	.40
4	Keith Hernandez	1.50	1.25	.60
5	George Brett	2.50	2.00	1.00
6	Don Mattingly	3.50	2.75	1.50
7	Ozzie Smith	1.00	.70	.40
8	Cal Ripken	2.50	2.00	1.00
9	Dwight Gooden	3.00	2.25	1.25
10	Pedro Guerrero	1.00	.70	.40
11	Lou Whitaker	1.00	.70	.40
12	Roger Clemens	3.00	2.25	1.25
13	Lance Parrish	1.00	.70	.40
14	Rickey Henderson	2.50	2.00	1.00
15	Fernando Valenzuela	1.25	.90	.50
16	Mike Schmidt	2.50	2.00	1.00
17	Darryl Strawberry	2.75	2.00	1.00
18	Mike Scott	1.00	.70	.40
19	Jim Rice	2.75	2.00	1.00
20	Wade Boggs	2.50	2.00	1.00

1988 Jiffy Pop

This 20-disc set is the third Jiffy Pop issue spotlighting leading players. Discs are 2-/12" in diameter, with a semi-gloss finish, and feature full-color closeups on white stock. Team logos have been airbrushed off the player's caps. The Jiffy Pop logo appears in red at the top of the disc; a banner running across the bottom encloses a "1988" and player name, also in red. The circular border is blue, with two large baseballs streaking toward the top logo. A third baseball appears lower right under the curved label "3rd Annual Collector's Edition." Dsic backs are white, with dark blue lettering, and contain player information and disc number.

	MT	NR MT	EX
Complete Set:	18.00	13.50	7.25

		MT .60	NR MT .45	EX .25
	Common Player:			
1	Buddy Bell	.60	.45	.25
2	Wade Boggs	2.25	1.75	.90
3	Gary Carter	1.50	1.25	.60
4	Jack Clark	.80	.60	.30
5	Will Clark	1.50	1.25	.60
6	Roger Clemens	2.25	1.75	.90
7	Vince Coleman	.80	.60	.30
8	Andre Dawson	1.25	.90	.50
9	Keith Hernandez	1.25	.90	.50
10	Kent Hrbek	1.25	.90	.50
11	Wally Joyner	1.50	1.25	.60
12	Paul Molitor	.80	.60	.30
13	Eddie Murray	1.50	1.25	.60
14	Tim Raines	1.50	1.25	.60
15	Bret Saberhagen	1.25	.90	.50
16	Alan Trammell	1.25	.90	.50
17	Ozzie Virgil	.60	.45	.25
18	Tim Wallach	.60	.45	.25
19	Dave Winfield	1.50	1.25	.60
20	Robin Yount	1.25	.90	.50

**Definitions for grading conditions are located
in the Introduction of this price guide.**

1953 Johnston Cookies Braves

The first and most common of three annual issues, the '53 Johnston's were inserted into boxes of cookies on a regional basis. Complete sets were also available from the company, whose factory sits in the shadow of Milwaukee County Stadium. While at first glance appearing to be color photos, the pictures on the 25 cards in the set are actually well-done colorizations of black and white photos. Cards measure 2-9/16" by 3-5/8". Write-ups on the backs were "borrowed" from the Braves' 1953 yearbook.

		NR MT 325.00	EX 175.00	VG 100.00
	Complete Set:			
	Common Player:	8.00	4.00	2.50
1	Charlie Grimm	10.00	5.00	3.00
2	John Antonelli	10.00	5.00	3.00
3	Vern Bickford	8.00	4.00	2.50
4	Bob Buhl	10.00	5.00	3.00
5	Lew Burdette	15.00	7.50	4.50
6	Dave Cole	8.00	4.00	2.50
7	Ernie Johnson	8.00	4.00	2.50
8	Dave Jolly	8.00	4.00	2.50
9	Don Liddle	8.00	4.00	2.50
10	Warren Spahn	55.00	27.00	16.50
11	Max Surkont	8.00	4.00	2.50
12	Jim Wilson	8.00	4.00	2.50
13	Sibby Sisti	8.00	4.00	2.50
14	Walker Cooper	8.00	4.00	2.50
15	Del Crandall	15.00	7.50	4.50
16	Ebba St. Claire	8.00	4.00	2.50
17	Joe Adcock	15.00	7.50	4.50
18	George Crowe	8.00	4.00	2.50
19	Jack Dittmer	8.00	4.00	2.50
20	Johnny Logan	10.00	5.00	3.00
21	Ed Mathews	55.00	27.00	16.50
22	Bill Bruton	10.00	5.00	3.00
23	Sid Gordon	8.00	4.00	2.50
24	Andy Pafko	10.00	5.00	3.00
25	Jim Pendleton	8.00	4.00	2.50

1954 Johnston Cookies Braves

In its second of three annual issues, Johnston's increased the number of cards in its 1954 Braves issue to 35, and switched to an unusual size, a narrow format, 2" by 3-7/8". Besides the players and managers, the '54 set also includes unnumbered cards of the team trainer and equipment manager. Other cards are numbered by uniform number. After his early-season injury—which gave Hank Aaron a chance to play regularly), Bobby Thomson's card was withdrawn, accounting for its scarcity and high value. A cardboard wall-hanging display into which cards could be inserted was available as a premium offer.

		NR MT 1250.00	EX 625.00	VG 375.00
	Complete Set:			
	Common Player:	10.00	5.00	3.00
1	Del Crandall	15.00	7.50	4.50
3	Jim Pendleton	10.00	5.00	3.00
4	Danny O'Connell	10.00	5.00	3.00
5	Henry Aaron	500.00	250.00	150.00
6	Jack Dittmer	10.00	5.00	3.00
9	Joe Adcock	15.00	7.50	4.50
10	Robert Buhl	15.00	7.50	4.50
11	Phillip Paine (Phillips)	10.00	5.00	3.00
12	Ben Johnson	10.00	5.00	3.00
13	Sibby Sisti	10.00	5.00	3.00
15	Charles Gorin	10.00	5.00	3.00
16	Chet Nichols	10.00	5.00	3.00
17	Dave Jolly	10.00	5.00	3.00
19	Jim Wilson	10.00	5.00	3.00
20	Ray Crone	10.00	5.00	3.00
21	Warren Spahn	65.00	32.00	19.50
22	Gene Conley	10.00	5.00	3.00
23	Johnny Logan	12.00	6.00	3.50
24	Charlie White	10.00	5.00	3.00
27	George Metkovich	10.00	5.00	3.00
28	John Cooney	10.00	5.00	3.00
29	Paul Burris	10.00	5.00	3.00
31	Wm. Walters	10.00	5.00	3.00
32	Ernest T. Johnson	10.00	5.00	3.00
33	Lew Burdette	20.00	10.00	6.00
34	Bob Thomson	200.00	100.00	60.00
35	Robert Keely	10.00	5.00	3.00
38	Billy Bruton	10.00	5.00	3.00
40	Charles Grimm	10.00	5.00	3.00
41	Ed Mathews	65.00	32.00	19.50
42	Sam Calderone	10.00	5.00	3.00
47	Joey Jay	10.00	5.00	3.00
48	Andy Pafko	12.00	6.00	3.50
-----	Dr. Charles Lacks (trainer)	10.00	5.00	3.00
-----	Joseph F. Taylor (asst. trainer)	10.00	5.00	3.00

1955 Johnston Cookies Braves

A third change in size and format was undertaken in the third and final year of Braves sets produced by Johnston's. The 35 cards in the 1955 set were issued in six fold-out panels of six cards each (Andy Pafko was double-printed). As in 1954, cards are numbered by uniform number, except those of the team equipment manager, trainer and road secretary (former Boston star Duffy Lewis). Single cards measure 2-7/8" by 4". Besides including panels in boxes of cookies, the '55 Johnston's could be ordered for 5¢ per panel by mail. The scarcest of the Johnston's issues, the 1955 set can be found today still in complete panels, or as single cards.

		NR MT	EX	VG
Complete Folder Set:		1500.00	750.00	450.00
Complete Singles Set:		1000.00	500.00	300.00
Common Player:		15.00	7.50	4.50
Common Folder:		125.00	62.00	37.00
1	Del Crandall	25.00	12.50	7.50
3	Jim Pendleton	15.00	7.50	4.50
4	Danny O'Connell	15.00	7.50	4.50
6	Jack Dittmer	15.00	7.50	4.50
9	Joe Adcock	25.00	12.50	7.50
10	Bob Buhl	20.00	10.00	6.00
11	Phil Paine	15.00	7.50	4.50
12	Ray Crone	15.00	7.50	4.50
15	Charlie Gorin	15.00	7.50	4.50
16	Dave Jolly	15.00	7.50	4.50
17	Chet Nichols	15.00	7.50	4.50
18	Chuck Tanner	25.00	12.50	7.50
19	Jim Wilson	15.00	7.50	4.50
20	Dave Koslo	15.00	7.50	4.50
21	Warren Spahn	80.00	40.00	24.00
22	Gene Conley	20.00	10.00	6.00
23	John Logan	20.00	10.00	6.00
24	Charlie White	15.00	7.50	4.50
28	Johnny Cooney	15.00	7.50	4.50
30	Roy Smalley	15.00	7.50	4.50
31	Bucky Walters	15.00	7.50	4.50
32	Ernie Johnson	15.00	7.50	4.50
33	Lew Burdette	25.00	12.50	7.50
34	Bobby Thomson	25.00	12.50	7.50
35	Bob Keely	15.00	7.50	4.50
38	Billy Bruton	20.00	10.00	6.00
39	George Crowe	15.00	7.50	4.50
40	Charlie Grimm	20.00	10.00	6.00
41	Eddie Mathews	80.00	40.00	24.00
44	Hank Aaron	400.00	200.00	120.00
47	Joe Jay	15.00	7.50	4.50
48	Andy Pafko	20.00	10.00	6.00
----	Dr. Charles K. Lacks	15.00	7.50	4.50
----	Duffy Lewis	15.00	7.50	4.50
----	Joe Taylor	15.00	7.50	4.50
----	Series 1 Folder (Hank Aaron, Lew Burdette, Del Crandall, Charlie Gorin, Bob Keely, Danny O'Connell)	400.00	200.00	120.00
----	Series 2 Folder (Joe Adcock, Joe Jay, Dr. Charles K. Lacks, Chet Nichols, Andy Pafko, Charlie White)	125.00	62.00	37.00
----	Series 3 Folder (Gene Conley, George Crowe, Jim Pendleton, Roy Smalley, Warren Spahn, Joe Taylor)	175.00	87.00	52.00
----	Series 4 Folder (Billy Bruton, John Cooney, Dave Jolly, Dave Koslo, Johnny Logan, Andy Pafko)	125.00	62.00	37.00
----	Series 5 Folder (Ray Crone, Ernie Johnson, Duffy Lewis, Eddie Mathews, Phil Paine, Chuck Tanner)	200.00	100.00	60.00
----	Series 6 Folder (Bob Buhl, Jack Dittmer, Charlie Grimm, Bobby Thomson, Bucky Walters, Jim Wilson)	125.00	62.00	37.00

1982 K-Mart

The first of what became dozens of boxed sets specially produced for retail chain stores by the major card producers, the 1982 K-Mart set has not enjoyed any collector popularity. The theme of the set is Most Valuable Players and selected record-breaking performances of the 1962-1981 seasons. The design used miniature reproductions of Topps cards of the era, except in a few cases where designs had to be created because original cards were never issued (1962 Maury Wills, 1975 Fred Lynn.) Originally sold for about $2 per boxed set of 44, large quantities were bought up by speculators who got burned when over-production and lack of demand caused the set to drop as low as 10¢. The 2-1/2" by 3-1/2" cards were printed by Topps.

		MT	NR MT	EX
Complete Set:		1.00	.70	.40
Common Player:		.03	.02	.01
1	Mickey Mantle	.25	.20	.10
2	Maury Wills	.05	.04	.02
3	Elston Howard	.03	.02	.01
4	Sandy Koufax	.10	.08	.04
5	Brooks Robinson	.05	.04	.02
6	Ken Boyer	.03	.02	.01
7	Zoilo Versalles	.03	.02	.01
8	Willie Mays	.10	.08	.04
9	Frank Robinson	.05	.04	.02
10	Bob Clemente	.10	.08	.04
11	Carl Yastrzemski	.10	.08	.04
12	Orlando Cepeda	.03	.02	.01
13	Denny McLain	.03	.02	.01
14	Bob Gibson	.05	.04	.02
15	Harmon Killebrew	.05	.04	.02
16	Willie McCovey	.05	.04	.02
17	Boog Powell	.03	.02	.01
18	Johnny Bench	.07	.05	.03
19	Vida Blue	.03	.02	.01
20	Joe Torre	.03	.02	.01
21	Rich Allen	.03	.02	.01
22	Johnny Bench	.07	.05	.03
23	Reggie Jackson	.07	.05	.03
24	Pete Rose	.12	.09	.05
25	Jeff Burroughs	.03	.02	.01
26	Steve Garvey	.07	.05	.03
27	Fred Lynn	.03	.02	.01
28	Joe Morgan	.05	.04	.02
29	Thurman Munson	.05	.04	.02
30	Joe Morgan	.05	.04	.02
31	Rod Carew	.07	.05	.03
32	George Foster	.03	.02	.01
33	Jim Rice	.05	.04	.02
34	Dave Parker	.05	.04	.02
35	Don Baylor	.03	.02	.01
36	Keith Hernandez	.03	.02	.01
37	Willie Stargell	.05	.04	.02
38	George Brett	.07	.05	.03
39	Mike Schmidt	.07	.05	.03
40	Rollie Fingers	.05	.04	.02
41	Mike Schmidt	.07	.05	.03
42	Don Drysdale	.05	.04	.02
43	Hank Aaron	.10	.08	.04
44	Pete Rose	.12	.09	.05

1987 K-Mart

Produced by Topps for K-Mart, the 1987 K-Mart set was distributed by the department stores to celebrate their 25th anniversary. Entitled "Baseball's Stars of the Decades," the 33-card set was issued in a special cardboard box with one stick of bubblegum. The card fronts feature a full-color photo set diagonally against a red background. The backs contain career highlights plus pitching or batting statistics for the decade in which the player enjoyed his greatest success. Cards are the standard 2-1/2" by 3-1/2" size.

		MT	NR MT	EX
Complete Set:		4.00	3.00	1.50
Common Player:		.10	.08	.04
1	Hank Aaron	.50	.40	.20
2	Roberto Clemente	.40	.30	.15
3	Bob Gibson	.10	.08	.04
4	Harmon Killebrew	.10	.08	.04
5	Mickey Mantle	1.00	.70	.40
6	Juan Marichal	.10	.08	.04
7	Roger Maris	.30	.25	.12
8	Willie Mays	.50	.40	.20
9	Brooks Robinson	.30	.25	.12
10	Frank Robinson	.20	.15	.08
11	Carl Yastrzemski	.50	.40	.20
12	Johnny Bench	.30	.25	.12
13	Lou Brock	.20	.15	.08
14	Rod Carew	.30	.25	.12
15	Steve Carlton	.20	.15	.08
16	Reggie Jackson	.30	.25	.12
17	Jim Palmer	.10	.08	.04
18	Jim Rice	.10	.08	.04
19	Pete Rose	.50	.40	.20
20	Nolan Ryan	.20	.15	.08
21	Tom Seaver	.20	.15	.08
22	Willie Stargell	.10	.08	.04
23	Wade Boggs	.50	.40	.20
24	George Brett	.40	.30	.15
25	Gary Carter	.20	.15	.08
26	Dwight Gooden	.50	.40	.20
27	Rickey Henderson	.35	.25	.12
28	Don Mattingly	.50	.40	.20
29	Dale Murphy	.40	.30	.15
30	Eddie Murray	.20	.15	.08
31	Mike Schmidt	.30	.25	.12
32	Darryl Strawberry	.40	.30	.15
33	Fernando Valenzuela	.10	.08	.04

1988 K-Mart

This 33-card boxed set, titled "Memorable Moments," was produced by Topps for distribution via K-Mart. Two previous Topps K-Mart sets were issued: a 44-card set in 1982 in honor of K-Mart's 20th anniversary and a 33-card set in 1987 for the company's 25th anniversary. The 1988 cards are standard-size with red, white and blue borders and a super glossy coating. Numbered card backs are printed in red and blue on white and highlight special events in the featured players' careers. The set was marketed in a bright yellow and green checklist box

(gum included).

		MT	NR MT	EX
Complete Set:		3.00	2.25	1.25
Common Player:		.10	.08	.04
1	George Bell	.20	.15	.08
2	Wade Boggs	.50	.40	.20
3	George Brett	.30	.25	.12
4	Jose Canseco	.50	.40	.20
5	Jack Clark	.15	.11	.06
6	Will Clark	.25	.20	.10
7	Roger Clemens	.40	.30	.15
8	Vince Coleman	.15	.11	.06
9	Andre Dawson	.15	.11	.06
10	Dwight Gooden	.40	.30	.15
11	Pedro Guerrero	.15	.11	.06
12	Tony Gwynn	.25	.20	.10
13	Rickey Henderson	.25	.20	.10
14	Keith Hernandez	.15	.11	.06
15	Don Mattingly	.40	.30	.15
16	Mark McGwire	.40	.30	.15
17	Paul Molitor	.12	.09	.05
18	Dale Murphy	.20	.15	.08
19	Tim Raines	.20	.15	.08
20	Dave Righetti	.12	.09	.05
21	Cal Ripken	.25	.20	.10
22	Pete Rose	.50	.40	.20
23	Nolan Ryan	.25	.20	.10
24	Benny Santiago	.25	.20	.10
25	Mike Schmidt	.30	.25	.12
26	Mike Scott	.10	.08	.04
27	Kevin Seitzer	.25	.20	.10
28	Ozzie Smith	.15	.11	.06
29	Darryl Strawberry	.30	.25	.12
30	Rick Sutcliffe	.10	.08	.04
31	Fernando Valenzuela	.15	.11	.06
32	Todd Worrell	.10	.08	.04
33	Robin Yount	.15	.11	.06

1989 K-Mart

This 33-card, glossy set was produced by Topps for K-Mart, where it was sold in stores nationwide. The standard-size cards feature mostly action shots on the front, and include the Topps "Dream Team" logo at the top, with the K-Mart logo in the lower right corner. The first 11 cards in the set picture the top rookies of 1988, while next 11 picture the top A.L. rookies of the '80s, and the final 11 cards highlight the top N.L. rookies of the decade.

		MT	NR MT	EX
Complete Set:		4.00	3.00	1.50
Common Player:		.10	.08	.04
1	Mark Grace	.50	.40	.20
2	Ron Gant	.15	.11	.06
3	Chris Sabo	.15	.11	.06
4	Walt Weiss	.15	.11	.06
5	Jay Buhner	.15	.11	.06
6	Cecil Espy	.10	.08	.04
7	Dave Gallagher	.15	.11	.06
8	Damon Berryhill	.10	.08	.04
9	Tim Belcher	.20	.15	.08
10	Paul Gibson	.10	.08	.04
11	Gregg Jefferies	.50	.40	.20
12	Don Mattingly	1.00	.70	.40
13	Harold Reynolds	.15	.11	.06
14	Wade Boggs	.50	.40	.20
15	Cal Ripken	.25	.20	.10
16	Kirby Puckett	.40	.30	.15
17	George Bell	.15	.11	.06
18	Jose Canseco	.50	.40	.20
19	Terry Steinbach	.20	.15	.08
20	Roger Clemens	.40	.30	.15
21	Mark Langston	.20	.15	.08
22	Harold Baines	.15	.11	.06
23	Will Clark	.50	.40	.20
24	Ryne Sanberg	.25	.20	.10
25	Tim Wallach	.10	.08	.04
26	Shawon Dunston	.10	.08	.04
27	Rock Raines	.15	.11	.06
28	Darryl Strawberry	.35	.25	.14
29	Tony Gwynn	.35	.25	.14
30	Tony Pena	.10	.08	.04
31	Doc Gooden	.35	.25	.12
32	Fernando Valenzuela	.15	.11	.06
33	Pedro Guerrero	.15	.11	.06

		MT	NR MT	EX
16	Glenn Davis	.15	.11	.06
17	Don Mattingly	.25	.20	.10
18	Julio Franco	.10	.08	.04
19	Wade Boggs	.20	.15	.08
20	Cal Ripken	.15	.11	.06
21	Jose Canseco	.40	.30	.15
22	Kirby Puckett	.20	.15	.08
23	Rickey Henderson	.25	.20	.10
24	Mickey Tettleton	.08	.06	.03
25	Nolan Ryan	.25	.20	.10
26	Bret Saberhagen	.10	.08	.04
27	Jeff Ballard	.08	.06	.03
28	Chuck Finley	.08	.06	.03
29	Dennis Eckersley	.15	.11	.06
30	Dan Plesac	.08	.06	.03
31	Fred McGriff	.15	.11	.06
32	Mark McGwire	.20	.15	.08
33	Managers (Tony LaRussa, Roger Craig)			
		.08	.06	.03

1955 Kahn's Wieners Reds

Compliments of Kahn's Wieners
"THE WIENER THE WORLD AWAITED"

The first of what would become 15 successive years of baseball card issues by the Kahn's meat company of Cincinnati is also the rarest. The set consists of six Cincinnati Redlegs player cards, 3-1/4" by 4". Printed in black and white, with blank backs, the '55 Kahn's cards were distributed at a one-day promotional event at a Cincinnati amusement park, where the featured players were on hand to sign autographs. Like the other Kahn's issues through 1963, the '55 cards have a 1/2" white panel containing an advertising message below the player photo. These cards are sometimes found with this portion cut off, greatly reducing the value of the card.

		NR MT	EX	VG
Complete Set:		3100.00	1550.00	930.00
Common Player:		450.00	225.00	135.00
(1)	Gus Bell	800.00	400.00	240.00
(2)	Ted Kluszewski	750.00	375.00	225.00
(3)	Roy McMillan	450.00	225.00	135.00
(4)	Joe Nuxhall	450.00	225.00	135.00
(5)	Wally Post	450.00	225.00	135.00
(6)	Johnny Temple	450.00	225.00	135.00

1990 K-Mart

This 33-card, glossy set was produced by Topps for K-Mart, where it was available nationwide. The set is subtitled "Superstars" and features sixteen A.L. players, sixteen N.L. stars and a managers' card featuring both Tony LaRussa and Roger Craig. A special Superstars logo is featured on the card fronts. 1990 marks the fourth consecutive year that Topps has produced a set in cooperation with K-Mart.

		MT	NR MT	EX
Complete Set:		3.00	2.25	1.25
Common Player:		.08	.06	.03
1	Will Clark	.25	.20	.10
2	Ryne Sandberg	.25	.20	.10
3	Howard Johnson	.15	.11	.06
4	Ozzie Smith	.15	.11	.06
5	Tony Gwynn	.15	.11	.06
6	Kevin Mitchell	.20	.15	.08
7	Jerome Walton	.15	.11	.06
8	Craig Biggio	.08	.06	.03
9	Mike Scott	.08	.06	.03
10	Doc Gooden	.20	.15	.08
11	Sid Fernandez	.08	.06	.03
12	Joe Magrane	.08	.06	.03
13	Jay Howell	.08	.06	.03
14	Mark Davis	.08	.06	.03
15	Pedro Guerrero	.10	.08	.04

1956 Kahn's Wieners Reds

In 1956, Kahn's expanded its baseball card program to include 15 Redlegs players, and began issuing the cards one per pack in packages of hot dogs. Because the cards were packaged in direct contact with the meat, they are often found today in stained condition. In 3-1/4" by 4" format, black and white with blank backs, the '56 Kahn's cards can be distinguished from later issues by the presence of full stadium photographic backgrounds behind the player

"Compliments of Kahn's Wieners"
"THE WIENER THE WORLD AWAITED"

photos. Like all Kahn's issues, the 1956 set is unnumbered; the checklists are arranged alphabetically for convenience. The set features the first-ever baseball card of Hall of Famer Frank Robinson.

		NR MT	EX	VG
Complete Set:		1600.00	800.00	480.00
Common Player:		75.00	37.00	22.00
(1)	Ed Bailey	75.00	37.00	22.00
(2)	Gus Bell	100.00	50.00	30.00
(3)	Joe Black	100.00	50.00	30.00
(4)	"Smokey" Burgess	100.00	50.00	30.00
(5)	Art Fowler	75.00	37.00	22.00
(6)	Hershell Freeman	75.00	37.00	22.00
(7)	Ray Jablonski	75.00	37.00	22.00
(8)	John Klippstein	75.00	37.00	22.00
(9)	Ted Kluszewski	150.00	75.00	45.00
(10)	Brooks Lawrence	75.00	37.00	22.00
(11)	Roy McMillan	75.00	37.00	22.00
(12)	Joe Nuxhall	100.00	50.00	30.00
(13)	Wally Post	75.00	37.00	22.00
(14)	Frank Robinson	350.00	175.00	105.00
(15)	Johnny Temple	100.00	50.00	30.00

1957 Kahn's Wieners

"Compliments of Kahn's Wieners"
"THE WIENER THE WORLD AWAITED"

In its third season of baseball card issue, Kahn's kept the basic 3-1/4" by 4" format, with black and white photos and blank backs. The issue was expanded to 28 players, all Pirates or Reds. The last of the blank-backed Kahn's sets, the 1957 Reds players can be distinguished from the 1956 issue by the general lack of background photo detail, in favor of a neutral light gray background. The Dick Groat card appears with two name variations, a facsimile autograph, "Richard Groat," and a printed "Dick Groat." Both Groat varieties are included in the complete set price.

		NR MT	EX	VG
Complete Set		2600.00	1300.00	780.00
Common Player		50.00	25.00	15.00
(1)	Tom Acker	50.00	25.00	15.00

		NR MT	EX	VG
(2)	Ed Bailey	50.00	25.00	15.00
(3)	Gus Bell	70.00	35.00	21.00
(4)	Smokey Burgess	70.00	35.00	21.00
(5)	Roberto Clemente	650.00	325.00	195.00
(6)	George Crowe	50.00	25.00	15.00
(7)	Elroy Face	70.00	35.00	21.00
(8)	Hershell Freeman	50.00	25.00	15.00
(9)	Robert Friend	50.00	25.00	15.00
(10)	Don Gross	50.00	25.00	15.00
(11a)	Dick Groat	70.00	35.00	21.00
(11b)	Richard Groat	175.00	87.00	52.00
(12)	Warren Hacker	50.00	25.00	15.00
(13)	Don Hoak	70.00	35.00	21.00
(14)	Hal Jeffcoat	50.00	25.00	15.00
(15)	Ron Kline	50.00	25.00	15.00
(16)	John Klippstein	50.00	25.00	15.00
(17)	Ted Kluszewski	100.00	50.00	30.00
(18)	Brooks Lawrence	50.00	25.00	15.00
(19)	Dale Long	50.00	25.00	15.00
(20)	Wm. Mazeroski	100.00	50.00	30.00
(21)	Roy McMillan	50.00	25.00	15.00
(22)	Joe Nuxhall	50.00	25.00	15.00
(23)	Wally Post	50.00	25.00	15.00
(24)	Frank Robinson	250.00	125.00	75.00
(25)	Johnny Temple	50.00	25.00	15.00
(26)	Frank Thomas	50.00	25.00	15.00
(27)	Bob Thurman	50.00	25.00	15.00
(28)	Lee Walls	50.00	25.00	15.00

1958 Kahn's Wieners

"Compliments of Kahn's Wieners"
"THE WIENER THE WORLD AWAITED"

MY GREATEST THRILL IN BASEBALL
By GEORGE CROWE

I've had lots of big and little thrills in my baseball career, both in the minors and when I was playing with Milwaukee. Looking back, I think my biggest moment was really a whole season long. It was the 1957 season when I was playing first base for the Cincinnati Redlegs.

I played in 133 games that year. I managed to hit 31 home runs and drive in 92 runs, leading the Redlegs in both departments that year. No doubt about it—1957 was my top thrill in baseball.

Long-time Cincinnati favorite Wally Post became the only Philadelphia Phillies ballplayer to appear in the 15-year run of Kahn's issues when he was traded in 1958, but included as part of the otherwise exclusively Pirates-Reds set. Like previous years, the '58 Kahn's were 3-1/4" by 4", with black and white player photos. Unlike previous years, however, the cards had printing on the back, a story by the pictured player, titled "My Greatest Thrill in Baseball." Quite similar to the 1959 issue, the '58 Kahn's can be distinguished by the fact that the top line of the advertising panel at bottom has the word "Wieners" in 1958, but not in 1959.

		NR MT	EX	VG
Complete Set:		2600.00	1300.00	780.00
Common Player:		50.00	25.00	15.00
(1)	Ed Bailey	50.00	25.00	15.00
(2)	Gene Baker	50.00	25.00	15.00
(3)	Gus Bell	60.00	30.00	18.00
(4)	Smokey Burgess	60.00	30.00	18.00
(5)	Roberto Clemente	500.00	250.00	150.00
(6)	George Crowe	50.00	25.00	15.00
(7)	Elroy Face	60.00	30.00	18.00
(8)	Henry Foiles	50.00	25.00	15.00
(9)	Dee Fondy	50.00	25.00	15.00
(10)	Robert Friend	60.00	30.00	18.00
(11)	Richard Groat	100.00	50.00	30.00
(12)	Harvey Haddix	60.00	30.00	18.00
(13)	Don Hoak	60.00	30.00	18.00
(14)	Hal Jeffcoat	60.00	30.00	18.00
(15)	Ronald L. Kline	60.00	30.00	18.00
(16)	Ted Kluszewski	100.00	50.00	30.00
(17)	Vernon Law	60.00	30.00	18.00
(18)	Brooks Lawrence	50.00	25.00	15.00
(19)	William Mazeroski	100.00	50.00	30.00
(20)	Roy McMillan	50.00	25.00	15.00
(21)	Joe Nuxhall	60.00	30.00	18.00

		NR MT	EX	VG
(22)	Wally Post	275.00	137.00	80.00
(23)	John Powers	50.00	25.00	15.00
(24)	Robert T. Purkey	50.00	25.00	15.00
(25)	Charles Rabe	275.00	137.00	80.00
(26)	Frank Robinson	275.00	137.00	80.00
(27)	Robert Skinner	50.00	25.00	15.00
(28)	Johnny Temple	50.00	25.00	15.00
(29)	Frank Thomas	275.00	137.00	80.00

1959 Kahn's Wieners

A third team was added to the Kahn's lineup in 1959, the Cleveland Indians joining the Pirates and Reds, bringing the number of cards in the set to 38. Again printed in black and white in the 3-1/4" by 4" size, the 1959 Kahn's cards can be differentiated from the previous issue by the lack of the word "Wieners" on the top line of the advertising panel at bottom. Backs again featured a story written by the pictured player, titled "The Toughest Play I Had to Make," "My Most Difficult Moment in Baseball," or "The Toughest Batters I Have to Face."

		NR MT	EX	VG
Complete Set:		4250.00	2125.00	1275.
Common Player:		45.00	22.00	13.50
(1)	Ed Bailey	45.00	22.00	13.50
(2)	Gary Bell	45.00	22.00	13.50
(3)	Gus Bell	50.00	25.00	15.00
(4)	Richard Brodowski	500.00	250.00	150.00
(5)	Forrest Burgess	50.00	25.00	15.00
(6)	Roberto Clemente	450.00	225.00	135.00
(7)	Rocky Colavito	75.00	37.00	22.00
(8)	ElRoy Face	50.00	25.00	15.00
(9)	Robert Friend	50.00	25.00	15.00
(10)	Joe Gordon	50.00	25.00	15.00
(11)	Jim Grant	45.00	22.00	13.50
(12)	Richard M. Groat	60.00	30.00	18.00
(13)	Harvey Haddix	350.00	175.00	105.00
(14)	Woodie Held	350.00	175.00	105.00
(15)	Don Hoak	50.00	25.00	15.00
(16)	Ronald Kline	45.00	22.00	13.50
(17)	Ted Kluszewski	75.00	37.00	22.00
(18)	Vernon Law	50.00	25.00	15.00
(19)	Jerry Lynch	45.00	22.00	13.50
(20)	Billy Martin	75.00	37.00	22.00
(21)	William Mazeroski	50.00	25.00	15.00
(22)	Cal McLish	350.00	175.00	105.00
(23)	Roy McMillan	45.00	22.00	13.50
(24)	Minnie Minoso	60.00	30.00	18.00
(25)	Russell Nixon	45.00	22.00	13.50
(26)	Joe Nuxhall	50.00	25.00	15.00
(27)	Jim Perry	50.00	25.00	15.00
(28)	Vada Pinson	60.00	30.00	18.00
(29)	Vic Power	45.00	22.00	13.50
(30)	Robert Purkey	45.00	22.00	13.50
(31)	Frank Robinson	175.00	87.00	52.00
(32)	Herb Score	50.00	25.00	15.00
(33)	Robert Skinner	45.00	22.00	13.50
(34)	George Strickland	45.00	22.00	13.50
(35)	Richard L. Stuart	50.00	25.00	15.00
(36)	John Temple	45.00	22.00	13.50
(37)	Frank Thomas	50.00	25.00	15.00
(38)	George A. Witt	45.00	22.00	13.50

1960 Kahn's Wieners

Three more teams joined the Kahn's roster in 1960, the Chicago Cubs, Chicago White Sox and St. Louis Cardinals. A total of 42 different players are represented in the set. Again 3-1/4" by 4" with black and white photos, the 1960 Kahn's cards featured for the first time player stats and personal data on the back, except Harvey Kuenn, which was issued with blank back, probably because of the lateness of his trade to the Indians.

		NR MT	EX	VG
Complete Set:		2000.00	1000.00	600.00
Common Player:		30.00	15.00	9.00
(1)	Ed Bailey	30.00	15.00	9.00
(2)	Gary Bell	30.00	15.00	9.00
(3)	Gus Bell	35.00	17.50	10.50
(4)	Forrest Burgess	35.00	17.50	10.50
(5)	Gino N. Cimoli	30.00	15.00	9.00
(6)	Roberto Clemente	300.00	150.00	90.00
(7)	ElRoy Face	35.00	17.50	10.50
(8)	Tito Francona	35.00	17.50	10.50
(9)	Robert Friend	35.00	17.50	10.50
(10)	Jim Grant	30.00	15.00	9.00
(11)	Richard Groat	40.00	20.00	12.00
(12)	Harvey Haddix	35.00	17.50	10.50
(13)	Woodie Held	30.00	15.00	9.00
(14)	Bill Henry	30.00	15.00	9.00
(15)	Don Hoak	35.00	17.50	10.50
(16)	Jay Hook	30.00	15.00	9.00
(17)	Eddie Kasko	30.00	15.00	9.00
(18)	Ronnie Kline	40.00	20.00	12.00
(19)	Ted Kluszewski	50.00	25.00	15.00
(20)	Harvey Kuenn	300.00	150.00	90.00
(21)	Vernon S. Law	35.00	17.50	10.50
(22)	Brooks Lawrence	30.00	15.00	9.00
(23)	Jerry Lynch	30.00	15.00	9.00
(24)	Billy Martin	60.00	30.00	18.00
(25)	William Mazeroski	40.00	20.00	12.00
(26)	Cal McLish	30.00	15.00	9.00
(27)	Roy McMillan	30.00	15.00	9.00
(28)	Don Newcombe	35.00	17.50	10.50
(29)	Russ Nixon	30.00	15.00	9.00
(30)	Joe Nuxhall	35.00	17.50	10.50
(31)	James J. O'Toole	30.00	15.00	9.00
(32)	Jim Perry	35.00	17.50	10.50
(33)	Vada Pinson	40.00	20.00	12.00
(34)	Vic Power	30.00	15.00	9.00
(35)	Robert T. Purkey	30.00	15.00	9.00
(36)	Frank Robinson	150.00	75.00	45.00
(37)	Herb Score	35.00	17.50	10.50
(38)	Robert R. Skinner	30.00	15.00	9.00
(39)	Richard L. Stuart	35.00	17.50	10.50
(40)	John Temple	30.00	15.00	9.00
(41)	Frank Thomas	40.00	20.00	12.00
(42)	Lee Walls	35.00	17.50	10.50

1961 Kahn's Wieners

After a single season, the Chicago and St. Louis teams dropped out of the Kahn's program, but the 1961 set was larger than ever, at 43 cards. The same basic format - 3-1/4" by 4" size, black and white photos and statistical information on the back - was

Compliments of Kahn's
"THE WIENER THE WORLD AWAITED"

retained. For the first time in '61, the meat company made complete sets of the Kahn's cards available to collectors via a mail-in offer. This makes the 1961 and later Kahn's cards considerably easier to obtain than the earlier issues.

Power cards, each Cleveland player can be found with two back variations, listing the team either as "Cleveland" or "Cleveland Indians." The complete set values listed below include all variations.

		NR MT	EX	VG
Complete Set:		1000.00	500.00	300.00
Common Player:		18.00	9.00	5.50
(1)	John A. Antonelli	20.00	10.00	6.00
(2)	Ed Bailey	18.00	9.00	5.50
(3)	Gary Bell	18.00	9.00	5.50
(4)	Gus Bell	20.00	10.00	6.00
(5)	James P. Brosnan	18.00	9.00	5.50
(6)	Forrest Burgess	20.00	10.00	6.00
(7)	Gino Cimoli	18.00	9.00	5.50
(8)	Roberto Clemente	200.00	100.00	60.00
(9)	Gordon Coleman	18.00	9.00	5.50
(10)	Jimmie Dykes	20.00	10.00	6.00
(11)	ElRoy Face	25.00	12.50	7.50
(12)	Tito Francona	20.00	10.00	6.00
(13)	Robert Friend	20.00	10.00	6.00
(14)	Gene L. Freese	18.00	9.00	5.50
(15)	Jim Grant	18.00	9.00	5.50
(16)	Richard M. Groat	30.00	15.00	9.00
(17)	Harvey Haddix	20.00	10.00	6.00
(18)	Woodie Held	18.00	9.00	5.50
(19)	Don Hoak	20.00	10.00	6.00
(20)	Jay Hook	18.00	9.00	5.50
(21)	Joe Jay	18.00	9.00	5.50
(22)	Eddie Kasko	18.00	9.00	5.50
(23)	Willie Kirkland	18.00	9.00	5.50
(24)	Vernon S. Law	25.00	12.50	7.50
(25)	Jerry Lynch	18.00	9.00	5.50
(26)	Jim Maloney	25.00	12.50	7.50
(27)	William Mazeroski	30.00	15.00	9.00
(28)	Wilmer D. Mizell	20.00	10.00	6.00
(29)	Glenn R. Nelson	18.00	9.00	5.50
(30)	James J. O'Toole	18.00	9.00	5.50
(31)	Jim Perry	20.00	10.00	6.00
(32)	John M. Phillips	18.00	9.00	5.50
(33)	Vada E. Pinson Jr.	30.00	15.00	9.00
(34)	Wally Post	18.00	9.00	5.50
(35)	Vic Power	18.00	9.00	5.50
(36)	Robert T. Purkey	18.00	9.00	5.50
(37)	Frank Robinson	125.00	62.00	37.00
(38)	John A. Romano Jr.	18.00	9.00	5.50
(39)	Dick Schofield	18.00	9.00	5.50
(40)	Robert Skinner	18.00	9.00	5.50
(41)	Hal Smith	18.00	9.00	5.50
(42)	Richard Stuart	20.00	10.00	6.00
(43)	John E. Temple	18.00	9.00	5.50

NOTE: A card number in parentheses ( ) indicates the set is unnumbered.

1962 Kahn's Wieners

Besides the familiar Reds, Pirates and Indians players in the 1962 Kahn's set, a fourth team was added, the Minnesota Twins, though the overall size of the set was decreased from the previous year, to 38 players in 1962. The cards retained the 3-1/4" by 4" black and white format of previous years. The '62 Kahn's set is awash in variations. Besides the photo and front design variations on the Bell, Purkey and

		NR MT	EX	VG
Complete Set:		2000.00	1000.00	600.00
Common Player:		15.00	7.50	4.50
(1a)	Gary Bell (fat man in background)	150.00	75.00	45.00
(1b)	Gary Bell (no fat man)	40.00	20.00	12.00
(2)	James P. Brosnan	15.00	7.50	4.50
(3)	Forrest Burgess	20.00	10.00	6.00
(4)	Leonardo Cardenas	15.00	7.50	4.50
(5)	Roberto Clemente	150.00	75.00	45.00
(6a)	Ty Cline (Cleveland Indians back)	75.00	37.00	22.00
(6b)	Ty Cline (Cleveland back)	30.00	15.00	9.00
(7)	Gordon Coleman	15.00	7.50	4.50
(8)	Dick Donovan	30.00	15.00	9.00
(9)	John Edwards	15.00	7.50	4.50
(10a)	Tito Francona (Cleveland Indians back)	75.00	37.00	22.00
(10b)	Tito Francona (Cleveland back)	30.00	15.00	9.00
(11)	Gene Freese	15.00	7.50	4.50
(12)	Robert B. Friend	20.00	10.00	6.00
(13)	Joe Gibbon	90.00	45.00	27.00
(14a)	Jim Grant (Cleveland Indians back)	75.00	37.00	22.00
(14b)	Jim Grant (Cleveland back)	30.00	15.00	9.00
(15)	Richard M. Groat	25.00	12.50	7.50
(16)	Harvey Haddix	20.00	10.00	6.00
(17a)	Woodie Held (Cleveland Indians back)	90.00	45.00	27.00
(17b)	Woodie Held (Cleveland back)	30.00	15.00	9.00
(18)	Bill Henry	15.00	7.50	4.50
(19)	Don Hoak	20.00	10.00	6.00
(20)	Ken Hunt	15.00	7.50	4.50
(21)	Joseph R. Jay	15.00	7.50	4.50
(22)	Eddie Kasko	15.00	7.50	4.50
(23a)	Willie Kirkland (Cleveland Indians back)	75.00	37.00	22.00
(23b)	Willie Kirkland (Cleveland back)	30.00	15.00	9.00
(24a)	Barry Latman (Cleveland Indians back)	75.00	37.00	22.00
(24b)	Barry Latman (Cleveland back)	30.00	15.00	9.00
(25)	Jerry Lynch	15.00	7.50	4.50
(26)	Jim Maloney	20.00	10.00	6.00
(27)	William Mazeroski	25.00	12.50	7.50
(28)	Jim O'Toole	15.00	7.50	4.50
(29a)	Jim Perry (Cleveland Indians back)	90.00	45.00	27.00
(29b)	Jim Perry (Cleveland back)	30.00	15.00	9.00
(30a)	John M. Phillips (Cleveland Indians back)	75.00	37.00	22.00
(30b)	John M. Phillips (Cleveland back)	30.00	15.00	9.00
(31)	Vada E. Pinson	25.00	12.50	7.50
(32)	Wally Post	15.00	7.50	4.50
(33a)	Vic Power (Cleveland Indians back)	75.00	37.00	22.00
(33b)	Vic Power (Cleveland back)	30.00	15.00	9.00
(33c)	Vic Power (Minnesota Twins back)	150.00	75.00	45.00
(34a)	Robert T. Purkey (no autograph)	150.00	75.00	45.00
(34b)	Robert T. Purkey (with autograph)	40.00	20.00	12.00
(35)	Frank Robinson	80.00	40.00	24.00
(36a)	John Romano (Cleveland Indians back)	75.00	37.00	22.00
(36b)	John Romano (Cleveland back)	30.00	15.00	9.00

		NR MT	EX	VG
(37)	Dick Stuart	20.00	10.00	6.00
(38)	Bill Virdon	20.00	10.00	6.00

1963 Kahn's Wieners

Compliments of Kahn's
"THE WIENER THE WORLD AWAITED"

In 1963, for the first time since Kahn's began issuing baseball cards in 1955, the design underwent a significant change, white borders were added to the top and sides of the card. Also, the card size was changed to 3-3/16" by 4-1/4". Statistical and personal data continued to be printed on the card backs. Joining traditional Reds, Pirates and Indians personnel in the 30-card 1963 set were a handful of New York Yankees and Dick Groat, in his new identity as a St. Louis Cardinal.

		NR MT	EX	VG
Complete Set:		800.00	400.00	240.00
Common Player:		15.00	7.50	4.50
(1)	Robert Bailey	15.00	7.50	4.50
(2)	Don Blasingame	15.00	7.50	4.50
(3)	Clete Boyer	25.00	12.50	7.50
(4)	Forrest Burgess	20.00	10.00	6.00
(5)	Leonardo Cardenas	15.00	7.50	4.50
(6)	Roberto Clemente	150.00	75.00	45.00
(7)	Don Clendennon (Donn Clendenon)			
		15.00	7.50	4.50
(8)	Gordon Coleman	15.00	7.50	4.50
(9)	John A. Edwards	15.00	7.50	4.50
(10)	Gene Freese	15.00	7.50	4.50
(11)	Robert B. Friend	20.00	10.00	6.00
(12)	Joe Gibbon	15.00	7.50	4.50
(13)	Dick Groat	25.00	12.50	7.50
(14)	Harvey Haddix	20.00	10.00	6.00
(15)	Elston Howard	30.00	15.00	9.00
(16)	Joey Jay	15.00	7.50	4.50
(17)	Eddie Kasko	15.00	7.50	4.50
(18)	Tony Kubek	30.00	15.00	9.00
(19)	Jerry Lynch	15.00	7.50	4.50
(20)	Jim Maloney	20.00	10.00	6.00
(21)	William Mazeroski	25.00	12.50	7.50
(22)	Joe Nuxhall	20.00	10.00	6.00
(23)	Jim O'Toole	15.00	7.50	4.50
(24)	Vada E. Pinson	25.00	12.50	7.50
(25)	Robert T. Purkey	15.00	7.50	4.50
(26)	Bob Richardson	30.00	15.00	9.00
(27)	Frank Robinson	70.00	35.00	21.00
(28)	Bill Stafford	20.00	10.00	6.00
(29)	Ralph W. Terry	25.00	12.50	7.50
(30)	Bill Virdon	20.00	10.00	6.00

1964 Kahn's Wieners

After nearly a decade of virtually identical card issues, the 1964 Kahn's issue was an abrupt change. In a new size, 3" by 3-1/2", the nearly square cards featured a borderless color photo. The only other design element on the front of the card was a facsimile autograph. The advertising slogan which had traditionally appeared on the front of the card was moved to the back, where it joined the player's stats and personal data. The teams in the 1964 issue

once again reverted to the Reds, Pirates and Indians, for a total of 31 cards.

		NR MT	EX	VG
Complete Set:		900.00	450.00	270.00
Common Player:		9.00	4.50	2.75
(1)	Max Alvis	9.00	4.50	2.75
(2)	Bob Bailey	9.00	4.50	2.75
(3)	Leonardo Cardenas	9.00	4.50	2.75
(4)	Roberto Clemente	150.00	75.00	45.00
(5)	Donn A. Clendenon	9.00	4.50	2.75
(6)	Victor Davalillo	9.00	4.50	2.75
(7)	Dick Donovan	9.00	4.50	2.75
(8)	John A. Edwards	9.00	4.50	2.75
(9)	Robert Friend	15.00	7.50	4.50
(10)	Jim Grant	9.00	4.50	2.75
(11)	Tommy Harper	9.00	4.50	2.75
(12)	Woodie Held	9.00	4.50	2.75
(13)	Joey Jay	9.00	4.50	2.75
(14)	Jack Kralick	9.00	4.50	2.75
(15)	Jerry Lynch	9.00	4.50	2.75
(16)	Jim Maloney	15.00	7.50	4.50
(17)	William S. Mazeroski	20.00	10.00	6.00
(18)	Alvin McBean	9.00	4.50	2.75
(19)	Joe Nuxhall	15.00	7.50	4.50
(20)	Jim Pagliaroni	9.00	4.50	2.75
(21)	Vada E. Pinson Jr.	20.00	10.00	6.00
(22)	Robert T. Purkey	9.00	4.50	2.75
(23)	Pedro Ramos	9.00	4.50	2.75
(24)	Frank Robinson	70.00	35.00	21.00
(25)	John Romano	9.00	4.50	2.75
(26)	Pete Rose	400.00	200.00	120.00
(27)	John Tsitouris	9.00	4.50	2.75
(28)	Robert A. Veale Jr.	9.00	4.50	2.75
(29)	Bill Virdon	15.00	7.50	4.50
(30)	Leon Wagner	9.00	4.50	2.75
(31)	Fred Whitfield	9.00	4.50	2.75

NOTE: A card number in parentheses ( ) indicates the set is unnumbered.

1965 Kahn's Wieners

There was little change for the Kahn's issue in 1965 beyond the addition of Milwaukee Braves players to the Reds, Pirates and Indians traditionally included in the set. At 45 players, the 1965 issue was the largest of the Kahn's sets. Once again in 3" by 3-1/2" size, the 1965s retained the borderless color photo design of the previous season. A look at the stats on the back will confirm the year of issue, however, since the last year of statistics is the year prior to the card's issue.

		NR MT	EX	VG
Complete Set:		1100.00	550.00	330.00
Common Player:		12.00	6.00	3.50
(1)	Hank Aaron	125.00	62.00	37.00
(2)	Max Alvis	12.00	6.00	3.50
(3)	Jose Azcue	12.00	6.00	3.50
(4)	Bob Bailey	12.00	6.00	3.50
(5)	Frank Bolling	12.00	6.00	3.50
(6)	Leonardo Cardenas	12.00	6.00	3.50
(7)	Rico Ricardo Carty	15.00	7.50	4.50
(8)	Donn A. Clendenon	12.00	6.00	3.50
(9)	Tony Cloninger	12.00	6.00	3.50
(10)	Gordon Coleman	12.00	6.00	3.50
(11)	Victor Davalillo	12.00	6.00	3.50
(12)	John A. Edwards	12.00	6.00	3.50
(13)	Sam Ellis	12.00	6.00	3.50
(14)	Robert Friend	15.00	7.50	4.50
(15)	Tommy Harper	12.00	6.00	3.50
(16)	Chuck Hinton	12.00	6.00	3.50
(17)	Dick Howser	15.00	7.50	4.50
(18)	Joey Jay	12.00	6.00	3.50
(19)	Deron Johnson	12.00	6.00	3.50
(20)	Jack Kralick	12.00	6.00	3.50
(21)	Denny Lemaster	12.00	6.00	3.50
(22)	Jerry Lynch	12.00	6.00	3.50
(23)	Jim Maloney	15.00	7.50	4.50
(24)	Lee Maye	12.00	6.00	3.50
(25)	William S. Mazeroski	20.00	10.00	6.00
(26)	Alvin McBean	12.00	6.00	3.50
(27)	Bill McCool	12.00	6.00	3.50
(28)	Sam McDowell	15.00	7.50	4.50
(29)	Donald McMahon	12.00	6.00	3.50
(30)	Denis Menke	12.00	6.00	3.50
(31)	Joe Nuxhall	15.00	7.50	4.50
(32)	Gene Oliver	12.00	6.00	3.50
(33)	Jim O'Toole	12.00	6.00	3.50
(34)	Jim Pagliaroni	12.00	6.00	3.50
(35)	Vada E. Pinson Jr.	20.00	10.00	6.00
(36)	Frank Robinson	100.00	50.00	30.00
(37)	Pete Rose	250.00	125.00	75.00
(38)	Willie Stargell	100.00	50.00	30.00
(39)	Ralph W. Terry	12.00	6.00	3.50
(40)	Luis Tiant	20.00	10.00	6.00
(41)	Joe Torre	25.00	12.50	7.50
(42)	John Tsitouris	12.00	6.00	3.50
(43)	Robert A. Veale Jr.	12.00	6.00	3.50
(44)	Bill Virdon	15.00	7.50	4.50
(45)	Leon Wagner	12.00	6.00	3.50

1966 Kahn's Wieners

The fourth new format in five years greeted collector's with the introduction of Kahn's 1966 issue of 32 cards. The design consisted of a color photo bordered by white and yellow vertical stripes. The player's name was printed above the photo, and a facsimile autograph appeared across the photo. As printed, the cards were 2-13/16" by 4" in size. However, the top portion consisted of a 2-13/16" by 1-3/8" advertising panel with a red rose logo and the word "Kahn's," separated from the player portion of the card by a black dotted line. Naturally, many of the cards are found today with the top portion cut off.

Values listed here are for cards with the top portion intact. Players from the Cincinnati Reds, Pittsburgh Pirates, Cleveland Indians and Atlanta Braves were included in the set. Since the cards are blank-backed, collectors must learn to differentiate player poses to determine year of issue for some cards.

		NR MT	EX	VG
Complete Set:		1000.00	500.00	300.00
Common Player:		15.00	7.50	4.50
(1)	Henry Aaron	125.00	62.00	37.00
(2)	Felipe Alou	24.00	12.00	7.25
(3)	Max Alvis	15.00	7.50	4.50
(4)	Robert Bailey	15.00	7.50	4.50
(5)	Wade Blasingame	15.00	7.50	4.50
(6)	Frank Bolling	15.00	7.50	4.50
(7)	Leo Cardenas	15.00	7.50	4.50
(8)	Roberto Clemente	125.00	62.00	37.00
(9)	Tony Cloninger	15.00	7.50	4.50
(10)	Vic Davalillo	15.00	7.50	4.50
(11)	John Edwards	15.00	7.50	4.50
(12)	Sam Ellis	15.00	7.50	4.50
(13)	Pedro Gonzalez	15.00	7.50	4.50
(14)	Tommy Harper	15.00	7.50	4.50
(15)	Deron Johnson	15.00	7.50	4.50
(16)	Mack Jones	15.00	7.50	4.50
(17)	Denny Lemaster	15.00	7.50	4.50
(18)	Jim Maloney	24.00	12.00	7.25
(19)	William Mazeroski	28.00	14.00	8.50
(20)	Bill McCool	15.00	7.50	4.50
(21)	Sam McDowell	24.00	12.00	7.25
(22)	Denis Menke	15.00	7.50	4.50
(23)	Joe Nuxhall	24.00	12.00	7.25
(24)	Jim Pagliaroni	15.00	7.50	4.50
(25)	Milt Pappas	24.00	12.00	7.25
(26)	Vada Pinson	28.00	14.00	8.50
(27)	Pete Rose	200.00	100.00	60.00
(28)	Sonny Siebert	15.00	7.50	4.50
(29)	Willie Stargell	80.00	40.00	24.00
(30)	Joe Torre	28.00	14.00	8.50
(31)	Bob Veale	15.00	7.50	4.50
(32)	Fred Whitfield	15.00	7.50	4.50

1967 Kahn's Wieners

Retaining the basic format of the 1966 set (see listing for description), the '67 Kahn's set was expanded to 41 players through the addition of several New York Mets players to the previous season's lineup of Reds, Pirates, Indians and Braves. Making the 1967 set especially challenging for collectors is the fact that some cards are found in a smaller size and/or with different colored stripes bordering the color player photo. On the majority of cards, the size remained 2-13/16" by 4" (with ad at top; 2-13/16" by 2-5/8" without ad at top). However, because of packing in different products, the Ellis, Helms and Torre cards can be found in 2-13/16" by 3-1/4" size (with ad; 2-13/16" by 2-1/8" without ad). The handful of known border stripe variations are listed below. Values quoted are for cards with the top ad panel intact. All variation cards are included in the valuations given below for complete sets.

		NR MT	EX	VG
	Complete Set:	1100.00	550.00	330.00
	Common Player:	15.00	7.50	4.50
(1)	Henry Aaron	125.00	62.00	37.00
(2)	Gene Alley	15.00	7.50	4.50
(3)	Felipe Alou	24.00	12.00	7.25
(4a)	Matty Alou (yellow & white striped border)			
		24.00	12.00	7.25
(4b)	Matty Alou (red & white striped border)			
		28.00	14.00	8.50
(5)	Max Alvis	15.00	7.50	4.50
(6a)	Ken Boyer (yellow & white striped border)			
		30.00	15.00	9.00
(6b)	Ken Boyer (red & white striped border)			
		35.00	17.50	10.50
(7)	Leo Cardenas	15.00	7.50	4.50
(8)	Rico Carty	24.00	12.00	7.25
(9)	Tony Cloninger	15.00	7.50	4.50
(10)	Tommy Davis	24.00	12.00	7.25
(11)	John Edwards	15.00	7.50	4.50
(12a)	Sam Ellis (large size)	15.00	7.50	4.50
(12b)	Sam Ellis (small size)	28.00	14.00	8.50
(13)	Jack Fisher	15.00	7.50	4.50
(14)	Steve Hargan	15.00	7.50	4.50
(15)	Tom Harper	15.00	7.50	4.50
(16a)	Tom Helms (large size)	15.00	7.50	4.50
(16b)	Tom Helms (small size)	28.00	14.00	8.50
(17)	Deron Johnson	15.00	7.50	4.50
(18)	Ken Johnson	15.00	7.50	4.50
(19)	Cleon Jones	15.00	7.50	4.50
(20a)	Ed Kranepool (yellow & white striped border)	15.00	7.50	4.50
(20b)	Ed Kranepool (red & white striped border)			
		25.00	12.50	7.50
(21a)	James Maloney (yellow & white striped border)	24.00	12.00	7.25
(21b)	James Maloney (red & white striped border)	28.00	14.00	8.50
(22)	Lee May	24.00	12.00	7.25
(23)	Wm. Mazeroski	28.00	14.00	8.50
(24)	Wm. McCool	15.00	7.50	4.50
(25)	Sam McDowell	24.00	12.00	7.25
(26)	Dennis Menke (Denis)	15.00	7.50	4.50
(27)	Jim Pagliaroni	15.00	7.50	4.50
(28)	Don Pavletich	15.00	7.50	4.50
(29)	Tony Perez	35.00	17.50	10.50
(30)	Vada Pinson	28.00	14.00	8.50
(31)	Dennis Ribant	15.00	7.50	4.50
(32)	Pete Rose	175.00	87.00	52.00
(33)	Art Shamsky	15.00	7.50	4.50
(34)	Bob Shaw	15.00	7.50	4.50
(35)	Sonny Siebert	15.00	7.50	4.50
(36)	Wm. Stargell (first name actually Wilver)			
		80.00	40.00	24.00
(37a)	Joe Torre (large size)	28.00	14.00	8.50
(37b)	Joe Torre (small size)	32.00	16.00	9.50
(38)	Bob Veale	15.00	7.50	4.50
(39)	Leon Wagner	15.00	7.50	4.50
(40)	Fred Whitfield	15.00	7.50	4.50
(41)	Woody Woodward	15.00	7.50	4.50

1968 Kahn's Wieners

The number of card size and stripe color variations increased with the 1968 Kahn's issue (see 1967 listing), though the basic card design was retained from the previous two seasons: 2-13/16" by 4" size (with ad panel at top; 2-13/16" by 2-5/8" with ad panel cut off), color photo bordered by yellow and white vertical stripes. In addition to the basic issue, a number of the cards appear in a smaller, 2-13/16" by 3-1/4", size, while some of them, and others, appear with variations in the color of border stripes. One card, Maloney, can be found with a top portion advertising Blue Mountain brand meats, as well as Kahn's. All in all, quite a challenge for the specialist. The 1968 set featured the largest number of teams represented in any Kahn's issue: Atlanta Braves, Chicago Cubs and White Sox, Cincinnati Reds, Cleveland Indians, Detroit Tigers, New York Mets and Pittsburgh Pirates. Values quoted below are for cards with the ad panel at top; complete set prices include all variations.

		NR MT	EX	VG
	Complete Set:	1600.00	800.00	480.00
	Common Player:	15.00	7.50	4.50
(1a)	Hank Aaron (large size)	125.00	62.00	37.00
(1b)	Hank Aaron (small size)	150.00	75.00	45.00
(2)	Tommy Agee	15.00	7.50	4.50
(3a)	Gene Alley (large size)	15.00	7.50	4.50
(3b)	Gene Alley (small size)	24.00	12.00	7.25
(4)	Felipe Alou	24.00	12.00	7.25
(5a)	Matty Alou (yellow striped border)			
		24.00	12.00	7.25
(5b)	Matty Alou (red striped border)	28.00	14.00	8.50
(6a)	Max Alvis (large size)	15.00	7.50	4.50
(6b)	Max Alvis (small size)	24.00	12.00	7.25
(7)	Gerry Arrigo	15.00	7.50	4.50
(8)	John Bench	400.00	200.00	120.00
(9a)	Clete Boyer (large size)	15.00	7.50	4.50
(9b)	Clete Boyer (small size)	24.00	12.00	7.25
(10)	Larry Brown	15.00	7.50	4.50
(11a)	Leo Cardenas (large size)	15.00	7.50	4.50
(11b)	Leo Cardenas (small size)	24.00	12.00	7.25
(12a)	Bill Freehan (large size)	24.00	12.00	7.25
(12b)	Bill Freehan (small size)	28.00	14.00	8.50
(13)	Steve Hargan	15.00	7.50	4.50
(14)	Joel Horlen	15.00	7.50	4.50
(15)	Tony Horton	24.00	12.00	7.25
(16)	Willie Horton	24.00	12.00	7.25
(17)	Ferguson Jenkins	32.00	16.00	9.50
(18)	Deron Johnson	15.00	7.50	4.50
(19)	Mack Jones	15.00	7.50	4.50
(20)	Bob Lee	15.00	7.50	4.50
(21a)	Jim Maloney (large size, rose logo)			
		24.00	12.00	7.25
(21b)	Jim Maloney (large size, blue mountain logo)	28.00	14.00	8.50
(21c)	Jim Maloney (small size, yellow & white striped border)	28.00	14.00	8.50
(21d)	Jim Maloney (small size, yellow, white & green striped border)	28.00	14.00	8.50
(22a)	Lee May (large size)	24.00	12.00	7.25
(22b)	Lee May (small size)	28.00	14.00	8.50
(23a)	Wm. Mazeroski (large size)	24.00	12.00	7.25
(23b)	Wm. Mazeroski (small size)	28.00	14.00	8.50
(24)	Dick McAuliffe	15.00	7.50	4.50
(25)	Bill McCool	15.00	7.50	4.50
(26a)	Sam McDowell (yellow striped border)			
		24.00	12.00	7.25
(26b)	Sam McDowell (red striped border)			
		28.00	14.00	8.50
(27a)	Tony Perez (yellow striped border)			
		35.00	17.50	10.50
(27b)	Tony Perez (red striped border)	40.00	20.00	12.00
(28)	Gary Peters	15.00	7.50	4.50
(29a)	Vada Pinson (large size)	24.00	12.00	7.25
(29b)	Vada Pinson (small size)	28.00	14.00	8.50
(30)	Chico Ruiz	15.00	7.50	4.50
(31a)	Ron Santo (yellow striped border)			
		24.00	12.00	7.25
(31b)	Ron Santo (red striped border)	28.00	14.00	8.50
(32)	Art Shamsky	15.00	7.50	4.50
(33)	Luis Tiant	24.00	12.00	7.25
(34a)	Joe Torre (large size)	28.00	14.00	8.50
(34b)	Joe Torre (small size)	32.00	16.00	9.50
(35a)	Bob Veale (large size)	15.00	7.50	4.50
(35b)	Bob Veale (small size)	24.00	12.00	7.25
(36)	Leon Wagner	15.00	7.50	4.50
(37)	Billy Williams	50.00	25.00	15.00
(38)	Earl Wilson	15.00	7.50	4.50

Regional interest may affect the value of a card.

1969 Kahn's Wieners

1987 Kahn's Wieners Reds

(44) ERIC DAVIS, OF

In its 15th consecutive year of baseball card issuing, Kahn's continued the basic format adopted in 1966. The basic card issue of 22 players was printed in 2-13/16" by 4" size (with ad panel at top; 2-13/16" by 2-5/8" without panel) and are blanked-backed. Teams represented in the set included the Braves, Cubs, White Sox, Reds, Cardinals, Indians and Pirates. The cards featured a color photo and facsimile autograph bordered by yellow and white vertical stripes. At top was an ad panel consisting of the Kahn's red rose logo. However, because some cards were produced for inclusion in packages other than the standard hot dogs, a number of variations in card size and stripe color were created, as noted in the listings below. The smaller size cards, 2-13/16" by 3-1/4" with ad, 2-13/16" by 2-1/8" without ad, were created by more closely cropping the player photo at top and bottom. Values quoted below are for cards with the top logo panel intact. Complete set values include all the variations.

		NR MT	EX	VG
Complete Set:		800.00	400.00	240.00
Common Player:		15.00	7.50	4.50
(1a)	Hank Aaron (large size)	125.00	62.00	37.00
(1b)	Hank Aaron (small size)	150.00	75.00	45.00
(2)	Matty Alou	24.00	12.00	7.25
(3)	Max Alvis	15.00	7.50	4.50
(4)	Gerry Arrigo	15.00	7.50	4.50
(5)	Steve Blass	15.00	7.50	4.50
(6)	Clay Carroll	15.00	7.50	4.50
(7)	Tony Cloninger	15.00	7.50	4.50
(8)	George Culver	15.00	7.50	4.50
(9)	Joel Horlen	15.00	7.50	4.50
(10)	Tony Horton	24.00	12.00	7.25
(11)	Alex Johnson	15.00	7.50	4.50
(12a)	Jim Maloney (large size)	24.00	12.00	7.25
(12b)	Jim Maloney (small size)	28.00	14.00	8.50
(13a)	Lee May (yellow striped border)	24.00	12.00	7.25
(13b)	Lee May (red striped border)	28.00	14.00	8.50
(14a)	Wm. Mazeroski (yellow striped border) 24.00		12.00	7.25
(14b)	Wm. Mazeroski (red striped border) 28.00		14.00	8.50
(15a)	Sam McDowell (yellow striped border) 24.00		12.00	7.25
(15b)	Sam McDowell (red striped border) 28.00		14.00	8.50
(16a)	Tony Perez (large size)	35.00	17.50	10.50
(16b)	Tony Perez (small size)	40.00	20.00	12.00
(17)	Gary Peters	15.00	7.50	4.50
(18a)	Ron Santo (yellow striped border) 24.00		12.00	7.25
(18b)	Ron Santo (red striped border)	28.00	14.00	8.50
(19)	Luis Tiant	24.00	12.00	7.25
(20)	Joe Torre	28.00	14.00	8.50
(21)	Bob Veale	15.00	7.50	4.50
(22)	Billy Williams	50.00	25.00	15.00

The values quoted are intended to reflect the market price.

After a nearly 20-year layoff, Kahn's Wieners produced a baseball card set. Kahn's, who produced card sets between 1955 and 1968, sponsored a 28-card 9set that was distributed to fans attending the August 2nd game at Riverfront Stadium. The cards are the standard 2-1/2" by 3-1/2" size. The fronts offer a full-color player photo bordered in red and white. The backs carry the Kahn's logo and a head shot of the player.

		MT	NR MT	EX
Complete Set:		15.00	11.00	6.00
Common Player:		.25	.20	.10
6	Bo Diaz	.25	.20	.10
10	Terry Francona	.25	.20	.10
11	Kurt Stillwell	.50	.40	.20
12	Nick Esasky	.50	.40	.20
13	Dave Concepcion	.50	.40	.20
15	Barry Larkin	2.00	1.50	.80
16	Ron Oester	.25	.20	.10
21	Paul O'Neill	1.00	.70	.40
23	Lloyd McClendon	.40	.30	.15
25	Buddy Bell	.35	.25	.14
28	Kal Daniels	1.00	.70	.40
29	Tracy Jones	.50	.40	.20
30	Guy Hoffman	.25	.20	.10
31	John Franco	.80	.60	.30
32	Tom Browning	.80	.60	.30
33	Ron Robinson	.25	.20	.10
34	Bill Gullickson	.25	.20	.10
35	Pat Pacillo	.30	.25	.12
39	Dave Parker	.80	.60	.30
43	Bill Landrum	.50	.40	.20
44	Eric Davis	2.50	2.00	1.00
46	Rob Murphy	.40	.30	.15
47	Frank Williams	.25	.20	.10
48	Ted Power	.25	.20	.10

1988 Kahn's Wieners Mets

Approximately 50,000 Mets fans received this complimentary card set during a ballpark promotion sponsored by Kahn's Wieners. Twenty-five players are featured in the set, along with manager Davey

Johnson, four coaches and a team photo. Card fronts have a dark blue border with an orange rectangle framing the full-color player photo. Card numbers reflecting the players' uniform numbers, are printed in white in the upper right corner of the card face, beside the team logo. The player name appears upper left and the player position is centered in the bottom margin. The card backs are black and white with red line accents. In addition to player acquisition date, birthday and residence, a paragraph-style career summary is included. The cards measure 2-1/2" by 3-1/2".

		MT	NR MT	EX
Complete Set:		14.00	10.50	5.50
Common Player:		.20	.15	.08
1	Mookie Wilson	.35	.25	.14
2	Mackey Sasser	.30	.25	.12
3	Bud Harrelson	.20	.15	.08
4	Lenny Dykstra	.40	.30	.15
5	Davey Johnson	.30	.25	.12
6	Wally Backman	.20	.15	.08
8	Gary Carter	1.00	.70	.40
11	Tim Teufel	.20	.15	.08
12	Ron Darling	.60	.45	.25
13	Lee Mazzilli	.20	.15	.08
15	Rick Aguilera	.20	.15	.08
16	Dwight Gooden	1.00	.70	.40
17	Keith Hernandez	1.00	.70	.40
18	Darryl Strawberry	2.00	1.50	.80
19	Bob Ojeda	.35	.25	.14
20	Howard Johnson	1.00	.70	.40
21	Kevin Elster	.50	.40	.20
22	Kevin McReynolds	.60	.45	.25
26	Terry Leach	.20	.15	.08
28	Bill Robinson	.20	.15	.08
29	Dave Magadan	.40	.30	.15
30	Mel Stottlemyre	.20	.15	.08
31	Gene Walter	.20	.15	.08
33	Barry Lyons	.20	.15	.08
34	Sam Perlozzo	.20	.15	.08
42	Roger McDowell	.30	.25	.12
44	David Cone	.70	.50	.30
48	Randy Myers	.50	.40	.20
50	Sid Fernandez	.35	.25	.14
52	Greg Pavlick	.20	.15	.08
----	Team Photo	.20	.15	.08

1988 Kahn's Wieners Reds

This 26-card set was a one-time giveaway during the August 14th, 1988 Cincinnati Reds game. The glossy cards (2-1/2" by 3-1/2") feature full-color action photos inside red and white borders. The Reds logo, player uniform number, name and position are printed below the photo. The backs are black and white, with small player close-ups and career stats. A promotional 25-cent coupon for Kahn's Wieners was included with each set.

		MT	NR MT	EX
Complete Set:		14.00	10.50	5.50
Common Player:		.25	.20	.10
6	Bo Diaz	.25	.20	.10

		MT	NR MT	EX
8	Terry McGriff	.25	.20	.10
9	Eddie Milner	.25	.20	.10
10	Leon Durham	.30	.25	.12
11	Barry Larkin	.70	.50	.30
12	Nick Esasky	.30	.25	.12
13	Dave Concepcion	.40	.30	.15
14	Pete Rose	1.25	.90	.50
15	Jeff Treadway	.50	.40	.20
17	Chris Sabo	1.50	1.25	.60
20	Danny Jackson	.60	.45	.25
21	Paul O'Neill	.30	.25	.12
22	Dave Collins	.25	.20	.10
27	Jose Rijo	.35	.25	.14
28	Kal Daniels	.70	.50	.30
29	Tracy Jones	.50	.40	.20
30	Lloyd McClendon	.25	.20	.10
31	John Franco	.50	.40	.20
32	Tom Browning	.50	.40	.20
33	Ron Robinson	.25	.20	.10
40	Jack Armstrong	.25	.20	.10
44	Eric Davis	1.50	1.25	.60
46	Rob Murphy	.25	.20	.10
47	Frank Williams	.25	.20	.10
48	Tim Birtsas	.25	.20	.10
----	Coaches (Scott Breeden, Tommy Helms, Bruce Kimm, Jim Lett, Lee May, Tony Perez)			
		.25	.20	.10

1989 Kahn's-Hillshire Farms

This 11-player card set was available through a mail-in offer. One dollar and three proofs of purchase from Hillshire Farms were needed to obtain the set. The card fronts feature paintings of recent Hall of Fame inductees. A coupon card was also included with each set.

		MT	NR MT	EX
Complete Set:		6.00	4.50	2.50
Common Player:		.40	.30	.10
(1)	Cool Papa Bell	.40	.30	.15
(2)	Johnny Bench	.80	.60	.30
(3)	Lou Brock	.80	.60	.30
(4)	Whitey Ford	.80	.60	.30
(5)	Bob Gibson	.80	.60	.30
(6)	Billy Herman	.40	.30	.15
(7)	Harmon Killebrew	.80	.60	.30
(8)	Eddie Mathews	1.00	.70	.40
(9)	Brooks Robinson	1.00	.70	.40
(10)	Willie Stargell	.80	.60	.30
(11)	Carl Yastrzemski	.80	.60	.30

1989 Kahn's Wieners Mets

This 30-card New York Mets team set was sponsored by Kahn's Wieners and was given to fans attending the July 6, 1989 Mets game at Shea Stadium. The standard-size cards feature a full-color photo surrounded by a blue and orange border with the player's name and uniform number across the top. The backs include the Kahn's logo, along with player information and complete Major League stats. Four update cards were later added to the set.

		MT	NR MT	EX
Complete Set:		15.00	11.00	6.00
Common Player:		.20	.15	.08
1	Mookie Wilson	.35	.25	.14
2	Mackey Sasser	.25	.20	.10
3	Bud Harrelson	.20	.15	.08
5	Davey Johnson	.25	.20	.10
7	Juan Samuel	.40	.30	.15
8	Gary Carter	.50	.40	.20
9	Gregg Jefferies	1.00	.70	.40
12	Ron Darling	.50	.40	.20
13	Lee Mazzilli	.20	.15	.08
16	Dwight Gooden	1.75	1.50	.70
17	Keith Hernandez	.60	.45	.25
18	Darryl Strawberry	1.25	.90	.50
19	Bob Ojeda	.25	.20	.10
20	Howard Johnson	.70	.50	.30
21	Kevin Elster	.35	.25	.14
22	Kevin McReynolds	.50	.40	.20
28	Bill Robinson	.20	.15	.08
29	Dave Magadan	.40	.30	.15
30	Mel Stottlemyre	.20	.15	.08
32	Mark Carreon	.40	.30	.15
33	Barry Lyons	.20	.15	.08
34	Sam Perlozzo	.20	.15	.08
38	Rick Aguilera	.20	.15	.08
44	David Cone	.50	.40	.20
46	Dave West	.60	.45	.25
48	Randy Myers	.35	.25	.14
50	Sid Fernandez	.35	.25	.14
51	Don Aase	.20	.15	.08
52	Greg Pavlick	.20	.15	.08
----	Team Card	.20	.15	.08
----	Jeff Innis	.90	.70	.50
----	Keith Miller	.70	.50	.30
----	Jeff Musselman	.70	.50	.30
----	Frank Viola	1.50	1.25	.60

Regional interest may affect the value of a card.

1989 Kahn's Wieners Reds

This 26-card Cincinnati Reds team set, sponsored by Kahn's Wieners, was distributed to fans attending the Aug. 6 Reds game at Riverfront Stadium. The standard-size, red-bordered cards feature action photos with the player's name in the upper left corner, his uniform number in the upper right and the Reds logo in the middle. The backs include a black-and-white head shot, player data and complete major and minor league stats. The Kahn's logo appears in the upper right corner of the back.

		MT	NR MT	EX
Complete Set:		12.00	9.00	4.75
Common Player:		.20	.15	.08
6	Bo Diaz	.20	.15	.08
7	Lenny Harris	.40	.30	.15
11	Barry Larkin	1.00	.70	.40
12	Joel Youngblood	.20	.15	.08
14	Pete Rose	1.00	.70	.40
16	Ron Oester	.25	.20	.10
17	Chris Sabo	.40	.30	.15
20	Danny Jackson	.25	.20	.15
21	Paul O'Neill	.25	.20	.15
25	Todd Benzinger	.40	.30	.15
27	Jose Rijo	.25	.20	.10
28	Kal Daniels	.40	.30	.15
29	Herm Winningham	.20	.15	.08
30	Ken Griffey	.30	.25	.12
31	John Franco	.30	.25	.12
32	Tom Browning	.35	.25	.14
33	Ron Robinson	.20	.15	.08
34	Jeff Reed	.20	.15	.08
36	Rolando Roomes	.70	.50	.30
37	Norm Charlton	.50	.40	.20
42	Rick Mahler	.25	.20	.10
43	Kent Tekulve	.20	.15	.08
44	Eric Davis	1.50	1.25	.60
48	Tim Birtsas	.20	.15	.08
49	Rob Dibble	.60	.45	.25
----	Coaches Card	.20	.15	.08

1990 Kahn's Wieners Mets

For the third consecutive year, Kahn's issued a set of baseball cards of members of the New York Mets. The sets were given out at Shea Stadium on May 3- prior to the Mets/Reds game. The cards feature blue and orange highlights like the team colors and are numbered according to uniform number. Two coupon cards were also included with each set.

		MT	NR MT	EX
Complete Set:		9.00	6.75	3.50
Common Player:		.20	.15	.08
1	Lou Thornton	.20	.15	.08
2	Mackey Sasser	.25	.20	.10
3	Bud Harrelson	.20	.15	.08
4	Mike Cubbage	.20	.15	.08
5	Davey Johnson	.20	.15	.08
6	Mike Marshall	.25	.20	.10
9	Gregg Jefferies	.80	.60	.30
10	Dave Magadan	.40	.30	.15
11	Tim Teufel	.20	.15	.08
13	Jeff Musselman	.20	.15	.08
15	Ron Darling	.30	.25	.12
16	Dwight Gooden	.80	.60	.30
18	Darryl Strawberry	1.00	.70	.40
19	Bob Ojeda	.20	.15	.08
20	Howard Johnson	.50	.40	.20
21	Kevin Elster	.25	.20	.10
22	Kevin McReynolds	.40	.30	.15
25	Keith Miller	.25	.20	.10

		MT	NR MT	EX
26	Alejandro Pena	.20	.15	.08
27	Tom O'Malley	.20	.15	.08
29	Frank Viola	.80	.60	.30
30	Mel Stottlemyre	.20	.15	.08
31	John Franco	.40	.30	.15
32	Doc Edwards	.20	.15	.08
33	Barry Lyons	.20	.15	.08
35	Orlando Mercado	.20	.15	.08
40	Jeff Innis	.25	.20	.15
44	David Cone	.40	.30	.15
45	Mark Carreon	.30	.25	.12
47	Wally Whitehurst	.30	.25	.12
48	Julio Machado	.30	.25	.12
50	Sid Fernandez	.35	.25	.14
52	Greg Pavlick	.20	.15	.08
----	Team Card	.20	.15	.08

Values quoted in this guide reflect the retail price of a card — the price a collector can expect to pay when buying a card from a dealer — the wholesale price — that which a collector can expect to receive from a dealer when selling cards — will be significantly lower, depending on desirability and condition.

1990 Kahn's Wieners Reds

This 27-card set marks the fourth consecutive year in which Kahn's released a modern Reds issue. The cards feature full-color photos, red and white borders and the player's name, number, and postion on the card front. The flip sides feature biographical information, statistics, a posed photo and the Kahn's logo. The set is numbered by uniform.

		MT	NR MT	EX
Complete Set:		10.00	7.50	4.00
Common Player:		.25	.20	.10
7	Mariano Duncan	.40	.30	.15
9	Joe Oliver	.40	.30	.15
10	Luis Quinones	.25	.20	.10
11	Barry Larkin	.80	.60	.30
15	Glenn Braggs	.30	.25	.12
16	Ron Oester	.25	.20	.10
17	Chris Sabo	.70	.50	.30
20	Danny Jackson	.30	.25	.12
21	Paul O'Neill	.40	.30	.15
22	Billy Hatcher	.25	.20	.10
23	Hal Morris	.80	.60	.30
25	Todd Benzinger	.30	.25	.12
27	Jose Rijo	.50	.40	.20
28	Randy Myers	.35	.25	.14
29	Herm Winningham	.25	.20	.10
30	Ken Griffey	.40	.30	.15
32	Tom Browning	.40	.30	.15
34	Jeff Reed	.25	.20	.10
37	Norm Charlton	.40	.30	.15
40	Jack Armstrong	.40	.30	.15
41	Lou Pinella	.40	.30	.15
42	Rick Mahler	.25	.20	.10
43	Tim Layana	.30	.25	.12
44	Eric Davis	1.00	.70	.40
48	Tim Birtsas	.25	.20	.10
49	Rob Dibble	.50	.40	.20
----	Reds Coaches	.25	.20	.10

1991 Kahn's Mets

Kahn's kept its tradition in 1991 with the release of this 33-card set featuring members of the New York Mets. The cards measure 2 1/2" by 3 1/2" and the fronts feature pinstripe design. The backs are printed horizontally and feature complete statistics. The

Values for recent cards and sets are listed in Mint (MT), Near Mint (NM) and Excellent (EX), reflecting the fact that many cards from recent years have been preserved in top condition. Recent cards and sets in less than Excellent condition have little collector interest.

cards are numbered according to uniform number. The complete set was distributed at a 1991 home game.

		MT	NR MT	EX
Complete Set:		8.00	6.00	3.25
Common Player:		.20	.15	.08
1	Vince Coleman	.50	.40	.20
2	Mackey Sasser	.20	.15	.08
3	Bud Harrelson	.20	.15	.08
4	Mike Cubbage	.20	.15	.08
5	Charlie O'Brien	.20	.15	.08
7	Hubie Brooks	.30	.25	.12
8	Daryl Boston	.20	.15	.08
9	Gregg Jefferies	.60	.45	.25
10	Dave Magadan	.30	.25	.12
11	Tim Teufel	.20	.15	.08
13	Rick Cerone	.20	.15	.08
15	Ron Darling	.25	.20	.10
16	Dwight Gooden	.60	.45	.25
17	David Cone	.50	.40	.20
20	Howard Johnson	.50	.40	.20
21	Kevin Elster	.20	.15	.08
22	Kevin McReynolds	.35	.25	.14
25	Keith Miller	.25	.20	.10
26	Alejandro Pena	.25	.20	.10
28	Tom Herr	.20	.15	.08
29	Frank Viola	.50	.40	.20
30	Mel Stottlemyre	.20	.15	.08
31	John Franco	.30	.25	.12
32	Doc Edwards	.20	.15	.08
40	Jeff Innis	.20	.15	.08
43	Doug Simons	.20	.15	.08
45	Mark Carreon	.20	.15	.08
47	Wally Whitehurst	.20	.15	.08
48	Pete Schourek	.20	.15	.08
50	Sid Fernandez	.30	.25	.12
51	Tom Spencer	.20	.15	.08
52	Greg Pavlick	.20	.15	.08
----	Team card	.20	.15	.08

1991 Kahn's Wieners Reds

The World Champion Cincinnati Reds are showcased in this 28-card set. The card fronts feature small full-color action photos on white stock. The backs feature statistics, biographical information and the Kahn's logo. A special card of Schottzie is included in this set.

		MT	NR MT	EX
Complete Set:		8.00	6.00	3.25
Common Player:		.25	.20	.10
	Schottzie	.25	.20	.10
7	Mariano Duncan	.30	.25	.12
9	Joe Oliver	.30	.25	.12
10	Luis Quinones	.25	.20	.10
11	Barry Larkin	.80	.60	.30
15	Glenn Braggs	.30	.25	.12
17	Chris Sabo	.60	.45	.25
19	Bill Doran	.35	.25	.14
21	Paul O'Neill	.40	.30	.15
22	Billy Hatcher	.25	.20	.10
23	Hal Morris	.80	.60	.30
25	Todd Benzinger	.30	.25	.12
27	Jose Rijo	.40	.30	.15
28	Randy Myers	.35	.25	.14
29	Herm Winningham	.25	.20	.10
32	Tom Browning	.35	.25	.14
34	Jeff Reed	.25	.20	.10
36	Don Carman	.25	.20	.10
37	Norm Charlton	.30	.25	.12
40	Jack Armstrong	.35	.25	.14
41	Lou Pinella	.35	.25	.14
44	Eric Davis	.80	.60	.30
45	Chris Hammond	.40	.30	.15
47	Scott Scudder	.30	.25	.12
48	Ted Power	.25	.20	.10
49	Rob Dibble	.50	.40	.20
57	Freddie Benavides	.40	.30	.15
-----	Reds Coaches	.25	.20	.10

1986 Kay Bee

One of the most-widely distributed of the specialty boxed sets of 1986, the Kay Bee toy store chain sets of "Young Superstars of Baseball" was produced by Topps. The 2-1/2" by 3-1/2" cards are printed on white stock with a glossy surface finish. Backs, printed in red and black, are strongly reminiscent of the 1971 Topps cards. While the set concentrated on "young" stars of the game, few of the year's top rookies were included.

		MT	NR MT	EX
Complete Set:		4.00	3.00	1.50
Common Player:		.05	.04	.02
1	Rick Aguilera	.12	.09	.05
2	Chris Brown	.15	.11	.06
3	Tom Browning	.07	.05	.03
4	Tom Brunansky	.07	.05	.03
5	Vince Coleman	.25	.20	.10
6	Ron Darling	.10	.08	.04
7	Alvin Davis	.10	.08	.04
8	Mariano Duncan	.07	.05	.03
9	Shawon Dunston	.07	.05	.03
10	Sid Fernandez	.10	.08	.04
11	Tony Fernandez	.10	.08	.04
12	Brian Fisher	.10	.08	.04
13	John Franco	.07	.05	.03
14	Julio Franco	.10	.08	.04
15	Dwight Gooden	.50	.40	.20
16	Ozzie Guillen	.15	.11	.06
17	Tony Gwynn	.30	.25	.12
18	Jimmy Key	.10	.08	.04
19	Don Mattingly	.80	.60	.30
20	Oddibe McDowell	.15	.11	.06

		MT	NR MT	EX
21	Roger McDowell	.15	.11	.06
22	Dan Pasqua	.10	.08	.04
23	Terry Pendleton	.07	.05	.03
24	Jim Presley	.10	.08	.04
25	Kirby Puckett	.25	.20	.10
26	Earnie Riles	.07	.05	.03
27	Bret Saberhagen	.15	.11	.06
28	Mark Salas	.05	.04	.02
29	Juan Samuel	.12	.09	.05
30	Jeff Stone	.05	.04	.02
31	Darryl Strawberry	.40	.30	.15
32	Andy Van Slyke	.10	.08	.04
33	Frank Viola	.12	.09	.05

1987 Kay Bee

For a second straight year, Topps produced a 33-card set for the Kay Bee toy store chain. Called "Superstars of Baseball," the cards in the set measure the standard 2-1/2" by 3-1/2" size. The glossy-coated card fronts carry a full-color player photo plus the Kay Bee logo. The card backs, reminiscent of those found in the 1971 Topps set, offer a black and white head shot of the player along with his name, postion, personal information, playing record and a brief biography. The set was packaged in a specially designed box.

		MT	NR MT	EX
Complete Set:		4.00	3.00	1.50
Common Player:		.05	.04	.02
1	Harold Baines	.10	.08	.04
2	Jesse Barfield	.12	.09	.05
3	Don Baylor	.10	.08	.04
4	Wade Boggs	1.00	.70	.40
5	George Brett	.40	.30	.15
6	Hubie Brooks	.07	.05	.03
7	Jose Canseco	1.00	.70	.40
8	Gary Carter	.20	.15	.08
9	Joe Carter	.12	.09	.05
10	Roger Clemens	.40	.30	.15
11	Vince Coleman	.15	.11	.06
12	Glenn Davis	.15	.11	.06
13	Dwight Gooden	.40	.30	.15
14	Pedro Guerrero	.15	.11	.06
15	Tony Gwynn	.25	.20	.10
16	Rickey Henderson	.25	.20	.10
17	Keith Hernandez	.20	.15	.08
18	Wally Joyner	.50	.40	.20
19	Don Mattingly	.80	.60	.30
20	Jack Morris	.15	.11	.06
21	Dale Murphy	.30	.25	.12
22	Eddie Murray	.25	.20	.10
23	Dave Parker	.15	.11	.06
24	Kirby Puckett	.25	.20	.10
25	Tim Raines	.25	.20	.10
26	Jim Rice	.25	.20	.10
27	Dave Righetti	.12	.09	.05
28	Ryne Sandberg	.40	.30	.15
29	Mike Schmidt	.30	.25	.12
30	Mike Scott	.12	.09	.05
31	Darryl Strawberry	.40	.30	.15
32	Fernando Valenzuela	.20	.15	.08
33	Dave Winfield	.20	.15	.08

1988 Kay Bee Superstars Of Baseball

This 33-card boxed set was produced by Topps for exclusive distribution via Kay Bee toy stores nationwide. Card fronts are super glossy and feature full-color player action photos below a bright red and yellow player name banner. Photos are framed in green above a large, cartoon-style Kay Bee logo. Card backs feature player closeups in a horizontal layout in blue ink on a green and white background. Card backs are numbered and carry a player name section that includes biographical information, career data and major league batting stats.

		MT	NR MT	EX
Complete Set:		4.00	3.00	1.50
Common Player:		.10	.08	.04
1	George Bell	.20	.15	.08
2	Wade Boggs	.60	.45	.25
3	Jose Canseco	1.00	.70	.40
4	Joe Carter	.12	.09	.05
5	Jack Clark	.15	.11	.06
6	Alvin Davis	.10	.08	.04
7	Eric Davis	.80	.60	.30
8	Andre Dawson	.15	.11	.06
9	Darrell Evans	.10	.08	.04
10	Dwight Evans	.10	.08	.04
11	Gary Gaetti	.12	.09	.05
12	Pedro Guerrero	.15	.11	.06
13	Tony Gwynn	.25	.20	.10
14	Howard Johnson	.12	.09	.05
15	Wally Joyner	.30	.25	.12
16	Don Mattingly	1.00	.70	.40
17	Willie McGee	.10	.08	.04
18	Mark McGwire	.60	.45	.25
19	Paul Molitor	.12	.09	.05
20	Dale Murphy	.30	.25	.12
21	Dave Parker	.15	.11	.06
22	Lance Parrish	.15	.11	.06
23	Kirby Puckett	.25	.20	.10
24	Tim Raines	.25	.20	.10
25	Cal Ripken	.50	.40	.20
26	Juan Samuel	.12	.09	.05
27	Mike Schmidt	.30	.25	.12
28	Ruben Sierra	.12	.09	.05
29	Darryl Strawberry	.40	.30	.15
30	Danny Tartabull	.12	.09	.05
31	Alan Trammell	.15	.11	.06
32	Tim Wallach	.10	.08	.04
33	Dave Winfield	.20	.15	.08

1988 Kay Bee Team Leaders

This first-year boxed edition of 44 player and 6 team logo cards was produced by Fleer for distribution by Kay Bee toy stores nationwide. Full-color player photos are framed in black against a bright red border. Lettering is blue, yellow and black. The "Fleer Team Leaders 1988" logo is printed vertically along the left side of the card front; the Kay Bee logo appears in the lower right corner of the photo; player's name, team and position are centered in the bottom margin. Card backs (red, white and pink) repeat the Team Leaders logo, followed by stats, personal data, team and major league baseball logos. The player's name, card number and position are listed on the lower border. The set includes six team logo sticker cards that feature black and white stadium photos on the backs.

		MT	NR MT	EX
Complete Set:		4.00	3.00	1.50
Common Player:		.05	.04	.02
1	George Bell	.20	.15	.08
2	Wade Boggs	.60	.45	.25
3	Jose Canseco	1.00	.70	.40
4	Will Clark	.25	.20	.10
5	Roger Clemens	.40	.30	.15
6	Eric Davis	.80	.60	.30
7	Andre Dawson	.15	.11	.06
8	Julio Franco	.07	.05	.03
9	Andres Galarraga	.15	.11	.06
10	Dwight Gooden	.40	.30	.15
11	Tony Gwynn	.25	.20	.10
12	Tom Henke	.05	.04	.02
13	Orel Hershiser	.10	.08	.04
14	Kent Hrbek	.15	.11	.06
15	Ted Higuera	.10	.08	.04
16	Wally Joyner	.30	.25	.12
17	Jimmy Key	.07	.05	.03
18	Mark Langston	.10	.08	.04
19	Don Mattingly	1.00	.70	.40
20	Willie McGee	.10	.08	.04
21	Mark McGwire	.60	.45	.25
22	Paul Molitor	.12	.09	.05
23	Jack Morris	.12	.09	.05
24	Dale Murphy	.30	.25	.12
25	Larry Parrish	.05	.04	.02
26	Kirby Puckett	.20	.15	.08
27	Tim Raines	.20	.15	.08
28	Jeff Reardon	.07	.05	.03
29	Dave Righetti	.12	.09	.05
30	Cal Ripken, Jr.	.50	.40	.20
31	Don Robinson	.05	.04	.02
32	Bret Saberhagen	.15	.11	.06
33	Juan Samuel	.12	.09	.05
34	Mike Schmidt	.30	.25	.12
35	Mike Scott	.12	.09	.05
36	Kevin Seitzer	.10	.08	.04
37	Dave Smith	.05	.04	.02
38	Ozzie Smith	.15	.11	.06
39	Zane Smith	.05	.04	.02
40	Darryl Strawberry	.40	.30	.15
41	Rick Sutcliffe	.10	.08	.04
42	Bobby Thigpen	.07	.05	.03
43	Alan Trammell	.15	.11	.06
44	Andy Van Slyke	.10	.08	.04

1989 Kay-Bee Superstars

The top stars of baseball were featured in this 33-card boxed set produced by Topps for the Kay-Bee Toy store chain. The glossy, standard-size cards display the Kay-Bee logo below the player photo on the front. The top of the card is headlined

"Superstars of Baseball," with the player's name underneath. The backs of the cards include a small black-and-white player photo and personal data.

		MT	NR MT	EX
Complete Set:		5.00	3.75	2.00
Common Player:		.10	.08	.04
1	Wade Boggs	.50	.40	.20
2	George Brett	.15	.11	.08
3	Jose Canseco	1.00	.70	.40
4	Gary Carter	.10	.08	.04
5	Jack Clark	.10	.08	.04
6	Will Clark	1.00	.70	.40
7	Roger Clemens	.50	.40	.20
8	Eric Davis	.40	.30	.15
9	Andre Dawson	.15	.11	.06
10	Dwight Evans	.10	.08	.04
11	Carlton Fisk	.15	.11	.06
12	Andres Galarraga	.10	.08	.04
13	Kirk Gibson	.10	.08	.04
14	Doc Gooden	.30	.25	.12
15	Mike Greenwell	.30	.25	.12
16	Pedro Guerrero	.15	.11	.08
17	Tony Gwynn	.25	.20	.10
18	Rickey Henderson	.50	.40	.20
19	Orel Hershiser	.15	.11	.06
20	Don Mattingly	.80	.60	.30
21	Mark McGwire	.40	.30	.15
22	Dale Murphy	.20	.15	.08
23	Eddie Murray	.15	.11	.06
24	Kirby Puckett	.25	.20	.10
25	Rock Raines	.15	.11	.06
26	Ryne Sanberg	.40	.30	.15
27	Mike Schmidt	.30	.25	.12
28	Ozzie Smith	.20	.15	.08
29	Darryl Strawberry	.30	.25	.12
30	Alan Trammell	.12	.09	.05
31	Frank Viola	.12	.09	.05
32	Dave Winfield	.12	.09	.05
33	Robin Yount	.20	.15	.08

1990 Kay Bee Kings of Baseball

This 33-card set marked the fifth straight produced by Topps for the Kay Bee store chain. The standard sized cards feature full-color action photos on the card fronts and complete statistics on the flip sides. The cards were numbered alphabetically.

		MT	NR MT	EX
Complete Set:		5.00	3.75	2.00
Common Player:		.08	.06	.03
1	Doyle Alexander	.08	.06	.03
2	Bert Blyleven	.12	.09	.05
3	Wade Boggs	.40	.30	.15
4	George Brett	.40	.30	.15
5	John Candelaria	.08	.06	.03
6	Gary Carter	.20	.15	.08
7	Vince Coleman	.20	.15	.08
8	Andre Dawson	.40	.30	.15
9	Dennis Eckersley	.40	.30	.15
10	Darrell Evans	.08	.06	.03
11	Dwight Evans	.10	.08	.04
12	Carlton Fisk	.20	.15	.08
13	Ken Griffey	.15	.11	.06
14	Tony Gwynn	.40	.30	.15
15	Rickey Henderson	.40	.30	.15
16	Keith Hernandez	.10	.08	.04
17	Charlie Hough	.08	.06	.03
18	Don Mattingly	.40	.30	.15
19	Jack Morris	.15	.11	.06
20	Dale Murphy	.15	.11	.06
21	Eddie Murray	.20	.15	.08
22	Dave Parker	.15	.11	.06
23	Kirby Puckett	.40	.30	.15
24	Tim Raines	.15	.11	.06
25	Rick Reuschel	.08	.06	.03
26	Jerry Reuss	.08	.06	.03
27	Jim Rice	.12	.09	.05
28	Nolan Ryan	1.00	.70	.40
29	Ozzie Smith	.20	.15	.08
30	Frank Tanana	.08	.06	.03
31	Willie Wilson	.08	.06	.03
32	Dave Winfield	.30	.25	.12
33	Robin Yount	.30	.25	.12

1970 Kellogg's

For 14 years in the 1970s and early 1980s, the Kellogg's cereal company provided Topps with virtually the only meaningful national competition in the baseball card market. Kellogg's kicked off its baseball card program in 1970 with a 75-player set of simulated 3-D cards. Single cards were available in selected brands of the company's cereal, while a mail-in program offered complete sets. The 3-D effect was achieved by the sandwiching of a clear color player photo between a purposely blurred stadium background scene and a layer of ribbed plastic. The relatively narrow dimension of the card, 2-1/4" by 3-1/2" and the nature of the plastic overlay seem to conspire to cause the cards to curl, often cracking the plastic layer, if not stored properly. Cards with major cracks in the plastic can be considered in Fair condition, at best.

		NR MT	EX	VG
Complete Set:		175.00	87.00	52.00
Common Player: 1-15		.90	.45	.25
Common Player: 16-30		1.00	.50	.30
Common Player: 31-75		.90	.45	.25
1	Ed Kranepool	1.50	.70	.45
2	Pete Rose	20.00	10.00	6.00

		NR MT	EX	VG
3	Cleon Jones	.90	.45	.25
4	Willie McCovey	3.50	1.75	1.00
5	Mel Stottlemyre	1.00	.50	.30
6	Frank Howard	1.25	.60	.40
7	Tom Seaver	10.00	5.00	3.00
8	Don Sutton	2.50	1.25	.70
9	Jim Wynn	.90	.45	.25
10	Jim Maloney	.90	.45	.25
11	Tommie Agee	.90	.45	.25
12	Willie Mays	10.00	5.00	3.00
13	Juan Marichal	3.00	1.50	.90
14	Dave McNally	1.00	.50	.30
15	Frank Robinson	3.50	1.75	1.00
16	Carlos May	1.00	.50	.30
17	Bill Singer	1.00	.50	.30
18	Rick Reichardt	1.00	.50	.30
19	Boog Powell	1.50	.70	.45
20	Gaylord Perry	3.50	1.75	1.00
21	Brooks Robinson	6.00	3.00	1.75
22	Luis Aparicio	3.50	1.75	1.00
23	Joel Horlen	1.00	.50	.30
24	Mike Epstein	1.00	.50	.30
25	Tom Haller	1.00	.50	.30
26	Willie Crawford	1.00	.50	.30
27	Roberto Clemente	10.00	5.00	3.00
28	Matty Alou	1.25	.60	.40
29	Willie Stargell	4.00	2.00	1.25
30	Tim Cullen	1.00	.50	.30
31	Randy Hundley	.90	.45	.25
32	Reggie Jackson	10.00	5.00	3.00
33	Rich Allen	1.25	.60	.40
34	Tim McCarver	1.00	.50	.30
35	Ray Culp	.90	.45	.25
36	Jim Fregosi	1.00	.50	.30
37	Billy Williams	3.00	1.50	.90
38	Johnny Odom	.90	.45	.25
39	Bert Campaneris	1.00	.50	.30
40	Ernie Banks	3.50	1.75	1.00
41	Chris Short	.90	.45	.25
42	Ron Santo	1.00	.50	.30
43	Glenn Beckert	.90	.45	.25
44	Lou Brock	3.50	1.75	1.00
45	Larry Hisle	.90	.45	.25
46	Reggie Smith	1.00	.50	.30
47	Rod Carew	4.00	2.00	1.25
48	Curt Flood	1.00	.50	.30
49	Jim Lonborg	.90	.45	.25
50	Sam McDowell	1.00	.50	.30
51	Sal Bando	1.00	.50	.30
52	Al Kaline	4.00	2.00	1.25
53	Gary Nolan	.90	.45	.25
54	Rico Petrocelli	.90	.45	.25
55	Ollie Brown	.90	.45	.25
56	Luis Tiant	1.25	.60	.40
57	Bill Freehan	1.00	.50	.30
58	Johnny Bench	10.00	5.00	3.00
59	Joe Pepitone	1.00	.50	.30
60	Bobby Murcer	1.00	.50	.30
61	Harmon Killebrew	3.50	1.75	1.00
62	Don Wilson	.90	.45	.25
63	Tony Oliva	1.25	.60	.40
64	Jim Perry	1.00	.50	.30
65	Mickey Lolich	1.25	.60	.40
66	Coco Laboy	.90	.45	.25
67	Dean Chance	.90	.45	.25
68	Ken Harrelson	1.00	.50	.30
69	Willie Horton	1.00	.50	.30
70	Wally Bunker	.90	.45	.25
71a	Bob Gibson (1959 IP blank)	5.00	2.50	1.50
71b	Bob Gibson (1959 IP 76)	3.00	1.50	.90
72	Joe Morgan	3.00	1.50	.90
73	Denny McLain	1.25	.60	.40
74	Tommy Harper	.90	.45	.25
75	Don Mincher	1.25	.60	.40

1971 Kellogg's

The scarcest and most valuable of the Kellogg's editions, the 75-card 1971 set was the only one not offered by the company on a mail-in basis; the only way to complete it was to buy ... and buy and buy ... boxes of cereal. Kellogg's again used the simulated 3-D effect in the cards' design, with the same result being many of the 2-1/4" by 3-1/2" cards are found today with cracks resulting from the cards' curling. A number of scarcer back variations are checklisted below. In addition, all 75 cards can be found with and

without the 1970 date before the "Xograph" copyright line on the back; though there is no difference in value.

		NR MT	EX	VG
Complete Set:		850.00	425.00	255.00
Common Player:		8.00	4.00	2.50
1a	Wayne Simpson (SO 120)	12.00	6.00	3.50
1b	Wayne Simpson (SO 119)	15.00	7.50	4.50
2	Tom Seaver	30.00	15.00	9.00
3a	Jim Perry (IP 2238)	10.00	5.00	3.00
3b	Jim Perry (IP 2239)	15.00	7.50	4.50
4a	Bob Robertson (RBI 94)	8.00	4.00	2.50
4b	Bob Robertson (RBI 95)	12.00	6.00	3.50
5	Roberto Clemente	35.00	17.50	10.50
6a	Gaylord Perry (IP 2014)	15.00	7.50	4.50
6b	Gaylord Perry (IP 2015)	20.00	10.00	6.00
7a	Felipe Alou (1970 Oakland NL)	15.00	7.50	4.50
7b	Felipe Alou (1970 Oakland AL)	10.00	5.00	3.00
8	Denis Menke	8.00	4.00	2.50
9a	Don Kessinger (Hits 849)	10.00	5.00	3.00
9b	Don Kessinger (Hits 850)	15.00	7.50	4.50
10	Willie Mays	35.00	17.50	10.50
11	Jim Hickman	8.00	4.00	2.50
12	Tony Oliva	12.00	6.00	3.50
13	Manny Sanguillen	8.00	4.00	2.50
14a	Frank Howard (1968 Washington NL)	18.00	9.00	5.50
14b	Frank Howard (1968 Washington AL)	12.00	6.00	3.50
15	Frank Robinson	25.00	12.50	7.50
16	Willie Davis	10.00	5.00	3.00
17	Lou Brock	20.00	10.00	6.00
18	Cesar Tovar	8.00	4.00	2.50
19	Luis Aparicio	15.00	7.50	4.50
20	Boog Powell	12.00	6.00	3.50
21a	Dick Selma (SO 584)	8.00	4.00	2.50
21b	Dick Selma (SO 587)	12.00	6.00	3.50
22	Danny Walton	8.00	4.00	2.50
23	Carl Morton	8.00	4.00	2.50
24a	Sonny Siebert (SO 1054)	8.00	4.00	2.50
24b	Sonny Siebert (SO 1055)	12.00	6.00	3.50
25	Jim Merritt	8.00	4.00	2.50
26a	Jose Cardenal (Hits 828)	8.00	4.00	2.50
26b	Jose Cardenal (Hits 829)	12.00	6.00	3.50
27	Don Mincher	8.00	4.00	2.50
28a	Clyde Wright (California state logo)	8.00	4.00	2.50
28b	Clyde Wright (Angels crest logo)	12.00	6.00	3.50
29	Les Cain	8.00	4.00	2.50
30	Danny Cater	8.00	4.00	2.50
31	Don Sutton	15.00	7.50	4.50
32	Chuck Dobson	8.00	4.00	2.50
33	Willie McCovey	20.00	10.00	6.00
34	Mike Epstein	8.00	4.00	2.50
35a	Paul Blair (Runs 386)	8.00	4.00	2.50
35b	Paul Blair (Runs 385)	12.00	6.00	3.50
36a	Gary Nolan (SO 577)	8.00	4.00	2.50
36b	Gary Nolan (SO 581)	12.00	6.00	3.50
37	Sam McDowell	10.00	5.00	3.00
38	Amos Otis	10.00	5.00	3.00
39a	Ray Fosse (RBI 69)	8.00	4.00	2.50
39b	Ray Fosse (RBI 70)	12.00	6.00	3.50
40	Mel Stottlenger	10.00	5.00	3.00
41	Cito Gaston	8.00	4.00	2.50
42	Dick Dietz	8.00	4.00	2.50
43	Roy White	10.00	5.00	3.00
44	Al Kaline	25.00	12.50	7.50
45	Carlos May	8.00	4.00	2.50
46a	Tommie Agee (RBI 313)	8.00	4.00	2.50

		NR MT	EX	VG
46b	Tommie Agee (RBI 314)	12.00	6.00	3.50
47	Tommy Harper	8.00	4.00	2.50
48	Larry Dierker	8.00	4.00	2.50
49	Mike Cuellar	10.00	5.00	3.00
50	Ernie Banks	25.00	12.50	7.50
51	Bob Gibson	20.00	10.00	6.00
52	Reggie Smith	10.00	5.00	3.00
53a	Matty Alou (RBI 273)	10.00	5.00	3.00
53b	Matty Alou (RBI 274)	15.00	7.50	4.50
54a	Alex Johnson (California state logo)	8.00	4.00	2.50
54b	Alex Johnson (Angels crest logo)	12.00	6.00	3.50
55	Harmon Killebrew	20.00	10.00	6.00
56	Billy Grabarkewitz	8.00	4.00	2.50
57	Rich Allen	12.00	6.00	3.50
58	Tony Perez	15.00	7.50	4.50
59a	Dave McNally (SO 1065)	10.00	5.00	3.00
59b	Dave McNally (SO 1067)	15.00	7.50	4.50
60a	Jim Palmer (SO 564)	15.00	7.50	4.50
60b	Jim Palmer (SO 567)	20.00	10.00	6.00
61	Billy Williams	15.00	7.50	4.50
62	Joe Torre	12.00	6.00	3.50
63a	Jim Northrup (AB 2773)	8.00	4.00	2.50
63b	Jim Northrup (AB 2772)	12.00	6.00	3.50
64a	Jim Fregosi (Calif. state logo - Hits 1326)	8.00	4.00	2.50
64b	Jim Fregosi (Calif. state logo - Hits 1327)	12.00	6.00	3.50
64c	Jim Fregosi (Angels crest logo)	12.00	6.00	3.50
65	Pete Rose	75.00	37.00	22.00
66a	Bud Harrelson (RBI 112)	8.00	4.00	2.50
66b	Bud Harrelson (RBI 113)	12.00	6.00	3.50
67	Tony Taylor	8.00	4.00	2.50
68	Willie Stargell	20.00	10.00	6.00
69	Tony Horton	8.50	4.25	2.50
70a	Claude Osteen (no number)	20.00	10.00	6.00
70b	Claude Osteen (#70 on back)	8.00	4.00	2.50
71	Glenn Beckert	10.00	5.00	3.00
72	Nate Colbert	8.00	4.00	2.50
73a	Rick Monday (AB 1705)	10.00	5.00	3.00
73b	Rick Monday (AB 1704)	15.00	7.50	4.50
74a	Tommy John (BB 444)	15.00	7.50	4.50
74b	Tommy John (BB 443)	20.00	10.00	6.00
75	Chris Short	12.00	6.00	3.50

1972 Kellogg's

For 1972, Kellogg's reduced both the number of cards in its set and the dimensions of each card, moving to a 2-1/8" by 3-1/4" size and fixing the set at 54 cards. Once again, the cards were produced to simulate a 3-D effect (see description for 1970 Kellogg's). The set was available via a mail-in offer. The checklist includes variations which resulted from the correction of erroneous statistics on the backs of some cards. The complete set values quoted do not include the scarcer variations.

		NR MT	EX	VG
Complete Set:		75.00	37.00	22.00
Common Player:		.70	.35	.20
1a	Tom Seaver (1970 ERA 2.85)	9.00	4.50	2.75
1b	Tom Seaver (1970 ERA 2.81)	6.50	3.25	2.00
2	Amos Otis	.80	.40	.25
3a	Willie Davis (Runs 842)	1.25	.60	.40
3b	Willie Davis (Runs 841)	.80	.40	.25

		NR MT	EX	VG
4	Wilbur Wood	.80	.40	.25
5	Bill Parsons	.70	.35	.20
6	Pete Rose	20.00	10.00	6.00
7a	Willie McCovey (HR 360)	5.00	2.50	1.50
7b	Willie McCovey (HR 370)	3.50	1.75	1.00
8	Fergie Jenkins	1.25	.60	.40
9a	Vida Blue (ERA 2.35)	1.50	.70	.45
9b	Vida Blue (ERA 2.31)	.90	.45	.25
10	Joe Torre	.90	.45	.25
11	Merv Rettenmund	.70	.35	.20
12	Bill Melton	.70	.35	.20
13a	Jim Palmer (Games 170)	4.75	2.50	1.50
13b	Jim Palmer (Games 168)	3.00	1.50	.90
14	Doug Rader	.70	.35	.20
15a	Dave Roberts (...Seaver, the NL leader...)	1.25	.60	.40
15b	Dave Roberts (...Seaver, the league leader...)	.70	.35	.20
16	Bobby Murcer	.80	.40	.25
17	Wes Parker	.70	.35	.20
18a	Joe Coleman (BB 394)	1.25	.60	.40
18b	Joe Coleman (BB 393)	.70	.35	.20
19	Manny Sanguillen	.70	.35	.20
20	Reggie Jackson	8.00	4.00	2.50
21	Ralph Garr	.70	.35	.20
22	Jim "Catfish" Hunter	2.50	1.25	.70
23	Rick Wise	.70	.35	.20
24	Glenn Beckert	.70	.35	.20
25	Tony Oliva	.90	.45	.25
26a	Bob Gibson (SO 2577)	4.75	2.50	1.50
26b	Bob Gibson (SO 2578)	3.00	1.50	.90
27a	Mike Cuellar (1971 ERA 3.80)	1.25	.60	.40
27b	Mike Cuellar (1971 ERA 3.08)	.80	.40	.25
28	Chris Speier	.70	.35	.20
29a	Dave McNally (ERA 3.18)	1.25	.60	.40
29b	Dave McNally (ERA 3.15)	.80	.40	.25
30	Chico Cardenas	.70	.35	.20
31a	Bill Freehan (AVG. .263)	1.25	.60	.40
31b	Bill Freehan (AVG. .262)	.80	.40	.25
32a	Bud Harrelson (Hits 634)	1.25	.60	.40
32b	Bud Harrelson (Hits 624)	.70	.35	.20
33a	Sam McDowell (...less than 200 innings...)	1.25	.60	.40
33b	Sam McDowell (...less than 225 innings...)	.80	.40	.25
34a	Claude Osteen (1971 ERA 3.25)	1.25	.60	.40
34b	Claude Osteen (1971 ERA 3.51)	.70	.35	.20
35	Reggie Smith	.80	.40	.25
36	Sonny Siebert	.70	.35	.20
37	Lee May	.80	.40	.25
38	Mickey Lolich	.90	.45	.25
39a	Cookie Rojas (2B 149)	1.25	.60	.40
39b	Cookie Rojas (2B 150)	.70	.35	.20
40	Dick Drago	.70	.35	.20
41	Nate Colbert	.70	.35	.20
42	Andy Messersmith	.70	.35	.20
43a	Dave Johnson (AVG. .262)	1.50	.70	.45
43b	Dave Johnson (AVG. .264)	.90	.45	.25
44	Steve Blass	.70	.35	.20
45	Bob Robertson	.70	.35	.20
46a	Billy Williams (...missed only one last season...)	5.00	2.50	1.50
46b	Billy Williams (phrase omitted)	3.00	1.50	.90
47	Juan Marichal	3.00	1.50	.90
48	Lou Brock	3.50	1.75	1.00
49	Roberto Clemente	7.00	3.50	2.00
50	Mel Stottlemyre	.80	.40	.25
51	Don Wilson	.70	.35	.20
52a	Sal Bando (RBI 355)	1.25	.60	.40
52b	Sal Bando (RBI 356)	.80	.40	.25
53a	Willie Stargell (2B 197)	5.00	2.50	1.50
53b	Willie Stargell (2B 196)	3.00	1.50	.90
54a	Willie Mays (RBI 1855)	18.00	9.00	5.50
54b	Willie Mays (RBI 1856)	10.00	5.00	3.00

1972 Kellogg's
All-Time Baseball Greats

Kellogg's issued a second baseball card set in 1972, inserted into packages of breakfast rolls. The 2-1/4" by 3-1/2" cards also featured a simulated 3-D effect, but the 15 players in the set were "All-Time Baseball Greats", rather than current players. The set is virtually identical to a Rold Gold pretzel issue of 1970; the only difference being the 1972 copyright date on the back of the Kellog's cards, while the pretzel issue bears a 1970 date. The pretzel cards are considerably scarcer than the Kellogg's.

		NR MT	EX	VG
	Complete Set:	15.00	7.50	4.50
	Common Player:	.50	.25	.15
1	Walter Johnson	1.25	.60	.40
2	Rogers Hornsby	.80	.40	.25
3	John McGraw	.50	.25	.15
4	Mickey Cochrane	.50	.25	.15
5	George Sisler	.50	.25	.15
6	Babe Ruth	4.00	2.00	1.25
7	Robert "Lefty" Grove	.70	.35	.20
8	Harold "Pie" Traynor	.50	.25	.15
9	Honus Wagner	1.00	.50	.30
10	Eddie Collins	.50	.25	.15
11	Tris Speaker	.70	.35	.20
12	Cy Young	.80	.40	.25
13	Lou Gehrig	2.00	1.00	.60
14	Babe Ruth	4.00	2.00	1.25
15	Ty Cobb	2.00	1.00	.60

		NR MT	EX	VG
10	Billy Williams	2.50	1.25	.70
11	Steve Blass	.50	.25	.15
12	Jon Matlack	.50	.25	.15
13	Cesar Cedeno	.70	.35	.20
14	Bob Gibson	2.50	1.25	.70
15	Sparky Lyle	.60	.30	.20
16	Nolan Ryan	15.00	7.50	4.50
17	Jim Palmer	2.50	1.25	.70
18	Ray Fosse	.50	.25	.15
19	Bobby Murcer	.60	.30	.20
20	Jim "Catfish" Hunter	2.50	1.25	.70
21	Tug McGraw	.80	.40	.25
22	Reggie Jackson	7.00	3.50	2.00
23	Bill Stoneman	.50	.25	.15
24	Lou Piniella	.80	.40	.25
25	Willie Stargell	2.50	1.25	.70
26	Dick Allen	.90	.45	.25
27	Carlton Fisk	1.25	.60	.40
28	Fergie Jenkins	.90	.45	.25
29	Phil Niekro	1.50	.70	.45
30	Gary Nolan	.50	.25	.15
31	Joe Torre	.80	.40	.25
32	Bobby Tolan	.50	.25	.15
33	Nate Colbert	.50	.25	.15
34	Joe Morgan	2.50	1.25	.70
35	Bert Blyleven	.90	.45	.25
36	Joe Rudi	.60	.30	.20
37	Ralph Garr	.50	.25	.15
38	Gaylord Perry	2.00	1.00	.60
39	Bobby Grich	.60	.30	.20
40	Lou Brock	2.50	1.25	.70
41	Pete Broberg	.50	.25	.15
42	Manny Sanguillen	.50	.25	.15
43	Willie Davis	.60	.30	.20
44	Dave Kingman	.90	.45	.25
45	Carlos May	.50	.25	.15
46	Tom Seaver	4.00	2.00	1.25
47	Mike Cuellar	.60	.30	.20
48	Joe Coleman	.50	.25	.15
49	Claude Osteen	.50	.25	.15
50	Steve Kline	.50	.25	.15
51	Rod Carew	4.00	2.00	1.25
52	Al Kaline	5.00	2.50	1.50
53	Larry Dierker	.50	.25	.15
54	Ron Santo	.70	.35	.20

1973 Kellogg's

The lone exception to Kellogg's long run of simulated 3-D effect cards came in 1973, when the cereal company's 54-card set was produced by "normal" printing methods. In 2'1/4" by 3-1/2" size, the design was otherwise quite compatible with the issues which preceded and succeeded it. Because it was available via a mail-in offer, it is not as scarce as some other Kellogg's issues.

		NR MT	EX	VG
	Complete Set:	75.00	37.00	22.00
	Common Player:	.50	.25	.15
1	Amos Otis	.60	.30	.20
2	Ellie Rodriguez	.50	.25	.15
3	Mickey Lolich	.80	.40	.25
4	Tony Oliva	.80	.40	.25
5	Don Sutton	1.25	.60	.40
6	Pete Rose	11.00	5.50	3.25
7	Steve Carlton	4.00	2.00	1.25
8	Bobby Bonds	.70	.35	.20
9	Wilbur Wood	.60	.30	.20

1974 Kellogg's

For 1974, Kellogg's returned to the use of simulated 3-D for its 54-player baseball card issue (see 1970 Kellogg's listing for description). In 2-1/8" by 3-1/4" size, the cards were available as a complete set via a mail-in offer.

		NR MT	EX	VG
	Complete Set:	65.00	32.00	19.50
	Common Player:	.50	.25	.15
1	Bob Gibson	5.00	2.50	1.50
2	Rick Monday	.70	.35	.20
3	Joe Coleman	.50	.25	.15
4	Bert Campaneris	.70	.35	.20
5	Carlton Fisk	1.25	.60	.40
6	Jim Palmer	2.50	1.25	.70
7a	Ron Santo (Chicago Cubs)	1.50	.70	.45
7b	Ron Santo (Chicago White Sox)	.80	.40	.25
8	Nolan Ryan	10.00	5.00	3.00
9	Greg Luzinski	.80	.40	.25

		NR MT	EX	VG
10a	Buddy Bell (Runs 134)	1.50	.70	.45
10b	Buddy Bell (Runs 135)	.80	.40	.25
11	Bob Watson	.50	.25	.15
12	Bill Singer	.50	.25	.15
13	Dave May	.50	.25	.15
14	Jim Brewer	.50	.25	.15
15	Manny Sanguillen	.50	.25	.15
16	Jeff Burroughs	.50	.25	.15
17	Amos Otis	.50	.25	.15
18	Ed Goodson	.50	.25	.15
19	Nate Colbert	.50	.25	.15
20	Reggie Jackson	4.00	2.00	1.25
21	Ted Simmons	.90	.45	.25
22	Bobby Murcer	.60	.30	.20
23	Willie Horton	.60	.30	.20
24	Orlando Cepeda	1.25	.60	.40
25	Ron Hunt	.50	.25	.15
26	Wayne Twitchell	.50	.25	.15
27	Ron Fairly	.50	.25	.15
28	Johnny Bench	5.00	2.50	1.50
29	John Mayberry	.50	.25	.15
30	Rod Carew	5.00	2.50	1.50
31	Ken Holtzman	.50	.25	.15
32	Billy Williams	2.50	1.25	.70
33	Dick Allen	.80	.40	.25
34a	Wilbur Wood (SO 959)	1.25	.60	.40
34b	Wilbur Wood (SO 960)	.70	.35	.20
35	Danny Thompson	.50	.25	.15
36	Joe Morgan	2.50	1.25	.70
37	Willie Stargell	3.00	1.50	.90
38	Pete Rose	13.00	6.50	4.00
39	Bobby Bonds	.70	.35	.20
40	Chris Speier	.50	.25	.15
41	Sparky Lyle	.60	.30	.20
42	Cookie Rojas	.50	.25	.15
43	Tommy Davis	.60	.30	.20
44	Jim "Catfish" Hunter	2.50	1.25	.70
45	Willie Davis	.60	.30	.20
46	Bert Blyleven	.90	.45	.25
47	Pat Kelly	.50	.25	.15
48	Ken Singleton	.60	.30	.20
49	Manny Mota	.60	.30	.20
50	Dave Johnson	.90	.45	.25
51	Sal Bando	.60	.30	.20
52	Tom Seaver	5.00	2.50	1.50
53	Felix Millan	.50	.25	.15
54	Ron Blomberg	.80	.40	.25

		NR MT	EX	VG
4b	Bob Grich (no "...1973 work...")	2.50	1.25	.70
5	Greg Gross	2.00	1.00	.60
6	Bob Watson	2.00	1.00	.60
7	Johnny Bench	11.00	5.50	3.25
8	Jeff Burroughs	2.00	1.00	.60
9	Elliott Maddox	2.00	1.00	.60
10	Jon Matlack	2.00	1.00	.60
11	Pete Rose	24.00	12.00	7.25
12	Leroy Stanton	2.00	1.00	.60
13	Bake McBride	2.00	1.00	.60
14	Jorge Orta	2.00	1.00	.60
15	Al Oliver	2.50	1.25	.70
16	John Briggs	2.00	1.00	.60
17	Steve Garvey	9.00	4.50	2.75
18	Brooks Robinson	10.00	5.00	3.00
19	John Hiller	2.00	1.00	.60
20	Lynn McGlothen	2.00	1.00	.60
21	Cleon Jones	2.00	1.00	.60
22	Fergie Jenkins	2.50	1.25	.70
23	Bill North	2.00	1.00	.60
24	Steve Busby	2.00	1.00	.60
25	Richie Zisk	2.00	1.00	.60
26	Nolan Ryan	20.00	10.00	6.00
27	Joe Morgan	6.50	3.25	2.00
28	Joe Rudi	2.50	1.25	.70
29	Jose Cardenal	2.00	1.00	.60
30	Andy Messersmith	2.00	1.00	.60
31	Willie Montanez	2.00	1.00	.60
32	Bill Buckner	2.50	1.25	.70
33	Rod Carew	10.00	5.00	3.00
34	Lou Piniella	2.50	1.25	.70
35	Ralph Garr	2.00	1.00	.60
36	Mike Marshall	2.00	1.00	.60
37	Garry Maddox	2.00	1.00	.60
38	Dwight Evans	3.00	1.50	.90
39	Lou Brock	9.00	4.50	2.75
40	Ken Singleton	2.50	1.25	.70
41	Steve Braun	2.00	1.00	.60
42	Dick Allen	2.50	1.25	.70
43	Johnny Grubb	2.00	1.00	.60
44a	Jim Hunter (Oakland)	12.00	6.00	3.50
44b	Jim Hunter (New York)	8.00	4.00	2.50
45	Gaylord Perry	6.50	3.25	2.00
46	George Hendrick	2.00	1.00	.60
47	Sparky Lyle	2.50	1.25	.70
48	Dave Cash	2.00	1.00	.60
49	Luis Tiant	2.50	1.25	.70
50	Cesar Geronimo	2.00	1.00	.60
51	Carl Yastrzemski	16.00	8.00	4.75
52	Ken Brett	2.00	1.00	.60
53	Hal McRae	2.50	1.25	.70
54	Reggie Jackson	12.00	6.00	3.50
55	Rollie Fingers	3.50	1.75	1.00
56	Mike Schmidt	14.00	7.00	4.25
57	Richie Hebner	2.50	1.25	.70

1975 Kellogg's

While the card size remained the same at 2-1/8" by 3-1/4", the size of the 1975 Kellogg's "3-D" set was increased by three, to 57 cards. Despite the fact cards could be obtained by a mail-in offer, as well as in cereal boxes, the '75 Kellogg's are noticeably scarcer than the company's other issues, with the exception of the 1971 set. Also helping to raise the value of the cards is the presence of an unusually large number of current and future Hall of Famers.

		NR MT	EX	VG
Complete Set:		150.00	75.00	45.00
Common Player:		2.00	1.00	.60
1	Roy White	3.50	1.75	1.00
2	Ross Grimsley	2.00	1.00	.60
3	Reggie Smith	2.50	1.25	.70
4a	Bob Grich ("...1973 work..." in last line)	4.00	2.00	1.25

1976 Kellogg's

A sizeable list of corrected errors and other variation cards dots the checklist for the 57-card 1976 Kellogg's 3-D set. Again containing 57 cards, the first three cards in the set are found far less often than cards #4-57, indicating they were short-printed in relation to the rest of the set. The complete set values quoted below do not include the scarcer variation cards. Card size remained at 2-1/8" by 3-1/4".

		NR MT	EX	VG
	Complete Set:	80.00	40.00	24.00
	Common Player:	1.25	.60	.40
1	Steve Hargan	10.00	5.00	3.00
2	Claudell Washington	10.00	5.00	3.00
3	Don Gullett	10.00	5.00	3.00
4	Randy Jones	1.25	.60	.40
5	Jim "Catfish" Hunter	6.50	3.25	2.00
6a	Clay Carroll (Cincinnati)	3.00	1.50	.90
6b	Clay Carroll (Chicago)	1.50	.70	.45
7	Joe Rudi	1.50	.70	.45
8	Reggie Jackson	10.00	5.00	3.00
9	Felix Millan	1.25	.60	.40
10	Jim Rice	8.00	4.00	2.50
11	Bert Blyleven	2.50	1.25	.70
12	Ken Singleton	1.50	.70	.45
13	Don Sutton	2.50	1.25	.70
14	Joe Morgan	5.00	2.50	1.50
15	Dave Parker	4.00	2.00	1.25
16	Dave Cash	1.25	.60	.40
17	Ron LeFlore	1.25	.60	.40
18	Greg Luzinski	2.00	1.00	.60
19	Dennis Eckersley	2.25	1.25	.70
20	Bill Madlock	2.25	1.25	.70
21	George Scott	1.25	.60	.40
22	Willie Stargell	6.50	3.25	2.00
23	Al Hrabosky	1.25	.60	.40
24	Carl Yastrzemski	13.00	6.50	4.00
25	Jim Kaat	2.50	1.25	.70
26	Marty Perez	1.25	.60	.40
27	Bob Watson	1.25	.60	.40
28	Eric Soderholm	1.25	.60	.40
29	Bill Lee	1.25	.60	.40
30a	Frank Tanana (1975 ERA 2.63)	2.50	1.25	.70
30b	Frank Tanana (1975 ERA 2.62)	1.50	.70	.45
31	Fred Lynn	3.50	1.75	1.00
32a	Tom Seaver (1967 PCT. 552)	10.00	5.00	3.00
32b	Tom Seaver (1967 Pct. .552)	8.00	4.00	2.50
33	Steve Busby	1.25	.60	.40
34	Gary Carter	10.00	5.00	3.00
35	Rick Wise	1.25	.60	.40
36	Johnny Bench	10.00	5.00	3.00
37	Jim Palmer	8.00	4.00	2.50
38	Bobby Murcer	2.00	1.00	.60
39	Von Joshua	1.25	.60	.40
40	Lou Brock	8.00	4.00	2.50
41a	Mickey Rivers (last line begins "In three...")	2.75	1.50	.80
41b	Mickey Rivers (last line begins "The Yankees...")	1.25	.60	.40
42	Manny Sanguillen	1.25	.60	.40
43	Jerry Reuss	1.50	.70	.45
44	Ken Griffey	1.50	.70	.45
45a	Jorge Orta (AB 1616)	2.25	1.25	.70
45b	Jorge Orta (AB 1615)	1.25	.60	.40
46	John Mayberry	1.25	.60	.40
47a	Vida Blue (2nd line reads "...pitched more innings...")	3.00	1.50	.90
47b	Vida Blue (2nd line reads "...struck out more...")	2.00	1.00	.60
48	Rod Carew	10.00	5.00	3.00
49a	Jon Matlack (1975 ER 87)	2.25	1.25	.70
49b	Jon Matlack (1975 ER 86)	1.25	.60	.40
50	Boog Powell	2.50	1.25	.70
51a	Mike Hargrove (AB 935)	2.25	1.25	.70
51b	Mike Hargrove (AB 934)	1.25	.60	.40
52a	Paul Lindblad (1975 ERA 2.72)	2.25	1.25	.70
52b	Paul Lindblad (1975 ERA 2.73)	1.25	.60	.40
53	Thurman Munson	6.50	3.25	2.00
54	Steve Garvey	8.00	4.00	2.50
55	Pete Rose	18.00	9.00	5.50
56a	Greg Gross (Games 302)	2.25	1.25	.70
56b	Greg Gross (Games 334)	1.25	.60	.40
57	Ted Simmons	2.50	1.25	.70

		NR MT	EX	VG
	Complete Set:	55.00	28.00	16.50
	Common Player:	.40	.20	.12
1	George Foster	.90	.45	.25
2	Bert Campaneris	.60	.30	.20
3	Fergie Jenkins	.90	.45	.25
4	Dock Ellis	.40	.20	.12
5	John Montefusco	.40	.20	.12
6	George Brett	8.50	4.25	2.50
7	John Candelaria	.50	.25	.15
8	Fred Norman	.40	.20	.12
9	Bill Travers	.40	.20	.12
10	Hal McRae	.60	.30	.20
11	Doug Rau	.40	.20	.12
12	Greg Luzinski	.70	.35	.20
13	Ralph Garr	.40	.20	.12
14	Steve Garvey	4.50	2.25	1.25
15	Rick Manning	.40	.20	.12
16	Lyman Bostock	.50	.25	.15
17	Randy Jones	.40	.20	.12
18a	Ron Cey (58 homers in first sentence)	1.00	.50	.30
18b	Ron Cey (48 homers in first sentence)	.60	.30	.20
19	Dave Parker	1.25	.60	.40
20	Pete Rose	11.00	5.50	3.25
21a	Wayne Garland (last line begins "Prior to...")	.90	.45	.25
21b	Wayne Garland (last line begins "There he...")	.40	.20	.12
22	Bill North	.40	.20	.12
23	Thurman Munson	2.50	1.25	.70
24	Tom Poquette	.40	.20	.12
25	Ron LeFlore	.50	.25	.15
26	Mark Fidrych	.50	.25	.15
27	Sixto Lezcano	.40	.20	.12
28	Dave Winfield	4.00	2.00	1.25
29	Jerry Koosman	.50	.25	.15
30	Mike Hargrove	.40	.20	.12
31	Willie Montanez	.40	.20	.12
32	Don Stanhouse	.40	.20	.12
33	Jay Johnstone	.50	.25	.15
34	Bake McBride	.40	.20	.12
35	Dave Kingman	.70	.35	.20
36	Freddie Patek	.40	.20	.12
37	Garry Maddox	.50	.25	.15
38a	Ken Reitz (last line begins "The previous...")	.90	.45	.25
38b	Ken Reitz (last line begins "In late...")	.40	.20	.12
39	Bobby Grich	.60	.30	.20
40	Cesar Geronimo	.40	.20	.12
41	Jim Lonborg	.40	.20	.12
42	Ed Figueroa	.40	.20	.12
43	Bill Madlock	.80	.40	.25
44	Jerry Remy	.40	.20	.12
45	Frank Tanana	.50	.25	.15
46	Al Oliver	.90	.45	.25
47	Charlie Hough	.50	.25	.15
48	Lou Piniella	.70	.35	.20
49	Ken Griffey	.60	.30	.20
50	Jose Cruz	.60	.30	.20
51	Rollie Fingers	1.25	.60	.40
52	Chris Chambliss	.50	.25	.15
53	Rod Carew	4.00	2.00	1.25
54	Andy Messersmith	.40	.20	.12
55	Mickey Rivers	.40	.20	.12
56	Butch Wynegar	.40	.20	.12
57	Steve Carlton	5.00	2.50	1.50

1977 Kellogg's

Other than another innovative card design to complement the simulated 3-D effect, there was little change in the 1977 Kellogg's issue. Set size remained at 57 cards, the set remained in the 2-1/8" by 3-1/4" format, and the cards were available either individually in boxes of cereal, or as a complete set via a mail-in box top offer. The 1977 set is the last in which Kellogg's used a player portrait photo on the back of the card.

1978 Kellogg's

Besides the substitution of a Tony the Tiger drawing for a player portrait photo on the back of the card, the 1978 Kellogg's set offered no major changes from the previous few years issues. Cards were once again in the 2-1/8" by 3-1/4" format, with 57 cards comprising a complete set. Single cards were available in selected brands of the company's cereal, while complete sets could be obtained by a mail-in offer.

		NR MT	EX	VG
Complete Set:		55.00	27.00	16.50
Common Player:		.40	.20	.12
1	Steve Carlton	4.00	2.00	1.25
2	Bucky Dent	.50	.25	.15
3	Mike Schmidt	4.00	2.00	1.25
4	Ken Griffey	.50	.25	.15
5	Al Cowens	.40	.20	.12
6	George Brett	5.00	2.50	1.50
7	Lou Brock	3.00	1.50	.90
8	Rich Gossage	1.25	.60	.40
9	Tom Johnson	.40	.20	.12
10	George Foster	.70	.35	.20
11	Dave Winfield	3.50	1.75	1.00
12	Dan Meyer	.40	.20	.12
13	Chris Chambliss	.50	.25	.15
14	Paul Dade	.40	.20	.12
15	Jeff Burroughs	.40	.20	.12
16	Jose Cruz	.60	.30	.20
17	Mickey Rivers	.40	.20	.12
18	John Candelaria	.50	.25	.15
19	Ellis Valentine	.40	.20	.12
20	Hal McRae	.50	.25	.15
21	Dave Rozema	.40	.20	.12
22	Lenny Randle	.40	.20	.12
23	Willie McCovey	3.00	1.50	.90
24	Ron Cey	.70	.35	.20
25	Eddie Murray	12.00	6.00	3.50
26	Larry Bowa	.60	.30	.20
27	Tom Seaver	3.50	1.75	1.00
28	Garry Maddox	.50	.25	.15
29	Rod Carew	4.00	2.00	1.25
30	Thurman Munson	2.50	1.25	.70
31	Garry Templeton	.60	.30	.20
32	Eric Soderholm	.40	.20	.12
33	Greg Luzinski	.70	.35	.20
34	Reggie Smith	.50	.25	.15
35	Dave Goltz	.40	.20	.12
36	Tommy John	1.25	.60	.40
37	Ralph Garr	.40	.20	.12
38	Alan Bannister	.40	.20	.12
39	Bob Bailor	.40	.20	.12
40	Reggie Jackson	5.00	2.50	1.50
41	Cecil Cooper	.80	.40	.25
42	Burt Hooton	.40	.20	.12
43	Sparky Lyle	.50	.25	.15
44	Steve Ontiveros	.40	.20	.12
45	Rick Reuschel	.60	.30	.20
46	Lyman Bostock	.50	.25	.15
47	Mitchell Page	.40	.20	.12
48	Bruce Sutter	.70	.35	.20
49	Jim Rice	3.50	1.75	1.00
50	Bob Forsch	.40	.20	.12
51	Nolan Ryan	8.00	4.00	2.50
52	Dave Parker	1.25	.60	.40
53	Bert Blyleven	.90	.45	.25
54	Frank Tanana	.50	.25	.15
55	Ken Singleton	.50	.25	.15
56	Mike Hargrove	.40	.20	.12
57	Don Sutton	2.50	1.25	.70

1979 Kellogg's

For its 1979 3-D issue, Kellogg's increased the size of the set to 60 cards, but reduced the width of the cards to 1-15/16". Depth stayed the same as in previous years, 3-1/4". The narrower card format seems to have compounded the problem of curling and subsequent cracking of the ribbed plastic surface which helps give the card a 3-D effect. Cards with major cracks can be graded no higher than VG. The complete set price in the checklist that follows does not include the scarcer variations. Numerous minor variations featuring copyright and trademark logos can be found in the set.

		NR MT	EX	VG
Complete Set:		35.00	17.50	10.50
Common Player:		.30	.15	.09
1	Bruce Sutter	.80	.40	.25
2	Ted Simmons	.70	.35	.20
3	Ross Grimsley	.30	.15	.09
4	Wayne Nordhagen	.30	.15	.09
5a	Jim Palmer (PCT. .649)	2.25	1.25	.70
5b	Jim Palmer (PCT. .650)	1.50	.70	.45
6	John Henry Johnson	.30	.15	.09
7	Jason Thompson	.30	.15	.09
8	Pat Zachry	.30	.15	.09
9	Dennis Eckersley	1.50	1.25	.60
10a	Paul Splittorff (IP 1665)	.60	.30	.20
10b	Paul Splittorff (IP 1666)	.30	.15	.09
11a	Ron Guidry (Hits 397)	2.00	1.00	.60
11b	Ron Guidry (Hits 396)	1.25	.60	.40
12	Jeff Burroughs	.30	.15	.09
13	Rod Carew	2.50	1.25	.70
14a	Buddy Bell (no trade line in bio)	1.25	.60	.40
14b	Buddy Bell (trade line in bio)	.60	.30	.20
15	Jim Rice	2.50	1.25	.70
16	Garry Maddox	.50	.25	.15
17	Willie McCovey	2.50	1.25	.70
18	Steve Carlton	2.50	1.25	.70
19a	J. R. Richard (stats begin with 1972)	.60	.30	.20
19b	J. R. Richard (stats begin with 1971)	.30	.15	.09
20	Paul Molitor	.90	.45	.25
21a	Dave Parker (AVG. .281)	2.00	1.00	.60
21b	Dave Parker (AVG. .318)	1.00	.50	.30
22a	Pete Rose (1978 3B 3)	12.00	6.00	3.50
22b	Pete Rose (1978 3B 33)	8.00	4.00	2.50
23a	Vida Blue (Runs 819)	1.25	.60	.40
23b	Vida Blue (Runs 818)	.60	.30	.20
24	Richie Zisk	.30	.15	.09
25a	Darrell Porter (2B 101)	.80	.40	.25
25b	Darrell Porter (2B 111)	.40	.20	.12
26a	Dan Driessen (Games 642)	.80	.40	.25
26b	Dan Driessen (Games 742)	.40	.20	.12
27a	Geoff Zahn (1978 Minnesota)	.60	.30	.20
27b	Geoff Zahn (1978 Minnesota)	.30	.15	.09
28	Phil Niekro	1.25	.60	.40
29	Tom Seaver	2.50	1.25	.70
30	Fred Lynn	1.00	.50	.30

		NR MT	EX	VG
31	Bill Bonham	.30	.15	.09
32	George Foster	.70	.35	.20
33a	Terry Puhl (last line of bio begins "Terry...")	.60	.30	.20
33b	Terry Puhl (last line of bio begins "His...")	.30	.15	.09
34a	John Candelaria (age is 24)	.90	.45	.25
34b	John Candelaria (age is 25)	.50	.25	.15
35	Bob Knepper	.40	.20	.12
36	Freddie Patek	.30	.15	.09
37	Chris Chambliss	.40	.20	.12
38a	Bob Forsch (1977 Games 86)	.80	.40	.25
38b	Bob Forsch (1977 Games 35)	.40	.20	.12
39a	Ken Griffey (1978 AB 674)	.90	.45	.25
39b	Ken Griffey (1978 AB 614)	.50	.25	.15
40	Jack Clark	.90	.45	.25
41a	Dwight Evans (1978 Hits 13)	1.50	.70	.45
41b	Dwight Evans (1978 Hits 123)	.90	.45	.25
42	Lee Mazzilli	.40	.20	.12
43	Mario Guerrero	.30	.15	.09
44	Larry Bowa	.50	.25	.15
45a	Carl Yastrzemski (Games 9930)	6.00	3.00	1.75
45b	Carl Yastrzemski (Games 9929)	4.00	2.00	1.25
46a	Reggie Jackson (1978 Games 162)	5.00	2.50	1.50
46b	Reggie Jackson (1978 Games 139)	3.00	1.50	.90
47	Rick Reuschel	.60	.30	.20
48a	Mike Flanagan (1976 SO 57)	.90	.45	.25
48b	Mike Flanagan (1976 SO 56)	.50	.25	.15
49a	Gaylord Perry (1973 Hits 325)	2.00	1.00	.60
49b	Gaylord Perry (1973 Hits 315)	1.25	.60	.40
50	George Brett	3.50	1.75	1.00
51a	Craig Reynolds (last line of bio begins "He spent...")	.60	.30	.20
51b	Craig Reynolds (last line of bio begins "In those...")	.30	.15	.09
52	Davey Lopes	.40	.20	.12
53a	Bill Almon (2B 31)	.60	.30	.20
53b	Bill Almon (2B 41)	.30	.15	.09
54	Roy Howell	.30	.15	.09
55	Frank Tanana	.50	.25	.15
56a	Doug Rau (1978 PCT. .577)	.60	.30	.20
56b	Doug Rau (1978 PCT. .625)	.30	.15	.09
57a	Rick Monday (1976 Runs 197)	.90	.45	.25
57b	Rick Monday (1976 Runs 107)	.50	.25	.15
58	Jon Matlack	.30	.15	.09
59a	Ron Jackson (last line of bio begins "His best...")	.60	.30	.20
59b	Ron Jackson (last line of bio begins "The Twins...")	.30	.15	.09
60	Jim Sundberg	.50	.25	.15

		NR MT	EX	VG
4	Ron Guidry	.90	.45	.25
5	Bert Blyleven	.80	.40	.25
6	Dave Kingman	.70	.35	.20
7	Jeff Newman	.30	.15	.09
8	Steve Rogers	.30	.15	.09
9	George Brett	4.00	2.00	1.25
10	Bruce Sutter	.70	.35	.20
11	Gorman Thomas	.40	.20	.12
12	Darrell Porter	.30	.15	.09
13	Roy Smalley	.30	.15	.09
14	Steve Carlton	1.75	.90	.50
15	Jim Palmer	1.50	.70	.45
16	Bob Bailor	.30	.15	.09
17	Jason Thompson	.30	.15	.09
18	Graig Nettles	.80	.40	.25
19	Ron Cey	.50	.25	.15
20	Nolan Ryan	5.00	2.50	1.50
21	Ellis Valentine	.30	.15	.09
22	Larry Hisle	.30	.15	.09
23	Dave Parker	.90	.45	.25
24	Eddie Murray	2.50	1.25	.70
25	Willie Stargell	1.75	.90	.50
26	Reggie Jackson	2.50	1.25	.70
27	Carl Yastrzemski	3.50	1.75	1.00
28	Andre Thornton	.40	.20	.12
29	Davey Lopes	.40	.20	.12
30	Ken Singleton	.40	.20	.12
31	Steve Garvey	2.50	1.25	.70
32	Dave Winfield	2.50	1.25	.70
33	Steve Kemp	.40	.20	.12
34	Claudell Washington	.40	.20	.12
35	Pete Rose	6.50	3.25	2.00
36	Cesar Cedeno	.40	.20	.12
37	John Stearns	.30	.15	.09
38	Lee Mazzilli	.30	.15	.09
39	Larry Bowa	.40	.20	.12
40	Fred Lynn	.80	.40	.25
41	Carlton Fisk	.90	.45	.25
42	Vida Blue	.50	.25	.15
43	Keith Hernandez	1.25	.60	.40
44	Jim Rice	1.75	.90	.50
45	Ted Simmons	.80	.40	.25
46	Chet Lemon	.30	.15	.09
47	Fergie Jenkins	.50	.25	.15
48	Gary Matthews	.40	.20	.12
49	Tom Seaver	2.50	1.25	.70
50	George Foster	.70	.35	.20
51	Phil Niekro	1.25	.60	.40
52	Johnny Bench	2.50	1.25	.70
53	Buddy Bell	.50	.25	.15
54	Lance Parrish	.90	.45	.25
55	Joaquin Andujar	.30	.15	.09
56	Don Baylor	.50	.25	.15
57	Jack Clark	.80	.40	.25
58	J.R. Richard	.30	.15	.09
59	Bruce Bochte	.30	.15	.09
60	Rod Carew	2.50	1.25	.70

1980 Kellogg's

The 1980 cereal company issue featured the narrowest format of any Kellogg's card, 1-7/8" by 3-1/4". For the second straight year, set size remained at 60 cards, available either singly in boxes of cereal, or as complete sets by a mail-in offer.

		NR MT	EX	VG
Complete Set:		25.00	12.50	7.50
Common Player:		.30	.15	.09
1	Ross Grimsley	.30	.15	.09
2	Mike Schmidt	4.00	2.00	1.25
3	Mike Flanagan	.40	.20	.12

1981 Kellogg's

"Bigger" is the word to best describe Kellogg's 1981 card set. Not only were the cards themselves larger than ever before (or since) at 2-1/2" by 3-1/2", but the size of the set was increased to 66, the largest since the 75-card issues of 1970-1971. The '81 Kellogg's set was available only as complete sets by mail. It is thought that the wider format of the 1981s may help prevent the problems of curling and cracking from which other years of Kellogg's issues suffer.

		MT	NR MT	EX
	Complete Set:	12.00	9.00	4.75
	Common Player:	.08	.04	.02
1	George Foster	.15	.08	.04
2	Jim Palmer	.30	.15	.08
3	Reggie Jackson	1.25	.90	.50
4	Al Oliver	.15	.08	.04
5	Mike Schmidt	1.25	.90	.50
6	Nolan Ryan	2.00	1.50	.80
7	Bucky Dent	.10	.05	.03
8	George Brett	1.25	.90	.50
9	Jim Rice	.35	.20	.09
10	Steve Garvey	.40	.20	.10
11	Willie Stargell	.30	.15	.08
12	Phil Niekro	.25	.13	.06
13	Dave Parker	.20	.10	.05
14	Cesar Cedeno	.10	.05	.03
15	Don Baylor	.10	.05	.03
16	J.R. Richard	.08	.04	.02
17	Tony Perez	.15	.08	.04
18	Eddie Murray	.80	.60	.30
19	Chet Lemon	.08	.04	.02
20	Ben Oglivie	.08	.04	.02
21	Dave Winfield	.50	.25	.13
22	Joe Morgan	.40	.30	.15
23	Vida Blue	.10	.05	.03
24	Willie Wilson	.15	.08	.04
25	Steve Henderson	.08	.04	.02
26	Rod Carew	1.00	.70	.40
27	Garry Templeton	.08	.04	.02
28	Dave Concepcion	.10	.05	.03
29	Davey Lopes	.08	.04	.02
30	Ken Landreaux	.08	.04	.02
31	Keith Hernandez	.40	.20	.10
32	Cecil Cooper	.10	.05	.03
33	Rickey Henderson	1.00	.70	.40
34	Frank White	.10	.05	.03
35	George Hendrick	.08	.04	.02
36	Reggie Smith	.10	.05	.03
37	Tug McGraw	.10	.05	.03
38	Tom Seaver	1.00	.70	.40
39	Ken Singleton	.10	.05	.03
40	Fred Lynn	.20	.10	.05
41	Rich "Goose" Gossage	.20	.10	.05
42	Terry Puhl	.08	.04	.02
43	Larry Bowa	.10	.05	.03
44	Phil Garner	.08	.04	.02
45	Ron Guidry	.20	.10	.05
46	Lee Mazzilli	.08	.04	.02
47	Dave Kingman	.15	.08	.04
48	Carl Yastrzemski	1.00	.70	.40
49	Rick Burleson	.08	.04	.02
50	Steve Carlton	.40	.20	.10
51	Alan Trammell	.30	.15	.08
52	Tommy John	.20	.10	.05
53	Paul Molitor	.20	.10	.05
54	Joe Charboneau	.08	.04	.02
55	Rick Langford	.08	.04	.02
56	Bruce Sutter	.10	.05	.03
57	Robin Yount	1.00	.70	.40
58	Steve Stone	.08	.04	.02
59	Larry Gura	.08	.04	.02
60	Mike Flanagan	.10	.05	.03
61	Bob Horner	.15	.08	.04
62	Bruce Bochte	.08	.04	.02
63	Pete Rose	1.00	.50	.25
64	Buddy Bell	.15	.08	.04
65	Johnny Bench	1.00	.70	.40
66	Mike Hargrove	.08	.04	.02

		MT	NR MT	EX
1	Richie Zisk	.12	.06	.03
2	Bill Buckner	.12	.06	.03
3	George Brett	1.00	.70	.40
4	Rickey Henderson	1.00	.70	.40
5	Jack Morris	.30	.15	.08
6	Ozzie Smith	.25	.13	.06
7	Rollie Fingers	.25	.13	.06
8	Tom Seaver	.50	.25	.13
9	Fernando Valenzuela	.60	.30	.15
10	Hubie Brooks	.12	.06	.03
11	Nolan Ryan	1.50	1.25	.60
12	Dave Winfield	.60	.30	.15
13	Bob Horner	.20	.10	.05
14	Reggie Jackson	1.00	.70	.40
15	Burt Hooton	.12	.06	.03
16	Mike Schmidt	1.00	.70	.40
17	Bruce Sutter	.20	.10	.05
18	Pete Rose	1.50	.70	.40
19	Dave Kingman	.20	.10	.05
20	Neil Allen	.12	.06	.03
21	Don Sutton	.25	.13	.06
22	Dave Concepcion	.20	.10	.05
23	Keith Hernandez	.50	.25	.13
24	Gary Carter	.70	.35	.20
25	Carlton Fisk	.30	.15	.08
26	Ron Guidry	.25	.13	.06
27	Steve Carlton	.50	.25	.13
28	Robin Yount	.60	.45	.25
29	John Castino	.12	.06	.03
30	Johnny Bench	1.00	.70	.40
31	Bob Knepper	.12	.06	.03
32	Rich "Goose" Gossage	.20	.10	.05
33	Buddy Bell	.20	.10	.05
34	Art Howe	.12	.06	.03
35	Tony Armas	.12	.06	.03
36	Phil Niekro	.30	.15	.08
37	Len Barker	.12	.06	.03
38	Bobby Grich	.20	.10	.05
39	Steve Kemp	.12	.06	.03
40	Kirk Gibson	.35	.20	.09
41	Carney Lansford	.20	.10	.05
42	Jim Palmer	.60	.45	.25
43	Carl Yastrzemski	1.00	.50	.25
44	Rick Burleson	.12	.06	.03
45	Dwight Evans	.25	.13	.06
46	Ron Cey	.20	.10	.05
47	Steve Garvey	.70	.35	.20
48	Dave Parker	.30	.15	.08
49	Mike Easler	.12	.06	.03
50	Dusty Baker	.12	.06	.03
51	Rod Carew	.70	.35	.20
52	Chris Chambliss	.12	.06	.03
53	Tim Raines	.70	.35	.20
54	Chet Lemon	.12	.06	.03
55	Bill Madlock	.20	.10	.05
56	George Foster	.20	.10	.05
57	Dwayne Murphy	.12	.06	.03
58	Ken Singleton	.20	.10	.05
59	Mike Norris	.12	.06	.03
60	Cecil Cooper	.20	.10	.05
61	Al Oliver	.20	.10	.05
62	Willie Wilson	.25	.13	.06
63	Vida Blue	.20	.10	.05
64	Eddie Murray	1.00	.70	.40

1982 Kellogg's

For the second straight year in 1982, Kellogg's cards were not inserted into cereal boxes, but had to be obtained by sending cash and box tops to the company for complete sets. The '82 cards were downsized both in number of cards in the set - 64 - and in physical dimensions, 2-1/8" by 3-1/4".

	MT	NR MT	EX
Complete Set:	16.00	12.00	6.50
Common Player:	.12	.06	.03

Regional interest may affect the value of a card.

1983 Kellogg's

In its 14th and final year of baseball card issue, Kellogg's returned to the policy of inserting single cards into cereal boxes, as well as offering complete sets by a mail-in box top redemption offer. The 3-D cards themselves returned to a narrow - 1-7/8" by 3-1/4" format, while the set size was reduced to 60 cards.

		MT	NR MT	EX
Complete Set:		15.00	11.00	6.00
Common Player:		.10	.08	.04
1	Rod Carew	.80	.60	.30
2	Rollie Fingers	.20	.15	.08
3	Reggie Jackson	.80	.60	.30
4	George Brett	.80	.60	.30
5	Hal McRae	.15	.11	.06
6	Pete Rose	1.25	.90	.50
7	Fernando Valenzuela	.35	.25	.14
8	Rickey Henderson	.80	.60	.30
9	Carl Yastrzemski	.80	.60	.30
10	Rich "Goose" Gossage	.20	.15	.08
11	Eddie Murray	.50	.40	.20
12	Buddy Bell	.15	.11	.06
13	Jim Rice	.40	.30	.15
14	Robin Yount	.80	.60	.30
15	Dave Winfield	.50	.40	.20
16	Harold Baines	.20	.15	.08
17	Garry Templeton	.15	.11	.06
18	Bill Madlock	.25	.20	.10
19	Pete Vuckovich	.10	.08	.04
20	Pedro Guerrero	.25	.20	.10
21	Ozzie Smith	.20	.15	.08
22	George Foster	.20	.15	.08
23	Willie Wilson	.20	.15	.08
24	Johnny Ray	.15	.11	.06
25	George Hendrick	.10	.08	.04
26	Andre Thornton	.10	.08	.04
27	Leon Durham	.10	.08	.04
28	Cecil Cooper	.15	.11	.06
29	Don Baylor	.15	.11	.06
30	Lonnie Smith	.10	.08	.04
31	Nolan Ryan	1.25	.90	.50
32	Dan Quiesenberry (Quisenberry)	.15	.11	.06
33	Len Barker	.10	.08	.04
34	Neil Allen	.10	.08	.04
35	Jack Morris	.30	.25	.12
36	Dave Stieb	.15	.11	.06
37	Bruce Sutter	.15	.11	.06
38	Jim Sundberg	.10	.08	.04
39	Jim Palmer	.35	.25	.14
40	Lance Parrish	.30	.25	.12
41	Floyd Bannister	.15	.11	.06
42	Larry Gura	.10	.08	.04
43	Britt Burns	.10	.08	.04
44	Toby Harrah	.10	.08	.04
45	Steve Carlton	.40	.30	.15
46	Greg Minton	.10	.08	.04
47	Gorman Thomas	.15	.11	.06
48	Jack Clark	.25	.20	.10
49	Keith Hernandez	.40	.30	.15
50	Greg Luzinski	.15	.11	.06
51	Fred Lynn	.25	.20	.10
52	Dale Murphy	.70	.50	.30
53	Kent Hrbek	.35	.25	.14

		MT	NR MT	EX
54	Bob Horner	.15	.11	.06
55	Gary Carter	.50	.40	.20
56	Carlton Fisk	.25	.20	.10
57	Dave Concepcion	.15	.11	.06
58	Mike Schmidt	.70	.50	.30
59	Bill Buckner	.15	.11	.06
60	Bobby Grich	.15	.11	.06

1986 Kitty Clover Potato Chips Royals

Twenty players of the 1985 World's Champion Kansas City Royals were featured in a round card set inserted into packages of potato chips in the K.C. area. The 2-7/8" discs were similar to a handful of snack issues produced by Mike Schecter Associates in that team logos have been airbrushed off the players' caps, and the photos of some of the players can be found on other regional issues of 1986.

		MT	NR MT	EX
Complete Set:		20.00	15.00	8.00
Common Player:		.70	.50	.30
1	Lonnie Smith	.70	.50	.30
2	Buddy Biancalana	.70	.50	.30
3	Bret Saberhagen	1.75	1.25	.70
4	Hal McRae	1.00	.70	.40
5	Onix Concepcion	.70	.50	.30
6	Jorge Orta	.70	.50	.30
7	Bud Black	.70	.50	.30
8	Dan Quisenberry	1.00	.70	.40
9	Dane Iorg	.70	.50	.30
10	Charlie Leibrandt	.80	.60	.30
11	Pat Sheridan	.70	.50	.30
12	John Wathan	.80	.60	.30
13	Frank White	1.00	.70	.40
14	Darryl Motley	.70	.50	.30
15	Willie Wilson	1.25	.90	.50
16	Danny Jackson	1.25	.90	.50
17	Steve Balboni	.80	.60	.30
18	Jim Sundberg	.70	.50	.30
19	Mark Gubicza	1.25	.90	.50
20	George Brett	3.25	2.50	1.25

1987 Kraft

Kraft Foods, Inc. issued a 48-card set on specially marked packages of their Macaroni & Cheese Dinners. Titled "Home Plate Heroes," 24 two-card panels measuring 3-1/2" by 7-1/8" make up the set.

individual cards measure 2-1/4" by 3-1/2" and are numbered 1 through 48. The blank-backed cards feature fronts with full-color photos, although all team insignias have been erased. In conjunction with the card set, Kraft offered a contest to "Win A Day With A Major Leaguer." Mike Schecter Associates produced the set for Kraft. 120 different panel combinatons can be found.

		MT	NR MT	EX
	Complete Set:	35.00	27.50	15.00
	Common Player:	.20	.15	.08
1	Eddie Murray	.75	.60	.30
2	Dale Murphy	.60	.45	.25
3	Cal Ripken	.75	.60	.30
4	Mike Scott	.35	.25	.14
5	Jim Rice	.50	.40	.20
6	Jody Davis	.20	.15	.08
7	Wade Boggs	1.00	.70	.40
8	Ryne Sandberg	1.00	.70	.40
9	Wally Joyner	1.00	.70	.40
10	Eric Davis	.80	.60	.30
11	Ozzie Guillen	.20	.15	.08
12	Tony Pena	.20	.15	.08
13	Harold Baines	.35	.25	.14
14	Johnny Ray	.20	.15	.08
15	Joe Carter	.35	.25	.14
16	Ozzie Smith	.35	.25	.14
17	Cory Snyder	.20	.15	.08
18	Vince Coleman	.35	.25	.14
19	Kirk Gibson	.50	.40	.20
20	Steve Garvey	.75	.60	.30
21	George Brett	1.00	.70	.40
22	John Tudor	.20	.15	.08
23	Robin Yount	1.00	.70	.40
24	Von Hayes	.35	.25	.14
25	Kent Hrbek	.50	.40	.20
26	Darryl Strawberry	1.00	.70	.40
27	Kirby Puckett	1.00	.70	.40
28	Ron Darling	.35	.25	.14
29	Don Mattingly	1.50	1.25	.60
30	Mike Schmidt	1.00	.70	.40
31	Rickey Henderson	1.00	.70	.40
32	Fernando Valenzuela	.50	.40	.20
33	Dave Winfield	.60	.45	.25
34	Pete Rose	1.25	.90	.50
35	Jose Canseco	2.00	1.50	.80
36	Glenn Davis	.35	.25	.14
37	Alvin Davis	.35	.25	.14
38	Steve Sax	.35	.25	.14
39	Pete Incaviglia	.30	.25	.12
40	Jeff Reardon	.35	.25	.14
41	Jesse Barfield	.35	.25	.14
42	Hubie Brooks	.20	.15	.08
43	George Bell	.50	.40	.20
44	Tony Gwynn	.75	.60	.30
45	Roger Clemens	1.00	.70	.40
46	Chili Davis	.20	.15	.08
47	Mike Witt	.20	.15	.08
48	Nolan Ryan	2.00	1.50	.80

1960 Lake To Lake Dairy Braves

This 28-card set of unnumbered 2-1/2" by 3-1/4" cards offers a special challenge for the condition-conscious collector. Originally issued by being stapled to milk cartons, the cards were redeemable for prizes ranging from pen and pencil sets to Braves tickets. When sent in for redemption, the cards had a hole punched in the corner. Naturally, collectors most desire cards without the staple or punch holes. Cards are printed in blue ink on front, red ink on back. Because he was traded in May, and his card withdrawn, the Ray Boone card is scarce; the Billy Bruton card is unaccountably scarcer still.

		NR MT	EX	VG
	Complete Set:	1200.00	600.00	360.00
	Common Player:	13.00	6.50	4.00
(1)	Henry Aaron	275.00	137.00	82.00
(2)	Joe Adcock	17.50	8.75	5.25
(3)	Ray Boone	125.00	62.00	37.00
(4)	Bill Bruton	275.00	137.00	82.00
(5)	Bob Buhl	17.50	8.75	5.25
(6)	Lou Burdette	20.00	10.00	6.00
(7)	Chuck Cottier	13.00	6.50	4.00
(8)	Wes Covington	15.00	7.50	4.50
(9)	Del Crandall	17.50	8.75	5.25
(10)	Charlie Dressen	15.00	7.50	4.50
(11)	Bob Giggie	13.00	6.50	4.00
(12)	Joey Jay	13.00	6.50	4.00
(13)	Johnny Logan	15.00	7.50	4.50
(14)	Felix Mantilla	13.00	6.50	4.00
(15)	Lee Maye	13.00	6.50	4.00
(16)	Don McMahon	13.00	6.50	4.00
(17)	George Myatt	13.00	6.50	4.00
(18)	Andy Pafko	15.00	7.50	4.50
(19)	Juan Pizarro	13.00	6.50	4.00
(20)	Mel Roach	13.00	6.50	4.00
(21)	Bob Rush	13.00	6.50	4.00
(22)	Bob Scheffing	13.00	6.50	4.00
(23)	Red Schoendienst	20.00	10.00	6.00
(24)	Warren Spahn	75.00	37.00	22.00
(25)	Al Spangler	13.00	6.50	4.00
(26)	Frank Torre	13.00	6.50	4.00
(27)	Carl Willey	13.00	6.50	4.00
(28)	Whitlow Wyatt	13.00	6.50	4.00

1948 Leaf

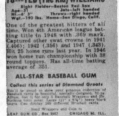

The first color baseball cards of the post-World War II era were the 98-card, 2-3/8" by 2-7/8", set produced by Chicago's Leaf Gum Company in 1948-1949. The color was crude, probably helping to make the set less popular than the Bowman issues of the same era. One of the toughest post-war sets to complete, exactly half of the Leaf issue - 49 of the cards - are significantly harder to find than the other 49. Probably intended to confound bubble gum buyers of the day, the set is skip-numbered between 1-168. Card backs contain offers of felt pennants, an album for the cards or 5-1/2" by 7-1/2" premium photos of Hall of Famers.

	NR MT	EX	VG
Complete Set:	30000.00	15000.00	9000.
Common Player:	25.00	12.50	7.50
Common Scarce Player:	300.00	150.00	90.00

#		NR MT	EX	VG
1	Joe DiMaggio	2000.00	1000.00	600.00
3	Babe Ruth	2200.00	1100.00	650.00
4	Stan Musial	700.00	350.00	200.00
5	Virgil Trucks	400.00	200.00	125.00
8	Leroy Paige	2000.00	1000.00	600.00
10	Paul Trout	25.00	12.50	7.50
11	Phil Rizzuto	150.00	75.00	45.00
13	Casimer Michaels	300.00	150.00	90.00
14	Billy Johnson	30.00	15.00	9.00
17	Frank Overmire	25.00	12.50	7.50
19	John Wyrostek	300.00	150.00	90.00
20	Hank Sauer	400.00	200.00	125.00
22	Al Evans	25.00	12.50	7.50
26	Sam Chapman	25.00	12.50	7.50
27	Mickey Harris	25.00	12.50	7.50
28	Jim Hegan	25.00	12.50	7.50
29	Elmer Valo	25.00	12.50	7.50
30	Bill Goodman	300.00	150.00	90.00
31	Lou Brissie	25.00	12.50	7.50
32	Warren Spahn	200.00	100.00	60.00
33	Harry Lowrey	300.00	150.00	90.00
36	Al Zarilla	300.00	150.00	90.00
38	Ted Kluszewski	80.00	40.00	25.00
39	Ewell Blackwell	50.00	25.00	15.00
42	Kent Peterson	25.00	12.50	7.50
43	Eddie Stevens	300.00	150.00	90.00
45	Ken Keltner	300.00	150.00	90.00
46	Johnny Mize	90.00	45.00	27.00
47	George Vico	25.00	12.50	7.50
48	Johnny Schmitz	300.00	150.00	90.00
49	Del Ennis	40.00	20.00	12.00
50	Dick Wakefield	25.00	12.50	7.50
51	Alvin Dark	400.00	200.00	125.00
53	John Vandermeer (Vander Meer)	40.00	20.00	12.00
54	Bobby Adams	300.00	150.00	90.00
55	Tommy Henrich	400.00	200.00	125.00
56	Larry Jensen (Jansen)	25.00	12.50	7.50
57	Bob McCall	25.00	12.50	7.50
59	Lucius Appling	80.00	40.00	25.00
61	Jake Early	25.00	12.50	7.50
62	Eddie Joost	300.00	150.00	90.00
63	Barney McCosky	300.00	150.00	90.00
65	Bob Elliot (Elliott)	25.00	12.50	7.50
66	Orval Grove	300.00	150.00	90.00
68	Ed Miller	300.00	150.00	90.00
70	John Wagner	250.00	125.00	75.00
72	Hank Edwards	25.00	12.50	7.50
73	Pat Seerey	25.00	12.50	7.50
75	Dom DiMaggio	500.00	250.00	150.00
76	Ted Williams	900.00	450.00	275.00
77	Roy Smalley	25.00	12.50	7.50
78	Walter Evers	300.00	150.00	90.00
79	Jackie Robinson	700.00	350.00	210.00
81	George Kurowski	300.00	150.00	90.00
82	Johnny Lindell	25.00	12.50	7.50
83	Bobby Doerr	100.00	50.00	30.00
84	Sid Hudson	25.00	12.50	7.50
85	Dave Philley	300.00	150.00	90.00
86	Ralph Weigel	25.00	12.50	7.50
88	Frank Gustine	300.00	150.00	90.00
91	Ralph Kiner	150.00	75.00	45.00
93	Bob Feller	1200.00	600.00	350.00
95	George Stirnweiss	25.00	12.50	7.50
97	Martin Marion	40.00	20.00	12.00
98	Hal Newhouser	500.00	250.00	150.00
102a	Gene Hermansk (incorrect spelling)	300.00	150.00	90.00
102b	Gene Hermanski (correct spelling)	25.00	12.50	7.50
104	Edward Stewart	300.00	150.00	90.00
106	Lou Boudreau	100.00	50.00	30.00
108	Matthew Batts	300.00	150.00	90.00
111	Gerald Priddy	25.00	12.50	7.50
113	Emil Leonard	300.00	150.00	90.00
117	Joe Gordon	25.00	12.50	7.50
120	George Kell	550.00	275.00	165.00
121	John Pesky	400.00	200.00	120.00
123	Clifford Fannin	300.00	150.00	90.00
125	Andy Pafko	25.00	12.50	7.50
127	Enos Slaughter	600.00	300.00	180.00
128	Warren Rosar	25.00	12.50	7.50
129	Kirby Higbe	300.00	150.00	90.00
131	Sid Gordon	300.00	150.00	90.00
133	Tommy Holmes	400.00	200.00	120.00
136a	Cliff Aberson (full sleeve)	25.00	12.50	7.50
136b	Cliff Aberson (short sleeve)	175.00	87.00	52.00
137	Harry Walker	300.00	150.00	90.00
138	Larry Doby	500.00	250.00	150.00
139	Johnny Hopp	25.00	12.50	7.50
142	Danny Murtaugh	300.00	150.00	90.00
143	Dick Sisler	300.00	150.00	90.00
144	Bob Dillinger	300.00	150.00	90.00
146	Harold Reiser	400.00	200.00	120.00
149	Henry Majeski	300.00	150.00	90.00
153	Floyd Baker	300.00	150.00	90.00
158	Harry Brecheen	400.00	200.00	120.00
159	Mizell Platt	25.00	12.50	7.50
160	Bob Scheffing	400.00	200.00	120.00
161	Vernon Stephens	400.00	200.00	120.00
163	Freddy Hutchinson	400.00	200.00	120.00
165	Dale Mitchell	400.00	200.00	120.00
168	Phil Cavaretta (Cavarretta)	400.00	200.00	120.00

1960 Leaf

While known to the hobby as "Leaf" cards, this set of 144 cards carries the copyright of Sports Novelties Inc., Chicago. The 2-1/2" by 3-1/2" cards feature black and white player portrait photos, with background airbrushed away. Cards were sold in 5¢ wax packs with a marble, rather than a piece of bubble gum. The second half of the set, cards #73-144, are very scarce and make the set a real challenge for the collector. Card #25, Jim Grant, is found in two versions, with his own picture (black cap) and with a photo of Brooks Lawrence (white cap). Eight cards (#'s 1, 12, 17, 23, 35, 58, 61 and 72) exist with close-up photos that are much rarer than the normal cap to chest photos. It is believed the scarce "face only" cards are proof cards prepared by Leaf as only a handful are known to exist.

		NR MT	EX	VG
Complete Set:		1800.00	900.00	550.00
Common Player: 1-72		4.00	2.00	1.25
Common Player: 73-144		15.00	7.50	4.50
1	Luis Aparicio	25.00	12.50	7.50
2	Woody Held	4.00	2.00	1.25
3	Frank Lary	3.00	1.50	.90
4	Camilo Pascual	3.00	1.50	.90
5	Frank Herrera	4.00	2.00	1.25
6	Felipe Alou	3.00	1.50	.90
7	Bennie Daniels	4.00	2.00	1.25
8	Roger Craig	3.00	1.50	.90
9	Eddie Kasko	4.00	2.00	1.25
10	Bob Grim	4.00	2.00	1.25
11	Jim Busby	4.00	2.00	1.25
12	Ken Boyer	4.00	2.00	1.25
13	Bob Boyd	4.00	2.00	1.25
14	Sam Jones	4.00	2.00	1.25
15	Larry Jackson	4.00	2.00	1.25
16	Roy Face	4.00	2.00	1.25
17	Walt Moryn	4.00	2.00	1.25
18	Jim Gilliam	4.00	2.00	1.25
19	Don Newcombe	3.00	1.50	.90
20	Glen Hobbie	4.00	2.00	1.25
21	Pedro Ramos	4.00	2.00	1.25
22	Ryne Duren	4.00	2.00	1.25
23	Joe Jay	4.00	2.00	1.25
24	Lou Berberet	4.00	2.00	1.25
25a	Jim Grant (white cap, photo actually Brooks Lawrence)	25.00	12.50	7.50
25b	Jim Grant (dark cap, correct photo)	50.00	25.00	15.00
26	Tom Borland	4.00	2.00	1.25
27	Brooks Robinson	50.00	25.00	15.00
28	Jerry Adair	3.00	1.50	.90

		NR MT	EX	VG
29	Ron Jackson	4.00	2.00	1.25
30	George Strickland	4.00	2.00	1.25
31	Rocky Bridges	4.00	2.00	1.25
32	Bill Tuttle	4.00	2.00	1.25
33	Ken Hunt	3.00	1.50	.90
34	Hal Griggs	4.00	2.00	1.25
35	Jim Coates	3.00	1.50	.90
36	Brooks Lawrence	4.00	2.00	1.25
37	Duke Snider	50.00	25.00	15.00
38	Al Spangler	4.00	2.00	1.25
39	Jim Owens	4.00	2.00	1.25
40	Bill Virdon	4.00	2.00	1.25
41	Ernie Broglio	4.00	2.00	1.25
42	Andre Rodgers	4.00	2.00	1.25
43	Julio Becquer	4.00	2.00	1.25
44	Tony Taylor	4.00	2.00	1.25
45	Jerry Lynch	3.00	1.50	.90
46	Cletis Boyer	4.00	2.00	1.25
47	Jerry Lumpe	3.00	1.50	.90
48	Charlie Maxwell	4.00	2.00	1.25
49	Jim Perry	3.00	1.50	.90
50	Danny McDevitt	4.00	2.00	1.25
51	Juan Pizarro	4.00	2.00	1.25
52	Dallas Green	4.00	2.00	1.25
53	Bob Friend	3.00	1.50	.90
54	Jack Sanford	3.00	1.50	.90
55	Jim Rivera	4.00	2.00	1.25
56	Ted Wills	4.00	2.00	1.25
57	Milt Pappas	3.00	1.50	.90
58a	Hal Smith (team & position on back)			
		4.00	2.00	1.25
58b	Hal Smith (team blackened out on back)			
		50.00	25.00	15.00
58c	Hal Smith (team missing on back)			
		50.00	25.00	15.00
59	Bob Avila	4.00	2.00	1.25
60	Clem Labine	3.00	1.50	.90
61	Vic Rehm	3.00	1.50	.90
62	John Gabler	3.00	1.50	.90
63	John Tsitouris	4.00	2.00	1.25
64	Dave Sisler	4.00	2.00	1.25
65	Vic Power	3.00	1.50	.90
66	Earl Battey	3.00	1.50	.90
67	Bob Purkey	3.00	1.50	.90
68	Moe Drabowsky	4.00	2.00	1.25
69	Hoyt Wilhelm	6.00	3.00	1.75
70	Humberto Robinson	4.00	2.00	1.25
71	Whitey Herzog	4.00	2.00	1.25
72	Dick Donovan	3.00	1.50	.90
73	Gordon Jones	15.00	7.50	4.50
74	Joe Hicks	15.00	7.50	4.50
75	Ray Culp	18.00	9.00	5.50
76	Dick Drott	15.00	7.50	4.50
77	Bob Duliba	15.00	7.50	4.50
78	Art Ditmar	18.00	9.00	5.50
79	Steve Korcheck	15.00	7.50	4.50
80	Henry Mason	15.00	7.50	4.50
81	Harry Simpson	15.00	7.50	4.50
82	Gene Green	15.00	7.50	4.50
83	Bob Shaw	15.00	7.50	4.50
84	Howard Reed	15.00	7.50	4.50
85	Dick Stigman	15.00	7.50	4.50
86	Rip Repulski	15.00	7.50	4.50
87	Seth Morehead	15.00	7.50	4.50
88	Camilo Carreon	15.00	7.50	4.50
89	John Blanchard	18.00	9.00	5.50
90	Billy Hoeft	15.00	7.50	4.50
91	Fred Hopke	18.00	9.00	5.50
92	Joe Martin	15.00	7.50	4.50
93	Wally Shannon	18.00	9.00	5.50
94	Baseball's Two Hal Smiths (Harold Raymond Smith, Harold Wayne Smith)			
		20.00	10.00	6.00
95	Al Schroll	15.00	7.50	4.50
96	John Kucks	15.00	7.50	4.50
97	Tom Morgan	15.00	7.50	4.50
98	Willie Jones	15.00	7.50	4.50
99	Marshall Renfroe	18.00	9.00	5.50
100	Willie Tasby	15.00	7.50	4.50
101	Irv Noren	15.00	7.50	4.50
102	Russ Snyder	15.00	7.50	4.50
103	Bob Turley	30.00	15.00	9.00
104	Jim Woods	15.00	7.50	4.50
105	Ronnie Kline	15.00	7.50	4.50
106	Steve Bilko	15.00	7.50	4.50
107	Elmer Valo	18.00	9.00	5.50
108	Tom McAvoy	18.00	9.00	5.50
109	Stan Williams	15.00	7.50	4.50
110	Earl Averill	15.00	7.50	4.50
111	Lee Walls	15.00	7.50	4.50
112	Paul Richards	18.00	9.00	5.50
113	Ed Sadowski	15.00	7.50	4.50

		NR MT	EX	VG
114	Stover McIlwain	18.00	9.00	5.50
115	Chuck Tanner (photo actually Ken Kuhn)			
		20.00	10.00	6.00
116	Lou Klimchock	15.00	7.50	4.50
117	Neil Chrisley	15.00	7.50	4.50
118	John Callison	20.00	10.00	6.00
119	Hal Smith	15.00	7.50	4.50
120	Carl Sawatski	15.00	7.50	4.50
121	Frank Leja	18.00	9.00	5.50
122	Earl Torgeson	15.00	7.50	4.50
123	Art Schult	15.00	7.50	4.50
124	Jim Brosnan	18.00	9.00	5.50
125	George Anderson	40.00	20.00	12.00
126	Joe Pignatano	15.00	7.50	4.50
127	Rocky Nelson	15.00	7.50	4.50
128	Orlando Cepeda	50.00	25.00	15.00
129	Daryl Spencer	15.00	7.50	4.50
130	Ralph Lumenti	15.00	7.50	4.50
131	Sam Taylor	15.00	7.50	4.50
132	Harry Brecheen	18.00	9.00	5.50
133	Johnny Groth	15.00	7.50	4.50
134	Wayne Terwilliger	15.00	7.50	4.50
135	Kent Hadley	18.00	9.00	5.50
136	Faye Throneberry	15.00	7.50	4.50
137	Jack Meyer	15.00	7.50	4.50
138	Chuck Cottier	15.00	7.50	4.50
139	Joe DeMaestri	18.00	9.00	5.50
140	Gene Freese	15.00	7.50	4.50
141	Curt Flood	40.00	20.00	12.00
142	Gino Cimoli	15.00	7.50	4.50
143	Clay Dalrymple	15.00	7.50	4.50
144	Jim Bunning	75.00	38.00	23.00

1990 Leaf

BRETT BUTLER OF

This 528-card set was issued in two 264-card series. The cards were printed on heavy quality stock and both the card fronts and backs have full color player photos. Cards also have an ultra-glossy finish on both the fronts and the backs. A high-tech foil Hall of Fame puzzle features former Yankee great Yogi Berra.

		MT	NR MT	EX
Complete Set:		300.00	225.00	125.00
Common Player:		.25	.20	.10
1	Introductory Card	.25	.20	.10
2	Mike Henneman	.25	.20	.10
3	Steve Bedrosian	.25	.20	.10
4	Mike Scott	.35	.25	.14
5	Allan Anderson	.25	.20	.10
6	Rick Sutcliffe	.35	.25	.14
7	Gregg Olson	.50	.40	.20
8	Kevin Elster	.25	.20	.10
9	Pete O'Brien	.30	.25	.12
10	Carlton Fisk	1.00	.70	.40
11	Joe Magrane	.40	.30	.15
12	Roger Clemens	4.00	3.00	1.50
13	Tom Glavine	8.00	6.00	3.25
14	Tom Gordon	.30	.25	.12
15	Todd Benzinger	.25	.20	.10
16	Hubie Brooks	.35	.25	.14
17	Roberto Kelly	.30	.25	.12
18	Barry Larkin	.50	.40	.20
19	Mike Boddicker	.25	.20	.10
20	Roger McDowell	.25	.20	.10
21	Nolan Ryan	7.00	5.25	2.75
22	John Farrell	.30	.25	.12

		MT	NR MT	EX				MT	NR MT	EX
23	Bruce Hurst	.25	.20	.10		114	Jay Buhner	.25	.20	.10
24	Wally Joyner	.40	.30	.15		115	Eric Show	.30	.25	.12
25	Greg Maddux	3.00	2.25	1.25		116	Bryan Harvey	.25	.20	.10
26	Chris Bosio	.30	.25	.12		117	Andy Van Slyke	.35	.25	.14
27	John Cerutti	.30	.25	.12		118	Jeff Ballard	.25	.20	.10
28	Tim Burke	.25	.20	.10		119	Barry Lyons	.30	.25	.12
29	Dennis Eckersley	.50	.40	.20		120	Kevin Mitchell	.50	.40	.20
30	Glenn Davis	.40	.30	.15		121	Mike Gallego	.30	.25	.12
31	Jim Abbott	2.00	1.50	.80		122	Dave Smith	.25	.20	.10
32	Mike LaValliere	.25	.20	.10		123	Kirby Puckett	3.00	2.25	1.25
33	Andres Thomas	.25	.20	.10		124	Jerome Walton	.40	.30	.15
34	Lou Whitaker	.35	.25	.14		125	Bo Jackson	3.00	2.25	1.25
35	Alvin Davis	.35	.25	.14		126	Harold Baines	.35	.25	.14
36	Melido Perez	.25	.20	.10		127	Scott Bankhead	.25	.20	.10
37	Craig Biggio	.80	.60	.30		128	Ozzie Guillen	.35	.25	.14
38	Rick Aguilera	.25	.20	.10		129	Jose Oquendo	.30	.25	.12
39	Pete Harnisch	.35	.25	.14		130	John Dopson	.30	.25	.12
40	David Cone	.35	.25	.14		131	Charlie Hayes	.25	.20	.10
41	Scott Garrelts	.25	.20	.10		132	Fred McGriff	.80	.60	.30
42	Jay Howell	.25	.20	.10		133	Chet Lemon	.25	.20	.10
43	Eric King	.25	.20	.10		134	Gary Carter	.35	.25	.14
44	Pedro Guerrero	.35	.25	.14		135	Rafael Ramirez	.30	.25	.12
45	Mike Bielecki	.25	.20	.10		136	Shane Mack	.25	.20	.10
46	Bob Boone	.25	.20	.10		137	Mark Grace	.50	.40	.20
47	Kevin Brown	.30	.25	.12		138	Phil Bradley	.25	.20	.10
48	Jerry Browne	.25	.20	.10		139	Dwight Gooden	.80	.60	.30
49	Mike Scioscia	.25	.20	.10		140	Harold Reynolds	.35	.25	.14
50	Chuck Cary	.30	.25	.12		141	Scott Fletcher	.30	.25	.12
51	Wade Boggs	2.00	1.50	.80		142	Ozzie Smith	.80	.60	.30
52	Von Hayes	.25	.20	.10		143	Mike Greenwell	.80	.60	.30
53	Tony Fernandez	.35	.25	.14		144	Pete Smith	.25	.20	.10
54	Dennis Martinez	.35	.25	.14		145	Mark Gubicza	.25	.20	.10
55	Tom Candiotti	.30	.25	.12		146	Chris Sabo	.25	.20	.10
56	Andy Benes	4.00	3.00	1.50		147	Ramon Martinez	3.00	2.25	1.25
57	Rob Dibble	.30	.25	.12		148	Dave Winfield	.40	.30	.15
58	Chuck Crim	.30	.25	.12		149	Randy Myers	.35	.25	.14
59	John Smoltz	2.50	2.00	1.00		150	Jody Reed	.25	.20	.10
60	Mike Heath	.30	.25	.12		151	Bruce Ruffin	.30	.25	.12
61	Kevin Gross	.25	.20	.10		152	Jeff Russell	.25	.20	.10
62	Mark McGwire	2.50	2.00	1.00		153	Doug Jones	.25	.20	.10
63	Bert Blyleven	.35	.25	.14		154	Tony Gwynn	1.00	.70	.40
64	Bob Walk	.30	.25	.12		155	Mark Langston	.35	.25	.14
65	Mickey Tettleton	.25	.20	.10		156	Mitch Williams	.25	.20	.10
66	Sid Fernandez	.35	.25	.14		157	Gary Sheffield	12.00	9.00	4.75
67	Terry Kennedy	.25	.20	.10		158	Tom Henke	.25	.20	.10
68	Fernando Valenzuela	.40	.30	.15		159	Oil Can Boyd	.25	.20	.10
69	Don Mattingly	1.50	1.25	.60		160	Rickey Henderson	2.00	1.50	.80
70	Paul O'Neill	.35	.25	.14		161	Bill Doran	.25	.20	.10
71	Robin Yount	1.00	.70	.40		162	Chuck Finley	.40	.30	.15
72	Bret Saberhagen	.30	.25	.12		163	Jeff King	.25	.20	.10
73	Geno Petralli	.30	.25	.12		164	Nick Esasky	.25	.20	.10
74	Brook Jacoby	.25	.20	.10		165	Cecil Fielder	2.50	2.00	1.00
75	Roberto Alomar	6.00	4.50	2.50		166	Dave Valle	.30	.25	.12
76	Devon White	.25	.20	.10		167	Robin Ventura	15.00	11.00	6.00
77	Jose Lind	.30	.25	.12		168	Jim Deshaies	.25	.20	.10
78	Pat Combs	.35	.25	.14		169	Juan Berenguer	.30	.25	.12
79	Dave Steib	.35	.25	.14		170	Craig Worthington	.35	.25	.14
80	Tim Wallach	.35	.25	.14		171	Gregg Jefferies	.50	.40	.30
81	Dave Stewart	.30	.25	.12		172	Will Clark	3.00	2.25	1.25
82	Eric Anthony	.50	.40	.20		173	Kirk Gibson	.35	.25	.14
83	Randy Bush	.30	.25	.12		174	Checklist	.30	.25	.12
84	Checklist	.30	.25	.12		175	Bobby Thigpen	.40	.30	.15
85	Jaime Navarro	.30	.25	.12		176	John Tudor	.25	.20	.10
86	Tommy Gregg	.30	.25	.12		177	Andre Dawson	.50	.40	.30
87	Frank Tanana	.25	.20	.10		178	George Brett	.80	.60	.30
88	Omar Vizquel	.30	.25	.12		179	Steve Buechele	.30	.25	.12
89	Ivan Calderon	.35	.25	.14		180	Joey Belle	7.00	5.25	2.75
90	Vince Coleman	.35	.25	.14		181	Eddie Murray	.50	.40	.20
91	Barry Bonds	2.00	1.50	.80		182	Bob Geren	.25	.20	.10
92	Randy Milligan	.35	.25	.14		183	Rob Murphy	.30	.25	.12
93	Frank Viola	.35	.25	.14		184	Tom Herr	.25	.20	.10
94	Matt Williams	.60	.45	.25		185	George Bell	.50	.40	.20
95	Alfredo Griffin	.30	.25	.12		186	Spike Owen	.25	.20	.10
96	Steve Sax	.35	.25	.14		187	Cory Snyder	.25	.20	.10
97	Gary Gaetti	.35	.25	.14		188	Fred Lynn	.25	.20	.10
98	Ryne Sandberg	4.00	3.00	1.50		189	Eric Davis	.60	.45	.25
99	Danny Tartabull	.35	.25	.14		190	Dave Parker	.30	.25	.12
100	Rafael Palmeiro	.60	.45	.25		191	Jeff Blauser	.30	.25	.12
101	Jesse Orosco	.25	.20	.10		192	Matt Nokes	.25	.20	.10
102	Garry Templeton	.25	.20	.10		193	Delino DeShields	.25	4.50	2.50
103	Frank DiPino	.25	.20	.10		194	Scott Sanderson	.25	.20	.10
104	Tony Pena	.25	.20	.10		195	Lance Parrish	.25	.20	.10
105	Dickie Thon	.30	.25	.12		196	Bobby Bonilla	.80	.60	.30
106	Kelly Gruber	.30	.25	.12		197	Cal Ripken	6.00	4.50	2.50
107	Marquis Grissom	6.00	4.50	2.50		198	Kevin McReynolds	.35	.25	.14
108	Jose Canseco	4.00	3.00	1.50		199	Robby Thompson	.25	.20	.10
109	Mike Blowers	.30	.25	.12		200	Tim Belcher	.25	.20	.10
110	Tom Browning	.25	.20	.10		201	Jesse Barfield	.25	.20	.10
111	Greg Vaughn	2.50	2.00	1.00		202	Mariano Duncan	.25	.20	.10
112	Oddibe McDowell	.25	.20	.10		203	Bill Spiers	.40	.30	.15
113	Gary Ward	.25	.20	.10		204	Frank White	.25	.20	.10

		MT	NR MT	EX			MT	NR MT	EX
205	Julio Franco	.35	.25	.14	296	Doug Drabek	.35	.25	.14
206	Greg Swindell	.25	.20	.10	297	Dave Justice	20.00	15.00	8.00
207	Benito Santiago	.30	.25	.12	298	Paul Gibson	.30	.25	.12
208	Johnny Ray	.30	.25	.12	299	Edgar Martinez	.50	.40	.20
209	Gary Redus	.30	.25	.12	300	Frank Thomas	50.00	37.00	20.00
210	Jeff Parrett	.30	.25	.12	301	Eric Yelding	.30	.25	.12
211	Jimmy Key	.25	.20	.10	302	Greg Gagne	.30	.25	.12
212	Tim Raines	.35	.25	.14	303	Brad Komminsk	.30	.25	.12
213	Carney Lansford	.25	.20	.10	304	Ron Darling	.25	.20	.10
214	Gerald Young	.30	.25	.12	305	Kevin Bass	.25	.20	.10
215	Gene Larkin	.30	.25	.12	306	Jeff Hamilton	.30	.25	.12
216	Dan Plesac	.25	.20	.10	307	Ron Karkovice	.30	.25	.12
217	Lonnie Smith	.25	.20	.10	308	Milt Thompson	.30	.25	.12
218	Alan Trammell	.40	.30	.15	309	Mike Harkey	.30	.25	.12
219	Jeffrey Leonard	.25	.20	.10	310	Mel Stottlemyre	.30	.25	.12
220	Sammy Sosa	1.50	1.25	.60	311	Kenny Rogers	.35	.25	.14
221	Todd Zeile	2.00	1.50	.80	312	Mitch Webster	.30	.25	.12
222	Bill Landrum	.25	.20	.10	313	Kal Daniels	.35	.25	.14
223	Mike Devereaux	.25	.20	.10	314	Matt Nokes	.25	.20	.10
224	Mike Marshall	.25	.20	.10	315	Dennis Lamp	.30	.25	.12
225	Jose Uribe	.30	.25	.12	316	Ken Howell	.30	.25	.12
226	Juan Samuel	.25	.20	.10	317	Glenallen Hill	.35	.25	.14
227	Mel Hall	.30	.25	.12	318	Dave Martinez	.30	.25	.12
228	Kent Hrbek	.40	.30	.15	319	Chris James	.25	.20	.10
229	Shawon Dunston	.40	.30	.15	320	Mike Pagliarulo	.25	.20	.10
230	Kevin Seitzer	.35	.25	.14	321	Hal Morris	6.00	4.50	2.50
231	Pete Incaviglia	.25	.20	.10	322	Rob Deer	.30	.25	.12
232	Sandy Alomar	.50	.40	.20	323	Greg Olson	.50	.40	.20
233	Bip Roberts	.25	.20	.10	324	Tony Phillips	.30	.25	.12
234	Scott Terry	.25	.20	.10	325	Larry Walker	6.00	4.50	2.50
235	Dwight Evans	.35	.25	.14	326	Ron Hassey	.30	.25	.12
236	Ricky Jordan	.35	.25	.14	327	Jack Howell	.30	.25	.12
237	John Olerud	6.00	4.50	2.50	328	John Smiley	.25	.20	.10
238	Zane Smith	.25	.20	.10	329	Steve Finley	.50	.40	.20
239	Walt Weiss	.25	.20	.10	330	Dave Magadan	.35	.25	.14
240	Alvaro Espinoza	.25	.20	.10	331	Greg Litton	.35	.25	.14
241	Billy Hatcher	.25	.20	.10	332	Mickey Hatcher	.30	.25	.12
242	Paul Molitor	.35	.25	.14	333	Lee Guetterman	.30	.25	.12
243	Dale Murphy	.50	.40	.20	334	Norm Charlton	.35	.25	.14
244	Dave Bergman	.30	.25	.12	335	Edgar Diaz	.25	.20	.10
245	Ken Griffey,Jr.	25.00	18.00	10.00	336	Willie Wilson	.25	.20	.10
246	Ed Whitson	.25	.20	.10	337	Bobby Witt	.35	.25	.14
247	Kirk McCaskill	.25	.20	.10	338	Candy Maldonado	.35	.25	.14
248	Jay Bell	.35	.25	.14	339	Craig Lefferts	.25	.20	.10
249	Ben McDonald	3.00	2.25	1.25	340	Dante Bichette	.25	.20	.10
250	Darryl Strawberry	1.75	1.25	.60	341	Wally Backman	.30	.25	.12
251	Brett Butler	.30	.25	.14	342	Dennis Cook	.25	.20	.10
252	Terry Steinbach	.25	.20	.10	343	Pat Borders	.25	.20	.10
253	Ken Caminiti	.30	.25	.12	344	Wallace Johnson	.30	.25	.12
254	Dan Gladden	.25	.20	.10	345	Willie Randolph	.25	.20	.10
255	Dwight Smith	.35	.25	.14	346	Danny Darwin	.25	.20	.10
256	Kurt Stillwell	.25	.20	.10	347	Al Newman	.30	.25	.12
257	Ruben Sierra	1.50	1.25	.60	348	Mark Knudson	.30	.25	.12
258	Mike Schooler	.25	.20	.10	349	Joe Boever	.30	.25	.12
259	Lance Johnson	.25	.20	.10	350	Larry Sheets	.30	.25	.12
260	Terry Pendleton	.30	.25	.14	351	Mike Jackson	.30	.25	.12
261	Ellis Burks	.40	.30	.15	352	Wayne Edwards	.30	.25	.12
262	Len Dykstra	.35	.25	.14	353	Bernard Gilkey	1.50	1.25	.60
263	Mookie Wilson	.25	.20	.10	354	Don Slaught	.30	.25	.12
264	Checklist	.50	.40	.20	355	Joe Orsulak	.30	.25	.12
265	No Hit King (Nolan Ryan)	6.00	4.50	2.50	356	John Franco	.35	.25	.14
266	Brian DuBois	.35	.25	.14	357	Jeff Brantley	.25	.20	.10
267	Don Robinson	.30	.25	.12	358	Mike Morgan	.30	.25	.12
268	Glenn Wilson	.30	.25	.12	359	Deion Sanders	6.00	4.50	2.50
269	Kevin Tapani	2.00	1.50	.80	360	Terry Leach	.30	.25	.12
270	Marvell Wynne	.30	.25	.12	361	Les Lancaster	.30	.25	.12
271	Billy Ripken	.30	.25	.12	362	Storm Davis	.25	.20	.10
272	Howard Johnson	.50	.40	.20	363	Scott Coolbaugh	.30	.25	.12
273	Brian Holman	.35	.25	.14	364	Checklist	.30	.25	.12
274	Dan Pasqua	.30	.25	.12	365	Cecilio Guante	.30	.25	.12
275	Ken Dayley	.30	.25	.12	366	Joey Cora	.30	.25	.12
276	Jeff Reardon	.25	.20	.10	367	Willie McGee	.35	.25	.14
277	Jim Presley	.25	.20	.10	368	Jerry Reed	.30	.25	.12
278	Jim Eisenreich	.30	.25	.12	369	Darren Daulton	.25	.20	.10
279	Danny Jackson	.25	.20	.10	370	Manny Lee	.25	.20	.10
280	Orel Hershiser	.35	.25	.14	371	Mark Gardner	.30	.25	.12
281	Andy Hawkins	.25	.20	.10	372	Rick Honeycutt	.30	.25	.12
282	Jose Rijo	.35	.25	.14	373	Steve Balboni	.30	.25	.12
283	Luis Rivera	.25	.20	.10	374	Jack Armstrong	.30	.25	.12
284	John Kruk	.25	.20	.10	375	Charlie O'Brien	.30	.25	.12
285	Jeff Huson	.30	.25	.12	376	Ron Gant	4.00	3.00	1.50
286	Joel Skinner	.30	.25	.12	377	Lloyd Moseby	.25	.20	.10
287	Jack Clark	.35	.25	.14	378	Gene Harris	.30	.25	.12
288	Chili Davis	.35	.25	.14	379	Joe Carter	.60	.45	.25
289	Joe Girardi	.25	.20	.10	380	Scott Bailes	.30	.25	.12
290	B.J. Surhoff	.25	.20	.10	381	R.J. Reynolds	.30	.25	.12
291	Luis Sojo	.30	.25	.12	382	Bob Melvin	.30	.25	.12
292	Tom Foley	.30	.25	.12	383	Tim Teufel	.30	.25	.12
293	Mike Moore	.25	.20	.10	384	John Burkett	.30	.25	.12
294	Ken Oberkfell	.30	.25	.12	385	Felix Jose	3.00	2.25	1.25
295	Luis Polonia	.30	.25	.12	386	Larry Andersen	.30	.25	.12

		MT	NR MT	EX
387	David West	.25	.20	.10
388	Luis Salazar	.30	.25	.12
389	Mike Macfarlane	.30	.25	.12
390	Charlie Hough	.25	.20	.10
391	Greg Briley	.35	.25	.14
392	Donn Pall	.30	.25	.12
393	Bryn Smith	.30	.25	.12
394	Carlos Quintana	.30	.25	.12
395	Steve Lake	.30	.25	.12
396	Mark Whiten	3.00	2.25	1.25
397	Edwin Nunez	.30	.25	.12
398	Rick Parker	.35	.25	.14
399	Mark Portugal	.30	.25	.12
400	Roy Smith	.30	.25	.12
401	Hector Villanueva	.30	.25	.12
402	Bob Milacki	.25	.20	.10
403	Alejandro Pena	.30	.25	.12
404	Scott Bradley	.30	.25	.12
405	Ron Kittle	.25	.20	.10
406	Bob Tewksbury	.30	.25	.12
407	Wes Gardner	.30	.25	.12
408	Ernie Whitt	.30	.25	.12
409	Terry Shumpert	.30	.25	.12
410	Tim Layana	.30	.25	.12
411	Chris Gwynn	.25	.20	.10
412	Jeff Robinson	.30	.25	.12
413	Scott Scudder	.30	.25	.12
414	Kevin Romine	.30	.25	.12
415	Jose DeJesus	.30	.25	.12
416	Mike Jeffcoat	.30	.25	.12
417	Rudy Seanez	.35	.25	.14
418	Mike Dunne	.30	.25	.12
419	Dick Schofield	.30	.25	.12
420	Steve Wilson	.35	.25	.14
421	Bill Krueger	.30	.25	.12
422	Junior Felix	.35	.25	.14
423	Drew Hall	.30	.25	.12
424	Curt Young	.30	.25	.12
425	Franklin Stubbs	.25	.20	.10
426	Dave Winfield	.50	.40	.20
427	Rick Reed	.30	.25	.12
428	Charlie Leibrandt	.25	.20	.10
429	Jeff Robinson	.30	.25	.12
430	Erik Hanson	.30	.25	.12
431	Barry Jones	.25	.20	.10
432	Alex Trevino	.30	.25	.12
433	John Moses	.30	.25	.12
434	Dave Johnson	.30	.25	.12
435	Mackey Sasser	.25	.20	.10
436	Rick Leach	.30	.25	.12
437	Lenny Harris	.35	.25	.14
438	Carlos Martinez	.25	.20	.10
439	Rex Hudler	.30	.25	.12
440	Domingo Ramos	.30	.25	.12
441	Gerald Perry	.30	.25	.12
442	John Russell	.30	.25	.12
443	Carlos Baerga	5.00	3.75	2.00
444	Checklist	.30	.25	.12
445	Stan Javier	.30	.25	.12
446	Kevin Maas	3.00	2.25	1.25
447	Tom Brunansky	.25	.20	.10
448	Carmelo Martinez	.30	.25	.12
449	Willie Blair	.30	.25	.12
450	Andres Galarraga	.35	.25	.14
451	Bud Black	.30	.25	.12
452	Greg Harris	.30	.25	.12
453	Joe Oliver	.30	.25	.12
454	Greg Brock	.30	.25	.12
455	Jeff Treadway	.25	.20	.10
456	Lance McCullers	.30	.25	.12
457	Dave Schmidt	.30	.25	.12
458	Todd Burns	.30	.25	.12
459	Max Venable	.30	.25	.12
460	Neal Heaton	.30	.25	.12
461	Mark Williamson	.30	.25	.12
462	Keith Miller	.30	.25	.12
463	Mike LaCoss	.30	.25	.12
464	Jose Offerman	1.00	.70	.40
465	Jim Leyritz	.25	.20	.10
466	Glenn Braggs	.30	.25	.12
467	Ron Robinson	.30	.25	.12
468	Mark Davis	.30	.25	.12
469	Gary Pettis	.30	.25	.12
470	Keith Hernandez	.25	.20	.10
471	Dennis Rasmussen	.25	.20	.10
472	Mark Eichhorn	.25	.20	.10
473	Ted Power	.25	.20	.10
474	Terry Mulholland	.25	.20	.10
475	Todd Stottlemyre	.25	.20	.10
476	Jerry Goff	.30	.25	.12
477	Gene Nelson	.30	.25	.12

		MT	NR MT	EX
478	Rich Gedman	.30	.25	.12
479	Brian Harper	.25	.20	.10
480	Mike Felder	.30	.25	.12
481	Steve Avery	15.00	11.00	6.00
482	Jack Morris	.40	.30	.15
483	Randy Johnson	.50	.40	.20
484	Scott Radinsky	.30	.25	.12
485	Jose DeLeon	.30	.25	.12
486	Stan Belinda	.30	.25	.12
487	Brain Holton	.30	.25	.12
488	Mark Carreon	.25	.20	.10
489	Trevor Wilson	.30	.25	.12
490	Mike Sharperson	.25	.20	.10
491	Alan Mills	.30	.25	.12
492	John Candelaria	.25	.20	.10
493	Paul Assenmacher	.30	.25	.12
494	Steve Crawford	.30	.25	.12
495	Brad Arnsberg	.25	.20	.10
496	Sergio Valdez	.30	.25	.12
497	Mark Parent	.30	.25	.12
498	Tom Pagnozzi	.30	.25	.12
499	Greg Harris	.30	.25	.12
500	Randy Ready	.30	.25	.12
501	Duane Ward	.30	.25	.12
502	Nelson Santovenia	.30	.25	.12
503	Joe Klink	.25	.20	.10
504	Eric Plunk	.30	.25	.12
505	Jeff Reed	.30	.25	.12
506	Ted Higuera	.35	.25	.14
507	Joe Hesketh	.30	.25	.12
508	Dan Petry	.30	.25	.12
509	Matt Young	.30	.25	.12
510	Jerald Clark	.25	.20	.10
511	John Orton	.35	.25	.14
512	Scott Ruskin	.30	.25	.12
513	Chris Hoiles	2.00	1.50	.80
514	Daryl Boston	.30	.25	.12
515	Francisco Oliveras	.35	.25	.14
516	Ozzie Canseco	.30	.25	.12
517	Xavier Hernandez	.35	.25	.14
518	Fred Manrique	.30	.25	.12
519	Shawn Boskie	.30	.25	.12
520	Jeff Montgomery	.25	.20	.10
521	Jack Daugherty	.30	.25	.12
522	Keith Comstock	.30	.25	.12
523	Greg Hibbard	.40	.30	.15
524	Lee Smith	.40	.30	.15
525	Dana Kiecker	.30	.25	.12
526	Darrel Akerfelds	.30	.25	.12
527	Greg Myers	.25	.20	.10
528	Checklist	.40	.30	.15

1991 Leaf

Silver borders and black insets surround the full-color action photos on the 1991 Leaf cards. The set was once again scheduled to be released in two series. Series I consists of cards 1-264. Card backs feature an additional player photo, biographical information, statistics and career highlights. The 1991 issue is not considered as scarce as the 1990 release. 1991 Leaf promo cards were first introduced in the 1991 Donruss factory sets.

	MT	NR MT	EX
Complete Set:	50.00	37.00	20.00
Common Player:	.08	.06	.03

		MT	NR MT	EX
1	The Leaf Card	.08	.06	.03
2	Kurt Stillwell	.08	.06	.03
3	Bobby Witt	.08	.06	.03
4	Tony Phillips	.08	.06	.03
5	Scott Garrelts	.08	.06	.03
6	Greg Swindell	.10	.08	.04
7	Billy Ripken	.08	.06	.03
8	Dave Martinez	.08	.06	.03
9	Kelly Gruber	.10	.08	.04
10	Juan Samuel	.10	.08	.04
11	Brian Holman	.08	.06	.03
12	Craig Biggio	.20	.15	.08
13	Lonnie Smith	.08	.06	.03
14	Ron Robinson	.08	.06	.03
15	Mike LaValliere	.08	.06	.03
16	Mark Davis	.08	.06	.03
17	Jack Daugherty	.08	.06	.03
18	Mike Henneman	.08	.06	.03
19	Mike Greenwell	.20	.15	.08
20	Dave Magadan	.12	.09	.05
21	Mark Williamson	.08	.06	.03
22	Marquis Grissom	.30	.25	.12
23	Pat Borders	.08	.06	.03
24	Mike Scioscia	.08	.06	.03
25	Shawon Dunston	.15	.11	.06
26	Randy Bush	.08	.06	.03
27	John Smoltz	.30	.25	.12
28	Chuck Crim	.08	.06	.03
29	Don Slaught	.08	.06	.03
30	Mike Macfarlane	.08	.06	.03
31	Wally Joyner	.20	.15	.08
32	Pat Combs	.10	.08	.04
33	Tony Pena	.10	.08	.04
34	Howard Johnson	.25	.20	.10
35	Leo Gomez	.50	.40	.20
36	Spike Owen	.08	.06	.03
37	Eric Davis	.30	.25	.12
38	Roberto Kelly	.20	.15	.08
39	Jerome Walton	.15	.11	.06
40	Shane Mack	.15	.11	.06
41	Kent Mercker	.10	.08	.04
42	B.J. Surhoff	.08	.06	.03
43	Jerry Browne	.08	.06	.03
44	Lee Smith	.10	.08	.04
45	Chuck Finley	.20	.15	.08
46	Terry Mulholland	.10	.08	.04
47	Tom Bolton	.08	.06	.03
48	Tom Herr	.08	.06	.03
49	Jim Deshaies	.08	.06	.03
50	Walt Weiss	.10	.08	.04
51	Hal Morris	.35	.25	.14
52	Lee Guetterman	.08	.06	.03
53	Paul Assenmacher	.08	.06	.03
54	Brian Harper	.10	.08	.04
55	Paul Gibson	.08	.06	.03
56	John Burkett	.08	.06	.03
57	Doug Jones	.08	.06	.03
58	Jose Oquendo	.08	.06	.03
59	Dick Schofield	.08	.06	.03
60	Dickie Thon	.08	.06	.03
61	Ramon Martinez	.50	.40	.20
62	Jay Buhner	.10	.08	.04
63	Mark Portugal	.08	.06	.03
64	Bob Welch	.10	.08	.04
65	Chris Sabo	.20	.15	.08
66	Chuck Cary	.08	.06	.03
67	Mark Langston	.15	.11	.06
68	Joe Boever	.08	.06	.03
69	Jody Reed	.10	.08	.04
70	Alejandro Pena	.08	.06	.03
71	Jeff King	.10	.08	.04
72	Tom Pagnozzi	.08	.06	.03
73	Joe Oliver	.08	.06	.03
74	Mike Witt	.08	.06	.03
75	Hector Villanueva	.15	.11	.06
76	Dan Gladden	.08	.06	.03
77	Dave Justice	2.00	1.50	.80
78	Mike Gallego	.08	.06	.03
79	Tom Candiotti	.08	.06	.03
80	Ozzie Smith	.40	.30	.15
81	Luis Polonia	.08	.06	.03
82	Randy Ready	.08	.06	.03
83	Greg Harris	.08	.06	.03
84	Checklist (Justice)	.25	.20	.10
85	Kevin Mitchell	.30	.25	.12
86	Mark McLemore	.08	.06	.03
87	Terry Steinbach	.08	.06	.03
88	Tom Browning	.10	.08	.04
89	Matt Nokes	.10	.08	.04
90	Mike Harkey	.12	.09	.05
91	Omar Vizquel	.08	.06	.03
92	Dave Bergman	.08	.06	.03
93	Matt Williams	.30	.25	.12
94	Steve Olin	.08	.06	.03
95	Craig Wilson	.20	.15	.08
96	Dave Stieb	.10	.08	.04
97	Ruben Sierra	.50	.40	.20
98	Jay Howell	.08	.06	.03
99	Scott Bradley	.08	.06	.03
100	Eric Yelding	.08	.06	.03
101	Rickey Henderson	.80	.60	.30
102	Jeff Reed	.08	.06	.03
103	Jimmy Key	.10	.08	.04
104	Terry Shumpert	.08	.06	.03
105	Kenny Rogers	.08	.06	.03
106	Cecil Fielder	.80	.60	.30
107	Robby Thompson	.08	.06	.03
108	Alex Cole	.10	.08	.04
109	Randy Milligan	.10	.08	.04
110	Andres Galarraga	.10	.08	.04
111	Bill Spiers	.08	.06	.03
112	Kal Daniels	.15	.11	.06
113	Henry Cotto	.08	.06	.03
114	Casy Candaele	.08	.06	.03
115	Jeff Blauser	.08	.06	.03
116	Robin Yount	.40	.30	.15
117	Ben McDonald	.30	.25	.12
118	Bret Saberhagen	.15	.11	.06
119	Juan Gonzalez	4.00	3.00	1.50
120	Lou Whitaker	.10	.08	.04
121	Ellis Burks	.20	.15	.08
122	Charlie O'Brien	.08	.06	.03
123	John Smiley	.10	.08	.04
124	Tim Burke	.08	.06	.03
125	John Olerud	.40	.30	.15
126	Eddie Murray	.30	.25	.12
127	Greg Maddux	.10	.08	.04
128	Kevin Tapani	.20	.15	.08
129	Ron Gant	.50	.40	.20
130	Jay Bell	.10	.08	.04
131	Chris Hoiles	.20	.15	.08
132	Tom Gordon	.10	.08	.04
133	Kevin Seitzer	.08	.06	.03
134	Jeff Huson	.10	.08	.04
135	Jerry Don Gleaton	.08	.06	.03
136	Jeff Brantley	.08	.06	.03
137	Felix Fermin	.08	.06	.03
138	Mike Devereaux	.10	.08	.04
139	Delino DeShields	.20	.15	.08
140	David Wells	.08	.06	.03
141	Tim Crews	.08	.06	.03
142	Erik Hanson	.15	.11	.06
143	Mark Davidson	.08	.06	.03
144	Tommy Gregg	.08	.06	.03
145	Jim Gantner	.08	.06	.03
146	Jose Lind	.08	.06	.03
147	Danny Tartabull	.15	.11	.06
148	Geno Petralli	.08	.06	.03
149	Travis Fryman	3.00	2.25	1.25
150	Tim Naehring	.20	.15	.08
151	Kevin McReynolds	.12	.09	.05
152	Joe Orsulak	.08	.06	.03
153	Steve Frey	.15	.11	.06
154	Duane Ward	.08	.06	.03
155	Stan Javier	.08	.06	.03
156	Damon Berryhill	.08	.06	.03
157	Gene Larkin	.08	.06	.03
158	Greg Olson	.10	.08	.04
159	Mark Knudson	.08	.06	.03
160	Carmelo Martinez	.08	.06	.03
161	Storm Davis	.08	.06	.03
162	Jim Abbott	.30	.25	.12
163	Len Dykstra	.15	.11	.06
164	Tom Brunansky	.08	.06	.03
165	Dwight Gooden	.25	.20	.10
166	Jose Mesa	.08	.06	.03
167	Oil Can Boyd	.08	.06	.03
168	Barry Larkin	.30	.25	.12
169	Scott Sanderson	.08	.06	.03
170	Mark Grace	.20	.15	.08
171	Mark Guthrie	.08	.06	.03
172	Tom Glavine	.40	.30	.15
173	Gary Sheffield	1.00	.70	.40
174	Checklist	.08	.06	.03
175	Chris James	.08	.06	.03
176	Milt Thompson	.08	.06	.03
177	Donnie Hill	.08	.06	.03
178	Wes Chamberlain	1.75	1.25	.70
179	John Marzano	.08	.06	.03
180	Frank Viola	.15	.11	.06
181	Eric Anthony	.15	.11	.06
182	Jose Canseco	1.00	.70	.40
183	Scott Scudder	.10	.08	.04

#	Player	MT	NR MT	EX		#	Player	MT	NR MT	EX
184	Dave Eiland	.08	.06	.03		276	Tony Fossas	.08	.06	.03
185	Luis Salazar	.08	.06	.03		277	Franklin Stubbs	.08	.06	.03
186	Pedro Munoz	1.25	.90	.50		278	John Kruk	.20	.15	.08
187	Steve Searcy	.08	.06	.03		279	Kevin Gross	.10	.08	.04
188	Don Robinson	.08	.06	.03		280	Von Hayes	.10	.08	.04
189	Sandy Alomar	.15	.11	.06		281	Frank Thomas	6.00	4.50	2.50
190	Jose DeLeon	.08	.06	.03		282	Rob Dibble	.15	.11	.06
191	John Orton	.08	.06	.03		283	Mel Hall	.10	.08	.04
192	Darren Daulton	.08	.06	.03		284	Rick Mahler	.08	.06	.03
193	Mike Morgan	.08	.06	.03		285	Dennis Eckersley	.20	.15	.08
194	Greg Briley	.08	.06	.03		286	Bernard Gilkey	.25	.20	.10
195	Karl Rhodes	.15	.11	.06		287	Dan Plesac	.08	.06	.03
196	Harold Baines	.10	.08	.04		288	Jason Grimsley	.10	.08	.04
197	Bill Doran	.10	.08	.04		289	Mark Lewis	.60	.45	.25
198	Alvaro Espinoza	.08	.06	.03		290	Tony Gwynn	.40	.30	.15
199	Kirk McCaskill	.10	.08	.04		291	Jeff Russell	.10	.08	.04
200	Jose DeJesus	.10	.08	.04		292	Curt Schilling	.10	.08	.04
201	Jack Clark	.10	.08	.04		293	Pascual Perez	.08	.06	.03
202	Daryl Boston	.08	.06	.03		294	Jack Morris	.15	.11	.06
203	Randy Tomlin	.40	.30	.15		295	Hubie Brooks	.10	.08	.04
204	Pedro Guerrero	.15	.11	.06		296	Alex Fernandez	.40	.30	.15
205	Billy Hatcher	.08	.06	.03		297	Harold Reynolds	.10	.08	.04
206	Tim Leary	.08	.06	.03		298	Craig Worthington	.08	.06	.03
207	Ryne Sandberg	.80	.60	.30		299	Willie Wilson	.08	.06	.03
208	Kirby Puckett	.50	.40	.20		300	Mike Maddux	.08	.06	.03
209	Charlie Leibrandt	.08	.06	.03		301	Dave Righetti	.10	.08	.04
210	Rick Honeycutt	.08	.06	.03		302	Paul Molitor	.15	.11	.06
211	Joel Skinner	.08	.06	.03		303	Gary Gaetti	.10	.08	.04
212	Rex Hudler	.08	.06	.03		304	Terry Pendleton	.20	.15	.08
213	Bryan Harvey	.10	.08	.04		305	Kevin Elster	.08	.06	.03
214	Charlie Hayes	.10	.08	.04		306	Scott Fletcher	.08	.06	.03
215	Matt Young	.08	.06	.03		307	Jeff Robinson	.08	.06	.03
216	Terry Kennedy	.08	.06	.03		308	Jesse Barfield	.10	.08	.04
217	Carl Nichols	.08	.06	.03		309	Mike LaCoss	.08	.06	.03
218	Mike Moore	.08	.06	.03		310	Andy Van Slyke	.15	.11	.06
219	Paul O'Neill	.10	.08	.04		311	Glenallen Hill	.15	.11	.06
220	Steve Sax	.10	.08	.04		312	Bud Black	.08	.06	.03
221	Shawn Boskie	.10	.08	.04		313	Kent Hrbek	.15	.11	.06
222	Rich DeLucia	.30	.25	.12		314	Tim Teufel	.08	.06	.03
223	Lloyd Moseby	.08	.06	.03		315	Tony Fernandez	.15	.11	.06
224	Mike Kingery	.08	.06	.03		316	Beau Allred	.08	.06	.03
225	Carlos Baerga	.25	.20	.10		317	Curtis Wilkerson	.08	.06	.03
226	Bryn Smith	.08	.06	.03		318	Bill Sampen	.08	.06	.03
227	Todd Stottlemyre	.10	.08	.04		319	Randy Johnson	.10	.08	.04
228	Julio Franco	.25	.20	.10		320	Mike Heath	.08	.06	.03
229	Jim Gott	.08	.06	.03		321	Sammy Sosa	.12	.09	.05
230	Mike Schooler	.10	.08	.04		322	Mickey Tettleton	.15	.11	.06
231	Steve Finley	.10	.08	.04		323	Jose Vizcaino	.08	.06	.03
232	Dave Henderson	.10	.08	.04		324	John Candelaria	.08	.06	.03
233	Luis Quinones	.08	.06	.03		325	David Howard	.20	.15	.08
234	Mark Whiten	.40	.30	.15		326	Jose Rijo	.10	.08	.04
235	Brian McRae	2.00	1.50	.80		327	Todd Zeile, Todd Zeile	.20	.15	.08
236	Rich Gossage	.10	.08	.04		328	Gene Nelson	.08	.06	.03
237	Rob Deer	.08	.06	.03		329	Dwayne Henry	.08	.06	.03
238	Will Clark	1.00	.70	.40		330	Mike Boddicker	.08	.06	.03
239	Albert Belle	1.00	.70	.40		331	Ozzie Guillen	.10	.08	.04
240	Bob Melvin	.08	.06	.03		332	Sam Horn	.08	.06	.03
241	Larry Walker	.15	.11	.06		333	Wally Whitehurst	.08	.06	.03
242	Dante Bichette	.08	.06	.03		334	Dave Parker	.10	.08	.04
243	Orel Hershiser	.15	.11	.06		335	George Brett, George Brett	.25	.20	.10
244	Pete O'Brien	.08	.06	.03		336	Bobby Thigpen	.10	.08	.04
245	Pete Harnisch	.10	.08	.04		337	Ed Whitson	.08	.06	.03
246	Jeff Treadway	.08	.06	.03		338	Ivan Calderon	.10	.08	.04
247	Julio Machado	.08	.06	.03		339	Mike Pagliarulo	.08	.06	.03
248	Dave Johnson	.08	.06	.03		340	Jack McDowell	.15	.11	.06
249	Kirk Gibson	.12	.09	.05		341	Dana Kiecker	.08	.06	.03
250	Kevin Brown	.08	.06	.03		342	Fred McGriff	.20	.15	.08
251	Milt Cuyler	.50	.40	.20		343	Mark Lee	.08	.06	.03
252	Jeff Reardon	.10	.08	.04		344	Alfredo Griffin	.08	.06	.03
253	David Cone	.15	.11	.06		345	Scott Bankhead	.08	.06	.03
254	Gary Redus	.08	.06	.03		346	Darrin Jackson	.10	.08	.04
255	Junior Noboa	.08	.06	.03		347	Rafael Palmeiro	.25	.20	.10
256	Greg Myers	.08	.06	.03		348	Steve Farr	.08	.06	.03
257	Dennis Cook	.08	.06	.03		349	Hensley Meulens	.10	.08	.04
258	Joe Girardi	.08	.06	.03		350	Danny Cox	.08	.06	.03
259	Allan Anderson	.08	.06	.03		351	Alan Trammell	.15	.11	.06
260	Paul Marak	.20	.15	.08		352	Edwin Nunez	.08	.06	.03
261	Barry Bonds	.50	.40	.20		353	Joe Carter	.25	.20	.10
262	Juan Bell	.10	.08	.04		354	Eric Show	.08	.06	.03
263	Russ Morman	.08	.06	.03		355	Vance Law	.08	.06	.03
264	Checklist (Brett)	.20	.15	.08		356	Jeff Gray	.08	.06	.03
265	Jerald Clark	.10	.08	.04		357	Bobby Bonilla	.30	.25	.12
266	Dwight Evans	.10	.08	.04		358	Ernest Riles	.08	.06	.03
267	Roberto Alomar	.70	.50	.30		359	Ron Hassey	.08	.06	.03
268	Danny Jackson	.08	.06	.03		360	Willie McGee	.12	.09	.05
269	Brian Downing	.08	.06	.03		361	Mackey Sasser	.08	.06	.03
270	John Cerutti	.08	.06	.03		362	Glenn Braggs	.08	.06	.03
271	Robin Ventura	1.50	1.25	.60		363	Mario Diaz	.08	.06	.03
272	Wade Boggs	.40	.30	.15		364	Checklist	.08	.06	.03
273	Dennis Martinez	.15	.11	.06		365	Kevin Bass	.08	.06	.03
274	Andy Benes	.20	.15	.08		366	Pete Incaviglia	.10	.08	.04

		MT	NR MT	EX
367	Luis Sojo	.10	.08	.04
368	Lance Parrish	.10	.08	.04
369	Mark Leonard	.20	.15	.08
370	Heathcliff Slocumb	.10	.08	.04
371	Jimmy Jones	.08	.06	.03
372	Ken Griffey, Jr.	3.00	2.25	1.25
373	Chris Hammond	.10	.08	.04
374	Chili Davis	.10	.08	.04
375	Joey Cora	.08	.06	.03
376	Ken Hill	.15	.11	.06
377	Darryl Strawberry	.50	.40	.20
378	Ron Darling	.08	.06	.03
379	Sid Bream	.08	.06	.03
380	Bill Swift	.10	.08	.04
381	Shawn Abner	.08	.06	.03
382	Eric King	.08	.06	.03
383	Mickey Morandini	.15	.11	.06
384	Carlton Fisk	.30	.25	.12
385	Steve Lake	.08	.06	.03
386	Mike Jeffcoat	.08	.06	.03
387	Darren Holmes	.08	.06	.03
388	Tim Wallach	.10	.08	.04
389	George Bell	.15	.11	.06
390	Craig Lefferts	.08	.06	.03
391	Ernie Whitt	.08	.06	.03
392	Felix Jose	.25	.20	.10
393	Kevin Maas	.30	.25	.12
394	Devon White	.10	.08	.04
395	Otis Nixon	.10	.08	.04
396	Chuck Knoblauch	2.00	1.50	.80
397	Scott Coolbaugh	.08	.06	.03
398	Glenn Davis	.12	.09	.05
399	Manny Lee	.08	.06	.03
400	Andre Dawson	.30	.25	.12
401	Scott Chiamparino	.10	.08	.04
402	Bill Gullickson	.10	.08	.04
403	Lance Johnson	.08	.06	.03
404	Juan Agosto	.08	.06	.03
405	Danny Darwin	.08	.06	.03
406	Barry Jones	.08	.06	.03
407	Larry Andersen	.08	.06	.03
408	Luis Rivera	.08	.06	.03
409	Jaime Navarro	.12	.09	.05
410	Roger McDowell	.08	.06	.03
411	Brett Butler	.10	.08	.04
412	Dale Murphy	.15	.11	.06
413	Tim Raines	.15	.11	.06
414	Norm Charlton	.10	.08	.04
415	Greg Cadaret	.08	.06	.03
416	Chris Nabholz	.15	.11	.06
417	Dave Stewart	.10	.08	.04
418	Rich Gedman	.08	.06	.03
419	Willie Randolph	.10	.08	.04
420	Mitch Williams	.10	.08	.04
421	Brook Jacoby	.08	.06	.03
422	Greg Harris	.08	.06	.03
423	Nolan Ryan	3.00	2.25	1.25
424	Dave Rohde	.10	.08	.04
425	Don Mattingly	.50	.40	.20
426	Greg Gagne	.08	.06	.03
427	Vince Coleman	.10	.08	.04
428	Dan Pasqua	.08	.06	.03
429	Alvin Davis	.08	.06	.03
430	Cal Ripken	1.50	1.25	.60
431	Jamie Quirk	.08	.06	.03
432	Benito Santiago	.15	.11	.06
433	Jose Uribe	.08	.06	.03
434	Candy Maldonado	.08	.06	.03
435	Junior Felix	.10	.08	.04
436	Deion Sanders	.20	.15	.08
437	John Franco	.10	.08	.04
438	Greg Hibbard	.08	.06	.03
439	Floyd Bannister	.08	.06	.03
440	Steve Howe	.08	.06	.03
441	Steve Decker	.25	.20	.10
442	Vicente Palacios	.08	.06	.03
443	Pat Tabler	.08	.06	.03
444	Checklist	.08	.06	.03
445	Mike Felder	.08	.06	.03
446	Al Newman	.08	.06	.03
447	Chris Donnels	.25	.20	.10
448	Rich Rodriguez	.10	.08	.04
449	Turner Ward	.15	.11	.06
450	Bob Walk	.08	.06	.03
451	Gilberto Reyes	.08	.06	.03
452	Mike Jackson	.08	.06	.03
453	Rafael Belliard	.08	.06	.03
454	Wayne Edwards	.08	.06	.03
455	Andy Allanson	.08	.06	.03
456	Dave Smith	.08	.06	.03
457	Gary Carter	.15	.11	.06

		MT	NR MT	EX
458	Warren Cromartie	.08	.06	.03
459	Jack Armstrong	.08	.06	.03
460	Bob Tewksbury	.10	.08	.04
461	Joe Klink	.08	.06	.03
462	Xavier Hernandez	.08	.06	.03
463	Scott Radinsky	.08	.06	.03
464	Jeff Robinson	.08	.06	.03
465	Gregg Jefferies	.15	.11	.06
466	Denny Neagle	.50	.40	.20
467	Carmelo Martinez	.08	.06	.03
468	Donn Pall	.08	.06	.03
469	Bruce Hurst	.10	.08	.04
470	Eric Bullock	.08	.06	.03
471	Rick Aguilera	.10	.08	.04
472	Charlie Hough	.08	.06	.03
473	Carlos Quintana	.08	.06	.03
474	Marty Barrett	.08	.06	.03
475	Kevin Brown	.10	.08	.04
476	Bobby Ojeda	.08	.06	.03
477	Edgar Martinez	.15	.11	.06
478	Bip Roberts	.08	.06	.03
479	Mike Flanagan	.08	.06	.03
480	John Habyan	.08	.06	.03
481	Larry Casian	.10	.08	.04
482	Wally Backman	.08	.06	.03
483	Doug Dascenzo	.08	.06	.03
484	Rick Dempsey	.08	.06	.03
485	Ed Sprague	.10	.08	.04
486	Steve Chitren	.10	.08	.04
487	Mark McGwire	.50	.40	.20
488	Roger Clemens	.70	.50	.30
489	Orlando Merced	.70	.50	.30
490	Rene Gonzales	.08	.06	.03
491	Mike Stanton	.08	.06	.03
492	Al Osuna	.15	.11	.06
493	Rick Cerone	.08	.06	.03
494	Mariano Duncan	.08	.06	.03
495	Zane Smith	.08	.06	.03
496	John Morris	.08	.06	.03
497	Frank Tanana	.08	.06	.03
498	Junior Ortiz	.08	.06	.03
499	Dave Winfield	.25	.20	.10
500	Gary Varsho	.08	.06	.03
501	Chico Walker	.08	.06	.03
502	Ken Caminiti	.08	.06	.03
503	Ken Griffey, Sr.	.10	.08	.04
504	Randy Myers	.10	.08	.04
505	Steve Bedrosian	.08	.06	.03
506	Cory Snyder	.10	.08	.04
507	Cris Carpenter	.08	.06	.03
508	Tim Belcher	.10	.08	.04
509	Jeff Hamilton	.08	.06	.03
510	Steve Avery	1.00	.70	.40
511	Dave Valle	.08	.06	.03
512	Tom Lampkin	.08	.06	.03
513	Shawn Hillegas	.08	.06	.03
514	Reggie Jefferson	.60	.45	.25
515	Ron Karkovice	.08	.06	.03
516	Doug Drabek	.10	.08	.04
517	Tom Henke	.10	.08	.04
518	Chris Bosio	.08	.06	.03
519	Gregg Olson	.12	.09	.05
520	Bob Scanlan	.10	.08	.04
521	Alonzo Powell	.10	.08	.04
522	Jeff Ballard	.08	.06	.03
523	Ray Lankford	1.50	1.25	.60
524	Tommy Greene	.15	.11	.06
525	Mike Timlin	.25	.20	.10
526	Juan Berenguer	.08	.06	.03
527	Scott Erickson	1.00	.70	.40
528	Checklist	.08	.06	.03

1991 Leaf Gold Bonus

Special gold rookie and gold bonus cards were randomly packed in 1991 Leaf packs. The card backs are designed in the same style as the regular Leaf cards with the exception of a gold back instead of silver. The card fronts feature a partial top inset with a banner on the bottom featuring the player's name and position. Variations of series I cards exist. They can be found numbered 265-276 as an extension of the first series. They actually are numbered with a "BC" designation, BC-1-BC12.

		MT	NR MT	EX
	Complete Set:	80.00	60.00	32.00
	Common Player:	2.00	1.50	.80
1	Scott Leius	2.00	1.50	.80
2	Luis Gonzalez	3.00	2.25	1.25
3	Wil Cordero	5.00	3.75	2.00
4	Gary Scott	2.50	2.00	1.00
5	Willie Banks	3.00	2.25	1.25
6	Arthur Rhodes	3.50	2.75	1.50
7	Mo Vaughn	6.00	4.50	2.50
8	Henry Rodriguez	2.00	1.50	.80
9	Todd Van Poppel	8.00	6.00	3.25
10	Reggie Sanders	12.00	9.00	4.75
11	Rico Brogna	4.00	3.00	1.50
12	Mike Mussina	12.00	9.00	4.75
13	Kirk Dressendorfer	3.00	2.25	1.25
14	Jeff Bagwell	12.00	9.00	4.75
15	Pete Schourek	2.00	1.50	.80
16	Wade Taylor	2.00	1.50	.80
17	Pat Kelly	4.00	3.00	1.50
18	Tim Costo, Tim Costo	2.50	2.00	1.00
19	Roger Salkeld	3.00	2.25	1.25
20	Andujar Cedeno	3.00	2.25	1.25
21	Ryan Klesko	9.00	6.75	3.50
22	Mike Huff	2.00	1.50	.80
23	Anthony Young	2.00	1.50	.80
24	Eddie Zosky	2.00	1.50	.80
25	Nolan Ryan	6.00	4.50	2.50
26	Rickey Henderson	5.00	3.75	2.00

The values quoted are intended to reflect the market price.

1992 Leaf

Two 264-card series comprise this 528-card set. The cards feature action photos on both the front and the back. Silver borders surround the photo on the card front. Each Leaf card was also produced in a gold foil version. One gold card was issued per pack and a complete Leaf Gold Edition set can be assembled. Traded players and free agents are shown in uniform with their new teams.

		MT	NR MT	EX
	Complete Set:	45.00	33.00	18.00
	Common Player:	.08	.06	.03
1	Jim Abbott	.20	.15	.08
2	Cal Eldred	.70	.50	.30
3	Bud Black	.08	.06	.03
4	Dave Howard	.08	.06	.03
5	Luis Sojo	.08	.06	.03
6	Gary Scott	.25	.20	.10
7	Joe Oliver	.10	.08	.04
8	Chris Gardner	.20	.15	.08
9	Sandy Alomar	.20	.15	.08
10	Greg Harris	.10	.08	.04
11	Doug Drabek	.15	.11	.06
12	Darryl Hamilton	.15	.11	.06
13	Mike Mussina	2.00	1.50	.80
14	Kevin Tapani	.15	.11	.06
15	Ron Gant	.50	.40	.20
16	Mark McGwire	.50	.40	.20
17	Robin Ventura	.80	.60	.30
18	Pedro Guerrero	.15	.11	.06
19	Roger Clemens	.60	.45	.25
20	Steve Farr	.08	.06	.03
21	Frank Tanana	.08	.06	.03
22	Joe Hesketh	.08	.06	.03
23	Erik Hanson	.12	.09	.05
24	Greg Cadaret	.08	.06	.03
25	Rex Hudler	.08	.06	.03
26	Mark Grace	.20	.15	.08
27	Kelly Gruber, Kelly Gruber	.10	.08	.04
28	Jeff Bagwell	.80	.60	.30
29	Darryl Strawberry	.50	.40	.20
30	Dave Smith	.08	.06	.03
31	Kevin Appier	.15	.11	.06
32	Steve Chitren	.08	.06	.03
33	Kevin Gross	.08	.06	.03
34	Rick Aguilera	.10	.08	.04
35	Juan Guzman	.70	.50	.30
36	Joe Orsulak	.08	.06	.03
37	Tim Raines	.15	.11	.06
38	Harold Reynolds	.10	.08	.04
39	Charlie Hough	.08	.06	.03
40	Tony Phillips	.10	.08	.04
41	Nolan Ryan	.80	.60	.30
42	Vince Coleman	.10	.08	.04
43	Andy Van Slyke	.15	.11	.06
44	Tim Burke	.08	.06	.03
45	Luis Polonia	.08	.06	.03
46	Tom Browning	.10	.08	.04
47	Willie McGee	.10	.08	.04
48	Gary DiSarcina	.10	.08	.04
49	Mark Lewis	.30	.25	.12
50	Phil Plantier	.50	.40	.20
51	Doug Dascenzo	.08	.06	.03
52	Cal Ripken	.80	.60	.30
53	Pedro Munoz	.50	.40	.20
54	Carlos Hernandez	.15	.11	.06
55	Jerald Clark	.10	.08	.04
56	Jeff Brantley	.08	.06	.03
57	Don Mattingly	.50	.40	.20
58	Roger McDowell	.08	.06	.03
59	Steve Avery	.80	.60	.30
60	John Olerud	.20	.15	.08
61	Bill Gullickson	.08	.06	.03
62	Juan Gonzalez	1.00	.70	.40
63	Felix Jose	.30	.25	.12
64	Robin Yount	.25	.20	.10
65	Greg Briley	.08	.06	.03
66	Steve Finley	.12	.09	.05
67	Checklist	.08	.06	.03
68	Tom Gordon	.08	.06	.03
69	Rob Dibble	.15	.11	.06
70	Glenallen Hill	.08	.06	.03
71	Calvin Jones	.08	.06	.03
72	Joe Girardi	.08	.06	.03
73	Barry Larkin	.30	.25	.12
74	Andy Benes	.20	.15	.08
75	Milt Cyler	.08	.06	.03
76	Kevin Bass	.08	.06	.03
77	Pete Harnisch	.10	.08	.04
78	Wilson Alvarez	.10	.08	.04
79	Mike Devereaux	.15	.11	.06
80	Doug Henry	.10	.08	.04
81	Orel Hershiser	.15	.11	.06
82	Shane Mack	.20	.15	.08
83	Mike Macfarlane	.10	.08	.04
84	Thomas Howard	.10	.08	.04
85	Alex Fernandez	.20	.15	.08
86	Reggie Jefferson	.30	.25	.12
87	Leo Gomez	.20	.15	.08
88	Mel Hall	.10	.08	.04

		MT	NR MT	EX
89	Mike Greenwell	.15	.11	.06
90	Jeff Russell	.10	.08	.04
91	Steve Buechele	.10	.08	.04
92	David Cone	.15	.11	.06
93	Kevin Reimer	.10	.08	.04
94	Mark Lemke	.10	.08	.04
95	Bob Tewksbury	.10	.08	.04
96	Zane Smith	.10	.08	.04
97	Mark Eichhorn	.08	.06	.03
98	Kirby Puckett	.80	.60	.30
99	Paul O'Neill	.12	.09	.05
100	Dennis Eckersley	.25	.20	.10
101	Duane Ward	.10	.08	.04
102	Matt Nokes	.10	.08	.04
103	Mo Vaughn	.30	.25	.12
104	Pat Kelly	.10	.08	.04
105	Ron Karkovice	.08	.06	.03
106	Bill Spiers	.08	.06	.03
107	Gary Gaetti	.10	.08	.04
108	Mackey Sasser	.08	.06	.03
109	Robby Thompson	.10	.08	.04
110	Marvin Freeman	.08	.06	.03
111	Jimmy Key	.10	.08	.04
112	Dwight Gooden	.25	.20	.10
113	Charlie Leibrandt	.08	.06	.03
114	Devon White	.10	.08	.04
115	Charles Nagy	.30	.25	.12
116	Rickey Henderson	.50	.40	.20
117	Paul Assenmacher	.08	.06	.03
118	Junior Felix	.10	.08	.04
119	Julio Franco	.20	.15	.08
120	Norm Charlton	.10	.08	.04
121	Scott Servais	.10	.08	.04
122	Gerald Perry	.08	.06	.03
123	Brian McRae	.30	.25	.12
124	Don Slaught	.08	.06	.03
125	Juan Samuel	.08	.06	.03
126	Harold Baines	.15	.11	.06
127	Scott Livingstone	.15	.11	.06
128	Jay Buhner	.10	.08	.04
129	Darrin Jackson	.10	.08	.04
130	Luis Mercedes	.20	.15	.08
131	Brian Harper	.10	.08	.04
132	Howard Johnson	.15	.11	.06
133	Checklist	.08	.06	.03
134	Dante Bichette	.08	.06	.03
135	Dave Righetti	.10	.08	.04
136	Jeff Montgomery	.10	.08	.04
137	Joe Grahe	.10	.08	.04
138	Delino DeShields	.25	.20	.10
139	Jose Rijo	.12	.09	.05
140	Ken Caminiti	.10	.08	.04
141	Steve Olin	.10	.08	.04
142	Kurt Stillwell	.10	.08	.04
143	Jay Bell	.12	.09	.05
144	Jaime Navarro	.12	.09	.05
145	Ben McDonald	.30	.25	.12
146	Greg Gagne	.08	.06	.03
147	Jeff Blauser	.10	.08	.04
148	Carney Lansford	.10	.08	.04
149	Ozzie Guillen	.10	.08	.04
150	Milt Thompson	.08	.06	.03
151	Jeff Reardon	.15	.11	.06
152	Scott Sanderson	.08	.06	.03
153	Cecil Fielder	.70	.50	.30
154	Greg Harris	.08	.06	.03
155	Rich DeLucia	.08	.06	.03
156	Roberto Kelly	.30	.25	.12
157	Bryn Smith	.08	.06	.03
158	Chuck McElroy	.08	.06	.03
159	Tom Henke	.12	.09	.05
160	Luis Gonzalez	.30	.25	.12
161	Steve Wilson	.08	.06	.03
162	Shawn Boskie	.08	.06	.03
163	Mark Davis	.08	.06	.03
164	Mike Moore	.10	.08	.04
165	Mike Scioscia	.10	.08	.04
166	Scott Erickson	.30	.25	.12
167	Todd Stottlemyre	.10	.08	.04
168	Alvin Davis	.10	.08	.04
169	Greg Hibbard	.10	.08	.04
170	David Valle	.08	.06	.03
171	Dave Winfield	.40	.30	.15
172	Alan Trammell	.12	.09	.05
173	Kenny Rogers	.08	.06	.03
174	John Franco	.10	.08	.04
175	Jose Lind	.08	.06	.03
176	Pete Schourek	.10	.08	.04
177	Von Hayes	.08	.06	.03
178	Chris Hammond	.10	.08	.04
179	John Burkett	.08	.06	.03
180	Dickie Thon	.08	.06	.03
181	Joel Skinner	.08	.06	.03
182	Scott Cooper	.12	.09	.05
183	Andre Dawson	.40	.30	.15
184	Billy Ripken	.08	.06	.03
185	Kevin Mitchell	.25	.20	.10
186	Brett Butler	.10	.08	.04
187	Tony Fernandez	.10	.08	.04
188	Cory Snyder	.10	.08	.04
189	John Habyan	.08	.06	.03
190	Dennis Martinez	.12	.09	.05
191	John Smoltz	.15	.11	.06
192	Greg Myers	.08	.06	.03
193	Rob Deer	.10	.08	.04
194	Ivan Rodriguez	.80	.60	.30
195	Ray Lankford	.50	.40	.20
196	Bill Wegman	.10	.08	.04
197	Edgar Martinez	.15	.11	.06
198	Darryl Kile	.10	.08	.04
199	Checklist	.08	.06	.03
200	Brent Mayne	.08	.06	.03
201	Larry Walker	.20	.15	.08
202	Carlos Baerga	.25	.20	.10
203	Russ Swan	.08	.06	.03
204	Mike Morgan	.10	.08	.04
205	Hal Morris	.20	.15	.08
206	Tony Gwynn	.60	.45	.25
207	Mark Leiter	.08	.06	.03
208	Kirt Manwaring	.08	.06	.03
209	Al Osuna	.08	.06	.03
210	Bobby Thigpen	.15	.11	.06
211	Chris Hoiles	.70	.50	.30
212	B.J. Surhoff	.10	.08	.04
213	Lenny Harris	.08	.06	.03
214	Scott Leius	.10	.08	.04
215	Gregg Jefferies	.25	.20	.10
216	Bruce Hurst	.10	.08	.04
217	Steve Sax	.12	.09	.05
218	Dave Otto	.08	.06	.03
219	Sam Horn	.08	.06	.03
220	Charlie Hayes	.10	.08	.04
221	Frank Viola	.30	.25	.12
222	Jose Guzman	.10	.08	.04
223	Gary Redus	.08	.06	.03
224	Dave Gallagher	.08	.06	.03
225	Dean Palmer	.60	.45	.25
226	Greg Olson	.10	.08	.04
227	Jose DeLeon	.08	.06	.03
228	Mike LaValliere	.08	.06	.03
229	Mark Langston	.15	.11	.06
230	Chuck Knoblauch	.80	.60	.30
231	Bill Doran	.10	.08	.04
232	Dave Henderson	.10	.08	.04
233	Roberto Alomar	.50	.40	.20
234	Scott Fletcher	.08	.06	.03
235	Tim Naehring	.08	.06	.03
236	Mike Gallego	.08	.06	.03
237	Lance Johnson	.10	.08	.04
238	Paul Molitor	.15	.11	.06
239	Dan Gladden	.08	.06	.03
240	Willie Randolph	.10	.08	.04
241	Will Clark	.70	.50	.30
242	Sid Bream	.08	.06	.03
243	Derek Bell	.50	.40	.20
244	Bill Pecota	.08	.06	.03
245	Terry Pendleton	.15	.11	.06
246	Randy Ready	.08	.06	.03
247	Jack Armstrong	.08	.06	.03
248	Todd Van Poppel	.70	.50	.30
249	Shawon Dunston	.10	.08	.04
250	Bobby Rose	.08	.06	.03
251	Jeff Huson	.08	.06	.03
252	Bip Roberts	.12	.09	.05
253	Doug Jones	.10	.08	.04
254	Lee Smith	.15	.11	.06
255	George Brett	.25	.20	.10
256	Randy Tomlin	.10	.08	.04
257	Todd Benzinger	.08	.06	.03
258	Dave Stewart	.15	.11	.06
259	Mark Carreon	.08	.06	.03
260	Pete O'Brien	.08	.06	.03
261	Tim Teufel	.08	.06	.03
262	Bob Milacki	.08	.06	.03
263	Mark Guthrie	.08	.06	.03
264	Darrin Fletcher	.08	.06	.03
265	Omar Vizquel	.08	.06	.03
266	Chris Bosio	.10	.08	.04
267	Jose Canseco	.60	.45	.25
268	Mike Boddicker	.08	.06	.03
269	Lance Parrish	.10	.08	.04
270	Jose Vizcaino	.08	.06	.03

		MT	NR MT	EX				MT	NR MT	EX
271	Chris Sabo	.15	.11	.06	363	Orlando Merced	.10	.08	.04
272	Royce Clayton	.20	.15	.08	364	Mike Bordick	.20	.15	.08
273	Marquis Grissom	.20	.15	.08	365	Dion James	.08	.06	.03
274	Fred McGriff	.20	.15	.08	366	Jack Clark	.10	.08	.04
275	Barry Bonds	.60	.45	.25	367	Mike Stanley	.08	.06	.03
277	Gregg Olson	.12	.09	.05	368	Randy Velarde	.08	.06	.03
278	Greg Vaughn, Dave Hollins	.20	.15	.08	369	Dan Pasqua	.08	.06	.03
279	Tom Glavine	.20	.15	.08	370	Pat Listach	1.75	1.25	.60
280	Bryan Hickerson	.15	.11	.06	371	Mike Fitzgerald	.08	.06	.03
281	Scott Radinsky	.08	.06	.03	372	Tom Foley	.08	.06	.03
282	Omar Olivares	.10	.08	.04	373	Matt Williams	.15	.11	.06
283	Ivan Calderon	.12	.09	.05	374	Brian Hunter	.15	.11	.06
284	Kevin Maas	.15	.11	.06	375	Joe Carter	.25	.20	.10
285	Mickey Tettleton	.15	.11	.06	376	Bret Saberhagen	.15	.11	.06
286	Wade Boggs	.30	.25	.12	377	Mike Stanton	.08	.06	.03
287	Stan Belinda	.08	.06	.03	378	Hubie Brooks	.08	.06	.03
288	Bret Barberie	.20	.15	.08	379	Eric Bell	.12	.09	.05
289	Jose Oquendo	.08	.06	.03	380	Walt Weiss	.10	.08	.04
290	Frank Castillo	.12	.09	.05	381	Danny Jackson	.08	.06	.03
291	Dave Stieb	.10	.08	.04	382	Manuel Lee	.08	.06	.03
292	Tommy Greene	.12	.09	.05	383	Ruben Sierra	.30	.25	.12
293	Eric Karros	1.00	.70	.40	384	Greg Swindell	.15	.11	.06
294	Greg Maddux	.25	.20	.10	385	Ryan Bowen	.12	.09	.05
295	Jim Eisenreich	.08	.06	.03	386	Kevin Ritz	.10	.08	.04
296	Rafael Palmeiro	.15	.11	.06	387	Curtis Wilkerson	.08	.06	.03
297	Ramon Martinez	.20	.15	.08	388	Gary Varsho	.08	.06	.03
298	Tim Wallach	.10	.08	.04	389	Dave Hansen	.08	.06	.03
299	Jim Thome	.50	.40	.20	390	Bob Welch	.10	.08	.04
300	Chito Martinez	.10	.08	.04	391	Lou Whitaker	.12	.09	.05
301	Mitch Williams	.12	.09	.05	392	Ken Griffey, Jr.	1.00	.70	.40
302	Randy Johnson	.10	.08	.04	393	Mike Maddux	.08	.06	.03
303	Carlton Fisk	.20	.15	.08	394	Arthur Rhodes	.15	.11	.06
304	Travis Fryman	.50	.40	.20	395	Chili Davis	.10	.08	.04
305	Bobby Witt	.10	.08	.04	396	Eddie Murray	.15	.11	.06
306	Dave Magadan	.10	.08	.04	397	Checklist	.08	.06	.03
307	Alex Cole	.08	.06	.03	398	Dave Cochrane	.08	.06	.03
308	Bobby Bonilla	.50	.40	.20	399	Kevin Seitzer	.10	.08	.04
309	Bryan Harvey	.12	.09	.05	400	Ozzie Smith	.20	.15	.08
310	Rafael Belliard	.08	.06	.03	401	Paul Sorrento	.10	.08	.04
311	Mariano Duncan	.08	.06	.03	402	Les Lancaster	.08	.06	.03
312	Chuck Crim	.08	.06	.03	403	Junior Noboa	.08	.06	.03
313	John Kruk	.15	.11	.06	404	Dave Justice	.40	.30	.15
314	Ellis Burks	.15	.11	.06	405	Andy Ashby	.12	.09	.05
315	Craig Biggio	.15	.11	.06	406	Danny Tartabull	.15	.11	.06
316	Glenn Davis	.10	.08	.04	407	Bill Swift	.10	.08	.04
317	Ryne Sandberg	.70	.50	.30	408	Craig Lefferts	.10	.08	.04
318	Mike Sharperson	.08	.06	.03	409	Tom Candiotti	.10	.08	.04
319	Rich Rodriguez	.08	.06	.03	410	Lance Blankenship	.08	.06	.03
320	Lee Guetterman	.08	.06	.03	411	Jeff Tackett	.15	.11	.06
321	Benito Santiago	.15	.11	.06	412	Sammy Sosa	.10	.08	.04
322	Jose Offerman	.12	.09	.05	413	Jody Reed	.10	.08	.04
323	Tony Pena	.10	.08	.04	414	Bruce Ruffin	.08	.06	.03
324	Pat Borders	.10	.08	.04	415	Gene Larkin	.08	.06	.03
325	Mike Henneman	.10	.08	.04	416	John Vanderwal	.20	.15	.08
326	Kevin Brown	.15	.11	.06	417	Tim Belcher	.10	.08	.04
327	Chris Nabholz	.10	.08	.04	418	Steve Frey	.08	.06	.03
328	Franklin Stubbs	.08	.06	.03	419	Dick Schofield	.08	.06	.03
329	Tino Martinez	.15	.11	.06	420	Jeff King	.10	.08	.04
330	Mickey Morandini	.15	.11	.06	421	Kim Batiste	.12	.09	.05
331	Checklist	.08	.06	.03	422	Jack McDowell	.15	.11	.06
332	Mark Gubicza	.10	.08	.04	423	Damon Berryhill	.08	.06	.03
333	Bill Landrum	.08	.06	.03	424	Gary Wayne	.08	.06	.03
334	Mark Whiten	.15	.11	.06	425	Jack Morris	.15	.11	.06
335	Darren Daulton	.20	.15	.08	426	Moises Alou	.20	.15	.08
336	Rick Wilkins	.12	.09	.05	427	Mark McLemore	.08	.06	.03
337	Brian Jordan	.50	.40	.20	428	Juan Guerrero	.15	.11	.06
338	Kevin Ward	.12	.09	.05	429	Scott Scudder	.08	.06	.03
339	Ruben Amaro	.12	.09	.05	430	Eric Davis	.20	.15	.08
340	Trevor Wilson	.10	.08	.04	431	Joe Slusarski	.10	.08	.04
341	Andujar Cedeno	.15	.11	.06	432	Todd Zeile	.15	.11	.06
342	Michael Huff	.08	.06	.03	433	Dwayne Henry	.08	.06	.03
343	Brady Anderson	.15	.11	.06	434	Cliff Brantley	.15	.11	.06
344	Craig Grebeck	.08	.06	.03	435	Butch Henry	.15	.11	.06
345	Bobby Ojeda	.08	.06	.03	436	Todd Worrell	.10	.08	.04
346	Mike Pagliarulo	.08	.06	.03	437	Bob Scanlan	.08	.06	.03
347	Terry Shumpert	.08	.06	.03	439	Wally Joyner, John Flaherty	.12	.09	.05
348	Dann Bilardello	.08	.06	.03	440	Brian Downing	.08	.06	.03
349	Frank Thomas	1.75	1.25	.70	441	Darren Lewis	.12	.09	.05
350	Albert Belle	.50	.40	.20	442	Gary Carter	.15	.11	.06
351	Jose Mesa	.08	.06	.03	443	Wally Ritchie	.08	.06	.03
352	Rich Monteleone	.08	.06	.03	444	Chris Jones	.10	.08	.04
353	Bob Walk	.08	.06	.03	445	Jeff Kent	.15	.11	.06
354	Monty Fariss	.10	.08	.04	446	Gary Sheffield	.30	.25	.12
355	Luis Rivera	.08	.06	.03	447	Ron Darling	.10	.08	.04
356	Anthony Young	.12	.09	.05	448	Deion Sanders	.30	.25	.12
357	Geno Petralli	.08	.06	.03	449	Andres Galarraga	.10	.08	.04
358	Otis Nixon	.10	.08	.04	450	Chuck Finley	.10	.08	.04
359	Tom Pagnozzi	.10	.08	.04	451	Derek Lilliquist	.08	.06	.03
360	Reggie Sanders	.50	.40	.20	452	Carl Willis	.08	.06	.03
361	Lee Stevens	.08	.06	.03	453	Wes Chamberlain	.10	.08	.04
362	Kent Hrbek	.15	.11	.06	454	Roger Mason	.08	.06	.03

		MT	NR MT	EX
455	Spike Owen	.08	.06	.03
456	Thomas Howard	.08	.06	.03
457	Dave Martinez	.08	.06	.03
458	Pete Incaviglia	.10	.08	.04
459	Keith Miller	.10	.08	.04
460	Mike Fetters	.08	.06	.03
461	Paul Gibson	.08	.06	.03
462	George Bell	.15	.11	.06
463	Checklist	.08	.06	.03
464	Terry Mulholland	.10	.08	.04
465	Storm Davis	.08	.06	.03
466	Gary Pettis	.08	.06	.03
467	Randy Bush	.08	.06	.03
468	Ken Hill	.12	.09	.05
469	Rheal Cormier	.12	.09	.05
470	Andy Stankiewicz	.25	.20	.10
471	Dave Burba	.08	.06	.03
472	Henry Cotto	.08	.06	.03
473	Dale Sveum	.08	.06	.03
474	Rich Gossage	.10	.08	.04
475	William Suero	.15	.11	.06
476	Doug Strange	.08	.06	.03
477	Bill Krueger	.10	.08	.04
478	John Wetteland	.15	.11	.06
479	Melido Perez	.10	.08	.04
480	Lonnie Smith	.10	.08	.04
481	Mike Jackson	.08	.06	.03
482	Mike Gardiner	.08	.06	.03
483	David Wells	.08	.06	.03
484	Barry Jones	.08	.06	.03
485	Scott Bankhead	.08	.06	.03
486	Terry Leach	.08	.06	.03
487	Vince Horseman	.15	.11	.06
488	Dave Eiland	.08	.06	.03
489	Alejandro Pena	.08	.06	.03
490	Julio Valera	.15	.11	.06
491	Joe Boever	.08	.06	.03
492	Paul Miller	.15	.11	.06
493	Arci Cianfrocco	.25	.20	.10
494	Dave Fleming	1.00	.70	.40
495	Kyle Abbott	.12	.09	.05
496	Chad Kreuter	.08	.06	.03
497	Chris James	.08	.06	.03
498	Donnie Hill	.08	.06	.03
499	Jacob Brumfield	.15	.11	.06
500	Ricky Bones	.10	.08	.04
501	Terry Steinbach	.10	.08	.04
502	Bernard Gilkey	.10	.08	.04
503	Dennis Cook	.08	.06	.03
504	Lenny Dykstra	.15	.11	.06
505	Mike Bielecki	.08	.06	.03
506	Bob Kipper	.08	.06	.03
507	Jose Melendez	.15	.11	.06
508	Rick Sutcliffe	.12	.09	.05
509	Ken Patterson	.08	.06	.03
510	Andy Allanson	.08	.06	.03
511	Al Newman	.08	.06	.03
512	Mark Gardner	.08	.06	.03
513	Jeff Schaefer	.08	.06	.03
514	Jim McNamara	.15	.11	.06
515	Peter Hoy	.12	.09	.05
516	Curt Schilling	.12	.09	.05
517	Kirk McCaskill	.10	.08	.04
518	Chris Gwynn	.08	.06	.03
519	Sid Fernandez	.12	.09	.05
520	Jeff Parrett	.08	.06	.03
521	Scott Ruskin	.08	.06	.03
522	Kevin McReynolds	.12	.09	.05
523	Rick Cerone	.08	.06	.03
524	Jesse Orosco	.08	.06	.03
525	Troy Afenir	.08	.06	.03
526	John Smiley	.12	.09	.05
527	Dale Murphy	.12	.09	.05
528	Leaf Set Card	.08	.06	.03

Values quoted in this guide reflect the retail price of a card — the price a collector can expect to pay when buying a card from a dealer. The wholesale price — that which a collector can expect to receive from a dealer when selling cards — will be significantly lower, depending on desirability and condition.

1992 Leaf Studio

Donruss introduced the Studio line in 1991 and released another 264-card set entitled Leaf Studio for 1992. The cards feature a unique player closeup with a large black and white photo behind the player. Tan borders surround the photos. The cards were only released in foil packs. Special Heritage insert cards featuring top players could be found in foil packs. Eight Heritage cards were released.

		MT	NR MT	EX
Complete Set:		30.00	22.00	12.00
Common Player:		.10	.08	.04
1	Steve Avery	.50	.40	.20
2	Sid Bream	.10	.08	.04
3	Ron Gant	.20	.15	.08
4	Tom Glavine	.30	.25	.12
5	David Justice	.50	.40	.20
6	Mark Lemke	.10	.08	.04
7	Greg Olson	.10	.08	.04
8	Terry Pendleton	.20	.15	.08
9	Deion Sanders	.30	.25	.12
10	John Smoltz	.15	.11	.06
11	Doug Dascenzo	.10	.08	.04
12	Andre Dawson	.20	.15	.08
13	Joe Girardi	.10	.08	.04
14	Mark Grace	.15	.11	.06
15	Greg Maddux	.20	.15	.08
16	Chuck McElroy	.10	.08	.04
17	Mike Morgan	.10	.08	.04
18	Ryne Sandberg	.80	.60	.30
19	Gary Scott	.20	.15	.08
20	Sammy Sosa	.12	.09	.05
21	Norm Charlton	.12	.09	.05
22	Rob Dibble	.15	.11	.06
23	Barry Larkin	.25	.20	.10
24	Hal Morris	.10	.08	.04
25	Paul O'Neill	.10	.08	.04
26	Jose Rijo	.12	.09	.05
27	Bip Roberts	.15	.11	.06
28	Chris Sabo	.15	.11	.06
29	Reggie Sanders	.80	.60	.30
30	Greg Swindell	.15	.11	.06
31	Jeff Bagwell	.80	.60	.30
32	Craig Biggio	.15	.11	.06
33	Ken Caminiti	.10	.08	.04
34	Andujar Cedeno	.15	.11	.06
35	Steve Finley	.15	.11	.06
36	Pete Harnisch	.12	.09	.05
37	Butch Henry	.15	.11	.06
38	Doug Jones	.10	.08	.04
39	Darryl Kile	.15	.11	.06
40	Eddie Taubensee	.15	.11	.06
41	Brett Butler	.12	.09	.05
42	Tom Candiotti	.12	.09	.05
43	Eric Davis	.15	.11	.06
44	Orel Hershiser	.15	.11	.06
45	Eric Karros	1.50	1.25	.60
46	Ramon Martinez	.15	.11	.06
47	Jose Offerman	.15	.11	.06
48	Mike Scioscia	.10	.08	.04
49	Mike Sharperson	.10	.08	.04
50	Darryl Strawberry	.25	.20	.10
51	Bret Barberie	.15	.11	.06
52	Ivan Calderon	.15	.11	.06
53	Gary Carter	.15	.11	.06
54	Delino DeShields	.15	.11	.06
55	Marquis Grissom	.20	.15	.08

		MT	NR MT	EX				MT	NR MT	EX
56	Ken Hill	.15	.11	.06		147	Von Hayes	.10	.08	.04
57	Dennis Martinez	.12	.09	.05		148	Mark Langston	.15	.11	.06
58	Spike Owen	.10	.08	.04		149	Lance Parrish	.10	.08	.04
59	Larry Walker	.25	.20	.10		150	Lee Stevens	.10	.08	.04
60	Tim Wallach	.12	.09	.05		151	George Bell	.15	.11	.06
61	Bobby Bonilla	.25	.20	.10		152	Alex Fernandez	.15	.11	.06
62	Tim Burke	.10	.08	.04		153	Greg Hibbard	.10	.08	.04
63	Vince Coleman	.15	.11	.06		154	Lance Johnson	.10	.08	.04
64	John Franco	.12	.09	.05		155	Kirk McCaskill	.10	.08	.04
65	Dwight Gooden	.25	.20	.10		156	Tim Raines	.15	.11	.06
66	Todd Hundley	.15	.11	.06		157	Steve Sax	.15	.11	.06
67	Howard Johnson	.15	.11	.06		158	Bobby Thigpen	.15	.11	.06
68	Eddie Murray	.15	.11	.06		159	Frank Thomas	3.00	2.25	1.25
69	Bret Saberhagen	.15	.11	.06		160	Robin Ventura	.60	.45	.25
70	Anthony Young	.15	.11	.06		161	Sandy Alomar, Jr.	.25	.20	.10
71	Kim Batiste	.15	.11	.06		162	Jack Armstrong	.10	.08	.04
72	Wes Chamberlain	.15	.11	.06		163	Carlos Baerga	.25	.20	.10
73	Darren Daulton	.25	.20	.10		164	Albert Belle	.25	.20	.10
74	Mariano Duncan	.10	.08	.04		165	Alex Cole	.10	.08	.04
75	Lenny Dykstra	.15	.11	.06		166	Glenallen Hill	.10	.08	.04
76	John Kruk	.15	.11	.06		167	Mark Lewis	.15	.11	.06
77	Mickey Morandini	.15	.11	.06		168	Kenny Lofton	.80	.60	.30
78	Terry Mulholland	.10	.08	.04		169	Paul Sorrento	.10	.08	.04
79	Dale Murphy	.15	.11	.06		170	Mark Whiten	.15	.11	.06
80	Mitch Williams	.15	.11	.06		171	Milt Cuyler	.10	.08	.04
81	Jay Bell	.15	.11	.06		172	Rob Deer	.10	.08	.04
82	Barry Bonds	.50	.40	.20		173	Cecil Fielder	.50	.40	.20
83	Steve Buechele	.10	.08	.04		174	Travis Fryman	1.25	.90	.50
84	Doug Drabek	.15	.11	.06		175	Mike Henneman	.10	.08	.04
85	Mike LaValliere	.10	.08	.04		176	Tony Phillips	.10	.08	.04
86	Jose Lind	.10	.08	.04		177	Frank Tanana	.10	.08	.04
87	Denny Neagle	.15	.11	.06		178	Mickey Tettleton	.15	.11	.06
88	Randy Tomlin	.15	.11	.06		179	Alan Trammell	.15	.11	.06
89	Andy Van Slyke	.15	.11	.06		180	Lou Whitaker	.15	.11	.06
90	Gary Varsho	.10	.08	.04		181	George Brett	.20	.15	.08
91	Pedro Guererro	.10	.08	.04		182	Tom Gordon	.10	.08	.04
92	Rex Hudler	.10	.08	.04		183	Mark Gubicza	.10	.08	.04
93	Brian Jordan	.50	.40	.20		184	Gregg Jefferies	.20	.15	.08
94	Felix Jose	.20	.15	.08		185	Wally Joyner	.20	.15	.08
95	Donovan Osborne	.20	.15	.08		186	Brent Mayne	.10	.08	.04
96	Tom Pagnozzi	.10	.08	.04		187	Brian McRae	.15	.11	.06
97	Lee Smith	.15	.11	.06		188	Kevin McReynolds	.15	.11	.06
98	Ozzie Smith	.25	.20	.10		189	Keith Miller	.10	.08	.04
99	Todd Worrell	.10	.08	.04		190	Jeff Montgomery	.10	.08	.04
100	Todd Zeile	.15	.11	.06		191	Dante Bichette	.10	.08	.04
101	Andy Benes	.15	.11	.06		192	Ricky Bones	.10	.08	.04
102	Jerald Clark	.10	.08	.04		193	Scott Fletcher	.10	.08	.04
103	Tony Fernandez	.10	.08	.04		194	Paul Molitor	.20	.15	.08
104	Tony Gwynn	.50	.40	.20		195	Jaime Navarro	.15	.11	.06
105	Greg Harris	.10	.08	.04		196	Franklin Stubbs	.10	.08	.04
106	Fred McGriff	.25	.20	.10		197	B.J. Surhoff	.10	.08	.04
107	Benito Santiago	.15	.11	.06		198	Greg Vaughn	.10	.08	.04
108	Gary Sheffield	.80	.60	.30		199	Bill Wegman	.10	.08	.04
109	Kurt Stillwell	.10	.08	.04		200	Robin Yount	.20	.15	.08
110	Tim Teufel	.10	.08	.04		201	Rick Aguilera	.12	.09	.05
111	Kevin Bass	.10	.08	.04		202	Scott Erickson	.15	.11	.06
112	Jeff Brantley	.10	.08	.04		203	Greg Gagne	.10	.08	.04
113	John Burkett	.10	.08	.04		204	Brian Harper	.10	.08	.04
114	Will Clark	.80	.60	.30		205	Kent Hrbek	.15	.11	.06
115	Royce Clayton	.20	.15	.08		206	Scott Leius	.10	.08	.04
116	Mike Jackson	.10	.08	.04		207	Shane Mack	.15	.11	.06
117	Darren Lewis	.12	.09	.05		208	Pat Mahomes	.50	.40	.20
118	Bill Swift	.10	.08	.04		209	Kirby Puckett	.80	.60	.30
119	Robby Thompson	.10	.08	.04		210	John Smiley	.10	.08	.04
120	Matt Williams	.15	.11	.06		211	Mike Gallego	.10	.08	.04
121	Brady Anderson	.20	.15	.08		212	Charlie Hayes	.10	.08	.04
122	Glenn Davis	.12	.09	.05		213	Pat Kelly	.12	.09	.05
123	Mike Devereaux	.15	.11	.06		214	Roberto Kelly	.15	.11	.06
124	Chris Hoiles	.20	.15	.08		215	Kevin Maas	.15	.11	.06
125	Sam Horn	.10	.08	.04		216	Don Mattingly	.20	.15	.08
126	Ben McDonald	.15	.11	.06		217	Matt Nokes	.10	.08	.04
127	Mike Mussina	2.00	1.50	.80		218	Melido Perez	.10	.08	.04
128	Gregg Olson	.15	.11	.06		219	Scott Sanderson	.10	.08	.04
129	Cal Ripken	1.00	.70	.40		220	Danny Tartabull	.15	.11	.06
130	Rick Sutcliffe	.15	.11	.06		221	Harold Baines	.15	.11	.06
131	Wade Boggs	.20	.15	.08		222	Jose Canseco	.80	.60	.30
132	Roger Clemens	.80	.60	.30		223	Dennis Eckersley	.20	.15	.08
133	Greg Harris	.10	.08	.04		224	Dave Henderson	.10	.08	.04
134	Tim Naehring	.10	.08	.04		225	Carney Lansford	.10	.08	.04
135	Tony Pena	.10	.08	.04		226	Mark McGwire	.80	.60	.30
136	Phil Plantier	.30	.25	.12		227	Mike Moore	.10	.08	.04
137	Jeff Reardon	.15	.11	.06		228	Randy Ready	.10	.08	.04
138	Jody Reed	.10	.08	.04		229	Terry Steinbach	.10	.08	.04
139	Mo Vaughn	.10	.08	.04		230	Dave Stewart	.15	.11	.06
140	Frank Viola	.20	.15	.08		231	Jay Buhner	.10	.08	.04
141	Jim Abbott	.20	.15	.08		232	Ken Griffey, Jr.	1.75	1.25	.70
142	Hubie Brooks	.10	.08	.04		233	Erik Hanson	.10	.08	.04
143	Chad Curtis	.20	.15	.08		234	Randy Johnson	.10	.08	.04
144	Gary DiSarcina	.10	.08	.04		235	Edgar Martinez	.15	.11	.06
145	Chuck Finley	.15	.11	.06		236	Tino Martinez	.15	.11	.06
146	Bryan Harvey	.15	.11	.06		237	Kevin Mitchell	.15	.11	.06

		MT	NR MT	EX
238	Pete O'Brien	.10	.08	.04
239	Harold Reynolds	.10	.08	.04
240	David Valle	.10	.08	.04
241	Julio Franco	.15	.11	.06
242	Juan Gonzalez	1.50	1.25	.60
243	Jose Guzman	.15	.11	.06
244	Rafael Palmeiro	.15	.11	.06
245	Dean Palmer	.15	.11	.06
246	Ivan Rodriguez	.80	.60	.30
247	Jeff Russell	.10	.08	.04
248	Nolan Ryan	1.50	1.25	.60
249	Ruben Sierra	.50	.40	.20
250	Dickie Thon	.10	.08	.04
251	Roberto Alomar	.60	.45	.25
252	Derek Bell	.20	.15	.08
253	Pat Borders	.10	.08	.04
254	Joe Carter	.25	.20	.10
255	Kelly Gruber	.10	.08	.04
256	Juan Guzman	2.00	1.50	.80
257	Jack Morris	.15	.11	.06
258	John Olerud	.20	.15	.08
259	Devon White	.10	.08	.04
260	Dave Winfield	.25	.20	.10
261	Checklist	.10	.08	.04
262	Checklist	.10	.08	.04
263	Checklist	.10	.08	.04
264	History Card	.10	.08	.04

Wrong backs, blank backs

Collectors occasionally find recent (1980s) cards which have wrong backs (player on front doesn't match bio/stats on back) or blank backs. Such cards result from mistakes in the printing process. They aren't very popular with collectors, so they have little, if any, premium value. Most collectors feel they are merely damaged cards and value them lower than correctly printed specimens. The only exception seems to be currently hot superstar or rookie cards, for which a few collectors are willing to pay premiums.

Collector-only issues

Collectors may find some recent issues not included in this volume. In most cases these are illegal, unauthorized "collector-only" issues. Such cards often show nothing but the player's photo and his name on the front, and his name and perhaps a line or two of statistics on the back. The sets usually lack a manufacturer's name. They are often sold at shows and in shops, and frequently carry high price tags.

The cards are not legitimate issues. They can be printed and reprinted at will, so they lack any scarcity value.

Card Company Addresses

AW Sports, 17842 Mitchell North, Suite 200, Irvine, CA 92714.
Action Packed, 851 N. Villa, Suite 101, Villa Park, Il 60181.
Bowman — See Topps.
Classic Games Inc., 8055 Troon Circle, Suite C, Austell, GA 30001.
Collector's Edge, P.O. Box 9010, Denver, CO 80209.
Courtside, 1247 Broadway Ave., Burlingame, CA 94010
Fleer Corporation, 1120 Rte. 73, Mt. Laurel, NJ 08054.
Front Row, 201 W. Main St., Dalton, PA 18414.
Kayo, One Meadowlands Plaza, Suite 1020, East Rutherford, NJ 07073.
Leaf/Donruss, 2355 Waukegan Road, Bannockburn, Il 60015.
Megacards, Inc., 5650 Wattsburg Rd., Erie, PA 16509
NBA Hoops, P.O. Box 14930, Research Triangle Park, NC 27709-4930.
O-Pee-Chee, P.O. Box 6306, London, Ontario, Canada, N5W 5S1.
Pacific Trading Cards, 18424 Hwy. 99, Lynwood, WA 98039.
Pro Line Portraits, P.O. Box 14930, Research Triangle Park, NC 27709-4930.
Pro Set, 17250 Dallas Parkway, Dallas, TX 75248.
Score, 25 Ford Road, Westport, CT 06880.
SilverStar Holograms, P.O. Box 8195, Van Nuys, CA 91406.
SkyBox Int'l., P.O. Box 14930, Research Triangle Park, NC 27709-4930.
Topps, 254 36th St., Brooklyn, NY 11232.
Upper Deck, 5909 Sea Otter Place, Carlsbad, CA 92008.
Wild Card, 2715 Dixie Highway, Hamilton, OH 45015.

1986 Lite Beer Astros

		MT	NR MT	EX
Complete Set:		70.00	52.00	37.00
Common Player:		1.50	1.25	.60
3	Phil Garner	1.50	1.25	.60
6	Mark Bailey	1.50	1.25	.60
10	Dickie Thon	2.00	1.50	.80
11	Frank DiPino	1.50	1.25	.60
12	Craig Reynolds	1.50	1.25	.60
14	Alan Ashby	1.50	1.25	.60
17	Kevin Bass	3.00	2.25	1.25
19	Bill Doran	3.00	2.25	1.25
20	Jim Pankovits	1.50	1.25	.60
21	Terry Puhl	1.50	1.25	.60
22	Hal Lanier	1.50	1.25	.60
25	Jose Cruz	3.00	2.25	1.25
27	Glenn Davis	7.00	5.25	2.75
28	Billy Hatcher	2.50	2.00	1.00
29	Denny Walling	1.50	1.25	.60
33	Mike Scott	4.00	3.00	1.50
34	Nolan Ryan	15.00	11.00	6.00
37	Charlie Kerfeld	2.00	1.50	.80
39	Bob Knepper	2.00	1.50	.80
43	Jim Deshaies	3.00	2.25	1.25
45	Dave Smith	2.00	1.50	.80
53	Mike Madden	1.50	1.25	.60

1986 Lite Beer Rangers

This postcard-size (approximately 4" by 6") regional set of 28 Texas Rangers cards was sponsored by Lite Beer and was available by mail directly from the Rangers. The fronts featured full-color photos surrounded by a wide, white border with the player's name, uniform number and position appearing below. The Rangers logo is displayed in the lower left corner, while the Lite Beer logo is in the lower right.

		MT	NR MT	EX
Complete Set:		60.00	45.00	24.00
Common Player:		1.50	1.25	.60
0	Oddibe McDowell	3.00	2.25	1.25

		MT	NR MT	EX
1	Scott Fletcher	2.00	1.50	.80
2	Bobby Valentine	2.00	1.50	.80
4	Don Slaught	1.50	1.25	.60
5	Pete Incaviglia	4.00	3.00	1.50
9	Pete O'Brien	3.00	2.25	1.25
10	Art Howe	1.50	1.25	.60
11	Toby Harrah	2.00	1.50	.80
12	Geno Petralli	1.50	1.25	.60
13	Joe Ferguson	1.50	1.25	.60
14	Tim Foli	1.50	1.25	.60
15	Larry Parrish	2.50	2.00	1.00
16	Mike Mason	1.50	1.25	.60
17	Darrell Porter	2.00	1.50	.80
18	Ed Correa	3.00	2.25	1.25
19	Curtis Wilkerson	1.50	1.25	.60
22	Steve Buechele	4.00	3.00	1.50
23	Jose Guzman	4.00	3.00	1.50
24	Ricky Wright	1.50	1.25	.60
27	Greg Harris	1.50	1.25	.60
31	Tom Robson	1.50	1.25	.60
32	Gary Ward	2.00	1.50	.80
35	Tom House	1.50	1.25	.60
44	Tom Paciorek	1.50	1.25	.60
45	Dwayne Henry	2.00	1.50	.80
48	Bobby Witt	5.00	3.75	2.00
49	Charlie Hough	3.00	2.25	1.25
----	Arlington Stadium	1.50	1.25	.60

1988 Louisville Slugger

Two more cards were added to the Hillerich & Bradsby hangtag collection in 1988. Hillerich & Bradsby, makers of Louisville Slugger bats and gloves, produced the cards to be attached to the company's baseball gloves. The 1988 Eric Davis and Mike Pagliarulo cards bring the total number of Hillerich & Bradsby hangtags issued since the first ones in 1981 (Graig Nettles and Steve Garvey) to 13. A small round hole is punched in the upper left corner of each standard-size card to enable them to be attached to the gloves, making it hard to find undamaged cards. The 1988 cards are numbered and follow the same basic design as previous issues - bright blue and green borders, player name and position above the full-color photo (with autograph overprint), yellow Louisville Slugger logo across the bottom border. Beneath the logo are the words "Member Louisville Slugger Bat & Glove Advisory Staff." The card backs are blue and green and include the player name, short biography and a list of personal records and information.

		MT	NR MT	EX
Complete Set:		150.00	112.00	60.00
Common Player:		5.00	3.75	2.00
(1)	Eric Davis (1988)	10.00	7.50	4.00
(2)	Steve Garvey (Dodgers-1981)	25.00	18.50	10.00
(3)	Steve Garvey (Padres - 1985)	12.00	9.00	4.75
(4)	Pedro Guerrero (1982)	12.00	9.00	4.75
(5)	Orel Hershiser (1986)	20.00	15.00	8.00
(6)	Ray Knight (Astros - 1984)	12.00	9.00	4.75
(7)	Ray Knight (Mets - 1984)	10.00	7.50	4.00
(8)	Fred Lynn (1982)	5.00	3.75	2.00
(9)	Gary Matthews (1985)	12.00	9.00	4.75
(10)	Graig Nettles (Yankees-1981)	12.00	9.00	4.75

		MT	NR MT	EX
(11)	Graig Nettles (Padres - 1984)	10.00	7.50	4.00
(12)	Mike Pagliarulo (1988)	5.00	3.75	2.00
(13)	Rick Rhoden (1985)	10.00	7.50	4.00

1987 M & M's

The M&M's "Star Lineup" set consists of 12 two card panels inserted in specially marked packages of large M&M's candy. The two-card panels measure 5" by 3-1/2" with individual cards measuring 2-1/2" by 3-1/2" in size. The full-color photos are enclosed by a wavy blue frame and a white border. Card backs are printed in red ink on white stock and carry the player's career statistics and highlights. All team insignias have been airbrushed away. The set was designed and produced by Mike Schechter and Associates.

		MT	NR MT	EX
Complete Panel Set:		20.00	15.00	8.00
Complete Singles Set:		10.00	7.50	4.00
Common Panel:		1.00	.70	.40
Common Single Player:		.10	.08	.04
	Panel	1.50	1.25	.60
1	Wally Joyner	.50	.40	.20
2	Tony Pena	.10	.08	.04
	Panel	1.50	1.25	.60
3	Mike Schmidt	.40	.30	.15
4	Ryne Sandberg	.40	.30	.15
	Panel	1.50	1.25	.60
5	Wade Boggs	.40	.30	.15
6	Jack Morris	.20	.15	.08
	Panel	1.25	.90	.50
7	Roger Clemens	.40	.30	.15
8	Harold Baines	.15	.11	.06
	Panel	2.75	2.00	1.00
9	Dale Murphy	.30	.25	.12
10	Jose Canseco	1.00	.70	.40
	Panel	3.25	2.50	1.25
11	Don Mattingly	1.25	.90	.50
12	Gary Carter	.20	.15	.08
	Panel	1.50	1.25	.60
13	Cal Ripken, Jr.	1.50	1.25	.60
14	George Brett	.30	.25	.12
	Panel	1.00	.70	.40
15	Kirby Puckett	.20	.15	.08
16	Joe Carter	.20	.15	.08
	Panel	1.00	.70	.40
17	Mike Witt	.15	.11	.06
18	Mike Scott	.15	.11	.06
	Panel	1.25	.90	.50
19	Fernando Valenzuela	.20	.15	.08
20	Steve Garvey	.20	.15	.08
	Panel	1.50	1.25	.60
21	Steve Sax	.15	.11	.06
22	Nolan Ryan	.70	.50	.30
	Panel	1.25	.90	.50
23	Tony Gwynn	.25	.20	.10
24	Ozzie Smith	.15	.11	.06

1989 Marathon Cubs

This colorful 25-card Cubs team set was sponsored by Marathon and was distributed as a stadium promotion to fans attending the August 10, 1989, game at Chicago's Wrigley Field. The oversize (2-3/4" by 4-1/4") feature an action photo inside a diagonal box on the card front, with the Chicago Cubs logo at the top and the player's uniform number, name and position along the bottom. The backs include a small black-and-white photo, player data and the Cubs and Marathon logos.

		MT	NR MT	EX
Complete Set:		8.00	6.00	3.25
Common Player:		.10	.08	.04
2	Vance Law	.10	.08	.04
4	Don Zimmer	.15	.11	.06
7	Joe Girardi	.50	.40	.20
8	Andre Dawson	.70	.50	.30
9	Damon Berryhill	.40	.30	.15
10	Lloyd McClendon	.50	.40	.20
12	Shawon Dunston	.50	.40	.20
15	Domingo Ramos	.10	.08	.04
17	Mark Grace	2.00	1.50	.80
18	Dwight Smith	.60	.45	.25
19	Curt Wilkerson	.10	.08	.04
20	Jerome Walton	1.50	1.25	.60
21	Scott Sanderson	.10	.08	.04
23	Ryne Sandberg	3.00	2.25	1.25
28	Mitch Williams	1.00	.70	.40
31	Greg Maddux	.70	.50	.30
32	Calvin Schiraldi	.10	.08	.04
33	Mitch Webster	.10	.08	.04
36	Mike Bielecki	.40	.30	.15
39	Paul Kilgus	.10	.08	.04
40	Rick Sutcliffe	.40	.30	.15
41	Jeff Pico	.25	.20	.10
44	Steve Wilson	.50	.40	.20
50	Les Lancaster	.15	.11	.06
-----	Coaches Card	.10	.08	.04

1989 Marathon Tigers

Marathon sponsored this give-away set for a 1989 Tigers home game. The oversized cards feature thin white stock and full-color player photos. The cards are numbered according to uniform number.

		MT	NR MT	EX
Complete Set:		7.00	5.25	2.75
Common Player:		.10	.08	.04
1	Lou Whitaker	.50	.40	.20
3	Alan Trammell	.60	.45	.25
8	Mike Heath	.10	.08	.04
9	Fred Lynn	.30	.25	.12
10	Keith Moreland	.15	.11	.06
11	Sparky Anderson	.40	.30	.15
12	Mike Brumley	.10	.08	.04
14	Dave Bergman	.10	.08	.04
15	Pat Sheridan	.10	.08	.04
17	Al Pedrique	.10	.08	.04
18	Ramon Pena	.15	.11	.06
19	Doyle Alexander	.20	.15	.08
21	Guillermo Hernandez	.20	.15	.08
23	Torey Lovullo	.30	.25	.12
24	Gary Pettis	.20	.15	.08
25	Ken Williams	.10	.08	.04
26	Frank Tanana	.20	.15	.08
27	Charles Hudson	.10	.08	.04
32	Gary Ward	.10	.08	.04
33	Matt Nokes	.40	.30	.15
34	Chet Lemon	.25	.20	.10
35	Rick Schu	.10	.08	.04
36	Frank Williams	.10	.08	.04
39	Mike Henneman	.30	.25	.12
44	Jeff Robinson	.20	.15	.08
47	Jack Morris	.40	.30	.15
48	Paul Gibson	.10	.08	.04
-----	Coaches	.10	.08	.04

1990 Marathon Cubs

Marathon sponsored its second consecutive Chicago Cubs team set. The oversized cards feature thin white stock and full-color photos. The cards are numbered according to uniform number, and were distributed at a Cubs home game.

		MT	NR MT	EX
Complete Set:		8.00	6.00	3.25
Common Player:		.10	.08	.04
4	Don Zimmer	.15	.11	.06
7	Joe Girardi	.20	.15	.08
8	Andre Dawson	.60	.45	.25
10	Lloyd McClendon	.10	.08	.04
11	Luis Salazar	.10	.08	.04
12	Shawon Dunston	.50	.40	.20
15	Domingo Ramos	.10	.08	.04
17	Mark Grace	1.50	1.25	.60
18	Dwight Smith	.40	.30	.15
19	Curtis Wilkerson	.10	.08	.04
20	Jerome Walton	1.00	.70	.40
22	Mike Harkey	.70	.50	.30
23	Ryne Sandberg	2.00	1.50	.80
25	Marvell Wynne	.10	.08	.04
28	Mitch Williams	.40	.30	.15
29	Doug Dascenzo	.20	.15	.08
30	Dave Clark	.15	.11	.06
31	Greg Maddux	.60	.45	.25
32	Hector Villanueva	.40	.30	.15
36	Mike Bielecki	.20	.15	.08
37	Bill Long	.10	.08	.04
40	Rick Sutcliffe	.30	.25	.12
41	Jeff Pico	.10	.08	.04

		MT	NR MT	EX
44	Steve Wilson	.30	.25	.12
45	Paul Assenmacher	.10	.08	.04
47	Shawn Boskie	.80	.60	.30
50	Les Lancaster	.10	.08	.04
-----	Coaches	.10	.08	.04

Values quoted in this guide reflect the retail price of a card — the price a collector can expect to pay when buying a card from a dealer. The wholesale price — that which a collector can expect to receive from a dealer when selling cards — will be significantly lower, depending on desirability and condition.

1991 Marathon Cubs

Marathon Oil once again sponsored a set featuring the Chicago Cubs. This 28-card release features oversized cards measuring 2 7/8" by 4 1/4". The card fronts feature full-color action photos. The flip sides feature complete statistics. The cards are numbered according to uniform number. This number appears on both the front and back of the card.

		MT	NR MT	EX
Complete Set:		7.00	5.25	2.75
Common Player:		.20	.15	.08
7	Joe Girardi	.25	.20	.10
8	Andre Dawson	.80	.60	.30
9	Damon Berryhill	.25	.20	.10
10	Luis Salazar	.20	.15	.08
11	George Bell	.35	.25	.14
12	Shawon Dunston	.35	.25	.14
16	Jose Vizcaino	.20	.15	.08
17	Mark Grace	.70	.50	.30
18	Dwight Smith	.25	.20	.10
19	Hector Villanueva	.25	.20	.10
20	Jerome Walton	.25	.20	.10
22	Mike Harkey	.30	.25	.12
23	Ryne Sandberg	1.25	.90	.50
24	Chico Walker	.25	.20	.10
29	Doug Dascenzo	.20	.15	.08
30	Bob Scanlan	.20	.15	.08
31	Greg Maddux	.50	.40	.20
32	Danny Jackson	.25	.20	.10
35	Chuck McElroy	.20	.15	.08
36	Mike Bielecki	.20	.15	.08
40	Rick Sutcliffe	.35	.25	.14
41	Jim Essian	.20	.15	.08
42	Dave Smith	.20	.15	.08
45	Paul Assenmacher	.20	.15	.08
47	Shawn Boskie	.30	.25	.12
50	Les Lancaster	.20	.15	.08
51	Heathcliff Slocumb	.25	.20	.10
-----	Coaches	.20	.15	.08

1988 Master Bread Twins

This set of 12 cardboard discs (2-3/4" diameter) features full-color photos of Minnesota Twins team members. Disc fronts have a bright blue background with red, yellow and black printing. A thin white line frames the player photo which is centered beneath a "Master Is Good Bread" headliner and a vivid yellow player/team name banner. Disc backs are black and white with five stars printed above the player's name, team, personal data, disc number, stats and "1988 Collector's Edition" banner. The discs were printed in Canada and marketed exclusively in Minnesota in packages of Master Bread, one disc per loaf.

	MT	NR MT	EX
Complete Set:	15.00	11.00	6.00
Common Player:	.50	.40	.20
1 Bert Blyleven	1.00	.70	.40
2 Frank Viola	2.25	1.75	.90
3 Juan Berenguer	.50	.40	.20
4 Jeff Reardon	.80	.60	.30
5 Tim Laudner	.50	.40	.20
6 Steve Lombardozzi	.50	.40	.20
7 Randy Bush	.50	.40	.20
8 Kirby Puckett	4.00	3.00	1.50
9 Gary Gaetti	1.75	1.25	.70
10 Kent Hrbek	1.75	1.25	.70
11 Greg Gagne	.70	.50	.30
12 Tom Brunansky	1.00	.70	.40

1986 Meadow Gold
Blank Back Set Of 16

This was the second set to be distributed by Meadow Gold Dairy (Beatrice Foods) in 1986. It was issued on Double Play ice cream cartons, one card per package. Full-color player photos have team logos and insignias airbrushed away. This 16-card set is very similar to the Meadow Gold popsicle set, but the photos are different in some instances. The cards measure 2-3/8" by 3-1/2". The Willie McGee card is reportedly tougher to find than other cards in the set.

	MT	NR MT	EX
Complete Set:	100.00	75.00	40.00
Common Player:	4.00	3.00	1.50
(1) George Brett	7.00	5.25	2.75
(2) Wade Boggs	7.00	5.25	2.75
(3) Carlton Fisk	7.00	5.25	2.75
(4) Steve Garvey	6.00	4.50	2.50
(5) Dwight Gooden	6.00	4.50	2.50
(6) Pedro Guerrero	4.00	3.00	1.50
(7) Reggie Jackson	8.00	6.00	3.25
(8) Don Mattingly	10.00	7.50	4.00
(9) Willie McGee	4.00	3.00	1.50
(10) Dale Murphy	5.00	3.75	1.50
(11) Cal Ripken	8.00	6.00	3.25
(12) Pete Rose	8.00	6.00	3.25
(13) Ryne Sandberg	8.00	6.00	3.25
(14) Mike Schmidt	8.00	6.00	3.25
(15) Fernando Valenzuela	5.00	3.75	2.00
(16) Dave Winfield	6.50	5.00	2.50

1986 Meadow Gold
Statistic Back Set Of 20

Beatrice Foods produced this set of 20 cards on specially marked boxes of Meadow Gold Double Play popsicles, fudgesicles and bubble gum coolers. They came in two-card panels and have full-color player pictures with player name, team and position printed below the photo. Card backs are printed in red ink and feature player career highlights. The cards measure 2-3/8" by 3-1/2" and were distributed in the West and Midwest. It is considered one of the toughest 1986 regional sets to complete.

	MT	NR MT	EX
Complete Panel Set:	40.00	30.00	15.00
Complete Singles Set:	20.00	15.00	8.00
Common Panel:	2.00	1.50	.80
Common Single Player:	.30	.25	.12
Panel 1	5.00	3.75	2.00
1 George Brett	1.50	1.25	.60
2 Fernando Valenzuela	.70	.50	.30
Panel 2	6.50	5.00	2.50
3 Dwight Gooden	2.00	1.50	.80
4 Dale Murphy	1.50	1.25	.60
Panel 3	8.00	6.00	3.25
5 Don Mattingly	3.00	2.25	1.25
6 Reggie Jackson	2.00	1.50	.80
Panel 4	6.50	5.00	2.50
7 Dave Winfield	1.00	.70	.40
8 Pete Rose	2.00	1.50	.80
Panel 5	5.00	3.75	2.00
9 Wade Boggs	2.00	1.50	.80
10 Willie McGee	.50	.40	.20
Panel 6	6.00	4.50	2.50
11 Cal Ripkin (Ripken)	2.00	1.50	.80
12 Ryne Sandberg	2.00	1.50	.80
Panel 7	5.00	3.75	2.00
13 Carlton Fisk	.80	.60	.30
14 Jim Rice	1.00	.70	.40
Panel 8	7.00	5.25	2.75
15 Steve Garvey	1.00	.70	.40
16 Mike Schmidt	2.00	1.50	.80
Panel 9	4.00	3.00	1.50
17 Bruce Sutter	.60	.45	.25
18 Pedro Guerrero	.60	.45	.25
Panel 10	4.00	3.00	1.50
19 Rick Sutcliff (Sutcliffe)	.60	.45	.25
20 Rich Gossage	.60	.45	.25

1986 Meadow Gold Milk

The third set from Meadow Gold from 1986 came on milk cartons; on pint, quart and half-gallon size containers. The cards measure 2-1/2" by 3-1/2" and feature drawings instead of photographs. Different dairies distributed the cards in various colors of ink. The cards can be found printed in red, brown or black ink. The crude drawings have prevented this rare set from being higher in price. It was believed that Don Mattingly and Fernando Valenzuela were part of the original set, but it has since been proven they were not.

	MT	NR MT	EX
Complete Set:	50.00	37.00	20.00
Common Player:	2.00	1.50	.80
(1) Wade Boggs	6.00	4.50	2.50
(2) George Brett	5.00	3.75	2.00
(3) Steve Carlton	3.00	2.25	1.25
(4) Dwight Gooden	6.00	4.50	2.50
(5) Willie McGee	2.00	1.50	.80
(6) Dale Murphy	5.00	3.75	2.00
(7) Cal Ripken, Jr.	6.00	4.50	2.50
(8) Pete Rose	10.00	7.50	4.00
(9) Ryne Sandberg	6.00	4.50	2.50
(10) Mike Schmidt	5.00	3.75	2.00

1971 Milk Duds

These cards were issued on the backs of five-cent packages of Milk Duds candy. Most collectors prefer to collect complete boxes, rather than cut-out cards, which measure approximately 1-13/16" by 2-5/8" when trimmed tightly. Values quoted below are for complete boxes. The set includes 37 National League and 32 American League players. Card numbers appear on the box flap, with each number from 1 through 24 being shared by three different players. A suffix (a, b and c) has been added for the collector's convenience. Harmon Killebrew, Brooks Robinson and Pete Rose were double-printed.

	NR MT	EX	VG
Complete Set:	1400.00	700.00	420.00
Common Player:	7.00	3.50	2.00
1a Frank Howard	11.00	5.50	3.25
1b Fritz Peterson	7.00	3.50	2.00
1c Pete Rose	80.00	40.00	24.00
2a Johnny Bench	30.00	15.00	9.00
2b Rico Carty	9.00	4.50	2.75
2c Pete Rose	80.00	40.00	24.00

	NR MT	EX	VG
3a Ken Holtzman	8.00	4.00	2.50
3b Willie Mays	60.00	30.00	18.00
3c Cesar Tovar	7.00	3.50	2.00
4a Willie Davis	9.00	4.50	2.75
4b Harmon Killebrew	20.00	10.00	6.00
4c Felix Millan	7.00	3.50	2.00
5a Billy Grabarkewitz	7.00	3.50	2.00
5b Andy Messersmith	8.00	4.00	2.50
5c Thurman Munson	20.00	10.00	6.00
6a Luis Aparicio	18.00	9.00	5.50
6b Lou Brock	25.00	12.50	7.50
6c Bill Melton	7.00	3.50	2.00
7a Ray Culp	7.00	3.50	2.00
7b Willie McCovey	25.00	12.50	7.50
7c Luke Walker	7.00	3.50	2.00
8a Roberto Clemente	40.00	20.00	12.00
8b Jim Merritt	7.00	3.50	2.00
8c Claud Osteen (Claude)	8.00	4.00	2.50
9a Stan Bahnsen	7.00	3.50	2.00
9b Sam McDowell	9.00	4.50	2.75
9c Billy Williams	18.00	9.00	5.50
10a Jim Hickman	7.00	3.50	2.00
10b Dave McNally	9.00	4.50	2.75
10c Tony Perez	13.00	6.50	4.00
11a Hank Aaron	60.00	30.00	18.00
11b Glen Beckert (Glenn)	8.00	4.00	2.50
11c Ray Fosse	7.00	3.50	2.00
12a Alex Johnson	7.00	3.50	2.00
12b Gaylord Perry	18.00	9.00	5.50
12c Wayne Simpson	7.00	3.50	2.00
13a Dave Johnson	9.00	4.50	2.75
13b George Scott	8.00	4.00	2.50
13c Tom Seaver	30.00	15.00	9.00
14a Bill Freehan	9.00	4.50	2.75
14b Bud Harrelson	8.00	4.00	2.50
14c Manny Sanguillen	7.00	3.50	2.00
15a Bob Gibson	25.00	12.50	7.50
15b Rusty Staub	11.00	5.50	3.25
15c Roy White	8.00	4.00	2.50
16a Jim Fregosi	9.00	4.50	2.75
16b Jim Hunter	18.00	9.00	5.50
16c Mel Stottlmyer (Stottlemyre)	8.00	4.00	2.50
17a Tommy Harper	7.00	3.50	2.00
17b Frank Robinson	25.00	12.50	7.50
17c Reggie Smith	9.00	4.50	2.75
18a Orlando Cepeda	13.00	6.50	4.00
18b Rico Petrocelli	8.00	4.00	2.50
18c Brooks Robinson	25.00	12.50	7.50
19a Tony Oliva	11.00	5.50	3.25
19b Milt Pappas	8.00	4.00	2.50
19c Bobby Tolan	7.00	3.50	2.00
20a Ernie Banks	25.00	12.50	7.50
20b Don Kessinger	8.00	4.00	2.50
20c Joe Torre	9.00	4.50	2.75
21a Fergie Jenkins	13.00	6.50	4.00
21b Jim Palmer	18.00	9.00	5.50
21c Ron Santo	9.00	4.50	2.75
22a Randy Hundley	7.00	3.50	2.00
22b Dennis Menke (Denis)	7.00	3.50	2.00
22c Boog Powell	11.00	5.50	3.25
23a Dick Dietz	7.00	3.50	2.00
23b Tommy John	13.00	6.50	4.00
23c Brooks Robinson	25.00	12.50	7.50
24a Danny Cater	7.00	3.50	2.00
24b Harmon Killebrew	18.00	9.00	5.50
24c Jim Perry	8.00	4.00	2.50

1984 Milton Bradley

In 1984 Milton Bradley printed their baseball game

cards in full-color and adopted the standard baseball card size of 2-1/2" by 3-1/2". A total of 30 cards were in the set. The card fronts show the player photos with the team insignias and logos airbrushed away. The game is called Championship Baseball. Card backs varied in style; some had player statistics plus game information, and others only game information.

		MT	NR MT	EX
Complete Set:		12.00	9.00	4.75
Common Player:		.25	.20	.10
(1)	Wade Boggs	.80	.60	.30
(2)	George Brett	1.00	.70	.40
(3)	Rod Carew	.50	.40	.20
(4)	Steve Carlton	.40	.30	.15
(5)	Gary Carter	.50	.40	.20
(6)	Dave Concepcion	.25	.20	.10
(7)	Cecil Cooper	.25	.20	.10
(8)	Andre Dawson	.50	.40	.20
(9)	Carlton Fisk	.40	.30	.15
(10)	Steve Garvey	.50	.40	.20
(11)	Pedro Guerrero	.35	.25	.14
(12)	Ron Guidry	.25	.20	.10
(13)	Rickey Henderson	1.00	.70	.40
(14)	Reggie Jackson	.50	.40	.20
(15)	Ron Kittle	.25	.20	.10
(16)	Bill Madlock	.25	.20	.10
(17)	Dale Murphy	.80	.60	.30
(18)	Al Oliver	.25	.20	.10
(19)	Darrell Porter	.25	.20	.10
(20)	Cal Ripken	1.00	.70	.40
(21)	Pete Rose	1.25	.90	.50
(22)	Steve Sax	.35	.25	.14
(23)	Mike Schmidt	.80	.60	.30
(24)	Ted Simmons	.25	.20	.10
(25)	Ozzie Smith	.35	.25	.14
(26)	Dave Stieb	.25	.20	.10
(27)	Fernando Valenzuela	.35	.25	.14
(28)	Lou Whitaker	.35	.25	.14
(29)	Dave Winfield	.50	.40	.20
(30)	Robin Yount	.40	.30	.15

1991 Mootown Snackers

Produced by the Sargento Cheese Co., this 24-card set features the superstars of baseball. Cards were available in Mootown Snacker packages or by sending in a special set redemption coupon from a package to obtain the entire set for $5.95 and three UPC codes. The card fronts feature full-color action photos, but uniform insignias are airbrushed. The backs feature statistics and a facsimile autograph. Sargento is located in Plymouth, Wis.

		MT	NR MT	EX
Complete Set:		8.00	6.00	3.25
Common Player:		.25	.20	.10
1	Jose Canseco	.60	.45	.25
2	Kirby Puckett	.35	.25	.14
3	Barry Bonds	.35	.25	.14
4	Ken Griffey, Jr.	1.25	.90	.50
5	Ryne Sandberg	.50	.40	.20

		MT	NR MT	EX
6	Tony Gwynn	.35	.25	.14
7	Kal Daniels	.25	.20	.10
8	Ozzie Smith	.35	.25	.14
9	Dave Justice	.80	.60	.30
10	Sandy Alomar, Jr.	.30	.25	.12
11	Wade Boggs	.35	.25	.14
12	Ozzie Guillen	.25	.20	.10
13	Dave Magadan	.25	.20	.10
14	Cal Ripken, Jr.	.50	.40	.20
15	Don Mattingly	.50	.40	.20
16	Ruben Sierra	.35	.25	.14
17	Robin Yount	.35	.25	.14
18	Len Dykstra	.25	.20	.10
19	George Brett	.35	.25	.14
20	Lance Parrish	.25	.20	.10
21	Chris Sabo	.25	.20	.10
22	Craig Biggio	.25	.20	.10
23	Kevin Mitchell	.30	.25	.12
24	Cecil Fielder	.50	.40	.20

1969 Nabisco Team Flakes

Frank Robinson—OF
Baltimore Orioles

This set of cards is seen in two different sizes: 1-15/16" by 3" and 1-3/4" by 2-15/16". This is explained by the varying widths of the card borders on the backs of Nabisco cereal packages. Cards are action color photos bordered in yellow. Twenty-four of the top players in the game are included in the set, which was issued in three series of eight cards each. No team insignias are visible on any of the cards. Packages described the cards as "Mini Posters."

		NR MT	EX	VG
Complete Set:		650.00	325.00	195.00
Common Player:		4.00	2.00	1.25
(1)	Hank Aaron	60.00	30.00	18.00
(2)	Richie Allen	7.00	3.50	2.00
(3)	Lou Brock	40.00	20.00	12.00
(4)	Paul Casanova	4.00	2.00	1.25
(5)	Roberto Clemente	60.00	30.00	18.00
(6)	Al Ferrara	4.00	2.00	1.25
(7)	Bill Freehan	5.00	2.50	1.50
(8)	Jim Fregosi	5.00	2.50	1.50
(9)	Bob Gibson	25.00	12.50	7.50
(10)	Tony Horton	5.00	2.50	1.50
(11)	Tommy John	10.00	5.00	3.00
(12)	Al Kaline	40.00	20.00	12.00
(13)	Jim Lonborg	4.00	2.00	1.25
(14)	Juan Marichal	25.00	12.50	7.50
(15)	Willie Mays	60.00	30.00	18.00
(16)	Rick Monday	5.00	2.50	1.50
(17)	Tony Oliva	6.00	3.00	1.75
(18)	Brooks Robinson	45.00	22.00	13.50
(19)	Frank Robinson	40.00	20.00	12.00
(20)	Pete Rose	65.00	32.00	19.50
(21)	Ron Santo	6.00	3.00	1.75
(22)	Tom Seaver	50.00	25.00	15.00
(23)	Rusty Staub	6.00	3.00	1.75
(24)	Mel Stottlemyre	5.00	2.50	1.50

1984 Nestle Dream Team

This set was issued by the Nestle candy company in conjunction with Topps.   Cards are in standard 2-1/2" by 3-1/2" size and feature the top 22 players of 1984, 11 from each league. This full-color "Dream Team" includes one player at each position, plus right- and left-handed starting pitchers and one reliever.   Card fronts have a Nestle logo in the upper-right corner and card backs have the candy company logo in the upper left. An unnumbered checklist was included with the set.

		MT	NR MT	EX
Complete Set:		18.00	13.50	7.25
Common Player:		.60	.45	.25
1	Eddie Murray	1.75	1.25	.70
2	Lou Whitaker	1.00	.70	.40
3	George Brett	2.25	1.75	.90
4	Cal Ripken	2.50	2.00	1.00
5	Jim Rice	1.25	.90	.50
6	Dave Winfield	1.50	1.25	.60
7	Lloyd Moseby	.60	.45	.25
8	Lance Parrish	1.00	.70	.40
9	LaMarr Hoyt	.60	.45	.25
10	Ron Guidry	.80	.60	.30
11	Dan Quisenberry	.60	.45	.25
12	Steve Garvey	1.50	1.25	.60
13	Johnny Ray	.60	.45	.25
14	Mike Schmidt	2.75	2.00	1.00
15	Ozzie Smith	.80	.60	.30
16	Andre Dawson	1.00	.70	.40
17	Tim Raines	1.50	1.25	.60
18	Dale Murphy	2.25	1.75	.90
19	Tony Pena	.60	.45	.25
20	John Denny	.60	.45	.25
21	Steve Carlton	1.25	.90	.50
22	Al Holland	.60	.45	.25
----	Checklist	.30	.25	.12

Definitions for grading conditions are located in the Introduction of this price guide.

1988 Nestle

This 44-card set was produced by Mike Schechter Associates for Nestle. "Dream Team" packets of 3 player cards and one checklist card were inserted in 6-packs of Nestle's chocolate candy bars. The 1988 issue, similar to the 33-card Nestle set produced by Topps, features current players divided into four Dream Teams (East and West teams for each league). The "1988 Nestle" header appears at the top of the red and yellow-bordered cards. Below the player closeup (in a plain airbrushed cap) is a blue oval player name banner. Card backs are red, white and blue with card numbers printed upper right above personal stats, career highlights and major league totals. The bright red, blue and yellow checklist card outlines two special offers; one for an uncut sheet of all 44 player cards and one for a 1988 replica autographed baseball.

		MT	NR MT	EX
Complete Set:		20.00	15.00	8.00
Common Player:		.25	.20	.10
1	Roger Clemens	1.00	.70	.40
2	Dale Murphy	.60	.45	.25
3	Eric Davis	.60	.45	.25
4	Gary Gaetti	.30	.25	.12
5	Ozzie Smith	.35	.25	.14
6	Mike Schmidt	1.00	.70	.40
7	Ozzie Guillen	.25	.20	.10
8	John Franco	.25	.20	.10
9	Andre Dawson	.50	.40	.20
10	Mark McGwire	.50	.40	.20
11	Bret Saberhagen	.35	.25	.14
12	Benny Santiago	.35	.25	.14
13	Jose Uribe	.25	.20	.10
14	Will Clark	1.75	1.25	.70
15	Don Mattingly	1.25	.90	.50
16	Juan Samuel	.30	.25	.12
17	Jack Clark	.35	.25	.14
18	Darryl Strawberry	.75	.60	.30
19	Bill Doran	.25	.20	.10
20	Pete Incaviglia	.30	.25	.12
21	Dwight Gooden	.75	.60	.30
22	Willie Randolph	.25	.20	.10
23	Tim Wallach	.25	.20	.10
24	Pedro Guerrero	.35	.25	.14
25	Steve Bedrosian	.25	.20	.10
26	Gary Carter	.50	.40	.20
27	Jeff Reardon	.25	.20	.10
28	Dave Righetti	.35	.25	.14
29	Frank White	.25	.20	.10
30	Buddy Bell	.25	.20	.10
31	Tim Raines	.50	.40	.20
32	Wade Boggs	1.00	.70	.40
33	Dave Winfield	.50	.40	.20
34	George Bell	.40	.30	.15
35	Alan Trammell	.40	.30	.15
36	Joe Carter	.30	.25	.12
37	Jose Canseco	1.50	1.25	.60
38	Carlton Fisk	.60	.45	.25
39	Kirby Puckett	1.00	.70	.40
40	Tony Gwynn	.50	.40	.20
41	Matt Nokes	.40	.30	.15
42	Keith Hernandez	.40	.30	.15
43	Nolan Ryan	2.00	1.50	.80
44	Wally Joyner	.50	.40	.20

1954 N.Y. Journal-American

Issued during the Golden Age of baseball in New York City, this 59-card set features only players from the three New York teams of the day - the Giants, Yankees and Dodgers. The 2" by 4" cards were issued at newsstands with the purchase of the now-extinct newspaper. Card fronts have promotional copy and a contest serial number in addition to the player's name and photo. Cards are black and white and unnumbered. Many of the game's top stars are included, such as Mickey Mantle, Willie Mays, Gil Hodges, Duke Snider, Jackie Robinson and Yogi Berra. Card backs featured team schedules. It has been theorized that a 60th Dodgers card should exist. Don Hoak and Bob Milliken have been suggested as the missing card, but the existence of either card has never been confirmed.

KEITH HERNANDEZ

		NR MT	EX	VG
Complete Set:		2250.00	1125.00	675.00
Common Player:		10.00	5.00	3.00
(1)	Johnny Antonelli	12.00	6.00	3.50
(2)	Hank Bauer	20.00	10.00	6.00
(3)	Yogi Berra	100.00	50.00	30.00
(4)	Joe Black	12.00	6.00	3.50
(5)	Harry Byrd	10.00	5.00	3.00
(6)	Roy Campanella	100.00	50.00	30.00
(7)	Andy Carey	10.00	5.00	3.00
(8)	Jerry Coleman	10.00	5.00	3.00
(9)	Joe Collins	10.00	5.00	3.00
(10)	Billy Cox	10.00	5.00	3.00
(11)	Al Dark	12.00	6.00	3.50
(12)	Carl Erskine	20.00	10.00	6.00
(13)	Whitey Ford	40.00	20.00	12.00
(14)	Carl Furillo	20.00	10.00	6.00
(15)	Junior Gilliam	20.00	10.00	6.00
(16)	Ruben Gomez	10.00	5.00	3.00
(17)	Marv Grissom	10.00	5.00	3.00
(18)	Jim Hearn	10.00	5.00	3.00
(19)	Gil Hodges	35.00	17.50	10.50
(20)	Bobby Hofman	10.00	5.00	3.00
(21)	Jim Hughes	10.00	5.00	3.00
(22)	Monte Irvin	25.00	12.50	7.50
(23)	Larry Jansen	10.00	5.00	3.00
(24)	Ray Katt	10.00	5.00	3.00
(25)	Steve Kraly	10.00	5.00	3.00
(26)	Bob Kuzava	10.00	5.00	3.00
(27)	Clem Labine	12.00	6.00	3.50
(28)	Frank Leja	10.00	5.00	3.00
(29)	Don Liddle	10.00	5.00	3.00
(30)	Whitey Lockman	10.00	5.00	3.00
(31)	Billy Loes	10.00	5.00	3.00
(32)	Eddie Lopat	20.00	10.00	6.00
(33)	Gil McDougald	20.00	10.00	6.00
(34)	Sal Maglie	12.00	6.00	3.50
(35)	Mickey Mantle	450.00	225.00	135.00
(36)	Willie Mays	200.00	100.00	60.00
(37)	Russ Meyer	10.00	5.00	3.00
(38)	Bill Miller	10.00	5.00	3.00
(39)	Tom Morgan	10.00	5.00	3.00
(40)	Don Mueller	10.00	5.00	3.00
(41)	Don Newcombe	20.00	10.00	6.00
(42)	Irv Noren	10.00	5.00	3.00
(43)	Erv Palica	10.00	5.00	3.00
(44)	PeeWee Reese	55.00	27.00	16.50
(45)	Allie Reynolds	20.00	10.00	6.00
(46)	Dusty Rhodes	10.00	5.00	3.00
(47)	Phil Rizzuto	35.00	17.50	10.50
(48)	Ed Robinson	10.00	5.00	3.00
(49)	Jackie Robinson	225.00	112.00	67.00
(50)	Preacher Roe	20.00	10.00	6.00
(51)	George Shuba	10.00	5.00	3.00
(52)	Duke Snider	150.00	75.00	45.00
(53)	Hank Thompson	10.00	5.00	3.00
(54)	Wes Westrum	10.00	5.00	3.00
(55)	Hoyt Wilhelm	30.00	15.00	9.00
(56)	Davey Williams	10.00	5.00	3.00
(57)	Dick Williams	12.00	6.00	3.50
(58)	Gene Woodling	12.00	6.00	3.50
(59)	Al Worthington	10.00	5.00	3.00

1986 N.Y. Mets Super Fan Club

This special nine-card panel was issued by the fan club of the 1986 World Champion New York Mets, along with other souvenir items gained with membership in the club. Included in the full-color set are eight top Mets players, with a promotional card in the center of the panel. Individual cards measure

2-1/2" by 3-1/2", and are perforated at the edges to facilitate separation. The full panel measures 70-1/2" by 10-1/2". Card fronts feature posed photos of each player, along with name, position and team logo. Backs feature career and personal data, and are printed in the team's blue and orange colors.

		MT	NR MT	EX
Complete Panel Set:		10.00	7.50	4.00
Complete Singles Set:		4.00	3.00	1.50
Common Single Player:		.15	.11	.06
	Panel	10.00	7.50	4.00
1	Wally Backman	.15	.11	.06
2	Gary Carter	.70	.50	.30
3	Ron Darling	.40	.30	.15
4	Dwight Gooden	1.25	.90	.50
5	Keith Hernandez	.60	.45	.25
6	Howard Johnson	.70	.50	.30
7	Roger McDowell	.40	.30	.15
8	Darryl Strawberry	1.25	.90	.50
----	Membership Card	.05	.04	.02

1960 Nu-Card

These large, 3-1/4" by 5-3/8" cards are printed in a mock newspaper format, with a headline, picture and story describing one of baseball's greatest events. There are 72 events featured in the set, which is printed in red and black. Each card is numbered in the upper left corner. The card backs offer a quiz question and answer. Certain cards in the set can be found with the fronts printed entirely in black. These cards may command a slight premium.

		NR MT	EX	VG
Complete Set:		225.00	112.00	67.00
Common Player:		1.25	.60	.40
1	Babe Hits 3 Homers In A Series Game	10.00	5.00	3.00
2	Podres Pitching Wins Series	1.25	.60	.40
3	Bevans Pitches No Hitter, Almost	1.25	.60	.40

		NR MT	EX	VG
4	Box Score Devised By Reporter	1.25	.60	.40
5	VanderMeer Pitches 2 No Hitters	1.25	.60	.40
6	Indians Take Bums	1.25	.60	.40
7	DiMag Comes Thru	10.00	5.00	3.00
8	Mathewson Pitches 3 W.S. Shutouts	1.75	.90	.50
9	Haddix Pitches 12 Perfect Innings	1.25	.60	.40
10	Thomson's Homer Sinks Dodgers	1.75	.90	.50
11	Hubbell Strikes Out 5 A.L. Stars	1.50	.70	.45
12	Pickoff Ends Series (Marty Marion)	1.25	.60	.40
13	Cards Take Series From Yanks (Grover Cleveland Alexander)	1.50	.70	.45
14	Dizzy And Daffy Win Series	3.50	1.75	1.00
15	Owen Drops 3rd Strike	1.25	.60	.40
16	Ruth Calls His Shot	8.00	4.00	2.50
17	Merkle Pulls Boner	1.25	.60	.40
18	Larsen Hurls Perfect World Series Game	1.50	.70	.45
19	Bean Ball Ends Career of Mickey Cochrane premium.	1.25	.60	.40
20	Banks Belts 47 Homers, Earns MVP Honors premium.	2.00	1.00	.60
21	Stan Musial Hits 5 Homers In 1 Day	3.50	1.75	1.00
22	Mickey Mantle Hits Longest Homer	12.00	6.00	3.50
23	Sievers Captures Home Run Title	1.25	.60	.40
24	Gehrig Consecutive Game Record Ends	10.00	5.00	3.00
25	Red Schoendienst Key Player In Victory	1.25	.60	.40
26	Midget Pinch-Hits For St. Louis Browns (Eddie Gaedel)	1.25	.60	.40
27	Willie Mays Makes Greatest Catch	4.00	2.00	1.25
28	Homer By Berra Puts Yanks In 1st Place	3.00	1.50	.90
29	Campy National League's MVP	3.00	1.50	.90
30	Bob Turley Hurls Yanks To Championship	1.25	.60	.40
31	Dodgers Take Series From Sox In Six	1.25	.60	.40
32	Furillo Hero As Dodgers Beat Chicago	1.25	.60	.40
33	Adcock Gets Four Homers And A Double	1.25	.60	.40
34	Dickey Chosen All Star Catcher	1.25	.60	.40
35	Burdette Beats Yanks In 3 Series Games	1.25	.60	.40
36	Umpires Clear White Sox Bench	1.25	.60	.40
37	Reese Honored As Greatest Dodger S.S.	2.50	1.25	.70
38	Joe DiMaggio Hits In 56 Straight Games	10.00	5.00	3.00
39	Ted Williams Hits .406 For Season	5.00	2.50	1.50
40	Johnson Pitches 56 Scoreless Innings	2.25	1.25	.70
41	Hodges Hits 4 Home Runs In Nite Game	1.75	.90	.50
42	Greenberg Returns To Tigers From Army	1.25	.60	.40
43	Ty Cobb Named Best Player Of All Time	10.00	5.00	3.00
44	Robin Roberts Wins 28 Games	1.25	.60	.40
45	Rizzuto's 2 Runs Save 1st Place	1.50	.70	.45
46	Tigers Beat Out Senators For Pennant (Hal Newhouser)	1.25	.60	.40
47	Babe Ruth Hits 60th Home Run	9.00	4.50	2.75
48	Cy Young Honored	1.75	.90	.50
49	Killebrew Starts Spring Training	1.75	.90	.50
50	Mantle Hits Longest Homer At Stadium	12.00	6.00	3.50
51	Braves Take Pennant (Hank Aaron)	3.50	1.75	1.00
52	Ted Williams Hero Of All Star Game	5.00	2.50	1.50
53	Robinson Saves Dodgers For Playoffs (Jackie Robinson)	3.50	1.75	1.00
54	Snodgrass Muffs A Fly Ball	1.25	.60	.40
55	Snider Belts 2 Homers	2.25	1.25	.70
56	New York Giants Win 26 Straight Games (Christy Mathewson)	1.75	.90	.50
57	Ted Kluszewski Stars In 1st Game Win	1.25	.60	.40
58	Ott Walks 5 Times In A Single Game (Mel Ott)	1.25	.60	.40
59	Harvey Kuenn Takes Batting Title	1.25	.60	.40
60	Bob Feller Hurls 3rd No-Hitter Of Career premium.	2.25	1.25	.70
61	Yanks Champs Again! (Casey Stengel)	1.50	.70	.45

		NR MT	EX	VG
62	Aaron's Bat Beats Yankees In Series	4.00	2.00	1.25
63	Warren Spahn Beats Yanks in World Series premium.	1.50	.70	.45
64	Ump's Wrong Call Helps Dodgers	1.25	.60	.40
65	Kaline Hits 3 Homers, 2 In Same Inning	2.00	1.00	.60
66	Bob Allison Named A.L. Rookie of Year	1.25	.60	.40
67	McCovey Blasts Way Into Giant Lineup	1.75	.90	.50
68	Colavito Hits Four Homers In One Game	1.25	.60	.40
69	Erskine Sets Strike Out Record In W.S.	1.25	.60	.40
70	Sal Maglie Pitches No-Hit Game	1.25	.60	.40
71	Early Wynn Victory Crushes Yanks	1.25	.60	.40
72	Nellie Fox American League's M.V.P.	3.00	1.50	.90

1961 Nu-Card

Very similar in style to their set of the year before, the Nu-Card Baseball Scoops were issued in a smaller 2-1/2" by 3-1/2" size, but still featured the mock newspaper card front. This 80-card set is numbered from 401 to 480, with numbers shown on both the card front and back. These cards, which commemorate great moments in individual players' careers, included only the headline and black and white photo on the fronts, with the descriptive story on the card backs. Cards are again printed in red and black. It appears the set may have been counterfeited, though when is not known. These cards can be determined by examining the card photo for unusual blurring and fuzziness.

		NR MT	EX	VG
Complete Set:		125.00	62.00	37.00
Common Player:		.50	.25	.15
401	Gentile Powers Birds Into 1st	1.00	.50	.30
402	Warren Spahn Hurls No-Hitter, Whiffs 15	1.00	.50	.30
403	Mazeroski's Homer Wins Series For Bucs	.75	.40	.25
404	Willie Mays' 3 Triples Paces Giants	4.00	2.00	1.25
405	Woodie Held Slugs 2 Homers, 6 RBIs	.50	.25	.15
406	Vern Law Winner Of Cy Young Award	.50	.25	.15
407	Runnels Makes 9 Hits in Twin-Bill	.50	.25	.15
408	Braves' Lew Burdette Wins No-Hitter, 1-0	.70	.35	.20
409	Dick Stuart Hits 3 Homers, Single	.50	.25	.15
410	Don Cardwell Of Cubs Pitches No-Hit Game	.50	.25	.15
411	Camilo Pascual Strikes Out 15 Bosox	.50	.25	.15
412	Eddie Mathews Blasts 300th Big League HR	1.00	.50	.30
413	Groat, NL Bat King, Named Loop's MVP	.70	.35	.20
414	AL Votes To Expand To 10 Teams (Gene Autry)	1.25	.60	.40

		NR MT	EX	VG
415	Bobby Richardson Sets Series Mark	.75	.40	.25
416	Maris Nips Mantle For AL MVP Award	2.50	1.25	.70
417	Merkle Pulls Boner	.50	.25	.15
418	Larsen Hurls Perefect World Series Game	.75	.40	.25
419	Bean Ball Ends Career Of Mickey Cochrane	.70	.35	.20
420	Banks Belts 47 Homers, Earns MVP Award	1.50	.70	.45
421	Stan Musial Hits 5 Homers In 1 Day	2.50	1.25	.70
422	Mickey Mantle Hits Longest Homer	10.00	5.00	3.00
423	Sievers Captures Home Run Title	.50	.25	.15
424	Gehrig Consecutive Game Record Ends	5.00	2.50	1.50
425	Red Schoendienst Key Player In Victory	.70	.35	.20
426	Midget Pinch-Hits For St. Louis Browns (Eddie Gaedel)	.75	.40	.25
427	Willie Mays Makes Greatest Catch	2.50	1.25	.70
428	Robinson Saves Dodgers For Playoffs	2.50	1.25	.70
429	Campy Most Valuable Player	2.50	1.25	.70
430	Turley Hurls Yanks To Championship	.50	.25	.15
431	Dodgers Take Series From Sox In Six (Larry Sherry)	.50	.25	.15
432	Furillo Hero In 3rd World Series Game	.70	.35	.20
433	Adcock Gets Four Homers, Double	.70	.35	.20
434	Dickey Chosen All Star Catcher	1.00	.50	.30
435	Burdette Beats Yanks In 3 Series Games	.75	.40	.25
436	Umpires Clear White Sox Bench	.50	.25	.15
437	Reese Honored As Greatest Dodgers S.S.	1.50	.70	.45
438	Joe DiMaggio Hits In 56 Straight Games	5.00	2.50	1.50
439	Ted Williams Hits .406 For Season	4.00	2.00	1.25
440	Johnson Pitches 56 Scoreless Innings	2.50	1.25	.70
441	Hodges Hits 4 Home Runs In Nite Game	1.50	.70	.45
442	Greenberg Returns To Tigers From Army	1.00	.50	.30
443	Ty Cobb Named Best Player Of All Time	4.00	2.00	1.25
444	Robin Roberts Wins 28 Games	1.00	.50	.30
445	Rizzuto's 2 Runs Save 1st Place	1.25	.60	.40
446	Tigers Beat Out Senators For Pennant (Hal Newhouser)	.50	.25	.15
447	Babe Ruth Hits 60th Home Run	6.00	3.00	1.75
448	Cy Young Honored	1.50	.70	.45
449	Killebrew Starts Spring Training	1.25	.60	.40
450	Mantle Hits Longest Homer At Stadium	9.00	4.50	2.75
451	Braves Take Pennant	.50	.25	.15
452	Ted Williams Hero Of All Star Game	2.50	1.25	.70
453	Homer By Berra Puts Yanks In 1st Place	2.50	1.25	.70
454	Snodgrass Muffs A Fly Ball	.50	.25	.15
455	Babe Hits 3 Homers In A Series Game	8.00	4.00	2.50
456	New York Wins 26 Straight Games	.50	.25	.15
457	Ted Kluszewski Stars In 1st Series Win	.50	.25	.15
458	Ott Walks 5 Times In A Single Game	1.00	.50	.30
459	Harvey Kuenn Takes Batting Title	.50	.25	.15
460	Bob Feller Hurls 3rd No-Hitter Of Career	2.50	1.25	.70
461	Yanks Champs Again! (Casey Stengel)	1.50	.70	.45
462	Aaron's Bat Beats Yankees In Series	2.50	1.25	.70
463	Warren Spahn Beats Yanks In World Series	1.00	.50	.30
464	Ump's Wrong Call Helps Dodgers	.50	.25	.15
465	Kaline Hits 3 Homers, 2 In Same Inning	1.50	.70	.45
466	Bob Allison Named A.L. Rookie Of Year	.50	.25	.15
467	DiMag Comes Thru	5.00	2.50	1.50
468	Colavito Hits Four Homers In One Game	.70	.35	.20
469	Erskine Sets Strike Out Record In W.S.	.70	.35	.20

		NR MT	EX	VG
470	Sal Maglie Pitches No-Hit Game	.70	.35	.20
471	Early Wynn Victory Crushes Yanks	1.00	.50	.30
472	Nellie Fox American League's MVP	.75	.40	.25
473	Pickoff Ends Series (Marty Marion)	.50	.25	.15
474	Podres Pitching Wins Series	.80	.40	.25
475	Owen Drops 3rd Strike	.50	.25	.15
476	Dizzy And Daffy Win Series	2.50	1.25	.70
477	Mathewson Pitches 3 W.S. Shutouts	1.50	.70	.45
478	Haddix Pitches 12 Perfect Innings	.50	.25	.15
479	Hubbell Strike Out 5 A.L. Stars	1.00	.50	.30
480	Homer Sinks Dodgers (Bobby Thomson)	1.25	.60	.40

1991 O-Pee-Chee Premier

The O-Pee-Chee Co. of London, Ontario, Canada produced this 132-card set. The card fronts feature action photos, while the flip sides display a posed photo and career statistics. The cards were packaged seven cards per pack in a tamper-proof foil wrap. Several Expo and Blue Jay players are featured. Two special cards are included in this set. Card #62 honors Rickey Henderson's stolen base record, while card #102 commemorates Nolan Ryan's seventh no-hitter. Traded players and free agents are featured with their new teams.

		MT	NR MT	EX
	Complete Set:	25.00	18.00	10.00
	Common Player:	.10	.08	.04
1	Roberto Alomar	.70	.50	.30
2	Sandy Alomar	.20	.15	.08
3	Moises Alou	.12	.09	.05
4	Brian Barnes	.25	.20	.10
5	Steve Bedrosian	.10	.08	.04
6	George Bell	.20	.15	.08
7	Juan Bell	.12	.09	.05
8	Albert Belle	.70	.50	.30
9	Bud Black	.10	.08	.04
10	Mike Boddicker	.10	.08	.04
11	Wade Boggs	.60	.45	.25
12	Barry Bonds	.60	.45	.25
13	Denis Boucher	.25	.20	.10
14	George Brett	.40	.30	.15
15	Hubie Brooks	.10	.08	.04
16	Brett Butler	.12	.09	.05
17	Ivan Calderon	.15	.11	.06
18	Jose Canseco	1.50	1.25	.60
19	Gary Carter	.20	.15	.08
20	Joe Carter	.25	.20	.10
21	Jack Clark	.15	.11	.06
22	Will Clark	1.50	1.25	.60
23	Roger Clemens	1.50	1.25	.60
24	Alex Cole	.15	.11	.06
25	Vince Coleman	.15	.11	.06
26	Jeff Conine	.20	.15	.08

		MT	NR MT	EX
27	Milt Cuyler	.60	.45	.25
28	Danny Darwin	.10	.08	.04
29	Eric Davis	.30	.25	.12
30	Glenn Davis	.15	.11	.06
31	Andre Dawson	.30	.25	.12
32	Ken Dayley	.10	.08	.04
33	Steve Decker	.50	.40	.20
34	Delino DeShields	.30	.25	.12
35	Lance Dickson	.50	.40	.20
36	Kirk Dressendorfer	.80	.60	.30
37	Shawon Dunston	.15	.11	.06
38	Dennis Eckersley	.15	.11	.06
39	Dwight Evans	.12	.09	.05
40	Howard Farmer	.20	.15	.08
41	Junior Felix	.15	.11	.06
42	Alex Fernandez	.50	.40	.20
43	Tony Fernandez	.12	.09	.05
44	Cecil Fielder	1.00	.70	.40
45	Carlton Fisk	.50	.40	.20
46	Willie Fraser	.10	.08	.04
47	Gary Gaetti	.12	.09	.05
48	Andres Galarraga	.10	.08	.04
49	Ron Gant	.80	.60	.30
50	Kirk Gibson	.15	.11	.06
51	Bernard Gilkey	.30	.25	.12
52	Leo Gomez	.50	.40	.20
53	Rene Gonzalez	.10	.08	.04
54	Juan Gonzalez	3.00	2.25	1.25
55	Doc Gooden	.40	.30	.15
56	Ken Griffey,Jr.	3.00	2.25	1.25
57	Kelly Gruber	.20	.15	.08
58	Pedro Guerrero	.15	.11	.06
59	Tony Gwynn	.60	.45	.25
60	Chris Hammond	.20	.15	.08
61	Ron Hassey	.10	.08	.04
62	Rickey Henderson	1.00	.70	.40
63	Tom Henke	.12	.09	.05
64	Orel Hershiser	.20	.15	.08
65	Chris Hoiles	.20	.15	.08
66	Todd Hundley	.30	.25	.12
67	Pete Incaviglia	.10	.08	.04
68	Danny Jackson	.10	.08	.04
69	Barry Jones	.10	.08	.04
70	David Justice	3.00	2.25	1.25
71	Jimmy Key	.12	.09	.05
72	Ray Lankford	1.00	.70	.40
73	Darren Lewis	.80	.60	.30
74	Kevin Maas	.60	.45	.25
75	Denny Martinez	.12	.09	.05
76	Tino Martinez	.50	.40	.20
77	Don Mattingly	1.00	.70	.40
78	Willie McGee	.15	.11	.06
79	Fred McGriff	.30	.25	.12
80	Hensley Meulens	.20	.15	.08
81	Kevin Mitchell	.30	.25	.12
82	Paul Molitor	.25	.20	.10
83	Mickey Morandini	.25	.20	.10
84	Jack Morris	.25	.20	.10
85	Dale Murphy	.25	.20	.10
86	Eddie Murray	.30	.25	.12
87	Chris Nabholz	.15	.11	.06
88	Tim Naehring	.20	.15	.08
89	Otis Nixon	.12	.09	.05
90	Jose Offerman	.20	.15	.08
91	Bob Ojeda	.10	.08	.04
92	John Olerud	.50	.40	.20
93	Gregg Olson	.15	.11	.06
94	Dave Parker	.15	.11	.06
95	Terry Pendleton	.20	.15	.08
96	Kirby Puckett	1.00	.70	.40
97	Rock Raines	.15	.11	.06
98	Jeff Reardon	.12	.09	.05
99	Dave Righetti	.12	.09	.05
100	Cal Ripken	3.00	2.25	1.25
101	Mel Rojas	.15	.11	.06
102	Nolan Ryan	4.00	3.00	1.50
103	Ryne Sandberg	2.00	1.50	.80
104	Scott Sanderson	.10	.08	.04
105	Benito Santiago	.15	.11	.06
106	Pete Schourek	.25	.20	.10
107	Gary Scott	.25	.20	.10
108	Terry Shumpert	.10	.08	.04
109	Ruben Sierra	.80	.60	.30
110	Doug Simons	.20	.15	.08
111	Dave Smith	.10	.08	.04
112	Ozzie Smith	.35	.25	.14
113	Cory Snyder	.10	.08	.04
114	Luis Sojo	.10	.08	.04
115	Dave Stewart	.15	.11	.06
116	Dave Stieb	.12	.09	.05
117	Darryl Strawberry	1.25	.90	.50

		MT	NR MT	EX
118	Pat Tabler	.10	.08	.04
119	Wade Taylor	.30	.25	.12
120	Bobby Thigpen	.15	.11	.06
121	Frank Thomas	6.00	4.50	2.50
122	Mike Timlin	.30	.25	.12
123	Alan Trammell	.20	.15	.08
124	Mo Vaughn	2.00	1.50	.80
125	Tim Wallach	.12	.09	.05
126	Devon White	.12	.09	.05
127	Mark Whiten	.60	.45	.25
128	Bernie Williams	1.25	.90	.50
129	Willie Wilson	.10	.08	.04
130	Dave Winfield	.30	.25	.12
131	Robin Yount	.60	.45	.25
132	Checklist	.10	.08	.04

1992 O-Pee-Chee Premier

JOHN KRUK

O-Pee-Chee increased the number of cards in its premier set to 198 for 1992. The cards feature white borders surrounding full-color player photos. The O-Pee-Chee banner appears at the top of the card and the player's name and position appear at the bottom. The backs feature an additional player photo, statistics and player information. Traded players and free agents are featured with their new teams.

		MT	NR MT	EX
Complete Set:		25.00	18.00	10.00
Common Player:		.08	.06	.03
1	Wade Boggs	.40	.30	.15
2	John Smiley	.10	.08	.04
3	Checklist	.08	.06	.03
4	Ron Gant	.20	.15	.08
5	Mike Bordick	.20	.15	.08
6	Charlie Hayes	.08	.06	.03
7	Kevin Morton	.08	.06	.03
8	Checklist	.08	.06	.03
9	Chris Gwynn	.08	.06	.03
10	Scott Bankhead	.08	.06	.03
11	Danny Gladden	.08	.06	.03
12	Brian McRae	.20	.15	.08
13	Denny Martinez	.10	.08	.04
14	Bob Scanlan	.15	.11	.06
15	Julio Franco	.10	.08	.04
16	Ruben Amaro	.15	.11	.06

Values quoted in this guide reflect the retail price of a card — the price a collector can expect to pay when buying a card from a dealer. The wholesale price — that which a collector can expect to receive from a dealer when selling cards — will be significantly lower, depending on desirability and condition.

#	Name	MT	NR MT	EX
17	Mo Sanford	.15	.11	.06
18	Melido Perez	.08	.06	.03
19	Dickie Thon	.08	.06	.03
20	Chris James	.08	.06	.03
21	Mike Huff	.08	.06	.03
22	Orlando Merced	.10	.08	.04
23	Chris Sabo	.15	.11	.06
24	Jose Canseco	.50	.40	.20
25	Reggie Sanders	.50	.40	.20
26	Chris Nabholz	.10	.08	.04
27	Kevin Seitzer	.08	.06	.03
28	Ryan Bowen	.15	.11	.06
29	Gary Carter	.15	.11	.06
30	Wayne Rosenthal	.08	.06	.03
31	Alan Trammell	.20	.15	.08
32	Doug Drabek	.20	.15	.08
33	Craig Shipley	.10	.08	.04
34	Ryne Sandberg	.30	.25	.12
35	Chuck Knoblauch	.25	.20	.10
36	Bret Barberie	.20	.15	.08
37	Tim Naehring	.12	.09	.05
38	Omar Olivares	.12	.09	.05
39	Royce Clayton	.25	.20	.10
40	Brent Mayne	.12	.09	.05
41	Darrin Fletcher	.08	.06	.03
42	Howard Johnson	.15	.11	.06
43	Steve Sax	.12	.09	.05
44	Greg Swindell	.20	.15	.08
45	Andre Dawson	.20	.15	.08
46	Kent Hrbek	.15	.11	.06
47	Doc Gooden	.35	.25	.14
48	Mark Leiter	.08	.06	.03
49	Tom Glavine	.20	.15	.08
50	Mo Vaughn	.20	.15	.08
51	Doug Jones	.08	.06	.03
52	Brian Barnes	.12	.09	.05
53	Rob Dibble	.15	.11	.06
54	Kevin McReynolds	.12	.09	.05
55	Ivan Rodriguez	.40	.30	.15
56	Scott Livingstone	.20	.15	.08
57	Mike Magnante	.12	.09	.05
58	Pete Schourek	.10	.08	.04
59	Frank Thomas	1.50	1.25	.60
61	Wally Joyner	.15	.11	.06
62	Rick Aguilera	.15	.11	.06
63	Eric Karros	2.00	1.50	.80
64	Tino Martinez	.20	.15	.08
65	Bryan Hickerson	.20	.15	.08
66	Ruben Sierra	.30	.25	.12
67	Willie Randolph	.10	.08	.04
68	Bill Landrum, Kirk McCaskill	.12	.09	.05
69	Bip Roberts	.15	.11	.06
70	Cecil Fielder	.40	.30	.15
71	Pat Kelly	.15	.11	.06
72	Kenny Lofton	.50	.40	.20
73	John Franco	.10	.08	.04
74	Phil Plantier	.20	.15	.08
75	Dave Martinez	.08	.06	.03
76	Warren Newson	.08	.06	.03
77	Chito Martinez	.15	.11	.06
78	Brian Hunter	.15	.11	.06
79	Jack Morris	.20	.15	.08
80	Eric king	.08	.06	.03
81	Nolan Ryan	.60	.45	.25
82	Bret Saberhagen	.15	.11	.06
83	Roberto Kelly	.15	.11	.06
84	Ozzie Smith	.20	.15	.08
85	Chuck McElroy	.08	.06	.03
86	Carlton Fisk	.25	.20	.10
87	Mike Mussina	1.00	.70	.40
88	Mark Carreon	.08	.06	.03
89	Ken Hill	.15	.11	.06
90	Rick Cerone	.08	.06	.03
91	Deion Sanders	.40	.30	.15
92	Don Mattingly	.40	.30	.15
93	Danny Tartabull	.15	.11	.06
94	Keith Miller	.12	.09	.05
95	Gregg Jefferies	.15	.11	.06
96	Barry Larkin	.20	.15	.08
97	Kevin Mitchell	.15	.11	.06
98	Rick Sutcliffe	.15	.11	.06
99	Mark McGwire	.30	.25	.12
100	Albert Belle	.30	.25	.12
101	Gregg Olson	.15	.11	.06
102	Kirby Puckett	.50	.40	.20
103	Luis Gonzalez	.20	.15	.08
104	Randy Myers	.10	.08	.04
105	Roger Clmens	.50	.40	.20
106	Tony Gwynn	.40	.30	.15
107	Jeff Bagwell	.50	.40	.20
108	John Wetteland	.15	.11	.06
109	Bernie Williams	.15	.11	.06
110	Scott Kamieniecki	.15	.11	.06
111	Robin Yount	.25	.20	.10
112	Dean Palmer	.15	.11	.06
113	Tim Belcher	.10	.08	.04
114	George Brett	.25	.20	.10
115	Frank Viola	.20	.15	.08
116	Kelly Gruber	.10	.08	.04
117	David Justice	.25	.20	.10
118	Scott Leuis	.10	.08	.04
119	Jeff Fassero	.10	.08	.04
120	Sammy Sosa	.12	.09	.05
121	Al Osuna	.08	.06	.03
122	Wilson Alvarez	.10	.08	.04
123	Jose Offerman	.15	.11	.06
124	Mel Rojas	.10	.08	.04
125	Shawon Dunston	.10	.08	.04
126	Pete Incaviglia	.10	.08	.04
127	Von Hayes	.08	.06	.03
128	Dave Gallagher	.08	.06	.03
129	Eric Davis	.15	.11	.06
130	Roberto Alomar	.50	.40	.20
131	Mike Gallego	.08	.06	.03
132	Robin Ventura	.40	.30	.15
133	Bill Swift	.10	.08	.04
134	John Kruk	.15	.11	.06
135	Craig Biggio	.15	.11	.06
136	Eddie Taubensee	.25	.20	.10
137	Cal Ripken	.60	.45	.25
138	Charles Nagy	.15	.11	.06
139	Jose Melendez	.20	.15	.08
140	Jim Abbott	.20	.15	.08
141	Paul Molitor	.20	.15	.08
142	Tom Candiotti	.08	.06	.03
143	Bobby Bonilla	.40	.30	.15
144	Matt Williams	.15	.11	.06
145	Brett Butler	.12	.09	.05
146	Will Clark	.50	.40	.20
147	Rickey Henderson	.30	.25	.12
148	Ray Lankford	.30	.25	.12
149	Bill Pecota	.08	.06	.03
150	Dave Winfield	.20	.15	.08
151	Darren Lewis	.10	.08	.04
152	Bob MacDonald	.10	.08	.04
153	David Segui	.10	.08	.04
154	Benny Santiago	.20	.15	.08
155	Chuck Finley	.12	.09	.05
156	Andujar Cedeno	.25	.20	.10
157	Barry Bonds	.50	.40	.20
158	Joe Grahe	.08	.06	.03
159	Frank Castillo	.15	.11	.06
160	Dave Burba	.08	.06	.03
161	Leo Gomez	.15	.11	.06
162	Orel Hershiser	.15	.11	.06
163	Delino DeShields	.20	.15	.08
164	Sandy Alomar	.30	.25	.12
165	Denny Neagle	.20	.15	.08
166	Fred McGriff	.25	.20	.10
167	Ken Griffey, Jr.	.80	.60	.30
168	Juan Guzman	.50	.40	.20
169	Bobby Rose	.08	.06	.03
170	Steve Avery	.15	.11	.06
171	Rich DeLucia	.10	.08	.04
172	Mike Timlin	.15	.11	.06
173	Randy Johnson	.10	.08	.04
174	Paul Gibson	.08	.06	.03
175	David Cone	.15	.11	.06
176	Marquis Grissom	.20	.15	.08
177	Kurt Stillwell	.08	.06	.03
178	Mark Whiten	.15	.11	.06
179	Darryl Strawberry	.25	.20	.10
180	Mike Morgan	.08	.06	.03
181	Scott Scudder	.08	.06	.03
182	George Bell	.15	.11	.06
183	Alvin Davis	.08	.06	.03
184	Len Dykstra	.15	.11	.06
185	Kyle Abbott	.15	.11	.06
186	Chris Haney	.15	.11	.06
187	Junior Noboa	.08	.06	.03
188	Dennis Eckersley	.20	.15	.08
189	Derek Bell	.35	.25	.14
190	Lee Smith	.12	.09	.05
191	Andres Galarraga	.10	.08	.04
192	Jack Armstrong	.08	.06	.03
193	Eddie Murray	.15	.11	.06
194	Joe Carter	.20	.15	.08
195	Terry Pendleton	.20	.15	.08
196	Darryl Kile	.15	.11	.06
197	Rod Beck	.15	.11	.06
198	Hubie Brooks	.08	.06	.03

1986 Oh Henry Indians

This 30-card set of Cleveland Indians players was distributed by the team at a special Photo/Baseball Card Day at Municipal Stadium. The cards were printed within a special three-panel, perforated fold-out piece which featured four action shots of the Indians on the cover. Unfolded, there are two panels containing the baseball cards and a third which contains a team photo. Cards measure 2-1/4" by 3-1/8" and are full-color studio portraits. Photos are framed in blue with a white border and list player name, number and position. Card fronts also include a picture of the sponsoring candy bar. Card backs include facsimile autograph and professional records. Each card is perforated for separation.

		MT	NR MT	EX
Complete Set:		10.00	7.50	4.00
Common Player:		.15	.11	.06
2	Brett Butler	.70	.50	.30
4	Tony Bernazard	.15	.11	.06
6	Andy Allanson	.25	.20	.10
7	Pat Corrales	.15	.11	.06
8	Carmen Castillo	.15	.11	.06
10	Pat Tabler	.30	.25	.12
13	Ernie Camacho	.15	.11	.06
14	Julio Franco	1.00	.70	.40
15	Dan Rohn	.15	.11	.06
18	Ken Schrom	.15	.11	.06
20	Otis Nixon	.20	.15	.08
22	Fran Mullins	.15	.11	.06
23	Chris Bando	.15	.11	.06
24	Ed Williams	.35	.25	.14
26	Brook Jacoby	.80	.60	.30
27	Mel Hall	.30	.25	.12
29	Andre Thornton	.30	.25	.12
30	Joe Carter	1.00	.70	.40
35	Phil Niekro	.80	.60	.30
36	Jamie Easterly	.15	.11	.06
37	Don Schulze	.15	.11	.06
42	Rich Yett	.20	.15	.08
43	Scott Bailes	.35	.25	.14
44	Neal Heaton	.15	.11	.06
46	Jim Kern	.15	.11	.06
48	Dickie Noles	.15	.11	.06
49	Tom Candiotti	.25	.20	.10
53	Reggie Ritter	.15	.11	.06
54	Tom Waddell	.15	.11	.06
----	Coaching Staff (Jack Aker, Bobby Bonds, Doc Edwards, Johnny Goryl)	.15	.11	.06

1963 Pepsi-Cola Colt .45'S

This 16-card set was distributed regionally in Texas in bottled six-packs of Pepsi. The cards were issued

on panels 2-3/8" by 9-1/8", which were fit in between the bottles in each carton. Values quoted in the checklist below are for complete panels. A standard 2-3/8" by 3-3/4" card was printed on each panel, which also included promos for Pepsi and the Colt .45's, as well as a team schedule. Card fronts were black and white posed action photos with blue and red trim. Player name and position and Pepsi logo are also included. Card backs offer player statistics and career highlights. The John Bateman card, which was apparently never distributed publicly, is among the rarest collectible baseball cards of the 1960s. The complete set price does not include the Bateman card.

		NR MT	EX	VG
Complete Set:		210.00	105.00	63.00
Common Player:		7.00	3.50	2.00
1	Bob Aspromonte	7.00	3.50	2.00
2	John Bateman	500.00	250.00	150.00
3	Bob Bruce	7.00	3.50	2.00
4	Jim Campbell	7.00	3.50	2.00
5	Dick Farrell	7.00	3.50	2.00
6	Ernie Fazio	7.00	3.50	2.00
7	Carroll Hardy	7.00	3.50	2.00
8	J.C. Hartman	7.00	3.50	2.00
9	Ken Johnson	7.00	3.50	2.00
10	Bob Lillis	7.00	3.50	2.00
11	Don McMahon	7.00	3.50	2.00
12	Pete Runnels	15.00	7.50	4.50
13	Al Spangler	7.00	3.50	2.00
14	Rusty Staub	30.00	15.00	9.00
15	Johnny Temple	7.00	3.50	2.00
16	Carl Warwick	60.00	30.00	18.00

Definitions for grading conditions are located in the Introduction of this price guide.

1988 Pepsi-Cola/Kroger Tigers

(41) DARRELL EVANS, IF

Approximately 38,000 sets of cards were given to fans at Tiger Stadium on July 30th, 1988. The set, sponsored by Pepsi-Cola and Kroger, includes 25 oversized (2-7/8" by 4-1/4") cards printed on glossy white stock with blue and orange borders. The card backs include small black and white close-up photos, the players' professional records and sponsor logos. The numbers in the following checklist refer to the players' uniform.

		MT	NR MT	EX
Complete Set:		8.00	6.00	3.25
Common Player:		.20	.15	.08
1	Lou Whitaker	.70	.50	.30
2	Alan Trammell	.90	.70	.35
8	Mike Heath	.20	.15	.08
11	Sparky Anderson	.40	.30	.15
12	Luis Salazar	.20	.15	.08
14	Dave Bergman	.20	.15	.08
15	Pat Sheridan	.20	.15	.08
16	Tom Brookens	.20	.15	.08
19	Doyle Alexander	.25	.20	.10
21	Guillermo Hernandez	.25	.20	.10
22	Ray Knight	.25	.20	.10
24	Gary Pettis	.20	.15	.08
25	Eric King	.30	.25	.12
26	Frank Tanana	.30	.25	.12
31	Larry Herndon	.20	.15	.08
32	Jim Walewander	.25	.20	.10
33	Matt Nokes	.90	.70	.35
34	Chet Lemon	.25	.20	.10
35	Walt Terrell	.25	.20	.10
39	Mike Henneman	.40	.30	.15
41	Darrell Evans	.40	.30	.15
44	Jeff Robinson	.50	.40	.20
47	Jack Morris	.70	.50	.30
48	Paul Gibson	.30	.25	.12
----	Coaches (Billy Consolo, Alex Grammas, Billy Muffett, Vada Pinson, Dick Tracewski)			
		.20	.15	.08

1990 Pepsi-Cola Red Sox

Pepsi combined with Score to produce this special 20-card Boston Red Sox team set. Cards were inserted regionally in 12-packs of Pepsi and Diet Pepsi. The card fronts feature full-color action photos with the team name across the top border and the player's name along the bottom border. The Pepsi and Diet Pepsi logos also appear on the bottom border. The card backs represent standard Score card backs, but are not numbered and also once again feature the Pepsi and Diet Pepsi logos.

		MT	NR MT	EX
Complete Set:		10.00	7.50	4.00
Common Player:		.25	.20	.10
(1)	Marty Barrett	.25	.20	.10
(2)	Mike Boddicker	.35	.25	.14
(3)	Wade Boggs	.80	.60	.30
(4)	Bill Buckner	.25	.20	.10
(5)	Ellis Burks	.80	.60	.30
(6)	Roger Clemens	1.50	1.25	.60
(7)	John Dopson	.25	.20	.10
(8)	Dwight Evans	.50	.40	.20
(9)	Wes Gardner	.25	.20	.10

		MT	NR MT	EX
(10)	Rich Gedman	.25	.20	.10
(11)	Mike Greenwell	.50	.40	.20
(12)	Dennis Lamp	.25	.20	.10
(13)	Rob Murphy	.25	.20	.10
(14)	Tony Pena	.50	.40	.20
(15)	Carlos Quintana	.50	.40	.20
(16)	Jeff Reardon	.40	.30	.15
(17)	Jody Reed	.50	.40	.20
(18)	Luis Rivera	.25	.20	.10
(19)	Kevin Romine	.25	.20	.10
(20)	Lee Smith	.40	.30	.15

1991 Pepsi-Cola Red Sox

For the second consecutive year, Pepsi/Diet Pepsi sponsored Boston Red Sox trading cards. The cards were inserted in specially marked packs of Pepsi and Diet Pepsi and were made available from July 1 through August 10. A consumer sweepstakes was also included with this promotion. Player jersey numbers are featured on the backs of the cards. Danny Darwin's jersey is incorrectly listed as #46. He actually wears #44 for the BoSox. Wade Boggs is not featured on a 1991 Pepsi-Cola Red Sox card.

		MT	NR MT	EX
Complete Set:		8.00	6.00	3.25
Common Player:		.25	.20	.10
2	Luis Rivera	.25	.20	.10
3	Jody Reed	.40	.30	.15
6	Tony Pena	.40	.30	.15
11	Tim Naehring	.50	.40	.20
12	Ellis Burks	.50	.40	.20
15	Dennis Lamp	.25	.20	.10
18	Carlos Quintana	.30	.25	.12
19	Dana Kiecker	.30	.25	.12
20	John Marzano	.25	.20	.10
21	Roger Clemens	1.00	.70	.40
23	Tom Brunansky	.30	.25	.12
25	Jack Clark	.40	.30	.15
27	Greg Harris	.25	.20	.10
29	Phil Plantier	1.25	.90	.50
30	Matt Young	.25	.20	.10
38	Jeff Gray	.30	.25	.12
39	Mike Greenwell	.50	.40	.20
41	Jeff Reardon	.40	.30	.15
46	Danny Darwin	.25	.20	.10
50	Tom Bolton	.25	.20	.10

1961 Peters Meats Twins

This set, featuring the first-year 1961 Minnesota Twins, is in a large, 4-5/8" by 3-1/2", format. Cards are on thick cardboard and heavily waxed, as they were used as partial packaging for the company's meat products. Card fronts feature full-color photos, team and Peters logos, and biographical information. The cards are blank-backed.

	NR MT	EX	VG
Complete Set:	650.00	325.00	195.00
Common Player:	15.00	7.50	4.50

		NR MT	EX	VG
1	Zoilo Versalles	20.00	10.00	6.00
2	Eddie Lopat	20.00	10.00	6.00
3	Pedro Ramos	15.00	7.50	4.50
4	Charles "Chuck" Stobbs	15.00	7.50	4.50
5	Don Mincher	20.00	10.00	6.00
6	Jack Kralick	15.00	7.50	4.50
7	Jim Kaat	50.00	25.00	15.00
8	Hal Naragon	15.00	7.50	4.50
9	Don Lee	15.00	7.50	4.50
10	Harry "Cookie" Lavagetto	15.00	7.50	4.50
11	Tom "Pete" Whisenant	15.00	7.50	4.50
12	Elmer Valo	15.00	7.50	4.50
13	Ray Moore	15.00	7.50	4.50
14	Billy Gardner	15.00	7.50	4.50
15	Lenny Green	15.00	7.50	4.50
16	Sam Mele	15.00	7.50	4.50
17	Jim Lemon	15.00	7.50	4.50
18	Harmon "Killer" Killebrew	150.00	75.00	45.00
19	Paul Giel	15.00	7.50	4.50
20	Reno Bertoia	15.00	7.50	4.50
21	Clyde McCullough	15.00	7.50	4.50
22	Earl Battey	20.00	10.00	6.00
23	Camilo Pascual	20.00	10.00	6.00
24	Dan Dobbek	15.00	7.50	4.50
25	Joe "Valvy" Valdivielso	15.00	7.50	4.50
26	Billy Consolo	15.00	7.50	4.50

1939 Play Ball

With the issuance of this card set by Gum Incorporated, a new era of baseball cards was born. Although the cards are black and white, the full-frame, actual photos on the card fronts are of better quality than previously seen, and the 2-1/2" by 3-1/4" size was larger and more popular than the smaller tobacco and caramel cards of the early 20th Century. Card backs featured player names and extensive biographies. There are 162 cards in the set, including superstars Joe DiMaggio and Ted Williams. Card number 126 was never issued. The complete set price does not include all back variations found in the low-numbered series.

	NR MT	EX	VG
Complete Set:	13500.00	6750.00	4250.
Common Player: 1-115	20.00	10.00	6.00
Common Player: 116-162	125.00	62.00	37.00

		NR MT	EX	VG
1	Alvin Jacob Powell	150.00	40.00	25.00
2a	Lee Theo Grissom (name in upper case letters)	25.00	9.00	5.50
2b	Lee Theo Grissom (name in upper and lower case)	35.00	12.50	7.50
3a	Charles Herbert Ruffing (name in upper case letters)	125.00	62.00	37.00
3b	Charles Herbert Ruffing (name in upper and lower case)	135.00	67.00	40.00
4a	Eldon LeRoy Auker (name in upper case letters)	20.00	10.00	6.00
4b	Eldon LeRoy Auker (name in upper and lower case)	22.00	11.00	6.50
5a	James Luther Sewell (name in upper case letters)	22.00	11.00	6.50
5b	James Luther Sewell (name in upper and lower case)	24.00	12.00	7.25
6a	Leo Ernest Durocher (name in upper case letters)	100.00	50.00	30.00
6b	Leo Ernest Durocher (name in upper and lower case)	125.00	62.00	37.00
7a	Robert Pershing Doerr (name in upper case letters)	100.00	50.00	30.00
7b	Robert Pershing Doerr (name in upper and lower case)	100.00	50.00	30.00
8	Henry Pippen	20.00	10.00	6.00
9a	James Tobin (name in upper case letters)	20.00	10.00	6.00
9b	James Tobin (name in upper and lower case)	22.00	11.00	6.50
10	James Brooklyn DeShong	20.00	10.00	6.00
11	John Costa Rizzo	20.00	10.00	6.00
12	Hershel Ray Martin (Herschel)	20.00	10.00	6.00
13a	Luke Daniel Hamlin (name in upper case letters)	20.00	10.00	6.00
13b	Luke Daniel Hamlin (name in upper and lower case)	22.00	11.00	6.50
14a	James R. Tabor ("...Tabor batted .295,...")	20.00	10.00	6.00
14b	James R. Tabor ("...Tabor batted 295,...")	22.00	11.00	6.50
15a	Paul Derringer (name in upper case letters)	22.00	11.00	6.50
15b	Paul Derringer (name in upper and lower case)	24.00	12.00	7.25
16	John Peacock	20.00	10.00	6.00
17	Emerson Dickman	20.00	10.00	6.00
18a	Harry Danning (name in upper case letters)	20.00	10.00	6.00
18b	Harry Danning (name in upper and lower case)	22.00	11.00	6.50
19	Paul Dean	35.00	17.50	10.50
20	Joseph Heving	20.00	10.00	6.00
21a	Emil Leonard (name in upper case letters)	20.00	10.00	6.00
21b	Emil Leonard (name in upper and lower case)	22.00	11.00	6.50
22a	William Henry Walters (name in upper case letters)	22.00	11.00	6.50
22b	William Henry Walters (name in upper and lower case)	24.00	12.00	7.25
23	Burgess U. Whitehead	20.00	10.00	6.00
24a	Richard S. Coffman (S. Richard) ("...Senators the same year.")	20.00	10.00	6.00
24b	Richard S. Coffman (S. Richard) ("...Browns the same year.")	35.00	17.50	10.50
25a	George Alexander Selkirk (name in upper case letters)	35.00	17.50	10.50
25b	George Alexander Selkirk (name in upper and lower case)	40.00	20.00	12.00
26a	Joseph Paul DiMaggio ("...206 hits in 1938 games...")	2000.00	1000.00	600.00
26b	Joseph Paul DiMaggio ("...206 hits in 138 games...")	2000.00	1000.00	600.00
27a	Fred Ray Ostermueller (name in upper case letters)	20.00	10.00	6.00
27b	Fred Ray Ostermueller (name in upper and lower case)	22.00	11.00	6.50
28	Sylvester Johnson	20.00	10.00	6.00
29a	John Francis Wilson (name in upper case letters)	20.00	10.00	6.00
29b	John Francis Wilson (name in upper and lower case)	22.00	11.00	6.50
30a	William Malcolm Dickey (name in upper case letters)	200.00	100.00	60.00
30b	William Malcolm Dickey (name in upper and lower case)	225.00	125.00	70.00
31a	Samuel West (name in upper case letters)	20.00	10.00	6.00
31b	Samuel West (name in upper and lower case)	22.00	11.00	6.50

	NR MT	EX	VG
32 Robert I. Seeds	20.00	10.00	6.00
33 Del Howard Young (name actually Del Edward)	20.00	10.00	6.00
34a Frank Joseph Demaree (Joseph Franklin) (name in upper case letters)	20.00	10.00	6.00
34b Frank Joseph Demaree (Joseph Franklin) (name in upper case letter)	22.00	11.00	6.50
35a William Frederick Jurges (name in upper case letters)	22.00	11.00	6.50
35b William Frederick Jurges (name in upper and lower case)	24.00	12.00	7.25
36a Frank Andrew McCormick (name in upper case letters)	20.00	10.00	6.00
36b Frank Andrew McCormick (name in upper and lower case)	22.00	11.00	6.50
37 Virgil Lawrence Davis	20.00	10.00	6.00
38a William Harrison Myers (name in upper case letters)	20.00	10.00	6.00
38b William Harrison Myers (name in upper and lower case)	22.00	11.00	6.50
39a Richard Benjamin Ferrell (name in upper case letters)	100.00	50.00	30.00
39b Richard Benjamin Ferrell (name in upper and lower case)	125.00	62.00	37.00
40 James Charles Bagby Jr.	20.00	10.00	6.00
41a Lonnie Warneke ("...the earned run department...")	20.00	10.00	6.00
41b Lonnie Warneke ("...the earned-run department...")	22.00	11.00	6.50
42 Arndt Jorgens	24.00	12.00	7.25
43 Melo Almada	20.00	10.00	6.00
44 Donald Henry Heffner	20.00	10.00	6.00
45a Merrill May (name in upper case letters)	20.00	10.00	6.00
45b Merrill May (name in upper and lower case)	22.00	11.00	6.50
46a Morris Arnovich (name in upper case letters)	20.00	10.00	6.00
46b Morris Arnovich (name in upper and lower case)	22.00	11.00	6.50
47a John Kelly Lewis, Jr. (name in upper case letters)	20.00	10.00	6.00
47b John Kelly Lewis, Jr. (name in upper and lower case)	22.00	11.00	6.50
48a Vernon Gomez (name in upper case letters)	200.00	100.00	60.00
48b Vernon Gomez (name in upper and lower case)	225.00	125.00	70.00
49 Edward Miller	20.00	10.00	6.00
50a Charles Len Gehringer (name actually Charles Leonard) (name in upper case letters)	200.00	100.00	60.00
50b Charles Len Gehringer (name actually Charles Leonard) (name in upper & lower case)	225.00	125.00	70.00
51a Melvin Thomas Ott (name in upper case)	200.00	100.00	60.00
51b Melvin Thomas Ott (name in upper and lower case)	225.00	125.00	70.00
52a Thomas D. Henrich (name in upper case letters)	40.00	20.00	12.00
52b Thomas D. Henrich (name in upper and lower case)	45.00	22.00	13.50
53a Carl Owen Hubbell (name in upper case letters)	200.00	100.00	60.00
53b Carl Owen Hubbell (name in upper and lower case)	225.00	125.00	70.00
54a Harry Edward Gumbert (name in upper case letters)	20.00	10.00	6.00
54b Harry Edward Gumbert (name in upper and lower case)	22.00	11.00	6.50
55a Floyd E. Vaughan (Joseph Floyd) (name in upper case letters)	125.00	62.00	37.00
55b Floyd E. Vaughan (Joseph Floyd) (name in upper and lower case)	125.00	62.00	37.00
56a Henry Greenberg (name in upper case letters)	150.00	75.00	45.00
56b Henry Greenberg (name in upper and lower case)	160.00	80.00	48.00
57a John A. Hassett (name in upper case letters)	20.00	10.00	6.00
57b John A. Hassett (name in upper and lower case)	22.00	11.00	6.50
58 Louis Peo Chiozza	20.00	10.00	6.00
59 Kendall Chase	20.00	10.00	6.00
60a Lynwood Thomas Rowe (name in upper case letters)	22.00	11.00	6.50
60b Lynwood Thomas Rowe (name in upper and lower case)	24.00	12.00	7.25
61a Anthony F. Cuccinello (name in upper case letters)	20.00	10.00	6.00
61b Anthony F. Cuccinello (name in upper and lower case)	22.00	11.00	6.50
62 Thomas Carey	20.00	10.00	6.00
63 Emmett Mueller	20.00	10.00	6.00
64a Wallace Moses, Jr. (name in upper case letters)	20.00	10.00	6.00
64b Wallace Moses, Jr. (name in upper and lower case)	22.00	11.00	6.50
65a Harry Francis Craft (name in upper case letters)	20.00	10.00	6.00
65b Harry Francis Craft (name in upper and lower case)	22.00	11.00	6.50
66 James A. Ripple	20.00	10.00	6.00
67 Edwin Joost	20.00	10.00	6.00
68 Fred Singleton	20.00	10.00	6.00
69 Elbert Preston Fletcher (Elburt)	20.00	10.00	6.00
70 Fred Maloy Frankhouse (Meloy)	20.00	10.00	6.00
71a Marcellus Monte Pearson (name actually Montgomery Marcellus) (name in upper case)	24.00	12.00	7.25
71b Marcellus Monte Pearson (name actually Montgomery Marcellus) (name in upper & lower)	35.00	17.50	10.50
72a Debs Garms (Born: Bango, Tex.)	20.00	10.00	6.00
72b Debs Garms (Born: Bangs, Tex.)	25.00	12.50	7.50
73a Harold H. Schumacher (Born: Dolgville, N.Y.)	22.00	11.00	6.50
73b Harold H. Schumacher (Born: Dolgville, N.Y.)	40.00	20.00	12.00
74a Harry A. Lavagetto (name in upper case letters)	24.00	12.00	7.25
74b Harry A. Lavagetto (name in upper and lower case)	15.00	7.50	4.50
75a Stanley Bordagaray (name in upper case letters)	20.00	10.00	6.00
75b Stanley Bordagaray (name in upper and lower case)	22.00	11.00	6.50
76 Goodwin George Rosen	20.00	10.00	6.00
77 Lewis Sidney Riggs	20.00	10.00	6.00
78a Julius Joseph Solters (name in upper case letters)	20.00	10.00	6.00
78b Julius Joseph Solters (name in upper and lower case)	22.00	11.00	6.50
79a Joseph Gregg Moore (given name is Joe) (Weight: 157 lbs.)	20.00	10.00	6.00
79b Joseph Gregg Moore (given name is Joe) (Weight: 175 lbs.)	25.00	12.50	7.50
80a Irwin Fox (Ervin) (Weight: 165 lbs.)	20.00	10.00	6.00
80b Irwin Fox (Ervin) (Weight: 157 lbs.)	25.00	12.50	7.50
81a Ellsworth Dahlgren (name in upper case letters)	24.00	12.00	7.25
81b Ellsworth Dahlgren (name in upper and lower case)	35.00	17.50	10.50
82a Charles Herbert Klein (name in upper case letters)	165.00	82.00	49.00
82b Charles Herbert Klein (name in upper and lower case)	175.00	87.00	52.00
83a August Richard Suhr (name in upper case letters)	20.00	10.00	6.00
83b August Richard Suhr (name in upper and lower case)	22.00	11.00	6.50
84 Lamar Newsome	20.00	10.00	6.00
85 John Walter Cooney	20.00	10.00	6.00
86a Adolph Camilli (Adolf) ("...start of the 1928 season,...")	22.00	11.00	6.50
86b Adolph Camilli (Adolf) ("...start of the 1938 season,...")	35.00	17.50	10.50
87 Milburn G. Shoffner (middle initial actually J.)	20.00	10.00	6.00
88 Charles Keller	50.00	25.00	15.00
89a Lloyd James Waner (name in upper case letters)	125.00	62.00	37.00
89b Lloyd James Waner (name in upper and lower case)	135.00	67.00	40.00
90a Robert H. Klinger (name in upper case letters)	20.00	10.00	6.00
90b Robert H. Klinger (name in upper and lower case)	22.00	11.00	6.50
91a John H. Knott (name in upper case letters)	20.00	10.00	6.00
91b John H. Knott (name in upper and lower case)	22.00	11.00	6.50
92a Ted Williams (name in upper case letters)	1800.00	900.00	540.00
92b Ted Williams (name in upper and lower case)	2000.00	1000.00	600.00
93 Charles M. Gelbert	20.00	10.00	6.00
94 Henry E. Manush	125.00	62.00	37.00
95a Whitlow Wyatt (name in upper case letters)	22.00	11.00	6.50

		NR MT	EX	VG
95b	Whitlow Wyatt (name in upper and lower case)	24.00	12.00	7.25
96a	Ernest Gordon Phelps (name in upper case letters)	22.00	11.00	6.50
96b	Ernest Gordon Phelps (name in upper and lower case)	24.00	12.00	7.25
97a	Robert Lee Johnson (name in upper case letters)	20.00	10.00	6.00
97b	Robert Lee Johnson (name in upper and lower case)	22.00	11.00	6.50
98	Arthur Carter Whitney	20.00	10.00	6.00
99a	Walter Anton Berger (name in upper case letters)	22.00	11.00	6.50
99b	Walter Anton Berger (name in upper and lower case)	24.00	12.00	7.25
100a	Charles Solomon Myer (name in upper case letters)	20.00	10.00	6.00
100b	Charles Solomon Myer (name in upper and lower case)	22.00	11.00	6.50
101a	Roger M. Cramer ("...the Martinburg Club...")	20.00	10.00	6.00
101b	Roger M. Cramer ("...the Martinsburg Club...")	25.00	12.50	7.50
102a	Lemuel Floyd Young (name in upper case letters)	20.00	10.00	6.00
102b	Lemuel Floyd Young (name in upper and lower case)	22.00	11.00	6.50
103	Morris Berg	22.00	11.00	6.50
104a	Thomas Davis Bridges ("...280 games, winning 283,...")	22.00	11.00	6.50
104b	Thomas Davis Bridges ("...280 games, winning 133,....")	35.00	17.50	10.50
105a	Donald Eric McNair (name in upper case letters)	20.00	10.00	6.00
105b	Donald Eric McNair (name in upper and lower case)	22.00	11.00	6.50
106	Albert Stark	20.00	10.00	6.00
107	Joseph Franklin Vosmik	20.00	10.00	6.00
108a	Frank Witman Hayes (name in upper case letters)	20.00	10.00	6.00
108b	Frank Witman Hayes (name in upper and lower case)	22.00	11.00	6.50
109a	Myril Hoag (name in upper case letters)	20.00	10.00	6.00
109b	Myril Hoag (name in upper and lower case)	22.00	11.00	6.50
110	Fred L. Fitzsimmons	22.00	11.00	6.50
111a	Van Lingle Mungo (name in upper case letters)	35.00	17.50	10.50
111b	Van Lingle Mungo (name in upper and lower case)	40.00	20.00	12.00
112a	Paul Glee Waner ("...Waner, the older...")	125.00	62.00	37.00
112b	Paul Glee Waner ("...Waner, the elder...")	150.00	75.00	45.00
113	Al Schacht	25.00	12.50	7.50
114a	Cecil Travis (name in upper case letters)	20.00	10.00	6.00
114b	Cecil Travis (name in upper and lower case)	22.00	11.00	6.50
115a	Ralph Kress (name in upper case letters)	20.00	10.00	6.00
115b	Ralph Kress (name in upper and lower case)	22.00	11.00	6.50
116	Eugene A. Desautels	125.00	62.00	37.00
117	Wayne Ambler	125.00	62.00	37.00
118	Lynn Nelson	125.00	62.00	37.00
119	Willard McKee Hershberger	125.00	62.00	37.00
120	Harold Benton Warstler (middle name actually Burton)	125.00	62.00	37.00
121	William J. Posedel	125.00	62.00	37.00
122	George Hartley McQuinn	125.00	62.00	37.00
123	Ray T. Davis	125.00	62.00	37.00
124	Walter George Brown	125.00	62.00	37.00
125	Clifford George Melton	125.00	62.00	37.00
126	Not Issued			
127	Gilbert Herman Brack	125.00	62.00	37.00
128	Joseph Emil Bowman	125.00	62.00	37.00
129	William Swift	125.00	62.00	37.00
130	Wilbur Lee Brubaker	125.00	62.00	37.00
131	Morton Cecil Cooper	125.00	62.00	37.00
132	James Roberson Brown	125.00	62.00	37.00
133	Lynn Myers	125.00	62.00	37.00
134	Forrest Pressnell	125.00	62.00	37.00
135	Arnold Malcolm Owen	125.00	62.00	37.00
136	Roy Chester Bell	125.00	62.00	37.00
137	Peter William Appleton	125.00	62.00	37.00
138	George Washington Case Jr.	125.00	62.00	37.00
139	Vitautas C. Tamulis	125.00	62.00	37.00
140	Raymond Hall Hayworth	125.00	62.00	37.00
141	Peter Coscarart	125.00	62.00	37.00

		NR MT	EX	VG
142	Ira Kendall Hutchinson	125.00	62.00	37.00
143	Howard Earl Averill	275.00	140.00	85.00
144	Henry J. Bonura	125.00	62.00	37.00
145	Hugh Noyes Mulcahy	125.00	62.00	37.00
146	Thomas Sunkel	125.00	62.00	37.00
147	George D. Coffman	125.00	62.00	37.00
148	William Trotter	125.00	62.00	37.00
149	Max Edward West	125.00	62.00	37.00
150	James Elton Walkup	125.00	62.00	37.00
151	Hugh Thomas Casey	125.00	62.00	37.00
152	Roy Weatherly	125.00	62.00	37.00
153	Paul H. Trout	150.00	75.00	45.00
154	John W. Hudson	125.00	62.00	37.00
155	James Paul Outlaw (middle name actually Paulus)	125.00	62.00	37.00
156	Raymond Berres	125.00	62.00	37.00
157	Donald Willard Padgett (middle name actually Wilson)	125.00	62.00	37.00
158	Luther Baxter Thomas	125.00	62.00	37.00
159	Russell E. Evans	125.00	62.00	37.00
160	Eugene Moore Jr.	125.00	62.00	37.00
161	Linus Reinhard Frey	135.00	67.00	40.00
162	Lloyd Albert Moore	250.00	90.00	55.00

1940 Play Ball

Following the success of their initial effort in 1939, Gum Incorporated issued a bigger and better set in 1940. The 240 black and white cards are once again in the 2-1/2" by 3-1/8" size, but the photos on the card fronts are enclosed by a frame which listed the player's name. Card backs again offer extensive biographies. Backs are also dated. A number of old-timers were issued along with the current day's players, and many Hall of Famers are included. The final 60 cards of the set are more difficult to obtain.

		NR MT	EX	VG
Complete Set:		20000.00	10000.00	6000.
Common Player: 1-120		22.00	11.00	6.50
Common Player: 121-180		25.00	12.50	7.50
Common Player: 181-240		80.00	40.00	24.00
1	Joe DiMaggio	2500.00	1250.00	750.00
2	"Art" Jorgens	25.00	12.50	7.50
3	"Babe" Dahlgren	25.00	12.50	7.50
4	"Tommy" Henrich	35.00	17.50	10.50
5	"Monte" Pearson	25.00	12.50	7.50
6	"Lefty" Gomez	200.00	100.00	60.00
7	"Bill" Dickey	200.00	100.00	60.00
8	"Twinkletoes" Selkirk	25.00	12.50	7.50
9	"Charley" Keller	35.00	17.50	10.50
10	"Red" Ruffing	75.00	37.00	22.00
11	"Jake" Powell	25.00	12.50	7.50
12	"Johnny" Schulte	25.00	12.50	7.50
13	"Jack" Knott	22.00	11.00	6.50
14	"Rabbit" McNair	22.00	11.00	6.50
15	George Case	22.00	11.00	6.50
16	Cecil Travis	22.00	11.00	6.50
17	"Buddy" Myer	22.00	11.00	6.50
18	"Charley" Gelbert	22.00	11.00	6.50
19	"Ken" Chase	22.00	11.00	6.50
20	"Buddy" Lewis	22.00	11.00	6.50
21	"Rick" Ferrell	65.00	32.00	19.50
22	"Sammy" West	22.00	11.00	6.50
23	"Dutch" Leonard	22.00	11.00	6.50
24	Frank "Blimp" Hayes	22.00	11.00	6.50

#	Name	NR MT	EX	VG
25	"Cherokee" Bob Johnson	22.00	11.00	6.50
26	"Wally" Moses	22.00	11.00	6.50
27	"Ted" Williams	1800.00	900.00	550.00
28	"Gene" Desautels	22.00	11.00	6.50
29	"Doc" Cramer	22.00	11.00	6.50
30	"Moe" Berg	25.00	12.50	7.50
31	"Jack" Wilson	22.00	11.00	6.50
32	"Jim" Bagby	22.00	11.00	6.50
33	"Fritz" Ostermueller	22.00	11.00	6.50
34	John Peacock	22.00	11.00	6.50
35	"Joe" Heving	22.00	11.00	6.50
36	"Jim" Tabor	22.00	11.00	6.50
37	Emerson Dickman	22.00	11.00	6.50
38	"Bobby" Doerr	100.00	50.00	30.00
39	"Tom" Carey	22.00	11.00	6.50
40	"Hank" Greenberg	250.00	125.00	75.00
41	"Charley" Gehringer	150.00	75.00	45.00
42	"Bud" Thomas	22.00	11.00	6.50
43	Pete Fox	22.00	11.00	6.50
44	"Dizzy" Trout	25.00	12.50	7.50
45	"Red" Kress	22.00	11.00	6.50
46	Earl Averill	100.00	50.00	30.00
47	"Old Os" Vitt	22.00	11.00	6.50
48	"Luke" Sewell	25.00	12.50	7.50
49	"Stormy Weather" Weatherly	22.00	11.00	6.50
50	"Hal" Trosky	22.00	11.00	6.50
51	"Don" Heffner	22.00	11.00	6.50
52	Myril Hoag	22.00	11.00	6.50
53	"Mac" McQuinn	22.00	11.00	6.50
54	"Bill" Trotter	22.00	11.00	6.50
55	"Slick" Coffman	22.00	11.00	6.50
56	"Eddie" Miller	22.00	11.00	6.50
57	Max West	22.00	11.00	6.50
58	"Bill" Posedel	22.00	11.00	6.50
59	"Rabbit" Warstler	22.00	11.00	6.50
60	John Cooney	22.00	11.00	6.50
61	"Tony" Cuccinello	22.00	11.00	6.50
62	"Buddy" Hassett	22.00	11.00	6.50
63	"Pete" Cascarart	22.00	11.00	6.50
64	"Van" Mungo	30.00	15.00	9.00
65	"Fitz" Fitzsimmons	25.00	12.50	7.50
66	"Babe" Phelps	25.00	12.50	7.50
67	"Whit" Wyatt	25.00	12.50	7.50
68	"Dolph" Camilli	25.00	12.50	7.50
69	"Cookie" Lavagetto	25.00	12.50	7.50
70	"Hot Potato" Hamlin	22.00	11.00	6.50
71	"Mel" Almada	22.00	11.00	6.50
72	"Chuck" Dressen	25.00	12.50	7.50
73	"Bucky" Walters	25.00	12.50	7.50
74	"Duke" Derringer	25.00	12.50	7.50
75	"Buck" McCormick	22.00	11.00	6.50
76	"Lonny" Frey	22.00	11.00	6.50
77	"Bill" Hershberger	22.00	11.00	6.50
78	"Lew" Riggs	22.00	11.00	6.50
79	"Wildfire" Craft	22.00	11.00	6.50
80	"Bill" Myers	22.00	11.00	6.50
81	"Wally" Berger	25.00	12.50	7.50
82	"Hank" Gowdy	22.00	11.00	6.50
83	"Clif" Melton (Cliff)	22.00	11.00	6.50
84	"Jo-Jo" Moore	22.00	11.00	6.50
85	"Hal" Schumacher	25.00	12.50	7.50
86	Harry Gumbert	22.00	11.00	6.50
87	Carl Hubbell	200.00	100.00	60.00
88	"Mel" Ott	200.00	100.00	60.00
89	"Bill" Jurges	25.00	12.50	7.50
90	Frank Demaree	22.00	11.00	6.50
91	Bob "Suitcase" Seeds	22.00	11.00	6.50
92	"Whitey" Whitehead	22.00	11.00	6.50
93	Harry "The Horse" Danning	22.00	11.00	6.50
94	"Gus" Suhr	22.00	11.00	6.50
95	"Mul" Mulcahy	22.00	11.00	6.50
96	"Heinie" Mueller	22.00	11.00	6.50
97	"Morry" Arnovich	22.00	11.00	6.50
98	"Pinky" May	22.00	11.00	6.50
99	"Syl" Johnson	22.00	11.00	6.50
100	"Hersh" Martin	22.00	11.00	6.50
101	"Del" Young	22.00	11.00	6.50
102	"Chuck" Klein	150.00	75.00	45.00
103	"Elbie" Fletcher	22.00	11.00	6.50
104	"Big Poison" Waner	150.00	75.00	45.00
105	"Little Poison" Waner	150.00	75.00	45.00
106	"Pep" Young	22.00	11.00	6.50
107	"Arky" Vaughan	100.00	50.00	30.00
108	"Johnny" Rizzo	22.00	11.00	6.50
109	"Don" Padgett	22.00	11.00	6.50
110	"Tom" Sunkel	22.00	11.00	6.50
111	"Mickey" Owen	22.00	11.00	6.50
112	"Jimmy" Brown	22.00	11.00	6.50
113	"Mort" Cooper	22.00	11.00	6.50
114	"Lon" Warneke	22.00	11.00	6.50
115	"Mike" Gonzales (Gonzalez)	22.00	11.00	6.50
116	"Al" Schacht	25.00	12.50	7.50
117	"Dolly" Stark	22.00	11.00	6.50
118	"Schoolboy" Hoyt	100.00	50.00	30.00
119	"Ol Pete" Alexander	180.00	90.00	54.00
120	Walter "Big Train" Johnson	275.00	137.00	82.00
121	Atley Donald	25.00	12.50	7.50
122	"Sandy" Sundra	25.00	12.50	7.50
123	"Hildy" Hildebrand	25.00	12.50	7.50
124	"Colonel" Combs	135.00	67.00	40.00
125	"Art" Fletcher	25.00	12.50	7.50
126	"Jake" Solters	25.00	12.50	7.50
127	"Muddy" Ruel	25.00	12.50	7.50
128	"Pete" Appleton	25.00	12.50	7.50
129	"Bucky" Harris	100.00	50.00	30.00
130	"Deerfoot" Milan	25.00	12.50	7.50
131	"Zeke" Bonura	25.00	12.50	7.50
132	Connie Mack	225.00	112.00	67.00
133	"Jimmie" Foxx	275.00	137.00	82.00
134	"Joe" Cronin	150.00	75.00	45.00
135	"Line Drive" Nelson	25.00	12.50	7.50
136	"Cotton" Pippen	25.00	12.50	7.50
137	"Bing" Miller	25.00	12.50	7.50
138	"Beau" Bell	25.00	12.50	7.50
139	Elden Auker (Eldon)	25.00	12.50	7.50
140	"Dick" Coffman	25.00	12.50	7.50
141	"Casey" Stengel	200.00	100.00	60.00
142	"Highpockets" Kelly	100.00	50.00	30.00
143	"Gene" Moore	25.00	12.50	7.50
144	"Joe" Vosmik	25.00	12.50	7.50
145	"Vito" Tamulis	25.00	12.50	7.50
146	"Tot" Pressnell	25.00	12.50	7.50
147	"Johnny" Hudson	25.00	12.50	7.50
148	"Hugh" Casey	25.00	12.50	7.50
149	"Pinky" Shoffner	25.00	12.50	7.50
150	"Whitey" Moore	25.00	12.50	7.50
151	Edwin Joost	25.00	12.50	7.50
152	"Jimmy" Wilson	25.00	12.50	7.50
153	"Bill" McKechnie	100.00	50.00	30.00
154	"Jumbo" Brown	25.00	12.50	7.50
155	"Ray" Hayworth	25.00	12.50	7.50
156	"Daffy" Dean	30.00	15.00	9.00
157	"Lou" Chiozza	25.00	12.50	7.50
158	"Stonewall" Jackson	100.00	50.00	30.00
159	"Pancho" Snyder	25.00	12.50	7.50
160	"Hans" Lobert	25.00	12.50	7.50
161	"Debs" Garms	25.00	12.50	7.50
162	"Joe" Bowman	25.00	12.50	7.50
163	"Spud" Davis	25.00	12.50	7.50
164	"Ray" Berres	25.00	12.50	7.50
165	"Bob" Klinger	25.00	12.50	7.50
166	"Bill" Brubaker	25.00	12.50	7.50
167	"Frankie" Frisch	150.00	75.00	45.00
168	"Honus" Wagner	275.00	137.00	82.00
169	"Gabby" Street	25.00	12.50	7.50
170	"Tris" Speaker	250.00	125.00	75.00
171	Harry Heilmann	150.00	75.00	45.00
172	"Chief" Bender	150.00	75.00	45.00
173	"Larry" Lajoie	275.00	137.00	82.00
174	"Johnny" Evers	150.00	75.00	45.00
175	"Christy" Mathewson	275.00	137.00	82.00
176	"Heinie" Manush	150.00	75.00	45.00
177	Frank "Homerun" Baker	150.00	75.00	45.00
178	Max Carey	150.00	75.00	45.00
179	George Sisler	135.00	67.00	40.00
180	"Mickey" Cochrane	150.00	75.00	45.00
181	"Spud" Chandler	80.00	40.00	25.00
182	"Knick" Knickerbocker	80.00	40.00	25.00
183	Marvin Breuer	80.00	40.00	25.00
184	"Mule" Haas	80.00	40.00	24.00
185	"Joe" Kuhel	80.00	40.00	24.00
186	Taft Wright	80.00	40.00	24.00
187	"Jimmy" Dykes	60.00	30.00	18.00
188	"Joe" Krakauskas	80.00	40.00	24.00
189	"Jim" Bloodworth	80.00	40.00	24.00
190	"Charley" Berry	80.00	40.00	24.00
191	John Babich	80.00	40.00	24.00
192	"Dick" Siebert	80.00	40.00	24.00
193	"Chubby" Dean	80.00	40.00	24.00
194	"Sam" Chapman	80.00	40.00	24.00
195	"Dee" Miles	80.00	40.00	24.00
196	"Nonny" Nonnenkamp	80.00	40.00	24.00
197	"Lou" Finney	80.00	40.00	24.00
198	"Denny" Galehouse	80.00	40.00	24.00
199	"Pinky" Higgins	80.00	40.00	24.00
200	"Soupy" Campbell	80.00	40.00	24.00
201	Barney McCosky	80.00	40.00	24.00
202	"Al" Milnar	80.00	40.00	24.00
203	"Bad News" Hale	80.00	40.00	24.00
204	Harry Eisenstat	80.00	40.00	24.00
205	"Rollie" Hemsley	80.00	40.00	24.00
206	"Chet" Laabs	80.00	40.00	24.00

		NR MT	EX	VG
207	"Gus" Mancuso	80.00	40.00	24.00
208	Lee Gamble	80.00	40.00	24.00
209	"Hy" Vandenberg	80.00	40.00	24.00
210	"Bill" Lohrman	80.00	40.00	24.00
211	"Pop" Joiner	80.00	40.00	24.00
212	"Babe" Young	80.00	40.00	24.00
213	John Rucker	80.00	40.00	24.00
214	"Ken" O'Dea	80.00	40.00	24.00
215	"Johnnie" McCarthy	80.00	40.00	24.00
216	"Joe" Marty	80.00	40.00	24.00
217	Walter Beck	80.00	40.00	24.00
218	"Wally" Millies	80.00	40.00	24.00
219	"Russ" Bauers	80.00	40.00	24.00
220	Mace Brown	80.00	40.00	24.00
221	Lee Handley	80.00	40.00	24.00
222	"Max" Butcher	80.00	40.00	24.00
223	Hugh "Ee-Yah" Jennings	150.00	75.00	45.00
224	"Pie" Traynor	250.00	125.00	75.00
225	"Shoeless Joe" Jackson	2500.00	1250.00	750.00
226	Harry Hooper	150.00	75.00	45.00
227	"Pop" Haines	150.00	75.00	45.00
228	"Charley" Grimm	80.00	40.00	25.00
229	"Buck" Herzog	80.00	40.00	24.00
230	"Red" Faber	150.00	75.00	45.00
231	"Dolf" Luque	80.00	40.00	24.00
232	"Goose" Goslin	150.00	75.00	45.00
233	"Moose" Earnshaw	80.00	40.00	24.00
234	Frank "Husk" Chance	200.00	100.00	60.00
235	John J. McGraw	250.00	125.00	75.00
236	"Sunny Jim" Bottomley	150.00	75.00	45.00
237	"Wee Willie" Keeler	225.00	112.00	67.00
238	"Poosh 'Em Up Tony" Lazzeri	100.00	50.00	30.00
239	George Uhle	80.00	40.00	25.00
240	"Bill" Atwood	200.00	60.00	35.00

1941 Play Ball

"DUKE" DERRINGER

While the card backs are quite similar to the black and white cards Gum Incorporated issued in 1940, the card fronts in the 1941 set are printed in color. Many of the card photos, however, are just color versions of the player's 1940 card. The cards are still in the 2-1/2" by 3-1/8" size, but only 72 cards are included in the set. Joe DiMaggio and Ted Williams continue to be the key players in the set, while card numbers 49-72 are rarer than the lower-numbered cards. The cards were printed in sheets, and can still be found that way, or in paper strips, lacking the cardboard backing.

		NR MT	EX	VG
Complete Set:		14500.00	6500.00	4000.
Common Player: 1-48		55.00	27.00	16.50
Common Player: 49-72		75.00	37.00	22.00
1	"Eddie" Miller	200.00	100.00	60.00
2	Max West	55.00	27.00	16.50
3	"Bucky" Walters	55.00	27.00	16.50
4	"Duke" Derringer	75.00	37.00	22.00
5	"Buck" McCormick	55.00	27.00	16.50
6	Carl Hubbell	250.00	125.00	75.00
7	"The Horse" Danning	55.00	27.00	16.50
8	"Mel" Ott	300.00	150.00	90.00
9	"Pinky" May	55.00	27.00	16.50
10	"Arky" Vaughan	75.00	37.00	22.00
11	Debs Garms	55.00	27.00	16.50
12	"Jimmy" Brown	55.00	27.00	16.50

		NR MT	EX	VG
13	"Jimmie" Foxx	375.00	187.00	110.00
14	"Ted" Williams	2000.00	1000.00	600.00
15	"Joe" Cronin	175.00	87.00	50.00
16	"Hal" Trosky	55.00	27.00	16.50
17	"Stormy" Weatherly	55.00	27.00	16.50
18	"Hank" Greenberg	350.00	175.00	105.00
19	"Charley" Gehringer	250.00	125.00	75.00
20	"Red" Ruffing	175.00	87.00	50.00
21	"Charlie" Keller	75.00	37.00	22.00
22	"Indian Bob" Johnson	55.00	27.00	16.50
23	"Mac" McQuinn	55.00	27.00	16.50
24	"Dutch" Leonard	55.00	27.00	16.50
25	"Gene" Moore	55.00	27.00	16.50
26	Harry "Gunboat" Gumbert	55.00	27.00	16.50
27	"Babe" Young	55.00	27.00	16.50
28	"Joe" Marty	55.00	27.00	16.50
29	"Jack" Wilson	55.00	27.00	16.50
30	"Lou" Finney	55.00	27.00	16.50
31	"Joe" Kuhel	55.00	27.00	16.50
32	Taft Wright	55.00	27.00	16.50
33	"Happy" Milnar	55.00	27.00	16.50
34	"Rollie" Hemsley	55.00	27.00	16.50
35	"Pinky" Higgins	55.00	27.00	16.50
36	Barney McCosky	55.00	27.00	16.50
37	"Soupy" Campbell	55.00	27.00	16.50
38	Atley Donald	75.00	37.00	22.00
39	"Tommy" Henrich	75.00	37.00	22.00
40	"Johnny" Babich	55.00	27.00	16.50
41	Frank "Blimp" Hayes	55.00	27.00	16.50
42	"Wally" Moses	55.00	27.00	16.50
43	Albert "Bronk" Brancato	55.00	27.00	16.50
44	"Sam" Chapman	55.00	27.00	16.50
45	Elden Auker (Eldon)	55.00	27.00	16.50
46	"Sid" Hudson	55.00	27.00	16.50
47	"Buddy" Lewis	55.00	27.00	16.50
48	Cecil Travis	55.00	27.00	16.50
49	"Babe" Dahlgren	75.00	37.00	22.00
50	"Johnny" Cooney	75.00	37.00	22.00
51	"Dolph" Camilli	55.00	27.00	16.50
52	Kirby Higbe	75.00	37.00	22.00
53	Luke "Hot Potato" Hamlin	75.00	37.00	22.00
54	"Pee Wee" Reese	750.00	375.00	225.00
55	"Whit" Wyatt	75.00	37.00	22.00
56	"Vandy" Vander Meer	75.00	37.00	22.00
57	"Moe" Arnovich	75.00	37.00	22.00
58	"Frank" Demaree	75.00	37.00	22.00
59	"Bill" Jurges	75.00	37.00	22.00
60	"Chuck" Klein	250.00	125.00	75.00
61	"Vince" DiMaggio	200.00	100.00	60.00
62	"Elbie" Fletcher	75.00	37.00	22.00
63	"Dom" DiMaggio	200.00	100.00	60.00
64	"Bobby" Doerr	225.00	112.00	70.00
65	"Tommy" Bridges	75.00	37.00	22.00
66	Harland Clift (Harland)	75.00	37.00	22.00
67	"Walt" Judnich	75.00	37.00	22.00
68	"Jack" Knott	75.00	37.00	22.00
69	George Case	75.00	37.00	22.00
70	"Bill" Dickey	650.00	325.00	200.00
71	"Joe" DiMaggio	2500.00	1250.00	750.00
72	"Lefty" Gomez	600.00	300.00	180.00

1960 Post Cereal

These cards were issued on the backs of Grape Nuts cereal and measure an oversized 7" by 8-3/4". The nine cards in the set include five baseball players (Al Kaline, Mickey Mantle, Don Drysdale, Harmon Killebrew and Ed Mathews) as well as two football and two basketball players. The full-color photos were placed on a color background and bordered by a wood frame design. The cards covered the entire back of the cereal box and were blank backed. Card fronts also include the player's name and team and a facsimile autograph. A panel on the side of the box contains player biographical information. A scarce set, the cards are very difficult to obtain in mint condition.

		NR MT	EX	VG
Complete Set:		4500.00	2250.00	1350.
Common Player:		350.00	175.00	105.00
(1)	Bob Cousy	350.00	175.00	105.00
(2)	Don Drysdale	400.00	200.00	120.00
(3)	Frank Gifford	400.00	200.00	120.00
(4)	Al Kaline	450.00	225.00	135.00
(5)	Harmon Killebrew	400.00	200.00	120.00
(6)	Ed Mathews	400.00	200.00	120.00
(7)	Mickey Mantle	1500.00	750.00	450.00
(8)	Bob Pettit	350.00	175.00	105.00
(9)	John Unitas	350.00	175.00	105.00

1961 Post Cereal

Two hundred different players are included in this set, but with variations the number of different cards exceeds 350. This was the first large-scale card set by the cereal company and it proved very popular with fans. Cards were issued both singly and in various panel sizes on the thick cardboard stock of cereal boxes, as well on thinner stock, in team sheets issued directly by Post via a mail-in offer. About 10 cards in the set were issued in significantly smaller quantities, making their prices much higher than other comparable players in the set. Individual cards measure a 3-1/2" by 2-1/2", and all cards are numbered in the upper left corner. Card fronts have full-color portait photos of the player, along with biographical information and 1960 and career statistics. Card backs are blank. The complete set price includes does not include the scarcer variations.

		NR MT	EX	VG
Complete Set:		1750.00	875.00	525.00
Common Player:		2.00	1.00	.60
1a	Yogi Berra (box)	25.00	12.50	7.50
1b	Yogi Berra (company)	15.00	7.50	4.50
2a	Elston Howard (box)	5.00	2.50	1.50
2b	Elston Howard (company)	3.00	1.50	.90
3a	Bill Skowron (box)	2.50	1.25	.70
3b	Bill Skowron (company)	2.50	1.25	.70
4a	Mickey Mantle (box)	100.00	50.00	30.00
4b	Mickey Mantle (company)	100.00	50.00	30.00
5	Bob Turley (company)	25.00	12.50	7.50
6a	Whitey Ford (box)	8.00	4.00	2.50
6b	Whitey Ford (company)	8.00	4.00	2.50
7a	Roger Maris (box)	25.00	12.50	7.50
7b	Roger Maris (company)	25.00	12.50	7.50
8a	Bobby Richardson (box)	3.00	1.50	.90
8b	Bobby Richardson (company)	3.00	1.50	.90
9a	Tony Kubek (box)	3.00	1.50	.90
9b	Tony Kubek (company)	3.00	1.50	.90
10	Gil McDougald (box)	35.00	17.50	10.50

		NR MT	EX	VG
11	Cletis Boyer (box)	2.00	1.00	.60
12a	Hector Lopez (box)	2.00	1.00	.60
12b	Hector Lopez (company)	2.00	1.00	.60
13	Bob Cerv (box)	2.00	1.00	.60
14	Ryne Duren (box)	2.00	1.00	.60
15	Bobby Shantz (box)	2.00	1.00	.60
16	Art Ditmar (box)	2.00	1.00	.60
17	Jim Coates (box)	2.00	1.00	.60
18	John Blanchard (box)	2.00	1.00	.60
19a	Luis Aparicio (box)	5.00	2.50	1.50
19b	Luis Aparicio (company)	5.00	2.50	1.50
20a	Nelson Fox (box)	4.00	2.00	1.25
20b	Nelson Fox (company)	4.00	2.00	1.25
21a	Bill Pierce (box)	6.00	3.00	1.75
21b	Bill Pierce (company)	3.50	1.75	1.00
22a	Early Wynn (box)	7.00	3.50	2.00
22b	Early Wynn (company)	25.00	12.50	7.50
23	Bob Shaw (box)	100.00	50.00	30.00
24a	Al Smith (box)	3.00	1.50	.90
24b	Al Smith (company)	2.00	1.00	.60
25a	Minnie Minoso (box)	2.50	1.25	.70
25b	Minnie Minoso (company)	2.50	1.25	.70
26a	Roy Sievers (box)	2.25	1.25	.70
26b	Roy Sievers (company)	2.25	1.25	.70
27a	Jim Landis (box)	2.00	1.00	.60
27b	Jim Landis (company)	2.00	1.00	.60
28a	Sherman Lollar (box)	3.00	1.50	.90
28b	Sherman Lollar (company)	2.00	1.00	.60
29	Gerry Staley (box)	2.00	1.00	.60
30a	Gene Freese (box, White Sox)	2.00	1.00	.60
30b	Gene Freese (company, Reds)	6.00	3.00	1.75
31	Ted Kluszewski (box)	3.00	1.50	.90
32	Turk Lown (box)	2.00	1.00	.60
33a	Jim Rivera (box)	2.00	1.00	.60
33b	Jim Rivera (company)	2.00	1.00	.60
34	Frank Baumann (box)	2.00	1.00	.60
35a	Al Kaline (box)	25.00	12.50	7.50
35b	Al Kaline (company)	25.00	12.50	7.50
36a	Rocky Colavito (box)	6.00	3.00	1.75
36b	Rocky Colavito (company)	3.50	1.75	1.00
37a	Charley Maxwell (box)	4.00	2.00	1.25
37b	Charley Maxwell (company)	2.00	1.00	.60
38a	Frank Lary (box)	2.00	1.00	.60
38b	Frank Lary (company)	2.00	1.00	.60
39a	Jim Bunning (box)	4.00	2.00	1.25
39b	Jim Bunning (company)	4.00	2.00	1.25
40a	Norm Cash (box)	2.00	1.00	.60
40b	Norm Cash (company)	2.00	1.00	.60
41a	Frank Bolling (box, Tigers)	8.00	4.00	2.50
41b	Frank Bolling (company, Braves)	5.00	2.50	1.50
42a	Don Mossi (box)	2.00	1.00	.60
42b	Don Mossi (company)	2.00	1.00	.60
43a	Lou Berberet (box)	2.00	1.00	.60
43b	Lou Berberet (company)	2.00	1.00	.60
44	Dave Sisler (box)	2.00	1.00	.60
45	Ed Yost (box)	2.00	1.00	.60
46	Pete Burnside (box)	2.00	1.00	.60
47a	Pete Runnels (box)	3.00	1.50	.90
47b	Pete Runnnels (company)	2.25	1.25	.70
48a	Frank Malzone (box)	2.00	1.00	.60
48b	Frank Malzone (company)	2.00	1.00	.60
49a	Vic Wertz (box)	5.00	2.50	1.50
49b	Vic Wertz (company)	3.00	1.50	.90
50a	Tom Brewer (box)	2.50	1.25	.70
50b	Tom Brewer (company)	2.00	1.00	.60
51a	Willie Tasby (box, no sold line)	8.00	4.00	2.50
51b	Willie Tasby (company, sold line)	2.00	1.00	.60
52a	Russ Nixon (box)	2.00	1.00	.60
52b	Russ Nixon (company)	2.00	1.00	.60
53a	Don Buddin (box)	2.00	1.00	.60
53b	Don Buddin (company)	2.00	1.00	.60
54a	Bill Monbouquette (box)	2.00	1.00	.60
54b	Bill Monbouquette (company)	2.00	1.00	.60
55a	Frank Sullivan (box, Red Sox)	2.00	1.00	.60
55b	Frank Sullivan (company, Phillies)	25.00	12.50	7.50
56a	Haywood Sullivan (box)	2.00	1.00	.60
56b	Haywood Sullivan (company)	2.00	1.00	.60
57a	Harvey Kuenn (box, Indians)	3.00	1.50	.90
57b	Harvey Kuenn (company, Giants)	6.00	3.00	1.75
58a	Gary Bell (box)	5.00	2.50	1.50
58b	Gary Bell (company)	2.25	1.25	.70
59a	Jim Perry (box)	2.25	1.25	.70
59b	Jim Perry (company)	2.25	1.25	.70
60a	Jim Grant (box)	3.00	1.50	.90
60b	Jim Grant (company)	2.25	1.25	.70
61a	Johnny Temple (box)	2.00	1.00	.60
61b	Johnny Temple (company)	2.00	1.00	.60
62a	Paul Foytack (box)	2.00	1.00	.60
62b	Paul Foytack (company)	2.00	1.00	.60
63a	Vic Power (box)	2.00	1.00	.60

#	Player	NR MT	EX	VG
63b	Vic Power (company)	2.00	1.00	.60
64a	Tito Francona (box)	2.00	1.00	.60
64b	Tito Francona (company)	2.00	1.00	.60
65a	Ken Aspromonte (box, no sold line)	6.00	3.00	1.75
65b	Ken Aspromonte (company, sold line)	6.00	3.00	1.75
66	Bob Wilson (box)	2.00	1.00	.60
67a	John Romano (box)	2.00	1.00	.60
67b	John Romano (company)	2.00	1.00	.60
68a	Jim Gentile (box)	2.50	1.25	.70
68b	Jim Gentile (company)	2.00	1.00	.60
69a	Gus Triandos (box)	3.00	1.50	.90
69b	Gus Triandos (company)	2.00	1.00	.60
70	Gene Woodling (box)	15.00	7.50	4.50
71a	Milt Pappas (box)	3.00	1.50	.90
71b	Milt Pappas (company)	2.00	1.00	.60
72a	Ron Hansen (box)	3.00	1.50	.90
72b	Ron Hansen (company)	2.00	1.00	.60
73	Chuck Estrada (company)	100.00	50.00	30.00
74a	Steve Barber (box)	2.00	1.00	.60
74b	Steve Barber (company)	2.00	1.00	.60
75a	Brooks Robinson (box)	25.00	12.50	7.50
75b	Brooks Robinson (company)	25.00	12.50	7.50
76a	Jackie Brandt (box)	2.00	1.00	.60
76b	Jackie Brandt (company)	2.00	1.00	.60
77a	Marv Breeding (box)	2.00	1.00	.60
77b	Marv Breeding (company)	2.00	1.00	.60
78	Hal Brown (box)	2.00	1.00	.60
79	Billy Klaus (box)	2.00	1.00	.60
80a	Hoyt Wilhelm (box)	5.00	2.50	1.50
80b	Hoyt Wilhelm (company)	6.00	3.00	1.75
81a	Jerry Lumpe (box)	6.00	3.00	1.75
81b	Jerry Lumpe (company)	4.00	2.00	1.25
82a	Norm Siebern (box)	2.00	1.00	.60
82b	Norm Siebern (company)	2.00	1.00	.60
83a	Bud Daley (box)	2.25	1.25	.70
83b	Bud Daley (company)	2.50	1.25	.70
84a	Bill Tuttle (box)	2.00	1.00	.60
84b	Bill Tuttle (company)	2.00	1.00	.60
85a	Marv Throneberry (box)	2.50	1.25	.70
85b	Marv Throneberry (company)	2.50	1.25	.70
86a	Dick Williams (box)	2.25	1.25	.70
86b	Dick Williams (company)	2.00	1.00	.60
87a	Ray Herbert (box)	2.00	1.00	.60
87b	Ray Herbert (company)	2.00	1.00	.60
88a	Whitey Herzog (box)	2.00	1.00	.60
88b	Whitey Herzog (company)	2.00	1.00	.60
89a	Ken Hamlin (box, no sold line)	2.00	1.00	.60
89b	Ken Hamlin (company, sold line)	8.00	4.00	2.50
90a	Hank Bauer (box)	2.00	1.00	.60
90b	Hank Bauer (company)	2.00	1.00	.60
91a	Bob Allison (box, Minneapolis)	4.00	2.00	1.25
91b	Bob Allison (company, Minnesota)	5.00	2.50	1.50
92a	Harmon Killebrew (box, Minneapolis)	25.00	12.50	7.50
92b	Harmon Killebrew (company, Minnesota)	25.00	12.50	7.50
93a	Jim Lemon (box, Minneapolis)	50.00	25.00	15.00
93b	Jim Lemon (company, Minnesota)	5.00	2.50	1.50
94	Chuck Stobbs (company)	150.00	75.00	45.00
95a	Reno Bertoia (box, Minneapolis)	2.00	1.00	.60
95b	Reno Bertoia (company, Minnesota)	4.00	2.00	1.25
96a	Billy Gardner (box, Minneapolis)	2.00	1.00	.60
96b	Billy Gardner (company, Minnesota)	4.00	2.00	1.25
97a	Earl Battey (box, Minneapolis)	4.00	2.00	1.25
97b	Earl Battey (company, Minnesota)	4.00	2.00	1.25
98a	Pedro Ramos (box, Minneapolis)	2.00	1.00	.60
98b	Pedro Ramos (company, Minnesota)	4.00	2.00	1.25
99a	Camilio Pascual (Camilo) (box, Minneapolis)	2.00	1.00	.60
99b	Camilio Pascual (Camilo) (company, Minnesota)	4.00	2.00	1.25
100a	Billy Consolo (box, Minneapolis)	2.00	1.00	.60
100b	Billy Consolo (company, Minnesota)	4.00	2.00	1.25
101a	Warren Spahn (box)	15.00	7.50	4.50
101b	Warren Spahn (company)	8.00	4.00	2.50
102a	Lew Burdette (box)	2.50	1.25	.70
102b	Lew Burdette (company)	2.50	1.25	.70
103a	Bob Buhl (box)	2.00	1.00	.60
103b	Bob Buhl (company)	2.00	1.00	.60
104a	Joe Adcock (box)	4.00	2.00	1.25
104b	Joe Adcock (company)	2.50	1.25	.70
105a	John Logan (box)	4.00	2.00	1.25
105b	John Logan (company)	2.25	1.25	.70
106	Ed Mathews (company)	35.00	17.50	10.50
107a	Hank Aaron (box)	25.00	12.50	7.50
107b	Hank Aaron (company)	25.00	12.50	7.50
108a	Wes Covington (box)	2.00	1.00	.60
108b	Wes Covington (company)	2.00	1.00	.60
109a	Bill Bruton (box, Braves)	6.00	3.00	1.75
109b	Bill Bruton (company, Tigers)	8.00	4.00	2.50
110a	Del Crandall (box)	4.00	2.00	1.25
110b	Del Crandall (company)	2.25	1.25	.70
111	Red Schoendienst (box)	5.00	2.50	1.50
112	Juan Pizarro (box)	2.00	1.00	.60
113	Chuck Cottier (box)	8.00	4.00	2.50
114	Al Spangler (box)	2.00	1.00	.60
115a	Dick Farrell (box)	6.00	3.00	1.75
115b	Dick Farrell (company)	4.00	2.00	1.25
116a	Jim Owens (box)	6.00	3.00	1.75
116b	Jim Owens (company)	4.00	2.00	1.25
117a	Robin Roberts (box)	6.00	3.00	1.75
117b	Robin Roberts (company)	6.00	3.00	1.75
118a	Tony Taylor (box)	2.00	1.00	.60
118b	Tony Taylor (company)	2.00	1.00	.60
119a	Lee Walls (box)	2.00	1.00	.60
119b	Lee Walls (company)	2.00	1.00	.60
120a	Tony Curry (box)	2.00	1.00	.60
120b	Tony Curry (company)	2.00	1.00	.60
121a	Pancho Herrera (box)	2.00	1.00	.60
121b	Pancho Herrera (company)	2.00	1.00	.60
122a	Ken Walters (box)	2.00	1.00	.60
122b	Ken Walters (company)	2.00	1.00	.60
123a	John Callison (box)	2.00	1.00	.60
123b	John Callison (company)	2.00	1.00	.60
124a	Gene Conley (box, Phillies)	2.00	1.00	.60
124b	Gene Conley (company, Red Sox)	15.00	7.50	4.50
125a	Bob Friend (box)	4.00	2.00	1.25
125b	Bob Friend (company)	2.00	1.00	.60
126a	Vernon Law (box)	4.00	2.00	1.25
126b	Vernon Law (company)	2.00	1.00	.60
127a	Dick Stuart (box)	2.00	1.00	.60
127b	Dick Stuart (company)	2.00	1.00	.60
128a	Bill Mazeroski (box)	2.50	1.25	.70
128b	Bill Mazeroski (company)	2.50	1.25	.70
129a	Dick Groat (box)	3.00	1.50	.90
129b	Dick Groat (company)	2.00	1.00	.60
130a	Don Hoak (box)	2.00	1.00	.60
130b	Don Hoak (company)	2.00	1.00	.60
131a	Bob Skinner (box)	2.00	1.00	.60
131b	Bob Skinner (company)	2.00	1.00	.60
132a	Bob Clemente (box)	25.00	12.50	7.50
132b	Bob Clemente (company)	25.00	12.50	7.50
133	Roy Face (box)	3.00	1.50	.90
134	Harvey Haddix (box)	2.25	1.25	.70
135	Bill Virdon (box)	35.00	17.50	10.50
136a	Gino Cimoli (box)	2.00	1.00	.60
136b	Gino Cimoli (company)	2.00	1.00	.60
137	Rocky Nelson (box)	2.00	1.00	.60
138a	Smoky Burgess (box)	2.25	1.25	.70
138b	Smoky Burgess (company)	2.25	1.25	.70
139	Hal Smith (box)	2.00	1.00	.60
140	Wilmer Mizell (box)	2.00	1.00	.60
141a	Mike McCormick (box)	2.00	1.00	.60
141b	Mike McCormick (company)	2.00	1.00	.60
142a	John Antonelli (box, Giants)	3.00	1.50	.90
142b	John Antonelli (company, Indians)	4.00	2.00	1.25
143a	Sam Jones (box)	4.00	2.00	1.25
143b	Sam Jones (company)	2.00	1.00	.60
144a	Orlando Cepeda (box)	5.00	2.50	1.50
144b	Orlando Cepeda (company)	5.00	2.50	1.50
145a	Willie Mays (box)	25.00	12.50	7.50
145b	Willie Mays (company)	25.00	12.50	7.50
146a	Willie Kirkland (box, Giants)	5.00	2.50	1.50
146b	Willie Kirkland (company, Indians)	5.00	2.50	1.50
147a	Willie McCovey (box)	7.00	3.50	2.00
147b	Willie McCovey (company)	25.00	12.50	7.50
148a	Don Blasingame (box)	2.00	1.00	.60
148b	Don Blasingame (company)	2.00	1.00	.60
149a	Jim Davenport (box)	2.00	1.00	.60
149b	Jim Davenport (company)	2.00	1.00	.60
150a	Hobie Landrith (box)	2.00	1.00	.60
150b	Hobie Landrith (company)	2.00	1.00	.60
151	Bob Schmidt (box)	2.00	1.00	.60
152a	Ed Bressoud (box)	2.00	1.00	.60
152b	Ed Bressoud (company)	2.00	1.00	.60
153a	Andre Rodgers (box, no traded line)	6.00	3.00	1.75
153b	Andre Rodgers (box, traded line)	2.00	1.00	.60
154	Jack Sanford (box)	2.00	1.00	.60
155	Billy O'Dell (box)	2.00	1.00	.60
156a	Norm Larker (box)	2.50	1.25	.70

		NR MT	EX	VG
156b	Norm Larker (company)	2.50	1.25	.70
157a	Charlie Neal (box)	2.00	1.00	.60
157b	Charlie Neal (company)	2.00	1.00	.60
158a	Jim Gilliam (box)	4.00	2.00	1.25
158b	Jim Gilliam (company)	2.50	1.25	.70
159a	Wally Moon (box)	2.00	1.00	.60
159b	Wally Moon (company)	2.00	1.00	.60
160a	Don Drysdale (box)	7.00	3.50	2.00
160b	Don Drysdale (company)	8.00	4.00	2.50
161a	Larry Sherry (box)	2.00	1.00	.60
161b	Larry Sherry (company)	2.00	1.00	.60
162	Stan Williams (box)	5.00	2.50	1.50
163	Mel Roach (box)	50.00	25.00	15.00
164a	Maury Wills (box)	4.00	2.00	1.25
164b	Maury Wills (company)	4.00	2.00	1.25
165	Tom Davis (box)	2.00	1.00	.60
166a	John Roseboro (box)	2.00	1.00	.60
166b	John Roseboro (company)	2.00	1.00	.60
167a	Duke Snider (box)	8.00	4.00	2.50
167b	Duke Snider (company)	25.00	12.50	7.50
168a	Gil Hodges (box)	5.00	2.50	1.50
168b	Gil Hodges (company)	6.00	3.00	1.75
169	John Podres (box)	2.50	1.25	.70
170	Ed Roebuck (box)	2.00	1.00	.60
171a	Ken Boyer (box)	6.00	3.00	1.75
171b	Ken Boyer (company)	4.00	2.00	1.25
172a	Joe Cunningham (box)	2.00	1.00	.60
172b	Joe Cunningham (company)	2.00	1.00	.60
173a	Daryl Spencer (box)	2.00	1.00	.60
173b	Daryl Spencer (company)	2.00	1.00	.60
174a	Larry Jackson (box)	2.00	1.00	.60
174b	Larry Jackson (company)	2.00	1.00	.60
175a	Lindy McDaniel (box)	2.00	1.00	.60
175b	Lindy McDaniel (company)	2.00	1.00	.60
176a	Bill White (box)	2.25	1.25	.70
176b	Bill White (company)	2.25	1.25	.70
177a	Alex Grammas (box)	2.00	1.00	.60
177b	Alex Grammas (company)	2.00	1.00	.60
178a	Curt Flood (box)	2.00	1.00	.60
178b	Curt Flood (company)	2.00	1.00	.60
179a	Ernie Broglio (box)	2.00	1.00	.60
179b	Ernie Broglio (company)	2.00	1.00	.60
180a	Hal Smith (box)	2.00	1.00	.60
180b	Hal Smith (company)	2.00	1.00	.60
181a	Vada Pinson (box)	2.50	1.25	.70
181b	Vada Pinson (company)	2.50	1.25	.70
182a	Frank Robinson (box)	25.00	12.50	7.50
182b	Frank Robinson (company)	25.00	12.50	7.50
183	Roy McMillan (box)	70.00	35.00	21.00
184a	Bob Purkey (box)	2.00	1.00	.60
184b	Bob Purkey (company)	2.00	1.00	.60
185a	Ed Kasko (box)	2.00	1.00	.60
185b	Ed Kasko (company)	2.00	1.00	.60
186a	Gus Bell (box)	2.00	1.00	.60
186b	Gus Bell (company)	2.00	1.00	.60
187a	Jerry Lynch (box)	2.00	1.00	.60
187b	Jerry Lynch (company)	2.00	1.00	.60
188a	Ed Bailey (box)	2.00	1.00	.60
188b	Ed Bailey (company)	2.00	1.00	.60
189a	Jim O'Toole (box)	2.00	1.00	.60
189b	Jim O'Toole (company)	2.00	1.00	.60
190a	Billy Martin (box, no sold line)	3.00	1.50	.90
190b	Billy Martin (company, sold line)	9.00	4.50	2.75
191a	Ernie Banks (box)	9.00	4.50	2.75
191b	Ernie Banks (company)	9.00	4.50	2.75
192a	Richie Ashburn (box)	3.00	1.50	.90
192b	Richie Ashburn (company)	3.00	1.50	.90
193a	Frank Thomas (box)	35.00	17.50	10.50
193b	Frank Thomas (company)	5.00	2.50	1.50
194a	Don Cardwell (box)	2.00	1.00	.60
194b	Don Cardwell (company)	2.00	1.00	.60
195a	George Altman (box)	2.00	1.00	.60
195b	George Altman (company)	2.00	1.00	.60
196a	Ron Santo (box)	3.00	1.50	.90
196b	Ron Santo (company)	3.00	1.50	.90
197a	Glen Hobbie (box)	2.00	1.00	.60
197b	Glen Hobbie (company)	2.00	1.00	.60
198a	Sam Taylor (box)	2.00	1.00	.60
198b	Sam Taylor (company)	2.00	1.00	.60
199a	Jerry Kindall (box)	2.00	1.00	.60
199b	Jerry Kindall (company)	2.00	1.00	.60
200a	Don Elston (box)	3.00	1.50	.90
200b	Don Elston (company)	3.00	1.50	.90

**Regional interest may affect
the value of a card.**

1962 Post Cereal

Like the 1961 Post set, there are 200 players pictured in the set of 3-1/2" by 2-1/2" cards. Differences include a Post logo on the card fronts and the player's name in script lettering. Cards are again blank backed and were issued in panels of five to seven cards on cereal boxes. American League players are numbered 1-100 and National League players 101-200. With variations there are 210 of the full-color cards known. A handful of the '62 cards were also issued in smaller quantities. The cards of Mickey Mantle and Roger Maris were reproduced in a special two-card panel for a Life magazine insert. the card stock for this insert is slightly thinner, with white margins. The 1962 Post Canadian and Jell-O sets have virtually the same checklist as this set. The complete set price does not include the scarcer variations.

		NR MT	EX	VG
Complete Set:		1500.00	750.00	450.00
Common Player:		1.50	.70	.45
1	Bill Skowron	4.00	2.00	1.25
2	Bobby Richardson	3.00	1.50	.90
3	Cletis Boyer	2.00	1.00	.60
4	Tony Kubek	3.00	1.50	.90
5a	Mickey Mantle (from box, no printing on back)	80.00	40.00	24.00
5b	Mickey Mantle (from ad, printing on back)	90.00	45.00	27.00
6a	Roger Maris (from box, no printing on back)	15.00	7.50	4.50
6b	Roger Maris (from ad, printing on back)	20.00	10.00	6.00
7	Yogi Berra	15.00	7.50	4.50
8	Elston Howard	3.00	1.50	.90
9	Whitey Ford	7.00	3.50	2.00
10	Ralph Terry	2.00	1.00	.60
11	John Blanchard	2.00	1.00	.60
12	Luis Arroyo	2.00	1.00	.60
13	Bill Stafford	2.00	1.00	.60
14a	Norm Cash (Throws: Right)	2.00	1.00	.60
14b	Norm Cash (Throws: Left)	5.00	2.50	1.50
15	Jake Wood	1.50	.70	.45
16	Steve Boros	1.50	.70	.45
17	Chico Fernandez	1.50	.70	.45
18	Bill Bruton	1.50	.70	.45
19	Rocky Colavito	3.00	1.50	.90
20	Al Kaline	8.00	4.00	2.50
21	Dick Brown	1.50	.70	.45
22	Frank Lary	1.50	.70	.45
23	Don Mossi	1.50	.70	.45
24	Phil Regan	1.50	.70	.45
25	Charley Maxwell	1.50	.70	.45
26	Jim Bunning	3.00	1.50	.90
27a	Jim Gentile (Home: Baltimore)	1.50	.70	.45
27b	Jim Gentile (Home: San Lorenzo)	5.00	2.50	1.50
28	Marv Breeding	1.50	.70	.45
29	Brooks Robinson	8.00	4.00	2.50
30	Ron Hansen	1.50	.70	.45
31	Jackie Brandt	1.50	.70	.45
32	Dick Williams	1.75	.90	.50
33	Gus Triandos	1.50	.70	.45
34	Milt Pappas	1.50	.70	.45
35	Hoyt Wilhelm	4.00	2.00	1.25
36	Chuck Estrada	5.00	2.50	1.50

#	Player	NR MT	EX	VG
37	Vic Power	1.50	.70	.45
38	Johnny Temple	1.50	.70	.45
39	Bubba Phillips	1.50	.70	.45
40	Tito Francona	1.50	.70	.45
41	Willie Kirkland	1.50	.70	.45
42	John Romano	1.50	.70	.45
43	Jim Perry	1.75	.90	.50
44	Woodie Held	1.50	.70	.45
45	Chuck Essegian	1.50	.70	.45
46	Roy Sievers	1.75	.90	.50
47	Nellie Fox	3.50	1.75	1.00
48	Al Smith	1.50	.70	.45
49	Luis Aparicio	4.00	2.00	1.25
50	Jim Landis	1.50	.70	.45
51	Minnie Minoso	2.00	1.00	.60
52	Andy Carey	1.50	.70	.45
53	Sherman Lollar	1.50	.70	.45
54	Bill Pierce	1.75	.90	.50
55	Early Wynn	40.00	20.00	12.00
56	Chuck Schilling	1.50	.70	.45
57	Pete Runnels	1.50	.70	.45
58	Frank Malzone	1.50	.70	.45
59	Don Buddin	1.50	.70	.45
60	Gary Geiger	1.50	.70	.45
61	Carl Yastrzemski	45.00	22.00	13.50
62	Jackie Jensen	2.00	1.00	.60
63	Jim Pagliaroni	1.50	.70	.45
64	Don Schwall	1.50	.70	.45
65	Dale Long	1.50	.70	.45
66	Chuck Cottier	1.50	.70	.45
67	Billy Klaus	1.50	.70	.45
68	Coot Veal	1.50	.70	.45
69	Marty Keough	40.00	20.00	12.00
70	Willie Tasby	1.50	.70	.45
71	Gene Woodling	1.50	.70	.45
72	Gene Green	1.50	.70	.45
73	Dick Donovan	1.50	.70	.45
74	Steve Bilko	1.50	.70	.45
75	Rocky Bridges	1.50	.70	.45
76	Eddie Yost	1.50	.70	.45
77	Leon Wagner	1.50	.70	.45
78	Albie Pearson	1.50	.70	.45
79	Ken Hunt	1.50	.70	.45
80	Earl Averill	1.50	.70	.45
81	Ryne Duren	1.50	.70	.45
82	Ted Kluszewski	2.50	1.25	.70
83	Bob Allison	35.00	17.50	10.50
84	Billy Martin	3.50	1.75	1.00
85	Harmon Killebrew	7.00	3.50	2.00
86	Zoilo Versalles	1.50	.70	.45
87	Lenny Green	1.50	.70	.45
88	Bill Tuttle	1.50	.70	.45
89	Jim Lemon	1.50	.70	.45
90	Earl Battey	1.50	.70	.45
91	Camilo Pascual	1.50	.70	.45
92	Norm Siebern	60.00	30.00	18.00
93	Jerry Lumpe	1.50	.70	.45
94	Dick Howser	2.00	1.00	.60
95a	Gene Stephens (Born: Jan. 5)	1.50	.70	.45
95b	Gene Stephens (Born: Jan. 20)	5.00	2.50	1.50
96	Leo Posada	1.50	.70	.45
97	Joe Pignatano	1.50	.70	.45
98	Jim Archer	1.50	.70	.45
99	Haywood Sullivan	1.50	.70	.45
100	Art Ditmar	1.50	.70	.45
101	Gil Hodges	65.00	32.00	19.50
102	Charlie Neal	1.50	.70	.45
103	Daryl Spencer	25.00	12.50	7.50
104	Maury Wills	4.00	2.00	1.25
105	Tommy Davis	2.00	1.00	.60
106	Willie Davis	1.75	.90	.50
107	John Roseboro	1.50	.70	.45
108	John Podres	2.50	1.25	.70
109a	Sandy Koufax (blue lines around stats)	40.00	20.00	12.00
109b	Sandy Koufax (red lines around stats)	25.00	12.50	7.50
110	Don Drysdale	7.00	3.50	2.00
111	Larry Sherry	1.50	.70	.45
112	Jim Gilliam	2.50	1.25	.70
113	Norm Larker	40.00	20.00	12.00
114	Duke Snider	8.00	4.00	2.50
115	Stan Williams	1.50	.70	.45
116	Gordy Coleman	80.00	40.00	24.00
117	Don Blasingame	1.50	.70	.45
118	Gene Freese	1.50	.70	.45
119	Ed Kasko	1.50	.70	.45
120	Gus Bell	1.50	.70	.45
121	Vada Pinson	2.50	1.25	.70
122	Frank Robinson	25.00	12.50	7.50
123	Bob Purkey	1.50	.70	.45
124a	Joey Jay (blue lines around stats)	8.00	4.00	2.50
124b	Joey Jay (red lines around stats)	1.50	.70	.45
125	Jim Brosnan	25.00	12.50	7.50
126	Jim O'Toole	1.50	.70	.45
127	Jerry Lynch	60.00	30.00	18.00
128	Wally Post	1.50	.70	.45
129	Ken Hunt	1.50	.70	.45
130	Jerry Zimmerman	1.50	.70	.45
131	Willie McCovey	80.00	40.00	24.00
132	Jose Pagan	1.50	.70	.45
133	Felipe Alou	1.75	.90	.50
134	Jim Davenport	1.50	.70	.45
135	Harvey Kuenn	2.00	1.00	.60
136	Orlando Cepeda	3.50	1.75	1.00
137	Ed Bailey	1.50	.70	.45
138	Sam Jones	1.50	.70	.45
139	Mike McCormick	1.50	.70	.45
140	Juan Marichal	80.00	40.00	24.00
141	Jack Sanford	1.50	.70	.45
142	Willie Mays	35.00	17.50	10.50
143	Stu Miller (photo actually Chuck Hiller)	6.00	3.00	1.75
144	Joe Amalfitano	15.00	7.50	4.50
145a	Joe Adock (name incorrect)	40.00	20.00	12.00
145b	Joe Adcock (name correct)	2.00	1.00	.60
146	Frank Bolling	1.50	.70	.45
147	Ed Mathews	7.00	3.50	2.00
148	Roy McMillan	1.50	.70	.45
149	Hank Aaron	45.00	22.00	13.50
150	Gino Cimoli	1.50	.70	.45
151	Frank Thomas	1.50	.70	.45
152	Joe Torre	3.00	1.50	.90
153	Lou Burdette	2.50	1.25	.70
154	Bob Buhl	1.50	.70	.45
155	Carlton Willey	1.50	.70	.45
156	Lee Maye	1.50	.70	.45
157	Al Spangler	1.50	.70	.45
158	Bill White	45.00	22.00	13.50
159	Ken Boyer	3.00	1.50	.90
160	Joe Cunningham	1.50	.70	.45
161	Carl Warwick	1.50	.70	.45
162	Carl Sawatski	1.50	.70	.45
163	Lindy McDaniel	1.50	.70	.45
164	Ernie Broglio	1.50	.70	.45
165	Larry Jackson	1.50	.70	.45
166	Curt Flood	2.00	1.00	.60
167	Curt Simmons	1.50	.70	.45
168	Alex Grammas	1.50	.70	.45
169	Dick Stuart	1.50	.70	.45
170	Bill Mazeroski	2.50	1.25	.70
171	Don Hoak	1.50	.70	.45
172	Dick Groat	2.00	1.00	.60
173a	Roberto Clemente (blue lines around stats)	40.00	20.00	12.00
173b	Roberto Clemente (red lines around stats)	25.00	12.50	7.50
174	Bob Skinner	1.50	.70	.45
175	Bill Virdon	1.75	.90	.50
176	Smoky Burgess	1.75	.90	.50
177	Elroy Face	1.75	.90	.50
178	Bob Friend	1.50	.70	.45
179	Vernon Law	1.50	.70	.45
180	Harvey Haddix	1.50	.70	.45
181	Hal Smith	1.50	.70	.45
182	Ed Bouchee	1.50	.70	.45
183	Don Zimmer	1.50	.70	.45
184	Ron Santo	2.50	1.25	.70
185	Andre Rodgers	1.50	.70	.45
186	Richie Ashburn	3.00	1.50	.90
187a	George Altman (last line is "...1955.)	1.50	.70	.45
187b	George Altman (last line is "...1955.")	3.00	1.50	.90
188	Ernie Banks	15.00	7.50	4.50
189	Sam Taylor	1.50	.70	.45
190	Don Elston	1.50	.70	.45
191	Jerry Kindall	1.50	.70	.45
192	Pancho Herrera	1.50	.70	.45
193	Tony Taylor	1.50	.70	.45
194	Ruben Amaro	1.50	.70	.45
195	Don Demeter	1.50	.70	.45
196	Bobby Gene Smith	1.50	.70	.45
197	Clay Dalrymple	1.50	.70	.45
198	Robin Roberts	5.00	2.50	1.50
199	Art Mahaffey	1.50	.70	.45
200	John Buzhardt	2.50	1.25	.70

The values quoted are intended to reflect the market price.

Definitions for grading conditions are located in the Introduction of this price guide.

1962 Post Cereal Canadian

This Canadian set of cards is scarce due to the much more limited distribution in Canada. The cards were printed on the back of the cereal box itself and contains a full-color player photo with biography and statistics given in both French and English. The card backs are blank. Cards measure 3-1/2" by 2-1/2". This 200-card set is very similar to the Post Cereal cards printed in the United States. the Post logo appears at the upper left corner in the Canadian issue. Several cards are scarce because of limited distribution and there are two Whitey Ford cards, the corrected version being the most scarce. The complete set price does not include the scarcer variations.

		NR MT	EX	VG
Complete Set:		2500.00	1250.00	750.00
Common Player:		3.00	1.50	.90
1	Bill Skowron	8.00	4.00	2.50
2	Bobby Richardson	6.00	3.00	1.75
3	Cletis Boyer	3.50	1.75	1.00
4	Tony Kubek	6.00	3.00	1.75
5a	Mickey Mantle (script name large)	200.00	100.00	60.00
5b	Mickey Mantle (script name small)	125.00	62.00	37.00
6	Roger Maris	25.00	12.50	7.50
7	Yogi Berra	25.00	12.50	7.50
8	Elston Howard	4.00	2.00	1.25
9a	Whitey Ford (Dodgers)	30.00	15.00	9.00
9b	Whitey Ford (Yankees)	50.00	25.00	15.00
10	Ralph Terry	35.00	17.50	10.50
11	John Blanchard	3.50	1.75	1.00
12	Luis Arroyo	3.50	1.75	1.00
13	Bill Stafford	3.50	1.75	1.00
14	Norm Cash	4.00	2.00	1.25
15	Jake Wood	3.00	1.50	.90
16	Steve Boros	3.00	1.50	.90
17	Chico Fernandez	3.00	1.50	.90
18	Bill Bruton	3.00	1.50	.90
19a	Rocky Colavito (script name large)	7.00	3.50	2.00
19b	Rocky Colavito (script name small)	7.00	3.50	2.00
20	Al Kaline	25.00	12.50	7.50
21	Dick Brown	7.00	3.50	2.00
22a	Frank Lary (French bio variation)	7.00	3.50	2.00
22b	Frank Lary (French bio variation)	7.00	3.50	2.00
23	Don Mossi	3.00	1.50	.90
24	Phil Regan	3.00	1.50	.90
25	Charley Maxwell	3.00	1.50	.90
26	Jim Bunning	6.00	3.00	1.75
27a	Jim Gentile (French bio variation)	5.00	2.50	1.50
27b	Jim Gentile (French bio variation)	5.00	2.50	1.50
28	Marv Breeding	3.00	1.50	.90
29	Brooks Robinson	35.00	17.50	10.50
30	Ron Hansen	3.00	1.50	.90
31	Jackie Brandt	3.00	1.50	.90
32	Dick Williams	35.00	17.50	10.50
33	Gus Triandos	3.00	1.50	.90
34	Milt Pappas	3.50	1.75	1.00
35	Hoyt Wilhelm	25.00	12.50	7.50
36	Chuck Estrada	3.00	1.50	.90
37	Vic Power	3.00	1.50	.90
38	Johnny Temple	3.00	1.50	.90
39	Bubba Phillips	35.00	17.50	10.50

		NR MT	EX	VG
40	Tito Francona	3.00	1.50	.90
41	Willie Kirkland	7.00	3.50	2.00
42	John Romano	7.00	3.50	2.00
43	Jim Perry	4.00	2.00	1.25
44	Woodie Held	3.00	1.50	.90
45	Chuck Essegian	3.00	1.50	.90
46	Roy Sievers	3.50	1.75	1.00
47	Nellie Fox	6.00	3.00	1.75
48	Al Smith	3.00	1.50	.90
49	Luis Aparicio	25.00	12.50	7.50
50	Jim Landis	3.00	1.50	.90
51	Minnie Minoso	35.00	17.50	10.50
52	Andy Carey	7.00	3.50	2.00
53	Sherman Lollar	3.00	1.50	.90
54	Bill Pierce	3.50	1.75	1.00
55	Early Wynn	20.00	10.00	6.00
56	Chuck Schilling	3.00	1.50	.90
57	Pete Runnels	3.50	1.75	1.00
58	Frank Malzone	3.00	1.50	.90
59	Don Buddin	7.00	3.50	2.00
60	Gary Geiger	3.00	1.50	.90
61	Carl Yastrzemski	50.00	25.00	15.00
62	Jackie Jensen	9.00	4.50	2.75
63	Jim Pagliaroni	3.00	1.50	.90
64	Don Schwall	3.00	1.50	.90
65	Dale Long	3.00	1.50	.90
66	Chuck Cottier	3.00	1.50	.90
67	Billy Klaus	3.00	1.50	.90
68	Coot Veal	3.00	1.50	.90
69	Marty Keough	3.00	1.50	.90
70	Willie Tasby	35.00	17.50	10.50
71	Gene Woodling (photo reversed)	3.50	1.75	1.00
72	Gene Green	3.00	1.50	.90
73	Dick Donovan	3.00	1.50	.90
74	Steve Bilko	3.00	1.50	.90
75	Rocky Bridges	6.00	3.00	1.75
76	Eddie Yost	3.00	1.50	.90
77	Leon Wagner	35.00	17.50	10.50
78	Albie Pearson	7.00	3.50	2.00
79	Ken Hunt	3.00	1.50	.90
80	Earl Averill	3.00	1.50	.90
81	Ryne Duren	4.00	2.00	1.25
82	Ted Kluszewski	4.00	2.00	1.25
83	Bob Allison	3.50	1.75	1.00
84	Billy Martin	6.00	3.00	1.75
85	Harmon Killebrew	20.00	10.00	6.00
86	Zoilo Versalles	3.00	1.50	.90
87	Lenny Green	3.00	1.50	.90
88	Bill Tuttle	3.00	1.50	.90
89	Jim Lemon	3.00	1.50	.90
90	Earl Battey	3.00	1.50	.90
91	Camilo Pascual	3.50	1.75	1.00
92	Norm Siebern	3.00	1.50	.90
93	Jerry Lumpe	3.00	1.50	.90
94	Dick Howser	35.00	17.50	10.50
95	Gene Stephens	3.00	1.50	.90
96	Leo Posada	3.00	1.50	.90
97	Joe Pignatano	3.00	1.50	.90
98	Jim Archer	3.00	1.50	.90
99	Haywood Sullivan	35.00	17.50	10.50
100	Art Ditmar	35.00	17.50	10.50
101	Gil Hodges	20.00	10.00	6.00
102	Charlie Neal	3.00	1.50	.90
103	Daryl Spencer	3.00	1.50	.90
104	Maury Wills	5.00	2.50	1.50
105	Tommy Davis	9.00	4.50	2.75
106	Willie Davis	4.00	2.00	1.25
107	John Roseboro	3.50	1.75	1.00
108	John Podres	4.00	2.00	1.25
109	Sandy Koufax	30.00	15.00	9.00
110	Don Drysdale	25.00	12.50	7.50
111	Larry Sherry	35.00	17.50	10.50
112	Jim Gilliam	35.00	17.50	10.50
113	Norm Larker	3.00	1.50	.90
114	Duke Snider	35.00	17.50	10.50
115	Stan Williams	3.00	1.50	.90
116	Gordy Coleman	3.00	1.50	.90
117	Don Blasingame	35.00	17.50	10.50
118	Gene Freese	7.00	3.50	2.00
119	Ed Kasko	3.00	1.50	.90
120	Gus Bell	3.00	1.50	.90
121	Vada Pinson	5.00	2.50	1.50
122	Frank Robinson	25.00	12.50	7.50
123	Bob Purkey	35.00	17.50	10.50
124	Joey Jay	3.00	1.50	.90
125	Jim Brosnan	3.50	1.75	1.00
126	Jim O'Toole	3.00	1.50	.90
127	Jerry Lynch	3.00	1.50	.90
128	Wally Post	70.00	35.00	21.00
129	Ken Hunt	3.00	1.50	.90
130	Jerry Zimmerman	3.00	1.50	.90
131	Willie McCovey	25.00	12.50	7.50

		NR MT	EX	VG
132	Jose Pagan	3.00	1.50	.90
133	Felipe Alou	3.50	1.75	1.00
134	Jim Davenport	3.00	1.50	.90
135	Harvey Kuenn	4.00	2.00	1.25
136	Orlando Cepeda	6.00	3.00	1.75
137	Ed Bailey	35.00	17.50	10.50
138	Sam Jones	35.00	17.50	10.50
139	Mike McCormick	3.00	1.50	.90
140	Juan Marichal	25.00	12.50	7.50
141	Jack Sanford	3.00	1.50	.90
142a	Willie Mays (big head)	50.00	25.00	15.00
142b	Willie Mays (small head)	60.00	30.00	18.00
143	Stu Miller	3.00	1.50	.90
144	Joe Amalfitano	35.00	17.50	10.50
145	Joe Adcock	4.00	2.00	1.25
146	Frank Bolling	3.00	1.50	.90
147	Ed Mathews	20.00	10.00	6.00
148	Roy McMillan	3.00	1.50	.90
149a	Hank Aaron (script name large)	50.00	25.00	15.00
149b	Hank Aaron (script name small)	50.00	25.00	15.00
150	Gino Cimoli	3.00	1.50	.90
151	Frank Thomas	3.00	1.50	.90
152	Joe Torre	5.00	2.50	1.50
153	Lou Burdette	5.00	2.50	1.50
154	Bob Buhl	3.50	1.75	1.00
155	Carlton Willey	3.00	1.50	.90
156	Lee Maye	3.00	1.50	.90
157	Al Spangler	3.00	1.50	.90
158	Bill White	3.50	1.75	1.00
159	Ken Boyer	30.00	15.00	9.00
160	Joe Cunningham	3.00	1.50	.90
161	Carl Warwick	7.00	3.50	2.00
162	Carl Sawatski	3.00	1.50	.90
163	Lindy McDaniel	3.00	1.50	.90
164	Ernie Broglio	3.00	1.50	.90
165	Larry Jackson	3.00	1.50	.90
166	Curt Flood	4.00	2.00	1.25
167	Curt Simmons	8.00	4.00	2.50
168	Alex Grammas	3.00	1.50	.90
169	Dick Stuart	3.50	1.75	1.00
170	Bill Mazeroski	35.00	17.50	10.50
171	Don Hoak	3.00	1.50	.90
172	Dick Groat	9.00	4.50	2.75
173	Roberto Clemente	30.00	15.00	9.00
174	Bob Skinner	3.00	1.50	.90
175	Bill Virdon	4.00	2.00	1.25
176	Smoky Burgess	8.00	4.00	2.50
177	Elroy Face	8.00	4.00	2.50
178	Bob Friend	3.50	1.75	1.00
179	Vernon Law	3.50	1.75	1.00
180	Harvey Haddix	3.50	1.75	1.00
181	Hal Smith	35.00	17.50	10.50
182	Ed Bouchee	3.00	1.50	.90
183	Don Zimmer	4.00	2.00	1.25
184	Ron Santo	5.00	2.50	1.50
185	Andre Rodgers	3.00	1.50	.90
186	Richie Ashburn	6.00	3.00	1.75
187	George Altman	3.00	1.50	.90
188	Ernie Banks	35.00	17.50	10.50
189	Sam Taylor	3.00	1.50	.90
190	Don Elston	3.00	1.50	.90
191	Jerry Kindall	3.00	1.50	.90
192	Pancho Herrera	3.00	1.50	.90
193	Tony Taylor	3.00	1.50	.90
194	Ruben Amaro	3.00	1.50	.90
195	Don Demeter	35.00	17.50	10.50
196	Bobby Gene Smith	3.00	1.50	.90
197	Clay Dalrymple	3.00	1.50	.90
198	Robin Roberts	20.00	10.00	6.00
199	Art Mahaffey	3.00	1.50	.90
200	John Buzhardt	5.00	2.50	1.50

1963 Post Cereal

Another 200-player, 3-1/2" by 2-1/2" set that, with variations, totals more than 205 cards. Numerous color variations also exist due to the different cereal boxes on which the cards were printed. As many as 25 cards in the set are considered scarce, making it much more difficult to complete than the other major Post sets. Star cards also command higher prices than in the '61 or '62 Post cards. The 1963 Post cards are almost identical to the '63 Jell-O set, which is a slight 1/4" narrower. Cards are still blank backed, with a color player photo, biographies and statistics on the numbered card fronts. No Post logo appears on the '63 cards. The complete set price does not include the scarcer variations.

		NR MT	EX	VG
	Complete Set:	3600.00	1800.00	1080.
	Common Player:	2.00	1.00	.60
1	Vic Power	3.50	1.75	1.00
2	Bernie Allen	2.00	1.00	.60
3	Zoilo Versalles	2.00	1.00	.60
4	Rich Rollins	2.00	1.00	.60
5	Harmon Killebrew	12.00	6.00	3.50
6	Lenny Green	35.00	17.50	10.50
7	Bob Allison	1.75	.90	.50
8	Earl Battey	2.00	1.00	.60
9	Camilo Pascual	2.00	1.00	.60
10	Jim Kaat	3.00	1.50	.90
11	Jack Kralick	2.00	1.00	.60
12	Bill Skowron	2.50	1.25	.70
13	Bobby Richardson	3.00	1.50	.90
14	Cletis Boyer	2.50	1.25	.70
15	Mickey Mantle	325.00	162.00	97.00
16	Roger Maris	150.00	75.00	45.00
17	Yogi Berra	15.00	7.50	4.50
18	Elston Howard	3.00	1.50	.90
19	Whitey Ford	8.00	4.00	2.50
20	Ralph Terry	2.50	1.25	.70
21	John Blanchard	2.50	1.25	.70
22	Bill Stafford	2.50	1.25	.70
23	Tom Tresh	2.50	1.25	.70
24	Steve Bilko	2.00	1.00	.60
25	Bill Moran	2.00	1.00	.60
26a	Joe Koppe (1962 Avg. is .277)	2.00	1.00	.60
26b	Joe Koppe (1962 Avg. is .227)	12.00	6.00	3.50
27	Felix Torres	2.00	1.00	.60
28a	Leon Wagner (lifetime Avg. is .278)	2.00	1.00	.60
28b	Leon Wagner (lifetime Avg. is .272)	12.00	6.00	3.50
29	Albie Pearson	2.00	1.00	.60
30	Lee Thomas (photo actually George Thomas)	70.00	35.00	21.00
31	Bob Rodgers	2.00	1.00	.60
32	Dean Chance	2.00	1.00	.60
33	Ken McBride	2.00	1.00	.60
34	George Thomas (photo actually Lee Thomas)	2.00	1.00	.60
35	Joe Cunningham	2.00	1.00	.60
36a	Nelson Fox (no bat showing)	3.50	1.75	1.00
36b	Nelson Fox (part of bat showing)	10.00	5.00	3.00
37	Luis Aparicio	4.00	2.00	1.25
38	Al Smith	25.00	12.50	7.50
39	Floyd Robinson	80.00	40.00	24.00
40	Jim Landis	2.00	1.00	.60
41	Charlie Maxwell	2.00	1.00	.60
42	Sherman Lollar	2.00	1.00	.60
43	Early Wynn	6.00	3.00	1.75
44	Juan Pizarro	2.00	1.00	.60
45	Ray Herbert	2.00	1.00	.60
46	Norm Cash	2.50	1.25	.70
47	Steve Boros	2.00	1.00	.60
48	Dick McAuliffe	25.00	12.50	7.50
49	Bill Bruton	2.00	1.00	.60
50	Rocky Colavito	3.00	1.50	.90
51	Al Kaline	10.00	5.00	3.00
52	Dick Brown	2.00	1.00	.60
53	Jim Bunning	110.00	55.00	33.00
54	Hank Aguirre	2.00	1.00	.60
55	Frank Lary	2.00	1.00	.60
56	Don Mossi	2.00	1.00	.60
57	Jim Gentile	2.00	1.00	.60
58	Jackie Brandt	2.00	1.00	.60
59	Brooks Robinson	10.00	5.00	3.00
60	Ron Hansen	2.00	1.00	.60
61	Jerry Adair	150.00	75.00	45.00
62	John Powell	3.00	1.50	.90

		NR MT	EX	VG
63	Russ Snyder	2.00	1.00	.60
64	Steve Barber	2.00	1.00	.60
65	Milt Pappas	2.00	1.00	.60
66	Robin Roberts	4.00	2.00	1.25
67	Tito Francona	2.00	1.00	.60
68	Jerry Kindall	2.00	1.00	.60
69	Woodie Held	2.00	1.00	.60
70	Bubba Phillips	15.00	7.50	4.50
71	Chuck Essegian	2.00	1.00	.60
72	Willie Kirkland	2.00	1.00	.60
73	Al Luplow	2.00	1.00	.60
74	Ty Cline	2.00	1.00	.60
75	Dick Donovan	2.00	1.00	.60
76	John Romano	2.00	1.00	.60
77	Pete Runnels	2.00	1.00	.60
78	Ed Bressoud	2.00	1.00	.60
79	Frank Malzone	2.00	1.00	.60
80	Carl Yastrzemski	325.00	162.00	97.00
81	Gary Geiger	2.00	1.00	.60
82	Lou Clinton	2.00	1.00	.60
83	Earl Wilson	2.00	1.00	.60
84	Bill Monbouquette	2.00	1.00	.60
85	Norm Siebern	2.00	1.00	.60
86	Jerry Lumpe	80.00	40.00	24.00
87	Manny Jimenez	80.00	40.00	24.00
88	Gino Cimoli	2.00	1.00	.60
89	Ed Charles	2.00	1.00	.60
90	Ed Rakow	2.00	1.00	.60
91	Bob Del Greco	2.00	1.00	.60
92	Haywood Sullivan	2.00	1.00	.60
93	Chuck Hinton	2.00	1.00	.60
94	Ken Retzer	2.00	1.00	.60
95	Harry Bright	2.00	1.00	.60
96	Bob Johnson	2.00	1.00	.60
97	Dave Stenhouse	15.00	7.50	4.50
98	Chuck Cottier	25.00	12.50	7.50
99	Tom Cheney	2.00	1.00	.60
100	Claude Osteen	15.00	7.50	4.50
101	Orlando Cepeda	3.00	1.50	.90
102	Charley Hiller	2.00	1.00	.60
103	Jose Pagan	2.00	1.00	.60
104	Jim Davenport	2.00	1.00	.60
105	Harvey Kuenn	2.50	1.25	.70
106	Willie Mays	25.00	12.50	7.50
107	Felipe Alou	1.75	.90	.50
108	Tom Haller	110.00	55.00	33.00
109	Juan Marichal	6.00	3.00	1.75
110	Jack Sanford	2.00	1.00	.60
111	Bill O'Dell	2.00	1.00	.60
112	Willie McCovey	7.00	3.50	2.00
113	Lee Walls	2.00	1.00	.60
114	Jim Gilliam	3.00	1.50	.90
115	Maury Wills	3.00	1.50	.90
116	Ron Fairly	2.00	1.00	.60
117	Tommy Davis	2.50	1.25	.70
118	Duke Snider	8.00	4.00	2.50
119	Willie Davis	150.00	75.00	45.00
120	John Roseboro	2.00	1.00	.60
121	Sandy Koufax	15.00	7.50	4.50
122	Stan Williams	2.00	1.00	.60
123	Don Drysdale	7.00	3.50	2.00
124a	Daryl Spencer (no arm showing)	2.00	1.00	.60
124b	Daryl Spencer (part of arm showing)	10.00	5.00	3.00
125	Gordy Coleman	2.00	1.00	.60
126	Don Blasingame	2.00	1.00	.60
127	Leo Cardenas	2.00	1.00	.60
128	Eddie Kasko	150.00	75.00	45.00
129	Jerry Lynch	15.00	7.50	4.50
130	Vada Pinson	2.50	1.25	.70
131a	Frank Robinson (no stripes on hat)	8.00	4.00	2.50
131b	Frank Robinson (stripes on hat)	15.00	7.50	4.50
132	John Edwards	2.00	1.00	.60
133	Joey Jay	2.00	1.00	.60
134	Bob Purkey	2.00	1.00	.60
135	Marty Keough	15.00	7.50	4.50
136	Jim O'Toole	2.00	1.00	.60
137	Dick Stuart	2.00	1.00	.60
138	Bill Mazeroski	2.50	1.25	.70
139	Dick Groat	2.50	1.25	.70
140	Don Hoak	30.00	15.00	9.00
141	Bob Skinner	15.00	7.50	4.50
142	Bill Virdon	2.50	1.25	.70
143	Roberto Clemente	20.00	10.00	6.00
144	Smoky Burgess	1.75	.90	.50
145	Bob Friend	2.00	1.00	.60
146	Al McBean	2.00	1.00	.60
147	El Roy Face (Elroy)	2.50	1.25	.70
148	Joe Adcock	2.50	1.25	.70
149	Frank Bolling	2.00	1.00	.60

		NR MT	EX	VG
150	Roy McMillan	2.00	1.00	.60
151	Eddie Mathews	6.00	3.00	1.75
152	Hank Aaron	70.00	35.00	21.00
153	Del Crandall	30.00	15.00	9.00
154a	Bob Shaw (third sentence has "In 1959" twice)	10.00	5.00	3.00
154b	Bob Shaw (third sentence has "In 1959" once)	2.00	1.00	.60
155	Lew Burdette	2.50	1.25	.70
156	Joe Torre	3.00	1.50	.90
157	Tony Cloninger	2.00	1.00	.60
158	Bill White	2.50	1.25	.70
159	Julian Javier	2.00	1.00	.60
160	Ken Boyer	3.00	1.50	.90
161	Julio Gotay	2.00	1.00	.60
162	Curt Flood	110.00	55.00	33.00
163	Charlie James	2.00	1.00	.60
164	Gene Oliver	2.00	1.00	.60
165	Ernie Broglio	2.00	1.00	.60
166	Bob Gibson	7.00	3.50	2.00
167a	Lindy McDaniel (asterisk before trade line)	2.00	1.00	.60
167b	Lindy McDaniel (no asterisk before trade line)	5.00	2.50	1.50
168	Ray Washburn	2.00	1.00	.60
169	Ernie Banks	8.00	4.00	2.50
170	Ron Santo	2.50	1.25	.70
171	George Altman	2.00	1.00	.60
172	Billy Williams	110.00	55.00	33.00
173	Andre Rodgers	6.00	3.00	1.75
174	Ken Hubbs	20.00	10.00	6.00
175	Don Landrum	2.00	1.00	.60
176	Dick Bertell	15.00	7.50	4.50
177	Roy Sievers	1.75	.90	.50
178	Tony Taylor	2.00	1.00	.60
179	John Callison	1.75	.90	.50
180	Don Demeter	2.00	1.00	.60
181	Tony Gonzalez	2.00	1.00	.60
182	Wes Covington	20.00	10.00	6.00
183	Art Mahaffey	2.00	1.00	.60
184	Clay Dalrymple	2.00	1.00	.60
185	Al Spangler	2.00	1.00	.60
186	Roman Mejias	2.00	1.00	.60
187	Bob Aspromonte	325.00	162.00	97.00
188	Norm Larker	30.00	15.00	9.00
189	Johnny Temple	2.00	1.00	.60
190	Carl Warwick	2.00	1.00	.60
191	Bob Lillis	2.00	1.00	.60
192	Dick Farrell	2.00	1.00	.60
193	Gil Hodges	7.00	3.50	2.00
194	Marv Throneberry	3.00	1.50	.90
195	Charlie Neal	10.00	5.00	3.00
196	Frank Thomas	150.00	75.00	45.00
197	Richie Ashburn	20.00	10.00	6.00
198	Felix Mantilla	2.00	1.00	.60
199	Rod Kanehl	20.00	10.00	6.00
200	Roger Craig	3.00	1.50	.90

1990 Post Cereal

Post Cereal returned in 1990 with a 30-card set. The card fronts feature borders in white, red and blue, with the post logo in the upper left and the Major League Baseball logo in the upper right. Below the full-color shot of the player is his name in red. Backs of the cards show complete major league statistics; underneath is a facsimile autograph. The player photos do not display team logos. Cards were included three per box, inside Alpha-Bits cereal.

Considered a difficult set to complete, the insert offer was only available for a limited time.

		MT	NR MT	EX
Complete Set:		30.00	22.00	12.00
Common Player:		.30	.25	.12
1	Don Mattingly	.80	.60	.30
2	Roger Clemens	.80	.60	.30
3	Kirby Puckett	.60	.45	.25
4	George Brett	.60	.45	.25
5	Tony Gwynn	.50	.40	.20
6	Ozzie Smith	.50	.40	.20
7	Will Clark	.80	.60	.30
8	Orel Hershiser	.40	.30	.15
9	Ryne Sandberg	1.00	.70	.40
10	Darryl Strawberry	.80	.60	.30
11	Nolan Ryan	1.50	1.25	.60
12	Mark McGwire	.40	.30	.15
13	Jim Abbott	.30	.25	.12
14	Bo Jackson	1.00	.90	.50
15	Kevin Mitchell	.40	.30	.15
16	Jose Canseco	1.25	.90	.50
17	Wade Boggs	.40	.30	.15
18	Dale Murphy	.40	.30	.15
19	Mark Grace	.40	.30	.15
20	Mike Scott	.30	.25	.12
21	Cal Ripken,Jr.	.80	.60	.30
22	Pedro Guerrero	.30	.25	.12
23	Ken Griffey,Jr.	2.00	1.50	.80
24	Eric Davis	.60	.45	.25
25	Rickey Henderson	.80	.60	.30
26	Robin Yount	.40	.30	.15
27	Von Hayes	.30	.25	.12
28	Alan Trammell	.40	.30	.15
29	Dwight Gooden	.80	.60	.30
30	Joe Carter	.40	.30	.15

1991 Post Cereal

These superstar trading cards were inserted in Post Honeycomb, Super Golden Crisp, Cocoa Pebbles, Fruity Pebbles, Alpha-Bits and Marshmallow Alpha-Bits children's cereals. The complete set features 30 cards of baseball's top players. The cards were produced by Mike Schechter Associates, Inc. and are authorized by The Major League Baseball Players Association. The card fronts feature a player photo, the Post logo and the MLBPA logo. The flip sides feature statistics and a facsimile autograph.

		MT	NR MT	EX
Complete Set:		25.00	20.00	10.00
Common Player:		.30	.25	.12
1	Dave Justice	1.75	1.25	.70
2	Mark McGwire	.40	.30	.15
3	Will Clark	.80	.60	.30
4	Jose Canseco	1.00	.70	.40
5	Vince Coleman	.30	.25	.12
6	Sandy Alomar,Jr.	.40	.30	.15
7	Darryl Strawberry	.50	.40	.20
8	Len Dykstra	.30	.25	.12
9	Gregg Jefferies	.50	.40	.20
10	Tony Gwynn	.40	.30	.15
11	Ken Griffey,Jr.	2.00	1.50	.80
12	Roger Clemens	.80	.60	.30

		MT	NR MT	EX
13	Chris Sabo	.30	.25	.12
14	Bobby Bonilla	.40	.30	.15
15	Gary Sheffield	.50	.40	.20
16	Ryne Sandberg	1.00	.70	.40
17	Nolan Ryan	1.25	.90	.50
18	Barry Larkin	.50	.40	.20
19	Cal Ripken,Jr.	1.00	.70	.40
20	Jim Abbott	.40	.30	.15
21	Barry Bonds	.50	.40	.20
22	Mark Grace	.40	.30	.15
23	Cecil Fielder	1.00	.70	.40
24	Kevin Mitchell	.40	.30	.15
25	Todd Zeile	.60	.45	.25
26	George Brett	.60	.45	.25
27	Rickey Henderson	.80	.60	.30
28	Kirby Puckett	.50	.40	.20
29	Don Mattingly	.80	.60	.30
30	Kevin Maas	.60	.45	.25

1986 Quaker Oats

The Quaker Company, in conjunction with Topps, produced this 33-card set of current baseball stars for packaging in groups of three in Chewy Granola Bars packages. The cards are noted as the "1st Annual Collectors Edition." They are numbered and measure 2-1/2" by 3-1/2". Card fronts feature full-color player photos with the product name at the top and the player name, team and position below the photo. The complete set was offered via mail order by the Quaker Company.

		MT	NR MT	EX
Complete Set:		8.00	6.00	3.25
Common Player:		.15	.11	.06
1	Willie McGee	.15	.11	.06
2	Dwight Gooden	1.00	.70	.40
3	Vince Coleman	.30	.25	.12
4	Gary Carter	.25	.20	.10
5	Jack Clark	.15	.11	.06
6	Steve Garvey	.25	.20	.10
7	Tony Gwynn	.35	.25	.14
8	Dale Murphy	.40	.30	.15
9	Dave Parker	.15	.11	.06
10	Tim Raines	.25	.20	.10
11	Pete Rose	1.00	.70	.40
12	Nolan Ryan	1.00	.70	.40
13	Ryne Sandberg	1.00	.70	.40
14	Mike Schmidt	.40	.30	.15
15	Ozzie Smith	.15	.11	.06
16	Darryl Strawberry	.40	.30	.15
17	Fernando Valenzuela	.20	.15	.08
18	Don Mattingly	1.00	.70	.40
19	Bret Saberhagen	.20	.15	.08
20	Ozzie Guillen	.15	.11	.06
21	Bert Blyleven	.15	.11	.06
22	Wade Boggs	.80	.60	.30
23	George Brett	.40	.30	.15
24	Darrell Evans	.15	.11	.06

		MT	NR MT	EX
25	Rickey Henderson	1.00	.70	.40
26	Reggie Jackson	.30	.25	.12
27	Eddie Murray	.30	.25	.12
28	Phil Niekro	.20	.15	.08
29	Dan Quisenberry	.15	.11	.06
30	Jim Rice	.25	.20	.10
31	Cal Ripken	.30	.25	.12
32	Tom Seaver	.25	.20	.10
33	Dave Winfield	.25	.20	.10
-----	Offer Card	.03	.02	.01

1984 Ralston Purina

This set, produced in conjunction with Topps, has 33 of the game's top players, and is titled "1st Annual Collector's Edition." The full-color photos on the 2-1/2" by 3-1/2" cards are all close-up poses. Topps' logo appears only on the card fronts, and the backs are completely different from Topps' regular issue of 1984. Card backs feature a checkerboard look, coinciding with the well-known Ralston Purina logo. Cards are numbered 1-33, with odd numbers for American Leaguers and even numbers for National League players. Four cards were packed in boxes of Cookie Crisp and Donkey Kong Junior brand cereals, and the complete set was available via a mail-in offer.

		MT	NR MT	EX
Complete Set:		5.00	3.75	2.00
Common Player:		.10	.08	.04
1	Eddie Murray	.30	.25	.12
2	Ozzie Smith	.10	.08	.04
3	Ted Simmons	.10	.08	.04
4	Pete Rose	.80	.60	.30
5	Greg Luzinski	.10	.08	.04
6	Andre Dawson	.15	.11	.06
7	Dave Winfield	.25	.20	.10
8	Tom Seaver	.25	.20	.10
9	Jim Rice	.25	.20	.10
10	Fernando Valenzuela	.20	.15	.08
11	Wade Boggs	.60	.45	.25
12	Dale Murphy	.35	.25	.14
13	George Brett	.35	.25	.14
14	Nolan Ryan	.80	.60	.30
15	Rickey Henderson	.80	.60	.30
16	Steve Carlton	.30	.25	.12
17	Rod Carew	.30	.25	.12
18	Steve Garvey	.25	.20	.10
19	Reggie Jackson	.30	.25	.12
20	Dave Concepcion	.10	.08	.04
21	Robin Yount	.20	.15	.08
22	Mike Schmidt	.35	.25	.14
23	Jim Palmer	.20	.15	.08
24	Bruce Sutter	.10	.08	.04
25	Dan Quisenberry	.10	.08	.04
26	Bill Madlock	.10	.08	.04
27	Cecil Cooper	.10	.08	.04

		MT	NR MT	EX
28	Gary Carter	.25	.20	.10
29	Fred Lynn	.15	.11	.06
30	Pedro Guerrero	.15	.11	.06
31	Ron Guidry	.15	.11	.06
32	Keith Hernandez	.20	.15	.08
33	Carlton Fisk	.20	.15	.08

1987 Ralston Purina

The Ralston Purina Company, in conjunction with Mike Schecter Associates, issued a 15-card set in specially marked boxes of Cookie Crisp and Honey Graham Chex brands of cereal. Three different cards, each measuring 2-1/2" by 3-1/2" and wrapped in cellophane, were inserted in each box. The card fronts contain a full-color photo with the team insignia airbrushed away. Above the photo are two yellow crossed bats and a star, with the player's uniform number inside the star. The card backs are grey with red printing and contain the set name, card number, player's name, personal information and career major league statistics. As part of the Ralston Purina promotion, the company advertised an uncut sheet of cards which was available by finding an "instant-winner" game card or sending $1 plus two non-winning cards. Cards on the uncut sheet are identical in design to the single cards, save the omission of the words "1987 Collectors Edition" in the upper right corner. A complete uncut sheet in mint condition is valued at $10.

		MT	NR MT	EX
Complete Set:		15.00	11.00	6.00
Common Player:		1.00	.70	.40
1	Nolan Ryan	2.00	1.50	.80
2	Steve Garvey	1.25	.90	.50
3	Wade Boggs	1.25	.90	.50
4	Dave Winfield	1.25	.90	.50
5	Don Mattingly	2.00	1.50	.80
6	Don Sutton	1.00	.70	.40
7	Dave Parker	1.00	.70	.40
8	Eddie Murray	1.25	.90	.50
9	Gary Carter	1.25	.90	.50
10	Roger Clemens	2.00	1.50	.80
11	Fernando Valenzuela	1.25	.90	.50
12	Cal Ripken Jr.	2.00	1.50	.80
13	Ozzie Smith	1.00	.70	.40
14	Mike Schmidt	1.50	1.25	.60
15	Ryne Sandberg	2.00	1.50	.80

1989 Ralston Purina

The Ralston Purina Co., in conjunction with Mike Schechter Associates, issued a 12-card "Superstars" set in 1989. As part of a late-spring and early-summer promotion, the standard-size cards were inserted, two per box, in specially-marked boxes of Crisp Crunch, Honey Nut O's, Fruit Rings and Frosted Flakes in most parts of the country. Ads on cereal boxes also offered complete sets through a mail-in offer. The fronts of the cards feature full-color player photos flanked by stars in all four corners. "Super Stars" appears at the top; the player's name and position are at the bottom. The backs include player stats and data, the card number and copyright line.

		MT	NR MT	EX
Complete Set:		8.00	6.00	3.25
Common Player:		.80	.60	.30
1	Ozzie Smith	.80	.60	.30
2	Andre Dawson	.80	.60	.30
3	Darryl Strawberry	1.00	.70	.40
4	Mike Schmidt	1.25	.90	.50
5	Orel Hershiser	.90	.70	.35
6	Tim Raines	.80	.60	.30
7	Roger Clemens	1.25	.90	.50
8	Kirby Puckett	1.00	.70	.40
9	George Brett	1.00	.70	.40
10	Alan Trammell	.80	.60	.30
11	Don Mattingly	1.00	.70	.40
12	Jose Canseco	2.00	1.50	.80

1954 Red Heart Dog Food

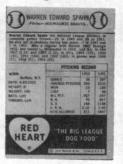

This set of 33 cards was issued in three color-coded series by the Red Heart Dog Food Co. Card fronts feature hand-colored photos on either a blue, green or red background. The 11 red-background cards are scarcer than the 11-card blue or green series. Backs of the 2-5/8" by 3-3/4" cards contain biographical and statistical information along with a Red Heart ad. Each 11-card series was available via a mail-in offer. As late as the early 1970s, the company was still sending cards to collectors who requested them.

		NR MT	EX	VG
Complete Set:		2500.00	1250.00	750.00
Common Player:		25.00	12.50	7.50
(1)	Richie Ashburn	40.00	20.00	12.00
(2)	Frankie Baumholtz	30.00	15.00	9.00
(3)	Gus Bell	25.00	12.50	7.50
(4)	Billy Cox	30.00	15.00	9.00
(5)	Alvin Dark	30.00	15.00	9.00
(6)	Carl Erskine	35.00	17.50	10.50
(7)	Ferris Fain	25.00	12.50	7.50
(8)	Dee Fondy	25.00	12.50	7.50
(9)	Nelson Fox	35.00	17.50	10.50

		NR MT	EX	VG
(10)	Jim Gilliam	35.00	17.50	10.50
(11)	Jim Hegan	30.00	15.00	9.00
(12)	George Kell	35.00	17.50	10.50
(13)	Ted Kluszewski	35.00	17.50	10.50
(14)	Ralph Kiner	55.00	27.00	16.50
(15)	Harvey Kuenn	30.00	15.00	9.00
(16)	Bob Lemon	55.00	27.00	16.50
(17)	Sherman Lollar	25.00	12.50	7.50
(18)	Mickey Mantle	450.00	225.00	135.00
(19)	Billy Martin	55.00	27.00	16.50
(20)	Gil McDougald	35.00	17.50	10.50
(21)	Roy McMillan	25.00	12.50	7.50
(22)	Minnie Minoso	30.00	15.00	9.00
(23)	Stan Musial	300.00	150.00	90.00
(24)	Billy Pierce	30.00	15.00	9.00
(25)	Al Rosen	35.00	17.50	10.50
(26)	Hank Sauer	25.00	12.50	7.50
(27)	Red Schoendienst	35.00	17.50	10.50
(28)	Enos Slaughter	35.00	17.50	10.50
(29)	Duke Snider	100.00	50.00	30.00
(30)	Warren Spahn	60.00	30.00	18.00
(31)	Sammy White	25.00	12.50	7.50
(32)	Eddie Yost	25.00	12.50	7.50
(33)	Gus Zernial	25.00	12.50	7.50

1982 Red Lobster Cubs

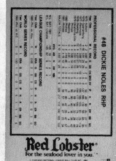

This 28-card set was co-sponsored by the team and a seafood restaurant chain for distribution at a 1982 Cubs promotional game. Card fronts are unbordered color photos, with player name, number, position and a superimposed facsimile autograph. The set includes 25 players on the 2-1/4" by 3-1/2" cards, along with a card for manager Lee Elia, an unnumbered card for the coaching staff and a team picture. Card backs have complete player statistics and a Red Lobster ad.

		MT	NR MT	EX
Complete Set:		12.00	9.00	4.75
Common Player:		.20	.15	.08
1	Larry Bowa	.40	.30	.15
4	Lee Elia	.20	.15	.08
6	Keith Moreland	.40	.30	.15
7	Jody Davis	.40	.30	.15
10	Leon Durham	.40	.30	.15
15	Junior Kennedy	.20	.15	.08
17	Bump Wills	.20	.15	.08
18	Scot Thompson	.20	.15	.08
21	Jay Johnstone	.25	.20	.10
22	Bill Buckner	.40	.30	.15
23	Ryne Sandberg	4.00	3.00	1.50
24	Jerry Morales	.20	.15	.08
25	Gary Woods	.20	.15	.08
28	Steve Henderson	.20	.15	.08
29	Bob Molinaro	.20	.15	.08
31	Fergie Jenkins	1.50	1.25	.60
33	Al Ripley	.20	.15	.08
34	Randy Martz	.20	.15	.08
36	Mike Proly	.20	.15	.08
37	Ken Kravec	.20	.15	.08
38	Willie Hernandez	.30	.25	.12

		MT	NR MT	EX
39	Bill Campbell	.20	.15	.08
41	Dick Tidrow	.20	.15	.08
46	Lee Smith	.50	.40	.20
47	Doug Bird	.20	.15	.08
48	Dickie Noles	.20	.15	.08
----	Team Photo	.20	.15	.08
----	Coaching Staff (Billy Connors, Tom Harmon, Gordy MacKenzie, John Vuckovich, Billy Williams)	.25	.20	.10

1952 Red Man Tobacco

This was the first national set of tobacco cards produced since the golden days of tobacco sets in the early part of the century. There are 52 cards in the set, with 25 top players and one manager from each league. Player selection was made by editor J.G. Taylor Spink of The Sporting News. Cards measure 3-1/2"by 4", including a 1/2" tab at the bottom of each card. These tabs were redeemable for a free baseball cap from Red Man. Cards are harder to find with tabs intact, and thus more valuable in that form. Values quoted here are for cards with tabs. Cards with the tabs removed would be valued about 35-40 percent of the quoted figures. Card fronts are full color paintings of each player with biographical information inset in the portrait area. Card backs contain company advertising. Cards are numbered and dated only on the tabs.

		NR MT	EX	VG
Complete Set:		2000.00	1000.00	600.00
Common Player:		20.00	10.00	6.00
1A	Casey Stengel	55.00	27.00	16.50
1N	Leo Durocher	40.00	20.00	12.00
2A	Roberto Avila	20.00	10.00	6.00
2N	Richie Ashburn	35.00	17.50	10.50
3A	Larry "Yogi" Berra	80.00	40.00	24.00
3N	Ewell Blackwell	25.00	12.50	7.50
4A	Gil Coan	20.00	10.00	6.00
4N	Cliff Chambers	20.00	10.00	6.00
5A	Dom DiMaggio	30.00	15.00	9.00
5N	Murry Dickson	20.00	10.00	6.00
6A	Larry Doby	30.00	15.00	9.00
6N	Sid Gordon	20.00	10.00	6.00
7A	Ferris Fain	25.00	12.50	7.50
7N	Granny Hamner	20.00	10.00	6.00
8A	Bob Feller	80.00	40.00	24.00
8N	Jim Hearn	20.00	10.00	6.00
9A	Nelson Fox	35.00	17.50	10.50
9N	Monte Irvin	50.00	25.00	15.00
10A	Johnny Groth	20.00	10.00	6.00
10N	Larry Jansen	20.00	10.00	6.00
11A	Jim Hegan	20.00	10.00	6.00
11N	Willie Jones	20.00	10.00	6.00
12A	Eddie Joost	20.00	10.00	6.00
12N	Ralph Kiner	50.00	25.00	15.00
13A	George Kell	50.00	25.00	15.00
13N	Whitey Lockman	20.00	10.00	6.00
14A	Gil McDougald	30.00	15.00	9.00
14N	Sal Maglie	25.00	12.50	7.50
15A	Orestes Minoso	25.00	12.50	7.50
15N	Willie Mays	150.00	75.00	45.00
16A	Bill Pierce	25.00	12.50	7.50
16N	Stan Musial	150.00	75.00	45.00

		NR MT	EX	VG
17A	Bob Porterfield	20.00	10.00	6.00
17N	Pee Wee Reese	75.00	37.00	22.00
18A	Eddie Robinson	20.00	10.00	6.00
18N	Robin Roberts	50.00	25.00	15.00
19A	Saul Rogovin	20.00	10.00	6.00
19N	Al Schoendienst	30.00	15.00	9.00
20A	Bobby Shantz	25.00	12.50	7.50
20N	Enos Slaughter	50.00	25.00	15.00
21A	Vern Stephens	20.00	10.00	6.00
21N	Duke Snider	100.00	50.00	30.00
22A	Vic Wertz	20.00	10.00	6.00
22N	Warren Spahn	60.00	30.00	18.00
23A	Ted Williams	175.00	87.00	52.00
23N	Eddie Stanky	25.00	12.50	7.50
24A	Early Wynn	50.00	25.00	15.00
24N	Bobby Thomson	30.00	15.00	9.00
25A	Eddie Yost	20.00	10.00	6.00
25N	Earl Torgeson	20.00	10.00	6.00
26A	Gus Zernial	20.00	10.00	6.00
26N	Wes Westrum	20.00	10.00	6.00

1953 Red Man Tobacco

This was the chewing tobacco company's second annual set of 3-1/2" by 4" cards, including the tabs at the bottom of the cards. Formats for both the fronts and backs are similar to the '52 edition. The 1953 Red Man cards, however, include card numbers within the player biographical section, and the card backs are headlined "New for '53." Once again, cards with intact tabs (which were redeemable for a free cap) are more valuable. Prices below are for cards with tabs. Cards with tabs removed are worth about 35-40 percent of the stated values. Each league is represented by 25 players and a manager on the full-color cards, a total of 52.

		NR MT	EX	VG
Complete Set:		1800.00	900.00	540.00
Common Player:		20.00	10.00	6.00
1A	Casey Stengel	55.00	27.00	16.50
1N	Charlie Dressen	25.00	12.50	7.50
2A	Hank Bauer	25.00	12.50	7.50
2N	Bobby Adams	20.00	10.00	6.00
3A	Larry "Yogi" Berra	80.00	40.00	24.00
3N	Richie Ashburn	35.00	17.50	10.50
4A	Walt Dropo	20.00	10.00	6.00
4N	Joe Black	25.00	12.50	7.50
5A	Nelson Fox	35.00	17.50	10.50
5N	Roy Campanella	80.00	40.00	24.00
6A	Jackie Jensen	25.00	12.50	7.50
6N	Ted Kluszewski	30.00	15.00	9.00
7A	Eddie Joost	20.00	10.00	6.00
7N	Whitey Lockman	20.00	10.00	6.00
8A	George Kell	50.00	25.00	15.00
8N	Sal Maglie	25.00	12.50	7.50
9A	Dale Mitchell	20.00	10.00	6.00
9N	Andy Pafko	25.00	12.50	7.50
10A	Phil Rizzuto	60.00	30.00	18.00
10N	Pee Wee Reese	75.00	37.00	22.00
11A	Eddie Robinson	20.00	10.00	6.00
11N	Robin Roberts	50.00	25.00	15.00
12A	Gene Woodling	25.00	12.50	7.50
12N	Al Schoendienst	30.00	15.00	9.00
13A	Gus Zernial	20.00	10.00	6.00
13N	Enos Slaughter	50.00	25.00	15.00

		NR MT	EX	VG
14A	Early Wynn	50.00	25.00	15.00
14N	Edwin "Duke" Snider	100.00	50.00	30.00
15A	Joe Dobson	20.00	10.00	6.00
15N	Ralph Kiner	50.00	25.00	15.00
16A	Billy Pierce	25.00	12.50	7.50
16N	Hank Sauer	20.00	10.00	6.00
17A	Bob Lemon	50.00	25.00	15.00
17N	Del Ennis	20.00	10.00	6.00
18A	Johnny Mize	50.00	25.00	15.00
18N	Granny Hamner	20.00	10.00	6.00
19A	Bob Porterfield	20.00	10.00	6.00
19N	Warren Spahn	60.00	30.00	18.00
20A	Bobby Shantz	25.00	12.50	7.50
20N	Wes Westrum	20.00	10.00	6.00
21A	"Mickey" Vernon	25.00	12.50	7.50
21N	Hoyt Wilhelm	50.00	25.00	15.00
22A	Dom DiMaggio	30.00	15.00	9.00
22N	Murry Dickson	20.00	10.00	6.00
23A	Gil McDougald	30.00	15.00	9.00
23N	Warren Hacker	20.00	10.00	6.00
24A	Al Rosen	30.00	15.00	9.00
24N	Gerry Staley	20.00	10.00	6.00
25A	Mel Parnell	20.00	10.00	6.00
25N	Bobby Thomson	25.00	12.50	7.50
26A	Roberto Avila	20.00	10.00	6.00
26N	Stan Musial	150.00	75.00	45.00

		NR MT	EX	VG
9Ab	Dave Philley (Philadelphia)	75.00	37.00	22.00
9N	Del Rice	20.00	10.00	6.00
10A	Billy Pierce	25.00	12.50	7.50
10N	Al Schoendienst	30.00	15.00	9.00
11A	Jim Piersall	25.00	12.50	7.50
11N	Warren Spahn	60.00	30.00	18.00
12A	Al Rosen	30.00	15.00	9.00
12N	Curt Simmons	25.00	12.50	7.50
13A	"Mickey" Vernon	25.00	12.50	7.50
13N	Roy Campanella	80.00	40.00	24.00
14A	Sammy White	20.00	10.00	6.00
14N	Jim Gilliam	30.00	15.00	9.00
15A	Gene Woodling	25.00	12.50	7.50
15N	"Pee Wee" Reese	75.00	37.00	22.00
16A	Ed "Whitey" Ford	65.00	32.00	19.50
16N	Edwin "Duke" Snider	100.00	50.00	30.00
17A	Phil Rizzuto	60.00	30.00	18.00
17N	Rip Repulski	20.00	10.00	6.00
18A	Bob Porterfield	20.00	10.00	6.00
18N	Robin Roberts	50.00	25.00	15.00
19A	Al "Chico" Carrasquel	20.00	10.00	6.00
19Na	Enos Slaughter	90.00	45.00	27.00
19Nb	Gus Bell	90.00	45.00	27.00
20A	Larry "Yogi" Berra	80.00	40.00	24.00
20N	Johnny Logan	20.00	10.00	6.00
21A	Bob Lemon	50.00	25.00	15.00
21N	Johnny Antonelli	25.00	12.50	7.50
22A	Ferris Fain	25.00	12.50	7.50
22N	Gil Hodges	55.00	27.00	16.50
23A	Hank Bauer	25.00	12.50	7.50
23N	Eddie Mathews	55.00	27.00	16.50
24A	Jim Delsing	20.00	10.00	6.00
24N	Lew Burdette	30.00	15.00	9.00
25A	Gil McDougald	30.00	15.00	9.00
25N	Willie Mays	150.00	75.00	45.00

1954 Red Man Tobacco

In 1954, the Red Man set eliminated managers from the set, and issued only 25 player cards for each league. There are, however, four variations which bring the total set size to 54 full-color cards. Two cards exist for Gus Bell and Enos Slaughter, while American Leaguers George Kell, Sam Mele and Dave Philley are each shown with two different teams. Complete set prices quoted below do not include the scarcer of the variation pairs. Cards still measure 3-1/2" by 4" with tabs intact. Cards without tabs are worth about 35-40 per cent of the values quoted below. Formats for the cards remain virtually unchanged, with card numbers included within the player information boxes as well as on the tabs.

		NR MT	EX	VG
Complete Set:		1600.00	800.00	480.00
Common Player:		20.00	10.00	6.00
1A	Bobby Avila	20.00	10.00	6.00
1N	Richie Ashburn	35.00	17.50	10.50
2A	Jim Busby	20.00	10.00	6.00
2N	Billy Cox	25.00	12.50	7.50
3A	Nelson Fox	35.00	17.50	10.50
3N	Del Crandall	25.00	12.50	7.50
4Aa	George Kell (Boston)	65.00	32.00	19.50
4Ab	George Kell (Chicago)	75.00	37.00	22.00
4N	Carl Erskine	30.00	15.00	9.00
5A	Sherman Lollar	20.00	10.00	6.00
5N	Monte Irvin	50.00	25.00	15.00
6Aa	Sam Mele (Baltimore)	50.00	25.00	15.00
6Ab	Sam Mele (Chicago)	75.00	37.00	22.00
6N	Ted Kluszewski	30.00	15.00	9.00
7A	Orestes Minoso	25.00	12.50	7.50
7N	Don Mueller	20.00	10.00	6.00
8A	Mel Parnell	20.00	10.00	6.00
8N	Andy Pafko	25.00	12.50	7.50
9Aa	Dave Philley (Cleveland)	50.00	25.00	15.00

1955 Red Man Tobacco

These 50 cards are quite similar to the 1954 edition, with card fronts virtually unchanged except for the data in the biographical box on the color picture area. This set of the 3-1/2" by 4" cards includes 25 players from each league, with no known variations. As with all Red Man sets, those cards complete with the redeemable tabs are more valuable. Values quoted below are for cards with tabs. Cards with the tabs removed are worth about 35-40 percent of those figures.

		NR MT	EX	VG
Complete Set:		1500.00	750.00	450.00
Common Player:		20.00	10.00	6.00
1A	Ray Boone	20.00	10.00	6.00
1N	Richie Ashburn	35.00	17.50	10.50
2A	Jim Busby	20.00	10.00	6.00
2N	Del Crandall	25.00	12.50	7.50
3A	Ed "Whitey" Ford	55.00	27.00	16.50
3N	Gil Hodges	65.00	32.00	19.50
4A	Nelson Fox	35.00	17.50	10.50
4N	Brooks Lawrence	20.00	10.00	6.00
5A	Bob Grim	20.00	10.00	6.00
5N	Johnny Logan	20.00	10.00	6.00
6A	Jack Harshman	20.00	10.00	6.00
6N	Sal Maglie	25.00	12.50	7.50
7A	Jim Hegan	20.00	10.00	6.00
7N	Willie Mays	150.00	75.00	45.00

		NR MT	EX	VG
8A	Bob Lemon	50.00	25.00	15.00
8N	Don Mueller	20.00	10.00	6.00
9A	Irv Noren	20.00	10.00	6.00
9N	Bill Sarni	20.00	10.00	6.00
10A	Bob Porterfield	20.00	10.00	6.00
10N	Warren Spahn	60.00	30.00	18.00
11A	Al Rosen	30.00	15.00	9.00
11N	Henry Thompson	20.00	10.00	6.00
12A	"Mickey" Vernon	25.00	12.50	7.50
12N	Hoyt Wilhelm	50.00	25.00	15.00
13A	Vic Wertz	20.00	10.00	6.00
13N	Johnny Antonelli	25.00	12.50	7.50
14A	Early Wynn	50.00	25.00	15.00
14N	Carl Erskine	30.00	15.00	9.00
15A	Bobby Avila	20.00	10.00	6.00
15N	Granny Hamner	20.00	10.00	6.00
16A	Larry "Yogi" Berra	80.00	40.00	24.00
16N	Ted Kluszewski	30.00	15.00	9.00
17A	Joe Coleman	20.00	10.00	6.00
17N	Pee Wee Reese	75.00	37.00	22.00
18A	Larry Doby	30.00	15.00	9.00
18N	Al Schoendienst	30.00	15.00	9.00
19A	Jackie Jensen	25.00	12.50	7.50
19N	Duke Snider	100.00	50.00	30.00
20A	Pete Runnels	20.00	10.00	6.00
20N	Frank Thomas	20.00	10.00	6.00
21A	Jim Piersall	25.00	12.50	7.50
21N	Ray Jablonski	20.00	10.00	6.00
22A	Hank Bauer	25.00	12.50	7.50
22N	James "Dusty" Rhodes	20.00	10.00	6.00
23A	"Chico" Carrasquel	20.00	10.00	6.00
23N	Gus Bell	20.00	10.00	6.00
24A	Orestes Minoso	25.00	12.50	7.50
24N	Curt Simmons	25.00	12.50	7.50
25A	Sandy Consuegra	20.00	10.00	6.00
25N	Marvin Grissom	20.00	10.00	6.00

		MT	NR MT	EX
10	Kent Tekulve	.05	.04	.02
11	Steve Bedrosian	.10	.08	.04
12	Orel Hershiser	.10	.08	.04
13	Rick Rueschel	.07	.05	.03
14	Fernando Valenzuela	.20	.15	.08
15	Bob Welch	.10	.08	.04
16	Wade Boggs	.50	.40	.20
17	Mark McGwire	.50	.40	.20
18	George Bell	.20	.15	.08
19	Harold Reynolds	.05	.04	.02
20	Paul Molitor	.12	.09	.05
21	Kirby Puckett	.25	.20	.10
22	Kevin Seitzer	.20	.15	.08
23	Brian Downing	.05	.04	.02
24	Dwight Evans	.10	.08	.04
25	Willie Wilson	.07	.05	.03
26	Danny Tartabull	.20	.15	.08
27	Jimmy Key	.07	.05	.03
28	Roger Clemens	.80	.60	.30
29	Dave Stewart	.25	.20	.10
30	Mark Eichhorn	.05	.04	.02
31	Tom Henke	.05	.04	.02
32	Charlie Hough	.05	.04	.02
33	Mark Langston	.10	.08	.04

1988 Rite Aid

This premiere edition was produced by Topps for distribution by Rite Aid drug and discount stores in the Eastern United States. The boxed set includes 33 standard-size full-color cards with at least one card for each major league team. Four cards in the set highlight MVP's from the 1987 season. Card fronts have white borders and carry a yellow "Team MVP's" header above the player photo which is outlined in red and blue. A large Rite Aid logo appears upper left; the players name appears bottom center. The numbered card backs are black on blue and white card stock in a horizontal layout containing the player name, biography and statistics.

		MT	NR MT	EX
Complete Set:		4.00	3.00	1.50
Common Player:		.05	.04	.02
1	Dale Murphy	.20	.15	.08
2	Andre Dawson	.20	.15	.08
3	Eric Davis	.50	.40	.20
4	Mike Scott	.10	.08	.04
5	Pedro Guerrero	.15	.11	.06
6	Tim Raines	.25	.20	.10
7	Darryl Strawberry	.40	.30	.15
8	Mike Schmidt	.30	.25	.12
9	Mike Dunne	.05	.04	.02
10	Jack Clark	.15	.11	.06
11	Tony Gwynn	.25	.20	.10
12	Will Clark	.30	.25	.12
13	Cal Ripken	.60	.45	.25
14	Wade Boggs	.60	.45	.25
15	Wally Joyner	.30	.25	.12
16	Harold Baines	.12	.09	.05
17	Joe Carter	.12	.09	.05
18	Alan Trammell	.15	.11	.06
19	Kevin Seitzer	.15	.11	.06
20	Paul Molitor	.12	.09	.05
21	Kirby Puckett	.25	.20	.10
22	Don Mattingly	.80	.60	.30

1988 Revco

This super-glossy boxed set of 33 standard-size cards was produced by Topps for exclusive distribution by Revco stores east of the Mississippi River. Card fronts feature a large blue Revco logo in the upper left corner opposite a yellow and black boxed "Topps League Leader" label. Player photos are framed in black and orange with a diagonal player name banner in the lower right corner that lists the player's name, team and position on white, orange and gold stripes. The numbered card backs are horizontal, printed in red and black on white stock and include the player name, followed by personal biographical data, batting/pitching stats and a brief career summary.

		MT	NR MT	EX
Complete Set:		5.00	3.75	2.00
Common Player:		.05	.04	.02
1	Tony Gwynn	.25	.20	.10
2	Andre Dawson	.15	.11	.06
3	Vince Coleman	.15	.11	.06
4	Jack Clark	.15	.11	.06
5	Tim Raines	.25	.20	.10
6	Tim Wallach	.10	.08	.04
7	Juan Samuel	.10	.08	.04
8	Nolan Ryan	.80	.60	.30
9	Rick Sutcliffe	.10	.08	.04

		MT	NR MT	EX
23	Mark McGwire	.50	.40	.20
24	Alvin Davis	.10	.08	.04
25	Ruben Sierra	.35	.25	.14
26	George Bell	.20	.15	.08
27	Jack Morris	.12	.09	.05
28	Jeff Reardon	.07	.05	.03
29	John Tudor	.07	.05	.03
30	Rick Rueschel	.07	.05	.03
31	Gary Gaetti	.12	.09	.05
32	Jeffrey Leonard	.05	.04	.02
33	Frank Viola	.12	.09	.05

1955 Rodeo Meats Athletics

Cloyd Boyer

This set of 2-1/2" by 3-1/2" color cards was issued by a local meat company to commemorate the first year of the Athletics in Kansas City. There are 38 different players included in the set, with nine players known to apppear in two different variations for a total of 47 cards in the set. Most variations are in background colors, although Bobby Shantz is also listed incorrectly as "Schantz" on one variation. The cards are unnumbered, with the Rodeo logo and player name on the fronts, and an ad for a scrapbook album listed on the backs.

		NR MT	EX	VG
	Complete Set:	4250.00	2125.00	1275.
	Common Player:	70.00	35.00	21.00
(1)	Joe Astroth	70.00	35.00	21.00
(2)	Harold Bevan	100.00	50.00	30.00
(3)	Charles Bishop	100.00	50.00	30.00
(4)	Don Bollweg	100.00	50.00	30.00
(5)	Lou Boudreau	250.00	125.00	75.00
(6)	Cloyd Boyer (blue background)	100.00	50.00	30.00
(7)	Cloyd Boyer (pink background)	70.00	35.00	21.00
(8)	Ed Burtschy	100.00	50.00	30.00
(9)	Art Ceccarelli	70.00	35.00	21.00
(10)	Joe DeMaestri (pea green background)	100.00	50.00	30.00
(11)	Joe DeMaestri (light green background)	70.00	35.00	21.00
(12)	Art Ditmar	70.00	35.00	21.00
(13)	John Dixon	100.00	50.00	30.00
(14)	Jim Finigan	70.00	35.00	21.00
(15)	Marion Fricano	100.00	50.00	30.00
(16)	John Gray	100.00	50.00	30.00
(17)	Tom Gorman	70.00	35.00	21.00
(18)	Ray Herbert	70.00	35.00	21.00
(19)	Forest "Spook" Jacobs (Forrest)	100.00	50.00	30.00
(20)	Alex Kellner	100.00	50.00	30.00
(21)	Harry Kraft (Craft)	70.00	35.00	21.00
(22)	Jack Littrell	70.00	35.00	21.00
(23)	Hector Lopez	80.00	40.00	24.00
(24)	Oscar Melillo	70.00	35.00	21.00
(25)	Arnold Portocarrero (purple background)	100.00	50.00	30.00
(26)	Arnold Portocarrero (grey background)	70.00	35.00	21.00
(27)	Vic Power (pink background)	125.00	62.00	37.00
(28)	Vic Power (yellow background)	80.00	40.00	24.00
(29)	Vic Raschi	100.00	50.00	30.00
(30)	Bill Renna (dark pink background)	100.00	50.00	30.00
(31)	Bill Renna (light pink background)	70.00	35.00	21.00

		NR MT	EX	VG
(32)	Al Robertson	100.00	50.00	30.00
(33)	Johnny Sain	125.00	62.00	37.00
(34a)	Bobby Schantz (incorrect spelling)	250.00	125.00	75.00
(34b)	Bobby Shantz (correct spelling)	125.00	62.00	37.00
(35)	Wilmer Shantz (orange background)	100.00	50.00	30.00
(36)	Wilmer Shantz (purple background)	70.00	35.00	21.00
(37)	Harry Simpson	70.00	35.00	21.00
(38)	Enos Slaughter	300.00	150.00	90.00
(39)	Lou Sleater	70.00	35.00	21.00
(40)	George Susce	70.00	35.00	21.00
(41)	Bob Trice	100.00	50.00	30.00
(42)	Elmer Valo (yellow background)	100.00	50.00	30.00
(43)	Elmer Valo (green background)	70.00	35.00	21.00
(44)	Bill Wilson (yellow background)	100.00	50.00	30.00
(45)	Bill Wilson (purple background)	70.00	35.00	21.00
(46)	Gus Zernial	80.00	40.00	24.00

1956 Rodeo Meats Athletics

Gus Zernial

Rodeo Meats issued another Kansas City Athletics set in 1956, but this one was a much smaller 13-card set. The 2-1/2" by 3-1/2" cards are again unnumbered, with the player name and Rodeo logo on the fronts. Card backs feature some of the same graphics and copy as the 1955 cards, but the album offer is omitted. The full-color cards were only available in packages of Rodeo hot dogs.

		NR MT	EX	VG
	Complete Set:	1250.00	625.00	375.00
	Common Player:	70.00	35.00	21.00
(1)	Joe Astroth	70.00	35.00	21.00
(2)	Lou Boudreau	250.00	125.00	75.00
(3)	Joe DeMaestri	70.00	35.00	21.00
(4)	Art Ditmar	70.00	35.00	21.00
(5)	Jim Finigan	70.00	35.00	21.00
(6)	Hector Lopez	80.00	40.00	24.00
(7)	Vic Power	80.00	40.00	24.00
(8)	Bobby Shantz	125.00	62.00	37.00
(9)	Harry Simpson	70.00	35.00	21.00
(10)	Enos Slaughter	250.00	125.00	75.00
(11)	Elmer Valo	70.00	35.00	21.00
(12)	Gus Zernial	80.00	40.00	24.00

1970 Rold Gold Pretzels

The 1970 Rold Gold Pretzels set of 15 cards honors the "Greatest Players Ever" as chosen by the Baseball Writers of America. The cards, which measure 2-1/4" by 3-1/2" in size, feature a simulated 3-D effect. The set was re-released in 1972 by Kellogg's in packages of Danish-Go-Rounds. Rold Gold cards can be differentiated from the Kellogg's cards of 1972 by the 1970 copyright date found on the card reverse.

		NR MT	EX	VG
	Complete Set:	50.00	25.00	15.00
	Common Player:	1.00	.50	.30
1	Walter Johnson	2.50	1.25	.70
2	Rogers Hornsby	1.50	.70	.45
3	John McGraw	1.00	.50	.30
4	Mickey Cochrane	1.00	.50	.30
5	George Sisler	1.00	.50	.30
6	Babe Ruth	15.00	7.50	4.50
7	Robert "Lefty" Grove	1.50	.70	.45
8	Harold "Pie" Traynor	1.00	.50	.30
9	Honus Wagner	1.75	.90	.50
10	Eddie Collins	1.00	.50	.30
11	Tris Speaker	1.50	.70	.45
12	Cy Young	1.00	.50	.30
13	Lou Gehrig	8.00	4.00	2.50
14	Babe Ruth	15.00	7.50	4.50
15	Ty Cobb	8.00	4.00	2.50

1950 Royal Desserts

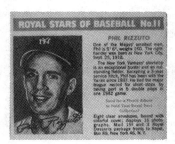

This set of 24 cards was issued one per box on the backs of various Royal Dessert products over a period of three years. The basic set contains 24 players, however a number of variations create the much higher total for the set. In 1950, Royal issued cards with two different tints - black and white with red, or blue and white with red. Over the next two years, various sentences of the cards' biographies were updated up to three times in some cases. Some players from the set left the majors after 1950 and others were apparently never updated, but the 23 biography updates that do exist, added to the original 24 cards issued in 1950, give the set a total of 47 cards. The 2-1/2" by 3-1/2" cards are blank-backed with personal and playing biographies alongside the card front photos.

	NR MT	EX	VG
Complete Set:	1200.00	600.00	360.00
Common Player:	20.00	10.00	6.00
1a Stan Musial (2nd paragraph begins "Musial's 207...")	125.00	62.00	37.00
1b Stan Musial (2nd paragraph begins "Musial batted...")	125.00	62.00	37.00
2a Pee Wee Reese (2nd paragraph begins "Pee Wee's...")	70.00	35.00	21.00

	NR MT	EX	VG
2b Pee Wee Reese (2nd paragraph begins "Captain...")	70.00	35.00	21.00
3a George Kell (2nd paragraph ends "...in 1945, '46.")	35.00	17.50	10.50
3b George Kell (2nd paragraph ends "...two base hits, 56.")	35.00	17.50	10.50
4a Dom DiMaggio (2nd paragraph ends "...during 1947.")	30.00	15.00	9.00
4b Dom DiMaggio (2nd paragraph ends "...with 11.")	30.00	15.00	9.00
5a Warren Spahn (2nd paragraph ends "...shutouts 7.")	50.00	25.00	15.00
5b Warren Spahn (2nd paragraph ends "...with 191.")	50.00	25.00	15.00
6a Andy Pafko (2nd paragraph ends "...7 games.")	25.00	12.50	7.50
6b Andy Pafko (2nd paragraph ends "...National League.")	25.00	12.50	7.50
6c Andy Pafko (2nd paragraph ends "...weighs 190.")	25.00	12.50	7.50
7a Andy Seminick (2nd paragraph ends "...as outfield.")	20.00	10.00	6.00
7b Andy Seminick (2nd paragraph ends "...since 1916.")	20.00	10.00	6.00
7c Andy Seminick (2nd paragraph ends "...in the outfield.")	20.00	10.00	6.00
7d Andy Seminick (2nd paragraph ends "...right handed.")	20.00	10.00	6.00
8a Lou Brissie (2nd paragraph ends "...when pitching.")	20.00	10.00	6.00
8b Lou Brissie (2nd paragraph ends "...weighs 215.")	20.00	10.00	6.00
9a Ewell Blackwell (2nd paragraph begins "Despite recent illness...")	25.00	12.50	7.50
9b Ewell Blackwell (2nd paragraph begins "Blackwell's...")	25.00	12.50	7.50
10a Bobby Thomson (2nd paragraph begins "In 1949...")	25.00	12.50	7.50
10b Bobby Thomson (2nd paragraph begins "Thomson is...")	25.00	12.50	7.50
11a Phil Rizzuto (2nd paragraph ends "...one 1942 game.")	60.00	30.00	18.00
11b Phil Rizzuto (2nd paragraph ends "...Most Valuable Player.")	60.00	30.00	18.00
12 Tommy Henrich	30.00	15.00	9.00
13 Joe Gordon	25.00	12.50	7.50
14a Ray Scarborough (Senators)	20.00	10.00	6.00
14b Ray Scarborough (White Sox, 2nd paragraph ends "...military service.")	20.00	10.00	6.00
14c Ray Scarborough (White Sox, 2nd paragraph ends "...the season.")	20.00	10.00	6.00
14d Ray Scarborough (Red Sox)	20.00	10.00	6.00
15a Stan Rojek (Pirates)	20.00	10.00	6.00
15b Stan Rojek (Browns)	20.00	10.00	6.00
16 Luke Appling	30.00	15.00	9.00
17 Willard Marshall	20.00	10.00	6.00
18 Alvin Dark	30.00	15.00	9.00
19a Dick Sisler (2nd paragraph ends "...service record.")	20.00	10.00	6.00
19b Dick Sisler (2nd paragraph ends "...National League flag.")	20.00	10.00	6.00
19c Dick Sisler (2nd paragraph ends "...Nov. 2, 1920.")	20.00	10.00	6.00
19d Dick Sisler (2nd paragraph ends "...from '46 to '48.")	20.00	10.00	6.00
20 Johnny Ostrowski	20.00	10.00	6.00
21a Virgil Trucks (2nd paragraph ends "...in military service.")	25.00	12.50	7.50
21b Virgil Trucks (2nd paragraph ends "...that year.")	25.00	12.50	7.50
21c Virgil Trucks (2nd paragraph ends "...for military service.")	25.00	12.50	7.50
22 Eddie Robinson	20.00	10.00	6.00
23 Nanny Fernandez	20.00	10.00	6.00
24 Ferris Fain	25.00	12.50	7.50

1952 Royal Desserts

This set, issued as a premium by Royal Desserts in 1952, consists of 16 unnumbered black and white cards, each measuring 5" by 7". The cards include the inscription "To A Royal Fan" along with the player's facsimile autograph.

	NR MT	EX	VG
Complete Set:	450.00	225.00	135.00

		NR MT	EX	VG
Common Player:		15.00	7.50	4.50
(1)	Ewell Blackwell	18.00	9.00	5.50
(2)	Leland V. Brissie Jr.	15.00	7.50	4.50
(3)	Alvin Dark	18.00	9.00	5.50
(4)	Dom DiMaggio	25.00	12.50	7.50
(5)	Ferris Fain	15.00	7.50	4.50
(6)	George Kell	28.00	14.00	8.50
(7)	Stan Musial	75.00	37.00	22.00
(8)	Andy Pafko	18.00	9.00	5.50
(9)	Pee Wee Reese	40.00	20.00	12.00
(10)	Phil Rizzuto	40.00	20.00	12.00
(11)	Eddie Robinson	15.00	7.50	4.50
(12)	Ray Scarborough	15.00	7.50	4.50
(13)	Andy Seminick	15.00	7.50	4.50
(14)	Dick Sisler	15.00	7.50	4.50
(15)	Warren Spahn	40.00	20.00	12.00
(16)	Bobby Thomson	25.00	12.50	7.50

1988 Score

A fifth member joined the group of nationally distributed baseball cards in 1988. Titled "Score," the new cards are characterized by extremely sharp and excellent full-color photography and printing. Card backs are full-color also and carry a player head-shot, along with a brief biography and player personal and statistical information. The 660 cards in the set each measure 2-1/2" by 3-1/2" in size. The fronts come with one of six different border colors - blue, red, green, purple, orange and gold - which are equally divided at 110 cards per color. The Score set was produced by Major League Marketing, the same company that markets the "triple-action" Sportflics card sets.

	MT	NR MT	EX
Complete Set:	20.00	15.00	8.00
Common Player:	.04	.03	.02

		MT	NR MT	EX
1	Don Mattingly	.30	.25	.12
2	Wade Boggs	.40	.30	.15
3	Tim Raines	.20	.15	.08
4	Andre Dawson	.15	.11	.06
5	Mark McGwire	.70	.50	.30
6	Kevin Seitzer	.30	.25	.12
7	Wally Joyner	.35	.25	.14
8	Jesse Barfield	.10	.08	.04
9	Pedro Guerrero	.15	.11	.06
10	Eric Davis	.30	.25	.12
11	George Brett	.30	.25	.12
12	Ozzie Smith	.12	.09	.05
13	Rickey Henderson	.40	.30	.15
14	Jim Rice	.20	.15	.08
15	*Matt Nokes*	.30	.25	.12
16	Mike Schmidt	.40	.30	.15
17	Dave Parker	.12	.09	.05
18	Eddie Murray	.25	.20	.10
19	Andres Galarraga	.12	.09	.05
20	Tony Fernandez	.10	.08	.04
21	Kevin McReynolds	.12	.09	.05
22	B.J. Surhoff	.10	.08	.04
23	Pat Tabler	.06	.05	.02
24	Kirby Puckett	.25	.20	.10
25	Benny Santiago	.25	.20	.10
26	Ryne Sandberg	.40	.30	.15
27	Kelly Downs	.08	.06	.03
28	Jose Cruz	.06	.05	.02
29	Pete O'Brien	.06	.05	.02
30	Mark Langston	.10	.08	.04
31	Lee Smith	.08	.06	.03
32	Juan Samuel	.10	.08	.04
33	Kevin Bass	.06	.05	.02
34	R.J. Reynolds	.04	.03	.02
35	Steve Sax	.12	.09	.05
36	John Kruk	.08	.06	.03
37	Alan Trammell	.15	.11	.06
38	Chris Bosio	.06	.05	.02
39	Brook Jacoby	.08	.06	.03
40	Willie McGee	.10	.08	.04
41	Dave Magadan	.10	.08	.04
42	Fred Lynn	.10	.08	.04
43	Kent Hrbek	.12	.09	.05
44	Brian Downing	.06	.05	.02
45	Jose Canseco	.80	.60	.30
46	Jim Presley	.08	.06	.03
47	Mike Stanley	.06	.05	.02
48	Tony Pena	.06	.05	.02
49	David Cone	.40	.30	.15
50	Rick Sutcliffe	.08	.06	.03
51	Doug Drabek	.10	.08	.04
52	Bill Doran	.06	.05	.02
53	Mike Scioscia	.06	.05	.02
54	Candy Maldonado	.06	.05	.02
55	Dave Winfield	.20	.15	.08
56	Lou Whitaker	.20	.15	.08
57	Tom Henke	.06	.05	.02
58	Ken Gerhart	.06	.05	.02
59	Glenn Braggs	.08	.06	.03
60	Julio Franco	.08	.06	.03
61	Charlie Leibrandt	.06	.05	.02
62	Gary Gaetti	.10	.08	.04
63	Bob Boone	.06	.05	.02
64	*Luis Polonia*	.35	.25	.14
65	Dwight Evans	.10	.08	.04
66	Phil Bradley	.08	.06	.03
67	Mike Boddicker	.06	.05	.02
68	Vince Coleman	.15	.11	.06
69	Howard Johnson	.08	.06	.03
70	Tim Wallach	.08	.06	.03
71	Keith Moreland	.06	.05	.02
72	Barry Larkin	.40	.30	.15
73	Alan Ashby	.04	.03	.02
74	Rick Rhoden	.06	.05	.02
75	Darrell Evans	.08	.06	.03
76	Dave Stieb	.08	.06	.03
77	Dan Plesac	.08	.06	.03
78	Will Clark	.80	.60	.30
79	Frank White	.06	.05	.02
80	Joe Carter	.25	.20	.10
81	Mike Witt	.06	.05	.02
82	Terry Steinbach	.10	.08	.04
83	Alvin Davis	.10	.08	.04
84	Tom Herr	.06	.05	.02
85	Vance Law	.06	.05	.02
86	Kal Daniels	.15	.11	.06
87	Rick Honeycutt	.04	.03	.02
88	Alfredo Griffin	.06	.05	.02
89	Bret Saberhagen	.20	.15	.08
90	Bert Blyleven	.10	.08	.04
91	Jeff Reardon	.08	.06	.03
92	Cory Snyder	.15	.11	.06

		MT	NR MT	EX			MT	NR MT	EX
93	Greg Walker	.06	.05	.02	180	Bo Jackson	.70	.50	.30
94	*Joe Magrane*	.30	.25	.12	181	Carmelo Martinez	.06	.05	.02
95	Rob Deer	.06	.05	.02	182	Alex Trevino	.04	.03	.02
96	Ray Knight	.06	.05	.02	183	Ron Oester	.04	.03	.02
97	Casey Candaele	.04	.03	.02	184	Danny Darwin	.04	.03	.02
98	John Cerutti	.06	.05	.02	185	Mike Krukow	.06	.05	.02
99	Buddy Bell	.08	.06	.03	186	Rafael Palmeiro	.50	.40	.20
100	Jack Clark	.12	.09	.05	187	Tim Burke	.04	.03	.02
101	Eric Bell	.06	.05	.02	188	Roger McDowell	.08	.06	.03
102	Willie Wilson	.08	.06	.03	189	Garry Templeton	.06	.05	.02
103	Dave Schmidt	.04	.03	.02	190	Terry Pendleton	.06	.05	.02
104	Dennis Eckersley	.10	.08	.04	191	Larry Parrish	.06	.05	.02
105	Don Sutton	.12	.09	.05	192	Rey Quinones	.04	.03	.02
106	Danny Tartabull	.15	.11	.06	193	Joaquin Andujar	.06	.05	.02
107	Fred McGriff	.80	.60	.30	194	Tom Brunansky	.08	.06	.03
108	*Les Straker*	.15	.11	.06	195	Donnie Moore	.04	.03	.02
109	Lloyd Moseby	.06	.05	.02	196	Dan Pasqua	.08	.06	.03
110	Roger Clemens	.50	.40	.20	197	Jim Gantner	.04	.03	.02
111	Glenn Hubbard	.04	.03	.02	198	Mark Eichhorn	.06	.05	.02
112	*Ken Williams*	.20	.15	.08	199	John Grubb	.04	.03	.02
113	Ruben Sierra	.35	.25	.14	200	*Bill Ripken*	.20	.15	.08
114	Stan Jefferson	.06	.05	.02	201	*Sam Horn*	.30	.25	.12
115	Milt Thompson	.04	.03	.02	202	Todd Worrell	.08	.06	.03
116	Bobby Bonilla	.40	.30	.15	203	Terry Leach	.04	.03	.02
117	Wayne Tolleson	.04	.03	.02	204	Garth Iorg	.04	.03	.02
118	*Matt Williams*	2.00	1.50	.80	205	Brian Dayett	.04	.03	.02
119	Chet Lemon	.06	.05	.02	206	Bo Diaz	.06	.05	.02
120	Dale Sveum	.06	.05	.02	207	Craig Reynolds	.04	.03	.02
121	Dennis Boyd	.06	.05	.02	208	Brian Holton	.08	.06	.03
122	Brett Butler	.06	.05	.02	209	Marvelle Wynne (Marvell)	.04	.03	.02
123	Terry Kennedy	.06	.05	.02	210	Dave Concepcion	.06	.05	.02
124	Jack Howell	.06	.05	.02	211	Mike Davis	.06	.05	.02
125	Curt Young	.06	.05	.02	212	Devon White	.15	.11	.06
126a	Dale Valle (first name incorrect)	.25	.20	.10	213	Mickey Brantley	.04	.03	.02
126b	Dave Valle (correct spelling)	.06	.05	.02	214	Greg Gagne	.04	.03	.02
127	Curt Wilkerson	.04	.03	.02	215	Oddibe McDowell	.06	.05	.02
128	Tim Teufel	.04	.03	.02	216	Jimmy Key	.08	.06	.03
129	Ozzie Virgil	.04	.03	.02	217	Dave Bergman	.04	.03	.02
130	Brian Fisher	.06	.05	.02	218	Calvin Schiraldi	.04	.03	.02
131	Lance Parrish	.12	.09	.05	219	Larry Sheets	.06	.05	.02
132	Tom Browning	.08	.06	.03	220	Mike Easler	.06	.05	.02
133a	Larry Anderson (incorrect spelling)	.25	.20	.10	221	Kurt Stillwell	.08	.06	.03
133b	Larry Andersen (correct spelling)	.06	.05	.02	222	*Chuck Jackson*	.15	.11	.06
134a	Bob Brenley (incorrect spelling)	.25	.20	.10	223	Dave Martinez	.08	.06	.03
134b	Bob Brenly (correct spelling)	.06	.05	.02	224	Tim Leary	.06	.05	.02
135	Mike Marshall	.10	.08	.04	225	Steve Garvey	.20	.15	.08
136	Gerald Perry	.08	.06	.03	226	Greg Mathews	.06	.05	.02
137	Bobby Meacham	.04	.03	.02	227	Doug Sisk	.04	.03	.02
138	Larry Herndon	.04	.03	.02	228	Dave Henderson	.08	.06	.03
139	*Fred Manrique*	.12	.09	.05	229	Jimmy Dwyer	.04	.03	.02
140	Charlie Hough	.06	.05	.02	230	Larry Owen	.04	.03	.02
141	Ron Darling	.10	.08	.04	231	Andre Thornton	.06	.05	.02
142	Herm Winningham	.04	.03	.02	232	Mark Salas	.04	.03	.02
143	Mike Diaz	.06	.05	.02	233	Tom Brookens	.04	.03	.02
144	*Mike Jackson*	.15	.11	.06	234	Greg Brock	.06	.05	.02
145	Denny Walling	.04	.03	.02	235	Rance Mulliniks	.04	.03	.02
146	Rob Thompson	.06	.05	.02	236	Bob Brower	.06	.05	.02
147	Franklin Stubbs	.06	.05	.02	237	Joe Niekro	.06	.05	.02
148	Albert Hall	.04	.03	.02	238	Scott Bankhead	.04	.03	.02
149	Bobby Witt	.08	.06	.03	239	Doug DeCinces	.06	.05	.02
150	Lance McCullers	.06	.05	.02	240	Tommy John	.12	.09	.05
151	Scott Bradley	.04	.03	.02	241	Rich Gedman	.06	.05	.02
152	Mark McLemore	.04	.03	.02	242	Ted Power	.04	.03	.02
153	Tim Laudner	.04	.03	.02	243	*Dave Meads*	.12	.09	.05
154	Greg Swindell	.15	.11	.06	244	Jim Sundberg	.06	.05	.02
155	Marty Barrett	.06	.05	.02	245	Ken Oberkfell	.04	.03	.02
156	Mike Heath	.04	.03	.02	246	Jimmy Jones	.08	.06	.03
157	Gary Ward	.06	.05	.02	247	Ken Landreaux	.04	.03	.02
158a	Lee Mazilli (incorrect spelling)	.25	.20	.10	248	Jose Oquendo	.04	.03	.02
158b	Lee Mazzilli (correct spelling)	.08	.06	.03	249	*John Mitchell*	.15	.11	.06
159	Tom Foley	.04	.03	.02	250	Don Baylor	.08	.06	.03
160	Robin Yount	.30	.25	.12	251	Scott Fletcher	.06	.05	.02
161	Steve Bedrosian	.10	.08	.04	252	Al Newman	.04	.03	.02
162	Bob Walk	.04	.03	.02	253	Carney Lansford	.08	.06	.03
163	Nick Esasky	.06	.05	.02	254	Johnny Ray	.06	.05	.02
164	*Ken Caminiti*	.25	.20	.10	255	Gary Pettis	.04	.03	.02
165	Jose Uribe	.04	.03	.02	256	Ken Phelps	.06	.05	.02
166	Dave Anderson	.04	.03	.02	257	Rick Leach	.04	.03	.02
167	Ed Whitson	.04	.03	.02	258	Tim Stoddard	.04	.03	.02
168	Ernie Whitt	.06	.05	.02	259	Ed Romero	.04	.03	.02
169	Cecil Cooper	.08	.06	.03	260	Sid Bream	.06	.05	.02
170	Mike Pagliarulo	.08	.06	.03	261a	Tom Neidenfuer (incorrect spelling)			
171	Pat Sheridan	.04	.03	.02			.25	.20	.10
172	Chris Bando	.04	.03	.02	261b	Tom Niedenfuer (correct spelling)	.06	.05	.02
173	Lee Lacy	.04	.03	.02	262	Rick Dempsey	.06	.05	.02
174	Steve Lombardozzi	.04	.03	.02	263	Lonnie Smith	.06	.05	.02
175	Mike Greenwell	.70	.50	.30	264	Bob Forsch	.06	.05	.02
176	Greg Minton	.04	.03	.02	265	Barry Bonds	.40	.30	.15
177	Moose Haas	.04	.03	.02	266	Willie Randolph	.06	.05	.02
178	Mike Kingery	.04	.03	.02	267	Mike Ramsey	.04	.03	.02
179	Greg Harris	.04	.03	.02	268	Don Slaught	.04	.03	.02

#	Player	MT	NR MT	EX
269	Mickey Tettleton	.04	.03	.02
270	Jerry Reuss	.06	.05	.02
271	Marc Sullivan	.04	.03	.02
272	Jim Morrison	.04	.03	.02
273	Steve Balboni	.06	.05	.02
274	Dick Schofield	.04	.03	.02
275	John Tudor	.08	.06	.03
276	*Gene Larkin*	.20	.15	.08
277	Harold Reynolds	.06	.05	.02
278	Jerry Browne	.06	.05	.02
279	Willie Upshaw	.06	.05	.02
280	Ted Higuera	.08	.06	.03
281	Terry McGriff	.04	.03	.02
282	Terry Puhl	.04	.03	.02
283	*Mark Wasinger*	.12	.09	.05
284	Luis Salazar	.04	.03	.02
285	Ted Simmons	.08	.06	.03
286	John Shelby	.04	.03	.02
287	*John Smiley*	.50	.40	.20
288	Curt Ford	.04	.03	.02
289	Steve Crawford	.04	.03	.02
290	Dan Quisenberry	.06	.05	.02
291	Alan Wiggins	.04	.03	.02
292	Randy Bush	.04	.03	.02
293	John Candelaria	.06	.05	.02
294	Tony Phillips	.04	.03	.02
295	Mike Morgan	.04	.03	.02
296	Bill Wegman	.04	.03	.02
297a	Terry Franconia (incorrect spelling)	.25	.20	.10
297b	Terry Francona (correct spelling)	.06	.05	.02
298	Mickey Hatcher	.04	.03	.02
299	Andres Thomas	.06	.05	.02
300	Bob Stanley	.04	.03	.02
301	*Alfredo Pedrique*	.12	.09	.05
302	Jim Lindeman	.06	.05	.02
303	Wally Backman	.06	.05	.02
304	Paul O'Neill	.06	.05	.02
305	Hubie Brooks	.08	.06	.03
306	Steve Buechele	.04	.03	.02
307	Bobby Thigpen	.08	.06	.03
308	George Hendrick	.06	.05	.02
309	John Moses	.04	.03	.02
310	Ron Guidry	.12	.09	.05
311	Bill Schroeder	.04	.03	.02
312	*Jose Nunez*	.08	.06	.03
313	Bud Black	.04	.03	.02
314	Joe Sambito	.04	.03	.02
315	Scott McGregor	.06	.05	.02
316	Rafael Santana	.04	.03	.02
317	Frank Williams	.04	.03	.02
318	Mike Fitzgerald	.04	.03	.02
319	Rick Mahler	.04	.03	.02
320	Jim Gott	.04	.03	.02
321	Mariano Duncan	.04	.03	.02
322	Jose Guzman	.06	.05	.02
323	Lee Guetterman	.04	.03	.02
324	Dan Gladden	.04	.03	.02
325	Gary Carter	.15	.11	.06
326	Tracy Jones	.10	.08	.04
327	Floyd Youmans	.04	.03	.02
328	Bill Dawley	.04	.03	.02
329	*Paul Noce*	.10	.08	.04
330	Angel Salazar	.04	.03	.02
331	Goose Gossage	.12	.09	.05
332	George Frazier	.04	.03	.02
333	Ruppert Jones	.04	.03	.02
334	Billy Jo Robidoux	.04	.03	.02
335	Mike Scott	.10	.08	.04
336	Randy Myers	.10	.08	.04
337	Bob Sebra	.04	.03	.02
338	Eric Show	.06	.05	.02
339	Mitch Williams	.06	.05	.02
340	Paul Molitor	.10	.08	.04
341	Gus Polidor	.04	.03	.02
342	Steve Trout	.04	.03	.02
343	Jerry Don Gleaton	.04	.03	.02
344	Bob Knepper	.06	.05	.02
345	Mitch Webster	.06	.05	.02
346	John Morris	.04	.03	.02
347	Andy Hawkins	.04	.03	.02
348	Dave Leiper	.04	.03	.02
349	Ernest Riles	.04	.03	.02
350	Dwight Gooden	.40	.30	.15
351	Dave Righetti	.12	.09	.05
352	Pat Dodson	.04	.03	.02
353	John Habyan	.04	.03	.02
354	Jim Deshaies	.06	.05	.02
355	Butch Wynegar	.04	.03	.02
356	Bryn Smith	.04	.03	.02
357	Matt Young	.04	.03	.02

#	Player	MT	NR MT	EX
358	*Tom Pagnozzi*	.25	.20	.10
359	Floyd Rayford	.04	.03	.02
360	Darryl Strawberry	.30	.25	.12
361	Sal Butera	.04	.03	.02
362	Domingo Ramos	.04	.03	.02
363	Chris Brown	.06	.05	.02
364	Jose Gonzalez	.04	.03	.02
365	Dave Smith	.06	.05	.02
366	Andy McGaffigan	.04	.03	.02
367	Stan Javier	.04	.03	.02
368	Henry Cotto	.04	.03	.02
369	Mike Birkbeck	.06	.05	.02
370	Len Dykstra	.08	.06	.03
371	Dave Collins	.06	.05	.02
372	Spike Owen	.04	.03	.02
373	Geno Petralli	.04	.03	.02
374	Ron Karkovice	.04	.03	.02
375	Shane Rawley	.06	.05	.02
376	*DeWayne Buice*	.15	.11	.06
377	*Bill Pecota*	.15	.11	.06
378	Leon Durham	.06	.05	.02
379	Ed Olwine	.04	.03	.02
380	Bruce Hurst	.08	.06	.03
381	Bob McClure	.04	.03	.02
382	Mark Thurmond	.04	.03	.02
383	Buddy Biancalana	.04	.03	.02
384	Tim Conroy	.04	.03	.02
385	Tony Gwynn	.25	.20	.10
386	Greg Gross	.04	.03	.02
387	*Barry Lyons*	.12	.09	.05
388	Mike Felder	.04	.03	.02
389	Pat Clements	.04	.03	.02
390	Ken Griffey	.06	.05	.02
391	Mark Davis	.04	.03	.02
392	Jose Rijo	.06	.05	.02
393	Mike Young	.04	.03	.02
394	Willie Fraser	.06	.05	.02
395	Dion James	.06	.05	.02
396	*Steve Shields*	.12	.09	.05
397	Randy St. Claire	.04	.03	.02
398	Danny Jackson	.12	.09	.05
399	Cecil Fielder	.60	.45	.25
400	Keith Hernandez	.15	.11	.06
401	Don Carman	.06	.05	.02
402	*Chuck Crim*	.12	.09	.05
403	Rob Woodward	.04	.03	.02
404	Junior Ortiz	.04	.03	.02
405	Glenn Wilson	.06	.05	.02
406	Ken Howell	.04	.03	.02
407	Jeff Kunkel	.04	.03	.02
408	Jeff Reed	.04	.03	.02
409	Chris James	.10	.08	.04
410	Zane Smith	.06	.05	.02
411	Ken Dixon	.04	.03	.02
412	Ricky Horton	.06	.05	.02
413	Frank DiPino	.04	.03	.02
414	*Shane Mack*	.25	.20	.10
415	Danny Cox	.06	.05	.02
416	Andy Van Slyke	.10	.08	.04
417	Danny Heep	.04	.03	.02
418	John Cangelosi	.04	.03	.02
419a	John Christiansen (incorrect spelling)	.25	.20	.10
419b	John Christensen (correct spelling)	.06	.05	.02
420	*Joey Cora*	.12	.09	.05
421	Mike LaValliere	.06	.05	.02
422	Kelly Gruber	.35	.25	.14
423	Bruce Benedict	.04	.03	.02
424	Len Matuszek	.04	.03	.02
425	Kent Tekulve	.06	.05	.02
426	Rafael Ramirez	.04	.03	.02
427	Mike Flanagan	.06	.05	.02
428	Mike Gallego	.04	.03	.02
429	Juan Castillo	.04	.03	.02
430	Neal Heaton	.04	.03	.02
431	Phil Garner	.04	.03	.02
432	*Mike Dunne*	.12	.09	.05
433	Wallace Johnson	.04	.03	.02
434	Jack O'Connor	.04	.03	.02
435	Steve Jeltz	.04	.03	.02
436	*Donnell Nixon*	.15	.11	.06
437	Jack Lazorko	.04	.03	.02
438	*Keith Comstock*	.12	.09	.05
439	Jeff Robinson	.04	.03	.02
440	Graig Nettles	.08	.06	.03
441	Mel Hall	.06	.05	.02
442	*Gerald Young*	.15	.11	.06
443	Gary Redus	.04	.03	.02
444	Charlie Moore	.04	.03	.02
445	Bill Madlock	.08	.06	.03
446	Mark Clear	.04	.03	.02

#	Player	MT	NR MT	EX
447	Greg Booker	.04	.03	.02
448	Rick Schu	.04	.03	.02
449	Ron Kittle	.06	.05	.02
450	Dale Murphy	.30	.25	.12
451	Bob Dernier	.04	.03	.02
452	Dale Mohorcic	.06	.05	.02
453	Rafael Belliard	.04	.03	.02
454	Charlie Puleo	.04	.03	.02
455	Dwayne Murphy	.06	.05	.02
456	Jim Eisenreich	.04	.03	.02
457	David Palmer	.04	.03	.02
458	Dave Stewart	.08	.06	.03
459	Pascual Perez	.06	.05	.02
460	Glenn Davis	.12	.09	.05
461	Dan Petry	.06	.05	.02
462	Jim Winn	.04	.03	.02
463	Darrell Miller	.04	.03	.02
464	Mike Moore	.04	.03	.02
465	Mike LaCoss	.04	.03	.02
466	Steve Farr	.04	.03	.02
467	Jerry Mumphrey	.04	.03	.02
468	Kevin Gross	.06	.05	.02
469	Bruce Bochy	.04	.03	.02
470	Orel Hershiser	.20	.15	.08
471	Eric King	.06	.05	.02
472	*Ellis Burks*	.80	.60	.30
473	Darren Daulton	.04	.03	.02
474	Mookie Wilson	.06	.05	.02
475	Frank Viola	.12	.09	.05
476	Ron Robinson	.04	.03	.02
477	Bob Melvin	.04	.03	.02
478	Jeff Musselman	.06	.05	.02
479	Charlie Kerfeld	.04	.03	.02
480	Richard Dotson	.06	.05	.02
481	Kevin Mitchell	.50	.40	.20
482	Gary Roenicke	.04	.03	.02
483	Tim Flannery	.04	.03	.02
484	Rich Yett	.04	.03	.02
485	Pete Incaviglia	.12	.09	.05
486	Rick Cerone	.04	.03	.02
487	Tony Armas	.06	.05	.02
488	Jerry Reed	.04	.03	.02
489	Davey Lopes	.06	.05	.02
490	Frank Tanana	.06	.05	.02
491	Mike Loynd	.04	.03	.02
492	Bruce Ruffin	.06	.05	.02
493	Chris Speier	.04	.03	.02
494	Tom Hume	.04	.03	.02
495	Jesse Orosco	.06	.05	.02
496	*Robby Wine, Jr.*	.12	.09	.05
497	*Jeff Montgomery*	.25	.20	.10
498	Jeff Dedmon	.04	.03	.02
499	Luis Aguayo	.04	.03	.02
500	Reggie Jackson (1968-75 Oakland Athletics)	.20	.15	.08
501	Reggie Jackson (1976 Baltimore Orioles)	.20	.15	.08
502	Reggie Jackson (1977-81 New York Yankees)	.20	.15	.08
503	Reggie Jackson (1982-86 California Angels)	.20	.15	.08
504	Reggie Jackson (1987 Oakland Athletics)	.20	.15	.08
505	Billy Hatcher	.06	.05	.02
506	Ed Lynch	.04	.03	.02
507	Willie Hernandez	.06	.05	.02
508	Jose DeLeon	.06	.05	.02
509	Joel Youngblood	.04	.03	.02
510	Bob Welch	.08	.06	.03
511	Steve Ontiveros	.04	.03	.02
512	Randy Ready	.04	.03	.02
513	Juan Nieves	.06	.05	.02
514	Jeff Russell	.04	.03	.02
515	Von Hayes	.06	.05	.02
516	Mark Gubicza	.10	.08	.04
517	Ken Dayley	.04	.03	.02
518	Don Aase	.04	.03	.02
519	Rick Reuschel	.08	.06	.03
520	*Mike Henneman*	.25	.20	.10
521	Rick Aguilera	.04	.03	.02
522	Jay Howell	.06	.05	.02
523	Ed Correa	.04	.03	.02
524	Manny Trillo	.06	.05	.02
525	Kirk Gibson	.15	.11	.06
526	*Wally Ritchie*	.12	.09	.05
527	Al Nipper	.04	.03	.02
528	Atlee Hammaker	.04	.03	.02
529	Shawon Dunston	.08	.06	.03
530	Jim Clancy	.06	.05	.02
531	Tom Paciorek	.04	.03	.02
532	Joel Skinner	.04	.03	.02
533	Scott Garrelts	.04	.03	.02
534	Tom O'Malley	.04	.03	.02
535	John Franco	.08	.06	.03
536	*Paul Kilgus*	.20	.15	.08
537	Darrell Porter	.06	.05	.02
538	Walt Terrell	.06	.05	.02
539	Bill Long	.15	.11	.06
540	George Bell	.20	.15	.08
541	Jeff Sellers	.06	.05	.02
542	*Joe Boever*	.12	.09	.05
543	Steve Howe	.06	.05	.02
544	Scott Sanderson	.04	.03	.02
545	Jack Morris	.15	.11	.06
546	*Todd Benzinger*	.30	.25	.12
547	Steve Henderson	.04	.03	.02
548	Eddie Milner	.04	.03	.02
549	*Jeff Robinson*	.25	.20	.10
550	Cal Ripken, Jr.	.40	.30	.15
551	Jody Davis	.06	.05	.02
552	Kirk McCaskill	.06	.05	.02
553	Craig Lefferts	.04	.03	.02
554	Darnell Coles	.06	.05	.02
555	Phil Niekro	.15	.11	.06
556	Mike Aldrete	.06	.05	.02
557	Pat Perry	.04	.03	.02
558	Juan Agosto	.04	.03	.02
559	Rob Murphy	.06	.05	.02
560	Dennis Rasmussen	.08	.06	.03
561	Manny Lee	.04	.03	.02
562	*Jeff Blauser*	.20	.15	.08
563	Bob Ojeda	.06	.05	.02
564	Dave Dravecky	.06	.05	.02
565	Gene Garber	.04	.03	.02
566	Ron Roenicke	.04	.03	.02
567	*Tommy Hinzo*	.12	.09	.05
568	*Eric Nolte*	.12	.09	.05
569	Ed Hearn	.04	.03	.02
570	*Mark Davidson*	.12	.09	.05
571	*Jim Walewander*	.12	.09	.05
572	Donnie Hill	.04	.03	.02
573	Jamie Moyer	.06	.05	.02
574	Ken Schrom	.04	.03	.02
575	Nolan Ryan	.60	.45	.25
576	Jim Acker	.04	.03	.02
577	Jamie Quirk	.04	.03	.02
578	*Jay Aldrich*	.10	.08	.04
579	Claudell Washington	.06	.05	.02
580	Jeff Leonard	.06	.05	.02
581	Carmen Castillo	.04	.03	.02
582	Daryl Boston	.04	.03	.02
583	*Jeff DeWillis*	.15	.11	.06
584	*John Marzano*	.20	.15	.08
585	Bill Gullickson	.06	.05	.02
586	Andy Allanson	.08	.06	.03
587	Lee Tunnell	.04	.03	.02
588	Gene Nelson	.04	.03	.02
589	Dave LaPoint	.06	.05	.02
590	Harold Baines	.10	.08	.04
591	Bill Buckner	.08	.06	.03
592	Carlton Fisk	.20	.15	.08
593	Rick Manning	.04	.03	.02
594	*Doug Jones*	.20	.15	.08
595	Tom Candiotti	.04	.03	.02
596	Steve Lake	.04	.03	.02
597	*Jose Lind*	.25	.20	.10
598	*Ross Jones*	.12	.09	.05
599	Gary Matthews	.06	.05	.02
600	Fernando Valezuela	.15	.11	.06
601	Dennis Martinez	.06	.05	.02
602	*Les Lancaster*	.15	.11	.06
603	Ozzie Guillen	.06	.05	.02
604	Tony Bernazard	.04	.03	.02
605	Chili Davis	.06	.05	.02
606	Roy Smalley	.04	.03	.02
607	Ivan Calderon	.08	.06	.03
608	Jay Tibbs	.04	.03	.02
609	Guy Hoffman	.04	.03	.02
610	Doyle Alexander	.06	.05	.02
611	Mike Bielecki	.04	.03	.02
612	*Shawn Hillegas*	.20	.15	.08
613	Keith Atherton	.04	.03	.02
614	Eric Plunk	.04	.03	.02
615	Sid Fernandez	.08	.06	.03
616	Dennis Lamp	.04	.03	.02
617	Dave Engle	.04	.03	.02
618	Harry Spilman	.04	.03	.02
619	Don Robinson	.06	.05	.02
620	*John Farrell*	.20	.15	.08
621	*Nelson Liriano*	.15	.11	.06
622	Floyd Bannister	.06	.05	.02
623	Rookie Prospect *(Randy Milligan)*	.60	.45	.25

		MT	NR MT	EX
624	Rookie Prospect (Kevin Elster)	.25	.20	.10
625	Rookie Prospect (Jody Reed)	.40	.30	.15
626	Rookie Prospect (Shawn Abner)	.20	.15	.08
627	Rookie Prospect (Kirt Manwaring)	.20	.15	.08
628	Rookie Prospect (Pete Stanicek)	.15	.11	.06
629	Rookie Prospect (Rob Ducey)	.12	.09	.05
630	Rookie Prospect (Steve Kiefer)	.04	.03	.02
631	Rookie Prospect (Gary Thurman)	.20	.15	.08
632	Rookie Prospect (Darrel Akerfelds)	.12	.09	.05
633	Rookie Prospect (Dave Clark)	.10	.08	.04
634	Rookie Prospect (Roberto Kelly)	1.00	.70	.40
635	Rookie Prospect (Keith Hughes)	.15	.11	.06
636	Rookie Prospect (John Davis)	.15	.11	.06
637	Rookie Prospect (Mike Devereaux)	.50	.40	.20
638	Rookie Prospect (Tom Glavine)	2.00	1.50	.80
639	Rookie Prospect (Keith Miller)	.20	.15	.08
640	Rookie Prospect (Chris Gwynn)	.20	.15	.08
641	Rookie Prospect (Tim Crews)	.15	.11	.06
642	Rookie Prospect (Mackey Sasser)	.20	.15	.08
643	Rookie Prospect (Vicente Palacios)	.15	.11	.06
644	Rookie Prospect (Kevin Romine)	.06	.05	.02
645	Rookie Prospect (Gregg Jefferies)	1.00	.70	.40
646	Rookie Prospect (Jeff Treadway)	.25	.20	.10
647	Rookie Prospect (Ronnie Gant)	4.00	3.00	1.50
648	Rookie Sluggers (Mark McGwire, Matt Nokes)	.30	.25	.12
649	Speed and Power (Eric Davis, Tim Raines)	.25	.20	.10
650	Game Breakers (Jack Clark, Don Mattingly)	.20	.15	.08
651	Super Shortstops (Tony Fernandez, Cal Ripken, Jr., Alan Trammell)	.20	.15	.08
652	1987 Highlights (Vince Coleman)	.08	.06	.03
653	1987 Highlights (Kirby Puckett)	.12	.09	.05
654	1987 Highlights (Benito Santiago)	.10	.08	.04
655	1987 Highlights (Juan Nieves)	.06	.05	.02
656	1987 Highlights (Steve Bedrosian)	.06	.05	.02
657	1987 Highlights (Mike Schmidt)	.20	.15	.08
658	1987 Highlights (Don Mattingly)	.30	.25	.12
659	1987 Highlights (Mark McGwire)	.15	.11	.06
660	1987 Highlights (Paul Molitor)	.08	.06	.03

		MT	NR MT	EX
15	Eric Davis	.40	.30	.15
	Panel	1.75	1.25	.70
3	Don Mattingly	.60	.45	.25
5	Cal Ripken, Jr.	.50	.40	.20
11	Jack Clark	.25	.20	.10
	Panel	2.00	1.50	.80
4	Wade Boggs	.50	.40	.20
9	Bret Saberhagen	.20	.15	.08
12	Ryne Sandberg	.60	.45	.25
	Panel	1.50	1.25	.60
6	George Bell	.25	.20	.10
13	Mike Schmidt	.35	.25	.14
18	Mike Scott	.15	.11	.06
	Panel	2.00	1.50	.80
7	Rickey Henderson	.60	.45	.25
16	Andre Dawson	.25	.20	.10
17	Darryl Strawberry	.40	.30	.15
	Panel	1.50	1.25	.60
8	Dave Winfield	.25	.20	.10
10	Gary Carter	.20	.15	.08
14	Ozzie Smith	.25	.20	.10

1988 Score Traded

This 110-card set featuring new rookies and traded veterans is similar in design to the 1988 Score set, except for a change in border color. Individual standard-size player cards (2-1/2" by 3-1/2") feature a bright orange border framing full-figure action photos highlighted by a thin white outline. The player name (in white) is centered in the bottom margin, flanked by three yellow stars lower left and a yellow Score logo lower right. The backs carry full-color player close-ups on a cream-colored background, followed by card number, team name and logo, player personal information and a purple stats chart that lists year-by-year and major league totals. A brief player profile follows the stats chart and, on some cards, information is included about the player's trade or acquisition. The update set also includes 10 Magic Motion 3-D trivia cards.

1988 Score Box Panels

This 18-card set, produced by Major League Marketing and manufactured by Optigraphics, is the premiere box-bottom set issued under the Score trademark. The set features 1987 major league All-Star players in full-color action poses, framed by a white border. A "1987 All-Star" banner (red or purple) curves above an orange player name block beneath the player photo. Card backs are printed in red, blue, gold and black and carry the card number, player name and position and league logo. Six colorful "Great Moments in Baseball" trivia cards are also included in this set. Each trivia card highlights an historical event at a famous ballpark.

		MT	NR MT	EX
Complete Panel Set:		8.00	6.00	3.25
Complete Singles Set:		3.00	2.25	1.25
Common Panel:		1.50	1.25	.60
Common Single Player:		.15	.11	.06
	Panel	1.50	1.25	.60
1	Terry Kennedy	.15	.11	.06
3	Willie Randolph	.15	.11	.06

		MT	NR MT	EX
Complete Set:		90.00	67.00	35.00
Common Player:		.08	.06	.03
1T	Jack Clark	.20	.15	.08
2T	Danny Jackson	.20	.15	.08
3T	Brett Butler	.10	.08	.04
4T	Kurt Stillwell	.12	.09	.05
5T	Tom Brunansky	.15	.11	.06
6T	Dennis Lamp	.08	.06	.03
7T	Jose DeLeon	.10	.08	.04
8T	Tom Herr	.12	.09	.05
9T	Keith Moreland	.10	.08	.04
10T	Kirk Gibson	.20	.15	.08
11T	Bud Black	.08	.06	.03
12T	Rafael Ramirez	.08	.06	.03
13T	Luis Salazar	.08	.06	.03
14T	Goose Gossage	.15	.11	.06
15T	Bob Welch	.15	.11	.06
16T	Vance Law	.10	.08	.04
17T	Ray Knight	.10	.08	.04
18T	Dan Quisenberry	.10	.08	.04
19T	Don Slaught	.08	.06	.03
20T	Lee Smith	.25	.20	.10

		MT	NR MT	EX
21T	Rick Cerone	.08	.06	.03
22T	Pat Tabler	.10	.08	.04
23T	Larry McWilliams	.08	.06	.03
24T	Rick Horton	.10	.08	.04
25T	Graig Nettles	.12	.09	.05
26T	Dan Petry	.10	.08	.04
27T	Joe Rijo	.10	.08	.04
28T	Chili Davis	.10	.08	.04
29T	Dickie Thon	.10	.08	.04
30T	Mackey Sasser(FC)	.15	.11	.06
31T	Mickey Tettleton	.08	.06	.03
32T	Rick Dempsey	.08	.06	.03
33T	Ron Hassey	.08	.06	.03
34T	Phil Bradley	.12	.09	.05
35T	Jay Howell	.10	.08	.04
36T	Bill Buckner	.12	.09	.05
37T	Alfredo Griffin	.10	.08	.04
38T	Gary Pettis	.08	.06	.03
39T	Calvin Schiraldi	.08	.06	.03
40T	John Candelaria	.10	.08	.04
41T	Joe Orsulak	.08	.06	.03
42T	Willie Upshaw	.10	.08	.04
43T	Herm Winningham	.08	.06	.03
44T	Ron Kittle	.12	.09	.05
45T	Bob Dernier	.08	.06	.03
46T	Steve Balboni	.10	.08	.04
47T	Steve Shields	.08	.06	.03
48T	Henry Cotto	.08	.06	.03
49T	Dave Henderson	.10	.08	.04
50T	Dave Parker	.15	.11	.06
51T	Mike Young	.08	.06	.03
52T	Mark Salas	.08	.06	.03
53T	Mike Davis	.08	.06	.03
54T	Rafael Santana	.08	.06	.03
55T	Don Baylor	.15	.11	.06
56T	Dan Pasqua	.12	.09	.05
57T	Ernest Riles	.08	.06	.03
58T	Glenn Hubbard	.08	.06	.03
59T	Mike Smithson	.08	.06	.03
60T	Richard Dotson	.10	.08	.04
61T	Jerry Reuss	.10	.08	.04
62T	Mike Jackson	.10	.08	.04
63T	Floyd Bannister	.10	.08	.04
64T	Jesse Orosco	.10	.08	.04
65T	Larry Parrish	.10	.08	.04
66T	Jeff Bittiger(FC)	.20	.15	.08
67T	Ray Hayward(FC)	.10	.08	.04
68T	Ricky Jordan(FC)	.60	.45	.25
69T	Tommy Gregg(FC)	.12	.09	.05
70T	Brady Anderson(FC)	7.00	5.25	2.75
71T	Jeff Montgomery	.08	.06	.03
72T	Darryl Hamilton(FC)	.75	.55	.35
73T	Cecil Espy(FC)	.10	.08	.04
74T	Greg Briley(FC)	.50	.40	.20
75T	Joey Meyer(FC)	.20	.15	.08
76T	Mike Macfarlane(FC)	.40	.30	.15
77T	Oswald Peraza(FC)	.20	.15	.08
78T	Jack Armstrong(FC)	.60	.45	.25
79T	Don Heinkel(FC)	.20	.15	.08
80T	Mark Grace(FC)	15.00	11.00	6.00
81T	Steve Curry(FC)	.20	.15	.08
82T	Damon Berryhill(FC)	.40	.30	.15
83T	Steve Ellsworth(FC)	.20	.15	.08
84T	Pete Smith(FC)	.12	.09	.05
85T	Jack McDowell	12.00	9.00	4.75
86T	Rob Dibble(FC)	3.00	2.25	1.25
87T	Brian Harvey(FC)	2.00	1.50	.80
88T	John Dopson(FC)	.25	.20	.10
89T	Dave Gallagher(FC)	.25	.20	.10
90T	Todd Stottlemyre(FC)	2.50	2.00	1.00
91T	Mike Schooler(FC)	1.00	.70	.40
92T	Don Gordon(FC)	.08	.06	.03
93T	Sil Campusano(FC)	.25	.20	.10
94T	Jeff Pico(FC)	.25	.20	.10
95T	Jay Buhner(FC)	2.00	1.50	.80
96T	Nelson Santovenia(FC)	.25	.20	.10
97T	Al Leiter(FC)	.30	.25	.12
98T	Luis Alicea(FC)	.20	.15	.08
99T	Pat Borders(FC)	1.00	.70	.40
100T	Chris Sabo(FC)	4.00	3.00	1.50
101T	Tim Belcher(FC)	.70	.50	.30
102T	Walt Weiss(FC)	.80	.60	.30
103T	Craig Biggio(FC)	5.00	3.75	2.00
104T	Don August(FC)	.25	.20	.10
105T	Roberto Alomar(FC)	60.00	45.00	25.00
106T	Todd Burns(FC)	.30	.25	.12
107T	John Costello(FC)	.20	.15	.08
108T	Melido Perez(FC)	.60	.45	.25
109T	Darrin Jackson(FC)	.12	.09	.05
110T	Orestes Destrade(FC)	.15	.11	.06

1988 Score
Young Superstar - Series I

This 40-card standard-size set (2-1/2" by 3-1/2" cards) from Optigraphics was divided into five separate 8-card sets. Similar to the company's regular issue, these cards are distinguished by excellent full-color photography on both front and back. The glossy player photos, with team logo in the lower right corner, are centered on a white background and framed by a vivid blue and green border. A player name banner beneath the photo includes the name, position and uniform number. The card backs feature ful-color player closeups beneath a hot pink player name/Score logo banner. Hot pink also frames the personal stats (in green), career stats (in black) and career biography (in blue). The backs also include quotes from well-known baseball authorities discussing player performance. This set was distributed via a write-in offer printed on 1988 Score 17-card package wrappers.

		MT	NR MT	EX
Complete Set:		8.00	6.00	3.25
Common Player:		.10	.08	.04
1	Mark McGwire	.70	.50	.30
2	Benito Santiago	.30	.25	.12
3	Sam Horn	.10	.08	.04
4	Chris Bosio	.10	.08	.04
5	Matt Nokes	.25	.20	.10
6	Ken Williams	.10	.08	.04
7	Dion James	.10	.08	.04
8	B.J. Surhoff	.25	.20	.10
9	Joe Margrane	.20	.15	.08
10	Kevin Seitzer	.10	.08	.04
11	Stanley Jefferson	.10	.08	.04
12	Devon White	.30	.25	.12
13	Nelson Liriano	.10	.08	.04
14	Chris James	.10	.08	.04
15	Mike Henneman	.15	.11	.06
16	Terry Steinbach	.20	.15	.08
17	John Kruk	.25	.20	.10
18	Matt Williams	.60	.45	.25
19	Kelly Downs	.10	.08	.04
20	Bill Ripken	.10	.08	.04
21	Ozzie Guillen	.10	.08	.04
22	Luis Polonia	.10	.08	.04
23	Dave Magadan	.40	.30	.15
24	Mike Greenwell	.50	.40	.20
25	Will Clark	1.00	.70	.40
26	Mike Dunne	.10	.08	.04
27	Wally Joyner	.50	.40	.20
28	Robby Thompson	.10	.08	.04
29	Ken Caminiti	.20	.15	.08
30	Jose Canseco	2.00	1.50	.80
31	Todd Benzinger	.30	.25	.12
32	Pete Incaviglia	.20	.15	.08
33	John Farrell	.10	.08	.04
34	Casey Candaele	.10	.08	.04
35	Mike Aldrete	.10	.08	.04
36	Ruben Sierra	.40	.30	.15
37	Ellis Burks	.60	.45	.25
38	Tracy Jones	.10	.08	.04
39	Kal Daniels	.30	.25	.12
40	Cory Snyder	.10	.08	.04

A player's name in italic indicates a rookie card. An (FC) indicates a player's first card for that particular card company.

1989 Score Traded

1988 Score
Young Superstar - Series II

This set of 40 standard-size cards (2-1/2" by 3-1/2") and five Magic trivia cards is part of a double series issued by Score. Each series is divided into five smaller sets of eight baseball cards and one trivia card. The design on both series is similar, except for border color. Series I has blue and green borders. Series II has red and blue borders framing full-color player photos with the player name and team logo printed beneath the photo. The card backs carry full-color head shots and stats in a variety of colors. Young Superstar series were offered via a write-in offer on the backs of 1988 Score card package wrappers. For each 8-card subset, collectors were instructed to send two Score wrappers and $1. Complete sets were offered by a number of hobby dealers nationwide.

		MT	NR MT	EX
Complete Set:		7.00	5.25	2.75
Common Player:		.10	.08	.04
1	Don Mattingly	1.00	.70	.40
2	Glenn Braggs	.15	.11	.06
3	Dwight Gooden	.50	.40	.20
4	Jose Lind	.10	.08	.04
5	Danny Tartabull	.30	.25	.12
6	Tony Fernandez	.15	.11	.06
7	Julio Franco	.15	.11	.06
8	Andres Galarraga	.15	.11	.06
9	Bobby Bonilla	.40	.30	.15
10	Eric Davis	.40	.30	.15
11	Gerald Young	.10	.08	.04
12	Barry Bonds	.40	.30	.15
13	Jerry Browne	.10	.08	.04
14	Jeff Blauser	.10	.08	.04
15	Mickey Brantley	.10	.08	.04
16	Floyd Youmans	.10	.08	.04
17	Bret Saberhagen	.25	.20	.10
18	Shawon Dunston	.20	.15	.08
19	Len Dykstra	.15	.11	.06
20	Darryl Strawberry	.40	.30	.15
21	Rick Aguilera	.10	.08	.04
22	Ivan Calderon	.10	.08	.04
23	Roger Clemens	.70	.50	.30
24	Vince Coleman	.30	.25	.12
25	Gary Thurman	.10	.08	.04
26	Jeff Treadway	.10	.08	.04
27	Oddibe McDowell	.10	.08	.04
28	Fred McGriff	.40	.30	.15
29	Mark McLemore	.10	.08	.04
30	Jeff Musselman	.10	.08	.04
31	Mitch Williams	.10	.08	.04
32	Dan Plesac	.10	.08	.04
33	Juan Nieves	.10	.08	.04
34	Barry Larkin	.30	.25	.12
35	Greg Mathews	.10	.08	.04
36	Shane Mack	.10	.08	.04
37	Scott Bankhead	.10	.08	.04
38	Eric Bell	.10	.08	.04
39	Greg Swindell	.25	.20	.10
40	Kevin Elster	.10	.08	.04

Score issued its second consecutive traded set in 1989 to supplement and update its regular set. The 110-card traded set features the same basic card design as the regular 1989 Score set. The set consists of rookies and traded players pictured with correct teams. The set was sold by hobby dealers in a special box that included an assortment of "Magic Motion" trivia cards.

		MT	NR MT	EX
Complete Set:		8.00	6.00	3.25
Common Player:		.06	.05	.02
1T	Rafael Palmeiro	.10	.08	.04
2T	Nolan Ryan	1.50	1.25	.60
3T	Jack Clark	.10	.08	.04
4T	Dave LaPoint	.06	.05	.02
5T	Mike Moore	.08	.06	.03
6T	Pete O'Brien	.06	.05	.02
7T	Jeffrey Leonard	.06	.05	.02
8T	Rob Murphy	.06	.05	.02
9T	Tom Herr	.06	.05	.02
10T	Claudell Washington	.06	.05	.02
11T	Mike Pagliarulo	.06	.05	.02
12T	Steve Lake	.06	.05	.02
13T	Spike Owen	.06	.05	.02
14T	Andy Hawkins	.06	.05	.02
15T	Todd Benzinger	.06	.05	.02
16T	Mookie Wilson	.06	.05	.03
17T	Bert Blyleven	.08	.06	.03
18T	Jeff Treadway	.06	.05	.02
19T	Bruce Hurst	.08	.06	.03
20T	Steve Sax	.12	.09	.05
21T	Juan Samuel	.06	.05	.02
22T	Jesse Barfield	.06	.05	.02
23T	Carmelo Castillo	.06	.05	.02
24T	Terry Leach	.06	.05	.02
25T	Mark Langston	.12	.09	.05
26T	Eric King	.06	.05	.02
27T	Steve Balboni	.06	.05	.02
28T	Len Dykstra	.06	.05	.02
29T	Keith Moreland	.06	.05	.02
30T	Terry Kennedy	.06	.05	.02
31T	Eddie Murray	.12	.09	.05
32T	Mitch Williams	.10	.08	.04
33T	Jeff Parrett	.06	.05	.02
34T	Wally Backman	.06	.05	.02
35T	Julio Franco	.10	.08	.04
36T	Lance Parrish	.06	.05	.02
37T	Nick Esasky	.06	.05	.02
38T	Luis Polonia	.06	.05	.02
39T	Kevin Gross	.06	.05	.02
40T	John Dopson	.06	.05	.02
41T	Willie Randolph	.08	.06	.03
42T	Jim Clancy	.06	.05	.02
43T	Tracy Jones	.06	.05	.02
44T	Phil Bradley	.06	.05	.02
45T	Milt Thompson	.06	.05	.02
46T	Chris James	.06	.05	.02
47T	Scott Fletcher	.06	.05	.02
48T	Kal Daniels	.08	.06	.03
49T	Steve Bedrosian	.06	.05	.02
50T	Rickey Henderson	.50	.40	.20
51T	Dion James	.06	.05	.02
52T	Tim Leary	.06	.05	.02
53T	Roger McDowell	.06	.05	.02
54T	Mel Hall	.06	.05	.02
55T	Dickie Thon	.06	.05	.02

		MT	NR MT	EX
56T	Zane Smith	.06	.05	.02
57T	Danny Heep	.06	.05	.02
58T	Bob McClure	.06	.05	.02
59T	Brian Holton	.06	.05	.02
60T	Randy Ready	.06	.05	.02
61T	Bob Melvin	.06	.05	.02
62T	Harold Baines	.08	.06	.03
63T	Lance McCullers	.06	.05	.02
64T	Jody Davis	.06	.05	.02
65T	Darrell Evans	.06	.05	.02
66T	Joel Youngblood	.08	.06	.03
67T	Frank Viola	.08	.06	.03
68T	Mike Aldrete	.06	.05	.02
69T	Greg Cadaret	.06	.05	.02
70T	John Kruk	.06	.05	.02
71T	Pat Sheridan	.06	.05	.02
72T	Oddibe McDowell	.06	.05	.02
73T	Tom Brookens	.06	.05	.02
74T	Bob Boone	.08	.06	.03
75T	Walt Terrell	.06	.05	.02
76T	Joel Skinner	.06	.05	.02
77T	Randy Johnson	.10	.08	.04
78T	Felix Fermin	.06	.05	.03
79T	Rick Mahler	.06	.05	.03
80T	Rich Dotson	.06	.05	.03
81T	Cris Carpenter(FC)	.20	.15	.08
82T	Bill Spiers(FC)	.25	.20	.10
83T	Junior Felix(FC)	.25	.20	.10
84T	Joe Girardi(FC)	.20	.15	.08
85T	Jerome Walton(FC)	.25	.20	.10
86T	Greg Litton(FC)	.25	.20	.10
87T	Greg Harris(FC)	.20	.15	.08
88T	Jim Abbott(FC)	1.00	.70	.40
89T	Kevin Brown(FC)	.20	.15	.08
90T	John Wetteland(FC)	.20	.15	.08
91T	Gary Wayne(FC)	.15	.11	.06
92T	Rich Monteleone(FC)	.15	.11	.06
93T	Bob Geren(FC)	.20	.15	.08
94T	Clay Parker(FC)	.15	.11	.06
95T	Steve Finley(FC)	.40	.30	.15
96T	Gregg Olson(FC)	.35	.25	.14
97T	Ken Patterson(FC)	.15	.11	.06
98T	Ken Hill(FC)	.30	.25	.12
99T	Scott Scudder(FC)	.25	.20	.10
100T	Ken Griffey, Jr.(FC)	5.00	3.75	2.00
101T	Jeff Brantley(FC)	.25	.20	.10
102T	Donn Pall(FC)	.15	.11	.06
103T	Carlos Martinez(FC)	.20	.15	.08
104T	Joe Oliver(FC)	.30	.25	.12
105T	Omar Vizquel(FC)	.15	.11	.06
106T	Joey Belle(FC)	2.50	2.00	1.00
107T	Kenny Rogers(FC)	.20	.15	.08
108T	Mark Carreon(FC)	.15	.11	.06
109T	Rolando Roomes(FC)	.15	.11	.06
110T	Pete Harnsisch(FC)	.35	.25	.14

1989 Score Young Superstar-Series I

This standard-size card set (2-1/2" by 3-1/2") displays full-color action photos with a high gloss finish. The card fronts feature a red and blue border surrounding the photo with the team logo in the lower right. A red band beneath the photo provided the setting for the player ID including name, position, and team number. The flip side features a red "Young Superstar" headline above a close-up photo. Above the headline, appears the player's personal information and statistics in orange and black ink respect-

ively.

The top of the flip side highlights the player's name and the Score logo in white within a purple band. To the right of the close-up photo a condensed scouting report and career hightlights are revealed. The card number and related logos appear on the bottom portion. Five trivia cards featuring "A Year to Remember" accompanied the series. Each trivia card relates to a highlight from the past 56 years. This set was distributed via a write-in offer with Score card wrappers.

		MT	NR MT	EX
	Complete Set:	9.00	6.75	3.50
	Common Player:	.10	.08	.04
1	Gregg Jefferies	.40	.30	.15
2	Jody Reed	.10	.08	.04
3	Mark Grace	.40	.30	.15
4	Dave Gallagher	.15	.11	.06
5	Bo Jackson	1.25	.90	.50
6	Jay Buhner	.10	.08	.04
7	Melido Perez	.10	.08	.04
8	Bobby Witt	.10	.08	.04
9	David Cone	.15	.11	.06
10	Chris Sabo	.15	.11	.06
11	Pat Borders	.10	.08	.04
12	Mark Grant	.10	.08	.04
13	Mike Macfarlane	.10	.08	.04
14	Mike Jackson	.10	.08	.04
15	Ricky Jordan	.30	.25	.12
16	Ron Gant	.50	.40	.20
17	Al Leiter	.10	.08	.04
18	Jeff Parrett	.10	.08	.04
19	Pete Smith	.10	.08	.04
20	Walt Weiss	.15	.11	.06
21	Doug Drabek	.12	.09	.05
22	Kirt Manwaring	.15	.11	.06
23	Keith Miller	.10	.08	.04
24	Damon Berryhill	.12	.09	.05
25	Gary Sheffield	.50	.40	.20
26	Brady Anderson	.10	.08	.04
27	Mitch Williams	.15	.11	.06
28	Roberto Alomar	.30	.25	.12
29	Bobby Thigpen	.12	.09	.05
30	Bryan Harvey	.10	.08	.04
31	Jose Rijo	.15	.11	.06
32	Dave West	.10	.08	.04
33	Joey Meyer	.10	.08	.04
34	Allan Anderson	.12	.09	.05
35	Rafael Palmeiro	.20	.15	.08
36	Tim Belcher	.30	.25	.12
37	John Smiley	.15	.11	.06
38	Mackey Sasser	.10	.08	.04
39	Greg Maddux	.30	.25	.12
40	Ramon Martinez	1.00	.70	.40
41	Randy Myers	.12	.09	.05
42	Scott Bankhead	.15	.11	.06

1989 Score Young Superstar-Series II

Score followed up with a second series of Young Superstars in 1989. The second series also included 42 cards and featured the same design as the first series. The set was also distributed via a write-in offer with Score card wrappers.

		MT	NR MT	EX
Complete Set:		5.00	3.75	2.00
Common Player:		.10	.08	.04

		MT	NR MT	EX
1	Sandy Alomar	.40	.30	.15
2	Tom Gordon	.40	.30	.15
3	Ron Jones	.10	.08	.04
4	Todd Burns	.10	.08	.04
5	Paul O'Neill	.10	.08	.04
6	Gene Larkin	.10	.08	.04
7	Eric King	.10	.08	.04
8	Jeff Robinson	.10	.08	.04
9	Bill Wegman	.10	.08	.04
10	Cecil Espy	.10	.08	.04
11	Jose Guzman	.10	.08	.04
12	Kelly Gruber	.20	.15	.08
13	Duane Ward	.10	.08	.04
14	Mark Gubicza	.25	.20	.10
15	Norm Charlton	.20	.15	.08
16	Jose Oquendo	.10	.08	.04
17	Geronimo Berroa	.10	.08	.04
18	Dwight Smith	.20	.15	.08
19	Lance McCullers	.10	.08	.04
20	Jimmy Jones	.10	.08	.04
21	Craig Worthington	.25	.20	.10
22	Mike Devereaux	.12	.09	.05
23	Bob Milacki	.15	.11	.06
24	Dale Sveum	.10	.08	.04
25	Carlos Quintana	.20	.15	.08
26	Luis Medina	.20	.15	.08
27	Steve Searcy	.20	.15	.08
28	Don August	.10	.08	.04
29	Shawn Hillegas	.10	.08	.04
30	Mike Campbell	.10	.08	.04
31	Mike Harkey	.25	.20	.10
32	Randy Johnson	.20	.15	.08
33	Craig Biggio	.35	.25	.12
34	Mike Schooler	.12	.09	.05
35	Andres Thomas	.10	.08	.04
36	Van Snider	.20	.15	.08
37	Cameron Drew	.20	.15	.08
38	Kevin Mitchell	.40	.30	.15
39	Lance Johnson	.15	.11	.06
40	Chad Kreuter	.10	.08	.04
41	Danny Jackson	.10	.08	.04
42	Kurt Stillwell	.10	.08	.04

1989 Score Rising Star

Similar in design to the Score Superstar set, this 100-card set showcased a host of rookies including Gary Sheffield and Gregg Jefferies. The full-color action photos are surrounded by a bright blue border with a green inner highlight line. The Score logo appears in the upper left in green and white. The player's name, position and team are found at the bottom. The flip sides display a full-color close-up of the player above his name and career highlights. The card number and player's rookie year are featured to the right. A "Rising Star" headline highlights the top border. Like the "Score Superstar" the Score "Rising Star" set was marketed as a combination with a related magazine. "1988-89 Baseball's 100 Hottest Rookies" accompanies the set which also includes six Magic Motion baseball trivia cards featuring "Rookies to Remember." The magazine/card sets were available at a select group of retailers.

		MT	NR MT	EX
Complete Set:		10.00	7.50	4.00
Common Player:		.07	.05	.03

		MT	NR MT	EX
1	Gregg Jefferies	.40	.30	.15
2	Vicente Palacios	.15	.11	.06
3	Cameron Drew	.10	.08	.04
4	Doug Dascenzo	.12	.09	.05
5	Luis Medina	.12	.09	.05
6	Craig Worthington	.20	.15	.08
7	Rob Ducey	.08	.06	.04
8	Hal Morris	.60	.45	.25
9	Bill Brennan	.07	.05	.03
10	Gary Sheffield	.40	.30	.15
11	Mike Devereaux	.10	.08	.04
12	Hensley Meulens	.40	.30	.15
13	Carlos Quintana	.20	.15	.08
14	Todd Frohwirth	.07	.05	.03
15	Scott Lusader	.09	.07	.04
16	Mark Carreon	.15	.11	.06
17	Torey Lovullo	.20	.15	.08
18	Randy Velarde	.12	.09	.05
19	Billy Bean	.09	.07	.04
20	Lance Blankenship	.15	.11	.06
21	Chris Gwynn	.15	.11	.06
22	Felix Jose	.20	.15	.08
23	Derek Lilliquist	.20	.15	.08
24	Gary Thurman	.07	.05	.03
25	Ron Jones	.20	.15	.08
26	Dave Justice	1.00	.70	.40
27	Johnny Paredes	.08	.06	.03
28	Tim Jones	.10	.08	.04
29	Jose Gonzalez	.10	.08	.04
30	Geronimo Berroa	.15	.11	.06
31	Trevor Wilson	.12	.09	.05
32	Morris Madden	.10	.08	.04
33	Lance Johnson	.15	.11	.06
34	Marvin Freeman	.07	.05	.03
35	Jose Cecena	.07	.05	.03
36	Jim Corsi	.07	.05	.03
37	Rolando Roomes	.10	.08	.04
38	Scott Medvin	.07	.05	.03
39	Charlie Hayes	.20	.15	.08
40	Edgar Martinez	.15	.11	.06
41	Van Snider	.20	.15	.08
42	John Fishel	.07	.05	.02
43	Bruce Fields	.07	.05	.03
44	Darryl Hamilton	.09	.07	.04
45	Tom Prince	.09	.07	.03
46	Kirt Manwaring	.20	.15	.08
47	Steve Searcy	.12	.09	.05
48	Mike Harkey	.20	.15	.08
49	German Gonzalez	.07	.05	.03
50	Tony Perezchica	.07	.05	.03
51	Chad Kreuter	.15	.11	.06
52	Luis de los Santos	.10	.08	.04
53	Steve Curry	.07	.05	.03
54	Greg Bailey	.10	.08	.04
55	Ramon Martinez	.60	.45	.25
56	Ron Tingley	.07	.05	.03
57	Randy Kramer	.07	.05	.03
58	Alex Madrid	.07	.05	.03
59	Kevin Reimer	.15	.11	.06
60	Dave Otto	.07	.05	.03
61	Ken Patterson	.07	.05	.03
62	Keith Miller	.10	.08	.04
63	Randy Johnson	.10	.08	.04
64	Dwight Smith	.20	.15	.08
65	Eric Yelding	.20	.15	.08
66	Bob Geren	.40	.30	.15
67	Shane Turner	.25	.20	.10
68	Tom Gordon	.40	.30	.15
69	Jeff Huson	.30	.25	.12
70	Marty Brown	.25	.20	.10
71	Nelson Santovenia	.20	.15	.08
72	Roberto Alomar	.40	.30	.15
73	Mike Schooler	.15	.11	.06
74	Pete Smith	.10	.08	.04
75	John Costello	.07	.05	.03
76	Chris Sabo	.20	.15	.08
77	Damon Berryhill	.09	.07	.04
78	Mark Grace	.40	.30	.15
79	Melido Perez	.07	.05	.03
80	Al Leiter	.07	.05	.03
81	Todd Stottlemyre	.20	.15	.08
82	Mackey Sasser	.07	.05	.03
83	Don August	.07	.05	.03
84	Jeff Treadway	.07	.05	.03
85	Jody Reed	.09	.07	.05
86	Mike Campbell	.07	.05	.03
87	Ron Gant	.60	.45	.25
88	Ricky Jordan	.30	.25	.12
89	Terry Clark	.07	.05	.03

		MT	NR MT	EX
90	Roberto Kelly	.20	.15	.08
91	Pat Borders	.20	.15	.08
92	Bryan Harvey	.20	.15	.08
93	Joey Meyer	.10	.08	.04
94	Tim Belcher	.25	.20	.10
95	Walt Weiss	.15	.11	.06
96	Dave Gallagher	.15	.11	.06
97	Mike Macfarlane	.07	.05	.03
98	Craig Biggio	.30	.25	.12
99	Jack Armstrong	.15	.11	.06
100	Todd Burns	.07	.05	.03

1989 Score Superstar

This 100-card set features full-color action photos of baseball's superstars, and also includes six Magic Motion "Rookies to Remember" baseball trivia cards. The card fronts contain a bright red border with a blue line inside highlighting the photo. The Score logo appears in the bottom left corner. The player ID is displayed in unique fashion using overlapping triangles in white, green, and yellow. The flip side features a full-color player close-up directly beneath a bright red "Superstar" headline. The set was marketed along with the magazine "1989 Baseball's 100 Hottest Players". The magazine/card set combo was available at select retailers.

		MT	NR MT	EX
Complete Set:		8.00	6.00	3.25
Common Player:		.06	.05	.02
1	Jose Canseco	1.00	.70	.40
2	David Cone	.15	.11	.06
3	Dave Winfield	.15	.11	.06
4	George Brett	.15	.11	.06
5	Frank Viola	.09	.07	.05
6	Cory Snyder	.06	.05	.02
7	Alan Trammell	.09	.07	.04
8	Dwight Evans	.09	.07	.04
9	Tim Leary	.06	.05	.03
10	Don Mattingly	.80	.60	.30
11	Kirby Puckett	.30	.25	.12
12	Carney Lansford	.06	.05	.02
13	Dennis Martinez	.06	.05	.02
14	Kent Hrbek	.10	.08	.04
15	Doc Gooden	.30	.25	.12
16	Dennis Eckersley	.08	.06	.03
17	Kevin Seitzer	.08	.06	.03
18	Lee Smith	.06	.05	.02
19	Danny Tartabull	.15	.11	.06
20	Gerald Perry	.06	.05	.02
21	Gary Gaetti	.10	.08	.04
22	Rick Reuschel	.08	.06	.03
23	Keith Hernandez	.08	.06	.03
24	Jeff Reardon	.06	.05	.02
25	Mark McGwire	.50	.40	.20
26	Juan Samuel	.06	.05	.02
27	Jack Clark	.06	.05	.02
28	Robin Yount	.15	.11	.06
29	Steve Bedrosian	.06	.05	.02
30	Kirk Gibson	.08	.06	.03
31	Barry Bonds	.08	.06	.03
32	Dan Plesac	.06	.05	.02
33	Steve Sax	.06	.05	.02
34	Jeff Robinson	.06	.05	.02
35	Orel Hershiser	.10	.08	.04
36	Julio Franco	.08	.06	.03

		MT	NR MT	EX
37	Dave Righetti	.06	.05	.02
38	Bob Knepper	.06	.05	.02
39	Carlton Fisk	.08	.06	.03
41	Doug Jones	.06	.05	.02
42	Bobby Bonilla	.20	.15	.08
43	Ellis Burks	.30	.25	.12
44	Pedro Guerrero	.15	.11	.06
45	Rickey Henderson	.25	.20	.12
46	Glenn Davis	.10	.08	.04
47	Benny Santiago	.15	.11	.06
48	Greg Maddux	.20	.15	.08
49	Teddy Higuera	.06	.05	.02
50	Darryl Strawberry	.30	.25	.12
51	Mike Scott	.08	.06	.03
52	Mike Henneman	.06	.05	.02
53	Eric Davis	.35	.25	.12
54	Paul Molitor	.09	.07	.04
55	Rafael Palmeiro	.06	.05	.02
56	Joe Carter	.09	.07	.05
57	Ryne Sandberg	.15	.11	.06
58	Tony Fernandez	.08	.06	.03
59	Barry Larkin	.10	.08	.04
60	Ozzie Guillen	.06	.05	.02
61	Tom Browning	.06	.05	.02
62	Mark Davis	.08	.06	.03
63	Tom Henke	.06	.05	.02
64	Nolan Ryan	.80	.60	.30
65	Fred McGriff	.30	.25	.12
66	Dale Murphy	.10	.08	.06
67	Mark Langston	.10	.08	.06
68	Bobby Thigpen	.06	.05	.02
69	Mark Gubicza	.08	.06	.03
70	Mike Greenwell	.50	.40	.20
71	Ron Darling	.06	.05	.02
72	Gerald Young	.06	.05	.02
73	Wally Joyner	.10	.08	.04
74	Andres Galarraga	.10	.08	.04
75	Danny Jackson	.06	.05	.02
76	Mike Schmidt	.25	.20	.10
77	Cal Ripken, Jr.	.15	.11	.06
78	Alvin Davis	.08	.06	.03
79	Bruce Hurst	.06	.05	.02
80	Andre Dawson	.12	.09	.05
81	Bob Boone	.06	.05	.02
82	Harold Reynolds	.06	.05	.02
83	Eddie Murray	.06	.05	.02
84	Robby Thompson	.06	.05	.02
85	Will Clark	.80	.60	.30
86	Vince Coleman	.09	.07	.04
87	Doug Drabek	.06	.05	.02
88	Ozzie Smith	.08	.06	.03
89	Bob Welch	.06	.05	.02
90	Roger Clemens	.25	.20	.10
91	George Bell	.08	.06	.03
92	Andy Van Slyke	.08	.06	.03
93	Willie McGee	.06	.05	.02
94	Todd Worrell	.06	.05	.02
95	Tim Raines	.06	.05	.02
96	Kevin McReynolds	.10	.08	.04
97	John Franco	.06	.05	.02
98	Jim Gott	.06	.05	.02
99	Johnny Ray	.06	.05	.02
100	Wade Boggs	.50	.40	.20

1989 Score Yankees

This 33-card New York Yankee team set was produced by Score as an in-stadium promotion in 1989 and was distributed to fans attending the July

29 game at Yankee Stadium. The standard-size cards include a full-color player photo with a line drawing of the famous Yankee Stadium facade running along the top of the card. The player's name, "New York Yankees" and position appear below the photo. A second full-color photo is included on the back of the card, along with stats, data and a brief player profile. The set includes a special Thurman Munson commemorative card.

		MT	NR MT	EX
Complete Set:		8.00	6.00	3.25
Common Player:		.15	.11	.06
1	Don Mattingly	1.75	1.25	.70
2	Steve Sax	.30	.25	.12
3	Alvaro Espinoza	.25	.20	.10
4	Luis Polonia	.20	.15	.08
5	Jesse Barfield	.25	.20	.10
6	Dave Righetti	.25	.20	.10
7	Dave Winfield	.50	.40	.20
8	John Candelaria	.15	.11	.06
9	Wayne Tolleson	.15	.11	.06
10	Ken Phelps	.15	.11	.06
11	Rafael Santana	.15	.11	.06
12	Don Slaught	.15	.11	.06
13	Mike Pagliarulo	.20	.15	.08
14	Lance McCullers	.15	.11	.06
15	Dave LaPoint	.15	.11	.06
16	Dale Mohorcic	.15	.11	.06
17	Steve Balboni	.15	.11	.06
18	Roberto Kelly	.50	.40	.20
19	Andy Hawkins	.25	.20	.10
20	Mel Hall	.20	.15	.08
21	Tom Brookens	.15	.11	.06
22	Deion Sanders	.70	.50	.30
23	Richard Dotson	.15	.11	.06
24	Lee Guetterman	.15	.11	.06
25	Bob Geren	.30	.25	.12
26	Jimmy Jones	.15	.11	.06
27	Chuck Cary	.15	.11	.06
28	Ron Guidry	.25	.20	.10
29	Hal Morris	1.00	.70	.40
30	Clay Parker	.25	.20	.10
31	Dallas Green	.20	.15	.08
32	Thurman Munson	.70	.50	.30
33	Sponsor Card	.15	.11	.06

1990 Score

The regular Score set increased to 704 cards in 1990. Included were a series of cards picturing first-round draft picks, an expanded subset of rookie cards, four World Series specials, five Highlight cards, and a 13-card "Dream Team" series featuring the game's top players pictured on old tobacco-style cards. For the first time in a Score set, team logos are displayed on the card fronts in the lower right corner. Card backs again include a full-color portrait photo with player data. A one-paragraph write-up of each player was again provided by former Sports Illustrated editor Les Woodcock. The Score set was again distributed with "Magic Motion" triva cards, this year using "Baseball's Most Valuable Players" as its theme.

		MT	NR MT	EX
Complete Set:		20.00	15.00	8.00
Common Player:		.04	.03	.02
1	Don Mattingly	.35	.25	.14
2	Cal Ripken, Jr.	.40	.30	.15
3	Dwight Evans	.08	.06	.03
4	Barry Bonds	.12	.09	.05
5	Kevin McReynolds	.12	.09	.05
6	Ozzie Guillen	.05	.04	.02
7	Terry Kennedy	.04	.03	.02
8	Bryan Harvey	.06	.05	.02
9	Alan Trammell	.09	.07	.04
10	Cory Snyder	.09	.07	.04
11	Jody Reed	.05	.04	.02
12	Roberto Alomar	.30	.25	.12
13	Pedro Guerrero	.09	.07	.04
14	Gary Redus	.04	.03	.02
15	Marty Barrett	.05	.04	.02
16	Ricky Jordan	.20	.15	.08
17	Joe Magrane	.07	.05	.03
18	Sid Fernandez	.07	.05	.03
19	Rich Dotson	.04	.03	.02
20	Jack Clark	.09	.07	.04
21	Bob Walk	.05	.04	.02
22	Ron Karkovice	.04	.03	.02
23	Lenny Harris(FC)	.10	.07	.04
24	Phil Bradley	.06	.05	.02
25	Andres Galarraga	.15	.11	.06
26	Brian Downing	.06	.05	.02
27	Dave Martinez	.06	.05	.02
28	Eric King	.04	.03	.02
29	Barry Lyons	.04	.03	.02
30	Dave Schmidt	.04	.03	.02
31	Mike Boddicker	.06	.05	.04
32	Tom Foley	.04	.03	.02
33	Brady Anderson	.07	.05	.03
34	Jim Presley	.05	.04	.02
35	Lance Parrish	.06	.05	.02
36	Von Hayes	.09	.07	.03
37	Lee Smith	.06	.05	.02
38	Herm Winningham	.04	.03	.02
39	Alejandro Pena	.04	.03	.02
40	Mike Scott	.09	.07	.04
41	Joe Orsulak	.04	.03	.02
42	Rafael Ramirez	.05	.04	.02
43	Gerald Young	.05	.04	.02
44	Dick Schofield	.05	.04	.02
45	Dave Smith	.06	.05	.02
46	Dave Magadan	.07	.05	.03
47	Dennis Martinez	.06	.05	.02
48	Greg Minton	.04	.03	.02
49	Milt Thompson	.04	.03	.02
50	Orel Hershiser	.12	.09	.05
51	Bip Roberts(FC)	.09	.07	.04
52	Jerry Browne	.09	.07	.04
53	Bob Ojeda	.05	.04	.02
54	Fernando Valenzuela	.09	.07	.04
55	Matt Nokes	.09	.07	.04
56	Brook Jacoby	.08	.06	.03
57	Frank Tanana	.05	.04	.02
58	Scott Fletcher	.05	.04	.02
59	Ron Oester	.05	.04	.02
60	Bob Boone	.08	.06	.03
61	Dan Gladden	.08	.06	.03
62	Darnell Coles	.04	.03	.02
63	Gregg Olson	.25	.20	.10
64	Todd Burns	.05	.04	.02
65	Todd Benzinger	.07	.05	.03
66	Dale Murphy	.12	.09	.05
67	Mike Flanagan	.06	.05	.02
68	Jose Oquendo	.06	.05	.02
69	Cecil Espy	.08	.06	.03
70	Chris Sabo	.10	.07	.04
71	Shane Rawley	.05	.04	.02
72	Tom Brunansky	.08	.06	.03
73	Vance Law	.05	.04	.02
74	B.J. Surhoff	.08	.06	.03
75	Lou Whitaker	.09	.07	.04
76	Ken Caminiti	.09	.07	.04
77	Nelson Liriano	.04	.03	.02
78	Tommy Gregg	.09	.07	.04
79	Don Slaught	.05	.04	.02
80	Eddie Murray	.12	.09	.05
81	Joe Boever	.08	.06	.02
82	Charlie Leibrandt	.06	.05	.02
83	Jose Lind	.06	.05	.02
84	Tony Phillips	.05	.04	.02
85	Mitch Webster	.04	.03	.02
86	Dan Plesac	.07	.05	.02
87	Rick Mahler	.05	.04	.02
88	Steve Lyons	.05	.04	.02
89	Tony Fernandez	.09	.07	.04

#	Player	MT	NR MT	EX
90	Ryne Sandberg	.30	.25	.12
91	Nick Esasky	.09	.07	.04
92	Luis Salazar	.04	.03	.02
93	Pete Incaviglia	.08	.06	.03
94	Ivan Calderon	.06	.05	.02
95	Jeff Treadway	.06	.05	.02
96	Kurt Stillwell	.06	.05	.02
97	Gary Sheffield	.25	.20	.10
98	Jeffrey Leonard	.07	.05	.03
99	Andres Thomas	.05	.04	.02
100	Roberto Kelly	.15	.11	.06
101	Alvaro Espinoza(FC)	.15	.11	.06
102	Greg Gagne	.05	.04	.02
103	John Farrell	.05	.04	.02
104	Willie Wilson	.05	.04	.02
105	Glenn Braggs	.08	.06	.03
106	Chet Lemon	.06	.05	.02
107	Jamie Moyer	.06	.05	.02
108	Chuck Crim	.04	.03	.02
109	Dave Valle	.04	.03	.02
110	Walt Weiss	.10	.07	.04
111	Larry Sheets	.04	.03	.02
112	Don Robinson	.05	.04	.02
113	Danny Heep	.04	.03	.02
114	Carmelo Martinez	.06	.05	.02
115	Dave Gallagher	.08	.06	.03
116	Mike LaValliere	.05	.04	.02
117	Bob McClure	.04	.03	.02
118	Rene Gonzales	.04	.03	.02
119	Mark Parent	.05	.04	.02
120	Wally Joyner	.15	.11	.06
121	Mark Gubicza	.09	.07	.04
122	Tony Pena	.08	.06	.03
123	Carmen Castillo	.04	.03	.02
124	Howard Johnson	.20	.15	.08
125	Steve Sax	.10	.08	.04
126	Tim Belcher	.10	.08	.04
127	Tim Burke	.06	.05	.02
128	Al Newman	.04	.03	.02
129	Dennis Rasmussen	.05	.04	.02
130	Doug Jones	.06	.05	.02
131	Fred Lynn	.09	.07	.04
132	Jeff Hamilton	.06	.05	.02
133	German Gonzalez	.05	.04	.02
134	John Morris	.05	.04	.02
135	Dave Parker	.10	.08	.04
136	Gary Pettis	.05	.04	.02
137	Dennis Boyd	.07	.05	.02
138	Candy Maldonado	.06	.05	.02
139	Rick Cerone	.04	.03	.02
140	George Brett	.15	.11	.06
141	Dave Clark	.05	.04	.02
142	Dickie Thon	.05	.04	.02
143	Junior Ortiz	.04	.03	.02
144	Don August	.06	.05	.02
145	Gary Gaetti	.10	.08	.04
146	Kirt Manwaring	.12	.09	.05
147	Jeff Reed	.04	.03	.02
148	Jose Alvarez(FC)	.08	.06	.03
149	Mike Schooler	.08	.06	.03
150	Mark Grace	.25	.20	.10
151	Geronimo Berroa	.08	.06	.03
152	Barry Jones	.04	.03	.02
153	Geno Petralli	.05	.04	.02
154	Jim Deshaies	.08	.06	.03
155	Barry Larkin	.15	.11	.06
156	Alfredo Griffin	.05	.04	.02
157	Tom Henke	.06	.05	.02
158	Mike Jeffcoat(FC)	.05	.04	.02
159	Bob Welch	.09	.07	.04
160	Julio Franco	.10	.08	.04
161	Henry Cotto	.04	.03	.02
162	Terry Steinbach	.10	.08	.04
163	Damon Berryhill	.08	.06	.03
164	Tim Crews	.04	.03	.02
165	Tom Browning	.09	.07	.04
166	Frd Manrique	.04	.03	.02
167	Harold Reynolds	.09	.07	.04
168	Ron Hassey	.05	.04	.02
169	Shawon Dunston	.08	.06	.03
170	Bobby Bonilla	.15	.11	.06
171	Tom Herr	.07	.05	.03
172	Mike Heath	.04	.03	.02
173	Rich Gedman	.05	.04	.02
174	Bill Ripken	.05	.04	.02
175	Pete O'Brien	.07	.05	.03
176a	Lloyd McClendon (uniform number 1 on back)	1.00	.70	.40
176b	Lloyd McClendon (uniform number 10 on back)	.20	.15	.08
177	Brian Holton	.05	.04	.02

#	Player	MT	NR MT	EX
178	Jeff Blauser	.05	.04	.02
179	Jim Eisenreich	.05	.04	.02
180	Bert Blyleven	.09	.07	.04
181	Rob Murphy	.05	.04	.02
182	Bill Doran	.07	.05	.03
183	Curt Ford	.04	.03	.02
184	Mike Henneman	.06	.05	.02
185	Eric Davis	.20	.15	.08
186	Lance McCullers	.06	.05	.03
187	*Steve Davis*(FC)	.15	.11	.06
188	Bill Wegman	.05	.04	.02
189	Brian Harper	.06	.05	.02
190	Mike Moore	.09	.07	.04
191	Dale Mohorcic	.04	.03	.02
192	Tim Wallach	.09	.07	.04
193	Keith Hernandez	.09	.07	.04
194	Dave Righetti	.07	.05	.03
195a	Bret Saberhagen ("joke" on card back)	.25	.20	.10
195b	Bret Saberhagen ("joker" on card back)	.30	.25	.12
196	Paul Kilgus	.04	.03	.02
197	Bud Black	.05	.04	.02
198	Juan Samuel	.09	.07	.04
199	Kevin Seitzer	.15	.11	.06
200	Darryl Strawberry	.30	.25	.12
201	Dave Steib	.09	.07	.04
202	Charlie Hough	.06	.05	.02
203	Jack Morris	.08	.06	.03
204	Rance Mulliniks	.04	.03	.02
205	Alvin Davis	.10	.08	.04
206	Jack Howell	.06	.05	.02
207	Ken Patterson(FC)	.06	.05	.02
208	Terry Pendleton	.09	.07	.03
209	Craig Lefferts	.06	.05	.02
210	Kevin Brown(FC)	.10	.08	.04
211	Dan Petry	.04	.03	.02
212	Dave Leiper	.06	.05	.02
213	Daryl Boston	.04	.03	.02
214	Kevin Hickey(FC)	.08	.06	.03
215	Mike Krukow	.06	.05	.02
216	Terry Francona	.04	.03	.02
217	Kirk McCaskill	.08	.06	.03
218	Scott Bailes	.05	.04	.02
219	Bob Forsch	.04	.03	.02
220	Mike Aldrete	.05	.04	.02
221	Steve Buechele	.06	.05	.02
222	Jesse Barfield	.09	.07	.05
223	Juan Berenguer	.06	.05	.02
224	Andy McGaffigan	.06	.05	.02
225	Pete Smith	.09	.07	.04
226	Mike Witt	.06	.05	.02
227	Jay Howell	.08	.06	.03
228	Scott Bradley	.05	.04	.02
229	*Jerome Walton*	.15	.11	.06
230	Greg Swindell	.15	.11	.06
231	Atlee Hammaker	.04	.03	.02
232	Mike Devereaux	.09	.07	.04
233	Ken Hill	.09	.07	.04
234	Craig Worthington	.15	.11	.06
235	Scott Terry	.08	.06	.03
236	Brett Butler	.09	.07	.04
237	Doyle Alexander	.07	.05	.03
238	Dave Anderson	.04	.03	.02
239	Bob Milacki	.10	.08	.04
240	Dwight Smith	.50	.40	.20
241	Otis Nixon	.04	.03	.02
242	Pat Tabler	.06	.05	.02
243	Derek Lilliquist	.12	.09	.05
244	Danny Tartabull	.15	.11	.06
245	Wade Boggs	.30	.25	.12
246	Scott Garrelts	.08	.06	.03
247	Spike Owen	.04	.03	.02
248	Norm Charlton	.12	.09	.05
249	Gerald Perry	.06	.05	.02
250	Nolan Ryan	.50	.40	.20
251	Kevin Gross	.07	.05	.03
252	Randy Milligan	.07	.05	.03
253	Mike LaCoss	.05	.04	.02
254	Dave Bergman	.04	.03	.02
255	Tony Gwynn	.35	.25	.12
256	Felix Fermin	.04	.03	.02
257	Greg Harris	.10	.08	.04
258	*Junior Felix*	.20	.15	.08
259	Mark Davis	.09	.07	.04
260	Vince Coleman	.15	.11	.06
261	Paul Gibson	.10	.08	.04
262	Mitch Williams	.10	.08	.04
263	Jeff Russell	.08	.06	.03
264	*Omar Vizquel*	.10	.07	.04
265	Andre Dawson	.12	.09	.05

#	Player	MT	NR MT	EX
266	Storm Davis	.08	.06	.03
267	Guillermo Hernandez	.04	.03	.02
268	Mike Felder	.05	.04	.02
269	Tom Candiotti	.05	.04	.02
270	Bruce Hurst	.09	.07	.04
271	Fred McGriff	.30	.25	.12
272	Glenn Davis	.15	.11	.60
273	John Franco	.09	.07	.04
274	Rich Yett	.04	.03	.02
275	Craig Biggio	.15	.11	.06
276	Gene Larkin	.05	.04	.02
277	Rob Dibble	.15	.11	.06
278	Randy Bush	.05	.04	.02
279	Kevin Bass	.08	.06	.03
280a	Bo Jackson ("Watham" on card back)	.60	.45	.25
280b	Bo Jackson ("Wathan" on card back)	1.00	.70	.40
281	Wally Backman	.06	.05	.02
282	Larry Andersen	.04	.03	.02
283	Chris Bosio	.09	.07	.04
284	Juan Agosto	.04	.03	.02
285	Ozzie Smith	.10	.08	.04
286	George Bell	.10	.08	.04
287	Rex Hudler	.05	.04	.02
288	Pat Borders	.10	.08	.04
289	Danny Jackson	.07	.05	.03
290	Carlton Fisk	.09	.07	.04
291	Tracy Jones	.05	.04	.02
292	Allan Anderson	.07	.05	.03
293	Johnny Ray	.07	.05	.03
294	Lee Guetterman	.04	.03	.02
295	Paul O'Neill	.09	.07	.05
296	Carney Lansford	.08	.06	.03
297	Tom Brookens	.04	.03	.02
298	Claudell Washington	.08	.06	.03
299	Hubie Brooks	.08	.06	.03
300	Will Clark	.60	.45	.25
301	*Kenny Rogers*	.20	.15	.08
302	Darrell Evans	.07	.05	.03
303	Greg Briley	.25	.20	.10
304	Donn Pall	.09	.07	.04
305	Teddy Higuera	.09	.07	.04
306	Dan Pasqua	.07	.05	.02
307	Dave Winfield	.15	.11	.06
308	Dennis Powell	.04	.03	.02
309	Jose DeLeon	.08	.06	.03
310	Roger Clemens	.25	.20	.10
311	Melido Perez	.09	.07	.04
312	Devon White	.09	.07	.04
313	Doc Gooden	.25	.20	.10
314	*Carlos Martinez*	.20	.15	.08
315	Dennis Eckersley	.10	.08	.04
316	Clay Parker	.12	.09	.05
317	Rick Honeycutt	.05	.04	.02
318	Tim Laudner	.05	.04	.02
319	Joe Carter	.10	.08	.04
320	Robin Yount	.20	.15	.08
321	Felix Jose	.30	.25	.15
322	Mickey Tettleton	.09	.07	.04
323	Mike Gallego	.04	.03	.02
324	Edgar Martinez	.09	.07	.04
325	Dave Henderson	.09	.07	.04
326	Chili Davis	.09	.07	.04
327	Steve Balboni	.05	.04	.02
328	Jody Davis	.04	.03	.02
329	Shawn Hillegas	.04	.03	.02
330	Jim Abbott	.35	.25	.12
331	John Dopson	.10	.08	.04
332	Mark Williamson	.04	.03	.02
333	Jeff Robinson	.08	.06	.03
334	John Smiley	.09	.07	.04
335	Bobby Thigpen	.07	.05	.03
336	Garry Templeton	.05	.04	.02
337	Marvell Wynne	.05	.04	.02
338a	Ken Griffey, Sr. (uniform number 25 on card back)	.25	.20	.10
338b	Ken Griffey, Sr. (uniform number 30 on card back)	3.00	2.25	1.25
339	*Steve Finley*	.25	.20	.10
340	Ellis Burks	.25	.20	.10
341	Frank Williams	.04	.03	.02
342	Mike Morgan	.05	.04	.02
343	Kevin Mitchell	.35	.25	.12
344	Joel Youngblood	.04	.03	.02
345	Mike Greenwell	.25	.20	.10
346	Glenn Wilson	.05	.04	.02
347	John Costello	.05	.04	.02
348	Wes Gardner	.04	.03	.02
349	Jeff Ballard	.09	.07	.04
350	Mark Thurmond	.04	.03	.02
351	Randy Myers	.07	.05	.03
352	Shawn Abner	.07	.05	.03
353	Jesse Orosco	.04	.03	.02
354	Greg Walker	.05	.04	.02
355	Pete Harnisch	.15	.11	.06
356	Steve Farr	.05	.04	.02
357	Dave LaPoint	.05	.04	.02
358	Willie Fraser	.05	.04	.02
359	Mickey Hatcher	.04	.03	.02
360	Rickey Henderson	.30	.25	.12
361	Mike Fitzgerald	.04	.03	.02
362	Bill Schroeder	.04	.03	.02
363	Mark Carreon	.10	.08	.04
364	Ron Jones	.10	.08	.04
365	Jeff Montgomery	.06	.05	.02
366	Bill Krueger(FC)	.04	.03	.02
367	John Cangelosi	.04	.03	.02
368	Jose Gonzalez	.10	.08	.04
369	*Greg Hibbard*(FC)	.30	.25	.12
370	John Smoltz	.15	.11	.06
371	*Jeff Brantley*	.15	.11	.06
372	Frank White	.08	.06	.03
373	Ed Whitson	.06	.05	.02
374	Willie McGee	.09	.07	.04
375	Jose Canseco	.70	.50	.30
376	Randy Ready	.04	.03	.02
377	Don Aase	.04	.03	.02
378	Tony Armas	.05	.04	.02
379	Steve Bedrosian	.07	.05	.03
380	Chuck Finley	.07	.05	.03
381	Kent Hrbek	.12	.09	.05
382	Jim Gantner	.06	.05	.02
383	Mel Hall	.06	.05	.02
384	Mike Marshall	.07	.05	.03
385	Mark McGwire	.20	.15	.08
386	Wayne Tolleson	.04	.03	.02
387	Brian Holton	.05	.04	.02
388	*John Wetteland*	.20	.15	.08
389	Darren Daulton	.04	.03	.02
390	Rob Deer	.07	.05	.03
391	John Moses	.04	.03	.02
392	Todd Worrell	.07	.05	.03
393	Chuck Cary(FC)	.10	.08	.04
394	Stan Javier	.05	.04	.02
395	Willie Randolph	.09	.07	.04
396	Bill Buckner	.06	.05	.02
397	Robby Thompson	.07	.05	.02
398	Mike Scioscia	.07	.05	.03
399	Lonnie Smith	.09	.07	.04
400	Kirby Puckett	.40	.30	.15
401	Mark Langston	.15	.11	.06
402	Danny Darwin	.04	.03	.02
403	Greg Maddux	.15	.11	.06
404	Lloyd Moseby	.07	.05	.02
405	Rafael Palmeiro	.09	.07	.04
406	Chad Kreuter	.10	.08	.04
407	Jimmy Key	.09	.07	.05
408	Tim Birtsas	.04	.03	.02
409	Tim Raines	.10	.08	.04
410	Dave Stewart	.09	.07	.04
411	*Eric Yelding*(FC)	.15	.11	.06
412	*Kent Anderson*(FC)	.15	.11	.06
413	Les Lancaster	.05	.04	.02
414	Rick Dempsey	.04	.03	.02
415	Randy Johnson	.10	.08	.04
416	Gary Carter	.07	.05	.03
417	Rolando Roomes	.15	.11	.06
418	Dan Schatzeder	.04	.03	.02
419	Bryn Smith	.07	.05	.03
420	Ruben Sierra	.20	.15	.08
421	Steve Jeltz	.04	.03	.02
422	Ken Oberkfell	.04	.03	.02
423	Sid Bream	.04	.03	.02
424	Jim Clancy	.04	.03	.02
425	Kelly Gruber	.09	.07	.04
426	Rick Leach	.04	.03	.02
427	Lenny Dykstra	.07	.05	.03
428	Jeff Pico	.06	.05	.02
429	John Cerutti	.06	.05	.02
430	David Cone	.15	.11	.06
431	Jeff Kunkel	.04	.03	.02
432	Luis Aquino	.05	.04	.02
433	Ernie Whitt	.05	.04	.02
434	Bo Diaz	.05	.04	.02
435	Steve Lake	.04	.03	.02
436	Pat Perry	.04	.03	.02
437	Mike Davis	.05	.04	.02
438	Cecilio Guante	.04	.03	.02
439	Duane Ward	.04	.03	.02
440	Andy Van Slyke	.10	.08	.04
441	Gene Nelson	.04	.03	.02

		MT	NR MT	EX
442	Luis Polonia	.06	.05	.02
443	Kevin Elster	.06	.05	.02
444	Keith Moreland	.06	.05	.02
445	Roger McDowell	.06	.05	.02
446	Ron Darling	.08	.06	.03
447	Ernest Riles	.04	.03	.02
448	Mookie Wilson	.08	.06	.03
449a	Bill Spiers (66 missing for year of birth)	1.25	.90	.50
449b	Bill Spiers (1966 for birth year)	.30	.25	.12
450	Rick Sutcliffe	.07	.05	.03
451	Nelson Santovenia	.10	.08	.04
452	Andy Allanson	.04	.03	.02
453	Bob Melvin	.04	.03	.02
454	Benny Santiago	.12	.09	.05
455	Jose Uribe	.05	.04	.02
456	Bill Landrum(FC)	.08	.06	.03
457	Bobby Witt	.07	.05	.03
458	Kevin Romine	.07	.05	.03
459	Lee Mazzilli	.04	.03	.02
460	Paul Molitor	.10	.08	.04
461	Ramon Martinez(FC)	.60	.45	.25
462	Frank DiPino	.04	.03	.02
463	Walt Terrell	.06	.05	.02
464	Bob Geren	.30	.25	.12
465	Rick Reuchel	.09	.07	.04
466	Mark Grant	.06	.05	.02
467	John Kruk	.07	.05	.03
468	Gregg Jefferies	.60	.45	.25
469	R.J. Reynolds	.04	.03	.02
470	Harold Baines	.09	.07	.04
471	Dennis Lamp	.04	.03	.02
472	Tom Gordon	.20	.15	.08
473	Terry Puhl	.04	.03	.02
474	Curtis Wilkerson	.04	.03	.02
475	Dan Quisenberry	.05	.04	.02
476	Oddibe McDowell	.07	.05	.03
477	Zane Smith	.04	.03	.02
478	Franklin Stubbs	.04	.03	.02
479	Wallace Johnson	.04	.03	.02
480	Jay Tibbs	.04	.03	.02
481	Tom Glavine	.09	.07	.03
482	Manny Lee	.05	.04	.02
483	Joe Hesketh	.04	.03	.02
484	Mike Bielecki	.07	.05	.03
485	Greg Brock	.06	.05	.02
486	Pascual Perez	.06	.05	.02
487	Kirk Gibson	.09	.07	.04
488	Scott Sanderson	.05	.04	.02
489	Domingo Ramos	.04	.03	.02
490	Kal Daniels	.10	.08	.04
491a	David Wells (Reverse negative on back photo)	3.00	2.25	1.25
491b	David Wells (Corrected)	.05	.04	.02
492	Jerry Reed	.04	.03	.02
493	Eric Show	.06	.05	.02
494	Mike Pagliarulo	.06	.05	.02
495	Ron Robinson	.05	.04	.02
496	Brad Komminsk	.04	.03	.02
497	Greg Litton	.15	.11	.06
498	Chris James	.07	.05	.02
499	Luis Quinones(FC)	.05	.04	.02
500	Frank Viola	.10	.08	.04
501	Tim Teufel	.05	.04	.02
502	Terry Leach	.04	.03	.02
503	Matt Williams	.20	.15	.08
504	Tim Leary	.06	.05	.02
505	Doug Drabek	.06	.05	.02
506	Mariano Duncan	.06	.05	.02
507	Charlie Hayes	.10	.08	.04
508	Joey Belle	.70	.50	.30
509	Pat Sheridan	.05	.04	.02
510	Mackey Sasser	.05	.04	.02
511	Jose Rijo	.09	.07	.04
512	Mike Smithson	.04	.03	.02
513	Gary Ward	.04	.03	.02
514	Dion James	.06	.05	.02
515	Jim Gott	.06	.05	.02
516	Drew Hall(FC)	.07	.05	.03
517	Doug Bair	.04	.03	.02
518	Scott Scudder	.20	.15	.08
519	Rick Aguilera	.06	.05	.02
520	Rafael Belliard	.05	.04	.02
521	Jay Buhner	.10	.08	.04
522	Jeff Reardon	.06	.05	.02
523	Steve Rosenberg(FC)	.09	.07	.04
524	Randy Velarde(FC)	.09	.07	.04
525	Jeff Musselman	.09	.07	.04
526	Bill Long	.06	.05	.02
527	Gary Wayne	.10	.08	.04
528	Dave Johnson(FC)	.15	.11	.06

		MT	NR MT	EX
529	Ron Kittle	.08	.06	.03
530	Erik Hanson(FC)	.20	.15	.08
531	Steve Wilson(FC)	.20	.15	.08
532	Joey Meyer	.04	.03	.02
533	Curt Young	.04	.03	.02
534	Kelly Downs	.06	.05	.02
535	Joe Girardi	.20	.15	.08
536	Lance Blankenship	.09	.07	.04
537	Greg Mathews	.05	.04	.02
538	Donell Nixon	.04	.03	.02
539	Mark Knudson(FC)	.09	.07	.04
540	Jeff Wetherby(FC)	.15	.11	.06
541	Darrin Jackson	.04	.03	.02
542	Terry Mulholland	.09	.07	.03
543	Eric Hetzel(FC)	.15	.11	.06
544	Rick Reed(FC)	.15	.11	.06
545	Dennis Cook(FC)	.20	.15	.08
546	Mike Jackson	.05	.04	.02
547	Brian Fisher	.06	.05	.02
548	Gene Harris(FC)	.20	.15	.08
549	Jeff King(FC)	.20	.15	.08
550	Dave Dravecky (Salute)	.10	.08	.04
551	Randy Kutcher(FC)	.08	.06	.03
552	Mark Portugal	.06	.05	.02
553	Jim Corsi(FC)	.12	.09	.05
554	Todd Stottlemyre	.12	.09	.05
555	Scott Bankhead	.09	.07	.04
556	Ken Dayley	.05	.04	.02
557	Rick Wrona(FC)	.15	.11	.06
558	Sammy Sosa(FC)	.40	.30	.15
559	Keith Miller	.08	.06	.03
560	Ken Griffey Jr.	2.00	1.50	.80
561a	Ryne Sandberg (No Errors- 3B Position designation)	10.00	7.50	4.00
561b	Ryne Sandberg (No Errors- No position designation)	.50	.40	.20
562	Billy Hatcher	.06	.05	.02
563	Jay Bell(FC)	.09	.07	.04
564	Jack Daugherty(FC)	.15	.11	.06
565	Rich Monteleone	.20	.15	.08
566	Bo Jackson (All-Star MVP)	.30	.25	.12
567	Tony Fossas(FC)	.10	.08	.04
568	Roy Smith(FC)	.15	.11	.06
569	Jaime Navarro(FC)	.25	.20	.10
570	Lance Johnson(FC)	.15	.11	.06
571	Mike Dyer(FC)	.25	.20	.10
572	Kevin Ritz(FC)	.20	.15	.08
573	Dave West	.15	.11	.06
574	Gary Mielke(FC)	.25	.20	.10
575	Scott Lusader(FC)	.09	.07	.04
576	Joe Oliver	.30	.25	.12
577	Sandy Alomar, Jr.	.25	.20	.10
578	Andy Benes(FC)	.30	.25	.12
579	Tim Jones	.07	.05	.03
580	Randy McCament(FC)	.15	.11	.06
581	Curt Schilling(FC)	.15	.11	.06
582	John Orton(FC)	.15	.11	.06
583a	Milt Cuyler (played in 998 games)(FC)	2.00	1.50	.80
583b	Milt Cuyler (played in 98 games)(FC)	.40	.30	.15
584	Eric Anthony(FC)	.25	.20	.10
585	Greg Vaughn(FC)	.60	.45	.25
586	Deion Sanders(FC)	.50	.40	.20
587	Jose DeJesus(FC)	.15	.11	.06
588	Chip Hale(FC)	.15	.11	.06
589	John Olerud(FC)	.70	.50	.30
590	Steve Olin(FC)	.20	.15	.08
591	Marquis Grissom(FC)	.60	.45	.25
592	Moises Alou(FC)	.50	.40	.20
593	Mark Lemke(FC)	.10	.08	.04
594	Dean Palmer(FC)	.80	.60	.30
595	Robin Ventura(FC)	1.00	.70	.40
596	Tino Martinez(FC)	.50	.40	.20
597	Mike Huff(FC)	.25	.20	.10
598	Scott Hemond(FC)	.25	.20	.10
599	Wally Whitehurst(FC)	.20	.15	.08
600	Todd Zeile(FC)	.50	.40	.20
601	Glenallen Hill(FC)	.35	.25	.14
602	Hal Morris(FC)	.15	.11	.06
603	Juan Bell(FC)	.15	.11	.06
604	Bobby Rose(FC)	.25	.20	.10
605	Matt Merullo(FC)	.20	.15	.08
606	Kevin Maas(FC)	.50	.40	.20
607	Randy Nosek(FC)	.15	.11	.06
608	Billy Bates(FC)	.15	.11	.06
609	Mike Stanton(FC)	.25	.20	.10
610	Goose Gozzo(FC)	.20	.15	.08
611	Charles Nagy(FC)	.40	.30	.15
612	Scott Coolbaugh(FC)	.20	.15	.08
613	Jose Vizcaino(FC)	.25	.20	.10

		MT	NR MT	EX
614	Greg Smith(FC)	.20	.15	.08
615	Jeff Huson(FC)	.25	.20	.10
616	Mickey Weston(FC)	.15	.11	.06
617	John Pawlowski(FC)	.15	.11	.06
618a	Joe Skalski (uniform #27)(FC)	.15	.11	.06
618b	Joe Skalski (uniform #67)(FC)	2.00	1.50	.80
619	Bernie Williams(FC)	.60	.45	.25
620	Shawn Holman(FC)	.15	.11	.06
621	Gary Eave(FC)	.15	.11	.06
622	Darrin Fletcher(FC)	.25	.20	.10
623	Pat Combs(FC)	.20	.15	.08
624	Mike Blowers(FC)	.25	.20	.10
625	Kevin Appier(FC)	.30	.25	.12
626	Pat Austin(FC)	.15	.11	.06
627	Kelly Mann(FC)	.20	.15	.08
628	Matt Kinzer(FC)	.15	.11	.06
629	Chris Hammond(FC)	.25	.20	.10
630	Dean Wilkins(FC)	.15	.11	.06
631	Larry Walker(FC)	.60	.45	.25
632	Blaine Beatty(FC)	.20	.15	.08
633a	Tom Barrett (uniform #29)(FC)	.15	.11	.06
633b	Tom Barrett (uniform #14)(FC)	4.00	3.00	1.50
634	Stan Belinda(FC)	.35	.25	.14
635	Tex Smith(FC)	.15	.11	.06
636	Hensley Meulens(FC)	.15	.11	.06
637	Juan Gonzalez(FC)	3.00	2.25	1.25
638	Lenny Webster(FC)	.20	.15	.08
639	Mark Gardner(FC)	.25	.20	.10
640	Tommy Greene(FC)	.20	.15	.08
641	Mike Hartley(FC)	.20	.15	.08
642	Phil Stephenson(FC)	.15	.11	.06
643	Kevin Mmahat(FC)	.15	.11	.06
644	Ed Whited(FC)	.15	.11	.06
645	Delino DeShields(FC)	.40	.30	.15
646	Kevin Blankenship(FC)	.15	.11	.06
647	Paul Sorrento(FC)	.40	.30	.15
648	Mike Roesler(FC)	.15	.11	.06
649	Jason Grimsley(FC)	.25	.20	.10
650	Dave Justice(FC)	2.00	1.50	.80
651	Scott Cooper(FC)	.25	.20	.10
652	Dave Eiland(FC)	.15	.11	.06
653	Mike Munoz(FC)	.20	.15	.08
654	Jeff Fischer(FC)	.15	.11	.06
655	Terry Jorgenson(FC)	.20	.15	.08
656	George Canale(FC)	.20	.15	.08
657	Brian DuBois(FC)	.15	.11	.06
658	Carlos Quintana	.10	.08	.04
659	Luis De los santos	.10	.08	.04
660	Jerald Clark	.10	.08	.04
661	#1 Draft Pick (Donald Harris)(FC)	.20	.15	.08
662	#1 Draft Pick (Paul Coleman)(FC)	.20	.15	.08
663	#1 Draft Pick (Frank Thomas)(FC)	7.00	5.25	2.75
664	#1 Draft Pick (Brent Mayne)(FC)	.30	.25	.12
665	#1 Draft Pick (Eddie Zosky)(FC)	.25	.20	.10
666	#1 Draft Pick (Steve Hosey)(FC)	.20	.15	.08
667	#1 Draft Pick (Scott Bryant)(FC)	.20	.15	.08
668	#1 Draft Pick (Tom Goodwin)(FC)	.40	.30	.15
669	#1 Draft Pick (Cal Eldred)(FC)	1.50	1.25	.60
670	#1 Draft Pick (Earl Cunningham)(FC)	.25	.20	.10
671	#1 Draft Pick (Alan Zinter)(FC)	.25	.20	.10
672	#1 Draft Pick (Chuck Knoblauch)(FC)	2.00	1.50	.80
673	#1 Draft Pick (Kyle Abbott)(FC)	.25	.20	.10
674	#1 Draft Pick (Roger Salkeld)(FC)	.60	.45	.25
675	#1 Draft Pick (Maurice Vaughn)(FC)	.60	.45	.25
676	#1 Draft Pick (Kiki Jones)(FC)	.20	.15	.08
677	#1 Draft Pick (Tyler Houston)(FC)	.25	.20	.10
678	#1 Draft Pick (Jeff Jackson)(FC)	.15	.11	.06
679	#1 Draft Pick (Greg Gohr) (#1 Draft Pick)(FC)	.25	.20	.10
680	#1 Draft Pick (Ben McDonald) (#1 Draft Pick)(FC)	.60	.45	.25
681	#1 Draft Pick (Greg Blosser) (#1 Draft Pick)(FC)	.50	.40	.20
682	#1 Draft Pick (Willie Green) (#1 Draft Pick)(FC)	.25	.20	.10
683	Dream Team (Wade Boggs)	.20	.15	.08
684	Dream Team (Will Clark)	.20	.15	.08
685	Dream Team (Tony Gwynn)	.20	.15	.08
686	Dream Team (Rickey Henderson)	.20	.15	.08
687	Dream Team (Bo Jackson)	.30	.25	.12
688	Dream Team (Mark Langston)	.20	.15	.11
689	Dream Team (Barry Larkin)	.20	.15	.11
690	Dream Team (Kirby Puckett)	.20	.15	.11
691	Dream Team (Ryne Sandberg)	.30	.25	.12
692	Dream Team (Mike Scott)	.20	.15	.11
693	Dream Team (Terry Steinbach)	.20	.15	.11
694	Dream Team (Bobby Thigpen)	.20	.15	.11

		MT	NR MT	EX
695	Dream Team (Mitch Williams)	.20	.15	.11
696	5000 K (Nolan Ryan)	.50	.40	.20
697	FB/BB NIKE (Bo Jackson)	2.00	1.50	.80
698	ALCS MVP (Rickey Henderson)	.25	.20	.10
699	NLCS MVP (Will Clark)	.25	.20	.10
700	World Series 1,2	.30	.25	.12
701	Candlestick	.30	.25	.12
702	World Series Game 3	.30	.25	.12
703	World Series Wrap-up	.30	.25	.12
704	200 Hit (Wade Boggs)	.25	.20	.10
-----	A. Bartlett Giamatti (Bonus-Dream Team)	2.00	1.50	.80
-----	Pat Combs (Bonus-Dream Team)	.30	.25	.12
-----	Todd Zeile (Bonus-Dream Team)	2.00	1.50	.80
-----	Luis de los Santos (Bonus-Dream Team)	.30	.25	.12
-----	Mark Lemke (Bonus-Dream Team)	.50	.40	.20
-----	Robin Ventura (Bonus-Dream Team)	8.00	6.00	3.00
-----	Jeff Huson (Bonus-Dream Team)	.30	.25	.12
-----	Greg Vaughn (Bonus-Dream Team)	3.00	2.25	1.25
-----	Marquis Grissom (Bonus-Dream Team)	3.00	2.25	1.25
-----	Eric Anthony (Bonus-Dream Team)	.60	.45	.25

1990 Score McDonald's

This 25-card set was released exclusively in the Boise, Idaho area. The set features baseball all-stars and was very limited in production. The cards are styled after the regular 1990 Score issue. The McDonald's logo appears on the front and back of the cards.

		MT	NR MT	EX
	Complete Set:	200.00	150.00	80.00
	Common Player:	4.00	3.00	1.50
1	Will Clark	25.00	18.00	10.00
2	Sandy Alomar, Jr.	5.00	3.75	2.00
3	Julio Franco	6.00	4.50	2.50
4	Carlton Fisk	10.00	7.50	4.00
5	Rickey Henderson	20.00	15.00	8.00
6	Matt Williams	7.00	5.25	2.75
7	John Franco	4.00	3.00	1.50
8	Ryne Sandberg	25.00	18.00	10.00
9	Kelly Gruber	4.00	3.00	1.50
10	Andre Dawson	8.00	6.00	3.25
11	Barry Bonds	8.00	6.00	3.25
12	Gary Sheffield	10.00	7.50	4.00
13	Ramon Martinez	5.00	3.75	2.00
14	Len Dykstra	5.00	3.75	2.00
15	Benito Santiago	4.00	3.00	1.50
16	Cecil Fielder	12.00	9.00	4.75
17	John Olerud	6.00	4.50	2.50
18	Roger Clemens	18.00	13.50	7.25
19	George Brett	15.00	11.00	6.00
20	George Bell	4.00	3.00	1.50
21	Ozzie Guillen	4.00	3.00	1.50
22	Steve Sax	4.00	3.00	1.50
23	Dave Stewart	5.00	3.75	2.00
24	Ozzie Smith	10.00	7.50	4.00
25	Robin Yount	15.00	11.00	6.00

1990 Score Rising Stars

For the second consecutive year Score produced a 100-card "Rising Stars" set. The 1990 Score Rising Stars were made available as a boxed set and were also marketed with a related magazine like the 1989 issue. Magic Motion trivia cards featuring past MVP's accompany the card set. The cards feature full- color action photos on the front and posed shots on the flip sides.

		MT	NR MT	EX
	Complete Set:	12.00	9.00	4.75
	Common Player:	.08	.06	.03
1	Tom Gordon	.25	.20	.10
2	Jerome Walton	.25	.20	.10
3	Ken Griffey,Jr.	3.00	2.25	1.25
4	Dwight Smith	.25	.20	.10
5	Jim Abbott	.25	.20	.10
6	Todd Zeile	.40	.30	.15
7	Donn Pall	.08	.06	.03
8	Rick Reed	.08	.06	.03
9	Joey Belle	.15	.11	.06
10	Gregg Jefferies	.35	.25	.14
11	Kevin Ritz	.10	.08	.04
12	Charlie Hayes	.15	.11	.06
13	Kevin Appier	.30	.25	.12
14	Jeff Huson	.15	.11	.06
15	Gary Wayne	.08	.06	.03
16	Eric Yelding	.15	.11	.06
17	Clay Parker	.08	.06	.03
18	Junior Felix	.30	.25	.12
19	Derek Lilliquist	.08	.06	.03
20	Gary Sheffield	.30	.25	.12
21	Craig Worthington	.08	.06	.03
22	Jeff Brantley	.10	.08	.04
23	Eric Hetzel	.10	.08	.04
24	Greg Harris	.08	.06	.03
25	John Wetteland	.20	.15	.08
26	Joe Oliver	.15	.11	.06
27	Kevin Maas	.80	.60	.30
28	Kevin Brown	.10	.08	.04
29	Mike Stanton	.15	.11	.06
30	Greg Vaughn	.40	.30	.15
31	Ron Jones	.08	.06	.03
32	Gregg Olson	.20	.15	.08
33	Joe Girardi	.10	.08	.04
34	Ken Hill	.08	.06	.03
35	Sammy Sosa	.35	.25	.14
36	Geronimo Berroa	.08	.06	.03
37	Omar Vizquel	.10	.08	.04
38	Dean Palmer	.10	.08	.04
39	John Olerud	.70	.50	.30
40	Deion Sanders	.25	.20	.10
41	Randy Kramer	.08	.06	.03
42	Scott Lusader	.08	.06	.03
43	Dave Johnson	.08	.06	.03
44	Jeff Wetherby	.08	.06	.03
45	Eric Anthony	.40	.30	.15
46	Kenny Rogers	.10	.08	.04
47	Matt Winters	.08	.06	.03
48	Goose Gozzo	.10	.08	.04
49	Carlos Quintana	.15	.11	.06
50	Bob Geren	.10	.08	.04
51	Chad Kreuter	.08	.06	.03
52	Randy Johnson	.10	.08	.04
53	Hensley Meulens	.15	.11	.06
54	Gene Harris	.10	.08	.04
55	Bill Spiers	.10	.08	.04
56	Kelly Mann	.15	.11	.06
57	Tom McCarthy	.08	.06	.03
58	Steve Finley	.10	.08	.04
59	Ramon Martinez	.50	.40	.20
60	Greg Briley	.08	.06	.03
61	Jack Daugherty	.10	.08	.04
62	Tim Jones	.08	.06	.03
63	Doug Strange	.08	.06	.03
64	John Orton	.08	.06	.03
65	Scott Scudder	.15	.11	.06
66	Mark Gardner	.20	.15	.08
67	Mark Carreon	.08	.06	.03
68	Bob Milacki	.08	.06	.03
69	Andy Benes	.10	.08	.04
70	Carlos Martinez	.10	.08	.04
71	Jeff King	.10	.08	.04
72	Brad Arnsberg	.08	.06	.03
73	Rick Wrona	.08	.06	.03
74	Cris Carpenter	.08	.06	.03
75	Dennis Cook	.08	.06	.03
76	Pete Harnisch	.10	.08	.04
77	Greg Hibbard	.15	.11	.06
78	Ed Whited	.08	.06	.03
79	Scott Coolbaugh	.15	.11	.06
80	Billy Bates	.08	.06	.03
81	German Gonzalez	.08	.06	.03
82	Lance Blankenship	.08	.06	.03
83	Lenny Harris	.10	.08	.04
84	Milt Cuyler	.20	.15	.08
85	Erik Hanson	.20	.15	.08
86	Kent Anderson	.08	.06	.03
87	Hal Morris	.40	.30	.15
88	Mike Brumley	.08	.06	.03
89	Ken Patterson	.08	.06	.03
90	Mike Devereaux	.08	.06	.03
91	Greg Litton	.10	.08	.04
92	Rolando Roomes	.08	.06	.03
93	Ben McDonald	.60	.45	.25
94	Curt Schilling	.10	.08	.04
95	Jose DeJesus	.15	.11	.06
96	Robin Ventura	.30	.25	.12
97	Steve Searcy	.08	.06	.03
98	Chip Hale	.10	.08	.04
99	Marquis Grissom	.40	.30	.15
100	Luis de los Santos	.10	.08	.04

1990 Score Superstar

100 of the game's top players are featured in this set. The card fronts feature full-color action photos and are similar in style to the past Score Superstar set. The set was marketed as a boxed set and with a special magazine devoted to baseball's 100 hottest players. Each set includes a series of Magic Motion cards honoring past MVP winners. The player cards measure 2-1/2" by 3-1/2" in size.

		MT	NR MT	EX
	Complete Set:	8.00	6.00	3.25
	Common Player:	.08	.06	.03
1	Kirby Puckett	.30	.25	.12
2	Steve Sax	.10	.08	.04
3	Tony Gwynn	.15	.11	.06
4	Willie Randolph	.08	.06	.03
5	Jose Canseco	.70	.50	.30
6	Ozzie Smith	.10	.08	.04
7	Rick Reuschel	.08	.06	.03

		MT	NR MT	EX
8	Bill Doran	.08	.06	.03
9	Mickey Tettleton	.08	.06	.03
10	Don Mattingly	.50	.40	.20
11	Greg Swindell	.08	.06	.03
12	Bert Blyleven	.10	.08	.04
13	Dave Stewart	.15	.11	.06
14	Andres Galarraga	.10	.08	.04
15	Darryl Strawberry	.30	.25	.12
16	Ellis Burks	.20	.15	.08
17	Paul O'Neill	.08	.06	.03
18	Bruce Hurst	.08	.06	.03
19	Dave Smith	.08	.06	.03
20	Carney Lansford	.08	.06	.03
21	Robby Thompson	.08	.06	.03
22	Gary Gaetti	.10	.08	.04
23	Jeff Russell	.08	.06	.03
24	Chuck Finley	.10	.08	.04
25	Mark McGwire	.35	.25	.14
26	Alvin Davis	.10	.08	.04
27	George Bell	.10	.08	.04
28	Cory Snyder	.08	.06	.03
29	Keith Hernandez	.08	.06	.03
30	Will Clark	.40	.30	.15
31	Steve Bedrosian	.08	.06	.03
32	Ryne Sandberg	.40	.30	.15
33	Tom Browning	.08	.06	.03
34	Tim Burke	.08	.06	.03
35	John Smoltz	.10	.08	.04
36	Phil Bradley	.08	.06	.03
37	Bobby Bonilla	.15	.11	.06
38	Kirk McCaskill	.08	.06	.03
39	Dave Righetti	.10	.08	.04
40	Bo Jackson	.70	.50	.30
41	Alan Trammell	.10	.08	.04
42	Mike Moore	.08	.06	.03
43	Harold Reynolds	.08	.06	.03
44	Nolan Ryan	.80	.60	.30
45	Fred McGriff	.25	.20	.10
46	Brian Downing	.08	.06	.03
47	Brett Butler	.08	.06	.03
48	Mike Scioscia	.08	.06	.03
49	John Franco	.08	.06	.03
50	Kevin Mitchell	.30	.25	.12
51	Mark Davis	.08	.06	.03
52	Glenn Davis	.15	.11	.06
53	Barry Bonds	.20	.15	.08
54	Dwight Evans	.10	.08	.04
55	Terry Steinbach	.08	.06	.03
56	Dave Gallagher	.08	.06	.03
57	Roberto Kelly	.10	.08	.04
58	Rafael Palmeiro	.10	.08	.04
59	Joe Carter	.10	.08	.04
60	Mark Grace	.20	.15	.08
61	Pedro Guerrero	.10	.08	.04
62	Von Hayes	.08	.06	.03
63	Benny Santiago	.15	.11	.06
64	Dale Murphy	.10	.08	.04
65	John Smiley	.08	.06	.03
66	Cal Ripken, Jr.	.40	.30	.15
67	Mike Greenwell	.25	.20	.10
68	Devon White	.08	.06	.03
69	Ed Whitson	.08	.06	.03
70	Carlton Fisk	.15	.11	.06
71	Lou Whitaker	.10	.08	.04
72	Danny Tartabull	.10	.08	.04
73	Vince Coleman	.10	.08	.04
74	Andre Dawson	.15	.11	.06
75	Tim Raines	.10	.08	.04
76	George Brett	.15	.11	.06
77	Tom Herr	.08	.06	.03
78	Andy Van Slyke	.10	.08	.04
79	Roger Clemens	.30	.25	.12
80	Wade Boggs	.30	.25	.12
81	Wally Joyner	.10	.08	.04
82	Lonnie Smith	.08	.06	.03
83	Howard Johnson	.15	.11	.06
84	Julio Franco	.15	.11	.06
85	Ruben Sierra	.20	.15	.08
86	Dan Plesac	.08	.06	.03
87	Bobby Thigpen	.15	.11	.06
88	Kevin Seitzer	.10	.08	.04
89	Dave Steib	.10	.08	.04
90	Rickey Henderson	.30	.25	.12
91	Jeffrey Leonard	.08	.06	.03
92	Robin Yount	.15	.11	.06
93	Mitch Williams	.10	.08	.04
94	Orel Hershiser	.20	.15	.08
95	Eric Davis	.25	.20	.10
96	Mark Langston	.10	.08	.04
97	Mike Scott	.08	.06	.03
98	Paul Molitor	.10	.08	.04

		MT	NR MT	EX
99	Doc Gooden	.25	.20	.10
100	Kevin Bass	.08	.06	.03

1990 Score Traded

This 110-card set features players with new teams as well as 1990 Major League rookies. The cards feature full-color action photos framed in yellow with an orange border. The player's name and position appear in green print below the photo. The team logo is displayed next to the player's name. The card backs feature posed player photos and follow the style of the regular 1990 Score issue. The cards are numbered 1T-110T. Young hockey phenom Eric Lindros is featured trying out for the Toronto Blue Jays.

		MT	NR MT	EX
Complete Set:		12.00	9.00	4.75
Common Player:		.06	.05	.02
1T	Dave Winfield	.15	.11	.06
2T	Kevin Bass	.06	.05	.02
3T	Nick Esasky	.06	.05	.02
4T	Mitch Webster	.06	.05	.02
5T	Pascual Perez	.06	.05	.02
6T	Gary Pettis	.06	.05	.02
7T	Tony Pena	.08	.06	.03
8T	Candy Maldonado	.08	.06	.03
9T	Cecil Fielder	.30	.25	.12
10T	Carmelo Martinez	.06	.05	.02
11T	Mark Langston	.08	.06	.03
12T	Dave Parker	.15	.11	.06
13T	Don Slaught	.06	.05	.02
14T	Tony Phillips	.06	.05	.02
15T	John Franco	.08	.06	.03
16T	Randy Myers	.08	.06	.03
17T	Jeff Reardon	.08	.06	.03
18T	Sandy Alomar, Jr.	.20	.15	.08
19T	Joe Carter	.10	.08	.04
20T	Fred Lynn	.06	.05	.02
21T	Storm Davis	.06	.05	.02
22T	Craig Lefferts	.06	.05	.02
23T	Pete O'Brien	.06	.05	.02
24T	Dennis Boyd	.06	.05	.02
25T	Lloyd Moseby	.06	.05	.02
26T	Mark Davis	.06	.05	.02
27T	Tim Leary	.06	.05	.02
28T	Gerald Perry	.06	.05	.02
29T	Don Aase	.06	.05	.02
30T	Ernie Whitt	.06	.05	.02
31T	Dale Murphy	.10	.08	.04
32T	Alejandro Pena	.06	.05	.02
33T	Juan Samuel	.08	.06	.03
34T	Hubie Brooks	.08	.06	.03
35T	Gary Carter	.10	.08	.04
36T	Jim Presley	.06	.05	.02
37T	Wally Backman	.06	.05	.02
38T	Matt Nokes	.06	.05	.02
39T	Dan Petry	.06	.05	.02
40T	Franklin Stubbs	.06	.05	.02
41T	Jeff Huson	.15	.11	.06
42T	Billy Hatcher	.06	.05	.02
43T	Terry Leach	.06	.05	.02
44T	Phil Bradley	.06	.05	.02
45T	Claudell Washington	.06	.05	.02
46T	Luis Polonia	.06	.05	.02
47T	Daryl Boston	.06	.05	.02

		MT	NR MT	EX
48T	Lee Smith	.08	.06	.03
49T	Tom Brunansky	.08	.06	.03
50T	Mike Witt	.06	.05	.02
51T	Willie Randolph	.08	.06	.03
52T	Stan Javier	.06	.05	.02
53T	Brad Komminsk	.06	.05	.02
54T	John Candelaria	.06	.05	.02
55T	Bryn Smith	.06	.05	.02
56T	Glenn Braggs	.06	.05	.02
57T	Keith Hernandez	.08	.06	.03
58T	Ken Oberkfell	.06	.05	.02
59T	Steve Jeltz	.06	.05	.02
60T	Chris James	.06	.05	.02
61T	Scott Sanderson	.06	.05	.02
62T	Bill Long	.06	.05	.02
63T	Rick Cerone	.06	.05	.02
64T	Scott Bailes	.06	.05	.02
65T	Larry Sheets	.06	.05	.02
66T	Junior Ortiz	.06	.05	.02
67T	Francisco Cabrera(FC)	.20	.15	.08
68T	Gary DiSarcina(FC)	.15	.11	.06
69T	Greg Olson(FC)	.20	.15	.08
70T	Beau Allred(FC)	.20	.15	.11
71T	Oscar Azocar(FC)	.15	.11	.06
72T	Kent Mercker(FC)	.25	.20	.10
73T	John Burkett(FC)	.20	.15	.08
74T	Carlos Baerga(FC)	1.00	.70	.40
75T	Dave Hollins(FC)	.30	.25	.12
76T	Todd Hundley(FC)	.20	.15	.08
77T	Rick Parker(FC)	.15	.11	.06
78T	Steve Cummings(FC)	.15	.11	.06
79T	Bill Sampen(FC)	.25	.20	.10
80T	Jerry Kutzler(FC)	.15	.11	.06
81T	Derek Bell(FC)	1.00	.70	.40
82T	Kevin Tapani(FC)	.35	.25	.14
83T	Jim Leyritz(FC)	.25	.20	.10
84T	Ray Lankford(FC)	1.25	.90	.50
85T	Wayne Edwards(FC)	.15	.11	.06
86T	Frank Thomas	7.00	5.25	2.75
87T	Tim Naehring(FC)	.20	.15	.08
88T	Willie Blair(FC)	.15	.11	.06
89T	Alan Mills(FC)	.25	.20	.10
90T	Scott Radinsky(FC)	.25	.20	.10
91T	Howard Farmer(FC)	.25	.20	.10
92T	Julio Machado(FC)	.15	.11	.06
93T	Rafael Valdez(FC)	.15	.11	.06
94T	Shawn Boskie(FC)	.25	.20	.10
95T	David Segui(FC)	.20	.15	.08
96T	Chris Hoiles(FC)	.30	.25	.12
97T	D.J. Dozier(FC)	.50	.40	.20
98T	Hector Villanueva(FC)	.25	.20	.10
99T	Eric Gunderson(FC)	.25	.20	.10
100T	Eric Lindros(FC)	6.00	4.50	2.50
101T	Dave Otto(FC)	.12	.09	.05
102T	Dana Kiecker(FC)	.20	.15	.08
103T	Tim Drummond(FC)	.15	.11	.06
104T	Mickey Pina(FC)	.25	.20	.10
105T	Craig Grebeck(FC)	.20	.15	.08
106T	Bernard Gilkey(FC)	.50	.40	.20
107T	Tim Layana(FC)	.25	.20	.10
108T	Scott Chiamparino(FC)	.30	.25	.12
109T	Steve Avery(FC)	2.00	1.50	.80
110T	Terry Shumpert(FC)	.20	.15	.08

1991 Score

Score introduced a two series format in 1991. The first series includes cards 1-441. Score cards once again feature multiple border colors within the set,

several subsets (Master Blaster, K-Man, Highlights and Rifleman), full-color action photos on the front, posed photos on the flip side. Score eliminated providing the player's uniform number on the 1991 cards. Card number 441 of Series I features a Jose Canseco Vanity Fair photo. All of the 1991 Dream Team cards feature this style. The 1991 Score set when complete with Series II will mark its biggest issue. Rookie prospects and #1 Draft Picks highlight the 1991 Score set. The second series was due for release in February of 1991.

		MT	NR MT	EX
Complete Set:		20.00	15.00	8.00
Common Player:		.04	.03	.02
1	Jose Canseco	.35	.25	.14
2	Ken Griffey, Jr.	.80	.60	.30
3	Ryne Sandberg	.20	.15	.08
4	Nolan Ryan	.30	.25	.12
5	Bo Jackson	.30	.25	.12
6	Bret Saberhagen	.12	.09	.05
7	Will Clark	.20	.15	.08
8	Ellis Burks	.15	.11	.06
9	Joe Carter	.15	.11	.06
10	Rickey Henderson	.25	.20	.10
11	Ozzie Guillen	.10	.08	.04
12	Wade Boggs	.20	.15	.08
13	Jerome Walton	.15	.11	.06
14	John Franco	.10	.08	.04
15	Ricky Jordan	.08	.06	.03
16	Wally Backman	.04	.03	.02
17	Rob Dibble	.10	.08	.04
18	Glenn Braggs	.05	.04	.02
19	Cory Snyder	.10	.08	.04
20	Kal Daniels	.10	.08	.04
21	Mark Langston	.10	.08	.04
22	Kevin Gross	.06	.05	.02
23	Don Mattingly	.25	.20	.10
24	Dave Righetti	.08	.06	.03
25	Roberto Alomar	.25	.20	.10
26	Robby Thompson	.06	.05	.02
27	Jack McDowell	.08	.06	.03
28	Bip Roberts	.08	.06	.03
29	Jay Howell	.05	.04	.02
30	Dave Steib	.08	.06	.03
31	Johnny Ray	.04	.03	.02
32	Steve Sax	.10	.08	.04
33	Terry Mulholland	.08	.06	.03
34	Lee Guetterman	.04	.03	.02
35	Tim Raines	.12	.09	.05
36	Scott Fletcher	.04	.03	.02
37	Lance Parrish	.08	.06	.03
38	Tony Phillips	.05	.04	.02
39	Todd Stottlemyre	.06	.05	.02
40	Alan Trammell	.12	.09	.05
41	Todd Burns	.04	.03	.02
42	Mookie Wilson	.06	.05	.02
43	Chris Bosio	.05	.04	.02
44	Jeffrey Leonard	.06	.05	.02
45	Doug Jones	.08	.06	.03
46	Mike Scott	.08	.06	.03
47	Andy Hawkins	.05	.04	.02
48	Harold Reynolds	.08	.06	.03
49	Paul Molitor	.12	.09	.05
50	John Farrell	.05	.04	.02
51	Danny Darwin	.06	.05	.02
52	Jeff Blauser	.04	.03	.02
53	John Tudor	.05	.04	.02
54	Milt Thompson	.04	.03	.02
55	Dave Justice	.30	.25	.12
56	Greg Olson	.12	.09	.05
57	Willie Blair	.12	.09	.05
58	Rick Parker	.10	.08	.04
59	Shawn Boskie	.15	.11	.06
60	Kevin Tapani	.10	.08	.04
61	Dave Hollins	.20	.15	.08
62	Scott Radinsky	.12	.09	.05
63	Francisco Cabrera	.10	.08	.04
64	Tim Layana	.12	.09	.05
65	Jim Leyritz	.12	.09	.05
66	Wayne Edwards	.08	.06	.03
67	Lee Stevens(FC)	.15	.11	.06
68	Bill Sampen	.15	.11	.06
69	Craig Grebeck	.10	.08	.04
70	John Burkett	.15	.11	.06
71	Hector Villanueva	.15	.11	.06
72	Oscar Azocar	.15	.11	.06
73	Alan Mills	.15	.11	.06

#	Name	MT	NR MT	EX		#	Name	MT	NR MT	EX
74	*Carlos Baerga*	.25	.20	.10		165	Mark Carreon	.05	.04	.02
75	Charles Nagy	.08	.06	.03		166	Mel Hall	.05	.04	.02
76	Tim Drummond	.08	.06	.03		167	Gary Mielke	.06	.05	.02
77	*Dana Kiecker*	.15	.11	.06		168	Cecil Fielder	.25	.20	.10
78	*Tom Edens*(FC)	.10	.08	.04		169	Darrin Jackson	.04	.03	.02
79	Kent Mercker	.10	.08	.04		170	Rick Aguilera	.06	.05	.02
80	Steve Avery	.20	.15	.08		171	Walt Weiss	.06	.05	.02
81	Lee Smith	.08	.06	.03		172	Steve Farr	.05	.04	.02
82	Dave Martinez	.05	.04	.02		173	Jody Reed	.06	.05	.02
83	Dave Winfield	.12	.09	.05		174	Mike Jeffcoat	.04	.03	.02
84	Bill Spiers	.06	.05	.02		175	Mark Grace	.15	.11	.06
85	Dan Pasqua	.05	.04	.02		176	Larry Sheets	.04	.03	.02
86	Randy Milligan	.06	.05	.02		177	Bill Gullickson	.05	.04	.02
87	Tracy Jones	.04	.03	.02		178	Chris Gwynn	.06	.05	.02
88	Greg Myers(FC)	.06	.05	.02		179	Melido Perez	.06	.05	.02
89	Keith Hernandez	.06	.05	.02		180	Sid Fernandez	.08	.06	.03
90	Todd Benzinger	.06	.05	.02		181	Tim Burke	.06	.05	.02
91	Mike Jackson	.05	.04	.02		182	Gary Pettis	.05	.04	.02
92	Mike Stanley	.04	.03	.02		183	Rob Murphy	.04	.03	.02
93	Candy Maldonado	.06	.05	.02		184	Craig Lefferts	.06	.05	.02
94	John Kruk	.05	.04	.02		185	Howard Johnson	.10	.08	.04
95	Cal Ripken,Jr.	.30	.25	.12		186	Ken Caminiti	.05	.04	.02
96	Willie Fraser	.04	.03	.02		187	Tim Belcher	.06	.05	.02
97	Mike Felder	.04	.03	.02		188	Greg Cadaret	.04	.03	.02
98	Bill Landrum	.05	.04	.02		189	Matt Williams	.15	.11	.06
99	Chuck Crim	.04	.03	.02		190	Dave Magadan	.08	.06	.03
100	Chuck Finley	.08	.06	.03		191	Geno Petralli	.04	.03	.02
101	Kirt Manwaring	.06	.05	.02		192	Jeff Robinson	.05	.04	.02
102	Jaime Navarro	.08	.06	.03		193	Jim Deshaies	.05	.04	.02
103	Dickie Thon	.04	.03	.02		194	Willie Randolph	.06	.05	.02
104	Brian Downing	.05	.04	.02		195	George Bell	.10	.08	.04
105	Jim Abbott	.12	.09	.05		196	Hubie Brooks	.10	.08	.04
106	Tom Brookens	.04	.03	.02		197	Tom Gordon	.10	.08	.04
107	Darryl Hamilton	.06	.05	.02		198	Mike Fitzgerald	.04	.03	.02
108	Bryan Harvey	.06	.05	.02		199	Mike Pagliarulo	.05	.04	.02
109	Greg Harris	.04	.03	.02		200	Kirby Puckett	.15	.11	.06
110	Greg Swindell	.08	.06	.03		201	Shawon Dunston	.08	.06	.03
111	Juan Berenguer	.04	.03	.02		202	Dennis Boyd	.05	.04	.02
112	Mike Heath	.04	.03	.02		203	Junior Felix	.08	.06	.03
113	Scott Bradley	.04	.03	.02		204	Alejandro Pena	.04	.03	.02
114	Jack Morris	.08	.06	.03		205	Pete Smith	.05	.04	.02
115	Barry Jones	.05	.04	.02		206	Tom Glavine	.06	.05	.02
116	Kevin Romine	.04	.03	.02		207	Luis Salazar	.04	.03	.02
117	Garry Templeton	.05	.04	.02		208	John Smoltz	.08	.06	.03
118	Scott Sanderson	.05	.04	.02		209	Doug Dascenzo	.05	.04	.02
119	Roberto Kelly	.08	.06	.03		210	Tim Wallach	.08	.06	.03
120	George Brett	.15	.11	.06		211	Greg Gagne	.05	.04	.02
121	Oddibe McDowell	.05	.04	.02		212	Mark Gubicza	.08	.06	.03
122	Jim Acker	.04	.03	.02		213	Mark Parent	.04	.03	.02
123	Bill Swift	.05	.04	.02		214	Ken Oberkfell	.04	.03	.02
124	Eric King	.05	.04	.02		215	Gary Carter	.08	.06	.03
125	Jay Buhner	.06	.05	.02		216	Rafael Palmeiro	.10	.08	.04
126	Matt Young	.04	.03	.02		217	Tom Niedenfuer	.04	.03	.02
127	Alvaro Espinoza	.05	.04	.02		218	Dave LaPoint	.05	.04	.02
128	Greg Hibbard	.08	.06	.03		219	Jeff Treadway	.05	.04	.02
129	Jeff Robinson	.05	.04	.02		220	Mitch Williams	.06	.05	.02
130	Mike Greenwell	.15	.11	.06		221	Jose DeLeon	.05	.04	.02
131	Dion James	.04	.03	.02		222	Mike LaValliere	.05	.04	.02
132	Donn Pall	.04	.03	.02		223	Darrel Akerfelds	.04	.03	.02
133	Lloyd Moseby	.06	.05	.02		224	Kent Anderson	.05	.04	.02
134	Randy Velarde	.04	.03	.02		225	Dwight Evans	.08	.06	.03
135	Allan Anderson	.05	.04	.02		226	Gary Redus	.04	.03	.02
136	Mark Davis	.06	.05	.02		227	Paul O'Neill	.06	.05	.02
137	Eric Davis	.15	.11	.06		228	Marty Barrett	.05	.04	.02
138	Phil Stephenson	.04	.03	.02		229	Tom Browning	.06	.05	.02
139	Felix Fermin	.04	.03	.02		230	Terry Pendleton	.06	.05	.02
140	Pedro Guerrero	.08	.06	.03		231	Jack Armstrong	.08	.06	.03
141	Charlie Hough	.05	.04	.02		232	Mike Boddicker	.06	.05	.02
142	Mike Henneman	.06	.05	.02		233	Neal Heaton	.05	.04	.02
143	Jeff Montgomery	.06	.05	.02		234	Marquis Grissom	.10	.08	.04
144	Lenny Harris	.06	.05	.02		235	Bert Blyleven	.08	.06	.03
145	Bruce Hurst	.06	.05	.02		236	Curt Young	.05	.04	.02
146	Eric Anthony	.15	.11	.06		237	Don Carman	.05	.04	.02
147	Paul Assenmacher	.04	.03	.02		238	Charlie Hayes	.06	.05	.02
148	Jesse Barfield	.06	.05	.02		239	Mark Knudson	.04	.03	.02
149	Carlos Quintana	.08	.06	.03		240	Todd Zeile	.20	.15	.08
150	Dave Stewart	.12	.09	.05		241	Larry Walker	.10	.08	.04
151	Roy Smith	.04	.03	.02		242	Jerald Clark	.06	.05	.02
152	Paul Gibson	.04	.03	.02		243	Jeff Ballard	.05	.04	.02
153	Mickey Hatcher	.04	.03	.02		244	Jeff King	.06	.05	.02
154	Jim Eisenreich	.04	.03	.02		245	Tom Brunansky	.08	.06	.03
155	Kenny Rogers	.06	.05	.02		246	Darren Daulton	.06	.05	.02
156	Dave Schmidt	.04	.03	.02		247	Scott Terry	.04	.03	.02
157	Lance Johnson	.06	.05	.02		248	Rob Deer	.06	.05	.02
158	Dave West	.05	.04	.02		249	Brady Anderson	.04	.03	.02
159	Steve Balboni	.04	.03	.02		250	Lenny Dykstra	.08	.06	.03
160	Jeff Brantley	.08	.06	.03		251	Greg Harris	.06	.05	.02
161	Craig Biggio	.06	.05	.02		252	Mike Hartley	.08	.06	.03
162	Brook Jacoby	.06	.05	.02		253	Joey Cora	.04	.03	.02
163	Dan Gladden	.05	.04	.02		254	Ivan Calderon	.08	.06	.03
164	Jeff Reardon	.08	.06	.03		255	Ted Power			

#	Player	MT	NR MT	EX		#	Player	MT	NR MT	EX
256	Sammy Sosa	.15	.11	.06		347	Tim McIntosh(FC)	.15	.11	.06
257	Steve Buechele	.05	.04	.02		348	Phil Plantier(FC)	.80	.60	.30
258	Mike Devereaux	.05	.04	.02		349	Terry Shumpert	.15	.11	.06
259	Brad Komminsk	.04	.03	.02		350	Darren Lewis(FC)	.30	.25	.12
260	Teddy Higuera	.08	.06	.03		351	David Walsh(FC)	.20	.15	.08
261	Shawn Abner	.05	.04	.02		352	Scott Chiamparino	.15	.11	.06
262	Dave Valle	.05	.04	.02		353	Julio Valera(FC)	.15	.11	.06
263	Jeff Huson	.06	.05	.02		354	Anthony Telford(FC)	.20	.15	.08
264	Edgar Martinez	.06	.05	.02		355	Kevin Wickander(FC)	.10	.08	.04
265	Carlton Fisk	.10	.08	.04		356	Tim Naehring	.20	.15	.08
266	Steve Finley	.06	.05	.02		357	Jim Poole(FC)	.20	.15	.08
267	John Wetteland	.06	.05	.02		358	Mark Whiten(FC)	.40	.30	.15
268	Kevin Appier	.08	.06	.03		359	Terry Wells(FC)	.20	.15	.08
269	Steve Lyons	.04	.03	.02		360	Rafael Valdez	.10	.08	.04
270	Mickey Tettleton	.05	.04	.02		361	Mel Stottlemyre(FC)	.15	.11	.06
271	Luis Rivera	.04	.03	.02		362	David Segui	.20	.15	.08
272	Steve Jeltz	.04	.03	.02		363	Paul Abbott	.15	.11	.06
273	R.J. Reynolds	.04	.03	.02		364	Steve Howard(FC)	.15	.11	.06
274	Carlos Martinez	.05	.04	.02		365	Karl Rhodes(FC)	.25	.20	.10
275	Dan Plesac	.06	.05	.02		366	Rafael Novoa(FC)	.15	.11	.06
276	Mike Morgan	.04	.03	.02		367	Joe Grahe(FC)	.15	.11	.06
277	Jeff Russell	.06	.05	.02		368	Darren Reed(FC)	.15	.11	.06
278	Pete Incaviglia	.06	.05	.02		369	Jeff McKnight(FC)	.10	.08	.04
279	Kevin Seitzer	.08	.06	.03		370	Scott Leius(FC)	.10	.08	.04
280	Bobby Thigpen	.08	.06	.03		371	Mark Dewey(FC)	.15	.11	.06
281	Stan Javier	.04	.03	.02		372	Mark Lee(FC)	.15	.11	.06
282	Henry Cotto	.04	.03	.02		373	Rosario Rodriguez(FC)	.15	.11	.06
283	Gary Wayne	.05	.04	.02		374	Chuck McElroy(FC)	.10	.08	.04
284	Shane Mack	.05	.04	.02		375	Mike Bell(FC)	.15	.11	.06
285	Brian Holman	.06	.05	.02		376	Mickey Morandini(FC)	.10	.08	.04
286	Gerald Perry	.05	.04	.02		377	Bill Haselman(FC)	.15	.11	.06
287	Steve Crawford	.04	.03	.02		378	Dave Pavlas(FC)	.15	.11	.06
288	Nelson Liriano	.04	.03	.02		379	Derrick May(FC)	.30	.25	.12
289	Don Aase	.04	.03	.02		380	Jeromy Burnitz (#1 Draft Pick)(FC)			
290	Randy Johnson	.06	.05	.02				.80	.60	.30
291	Harold Baines	.08	.06	.03		381	Donald Peters (#1 Draft Pick)(FC)	.25	.20	.10
292	Kent Hrbek	.08	.06	.03		382	Alex Fernandez (#1 Draft Pick)(FC)	.30	.25	.12
293	Les Lancaster	.04	.03	.02		383	Michael Mussina (#1 Draft Pick)(FC)			
294	Jeff Musselman	.04	.03	.02				1.50	1.25	.60
295	Kurt Stillwell	.06	.05	.02		384	Daniel Smith (#1 Draft Pick)(FC)	.25	.20	.10
296	Stan Belinda	.06	.05	.02		385	Lance Dickson (#1 Draft Pick)(FC)	.40	.30	.15
297	Lou Whitaker	.08	.06	.03		386	Carl Everett (#1 Draft Pick)(FC)	.40	.30	.15
298	Glenn Wilson	.05	.04	.02		387	Thomas Nevers (#1 Draft Pick)(FC)			
299	Omar Vizquel	.04	.03	.02				.30	.25	.12
300	Ramon Martinez	.20	.15	.08		388	Adam Hyzdu (#1 Draft Pick)(FC)	.40	.30	.15
301	Dwight Smith	.06	.05	.02		389	Todd Van Poppel (#1 Draft Pick)(FC)			
302	Tim Crews	.04	.03	.02				1.00	.70	.40
303	Lance Blankenship	.05	.04	.02		390	Rondell White (#1 Draft Pick)(FC)	.60	.45	.25
304	Sid Bream	.06	.05	.02		391	Marc Newfield (#1 Draft Pick)(FC)			
305	Rafael Ramirez	.04	.03	.02				1.25	.90	.50
306	Steve Wilson	.06	.05	.02		392	Julio Franco (AS)	.10	.08	.04
307	Mackey Sasser	.06	.05	.02		393	Wade Boggs (AS)	.20	.15	.08
308	Franklin Stubbs	.06	.05	.02		394	Ozzie Guillen (AS)	.10	.08	.04
309	Jack Daugherty	.06	.05	.02		395	Cecil Fielder (AS)	.20	.15	.08
310	Eddie Murray	.10	.08	.04		396	Ken Griffey, Jr. (AS)	.40	.30	.15
311	Bob Welch	.08	.06	.03		397	Rickey Henderson (AS)	.20	.15	.08
312	Brian Harper	.06	.05	.02		398	Jose Canseco (AS)	.30	.25	.12
313	Lance McCullers	.04	.03	.02		399	Roger Clemens (AS)	.15	.11	.06
314	Dave Smith	.06	.05	.02		400	Sandy Alomar, Jr. (AS)	.10	.08	.04
315	Bobby Bonilla	.15	.11	.06		401	Bobby Thigpen (AS)	.10	.08	.04
316	Jerry Don Gleaton	.04	.03	.02		402	Bobby Bonilla (Master Blaster)	.10	.08	.04
317	Greg Maddux	.08	.06	.03		403	Eric Davis (Master Blaster)	.10	.08	.04
318	Keith Miller	.05	.04	.03		404	Fred McGriff (Master Blaster)	.10	.08	.04
319	Mark Portugal	.04	.03	.02		405	Glenn Davis (Master Blaster)	.10	.08	.04
320	Robin Ventura	.25	.20	.10		406	Kevin Mitchell (Master Blaster)	.10	.08	.04
321	Bob Ojeda	.04	.03	.02		407	Rob Dibble (K-Man)	.10	.08	.04
322	Mike Harkey	.08	.06	.03		408	Ramon Martinez (K-Man)	.15	.11	.06
323	Jay Bell	.06	.05	.02		409	David Cone (K-Man)	.10	.08	.04
324	Mark McGwire	.20	.15	.08		410	Bobby Witt (K-Man)	.10	.08	.04
325	Gary Gaetti	.10	.08	.04		411	Mark Langston (K-Man)	.10	.08	.04
326	Jeff Pico	.04	.03	.02		412	Bo Jackson (Rifleman)	.30	.25	.12
327	Kevin McReynolds	.08	.06	.03		413	Shawon Dunston (Rifleman)	.10	.08	.04
328	Frank Tanana	.05	.04	.02		414	Jesse Barfield (Rifleman)	.08	.06	.03
329	Eric Yelding	.06	.05	.02		415	Ken Caminiti (Rifleman)	.08	.06	.03
330	Barry Bonds	.20	.15	.08		416	Benito Santiago (Rifleman)	.10	.08	.04
331	Brian McRae(FC)	.30	.25	.12		417	Nolan Ryan (Highlight)	.30	.25	.12
332	Pedro Munoz(FC)	.40	.30	.15		418	Bobby Thigpen (Highlight)	.10	.08	.04
333	Daryl Irvine(FC)	.15	.11	.06		419	Ramon Martinez (Highlight)	.15	.11	.06
334	Chris Hoiles	.25	.20	.10		420	Bo Jackson (Highlight)	.20	.15	.08
335	Thomas Howard(FC)	.20	.15	.08		421	Carlton Fisk (Highlight)	.10	.08	.04
336	Jeff Schulz(FC)	.15	.11	.06		422	Jimmy Key	.06	.05	.02
337	Jeff Manto(FC)	.15	.11	.06		423	Junior Noboa(FC)	.05	.04	.02
338	Beau Allred	.10	.08	.04		424	Al Newman	.04	.03	.02
339	Mike Bordick(FC)	.15	.11	.06		425	Pat Borders	.05	.04	.02
340	Todd Hundley	.15	.11	.06		426	Von Hayes	.08	.06	.03
341	Jim Vatcher(FC)	.15	.11	.06		427	Tim Teufel	.04	.03	.02
342	Luis Sojo(FC)	.10	.08	.04		428	Eric Plunk	.04	.03	.02
343	Jose Offerman(FC)	.30	.25	.12		429	John Moses	.04	.03	.02
344	Pete Coachman(FC)	.15	.11	.06		430	Mike Witt	.05	.04	.02
345	Mike Benjamin(FC)	.10	.08	.04		431	Otis Nixon	.04	.03	.02
346	Ozzie Canseco(FC)	.15	.11	.06		432	Tony Fernandez	.08	.06	.03

	MT	NR MT	EX			MT	NR MT	EX
433 Rance Mulliniks	.04	.03	.02	524 Bruce Ruffin	.05	.04	.02
434 Dan Petry	.04	.03	.02	525 Robin Yount	.15	.11	.06
435 Bob Geren	.05	.04	.02	526 Tom Foley	.04	.03	.02
436 Steve Frey(FC)	.06	.05	.02	527 Pat Perry	.04	.03	.02
437 Jamie Moyer	.05	.04	.02	528 Greg Vaughn	.15	.11	.06
438 Junior Ortiz	.04	.03	.02	529 Wally Whitehurst	.06	.05	.02
439 Tom O'Malley	.04	.03	.02	530 Norm Charlton	.06	.05	.02
440 Pat Combs	.06	.05	.02	531 Marvell Wynne	.04	.03	.02
441 Jose Canseco (Dream Team)	2.00	1.50	.80	532 Jim Gantner	.05	.04	.02
442 Alfredo Griffin	.04	.03	.02	533 Greg Litton	.04	.03	.02
443 Andres Galarraga	.08	.06	.03	534 Manny Lee	.05	.04	.02
444 Bryn Smith	.04	.03	.02	535 Scott Bailes	.04	.03	.02
445 Andre Dawson	.12	.09	.05	536 Charlie Leibrandt	.04	.03	.02
446 Juan Samuel	.06	.05	.02	537 Roger McDowell	.05	.04	.02
447 Mike Aldrete	.04	.03	.02	538 Andy Benes	.15	.11	.06
448 Ron Gant	.12	.09	.05	539 Rick Honeycutt	.04	.03	.02
449 Fernando Valenzuela	.08	.06	.03	540 Doc Gooden	.15	.11	.06
450 Vince Coleman	.08	.06	.03	541 Scott Garrelts	.04	.03	.02
451 Kevin Mitchell	.15	.11	.06	542 Dave Clark	.04	.03	.02
452 Spike Owen	.04	.03	.02	543 Lonnie Smith	.04	.03	.02
453 Mike Bielecki	.04	.03	.02	544 Rick Rueschel	.05	.04	.02
454 Dennis Martinez	.08	.06	.03	545 Delino DeShields	.20	.15	.08
455 Brett Butler	.08	.06	.03	546 Mike Sharperson	.04	.03	.02
456 Ron Darling	.06	.05	.02	547 Mike Kingery	.04	.03	.02
457 Dennis Rasmussen	.04	.03	.02	548 Terry Kennedy	.04	.03	.02
458 Ken Howell	.04	.03	.02	549 David Cone	.08	.06	.03
459 Steve Bedrosian	.05	.04	.02	550 Orel Hershiser	.12	.09	.05
460 Frank Viola	.12	.09	.05	551 Matt Nokes	.06	.05	.02
461 Jose Lind	.04	.03	.02	552 Eddie Williams	.04	.03	.02
462 Chris Sabo	.08	.06	.03	553 Frank DiPino	.04	.03	.02
463 Dante Bichette	.05	.04	.02	554 Fred Lynn	.05	.04	.02
464 Rick Mahler	.04	.03	.02	555 Alex Cole(FC)	.25	.20	.10
465 John Smiley	.06	.05	.02	556 Terry Leach	.04	.03	.02
466 Devon White	.06	.05	.02	557 Chet Lemon	.04	.03	.02
467 John Orton	.04	.03	.02	558 Paul Mirabella	.04	.03	.02
468 Mike Stanton	.08	.06	.03	559 Bill Long	.04	.03	.02
469 Billy Hatcher	.04	.03	.02	560 Phil Bradley	.05	.04	.02
470 Wally Joyner	.12	.09	.05	561 Duane Ward	.05	.04	.02
471 Gene Larkin	.05	.04	.02	562 Dave Bergman	.04	.03	.02
472 Doug Drabek	.08	.06	.03	563 Eric Show	.04	.03	.02
473 Gary Sheffield	.15	.11	.06	564 Xavier Hernandez(FC)	.08	.06	.03
474 David Wells	.04	.03	.02	565 Jeff Parrett	.04	.03	.02
475 Andy Van Slyke	.08	.06	.03	566 Chuck Cary	.04	.03	.02
476 Mike Gallego	.05	.04	.02	567 Ken Hill	.06	.05	.02
477 B.J. Surhoff	.08	.06	.03	568 Bob Welch	.08	.06	.03
478 Gene Nelson	.04	.03	.02	569 John Mitchell	.04	.03	.02
479 Mariano Duncan	.05	.04	.02	570 *Travis Fryman*(FC)	.60	.45	.25
480 Fred McGriff	.12	.09	.05	571 Derek Lilliquist	.04	.03	.02
481 Jerry Browne	.04	.03	.02	572 Steve Lake	.04	.03	.02
482 Alvin Davis	.06	.05	.02	573 *John Barfield*(FC)	.10	.08	.04
483 Bill Wegman	.05	.04	.02	574 Randy Bush	.04	.03	.02
484 Dave Parker	.08	.06	.03	575 Joe Magrane	.06	.05	.02
485 Dennis Eckersley	.12	.09	.05	576 Edgar Diaz	.04	.03	.02
486 Erik Hanson	.12	.09	.05	577 Casy Candaele	.04	.03	.02
487 Bill Ripken	.04	.03	.02	578 Jesse Orosco	.04	.03	.02
488 Tom Candiotti	.05	.04	.02	579 Tom Henke	.06	.05	.02
489 Mike Schooler	.06	.05	.02	580 Rick Cerone	.04	.03	.02
490 Gregg Olson	.12	.09	.05	581 Drew Hall	.04	.03	.02
491 Chris James	.05	.04	.02	582 Tony Castillo	.04	.03	.02
492 Pete Harnisch	.06	.05	.02	583 Jimmy Jones	.04	.03	.02
493 Julio Franco	.10	.08	.04	584 Rick Reed	.04	.03	.02
494 Greg Briley	.05	.04	.02	585 Joe Girardi	.05	.04	.02
495 Ruben Sierra	.15	.11	.06	586 *Jeff Gray*(FC)	.15	.11	.06
496 Steve Olin	.05	.04	.02	587 Luis Polonia	.06	.05	.02
497 Mike Fetters	.05	.04	.02	588 Joe Klink(FC)	.08	.06	.03
498 Mark Williamson	.04	.03	.02	589 Rex Hudler	.05	.04	.02
499 Bob Tewksbury	.04	.03	.02	590 Kirk McCaskill	.06	.05	.02
500 Tony Gwynn	.15	.11	.06	591 Juan Agosto	.04	.03	.02
501 Randy Myers	.08	.06	.03	592 Wes Gardner	.04	.03	.02
502 Keith Comstock	.04	.03	.02	593 *Rich Rodriguez*(FC)	.12	.09	.05
503 Craig Worthington	.08	.06	.03	594 Mitch Webster	.04	.03	.02
504 Mark Eichhorn	.04	.03	.02	595 Kelly Gruber	.12	.09	.05
505 Barry Larkin	.12	.09	.05	596 Dale Mohorcic	.04	.03	.02
506 Dave Johnson	.04	.03	.02	597 Willie McGee	.08	.06	.03
507 Bobby Witt	.06	.05	.02	598 Bill Krueger	.05	.04	.02
508 Joe Orsulak	.04	.03	.02	599 Bob Walk	.04	.03	.02
509 Pete O'Brien	.04	.03	.02	600 Kevin Maas	.30	.25	.12
510 Brad Arnsberg	.05	.04	.02	601 Danny Jackson	.06	.05	.02
511 Storm Davis	.05	.04	.02	602 Craig McMurtry	.04	.03	.02
512 Bob Milacki	.05	.04	.02	603 Curtis Wilkerson	.04	.03	.02
513 Bill Pecota	.05	.04	.02	604 Adam Peterson	.04	.03	.02
514 Glenallen Hill	.08	.06	.03	605 Sam Horn	.06	.05	.02
515 Danny Tartabull	.10	.08	.04	606 Tommy Gregg	.04	.03	.02
516 Mike Moore	.05	.04	.02	607 Ken Dayley	.04	.03	.02
517 Ron Robinson	.04	.03	.02	608 Carmelo Castillo	.04	.03	.02
518 Mark Gardner	.08	.06	.03	609 John Shelby	.04	.03	.02
519 Rick Wrona	.04	.03	.02	610 Don Slaught	.04	.03	.02
520 Mike Scioscia	.06	.05	.02	611 Calvin Schiraldi	.04	.03	.02
521 Frank Wills	.04	.03	.02	612 Dennis Lamp	.04	.03	.02
522 Greg Brock	.04	.03	.02	613 Andres Thomas	.04	.03	.02
523 Jack Clark	.08	.06	.03	614 Jose Gonzales	.04	.03	.02

		MT	NR MT	EX
615	Randy Ready	.04	.03	.02
616	Kevin Bass	.06	.05	.02
617	Mike Marshall	.05	.04	.02
618	Daryl Boston	.04	.03	.02
619	Andy McGaffigan	.04	.03	.02
620	Joe Oliver	.06	.05	.02
621	Jim Gott	.04	.03	.02
622	Jose Oquendo	.04	.03	.02
623	Jose DeJesus	.06	.05	.02
624	Mike Brumley	.04	.03	.02
625	John Olerud	.30	.25	.12
626	Ernest Riles	.04	.03	.02
627	Gene Harris	.05	.04	.02
628	Jose Uribe	.04	.03	.02
629	Darnell Coles	.04	.03	.02
630	Carney Lansford	.06	.05	.02
631	Tim Leary	.05	.04	.02
632	Tim Hulett	.04	.03	.02
633	Kevin Elster	.06	.05	.02
634	Tony Fossas	.04	.03	.02
635	Francisco Oliveras	.04	.03	.02
636	Bob Patterson	.04	.03	.02
637	Gary Ward	.04	.03	.02
638	Rene Gonzales	.04	.03	.02
639	Don Robinson	.04	.03	.02
640	Darryl Strawberry	.20	.15	.08
641	Dave Anderson	.04	.03	.02
642	Scott Scudder	.06	.05	.02
643	Reggie Harris(FC)	.20	.15	.08
644	Dave Henderson	.08	.06	.03
645	Ben McDonald	.35	.25	.14
646	Bob Kipper	.04	.03	.02
647	Hal Morris	.15	.11	.06
648	Tim Birtsas	.04	.03	.02
649	Steve Searcy	.04	.03	.02
650	Dale Murphy	.12	.09	.05
651	Ron Oester	.04	.03	.02
652	Mike LaCoss	.04	.03	.02
653	Ron Jones	.05	.04	.02
654	Kelly Downs	.04	.03	.02
655	Roger Clemens	.20	.15	.08
656	Herm Winningham	.04	.03	.02
657	Trevor Wilson	.06	.05	.02
658	Jose Rijo	.08	.06	.03
659	Dann Bilardello	.04	.03	.02
660	Gregg Jefferies	.15	.11	.06
661	Doug Drabek (AS)	.08	.06	.03
662	Randy Myers (AS)	.06	.05	.02
663	Benito Santiago (AS)	.08	.06	.03
664	Will Clark (AS)	.15	.11	.06
665	Ryne Sandberg (AS)	.15	.11	.06
666	Barry Larkin (AS)	.08	.06	.03
667	Matt Williams (AS)	.08	.06	.03
668	Barry Bonds (AS)	.12	.09	.05
669	Eric Davis	.12	.09	.05
670	Bobby Bonilla (AS)	.08	.06	.03
671	#1 Draft Pick (Chipper Jones)(FC)	.50	.40	.20
672	#1 Draft Pick (Eric Christopherson)(FC)	.15	.11	.06
673	#1 Draft Pick (Robbie Beckett)(FC)	.15	.11	.06
674	#1 Draft Pick (Shane Andrews)(FC)	.20	.15	.08
675	#1 Draft Pick (Steve Karsay)(FC)	.40	.30	.15
676	#1 Draft Pick (Aaron Holbert)(FC)	.20	.15	.08
677	#1 Draft Pick (Donovan Osborne)(FC)	.60	.45	.25
678	#1 Draft Pick (Todd Ritchie)(FC)	.15	.11	.06
679	#1 Draft Pick (Ron Walden)(FC)	.20	.15	.08
680	#1 Draft Pick (Tim Costo)(FC)	.40	.30	.15
681	#1 Draft Pick (Dan Wilson)(FC)	.40	.30	.15
682	#1 Draft Pick (Kurt Miller)(FC)	.15	.11	.06
683	#1 Draft Pick (Mike Lieberthal)(FC)	.25	.20	.10
684	Roger Clemens (K-Man)(FC)	.15	.11	.06
685	Doc Gooden (K-Man)	.15	.11	.06
686	Nolan Ryan (K-Man)	.20	.15	.08
687	Frank Viola (K-Man)	.08	.06	.03
688	Erik Hanson (K-Man)	.08	.06	.03
689	Matt Williams (Master Blaster)	.10	.08	.04
690	Jose Canseco (Master Blaster)	.20	.15	.08
691	Darryl Strawberry (Master Blaster)	.15	.11	.06
692	Bo Jackson (Master Blaster)	.30	.25	.12
693	Cecil Fielder (Master Blaster)	.20	.15	.08
694	Sandy Alomar, Jr. (Rifleman)	.08	.06	.03
695	Cory Snyder (Rifleman)	.05	.04	.02
696	Eric Davis, Eric Davis (Rifleman)	.08	.06	.03
697	Ken Griffey, Jr. (Rifleman)	.30	.25	.12
698	Andy Van Slyke (Rifleman)	.08	.06	.03
699	Langston/Witt (No-Hit Club)	.08	.06	.03
700	Randy Johnson (No-Hit Club)	.08	.06	.03
701	Nolan Ryan (No-Hit Club)	.20	.15	.08
702	Dave Stewart (No-Hit Club)	.08	.06	.03
703	Fernando Valenzuela (No-Hit Club)	.06	.05	.02
704	Andy Hawkins (No-Hit Club)	.04	.03	.02
705	Melido Perez (No-Hit Club)	.04	.03	.02
706	Terry Mulholland (No-Hit Club)	.06	.05	.02
707	Dave Stieb (No-Hit Club)	.06	.05	.02
708	Brian Barnes(FC)	.20	.15	.08
709	Bernard Gilkey	.30	.25	.12
710	Steve Decker(FC)	.25	.20	.10
711	Paul Faries(FC)	.12	.09	.05
712	Paul Marak(FC)	.10	.08	.04
713	Wes Chamberlain(FC)	.40	.30	.15
714	Kevin Belcher(FC)	.10	.08	.04
715	Dan Boone(FC)	.05	.04	.02
716	Steve Adkins(FC)	.10	.08	.04
717	Geronimo Pena(FC)	.10	.08	.04
718	Howard Farmer(FC)	.08	.06	.03
719	Mark Leonard(FC)	.25	.20	.10
720	Tom Lampkin	.04	.03	.02
721	Mike Gardiner(FC)	.15	.11	.06
722	Jeff Conine(FC)	.15	.11	.06
723	Efrain Valdez(FC)	.10	.08	.04
724	Chuck Malone(FC)	.08	.06	.03
725	Leo Gomez(FC)	.30	.25	.12
726	Paul McClellan(FC)	.15	.11	.06
727	Mark Leiter(FC)	.10	.08	.04
728	Rich DeLucia(FC)	.15	.11	.06
729	Mel Rojas(FC)	.08	.06	.03
730	Hector Wagner(FC)	.10	.08	.04
731	Ray Lankford	.40	.30	.15
732	Turner Ward(FC)	.25	.20	.10
733	Gerald Alexander(FC)	.10	.08	.04
734	Scott Anderson(FC)	.10	.08	.04
735	Tony Perezchica(FC)	.05	.04	.02
736	Jimmy Kremers(FC)	.08	.06	.03
737	American Flag	.30	.25	.12
738	Mike York(FC)	.10	.08	.04
739	Mike Rochford(FC)	.06	.05	.02
740	Scott Aldred(FC)	.08	.06	.03
741	Rico Brogna(FC)	.25	.20	.10
742	Dave Burba(FC)	.10	.08	.04
743	Ray Stephens(FC)	.10	.08	.04
744	Eric Gunderson	.08	.06	.03
745	Troy Afenir(FC)	.08	.06	.03
746	Jeff Shaw(FC)	.08	.06	.03
747	Orlando Merced(FC)	.35	.25	.14
748	Omar Oliveras(FC)	.10	.08	.04
749	Jerry Kutzler(FC)	.06	.05	.02
750	Maurice Vaughn	.35	.25	.12
751	Matt Stark(FC)	.20	.15	.08
752	Randy Hennis(FC)	.10	.08	.04
753	Andujar Cedeno(FC)	.30	.25	.12
754	Kelvin Torve(FC)	.08	.06	.03
755	Joe Kraemer(FC)	.08	.06	.03
756	Phil Clark(FC)	.15	.11	.06
757	Ed Vosberg(FC)	.10	.08	.04
758	Mike Perez(FC)	.10	.08	.04
759	Scott Lewis(FC)	.10	.08	.04
760	Steve Chitren(FC)	.10	.08	.04
761	Ray Young(FC)	.10	.08	.04
762	Andres Santana(FC)	.15	.11	.06
763	Rodney McCray(FC)	.10	.08	.04
764	Sean Berry(FC)	.10	.08	.04
765	Brent Mayne	.08	.06	.03
766	Mike Simms(FC)	.15	.11	.06
767	Glenn Sutko(FC)	.10	.08	.04
768	Gary Disarcina	.06	.05	.02
769	George Brett (Highlight)	.08	.06	.03
770	Cecil Fielder (Highlight)	.08	.06	.03
771	Jim Presley	.05	.04	.02
772	John Dopson	.05	.04	.02
773	Bo Jackson (Bo Breaker)	.35	.25	.14
774	Brent Knackert(FC)	.08	.06	.03
775	Bill Doran	.06	.05	.02
776	Dick Schofield	.04	.03	.02
777	Nelson Santovenia	.04	.03	.02
778	Mark Guthrie(FC)	.08	.06	.03
779	Mark Lemke	.08	.06	.03
780	Terry Steinbach	.06	.05	.02
781	Tom Bolton	.05	.04	.02
782	Randy Tomlin(FC)	.20	.15	.08
783	Jeff Kunkel	.04	.03	.02
784	Felix Jose	.10	.08	.04
785	Rick Sutcliffe	.05	.04	.02
786	John Cerutti	.04	.03	.02
787	Jose Vizcaino	.05	.04	.02
788	Curt Schilling	.06	.05	.02
789	Ed Whitson	.05	.04	.02
790	Tony Pena	.06	.05	.02
791	John Candelaria	.04	.03	.02

		MT	NR MT	EX
792	Carmelo Martinez	.04	.03	.02
793	Sandy Alomar, Jr.	.08	.06	.03
794	*Jim Neidlinger*(FC)	.08	.06	.03
795	Red's October	.08	.06	.03
796	Paul Sorrento	.05	.04	.02
797	Tom Pagnozzi	.06	.05	.02
798	Tino Martinez	.15	.11	.06
799	Scott Ruskin(FC)	.08	.06	.03
800	Kirk Gibson	.08	.06	.03
801	Walt Terrell	.04	.03	.02
802	John Russell	.04	.03	.02
803	Chili Davis	.08	.06	.03
804	Chris Nabholz(FC)	.08	.06	.03
805	Juan Gonzalez	.30	.25	.12
806	Ron Hassey	.04	.03	.02
807	Todd Worrell	.06	.05	.02
808	Tommy Greene	.06	.05	.02
809	Joel Skinner	.04	.03	.02
810	Benito Santiago	.08	.06	.03
811	Pat Tabler	.04	.03	.02
812	*Scott Erickson*(FC)	.50	.40	.20
813	Moises Alou	.06	.05	.02
814	Dale Sveum	.04	.03	.02
815	Ryne Sandberg (Man of the Year)	.20	.15	.08
816	Rick Dempsey	.04	.03	.02
817	Scott Bankhead	.05	.04	.02
818	Jason Grimsley	.05	.04	.02
819	Doug Jennings	.04	.03	.02
820	Tom Herr	.05	.04	.02
821	Rob Ducey	.04	.03	.02
822	Luis Quinones	.04	.03	.02
823	Greg Minton	.04	.03	.02
824	Mark Grant	.04	.03	.02
825	Ozzie Smith	.10	.08	.04
826	Dave Eiland	.04	.03	.02
827	Danny Heep	.04	.03	.02
828	Hensley Meulens	.08	.06	.03
829	Charlie O'Brien	.04	.03	.02
830	Glenn Davis	.08	.06	.03
831	John Marzano	.04	.03	.02
832	Steve Ontiveros	.04	.03	.02
833	Ron Karkovice	.04	.03	.02
834	Jerry Goff(FC)	.08	.06	.03
835	Ken Griffey, Sr.	.08	.06	.03
836	Kevin Reimer(FC)	.10	.08	.04
837	Randy Kutcher	.04	.03	.02
838	Mike Blowers	.05	.04	.02
839	Mike Macfarlane	.05	.04	.02
840	Frank Thomas	1.25	.90	.50
841	Ken Griffey, Jr. & Sr. (FS)	1.25	.90	.50
842	Jack Howell	.04	.03	.02
843	Mauro Gozzo(FC)	.06	.05	.02
844	Gerald Young	.04	.03	.02
845	Zane Smith	.05	.04	.02
846	Kevin Brown	.05	.04	.02
847	Sil Campusano	.04	.03	.02
848	Larry Andersen	.04	.03	.02
849	Cal Ripken, Jr. (FR)	.12	.09	.05
850	Roger Clemens (FR)	.12	.09	.05
851	Sandy Alomar, Jr. (FR)	.08	.06	.03
852	Alan Trammell (FR)	.08	.06	.03
853	George Brett (FR)	.08	.06	.03
854	Robin Yount (FR)	.08	.06	.03
855	Kirby Puckett (FR)	.08	.06	.03
856	Don Mattingly (FR)	.15	.11	.06
857	Rickey Henderson (FR)	.15	.11	.06
858	Ken Griffey,Jr. (FR)	1.00	.70	.40
859	Ruben Sierra (FR)	.10	.08	.04
860	John Olerud (FR)	.10	.08	.04
861	Dave Justice (FR)	.50	.40	.20
862	Ryne Sandberg (FR)	.15	.11	.06
863	Eric Davis (FR)	.08	.06	.03
864	Darryl Strawberry (FR)	.10	.08	.04
865	Tim Wallach (FR)	.05	.04	.02
866	Doc Gooden (FR)	.08	.06	.03
867	Lenny Dykstra (FR)	.06	.05	.02
868	Barry Bonds (FR)	.10	.08	.04
869	Todd Zeile (FR)	.10	.08	.04
870	Benito Santiago (FR)	.08	.06	.03
871	Will Clark (FR)	.20	.15	.08
872	Craig Biggio (FR)	.08	.06	.03
873	Wally Joyner (FR)	.08	.06	.03
874	Frank Thomas (FR)	.60	.45	.25
875	Rickey Henderson (MVP)	.10	.08	.04
876	Barry Bonds (MVP)	.10	.08	.04
877	Bob Welch (Cy Young)	.05	.04	.02
878	Doug Drabek (Cy Young)	.06	.05	.02
879	Sandy Alomar, Jr. (ROY)	.08	.06	.03
880	Dave Justice (ROY)	.25	.20	.10
881	Damon Berryhill	.05	.04	.02
882	Frank Viola (Dream Team)	.10	.08	.04

		MT	NR MT	EX
883	Dave Stewart (Dream Team)	.10	.08	.04
884	Doug Jones (Dream Team)	.05	.04	.02
885	Randy Myers (Dream Team)	.06	.05	.02
886	Will Clark (Dream Team)	.30	.25	.12
887	Roberto Alomar (Dream Team)	.08	.06	.03
888	Barry Larkin (Dream Team)	.12	.09	.05
889	Wade Boggs (Dream Team)	.20	.15	.08
890	Rickey Henderson (Dream Team)	.80	.60	.30
891	Kirby Puckett (Dream Team)	.20	.15	.08
892	Ken Griffey,Jr. (Dream Team)	1.50	1.25	.60
893	Benito Santiago (Dream Team)	.10	.08	.04

1991 Score Rising Star

Marketed along with "1990-91 "Baseball's Hottest Rookies" magazine, this 100-card set features top rookies and young players such as Alex Fernandez and Frank Thomas. The cards are similar in design to the Score Superstar set. The magazine/card sets were available to a select group of retailers.

		MT	NR MT	EX
Complete Set:		10.00	7.50	4.00
Common Player:		.08	.06	.03
1	Sandy Alomar,Jr.	.15	.11	.06
2	Tom Edens	.08	.06	.03
3	Terry Shumpert	.15	.11	.06
4	Shawn Boskie	.20	.15	.08
5	Steve Avery	.70	.50	.30
6	Deion Sanders	.10	.08	.04
7	John Burkett	.10	.08	.04
8	Stan Belinda	.08	.06	.03
9	Thomas Howard	.15	.11	.06
10	Wayne Edwards	.08	.06	.03
11	Rick Parker	.08	.06	.03
12	Randy Veres	.08	.06	.03
13	Alex Cole	.15	.11	.06
14	Scott Chaimparino	.10	.08	.04
15	Greg Olson	.08	.06	.03
16	Jose DeJesus	.10	.08	.04
17	Mike Blowers	.08	.06	.03
18	Jeff Huson	.08	.06	.03
19	Willie Blair	.10	.08	.04
20	Howard Farmer	.10	.08	.04
21	Larry Walker	.15	.11	.06
22	Scott Hemond	.08	.06	.03
23	Mel Stottlemyre	.10	.08	.04
24	Mark Whiten	.25	.20	.10
25	Jeff Schulz	.10	.08	.04
26	Gary Disarcina	.08	.06	.03
27	George Canale	.08	.06	.03
28	Dean Palmer	.10	.08	.04
29	Jim Leyritz	.20	.15	.08
30	Carlos Baerga	.20	.15	.08
31	Rafael Valdez	.15	.11	.06
32	Derek Bell	.20	.15	.08
33	Francisco Cabrera	.08	.06	.03
34	Chris Hoiles	.20	.15	.08
35	Craig Grebeck	.08	.06	.03
36	Scott Coolbaugh	.08	.06	.03
37	Kevin Wickander	.10	.08	.04
38	Marquis Grissom	.15	.11	.06
39	Chip Hale	.08	.06	.03
40	Kevin Maas	.50	.40	.20
41	Juan Gonzalez	1.25	.90	.50
42	Eric Anthony	.25	.20	.10
43	Luis Sojo	.10	.08	.04

		MT	NR MT	EX
44	Paul Sorrento	.08	.06	.03
45	Dave Justice	1.00	.70	.40
46	Oscar Azocar	.08	.06	.03
47	Charles Nagy	.08	.06	.03
48	Robin Ventura	.20	.15	.08
49	Reggie Harris	.15	.11	.06
50	Ben McDonald	.50	.40	.20
51	Hector Villanueva	.15	.11	.06
52	Kevin Tapani	.15	.11	.06
53	Brian Bohanon	.08	.06	.03
54	Tim Layana	.10	.08	.04
55	Delino DeShields	.25	.20	.10
56	Beau Allred	.08	.06	.03
57	Eric Gunderson	.20	.15	.08
58	Kent Mercker	.10	.08	.04
59	Juan Bell	.10	.08	.04
60	Glenallen Hill	.10	.08	.04
61	David Segui	.30	.25	.12
62	Alan Mills	.15	.11	.06
63	Mike Harkey	.15	.11	.06
64	Bill Sampen	.15	.11	.06
65	Greg Vaughn	.20	.15	.08
66	Alex Fernandez	.50	.40	.20
67	Mike Hartley	.08	.06	.03
68	Travis Fryman	.40	.30	.15
69	Dave Rohde	.10	.08	.04
70	Tom Lampkin	.08	.06	.03
71	Mark Gardner	.15	.11	.06
72	Pat Combs	.10	.08	.04
73	Kevin Appier	.15	.11	.06
74	Mike Fetters	.08	.06	.03
75	Greg Myers	.08	.06	.03
76	Steve Searcy	.08	.06	.03
77	Tim Naehring	.25	.20	.10
78	Frank Thomas	2.50	2.00	1.00
79	Todd Hundley	.10	.08	.04
80	Ed Vosburg	.15	.11	.06
81	Todd Zeile	.20	.15	.08
82	Lee Stevens	.10	.08	.04
83	Scott Radinsky	.10	.08	.04
84	Hensley Meulens	.10	.08	.04
85	Brian DuBois	.08	.06	.03
86	Steve Olin	.08	.06	.03
87	Julio Machado	.10	.08	.04
88	Jose Vizcaino	.08	.06	.03
89	Mark Lemke	.10	.08	.04
90	Felix Jose	.08	.06	.03
91	Wally Whitehurst	.08	.06	.03
92	Dana Kiecker	.10	.08	.04
93	Mike Munoz	.08	.06	.03
94	Adam Peterson	.08	.06	.03
95	Tim Drummond	.08	.06	.03
96	Dave Hollins	.10	.08	.04
97	Craig Wilson	.10	.08	.04
98	Hal Morris	.20	.15	.08
99	Jose Offerman	.30	.25	.12
100	John Olerud	.30	.25	.12

1991 Score Superstar

This 100-card set features full-color action photos on the card fronts and posed shots on the flip sides. The set was marketed along with the magazine "1991 Baseball's Hottest Players". The cards feature red, white, and blue borders and display the player's name and position below the photo on the card front. The backs contain brief career highlights of the player. The magazine/card set combo was available to select retailers.

		MT	NR MT	EX
Complete Set:		10.00	7.50	4.00
Common Player:		.08	.06	.03
1	Jose Canseco	.30	.25	.12
2	Bo Jackson	.30	.25	.12
3	Wade Boggs	.15	.11	.06
4	Will Clark	.35	.25	.14
5	Ken Griffey,Jr.	1.50	1.25	.60
6	Doug Drabek	.10	.08	.04
7	Kirby Puckett	.15	.11	.06
8	Joe Orsulak	.08	.06	.03
9	Eric Davis	.15	.11	.06
10	Rickey Henderson	.20	.15	.08
11	Lenny Dykstra	.10	.08	.04
12	Ruben Sierra	.10	.08	.04
13	Paul Molitor	.10	.08	.04
14	Ron Gant	.35	.25	.14
15	Ozzie Guillen	.10	.08	.04
16	Ramon Martinez	.20	.15	.08
17	Edgar Martinez	.08	.06	.03
18	Ozzie Smith	.10	.08	.04
19	Charlie Hayes	.08	.06	.03
20	Barry Larkin	.15	.11	.06
21	Cal Ripken,Jr.	.30	.25	.12
22	Andy Van Slyke	.10	.08	.04
23	Don Mattingly	.25	.20	.10
24	Dave Stewart	.15	.11	.06
25	Nolan Ryan	.30	.25	.12
26	Barry Bonds	.20	.15	.08
27	Gregg Olson	.10	.08	.04
28	Chris Sabo	.10	.08	.04
29	John Franco	.10	.08	.04
30	Gary Sheffield	.20	.15	.08
31	Jeff Treadway	.08	.06	.03
32	Tom Browning	.08	.06	.03
33	Jose Lind	.08	.06	.03
34	Dave Magadan	.10	.08	.04
35	Dale Murphy	.10	.08	.04
36	Tom Candiotti	.08	.06	.03
37	Willie McGee	.10	.08	.04
38	Robin Yount	.15	.11	.06
39	Mark McGwire	.20	.15	.08
40	George Bell	.10	.08	.04
41	Carlton Fisk	.10	.08	.04
42	Bobby Bonilla	.10	.08	.04
43	Randy Milligan	.08	.06	.03
44	Dave Parker	.15	.11	.06
45	Shawon Dunston	.10	.08	.04
46	Brian Harper	.08	.06	.03
47	John Tudor	.08	.06	.03
48	Ellis Burks	.15	.11	.06
49	Bob Welch	.10	.08	.04
50	Roger Clemens	.20	.15	.08
51	Mike Henneman	.08	.06	.03
52	Eddie Murray	.15	.11	.06
53	Kal Daniels	.10	.08	.04
54	Doug Jones	.10	.08	.04
55	Craig Biggio	.10	.08	.04
56	Rafael Palmeiro	.15	.11	.06
57	Wally Joyner	.10	.08	.04
58	Tim Wallach	.10	.08	.04
59	Bret Saberhagen	.15	.11	.06
60	Ryne Sandberg	.20	.15	.08
61	Benito Santiago	.10	.08	.04
62	Darryl Strawberry	.20	.15	.08
63	Alan Trammell	.10	.08	.04
64	Kelly Gruber	.15	.11	.06
65	Dwight Gooden	.20	.15	.08
66	Dave Winfield	.10	.08	.04
67	Rick Aguilera	.08	.06	.03
68	Dave Righetti	.10	.08	.04
69	Jim Abbott	.10	.08	.04
70	Frank Viola	.15	.11	.06
71	Fred McGriff	.20	.15	.08
72	Steve Sax	.10	.08	.04
73	Dennis Eckersley	.15	.11	.06
74	Cory Snyder	.08	.06	.03
75	Mackey Sasser	.08	.06	.03
76	Candy Maldonado	.10	.08	.04
77	Matt Williams	.15	.11	.06
78	Kent Hrbek	.10	.08	.04
79	Randy Myers	.10	.08	.04
80	Gregg Jefferies	.20	.15	.08
81	Joe Carter	.10	.08	.04
82	Mike Greenwell	.15	.11	.06
83	Jack Armstrong	.10	.08	.04
84	Julio Franco	.10	.08	.04
85	George Brett	.15	.11	.06
86	Howard Johnson	.10	.08	.04
87	Andre Dawson	.15	.11	.06

		MT	NR MT	EX
88	Cecil Fielder	.25	.20	.10
89	Tim Raines	.10	.08	.04
90	Chuck Finley	.10	.08	.04
91	Mark Grace	.15	.11	.06
92	Brook Jacoby	.10	.08	.04
93	Dave Steib	.10	.08	.04
94	Tony Gwynn	.15	.11	.06
95	Bobby Thigpen	.10	.08	.04
96	Roberto Kelly	.10	.08	.04
97	Kevin Seitzer	.10	.08	.04
98	Kevin Mitchell	.15	.11	.06
99	Dwight Evans	.10	.08	.04
100	Roberto Alomar	.10	.08	.04

1991 Score Rookies

This 40-card boxed set did not receive much attention in the hobby world, but features some of the top young players of 1991. The card fronts feature full-color action photos with a "Rookies" banner along the side border of the card. The backs feature statistics and a player profile. This set was available through hobby dealers and is Score's first release of its kind.

		MT	NR MT	EX
Complete Set:		8.00	6.00	3.25
Common Player:		.10	.08	.04
1	Mel Rojas	.15	.11	.06
2	Ray Lankford	.30	.25	.12
3	Scott Aldred	.10	.08	.04
4	Turner Ward	.15	.11	.06
5	Omar Olivares	.10	.08	.04
6	Mo Vaughn	.50	.40	.20
7	Phil Clark	.15	.11	.06
8	Brent Mayne	.10	.08	.04
9	Scott Lewis	.15	.11	.06
10	Brian Barnes	.20	.15	.08
11	Bernard Gilkey	.20	.15	.08
12	Steve Decker	.25	.20	.10
13	Paul Marak	.15	.11	.06
14	Wes Chamberlain	.40	.30	.15
15	Kevin Belcher	.10	.08	.04
16	Steve Adkins	.10	.08	.04
17	Geronimo Pena	.20	.15	.08
18	Mark Leonard	.15	.11	.06
19	Jeff Conine	.20	.15	.08
20	Leo Gomez	.25	.20	.10
21	Chuck Malone	.10	.08	.04
22	Beau Allred	.10	.08	.04
23	Todd Hundley	.20	.15	.08
24	Lance Dickson	.20	.15	.08
25	Mike Benjamin	.10	.08	.04
26	Jose Offerman	.25	.20	.10
27	Terry Shumpert	.10	.08	.04
28	Darren Lewis	.25	.20	.10
29	Scott Chiamparino	.10	.08	.04
30	Tim Naehring	.20	.15	.08
31	David Segui	.15	.11	.06
32	Karl Rhodes	.15	.11	.06
33	Mickey Morandini	.15	.11	.06
34	Chuck McElroy	.10	.08	.04
35	Tim McIntosh	.10	.08	.04
36	Derrick May	.30	.25	.12
37	Rich DeLucia	.10	.08	.04
38	Tino Martinez	.20	.15	.08
39	Hensley Meulens	.15	.11	.06
40	Andujar Cedeno	.40	.30	.15

1991 Score Traded

This 110-card set features players with new teams as well as 1991 Major League rookies. The cards are designed in the same style as the regular 1991 Score issue. The cards once again feature a "T" designation along with the card number. The complete set was sold at hobby shops in a special box.

		MT	NR MT	EX
Complete Set:		6.00	4.50	2.50
Common Player:		.06	.05	.02
1	Bo Jackson	.35	.25	.14
2	Mike Flanagan	.06	.05	.02
3	Pete Incaviglia	.08	.06	.03
4	Jack Clark	.10	.08	.04
5	Hubie Brooks	.08	.06	.03
6	Ivan Calderon	.12	.09	.05
7	Glenn Davis	.12	.09	.05
8	Wally Backman	.06	.05	.02
9	Dave Smith	.08	.06	.03
10	Tim Raines	.15	.11	.06
11	Joe Carter	.15	.11	.06
12	Sid Bream	.08	.06	.03
13	George Bell	.12	.09	.05
14	Steve Bedrosian	.06	.05	.02
15	Willie Wilson	.06	.05	.02
16	Darryl Strawberry	.30	.25	.12
17	Danny Jackson	.06	.05	.02
18	Kirk Gibson	.08	.06	.03
19	Willie McGee	.10	.08	.04
20	Junior Felix	.08	.06	.03
21	Steve Farr	.06	.05	.02
22	Pat Tabler	.06	.05	.02
23	Brett Butler	.10	.08	.04
24	Danny Darwin	.06	.05	.02
25	Mikey Tettleton	.08	.06	.03
26	Gary Carter	.10	.08	.04
27	Mitch Williams	.08	.06	.03
28	Candy Maldonado	.08	.06	.03
29	Otis Nixon	.08	.06	.03
30	Brian Downing	.06	.05	.02
31	Tom Candiotti	.06	.05	.02
32	John Candelaria	.06	.05	.02
33	Rob Murphy	.06	.05	.02
34	Deion Sanders	.20	.15	.08
35	Willie Randolph	.08	.06	.03
36	Pete Harnisch	.08	.06	.03
37	Dante Bichette	.06	.05	.02
38	Garry Templeton	.08	.06	.03
39	Gary Gaetti	.08	.06	.03
40	John Cerutti	.06	.05	.02
41	Rick Cerone	.06	.05	.02
42	Mike Pagliarulo	.06	.05	.02
43	Ron Hassey	.06	.05	.02
44	Roberto Alomar	.30	.25	.12
45	Mike Boddicker	.08	.06	.03
46	Bud Black	.06	.05	.02
47	Rob Deer	.06	.05	.02
48	Devon White	.08	.06	.03
49	Luis Sojo	.06	.05	.02
50	Terry Pendleton	.08	.06	.03
51	Kevin Gross	.06	.05	.02
52	Mike Huff	.08	.06	.03
53	Dave Righetti	.08	.06	.03
54	Matt Young	.06	.05	.02
55	Ernest Riles	.06	.05	.02
56	Bill Gullickson	.08	.06	.03

		MT	NR MT	EX
57	Vince Coleman	.10	.08	.04
58	Fred McGriff	.12	.09	.05
59	Franklin Stubbs	.06	.05	.02
60	Eric King	.06	.05	.02
61	Cory Snyder	.06	.05	.02
62	Dwight Evans	.08	.06	.03
63	Gerald Perry	.06	.05	.02
64	Eric Show	.06	.05	.02
65	Shawn Hillegas	.06	.05	.02
66	Tony Fernandez	.08	.06	.03
67	Tim Teufel	.06	.05	.02
68	Mitch Webster	.06	.05	.02
69	Mike Heath	.06	.05	.02
70	Chili Davis	.08	.06	.03
71	Larry Andersen	.06	.05	.02
72	Gary Varsho	.06	.05	.02
73	Juan Berenguer	.06	.05	.02
74	Jack Morris	.08	.06	.03
75	Barry Jones	.06	.05	.02
76	Rafael Belliard	.06	.05	.02
77	Steve Buechele	.06	.05	.02
78	Scott Sanderson	.06	.05	.02
79	Bob Ojeda	.06	.05	.02
80	Curt Schilling	.06	.05	.02
81	Brian Drahman(FC)	.15	.11	.06
82	Ivan Rodriguez(FC)	1.00	.70	.40
83	David Howard(FC)	.20	.15	.08
84	Heath Slocumb(FC)	.15	.11	.06
85	Mike Timlin(FC)	.20	.15	.08
86	Darruyl Kile(FC)	.20	.15	.08
87	Pete Schourek(FC)	.20	.15	.08
88	Bruce Walton(FC)	.12	.09	.05
89	Al Osuna(FC)	.15	.11	.06
90	Gary Scott(FC)	.35	.25	.14
91	Doug Simons(FC)	.15	.11	.06
92	Chris Jones(FC)	.25	.20	.10
93	Chuck Knoblauch	.40	.30	.15
94	Dana Allison(FC)	.15	.11	.06
95	Erik Pappas(FC)	.20	.15	.08
96	Jeff Bagwell(FC)	1.25	.90	.50
97	Kirk Dressendorfer(FC)	.35	.25	.14
98	Freddie Benavides(FC)	.20	.15	.08
99	Luis Gonzalez(FC)	.40	.30	.15
100	Wade Taylor(FC)	.20	.15	.08
101	Ed Sprague(FC)	.15	.11	.06
102	Bob Scanlan(FC)	.15	.11	.06
103	Rick Wilkins(FC)	.30	.25	.12
104	Chris Donnels(FC)	.20	.15	.08
105	Joe Slusarski(FC)	.20	.15	.08
106	Mark Lewis(FC)	.30	.25	.12
107	Pat Kelly(FC)	.25	.20	.10
108	John Briscoe(FC)	.15	.11	.06
109	Luis Lopez(FC)	.20	.15	.08
110	Jeff Johnson(FC)	.25	.20	.10

1992 Score

Score used a two series format for the second consecutive year in 1992. Cards 1-442 are featured in the first series. The card fronts feature full-color game action photos. The player's name, in white lettering, is across the top with the team logo on the upper-right corner. The player's position is across the bottom. Four-color borders are used. Card backs feature color head shots of the players, team logo and career stats on a vertical layout. Several subsets are included in 1992, including a five-card Joe DiMaggio set. DiMaggio autographed cards were also inserted into random packs. Cards 736-772 can be found with or without a "Rookie Prospects"

banner on the card front.

		MT	NR MT	EX
Complete Set:		20.00	15.00	8.00
Common Player:		.04	.03	.02
1	Ken Griffey, Jr.	.50	.40	.20
2	Nolan Ryan	.25	.20	.10
3	Will Clark	.25	.20	.10
4	Dave Justice	.30	.25	.12
5	Dave Henderson	.08	.06	.03
6	Bret Saberhagen	.08	.06	.03
7	Fred McGriff	.08	.06	.03
8	Erik Hanson	.08	.06	.03
9	Darryl Strawberry	.20	.15	.08
10	Doc Gooden	.12	.09	.05
11	Juan Gonzalez	.20	.15	.08
12	Mark Langston	.08	.06	.03
13	Lonnie Smith	.04	.03	.02
14	Jeff Montgomery	.05	.04	.02
15	Roberto Alomar	.15	.11	.06
16	Delino DeShields	.08	.06	.03
17	Steve Bedrosian	.04	.03	.02
18	Terry Pendleton	.08	.06	.03
19	Mark Carreon	.04	.03	.02
20	Mark McGwire	.15	.11	.06
21	Roger Clemens	.15	.11	.06
22	Chuck Crim	.04	.03	.02
23	Don Mattingly	.25	.20	.10
24	Dickie Thon	.04	.03	.02
25	Ron Gant	.15	.11	.06
26	Milt Cuyler	.10	.08	.04
27	Mike Macfarlane	.05	.04	.02
28	Dan Gladden	.04	.03	.02
29	Melido Perez	.04	.03	.02
30	Willie Randolph	.05	.04	.02
31	Albert Belle	.20	.15	.08
32	Dave Winfield	.08	.06	.03
33	Jimmy Jones	.04	.03	.02
34	Kevin Gross	.04	.03	.02
35	Andres Galarraga	.06	.05	.02
36	Mike Devereaux	.05	.04	.02
37	Chris Bosio	.05	.04	.02
38	Mike LaValliere	.05	.04	.02
39	Gary Gaetti	.08	.06	.03
40	Felix Jose	.10	.08	.04
41	Alvaro Espinoza	.04	.03	.02
42	Rick Aguilera	.06	.05	.02
43	Mike Gallego	.04	.03	.02
44	Eric Davis	.12	.09	.05
45	George Bell	.08	.06	.03
46	Tom Brunansky	.06	.05	.02
47	Steve Farr	.04	.03	.02
48	Duane Ward	.05	.04	.02
49	David Wells	.04	.03	.02
50	Cecil Fielder	.20	.15	.08
51	Walt Weiss	.06	.05	.02
52	Todd Zeile	.10	.08	.04
53	Doug Jones	.04	.03	.02
54	Bob Walk	.04	.03	.02
55	Rafael Palmeiro	.08	.06	.03
56	Rob Deer	.04	.03	.02
57	Paul O'Neill	.08	.06	.03
58	Jeff Reardon	.08	.06	.03
59	Randy Ready	.04	.03	.02
60	Scott Erickson	.20	.15	.08
61	Paul Molitor	.08	.06	.03
62	Jack McDowell	.08	.06	.03
63	Jim Acker	.04	.03	.02
64	Jay Buhner	.06	.05	.02
65	Travis Fryman	.20	.15	.08
66	Marquis Grissom	.10	.08	.04
67	Mike Harkey	.05	.04	.02
68	Luis Polonia	.05	.04	.02
69	Ken Caminiti	.05	.04	.02
70	Chris Sabo	.08	.06	.03
71	Gregg Olson	.08	.06	.03
72	Carlton Fisk	.12	.09	.05
73	Juan Samuel	.06	.05	.02
74	Todd Stottlemyre	.06	.05	.02
75	Andre Dawson	.12	.09	.05
76	Alvin Davis	.06	.05	.02
77	Bill Doran	.06	.05	.02
78	B.J. Surhoff	.06	.05	.02
79	Kirk McCaskill	.06	.05	.02
80	Dale Murphy	.12	.09	.05
81	Jose DeLeon	.05	.04	.02
82	Alex Fernandez	.20	.15	.08
83	Ivan Calderon	.08	.06	.03
84	Brent Mayne	.06	.05	.02
85	Jody Reed	.06	.05	.02

#	Player	MT	NR MT	EX
86	Randy Tomlin	.06	.05	.02
87	Randy Milligan	.06	.05	.02
88	Pascual Perez	.04	.03	.02
89	Hensley Meulens	.08	.06	.03
90	Joe Carter	.10	.08	.04
91	Mike Moore	.05	.04	.02
92	Ozzie Guillen	.08	.06	.03
93	Shawn Hillegas	.04	.03	.02
94	Chili Davis	.08	.06	.03
95	Vince Coleman	.08	.06	.03
96	Jimmy Key	.06	.05	.02
97	Billy Ripken	.04	.03	.02
98	Dave Smith	.06	.05	.02
99	Tom Bolton	.04	.03	.02
100	Barry Larkin	.12	.09	.05
101	Kenny Rogers	.04	.03	.02
102	Mike Boddicker	.06	.05	.02
103	Kevin Elster	.04	.03	.02
104	Ken Hill	.06	.05	.02
105	Charlie Leibrandt	.04	.03	.02
106	Pat Combs	.06	.05	.02
107	Hubie Brooks	.06	.05	.02
108	Julio Franco	.10	.08	.04
109	Vicente Palacios	.04	.03	.02
110	Kal Daniels	.08	.06	.03
111	Bruce Hurst	.06	.05	.02
112	Willie McGee	.08	.06	.03
113	Ted Power	.04	.03	.02
114	Milt Thompson	.04	.03	.02
115	Doug Drabek	.08	.06	.03
116	Rafael Belliard	.04	.03	.02
117	Scott Garrelts	.04	.03	.02
118	Terry Mulholland	.06	.05	.02
119	Jay Howell	.05	.04	.02
120	Danny Jackson	.05	.04	.02
121	Scott Ruskin	.05	.04	.02
122	Robin Ventura	.15	.11	.06
123	Bip Roberts	.06	.05	.02
124	Jeff Russell	.05	.04	.02
125	Hal Morris	.12	.09	.05
126	Teddy Higuera	.06	.05	.02
127	Luis Sojo	.05	.04	.02
128	Carlos Baerga	.10	.08	.04
129	Jeff Ballard	.04	.03	.02
130	Tom Gordon	.08	.06	.03
131	Sid Bream	.06	.05	.02
132	Rance Mulliniks	.04	.03	.02
133	Andy Benes	.10	.08	.04
134	Mickey Tettleton	.08	.06	.03
135	Rich DeLucia	.06	.05	.02
136	Tom Pagnozzi	.06	.05	.02
137	Harold Baines	.08	.06	.03
138	Danny Darwin	.04	.03	.02
139	Kevin Bass	.06	.05	.02
140	Chris Nabholz	.06	.05	.02
141	Pete O'Brien	.04	.03	.02
142	Jeff Treadway	.05	.04	.02
143	Mickey Morandini	.08	.06	.03
144	Eric King	.04	.03	.02
145	Danny Tartabull	.08	.06	.03
146	Lance Johnson	.04	.03	.02
147	Casey Candaele	.04	.03	.02
148	Felix Fermin	.04	.03	.02
149	Rich Rodriguez	.06	.05	.02
150	Dwight Evans	.08	.06	.03
151	Joe Klink	.04	.03	.02
152	Kevin Reimer	.08	.06	.03
153	Orlando Merced	.20	.15	.08
154	Mel Hall	.05	.04	.02
155	Randy Myers	.06	.05	.02
156	Greg Harris	.04	.03	.02
157	Jeff Brantley	.05	.04	.02
158	Jim Eisenreich	.05	.04	.02
159	Luis Rivera	.04	.03	.02
160	Cris Carpenter	.05	.04	.02
161	Bruce Ruffin	.04	.03	.02
162	Omar Vizquel	.04	.03	.02
163	Gerald Alexander	.05	.04	.02
164	Mark Guthrie	.06	.05	.02
165	Scott Lewis	.06	.05	.02
166	Bill Sampen	.06	.05	.02
167	Dave Anderson	.04	.03	.02
168	Kevin McReynolds	.08	.06	.03
169	Jose Vizcaino	.04	.03	.02
170	Bob Geren	.04	.03	.02
171	Mike Morgan	.05	.04	.02
172	Jim Gott	.04	.03	.02
173	Mike Pagliarulo	.05	.04	.02
174	Mike Jeffcoat	.04	.03	.02
175	Craig Lefferts	.05	.04	.02
176	Steve Finley	.08	.06	.03
177	Wally Backman	.04	.03	.02
178	Kent Mercker	.06	.05	.02
179	John Cerutti	.04	.03	.02
180	Jay Bell	.06	.05	.02
181	Dale Sveum	.04	.03	.02
182	Greg Gagne	.04	.03	.02
183	Donnie Hill	.04	.03	.02
184	Rex Hudler	.04	.03	.02
185	Pat Kelly	.25	.20	.10
186	Jeff Robinson	.04	.03	.02
187	Jeff Gray	.08	.06	.03
188	Jerry Willard	.04	.03	.02
189	Carlos Quintana	.08	.06	.03
190	Dennis Eckersley	.08	.06	.03
191	Kelly Downs	.04	.03	.02
192	Gregg Jefferies	.12	.09	.05
193	Darrin Fletcher	.05	.04	.02
194	Mike Jackson	.05	.04	.02
195	Eddie Murray	.12	.09	.05
196	Billy Landrum	.04	.03	.02
197	Eric Yelding	.04	.03	.02
198	Devon White	.06	.05	.02
199	Larry Walker	.08	.06	.03
200	Ryne Sandberg	.20	.15	.08
201	Dave Magadan	.08	.06	.03
202	Steve Chitren	.06	.05	.02
203	Scott Fletcher	.04	.03	.02
204	Dwayne Henry	.04	.03	.02
205	Scott Coolbaugh	.06	.05	.02
206	Tracy Jones	.04	.03	.02
207	Von Hayes	.06	.05	.02
208	Bob Melvin	.04	.03	.02
209	Scott Scudder	.05	.04	.02
210	Luis Gonzalez	.20	.15	.08
211	Scott Sanderson	.05	.04	.02
212	*Chris Donnels*	.05	.04	.02
213	*Heath Slocumb*	.08	.06	.03
214	Mike Timlin	.12	.09	.05
215	Brian Harper	.06	.05	.02
216	Juan Berenguer	.04	.03	.02
217	Mike Henneman	.06	.05	.02
218	Bill Spiers	.04	.03	.02
219	Scott Terry	.04	.03	.02
220	Frank Viola	.12	.09	.05
221	Mark Eichhorn	.04	.03	.02
222	Ernest Riles	.04	.03	.02
223	Ray Lankford	.20	.15	.08
224	Pete Harnisch	.06	.05	.02
225	Bobby Bonilla	.12	.09	.05
226	Mike Scioscia	.05	.04	.02
227	Joel Skinner	.04	.03	.02
228	Brian Holman	.05	.04	.02
229	Gilberto Reyes(FC)	.06	.05	.02
230	Matt Williams	.15	.11	.06
231	Jaime Navarro	.06	.05	.02
232	Jose Rijo	.08	.06	.03
233	Atlee Hammaker	.04	.03	.02
234	Tim Teufel	.04	.03	.02
235	John Kruk	.08	.06	.03
236	Kurt Stillwell	.05	.04	.02
237	Dan Pasqua	.05	.04	.02
238	Tim Crews	.04	.03	.02
239	Dave Gallagher	.05	.04	.02
240	Leo Gomez	.15	.11	.06
241	Steve Avery	.25	.20	.10
242	Bill Gullickson	.06	.05	.02
243	Mark Portugal	.04	.03	.02
244	Lee Guetterman	.04	.03	.02
245	Benny Santiago	.08	.06	.03
246	Jim Gantner	.04	.03	.02
247	Robby Thompson	.05	.04	.02
248	Terry Shumpert	.04	.03	.02
249	*Mike Bell*(FC)	.15	.11	.06
250	Harold Reynolds	.06	.05	.02
251	Mike Felder	.04	.03	.02
252	Bill Pecota	.04	.03	.02
253	Bill Krueger	.04	.03	.02
254	Alfredo Griffin	.04	.03	.02
255	Lou Whitaker	.08	.06	.03
256	Roy Smith	.04	.03	.02
257	Jerald Clark	.05	.04	.02
258	Sammy Sosa	.08	.06	.03
259	Tim Naehring	.15	.11	.06
260	Dave Righetti	.08	.06	.03
261	Paul Gibson	.04	.03	.02
262	Chris James	.05	.04	.02
263	Larry Andersen	.04	.03	.02
264	Storm Davis	.05	.04	.02
265	Jose Lind	.04	.03	.02
266	Greg Hibbard	.06	.05	.02
267	Norm Charlton	.06	.05	.02

		MT	NR MT	EX
268	Paul Kilgus	.04	.03	.02
269	Greg Maddux	.06	.05	.02
270	Ellis Burks	.12	.09	.05
271	Frank Tanana	.05	.04	.02
272	Gene Larkin	.05	.04	.02
273	Ron Hassey	.04	.03	.02
274	Jeff Robinson	.04	.03	.02
275	Steve Howe	.05	.04	.02
276	Daryl Boston	.04	.03	.02
277	Mark Lee	.04	.03	.02
278	*Jose Segura* (FC)	.12	.09	.05
279	Lance Blankenship	.04	.03	.02
280	Don Slaught	.04	.03	.02
281	Russ Swan	.08	.06	.03
282	Bob Tewksbury	.04	.03	.02
283	Geno Petralli	.04	.03	.02
284	Shane Mack	.08	.06	.03
285	Bob Scanlan	.25	.20	.10
286	Tim Leary	.05	.04	.02
287	John Smoltz	.15	.11	.06
288	Pat Borders	.05	.04	.02
289	Mark Davidson	.04	.03	.02
290	Sam Horn	.06	.05	.02
291	Lenny Harris	.05	.04	.02
292	Franklin Stubbs	.04	.03	.02
293	Thomas Howard	.05	.04	.02
294	Steve Lyons	.04	.03	.02
295	Francisco Oliveras	.04	.03	.02
296	Terry Leach	.04	.03	.02
297	Barry Jones	.04	.03	.02
298	Lance Parrish	.08	.06	.03
299	Wally Whitehurst	.06	.05	.02
300	Bob Welch	.06	.05	.02
301	Charlie Hayes	.05	.04	.02
302	Charlie Hough	.05	.04	.02
303	Gary Redus	.04	.03	.02
304	Scott Bradley	.04	.03	.02
305	Jose Oquendo	.04	.03	.02
306	Pete Incaviglia	.06	.05	.02
307	Marvin Freeman	.04	.03	.02
308	Gary Pettis	.04	.03	.02
309	Joe Slusarski	.25	.20	.10
310	Kevin Seitzer	.05	.04	.02
311	Jeff Reed	.04	.03	.02
312	Pat Tabler	.04	.03	.02
313	Mike Maddux	.04	.03	.02
314	Bob Milacki	.04	.03	.02
315	Eric Anthony	.10	.08	.04
316	Dante Bichette	.05	.04	.02
317	Steve Decker	.15	.11	.06
318	Jack Clark	.08	.06	.03
319	Doug Dascenzo	.04	.03	.02
320	Scott Leius	.10	.08	.04
321	Jim Lindeman	.04	.03	.02
322	Bryan Harvey	.08	.06	.03
323	Spike Owen	.04	.03	.02
324	Roberto Kelly	.12	.09	.05
325	Stan Belinda	.05	.04	.02
326	Joey Cora	.04	.03	.02
327	Jeff Innis	.04	.03	.02
328	Willie Wilson	.05	.04	.02
329	Juan Agosto	.04	.03	.02
330	Charles Nagy	.10	.08	.04
331	Scott Bailes	.04	.03	.02
332	*Pete Schourek*	.12	.09	.05
333	Mike Flanagan	.04	.03	.02
334	Omar Olivares	.10	.08	.04
335	Dennis Lamp	.04	.03	.02
336	Tommy Greene	.06	.05	.02
337	Randy Velarde	.04	.03	.02
338	Tom Lampkin	.04	.03	.02
339	John Russell	.04	.03	.02
340	Bob Kipper	.04	.03	.02
341	Todd Burns	.04	.03	.02
342	Ron Jones	.05	.04	.02
343	Dave Valle	.04	.03	.02
344	Mike Heath	.04	.03	.02
345	John Olerud	.15	.11	.06
346	Gerald Young	.04	.03	.02
347	Ken Patterson	.04	.03	.02
348	Les Lancaster	.04	.03	.02
349	Steve Crawford	.04	.03	.02
350	John Candelaria	.04	.03	.02
351	Mike Aldrete	.04	.03	.02
352	Mariano Duncan	.05	.04	.02
353	Julio Machado	.04	.03	.02
354	Ken Williams	.04	.03	.02
355	Walt Terrell	.04	.03	.02
356	Mitch Williams	.08	.06	.03
357	Al Newman	.04	.03	.02
358	Bud Black	.05	.04	.02

		MT	NR MT	EX
359	Joe Hesketh	.04	.03	.02
360	Paul Assenmacher	.05	.04	.02
361	Bo Jackson	.25	.20	.10
362	Jeff Blauser	.04	.03	.02
363	Mike Brumley	.04	.03	.02
364	Jim Deshaies	.04	.03	.02
365	Brady Anderson	.04	.03	.02
366	Chuck McElroy	.04	.03	.02
367	Matt Merullo	.04	.03	.02
368	Tim Belcher	.06	.05	.02
369	Luis Aquino	.04	.03	.02
370	Joe Oliver	.05	.04	.02
371	Greg Swindell	.08	.06	.03
372	Lee Stevens	.10	.08	.04
373	Mark Knudson	.04	.03	.02
374	Bill Wegman	.05	.04	.02
375	Jerry Don Gleaton	.04	.03	.02
376	Pedro Guerrero	.10	.08	.04
377	Randy Bush	.04	.03	.02
378	Greg Harris	.04	.03	.02
379	Eric Plunk	.04	.03	.02
380	Jose DeJesus	.08	.06	.03
381	Bobby Witt	.06	.05	.02
382	Curtis Wilkerson	.04	.03	.02
383	Gene Nelson	.04	.03	.02
384	Wes Chamberlain	.20	.15	.08
385	Tom Henke	.06	.05	.02
386	Mark Lemke	.06	.05	.02
387	Greg Briley	.04	.03	.02
388	Rafael Ramirez	.04	.03	.02
389	Tony Fossas	.04	.03	.02
390	Henry Cotto	.04	.03	.02
391	Tim Hulett	.04	.03	.02
392	Dean Palmer	.25	.20	.10
393	Glenn Braggs	.05	.04	.02
394	Mark Salas	.04	.03	.02
395	Rusty Meacham (FC)	.20	.15	.08
396	*Andy Ashby* (FC)	.15	.11	.06
397	*Jose Melendez* (FC)	.20	.15	.08
398	*Warren Newson* (FC)	.20	.15	.08
399	*Frank Castillo* (FC)	.15	.11	.06
400	*Chito Martinez* (FC)	.25	.20	.10
401	Bernie Williams	.20	.15	.08
402	Derek Bell (FC)	.20	.15	.08
403	*Javier Ortiz* (FC)	.15	.11	.06
404	*Tim Sherrill* (FC)	.12	.09	.05
405	Rob MacDonald (FC)	.15	.11	.06
406	Phil Plantier	.40	.30	.15
407	Troy Afenir	.10	.08	.04
408	*Gino Minutelli* (FC)	.10	.08	.04
409	*Reggie Jefferson* (FC)	.20	.15	.08
410	*Mike Remlinger* (FC)	.15	.11	.06
411	*Carlos Rodriguez* (FC)	.15	.11	.06
412	*Joe Redfield* (FC)	.20	.15	.08
413	Alonzo Powell (FC)	.08	.06	.03
414	*Scott Livingstone* (FC)	.30	.25	.12
415	Scott Kamieniecki (FC)	.15	.11	.06
416	*Tim Spehr* (FC)	.20	.15	.08
417	*Brian Hunter* (FC)	.30	.25	.12
418	*Ced Landrum* (FC)	.15	.11	.06
419	*Bret Barberie* (FC)	.15	.11	.06
420	Kevin Morton (FC)	.20	.15	.08
421	*Doug Henry* (FC)	.20	.15	.08
422	*Doug Piatt* (FC)	.15	.11	.06
423	Pat Rice (FC)	.15	.11	.06
424	*Juan Guzman* (FC)	.60	.45	.25
425	Nolan Ryan (No-Hit Club)	.30	.25	.12
426	Tommy Greene (No-Hit Club)	.10	.08	.04
427	Milacki/Flanagan/Williamson (No-Hit Club)	.10	.08	.04
428	Wilson Alvarez (No-Hit Club)	.20	.15	.08
429	Otis Nixon (Highlight)	.08	.06	.03
430	Rickey Henderson (Highlight)	.20	.15	.08
431	Cecil Fielder (AS)	.10	.08	.04
432	Julio Franco (AS)	.08	.06	.03
433	Cal Ripken, Jr. (AS)	.15	.11	.06
434	Wade Boggs (AS)	.10	.08	.04
435	Joe Carter (AS)	.10	.08	.04
436	Ken Griffey, Jr. (AS)	.40	.30	.15
437	Ruben Sierra (AS)	.10	.08	.04
438	Scott Erickson (AS)	.15	.11	.06
439	Tom Henke (AS)	.05	.04	.02
440	Terry Steinbach (AS)	.05	.04	.02
441	Rickey Henderson (Dream Team)	.25	.20	.10
442	Ryne Sandberg (Dream Team)	.35	.25	.14
443	Otis Nixon	.06	.05	.02
444	Scott Radinsky	.04	.03	.02
445	Mark Grace	.08	.06	.03
446	Tony Pena	.06	.05	.02
447	Billy Hatcher	.04	.03	.02
448	Glenallen Hill	.06	.05	.02

#	Player	MT	NR MT	EX		#	Player	MT	NR MT	EX
449	Chris Gwynn	.04	.03	.02		540	Cal Ripken	.20	.15	.08
450	Tom Glavine	.08	.06	.03		541	Bill Swift	.06	.05	.02
451	John Habyan	.04	.03	.02		542	Kevin Appier	.06	.05	.02
452	Al Osuna	.04	.03	.02		543	Dave Bergman	.04	.03	.02
453	Tony Phillips	.06	.05	.02		544	Bernard Gilkey	.10	.08	.04
454	Greg Cadaret	.04	.03	.02		545	Mike Greenwell	.08	.06	.03
455	Rob Dibble	.08	.06	.03		546	Jose Uribe	.04	.03	.02
456	Rick Honeycutt	.04	.03	.02		547	Jesse Orosco	.04	.03	.02
457	Jerome Walton	.04	.03	.02		548	Bob Patterson	.04	.03	.02
458	Mookie Wilson	.04	.03	.02		549	Mike Stanley	.04	.03	.02
459	Mark Gubicza	.04	.03	.02		550	Howard Johnson	.08	.06	.03
460	Craig Biggio	.08	.06	.03		551	Joe Orsulak	.04	.03	.02
461	Dave Cochrane	.04	.03	.02		552	Dick Schofield	.04	.03	.02
462	Keith Miller	.04	.03	.02		553	Dave Hollins	.08	.06	.03
463	Alex Cole	.06	.05	.02		554	David Segui	.06	.05	.02
464	Pete Smith	.04	.03	.02		555	Barry Bonds	.20	.15	.08
465	Brett Butler	.06	.05	.02		556	Mo Vaughn	.20	.15	.08
466	Jeff Huson	.04	.03	.02		557	Craig Wilson	.06	.05	.02
467	Steve Lake	.04	.03	.02		558	Bobby Rose	.04	.03	.02
468	Lloyd Moseby	.04	.03	.02		559	Rod Nichols	.04	.03	.02
469	Tim McIntosh	.04	.03	.02		560	Len Dykstra	.08	.06	.03
470	Dennis Martinez	.06	.05	.02		561	Craig Grebeck	.04	.03	.02
471	Greg Myers	.04	.03	.02		562	Darren Lewis	.10	.08	.04
472	Mackey Sasser	.04	.03	.02		563	Todd Benzinger	.04	.03	.02
473	Junior Ortiz	.04	.03	.02		564	Ed Whitson	.04	.03	.02
474	Greg Olson	.04	.03	.02		565	Jesse Barfield	.04	.03	.02
475	Steve Sax	.06	.05	.02		566	Lloyd McClendon	.04	.03	.02
476	Ricky Jordan	.06	.05	.02		567	Dan Plesac	.04	.03	.02
477	Max Venable	.04	.03	.02		568	Danny Cox	.04	.03	.02
478	Brian McRae	.10	.08	.04		569	Skeeter Barnes	.04	.03	.02
479	Doug Simons	.04	.03	.02		570	Bobby Thigpen	.08	.06	.03
480	Rickey Henderson	.15	.11	.06		571	Deion Sanders	.10	.08	.04
481	Gary Varsho	.04	.03	.02		572	Chuck Knoblauch	.20	.15	.08
482	Carl Willis	.04	.03	.02		573	Matt Nokes	.06	.05	.02
483	*Rick Wilkins*	.10	.08	.04		574	Herm Winningham	.04	.03	.02
484	Donn Pall	.04	.03	.02		575	Tom Candiotti	.06	.05	.02
485	Edgar Martinez	.08	.06	.03		576	*Jeff Bagwell*	.50	.40	.20
486	Tom Foley	.08	.06	.03		577	Brook Jacoby	.04	.03	.02
487	Mark Williamson	.08	.06	.03		578	Chico Walker	.04	.03	.02
488	Jack Armstrong	.08	.06	.03		579	Brian Downing	.04	.03	.02
489	Gary Carter	.08	.06	.03		580	Dave Stewart	.06	.05	.02
490	Ruben Sierra	.15	.11	.06		581	Francisco Cabrera	.04	.03	.02
491	Gerald Perry	.04	.03	.02		582	Rene Gonzales	.04	.03	.02
492	Rob Murphy	.04	.03	.02		583	Stan Javier	.04	.03	.02
493	Zane Smith	.04	.03	.02		584	Randy Johnson	.06	.05	.02
494	*Darryl Kile*	.10	.08	.04		585	Chuck Finley	.06	.05	.02
495	Kelly Gruber	.06	.05	.02		586	Mark Gardner	.04	.03	.02
496	Jerry Browne	.04	.03	.02		587	Mark Whiten	.10	.08	.04
497	Darryl Hamilton	.06	.05	.02		588	Garry Templeton	.04	.03	.02
498	Mike Stanton	.04	.03	.02		589	Gary Sheffield	.20	.15	.08
499	Mark Leonard	.04	.03	.02		590	Ozzie Smith	.08	.06	.03
500	Jose Canseco	.20	.15	.08		591	Candy Maldonado	.04	.03	.02
501	Dave Martinez	.04	.03	.02		592	Mike Sharperson	.04	.03	.02
502	Jose Guzman	.04	.03	.02		593	Carlos Martinez	.04	.03	.02
503	Terry Kennedy	.04	.03	.02		594	Scott Bankhead	.04	.03	.02
504	*Ed Sprague*	.08	.06	.03		595	Tim Wallach	.06	.05	.02
505	Frank Thomas	.60	.45	.25		596	Tino Martinez	.08	.06	.03
506	Darren Daulton	.06	.05	.02		597	Roger McDowell	.04	.03	.02
507	Kevin Tapani	.06	.05	.02		598	Cory Snyder	.06	.05	.02
508	Luis Salazar	.04	.03	.02		599	Andujar Cedeno	.10	.08	.04
509	Paul Faries	.04	.03	.02		600	Kirby Puckett	.15	.11	.06
510	Sandy Alomar, Jr.	.08	.06	.03		601	Rick Parker	.04	.03	.02
511	Jeff King	.04	.03	.02		602	Todd Hundley	.08	.06	.03
512	Gary Thurman	.04	.03	.02		603	Greg Litton	.04	.03	.02
513	Chris Hammond	.06	.05	.02		604	Dave Johnson	.04	.03	.02
514	*Pedro Munoz*	.15	.11	.06		605	John Franco	.04	.03	.02
515	Alan Trammell	.08	.06	.03		606	Mike Fetters	.04	.03	.02
516	Geronimo Pena	.06	.05	.02		607	Luis Alicea	.04	.03	.02
517	Rodney McCray	.04	.03	.02		608	Trevor Wilson	.04	.03	.02
518	Manny Lee	.04	.03	.02		609	Rob Ducey	.04	.03	.02
519	Junior Felix	.06	.05	.02		610	Ramon Martinez	.08	.06	.03
520	Kirk Gibson	.06	.05	.02		611	Dave Burba	.04	.03	.02
521	Darrin Jackson	.06	.05	.02		612	Dwight Smith	.04	.03	.02
522	John Burkett	.06	.05	.02		613	Kevin Maas	.08	.06	.03
523	Jeff Johnson	.06	.05	.02		614	John Costello	.04	.03	.02
524	Jim Corsi	.04	.03	.02		615	Glenn Davis	.06	.05	.02
525	Robin Yount	.12	.09	.05		616	Shawn Abner	.04	.03	.02
526	Jamie Quirk	.04	.03	.02		617	Scott Hemond	.04	.03	.02
527	Bob Ojeda	.04	.03	.02		618	Tom Prince	.04	.03	.02
528	Mark Lewis	.10	.08	.04		619	Wally Ritchie	.04	.03	.02
529	Bryn Smith	.04	.03	.02		620	Jim Abbott	.08	.06	.03
530	Kent Hrbek	.06	.05	.02		621	Charlie O'Brien	.04	.03	.02
531	Dennis Boyd	.04	.03	.02		622	Jack Daugherty	.04	.03	.02
532	Ron Karkovice	.04	.03	.02		623	Tommy Gregg	.04	.03	.02
533	Don August	.04	.03	.02		624	Jeff Shaw	.04	.03	.02
534	Todd Frohwirth	.04	.03	.02		625	Tony Gwynn	.15	.11	.06
535	Wally Joyner	.08	.06	.03		626	Mark Leiter	.04	.03	.02
536	Dennis Rasmussen	.04	.03	.02		627	Jim Clancy	.04	.03	.02
537	Andy Allanson	.04	.03	.02		628	Tim Layana	.04	.03	.02
538	Rich Gossage	.04	.03	.02		629	Jeff Schaefer	.04	.03	.02
539	John Marzano	.04	.03	.02		630	Lee Smith	.06	.05	.02

		MT	NR MT	EX			MT	NR MT	EX
631	Wade Taylor	.06	.05	.02	722	Curt Young	.04	.03	.02
632	Mike Simms	.06	.05	.02	723	Neal Heaton	.04	.03	.02
633	Terry Steinbach	.04	.03	.02	724	Craig Worthington	.04	.03	.02
634	Shawon Dunston	.06	.05	.02	725	Mel Rojas	.04	.03	.02
635	Tim Raines	.06	.05	.02	726	Daryl Irvine	.04	.03	.02
636	Kirt Manwaring	.04	.03	.02	727	Roger Mason	.04	.03	.02
637	Warren Cromartie	.04	.03	.02	728	Kirk Dressendorfer	.08	.06	.03
638	Luis Quinones	.04	.03	.02	729	Scott Aldred	.04	.03	.02
639	Greg Vaughn	.08	.06	.03	730	Willie Blair	.04	.03	.02
640	Kevin Mitchell	.08	.06	.03	731	Allan Anderson	.04	.03	.02
641	Chris Hoiles	.10	.08	.04	732	Dana Kiecker	.04	.03	.02
642	Tom Browning	.04	.03	.02	733	Jose Gonzalez	.04	.03	.02
643	Mitch Webster	.04	.03	.02	734	Brian Drahman	.04	.03	.03
644	Steve Olin	.06	.05	.02	735	Brad Komminsk	.04	.03	.03
645	Tony Fernandez	.06	.05	.02	736	Arthur Rhodes(FC)	.15	.11	.06
646	Juan Bell	.04	.03	.02	737	Terry Mathews(FC)	.10	.08	.04
647	Joe Boever	.04	.03	.02	738	Jeff Fassero(FC)	.08	.06	.03
648	Carney Lansford	.06	.05	.02	739	Mike Magnante(FC)	.08	.06	.03
649	Mike Benjamin	.04	.03	.02	740	Kip Gross(FC)	.08	.06	.03
650	George Brett	.10	.08	.04	741	Jim Hunter(FC)	.06	.05	.02
651	Tim Burke	.04	.03	.02	742	Jose Mota(FC)	.08	.06	.03
652	Jack Morris	.06	.05	.02	743	Joe Bitker	.04	.03	.02
653	Orel Hershiser	.06	.05	.02	744	Tim Mauser(FC)	.08	.06	.03
654	Mike Schooler	.04	.03	.02	745	Ramon Garcia(FC)	.08	.06	.03
655	Andy Van Slyke	.08	.06	.03	746	Rod Beck(FC)	.08	.06	.03
656	Dave Stieb	.06	.05	.02	747	Jim Austin(FC)	.08	.06	.03
657	Dave Clark	.04	.03	.02	748	Keith Mitchell(FC)	.10	.08	.04
658	Ben McDonald	.10	.08	.04	749	Wayne Rosenthal(FC)	.06	.05	.02
659	John Smiley	.06	.05	.02	750	Bryan Hickerson(FC)	.08	.06	.03
660	Wade Boggs	.12	.09	.05	751	Bruce Egloff(FC)	.08	.06	.03
661	Eric Bullock	.04	.03	.02	752	John Wehner(FC)	.08	.06	.03
662	Eric Show	.04	.03	.02	753	Darren Holmes(FC)	.05	.04	.02
663	Lenny Webster	.06	.05	.02	754	Dave Hansen	.06	.05	.02
664	Mike Huff	.04	.03	.02	755	Mike Mussina(FC)	.20	.15	.08
665	Rick Sutcliffe	.06	.05	.02	756	Anthony Young(FC)	.10	.08	.04
666	Jeff Manto	.04	.03	.02	757	Ron Tingley	.04	.03	.02
667	Mike Fitzgerald	.04	.03	.02	758	Ricky Bones(FC)	.10	.08	.04
668	Matt Young	.04	.03	.02	759	Mark Wohlers(FC)	.25	.20	.10
669	Dave West	.04	.03	.02	760	Wilson Alvarez(FC)	.08	.06	.03
670	Mike Hartley	.04	.03	.02	761	Harvey Pulliam(FC)	.08	.06	.03
671	Curt Schilling	.06	.05	.02	762	Ryan Bowen(FC)	.10	.08	.04
672	Brian Bohanon	.04	.03	.02	763	Terry Bross(FC)	.04	.03	.02
673	Cecil Espy	.04	.03	.02	764	Joel Johnston(FC)	.08	.06	.03
674	Joe Grahe	.04	.03	.02	765	Terry McDaniel(FC)	.10	.08	.04
675	Sid Fernandez	.06	.05	.02	766	Esteban Beltre(FC)	.08	.06	.03
676	Edwin Nunez	.04	.03	.02	767	Rob Maurer(FC)	.20	.15	.08
677	Hector Villanueva	.04	.03	.02	768	Ted Wood	.20	.15	.08
678	Sean Berry	.06	.05	.02	769	Mo Sanford(FC)	.10	.08	.04
679	Dave Eiland	.04	.03	.02	770	Jeff Carter(FC)	.08	.06	.03
680	David Cone	.08	.06	.03	771	Gil Heredia(FC)	.08	.06	.03
681	Mike Bordick	.06	.05	.02	772	Monty Fariss(FC)	.08	.06	.03
682	Tony Castillo	.04	.03	.02	773	Will Clark (AS)	.10	.08	.04
683	John Barfield	.04	.03	.02	774	Ryne Sandberg (AS)	.10	.08	.04
684	Jeff Hamilton	.04	.03	.02	775	Barry Larkin (AS)	.08	.06	.03
685	Ken Dayley	.04	.03	.02	776	Howard Johnson (AS)	.08	.06	.03
686	Carmelo Martinez	.04	.03	.02	777	Barry Bonds (AS)	.10	.08	.04
687	Mike Capel	.04	.03	.02	778	Brett Butler (AS)	.06	.05	.02
688	Scott Chiamparino	.04	.03	.02	779	Tony Gwynn (AS)	.10	.08	.04
689	Rich Gedman	.04	.03	.02	780	Ramon Martinez (AS)	.06	.05	.02
690	Rich Monteleone	.04	.03	.02	781	Lee Smith (AS)	.06	.05	.02
691	Alejandro Pena	.04	.03	.02	782	Mike Scioscia (AS)	.04	.03	.02
692	Oscar Azocar	.04	.03	.02	783	Dennis Martinez (Highlight)	.04	.03	.02
693	Jim Poole	.04	.03	.02	784	Dennis Martinez (No-Hit Club)	.04	.03	.02
694	Mike Gardiner	.04	.03	.02	785	Mark Gardner (No-Hit Club)	.04	.03	.02
695	Steve Buechele	.04	.03	.02	786	Bret Saberhagen (No-Hit Club)	.06	.05	.02
696	Rudy Seanez	.04	.03	.02	787	Kent Mercker, Mark Wohlers, Alejandro			
697	Paul Abbott	.04	.03	.02		Pena (No-Hit Club)	.06	.05	.02
698	Steve Searcy	.04	.03	.02	788	Cal Ripken (MVP)	.10	.08	.04
699	Jose Offerman	.06	.05	.02	789	Terry Pendleton (MVP)	.08	.06	.03
700	Ivan Rodriguez	.50	.40	.20	790	Roger Clemens (CY YOUNG)	.10	.08	.04
701	Joe Girardi	.04	.03	.02	791	Tom Glavine (CY YOUNG)	.08	.06	.03
702	Tony Perezchica	.04	.03	.02	792	Chuck Knoblauch (ROY)	.20	.15	.08
703	Paul McClellan	.05	.04	.02	793	Jeff Bagwell (ROY)	.30	.25	.12
704	David Howard	.06	.05	.02	794	Cal Ripken (Man of the Year)	.08	.06	.03
705	Dan Petry	.04	.03	.02	795	David Cone (Highlight)	.06	.05	.02
706	Jack Howell	.04	.03	.02	796	Kirby Puckett (Highlight)	.08	.06	.03
707	Jose Mesa	.04	.03	.02	797	Steve Avery (Highlight)	.10	.08	.04
708	Randy St. Claire	.04	.03	.02	798	Jack Morris (Highlight)	.06	.05	.02
709	Kevin Brown	.06	.05	.02	799	Allen Watson(FC)	.20	.15	.08
710	Ron Darling	.06	.05	.02	800	Manny Ramirez(FC)	.80	.60	.30
711	Jason Grimsley	.04	.03	.02	801	Cliff Floyd	.35	.25	.14
712	John Orton	.04	.03	.02	802	Al Shirley(FC)	.35	.25	.14
713	Shawn Boskie	.04	.03	.02	803	Brian Barber(FC)	.20	.15	.08
714	Pat Clements	.04	.03	.02	804	John Farrell(FC)	.20	.15	.08
715	Brian Barnes	.06	.05	.02	805	Brent Gates(FC)	.20	.15	.08
716	Luis Lopez(FC)	.08	.06	.03	806	Scott Ruffcorn(FC)	.20	.15	.08
717	Bob McClure	.04	.03	.02	807	Tyrone Hill(FC)	.30	.25	.12
718	Mark Davis	.04	.03	.02	808	Benji Gill(FC)	.30	.25	.12
719	Dann Billardello	.04	.03	.02	809	Aaron Sele(FC)	.30	.25	.12
720	Tom Edens	.04	.03	.02	810	Tyler Green(FC)	.70	.50	.30
721	Willie Fraser	.04	.03	.02	811	Chris Jones	.04	.03	.02

		MT	NR MT	EX
812	Steve Wilson	.04	.03	.02
813	*Cliff Young*	.08	.06	.03
814	*Don Wakamatsu*	.08	.06	.03
815	*Mike Humphreys*	.08	.06	.03
816	*Scott Servais*	.08	.06	.03
817	*Rico Rossy*	.08	.06	.03
818	*John Ramos*	.08	.06	.03
819	Rob Mallicoat	.06	.05	.02
820	*Milt Hill*	.08	.06	.03
821	Carlos Carcia	.06	.05	.02
822	Stan Royer	.06	.05	.02
823	*Jeff Plympton*(FC)	.15	.11	.06
824	*Braulio Castillo*(FC)	.20	.15	.08
825	*David Haas*(FC)	.08	.06	.03
826	*Luis Mercedes*(FC)	.10	.08	.04
827	*Eric Karros*(FC)	.25	.20	.10
828	*Shawn Hare*(FC)	.10	.08	.04
829	*Reggie Sanders*(FC)	.30	.25	.12
830	Tom Goodwin	.10	.08	.04
831	*Dan Gakeler*(FC)	.08	.06	.03
832	*Stacy Jones*(FC)	.08	.06	.03
833	*Kim Batiste*	.08	.06	.03
834	Cal Eldred	.08	.06	.03
835	*Chris George*(FC)	.10	.08	.04
836	*Wayne Housie*(FC)	.10	.08	.04
837	*Mike Ignasiak*(FC)	.10	.08	.04
838	*Josias Manzanillo*(FC)	.10	.08	.04
839	*Jim Olander*(FC)	.10	.08	.04
840	*Gary Cooper*(FC)	.10	.08	.04
841	*Royce Clayton*(FC)	.20	.15	.08
842	*Hector Fajardo*(FC)	.20	.15	.08
843	Blaine Beatty	.04	.03	.02
844	*Jorge Pedre*(FC)	.10	.08	.04
845	*Kenny Lofton*(FC)	.40	.30	.15
846	*Scott Brosius*(FC)	.08	.06	.03
847	*Chris Cron*(FC)	.08	.06	.03
848	Denis Boucher	.06	.05	.02
849	Kyle Abbott	.10	.08	.04
850	*Bob Zupcic*(FC)	.30	.25	.12
851	*Rheal Cormier*(FC)	.15	.11	.06
852	*Jim Lewis*(FC)	.08	.06	.03
853	Anthony Telford	.04	.03	.02
854	*Cliff Brantley*(FC)	.10	.08	.04
855	*Kevin Campbell*(FC)	.10	.08	.04
856	*Craig Shipley*(FC)	.08	.06	.03
857	Chuck Carr	.04	.03	.02
858	*Tony Eusebio*(FC)	.10	.08	.04
859	*Jim Thome*(FC)	.40	.30	.15
860	*Vinny Castilla*(FC)	.10	.08	.04
861	Dann Howitt	.04	.03	.02
862	*Kevin Ward*(FC)	.10	.08	.04
863	*Steve Wapnick*(FC)	.08	.06	.03
864	Rod Brewer	.08	.06	.03
865	Todd Van Poppel	.35	.25	.14
866	*Jose Hernandez*(FC)	.10	.08	.04
867	*Amalio Carreno*(FC)	.10	.08	.04
868	*Calvin Jones*(FC)	.10	.08	.04
869	*Jeff Gardner*(FC)	.10	.08	.04
870	*Jarvis Brown*(FC)	.10	.08	.04
871	*Eddie Taubensee*(FC)	.20	.15	.08
872	*Andy Mota*(FC)	.08	.06	.03
873	Chris Haney	.06	.05	.02
874	Roberto Hernandez	.10	.08	.04
875	*Laddie Renfroe*(FC)	.10	.08	.04
876	Scott Cooper	.08	.06	.03
877	*Armando Reynoso*(FC)	.10	.08	.04
878	Ty Cobb (Memorabilia)	.30	.25	.12
879	Babe Ruth (Memorabilia)	.40	.30	.15
880	Honus Wagner (Memorabilia)	.20	.15	.08
881	Lou Gehrig (Memorabilia)	.30	.25	.12
882	Satchel Paige (Memorabilia)	.20	.15	.08
883	Will Clark (Dream Team)	.20	.15	.08
884	Cal Ripken (Dream Team)	.30	.25	.12
885	Wade Boggs (Dream Team)	.20	.15	.08
886	Kirby Puckett (Dream Team)	.20	.15	.08
887	Tony Gwynn (Dream Team)	.20	.15	.08
889	Scott Erickson (Dream Team)	.25	.20	.10
890	Tom Glavine (Dream Team)	.10	.08	.04
891	Rob Dibble (Dream Team)	.08	.06	.03
892	Mitch Williams (Dream Team)	.06	.05	.02
893	Frank Thomas (Dream Team)	.80	.60	.30

1992 Score Pinnacle

Score entered the high end card market with the release of this 620-card set. The cards feature black borders surrounding a white frame with a full-color

action photo inside. The player extends beyond the natural background. The backs are horizontal and feature a closeup photo, statistics, team logo, biographical information and player information. Several subsets can be found within the set including idols, sidelines, grips, shades and technicians. Score produced Pinnacle lines in football and hockey as well as in baseball.

		MT	NR MT	EX
	Complete Set:	70.00	52.00	30.00
	Common Player:	.10	.08	.04
1	Frank Thomas	4.00	3.00	1.50
2	Benito Santiago	.15	.11	.06
3	Carlos Baerga	.20	.15	.08
4	Cecil Fielder	.50	.40	.20
5	Barry Larkin	.30	.25	.12
6	Ozzie Smith	.30	.25	.12
7	Willie McGee	.12	.09	.05
8	Paul Moltior	.12	.09	.05
9	Andy Van Slyke	.12	.09	.05
10	Ryne Sandberg	.60	.45	.25
11	Kevin Seitzer	.10	.08	.04
12	Lenny Dykstra	.12	.09	.05
13	Edgar Martinez	.15	.11	.06
14	Ruben Sierra	.25	.20	.10
15	Howard Johnson	.20	.15	.08
16	Dave Henderson	.10	.08	.04
17	Devon White	.10	.08	.04
18	Terry Pendleton	.15	.11	.06
19	Steve Finley	.10	.08	.04
20	Kirby Puckett	.50	.40	.20
21	Orel Hershiser	.10	.08	.04
22	Hal Morris	.10	.08	.04
23	Don Mattingly	.20	.15	.08
24	Delino DeShields	.15	.11	.06
25	Dennis Eckersley	.15	.11	.06
26	Ellis Burks	.10	.08	.04
27	Jay Buhner	.10	.08	.04
28	Matt Williams	.20	.15	.08
29	Lou Whitaker	.10	.08	.04
30	Alex Fernandez	.12	.09	.05
31	Albert Belle	.50	.40	.20
32	Todd Zeile	.12	.09	.05
33	Tony Pena	.10	.08	.04
34	Jay Bell	.10	.08	.04
35	Rafael Palmeiro	.25	.20	.10
36	Wes Chamberlain	.10	.08	.04
37	George Bell	.12	.09	.05
38	Robin Yount	.50	.40	.20
39	Vince Coleman	.10	.08	.04
40	Bruce Hurst	.10	.08	.04
41	Harold Baines	.12	.09	.05
42	Chuck Finley	.12	.09	.05
43	Ken Caminiti	.10	.08	.04
44	Ben McDonald	.40	.30	.15
45	Roberto Alomar	.50	.40	.20
46	Chili Davis	.10	.08	.04
47	Bill Doran	.10	.08	.04
48	Jerald Clark	.10	.08	.04
49	Jose Lind	.10	.08	.04
50	Nolan Ryan	1.25	.90	.50
51	Phil Plantier	.60	.45	.25
52	Gary DiSarcina	.10	.08	.04
53	Kevin Bass	.10	.08	.04
54	Pat Kelly	.10	.08	.04
55	Mark Wohlers	.30	.25	.12
56	Walt Weiss	.10	.08	.04
57	Lenny Harris	.10	.08	.04
58	Ivan Calderon	.10	.08	.04

#	Name	MT	NR MT	EX
59	Harold Reynolds	.10	.08	.04
60	George Brett	.40	.30	.15
61	Gregg Olson	.12	.09	.05
62	Orlando Merced	.10	.08	.04
63	Steve Decker	.10	.08	.04
64	John Franco	.10	.08	.04
65	Greg Maddux	.20	.15	.08
66	Alex Cole	.10	.08	.04
67	Dave Holins	.15	.11	.06
68	Kent Hrbek	.10	.08	.04
69	Tom Pagnozzi	.10	.08	.04
70	Jeff Bagwell	.60	.45	.25
71	Jim Gantner	.10	.08	.04
72	Matt Nokes	.10	.08	.04
73	Brian Harper	.10	.08	.04
74	Andy Benes	.20	.15	.08
75	Tom Glavine	.25	.20	.10
76	Terry Steinbach	.10	.08	.04
77	Dennis Martinez	.10	.08	.04
78	John Olerud	.20	.15	.08
79	Ozzie Guillen	.10	.08	.04
80	Darryl Strawberry	.40	.30	.15
81	Gary Gaetti	.10	.08	.04
82	Dave Righetti	.10	.08	.04
83	Chris Hoiles	.15	.11	.06
84	Andujar Cedeno	.20	.15	.08
85	Jack Clark	.10	.08	.04
86	David Howard	.10	.08	.04
87	Bill Gullickson	.10	.08	.04
88	Bernard Gilkey	.15	.11	.06
89	Kevin Elster	.10	.08	.04
90	Kevin Maas	.15	.11	.06
91	Mark Lewis	.15	.11	.06
92	Greg Vaughn	.20	.15	.08
93	Bret Barberie	.15	.11	.06
94	Dave Smith	.10	.08	.04
95	Roger Clemens	.60	.45	.25
96	Doug Drabek	.15	.11	.06
97	Omar Vizquel	.10	.08	.04
98	Jose Guzman	.10	.08	.04
99	Juan Samuel	.10	.08	.04
100	Dave Justice	.50	.40	.20
101	Tom Browning	.10	.08	.04
102	Mark Gubicza	.10	.08	.04
103	Mickey Morandini	.10	.08	.04
104	Ed Whitson	.10	.08	.04
105	Lance Parrish	.10	.08	.04
106	Scott Erickson	.40	.30	.15
107	Jack McDowell	.30	.25	.12
108	Dave Stieb	.10	.08	.04
109	Mike Moore	.10	.08	.04
110	Travis Fryman	.25	.20	.10
111	Doc Gooden	.35	.25	.14
112	Fred McGriff	.25	.20	.10
113	Alan Trammell	.20	.15	.08
114	Roberto Kelly	.15	.11	.06
115	Andre Dawson	.25	.20	.10
116	Bill Landrum	.10	.08	.04
117	Brian McRae	.20	.15	.08
119	Chuck Knoblauch	.50	.40	.20
120	Steve Olin	.12	.09	.05
121	Robin Ventura	.60	.45	.25
122	Will Clark	.80	.60	.30
123	Tino Martinez	.15	.11	.06
124	Dale Murphy	.15	.11	.06
125	Pete O'Brien	.10	.08	.04
126	Ray Lankford	.50	.40	.20
127	Juan Gonzalez	.70	.50	.30
128	Ron Gant	.70	.50	.30
129	Marquis Grissom	.30	.25	.12
130	Jose Canseco	.80	.60	.30
131	Mike Greenwell	.20	.15	.08
132	Mark Langston	.12	.09	.05
133	Brett Butler	.12	.09	.05
134	Kelly Gruber	.20	.15	.08
135	Chris Sabo	.20	.15	.08
136	Mark Grace	.20	.15	.08
137	Tony Fernandez	.12	.09	.05
138	Glenn Davis	.12	.09	.05
139	Pedro Munoz	.50	.40	.20
140	Craig Biggio, Craig Biggio	.15	.11	.06
141	Pete Schourek	.10	.08	.04
142	Mike Boddicker	.10	.08	.04
143	Robby Thompson	.10	.08	.04
144	Mel Hall	.12	.09	.05
145	Bryan Harvey	.12	.09	.05
146	Mike LaValliere	.10	.08	.04
147	John Kruk	.12	.09	.05
148	Joe Carter	.30	.25	.12
149	Greg Olson	.10	.08	.04
150	Julio Franco	.25	.20	.10
151	Darryl Hamilton	.12	.09	.05
152	Felix Fermin	.10	.08	.04
153	Jose Offerman	.12	.09	.05
154	Paul O'Neill	.12	.09	.05
155	Tommy Greene	.12	.09	.05
156	Ivan Rodriguez	1.00	.70	.40
157	Dave Stewart	.12	.09	.05
158	Jeff Reardon	.12	.09	.05
159	Felix Jose	.15	.11	.06
160	Doug Dascenzo	.10	.08	.04
161	Tim Wallach	.10	.08	.04
162	Dan Plesac	.10	.08	.04
163	Luis Gonzalez	.30	.25	.12
164	Mike Henneman	.12	.09	.05
165	Mike Devereaux	.12	.09	.05
166	Luis Polonia	.10	.08	.04
167	Mike Sharperson	.10	.08	.04
168	Chris Donnels	.10	.08	.04
169	Greg Harris	.10	.08	.04
170	Deion Sanders	.60	.45	.25
171	Mike Schooler	.10	.08	.04
172	Jose DeJesus	.10	.08	.04
173	Jeff Montgomery	.10	.08	.04
174	Milt Cuyler	.10	.08	.04
175	Wade Boggs	.40	.30	.15
176	Kevin Tapani	.15	.11	.06
177	Bill Spiers	.10	.08	.04
178	Tim Raines	.15	.11	.06
179	Randy Milligan	.10	.08	.04
180	Rob Dibble	.15	.11	.06
181	Kirt Manwaring	.10	.08	.04
182	Pascual Perez	.10	.08	.04
183	Juan Guzman	1.50	1.25	.60
184	John Smiley	.12	.09	.05
185	David Segui	.10	.08	.04
186	Omar Olivares	.10	.08	.04
187	Joe Slusarski	.10	.08	.04
188	Erik Hanson	.10	.08	.04
189	Mark Portugal	.10	.08	.04
190	Walt Terrell	.10	.08	.04
191	John Smoltz	.20	.15	.08
192	Wilson Alvarez	.10	.08	.04
193	Jimmy Key	.12	.09	.05
194	Larry Walker	.20	.15	.08
195	Lee Smith	.12	.09	.05
196	Pete Harnisch	.12	.09	.05
197	Mike Harkey	.10	.08	.04
198	Frank Tananna	.10	.08	.04
199	Terry Mulholland	.10	.08	.04
200	Cal Ripken, Jr.	1.00	.70	.40
201	Dave Magadan	.10	.08	.04
202	Bud Black	.10	.08	.04
203	Terry Shumpert	.10	.08	.04
204	Mike Mussina	2.00	1.50	.80
205	Mo Vaughn	.30	.25	.12
206	Steve Farr	.10	.08	.04
207	Darrin Jackson	.10	.08	.04
208	Jerry Browne	.10	.08	.04
209	Jeff Russell	.10	.08	.04
210	Mike Scioscia	.10	.08	.04
211	Rick Aguilera	.12	.09	.05
212	Jaime Navarro	.12	.09	.05
213	Randy Tomlin	.12	.09	.05
214	Bobby Thigpen	.20	.15	.08
215	Mark Gardner	.10	.08	.04
216	Norm Charlton	.12	.09	.05
217	Mark McGwire	.50	.40	.20
219	Bob Tewksbury	.12	.09	.05
220	Junior Felix	.10	.08	.04
221	Sam Horn	.10	.08	.04
222	Jody Reed	.10	.08	.04
223	Luis Sojo	.10	.08	.04
224	Jerome Walton	.10	.08	.04
225	Darryl Kile	.12	.09	.05
226	Mickey Tettleton	.15	.11	.06
227	Dan Pasqua	.10	.08	.04
228	Jim Gott	.10	.08	.04
229	Bernie Williams	.30	.25	.12
230	Shane Mack	.25	.20	.10
231	Steve Avery	.50	.40	.20
232	Dave Valle	.10	.08	.04
233	Mark Leonard	.10	.08	.04
234	Spike Owen	.10	.08	.04
235	Gary Sheffield	.70	.50	.30
236	Steve Chitren	.10	.08	.04
237	Zane Smith	.10	.08	.04
238	Tom Gordon	.10	.08	.04
239	Jose Oquendo	.10	.08	.04
240	Todd Stottlemyre	.10	.08	.04
241	Darren Daulton	.15	.11	.06
242	Tim Naehring	.12	.09	.05

#	Player	MT	NR MT	EX	#	Player	MT	NR MT	EX
243	Tony Phillips	.12	.09	.05	337	Scott Sanderson	.10	.08	.04
244	Shawon Dunston	.12	.09	.05	338	Dick Schofield	.10	.08	.04
245	Manuel Lee	.10	.08	.04	339	Bob Milacki	.10	.08	.04
246	Mike Pagliarulo	.10	.08	.04	340	Kevin Reimer	.10	.08	.04
247	Jim Thome	1.00	.70	.40	341	Jose DeLeon	.10	.08	.04
248	Luis Mercedes	.25	.20	.10	342	Henry Cotto	.10	.08	.04
249	Cal Eldred	.70	.50	.30	343	Daryl Boston	.10	.08	.04
250	Derek Bell	.50	.40	.20	344	Kevin Gross	.10	.08	.04
251	Arthur Lee Rhodes	.40	.30	.15	345	Milt Thompson	.10	.08	.04
252	Scott Cooper	.20	.15	.08	346	Luis Rivera	.10	.08	.04
253	Roberto Hernandez	.20	.15	.08	347	Al Osuna	.10	.08	.04
254	Mo Sanford	.30	.25	.12	348	Rob Deer	.10	.08	.04
255	Scott Servais	.25	.20	.10	349	Tim Leary	.10	.08	.04
256	Eric Karros	1.50	1.25	.60	350	Mike Stanton	.10	.08	.04
259	Joel Johnston	.12	.09	.05	351	Dean Palmer	.40	.30	.15
260	John Wehner	.12	.09	.05	352	Trevor Wilson	.10	.08	.04
261	Gino Minutelli	.12	.09	.05	353	Mark Eichhorn	.10	.08	.04
262	Greg Gagne	.10	.08	.04	354	Scott Aldred	.12	.09	.05
263	Stan Royer	.15	.11	.06	355	Mark Whiten	.20	.15	.08
264	Carlos Garcia	.15	.11	.06	356	Leo Gomez	.12	.09	.05
265	Andy Ashby	.12	.09	.05	357	Rafael Belliard	.10	.08	.04
266	Kim Batiste	.25	.20	.10	358	Carlos Quintana	.10	.08	.04
267	Julio Valera	.12	.09	.05	359	Mark Davis	.10	.08	.04
268	Royce Clayton	.40	.30	.15	360	Chris Nabholz	.10	.08	.04
269	Gary Scott	.30	.25	.12	361	Carlton Fisk	.20	.15	.08
270	Kirk Dressendorfer	.25	.20	.10	362	Joe Orsulak	.10	.08	.04
271	Sean Berry	.12	.09	.05	363	Eric Anthony	.12	.09	.05
272	Lance Dickson	.12	.09	.05	364	Greg Hibbard	.12	.09	.05
273	Rob Maurer	.20	.15	.08	365	Scott Leius	.12	.09	.05
274	Scott Brosius	.20	.15	.08	366	Hensley Meulens	.12	.09	.05
275	Dave Fleming	.80	.60	.30	367	Chris Bosio	.12	.09	.05
276	Lenny Webster	.12	.09	.05	368	Brian Downing	.10	.08	.04
278	Freddie Benavides	.12	.09	.05	369	Sammy Sosa	.12	.09	.05
279	Harvey Pulliam	.12	.09	.05	370	Stan Belinda	.10	.08	.04
280	Jeff Carter	.12	.09	.05	371	Joe Grahe	.10	.08	.04
281	Jim Abbott (I)	.15	.11	.06	372	Luis Salazar	.10	.08	.04
282	Wade Boggs (I)	.15	.11	.06	373	Lance Johnson	.10	.08	.04
283	Ken Griffey, Jr. (Idols)	2.50	2.00	1.00	374	Kal Daniels	.10	.08	.04
284	Wally Joyner (I)	.15	.11	.06	375	Dave Winfield	.25	.20	.10
285	Chuck Knoblauch (Idols)	.50	.40	.20	376	Brook Jacoby	.10	.08	.04
286	Robin Ventura (Idols)	.50	.40	.20	377	Mariano Duncan	.10	.08	.04
287	Robin Yount (Sidelines)	.30	.25	.12	378	Ron Darling	.12	.09	.05
288	Bob Tewksbury (S)	.12	.09	.05	379	Randy Johnson	.12	.09	.05
289	Kirby Puckett (Sidelines)	.40	.30	.15	380	Chito Martinez	.12	.09	.05
290	Kenny Lofton (Sidelines)	.60	.45	.25	381	Andres Galarraga	.12	.09	.05
291	Jack McDowell (Sidelines)	.30	.25	.12	382	Willie Randolph	.12	.09	.05
292	John Burkett (S)	.12	.09	.05	383	Charles Nagy	.25	.20	.10
293	Dwight Smith (S)	.12	.09	.05	384	Tim Belcher	.12	.09	.05
294	Nolan Ryan (Sidelines)	1.00	.70	.40	385	Duane Ward	.10	.08	.04
295	Manny Ramirez	2.50	2.00	1.00	386	Vicente Palacios	.10	.08	.04
296	Cliff Floyd	1.25	.90	.50	387	Mike Gallego	.10	.08	.04
297	Al Shirley	.50	.40	.20	388	Rich DeLucia	.10	.08	.04
298	Brian Barber	.40	.30	.15	389	Scott Radinsky	.10	.08	.04
299	Jon Farrell	.30	.25	.12	390	Damon Berryhill	.10	.08	.04
300	Scott Ruffcorn	.40	.30	.15	391	Kirk McCaskill	.10	.08	.04
301	Tyrone Hill	.40	.30	.15	392	Pedro Guerrero	.12	.09	.05
302	Benji Gil	.50	.40	.20	393	Kevin Mitchell	.20	.15	.08
303	Tyler Green	.80	.60	.30	394	Dickie Thon	.10	.08	.04
304	Allen Watson (SH)	.15	.11	.06	395	Bobby Bonilla	.30	.25	.12
305	Jay Buhner (SH)	.12	.09	.05	396	Bill Wegman	.10	.08	.04
306	Roberto Alomar (Shades)	.20	.15	.08	397	Dave Martinez	.10	.08	.04
307	Chuck Knoblauch (Shades)	.25	.20	.10	398	Rick Sutcliffe	.12	.09	.05
308	Darryl Strawberry (Shades)	.25	.20	.10	399	Larry Andersen	.10	.08	.04
309	DAnny Tartabull (SH)	.12	.09	.05	400	Tony Gwynn	.40	.30	.15
310	Bobby Bonilla (Shades)	.25	.20	.10	401	Rickey Henderson	.50	.40	.20
311	Mike Felder	.10	.08	.04	402	Greg Cadaret	.10	.08	.04
312	Storm Davis	.10	.08	.04	403	Keith Miller	.10	.08	.04
313	Tim Teufel	.10	.08	.04	404	Bip Roberts	.12	.09	.05
314	Tom Brunansky	.10	.08	.04	405	Kevin Brown	.12	.09	.05
315	Rex Hudler	.10	.08	.04	406	Mitch Williams	.20	.15	.08
316	Dave Otto	.10	.08	.04	407	Frank Viola	.20	.15	.08
317	Jeff King	.10	.08	.04	408	Darren Lewis	.20	.15	.08
318	Dan Gladden	.10	.08	.04	409	Bob Walk	.12	.09	.05
319	Bill Pecota	.10	.08	.04	410	Bob Walk	.10	.08	.04
320	Franklin Stubbs	.10	.08	.04	411	Todd Frohwirth	.10	.08	.04
321	Gary Carter	.15	.11	.06	412	Brian Hunter	.15	.11	.06
322	Melido Perez	.10	.08	.04	413	Ron Karkovice	.10	.08	.04
323	Eric Davis	.20	.15	.08	414	Mike Morgan	.10	.08	.04
324	Greg Myers	.10	.08	.04	415	Joe Hesketh	.10	.08	.04
325	Pete Incaviglia	.10	.08	.04	416	Don Slaught	.10	.08	.04
326	Von Hayes	.10	.08	.04	417	Tom Henke	.12	.09	.05
327	Greg Swindell	.15	.11	.06	418	Kurt Stillwell	.10	.08	.04
328	Steve Sax	.20	.15	.08	419	Hector Villanueva	.10	.08	.04
329	Chuck McElroy	.10	.08	.04	420	Glenallen Hill	.10	.08	.04
330	Gregg Jefferies	.20	.15	.08	421	Pat Borders	.10	.08	.04
331	Joe Oliver	.10	.08	.04	422	Charlie Hough	.10	.08	.04
332	Paul Faries	.10	.08	.04	423	Charlie Leibrandt	.10	.08	.04
333	David West	.10	.08	.04	424	Eddie Murray	.20	.15	.08
334	Craig Grebeck	.10	.08	.04	425	Jesse Barfield	.10	.08	.04
335	Chris Hammond	.10	.08	.04	426	Mark Lemke	.10	.08	.04
336	Billy Ripken	.10	.08	.04	427	Kevin McReynolds	.12	.09	.05

		MT	NR MT	EX			MT	NR MT	EX
428	Gilberto Reyes	.10	.08	.04	519	Otis Nixon	.12	.09	.05
429	Ramon Martinez	.20	.15	.08	520	Brian Holman	.10	.08	.04
430	Steve Buechele	.10	.08	.04	521	Chris Haney	.20	.15	.08
431	David Wells	.10	.08	.04	522	Jeff Kent	.15	.11	.06
432	Kyle Abbott	.15	.11	.06	523	Chad Curtis	.25	.20	.10
433	John Habyan	.10	.08	.04	524	Vince Horsman	.20	.15	.08
434	Kevin Appier	.15	.11	.06	525	Rod Nichols	.10	.08	.04
435	Gene Larkin	.10	.08	.04	526	Peter Hoy	.20	.15	.08
436	Sandy Alomar, Jr.	.20	.15	.08	527	Shawn Boskie	.12	.09	.05
437	Mike Jackson	.10	.08	.04	528	Alejandro Pena	.10	.08	.04
438	Todd Benzinger	.10	.08	.04	529	Dave Burba	.10	.08	.04
439	Teddy Higuera	.10	.08	.04	530	Ricky Jordan	.15	.11	.06
440	Reggie Sanders	.70	.50	.30	531	David Silvestri	.20	.15	.08
441	Mark Carreon	.10	.08	.04	532	John Patterson	.20	.15	.08
442	Bret Saberhagen	.20	.15	.08	533	Jeff Branson	.20	.15	.08
443	Gene Nelson	.10	.08	.04	534	Derrick May	.30	.25	.12
444	Jay Howell	.10	.08	.04	535	Esteban Beltre	.20	.15	.08
445	Roger McDowell	.10	.08	.04	536	Jose Melendez	.15	.11	.06
446	Sid Bream	.10	.08	.04	537	Wally Joyner	.20	.15	.08
447	Mackey Sasser	.10	.08	.04	538	Eddie Taubensee	.25	.20	.10
448	Bill Swift	.10	.08	.04	539	Jim Abbott	.20	.15	.08
449	Hubie Brooks	.10	.08	.04	540	Brian Williams	.25	.20	.10
450	David Cone	.20	.15	.08	541	Donovan Osborne	.40	.30	.15
451	Bobby Witt	.12	.09	.05	542	Patrick Lennon	.20	.15	.08
452	Brady Anderson	.20	.15	.08	543	Mike Groppuso	.20	.15	.08
453	Lee Stevens	.10	.08	.04	544	Jarvis Brown	.25	.20	.10
454	Luis Aquino	.10	.08	.04	545	Shawn Livesy	.20	.15	.08
455	Carney Lansford	.12	.09	.05	546	Jeff Ware	.25	.20	.10
456	Carlos Hernandez	.15	.11	.06	547	Danny Tartabull	.20	.15	.08
457	Danny Jackson	.10	.08	.04	548	Bobby Jones	.25	.20	.10
458	Gerald Young	.10	.08	.04	549	Ken Griffey, Jr.	2.00	1.50	.80
459	Tom Candiotti	.10	.08	.04	550	Rey Sanchez	.25	.20	.10
460	Billy Hatcher	.10	.08	.04	551	Eric Wedge	.20	.15	.08
461	John Wetteland	.15	.11	.06	552	Juan Guerrero	.20	.15	.08
462	Mike Bordick	.15	.11	.06	553	Jacob Brumfield	.25	.20	.10
463	Don Robinson	.10	.08	.04	554	Ben Rivera	.20	.15	.08
464	Jeff Johnson	.12	.09	.05	555	Brian Jordan	1.00	.70	.40
465	Lonnie Smith	.10	.08	.04	556	Denny Neagle	.25	.20	.10
466	Paul Assenmacher	.10	.08	.04	557	Cliff Brantley	.25	.20	.10
467	Alvin Davis	.10	.08	.04	558	Anthony Young	.25	.20	.10
468	Jim Eisenreich	.10	.08	.04	559	John VanderWal	.30	.25	.12
469	Brent Mayne	.10	.08	.04	560	Monty Fariss	.20	.15	.08
470	Jeff BRantley	.10	.08	.04	561	Russ Springer	.20	.15	.08
471	Tim Burke	.10	.08	.04	562	Pat Listach	3.00	2.25	1.25
472	Pat Mahomes	.40	.30	.15	563	Pat Hentgen	.20	.15	.08
473	Ryan Bowen	.20	.15	.08	564	Andy Stankiewicz	.40	.30	.15
474	Bryn Smith	.10	.08	.04	565	Mike Perez	.15	.11	.06
475	Mike Flanagan	.10	.08	.04	566	Mike Bielecki	.10	.08	.04
476	Reggie Jefferson	.15	.11	.06	567	Butch Henry	.25	.20	.10
477	Jeff Blauser	.10	.08	.04	568	Dave Nilsson	.50	.40	.20
478	Craig Lefferts	.10	.08	.04	569	Scott Hatteberg	.20	.15	.08
479	Todd Worrell	.10	.08	.04	570	Ruben Amaro, Jr.	.20	.15	.08
480	Scott Scudder	.10	.08	.04	571	Todd Hundley	.15	.11	.06
481	Kirk Gibson	.10	.08	.04	572	Moises Alou	.15	.11	.06
482	Kenny Rogers	.10	.08	.04	573	Hector Fajardo	.15	.11	.06
483	Jack Morris	.20	.15	.08	574	Todd Van Poppel	.60	.45	.25
484	Russ Swan	.10	.08	.04	575	Willie Banks	.15	.11	.06
485	Mike Huff	.10	.08	.04	576	Eddie Zosky	.15	.11	.06
486	Ken Hill	.15	.11	.06	577	J.J. Johnson	.30	.25	.12
487	Geronimo Pena	.12	.09	.05	578	John Burkett	.10	.08	.04
488	Charlie O'Brien	.10	.08	.04	579	Trever Miller	.25	.20	.10
489	Mike Maddux	.10	.08	.04	580	Scott Bankhead	.10	.08	.04
490	Scott Livingstone	.12	.09	.05	581	Rich Amaral	.20	.15	.08
491	Carl Willis	.10	.08	.04	582	Kenny Lofton	.60	.45	.25
492	Kelly Downs	.10	.08	.04	583	Matt Stairs	.20	.15	.08
493	Dennis Cook	.10	.08	.04	584	Don Mattingly (I)	.40	.30	.15
494	Joe Magrane	.10	.08	.04	585	Steve Avery (I)	.30	.25	.12
495	Bob Kipper	.10	.08	.04	586	Roberto Alomar (I)	.50	.40	.20
496	Jose Mesa	.10	.08	.04	587	Scott Sanderson (I)	.10	.08	.04
497	Charlie Hayes	.10	.08	.04	588	Dave Justice (I)	.30	.25	.12
498	Joe Girardi	.10	.08	.04	589	Rex Hudler (I)	.10	.08	.04
499	Doug Jones	.10	.08	.04	590	David Cone (I)	.20	.15	.08
500	Barry Bonds	.40	.30	.15	591	Tony Gwynn (I)	.25	.20	.10
501	Bill Krueger	.10	.08	.04	592	Orel Hershiser (I)	.15	.11	.06
502	Glenn Braggs	.10	.08	.04	593	John Wetteland (S)	.15	.11	.06
503	Eric King	.10	.08	.04	594	Tom Glavine (S)	.20	.15	.08
504	Frank Castillo	.10	.08	.04	595	Randy Johnson (S)	.10	.08	.04
505	Mike Gardiner	.10	.08	.04	596	Jim Gott (S)	.10	.08	.04
506	Cory Snyder	.10	.08	.04	597	Dan Weathers	.20	.15	.08
507	Steve Howe	.10	.08	.04	598	Shawn Hare	.35	.25	.14
508	Jose Rijo	.12	.09	.05	599	Chris Gardner	.25	.20	.10
509	Sid Fernandez	.12	.09	.05	600	Rusty Meacham	.30	.25	.12
510	Archi Cianfrocco	.40	.30	.15	601	Benito Santiago (SH)	.20	.15	.08
511	Mark Guthrie	.10	.08	.04	602	Eric Davis (SH)	.20	.15	.08
512	Bob Ojeda	.10	.08	.04	603	Jose Lind (SH)	.10	.08	.04
513	John Doherty	.15	.11	.06	604	Dave Justice (SH)	.30	.25	.12
514	Dante Bichette	.10	.08	.04	605	Tim Raines (SH)	.15	.11	.06
515	Juan Berenguer	.10	.08	.04	606	Randy Tomlin (G)	.15	.11	.06
516	Jeff Robinson	.10	.08	.04	607	Jack McDowell (G)	.20	.15	.08
517	Mike MacFarlane	.10	.08	.04	608	Greg Maddux (G)	.20	.15	.08
518	Matt Young	.10	.08	.04	609	Charles Nagy (G)	.35	.25	.14

		MT	NR MT	EX
610	Tom Candiotti (G)	.10	.08	.04
611	David Cone (G)	.20	.15	.08
612	Steve Avery (G)	.25	.20	.10
613	Rod Beck (G)	.10	.08	.04
614	Rickey Henderson (T)	.25	.20	.10
615	Benito Santiago (T)	.20	.15	.08
616	Ruben Sierra (T)	.20	.15	.08
617	Ryne Sandberg (T)	.40	.30	.15
618	Nolan Ryan (T)	.40	.30	.15
619	Brett Butler (T)	.10	.08	.04
620	Dave Justice (T)	.30	.25	.12

Values for recent cards and sets are listed in Mint (MT), Near Mint (NM) and Excellent (EX), reflecting the fact that many cards from recent years have been preserved in top condition. Recent cards and sets in less than Excellent condition have little collector interest.

1992 Score Pinnacle Rookies

Styled after the regular 1992 Score Pinnacle cards, this 30-card set features the top rookies of 1992. The cards feature black borders surrounding full-color player photos. The flip sides feature an additional player photo and background information.

		MT	NR MT	EX
Complete Set:		13.00	9.75	5.25
Common Player:		.20	.15	.08
1	Luis Mercedes	.25	.20	.10
2	Scott Cooper	.25	.20	.10
3	Kenny Lofton	1.00	.70	.40
4	John Doherty	.25	.20	.10
5	Pat Listach	2.00	1.50	.80
6	Andy Stankiewicz	.50	.40	.20
7	Derek Bell	.30	.25	.12
8	Gary DiSarcina	.20	.15	.08
9	Roberto Hernandez	.30	.25	.12
10	Joel Johnston	.25	.20	.10
11	Pat Mahomes	1.00	.70	.40
12	Todd Van Poppel	.50	.40	.20
13	Dave Fleming	1.00	.70	.40
14	Monty Fariss	.25	.20	.10
15	Gary Scott	.25	.20	.10
16	Moises Alou	.35	.25	.14
17	Todd Hundley	.25	.20	.10
18	Kim Batiste	.20	.15	.08
19	Denny Neagle	.25	.20	.10
20	Donovan Osborne	.35	.25	.14
21	Mark Wohlers	.20	.15	.08
22	Reggie Sanders	1.00	.70	.40
23	Brian Williams	.20	.15	.08
24	Eric Karros	1.50	1.25	.60
25	Frank Seminara	.25	.20	.10
26	Royce Clayton	.30	.25	.12
27	Dave Nilsson	.35	.25	.14
28	Matt Stairs	.20	.15	.08
29	Chad Curtis	.35	.25	.14
30	Carlos Hernandez	.25	.20	.10

1992 Score Rookie & Traded

This 110-card set features traded players, free agents and top rookies from 1992. The cards are styled after the regular 1992 Score cards. Cards 80-110 feature the rookies. The set was was released as a boxed set and was available at hobby shops and through hobby dealers.

		MT	NR MT	EX
Complete Set:		9.00	6.75	3.50
Common Player:		.05	.04	.02
1	Gary Sheffield	.20	.15	.08
2	Kevin Seitzer	.05	.04	.02
3	Danny Tartabull	.08	.06	.03
4	Steve Sax	.06	.05	.02
5	Bobby Bonilla	.10	.08	.04
6	Frank Viola	.08	.06	.03
7	Dave Winfield	.10	.08	.04
8	Rick Sutcliffe	.08	.04	.02
9	Jose Canseco	.25	.20	.10
10	Greg Swindell	.08	.04	.02
11	Eddie Murray	.08	.04	.02
12	Randy Myers	.06	.05	.02
13	Wally Joyner	.08	.06	.03
14	Kenny Lofton	.30	.25	.12
15	Jack Morris	.08	.06	.03
16	Charlie Hayes	.06	.05	.02
17	Pete Incaviglia	.06	.05	.02
18	Kevin Mitchell	.08	.06	.03
19	Kurt Stillwell	.05	.04	.02
20	Bret Saberhagen	.08	.06	.03
21	Steve Buechele	.05	.04	.02
22	John Smiley	.06	.05	.02
23	Sammy Sosa	.06	.05	.02
24	George Bell	.08	.06	.03
25	Curt Schilling	.08	.06	.03
26	Dick Schofield	.05	.04	.02
27	David Cone	.08	.06	.03
28	Dan Gladden	.05	.04	.02
29	Kirk McCaskill	.05	.04	.02
30	Mike Gallego	.05	.04	.02
31	Kevin McReynolds	.06	.05	.02
32	Bill Swift	.06	.05	.02
33	Dave Martinez	.05	.04	.02
34	Storm Davis	.05	.04	.02
35	Willie Randolph	.06	.05	.02
36	Melido Perez	.05	.04	.02
37	Mark Carreon	.05	.04	.02
38	Doug Jones	.05	.04	.02
39	Gregg Jefferies	.08	.06	.03
40	Mike Jackson	.05	.04	.02
41	Dickie Thon	.05	.04	.02
42	Eric King	.05	.04	.02
43	Herm Winningham	.05	.04	.02
44	Derek Lilliquist	.05	.04	.02
45	Dave Anderson	.05	.04	.02
46	Jeff Reardon	.08	.06	.03
47	Scott Bankhead	.05	.04	.02
48	Cory Snyder	.05	.04	.02
49	Al Newman	.05	.04	.02
50	Keith Miller	.05	.04	.02
51	Dave Burba	.05	.04	.02
52	Bill Pecota	.05	.04	.02
53	Chuck Crim	.05	.04	.02
54	Mariano Duncan	.05	.04	.02
55	Dave Gallagher	.05	.04	.02
56	Chris Gwynn	.05	.04	.02
57	Scott Ruskin	.05	.04	.02
58	Jack Armstrong	.05	.04	.02
59	Gary Carter	.12	.09	.05
60	Andres Galarraga	.06	.05	.02
61	Ken Hill	.08	.06	.03
62	Eric Davis	.08	.06	.03
63	Ruben Sierra	.12	.09	.05
64	Darrin Fletcher	.05	.04	.02
65	Tim Belcher	.06	.05	.02
66	Mike Morgan	.06	.05	.02
67	Scott Scudder	.05	.04	.02
68	Tom Candiotti	.05	.04	.02
69	Hubie Brooks	.05	.04	.02
70	Kal Daniels	.05	.04	.02
71	Bruce Ruffin	.05	.04	.02
72	Billy Hatcher	.05	.04	.02
73	Bob Melvin	.05	.04	.02
74	Lee Guetterman	.05	.04	.02
75	Rene Gonzales	.05	.04	.02
76	Kevin Bass	.05	.04	.02
77	Tom Bolton	.05	.04	.02
78	John Wetteland	.08	.06	.03
79	Bip Roberts	.08	.06	.03
80	Pat Listach(FC)	1.00	.70	.40
81	John Doherty(FC)	.12	.09	.05
82	Sam Militello(FC)	.50	.40	.20
83	Brian Jordan(FC)	.35	.25	.14
84	Jeff Kent(FC)	.20	.15	.08
85	Dave Fleming(FC)	.50	.40	.20
86	Jeff Tackett(FC)	.12	.09	.05
87	Chad Curtis(FC)	.15	.11	.06
88	Eric Fox	.12	.09	.05

		MT	NR MT	EX
89	Denny Neagle(FC)	.12	.09	.05
90	Donovan Osborne(FC)	.25	.20	.10
91	Carlos Hernandez(FC)	.12	.09	.05
92	Tim Wakefield(FC)	.35	.25	.14
93	Tim Salmon(FC)	.70	.50	.30
94	Dave Nilsson(FC)	.20	.15	.08
95	Mike Perez(FC)	.12	.09	.05
96	Pat Hentgen(FC)	.12	.09	.05
97	Frank Seminara(FC)	.12	.09	.05
98	Ruben Amaro, Jr.(FC)	.12	.09	.05
99	Archi Cianfrocco(FC)	.35	.25	.14
100	Andy Stankiewicz(FC)	.35	.25	.14
101	Jim Bullinger(FC)	.12	.09	.05
102	Pat Mahomes(FC)	.50	.40	.20
103	Hipolito Pichardo(FC)	.12	.09	.05
104	Bret Boone(FC)	.60	.45	.25
105	John Vander Wal(FC)	.12	.09	.05
106	Vince Horsman(FC)	.10	.08	.04
107	James Austin(FC)	.10	.08	.04
108	Brian Williams(FC)	.12	.09	.05
109	Dan Walters(FC)	.12	.09	.05
110	Wil Cordero(FC)	.35	.25	.12

1993 Score Select

This 400-card set from Score is designed for the mid-priced card market. The card fronts feature green borders on two sides of the card with the photo filling the remaining portion of the card front. "Score Select" appears within the photo. The backs feature an additional photo, player information and statistics. Cards numbered 271-360 are devoted to rookies and draft picks. Several cards from this set are printed horizontally. The cards are UV coated on both sides.

		MT	NR MT	EX
Complete Set:		30.00	22.00	12.00
Common Player:		.06	.05	.02
1	Barry Bonds	.20	.15	.08
2	Ken Griffey Jr.	.60	.45	.25
3	Will Clark	.20	.15	.08
4	Kirby Puckett	.25	.20	.10
5	Tony Gwynn	.20	.15	.08
6	Frank Thomas	1.00	.70	.40
7	Tom Glavine	.20	.15	.08
8	Roberto Alomar	.25	.20	.10
9	Andre Dawson	.15	.11	.06
10	Ron Darling	.08	.06	.03
11	Bobby Bonilla	.15	.11	.06
12	Danny Tartabull	.15	.11	.06
13	Darren Daulton	.12	.09	.05
14	Roger Clemens	.25	.20	.10
15	Ozzie Smith	.12	.09	.05
16	Mark McGwire	.40	.30	.15
17	Terry Pendleton	.15	.11	.06
18	Cal Ripken Jr.	.50	.40	.20
19	Fred McGriff	.20	.15	.08
20	Cecil Fielder	.25	.20	.10
21	Darryl Strawberry	.25	.20	.10
22	Robin Yount	.25	.20	.10
23	Barry Larkin	.20	.15	.08
24	Don Mattingly	.20	.15	.08
25	Craig Biggio	.10	.08	.04
26	Sandy Alomar Jr.	.15	.11	.06
27	Larry Walker	.15	.11	.06
28	Junior Felix	.06	.05	.02

		MT	NR MT	EX
29	Eddie Murray	.15	.11	.06
30	Robin Ventura	.15	.11	.06
31	Greg Maddux	.15	.11	.06
32	Dave Winfield	.20	.15	.08
33	John Kruk	.12	.09	.05
34	Wally Joyner	.12	.09	.05
35	Andy Van Slyke	.12	.09	.05
36	Chuck Knoblauch	.15	.11	.06
37	Tom Pagnozzi	.08	.06	.03
38	Dennis Eckersley	.15	.11	.06
39	Dave Justice	.20	.15	.08
40	Juan Gonzalez	.35	.25	.14
41	Gary Sheffield	.20	.15	.08
42	Paul Molitor	.15	.11	.06
43	Delino DeShields	.12	.09	.05
44	Travis Fryman	.25	.20	.10
45	Hal Morris	.10	.08	.04
46	Gregg Olson	.10	.08	.04
47	Ken Caminiti	.08	.06	.03
48	Wade Boggs	.15	.11	.06
49	Orel Hershiser	.12	.09	.05
50	Albert Belle	.15	.11	.06
51	Bill Swift	.08	.06	.03
52	Mark Langston	.12	.09	.05
53	Joe Girardi	.06	.05	.02
54	Keith Miller	.06	.05	.02
55	Gary Carter	.12	.09	.05
56	Brady Anderson	.15	.11	.06
57	Doc Gooden	.15	.11	.06
58	Julio Franco	.10	.08	.04
59	Lenny Dykstra	.10	.08	.04
60	Mickey Tettleton	.10	.08	.04
61	Randy Tomlin	.10	.08	.04
62	B.J. Surhoff	.08	.06	.03
63	Todd Zeile	.08	.06	.03
64	Roberto Kelly	.10	.08	.04
65	Rob Dibble	.10	.08	.04
66	Leo Gomez	.10	.08	.04
67	Doug Jones	.06	.05	.02
68	Ellis Burks	.12	.09	.05
69	Mike Scioscia	.06	.05	.02
70	Charles Nagy	.12	.09	.05
71	Cory Snyder	.06	.05	.02
72	Devon White	.08	.06	.03
73	Mark Grace	.12	.09	.05
74	Luis Polonia	.06	.05	.02
75	John Smiley	.08	.06	.03
76	Carlton Fisk	.15	.11	.06
77	Luis Sojo	.06	.05	.02
78	George Brett	.20	.15	.08
79	Mitch Williams	.10	.08	.04
80	Kent Hrbek	.10	.08	.04
81	Jay Bell	.10	.08	.04
82	Edgar Martinez	.15	.11	.06
83	Lee Smith	.10	.08	.04
84	Deion Sanders	.20	.15	.08
85	Bill Gullickson	.08	.06	.03
86	Paul O'Neill	.08	.06	.03
87	Kevin Seitzer	.08	.06	.03
88	Steve Finley	.08	.06	.03
89	Mel Hall	.08	.06	.03
90	Nolan Ryan	.50	.40	.20
91	Eric Davis	.15	.11	.06
92	Mike Mussina	.50	.40	.20
93	Tony Fernandez	.08	.06	.03
94	Frank Viola	.12	.09	.05
95	Matt Williams	.12	.09	.05
96	Joe Carter	.15	.11	.06
97	Ryne Sandberg	.35	.25	.14
98	Jim Abbott	.15	.11	.06
99	Marquis Grissom	.15	.11	.06
100	George Bell	.15	.11	.06
101	Howard Johnson	.10	.08	.04
102	Kevin Appier	.12	.09	.05
103	Dale Murphy	.12	.09	.05
104	Shane Mack	.10	.08	.04
105	Jose Lind	.08	.06	.03
106	Rickey Henderson	.30	.25	.12
107	Bob Tewksbury	.08	.06	.03
108	Kevin Mitchell	.12	.09	.05
109	Steve Avery	.15	.11	.06
110	Candy Maldonado	.08	.06	.03
111	Bip Roberts	.10	.08	.04
112	Lou Whitaker	.10	.08	.04
113	Jeff Bagwell	.25	.20	.10
114	Dante Bichette	.06	.05	.02
115	Brett Butler	.10	.08	.04
116	Melido Perez	.06	.05	.02
117	Andy Benes	.12	.09	.05
118	Randy Johnson	.08	.06	.03
119	Willie McGee	.08	.06	.03

#	Player	MT	NR MT	EX
120	Jody Reed	.08	.06	.03
121	Shawon Dunston	.08	.06	.03
122	Carlos Baerga	.20	.15	.08
123	Bret Saberhagen	.12	.09	.05
124	John Olerud	.15	.11	.06
125	Ivan Calderon	.08	.06	.03
126	Bryan Harvey	.10	.08	.04
127	Terry Mulholland	.08	.06	.03
128	Ozzie Guillen	.10	.08	.04
129	Steve Buechele	.08	.06	.03
130	Kevin Tapani	.08	.06	.03
131	Felix Jose	.12	.09	.05
132	Terry Steinbach	.08	.06	.03
133	Ron Gant	.12	.09	.05
134	Harold Reynolds	.08	.06	.03
135	Chris Sabo	.10	.08	.04
136	Ivan Rodriguez	.20	.15	.08
137	Eric Anthony	.08	.06	.03
138	Mike Henneman	.08	.06	.03
139	Robby Thompson	.08	.06	.03
140	Scott Fletcher	.06	.05	.02
141	Bruce Hurst	.08	.06	.03
142	Kevin Maas	.08	.06	.03
143	Tom Candiotti	.08	.06	.03
144	Chris Hoiles	.20	.15	.08
145	Mike Morgan	.08	.06	.03
146	Mark Whiten	.15	.11	.06
147	Dennis Martinez	.10	.08	.04
148	Tony Pena	.08	.06	.03
149	Dave Magadan	.08	.06	.03
150	Mark Lewis	.10	.08	.04
151	Mariano Duncan	.06	.05	.02
152	Gregg Jefferies	.15	.11	.06
153	Doug Drabek	.12	.09	.05
154	Brian Harper	.12	.09	.05
155	Ray Lankford	.20	.15	.08
156	Carney Lansford	.08	.06	.03
157	Mike Sharperson	.08	.06	.03
158	Jack Morris	.15	.11	.06
159	Otis Nixon	.10	.08	.04
160	Steve Sax	.10	.08	.04
161	Mark Lemke	.08	.06	.03
162	Rafael Palmeiro	.12	.09	.05
163	Jose Rijo	.12	.09	.05
164	Omar Vizquel	.06	.05	.02
165	Sammy Sosa	.08	.06	.03
166	Milt Cuyler	.08	.06	.03
167	John Franco	.08	.06	.03
168	Darryl Hamilton	.08	.06	.03
169	Ken Hill	.10	.08	.04
170	Mike Devereaux	.10	.08	.04
171	Don Slaught	.06	.05	.02
172	Steve Farr	.06	.05	.02
173	Bernard Gilkey	.10	.08	.04
174	Mike Fetters	.06	.05	.02
175	Vince Coleman	.08	.06	.03
176	Kevin McReynolds	.10	.08	.04
177	John Smoltz	.15	.11	.06
178	Greg Gagne	.08	.06	.03
179	Greg Swindell	.15	.11	.06
180	Juan Guzman	.20	.15	.08
181	Kal Daniels	.08	.06	.03
182	Rick Sutcliffe	.12	.09	.05
183	Orlando Merced	.12	.09	.05
184	Bill Wegman	.08	.06	.03
185	Mark Gardner	.08	.06	.03
186	Rob Deer	.08	.06	.03
187	Dave Hollins	.15	.11	.06
188	Jack Clark	.08	.06	.03
189	Brian Hunter	.15	.11	.06
190	Tim Wallach	.08	.06	.03
191	Tim Belcher	.08	.06	.03
192	Walt Weiss	.08	.06	.03
193	Kurt Stillwell	.06	.05	.02
194	Charlie Hayes	.08	.06	.03
195	Willie Randolph	.08	.06	.03
196	Jack McDowell	.15	.11	.06
197	Jose Offerman	.10	.08	.04
198	Chuck Finley	.10	.08	.04
199	Darrin Jackson	.08	.06	.03
200	Kelly Gruber	.08	.06	.03
201	John Wetteland	.12	.09	.05
202	Jay Buhner	.08	.06	.03
203	Mike LaValliere	.06	.05	.02
204	Kevin Brown	.12	.09	.05
205	Luis Gonzalez	.12	.09	.05
206	Rick Aguilera	.12	.09	.05
207	Norm Charlton	.12	.09	.05
208	Mike Bordick	.12	.09	.05
209	Charlie Leibrandt	.06	.05	.02
210	Tom Brunansky	.08	.06	.03
211	Tom Henke	.10	.08	.04
212	Randy Milligan	.06	.05	.02
213	Ramon Martinez	.15	.11	.06
214	Mo Vaughn	.08	.06	.03
215	Randy Myers	.08	.06	.03
216	Greg Hibbard	.08	.06	.03
217	Wes Chamberlain	.10	.08	.04
218	Tony Phillips	.10	.08	.04
219	Pete Harnisch	.10	.08	.04
220	Mike Gallego	.06	.05	.02
221	Bud Black	.06	.05	.02
222	Greg Vaughn	.10	.08	.04
223	Milt Thompson	.06	.05	.02
224	Ben McDonald	.15	.11	.06
225	Billy Hatcher	.06	.05	.02
226	Paul Sorrento	.08	.06	.03
227	Mark Gubicza	.08	.06	.03
228	Mike Greenwell	.08	.06	.03
229	Curt Schilling	.08	.06	.03
230	Alan Trammell	.10	.08	.04
231	Zane Smith	.08	.06	.03
232	Bobby Thigpen	.10	.08	.04
233	Greg Olson	.06	.05	.02
234	Joe Orsulak	.06	.05	.02
235	Joe Oliver	.06	.05	.02
236	Tim Raines	.12	.09	.05
237	Juan Samuel	.06	.05	.02
238	Chili Davis	.08	.06	.03
239	Spike Owen	.06	.05	.02
240	Dave Stewart	.12	.09	.05
241	Jim Eisenreich	.06	.05	.02
242	Phil Plantier	.20	.15	.08
243	Sid Fernandez	.10	.08	.04
244	Dan Gladden	.06	.03	.02
245	Mickey Morandini	.12	.09	.05
246	Tino Martinez	.12	.09	.05
247	Kirt Manwaring	.06	.05	.02
248	Dean Palmer	.12	.09	.05
249	Tom Browning	.08	.06	.03
250	Brian McRae	.12	.09	.05
251	Scott Leius	.08	.06	.03
252	Bert Blyleven	.08	.06	.03
253	Scott Erickson	.10	.08	.04
254	Bob Welch	.10	.08	.04
255	Pat Kelly	.10	.08	.04
256	Felix Fermin	.06	.05	.02
257	Harold Baines	.12	.09	.05
258	Duane Ward	.08	.06	.03
259	Bill Spiers	.08	.06	.03
260	Jaime Navarro	.10	.08	.04
261	Scott Sanderson	.08	.06	.03
262	Gary Gaetti	.08	.06	.03
263	Bob Ojeda	.06	.05	.02
264	Jeff Montgomery	.08	.06	.03
265	Scott Bankhead	.08	.06	.03
266	Lance Johnson	.08	.06	.03
267	Rafael Belliard	.06	.05	.02
268	Kevin Reimer	.08	.06	.03
269	Benito Santiago	.12	.09	.05
270	Mike Moore	.08	.06	.03
271	Dave Fleming	.15	.11	.06
272	Moises Alou	.15	.11	.06
273	Pat Listach	.40	.30	.15
274	Reggie Sanders	.30	.25	.12
275	Kenny Lofton	.30	.25	.12
276	Donovan Osborne	.20	.15	.08
277	Rusty Meacham	.20	.15	.08
278	Eric Karros	.40	.30	.15
279	Andy Stankiewicz	.15	.11	.06
280	Brian Jordan	.25	.20	.10
281	Gary DiSarcina	.08	.06	.03
282	Mark Wohlers	.08	.06	.03
283	Dave Nilsson	.20	.15	.08
284	Anthony Young	.10	.08	.04
285	Jim Bullinger	.12	.09	.05
286	Derek Bell	.20	.15	.08
287	Brian Williams	.15	.11	.06
288	Julio Valera	.15	.11	.06
289	Dan Walters	.15	.11	.06
290	Chad Curtis	.25	.20	.10
291	Michael Tucker	.25	.20	.10
292	Bob Zupcic	.15	.11	.06
293	Todd Hundley	.15	.11	.06
294	Jeff Tackett	.15	.11	.06
295	Greg Colbrunn	.15	.11	.06
296	Cal Eldred	.40	.30	.15
297	Chris Roberts	.20	.15	.08
298	John Doherty	.20	.15	.08
299	Denny Neagle	.12	.09	.05
300	Arthur Rhodes	.20	.15	.08
301	Mark Clark	.20	.15	.08

		MT	NR MT	EX
302	Scott Cooper	.20	.15	.08
303	Jamie Arnold	.20	.15	.08
304	Jim Thome	.15	.11	.06
305	Frank Seminara	.15	.11	.06
306	Kurt Knudsen	.15	.11	.06
307	Tim Wakefield	.30	.25	.12
308	John Jaha	.20	.15	.08
309	Pat Hentgen	.15	.11	.06
310	B.J. Wallace	.20	.15	.08
311	Roberto Hernandez	.20	.15	.08
312	Hipolito Pichardo	.20	.15	.08
313	Eric Fox	.15	.11	.06
314	Willie Banks	.15	.11	.06
315	Sam Millitello	.20	.15	.08
316	Vince Horsman	.15	.11	.06
317	Carlos Hernandez	.15	.11	.06
318	Jeff Kent	.20	.15	.08
319	Mike Perez	.12	.09	.05
320	Scott Livingstone	.15	.11	.06
321	Jeff Conine	.15	.11	.06
322	James Austin	.15	.11	.06
323	John Vander Wal	.15	.11	.06
324	Pat Mahomes	.25	.20	.10
325	Pedro Astacio	.25	.20	.10
326	Bret Boone	.25	.20	.10
327	Matt Stairs	.15	.11	.06
328	Damion Easley	.20	.15	.08
329	Ben Rivera	.20	.15	.08
330	Reggie Jefferson	.20	.15	.08
331	Luis Mercedes	.20	.15	.08
332	Kyle Abbott	.20	.15	.08
333	Eddie Taubensee	.20	.15	.08
334	Tim McIntosh	.10	.08	.04
335	Phil Clark	.10	.08	.04
336	Will Cordero	.20	.15	.08
337	Russ Springer	.15	.11	.06
338	Craig Colbert	.10	.08	.04
339	Tim Salmon	.20	.15	.08
340	Braulio Castillo	.20	.15	.08
341	Donald Harris	.12	.09	.05
342	Eric Young	.20	.15	.08
343	Bob Wickman	.25	.20	.10
344	John Valentin	.15	.11	.06
345	Dan Wilson	.15	.11	.06
346	Steve Hosey	.15	.11	.06
347	Mike Piazza	.30	.25	.12
348	Willie Greene	.20	.15	.08
349	Tom Goodwin	.10	.08	.04
350	Eric Hillman	.15	.11	.06
351	Steve Reed	.15	.11	.06
352	Dan Serafini	.25	.20	.10
353	Todd Steverson	.25	.20	.10
354	Benji Grigsby	.25	.20	.10
355	Shannon Stewart	.25	.20	.10
356	Sean Lowe	.25	.20	.10
357	Derek Wallace	.25	.20	.10
358	Rick Helling	.25	.20	.10
359	Jason Kendall	.25	.20	.10
360	Derek Jeter	.25	.20	.10
361	David Cone	.15	.11	.06
362	Jeff Reardon	.15	.11	.06
363	Bobby Witt	.08	.06	.03
364	Jose Canseco	.40	.30	.15
365	Jeff Russell	.08	.06	.03
366	Ruben Sierra	.25	.20	.10
367	Alan Mills	.06	.05	.02
368	Matt Nokes	.08	.06	.03
369	Pat Borders	.08	.06	.03
370	Pedro Munoz	.12	.09	.05
371	Danny Jackson	.06	.05	.02
372	Geronimo Pena	.10	.08	.04
373	Craig Lefferts	.08	.06	.03
374	Joe Grahe	.08	.06	.03
375	Roger McDowell	.06	.05	.02
376	Jimmy Key	.10	.08	.04
377	Steve Olin	.10	.08	.04
378	Glenn Davis	.10	.08	.04
379	Rene Gonzales	.06	.05	.02
380	Manuel Lee	.06	.05	.02
381	Ron Karkovice	.06	.05	.02
382	Sid Bream	.06	.05	.02
383	Gerald Williams	.12	.09	.05
384	Lenny Harris	.06	.05	.02
385	J.T. Snow	.20	.15	.08
386	Dave Stieb	.08	.06	.03
387	Kirk McCaskill	.08	.06	.03
388	Lance Parrish	.08	.06	.03
389	Craig Greback	.06	.05	.02
390	Rick Wilkins	.12	.09	.05
391	Manny Alexander	.25	.20	.10
392	Mike Schooler	.06	.05	.02

		MT	NR MT	EX
393	Bernie Williams	.12	.09	.05
394	Kevin Koslofski	.20	.15	.08
395	Willie Wilson	.08	.06	.03
396	Jeff Parrett	.06	.05	.02
397	Mike Harkey	.08	.06	.03
398	Frank Tanana	.08	.06	.03
399	Doug Henry	.08	.06	.03
400	Royce Clayton	.15	.11	.06
401	Eric Wedge	.12	.09	.05
402	Derrick May	.12	.09	.05
403	Carlos Garcia	.15	.11	.06
404	Henry Rodriguez	.12	.09	.05
405	Ryan Klesko	.20	.15	.08

1986 Sportflics

The premiere issue from Sportflics was distributed nationally by Amurol Division of Wrigley Gum Company. These high quality, three-phase "Magic Motion" cards depict three different photos per card, with each visible separately as the card is tilted. The 1986 issue features 200 full-color baseball cards plus 133 trivia cards. The cards come in the standard 2-1/2" by 3-1/2" size with the backs containing player stats and personal information. There are three different types of picture cards: 1) Tri-Star cards - 50 cards feature three players on one card; 2) Big Six cards - 10 cards which have six players in special categories; and 3) the Big Twelve card of 12 World Series players from the Kansas City Royals. The trivia cards are 1-3/4" by 2" and do not have player photos.

		MT	NR MT	EX
	Complete Set:	40.00	30.00	16.00
	Common Player:	.10	.08	.04
1	George Brett	1.00	.70	.40
2	Don Mattingly	2.00	1.50	.80
3	Wade Boggs	1.50	1.25	.60
4	Eddie Murray	.60	.45	.25
5	Dale Murphy	.50	.40	.20
6	Rickey Henderson	1.50	1.25	.60
7	Harold Baines	.20	.15	.08
8	Cal Ripken, Jr.	2.00	1.50	.80
9	Orel Hershiser	.40	.30	.15
10	Bret Saberhagen	.30	.25	.12
11	Tim Raines	.40	.30	.15
12	Fernando Valenzuela	.30	.25	.12
13	Tony Gwynn	.60	.45	.25
14	Pedro Guerrero	.25	.20	.10
15	Keith Hernandez	.35	.25	.14
16	Ernest Riles	.20	.15	.08
17	Jim Rice	.30	.25	.12
18	Ron Guidry	.25	.20	.10
19	Willie McGee	.25	.20	.10
20	Ryne Sandberg	2.00	1.50	.80
21	Kirk Gibson	.35	.25	.14
22	Ozzie Guillen	.30	.25	.12
23	Dave Parker	.25	.20	.10
24	Vince Coleman	2.00	1.50	.80
25	Tom Seaver	.40	.30	.15
26	Brett Butler	.10	.08	.04
27	Steve Carlton	.50	.40	.20
28	Gary Carter	.35	.25	.14

		MT	NR MT	EX
29	Cecil Cooper	.15	.11	.06
30	Jose Cruz	.10	.08	.04
31	Alvin Davis	.20	.15	.08
32	Dwight Evans	.15	.11	.06
33	Julio Franco	.15	.11	.06
34	Damaso Garcia	.10	.08	.04
35	Steve Garvey	.40	.30	.15
36	Kent Hrbek	.25	.20	.10
37	Reggie Jackson	.70	.50	.30
38	Fred Lynn	.20	.15	.08
39	Paul Molitor	.15	.11	.06
40	Jim Presley	.15	.11	.06
41	Dave Righetti	.20	.15	.08
42a	Robin Yount (Yankees logo on back)	300.00	225.00	125.00
42b	Robin Yount (Brewers logo on back)	.60	.45	.25
43	Nolan Ryan	2.00	1.50	.80
44	Mike Schmidt	1.25	.90	.50
45	Lee Smith	.10	.08	.04
46	Rick Sutcliffe	.15	.11	.06
47	Bruce Sutter	.15	.11	.06
48	Lou Whitaker	.20	.15	.08
49	Dave Winfield	.60	.45	.25
50	Pete Rose	1.50	1.25	.60
51	National League MVPs (Steve Garvey, Pete Rose, Ryne Sandberg)	.70	.50	.30
52	Slugging Stars (Harold Baines, George Brett, Jim Rice)	.35	.25	.14
53	No-Hitters (Phil Niekro, Jerry Reuss, Mike Witt)	.15	.11	.06
54	Big Hitters (Don Mattingly, Cal Ripken, Jr., Robin Yount)	1.25	.90	.50
55	Bullpen Aces (Goose Gossage, Dan Quisenberry, Lee Smith)	.10	.08	.04
56	Rookies of the Year (Pete Rose, Steve Sax, Darryl Strawberry)	.80	.60	.30
57	American League MVPs (Don Baylor, Reggie Jackson, Cal Ripken, Jr.)	.35	.25	.14
58	Repeat Batting Champs (Bill Madlock, Dave Parker, Pete Rose)	.60	.45	.25
59	Cy Young Winners (Mike Flanagan, Ron Guidry, LaMarr Hoyt)	.10	.08	.04
60	Double Award Winners (Tom Seaver, Rick Sutcliffe, Fernando Valenzuela)	.20	.15	.08
61	Home Run Champs (Tony Armas, Reggie Jackson, Jim Rice)	.25	.20	.10
62	National League MVPs (Keith Hernandez, Dale Murphy, Mike Schmidt)	.50	.40	.20
63	American League MVPs (George Brett, Fred Lynn, Robin Yount)	.30	.25	.12
64	Comeback Players (Bert Blyleven, John Denny, Jerry Koosman)	.10	.08	.04
65	Cy Young Relievers (Rollie Fingers, Willie Hernandez, Bruce Sutter)	.15	.11	.06
66	Rookies Of The Year (Andre Dawson, Bob Horner, Gary Matthews)	.15	.11	.06
67	Rookies Of The Year (Carlton Fisk, Ron Kittle, Tom Seaver)	.15	.11	.06
68	Home Run Champs (George Foster, Dave Kingman, Mike Schmidt)	.30	.25	.12
69	Double Award Winners (Rod Carew, Cal Ripken, Jr., Pete Rose)	1.00	.70	.40
70	Cy Young Winners (Steve Carlton, Tom Seaver, Rick Sutcliffe)	.25	.20	.10
71	Top Sluggers (Reggie Jackson, Fred Lynn, Robin Yount)	.30	.25	.12
72	Rookies of the Year (Dave Righetti, Rick Sutcliffe, Fernando Valenzuela)	.15	.11	.06
73	Rookies Of The Year (Fred Lynn, Eddie Murray, Cal Ripken, Jr.)	.25	.20	.10
74	Rookies Of The Year (Rod Carew, Alvin Davis, Lou Whitaker)	.20	.15	.08
75	Batting Champs (Wade Boggs, Carney Lansford, Don Mattingly)	1.50	1.25	.60
76	Jesse Barfield	.20	.15	.08
77	Phil Bradley	.15	.11	.06
78	Chris Brown	.25	.20	.10
79	Tom Browning	.30	.25	.12
80	Tom Brunansky	.15	.11	.06
81	Bill Buckner	.10	.08	.04
82	Chili Davis	.10	.08	.04
83	Mike Davis	.10	.08	.04
84	Rich Gedman	.10	.08	.04
85	Willie Hernandez	.10	.08	.04
86	Ron Kittle	.10	.08	.04
87	Lee Lacy	.10	.08	.04
88	Bill Madlock	.15	.11	.06
89	Mike Marshall	.15	.11	.06
90	Keith Moreland	.10	.08	.04
91	Graig Nettles	.15	.11	.06

		MT	NR MT	EX
92	Lance Parrish	.20	.15	.08
93	Kirby Puckett	2.00	1.50	.80
94	Juan Samuel	.20	.15	.08
95	Steve Sax	.20	.15	.08
96	Dave Stieb	.10	.08	.04
97	Darryl Strawberry	2.00	1.50	.80
98	Willie Upshaw	.10	.08	.04
99	Frank Viola	.50	.40	.20
100	Dwight Gooden	2.00	1.50	.80
101	Joaquin Andujar	.10	.08	.04
102	George Bell	.40	.30	.15
103	Bert Blyleven	.15	.11	.06
104	Mike Boddicker	.10	.08	.04
105	Britt Burns	.10	.08	.04
106	Rod Carew	1.25	.90	.50
107	Jack Clark	.25	.20	.10
108	Danny Cox	.10	.08	.04
109	Ron Darling	.15	.11	.06
110	Andre Dawson	.25	.20	.10
111	Leon Durham	.10	.08	.04
112	Tony Fernandez	.15	.11	.06
113	Tom Herr	.10	.08	.04
114	Teddy Higuera	.80	.60	.30
115	Bob Horner	.15	.11	.06
116	Dave Kingman	.15	.11	.06
117	Jack Morris	.20	.15	.08
118	Dan Quisenberry	.10	.08	.04
119	Jeff Reardon	.15	.11	.06
120	Bryn Smith	.10	.08	.04
121	Ozzie Smith	.25	.20	.10
122	John Tudor	.15	.11	.06
123	Tim Wallach	.15	.11	.06
124	Willie Wilson	.15	.11	.06
125	Carlton Fisk	.25	.20	.10
126	RBI Sluggers (Gary Carter, George Foster, Al Oliver)	.15	.11	.06
127	Run Scorers (Keith Hernandez, Tim Raines, Ryne Sandberg)	.25	.20	.10
128	Run Scorers (Paul Molitor, Cal Ripken, Jr., Willie Wilson)	.20	.15	.08
129	No-Hitters (John Candelaria, Dennis Eckersley, Bob Forsch)	.10	.08	.04
130	World Series MVPs (Ron Cey, Rollie Fingers, Pete Rose)	.50	.40	.20
131	All-Star Game MVPs (Dave Concepcion, George Foster, Bill Madlock)	.10	.08	.04
132	Cy Young Winners (Vida Blue, John Denny, Fernando Valenzuela)	.15	.11	.06
133	Comeback Players (Doyle Alexander, Joaquin Andujar, Richard Dotson)	.10	.08	.04
134	Big Winners (John Denny, Tom Seaver, Rick Sutcliffe)	.15	.11	.06
135	Veteran Pitchers (Phil Niekro, Tom Seaver, Don Sutton)	.25	.20	.10
136	Rookies Of The Year (Vince Coleman, Dwight Gooden, Alfredo Griffin)	.80	.60	.30
137	All-Star Game MVPs (Gary Carter, Steve Garvey, Fred Lynn)	.20	.15	.08
138	Veteran Hitters (Tony Perez, Pete Rose, Rusty Staub)	.50	.40	.20
139	Power Hitters (George Foster, Jim Rice, Mike Schmidt)	.30	.25	.12
140	Batting Champs (Bill Buckner, Tony Gwynn, Al Oliver)	.20	.15	.08
141	No-Hitters (Jack Morris, Dave Righetti, Nolan Ryan)	.20	.15	.08
142	No-Hitters (Vida Blue, Bert Blyleven, Tom Seaver)	.15	.11	.06
143	Strikeout Kings (Dwight Gooden, Nolan Ryan, Fernando Valenzuela)	1.25	.90	.50
144	Base Stealers (Dave Lopes, Tim Raines, Willie Wilson)	.15	.11	.06
145	RBI Sluggers (Tony Armas, Cecil Cooper, Eddie Murray)	.15	.11	.06
146	American League MVPs (Rod Carew, Rollie Fingers, Jim Rice)	.25	.20	.10
147	World Series MVPs (Rick Dempsey, Reggie Jackson, Alan Trammell)	.25	.20	.10
148	World Series MVPs (Pedro Guerrero, Darrell Porter, Mike Schmidt)	.20	.15	.08
149	ERA Leaders (Mike Boddicker, Ron Guidry, Rick Sutcliffe)	.10	.08	.04
150	Comeback Players (Reggie Jackson, Dave Kingman, Fred Lynn)	.20	.15	.08
151	Buddy Bell	.15	.11	.06
152	Dennis Boyd	.10	.08	.04
153	Dave Concepcion	.15	.11	.06
154	Brian Downing	.10	.08	.04
155	Shawon Dunston	.15	.11	.06
156	John Franco	.15	.11	.06
157	Scott Garrelts	.10	.08	.04

		MT	NR MT	EX
158	Bob James	.10	.08	.04
159	Charlie Leibrandt	.10	.08	.04
160	Oddibe McDowell	.30	.25	.12
161	Roger McDowell	.50	.40	.20
162	Mike Moore	.10	.08	.04
163	Phil Niekro	.25	.20	.10
164	Al Oliver	.15	.11	.06
165	Tony Pena	.10	.08	.04
166	Ted Power	.10	.08	.04
167	Mike Scioscia	.10	.08	.04
168	Mario Soto	.10	.08	.04
169	Bob Stanley	.10	.08	.04
170	Garry Templeton	.10	.08	.04
171	Andre Thornton	.10	.08	.04
172	Alan Trammell	.30	.25	.12
173	Doug DeCinces	.10	.08	.04
174	Greg Walker	.10	.08	.04
175	Don Sutton	.25	.20	.10
176	1985 Award Winners (Vince Coleman, Dwight Gooden, Ozzie Guillen, Don Mattingly, Wille McGee, Bret Saberhagen)	1.25	.90	.50
177	1985 Hot Rookies (Stewart Cliburn, Brian Fisher, Joe Hesketh, Joe Orsulak, Mark Salas, Larry Sheets)	.20	.15	.08
178	Future Stars (Jose Canseco, Mark Funderburk, Mike Greenwell, Steve Lombardozzi, Billy Joe Robidoux, Dan Tartabull)	15.00	11.00	6.00
179	1985 Gold Glovers (George Brett, Ron Guidry, Keith Hernandez, Don Mattingly, Willie McGee, Dale Murphy)	1.25	.90	.50
180	Active .300 Hitters (Wade Boggs, George Brett, Rod Carew, Cecil Cooper, Don Mattingly, Willie Wilson)	1.25	.90	.50
181	Active .300 Hitters (Pedro Guerrero, Tony Gwynn, Keith Hernandez, Bill Madlock, Dave Parker, Pete Rose)	.70	.50	.30
182	1985 Milestones (Rod Carew, Phil Niekro, Pete Rose, Nolan Ryan, Tom Seaver, Matt Tallman)	1.50	1.25	.60
183	1985 Triple Crown (Wade Boggs, Darrell Evans, Don Mattingly, Willie McGee, Dale Murphy, Dave Parker)	1.25	.90	.50
184	1985 Highlights (Wade Boggs, Dwight Gooden, Rickey Henderson, Don Mattingly, Willie McGee, John Tudor)	1.50	1.25	.60
185	1985 20-Game Winners (Joaquin Andujar, Tom Browning, Dwight Gooden, Ron Guidry, Bret Saberhagen, John Tudor)	.60	.45	.25
186	Kansas City Royals (Steve Balboni, George Brett, Dane Iorg, Danny Jackson, Charlie Leibrandt, Darryl Motley, Dan Quisenberry, Bret Saberhagen, Lonnie Smith, Jim Sundberg, Frank White, Willie Wilson)	.40	.30	.15
187	Hubie Brooks	.10	.08	.04
188	Glenn Davis	.60	.45	.25
189	Darrell Evans	.10	.08	.04
190	Rich Gossage	.15	.11	.06
191	Andy Hawkins	.10	.08	.04
192	Jay Howell	.10	.08	.04
193	LaMarr Hoyt	.10	.08	.04
194	Davey Lopes	.10	.08	.04
195	Mike Scott	.20	.15	.08
196	Ted Simmons	.15	.11	.06
197	Gary Ward	.10	.08	.04
198	Bob Welch	.15	.11	.06
199	Mike Young	.10	.08	.04
200	Buddy Biancalana	.10	.08	.04

Values for recent cards and sets are listed in Mint (MT), Near Mint (NM) and Excellent (EX), reflecting the fact that many cards from recent years have been preserved in top condition. Recent cards and sets in less than Excellent condition have little collector interest.

1986 Sportflics Rookies

The 1986 Rookies set issued by Sportflics offers 50 cards and features 47 individual rookie players. In addition, there are two Tri-Star cards; one highlights former Rookies of the Year and the other features three prominent players. There is one "Big Six" card featuring six superstars. The full-color photos on the 2-1/2" by 3-1/2" cards use Sportflics three-phase "Magic Motion" animation. The set was packaged in an attractive collector box which also contained 34 trivia cards that measure 1-3/4" by 2". The set was distributed only by hobby dealers.

		MT	NR MT	EX
	Complete Set:	18.00	13.50	7.25
	Common Player:	.20	.15	.08
1	John Kruk	.80	.60	.30
2	Edwin Correa	.20	.15	.08
3	Pete Incaviglia	.25	.20	.10
4	Dale Sveum	.30	.25	.12
5	Juan Nieves	.30	.25	.12
6	Will Clark	3.00	2.25	1.25
7	Wally Joyner	2.00	1.50	.80
8	Lance McCullers	.20	.15	.08
9	Scott Bailes	.20	.15	.08
10	Dan Plesac	.40	.30	.15
11	Jose Canseco	3.00	2.25	1.25
12	Bobby Witt	.40	.30	.15
13	Barry Bonds	.70	.50	.30
14	Andres Thomas	.20	.15	.08
15	Jim Deshaies	.30	.25	.12
16	Ruben Sierra	2.00	1.50	.80
17	Steve Lombardozzi	.20	.15	.08
18	Cory Snyder	.25	.20	.10
19	Reggie Williams	.20	.15	.08
20	Mitch Williams	.20	.15	.08
21	Glenn Braggs	.30	.25	.12
22	Danny Tartabull	.80	.60	.30
23	Charlie Kerfeld	.20	.15	.08
24	Paul Assenmacher	.20	.15	.08
25	Robby Thompson	.30	.25	.12
26	Bobby Bonilla	.70	.50	.30
27	Andres Galarraga	.70	.50	.30
28	Billy Jo Robidoux	.20	.15	.08
29	Bruce Ruffin	.30	.25	.12
30	Greg Swindell	.60	.45	.25
31	John Cangelosi	.20	.15	.08
32	Jim Traber	.20	.15	.08
33	Russ Morman	.20	.15	.08
34	Barry Larkin	.60	.45	.25
35	Todd Worrell	.25	.20	.10
36	John Cerutti	.20	.15	.08
37	Mike Kingery	.20	.15	.08
38	Mark Eichhorn	.20	.15	.08
39	Scott Bankhead	.20	.15	.08
40	Bo Jackson	2.00	1.50	.80
41	Greg Mathews	.30	.25	.12
42	Eric King	.20	.15	.08
43	Kal Daniels	.80	.60	.30
44	Calvin Schiraldi	.20	.15	.08
45	Mickey Brantley	.20	.15	.08
46	Outstanding Rookie Seasons (Fred Lynn, Willie Mays, Pete Rose)	.80	.60	.30
47	Outstanding Rookie Seasons (Dwight Gooden, Tom Seaver, Fernando Valenzuela)	.80	.60	.30
48	Outstanding Rookie Seasons (Eddie Murray, Dave Righetti, Cal Ripken, Jr., Steve Sax, Darryl Strawberry, Lou Whitaker)	.60	.45	.25
49	Kevin Mitchell	2.00	1.50	.80
50	Mike Diaz	.20	.15	.08

1987 Sportflics

For its second season in the national baseball card market, Sportflics' basic issue was again a 200-card set of 2-1/2" by 3-1/2" "Magic Motion" cards, which offer three different photos on the same card, each visible in turn as the card is moved from top to bottom or side to side. Besides single-player cards, the '87 Sportflics set includes several three- and six-player cards, though not as many as in the 1986 set. The card backs feature a small player portrait photo on the single-player cards, an innovation for 1987.

		MT	NR MT	EX
	Complete Set:	30.00	22.00	12.00
	Common Player:	.10	.08	.04
1	Don Mattingly	2.00	1.50	.80
2	Wade Boggs	.70	.50	.30
3	Dale Murphy	.50	.40	.20
4	Rickey Henderson	1.00	.70	.40
5	George Brett	.70	.50	.30
6	Eddie Murray	.50	.40	.20
7	Kirby Puckett	.90	.70	.35
8	Ryne Sandberg	1.75	1.25	.70
9	Cal Ripken Jr.	1.00	.70	.40
10	Roger Clemens	1.50	1.25	.60
11	Ted Higuera	.15	.11	.06
12	Steve Sax	.20	.15	.08
13	Chris Brown	.10	.08	.04
14	Jesse Barfield	.15	.11	.06
15	Kent Hrbek	.20	.15	.08
16	Robin Yount	.30	.25	.12
17	Glenn Davis	.25	.20	.10
18	Hubie Brooks	.10	.08	.04
19	Mike Scott	.15	.11	.06
20	Darryl Strawberry	1.50	1.25	.60
21	Alvin Davis	.15	.11	.06
22	Eric Davis	.70	.50	.30
23	Danny Tartabull	.30	.25	.12
24a	Cory Snyder (Pat Tabler photo on back (facing front), 3/4 swing on front)	2.00	1.50	.80
24b	Cory Snyder (Pat Tabler photo on back (facing front), 1/4 swing on front)	2.00	1.50	.80
24c	Cory Snyder (Snyder photo on back (facing to side))	1.00	.70	.40
25	Pete Rose	1.25	.90	.50
26	Wally Joyner	1.00	.70	.40
27	Pedro Guerrero	.20	.15	.08
28	Tom Seaver	.60	.45	.25
29	Bob Knepper	.10	.08	.04
30	Mike Schmidt	1.00	.70	.40
31	Tony Gwynn	.70	.50	.30
32	Don Slaught	.10	.08	.04
33	Todd Worrell	.30	.25	.12
34	Tim Raines	.40	.30	.15
35	Dave Parker	.20	.15	.08
36	Bob Ojeda	.10	.08	.04
37	Pete Incaviglia	.50	.40	.20
38	Bruce Hurst	.15	.11	.06
39	Bobby Witt	.40	.30	.15
40	Steve Garvey	.40	.30	.15
41	Dave Winfield	.40	.30	.15
42	Jose Cruz	.10	.08	.04
43	Orel Hershiser	.40	.30	.15
44	Reggie Jackson	.70	.50	.30
45	Chili Davis	.10	.08	.04
46	Robby Thompson	.30	.25	.12
47	Dennis Boyd	.10	.08	.04
48	Kirk Gibson	.30	.25	.12
49	Fred Lynn	.20	.15	.08
50	Gary Carter	.30	.25	.12
51	George Bell	.40	.30	.15
52	Pete O'Brien	.10	.08	.04
53	Ron Darling	.15	.11	.06
54	Paul Molitor	.15	.11	.06
55	Mike Pagliarulo	.15	.11	.06
56	Mike Boddicker	.10	.08	.04
57	Dave Righetti	.20	.15	.08
58	Len Dykstra(FC)	.15	.11	.06

		MT	NR MT	EX
59	Mike Witt	.10	.08	.04
60	Tony Bernazard	.10	.08	.04
61	John Kruk	.30	.25	.12
62	Mike Krukow	.10	.08	.04
63	Sid Fernandez	.15	.11	.06
64	Gary Gaetti	.20	.15	.08
65	Vince Coleman	.30	.25	.12
66	Pat Tabler	.10	.08	.04
67	Mike Scioscia	.10	.08	.04
68	Scott Garrelts	.10	.08	.04
69	Brett Butler	.10	.08	.04
70	Bill Buckner	.10	.08	.04
71a	Dennis Rasmussen (John Montefusco photo on back)	.25	.20	.10
71b	Dennis Rasmussen (Rasmussen photo on back)	.15	.11	.06
72	Tim Wallach	.15	.11	.06
73	Bob Horner	.15	.11	.06
74	Willie McGee	.15	.11	.06
75	American League First Basemen (Wally Joyner, Don Mattingly, Eddie Murray)	1.00	.70	.40
76	Jesse Orosco	.10	.08	.04
77	National League Relief Pitchers (Jeff Reardon, Dave Smith, Todd Worrell)	.15	.11	.06
78	Candy Maldonado	.10	.08	.04
79	National League Shortstops (Hubie Brooks, Shawon Dunston, Ozzie Smith)	.15	.11	.06
80	American League Left Fielders (George Bell, Jose Canseco, Jim Rice)	1.25	.90	.50
81	Bert Blyleven	.15	.11	.06
82	Mike Marshall	.15	.11	.06
83	Ron Guidry	.20	.15	.08
84	Julio Franco	.15	.11	.06
85	Willie Wilson	.15	.11	.06
86	Lee Lacy	.10	.08	.04
87	Jack Morris	.20	.15	.08
88	Ray Knight	.10	.08	.04
89	Phil Bradley	.15	.11	.06
90	Jose Canseco	2.00	1.50	.80
91	Gary Ward	.10	.08	.04
92	Mike Easler	.10	.08	.04
93	Tony Pena	.10	.08	.04
94	Dave Smith	.10	.08	.04
95	Will Clark	2.50	2.00	1.00
96	Lloyd Moseby	.10	.08	.04
97	Jim Rice	.40	.30	.15
98	Shawon Dunston	.15	.11	.06
99	Don Sutton	.25	.20	.10
100	Dwight Gooden	1.00	.70	.40
101	Lance Parrish	.20	.15	.08
102	Mark Langston	.15	.11	.06
103	Floyd Youmans	.10	.08	.04
104	Lee Smith	.10	.08	.04
105	Willie Hernandez	.10	.08	.04
106	Doug DeCinces	.10	.08	.04
107	Ken Schrom	.10	.08	.04
108	Don Carman	.10	.08	.04
109	Brook Jacoby	.15	.11	.06
110	Steve Bedrosian	.15	.11	.06
111	American League Pitchers (Roger Clemens, Teddy Higuera, Jack Morris)	.50	.40	.20
112	American League Second Basemen (Marty Barrett, Tony Bernazard, Lou Whitaker)	.10	.08	.04
113	American League Shortstops (Tony Fernandez, Scott Fletcher, Cal Ripken)	.25	.20	.10
114	American League Third Basemen (Wade Boggs, George Brett, Gary Gaetti)	.60	.45	.25
115	National League Third Basemen (Chris Brown, Mike Schmidt, Tim Wallach)	.35	.25	.14
116	National League Second Basemen (Bill Doran, Johnny Ray, Ryne Sandberg)	.15	.11	.06
117	National League Right Fielders (Kevin Bass, Tony Gwynn, Dave Parker)	.25	.20	.10
118	Hot Rookie Prospects (David Clark, Pat Dodson, Ty Gainey, Phil Lombardi, Benito Santiago, Terry Steinbach)	1.25	.90	.50
119	1986 Season Highlights (Dave Righetti, Mike Scott, Fernando Valenzuela)	.15	.11	.06
120	National League Pitchers (Dwight Gooden, Mike Scott, Fernando Valenzuela)	.40	.30	.15
121	Johnny Ray	.10	.08	.04
122	Keith Moreland	.10	.08	.04
123	Juan Samuel	.15	.11	.06
124	Wally Backman	.10	.08	.04
125	Nolan Ryan	2.00	1.50	.80
126	Greg Harris	.10	.08	.04
127	Kirk McCaskill	.10	.08	.04

#	Player	MT	NR MT	EX
128	Dwight Evans	.15	.11	.06
129	Rick Rhoden	.10	.08	.04
130	Bill Madlock	.15	.11	.06
131	Oddibe McDowell	.10	.08	.04
132	Darrell Evans	.10	.08	.04
133	Keith Hernandez	.30	.25	.12
134	Tom Brunansky	.15	.11	.06
135	Kevin McReynolds	.20	.15	.08
136	Scott Fletcher	.10	.08	.04
137	Lou Whitaker	.20	.15	.08
138	Carney Lansford	.10	.08	.04
139	Andre Dawson	.25	.20	.10
140	Carlton Fisk	.20	.15	.08
141	Buddy Bell	.15	.11	.06
142	Ozzie Smith	.20	.15	.08
143	Dan Pasqua	.15	.11	.06
144	Kevin Mitchell	1.25	.90	.50
145	Bret Saberhagen	.25	.20	.10
146	Charlie Kerfeld	.10	.08	.04
147	Phil Niekro	.25	.20	.10
148	John Candelaria	.10	.08	.04
149	Rich Gedman	.10	.08	.04
150	Fernando Valenzuela	.30	.25	.12
151	National League Catchers (Gary Carter, Tony Pena, Mike Scioscia)	.15	.11	.06
152	National League Left Fielders (Vince Coleman, Jose Cruz, Tim Raines)	.20	.15	.08
153	American League Right Fielders (Harold Baines, Jesse Barfield, Dave Winfield)	.25	.20	.10
154	American League Catchers (Rich Gedman, Lance Parrish, Don Slaught)	.10	.08	.04
155	National League Center Fielders (Eric Davis, Kevin McReynolds, Dale Murphy)	.70	.50	.30
156	1986 Season Highlights (Jim Deshaies, Mike Schmidt, Don Sutton)	.30	.25	.12
157	American League Speedburners (John Cangelosi, Rickey Henderson, Gary Pettis)	.25	.20	.10
158	Hot Rookie Prospects (Randy Asadoor, Casey Candaele, Dave Cochrane, Rafael Palmeiro, Tim Pyznarski, Kevin Seitzer)	1.25	.90	.50
159	The Best of the Best (Roger Clemens, Dwight Gooden, Rickey Henderson, Don Mattingly, Dale Murphy, Eddie Murray)	1.25	.90	.50
160	Roger McDowell	.15	.11	.06
161	Brian Downing	.10	.08	.04
162	Bill Doran	.10	.08	.04
163	Don Baylor	.15	.11	.06
164	Alfredo Griffin	.10	.08	.04
165	Don Aase	.10	.08	.04
166	Glenn Wilson	.10	.08	.04
167	Dan Quisenberry	.10	.08	.04
168	Frank White	.10	.08	.04
169	Cecil Cooper	.15	.11	.06
170	Jody Davis	.10	.08	.04
171	Harold Baines	.20	.15	.08
172	Rob Deer	.10	.08	.04
173	John Tudor	.15	.11	.06
174	Larry Parrish	.10	.08	.04
175	Kevin Bass	.10	.08	.04
176	Joe Carter	.15	.11	.06
177	Mitch Webster	.10	.08	.04
178	Dave Kingman	.15	.11	.06
179	Jim Presley	.15	.11	.06
180	Mel Hall	.10	.08	.04
181	Shane Rawley	.10	.08	.04
182	Marty Barrett	.10	.08	.04
183	Damaso Garcia	.10	.08	.04
184	Bobby Grich	.10	.08	.04
185	Leon Durham	.10	.08	.04
186	Ozzie Guillen	.10	.08	.04
187	Tony Fernandez	.15	.11	.06
188	Alan Trammell	.30	.25	.12
189	Jim Clancy	.10	.08	.04
190	Bo Jackson	2.00	1.50	.80
191	Bob Forsch	.10	.08	.04
192	John Franco	.10	.08	.04
193	Von Hayes	.10	.08	.04
194	American League Relief Pitchers (Don Aase, Mark Eichhorn, Dave Righetti)	.10	.08	.04
195	National League First Basemen (Will Clark, Glenn Davis, Keith Hernandez)	1.00	.70	.40
196	1986 Season Highlights (Roger Clemens, Joe Cowley, Bob Horner)	.35	.25	.14
197	The Best of the Best (Wade Boggs, George Brett, Hubie Brooks, Tony Gwynn, Tim Raines, Ryne Sandberg)	.80	.60	.30
198	American League Center Fielders (Rickey Henderson, Fred Lynn, Kirby Puckett)	.25	.20	.10
199	National League Speedburners (Vince Coleman, Eric Davis, Tim Raines)	.50	.40	.20
200	Steve Carlton	.60	.45	.25

1987 Sportflics Rookie Prospects

The 1987 Sportflics Rookie Prospects set consists of 10 cards that are the standard 2-1/2" by 3-1/2" size. The card fronts feature Sportflics' "Magic Motion" process. Card backs contain a player photo plus a short biography and player personal and statistical information. The set was offered in two separately wrapped mylar packs of five cards to hobby dealers purchasing cases of Sportflics' Team Preview set. Twenty-four packs of "Rookie Prospects" cards were included with each case.

		MT	NR MT	EX
	Complete Set:	6.00	4.50	2.50
	Common Player:	.50	.40	.20
1	Terry Steinbach	.70	.50	.30
2	Rafael Palmeiro	1.50	1.25	.60
3	Dave Magadan	1.25	.90	.50
4	Marvin Freeman	.50	.40	.20
5	Brick Smith	.50	.40	.20
6	B.J. Surhoff	.70	.50	.30
7	John Smiley	.70	.50	.30
8	Alonzo Powell	.50	.40	.20
9	Benny Santiago	.80	.60	.30
10	Devon White	.70	.50	.30

1987 Sportflics Rookies

The 1987 Sportflics Rookies set was issued in two series of 25 cards. The first was released in July with the second series following in October. The cards, which are the standard 2-1/2" by 3-1/2", feature Sportflics' special "Magic Motion" process. The card fronts contain a full-color photo and present three different pictures, depending on how the card is held.

The backs also contain a full-color photo along with player statistics and a biography.

		MT	NR MT	EX
	Complete Set:	10.00	7.50	4.00
	Common Player:	.20	.15	.08
1	Eric Bell	.20	.15	.08
2	Chris Bosio	.20	.15	.08
3	Bob Brower	.20	.15	.08
4	Jerry Browne	.20	.15	.08
5	Ellis Burks	.80	.60	.30
6	Casey Candaele	.20	.15	.08
7	Joey Cora	.20	.15	.08
8	Ken Gerhart	.30	.25	.12
9	Mike Greenwell	1.00	.70	.40
10	Stan Jefferson	.20	.15	.08
11	Dave Magadan	.70	.50	.30
12	Joe Magrane	.40	.30	.15
13	Fred McGriff	.80	.60	.30
14	Mark McGwire	1.00	.70	.40
15	Mark McLemore	.20	.15	.08
16	Jeff Musselman	.20	.15	.08
17	Matt Nokes	.40	.30	.15
18	Paul O'Neill	.20	.15	.08
19	Luis Polonia	.20	.15	.08
20	Benny Santiago	.80	.60	.30
21	Kevin Seitzer	.80	.60	.30
22	Terry Steinbach	.30	.25	.12
23	B.J. Surhoff	.70	.50	.30
24	Devon White	.40	.30	.15
25	Matt Williams	.70	.50	.30
26	DeWayne Buice	.20	.15	.08
27	Willie Fraser	.20	.15	.08
28	Bill Ripken	.30	.25	.12
29	Mike Henneman	.30	.25	.12
30	Shawn Hillegas	.20	.15	.08
31	Shane Mack	.20	.15	.08
32	Rafael Palmeiro	.70	.50	.30
33	Mike Jackson	.20	.15	.08
34	Gene Larkin	.20	.15	.08
35	Jimmy Jones	.20	.15	.08
36	Gerald Young	.40	.30	.15
37	Ken Caminiti	.20	.15	.08
38	Sam Horn	.60	.45	.25
39	David Cone	.70	.50	.30
40	Mike Dunne	.50	.40	.20
41	Ken Williams	.30	.25	.12
42	John Morris	.20	.15	.08
43	Jim Lindeman	.30	.25	.12
44	Todd Benzinger	.70	.50	.30
45	Mike Stanley	.30	.25	.12
46	Les Straker	.20	.15	.08
47	Jeff Robinson	.50	.40	.20
48	Jeff Blauser	.30	.25	.12
49	John Marzano	.30	.25	.12
50	Keith Miller	.30	.25	.12

1988 Sportflics

BENNY SANTIAGO 9   CATCHER

The design of the 1988 Sportflics set differs greatly from the previous two years. Besides increasing the number of cards in the set to 225, Sportflics included the player name, team and uniform number on the card front. The triple-action color photos are surrounded by a red border. The backs are re-designed, also. Full-color action photos, plus extensive statistics and informative biographies are utilized. Three highlights cards and three rookie

prospects card are included in the set. The cards are the standard 2-1/2" by 3-1/2".

		MT	NR MT	EX
	Complete Set:	30.00	22.00	12.00
	Common Player:	.10	.08	.04
1	Don Mattingly	1.00	.70	.40
2	Tim Raines	.35	.25	.14
3	Andre Dawson	.25	.20	.10
4	George Bell	.30	.25	.12
5	Joe Carter	.15	.11	.06
6	Matt Nokes	.50	.40	.20
7	Dave Winfield	.35	.25	.14
8	Kirby Puckett	.50	.40	.20
9	Will Clark	1.00	.70	.40
10	Eric Davis	.60	.45	.25
11	Rickey Henderson	1.00	.70	.40
12	Ryne Sandberg	1.00	.70	.40
13	Jesse Barfield	.15	.11	.06
14	Ozzie Guillen	.10	.08	.04
15	Bret Saberhagen	.20	.15	.08
16	Tony Gwynn	.40	.30	.15
17	Kevin Seitzer	.30	.25	.12
18	Jack Clark	.20	.15	.08
19	Danny Tartabull	.30	.25	.12
20	Ted Higuera	.15	.11	.06
21	Charlie Leibrandt, Jr.	.10	.08	.04
22	Benny Santiago	.50	.40	.20
23	Fred Lynn	.15	.11	.06
24	Rob Thompson	.10	.08	.04
25	Alan Trammell	.25	.20	.10
26	Tony Fernandez	.15	.11	.06
27	Rick Sutcliffe	.15	.11	.06
28	Gary Carter	.25	.20	.10
29	Cory Snyder	.20	.15	.08
30	Lou Whitaker	.20	.15	.08
31	Keith Hernandez	.25	.20	.10
32	Mike Witt	.10	.08	.04
33	Harold Baines	.15	.11	.06
34	Robin Yount	.25	.20	.10
35	Mike Schmidt	.80	.60	.30
36	Dion James	.10	.08	.04
37	Tom Candiotti	.10	.08	.04
38	Tracy Jones	.15	.11	.06
39	Nolan Ryan	1.00	.70	.40
40	Fernando Valenzuela	.25	.20	.10
41	Vance Law	.10	.08	.04
42	Roger McDowell	.10	.08	.04
43	Carlton Fisk	.15	.11	.06
44	Scott Garrelts	.10	.08	.04
45	Lee Guetterman	.10	.08	.04
46	Mark Langston	.15	.11	.06
47	Willie Randolph	.10	.08	.04
48	Bill Doran	.10	.08	.04
49	Larry Parrish	.10	.08	.04
50	Wade Boggs	.70	.50	.30
51	Shane Rawley	.10	.08	.04
52	Alvin Davis	.15	.11	.06
53	Jeff Reardon	.15	.11	.06
54	Jim Presley	.10	.08	.04
55	Kevin Bass	.10	.08	.04
56	Kevin McReynolds	.20	.15	.08
57	B.J. Surhoff	.15	.11	.06
58	Julio Franco	.15	.11	.06
59	Eddie Murray	.40	.30	.15
60	Jody Davis	.10	.08	.04
61	Todd Worrell	.15	.11	.06
62	Von Hayes	.10	.08	.04
63	Billy Hatcher	.10	.08	.04
64	John Kruk	.15	.11	.06
65	Tom Henke	.10	.08	.04
66	Mike Scott	.15	.11	.06
67	Vince Coleman	.20	.15	.08
68	Ozzie Smith	.20	.15	.08
69	Ken Williams	.20	.15	.08
70	Steve Bedrosian	.15	.11	.06
71	Luis Polonia	.20	.15	.08
72	Brook Jacoby	.15	.11	.06
73	Ron Darling	.15	.11	.06
74	Lloyd Moseby	.10	.08	.04
75	Wally Joyner	.50	.40	.20
76	Dan Quisenberry	.10	.08	.04
77	Scott Fletcher	.10	.08	.04
78	Kirk McCaskill	.10	.08	.04
79	Paul Molitor	.15	.11	.06
80	Mike Aldrete	.10	.08	.04
81	Neal Heaton	.10	.08	.04
82	Jeffrey Leonard	.10	.08	.04
83	Dave Magadan	.15	.11	.06
84	Danny Cox	.10	.08	.04
85	Lance McCullers	.10	.08	.04

		MT	NR MT	EX
86	Jay Howell	.10	.08	.04
87	Charlie Hough	.10	.08	.04
88	Gene Garber	.10	.08	.04
89	Jesse Orosco	.10	.08	.04
90	Don Robinson	.10	.08	.04
91	Willie McGee	.15	.11	.06
92	Bert Blyleven	.15	.11	.06
93	Phil Bradley	.15	.11	.06
94	Terry Kennedy	.10	.08	.04
95	Kent Hrbek	.20	.15	.08
96	Juan Samuel	.15	.11	.06
97	Pedro Guerrero	.20	.15	.08
98	Sid Bream	.10	.08	.04
99	Devon White	.30	.25	.12
100	Mark McGwire	.80	.60	.30
101	Dave Parker	.15	.11	.06
102	Glenn Davis	.20	.15	.08
103	Greg Walker	.10	.08	.04
104	Rick Rhoden	.10	.08	.04
105	Mitch Webster	.10	.08	.04
106	Lenny Dykstra	.10	.08	.04
107	Gene Larkin	.15	.11	.06
108	Floyd Youmans	.10	.08	.04
109	Andy Van Slyke	.15	.11	.06
110	Mike Scioscia	.10	.08	.04
111	Kirk Gibson	.25	.20	.10
112	Kal Daniels	.30	.25	.12
113	Ruben Sierra	.80	.60	.30
114	Sam Horn	.30	.25	.12
115	Ray Knight	.10	.08	.04
116	Jimmy Key	.10	.08	.04
117	Bo Diaz	.10	.08	.04
118	Mike Greenwell	.60	.45	.25
119	Barry Bonds	.70	.50	.30
120	Reggie Jackson	.50	.40	.20
121	Mike Pagliarulo	.15	.11	.06
122	Tommy John	.20	.15	.08
123	Bill Madlock	.15	.11	.06
124	Ken Caminiti	.30	.25	.12
125	Gary Ward	.10	.08	.04
126	Candy Maldonado	.10	.08	.04
127	Harold Reynolds	.10	.08	.04
128	Joe Magrane	.30	.25	.12
129	Mike Henneman	.25	.20	.10
130	Jim Gantner	.10	.08	.04
131	Bobby Bonilla	.15	.11	.06
132	John Farrell	.30	.25	.12
133	Frank Tanana	.10	.08	.04
134	Zane Smith	.10	.08	.04
135	Dave Righetti	.20	.15	.08
136	Rick Reuschel	.10	.08	.04
137	Dwight Evans	.15	.11	.06
138	Howard Johnson	.10	.08	.04
139	Terry Leach	.10	.08	.04
140	Casey Candaele	.10	.08	.04
141	Tom Herr	.10	.08	.04
142	Tony Pena	.10	.08	.04
143	Lance Parrish	.20	.15	.08
144	Ellis Burks	1.00	.70	.40
145	Pete O'Brien	.10	.08	.04
146	Mike Boddicker	.10	.08	.04
147	Buddy Bell	.10	.08	.04
148	Bo Jackson	1.00	.70	.40
149	Frank White	.10	.08	.04
150	George Brett	.60	.45	.25
151	Tim Wallach	.10	.08	.04
152	Cal Ripken, Jr.	.80	.60	.30
153	Brett Butler	.10	.08	.04
154	Gary Gaetti	.15	.11	.06
155	Darryl Strawberry	.80	.60	.30
156	Alfredo Griffin	.10	.08	.04
157	Marty Barrett	.10	.08	.04
158	Jim Rice	.30	.25	.12
159	Terry Pendleton	.10	.08	.04
160	Orel Hershiser	.35	.25	.14
161	Larry Sheets	.10	.08	.04
162	Dave Stewart	.10	.08	.04
163	Shawon Dunston	.15	.11	.06
164	Keith Moreland	.10	.08	.04
165	Ken Oberkfell	.10	.08	.04
166	Ivan Calderon	.10	.08	.04
167	Bob Welch	.15	.11	.06
168	Fred McGriff	.40	.30	.15
169	Pete Incaviglia	.15	.11	.06
170	Dale Murphy	.40	.30	.15
171	Mike Dunne	.25	.20	.10
172	Chili Davis	.10	.08	.04
173	Milt Thompson	.10	.08	.04
174	Terry Steinbach	.15	.11	.06
175	Oddibe McDowell	.10	.08	.04
176	Jack Morris	.20	.15	.08

		MT	NR MT	EX
177	Sid Fernandez	.15	.11	.06
178	Ken Griffey	.10	.08	.04
179	Lee Smith	.10	.08	.04
180	1987 Highlights (Juan Nieves, Kirby Puckett, Mike Schmidt)	.25	.20	.10
181	Brian Downing	.10	.08	.04
182	Andres Galarraga	.20	.15	.08
183	Rob Deer	.10	.08	.04
184	Greg Brock	.10	.08	.04
185	Doug DeCinces	.10	.08	.04
186	Johnny Ray	.10	.08	.04
187	Hubie Brooks	.10	.08	.04
188	Darrell Evans	.10	.08	.04
189	Mel Hall	.10	.08	.04
190	Jim Deshaies	.10	.08	.04
191	Dan Plesac	.15	.11	.06
192	Willie Wilson	.15	.11	.06
193	Mike LaValliere	.10	.08	.04
194	Tom Brunansky	.15	.11	.06
195	John Franco	.15	.11	.06
196	Frank Viola	.20	.15	.08
197	Bruce Hurst	.10	.08	.04
198	John Tudor	.10	.08	.04
199	Bob Forsch	.10	.08	.04
200	Dwight Gooden	.60	.45	.25
201	Jose Canseco	1.00	.70	.40
202	Carney Lansford	.10	.08	.04
203	Kelly Downs	.10	.08	.04
204	Glenn Wilson	.10	.08	.04
205	Pat Tabler	.10	.08	.04
206	Mike Davis	.10	.08	.04
207	Roger Clemens	1.00	.70	.40
208	Dave Smith	.10	.08	.04
209	Curt Young	.10	.08	.04
210	Mark Eichhorn	.10	.08	.04
211	Juan Nieves	.10	.08	.04
212	Bob Boone	.10	.08	.04
213	Don Sutton	.20	.15	.08
214	Willie Upshaw	.10	.08	.04
215	Jim Clancy	.10	.08	.04
216	Bill Ripken	.25	.20	.10
217	Ozzie Virgil	.10	.08	.04
218	Dave Concepcion	.10	.08	.04
219	Alan Ashby	.10	.08	.04
220	Mike Marshall	.15	.11	.06
221	1987 Highlights (Vince Coleman, Mark McGwire, Paul Molitor)	.50	.40	.20
222	1987 Highlights (Steve Bedrosian, Don Mattingly, Benito Santiago)	.50	.40	.20
223	Hot Rookie Prospects (Shawn Abner, Jay Buhner, Gary Thurman)	.40	.30	.15
224	Hot Rookie Prospects (Tim Crews, John Davis, Vincente Palacios)	.30	.25	.12
225	Hot Rookie Prospects (Keith Miller, Jody Reed, Jeff Treadway)	.50	.40	.20

1989 Sportflics

This basic issue includes 225 standard-size player cards (2-1/2" by 3-1/2") and 153 trivia cards, all featuring the patented Magic Motion design. A 5-card sub-set of triple photo cards called "Tri-Star" features a mix of veterans and rookies. The card fronts feature a white outer border and double color inner border in one of six color schemes (i.e. red, blue, purple). The inner border color changes when the card is tilted and the bottom border carries a double stripe of colors. The player name appears in the top border, player postition and uniform number appear, alternately, in the bottom border. The card backs contain crisp 1-7/8" by 1-3/4" player action shots, along with personal information, stats and career highlights. "The Unforgettables" trivia cards in this set salute members of the Hall of Fame.

		MT	NR MT	EX
Complete Set:		30.00	22.00	12.50
Common Player:		.10	.08	.04
1	Jose Canseco	1.50	1.25	.60
2	Wally Joyner	.40	.30	.15
3	Roger Clemens	.60	.45	.25
4	Greg Swindell	.15	.11	.06
5	Jack Morris	.20	.15	.08
6	Mickey Brantley	.10	.08	.04
7	Jim Presley	.15	.11	.06
8	Pete O'Brien	.10	.08	.04
9	Jesse Barfield	.15	.11	.06
10	Frank Viola	.20	.15	.08
11	Kevin Bass	.10	.08	.04
12	Glenn Wilson	.10	.08	.04
13	Chris Sabo	.60	.45	.25
14	Fred McGriff	.50	.40	.20
15	Mark Grace	1.00	.70	.40
16	Devon White	.20	.15	.08
17	Juan Samuel	.15	.11	.06
18	Lou Whitaker	.25	.20	.10
19	Greg Walker	.10	.08	.04
20	Roberto Alomar	.50	.40	.20
21	Mike Schmidt	.60	.45	.25
22	Benny Santiago	.25	.20	.10
23	Dave Stewart	.10	.08	.04
24	Dave Winfield	.35	.25	.14
25	George Bell	.30	.25	.12
26	Jack Clark	.20	.15	.08
27	Doug Drabek	.10	.08	.04
28	Ron Gant	.15	.11	.06
29	Glenn Braggs	.10	.08	.04
30	Rafael Palmeiro	.20	.15	.08
31	Brett Butler	.10	.08	.04
32	Ron Darling	.15	.11	.06
33	Alvin Davis	.15	.11	.06
34	Bob Walk	.10	.08	.04
35	Dave Stieb	.15	.11	.06
36	Orel Hershiser	.40	.30	.15
37	John Farrell	.15	.11	.06
38	Doug Jones	.10	.08	.04
39	Kelly Downs	.10	.08	.04
40	Bob Boone	.10	.08	.04
41	Gary Sheffield	.80	.60	.30
42	Doug Dascenzo	.30	.25	.12
43	Chad Krueter	.20	.15	.08
44	Ricky Jordan	.50	.40	.20
45	Dave West	.30	.25	.12
46	Danny Tartabull	.30	.25	.12
47	Teddy Higuera	.15	.11	.06
48	Gary Gaetti	.15	.11	.06
49	Dave Parker	.15	.11	.06
50	Don Mattingly	.80	.60	.30
51	David Cone	.25	.20	.10
52	Kal Daniels	.25	.20	.10
53	Carney Lansford	.10	.08	.04
54	Mike Marshall	.15	.11	.06
55	Kevin Seitzer	.30	.25	.12
56	Mike Henneman	.10	.08	.04
57	Bill Doran	.10	.08	.04
58	Steve Sax	.20	.15	.08
59	Lance Parrish	.15	.11	.06
60	Keith Hernandez	.25	.20	.10
61	Jose Uribe	.10	.08	.04
62	Jose Lind	.15	.11	.06
63	Steve Bedrosian	.15	.11	.06
64	George Brett	.60	.45	.25
65	Kirk Gibson	.25	.20	.10
66	Cal Ripken, Jr.	.60	.45	.25
67	Mitch Webster	.10	.08	.04
68	Fred Lynn	.15	.11	.06
69	Eric Davis	.50	.40	.20
70	Bo Jackson	1.75	1.25	.70
71	Kevin Elster	.15	.11	.06
72	Rick Reuschel	.10	.08	.04
73	Tim Burke	.10	.08	.04
74	Mark Davis	.10	.08	.04
75	Claudell Washington	.10	.08	.04
76	Lance McCullers	.10	.08	.04
77	Mike Moore	.10	.08	.04
78	Robby Thompson	.10	.08	.04
79	Roger McDowell	.10	.08	.04
80	Danny Jackson	.15	.11	.06

		MT	NR MT	EX
81	Tim Leary	.10	.08	.04
82	Bobby Witt	.15	.11	.06
83	Jim Gott	.10	.08	.04
84	Andy Hawkins	.10	.08	.04
85	Ozzie Guillen	.10	.08	.04
86	John Tudor	.15	.11	.06
87	Todd Burns	.25	.20	.10
88	Dave Gallagher	.25	.20	.10
89	Jay Buhner	.15	.11	.06
90	Gregg Jefferies	.80	.60	.30
91	Bob Welch	.15	.11	.06
92	Charlie Hough	.10	.08	.04
93	Tony Fernandez	.15	.11	.06
94	Ozzie Virgil	.10	.08	.04
95	Andre Dawson	.25	.20	.10
96	Hubie Brooks	.10	.08	.04
97	Kevin McReynolds	.20	.15	.08
98	Mike LaValliere	.10	.08	.04
99	Terry Pendleton	.10	.08	.04
100	Wade Boggs	.80	.60	.30
101	Dennis Eckersley	.15	.11	.06
102	Mark Gubicza	.15	.11	.06
103	Frank Tanana	.10	.08	.04
104	Joe Carter	.15	.11	.06
105	Ozzie Smith	.20	.15	.08
106	Dennis Martinez	.10	.08	.04
107	Jeff Treadway	.15	.11	.06
108	Greg Maddux	.15	.11	.06
109	Bret Saberhagen	.20	.15	.08
110	Dale Murphy	.40	.30	.15
111	Rob Deer	.10	.08	.04
112	Pete Incaviglia	.15	.11	.06
113	Vince Coleman	.20	.15	.08
114	Tim Wallach	.15	.11	.06
115	Nolan Ryan	1.00	.70	.40
116	Walt Weiss	.35	.25	.14
117	Brian Downing	.10	.08	.04
118	Melido Perez	.15	.11	.06
119	Terry Steinbach	.15	.11	.06
120	Mike Scott	.15	.11	.06
121	Tim Belcher	.15	.11	.06
122	Mike Boddicker	.10	.08	.04
123	Len Dykstra	.10	.08	.04
124	Fernando Valenzuela	.25	.20	.10
125	Gerald Young	.15	.11	.06
126	Tom Henke	.10	.08	.04
127	Dave Henderson	.10	.08	.04
128	Dan Plesac	.15	.11	.06
129	Chili Davis	.10	.08	.04
130	Bryan Harvey	.25	.20	.10
131	Don August	.15	.11	.06
132	Mike Harkey	.50	.40	.20
133	Luis Polonia	.10	.08	.04
134	Craig Worthington	.25	.20	.10
135	Joey Meyer	.15	.11	.06
136	Barry Larkin	.25	.20	.10
137	Glenn Davis	.20	.15	.08
138	Mike Scioscia	.10	.08	.04
139	Andres Galarraga	.20	.15	.08
140	Doc Gooden	.60	.45	.25
141	Keith Moreland	.10	.08	.04
142	Kevin Mitchell	.10	.08	.04
143	Mike Greenwell	.40	.30	.15
144	Mel Hall	.10	.08	.04
145	Rickey Henderson	.50	.40	.20
146	Barry Bonds	.20	.15	.08
147	Eddie Murray	.40	.30	.15
148	Lee Smith	.10	.08	.04
149	Julio Franco	.15	.11	.06
150	Tim Raines	.35	.25	.14
151	Mitch Williams	.10	.08	.04
152	Tim Laudner	.10	.08	.04
153	Mike Pagliarulo	.15	.11	.06
154	Floyd Bannister	.10	.08	.04
155	Gary Carter	.25	.20	.10
156	Kirby Puckett	.40	.30	.15
157	Harold Baines	.20	.15	.08
158	Dave Righetti	.20	.15	.08
159	Mark Langston	.15	.11	.06
160	Tony Gwynn	.50	.40	.20
161	Tom Brunansky	.15	.11	.06
162	Vance Law	.10	.08	.04
163	Kelly Gruber	.10	.08	.04
164	Gerald Perry	.15	.11	.06
165	Harold Reynolds	.10	.08	.04
166	Andy Van Slyke	.15	.11	.06
167	Jimmy Key	.15	.11	.06
168	Jeff Reardon	.15	.11	.06
169	Milt Thompson	.10	.08	.04
170	Will Clark	.80	.60	.30
171	Chet Lemon	.10	.08	.04

#	Player	MT	NR MT	EX
172	Pat Tabler	.10	.08	.04
173	Jim Rice	.30	.25	.12
174	Billy Hatcher	.10	.08	.04
175	Bruce Hurst	.15	.11	.06
176	John Franco	.15	.11	.06
177	Van Snider	.25	.20	.10
178	Ron Jones	.25	.20	.10
179	Jerald Clark	.30	.25	.12
180	Tom Browning	.15	.11	.06
181	Von Hayes	.10	.08	.04
182	Bobby Bonilla	.15	.11	.06
183	Todd Worrell	.15	.11	.06
184	John Kruk	.15	.11	.06
185	Scott Fletcher	.10	.08	.04
186	Willie Wilson	.15	.11	.06
187	Jody Davis	.10	.08	.04
188	Kent Hrbek	.20	.15	.08
189	Ruben Sierra	.35	.25	.14
190	Shawon Dunston	.15	.11	.06
191	Ellis Burks	.50	.40	.20
192	Brook Jacoby	.15	.11	.06
193	Jeff Robinson	.15	.11	.06
194	Rich Dotson	.10	.08	.04
195	Johnny Ray	.10	.08	.04
196	Cory Snyder	.25	.20	.10
197	Mike Witt	.10	.08	.04
198	Marty Barrett	.10	.08	.04
199	Robin Yount	.30	.25	.12
200	Mark McGwire	.50	.40	.20
201	Ryne Sandberg	.80	.60	.30
202	John Candelaria	.10	.08	.04
203	Matt Nokes	.20	.15	.08
204	Dwight Evans	.15	.11	.06
205	Darryl Strawberry	.60	.45	.25
206	Willie McGee	.15	.11	.06
207	Bobby Thigpen	.15	.11	.06
208	B.J. Surhoff	.15	.11	.06
209	Paul Molitor	.15	.11	.06
210	Jody Reed	.10	.08	.04
211	Doyle Alexander	.15	.11	.06
212	Dennis Rasmussen	.10	.08	.04
213	Kevin Gross	.10	.08	.04
214	Kirk McCaskill	.10	.08	.04
215	Alan Trammell	.30	.25	.12
216	Damon Berryhill	.15	.11	.06
217	Rick Sutcliffe	.15	.11	.06
218	Don Slaught	.10	.08	.04
219	Carlton Fisk	.30	.25	.12
220	Allan Anderson	.10	.08	.04
221	1988 Highlights (Wade Boggs, Jose Canseco, Mike Greenwell)	1.50	1.25	.60
222	1988 Highlights (Tom Browning, Dennis Eckersley, Orel Hershiser)	.25	.20	.10
223	Hot Rookie Prospects (Sandy Alomar, Gregg Jefferies, Gary Sheffield)	4.00	3.00	1.50
224	Hot Rookie Prospects (Randy Johnson, Ramon Martinez, Bob Milacki)	1.50	1.25	.60
225	Hot Rookie Prospects (Geronimo Berroa, Cameron Drew, Ron Jones)	.25	.20	.10

1990 Sportflics

The Sportflics set for 1990 again contained 225 cards. The cards feature the unique "Magic Motion" effect which displays either of two different photos depending on how the card is tilted. (Previous years' sets had used three photos per card.) The two-photo "Magic Motion" sequence is designed to depict sequential game-action, showing a batter following through on his swing, a pitcher completing his motion, etc. Sportflics also added a moving red and yellow "marquee" border on the cards to compliment the animation effect. The player's name, which appears below the animation, remains stationary. The set includes 19 special rookie cards. The backs contain a color player photo, team logo, player information and stats. The cards were distributed in non-transparent mylar packs with small MVP trivia cards.

	MT	NR MT	EX
Complete Set:	25.00	20.00	10.00
Common Player:	.10	.08	.04

#	Player	MT	NR MT	EX
1	Kevin Mitchell	.40	.30	.15
2	Wade Boggs	.50	.40	.20
3	Cory Snyder	.10	.08	.04
4	Paul O'Neill	.10	.08	.04
5	Will Clark	.80	.60	.30
6	Tony Fernandez	.10	.08	.04
7	Ken Griffey, Jr.	3.00	2.25	1.25
8	Nolan Ryan	1.00	.70	.40
9	Rafael Palmeiro	.10	.08	.04
10	Jesse Barfield	.10	.08	.04
11	Kirby Puckett	.40	.30	.15
12	Steve Sax	.10	.08	.04
13	Fred McGriff	.40	.30	.15
14	Gregg Jefferies	.50	.40	.20
15	Mark Grace	.90	.70	.35
16	Devon White	.10	.08	.04
17	Juan Samuel	.15	.11	.06
18	Robin Yount	.25	.20	.10
19	Glenn Davis	.10	.08	.04
20	Jeffrey Leonard	.10	.08	.04
21	Chili Davis	.10	.08	.04
22	Craig Biggio	.70	.50	.30
23	Jose Canseco	.50	.40	.20
24	Derek Lilliquist	.20	.15	.08
25	Chris Bosio	.10	.08	.04
26	Dave Steib	.10	.08	.04
27	Bobby Thigpen	.10	.08	.04
28	Jack Clark	.10	.08	.04
29	Kevin Ritz	.20	.15	.08
30	Tom Gordon	.40	.30	.15
31	Bryan Harvey	.10	.08	.04
32	Jim Deshaies	.10	.08	.04
33	Terry Steinbach	.15	.11	.06
34	Tom Glavine	.15	.11	.06
35	Bob Welch	.10	.08	.04
36	Charlie Hayes	.20	.15	.08
37	Jeff Reardon	.10	.08	.04
38	Joe Orsulak	.10	.08	.04
39	Scott Garrelts	.10	.08	.04
40	Bob Boone	.10	.08	.04
41	Scott Bankhead	.10	.08	.04
42	Tom Henke	.10	.08	.04
43	Greg Briley	.40	.30	.15
44	Teddy Higuera	.10	.08	.04
45	Pat Borders	.10	.08	.04
46	Kevin Seitzer	.15	.11	.06
47	Bruce Hurst	.15	.11	.06
48	Ozzie Guillen	.10	.08	.04
49	Wally Joyner	.50	.40	.20
50	Mike Greenwell	.40	.30	.15
51	Gary Gaetti	.12	.09	.05
52	Gary Sheffield	.50	.40	.20
53	Dennis Martinez	.10	.08	.04
54	Ryne Sandberg	.40	.30	.15
55	Mike Scott	.12	.09	.05
56	Todd Benzinger	.10	.08	.04
57	Kelly Gruber	.15	.11	.06
58	Jose Lind	.10	.08	.04
59	Allan Anderson	.10	.08	.04
60	Robby Thompson	.10	.08	.04
61	John Smoltz	.30	.25	.12
62	Mark Davis	.12	.09	.05
63	Tom Herr	.10	.08	.06
64	Randy Johnson	.20	.15	.08
65	Lonnie Smith	.10	.08	.04
66	Pedro Guerrero	.15	.11	.06
67	Jerome Walton	.50	.40	.20
68	Ramon Martinez	.60	.45	.25
69	Tim Raines	.12	.09	.05
70	Matt Williams	.20	.15	.08
71	Joe Oliver	.20	.15	.08
72	Nick Esasky	.12	.09	.05
73	Kevin Brown	.25	.20	.10
74	Walt Weiss	.12	.09	.05
75	Roger McDowell	.10	.08	.04
76	Jose DeLeon	.10	.08	.04
77	Brian Downing	.10	.08	.04
78	Jay Howell	.10	.08	.04
79	Jose Uribe	.10	.08	.04
80	Ellis Burks	.50	.40	.20
81	Sammy Sosa	.50	.40	.20
82	Johnny Ray	.20	.15	.08
83	Danny Darwin	.10	.08	.04
84	Carney Lansford	.12	.09	.05
85	Jose Oquendo	.10	.08	.04
86	John Cerutti	.10	.08	.04
87	Dave Winfield	.15	.11	.08
88	Dave Righetti	.10	.08	.04
89	Danny Jackson	.10	.08	.04
90	Andy Benes	.40	.30	.15
91	Tom Browning	.10	.08	.04

		MT	NR MT	EX
92	Pete O'Brien	.10	.08	.04
93	Roberto Alomar	.15	.11	.06
94	Bret Saberhagen	.15	.11	.06
95	Phil Bradley	.10	.08	.04
96	Doug Jones	.10	.08	.04
97	Eric Davis	.40	.30	.15
98	Tony Gwynn	.40	.30	.15
99	Jim Abbott	.40	.30	.15
100	Cal Ripken, Jr.	.15	.11	.06
101	Andy Van Slyke	.12	.09	.05
102	Dan Plesac	.10	.08	.04
103	Lou Whitaker	.10	.08	.04
104	Steve Bedrosian	.10	.08	.04
105	Dave Gallagher	.10	.08	.04
106	Keith Hernandez	.10	.08	.04
107	Duane Ward	.10	.08	.04
108	Andre Dawson	.15	.11	.08
109	Howard Johnson	.20	.15	.08
110	Mark Langston	.12	.09	.05
111	Jerry Browne	.10	.08	.04
112	Alvin Davis	.10	.08	.04
113	Sid Fernandez	.10	.08	.04
114	Mike Devereaux	.10	.08	.04
115	Benny Santiago	.12	.09	.05
116	Bip Roberts	.10	.08	.04
117	Craig Worthington	.15	.11	.06
118	Kevin Elster	.10	.08	.04
119	Harold Reynolds	.10	.08	.04
120	Joe Carter	.15	.11	.06
121	Brian Harper	.10	.08	.04
122	Frank Viola	.15	.11	.06
123	Jeff Ballard	.10	.08	.04
124	John Kruk	.10	.08	.04
125	Harold Baines	.10	.08	.04
126	Tom Candiotti	.10	.08	.04
127	Kevin McReynolds	.15	.11	.06
128	Mookie Wilson	.10	.08	.04
129	Danny Tartabull	.12	.09	.05
130	Craig Lefferts	.10	.08	.04
131	Jose DeJesus	.15	.11	.06
132	John Orton	.30	.20	.10
133	Curt Schilling	.20	.15	.08
134	Marquis Grissom	.70	.50	.30
135	Greg Vaughn	.80	.60	.30
136	Brett Butler	.10	.08	.04
137	Rob Deer	.10	.08	.04
138	John Franco	.10	.08	.04
139	Keith Moreland	.10	.08	.04
140	Dave Smith	.10	.08	.04
141	Mark McGwire	.60	.45	.25
142	Vince Coleman	.15	.11	.06
143	Barry Bonds	.15	.11	.06
144	Mike Henneman	.10	.08	.04
145	Doc Gooden	.30	.25	.12
146	Darryl Strawberry	.50	.40	.20
147	Von Hayes	.10	.08	.04
148	Andres Galarraga	.12	.09	.05
149	Roger Clemens	.25	.20	.10
150	Don Mattingly	.80	.60	.30
151	Joe Magrane	.10	.08	.04
152	Dwight Smith	.60	.45	.25
153	Ricky Jordan	.30	.25	.12
154	Alan Trammell	.10	.08	.04
155	Brook Jacoby	.10	.08	.04
156	Lenny Dykstra	.10	.08	.04
157	Mike LaValliere	.10	.08	.04
158	Julio Franco	.12	.09	.05
159	Joey Belle	.80	.60	.30
160	Barry Larkin	.15	.11	.06
161	Rick Reuschel	.10	.08	.04
162	Nelson Santovenia	.10	.08	.04
163	Mike Scioscia	.10	.08	.04
164	Damon Berryhill	.10	.08	.04
165	Todd Worrell	.10	.08	.04
166	Jim Eisenreich	.10	.08	.04
167	Ivan Calderon	.10	.08	.04
168	Goose Gozzo	.25	.20	.10
169	Kirk McCaskill	.10	.08	.04
170	Dennis Eckersley	.10	.08	.04
171	Mickey Tettleton	.12	.09	.05
172	Chuck Finley	.10	.08	.04
173	Dave Magadan	.10	.08	.04
174	Terry Pendleton	.10	.08	.04
175	Willie Randolph	.10	.08	.04
176	Jeff Huson	.25	.20	.10
177	Todd Zeile	.70	.50	.30
178	Steve Olin	.40	.30	.15
179	Eric Anthony	.60	.45	.25
180	Scott Coolbaugh	.30	.25	.12
181	Rick Sutcliffe	.10	.08	.04
182	Tim Wallach	.10	.08	.04

		MT	NR MT	EX
183	Paul Molitor	.12	.09	.05
184	Roberto Kelly	.12	.09	.05
185	Mike Moore	.10	.08	.04
186	Junior Felix	.40	.30	.15
187	Mike Schooler	.10	.08	.04
188	Ruben Sierra	.40	.30	.15
189	Dale Murphy	.12	.09	.05
190	Dan Gladden	.10	.08	.04
191	John Smiley	.10	.08	.04
192	Jeff Russell	.10	.08	.04
193	Bert Blyleven	.10	.08	.04
194	Dave Stewart	.12	.09	.05
195	Bobby Bonilla	.12	.09	.05
196	Mitch Williams	.10	.08	.04
197	Orel Hershiser	.20	.15	.08
198	Kevin Bass	.10	.08	.04
199	Tim Burke	.10	.08	.04
200	Bo Jackson	1.00	.70	.40
201	David Cone	.12	.09	.05
202	Gary Pettis	.10	.08	.04
203	Kent Hrbek	.10	.08	.04
204	Carlton Fisk	.10	.08	.04
205	Bob Geren	.20	.15	.08
206	Bill Spiers	.25	.20	.10
207	Oddibe McDowell	.10	.08	.04
208	Rickey Henderson	.40	.30	.15
209	Ken Caminiti	.10	.08	.04
210	Devon White	.10	.08	.04
211	Greg Maddux	.15	.11	.06
212	Ed Whitson	.10	.08	.04
213	Carlos Martinez	.25	.20	.10
214	George Brett	.25	.20	.10
215	Gregg Olson	.50	.40	.20
216	Kenny Rogers	.20	.15	.08
217	Dwight Evans	.10	.08	.04
218	Pat Tabler	.10	.08	.04
219	Jeff Treadway	.10	.08	.04
220	Scott Fletcher	.10	.08	.04
221	Deion Sanders	.70	.50	.30
222	Robin Ventura	1.00	.70	.40
223	Chip Hale	.20	.15	.08
224	Tommy Greene	.40	.30	.15
225	Dean Palmer	.50	.40	.20

1911 T3 Turkey Reds

Turkey Reds are the only cabinet cards the average collector can have a realistic chance to complete. Obtained by mailing in coupons found in Turkey Red, Fez and Old Mill brand cigarettes, the Turkey Reds measure 5 3/4" by 8", a size known to collectors as "cabinet cards." Turkey Reds feature full color lithograph fronts with wide gray frames. Backs carried either a numbered ordering list or an ad for Turkey Red cigarettes. The Turkey Red series consists of 25 boxers and 100 baseball players. Despite their cost, Turkey Reds remain very popular today as the most attractive of the cabinet sets.

		NR MT	EX	VG
Complete Set:		70000.00	35000.00	21000.
Common Player: 1-50		300.00	150.00	90.00
Common Player: 77-126		325.00	162.00	97.00
1	Mordecai Brown	1000.00	500.00	300.00
2	Bill Bergen	300.00	150.00	90.00
3	Tommy Leach	300.00	150.00	90.00
4	Roger Bresnahan	1200.00	600.00	360.00
5	Sam Crawford	1200.00	600.00	360.00
6	Hal Chase	400.00	200.00	125.00
7	Howie Camnitz	300.00	150.00	90.00
8	Fred Clarke	1000.00	500.00	300.00
9	Ty Cobb	8500.00	4250.00	2550.
10	Art Devlin	300.00	150.00	90.00
11	Bill Dahlen	300.00	150.00	90.00
12	Wil Bill Donovan	300.00	150.00	90.00
13	Larry Doyle	300.00	150.00	90.00
14	Red Dooin	300.00	150.00	90.00
15	Kid Elberfeld	300.00	150.00	90.00

		NR MT	EX	VG
16	Johnny Evers	1200.00	600.00	360.00
17	Clark Griffith	1200.00	600.00	360.00
18	Hughie Jennings	1200.00	600.00	360.00
19	Addie Joss	1200.00	600.00	360.00
20	Tim Jordan	300.00	150.00	90.00
21	Red Kleinow	300.00	150.00	90.00
22	Harry Krause	300.00	150.00	90.00
23	Nap Lajoie	2800.00	1400.00	840.00
24	Mike Mitchell	300.00	150.00	90.00
25	Matty McIntyre	300.00	150.00	90.00
26	John McGraw	1350.00	775.00	375.00
27	Christy Mathewson	3750.00	1875.00	1125.
28a	Harry McIntyre (Brooklyn)	300.00	150.00	90.00
28b	Harry McIntyre (Brooklyn and Chicago)			
		350.00	175.00	105.00
29	Amby McConnell	300.00	150.00	90.00
30	George Mullin	300.00	150.00	90.00
31	Sherry Magee	300.00	150.00	90.00
32	Orval Overall	300.00	150.00	90.00
33	Jake Pfeister	300.00	150.00	90.00
34	Nap Rucker	300.00	150.00	90.00
35	Joe Tinker	1200.00	600.00	360.00
36	Tris Speaker	2800.00	1400.00	840.00
37	Slim Sallee	300.00	150.00	90.00
38	Jake Stahl	300.00	150.00	90.00
39	Rube Waddell	1200.00	600.00	360.00
40a	Vic Willis (Pittsburg)	300.00	150.00	90.00
40b	Vic Willis (Pittsburg and St. Louis)			
		350.00	175.00	105.00
41	Hooks Wiltse	300.00	150.00	90.00
42	Cy Young	3500.00	1750.00	1050.
43	Out At Third	200.00	100.00	60.00
44	Trying To Catch Him Napping	200.00	100.00	60.00
45	Jordan & Herzog At First	300.00	150.00	90.00
46	Safe At Third	200.00	100.00	60.00
47	Frank Chance At Bat	1000.00	500.00	300.00
48	Jack Murray At Bat	300.00	150.00	90.00
49	A Close Play At Second	300.00	150.00	90.00
50	Chief Myers At Bat	300.00	150.00	90.00
77	Red Ames	325.00	162.00	97.00
78	Home Run Baker	1200.00	600.00	360.00
79	George Bell	325.00	162.00	97.00
80	Chief Bender	1000.00	500.00	300.00
81	Bob Bescher	325.00	162.00	97.00
82	Kitty Bransfield	325.00	162.00	97.00
83	Al Bridwell	325.00	162.00	97.00
84	George Browne	325.00	162.00	97.00
85	Bill Burns	325.00	162.00	97.00
86	Bill Carrigan	325.00	162.00	97.00
87	Eddie Collins	1000.00	500.00	300.00
88	Harry Coveleski	325.00	162.00	97.00
89	Lou Criger	325.00	162.00	97.00
90a	Mickey Doolin (name incorrect)			
		375.00	187.00	112.00
90b	Mickey Doolan (name correct)	325.00	162.00	97.00
91	Tom Downey	325.00	162.00	97.00
92	Jimmy Dygert	325.00	162.00	97.00
93	Art Fromme	325.00	162.00	97.00
94	George Gibson	325.00	162.00	97.00
95	Peaches Graham	325.00	162.00	97.00
96	Bob Groom	325.00	162.00	97.00
97	Dick Hoblitzell	325.00	162.00	97.00
98	Solly Hofman	325.00	162.00	97.00
99	Walter Johnson	4000.00	2000.00	1200.
100	Davy Jones	325.00	162.00	97.00
101	Wee Willie Keeler	450.00	225.00	135.00
102	Johnny Kling	325.00	162.00	97.00
103	Ed Konetchy	325.00	162.00	97.00
104	Ed Lennox	325.00	162.00	97.00
105	Hans Lobert	325.00	162.00	97.00
106	Harry Lord	325.00	162.00	97.00
107	Rube Manning	325.00	162.00	97.00
108	Fred Merkle	325.00	162.00	97.00
109	Pat Moran	325.00	162.00	97.00
110	George McBride	325.00	162.00	97.00
111	Harry Niles	325.00	162.00	97.00
112a	Dode Paskert (Cincinnati)	350.00	175.00	105.00
112b	Dode Paskert (Cincinnati and Philadelphia)			
		325.00	162.00	97.00
113	Bugs Raymond	325.00	162.00	97.00
114	Bob Rhoades (Rhoads)	350.00	175.00	105.00
115	Admiral Schlei	325.00	162.00	97.00
116	Boss Schmidt	325.00	162.00	97.00
117	Wildfire Schulte	325.00	162.00	97.00
118	Frank Smith	325.00	162.00	97.00
119	George Stone	325.00	162.00	97.00
120	Gabby Street	325.00	162.00	97.00
121	Billy Sullivan	325.00	162.00	97.00
122a	Fred Tenney (New York)	350.00	175.00	105.00
122b	Fred Tenney (New York and Boston)			
		325.00	162.00	97.00

		NR MT	EX	VG
123	Ira Thomas	325.00	162.00	97.00
124	Bobby Wallace	1000.00	500.00	300.00
125	Ed Walsh	1200.00	600.00	360.00
126	Owen Wilson	325.00	162.00	97.00

1911 T201 Mecca Double Folders

These cards found in packages of Mecca cigarettes feature one player when the card is open, and another when the card is folded; two players sharing the same pair of legs. Mecca Double Folders measure 2-1/4" by 4-11/16." The fronts are color lithographs with the player's name appearing in black script in the upper left. The backs are printed in red and contain an innovation in the form of player statistics. The 50-card set contains 100 different players including a number of Hall of Famers. The Mecca Double Folders, with two players (Topps "borrowed" the idea in 1955) and statistics, were one of the most innovative series of the tobacco card era.

		NR MT	EX	VG
Complete Set:		10000.00	5000.00	3000.
Common Player:		75.00	37.00	22.00
(1)	Abstein, Butler	75.00	37.00	22.00
(2)	Baker, Collins	400.00	200.00	125.00
(3)	Baker, Downie (Downey)	75.00	37.00	22.00
(4)	Barrett, McGlynn	75.00	37.00	22.00
(5)	Barry, Lapp	75.00	37.00	22.00
(6)	Bender, Oldring	250.00	125.00	75.00
(7)	Bergen, Wheat	250.00	125.00	75.00
(8)	Blair, Hartzell	75.00	37.00	22.00
(9)	Bresnahan, Huggins	500.00	250.00	150.00
(10)	Bridwell, Matthewson (Mathewson)			
		750.00	375.00	230.00
(11)	Brown, Hofman	250.00	125.00	75.00
(12)	Byrne, Clarke	200.00	100.00	60.00
(13)	Chance, Evers	450.00	225.00	135.00
(14)	Chase, Sweeney	125.00	62.00	37.00
(15)	Cicotte, Thoney	100.00	50.00	30.00
(16)	Clarke, Gaspar	75.00	37.00	22.00
(17)	Cobb, Crawford	2500.00	1250.00	750.00
(18)	Cole, Kling	75.00	37.00	22.00
(19)	Coombs, Thomas	75.00	37.00	22.00
(20)	Daubert, Rucker	100.00	50.00	30.00
(21)	Donovan, Stroud	75.00	37.00	22.00
(22)	Dooin, Titus	75.00	37.00	22.00
(23)	Dougherty, Lord	400.00	200.00	125.00
(24)	Downs, Odwell	75.00	37.00	22.00
(25)	Doyle, Meyers	75.00	37.00	22.00
(26)	Dygert, Seymour	75.00	37.00	22.00
(27)	Elberfeld, McBride	75.00	37.00	22.00
(28)	Falkenberg, Lajoie	500.00	250.00	150.00
(29)	Fitzpatrick, Killian	75.00	37.00	22.00

		NR MT	EX	VG
(30)	Ford, Johnson	75.00	37.00	22.00
(31)	Foster, Ward	75.00	37.00	22.00
(32)	Gardner, Speaker	150.00	75.00	45.00
(33)	Gibson, Leach	75.00	37.00	22.00
(34)	Graham, Mattern	75.00	37.00	22.00
(35)	Grant, McLean	75.00	37.00	22.00
(36)	Hauser, Lush	75.00	37.00	22.00
(37)	Herzog, Miller	75.00	37.00	22.00
(38)	Hickman, Hinchman	75.00	37.00	22.00
(39)	Jennings, Summers	250.00	125.00	75.00
(40)	Johnson, Street	750.00	375.00	230.00
(41)	LaPorte, Stephens	75.00	37.00	22.00
(42)	Lake, Wallace	200.00	100.00	60.00
(43)	Leifield, Simon	75.00	37.00	22.00
(44)	Lobert, Moore	75.00	37.00	22.00
(45)	McCabe, Starr	75.00	37.00	22.00
(46)	McCarty, McGinnity	200.00	100.00	60.00
(47)	Merkle, Wiltse	100.00	50.00	30.00
(48)	Payne, Walsh	250.00	125.00	75.00
(49)	Stovall, Turner	75.00	37.00	22.00
(50)	Williams, Woodruff	75.00	37.00	22.00

1912 T202 Hassan Triple Folders

Measuring 5-1/2" by 2-1/4", Hassan cigarette cards carried the concept of multiple-player cards even further than the innovative Mecca set of the previous year. Scored so that the two end cards - which are full-color and very close to exact duplicates of T205 "Gold Borders" - can fold over the black and white center panel, the Hassan Triple Folder appears like a booklet when closed. The two end cards are individual player cards, while the larger center panel contains an action scene. Usually the two player cards are not related to the action scene. The unique Hassan Triple Folders feature player biographies on the back of the two individual cards with a description of the action on the back of the center panel. Values depend on the player featured in the center panel, as well as the players featured on the end cards.

		NR MT	EX	VG
Complete Set of 132:		75000.00	37500.00	22500.
Common Player:		225.00	112.00	67.00
(1a)	A Close Play At The Home Plate (LaPorte, Wallace)	250.00	125.00	75.00
(1b)	A Close Play At The Home Plate (Pelty, Wallace)	250.00	125.00	75.00
(2)	A Desperate Slide For Third (Ty Cobb, O'Leary)	2500.00	1250.00	750.00
(3a)	A Great Batsman (Barger, Bergen)	225.00	112.00	67.00
(3b)	A Great Batsman (Bergen, Rucker)	225.00	112.00	67.00
(4)	Ambrose McConnell At Bat (Blair, Quinn)	225.00	112.00	67.00
(5)	A Wide Throw Saves Crawford (Mullin, Stanage)	225.00	112.00	67.00
(6)	Baker Gets His Man (Baker, Collins)	500.00	250.00	150.00
(7)	Birmingham Gets To Third (Johnson, Street)	750.00	375.00	225.00
(8)	Birmingham's Home Run (Birmingham, Turner)	800.00	400.00	250.00
(9)	Bush Just Misses Austin (Magee, Moran)	225.00	112.00	67.00

		NR MT	EX	VG
(10a)	Carrigan Blocks His Man (Gaspar, McLean)	225.00	112.00	67.00
(10b)	Carrigan Blocks His Man (Carrigan, Wagner)	225.00	112.00	67.00
(11)	Catching Him Napping (Bresnahan, Oakes)	400.00	200.00	120.00
(12)	Caught Asleep Off First (Bresnahan, Harmon)	400.00	200.00	120.00
(13a)	Chance Beats Out A Hit (Chance, Foxen)	400.00	200.00	120.00
(13b)	Chance Beats Out A Hit (Archer, McIntyre)	225.00	112.00	67.00
(13c)	Chance Beats Out A Hit (Archer, Overall)	225.00	112.00	67.00
(13d)	Chance Beats Out A Hit (Archer, Rowan)	225.00	112.00	67.00
(13e)	Chance Beats Out A Hit (Chance, Shean)	400.00	200.00	120.00
(14a)	Chase Dives Into Third (Chase, Wolter)	225.00	112.00	67.00
(14b)	Chase Dives Into Third (Clarke, Gibson)	250.00	125.00	75.00
(14c)	Chase Dives Into Third (Gibson, Phillippe)	225.00	112.00	67.00
(15a)	Chase Gets Ball Too Late (Egan, Mitchell)	225.00	112.00	67.00
(15b)	Chase Gets Ball Too Late (Chase, Wolter)	225.00	112.00	67.00
(16a)	Chase Guarding First (Chase, Wolter)	225.00	112.00	67.00
(16b)	Chase Guarding First (Clarke, Gibson)	250.00	125.00	75.00
(16c)	Chase Guarding First (Gibson, Leifield)	225.00	112.00	67.00
(17)	Chase Ready For The Squeeze Play (Magee, Paskert)	225.00	112.00	67.00
(18)	Chase Safe At Third (Baker, Barry)	400.00	200.00	120.00
(19)	Chief Bender Waiting For A Good One (Bender, Thomas)	400.00	200.00	120.00
(20)	Clarke Hikes For Home (Bridwell, Kling)	225.00	112.00	67.00
(21)	Close At First (Ball, Stovall)	225.00	112.00	67.00
(22a)	Close At The Plate (Payne, Walsh)	400.00	200.00	120.00
(22b)	Close At The Plate (Payne, White)	225.00	112.00	67.00
(23)	Close At Third - Speaker (Speaker, Wood)	500.00	250.00	150.00
(24)	Close At Third - Wagner (Carrigan, Wagner)	225.00	112.00	67.00
(25a)	Collins Easily Safe (Byrne, Clarke)	300.00	150.00	90.00
(25b)	Collins Easily Safe (Baker, Collins)	500.00	250.00	150.00
(25c)	Collins Easily Safe (Collins, Murphy)	400.00	200.00	120.00
(26)	Crawford About To Smash One (Stanage, Summers)	225.00	112.00	67.00
(27)	Cree Rolls Home (Daubert, Hummel)	225.00	112.00	67.00
(28)	Davy Jones' Great Slide (Delahanty, Jones)	225.00	112.00	67.00
(29a)	Devlin Gets His Man (Devlin (Giants), Mathewson)	1000.00	500.00	300.00
(29b)	Devlin Gets His Man (Devlin (Rustlers), Mathewson)	650.00	325.00	200.00
(29c)	Devlin Gets His Man (Fletcher, Mathewson)	650.00	325.00	200.00
(29d)	Devlin Gets His Man (Mathewson, Meyers)	650.00	325.00	200.00
(30a)	Donlin Out At First (Camnitz, Gibson)	225.00	112.00	67.00
(30b)	Donlin Out At First (Doyle, Merkle)	225.00	112.00	67.00
(30c)	Donlin Out At First (Leach, Wilson)	225.00	112.00	67.00
(30d)	Donlin Out At First (Dooin, Magee)	225.00	112.00	67.00
(30e)	Donlin Out At First (Gibson, Phillippe)	225.00	112.00	67.00
(31a)	Dooin Gets His Man (Dooin, Doolan)	225.00	112.00	67.00
(31b)	Dooin Gets His Man (Dooin, Lobert)	225.00	112.00	67.00
(31c)	Dooin Gets His Man (Dooin, Titus)	225.00	112.00	67.00
(32)	Easy For Larry (Doyle, Merkle)	225.00	112.00	67.00
(33)	Elberfeld Beats The Throw (Elberfeld, Milan)	225.00	112.00	67.00

	NR MT	EX	VG
(34) Elberfeld Gets His Man (Elberfeld, Milan)			
	225.00	112.00	67.00
(35) Engle In A Close Play (Engle, Speaker)			
	450.00	225.00	135.00
(36a) Evers Makes A Safe Slide (Archer, Evers)			
	400.00	200.00	120.00
(36b) Evers Makes A Safe Slide (Chance, Evers)			
	500.00	250.00	150.00
(36c) Evers Makes A Safe Slide (Archer, Overall)			
	225.00	112.00	67.00
(36d) Evers Makes A Safe Slide (Archer, Reulbach)			
	225.00	112.00	67.00
(36e) Evers Makes A Safe Slide (Chance, Tinker)			
	550.00	275.00	165.00
(37) Fast Work At Third (Cobb, O'Leary)			
	2500.00	1250.00	750.00
(38a) Ford Putting Over A Spitter (Ford, Vaughn)			
	225.00	112.00	67.00
(38b) Ford Putting Over A Spitter (Sweeney, Ford)			
	225.00	112.00	67.00
(39) Good Play At Third (Cobb, Moriarity)			
	2500.00	1250.00	750.00
(40) Grant Gets His Man (Grant, Hoblitzell)			
	225.00	112.00	67.00
(41a) Hal Chase Too Late (McConnell, McIntyre)			
	225.00	112.00	67.00
(41b) Hal Chase Too Late (McLean, Suggs)			
	225.00	112.00	67.00
(42) Harry Lord At Third (Lennox, Tinker)			
	150.00	75.00	45.00
(43) Hartzell Covering Third (Dahlen, Scanlan)			
	225.00	112.00	67.00
(44) Hartsel Strikes Out (Gray, Groom)			
	225.00	112.00	67.00
(45) Held At Third (Lord, Tannehill)	225.00	112.00	67.00
(46) Jake Stahl Guarding First (Cicotte, Stahl)			
	225.00	112.00	67.00
(47) Jim Delahanty At Bat (Delahanty, Jones)			
	225.00	112.00	67.00
(48a) Just Before The Battle (Ames, Meyers)			
	225.00	112.00	67.00
(48b) Just Before The Battle (Bresnahan, McGraw)			
	500.00	250.00	150.00
(48c) Just Before The Battle (Crandall, Meyers)			
	225.00	112.00	67.00
(48d) Just Before The Battle (Becker, Devore)			
	225.00	112.00	67.00
(48e) Just Before The Battle (Fletcher, Mathewson)			
	650.00	325.00	200.00
(48f) Just Before The Battle (Marquard, Meyers)			
	400.00	200.00	120.00
(48g) Just Before The Battle (Jennings, McGraw)			
	550.00	275.00	165.00
(48h) Just Before The Battle (Mathewson, Meyers)			
	650.00	325.00	200.00
(48i) Just Before The Battle (Murray, Snodgrass)			
	225.00	112.00	67.00
(48j) Just Before The Battle (Meyers, Wiltse)			
	225.00	112.00	67.00
(49) Knight Catches A Runner (Johnson, Knight)			
	750.00	375.00	225.00
(50a) Lobert Almost Caught (Bridwell, Kling)			
	225.00	112.00	67.00
(50b) Lobert Almost Caught (Kling, Young)			
	550.00	275.00	165.00
(50c) Lobert Almost Caught (Kling, Mattern)			
	225.00	112.00	67.00
(50d) Lobert Almost Caught (Kling, Steinfeldt)			
	225.00	112.00	67.00
(51) Lobert Gets Tenney (Dooin, Lobert)			
	225.00	112.00	67.00
(52) Lord Catches His Man (Lord, Tannehil)			
	225.00	112.00	67.00
(53) McConnell Caught (Needham, Richie)			
	225.00	112.00	67.00
(54) McIntyre At Bat (McConnell, McIntyre)			
	225.00	112.00	67.00
(55) Moriarty Spiked (Stanage, Willett)			
	225.00	112.00	67.00
(56) Nearly Caught (Bates, Bescher)			
	225.00	112.00	67.00
(57) Oldring Almost Home (Lord, Oldring)			
	225.00	112.00	67.00
(58) Schaefer On First (McBride, Milan)			
	225.00	112.00	67.00
(59) Schaefer Steals Second (Clark Griffith, McBride)			
	400.00	200.00	120.00
(60) Scoring From Second (Lord, Oldring)			
	225.00	112.00	67.00
(61a) Scrambling Back To First (Barger, Bergen)			
	225.00	112.00	67.00

	NR MT	EX	VG
(61b) Scrambling Back To First (Chase, Wolter)			
	225.00	112.00	67.00
(62) Speaker Almost Caught (Clarke, Miller)			
	300.00	150.00	90.00
(63) Speaker Rounding Third (Speaker, Wood)			
	500.00	250.00	150.00
(64) Speaker Scores (Engle, Speaker)			
	500.00	250.00	150.00
(65) Stahl Safe (Austin, Stovall)	225.00	112.00	67.00
(66) Stone About To Swing (Schulte, Sheckard)			
	225.00	112.00	67.00
(67a) Sullivan Puts Up A High One (Evans, Huggins)			
	400.00	200.00	125.00
(67b) Sullivan Puts Up A High One (Gray, Groom)			
	225.00	112.00	67.00
(68a) Sweeney Gets Stahl (Ford, Vaughn)			
	225.00	112.00	67.00
(68b) Sweeney Gets Stahl (Ford, Sweeney)			
	225.00	112.00	67.00
(69) Tenney Lands Safely (Latham, Raymond)			
	225.00	112.00	67.00
(70a) The Athletic Infield (Baker, Barry)			
	400.00	200.00	125.00
(70b) The Athletic Infield (Brown, Graham)			
	400.00	200.00	125.00
(70c) The Athletic Infield (Hauser, Konetchy)			
	150.00	75.00	45.00
(70d) The Athletic Infield (Krause, Thomas)			
	225.00	112.00	67.00
(71) The Pinch Hitter (Egan, Hoblitzell)			
	225.00	112.00	67.00
(72) The Scissors Slide (Birmingham, Turner)			
	225.00	112.00	67.00
(73a) Tom Jones At Bat (Fromme, McLean)			
	225.00	112.00	67.00
(73b) Tom Jones At Bat (Gaspar, McLean)			
	225.00	112.00	67.00
(74a) Too Late For Devlin (Ames, Meyers)			
	225.00	112.00	67.00
(74b) Too Late For Devlin (Crandall, Meyers)			
	225.00	112.00	67.00
(74c) Too Late For Devlin (Devlin (Giants), Mathewson)			
	850.00	425.00	265.00
(74d) Too Late For Devlin (Devlin (Rustlers), Mathewson)			
	650.00	325.00	200.00
(74e) Too Late For Devlin (Marquard, Meyers)			
	400.00	200.00	120.00
(74f) Too Late For Devlin (Meyers, Wiltse)			
	225.00	112.00	67.00
(75a) Ty Cobb Steals Third (Cobb, Jennings)			
	3000.00	1500.00	900.00
(75b) Ty Cobb Steals Third (Cobb, Moriarty)			
	2500.00	1250.00	750.00
(75c) Ty Cobb Steals Third (Austin, Stovall)			
	1200.00	600.00	350.00
(76) Wheat Strikes Out (Dahlen, Wheat)			
	450.00	225.00	135.00

1911 T205 Gold Border

Taking their hobby nickname from their border color, these cards were issued in a number of different cigarette brands. The cards measure

1-1/2" by 2-5/8". American League cards feature a color lithograph of the player inside a stylized baseball diamond. National League cards have head-and-shoulders portraits and a plain background, plus the first ever use of a facsimile autograph in a major card set. The 12 minor league players in the set feature three-quarter length portraits or action pictures in an elaborate frame of columns and other devices. Card backs of the major leaguers carry the player's full name (a first) and statistics. Card backs of the minor leaguers lack the statistics. The complete set price does not include the scarcer variations.

		NR MT	EX	VG
	Complete Set:	85000.00	42500.00	25500.
	Common Player:	120.00	60.00	36.00
(1)	Edward J. Abbaticchio	120.00	60.00	36.00
(2)	Doc Adkins	375.00	150.00	90.00
(3)	Leon K. Ames	120.00	60.00	36.00
(4)	Jas. P. Archer	120.00	60.00	36.00
(5)	Jimmy Austin	120.00	60.00	36.00
(6)	Bill Bailey	120.00	60.00	36.00
(7)	Home Run Baker	600.00	300.00	180.00
(8)	Neal Ball	800.00	400.00	240.00
(9)	E.B. Barger (full "B" on cap)	120.00	60.00	36.00
(10)	E.B. Barger (partial "B" on cap)	600.00	300.00	180.00
(11)	Jack Barry	120.00	60.00	36.00
(12)	Emil Batch	375.00	150.00	90.00
(13)	John W. Bates	120.00	60.00	36.00
(14)	Fred Beck	120.00	60.00	36.00
(15)	B. Becker	120.00	60.00	36.00
(16)	George G. Bell	120.00	60.00	36.00
(17)	Chas. Bender	800.00	400.00	240.00
(18)	William Bergen	120.00	60.00	36.00
(19)	Bob Bescher	120.00	60.00	36.00
(20)	Joe Birmingham	120.00	60.00	36.00
(21)	Lena Blackburne	120.00	60.00	36.00
(22)	William E. Bransfield	120.00	60.00	36.00
(23)	Roger P. Bresnahan (mouth closed)	800.00	400.00	240.00
(24)	Roger P. Bresnahan (mouth open)	750.00	300.00	180.00
(25)	A.H. Bridwell	120.00	60.00	36.00
(26)	Mordecai Brown	800.00	400.00	240.00
(27)	Robert Byrne	120.00	60.00	36.00
(28)	Hick Cady	375.00	150.00	90.00
(29)	H. Camnitz	120.00	60.00	36.00
(30)	Bill Carrigan	120.00	60.00	36.00
(31)	Frank J. Chance	800.00	400.00	240.00
(32a)	Hal Chase (both ears show, gold diamond frame extends below shoulders)	200.00	100.00	60.00
(32b)	Hal Chase (both ears show, gold diamond frame ends at shoulders)	200.00	100.00	60.00
(33)	Hal Chase (only left ear shows)	650.00	275.00	165.00
(34)	Ed Cicotte	150.00	75.00	45.00
(35)	Fred C. Clarke	350.00	137.00	82.00
(36)	Ty Cobb	7500.00	3750.00	2250.
(37)	Eddie Collins (mouth closed)	800.00	400.00	240.00
(38)	Eddie Collins (mouth open)	750.00	250.00	150.00
(39)	Jimmy Collins	800.00	400.00	240.00
(40)	Frank J. Corridon	120.00	60.00	36.00
(41a)	Otis Crandall ("t" not crossed in name)	120.00	60.00	36.00
(41b)	Otis Crandall ("t" crossed in name)	120.00	60.00	36.00
(42)	Lou Criger	120.00	60.00	36.00
(43)	W.F. Dahlen	325.00	137.00	82.00
(44)	Jake Daubert	125.00	55.00	33.00
(45)	Jim Delahanty	120.00	60.00	36.00
(46)	Arthur Devlin	120.00	60.00	36.00
(47)	Josh Devore	120.00	60.00	36.00
(48)	W.R. Dickson	120.00	60.00	36.00
(49)	Jiggs Donohue (Donahue)	600.00	300.00	180.00
(50)	Chas. S. Dooin	120.00	60.00	36.00
(51)	Michael J. Doolan	120.00	60.00	36.00
(52a)	Patsy Dougherty (red sock for team emblem)	120.00	60.00	36.00
(52b)	Patsy Dougherty (white sock for team emblem)	350.00	175.00	105.00
(53)	Thomas Downey	120.00	60.00	36.00
(54)	Larry Doyle	120.00	60.00	36.00
(55)	Hugh Duffy	800.00	400.00	240.00
(56)	Jack Dunn	375.00	150.00	90.00
(57)	Jimmy Dygert	120.00	60.00	36.00
(58)	R. Egan	120.00	60.00	36.00
(59)	Kid Elberfeld	120.00	60.00	36.00
(60)	Clyde Engle	120.00	60.00	36.00
(61)	Louis Evans	120.00	60.00	36.00
(62)	John J. Evers	600.00	300.00	180.00
(63)	Robert Ewing	120.00	60.00	36.00
(64)	G.C. Ferguson	120.00	60.00	36.00
(65)	Ray Fisher	450.00	175.00	105.00
(66)	Arthur Fletcher	120.00	60.00	36.00
(67)	John A. Flynn	120.00	60.00	36.00
(68)	Russ Ford (black cap)	120.00	60.00	36.00
(69)	Russ Ford (white cap)	450.00	175.00	105.00
(70)	Wm. A. Foxen	120.00	60.00	36.00
(71)	Jimmy Frick	375.00	150.00	90.00
(72)	Arthur Fromme	120.00	60.00	36.00
(73)	Earl Gardner	120.00	60.00	36.00
(74)	H.L. Gaspar	120.00	60.00	36.00
(75)	George Gibson	120.00	60.00	36.00
(76)	Wilbur Goode	120.00	60.00	36.00
(77)	George F. Graham (Rustlers)	120.00	60.00	36.00
(78)	George F. Graham (Cubs)	600.00	300.00	180.00
(79)	Edward L. Grant	450.00	200.00	120.00
(80a)	Dolly Gray (no stats on back)	120.00	60.00	36.00
(80b)	Dolly Gray (stats on back)	275.00	137.00	82.00
(81)	Clark Griffith	600.00	300.00	180.00
(82)	Bob Groom	120.00	60.00	36.00
(83)	Charlie Hanford	375.00	150.00	90.00
(84)	Bob Harmon (both ears show)	120.00	60.00	36.00
(85)	Bob Harmon (only left ear shows)	600.00	300.00	180.00
(86)	Topsy Hartsel	120.00	60.00	36.00
(87)	Arnold J. Hauser	120.00	60.00	36.00
(88)	Charlie Hemphill	120.00	60.00	36.00
(89)	C.L. Herzog	120.00	60.00	36.00
(90a)	R. Hoblitzell (no stats on back)	800.00	400.00	240.00
(90b)	R. Hoblitzell ("Cin." after 2nd 1908 in stats)	300.00	150.00	90.00
(90c)	R. Hoblitzel (name incorrect, no "Cin." after 1908 in stats)	120.00	60.00	36.00
(90d)	R. Hoblitzell (name correct, no "Cin." after 1908 in stats)	300.00	150.00	90.00
(91)	Danny Hoffman	120.00	60.00	36.00
(92)	Miller J. Huggins	450.00	225.00	135.00
(93)	John E. Hummel	120.00	60.00	36.00
(94)	Fred Jacklitsch	120.00	60.00	36.00
(95)	Hughie Jennings	800.00	400.00	240.00
(96)	Walter Johnson	2500.00	1250.00	750.00
(97)	D. Jones	120.00	60.00	36.00
(98)	Tom Jones	120.00	60.00	36.00
(99)	Addie Joss	800.00	300.00	180.00
(100)	Ed Karger	375.00	137.00	82.00
(101)	Ed Killian	120.00	60.00	36.00
(102)	Red Kleinow	375.00	137.00	82.00
(103)	John G. Kling	120.00	60.00	36.00
(104)	Jack Knight	120.00	60.00	36.00
(105)	Ed Konetchy	120.00	60.00	36.00
(106)	Harry Krause	120.00	60.00	36.00
(107)	Floyd M. Kroh	120.00	60.00	36.00
(108)	Frank LaPorte	120.00	60.00	36.00
(109)	Frank Lang (Lange)	120.00	60.00	36.00
(110a)	A. Latham (A. Latham on back)	120.00	60.00	36.00
(110b)	A. Latham (W.A. Latham on back)	120.00	60.00	36.00
(111)	Thomas W. Leach	120.00	60.00	36.00
(112)	Watty Lee	375.00	150.00	90.00
(113)	Sam Leever	120.00	60.00	36.00
(114a)	A. Leifield (initial "A." on front)	120.00	60.00	36.00
(114b)	A.P. Leifield (initials "A.P." on front)	120.00	60.00	36.00
(115)	Edgar Lennox	120.00	60.00	36.00
(116)	Paddy Livingston	120.00	60.00	36.00
(117)	John B. Lobert	120.00	60.00	36.00
(118)	Bris Lord (Athletics)	120.00	60.00	36.00
(119)	Harry Lord (White Sox)	120.00	60.00	36.00
(120)	Jno. C. Lush	120.00	60.00	36.00
(121)	Nick Maddox	120.00	60.00	36.00
(122)	Sherwood R. Magee	110.00	55.00	33.00
(123)	R.W. Marquard	550.00	200.00	120.00
(124)	C. Mathewson	1500.00	750.00	450.00
(125)	A.A. Mattern	120.00	60.00	36.00
(126)	Sport McAllister	375.00	150.00	90.00
(127)	George McBride	120.00	60.00	36.00
(128)	Amby McConnell	120.00	60.00	36.00
(129)	P.M. McElveen	120.00	60.00	36.00
(130)	J.J. McGraw	800.00	400.00	240.00
(131)	Harry McIntyre (Cubs)	120.00	60.00	36.00
(132)	Matty McIntyre (White Sox)	120.00	60.00	36.00
(133)	M.A. McLean (initials actually J.B.)	120.00	60.00	36.00
(134)	Fred Merkle	125.00	55.00	33.00
(135)	George Merritt	375.00	150.00	90.00
(136)	J.T. Meyers	120.00	60.00	36.00
(137)	Clyde Milan	120.00	60.00	36.00
(138)	J.D. Miller	120.00	60.00	36.00
(139)	M.F. Mitchell	120.00	60.00	36.00

	NR MT	EX	VG
(140a) P.J. Moran (stray line of type below stats)			
	120.00	60.00	36.00
(140b) P.J. Moran (no stray line)	120.00	60.00	36.00
(141) George Moriarty	120.00	60.00	36.00
(142) George Mullin	120.00	60.00	36.00
(143) Danny Murphy	120.00	60.00	36.00
(144) Jack Murray	120.00	60.00	36.00
(145) John Nee	375.00	150.00	90.00
(146) Thomas J. Needham	120.00	60.00	36.00
(147) Rebel Oakes	120.00	60.00	36.00
(148) Rube Oldring	120.00	60.00	36.00
(149) Charley O'Leary	120.00	60.00	36.00
(150) Fred Olmstead	120.00	60.00	36.00
(151) Orval Overall	120.00	60.00	36.00
(152) Freddy Parent	120.00	60.00	36.00
(153) George Paskert	120.00	60.00	36.00
(154) Billy Payne	120.00	60.00	36.00
(155) Barney Pelty	120.00	60.00	36.00
(156) John Pfeister	120.00	60.00	36.00
(157) Jimmy Phelan	375.00	150.00	90.00
(158) E.J. Phelps	120.00	60.00	36.00
(159) C. Phillippe	120.00	60.00	36.00
(160) Jack Quinn	120.00	60.00	36.00
(161) A.L. Raymond	600.00	300.00	180.00
(162) E.M. Reulbach	120.00	60.00	36.00
(163) Lewis Richie	120.00	60.00	36.00
(164) John A. Rowan	400.00	200.00	120.00
(165) George N. Rucker	120.00	60.00	36.00
(166) W.D. Scanlan	375.00	175.00	105.00
(167) Germany Schaefer	120.00	60.00	36.00
(168) George Schlei	120.00	60.00	36.00
(169) Boss Schmidt	120.00	60.00	36.00
(170) F.M. Schulte	120.00	60.00	36.00
(171) Jim Scott	120.00	60.00	36.00
(172) B.H. Sharpe	120.00	60.00	36.00
(173) David Shean (Rustlers)	120.00	60.00	36.00
(174) David Shean (Cubs)	600.00	300.00	180.00
(175) Jas. T. Sheckard	120.00	60.00	36.00
(176) Hack Simmons	120.00	60.00	36.00
(177) Tony Smith	120.00	60.00	36.00
(178) Fred C. Snodgrass	120.00	60.00	36.00
(179) Tris Speaker	725.00	300.00	180.00
(180) Jake Stahl	120.00	60.00	36.00
(181) Oscar Stanage	120.00	60.00	36.00
(182) Harry Steinfeldt	125.00	55.00	33.00
(183) George Stone	120.00	60.00	36.00
(184) George Stovall	120.00	60.00	36.00
(185) Gabby Street	120.00	60.00	36.00
(186) George F. Suggs	600.00	300.00	180.00
(187) Ed Summers	120.00	60.00	36.00
(188) Jeff Sweeney	400.00	175.00	105.00
(189) Lee Tannehill	120.00	60.00	36.00
(190) Ira Thomas	120.00	60.00	36.00
(191) Joe Tinker	800.00	400.00	240.00
(192) John Titus	120.00	60.00	36.00
(193) Terry Turner	600.00	300.00	180.00
(194) James Vaughn	120.00	60.00	36.00
(195) Heinie Wagner	400.00	175.00	105.00
(196) Bobby Wallace (with cap)	375.00	175.00	105.00
(197a) Bobby Wallace (no cap, one line of 1910 stats)			
	800.00	400.00	240.00
(197b) Bobby Wallace (no cap, two lines of 1910 stats)			
	625.00	275.00	165.00
(198) Ed Walsh	650.00	250.00	150.00
(199) Z.D. Wheat	600.00	300.00	180.00
(200) Doc White (White Sox)	120.00	60.00	36.00
(201) Kirb. White (Pirates)	400.00	200.00	120.00
(202) Irvin K. Wilhelm	600.00	300.00	180.00
(203) Ed Willett	120.00	60.00	36.00
(204) J. Owen Wilson	120.00	60.00	36.00
(205) George R. Wiltse (both ears show)			
	120.00	60.00	36.00
(206) George R. Wiltse (only right ear shows)			
	600.00	300.00	180.00
(207) Harry Wolter	120.00	60.00	36.00
(208) Cy Young	1500.00	750.00	450.00

1909-11 T206 White Border

The nearly 525 cards which make up the T206 set are the most popular of the early tobacco card issues. Players are depicted in a color lithograph against a variety of colorful backgrounds, surrounded by a white border. The player names on the 1-1/2" by 2-5/8" cards appear at the bottom with the city and league, when a city had more than one team. Backs contain an ad for one of 16 brands of

cigarettes. There are 389 major leaguer cards and 134 minor leaguer cards in the set, but with front/back varieties the number of potentially different cards runs into the thousands. The set features many expensive cards including a number of pose and/or team variations, along with the very scarce Eddie Plank card and the "King of Baseball Cards," the T206 Honus Wagner, the most avidly sought of all baseball cards. The complete set price does not include the Doyle (N.Y. Natl.), Magie, Plank and Wagner cards.

	NR MT	EX	VG
Complete Set:	1500.00	7500.00	2250.
Common Player:	100.00	50.00	30.00
Common Minor Leaguer:	105.00	52.00	31.00
Common Southern Leaguer:	225.00	112.00	67.00
(1) Ed Abbaticchio (blue sleeves)	150.00	75.00	45.00
(2) Ed Abbaticchio (brown sleeves)	100.00	50.00	30.00
(3) Fred Abbott	105.00	52.00	31.00
(4) Bill Abstein	100.00	50.00	30.00
(5) Doc Adkins	105.00	52.00	31.00
(6) Whitey Alperman	125.00	62.00	37.00
(7) Red Ames (hands at chest)	125.00	62.00	37.00
(8) Red Ames (hands above head)	125.00	62.00	37.00
(9) Red Ames (portrait)	100.00	50.00	30.00
(10) John Anderson	105.00	52.00	31.00
(11) Frank Arellanes	100.00	50.00	30.00
(12) Herman Armbruster	105.00	52.00	31.00
(13) Harry Arndt	105.00	52.00	31.00
(14) Jake Atz	100.00	50.00	30.00
(15) Home Run Baker	450.00	225.00	135.00
(16) Neal Ball (New York)	125.00	62.00	37.00
(17) Neal Ball (Cleveland)	100.00	50.00	30.00
(18) Jap Barbeau	125.00	62.00	37.00
(19) Cy Barger	105.00	52.00	31.00
(20) Jack Barry (Philadelphia)	100.00	50.00	30.00
(21) Shad Barry (Milwaukee)	105.00	52.00	31.00
(22) Jack Bastian	225.00	112.00	67.00
(23) Emil Batch	105.00	52.00	31.00
(24) Johnny Bates	125.00	62.00	37.00
(25) Harry Bay	300.00	150.00	90.00
(26) Ginger Beaumont	125.00	62.00	37.00
(27) Fred Beck	100.00	50.00	30.00
(28) Beals Becker	100.00	50.00	30.00
(29) Jake Beckley	300.00	150.00	90.00
(30) George Bell (hands above head)			
	125.00	62.00	37.00
(31) George Bell (pitching follow thru)			
	100.00	50.00	30.00
(32) Chief Bender (pitching, no trees in background)	400.00	200.00	120.00
(33) Chief Bender (pitching, trees in background)	400.00	200.00	120.00
(34) Chief Bender (portrait)	500.00	250.00	150.00
(35) Bill Bergen (batting)	125.00	62.00	37.00
(36) Bill Bergen (catching)	105.00	52.00	31.00
(37) Heinie Berger	100.00	50.00	30.00
(38) Bill Bernhard	225.00	112.00	67.00
(39) Bob Bescher (hands in air)	100.00	50.00	30.00
(40) Bob Bescher (portrait)	100.00	50.00	30.00
(41) Joe Birmingham	135.00	67.00	40.00
(42) Lena Blackburne	105.00	52.00	31.00
(43) Jack Bliss	100.00	50.00	30.00
(44) Frank Bowerman	125.00	62.00	37.00

No.	Player	NR MT	EX	VG
(45)	Bill Bradley (portrait)	125.00	62.00	37.00
(46)	Bill Bradley (with bat)	100.00	50.00	30.00
(47)	Dave Brain	105.00	52.00	31.00
(48)	Kitty Bransfield	125.00	62.00	37.00
(49)	Roy Brashear	105.00	52.00	31.00
(50)	Ted Breitenstein	225.00	112.00	67.00
(51)	Roger Bresnahan (portrait)	550.00	275.00	165.00
(52)	Roger Bresnahan (with bat)	400.00	200.00	120.00
(53)	Al Bridwell (portrait, no cap)	100.00	50.00	30.00
(54)	Al Bridwell (portrait, with cap)	125.00	62.00	37.00
(55a)	George Brown (Browne) (Chicago)	125.00	62.00	37.00
(55b)	George Brown (Browne) (Washington)	1000.00	500.00	300.00
(56)	Mordecai Brown (Chicago on shirt)	400.00	200.00	120.00
(57)	Mordecai Brown (Cubs on shirt)	550.00	275.00	165.00
(58)	Mordecai Brown (portrait)	450.00	225.00	135.00
(59)	Al Burch (batting)	275.00	137.00	80.00
(60)	Al Burch (fielding)	100.00	50.00	30.00
(61)	Fred Burchell	105.00	52.00	31.00
(62)	Jimmy Burke	105.00	52.00	31.00
(63)	Bill Burns	100.00	50.00	30.00
(64)	Donie Bush	100.00	50.00	30.00
(65)	John Butler	105.00	52.00	31.00
(66)	Bobby Byrne	100.00	50.00	30.00
(67)	Howie Camnitz (arm at side)	100.00	50.00	30.00
(68)	Howie Camnitz (arms folded)	125.00	62.00	37.00
(69)	Howie Camnitz (hands above head)	100.00	50.00	30.00
(70)	Billy Campbell	100.00	50.00	30.00
(71)	Scoops Carey	225.00	112.00	67.00
(72)	Charley Carr	105.00	52.00	31.00
(73)	Bill Carrigan	100.00	50.00	30.00
(74)	Doc Casey	105.00	52.00	31.00
(75)	Peter Cassidy	105.00	52.00	31.00
(76)	Frank Chance (batting)	400.00	200.00	120.00
(77)	Frank Chance (portrait, red background)	550.00	275.00	165.00
(78)	Frank Chance (portrait, yellow background)	450.00	225.00	135.00
(79)	Bill Chappelle	105.00	52.00	31.00
(80)	Chappie Charles	100.00	50.00	30.00
(81)	Hal Chase (holding trophy)	225.00	112.00	67.00
(82)	Hal Chase (portrait, blue background)	250.00	125.00	75.00
(83)	Hal Chase (portrait, pink background)	350.00	175.00	105.00
(84)	Hal Chase (throwing, dark cap)	200.00	100.00	60.00
(85)	Hal Chase (throwing, white cap)	475.00	237.00	145.00
(86)	Jack Chesbro	600.00	300.00	180.00
(87)	Ed Cicotte	175.00	87.00	52.00
(88)	Bill Clancy (Clancey)	105.00	52.00	31.00
(89)	Josh Clark (Clarke) (Columbus)	105.00	52.00	31.00
(90)	Fred Clarke (Pittsburg, holding bat)	400.00	200.00	120.00
(91)	Fred Clarke (Pittsburg, portrait)	450.00	225.00	135.00
(92)	Nig Clarke (Cleveland)	125.00	62.00	37.00
(93)	Bill Clymer	105.00	52.00	31.00
(94)	Ty Cobb (portrait, green background)	3250.00	1625.00	975.00
(95)	Ty Cobb (portrait, red background)	2500.00	1250.00	750.00
(96)	Ty Cobb (with bat off shoulder)	2500.00	1250.00	750.00
(97)	Ty Cobb (with bat on shoulder)	2500.00	1250.00	750.00
(98)	Cad Coles	225.00	112.00	67.00
(99)	Eddie Collins (Philadelphia)	500.00	250.00	150.00
(100)	Jimmy Collins (Minneapolis)	375.00	187.00	110.00
(101)	Bunk Congalton	105.00	52.00	31.00
(102)	Wid Conroy (fielding)	125.00	62.00	37.00
(103)	Wid Conroy (with bat)	100.00	50.00	30.00
(104)	Harry Covaleski (Coveleski)	125.00	62.00	37.00
(105)	Doc Crandall (portrait, no cap)	125.00	62.00	37.00
(106)	Doc Crandall (portrait, with cap)	100.00	50.00	30.00
(107)	Bill Cranston	250.00	125.00	75.00
(108)	Gavvy Cravath	175.00	87.00	52.00
(109)	Sam Crawford (throwing)	500.00	250.00	150.00
(110)	Sam Crawford (with bat)	450.00	225.00	135.00
(111)	Birdie Cree	100.00	50.00	30.00
(112)	Lou Criger	125.00	62.00	37.00
(113)	Dode Criss	125.00	62.00	37.00
(114)	Monte Cross	105.00	52.00	31.00
(115a)	Bill Dahlen (Boston)	150.00	75.00	45.00
(115b)	Bill Dahlen (Brooklyn)	600.00	300.00	175.00
(116)	Paul Davidson	105.00	52.00	31.00
(117)	George Davis (Chicago)	125.00	62.00	37.00
(118)	Harry Davis (Philadelphia, Davis on front)	100.00	50.00	30.00
(119)	Harry Davis (Philadelphia, H. Davis on front)	125.00	62.00	37.00
(120)	Frank Delehanty (Delahanty) (Louisville)	105.00	52.00	31.00
(121)	Jim Delehanty (Delahanty) (Washington)	125.00	62.00	37.00
(122a)	Ray Demmitt (New York)	100.00	50.00	30.00
(122b)	Ray Demmitt (St. Louis)	7500.00	3750.00	2300.
(123)	Rube Dessau	105.00	52.00	31.00
(124)	Art Devlin	125.00	62.00	37.00
(125)	Josh Devore	100.00	50.00	30.00
(126)	Bill Dineen (Dinneen)	100.00	50.00	30.00
(127)	Mike Donlin (fielding)	350.00	175.00	105.00
(128)	Mike Donlin (seated)	125.00	62.00	37.00
(129)	Mike Donlin (with bat)	100.00	50.00	30.00
(130)	Jiggs Donohue (Donahue)	125.00	62.00	37.00
(131)	Wild Bill Donovan (portrait)	125.00	62.00	37.00
(132)	Wild Bill Donovan (throwing)	100.00	50.00	30.00
(133)	Red Dooin	125.00	62.00	37.00
(134)	Mickey Doolan (batting)	100.00	50.00	30.00
(135)	Mickey Doolan (fielding)	100.00	50.00	30.00
(136)	Mickey Doolin (Doolan)	125.00	62.00	37.00
(137)	Gus Dorner	105.00	52.00	31.00
(138)	Patsy Dougherty (arm in air)	100.00	50.00	30.00
(139)	Patsy Dougherty (portrait)	125.00	62.00	37.00
(140)	Tom Downey (batting)	100.00	50.00	30.00
(141)	Tom Downey (fielding)	100.00	50.00	30.00
(142)	Jerry Downs	105.00	52.00	31.00
(143a)	Joe Doyle (N.Y. Natl., hands above head)	30000.00	15000.00	9000.
(143b)	Joe Doyle (N.Y., hands above head)	100.00	50.00	30.00
(144)	Larry Doyle (N.Y. Nat'l., portrait)	125.00	62.00	37.00
(145)	Larry Doyle (N.Y. Nat'l., throwing)	175.00	87.00	52.00
(146)	Larry Doyle (N.Y. Nat'l., with bat)	125.00	62.00	37.00
(147)	Jean Dubuc	100.00	50.00	30.00
(148)	Hugh Duffy	400.00	200.00	120.00
(149)	Jack Dunn (Baltimore)	105.00	52.00	31.00
(150)	Joe Dunn (Brooklyn)	100.00	50.00	30.00
(151)	Bull Durham	135.00	67.00	40.00
(152)	Jimmy Dygert	100.00	50.00	30.00
(153)	Ted Easterly	100.00	50.00	30.00
(154)	Dick Egan	100.00	50.00	30.00
(155a)	Kid Elberfeld (New York)	125.00	62.00	37.00
(155b)	Kid Elberfeld (Washington, portrait)	2500.00	1250.00	750.00
(156)	Kid Elberfeld (Washington, fielding)	100.00	50.00	30.00
(157)	Roy Ellam	250.00	125.00	75.00
(158)	Clyde Engle	100.00	50.00	30.00
(159)	Steve Evans	100.00	50.00	30.00
(160)	Johnny Evers (portrait)	650.00	325.00	200.00
(161)	Johnny Evers (with bat, Chicago on shirt)	400.00	200.00	120.00
(162)	Johnny Evers (with bat, Cubs on shirt)	500.00	250.00	150.00
(163)	Bob Ewing	125.00	62.00	37.00
(164)	Cecil Ferguson	100.00	50.00	30.00
(165)	Hobe Ferris	125.00	62.00	37.00
(166)	Lou Fiene (portrait)	100.00	50.00	30.00
(167)	Lou Fiene (throwing)	100.00	50.00	30.00
(168)	Steamer Flanagan	105.00	52.00	31.00
(169)	Art Fletcher	100.00	50.00	30.00
(170)	Elmer Flick	450.00	225.00	135.00
(171)	Russ Ford	100.00	50.00	30.00
(172)	Ed Foster	225.00	112.00	67.00
(173)	Jerry Freeman	105.00	52.00	31.00
(174)	John Frill	100.00	50.00	30.00
(175)	Charlie Fritz	225.00	112.00	67.00
(176)	Art Fromme	100.00	50.00	30.00
(177)	Chick Gandil	125.00	62.00	37.00
(178)	Bob Ganley	125.00	62.00	37.00
(179)	John Ganzel	105.00	52.00	31.00
(180)	Harry Gasper	100.00	50.00	30.00
(181)	Rube Geyer	100.00	50.00	30.00
(182)	George Gibson	125.00	62.00	37.00
(183)	Billy Gilbert	125.00	62.00	37.00
(184)	Wilbur Goode (Good)	125.00	62.00	37.00
(185)	Bill Graham (St. Louis)	100.00	50.00	30.00
(186)	Peaches Graham (Boston)	100.00	50.00	30.00
(187)	Dolly Gray	100.00	50.00	30.00
(188)	Ed Greminger	225.00	112.00	67.00
(189)	Clark Griffith (batting)	450.00	225.00	135.00
(190)	Clark Griffith (portrait)	500.00	250.00	150.00
(191)	Moose Grimshaw	105.00	52.00	31.00
(192)	Bob Groom	100.00	50.00	30.00

	NR MT	EX	VG
(193) Guiheen	250.00	125.00	75.00
(194) Ed Hahn	125.00	62.00	37.00
(195) Bob Hall	105.00	52.00	31.00
(196) Bill Hallman	105.00	52.00	31.00
(197) Jack Hannifan (Hannifin)	105.00	52.00	31.00
(198) Bill Hart (Little Rock)	300.00	150.00	90.00
(199) Jimmy Hart (Montgomery)	250.00	125.00	75.00
(200) Topsy Hartsel	100.00	50.00	30.00
(201) Jack Hayden	105.00	52.00	31.00
(202) J. Ross Helm	225.00	112.00	67.00
(203) Charlie Hemphill	125.00	62.00	37.00
(204) Buck Herzog (Boston)	100.00	50.00	30.00
(205) Buck Herzog (New York)	125.00	62.00	37.00
(206) Gordon Hickman	225.00	112.00	67.00
(207) Bill Hinchman (Cleveland)	125.00	62.00	37.00
(208) Harry Hinchman (Toledo)	105.00	52.00	31.00
(209) Dick Hoblitzell	100.00	50.00	30.00
(210) Danny Hoffman (St. Louis)	100.00	50.00	30.00
(211) Izzy Hoffman (Providence)	105.00	52.00	31.00
(212) Solly Hofman	100.00	50.00	30.00
(213) Bock Hooker	225.00	112.00	67.00
(214) Del Howard (Chicago)	100.00	50.00	30.00
(215) Ernie Howard (Savannah)	225.00	112.00	67.00
(216) Harry Howell (hand at waist)	100.00	50.00	30.00
(217) Harry Howell (portrait)	100.00	50.00	30.00
(218) Miller Huggins (hands at mouth)	400.00	200.00	120.00
(219) Miller Huggins (portrait)	450.00	225.00	135.00
(220) Rudy Hulswitt	100.00	50.00	30.00
(221) John Hummel	100.00	50.00	30.00
(222) George Hunter	100.00	50.00	30.00
(223) Frank Isbell	135.00	67.00	40.00
(224) Fred Jacklitsch	135.00	67.00	40.00
(225) Jimmy Jackson	105.00	52.00	31.00
(226) Hughie Jennings (one hand showing)	400.00	200.00	120.00
(227) Hughie Jennings (both hands showing)	400.00	200.00	120.00
(228) Hughie Jennings (portrait)	450.00	225.00	135.00
(229) Walter Johnson (hands at chest)	1250.00	625.00	375.00
(230) Walter Johnson (portrait)	1400.00	700.00	400.00
(231) Fielder Jones (Chicago, hands at hips)	125.00	62.00	37.00
(232) Fielder Jones (Chicago, portrait)	125.00	62.00	37.00
(233) Davy Jones (Detroit)	100.00	50.00	30.00
(234) Tom Jones (St. Louis)	125.00	62.00	37.00
(235) Dutch Jordan (Atlanta)	225.00	112.00	67.00
(236) Tim Jordan (Brooklyn, batting)	100.00	50.00	30.00
(237) Tim Jordan (Brooklyn, portrait)	125.00	62.00	37.00
(238) Addie Joss (hands at chest)	450.00	225.00	135.00
(239) Addie Joss (portrait)	550.00	275.00	165.00
(240) Ed Karger	125.00	62.00	37.00
(241) Willie Keeler (portrait)	750.00	375.00	225.00
(242) Willie Keeler (with bat)	700.00	350.00	210.00
(243) Joe Kelley	300.00	150.00	90.00
(244) J.F. Kiernan	225.00	112.00	67.00
(245) Ed Killian (hands at chest)	100.00	50.00	30.00
(246) Ed Killian (portrait)	125.00	62.00	37.00
(247) Frank King	225.00	112.00	67.00
(248) Rube Kisinger (Kissinger)	105.00	52.00	31.00
(249a) Red Kleinow (Boston)	1250.00	625.00	375.00
(249b) Red Kleinow (New York, catching)	100.00	50.00	30.00
(250) Red Kleinow (New York, with bat)	125.00	62.00	37.00
(251) Johnny Kling	125.00	62.00	37.00
(252) Otto Knabe	100.00	50.00	30.00
(253) Jack Knight (portrait)	100.00	50.00	30.00
(254) Jack Knight (with bat)	100.00	50.00	30.00
(255) Ed Konetchy (glove above head)	125.00	62.00	37.00
(256) Ed Konetchy (glove near ground)	100.00	50.00	30.00
(257) Harry Krause (pitching)	100.00	50.00	30.00
(258) Harry Krause (portrait)	100.00	50.00	30.00
(259) Rube Kroh	100.00	50.00	30.00
(260) Otto Kruger (Krueger)	105.00	52.00	31.00
(261) James Lafitte	225.00	112.00	67.00
(262) Nap Lajoie (portrait)	1250.00	625.00	375.00
(263) Nap Lajoie (throwing)	700.00	350.00	200.00
(264) Nap Lajoie (with bat)	700.00	350.00	200.00
(265) Joe Lake (New York)	125.00	62.00	37.00
(266) Joe Lake (St. Louis, ball in hand)	100.00	50.00	30.00
(267) Joe Lake (St. Louis, no ball in hand)	100.00	50.00	30.00
(268) Frank LaPorte	100.00	50.00	30.00
(269) Arlie Latham	100.00	50.00	30.00

	NR MT	EX	VG
(270) Bill Lattimore	105.00	52.00	31.00
(271) Jimmy Lavender	105.00	52.00	31.00
(272) Tommy Leach (bending over)	100.00	50.00	30.00
(273) Tommy Leach (portrait)	125.00	62.00	37.00
(274) Lefty Leifield (batting)	100.00	50.00	30.00
(275) Lefty Leifield (pitching)	125.00	62.00	37.00
(276) Ed Lennox	100.00	50.00	30.00
(277) Harry Lentz (Sentz)	225.00	112.00	67.00
(278) Glenn Liebhardt	125.00	62.00	37.00
(279) Vive Lindaman	125.00	62.00	37.00
(280) Perry Lipe	225.00	112.00	67.00
(281) Paddy Livingstone (Livingston)	100.00	50.00	30.00
(282) Hans Lobert	125.00	62.00	37.00
(283) Harry Lord	100.00	50.00	30.00
(284) Harry Lumley	125.00	62.00	37.00
(285a) Carl Lundgren (Chicago)	700.00	350.00	200.00
(285b) Carl Lundgren (Kansas City)	105.00	52.00	31.00
(286) Nick Maddox	100.00	50.00	30.00
(287a) Sherry Magie (Magee)	30000.00	15000.00	9000.
(287b) Sherry Magee (portrait)	175.00	87.00	52.00
(288) Sherry Magee (with bat)	125.00	62.00	37.00
(289) Bill Malarkey	105.00	52.00	31.00
(290) Billy Maloney	105.00	52.00	31.00
(291) George Manion	225.00	112.00	67.00
(292) Rube Manning (batting)	125.00	62.00	37.00
(293) Rube Manning (pitching)	100.00	50.00	30.00
(294) Rube Marquard (hands at thighs)	500.00	250.00	150.00
(295) Rube Marquard (pitching follow thru)	450.00	225.00	135.00
(296) Rube Marquard (portrait)	475.00	237.00	140.00
(297) Doc Marshall	100.00	50.00	30.00
(298) Christy Mathewson (dark cap)	800.00	400.00	250.00
(299) Christy Mathewson (portrait)	1400.00	700.00	400.00
(300) Christy Mathewson (white cap)	1200.00	600.00	350.00
(301) Al Mattern	100.00	50.00	30.00
(302) John McAleese	100.00	50.00	30.00
(303) George McBride	100.00	50.00	30.00
(304) Pat McCauley	225.00	112.00	67.00
(305) Moose McCormick	100.00	50.00	30.00
(306) Pryor McElveen	100.00	50.00	30.00
(307) Dan McGann	105.00	52.00	31.00
(308) Jim McGinley	105.00	52.00	31.00
(309) Iron Man McGinnity	350.00	175.00	105.00
(310) Stoney McGlynn	105.00	52.00	31.00
(311) John McGraw (finger in air)	500.00	250.00	150.00
(312) John McGraw (glove at hip)	475.00	237.00	140.00
(313) John McGraw (portrait, no cap)	600.00	300.00	175.00
(314) John McGraw (portrait, with cap)	400.00	200.00	120.00
(315) Harry McIntyre (Brooklyn)	125.00	62.00	37.00
(316) Harry McIntyre (Brooklyn & Chicago)	100.00	50.00	30.00
(317) Matty McIntyre (Detroit)	100.00	50.00	30.00
(318) Larry McLean	100.00	50.00	30.00
(319) George McQuillan (ball in hand)	125.00	62.00	37.00
(320) George McQuillan (with bat)	100.00	50.00	30.00
(321) Fred Merkle (portrait)	150.00	75.00	45.00
(322) Fred Merkle (throwing)	125.00	62.00	37.00
(323) George Merritt	105.00	52.00	31.00
(324) Chief Meyers	100.00	50.00	30.00
(325) Clyde Milan	100.00	50.00	30.00
(326) Dots Miller (Pittsburg)	100.00	50.00	30.00
(327) Molly Miller (Dallas)	225.00	112.00	67.00
(328) Bill Milligan	105.00	52.00	31.00
(329) Fred Mitchell (Toronto)	105.00	52.00	31.00
(330) Mike Mitchell (Cincinnati)	100.00	50.00	30.00
(331) Dan Moeller	105.00	52.00	31.00
(332) Carlton Molesworth	225.00	112.00	67.00
(333) Herbie Moran (Providence)	105.00	52.00	31.00
(334) Pat Moran (Chicago)	100.00	50.00	30.00
(335) George Moriarty	100.00	50.00	30.00
(336) Mike Mowrey	100.00	50.00	30.00
(337) Dom Mullaney	225.00	112.00	67.00
(338) George Mullen (Mullin)	100.00	50.00	30.00
(339) George Mullin (throwing)	125.00	62.00	37.00
(340) George Mullin (with bat)	100.00	50.00	30.00
(341) Danny Murphy (batting)	100.00	50.00	30.00
(342) Danny Murphy (throwing)	125.00	62.00	37.00
(343) Red Murray (batting)	100.00	50.00	30.00
(344) Red Murray (portrait)	100.00	50.00	30.00
(345) Chief Myers (Meyers) (batting)	100.00	50.00	30.00
(346) Chief Myers (Meyers) (fielding)	100.00	50.00	30.00
(347) Billy Nattress	105.00	52.00	31.00
(348) Tom Needham	100.00	50.00	30.00
(349) Simon Nicholls (hands on knees)	125.00	62.00	37.00
(350) Simon Nichols (Nicholls) (batting)	100.00	50.00	30.00
(351) Harry Niles	125.00	62.00	37.00

	NR MT	EX	VG
(352) Rebel Oakes	100.00	50.00	30.00
(353) Frank Oberlin	105.00	52.00	31.00
(354) Peter O'Brien	105.00	52.00	31.00
(355a) Bill O'Hara (New York)	100.00	50.00	30.00
(355b) Bill O'Hara (St. Louis)	7500.00	3750.00	2250.
(356) Rube Oldring (batting)	100.00	50.00	30.00
(357) Rube Oldring (fielding)	125.00	62.00	37.00
(358) Charley O'Leary (hands on knees)			
	100.00	50.00	30.00
(359) Charley O'Leary (portrait)	125.00	62.00	37.00
(360) William J. O'Neil	105.00	52.00	31.00
(361) Al Orth	225.00	112.00	67.00
(362) William Otey	225.00	112.00	67.00
(363) Orval Overall (hand face level)	100.00	50.00	30.00
(364) Orval Overall (hands waist level)			
	100.00	50.00	30.00
(365) Orval Overall (portrait)	125.00	62.00	37.00
(366) Frank Owen	125.00	62.00	37.00
(367) George Paige	225.00	112.00	67.00
(368) Fred Parent	125.00	62.00	37.00
(369) Dode Paskert	100.00	50.00	30.00
(370) Jim Pastorius	125.00	62.00	37.00
(371) Harry Pattee	550.00	275.00	165.00
(372) Billy Payne	100.00	50.00	30.00
(373) Barney Pelty (horizontal photo)			
	350.00	175.00	105.00
(374) Barney Pelty (vertical photo)	100.00	50.00	30.00
(375) Hub Perdue	225.00	112.00	67.00
(376) George Perring	100.00	50.00	30.00
(377) Arch Persons	225.00	112.00	67.00
(378) Francis (Big Jeff) Pfeffer	100.00	50.00	30.00
(379) Jake Pfeister (Pfiester) (seated)			
	100.00	50.00	30.00
(380) Jake Pfeister (Pfiester) (throwing)			
	100.00	50.00	30.00
(381) Jimmy Phelan	105.00	52.00	31.00
(382) Eddie Phelps	100.00	50.00	30.00
(383) Deacon Phillippe	100.00	50.00	30.00
(384) Ollie Pickering	105.00	52.00	31.00
(385) Eddie Plank	25000.00	12500.00	7500.
(386) Phil Poland	105.00	52.00	31.00
(387) Jack Powell	125.00	62.00	37.00
(388) Mike Powers	350.00	175.00	105.00
(389) Billy Purtell	100.00	50.00	30.00
(390) Ambrose Puttman (Puttmann)	105.00	52.00	31.00
(391) Lee Quillen (Quillin)	105.00	52.00	31.00
(392) Jack Quinn	100.00	50.00	30.00
(393) Newt Randall	105.00	52.00	31.00
(394) Bugs Raymond	100.00	50.00	30.00
(395) Ed Reagan	225.00	112.00	67.00
(396) Ed Reulbach (glove showing)	275.00	137.00	80.00
(397) Ed Reulbach (no glove showing)			
	100.00	50.00	30.00
(398) Dutch Revelle	225.00	112.00	67.00
(399) Bob Rhoades (Rhoads) (hands at chest)			
	100.00	50.00	30.00
(400) Bob Rhoades (Rhoads) (right arm extended)			
	100.00	50.00	30.00
(401) Charlie Rhodes	100.00	50.00	30.00
(402) Claude Ritchey	125.00	62.00	37.00
(403) Lou Ritter	105.00	52.00	31.00
(404) Ike Rockenfeld	225.00	112.00	67.00
(405) Claude Rossman	100.00	50.00	30.00
(406) Nap Rucker (portrait)	125.00	62.00	37.00
(407) Nap Rucker (throwing)	100.00	50.00	30.00
(408) Dick Rudolph	105.00	52.00	31.00
(409) Ray Ryan	225.00	112.00	67.00
(410) Germany Schaefer (Detroit)	125.00	62.00	37.00
(411) Germany Schaefer (Washington)			
	100.00	50.00	30.00
(412) George Schirm	105.00	52.00	31.00
(413) Larry Schlafly	105.00	52.00	31.00
(414) Admiral Schlei (batting)	100.00	50.00	30.00
(415) Admiral Schlei (catching)	125.00	62.00	37.00
(416) Admiral Schlei (portrait)	100.00	50.00	30.00
(417) Boss Schmidt (portrait)	100.00	50.00	30.00
(418) Boss Schmidt (throwing)	125.00	62.00	37.00
(419) Ossee Schreck (Schreckengost)			
	105.00	52.00	31.00
(420) Wildfire Schulte (front view)	125.00	62.00	37.00
(421) Wildfire Schulte (back view)	100.00	50.00	30.00
(422) Jim Scott	100.00	50.00	30.00
(423) Charles Seitz	225.00	112.00	67.00
(424) Cy Seymour (batting)	125.00	62.00	37.00
(425) Cy Seymour (portrait)	100.00	50.00	30.00
(426) Cy Seymour (throwing)	100.00	50.00	30.00
(427) Spike Shannon	105.00	52.00	31.00
(428) Bud Sharpe	105.00	52.00	31.00
(429) Shag Shaughnessy	225.00	112.00	67.00
(430) Al Shaw (St. Louis)	125.00	62.00	37.00
(431) Hunky Shaw (Providence)	105.00	52.00	31.00

	NR MT	EX	VG
(432) Jimmy Sheckard (glove showing)			
	100.00	50.00	30.00
(433) Jimmy Sheckard (no glove showing)			
	125.00	62.00	37.00
(434) Bill Shipke	125.00	62.00	37.00
(435) Jimmy Slagle	105.00	52.00	31.00
(436) Carlos Smith (Shreveport)	225.00	112.00	67.00
(437) Frank Smith (Chicago, F. Smith on front)			
	250.00	125.00	75.00
(438a) Frank Smith (Chicago, white cap)			
	100.00	50.00	30.00
(438b) Frank Smith (Chicago & Boston)			
	1250.00	625.00	375.00
(439) "Happy" Smith (Brooklyn)	100.00	50.00	30.00
(440) Heinie Smith (Buffalo)	105.00	52.00	31.00
(441) Sid Smith (Atlanta)	225.00	112.00	67.00
(442) Fred Snodgrass (batting)	125.00	62.00	37.00
(443) Fred Snodgrass (catching)	125.00	62.00	37.00
(444) Bob Spade	100.00	50.00	30.00
(445) Tris Speaker	1250.00	625.00	375.00
(446) Tubby Spencer	125.00	62.00	37.00
(447) Jake Stahl (glove shows)	100.00	50.00	30.00
(448) Jake Stahl (no glove shows)	125.00	62.00	37.00
(449) Oscar Stanage	100.00	50.00	30.00
(450) Dolly Stark	225.00	112.00	67.00
(451) Charlie Starr	100.00	50.00	30.00
(452) Harry Steinfeldt (portrait)	150.00	75.00	45.00
(453) Harry Steinfeldt (with bat)	125.00	62.00	37.00
(454) Jim Stephens	100.00	50.00	30.00
(455) George Stone	125.00	62.00	37.00
(456) George Stovall (batting)	100.00	50.00	30.00
(457) George Stovall (portrait)	125.00	62.00	37.00
(458) Sam Strang	105.00	52.00	31.00
(459) Gabby Street (catching)	100.00	50.00	30.00
(460) Gabby Street (portrait)	100.00	50.00	30.00
(461) Billy Sullivan	125.00	62.00	37.00
(462) Ed Summers	100.00	50.00	30.00
(463) Bill Sweeney (Boston)	100.00	50.00	30.00
(464) Jeff Sweeney (New York)	100.00	50.00	30.00
(465) Jesse Tannehill (Washington)	100.00	50.00	30.00
(466) Lee Tannehill (Chicago, L. Tannehill on front)			
	125.00	62.00	37.00
(467) Lee Tannehill (Chicago, Tannehill on front)			
	100.00	50.00	30.00
(468) Dummy Taylor	105.00	52.00	31.00
(469) Fred Tenney	125.00	62.00	37.00
(470) Tony Thebo	225.00	112.00	67.00
(471) Jake Thielman	105.00	52.00	31.00
(472) Ira Thomas	100.00	50.00	30.00
(473) Woodie Thornton	225.00	112.00	67.00
(474) Joe Tinker (bat off shoulder)	450.00	225.00	135.00
(475) Joe Tinker (bat on shoulder)	450.00	225.00	135.00
(476) Joe Tinker (hands on knees)	500.00	250.00	150.00
(477) Joe Tinker (portrait)	550.00	275.00	165.00
(478) John Titus	100.00	50.00	30.00
(479) Terry Turner	125.00	62.00	37.00
(480) Bob Unglaub	100.00	50.00	30.00
(481) Juan Violat (Viola)	225.00	112.00	67.00
(482) Rube Waddell (portrait)	500.00	250.00	150.00
(483) Rube Waddell (throwing)	500.00	250.00	150.00
(484) Heinie Wagner (bat on left shoulder)			
	125.00	67.00	40.00
(485) Heinie Wagner (bat on right shoulder)			
	100.00	50.00	30.00
(486) Honus Wagner	3000.00	1500.00	10500.
(487) Bobby Wallace	400.00	200.00	120.00
(488) Ed Walsh	550.00	275.00	165.00
(489) Jack Warhop	100.00	50.00	30.00
(490) Jake Weimer	125.00	62.00	37.00
(491) James Westlake	225.00	112.00	67.00
(492) Zack Wheat	550.00	275.00	165.00
(493) Doc White (Chicago, pitching)	100.00	50.00	30.00
(494) Doc White (Chicago, portrait)	125.00	62.00	37.00
(495) Foley White (Houston)	225.00	112.00	67.00
(496) Jack White (Buffalo)	105.00	52.00	31.00
(497) Kaiser Wilhelm (hands at chest)			
	125.00	62.00	37.00
(498) Kaiser Wilhelm (with bat)	100.00	50.00	30.00
(499) Ed Willett	100.00	50.00	30.00
(500) Ed Willetts (Willett)	100.00	50.00	30.00
(501) Jimmy Williams	125.00	62.00	37.00
(502) Vic Willis (Pittsburg)	100.00	50.00	30.00
(503) Vic Willis (St. Louis, throwing)	100.00	50.00	30.00
(504) Vic Willis (St. Louis, with bat)	100.00	50.00	30.00
(505) Owen Wilson	100.00	50.00	30.00
(506) Hooks Wiltse (pitching)	105.00	52.00	31.00
(507) Hooks Wiltse (portrait, no cap)	125.00	62.00	37.00
(508) Hooks Wiltse (portrait, with cap)			
	100.00	50.00	30.00
(509) Lucky Wright	105.00	52.00	31.00
(510) Cy Young (Cleveland, glove shows)			
	750.00	375.00	225.00

	NR MT	EX	VG
(511) Cy Young (Cleveland, bare hand shows)			
	750.00	375.00	225.00
(512) Cy Young (Cleveland, portrait)	1400.00	700.00	400.00
(513) Irv Young (Minneapolis)	105.00	52.00	31.00
(514) Heinie Zimmerman	100.00	50.00	30.00

1912 T207 Brown Background

Harry Lord

Harry Lord, the brilliant White Sox third baseman, came to Chicago in one of the queerest baseball deals ever recorded. Lord first achieved success in the New England League, where, in 1908, he was lifted to the Boston Americans. Although rated as a wonderful ball player, he fell out with the club management and was traded to Comiskey, who secured a star. Lord played wonderful ball in 1911 and is rated by many as the greatest third baseman now playing—a worthy successor to Bradley and Collins. Last season he batted .321, fielded .941 and led his club with stolen bases.

RECRUIT LITTLE CIGARS

LORD-CHICAGO-AMER.

These 1-1/2" by 2-5/8" cards take their name from the background color which frames the rather drab sepia and white player drawings. They have tan borders making them less colorful than the more popular issues of their era. Player pictures are also on the dull side, with a white strip containing the player's last name, team and league. The card backs have the player's full name, a baseball biography and an ad for one of several brands of cigarettes. The set features 200 players including stars and three classic rarities: Irving Lewis (Boston-Nat.), Ward Miller (Chicago-Nat.) and Louis Lowdermilk (St. Louis-Nat.). There are a number of other scarce cards in the set, including a higher than usual number of obscure players.

	NR MT	EX	VG
Complete Set:	40000.00	20000.00	12000.
Common Player:	90.00	45.00	27.00
(1) John B. Adams	250.00	125.00	75.00
(2) Edward Ainsmith	90.00	45.00	27.00
(3) Rafael Almeida	250.00	125.00	75.00
(4a) James Austin (insignia on shirt)	175.00	87.00	52.00
(4b) James Austin (no insignia on shirt)			
	250.00	125.00	75.00
(5) Neal Ball	90.00	45.00	27.00
(6) Eros Barger	90.00	45.00	27.00
(7) Jack Barry	90.00	45.00	27.00
(8) Charles Bauman	250.00	125.00	75.00
(9) Beals Becker	90.00	45.00	27.00
(10) Chief (Albert) Bender	550.00	275.00	165.00
(11) Joseph Benz	250.00	125.00	75.00
(12) Robert Bescher	90.00	45.00	27.00
(13) Joe Birmingham	250.00	125.00	75.00
(14) Russell Blackburne	250.00	125.00	75.00
(15) Fred Blanding	250.00	125.00	75.00
(16) Jimmy Block	90.00	45.00	27.00
(17) Ping Bodie	90.00	45.00	27.00
(18) Hugh Bradley	90.00	45.00	27.00
(19) Roger Bresnahan	550.00	275.00	165.00
(20) J.F. Bushelman	250.00	125.00	75.00
(21) Henry (Hank) Butcher	250.00	125.00	75.00
(22) Robert M. Byrne	90.00	45.00	27.00
(23) John James Callahan	90.00	45.00	27.00
(24) Howard Camnitz	90.00	45.00	27.00
(25) Max Carey	375.00	187.00	112.00
(26) William Carrigan	90.00	45.00	27.00
(27) George Chalmers	90.00	45.00	27.00
(28) Frank Leroy Chance	550.00	275.00	165.00
(29) Edward Cicotte	150.00	75.00	45.00
(30) Tom Clarke	90.00	45.00	27.00
(31) Leonard Cole	90.00	45.00	27.00
(32) John Collins	200.00	100.00	60.00

	NR MT	EX	VG
(33) Robert Coulson	90.00	45.00	27.00
(34) Tex Covington	90.00	45.00	27.00
(35) Otis Crandall	90.00	45.00	27.00
(36) William Cunningham	250.00	125.00	75.00
(37) Dave Danforth	90.00	45.00	27.00
(38) Bert Daniels	90.00	45.00	27.00
(39) John Daubert	150.00	75.00	45.00
(40a) Harry Davis (brown "C" on cap)			
	175.00	87.00	52.00
(40b) Harry Davis (blue "C" on cap)	175.00	87.00	52.00
(41) Jim Delehanty	90.00	45.00	27.00
(42) Claude Derrick	90.00	45.00	27.00
(43) Arthur Devlin	90.00	45.00	27.00
(44) Joshua Devore	90.00	45.00	27.00
(45) Mike Donlin	250.00	125.00	75.00
(46) Edward Donnelly	250.00	125.00	75.00
(47) Charles Dooin	90.00	45.00	27.00
(48) Tom Downey	250.00	125.00	75.00
(49) Lawrence Doyle	90.00	45.00	27.00
(50) Del Drake	90.00	45.00	27.00
(51) Ted Easterly	90.00	45.00	27.00
(52) George Ellis	90.00	45.00	27.00
(53) Clyde Engle	90.00	45.00	27.00
(54) R.E. Erwin	90.00	45.00	27.00
(55) Louis Evans	90.00	45.00	27.00
(56) John Ferry	90.00	45.00	27.00
(57a) Ray Fisher (blue cap)	175.00	87.00	52.00
(57b) Ray Fisher (white cap)	175.00	87.00	52.00
(58) Arthur Fletcher	90.00	45.00	27.00
(59) Jacques Fournier	250.00	125.00	75.00
(60) Arthur Fromme	90.00	45.00	27.00
(61) Del Gainor	90.00	45.00	27.00
(62) William Lawrence Gardner	90.00	45.00	27.00
(63) Lefty George	90.00	45.00	27.00
(64) Roy Golden	90.00	45.00	27.00
(65) Harry Gowdy	90.00	45.00	27.00
(66) George Graham	200.00	100.00	60.00
(67) J.G. Graney	90.00	45.00	27.00
(68) Vean Gregg	250.00	125.00	75.00
(69) Casey Hageman	90.00	45.00	27.00
(70) Charlie Hall	90.00	45.00	27.00
(71) E.S. Hallinan	90.00	45.00	27.00
(72) Earl Hamilton	90.00	45.00	27.00
(73) Robert Harmon	90.00	45.00	27.00
(74) Grover Hartley	250.00	125.00	75.00
(75) Olaf Henriksen	90.00	45.00	27.00
(76) John Henry	200.00	100.00	60.00
(77) Charles Herzog	250.00	125.00	75.00
(78) Robert Higgins	90.00	45.00	27.00
(79) Chester Hoff	250.00	125.00	75.00
(80) William Hogan	90.00	45.00	27.00
(81) Harry Hooper	650.00	325.00	200.00
(82) Ben Houser	250.00	125.00	75.00
(83) Hamilton Hyatt	250.00	125.00	75.00
(84) Walter Johnson	1500.00	750.00	450.00
(85) George Kaler	90.00	45.00	27.00
(86) William Kelly	250.00	125.00	75.00
(87) Jay Kirke	250.00	125.00	75.00
(88) John Kling	90.00	45.00	27.00
(89) Otto Knabe	90.00	45.00	27.00
(90) Elmer Knetzer	90.00	45.00	27.00
(91) Edward Konetchy	90.00	45.00	27.00
(92) Harry Krause	90.00	45.00	27.00
(93) "Red" Kuhn	250.00	125.00	75.00
(94) Joseph Kutina	250.00	125.00	75.00
(95) F.H. (Bill) Lange	250.00	125.00	75.00
(96) Jack Lapp	90.00	45.00	27.00
(97) W. Arlington Latham	90.00	45.00	27.00
(98) Thomas W. Leach	90.00	45.00	27.00
(99) Albert Leifield	90.00	45.00	27.00
(100) Edgar Lennox	90.00	45.00	27.00
(101) Duffy Lewis	90.00	45.00	27.00
(102a) Irving Lewis (no emblem on sleeve)			
	2000.00	1000.00	600.00
(102b) Irving Lewis (emblem on sleeve)			
	1800.00	900.00	540.00
(103) Jack Lively	90.00	45.00	27.00
(104a) Paddy Livingston ("A" on shirt)	550.00	275.00	165.00
(104b) Paddy Livingston (big "C" on shirt)			
	550.00	275.00	165.00
(104c) Paddy Livingston (little "C" on shirt)			
	175.00	87.00	52.00
(105) Briscoe Lord (Philadelphia)	90.00	45.00	27.00
(106) Harry Lord (Chicago)	90.00	45.00	27.00
(107) Louis Lowdermilk	4000.00	2000.00	1200.
(108) Richard Marquard	550.00	275.00	165.00
(109) Armando Marsans	90.00	45.00	27.00
(110) George McBride	90.00	45.00	27.00
(111) Alexander McCarthy	175.00	87.00	52.00
(112) Edward McDonald	90.00	45.00	27.00
(113) John J. McGraw	750.00	375.00	225.00
(114) Harry McIntire (McIntyre)	90.00	45.00	27.00

		NR MT	EX	VG
(115)	Matthew McIntyre	90.00	45.00	27.00
(116)	William McKechnie	400.00	200.00	120.00
(117)	Larry McLean	90.00	45.00	27.00
(118)	Clyde Milan	90.00	45.00	27.00
(119)	John B. Miller (Pittsburg)	90.00	45.00	27.00
(120)	Otto Miller (Brooklyn)	250.00	125.00	75.00
(121)	Roy Miller (Boston)	250.00	125.00	75.00
(122)	Ward Miller (Chicago)	200.00	100.00	60.00
(123)	Mike Mitchell (Cleveland, front depicts Willie Mitchell)	200.00	100.00	60.00
(124)	Mike Mitchell (Cincinnati)	90.00	45.00	27.00
(125)	Geo. Mogridge	250.00	125.00	75.00
(126)	Earl Moore	250.00	125.00	75.00
(127)	Patrick J. Moran	90.00	45.00	27.00
(128)	Cy Morgan (Philadelphia)	90.00	45.00	27.00
(129)	Ray Morgan (Washington)	90.00	45.00	27.00
(130)	George Moriarty	250.00	125.00	75.00
(131a)	George Mullin ("D" on cap)	175.00	87.00	52.00
(131b)	George Mullin (no "D" on cap)	175.00	87.00	52.00
(132)	Thomas Needham	90.00	45.00	27.00
(133)	Red Nelson	250.00	125.00	75.00
(134)	Herbert Northen	90.00	45.00	27.00
(135)	Leslie Nunamaker	90.00	45.00	27.00
(136)	Rebel Oakes	90.00	45.00	27.00
(137)	Buck O'Brien	90.00	45.00	27.00
(138)	Rube Oldring	90.00	45.00	27.00
(139)	Ivan Olson	90.00	45.00	27.00
(140)	Martin J. O'Toole	90.00	45.00	27.00
(141)	George Paskart (Paskert)	90.00	45.00	27.00
(142)	Barney Pelty	250.00	125.00	75.00
(143)	Herbert Perdue	90.00	45.00	27.00
(144)	O.C. Peters	250.00	125.00	75.00
(145)	Arthur Phelan	250.00	125.00	75.00
(146)	Jack Quinn	90.00	45.00	27.00
(147)	Don Carlos Ragan	225.00	112.00	67.00
(148)	Arthur Rasmussen	250.00	125.00	75.00
(149)	Morris Rath	250.00	125.00	75.00
(150)	Edward Reulbach	90.00	45.00	27.00
(151)	Napoleon Rucker	90.00	45.00	27.00
(152)	J.B. Ryan	250.00	125.00	75.00
(153)	Victor Saier	1500.00	750.00	450.00
(154)	William Scanlon	90.00	45.00	27.00
(155)	Germany Schaefer	90.00	45.00	27.00
(156)	Wilbur Schardt	90.00	45.00	27.00
(157)	Frank Schulte	90.00	45.00	27.00
(158)	Jim Scott	90.00	45.00	27.00
(159)	Henry Severoid (Severeid)	90.00	45.00	27.00
(160)	Mike Simon	90.00	45.00	27.00
(161)	Frank E. Smith (Cincinnati)	90.00	45.00	27.00
(162)	Wallace Smith (St. Louis)	90.00	45.00	27.00
(163)	Fred Snodgrass	90.00	45.00	27.00
(164)	Tristam Speaker	2000.00	1000.00	600.00
(165)	Harry Lee Spratt	90.00	45.00	27.00
(166)	Edward Stack	90.00	45.00	27.00
(167)	Oscar Stanage	90.00	45.00	27.00
(168)	William Steele	90.00	45.00	27.00
(169)	Harry Steinfeldt	90.00	45.00	27.00
(170)	George Stovall	90.00	45.00	27.00
(171)	Charles (Gabby) Street	90.00	45.00	27.00
(172)	Amos Strunk	90.00	45.00	27.00
(173)	William Sullivan	90.00	45.00	27.00
(174)	William J. Sweeney	250.00	125.00	75.00
(175)	Leeford Tannehill	90.00	45.00	27.00
(176)	C.D. Thomas	90.00	45.00	27.00
(177)	Joseph Tinker	550.00	275.00	165.00
(178)	Bert Tooley	90.00	45.00	27.00
(179)	Terence Turner (Terrence)	90.00	45.00	27.00
(180)	George Tyler	300.00	150.00	90.00
(181)	Jim Vaughn	90.00	45.00	27.00
(182)	Chas. (Heinie) Wagner	90.00	45.00	27.00
(183)	Ed (Dixie) Walker	90.00	45.00	27.00
(184)	Robert Wallace	375.00	187.00	112.00
(185)	John Warhop	90.00	45.00	27.00
(186)	George Weaver	250.00	125.00	75.00
(187)	Zach Wheat	450.00	225.00	135.00
(188)	G. Harris White	250.00	125.00	75.00
(189)	Ernest Wilie	250.00	125.00	75.00
(190)	Bob Williams	90.00	45.00	27.00
(191)	Arthur Wilson (New York)	250.00	125.00	75.00
(192)	Owen Wilson (Pittsburg)	90.00	45.00	27.00
(193)	George Wiltse	90.00	45.00	27.00
(194)	Ivey Wingo	90.00	45.00	27.00
(195)	Harry Wolverton	90.00	45.00	27.00
(196)	Joe Wood	200.00	100.00	60.00
(197)	Eugene Woodburn	250.00	125.00	75.00
(198)	Ralph Works	200.00	100.00	60.00
(199)	Stanley Yerkes	90.00	45.00	27.00
(200)	Rollie Zeider	200.00	100.00	60.00

NOTE: A card number in parentheses ( ) indicates the set is unnumbered.

1948 Topps Magic Photos

The first Topps baseball cards appeared as a subset of 19 cards from an issue of 252 "Magic Photos." The set takes its name from the self-developing nature of the cards. The cards were blank on the front when first taken from the wrapper. By spitting on the wrapper and holding it to the card while exposing it to light the black and white photo appeared. Measuring 7/8" by 1-1/2," the cards are very similar to Topps 1956 "Hocus Focus" issue.

		NR MT	EX	VG
Complete Set:		750.00	375.00	225.00
Common Player:		10.00	5.00	3.00
1	Lou Boudreau	20.00	10.00	6.00
2	Cleveland Indians	10.00	5.00	3.00
3	Bob Eliott	15.00	7.50	4.50
4	Cleveland Indians 4-3	10.00	5.00	3.00
5	Cleveland Indians 4-1 (Lou Boudreau Scoring)	20.00	10.00	6.00
6	"Babe" Ruth 714	200.00	100.00	60.00
7	Tris Speaker 793	25.00	12.50	7.50
8	Rogers Hornsby	50.00	25.00	15.00
9	Connie Mack	40.00	20.00	12.00
10	Christy Mathewson	50.00	25.00	15.00
11	Hans Wagner	50.00	25.00	15.00
12	Grover Alexander	30.00	15.00	9.00
13	Ty Cobb	100.00	50.00	30.00
14	Lou Gehrig	100.00	50.00	30.00
15	Walter Johnson	50.00	25.00	15.00
16	Cy Young	30.00	15.00	9.00
17	George Sisler 257	20.00	10.00	6.00
18	Tinker and Evers	20.00	10.00	6.00
19	Third Base Cleveland Indians	10.00	5.00	3.00

1951 Topps Blue Backs

Sold two cards in a package with a piece of candy for 1¢, the Topps Blue Backs are more scarce then their Red Back counterparts. The 2" by 2-5/8" cards carry a black and white player photograph on a red, white, yellow and green background along with the player's name and other information including their 1950 record on the front. The back is printed in blue on a white background. The 52-card set has varied baseball situations on them, making the playing of a rather elementary game of baseball possible.

Although scarce, Blue Backs were printed on thick cardboard and have survived quite well over the years. There are, however, few stars (Johnny Mize and Enos Slaughter are two) in the set. Despite being a Topps product, Blue Backs do not currently enjoy great popularity.

		NR MT	EX	VG
	Complete Set:	2100.00	1050.00	630.00
	Common Player:	30.00	15.00	9.00
1	Eddie Yost	30.00	15.00	9.00
2	Henry (Hank) Majeski	30.00	15.00	9.00
3	Richie Ashburn	50.00	25.00	15.00
4	Del Ennis	30.00	15.00	9.00
5	Johnny Pesky	25.00	12.50	7.50
6	Albert (Red) Schoendienst	35.00	17.50	10.50
7	Gerald Staley	30.00	15.00	9.00
8	Dick Sisler	30.00	15.00	9.00
9	Johnny Sain	35.00	17.50	10.50
10	Joe Page	30.00	15.00	9.00
11	Johnny Groth	30.00	15.00	9.00
12	Sam Jethroe	30.00	15.00	9.00
13	James (Mickey) Vernon	25.00	12.50	7.50
14	George Munger	30.00	15.00	9.00
15	Eddie Joost	30.00	15.00	9.00
16	Murry Dickson	30.00	15.00	9.00
17	Roy Smalley	30.00	15.00	9.00
18	Ned Garver	30.00	15.00	9.00
19	Phil Masi	30.00	15.00	9.00
20	Ralph Branca	30.00	15.00	9.00
21	Billy Johnson	30.00	15.00	9.00
22	Bob Kuzava	30.00	15.00	9.00
23	Paul (Dizzy) Trout	30.00	15.00	9.00
24	Sherman Lollar	30.00	15.00	9.00
25	Sam Mele	30.00	15.00	9.00
26	Chico Carresquel (Carrasquel)	30.00	15.00	9.00
27	Andy Pafko	25.00	12.50	7.50
28	Harry (The Cat) Brecheen	30.00	15.00	9.00
29	Granville Hamner	30.00	15.00	9.00
30	Enos (Country) Slaughter	60.00	30.00	18.00
31	Lou Brissie	30.00	15.00	9.00
32	Bob Elliott	30.00	15.00	9.00
33	Don Lenhardt	30.00	15.00	9.00
34	Earl Torgeson	30.00	15.00	9.00
35	Tommy Byrne	30.00	15.00	9.00
36	Cliff Fannin	30.00	15.00	9.00
37	Bobby Doerr	55.00	27.00	16.50
38	Irv Noren	30.00	15.00	9.00
39	Ed Lopat	30.00	15.00	9.00
40	Vic Wertz	25.00	12.50	7.50
41	Johnny Schmitz	30.00	15.00	9.00
42	Bruce Edwards	30.00	15.00	9.00
43	Willie (Puddin' Head) Jones	30.00	15.00	9.00
44	Johnny Wyrostek	30.00	15.00	9.00
45	Bill Pierce	25.00	12.50	7.50
46	Gerry Priddy	30.00	15.00	9.00
47	Herman Wehmeier	30.00	15.00	9.00
48	Billy Cox	30.00	15.00	9.00
49	Henry (Hank) Sauer	30.00	15.00	9.00
50	Johnny Mize	60.00	30.00	18.00
51	Eddie Waitkus	30.00	15.00	9.00
52	Sam Chapman	30.00	15.00	9.00

GRADING GUIDE

Mint (MT): A perfect card. Well-centered with all corners sharp and square. No creases, stains, edge nicks, surface marks, yellowing or fading.

Near Mint (NM): A nearly perfect card. At first glance, a NM card appears to be perfect. May be slightly off-center. No surface marks, creases or loss of gloss.

Excellent (EX): Corners are still fairly sharp with only moderate wear. Borders may be off-center. No creases or stains on fronts or backs, but may show slight loss of surface luster.

Very Good (VG): Shows obvious handling. May have rounded corners, minor creases, major gum or wax stains. No major creases, tape marks, writing, etc.

Good (G): A well-worn card, but exhibits no intentional damage. May have major or multiple creases. Corners may be rounded well beyond card border.

1951 Topps Red Backs

Like the Blue Backs, the Topps Red Backs which were sold at the same time, came two to a package for 1¢. Their black and white photographs appear on a red, white, blue and yellow background. The back printing is red on white. Their 2" by 2-5/8" size is the same as Blue Backs. Also identical is the set size (52 cards) and the game situations to be found on the fronts of the cards, for use in playing a card game of baseball. Red Backs are more common than the Blue Backs by virtue of a recent discovery of a large hoard of unopened boxes.

		NR MT	EX	VG
	Complete Set:	750.00	375.00	230.00
	Common Player:	9.00	4.50	2.75
1	Larry (Yogi) Berra	75.00	38.00	23.50
2	Sid Gordon	5.00	2.50	1.50
3	Ferris Fain	9.00	4.50	2.75
4	Verne Stephens (Vern)	9.00	4.50	2.75
5	Phil Rizzuto	25.00	12.50	7.50
6	Allie Reynolds	10.00	5.00	3.00
7	Howie Pollet	5.00	2.50	1.50
8	Early Wynn	25.00	12.50	7.50
9	Roy Sievers	9.00	4.50	2.75
10	Mel Parnell	9.00	4.50	2.75
11	Gene Hermanski	5.00	2.50	1.50
12	Jim Hegan	5.00	2.50	1.50
13	Dale Mitchell	5.00	2.50	1.50
14	Wayne Terwilliger	5.00	2.50	1.50
15	Ralph Kiner	25.00	12.50	7.50
16	Preacher Roe	8.00	4.00	2.50
17	Dave Bell	8.00	4.00	2.50
18	Gerry Coleman	8.00	4.00	2.50
19	Dick Kokos	5.00	2.50	1.50
20	Dominick DiMaggio (Dominic)	10.00	5.00	3.00
21	Larry Jansen	5.00	2.50	1.50
22	Bob Feller	25.00	12.50	7.50
23	Ray Boone	9.00	4.50	2.75
24	Hank Bauer	10.00	5.00	3.00
25	Cliff Chambers	5.00	2.50	1.50
26	Luke Easter	9.00	4.50	2.75
27	Wally Westlake	5.00	2.50	1.50
28	Elmer Valo	5.00	2.50	1.50
29	Bob Kennedy	5.00	2.50	1.50
30	Warren Spahn	25.00	12.50	7.50
31	Gil Hodges	25.00	12.50	7.50
32	Henry Thompson	5.00	2.50	1.50
33	William Werle	5.00	2.50	1.50
34	Grady Hatton	5.00	2.50	1.50
35	Al Rosen	10.00	5.00	3.00
36a	Gus Zernial (Chicago in bio)	20.00	10.00	6.00
36b	Gus Zernial (Philadelphia in bio)	12.00	6.00	3.50
37	Wes Westrum	9.00	4.50	2.75
38	Ed (Duke) Snider	60.00	30.00	17.50
39	Ted Kluszewski	10.00	5.00	3.00
40	Mike Garcia	9.00	4.50	2.75
41	Whitey Lockman	5.00	2.50	1.50
42	Ray Scarborough	5.00	2.50	1.50
43	Maurice McDermott	5.00	2.50	1.50
44	Sid Hudson	5.00	2.50	1.50
45	Andy Seminick	5.00	2.50	1.50
46	Billy Goodman	5.00	2.50	1.50
47	Tommy Glaviano	5.00	2.50	1.50
48	Eddie Stanky	9.00	4.50	2.75
49	Al Zarilla	5.00	2.50	1.50
50	Monte Irvin	25.00	12.50	7.50
51	Eddie Robinson	5.00	2.50	1.50
52a	Tommy Holmes (Boston in bio)	20.00	10.00	6.00
52b	Tommy Holmes (Hartford in bio)	20.00	10.00	6.00

1951 Topps
Connie Mack's All-Stars

A set of die-cut, 2-1/16" by 5-1/4" cards, all eleven players are Hall of Famers. The cards feature a black and white photograph of the player printed on a red background' with a red, white, blue, yellow and black plaque underneath. Like the "Current All-Stars," with which they were issued, the background could be removed making it possible for the card to stand up. This practice, however, resulted in the card's mutilation and lowers its condition in the eyes of today's collectors. Connie Mack All-Stars are scarce today and, despite being relatively expensive, retain a certain popularity as one of Topps first issues.

		NR MT	EX	VG
Complete Set:		9500.00	4500.00	1950.
Common Player:		350.00	150.00	60.00
(1)	Grover Cleveland Alexander	550.00	275.00	100.00
(2)	Gordon Stanley Cochrane	400.00	175.00	75.00
(3)	Edward Trowbridge Collins	350.00	150.00	60.00
(4)	James J. Collins	350.00	150.00	60.00
(5)	Henry Louis Gehrig	2000.00	1000.00	350.00
(6)	Walter Johnson	750.00	325.00	150.00
(7)	Connie Mack	400.00	175.00	75.00
(8)	Christopher Mathewson	750.00	325.00	135.00
(9)	George Herman Ruth	2250.00	1150.00	450.00
(10)	Tristram Speaker	575.00	275.00	100.00
(11)	John Peter Wagner	500.00	225.00	100.00

1951 Topps Current All-Stars

The Topps Current All-Stars are very similar to the Connie Mack All-Stars of the same year. The 2-1/16 by 5-1/4" cards have a black and white photograph on a red die-cut background. Most of the background could be folded over or removed so that the card would stand up. A plaque at the base carries brief biographical information. The set was to contain 11 cards, but only eight were actually issued in gum packs. Those of Jim Konstanty, Robin Roberts and

Eddie Stanky were not released and are very rare. A big problem with the set is that if the card was used as it was intended it was folded and, thus, damaged from a collector's viewpoint. That makes top quality examples of any players difficult to find and quite expensive.

		NR MT	EX	VG
Complete Set:		40000.00	20000.00	8500.
Common Player:		500.00	250.00	100.00
(1)	Lawrence (Yogi) Berra	1500.00	750.00	450.00
(2)	Lawrence Eugene Doby	750.00	375.00	150.00
(3)	Walter Dropo	750.00	375.00	150.00
(4)	Walter (Hoot) Evers	500.00	250.00	100.00
(5)	George Clyde Kell	1000.00	500.00	200.00
(6)	Ralph McPherran Kiner	1075.00	525.00	200.00
(7)	James Casimir Konstanty	8500.00	4250.00	2000.
(8)	Robert G. Lemon	1075.00	525.00	200.00
(9)	Phillip Rizzuto	1200.00	600.00	225.00
(10)	Robin Evan Roberts	9500.00	4750.00	2250.
(11)	Edward Raymond Stanky	8500.00	4250.00	2000.

1951 Topps Teams

An innovative issue for 1951, the Topps team cards were a nine-card set, 5-1/4" by 2-1/16," which carried a black and white picture of a major league team surrounded by a yellow border on the front. The back identifies team members with red printing on white cardboard. There are two versions of each card, with and without the date "1950" in the banner that carries the team name. Undated versions are valued slightly higher than the cards with dates. Strangely only nine teams were issued. Scarcity varies, with the Cardinals and Red Sox being the most difficult to obtain. The complete set price does not include the scarcer variations.

		NR MT	EX	VG
Complete Set:		4500.00	2200.00	975.00
Common Team:		150.00	70.00	30.00
(1a)	Boston Red Sox (1950)	250.00	100.00	50.00
(1b)	Boston Red Sox (without 1950)	300.00	125.00	60.00
(2a)	Brooklyn Dodgers (1950)	300.00	125.00	60.00
(2b)	Brooklyn Dodgers (without 1950)	350.00	150.00	70.00
(3a)	Chicago White Sox (1950)	150.00	75.00	45.00
(3b)	Chicago White Sox (without 1950)	200.00	85.00	40.00
(4a)	Cincinnati Reds (1950)	150.00	70.00	30.00
(4b)	Cincinnati Reds (without 1950)	200.00	85.00	40.00
(5a)	New York Giants (1950)	250.00	100.00	50.00
(5b)	New York Giants (without 1950)	300.00	125.00	60.00
(6a)	Philadelphia Athletics (1950)	150.00	70.00	30.00
(6b)	Philadelphia Athletics (without 1950)	200.00	85.00	40.00
(7a)	Philadelphia Phillies (1950)	150.00	70.00	30.00
(7b)	Philadelphia Phillies (without 1950)	200.00	85.00	40.00
(8a)	St. Louis Cardinals (1950)	150.00	70.00	30.00
(8b)	St. Louis Cardinals (without 1950)	200.00	85.00	40.00
(9a)	Washington Senators (1950)	150.00	70.00	30.00

	NR MT	EX	VG
(9b) Washington Senators (without 1950)	200.00	85.00	40.00

1952 Topps

At 407 cards, the 1952 Topps set was the largest set of its day, both in number of cards and physical dimensions of the cards. Cards are 2-5/8" by 3-3/4" with a hand-colored black and white photo on front. Major baseball card innovations presented in the set include the first-ever use of color team logos as part of the design, and the inclusion of stats for the previous season and overall career on the backs. A major variety in the set is that first 80 cards can be found with backs printed entirely in black or black and red. Backs entirely in black command a $10-15 premium. Card numbers 311-407 were printed in limited supplies and are extremely rare.

	NR MT	EX	VG
Complete Set:	70000.00	35000.00	20000.
Common Player: 1-80	50.00	25.00	15.00
Common Player: 81-250	25.00	12.50	7.50
Common Player: 251-280	40.00	20.00	12.00
Common Player: 281-300	50.00	25.00	15.00
Common Player: 301-310	40.00	20.00	12.00
Common Player: 311-407	175.00	87.00	52.00

#	Player	NR MT	EX	VG
1	Andy Pafko	1200.00	150.00	25.00
2	*James E. Runnels*	80.00	20.00	6.00
3	Hank Thompson	55.00	15.00	5.50
4	Don Lenhardt	55.00	15.00	5.50
5	Larry Jansen	55.00	15.00	5.50
6	Grady Hatton	55.00	15.00	5.50
7	Wayne Terwilliger	60.00	16.00	6.00
8	Fred Marsh	55.00	15.00	5.50
9	Bobby Hogue	65.00	18.00	6.50
10	Al Rosen	80.00	24.00	8.00
11	Phil Rizzuto	175.00	87.00	52.00
12	Monty Basgall	55.00	15.00	5.50
13	Johnny Wyrostek	55.00	15.00	5.50
14	Bob Elliott	55.00	15.00	5.50
15	Johnny Pesky	60.00	16.00	6.00
16	Gene Hermanski	55.00	15.00	5.50
17	Jim Hegan	55.00	15.00	5.50
18	Merrill Combs	55.00	15.00	5.50
19	Johnny Bucha	55.00	15.00	5.50
20	*Billy Loes*	110.00	55.00	32.00
21	Ferris Fain	60.00	16.00	6.00
22	Dom DiMaggio	90.00	45.00	27.00
23	Billy Goodman	55.00	15.00	5.50
24	Luke Easter	60.00	16.00	6.00
25	Johnny Groth	55.00	15.00	5.50
26	Monty Irvin	90.00	45.00	27.00
27	Sam Jethroe	55.00	15.00	5.50
28	Jerry Priddy	55.00	15.00	5.50
29	Ted Kluszewski	90.00	45.00	27.00
30	Mel Parnell	60.00	16.00	6.00
31	Gus Zernial	60.00	16.00	6.00
32	Eddie Robinson	55.00	15.00	5.50
33	Warren Spahn	225.00	112.00	67.00
34	Elmer Valo	55.00	15.00	5.50
35	Hank Sauer	60.00	16.00	6.00
36	Gil Hodges	150.00	75.00	45.00
37	Duke Snider	300.00	150.00	90.00
38	Wally Westlake	55.00	15.00	5.50
39	"Dizzy" Trout	60.00	16.00	6.00
40	Irv Noren	55.00	15.00	5.50
41	Bob Wellman	55.00	15.00	5.50
42	Lou Kretlow	55.00	15.00	5.50
43	Ray Scarborough	55.00	15.00	5.50
44	Con Dempsey	55.00	15.00	5.50
45	Eddie Joost	55.00	15.00	5.50
46	Gordon Goldsberry	55.00	15.00	5.50
47	Willie Jones	55.00	15.00	5.50
48a	Joe Page (Johnny Sain bio)	225.00	68.00	23.00
48b	Joe Page (correct bio)	80.00	24.00	8.00
49a	Johnny Sain (Joe Page bio)	225.00	68.00	23.00
49b	Johnny Sain (correct bio)	80.00	24.00	8.00
50	Marv Rickert	55.00	15.00	5.50
51	Jim Russell	60.00	16.00	6.00
52	Don Mueller	55.00	15.00	5.50
53	Chris Van Cuyk	60.00	16.00	6.00
54	Leo Kiely	55.00	15.00	5.50
55	Ray Boone	60.00	16.00	6.00
56	Tommy Glaviano	55.00	15.00	5.50
57	Ed Lopat	80.00	40.00	25.00
58	Bob Mahoney	55.00	15.00	5.50
59	Robin Roberts	125.00	62.00	37.00
60	Sid Hudson	55.00	15.00	5.50
61	"Tookie" Gilbert	55.00	15.00	5.50
62	Chuck Stobbs	55.00	15.00	5.50
63	Howie Pollet	55.00	15.00	5.50
64	Roy Sievers	65.00	18.00	6.50
65	Enos Slaughter	100.00	50.00	30.00
66	"Preacher" Roe	100.00	50.00	30.00
67	Allie Reynolds	90.00	45.00	27.00
68	Cliff Chambers	55.00	15.00	5.50
69	Virgil Stallcup	55.00	15.00	5.50
70	Al Zarilla	55.00	15.00	5.50
71	Tom Upton	55.00	15.00	5.50
72	Karl Olson	55.00	15.00	5.50
73	William Werle	55.00	15.00	5.50
74	Andy Hansen	55.00	15.00	5.50
75	Wes Westrum	60.00	16.00	6.00
76	Eddie Stanky	65.00	18.00	6.50
77	Bob Kennedy	55.00	15.00	5.50
78	Ellis Kinder	55.00	15.00	5.50
79	Gerald Staley	55.00	15.00	5.50
80	Herman Wehmeier	55.00	15.00	5.50
81	Vernon Law	25.00	11.00	6.25
82	Duane Pillette	25.00	12.50	7.50
83	Billy Johnson	25.00	12.50	7.50
84	Vern Stephens	25.00	12.50	7.50
85	Bob Kuzava	50.00	25.00	15.00
86	Ted Gray	25.00	12.50	7.50
87	Dale Coogan	25.00	12.50	7.50
88	Bob Feller	175.00	87.00	52.00
89	Johnny Lipon	25.00	12.50	7.50
90	Mickey Grasso	25.00	12.50	7.50
91	Al Schoendienst	80.00	20.00	6.00
92	Dale Mitchell	25.00	12.50	7.50
93	Al Sima	25.00	12.50	7.50
94	Sam Mele	25.00	12.50	7.50
95	Ken Holcombe	25.00	12.50	7.50
96	Willard Marshall	25.00	12.50	7.50
97	Earl Torgeson	25.00	12.50	7.50
98	Bill Pierce	25.00	11.00	6.25
99	Gene Woodling	50.00	25.00	15.00
100	Del Rice	25.00	12.50	7.50
101	Max Lanier	25.00	12.50	7.50
102	Bill Kennedy	25.00	12.50	7.50
103	Cliff Mapes	25.00	12.50	7.50
104	Don Kolloway	25.00	12.50	7.50
105	John Pramesa	25.00	12.50	7.50
106	Mickey Vernon	25.00	11.00	6.25
107	Connie Ryan	25.00	12.50	7.50
108	Jim Konstanty	25.00	11.00	6.25
109	Ted Wilks	25.00	12.50	7.50
110	Dutch Leonard	25.00	12.50	7.50
111	Harry Lowrey	25.00	12.50	7.50
112	Henry Majeski	25.00	12.50	7.50
113	Dick Sisler	25.00	12.50	7.50
114	Willard Ramsdell	25.00	12.50	7.50
115	George Munger	25.00	12.50	7.50
116	Carl Scheib	25.00	12.50	7.50
117	Sherman Lollar	25.00	11.00	6.25
118	Ken Raffensberger	25.00	12.50	7.50
119	Maurice McDermott	25.00	12.50	7.50
120	Bob Chakales	25.00	12.50	7.50
121	Gus Niarhos	25.00	12.50	7.50
122	Jack Jensen	70.00	35.00	21.00
123	Eddie Yost	25.00	11.00	6.25
124	Monte Kennedy	25.00	12.50	7.50
125	Bill Rigney	25.00	11.00	6.25
126	Fred Hutchinson	25.00	11.00	6.25
127	Paul Minner	25.00	12.50	7.50
128	Don Bollweg	50.00	25.00	15.00

		NR MT	EX	VG				NR MT	EX	VG
129	Johnny Mize	70.00	35.00	21.00		220	Joe Presko	25.00	12.50	7.50
130	Sheldon Jones	25.00	12.50	7.50		221	Granny Hamner	25.00	12.50	7.50
131	Morrie Martin	25.00	12.50	7.50		222	"Hoot" Evers	25.00	12.50	7.50
132	Clyde Kluttz	25.00	12.50	7.50		223	Del Ennis	25.00	11.00	6.25
133	Al Widmar	25.00	12.50	7.50		224	Bruce Edwards	25.00	12.50	7.50
134	Joe Tipton	25.00	12.50	7.50		225	Frank Baumholtz	25.00	12.50	7.50
135	Dixie Howell	25.00	12.50	7.50		226	Dave Philley	25.00	11.00	6.25
136	Johnny Schmitz	25.00	11.00	6.25		227	Joe Garagiola	100.00	50.00	30.00
137	*Roy McMillan*	25.00	11.00	6.25		228	Al Brazle	25.00	12.50	7.50
138	Bill MacDonald	25.00	12.50	7.50		229	Gene Bearden	25.00	12.50	7.50
139	Ken Wood	25.00	12.50	7.50		230	Matt Batts	25.00	12.50	7.50
140	John Antonelli	25.00	11.00	6.25		231	Sam Zoldak	25.00	12.50	7.50
141	Clint Hartung	25.00	12.50	7.50		232	Billy Cox	50.00	25.00	15.00
142	Harry Perkowski	25.00	12.50	7.50		233	*Bob Friend*	25.00	11.00	6.25
143	Les Moss	25.00	12.50	7.50		234	Steve Souchock	25.00	12.50	7.50
144	Ed Blake	25.00	12.50	7.50		235	Walt Dropo	25.00	11.00	6.25
145	Joe Haynes	25.00	12.50	7.50		236	Ed Fitz Gerald	25.00	12.50	7.50
146	Frank House	25.00	12.50	7.50		237	Jerry Coleman	50.00	25.00	15.00
147	Bob Young	25.00	12.50	7.50		238	Art Houtteman	25.00	12.50	7.50
148	Johnny Klippstein	25.00	12.50	7.50		239	Rocky Bridges	25.00	11.00	6.25
149	Dick Kryhoski	25.00	12.50	7.50		240	Jack Phillips	25.00	12.50	7.50
150	Ted Beard	25.00	12.50	7.50		241	Tommy Byrne	25.00	12.50	7.50
151	Wally Post	25.00	12.50	7.50		242	Tom Poholsky	25.00	12.50	7.50
152	Al Evans	25.00	12.50	7.50		243	Larry Doby	40.00	18.00	11.00
153	Bob Rush	25.00	12.50	7.50		244	Vic Wertz	25.00	11.00	6.25
154	Joe Muir	25.00	12.50	7.50		245	Sherry Robertson	25.00	12.50	7.50
155	Frank Overmire	50.00	25.00	15.00		246	George Kell	60.00	30.00	18.00
156	Frank Hiller	25.00	12.50	7.50		247	Randy Gumpert	25.00	12.50	7.50
157	Bob Usher	25.00	12.50	7.50		248	Frank Shea	25.00	12.50	7.50
158	Eddie Waitkus	25.00	12.50	7.50		249	Bobby Adams	25.00	12.50	7.50
159	Saul Rogovin	25.00	12.50	7.50		250	Carl Erskine	60.00	30.00	18.00
160	Owen Friend	25.00	12.50	7.50		251	Chico Carrasquel	40.00	20.00	12.00
161	Bud Byerly	25.00	12.50	7.50		252	Vern Bickford	40.00	20.00	12.00
162	Del Crandall	25.00	11.00	6.25		253	Johnny Berardino	50.00	25.00	15.00
163	Stan Rojek	25.00	12.50	7.50		254	Joe Dobson	40.00	20.00	12.00
164	Walt Dubiel	25.00	12.50	7.50		255	Clyde Vollmer	40.00	20.00	12.00
165	Eddie Kazak	25.00	12.50	7.50		256	Pete Suder	40.00	20.00	12.00
166	Paul LaPalme	25.00	12.50	7.50		257	Bobby Avila	40.00	20.00	12.00
167	Bill Howerton	25.00	12.50	7.50		258	Steve Gromek	40.00	20.00	12.00
168	Charlie Silvera	50.00	25.00	15.00		259	Bob Addis	40.00	20.00	12.00
169	Howie Judson	25.00	12.50	7.50		260	Pete Castiglione	40.00	20.00	12.00
170	Gus Bell	25.00	11.00	6.25		261	Willie Mays	2500.00	1250.00	750.00
171	Ed Erautt	25.00	12.50	7.50		262	Virgil Trucks	50.00	25.00	15.00
172	Eddie Miksis	25.00	12.50	7.50		263	Harry Brecheen	50.00	25.00	15.00
173	Roy Smalley	25.00	12.50	7.50		264	Roy Hartsfield	40.00	20.00	12.00
174	Clarence Marshall	25.00	12.50	7.50		265	Chuck Diering	40.00	20.00	12.00
175	*Billy Martin*	350.00	175.00	105.00		266	Murry Dickson	40.00	20.00	12.00
176	Hank Edwards	25.00	12.50	7.50		267	Sid Gordon	40.00	20.00	12.00
177	Bill Wight	25.00	12.50	7.50		268	Bob Lemon	200.00	100.00	60.00
178	Cass Michaels	25.00	12.50	7.50		269	Willard Nixon	40.00	20.00	12.00
179	Frank Smith	25.00	12.50	7.50		270	Lou Brissie	40.00	20.00	12.00
180	*Charley Maxwell*	25.00	11.00	6.25		271	Jim Delsing	40.00	20.00	12.00
181	Bob Swift	25.00	12.50	7.50		272	Mike Garcia	50.00	25.00	15.00
182	Billy Hitchcock	25.00	12.50	7.50		273	Erv Palica	50.00	25.00	15.00
183	Erv Dusak	25.00	12.50	7.50		274	Ralph Branca	70.00	35.00	21.00
184	Bob Ramazzotti	25.00	12.50	7.50		275	Pat Mullin	40.00	20.00	12.00
185	Bill Nicholson	25.00	12.50	7.50		276	Jim Wilson	40.00	20.00	12.00
186	Walt Masterson	25.00	12.50	7.50		277	Early Wynn	175.00	87.00	52.00
187	Bob Miller	25.00	12.50	7.50		278	Al Clark	40.00	20.00	12.00
188	Clarence Podbielan	25.00	11.00	6.25		279	Ed Stewart	40.00	20.00	12.00
189	Pete Reiser	25.00	11.00	6.25		280	Cloyd Boyer	40.00	20.00	12.00
190	Don Johnson	25.00	12.50	7.50		281	Tommy Brown	50.00	25.00	15.00
191	Yogi Berra	350.00	175.00	100.00		282	Birdie Tebbetts	50.00	25.00	15.00
192	Myron Ginsberg	25.00	12.50	7.50		283	Phil Masi	50.00	25.00	15.00
193	Harry Simpson	25.00	12.50	7.50		284	Hank Arft	50.00	25.00	15.00
194	Joe Hatten	25.00	12.50	7.50		285	Cliff Fannin	50.00	25.00	15.00
195	*Orestes Minoso*	125.00	62.00	37.00		286	Joe DeMaestri	50.00	25.00	15.00
196	Solly Hemus	25.00	12.50	7.50		287	Steve Bilko	50.00	25.00	15.00
197	George Strickland	25.00	12.50	7.50		288	Chet Nichols	50.00	25.00	15.00
198	Phil Haugstad	25.00	11.00	6.25		289	Tommy Holmes	55.00	25.00	8.25
199	George Zuverink	25.00	12.50	7.50		290	Joe Astroth	50.00	25.00	15.00
200	Ralph Houk	60.00	30.00	18.00		291	Gil Coan	50.00	25.00	15.00
201	Alex Kellner	25.00	12.50	7.50		292	Floyd Baker	50.00	25.00	15.00
202	Joe Collins	50.00	25.00	15.00		293	Sibby Sisti	50.00	25.00	15.00
203	Curt Simmons	25.00	11.00	6.25		294	Walker Cooper	50.00	25.00	15.00
204	Ron Northey	25.00	12.50	7.50		295	Phil Cavarretta	55.00	22.00	8.25
205	Clyde King	25.00	11.00	6.25		296	"Red" Rolfe	50.00	25.00	15.00
206	Joe Ostrowski	50.00	25.00	15.00		297	Andy Seminick	50.00	25.00	15.00
207	Mickey Harris	25.00	12.50	7.50		298	Bob Ross	50.00	25.00	15.00
208	Marlin Stuart	25.00	12.50	7.50		299	Ray Murray	50.00	25.00	15.00
209	Howie Fox	25.00	12.50	7.50		300	Barney McCosky	50.00	25.00	15.00
210	Dick Fowler	25.00	12.50	7.50		301	Bob Porterfield	40.00	20.00	12.00
211	Ray Coleman	25.00	12.50	7.50		302	Max Surkont	40.00	20.00	12.00
212	Ned Garver	25.00	12.50	7.50		303	Harry Dorish	40.00	20.00	12.00
213	Nippy Jones	25.00	12.50	7.50		304	Sam Dente	40.00	20.00	12.00
214	Johnny Hopp	50.00	25.00	15.00		305	Paul Richards	50.00	25.00	15.00
215	Hank Bauer	40.00	18.00	11.00		306	Lou Sleator	40.00	20.00	12.00
216	Richie Ashburn	80.00	40.00	25.00		307	Frank Campos	40.00	20.00	12.00
217	George Stirnweiss	25.00	12.50	7.50		308	Luis Aloma	40.00	20.00	12.00
218	Clyde McCullough	25.00	12.50	7.50		309	Jim Busby	40.00	20.00	12.00
219	Bobby Shantz	25.00	11.00	6.25		310	George Metkovich	40.00	20.00	12.00

		NR MT	EX	VG
311	Mickey Mantle	30000.00	15000.00	8000.
312	Jackie Robinson	1000.00	500.00	300.00
313	Bobby Thomson	175.00	87.00	52.00
314	Roy Campanella	1500.00	750.00	450.00
315	Leo Durocher	250.00	100.00	63.00
316	Davey Williams	175.00	87.00	52.00
317	Connie Marrero	175.00	87.00	52.00
318	Hal Gregg	175.00	87.00	52.00
319	Al Walker	175.00	87.00	52.00
320	John Rutherford	175.00	87.00	52.00
321	*Joe Black*	225.00	90.00	56.00
322	Randy Jackson	175.00	87.00	52.00
323	Bubba Church	175.00	87.00	52.00
324	Warren Hacker	175.00	87.00	52.00
325	Bill Serena	175.00	87.00	52.00
326	George Shuba	175.00	87.00	52.00
327	Archie Wilson	175.00	87.00	52.00
328	Bob Borkowski	175.00	87.00	52.00
329	Ivan Delock	175.00	87.00	52.00
330	Turk Lown	175.00	87.00	52.00
331	Tom Morgan	160.00	80.00	48.00
332	Tony Bartirome	175.00	87.00	52.00
333	Pee Wee Reese	1000.00	500.00	300.00
334	Wilmer Mizell	175.00	87.00	52.00
335	Ted Lepcio	175.00	87.00	52.00
336	Dave Koslo	175.00	87.00	52.00
337	Jim Hearn	175.00	87.00	52.00
338	Sal Yvars	175.00	87.00	52.00
339	Russ Meyer	175.00	87.00	52.00
340	Bob Hooper	175.00	87.00	52.00
341	Hal Jeffcoat	175.00	87.00	52.00
342	*Clem Labine*	200.00	90.00	52.00
343	Dick Gernert	175.00	87.00	52.00
344	Ewell Blackwell	160.00	80.00	48.00
345	Sam White	175.00	87.00	52.00
346	George Spencer	175.00	87.00	52.00
347	Joe Adcock	200.00	100.00	60.00
348	Bob Kelly	175.00	87.00	52.00
349	Bob Cain	175.00	87.00	52.00
350	Cal Abrams	175.00	87.00	52.00
351	Al Dark	175.00	87.00	52.00
352	Karl Drews	175.00	87.00	52.00
353	Bob Del Greco	175.00	87.00	52.00
354	Fred Hatfield	175.00	87.00	52.00
355	Bobby Morgan	175.00	87.00	52.00
356	Toby Atwell	175.00	87.00	52.00
357	Smoky Burgess	250.00	125.00	75.00
358	John Kucab	175.00	87.00	52.00
359	Dee Fondy	175.00	87.00	52.00
360	George Crowe	175.00	87.00	52.00
361	Bill Posedel	175.00	87.00	52.00
362	Ken Heintzelman	175.00	87.00	52.00
363	Dick Rozek	175.00	87.00	52.00
364	Clyde Sukeforth	175.00	87.00	52.00
365	"Cookie" Lavagetto	175.00	87.00	52.00
366	Dave Madison	175.00	87.00	52.00
367	Bob Thorpe	175.00	87.00	52.00
368	Ed Wright	175.00	87.00	52.00
369	*Dick Groat*	300.00	150.00	90.00
370	Billy Hoeft	175.00	87.00	52.00
371	Bob Hofman	175.00	87.00	52.00
372	*Gil McDougald*	300.00	150.00	90.00
373	Jim Turner	160.00	80.00	48.00
374	Al Benton	175.00	87.00	52.00
375	Jack Merson	175.00	87.00	52.00
376	Faye Throneberry	175.00	87.00	52.00
377	Chuck Dressen	175.00	90.00	52.00
378	Les Fusselman	175.00	87.00	52.00
379	Joe Rossi	175.00	87.00	52.00
380	Clem Koshorek	175.00	87.00	52.00
381	Milton Stock	175.00	87.00	52.00
382	Sam Jones	175.00	87.00	52.00
383	Del Wilber	175.00	87.00	52.00
384	Frank Crosetti	250.00	125.00	67.00
385	Herman Franks	175.00	87.00	52.00
386	Eddie Yuhas	175.00	87.00	52.00
387	Billy Meyer	175.00	87.00	52.00
388	Bob Chipman	175.00	87.00	52.00
389	Ben Wade	175.00	87.00	52.00
390	Glenn Nelson	175.00	87.00	52.00
391	Ben Chapman (photo actually Sam Chapman)	175.00	87.00	52.00
392	*Hoyt Wilhelm*	600.00	300.00	175.00
393	Ebba St. Claire	175.00	87.00	52.00
394	Billy Herman	250.00	125.00	75.00
395	Jake Pitler	175.00	87.00	52.00
396	*Dick Williams*	250.00	125.00	75.00
397	Forrest Main	175.00	87.00	52.00
398	Hal Rice	175.00	87.00	52.00
399	Jim Fridley	175.00	87.00	52.00
400	Bill Dickey	600.00	300.00	175.00

		NR MT	EX	VG
401	Bob Schultz	175.00	87.00	52.00
402	Earl Harrist	175.00	87.00	52.00
403	Bill Miller	160.00	80.00	48.00
404	Dick Brodowski	175.00	87.00	52.00
405	Eddie Pellagrini	175.00	87.00	52.00
406	*Joe Nuxhall*	200.00	100.00	60.00
407	*Ed Mathews*	3000.00	1500.00	900.00

1953 Topps

The 1953 Topps set reflects the company's continuing legal battles with Bowman. The set, originally intended to consist of 280 cards, is lacking six numbers (#'s 253, 261, 267, 268, 271 and 275) which probably represent players whose contracts were lost to the competition. The 2-5/8" by 3-3/4" cards feature painted player pictures. A color team logo appears at a bottom panel (red for American Leauge and black for National.) Card backs contain the first baseball trivia questions along with brief statistics and player biographies. In the red panel at the top which lists the player's personal data, cards from the 2nd Series (#'s 86-165 plus 10, 44, 61, 72 and 81) can be found with that data printed in either black or white, black being the scarcer variety. Card numbers 221-280 are the scarce high numbers.

		NR MT	EX	VG
Complete Set:		14000.00	7000.00	4000.
Common Player Singleprint: 1-165		25.00	12.50	7.50
Common Player: 1-165		16.00	8.00	4.75
Common Player: 166-220		16.00	8.00	4.75
Common Player Singleprint: 221-280		90.00	45.00	27.00
Common Player: 221-280		50.00	25.00	15.00
1	Jackie Robinson	650.00	275.00	175.00
2	Luke Easter	25.00	12.50	7.50
3	George Crowe	25.00	12.50	7.50
4	Ben Wade	25.00	12.50	7.50
5	Joe Dobson	25.00	12.50	7.50
6	Sam Jones	25.00	12.50	7.50
7	Bob Borkowski	16.00	8.00	4.75
8	Clem Koshorek	16.00	8.00	4.75
9	Joe Collins	30.00	15.00	9.00
10	Smoky Burgess	40.00	20.00	12.00
11	Sal Yvars	25.00	12.50	7.50
12	Howie Judson	16.00	8.00	4.75
13	Connie Marrero	16.00	8.00	4.75
14	Clem Labine	25.00	12.50	7.50
15	Bobo Newsom	25.00	12.50	7.50
16	Harry Lowrey	16.00	8.00	4.75
17	Billy Hitchcock	25.00	12.50	7.50
18	Ted Lepcio	16.00	8.00	4.75
19	Mel Parnell	25.00	12.50	7.50
20	Hank Thompson	25.00	12.50	7.50
21	Billy Johnson	25.00	12.50	7.50
22	Howie Fox	25.00	12.50	7.50
23	Toby Atwell	16.00	8.00	4.75
24	Ferris Fain	25.00	12.50	7.50
25	Ray Boone	25.00	12.50	7.50
26	Dale Mitchell	16.00	8.00	4.75
27	Roy Campanella	225.00	112.00	67.00
28	Eddie Pellagrini	25.00	12.50	7.50
29	Hal Jeffcoat	25.00	12.50	7.50
30	Willard Nixon	25.00	12.50	7.50
31	Ewell Blackwell	40.00	20.00	12.00
32	Clyde Vollmer	25.00	12.50	7.50

		NR MT	EX	VG			NR MT	EX	VG
33	Bob Kennedy	16.00	8.00	4.75	126	Bill Connelly	16.00	8.00	4.75
34	George Shuba	25.00	12.50	7.50	127	Clint Courtney	16.00	8.00	4.75
35	Irv Noren	25.00	12.50	7.50	128	Wilmer Mizell	16.00	8.00	4.75
36	Johnny Groth	16.00	8.00	4.75	129	Keith Thomas	16.00	8.00	4.75
37	Ed Mathews	115.00	57.50	34.50	130	Turk Lown	16.00	8.00	4.75
38	Jim Hearn	16.00	8.00	4.75	131	Harry Byrd	16.00	8.00	4.75
39	Eddie Miksis	25.00	12.50	7.50	132	Tom Morgan	25.00	12.50	7.50
40	John Lipon	25.00	12.50	7.50	133	Gil Coan	16.00	8.00	4.75
41	Enos Slaughter	90.00	45.00	27.00	134	Rube Walker	25.00	12.50	7.50
42	Gus Zernial	16.00	8.00	4.75	135	Al Rosen	35.00	17.50	10.50
43	Gil McDougald	50.00	25.00	15.00	136	Ken Heintzelman	16.00	8.00	4.75
44	Ellis Kinder	30.00	15.00	9.00	137	John Rutherford	25.00	12.50	7.50
45	Grady Hatton	16.00	8.00	4.75	138	George Kell	65.00	32.50	19.50
46	Johnny Klippstein	16.00	8.00	4.75	139	Sammy White	16.00	8.00	4.75
47	Bubba Church	16.00	8.00	4.75	140	Tommy Glaviano	16.00	8.00	4.75
48	Bob Del Greco	16.00	8.00	4.75	141	Allie Reynolds	35.00	17.50	10.50
49	Faye Throneberry	16.00	8.00	4.75	142	Vic Wertz	25.00	12.50	7.50
50	Chuck Dressen	25.00	12.50	7.50	143	Billy Pierce	25.00	12.50	7.50
51	Frank Campos	16.00	8.00	4.75	144	Bob Schultz	16.00	8.00	4.75
52	Ted Gray	16.00	8.00	4.75	145	Harry Dorish	16.00	8.00	4.75
53	Sherman Lollar	16.00	8.00	4.75	146	Granville Hamner	16.00	8.00	4.75
54	Bob Feller	125.00	67.00	37.00	147	Warren Spahn	150.00	75.00	45.00
55	Maurice McDermott	16.00	8.00	4.75	148	Mickey Grasso	16.00	8.00	4.75
56	Gerald Staley	16.00	8.00	4.75	149	Dom DiMaggio	30.00	15.00	9.00
57	Carl Scheib	25.00	12.50	7.50	150	Harry Simpson	16.00	8.00	4.75
58	George Metkovich	25.00	12.50	7.50	151	Hoyt Wilhelm	70.00	35.00	20.00
59	Karl Drews	16.00	8.00	4.75	152	Bob Adams	16.00	8.00	4.75
60	Cloyd Boyer	16.00	8.00	4.75	153	Andy Seminick	16.00	8.00	4.75
61	Early Wynn	80.00	40.00	25.00	154	Dick Groat	25.00	12.50	7.50
62	Monte Irvin	45.00	23.00	13.50	155	Dutch Leonard	16.00	8.00	4.75
63	Gus Niarhos	16.00	8.00	4.75	156	Jim Rivera	16.00	8.00	4.75
64	Dave Philley	25.00	12.50	7.50	157	Bob Addis	16.00	8.00	4.75
65	Earl Harrist	25.00	12.50	7.50	158	*John Logan*	25.00	12.50	7.50
66	Orestes Minoso	30.00	15.00	9.00	159	Wayne Terwilliger	16.00	8.00	4.75
67	Roy Sievers	25.00	12.50	7.50	160	Bob Young	16.00	8.00	4.75
68	Del Rice	25.00	12.50	7.50	161	Vern Bickford	16.00	8.00	4.75
69	Dick Brodowski	25.00	12.50	7.50	162	Ted Kluszewski	50.00	25.00	15.00
70	Ed Yuhas	25.00	12.50	7.50	163	Fred Hatfield	16.00	8.00	4.75
71	Tony Bartirome	25.00	12.50	7.50	164	Frank Shea	16.00	8.00	4.75
72	Fred Hutchinson	25.00	12.50	7.50	165	Billy Hoeft	16.00	8.00	4.75
73	Eddie Robinson	25.00	12.50	7.50	166	Bill Hunter	16.00	8.00	4.75
74	Joe Rossi	25.00	12.50	7.50	167	Art Schult	16.00	8.00	4.75
75	Mike Garcia	25.00	12.50	7.50	168	Willard Schmidt	16.00	8.00	4.75
76	Pee Wee Reese	175.00	87.00	52.00	169	Dizzy Trout	16.00	8.00	4.75
77	John Mize	60.00	30.00	18.00	170	Bill Werle	16.00	8.00	4.75
78	Al Schoendienst	65.00	33.00	20.00	171	Bill Glynn	16.00	8.00	4.75
79	Johnny Wyrostek	25.00	12.50	7.50	172	Rip Repulski	16.00	8.00	4.75
80	Jim Hegan	25.00	12.50	7.50	173	Preston Ward	16.00	8.00	4.75
82	Mickey Mantle	3000.00	1500.00	900.00	174	Billy Loes	16.00	8.00	4.75
83	Howie Pollet	25.00	12.50	7.50	175	Ron Kline	16.00	8.00	4.75
84	Bob Hooper	16.00	8.00	4.75	176	*Don Hoak*	16.00	8.00	4.75
85	Bobby Morgan	25.00	12.50	7.50	177	Jim Dyck	16.00	8.00	4.75
86	Billy Martin	125.00	67.00	37.00	178	Jim Waugh	16.00	8.00	4.75
87	Ed Lopat	35.00	17.50	10.50	179	Gene Hermanski	16.00	8.00	4.75
88	Willie Jones	16.00	8.00	4.75	180	Virgil Stallcup	16.00	8.00	4.75
89	Chuck Stobbs	16.00	8.00	4.75	181	Al Zarilla	16.00	8.00	4.75
90	Hank Edwards	16.00	8.00	4.75	182	Bob Hofman	16.00	8.00	4.75
91	Ebba St. Claire	16.00	8.00	4.75	183	*Stu Miller*	16.00	8.00	4.75
92	Paul Minner	16.00	8.00	4.75	184	*Hal Brown*	16.00	8.00	4.75
93	Hal Rice	16.00	8.00	4.75	185	Jim Pendleton	16.00	8.00	4.75
94	William Kennedy	16.00	8.00	4.75	186	Charlie Bishop	16.00	8.00	4.75
95	Willard Marshall	16.00	8.00	4.75	187	Jim Fridley	16.00	8.00	4.75
96	Virgil Trucks	25.00	12.50	7.50	188	*Andy Carey*	16.00	8.00	4.75
97	Don Kolloway	16.00	8.00	4.75	189	Ray Jablonski	16.00	8.00	4.75
98	Cal Abrams	16.00	8.00	4.75	190	Dixie Walker	16.00	8.00	4.75
99	Dave Madison	16.00	8.00	4.75	191	Ralph Kiner	70.00	35.00	21.00
100	Bill Miller	25.00	12.50	7.50	192	Wally Westlake	16.00	8.00	4.75
101	Ted Wilks	16.00	8.00	4.75	193	Mike Clark	16.00	8.00	4.75
102	Connie Ryan	16.00	8.00	4.75	194	Eddie Kazak	16.00	8.00	4.75
103	Joe Astroth	16.00	8.00	4.75	195	Ed McGhee	16.00	8.00	4.75
104	Yogi Berra	250.00	125.00	75.00	196	Bob Keegan	16.00	8.00	4.75
105	Joe Nuxhall	25.00	12.50	7.50	197	Del Crandall	16.00	8.00	4.75
106	Johnny Antonelli	25.00	12.50	7.50	198	Forrest Main	16.00	8.00	4.75
107	Danny O'Connell	16.00	8.00	4.75	199	Marion Fricano	16.00	8.00	4.75
108	Bob Porterfield	16.00	8.00	4.75	200	Gordon Goldsberry	16.00	8.00	4.75
109	Alvin Dark	30.00	15.00	9.00	201	Paul LaPalme	16.00	8.00	4.75
110	Herman Wehmeier	16.00	8.00	4.75	202	Carl Sawatski	16.00	8.00	4.75
111	Hank Sauer	16.00	8.00	4.75	203	Cliff Fannin	16.00	8.00	4.75
112	Ned Garver	16.00	8.00	4.75	204	Dick Bokelmann	16.00	8.00	4.75
113	Jerry Priddy	16.00	8.00	4.75	205	Vern Benson	16.00	8.00	4.75
114	Phil Rizzuto	125.00	62.00	37.00	206	*Ed Bailey*	16.00	8.00	4.75
115	George Spencer	16.00	8.00	4.75	207	Whitey Ford	150.00	75.00	45.00
116	Frank Smith	16.00	8.00	4.75	208	Jim Wilson	16.00	8.00	4.75
117	Sid Gordon	16.00	8.00	4.75	209	Jim Greengrass	16.00	8.00	4.75
118	Gus Bell	16.00	8.00	4.75	210	*Bob Cerv*	16.00	8.00	4.75
119	John Sain	40.00	20.00	12.00	211	J.W. Porter	16.00	8.00	4.75
120	Davey Williams	16.00	8.00	4.75	212	Jack Dittmer	16.00	8.00	4.75
121	Walt Dropo	16.00	8.00	4.75	213	Ray Scarborough	16.00	8.00	4.75
122	Elmer Valo	16.00	8.00	4.75	214	*Bill Bruton*	16.00	8.00	4.75
123	Tommy Byrne	16.00	8.00	4.75	215	*Gene Conley*	16.00	8.00	4.75
124	Sibby Sisti	16.00	8.00	4.75	216	Jim Hughes	16.00	8.00	4.75
125	Dick Williams	25.00	12.50	7.50					

		NR MT	EX	VG
217	Murray Wall	16.00	8.00	4.75
218	Les Fusselman	16.00	8.00	4.75
219	Pete Runnels (photo actually Don Johnson)	16.00	8.00	4.75
220	Satchell Paige	450.00	225.00	135.00
221	Bob Milliken	90.00	45.00	27.00
222	Vic Janowicz	50.00	25.00	15.00
223	John O'Brien	50.00	25.00	15.00
224	Lou Sleater	50.00	25.00	15.00
225	Bobby Shantz	100.00	50.00	30.00
226	Ed Erautt	90.00	45.00	27.00
227	Morris Martin	50.00	25.00	15.00
228	Hal Newhouser	125.00	67.00	37.00
229	Rocky Krsnich	90.00	45.00	27.00
230	Johnny Lindell	50.00	25.00	15.00
231	Solly Hemus	50.00	25.00	15.00
232	Dick Kokos	90.00	45.00	27.00
233	Al Aber	90.00	45.00	27.00
234	Ray Murray	50.00	25.00	15.00
235	John Hetki	50.00	25.00	15.00
236	Harry Perkowski	90.00	45.00	27.00
237	Clarence Podbielan	50.00	25.00	15.00
238	Cal Hogue	50.00	25.00	15.00
239	Jim Delsing	90.00	45.00	27.00
240	Freddie Marsh	50.00	25.00	15.00
241	Al Sima	50.00	25.00	15.00
242	Charlie Silvera	90.00	45.00	27.00
243	Carlos Bernier	50.00	25.00	15.00
244	Willie Mays	2500.00	1250.00	750.00
245	Bill Norman	90.00	45.00	27.00
246	*Roy Face*	80.00	40.00	25.00
247	Mike Sandlock	50.00	25.00	15.00
248	Gene Stephens	50.00	25.00	15.00
249	Ed O'Brien	50.00	25.00	15.00
250	Bob Wilson	90.00	45.00	27.00
251	Sid Hudson	90.00	45.00	27.00
252	Henry Foiles	90.00	45.00	27.00
253	Not Issued			
254	Preacher Roe	80.00	40.00	24.00
255	Dixie Howell	90.00	45.00	27.00
256	Les Peden	90.00	45.00	27.00
257	Bob Boyd	90.00	45.00	27.00
258	*Jim Gilliam*	300.00	150.00	90.00
259	Roy McMillan	90.00	45.00	27.00
260	Sam Calderone	90.00	45.00	27.00
261	Not Issued			
262	Bob Oldis	90.00	45.00	27.00
263	*John Podres*	250.00	125.00	70.00
264	Gene Woodling	70.00	35.00	20.00
265	Jackie Jensen	100.00	50.00	30.00
266	Bob Cain	90.00	45.00	27.00
267	Not Issued			
268	Not Issued			
269	Duane Pillette	90.00	45.00	27.00
270	Vern Stephens	90.00	45.00	27.00
271	Not Issued			
272	Bill Antonello	90.00	45.00	27.00
273	*Harvey Haddix*	125.00	62.00	37.00
274	John Riddle	90.00	45.00	27.00
275	Not Issued			
276	Ken Raffensberger	50.00	25.00	15.00
277	Don Lund	90.00	45.00	27.00
278	Willie Miranda	90.00	45.00	27.00
279	Joe Coleman	50.00	25.00	15.00
280	Milt Bolling	300.00	150.00	60.00

1954 Topps

color backgrounds frame both color head- and-shoulders and black and white action pictures of the player. The player's name, position, team and team logo appear at the top. Backs include an "Inside Baseball" cartoon regarding the player as well as statistics and biography. The 250-card, 2-5/8" by 3-3/4", set includes manager and coaches cards, and the first use of two players together on a modern card; the players were, appropriately, the O'Brien twins.

		NR MT	EX	VG
Complete Set:		8200.00	4100.00	2550.
Common Player: 1-50		13.00	6.50	4.00
Common Player: 51-75		30.00	15.00	9.00
Common Player: 76-250		13.00	6.50	4.00
1	Ted Williams	650.00	200.00	125.00
2	Gus Zernial	13.00	6.50	4.00
3	Monte Irvin	35.00	17.50	10.50
4	Hank Sauer	15.00	7.50	4.50
5	Ed Lopat	20.00	10.00	6.00
6	Pete Runnels	13.00	6.50	4.00
7	Ted Kluszewski	30.00	15.00	9.00
8	Bobby Young	13.00	6.50	4.00
9	Harvey Haddix	13.00	6.50	4.00
10	Jackie Robinson	300.00	150.00	90.00
11	Paul Smith	13.00	6.50	4.00
12	Del Crandall	13.00	6.50	4.00
13	Billy Martin	85.00	42.00	26.00
14	Preacher Roe	40.00	20.00	12.00
15	Al Rosen	20.00	10.00	6.00
16	Vic Janowicz	13.00	6.50	4.00
17	Phil Rizzuto	70.00	35.00	20.00
18	Walt Dropo	13.00	6.50	4.00
19	Johnny Lipon	13.00	6.50	4.00
20	Warren Spahn	110.00	55.00	33.00
21	Bobby Shantz	13.00	6.50	4.00
22	Jim Greengrass	13.00	6.50	4.00
23	Luke Easter	13.00	6.50	4.00
24	Granny Hamner	13.00	6.50	4.00
25	*Harvey Kuenn*	50.00	25.00	15.00
26	Ray Jablonski	13.00	6.50	4.00
27	Ferris Fain	13.00	6.50	4.00
28	Paul Minner	13.00	6.50	4.00
29	Jim Hegan	13.00	6.50	4.00
30	Ed Mathews	100.00	50.00	30.00
31	Johnny Klippstein	13.00	6.50	4.00
32	Duke Snider	150.00	75.00	45.00
33	Johnny Schmitz	13.00	6.50	4.00
34	Jim Rivera	13.00	6.50	4.00
35	Junior Gilliam	30.00	15.00	9.00
36	Hoyt Wilhelm	50.00	25.00	15.00
37	Whitey Ford	100.00	50.00	30.00
38	Eddie Stanky	13.00	6.50	4.00
39	Sherm Lollar	13.00	6.50	4.00
40	Mel Parnell	13.00	6.50	4.00
41	Willie Jones	13.00	6.50	4.00
42	Don Mueller	13.00	6.50	4.00
43	Dick Groat	13.00	6.50	4.00
44	Ned Garver	13.00	6.50	4.00
45	Richie Ashburn	40.00	20.00	12.00
46	Ken Raffensberger	13.00	6.50	4.00
47	Ellis Kinder	13.00	6.50	4.00
48	Billy Hunter	13.00	6.50	4.00
49	Ray Murray	13.00	6.50	4.00
50	Yogi Berra	260.00	130.00	78.00
51	Johnny Lindell	30.00	15.00	9.00
52	Vic Power	30.00	15.00	9.00
53	Jack Dittmer	30.00	15.00	9.00
54	Vern Stephens	30.00	15.00	9.00
55	Phil Cavarretta	30.00	15.00	9.00
56	Willie Miranda	30.00	15.00	9.00
57	Luis Aloma	30.00	15.00	9.00
58	Bob Wilson	30.00	15.00	9.00
59	Gene Conley	30.00	15.00	9.00
60	Frank Baumholtz	30.00	15.00	9.00
61	Bob Cain	30.00	15.00	9.00
62	Eddie Robinson	30.00	15.00	9.00
63	Johnny Pesky	30.00	15.00	9.00
64	Hank Thompson	30.00	15.00	9.00
65	Bob Swift	30.00	15.00	9.00
66	Ted Lepcio	30.00	15.00	9.00
67	Jim Willis	30.00	15.00	9.00
68	Sammy Calderone	30.00	15.00	9.00
69	Bud Podbielan	30.00	15.00	9.00
70	Larry Doby	70.00	35.00	21.00
71	Frank Smith	30.00	15.00	9.00
72	Preston Ward	30.00	15.00	9.00
73	Wayne Terwilliger	30.00	15.00	9.00

The first issue to use two player pictures on the front, the 1954 Topps set is very popular today. Solid

		NR MT	EX	VG
74	Bill Taylor	30.00	15.00	9.00
75	Fred Haney	30.00	15.00	9.00
76	Bob Scheffing	13.00	6.50	4.00
77	Ray Boone	13.00	6.50	4.00
78	Ted Kazanski	13.00	6.50	4.00
79	Andy Pafko	13.00	6.50	4.00
80	Jackie Jensen	13.00	6.50	4.00
81	Dave Hoskins	13.00	6.50	4.00
82	Milt Bolling	13.00	6.50	4.00
83	Joe Collins	13.00	6.50	4.00
84	Dick Cole	13.00	6.50	4.00
85	*Bob Turley*	13.00	6.50	4.00
86	Billy Herman	30.00	15.00	9.00
87	Roy Face	13.00	6.50	4.00
88	Matt Batts	13.00	6.50	4.00
89	Howie Pollet	13.00	6.50	4.00
90	Willie Mays	500.00	250.00	150.00
91	Bob Oldis	13.00	6.50	4.00
92	Wally Westlake	13.00	6.50	4.00
93	Sid Hudson	13.00	6.50	4.00
94	*Ernie Banks*	800.00	400.00	250.00
95	Hal Rice	13.00	6.50	4.00
96	Charlie Silvera	13.00	6.50	4.00
97	Jerry Lane	13.00	6.50	4.00
98	Joe Black	13.00	6.50	4.00
99	Bob Hofman	13.00	6.50	4.00
100	Bob Keegan	13.00	6.50	4.00
101	Gene Woodling	20.00	10.00	6.00
102	Gil Hodges	75.00	38.00	23.00
103	*Jim Lemon*	13.00	6.50	4.00
104	Mike Sandlock	13.00	6.50	4.00
105	Andy Carey	13.00	6.50	4.00
106	Dick Kokos	13.00	6.50	4.00
107	Duane Pillette	13.00	6.50	4.00
108	Thornton Kipper	13.00	6.50	4.00
109	Bill Bruton	13.00	6.50	4.00
110	Harry Dorish	13.00	6.50	4.00
111	Jim Delsing	13.00	6.50	4.00
112	Bill Renna	13.00	6.50	4.00
113	Bob Boyd	13.00	6.50	4.00
114	Dean Stone	13.00	6.50	4.00
115	"Rip" Repulski	13.00	6.50	4.00
116	Steve Bilko	13.00	6.50	4.00
117	Solly Hemus	13.00	6.50	4.00
118	Carl Scheib	13.00	6.50	4.00
119	Johnny Antonelli	13.00	6.50	4.00
120	Roy McMillan	13.00	6.50	4.00
121	Clem Labine	13.00	6.50	4.00
122	Johnny Logan	13.00	6.50	4.00
123	Bobby Adams	13.00	6.50	4.00
124	Marion Fricano	13.00	6.50	4.00
125	Harry Perkowski	13.00	6.50	4.00
126	Ben Wade	13.00	6.50	4.00
127	Steve O'Neill	13.00	6.50	4.00
128	*Henry Aaron*	2000.00	1000.00	600.00
129	Forrest Jacobs	13.00	6.50	4.00
130	Hank Bauer	30.00	15.00	9.00
131	Reno Bertoia	13.00	6.50	4.00
132	*Tom Lasorda*	175.00	87.00	50.00
133	Del Baker	13.00	6.50	4.00
134	Cal Hogue	13.00	6.50	4.00
135	Joe Presko	13.00	6.50	4.00
136	Connie Ryan	13.00	6.50	4.00
137	*Wally Moon*	13.00	6.50	4.00
138	Bob Borkowski	13.00	6.50	4.00
139	Ed & Johnny O'Brien	30.00	15.00	9.00
140	Tom Wright	13.00	6.50	4.00
141	*Joe Jay*	13.00	6.50	4.00
142	Tom Poholsky	13.00	6.50	4.00
143	Rollie Hemsley	13.00	6.50	4.00
144	Bill Werle	13.00	6.50	4.00
145	Elmer Valo	13.00	6.50	4.00
146	Don Johnson	13.00	6.50	4.00
147	John Riddle	13.00	6.50	4.00
148	Bob Trice	13.00	6.50	4.00
149	Jim Robertson	13.00	6.50	4.00
150	Dick Kryhoski	13.00	6.50	4.00
151	Alex Grammas	13.00	6.50	4.00
152	Mike Blyzka	13.00	6.50	4.00
153	"Rube" Walker	13.00	6.50	4.00
154	Mike Fornieles	13.00	6.50	4.00
155	Bob Kennedy	13.00	6.50	4.00
156	Joe Coleman	13.00	6.50	4.00
157	Don Lenhardt	13.00	6.50	4.00
158	"Peanuts" Lowrey	13.00	6.50	4.00
159	Dave Philley	13.00	6.50	4.00
160	"Red" Kress	13.00	6.50	4.00
161	John Hetki	13.00	6.50	4.00
162	Herman Wehmeier	13.00	6.50	4.00
163	Frank House	13.00	6.50	4.00
164	Stu Miller	13.00	6.50	4.00
165	Jim Pendleton	13.00	6.50	4.00
166	Johnny Podres	30.00	15.00	9.00
167	Don Lund	13.00	6.50	4.00
168	Morrie Martin	13.00	6.50	4.00
169	Jim Hughes	13.00	6.50	4.00
170	*Jim Rhodes*	13.00	6.50	4.00
171	Leo Kiely	13.00	6.50	4.00
172	Hal Brown	13.00	6.50	4.00
173	Jack Harshman	13.00	6.50	4.00
174	Tom Qualters	13.00	6.50	4.00
175	Frank Leja	13.00	6.50	4.00
176	Bob Keely	13.00	6.50	4.00
177	Bob Milliken	13.00	6.50	4.00
178	Bill Glynn (Glynn)	13.00	6.50	4.00
179	Gair Allie	13.00	6.50	4.00
180	Wes Westrum	13.00	6.50	4.00
181	Mel Roach	13.00	6.50	4.00
182	Chuck Harmon	13.00	6.50	4.00
183	Earle Combs	35.00	17.50	10.50
184	Ed Bailey	13.00	6.50	4.00
185	Chuck Stobbs	13.00	6.50	4.00
186	Karl Olson	13.00	6.50	4.00
187	"Heinie" Manush	35.00	17.50	10.50
188	Dave Jolly	13.00	6.50	4.00
189	Bob Ross	13.00	6.50	4.00
190	Ray Herbert	13.00	6.50	4.00
191	*Dick Schofield*	13.00	6.50	4.00
192	"Cot" Deal	13.00	6.50	4.00
193	Johnny Hopp	13.00	6.50	4.00
194	Bill Sarni	13.00	6.50	4.00
195	Bill Consolo	13.00	6.50	4.00
196	Stan Jok	13.00	6.50	4.00
197	"Schoolboy" Rowe	13.00	6.50	4.00
198	Carl Sawatski	13.00	6.50	4.00
199	"Rocky" Nelson	13.00	6.50	4.00
200	Larry Jansen	13.00	6.50	4.00
201	*Al Kaline*	800.00	400.00	250.00
202	*Bob Purkey*	13.00	6.50	4.00
203	Harry Brecheen	13.00	6.50	4.00
204	Angel Scull	13.00	6.50	4.00
205	Johnny Sain	35.00	17.50	10.50
206	Ray Crone	13.00	6.50	4.00
207	Tom Oliver	13.00	6.50	4.00
208	Grady Hatton	13.00	6.50	4.00
209	Charlie Thompson	13.00	6.50	4.00
210	*Bob Buhl*	13.00	6.50	4.00
211	Don Hoak	13.00	6.50	4.00
212	Mickey Micelotta	13.00	6.50	4.00
213	John Fitzpatrick	13.00	6.50	4.00
214	Arnold Portocarrero	13.00	6.50	4.00
215	Ed McGhee	13.00	6.50	4.00
216	Al Sima	13.00	6.50	4.00
217	Paul Schreiber	13.00	6.50	4.00
218	Fred Marsh	13.00	6.50	4.00
219	Charlie Kress	13.00	6.50	4.00
220	Ruben Gomez	13.00	6.50	4.00
221	Dick Brodowski	13.00	6.50	4.00
222	Bill Wilson	13.00	6.50	4.00
223	Joe Haynes	13.00	6.50	4.00
224	Dick Weik	13.00	6.50	4.00
225	Don Liddle	13.00	6.50	4.00
226	Jehosie Heard	13.00	6.50	4.00
227	Buster Mills	13.00	6.50	4.00
228	Gene Hermanski	13.00	6.50	4.00
229	Bob Talbot	13.00	6.50	4.00
230	Bob Kuzava	13.00	6.50	4.00
231	Roy Smalley	13.00	6.50	4.00
232	Lou Limmer	13.00	6.50	4.00
233	Augie Galan	13.00	6.50	4.00
234	*Jerry Lynch*	13.00	6.50	4.00
235	Vern Law	13.00	6.50	4.00
236	Paul Penson	13.00	6.50	4.00
237	Mike Ryba	13.00	6.50	4.00
238	Al Aber	13.00	6.50	4.00
239	*Bill Skowron*	90.00	45.00	27.00
240	Sam Mele	13.00	6.50	4.00
241	Bob Miller	13.00	6.50	4.00
242	Curt Roberts	13.00	6.50	4.00
243	Ray Blades	13.00	6.50	4.00
244	Leroy Wheat	13.00	6.50	4.00
245	Roy Sievers	13.00	6.50	4.00
246	Howie Fox	13.00	6.50	4.00
247	Eddie Mayo	13.00	6.50	4.00
248	*Al Smith*	13.00	6.50	4.00
249	Wilmer Mizell	13.00	6.50	4.00
250	Ted Williams	700.00	225.00	110.00

**Regional interest may affect
the value of a card.**

1955 Topps

MONTE IRVIN   outfield NEW YORK GIANTS

The 1955 Topps set is numerically the smallest of the regular issue Topps sets. The 3-3/4" by 2-5/8" cards mark the first time that Topps used a horizontal format. While that format was new, the design was not; they are very similar to the 1954 cards to the point many pictures appeared in both years. Although it was slated for a 210-card set, the 1955 Topps set turned out to be only 206 cards with numbers 175, 186, 203 and 209 never being released. The scarce high numbers in this set begin with #161.

	NR MT	EX	VG
Complete Set:	7500.00	3750.00	2250.
Common Player: 1-150	8.00	4.00	2.50
Common Player: 151-160	17.00	8.50	5.00
Common Player: 161-210	25.00	12.50	7.50

#	Player	NR MT	EX	VG
1	"Dusty" Rhodes	50.00	15.00	9.00
2	Ted Williams	400.00	200.00	125.00
3	Art Fowler	8.00	4.00	2.50
4	Al Kaline	200.00	100.00	60.00
5	Jim Gilliam	10.00	5.00	3.00
6	Stan Hack	8.00	4.00	2.50
7	Jim Hegan	8.00	4.00	2.50
8	Hal Smith	8.00	4.00	2.50
9	Bob Miller	8.00	4.00	2.50
10	Bob Keegan	8.00	4.00	2.50
11	Ferris Fain	8.00	4.00	2.50
12	"Jake" Thies	8.00	4.00	2.50
13	Fred Marsh	8.00	4.00	2.50
14	Jim Finigan	8.00	4.00	2.50
15	Jim Pendleton	8.00	4.00	2.50
16	Roy Sievers	15.00	7.50	4.50
17	Bobby Hofman	8.00	4.00	2.50
18	Russ Kemmerer	8.00	4.00	2.50
19	Billy Herman	12.00	6.00	3.50
20	Andy Carey	9.00	4.50	2.75
21	Alex Grammas	8.00	4.00	2.50
22	Bill Skowron	15.00	7.50	4.50
23	Jack Parks	8.00	4.00	2.50
24	Hal Newhouser	8.00	4.00	2.50
25	Johnny Podres	20.00	10.00	6.00
26	Dick Groat	15.00	7.50	4.50
27	Billy Gardner	8.00	4.00	2.50
28	Ernie Banks	225.00	112.00	67.00
29	Herman Wehmeier	8.00	4.00	2.50
30	Vic Power	8.00	4.00	2.50
31	Warren Spahn	80.00	40.00	25.00
32	Ed McGhee	8.00	4.00	2.50
33	Tom Qualters	8.00	4.00	2.50
34	Wayne Terwilliger	8.00	4.00	2.50
35	Dave Jolly	8.00	4.00	2.50
36	Leo Kiely	8.00	4.00	2.50
37	Joe Cunningham	10.00	5.00	3.00
38	Bob Turley	17.00	8.50	5.00
39	Bill Glynn	8.00	4.00	2.50
40	Don Hoak	10.00	5.00	3.00
41	Chuck Stobbs	8.00	4.00	2.50
42	"Windy" McCall	8.00	4.00	2.50
43	Harvey Haddix	8.00	4.00	2.50
44	"Corky" Valentine	8.00	4.00	2.50
45	Hank Sauer	8.00	4.00	2.50
46	Ted Kazanski	8.00	4.00	2.50
47	Hank Aaron	400.00	200.00	125.00
48	Bob Kennedy	8.00	4.00	2.50
49	J.W. Porter	8.00	4.00	2.50
50	Jackie Robinson	250.00	125.00	75.00
51	Jim Hughes	8.00	4.00	2.50
52	Bill Tremel	8.00	4.00	2.50
53	Bill Taylor	8.00	4.00	2.50
54	Lou Limmer	8.00	4.00	2.50
55	"Rip" Repulski	8.00	4.00	2.50
56	Ray Jablonski	8.00	4.00	2.50
57	Billy O'Dell	8.00	4.00	2.50
58	Jim Rivera	8.00	4.00	2.50
59	Gair Allie	8.00	4.00	2.50
60	Dean Stone	8.00	4.00	2.50
61	"Spook" Jacobs	8.00	4.00	2.50
62	Thornton Kipper	8.00	4.00	2.50
63	Joe Collins	9.00	4.50	2.75
64	Gus Triandos	10.00	5.00	3.00
65	Ray Boone	8.00	4.00	2.50
66	Ron Jackson	8.00	4.00	2.50
67	Wally Moon	8.00	4.00	2.50
68	Jim Davis	8.00	4.00	2.50
69	Ed Bailey	8.00	4.00	2.50
70	Al Rosen	17.00	8.50	5.00
71	Ruben Gomez	8.00	4.00	2.50
72	Karl Olson	8.00	4.00	2.50
73	Jack Shepard	8.00	4.00	2.50
74	Bob Borkowski	8.00	4.00	2.50
75	Sandy Amoros	8.00	4.00	2.50
76	Howie Pollet	8.00	4.00	2.50
77	Arnold Portocarrero	8.00	4.00	2.50
78	Gordon Jones	8.00	4.00	2.50
79	Danny Schell	8.00	4.00	2.50
80	Bob Grim	9.00	4.50	2.75
81	Gene Conley	8.00	4.00	2.50
82	Chuck Harmon	8.00	4.00	2.50
83	Tom Brewer	8.00	4.00	2.50
84	Camilo Pascual	8.00	4.00	2.50
85	Don Mossi	8.00	4.00	2.50
86	Bill Wilson	8.00	4.00	2.50
87	Frank House	8.00	4.00	2.50
88	Bob Skinner	8.00	4.00	2.50
89	Joe Frazier	8.00	4.00	2.50
90	Karl Spooner	9.00	4.50	2.75
91	Milt Bolling	8.00	4.00	2.50
92	Don Zimmer	40.00	20.00	12.00
93	Steve Bilko	8.00	4.00	2.50
94	Reno Bertoia	8.00	4.00	2.50
95	Preston Ward	8.00	4.00	2.50
96	Charlie Bishop	8.00	4.00	2.50
97	Carlos Paula	8.00	4.00	2.50
98	Johnny Riddle	8.00	4.00	2.50
99	Frank Leja	9.00	4.50	2.75
100	Monte Irvin	25.00	12.50	7.50
101	Johnny Gray	8.00	4.00	2.50
102	Wally Westlake	8.00	4.00	2.50
103	Charlie White	8.00	4.00	2.50
104	Jack Harshman	8.00	4.00	2.50
105	Chuck Diering	8.00	4.00	2.50
106	Frank Sullivan	8.00	4.00	2.50
107	Curt Roberts	8.00	4.00	2.50
108	"Rube" Walker	8.00	4.00	2.50
109	Ed Lopat	10.00	5.00	3.00
110	Gus Zernial	8.00	4.00	2.50
111	Bob Milliken	8.00	4.00	2.50
112	Nelson King	8.00	4.00	2.50
113	Harry Brecheen	8.00	4.00	2.50
114	Lou Ortiz	8.00	4.00	2.50
115	Ellis Kinder	8.00	4.00	2.50
116	Tom Hurd	8.00	4.00	2.50
117	Mel Roach	8.00	4.00	2.50
118	Bob Purkey	8.00	4.00	2.50
119	Bob Lennon	8.00	4.00	2.50
120	Ted Kluszewski	25.00	12.50	7.50
121	Bill Renna	8.00	4.00	2.50
122	Carl Sawatski	8.00	4.00	2.50
123	Sandy Koufax	1400.00	700.00	375.00
124	Harmon Killebrew	400.00	200.00	125.00
125	Ken Boyer	75.00	38.00	23.00
126	Dick Hall	8.00	4.00	2.50
127	Dale Long	8.00	4.00	2.50
128	Ted Lepcio	8.00	4.00	2.50
129	Elvin Tappe	8.00	4.00	2.50
130	Mayo Smith	8.00	4.00	2.50
131	Grady Hatton	8.00	4.00	2.50
132	Bob Trice	8.00	4.00	2.50
133	Dave Hoskins	8.00	4.00	2.50
134	Joe Jay	8.00	4.00	2.50
135	Johnny O'Brien	8.00	4.00	2.50
136	"Bunky" Stewart	8.00	4.00	2.50
137	Harry Elliott	8.00	4.00	2.50
138	Ray Herbert	8.00	4.00	2.50
139	Steve Kraly	9.00	4.50	2.75
140	Mel Parnell	8.00	4.00	2.50
141	Tom Wright	8.00	4.00	2.50

		NR MT	EX	VG
142	Jerry Lynch	8.00	4.00	2.50
143	Dick Schofield	8.00	4.00	2.50
144	Joe Amalfitano	8.00	4.00	2.50
145	Elmer Valo	8.00	4.00	2.50
146	*Dick Donovan*	8.00	4.00	2.50
147	Laurin Pepper	8.00	4.00	2.50
148	Hal Brown	8.00	4.00	2.50
149	Ray Crone	8.00	4.00	2.50
150	Mike Higgins	8.00	4.00	2.50
151	"Red" Kress	17.00	8.50	5.00
152	*Harry Agganis*	75.00	38.00	23.00
153	"Bud" Podbielan	17.00	8.50	5.00
154	Willie Miranda	17.00	8.50	5.00
155	Ed Mathews	125.00	67.00	37.00
156	Joe Black	20.00	10.00	6.00
157	Bob Miller	17.00	8.50	5.00
158	Tom Carroll	20.00	10.00	6.00
159	Johnny Schmitz	17.00	8.50	5.00
160	Ray Narleski	17.00	8.50	5.00
161	*Chuck Tanner*	30.00	15.00	9.00
162	Joe Coleman	25.00	12.50	7.50
163	Faye Throneberry	25.00	12.50	7.50
164	*Roberto Clemente*	1800.00	900.00	550.00
165	Don Johnson	25.00	12.50	7.50
166	Hank Bauer	40.00	20.00	12.00
167	Tom Casagrande	25.00	12.50	7.50
168	Duane Pillette	25.00	12.50	7.50
169	Bob Oldis	25.00	12.50	7.50
170	Jim Pearce	25.00	12.50	7.50
171	Dick Brodowski	25.00	12.50	7.50
172	Frank Baumholtz	25.00	12.50	7.50
173	Bob Kline	25.00	12.50	7.50
174	Rudy Minarcin	25.00	12.50	7.50
175	Not Issued			
176	Norm Zauchin	25.00	12.50	7.50
177	Jim Robertson	25.00	12.50	7.50
178	Bobby Adams	25.00	12.50	7.50
179	Jim Bolger	25.00	12.50	7.50
180	Clem Labine	25.00	12.50	7.50
181	Roy McMillan	25.00	12.50	7.50
182	Humberto Robinson	25.00	12.50	7.50
183	Tony Jacobs	25.00	12.50	7.50
184	Harry Perkowski	25.00	12.50	7.50
185	Don Ferrarese	25.00	12.50	7.50
186	Not Issued			
187	Gil Hodges	150.00	75.00	45.00
188	Charlie Silvera	25.00	12.50	7.50
189	Phil Rizzuto	150.00	75.00	45.00
190	Gene Woodling	25.00	12.50	7.50
191	Ed Stanky	25.00	12.50	7.50
192	Jim Delsing	25.00	12.50	7.50
193	Johnny Sain	40.00	20.00	12.00
194	Willie Mays	550.00	275.00	165.00
195	Ed Roebuck	25.00	12.50	7.50
196	Gale Wade	25.00	12.50	7.50
197	Al Smith	25.00	12.50	7.50
198	Yogi Berra	250.00	125.00	75.00
199	Bert Hamric	25.00	12.50	7.50
200	Jack Jensen	50.00	25.00	15.00
201	Sherm Lollar	25.00	12.50	7.50
202	Jim Owens	25.00	12.50	7.50
203	Not Issued			
204	Frank Smith	25.00	12.50	7.50
205	Gene Freese	25.00	12.50	7.50
206	Pete Daley	25.00	12.50	7.50
207	Bill Consolo	25.00	12.50	7.50
208	Ray Moore	25.00	12.50	7.50
209	Not Issued			
210	Duke Snider	500.00	200.00	110.00

1955 Topps Doubleheaders

This set is a throwback to the 1911 T201 Mecca

Double Folders. The cards were perforated allowing them to be folded. Open, there is a color painting of a player set against a ballpark background. When folded, a different stadium and player appears, although both share the same lower legs and feet. Back gives abbreviated career histories. Placed side by side in reverse numerical order, the backgrounds form a continuous stadium scene. When open, the cards measure 2-1/16" by 4-7/8." The 66 cards in the set mean 132 total players, all of whom also appeared in the lower number regular 1955 Topps set.

		NR MT	EX	VG
Complete Set:		3750.00	1875.00	1125.
Common Player:		30.00	15.00	9.00
1	Al Rosen			
2	Chuck Diering	30.00	15.00	9.00
3	Monte Irvin			
4	Russ Kemmerer	30.00	15.00	9.00
5	Ted Kazanski			
6	Gordon Jones	30.00	15.00	9.00
7	Bill Taylor			
8	Billy O'Dell	30.00	15.00	9.00
9	J.W. Porter			
10	Thornton Kipper	30.00	15.00	9.00
11	Curt Roberts			
12	Arnie Portocarrero	30.00	15.00	9.00
13	Wally Westlake			
14	Frank House	30.00	15.00	9.00
15	"Rube" Walker			
16	Lou Limmer	30.00	15.00	9.00
17	Dean Stone			
18	Charlie White	30.00	15.00	9.00
19	Karl Spooner			
20	Jim Hughes	30.00	15.00	9.00
21	Bill Skowron			
22	Frank Sullivan	30.00	15.00	9.00
23	Jack Shepard			
24	Stan Hack	30.00	15.00	9.00
25	Jackie Robinson			
26	Don Hoak	275.00	137.00	80.00
27	"Dusty" Rhodes			
28	Jim Davis	30.00	15.00	9.00
29	Vic Power			
30	Ed Bailey	30.00	15.00	9.00
31	Howie Pollet			
32	Ernie Banks	150.00	75.00	45.00
33	Jim Pendleton			
34	Gene Conley	30.00	15.00	9.00
35	Karl Olson	30.00	15.00	9.00
36	Andy Carey	30.00	15.00	9.00
37	Wally Moon	30.00	15.00	9.00
38	Joe Cunningham	30.00	15.00	9.00
39	Fred Marsh			
40	"Jake" Thies	30.00	15.00	9.00
41	Ed Lopat			
42	Harvey Haddix	30.00	15.00	9.00
43	Leo Kiely			
44	Chuck Stobbs	30.00	15.00	9.00
45	Al Kaline			
46	"Corky" Valentine	300.00	150.00	90.00
47	"Spook" Jacobs			
48	Johnny Gray	30.00	15.00	9.00
49	Ron Jackson			
50	Jim Finigan	30.00	15.00	9.00
51	Ray Jablonski			
52	Bob Keegan	30.00	15.00	9.00
53	Billy Herman			
54	Sandy Amoros	30.00	15.00	9.00
55	Chuck Harmon			
56	Bob Skinner	30.00	15.00	9.00
57	Dick Hall			
58	Bob Grim	30.00	15.00	9.00
59	Billy Glynn			
60	Bob Miller	30.00	15.00	9.00
61	Billy Gardner			
62	John Hetki	30.00	15.00	9.00
63	Bob Borkowski			
64	Bob Turley	30.00	15.00	9.00
65	Joe Collins			
66	Jack Harshman	30.00	15.00	9.00
67	Jim Hegan			
68	Jack Parks	30.00	15.00	9.00
69	Ted Williams			
70	Hal Smith	300.00	150.00	90.00
71	Gair Allie			
72	Grady Hatton	30.00	15.00	9.00
73	Jerry Lynch			

		NR MT	EX	VG
74	Harry Brecheen	30.00	15.00	9.00
75	Tom Wright			
76	"Bunky" Stewart	30.00	15.00	9.00
77	Dave Hoskins			
78	Ed McGhee	30.00	15.00	9.00
79	Roy Sievers			
80	Art Fowler	30.00	15.00	9.00
81	Danny Schell			
82	Gus Triandos	30.00	15.00	9.00
83	Joe Frazier			
84	Don Mossi	30.00	15.00	9.00
85	Elmer Valo			
86	Hal Brown	30.00	15.00	9.00
87	Bob Kennedy			
88	"Windy" McCall	30.00	15.00	9.00
89	Ruben Gomez			
90	Jim Rivera	30.00	15.00	9.00
91	Lou Ortiz			
92	Milt Bolling	30.00	15.00	9.00
93	Carl Sawatski			
94	Elvin Tappe	30.00	15.00	9.00
95	Dave Jolly			
96	Bobby Hofman	30.00	15.00	9.00
97	Preston Ward			
98	Don Zimmer	30.00	15.00	9.00
99	Bill Renna			
100	Dick Groat	30.00	15.00	9.00
101	Bill Wilson			
102	Bill Tremel	30.00	15.00	9.00
103	Hank Sauer			
104	Camilo Pascual	30.00	15.00	9.00
105	Hank Aaron			
106	Ray Herbert	450.00	225.00	135.00
107	Alex Grammas			
108	Tom Qualters	30.00	15.00	9.00
109	Hal Newhouser			
110	Charlie Bishop	30.00	15.00	9.00
111	Harmon Killebrew			
112	John Podres	250.00	125.00	75.00
113	Ray Boone			
114	Bob Purkey	30.00	15.00	9.00
115	Dale Long			
116	Ferris Fain	30.00	15.00	9.00
117	Steve Bilko			
118	Bob Milliken	30.00	15.00	9.00
119	Mel Parnell			
120	Tom Hurd	30.00	15.00	9.00
121	Ted Kluszewski			
122	Jim Owens	30.00	15.00	9.00
123	Gus Zernial			
124	Bob Trice	30.00	15.00	9.00
125	"Rip" Repulski			
126	Ted Lepcio	30.00	15.00	9.00
127	Warren Spahn			
128	Tom Brewer	200.00	100.00	60.00
129	Jim Gilliam			
130	Ellis Kinder	30.00	15.00	9.00
131	Herm Wehmeier			
132	Wayne Terwilliger	30.00	15.00	9.00

1956 Topps

This 340-card set is quite similar in design to the 1955 Topps set, again using both a portrait and an "action" picture. Some portraits are the same as those used in 1955 (and even 1954). Innovations found in the 1956 Topps set of 2-5/8" by 3-3/4" cards include team cards introduced as part of a regular set. Additionally, there are two unnumbered

checklist cards (the complete set price quoted below does not include the checklist cards). Finally, there are cards of the two league presidents, William Harridge and Warren Giles. On the backs, a three-panel cartoon depicts big moments from the player's career while biographical information appears above the cartoon and the statistics below. Card backs for numbers 1-180 can be found with either white or grey cardboard. Some dealers charge a premium for grey backs (#'s 1-100) and white backs (#'s 101-180).

		NR MT	EX	VG
Complete Set:		7500.00	3750.00	2250.
Common Player: 1-100		7.00	3.50	2.00
Common Player: 101-180		9.00	4.50	2.75
Common Player: 181-260		15.00	7.50	4.50
Common Player: 261-340		9.00	4.50	2.75
1	William Harridge	110.00	25.00	3.75
2	Warren Giles	15.00	7.50	4.50
3	Elmer Valo	7.00	3.50	2.00
4	Carlos Paula	7.00	3.50	2.00
5	Ted Williams	350.00	175.00	105.00
6	Ray Boone	9.00	4.50	2.75
7	Ron Negray	7.00	3.50	2.00
8	Walter Alston	40.00	20.00	12.00
9	Ruben Gomez	7.00	3.50	2.00
10	Warren Spahn	80.00	40.00	25.00
11a	Cubs Team (with date)	50.00	25.00	15.00
11b	Cubs Team (no date, name centered)	15.00	7.50	4.50
11c	Cubs Team (no date, name at left)	15.00	7.50	4.50
12	Andy Carey	10.00	5.00	3.00
13	Roy Face	10.00	5.00	3.00
14	Ken Boyer	15.00	7.50	4.50
15	Ernie Banks	125.00	62.00	37.00
16	*Hector Lopez*	10.00	5.00	3.00
17	Gene Conley	9.00	4.50	2.75
18	Dick Donovan	7.00	3.50	2.00
19	Chuck Diering	7.00	3.50	2.00
20	Al Kaline	100.00	50.00	30.00
21	Joe Collins	10.00	5.00	3.00
22	Jim Finigan	7.00	3.50	2.00
23	Freddie Marsh	7.00	3.50	2.00
24	Dick Groat	10.00	5.00	3.00
25	Ted Kluszewski	20.00	10.00	6.00
26	Grady Hatton	7.00	3.50	2.00
27	Nelson Burbrink	7.00	3.50	2.00
28	Bobby Hofman	7.00	3.50	2.00
29	Jack Harshman	7.00	3.50	2.00
30	Jackie Robinson	150.00	60.00	38.00
31	Hank Aaron	200.00	100.00	60.00
32	Frank House	7.00	3.50	2.00
33	Roberto Clemente	450.00	225.00	135.00
34	Tom Brewer	7.00	3.50	2.00
35	Al Rosen	15.00	7.50	4.50
36	Rudy Minarcin	7.00	3.50	2.00
37	Alex Grammas	7.00	3.50	2.00
38	Bob Kennedy	7.00	3.50	2.00
39	Don Mossi	9.00	4.50	2.75
40	Bob Turley	15.00	7.50	4.50
41	Hank Sauer	7.00	3.50	2.00
42	Sandy Amoros	9.00	4.50	2.75
43	Ray Moore	7.00	3.50	2.00
44	"Windy" McCall	7.00	3.50	2.00
45	Gus Zernial	9.00	4.50	2.75
46	Gene Freese	7.00	3.50	2.00
47	Art Fowler	7.00	3.50	2.00
48	Jim Hegan	7.00	3.50	2.00
49	*Pedro Ramos*	9.00	4.50	2.75
50	"Dusty" Rhodes	9.00	4.50	2.75
51	Ernie Oravetz	7.00	3.50	2.00
52	Bob Grim	10.00	5.00	3.00
53	Arnold Portocarrero	7.00	3.50	2.00
54	Bob Keegan	7.00	3.50	2.00
55	Wally Moon	9.00	4.50	2.75
56	Dale Long	9.00	4.50	2.75
57	"Duke" Maas	7.00	3.50	2.00
58	Ed Roebuck	9.00	4.50	2.75
59	Jose Santiago	7.00	3.50	2.00
60	Mayo Smith	7.00	3.50	2.00
61	Bill Skowron	15.00	7.50	4.50
62	Hal Smith	7.00	3.50	2.00
63	*Roger Craig*	30.00	15.00	9.00
64	Luis Arroyo	7.00	3.50	2.00
65	Johnny O'Brien	7.00	3.50	2.00
66	Bob Speake	7.00	3.50	2.00
67	Vic Power	7.00	3.50	2.00

#	Name	NR MT	EX	VG
68	Chuck Stobbs	7.00	3.50	2.00
69	Chuck Tanner	10.00	5.00	3.00
70	Jim Rivera	7.00	3.50	2.00
71	Frank Sullivan	7.00	3.50	2.00
72a	Phillies Team (with date)	50.00	25.00	15.00
72b	Phillies Team (no date, name centered)	15.00	7.50	4.50
72c	Philadelphia Phillies (no date, name at left)	15.00	7.50	4.50
73	Wayne Terwilliger	7.00	3.50	2.00
74	Jim King	7.00	3.50	2.00
75	Roy Sievers	9.00	4.50	2.75
76	Ray Crone	7.00	3.50	2.00
77	Harvey Haddix	9.00	4.50	2.75
78	Herman Wehmeier	7.00	3.50	2.00
79	Sandy Koufax	375.00	187.00	110.00
80	Gus Triandos	9.00	4.50	2.75
81	Wally Westlake	7.00	3.50	2.00
82	Bill Renna	7.00	3.50	2.00
83	Karl Spooner	9.00	4.50	2.75
84	"Babe" Birrer	7.00	3.50	2.00
85a	Indians Team (with date)	50.00	25.00	15.00
85b	Indians Team (no date, name centered)	15.00	7.50	4.50
85c	Indians Team (no date, name at left)	15.00	7.50	4.50
86	Ray Jablonski	7.00	3.50	2.00
87	Dean Stone	7.00	3.50	2.00
88	Johnny Kucks	10.00	5.00	3.00
89	Norm Zauchin	7.00	3.50	2.00
90a	Redlegs Team (with date)	50.00	25.00	15.00
90b	Redlegs Team (no date, name centered)	15.00	7.50	4.50
90c	Redlegs Team (no date, name at left)	15.00	7.50	4.50
91	Gail Harris	7.00	3.50	2.00
92	"Red" Wilson	7.00	3.50	2.00
93	George Susce, Jr.	7.00	3.50	2.00
94	Ronnie Kline	7.00	3.50	2.00
95a	Braves Team (with date)	50.00	25.00	15.00
95b	Braves Team (no date, name centered)	15.00	7.50	4.50
95c	Braves Team (no date, name at left)	15.00	7.50	4.50
96	Bill Tremel	7.00	3.50	2.00
97	Jerry Lynch	7.00	3.50	2.00
98	Camilo Pascual	9.00	4.50	2.75
99	Don Zimmer	15.00	7.50	4.50
100a	Orioles Team (with date)	40.00	20.00	12.00
100b	Orioles Team (no date, name centered)	15.00	7.50	4.50
100c	Orioles Team (no date, name at left)	15.00	7.50	4.50
101	Roy Campanella	150.00	75.00	45.00
102	Jim Davis	9.00	4.50	2.75
103	Willie Miranda	9.00	4.50	2.75
104	Bob Lennon	9.00	4.50	2.75
105	Al Smith	9.00	4.50	2.75
106	Joe Astroth	9.00	4.50	2.75
107	Ed Mathews	60.00	30.00	18.00
108	Laurin Pepper	9.00	4.50	2.75
109	Enos Slaughter	30.00	15.00	9.00
110	Yogi Berra	125.00	56.00	35.00
111	Red Sox Team	9.00	4.50	2.75
112	Dee Fondy	9.00	4.50	2.75
113	Phil Rizzuto	50.00	25.00	15.00
114	Jim Owens	9.00	4.50	2.75
115	Jackie Jensen	15.00	7.50	4.50
116	Eddie O'Brien	9.00	4.50	2.75
117	Virgil Trucks	9.00	4.50	2.75
118	"Nellie" Fox	30.00	15.00	9.00
119	*Larry Jackson*	9.00	4.50	2.75
120	Richie Ashburn	35.00	17.50	10.50
121	Pirates Team	15.00	7.50	4.50
122	Willard Nixon	9.00	4.50	2.75
123	Roy McMillan	9.00	4.50	2.75
124	Don Kaiser	9.00	4.50	2.75
125	"Minnie" Minoso	20.00	10.00	6.00
126	Jim Brady	9.00	4.50	2.75
127	Willie Jones	9.00	4.50	2.75
128	Eddie Yost	9.00	4.50	2.75
129	"Jake" Martin	9.00	4.50	2.75
130	Willie Mays	350.00	175.00	105.00
131	Bob Roselli	9.00	4.50	2.75
132	Bobby Avila	9.00	4.50	2.75
133	Ray Narleski	9.00	4.50	2.75
134	Cardinals Team	15.00	7.50	4.50
135	Mickey Mantle	1000.00	500.00	300.00
136	Johnny Logan	9.00	4.50	2.75
137	Al Silvera	9.00	4.50	2.75
138	Johnny Antonelli	9.00	4.50	2.75
139	Tommy Carroll	9.00	4.50	2.75
140	*Herb Score*	35.00	17.50	10.50
141	Joe Frazier	9.00	4.50	2.75
142	Gene Baker	9.00	4.50	2.75
143	Jim Piersall	9.00	4.50	2.75
144	Leroy Powell	9.00	4.50	2.75
145	Gil Hodges	45.00	23.00	13.50
146	Senators Team	15.00	7.50	4.50
147	Earl Torgeson	9.00	4.50	2.75
148	Alvin Dark	9.00	4.50	2.75
149	"Dixie" Howell	9.00	4.50	2.75
150	"Duke" Snider	100.00	45.00	27.00
151	"Spook" Jacobs	9.00	4.50	2.75
152	Billy Hoeft	9.00	4.50	2.75
153	Frank Thomas	9.00	4.50	2.75
154	Dave Pope	9.00	4.50	2.75
155	Harvey Kuenn	15.00	7.50	4.50
156	Wes Westrum	9.00	4.50	2.75
157	Dick Brodowski	9.00	4.50	2.75
158	Wally Post	9.00	4.50	2.75
159	Clint Courtney	9.00	4.50	2.75
160	Billy Pierce	15.00	7.50	4.50
161	Joe DeMaestri	9.00	4.50	2.75
162	"Gus" Bell	9.00	4.50	2.75
163	Gene Woodling	9.00	4.50	2.75
164	Harmon Killebrew	110.00	55.00	33.00
165	"Red" Schoendienst	30.00	15.00	9.00
166	Dodgers Team	200.00	100.00	60.00
167	Harry Dorish	9.00	4.50	2.75
168	Sammy White	9.00	4.50	2.75
169	Bob Nelson	9.00	4.50	2.75
170	Bill Virdon	15.00	7.50	4.50
171	Jim Wilson	9.00	4.50	2.75
172	*Frank Torre*	9.00	4.50	2.75
173	Johnny Podres	15.00	7.50	4.50
174	Glen Gorbous	9.00	4.50	2.75
175	Del Crandall	15.00	7.50	4.50
176	Alex Kellner	9.00	4.50	2.75
177	Hank Bauer	15.00	7.50	4.50
178	Joe Black	9.00	4.50	2.75
179	Harry Chiti	9.00	4.50	2.75
180	Robin Roberts	25.00	12.50	7.50
181	Billy Martin	110.00	55.00	33.00
182	Paul Minner	15.00	7.50	4.50
183	Stan Lopata	15.00	7.50	4.50
184	Don Bessent	15.00	7.50	4.50
185	Bill Bruton	15.00	7.50	4.50
186	Ron Jackson	15.00	7.50	4.50
187	Early Wynn	30.00	15.00	9.00
188	White Sox Team	15.00	7.50	4.50
189	Ned Garver	15.00	7.50	4.50
190	Carl Furillo	20.00	10.00	6.00
191	Frank Lary	15.00	7.50	4.50
192	"Smoky" Burgess	15.00	7.50	4.50
193	Wilmer Mizell	15.00	7.50	4.50
194	Monte Irvin	30.00	15.00	9.00
195	George Kell	30.00	15.00	9.00
196	Tom Poholsky	15.00	7.50	4.50
197	Granny Hamner	15.00	7.50	4.50
198	Ed Fitzgerald (Fitz Gerald)	15.00	7.50	4.50
199	Hank Thompson	15.00	7.50	4.50
200	Bob Feller	110.00	55.00	33.00
201	"Rip" Repulski	15.00	7.50	4.50
202	Jim Hearn	15.00	7.50	4.50
203	Bill Tuttle	15.00	7.50	4.50
204	Art Swanson	15.00	7.50	4.50
205	"Whitey" Lockman	15.00	7.50	4.50
206	Erv Palica	15.00	7.50	4.50
207	Jim Small	15.00	7.50	4.50
208	Elston Howard	30.00	15.00	9.00
209	Max Surkont	15.00	7.50	4.50
210	Mike Garcia	15.00	7.50	4.50
211	Murry Dickson	15.00	7.50	4.50
212	Johnny Temple	15.00	7.50	4.50
213	Tigers Team	50.00	25.00	15.00
214	Bob Rush	15.00	7.50	4.50
215	Tommy Byrne	15.00	7.50	4.50
216	Jerry Schoonmaker	15.00	7.50	4.50
217	Billy Klaus	15.00	7.50	4.50
218	Joe Nuxall (Nuxhall)	15.00	7.50	4.50
219	Lew Burdette	15.00	7.50	4.50
220	Del Ennis	15.00	7.50	4.50
221	Bob Friend	15.00	7.50	4.50
222	Dave Philley	15.00	7.50	4.50
223	Randy Jackson	15.00	7.50	4.50
224	"Bud" Podbielan	15.00	7.50	4.50
225	Gil McDougald	25.00	12.50	7.50
226	Giants Team	60.00	30.00	18.00
227	Russ Meyer	15.00	7.50	4.50
228	"Mickey" Vernon	15.00	7.50	4.50
229	Harry Brecheen	15.00	7.50	4.50

		NR MT	EX	VG
230	"Chico" Carrasquel	15.00	7.50	4.50
231	Bob Hale	15.00	7.50	4.50
232	"Toby" Atwell	15.00	7.50	4.50
233	Carl Erskine	20.00	10.00	6.00
234	"Pete" Runnels	15.00	7.50	4.50
235	Don Newcombe	50.00	25.00	15.00
236	Athletics Team	15.00	7.50	4.50
237	Jose Valdivielso	15.00	7.50	4.50
238	Walt Dropo	15.00	7.50	4.50
239	Harry Simpson	15.00	7.50	4.50
240	"Whitey" Ford	125.00	67.00	37.00
241	Don Mueller	15.00	7.50	4.50
242	Hershell Freeman	15.00	7.50	4.50
243	Sherm Lollar	15.00	7.50	4.50
244	Bob Buhl	15.00	7.50	4.50
245	Billy Goodman	15.00	7.50	4.50
246	Tom Gorman	15.00	7.50	4.50
247	Bill Sarni	15.00	7.50	4.50
248	Bob Porterfield	15.00	7.50	4.50
249	Johnny Klippstein	15.00	7.50	4.50
250	Larry Doby	20.00	10.00	6.00
251	Yankees Team	225.00	112.00	67.00
252	Vernon Law	15.00	7.50	4.50
253	Irv Noren	15.00	7.50	4.50
254	George Crowe	15.00	7.50	4.50
255	Bob Lemon	25.00	12.50	7.50
256	Tom Hurd	15.00	7.50	4.50
257	Bobby Thomson	15.00	7.50	4.50
258	Art Ditmar	15.00	7.50	4.50
259	Sam Jones	15.00	7.50	4.50
260	"Pee Wee" Reese	125.00	62.00	37.00
261	Bobby Shantz	9.00	4.50	2.75
262	Howie Pollet	9.00	4.50	2.75
263	Bob Miller	9.00	4.50	2.75
264	Ray Monzant	9.00	4.50	2.75
265	Sandy Consuegra	9.00	4.50	2.75
266	Don Ferrarese	9.00	4.50	2.75
267	Bob Nieman	9.00	4.50	2.75
268	Dale Mitchell	9.00	4.50	2.75
269	Jack Meyer	9.00	4.50	2.75
270	Billy Loes	9.00	4.50	2.75
271	Foster Castleman	9.00	4.50	2.75
272	Danny O'Connell	9.00	4.50	2.75
273	Walker Cooper	9.00	4.50	2.75
274	Frank Baumholtz	9.00	4.50	2.75
275	Jim Greengrass	9.00	4.50	2.75
276	George Zuverink	9.00	4.50	2.75
277	Daryl Spencer	9.00	4.50	2.75
278	Chet Nichols	9.00	4.50	2.75
279	Johnny Groth	9.00	4.50	2.75
280	Jim Gilliam	15.00	7.50	4.50
281	Art Houtteman	9.00	4.50	2.75
282	Warren Hacker	9.00	4.50	2.75
283	Hal Smith	9.00	4.50	2.75
284	Ike Delock	9.00	4.50	2.75
285	Eddie Miksis	9.00	4.50	2.75
286	Bill Wight	9.00	4.50	2.75
287	Bobby Adams	9.00	4.50	2.75
288	Bob Cerv	25.00	12.50	7.50
289	Hal Jeffcoat	9.00	4.50	2.75
290	Curt Simmons	9.00	4.50	2.75
291	Frank Kellert	9.00	4.50	2.75
292	*Luis Aparicio*	135.00	67.00	40.00
293	Stu Miller	9.00	4.50	2.75
294	Ernie Johnson	9.00	4.50	2.75
295	Clem Labine	9.00	4.50	2.75
296	Andy Seminick	9.00	4.50	2.75
297	Bob Skinner	9.00	4.50	2.75
298	Johnny Schmitz	9.00	4.50	2.75
299	Charley Neal	25.00	12.50	7.50
300	Vic Wertz	9.00	4.50	2.75
301	Marv Grissom	9.00	4.50	2.75
302	Eddie Robinson	15.00	7.50	4.50
303	Jim Dyck	9.00	4.50	2.75
304	Frank Malzone	9.00	4.50	2.75
305	Brooks Lawrence	9.00	4.50	2.75
306	Curt Roberts	9.00	4.50	2.75
307	Hoyt Wilhelm	35.00	17.50	10.50
308	"Chuck" Harmon	9.00	4.50	2.75
309	*Don Blasingame*	9.00	4.50	2.75
310	Steve Gromek	9.00	4.50	2.75
311	Hal Naragon	9.00	4.50	2.75
312	Andy Pafko	9.00	4.50	2.75
313	Gene Stephens	9.00	4.50	2.75
314	Hobie Landrith	9.00	4.50	2.75
315	Milt Bolling	9.00	4.50	2.75
316	Jerry Coleman	9.00	4.50	2.75
317	Al Aber	9.00	4.50	2.75
318	Fred Hatfield	9.00	4.50	2.75
319	Jack Crimian	9.00	4.50	2.75
320	Joe Adcock	9.00	4.50	2.75

		NR MT	EX	VG
321	Jim Konstanty	15.00	7.50	4.50
322	Karl Olson	9.00	4.50	2.75
323	Willard Schmidt	9.00	4.50	2.75
324	"Rocky" Bridges	9.00	4.50	2.75
325	Don Liddle	9.00	4.50	2.75
326	Connie Johnson	9.00	4.50	2.75
327	Bob Wiesler	9.00	4.50	2.75
328	Preston Ward	9.00	4.50	2.75
329	Lou Berberet	9.00	4.50	2.75
330	Jim Busby	9.00	4.50	2.75
331	Dick Hall	9.00	4.50	2.75
332	Don Larsen	35.00	17.50	10.50
333	Rube Walker	9.00	4.50	2.75
334	Bob Miller	9.00	4.50	2.75
335	Don Hoak	9.00	4.50	2.75
336	Ellis Kinder	9.00	4.50	2.75
337	Bobby Morgan	9.00	4.50	2.75
338	Jim Delsing	9.00	4.50	2.75
339	Rance Pless	9.00	4.50	2.75
340	Mickey McDermott	30.00	15.00	9.00
-----	Checklist 1/3	200.00	75.00	45.00
-----	Checklist 2/4	200.00	75.00	45.00

1956 Topps Hocus Focus Large

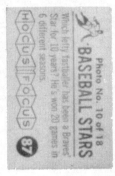

These sets are a direct descendant of the 1948 Topps Magic Photo" issue. Again, the baseball players were part of a larger overall series covering several topical areas. There are two distinct issues of Hocus Focus cards in 1956. The "large" cards, measuring 1" by 1-5/8", consists of 18 players. The "small" cards, 7/8 by 1-3/8," state on the back that they are a series of 23, though only 13 are known. Besides players on the cards themselves, the easiest way to distinguish Hocus Focus cards of 1956 from the Magic Photos series of 1948 is to remember that the 1956 cards actually have the words "Hocus Focus" on the back. The photos on these cards were developed by wetting the cards surface and exposing to light. Prices below are for cards with well-developed pictures. Cards with poorly developed photos are worth significantly less.

		NR MT	EX	VG
Complete Set:		525.00	262.00	157.00
Common Player:		12.00	6.00	3.50
1	Dick Groat	25.00	12.50	7.50
2	Ed Lopat	25.00	12.50	7.50
3	Hank Sauer	12.00	6.00	3.50
4	"Dusty" Rhodes	12.00	6.00	3.50
5	Ted Williams	125.00	62.00	37.00
6	Harvey Haddix	12.00	6.00	3.50
7	Ray Boone	12.00	6.00	3.50
8	Al Rosen	25.00	12.50	7.50
9	Mayo Smith	12.00	6.00	3.50
10	Warren Spahn	70.00	35.00	21.00
11	Jim Rivera	12.00	6.00	3.50
12	Ted Kluszewski	25.00	12.50	7.50
13	Gus Zernial	12.00	6.00	3.50
14	Jackie Robinson	125.00	62.00	37.00
15	Hal Smith	12.00	6.00	3.50
16	Johnny Schmitz	12.00	6.00	3.50
17	"Spook" Jacobs	12.00	6.00	3.50

		NR MT	EX	VG
18	Mel Parnell	12.00	6.00	3.50

1956 Topps Pins

One of Topps first specialty issues, the 60-pin set of ballplayers issued in 1956 contains a high percentage of big-name stars which, combined with the scarcity of the pins, makes collecting a complete set extremely challenging. Compounding the situation is the fact that some pins are seen far less often than others, though the reason is unknown. Chuck Stobbs, Hector Lopez and Chuck Diering are unaccountably scarce. Measuring 1-1/8" in diameter, the pins utilize the same portraits found on 1956 Topps baseball cards. The photos are set against a solid color background.

		NR MT	EX	VG
Complete Set:		2500.00	1250.00	750.00
Common Player:		15.00	7.50	4.50
(1)	Hank Aaron	100.00	50.00	30.00
(2)	Sandy Amoros	15.00	7.50	4.50
(3)	Luis Arroyo	15.00	7.50	4.50
(4)	Ernie Banks	50.00	25.00	15.00
(5)	Yogi Berra	70.00	35.00	21.00
(6)	Joe Black	15.00	7.50	4.50
(7)	Ray Boone	15.00	7.50	4.50
(8)	Ken Boyer	20.00	10.00	6.00
(9)	Joe Collins	15.00	7.50	4.50
(10)	Gene Conley	15.00	7.50	4.50
(11)	Chuck Diering	225.00	112.00	67.00
(12)	Dick Donovan	15.00	7.50	4.50
(13)	Jim Finigan	15.00	7.50	4.50
(14)	Art Fowler	15.00	7.50	4.50
(15)	Ruben Gomez	15.00	7.50	4.50
(16)	Dick Groat	20.00	10.00	6.00
(17)	Harvey Haddix	15.00	7.50	4.50
(18)	Jack Harshman	15.00	7.50	4.50
(19)	Grady Hatton	15.00	7.50	4.50
(20)	Jim Hegan	15.00	7.50	4.50
(21)	Gil Hodges	40.00	20.00	12.00
(22)	Bobby Hofman	15.00	7.50	4.50
(23)	Frank House	15.00	7.50	4.50
(24)	Jackie Jensen	20.00	10.00	6.00
(25)	Al Kaline	60.00	30.00	18.00
(26)	Bob Kennedy	15.00	7.50	4.50
(27)	Ted Kluszewski	25.00	12.50	7.50
(28)	Dale Long	15.00	7.50	4.50
(29)	Hector Lopez	200.00	100.00	60.00
(30)	Ed Mathews	40.00	20.00	12.00
(31)	Willie Mays	100.00	50.00	30.00
(32)	Roy McMillan	15.00	7.50	4.50
(33)	Willie Miranda	15.00	7.50	4.50
(34)	Wally Moon	15.00	7.50	4.50
(35)	Don Mossi	15.00	7.50	4.50
(36)	Ron Negray	15.00	7.50	4.50
(37)	Johnny O'Brien	15.00	7.50	4.50
(38)	Carlos Paula	15.00	7.50	4.50
(39)	Vic Power	15.00	7.50	4.50
(40)	Jim Rivera	15.00	7.50	4.50
(41)	Phil Rizzuto	40.00	20.00	12.00
(42)	Jackie Robinson	100.00	50.00	30.00
(43)	Al Rosen	25.00	12.50	7.50
(44)	Hank Sauer	15.00	7.50	4.50
(45)	Roy Sievers	15.00	7.50	4.50
(46)	Bill Skowron	20.00	10.00	6.00

		NR MT	EX	VG
(47)	Al Smith	15.00	7.50	4.50
(48)	Hal Smith	15.00	7.50	4.50
(49)	Mayo Smith	15.00	7.50	4.50
(50)	Duke Snider	70.00	35.00	21.00
(51)	Warren Spahn	50.00	25.00	15.00
(52)	Karl Spooner	15.00	7.50	4.50
(53)	Chuck Stobbs	175.00	87.00	52.00
(54)	Frank Sullivan	15.00	7.50	4.50
(55)	Bill Tremel	15.00	7.50	4.50
(56)	Gus Triandos	15.00	7.50	4.50
(57)	Bob Turley	20.00	10.00	6.00
(58)	Herman Wehmeier	15.00	7.50	4.50
(59)	Ted Williams	110.00	55.00	33.00
(60)	Gus Zernial	15.00	7.50	4.50

1957 Topps

For 1957, Topps reduced the size of its cards to the now-standard 2-1/2" by 3-1/2." Set size was increased to 407 cards. Another change came in the form of the use of real color photographs as opposed to the hand-colored black and whites of previous years. For the first time since 1954, there were also cards with more than one player. The two, "Dodger Sluggers" and "Yankees' Power Hitters" began a trend toward the increased use of mulitple-player cards. Another first-time innovation, found on the backs, is complete players statistics. The scarce cards in the set are not the highest numbers, but rather numbers 265-352. Four unnumbered checklist cards were issued along with the set. They are quite expensive and are not included in the complete set prices quoted below.

		NR MT	EX	VG
Complete Set:		7500.00	3750.00	2250.
Common Player: 1-264		7.00	3.50	2.00
Common Player: 265-352		18.00	9.00	5.50
Common Player: 353-407		7.00	3.50	2.00
1	Ted Williams	425.00	100.00	38.00
2	Yogi Berra	150.00	70.00	45.00
3	Dale Long	7.00	3.50	2.00
4	Johnny Logan	7.00	3.50	2.00
5	Sal Maglie	8.00	4.00	2.50
6	Hector Lopez	7.00	3.50	2.00
7	Luis Aparicio	30.00	15.00	9.00
8	Don Mossi	7.00	3.50	2.00
9	Johnny Temple	7.00	3.50	2.00
10	Willie Mays	250.00	125.00	75.00
11	George Zuverink	7.00	3.50	2.00
12	Dick Groat	6.00	3.00	1.75
13	Wally Burnette	7.00	3.50	2.00
14	Bob Nieman	7.00	3.50	2.00
15	Robin Roberts	20.00	10.00	6.00
16	Walt Moryn	7.00	3.50	2.00
17	Billy Gardner	7.00	3.50	2.00
18	*Don Drysdale*	200.00	100.00	60.00
19	Bob Wilson	7.00	3.50	2.00
20	Hank Aaron (photo reversed)	225.00	112.00	67.00
21	Frank Sullivan	7.00	3.50	2.00
22	Jerry Snyder (photo actually Ed Fitz Gerald)	7.00	3.50	2.00
23	Sherm Lollar	7.00	3.50	2.00
24	*Bill Mazeroski*	60.00	30.00	18.00
25	Whitey Ford	50.00	25.00	15.00
26	Bob Boyd	7.00	3.50	2.00

#	Player	NR MT	EX	VG		#	Player	NR MT	EX	VG
27	Ted Kazanski	7.00	3.50	2.00		118	Bob Porterfield	7.00	3.50	2.00
28	Gene Conley	7.00	3.50	2.00		119	Stan Lopata	7.00	3.50	2.00
29	*Whitey Herzog*	30.00	15.00	9.00		120	Bob Lemon	15.00	7.50	4.50
30	Pee Wee Reese	60.00	30.00	18.00		121	*Cletis Boyer*	15.00	7.50	4.50
31	Ron Northey	7.00	3.50	2.00		122	Ken Boyer	8.00	4.00	2.50
32	Hersh Freeman	7.00	3.50	2.00		123	Steve Ridzik	7.00	3.50	2.00
33	Jim Small	7.00	3.50	2.00		124	Dave Philley	7.00	3.50	2.00
34	Tom Sturdivant	6.00	3.00	1.75		125	Al Kaline	80.00	40.00	25.00
35	*Frank Robinson*	300.00	150.00	90.00		126	Bob Wiesler	7.00	3.50	2.00
36	Bob Grim	6.00	3.00	1.75		127	Bob Buhl	7.00	3.50	2.00
37	Frank Torre	7.00	3.50	2.00		128	Ed Bailey	7.00	3.50	2.00
38	Nellie Fox	20.00	10.00	6.00		129	Saul Rogovin	7.00	3.50	2.00
39	Al Worthington	7.00	3.50	2.00		130	Don Newcombe	10.00	5.00	3.00
40	Early Wynn	20.00	10.00	6.00		131	Milt Bolling	7.00	3.50	2.00
41	Hal Smith	7.00	3.50	2.00		132	Art Ditmar	6.00	3.00	1.75
42	Dee Fondy	7.00	3.50	2.00		133	Del Crandall	6.00	3.00	1.75
43	Connie Johnson	7.00	3.50	2.00		134	Don Kaiser	7.00	3.50	2.00
44	Joe DeMaestri	7.00	3.50	2.00		135	Bill Skowron	12.00	6.00	3.50
45	Carl Furillo	9.00	4.50	2.75		136	Jim Hegan	7.00	3.50	2.00
46	Bob Miller	7.00	3.50	2.00		137	Bob Rush	7.00	3.50	2.00
47	Don Blasingame	7.00	3.50	2.00		138	Minnie Minoso	8.00	4.00	2.50
48	Bill Bruton	7.00	3.50	2.00		139	Lou Kretlow	7.00	3.50	2.00
49	Daryl Spencer	7.00	3.50	2.00		140	Frank Thomas	7.00	3.50	2.00
50	Herb Score	6.00	3.00	1.75		141	Al Aber	7.00	3.50	2.00
51	Clint Courtney	7.00	3.50	2.00		142	Charley Thompson	7.00	3.50	2.00
52	Lee Walls	7.00	3.50	2.00		143	Andy Pafko	6.00	3.00	1.75
53	Clem Labine	6.00	3.00	1.75		144	Ray Narleski	7.00	3.50	2.00
54	Elmer Valo	7.00	3.50	2.00		145	Al Smith	7.00	3.50	2.00
55	Ernie Banks	110.00	55.00	33.00		146	Don Ferrarese	7.00	3.50	2.00
56	Dave Sisler	7.00	3.50	2.00		147	Al Walker	6.00	3.00	1.75
57	Jim Lemon	7.00	3.50	2.00		148	Don Mueller	7.00	3.50	2.00
58	Ruben Gomez	7.00	3.50	2.00		149	Bob Kennedy	7.00	3.50	2.00
59	Dick Williams	6.00	3.00	1.75		150	Bob Friend	6.00	3.00	1.75
60	Billy Hoeft	7.00	3.50	2.00		151	Willie Miranda	7.00	3.50	2.00
61	Dusty Rhodes	7.00	3.50	2.00		152	Jack Harshman	7.00	3.50	2.00
62	Billy Martin	50.00	25.00	15.00		153	Karl Olson	7.00	3.50	2.00
63	Ike Delock	7.00	3.50	2.00		154	Red Schoendienst	20.00	10.00	6.00
64	Pete Runnels	6.00	3.00	1.75		155	Jim Brosnan	7.00	3.50	2.00
65	Wally Moon	7.00	3.50	2.00		156	Gus Triandos	7.00	3.50	2.00
66	Brooks Lawrence	7.00	3.50	2.00		157	Wally Post	7.00	3.50	2.00
67	Chico Carrasquel	7.00	3.50	2.00		158	Curt Simmons	6.00	3.00	1.75
68	Ray Crone	7.00	3.50	2.00		159	Solly Drake	7.00	3.50	2.00
69	Roy McMillan	7.00	3.50	2.00		160	Billy Pierce	6.00	3.00	1.75
70	Richie Ashburn	25.00	12.50	7.50		161	Pirates Team	8.00	4.00	2.50
71	Murry Dickson	7.00	3.50	2.00		162	Jack Meyer	7.00	3.50	2.00
72	Bill Tuttle	7.00	3.50	2.00		163	Sammy White	7.00	3.50	2.00
73	George Crowe	7.00	3.50	2.00		164	Tommy Carroll	6.00	3.00	1.75
74	Vito Valentinetti	7.00	3.50	2.00		165	Ted Kluszewski	25.00	12.50	7.50
75	Jim Piersall	6.00	3.00	1.75		166	Roy Face	6.00	3.00	1.75
76	Bob Clemente	250.00	125.00	75.00		167	Vic Power	7.00	3.50	2.00
77	Paul Foytack	7.00	3.50	2.00		168	Frank Lary	6.00	3.00	1.75
78	Vic Wertz	6.00	3.00	1.75		169	Herb Plews	7.00	3.50	2.00
79	*Lindy McDaniel*	6.00	3.00	1.75		170	Duke Snider	100.00	50.00	30.00
80	Gil Hodges	50.00	30.00	15.00		171	Red Sox Team	9.00	4.50	2.75
81	Herm Wehmeier	7.00	3.50	2.00		172	Gene Woodling	6.00	3.00	1.75
82	Elston Howard	15.00	7.50	4.50		173	Roger Craig	8.00	4.00	2.50
83	Lou Skizas	7.00	3.50	2.00		174	Willie Jones	7.00	3.50	2.00
84	Moe Drabowsky	7.00	3.50	2.00		175	Don Larsen	8.00	4.00	2.50
85	Larry Doby	10.00	5.00	3.00		176	Gene Baker	7.00	3.50	2.00
86	Bill Sarni	7.00	3.50	2.00		177	Eddie Yost	7.00	3.50	2.00
87	Tom Gorman	7.00	3.50	2.00		178	Don Bessent	7.00	3.50	2.00
88	Harvey Kuenn	6.00	3.00	1.75		179	Ernie Oravetz	7.00	3.50	2.00
89	Roy Sievers	7.00	3.50	2.00		180	Gus Bell	7.00	3.50	2.00
90	Warren Spahn	75.00	38.00	23.00		181	Dick Donovan	7.00	3.50	2.00
91	Mack Burk	7.00	3.50	2.00		182	Hobie Landrith	7.00	3.50	2.00
92	Mickey Vernon	6.00	3.00	1.75		183	Cubs Team	8.00	4.00	2.50
93	Hal Jeffcoat	7.00	3.50	2.00		184	*Tito Francona*	6.00	3.00	1.75
94	Bobby Del Greco	7.00	3.50	2.00		185	Johnny Kucks	6.00	3.00	1.75
95	Mickey Mantle	900.00	450.00	275.00		186	Jim King	7.00	3.50	2.00
96	*Hank Aguirre*	6.00	3.00	1.75		187	Virgil Trucks	7.00	3.50	2.00
97	Yankees Team	40.00	20.00	12.00		188	Felix Mantilla	7.00	3.50	2.00
98	Al Dark	8.00	4.00	2.50		189	Willard Nixon	7.00	3.50	2.00
99	Bob Keegan	7.00	3.50	2.00		190	Randy Jackson	7.00	3.50	2.00
100	League Presidents (Warren Giles, William Harridge)	6.00	3.00	1.75		191	Joe Margoneri	7.00	3.50	2.00
101	Chuck Stobbs	7.00	3.50	2.00		192	Jerry Coleman	6.00	3.00	1.75
102	Ray Boone	7.00	3.50	2.00		193	Del Rice	7.00	3.50	2.00
103	Joe Nuxhall	6.00	3.00	1.75		194	Hal Brown	7.00	3.50	2.00
104	Hank Foiles	7.00	3.50	2.00		195	Bobby Avila	7.00	3.50	2.00
105	Johnny Antonelli	7.00	3.50	2.00		196	Larry Jackson	7.00	3.50	2.00
106	Ray Moore	7.00	3.50	2.00		197	Hank Sauer	7.00	3.50	2.00
107	Jim Rivera	7.00	3.50	2.00		198	Tigers Team	9.00	4.50	2.75
108	Tommy Byrne	6.00	3.00	1.75		199	Vernon Law	6.00	3.00	1.75
109	Hank Thompson	7.00	3.50	2.00		200	Gil McDougald	12.00	6.00	3.50
110	Bill Virdon	6.00	3.00	1.75		201	Sandy Amoros	7.00	3.50	2.00
111	Hal Smith	7.00	3.50	2.00		202	Dick Gernert	7.00	3.50	2.00
112	Tom Brewer	6.00	3.00	1.75		203	Hoyt Wilhelm	18.00	9.00	5.50
113	Wilmer Mizell	7.00	3.50	2.00		204	Athletics Team	8.00	4.00	2.50
114	Braves Team	10.00	5.00	3.00		205	Charley Maxwell	7.00	3.50	2.00
115	Jim Gilliam	10.00	5.00	3.00		206	Willard Schmidt	7.00	3.50	2.00
116	Mike Fornieles	7.00	3.50	2.00		207	Billy Hunter	7.00	3.50	2.00
117	Joe Adcock	6.00	3.00	1.75		208	Lew Burdette	6.00	3.00	1.75

		NR MT	EX	VG			NR MT	EX	VG
209	Bob Skinner	7.00	3.50	2.00	300	Mike Garcia	18.00	9.00	5.50
210	Roy Campanella	100.00	50.00	30.00	301	Sam Esposito	18.00	9.00	5.50
211	Camilo Pascual	7.00	3.50	2.00	302	Sandy Koufax	400.00	200.00	125.00
212	*Rocco Colavito*	135.00	67.00	40.00	303	Billy Goodman	18.00	9.00	5.50
213	Les Moss	7.00	3.50	2.00	304	Joe Cunningham	18.00	9.00	5.50
214	Phillies Team	8.00	4.00	2.50	305	Chico Fernandez	18.00	9.00	5.50
215	Enos Slaughter	20.00	10.00	6.00	306	Darrell Johnson	18.00	9.00	5.50
216	Marv Grissom	7.00	3.50	2.00	307	Jack Phillips	18.00	9.00	5.50
217	Gene Stephens	7.00	3.50	2.00	308	Dick Hall	18.00	9.00	5.50
218	Ray Jablonski	7.00	3.50	2.00	309	Jim Busby	18.00	9.00	5.50
219	Tom Acker	7.00	3.50	2.00	310	Max Surkont	18.00	9.00	5.50
220	Jackie Jensen	6.00	3.00	1.75	311	Al Pilarcik	18.00	9.00	5.50
221	Dixie Howell	7.00	3.50	2.00	312	*Tony Kubek*	135.00	67.00	40.00
222	Alex Grammas	7.00	3.50	2.00	313	Mel Parnell	18.00	9.00	5.50
223	Frank House	7.00	3.50	2.00	314	Ed Bouchee	18.00	9.00	5.50
224	Marv Blaylock	7.00	3.50	2.00	315	Lou Berberet	18.00	9.00	5.50
225	Harry Simpson	7.00	3.50	2.00	316	Billy O'Dell	18.00	9.00	5.50
226	Preston Ward	7.00	3.50	2.00	317	Giants Team	50.00	25.00	15.00
227	Jerry Staley	7.00	3.50	2.00	318	Mickey McDermott	18.00	9.00	5.50
228	Smoky Burgess	6.00	3.00	1.75	319	Gino Cimoli	18.00	9.00	5.50
229	George Susce	7.00	3.50	2.00	320	Neil Chrisley	18.00	9.00	5.50
230	George Kell	18.00	9.00	5.50	321	Red Murff	18.00	9.00	5.50
231	Solly Hemus	7.00	3.50	2.00	322	Redlegs Team	50.00	25.00	15.00
232	Whitey Lockman	7.00	3.50	2.00	323	Wes Westrum	18.00	9.00	5.50
233	Art Fowler	7.00	3.50	2.00	324	Dodgers Team	90.00	45.00	27.00
234	Dick Cole	7.00	3.50	2.00	325	Frank Bolling	18.00	9.00	5.50
235	Tom Poholsky	7.00	3.50	2.00	326	Pedro Ramos	18.00	9.00	5.50
236	Joe Ginsberg	7.00	3.50	2.00	327	Jim Pendleton	18.00	9.00	5.50
237	Foster Castleman	7.00	3.50	2.00	328	*Brooks Robinson*	400.00	200.00	125.00
238	Eddie Robinson	7.00	3.50	2.00	329	White Sox Team	35.00	17.50	10.50
239	Tom Morgan	7.00	3.50	2.00	330	Jim Wilson	18.00	9.00	5.50
240	Hank Bauer	10.00	5.00	3.00	331	Ray Katt	18.00	9.00	5.50
241	Joe Lonnett	7.00	3.50	2.00	332	Bob Bowman	18.00	9.00	5.50
242	Charley Neal	7.00	3.50	2.00	333	Ernie Johnson	18.00	9.00	5.50
243	Cardinals Team	8.00	4.00	2.50	334	Jerry Schoonmaker	18.00	9.00	5.50
244	Billy Loes	7.00	3.50	2.00	335	Granny Hamner	18.00	9.00	5.50
245	Rip Repulski	7.00	3.50	2.00	336	*Haywood Sullivan*	18.00	9.00	5.50
246	Jose Valdivielso	7.00	3.50	2.00	337	Rene Valdes	18.00	9.00	5.50
247	Turk Lown	7.00	3.50	2.00	338	*Jim Bunning*	125.00	62.00	37.00
248	Jim Finigan	7.00	3.50	2.00	339	Bob Speake	18.00	9.00	5.50
249	Dave Pope	7.00	3.50	2.00	340	Bill Wight	18.00	9.00	5.50
250	Ed Mathews	35.00	17.50	10.50	341	Don Gross	18.00	9.00	5.50
251	Orioles Team	8.00	4.00	2.50	342	Gene Mauch	18.00	9.00	5.50
252	Carl Erskine	10.00	5.00	3.00	343	Taylor Phillips	18.00	9.00	5.50
253	Gus Zernial	7.00	3.50	2.00	344	Paul LaPalme	18.00	9.00	5.50
254	Ron Negray	7.00	3.50	2.00	345	Paul Smith	18.00	9.00	5.50
255	Charlie Silvera	7.00	3.50	2.00	346	Dick Littlefield	18.00	9.00	5.50
256	Ronnie Kline	7.00	3.50	2.00	347	Hal Naragon	18.00	9.00	5.50
257	Walt Dropo	7.00	3.50	2.00	348	Jim Hearn	18.00	9.00	5.50
258	Steve Gromek	7.00	3.50	2.00	349	Nelson King	18.00	9.00	5.50
259	Eddie O'Brien	7.00	3.50	2.00	350	Eddie Miksis	18.00	9.00	5.50
260	Del Ennis	7.00	3.50	2.00	351	Dave Hillman	18.00	9.00	5.50
261	Bob Chakales	7.00	3.50	2.00	352	Ellis Kinder	18.00	9.00	5.50
262	Bobby Thomson	6.00	3.00	1.75	353	Cal Neeman	7.00	3.50	2.00
263	George Strickland	7.00	3.50	2.00	354	Rip Coleman	7.00	3.50	2.00
264	Bob Turley	8.00	4.00	2.50	355	Frank Malzone	7.00	3.50	2.00
265	Harvey Haddix	20.00	10.00	6.00	356	Faye Throneberry	7.00	3.50	2.00
266	Ken Kuhn	18.00	9.00	5.50	357	Earl Torgeson	7.00	3.50	2.00
267	Danny Kravitz	18.00	9.00	5.50	358	Jerry Lynch	7.00	3.50	2.00
268	Jackie Collum	18.00	9.00	5.50	359	Tom Cheney	7.00	3.50	2.00
269	Bob Cerv	18.00	9.00	5.50	360	Johnny Groth	7.00	3.50	2.00
270	Senators Team	25.00	12.50	7.50	361	Curt Barclay	7.00	3.50	2.00
271	Danny O'Connell	18.00	9.00	5.50	362	Roman Mejias	7.00	3.50	2.00
272	Bobby Shantz	25.00	12.50	7.50	363	Eddie Kasko	7.00	3.50	2.00
273	Jim Davis	18.00	9.00	5.50	364	Cal McLish	7.00	3.50	2.00
274	Don Hoak	18.00	9.00	5.50	365	Ossie Virgil	7.00	3.50	2.00
275	Indians Team	35.00	17.50	10.50	366	Ken Lehman	7.00	3.50	2.00
276	Jim Pyburn	18.00	9.00	5.50	367	Ed Fitz Gerald	7.00	3.50	2.00
277	Johnny Podres	50.00	25.00	15.00	368	Bob Purkey	7.00	3.50	2.00
278	Fred Hatfield	18.00	9.00	5.50	369	Milt Graff	7.00	3.50	2.00
279	Bob Thurman	18.00	9.00	5.50	370	Warren Hacker	7.00	3.50	2.00
280	Alex Kellner	18.00	9.00	5.50	371	Bob Lennon	7.00	3.50	2.00
281	Gail Harris	18.00	9.00	5.50	372	Norm Zauchin	7.00	3.50	2.00
282	Jack Dittmer	18.00	9.00	5.50	373	Pete Whisenant	7.00	3.50	2.00
283	*Wes Covington*	18.00	9.00	5.50	374	Don Cardwell	7.00	3.50	2.00
284	Don Zimmer	20.00	10.00	6.00	375	*Jim Landis*	6.00	3.00	1.75
285	Ned Garver	18.00	9.00	5.50	376	Don Elston	7.00	3.50	2.00
286	*Bobby Richardson*	125.00	67.00	37.00	377	Andre Rodgers	7.00	3.50	2.00
287	Sam Jones	18.00	9.00	5.50	378	Elmer Singleton	7.00	3.50	2.00
288	Ted Lepcio	18.00	9.00	5.50	379	Don Lee	7.00	3.50	2.00
289	Jim Bolger	18.00	9.00	5.50	380	Walker Cooper	7.00	3.50	2.00
290	Andy Carey	18.00	9.00	5.50	381	Dean Stone	7.00	3.50	2.00
291	Windy McCall	18.00	9.00	5.50	382	Jim Brideweser	7.00	3.50	2.00
292	Billy Klaus	18.00	9.00	5.50	383	*Juan Pizarro*	6.00	3.00	1.75
293	Ted Abernathy	18.00	9.00	5.50	384	Bobby Gene Smith	7.00	3.50	2.00
294	Rocky Bridges	18.00	9.00	5.50	385	Art Houtteman	7.00	3.50	2.00
295	Joe Collins	18.00	9.00	5.50	386	Lyle Luttrell	7.00	3.50	2.00
296	Johnny Klippstein	18.00	9.00	5.50	387	*Jack Sanford*	6.00	3.00	1.75
297	Jack Crimian	18.00	9.00	5.50	388	Pete Daley	7.00	3.50	2.00
298	Irv Noren	18.00	9.00	5.50	389	Dave Jolly	7.00	3.50	2.00
299	Chuck Harmon	18.00	9.00	5.50	390	Reno Bertoia	7.00	3.50	2.00

		NR MT	EX	VG
391	*Ralph Terry*	10.00	5.00	3.00
392	Chuck Tanner	6.00	3.00	1.75
393	Raul Sanchez	7.00	3.50	2.00
394	Luis Arroyo	7.00	3.50	2.00
395	Bubba Phillips	7.00	3.50	2.00
396	Casey Wise	7.00	3.50	2.00
397	Roy Smalley	7.00	3.50	2.00
398	Al Cicotte	6.00	3.00	1.75
399	Billy Consolo	7.00	3.50	2.00
400	Dodgers' Sluggers (Roy Campanella, Carl Furillo, Gil Hodges, Duke Snider)	200.00	100.00	60.00
401	*Earl Battey*	6.00	3.00	1.75
402	Jim Pisoni	7.00	3.50	2.00
403	Dick Hyde	7.00	3.50	2.00
404	Harry Anderson	7.00	3.50	2.00
405	Duke Maas	7.00	3.50	2.00
406	Bob Hale	7.00	3.50	2.00
407	Yankees' Power Hitters (Yogi Berra, Mickey Mantle)	400.00	200.00	125.00
---a	Checklist Series 1-2 (Big Blony ad on back)	175.00	87.00	52.00
---b	Checklist Series 1-2 (Bazooka ad on back)	175.00	87.00	52.00
---a	Checklist Series 2-3 (Big Blony ad on back)	300.00	150.00	90.00
---b	Checklist Series 2-3 (Bazooka ad on back)	300.00	150.00	90.00
---a	Checklist Series 3-4 (Big Blony ad on back)	500.00	250.00	150.00
---b	Checklist Series 3-4 (Bazooka ad on back)	500.00	250.00	150.00
---a	Checklist Series 4-5 (Big Blony ad on back)	750.00	325.00	225.00
---b	Checklist Series 4-5 (Bazooka ad on back)	750.00	325.00	225.00
----	Contest Card (Saturday, May 4th)	15.00	7.50	4.50
----	Contest Card (Saturday, May 25th)	15.00	7.50	4.50
----	Contest Card (Saturday, June 22nd)	15.00	7.50	4.50
----	Contest Card (Friday, July 19)	15.00	7.50	4.50
----	Lucky Penny Insert Card	15.00	7.50	4.50

1958 Topps

Topps continued to expand its set size in 1958 with the release of a 494-card set. One card (#145) was not issued after Ed Bouchee was suspended from baseball. Cards retained the 2-1/2" by 3-1/2" size. There are a number of variations, including yellow or white lettering on 33 cards between numbers 2-108 (higher priced yellow letter variations checklisted below are not included in the complete set prices). The number of multiple-player cards was increased. A major innovation is the addition of 20 "All-Star" cards. For the first time, checklists were incorporated into the numbered series, as the backs of team cards.

		NR MT	EX	VG
	Complete Set:	5000.00	2500.00	1500.
	Common Player: 1-110	7.00	3.50	2.00
	Common Player: 111-440	5.00	2.50	1.50
	Common Player: 441-495	4.00	2.00	1.25
1	Ted Williams	400.00	125.00	60.00
2a	Bob Lemon (yellow team letters)	35.00	17.50	10.50

		NR MT	EX	VG
2b	Bob Lemon (white team letters)	12.00	6.00	3.50
3	Alex Kellner	7.00	3.50	2.00
4	Hank Foiles	7.00	3.50	2.00
5	Willie Mays	160.00	80.00	50.00
6	George Zuverink	7.00	3.50	2.00
7	Dale Long	7.00	3.50	2.00
8a	Eddie Kasko (yellow name letters)	20.00	10.00	6.00
8b	Eddie Kasko (white name letters)	7.00	3.50	2.00
9	Hank Bauer	12.00	6.00	3.50
10	Lou Burdette	8.00	4.00	2.50
11a	Jim Rivera (yellow team letters)	20.00	10.00	6.00
11b	Jim Rivera (white team letters)	7.00	3.50	2.00
12	George Crowe	7.00	3.50	2.00
13a	Billy Hoeft (yellow name letters)	20.00	10.00	6.00
13b	Billy Hoeft (white name, orange triangle by foot)	7.00	3.50	2.00
13c	Billy Hoeft (white name, red triangle by foot)	7.00	3.50	2.00
14	Rip Repulski	7.00	3.50	2.00
15	Jim Lemon	7.00	3.50	2.00
16	Charley Neal	7.00	3.50	2.00
17	Felix Mantilla	7.00	3.50	2.00
18	Frank Sullivan	7.00	3.50	2.00
19	Giants Team/Checklist 1-88	10.00	5.00	3.00
20a	Gil McDougald (yellow name letters)	25.00	12.50	7.50
20b	Gil McDougald (white name letters)	9.00	4.50	2.75
21	Curt Barclay	7.00	3.50	2.00
22	Hal Naragon	7.00	3.50	2.00
23a	Bill Tuttle (yellow name letters)	20.00	10.00	6.00
23b	Bill Tuttle (white name letters)	7.00	3.50	2.00
24a	Hobie Landrith (yellow name letters)	20.00	10.00	6.00
24b	Hobie Landrith (white name letters)	7.00	3.50	2.00
25	Don Drysdale	60.00	30.00	18.00
26	Ron Jackson	7.00	3.50	2.00
27	Bud Freeman	7.00	3.50	2.00
28	Jim Busby	7.00	3.50	2.00
29	Ted Lepcio	7.00	3.50	2.00
30a	Hank Aaron (yellow name letters)	350.00	140.00	88.00
30b	Hank Aaron (white name letters)	175.00	87.00	52.00
31	Tex Clevenger	7.00	3.50	2.00
32a	J.W. Porter (yellow name letters)	20.00	10.00	6.00
32b	J.W. Porter (white name letters)	7.00	3.50	2.00
33a	Cal Neeman (yellow team letters)	20.00	10.00	6.00
33b	Cal Neeman (white team letters)	7.00	3.50	2.00
34	Bob Thurman	7.00	3.50	2.00
35a	Don Mossi (yellow name letters)	20.00	10.00	6.00
35b	Don Mossi (white name letters)	7.00	3.50	2.00
36	Ted Kazanski	7.00	3.50	2.00
37	*Mike McCormick* (photo actually Ray Monzant)	7.00	3.50	2.00
38	Dick Gernert	7.00	3.50	2.00
39	Bob Martyn	7.00	3.50	2.00
40	George Kell	15.00	7.50	4.50
41	Dave Hillman	7.00	3.50	2.00
42	*John Roseboro*	7.00	3.50	2.00
43	Sal Maglie	10.00	5.00	3.00
44	Senators Team/Checklist 1-88	10.00	5.00	3.00
45	Dick Groat	7.00	3.50	2.00
46a	Lou Sleater (yellow name letters)	20.00	10.00	6.00
46b	Lou Sleater (white name letters)	7.00	3.50	2.00
47	*Roger Maris*	450.00	225.00	135.00
48	Chuck Harmon	7.00	3.50	2.00
49	Smoky Burgess	7.00	3.50	2.00
50a	Billy Pierce (yellow name letters)	20.00	10.00	6.00
50b	Billy Pierce (white name letters)	7.00	3.50	2.00
51	Del Rice	7.00	3.50	2.00
52a	Bob Clemente (yellow team letters)	350.00	175.00	105.00
52b	Bob Clemente (white team letters)	225.00	112.00	67.00
53a	Morrie Martin (yellow name letters)	20.00	10.00	6.00
53b	Morrie Martin (white name letters)	7.00	3.50	2.00
54	*Norm Siebern*	7.00	3.50	2.00
55	Chico Carrasquel	7.00	3.50	2.00
56	Bill Fischer	7.00	3.50	2.00
57a	Tim Thompson (yellow name letters)	20.00	10.00	6.00
57b	Tim Thompson (white name letters)	7.00	3.50	2.00
58a	Art Schult (yellow team letters)	20.00	10.00	6.00

		NR MT	EX	VG
58b	Art Schult (white team letters)	7.00	3.50	2.00
59	Dave Sisler	7.00	3.50	2.00
60a	Del Ennis (yellow name letters)	20.00	10.00	6.00
60b	Del Ennis (white name letters)	7.00	3.50	2.00
61a	Darrell Johnson (yellow name letters)			
		20.00	10.00	6.00
61b	Darrell Johnson (white name letters)			
		7.00	3.50	2.00
62	Joe DeMaestri	7.00	3.50	2.00
63	Joe Nuxhall	7.00	3.50	2.00
64	Joe Lonnett	7.00	3.50	2.00
65a	Von McDaniel (yellow name letters)			
		20.00	10.00	6.00
65b	Von McDaniel (white name letters)			
		7.00	3.50	2.00
66	Lee Walls	7.00	3.50	2.00
67	Joe Ginsberg	7.00	3.50	2.00
68	Daryl Spencer	7.00	3.50	2.00
69	Wally Burnette	7.00	3.50	2.00
70a	Al Kaline (yellow name letters)	200.00	100.00	60.00
70b	Al Kaline (white name letters)	75.00	38.00	23.00
71	Dodgers Team/Checklist 1-88	20.00	10.00	6.00
72	Bud Byerly	7.00	3.50	2.00
73	Pete Daley	7.00	3.50	2.00
74	Roy Face	7.00	3.50	2.00
75	Gus Bell	7.00	3.50	2.00
76a	Dick Farrell (yellow team letters)			
		20.00	10.00	6.00
76b	Dick Farrell (white team letters)	7.00	3.50	2.00
77a	Don Zimmer (yellow team letters)			
		20.00	10.00	6.00
77b	Don Zimmer (white team letters)	7.00	3.50	2.00
78a	Ernie Johnson (yellow team letters)			
		20.00	10.00	6.00
78b	Ernie Johnson (white team letters)			
		7.00	3.50	2.00
79a	Dick Williams (yellow team letters)			
		20.00	10.00	6.00
79b	Dick Williams (white team letters)	7.00	3.50	2.00
80	Dick Drott	7.00	3.50	2.00
81a	*Steve Boros* (yellow team letters)			
		20.00	10.00	6.00
81b	*Steve Boros* (white team letters)	7.00	3.50	2.00
82	Ronnie Kline	7.00	3.50	2.00
83	Bob Hazle	7.00	3.50	2.00
84	Billy O'Dell	7.00	3.50	2.00
85a	Luis Aparicio (yellow team letters)			
		50.00	25.00	15.00
85b	Luis Aparicio (white team letters)			
		15.00	7.50	4.50
86	Valmy Thomas	7.00	3.50	2.00
87	Johnny Kucks	7.00	3.50	2.00
88	Duke Snider	75.00	38.00	23.00
89	Billy Klaus	7.00	3.50	2.00
90	Robin Roberts	20.00	10.00	6.00
91	Chuck Tanner	7.00	3.50	2.00
92a	Clint Courtney (yellow name letters)			
		20.00	10.00	6.00
92b	Clint Courtney (white name letters)			
		7.00	3.50	2.00
93	Sandy Amoros	7.00	3.50	2.00
94	Bob Skinner	7.00	3.50	2.00
95	Frank Bolling	7.00	3.50	2.00
96	Joe Durham	7.00	3.50	2.00
97a	Larry Jackson (yellow name letters)			
		20.00	10.00	6.00
97b	Larry Jackson (white name letters)			
		7.00	3.50	2.00
98a	Billy Hunter (yellow name letters)			
		20.00	10.00	6.00
98b	Billy Hunter (white name letters)	7.00	3.50	2.00
99	Bobby Adams	7.00	3.50	2.00
100a	Early Wynn (yellow team letters)	30.00	15.00	9.00
100b	Early Wynn (white team letters)	15.00	7.50	4.50
101a	Bobby Richardson (yellow name letters)			
		30.00	15.00	9.00
101b	Bobby Richardson (white name letters)			
		15.00	7.50	4.50
102	George Strickland	7.00	3.50	2.00
103	Jerry Lynch	7.00	3.50	2.00
104	Jim Pendleton	7.00	3.50	2.00
105	Billy Gardner	7.00	3.50	2.00
106	Dick Schofield	7.00	3.50	2.00
107	Ossie Virgil	7.00	3.50	2.00
108a	Jim Landis (yellow team letters)	20.00	10.00	6.00
108b	Jim Landis (white team letters)	7.00	3.50	2.00
109	Herb Plews	7.00	3.50	2.00
110	Johnny Logan	7.00	3.50	2.00
111	Stu Miller	5.00	2.50	1.50
112	Gus Zernial	5.50	2.75	1.75
113	Jerry Walker	5.00	2.50	1.50

		NR MT	EX	VG
114	Irv Noren	5.00	2.50	1.50
115	Jim Bunning	18.00	9.00	5.50
116	Dave Philley	5.50	2.75	1.75
117	Frank Torre	5.00	2.50	1.50
118	Harvey Haddix	5.00	2.50	1.50
119	Harry Chiti	5.00	2.50	1.50
120	Johnny Podres	7.00	3.50	2.00
121	Eddie Miksis	5.00	2.50	1.50
122	Walt Moryn	5.00	2.50	1.50
123	Dick Tomanek	5.00	2.50	1.50
124	Bobby Usher	5.00	2.50	1.50
125	Al Dark	7.00	3.50	2.00
126	Stan Palys	5.00	2.50	1.50
127	Tom Sturdivant	7.00	3.50	2.00
128	*Willie Kirkland*	5.50	2.75	1.75
129	Jim Derrington	5.00	2.50	1.50
130	Jackie Jensen	7.00	3.50	2.00
131	Bob Henrich	5.00	2.50	1.50
132	Vernon Law	6.00	3.00	1.75
133	Russ Nixon	5.00	2.50	1.50
134	Phillies Team/Checklist 89-176	8.00	4.00	2.50
135	Mike Drabowsky	5.00	2.50	1.50
136	Jim Finingan	5.00	2.50	1.50
137	Russ Kemmerer	5.00	2.50	1.50
138	Earl Torgeson	5.00	2.50	1.50
139	George Brunet	5.00	2.50	1.50
140	Wes Covington	5.50	2.75	1.75
141	Ken Lehman	5.00	2.50	1.50
142	Enos Slaughter	20.00	10.00	6.00
143	Billy Muffett		2.50	1.50
144	Bobby Morgan	5.00	2.50	1.50
145	Not Issued			
146	Dick Gray	5.00	2.50	1.50
147	*Don McMahon*	6.00	3.00	1.75
148	Billy Consolo	5.00	2.50	1.50
149	Tom Acker	5.00	2.50	1.50
150	Mickey Mantle	550.00	275.00	165.00
151	Buddy Pritchard	5.00	2.50	1.50
152	Johnny Antonelli	6.00	3.00	1.75
153	Les Moss	5.00	2.50	1.50
154	Harry Byrd	5.00	2.50	1.50
155	Hector Lopez	5.00	2.50	1.50
156	Dick Hyde	5.00	2.50	1.50
157	Dee Fondy	5.00	2.50	1.50
158	Indians Team/Checklist 177-264	7.00	3.50	2.00
159	Taylor Phillips	5.00	2.50	1.50
160	Don Hoak	5.50	2.75	1.75
161	Don Larsen	7.00	3.50	2.00
162	Gil Hodges	25.00	12.50	7.50
163	Jim Wilson	5.00	2.50	1.50
164	Bob Taylor	5.00	2.50	1.50
165	Bob Nieman	5.00	2.50	1.50
166	Danny O'Connell	5.00	2.50	1.50
167	Frank Baumann	5.00	2.50	1.50
168	Joe Cunningham	5.50	2.75	1.75
169	Ralph Terry	5.50	2.75	1.75
170	Vic Wertz	6.00	3.00	1.75
171	Harry Anderson	5.00	2.50	1.50
172	Don Gross	5.00	2.50	1.50
173	Eddie Yost	5.50	2.75	1.75
174	A's Team/Checklist 89-176	8.00	4.00	2.50
175	*Marv Throneberry*	12.00	6.00	3.50
176	Bob Buhl	5.50	2.75	1.75
177	Al Smith	5.00	2.50	1.50
178	Ted Kluszewski	5.00	2.50	1.50
179	Willy Miranda	5.00	2.50	1.50
180	Lindy McDaniel	5.00	2.50	1.50
181	Willie Jones	5.00	2.50	1.50
182	Joe Caffie	5.00	2.50	1.50
183	Dave Jolly	5.00	2.50	1.50
184	Elvin Tappe	5.00	2.50	1.50
185	Ray Boone	5.50	2.75	1.75
186	Jack Meyer	5.00	2.50	1.50
187	Sandy Koufax	135.00	67.00	40.00
188	Milt Bolling (photo actually Lou Berberet)			
		5.00	2.50	1.50
189	George Susce	5.00	2.50	1.50
190	Red Schoendienst	15.00	7.50	4.50
191	Art Ceccarelli	5.00	2.50	1.50
192	Milt Graff	5.00	2.50	1.50
193	*Jerry Lumpe*	5.00	2.50	1.50
194	Roger Craig	6.00	3.00	1.75
195	Whitey Lockman	5.00	2.50	1.50
196	Mike Garcia	5.50	2.75	1.75
197	Haywood Sullivan	5.50	2.75	1.75
198	Bill Virdon	6.00	3.00	1.75
199	Don Blasingame	5.00	2.50	1.50
200	Bob Keegan	5.00	2.50	1.50
201	Jim Bolger	5.00	2.50	1.50
202	*Woody Held*	6.00	3.00	1.75
203	Al Walker	5.00	2.50	1.50

		NR MT	EX	VG
204	Leo Kiely	5.00	2.50	1.50
205	Johnny Temple	5.00	2.50	1.50
206	Bob Shaw	6.00	3.00	1.75
207	Solly Hemus	5.00	2.50	1.50
208	Cal McLish	5.00	2.50	1.50
209	Bob Anderson	5.00	2.50	1.50
210	Wally Moon	5.50	2.75	1.75
211	Pete Burnside	5.00	2.50	1.50
212	Bubba Phillips	5.00	2.50	1.50
213	Red Wilson	5.00	2.50	1.50
214	Willard Schmidt	5.00	2.50	1.50
215	Jim Gilliam	5.00	2.50	1.50
216	Cards Team/Checklist 177-264	7.00	3.50	2.00
217	Jack Harshman	5.00	2.50	1.50
218	Dick Rand	5.00	2.50	1.50
219	Camilo Pascual	5.50	2.75	1.75
220	Tom Brewer	5.00	2.50	1.50
221	Jerry Kindall	5.00	2.50	1.50
222	Bud Daley	5.00	2.50	1.50
223	Andy Pafko	6.00	3.00	1.75
224	Bob Grim	7.00	3.50	2.00
225	Billy Goodman	5.00	2.50	1.50
226	Bob Smith (photo actually Bobby Gene Smith)	5.00	2.50	1.50
227	Gene Stephens	5.00	2.50	1.50
228	Duke Maas	5.00	2.50	1.50
229	Frank Zupo	5.00	2.50	1.50
230	Richie Ashburn	8.00	4.00	2.50
231	Lloyd Merritt	5.00	2.50	1.50
232	Reno Bertoia	5.00	2.50	1.50
233	Mickey Vernon	5.50	2.75	1.75
234	Carl Sawatski	5.00	2.50	1.50
235	Tom Gorman	5.00	2.50	1.50
236	Ed Fitz Gerald	5.00	2.50	1.50
237	Bill Wight	5.00	2.50	1.50
238	Bill Mazeroski	15.00	7.50	4.50
239	Chuck Stobbs	5.00	2.50	1.50
240	Moose Skowron	10.00	5.00	3.00
241	Dick Littlefield	5.00	2.50	1.50
242	Johnny Klippstein	5.00	2.50	1.50
243	Larry Raines	5.00	2.50	1.50
244	*Don Demeter*	5.50	2.75	1.75
245	*Frank Lary*	5.50	2.75	1.75
246	Yankees Team/Checklist 177-264	40.00	20.00	12.00
247	Casey Wise	5.00	2.50	1.50
248	Herm Wehmeier	5.00	2.50	1.50
249	Ray Moore	5.00	2.50	1.50
250	Roy Sievers	6.00	3.00	1.75
251	Warren Hacker	5.00	2.50	1.50
252	Bob Trowbridge	5.00	2.50	1.50
253	Don Mueller	5.00	2.50	1.50
254	Alex Grammas	5.00	2.50	1.50
255	Bob Turley	5.00	2.50	1.50
256	White Sox Team/Checklist 265-352	8.00	4.00	2.50
257	Hal Smith	5.00	2.50	1.50
258	Carl Erskine	5.00	2.50	1.50
259	Al Pilarcik	5.00	2.50	1.50
260	Frank Malzone	5.50	2.75	1.75
261	Turk Lown	5.00	2.50	1.50
262	Johnny Groth	5.00	2.50	1.50
263	Eddie Bressoud	5.50	2.75	1.75
264	Jack Sanford	5.50	2.75	1.75
265	Pete Runnels	5.50	2.75	1.75
266	Connie Johnson	5.00	2.50	1.50
267	Sherm Lollar	5.50	2.75	1.75
268	Granny Hamner	5.00	2.50	1.50
269	Paul Smith	5.00	2.50	1.50
270	Warren Spahn	50.00	25.00	15.00
271	Billy Martin	15.00	7.50	4.50
272	Ray Crone	5.00	2.50	1.50
273	Hal Smith	5.00	2.50	1.50
274	Rocky Bridges	5.00	2.50	1.50
275	Elston Howard	8.00	4.00	2.50
276	Bobby Avila	5.00	2.50	1.50
277	Virgil Trucks	5.50	2.75	1.75
278	Mack Burk	5.00	2.50	1.50
279	Bob Boyd	5.00	2.50	1.50
280	Jim Piersall	6.00	3.00	1.75
281	Sam Taylor	5.00	2.50	1.50
282	Paul Foytack	5.00	2.50	1.50
283	Ray Shearer	5.00	2.50	1.50
284	Ray Katt	5.00	2.50	1.50
285	Frank Robinson	65.00	33.00	20.00
286	Gino Cimoli	5.00	2.50	1.50
287	Sam Jones	5.00	2.50	1.50
288	Harmon Killebrew	50.00	30.00	15.00
289	Series Hurling Rivals (Lou Burdette, Bobby Shantz)	4.00	2.00	1.25
290	Dick Donovan	5.00	2.50	1.50
291	Don Landrum	5.00	2.50	1.50
292	Ned Garver	5.00	2.50	1.50
293	Gene Freese	5.00	2.50	1.50
294	Hal Jeffcoat	5.00	2.50	1.50
295	Minnie Minoso	4.00	2.00	1.25
296	*Ryne Duren*	12.00	6.00	3.50
297	Don Buddin	5.00	2.50	1.50
298	Jim Hearn	5.00	2.50	1.50
299	Harry Simpson	7.00	3.50	2.00
300	League Presidents (Warren Giles, William Harridge)	7.00	3.50	2.00
301	Randy Jackson	5.00	2.50	1.50
302	Mike Baxes	5.00	2.50	1.50
303	Neil Chrisley	5.00	2.50	1.50
304	Tigers' Big Bats (Al Kaline, Harvey Kuenn)	10.00	5.00	3.00
305	Clem Labine	5.50	2.75	1.75
306	Whammy Douglas	5.00	2.50	1.50
307	Brooks Robinson	90.00	45.00	27.00
308	Paul Giel	5.00	2.50	1.50
309	Gail Harris	5.00	2.50	1.50
310	Ernie Banks	90.00	45.00	27.00
311	Bob Purkey	5.00	2.50	1.50
312	Red Sox Team/Checklist 353-440	8.00	4.00	2.50
313	Bob Rush	5.00	2.50	1.50
314	Dodgers' Boss & Power (Walter Alston, Duke Snider)	15.00	7.50	4.50
315	Bob Friend	6.00	3.00	1.75
316	Tito Francona	5.50	2.75	1.75
317	*Albie Pearson*	6.00	3.00	1.75
318	Frank House	5.00	2.50	1.50
319	Lou Skizas	5.00	2.50	1.50
320	Whitey Ford	35.00	17.50	10.50
321	Sluggers Supreme (Ted Kluszewski, Ted Williams)	20.00	10.00	6.00
322	Harding Peterson	5.00	2.50	1.50
323	Elmer Valo	5.00	2.50	1.50
324	Hoyt Wilhelm	15.00	7.50	4.50
325	Joe Adcock	6.00	3.00	1.75
326	Bob Miller	5.00	2.50	1.50
327	Cubs Team/Checklist 265-352	8.00	4.00	2.50
328	Ike Delock	5.00	2.50	1.50
329	Bob Cerv	5.00	2.50	1.50
330	Ed Bailey	5.00	2.50	1.50
331	Pedro Ramos	5.00	2.50	1.50
332	Jim King	5.00	2.50	1.50
333	Andy Carey	7.00	3.50	2.00
334	Mound Aces (Bob Friend, Billy Pierce)	6.00	3.00	1.75
335	Ruben Gomez	5.00	2.50	1.50
336	Bert Hamric	5.00	2.50	1.50
337	Hank Aguirre	5.00	2.50	1.50
338	Walt Dropo	5.50	2.75	1.75
339	Fred Hatfield	5.00	2.50	1.50
340	Don Newcombe	7.00	3.50	2.00
341	Pirates Team/Checklist 265-352	8.00	4.00	2.50
342	Jim Brosnan	5.50	2.75	1.75
343	*Orlando Cepeda*	80.00	40.00	25.00
344	Bob Porterfield	5.00	2.50	1.50
345	Jim Hegan	5.00	2.50	1.50
346	Steve Bilko	5.00	2.50	1.50
347	Don Rudolph	5.00	2.50	1.50
348	Chico Fernandez	5.00	2.50	1.50
349	Murry Dickson	5.00	2.50	1.50
350	Ken Boyer	5.00	2.50	1.50
351	Braves' Fence Busters (Hank Aaron, Joe Adcock, Del Crandall, Ed Mathews)	20.00	10.00	6.00
352	Herb Score	7.00	3.50	2.00
353	Stan Lopata	5.00	2.50	1.50
354	Art Ditmar	7.00	3.50	2.00
355	Bill Bruton	5.50	2.75	1.75
356	Bob Malkmus	5.00	2.50	1.50
357	Danny McDevitt	5.00	2.50	1.50
358	Gene Baker	5.00	2.50	1.50
359	Billy Loes	5.00	2.50	1.50
360	Roy McMillan	5.00	2.50	1.50
361	Mike Fornieles	5.00	2.50	1.50
362	Ray Jablonski	5.00	2.50	1.50
363	Don Elston	5.00	2.50	1.50
364	Earl Battey	5.50	2.75	1.75
365	Tom Morgan	5.00	2.50	1.50
366	Gene Green	5.00	2.50	1.50
367	Jack Urban	5.00	2.50	1.50
368	Rocky Colavito	30.00	15.00	9.00
369	Ralph Lumenti	5.00	2.50	1.50
370	Yogi Berra	100.00	50.00	30.00
371	Marty Keough	5.00	2.50	1.50
372	Don Cardwell	5.00	2.50	1.50
373	Joe Pignatano	5.00	2.50	1.50
374	Brooks Lawrence	5.00	2.50	1.50

		NR MT	EX	VG
375	Pee Wee Reese	50.00	30.00	15.00
376	Charley Rabe	5.00	2.50	1.50
377a	Braves Team (alphabetical checklist on back)	9.00	4.50	2.75
377b	Braves Team (numerical checklist on back)	60.00	30.00	18.00
378	Hank Sauer	5.50	2.75	1.75
379	Ray Herbert	5.00	2.50	1.50
380	Charley Maxwell	5.00	2.50	1.50
381	Hal Brown	5.00	2.50	1.50
382	Al Cicotte	7.00	3.50	2.00
383	Lou Berberet	5.00	2.50	1.50
384	John Goryl	5.00	2.50	1.50
385	Wilmer Mizell	5.00	2.50	1.50
386	Birdie's Young Sluggers (Ed Bailey, Frank Robinson, Birdie Tebbetts)	7.00	3.50	2.00
387	Wally Post	5.00	2.50	1.50
388	Billy Moran	5.00	2.50	1.50
389	Bill Taylor	5.00	2.50	1.50
390	Del Crandall	6.00	3.00	1.75
391	Dave Melton	5.00	2.50	1.50
392	Bennie Daniels	5.00	2.50	1.50
393	Tony Kubek	20.00	10.00	6.00
394	*Jim Grant*	6.00	3.00	1.75
395	Willard Nixon	5.00	2.50	1.50
396	Dutch Dotterer	5.00	2.50	1.50
397a	Tigers Team (alphabetical checklist on back)	9.00	4.50	2.75
397b	Tigers Team (numerical checklist on back)	60.00	30.00	18.00
398	Gene Woodling	5.50	2.75	1.75
399	Marv Grissom	5.00	2.50	1.50
400	Nellie Fox	15.00	7.50	4.50
401	Don Bessent	5.00	2.50	1.50
402	Bobby Gene Smith	5.00	2.50	1.50
403	Steve Korcheck	5.00	2.50	1.50
404	Curt Simmons	6.00	3.00	1.75
405	Ken Aspromonte	5.00	2.50	1.50
406	Vic Power	5.00	2.50	1.50
407	Carlton Willey	5.00	2.50	1.50
408a	Orioles Team (alphabetical checklist on back)	8.00	4.00	2.50
408b	Orioles Team (numerical checklist on back)	60.00	30.00	18.00
409	Frank Thomas	5.00	2.50	1.50
410	Murray Wall	5.00	2.50	1.50
411	*Tony Taylor*	5.50	2.75	1.75
412	Jerry Staley	5.00	2.50	1.50
413	*Jim Davenport*	5.50	2.75	1.75
414	Sammy White	5.00	2.50	1.50
415	Bob Bowman	5.00	2.50	1.50
416	Foster Castleman	5.00	2.50	1.50
417	Carl Furillo	7.00	3.50	2.00
418	World Series Batting Foes (Hank Aaron, Mickey Mantle)	150.00	75.00	45.00
419	Bobby Shantz	7.00	3.50	2.00
420	*Vada Pinson*	25.00	12.50	7.50
421	Dixie Howell	5.00	2.50	1.50
422	Norm Zauchin	5.00	2.50	1.50
423	Phil Clark	5.00	2.50	1.50
424	Larry Doby	5.00	2.50	1.50
425	Sam Esposito	5.00	2.50	1.50
426	Johnny O'Brien	5.00	2.50	1.50
427	Al Worthington	5.00	2.50	1.50
428a	Redlegs Team (alphabetical checklist on back)	8.00	4.00	2.50
428b	Redlegs Team (numerical checklist on back)	50.00	25.00	15.00
429	Gus Triandos	5.50	2.75	1.75
430	Bobby Thomson	6.00	3.00	1.75
431	Gene Conley	5.50	2.75	1.75
432	John Powers	5.00	2.50	1.50
433	Pancho Herrera	5.00	2.50	1.50
434	Harvey Kuenn	6.00	3.00	1.75
435	Ed Roebuck	5.00	2.50	1.50
436	Rival Fence Busters (Willie Mays, Duke Snider)	55.00	28.00	16.50
437	Bob Speake	5.00	2.50	1.50
438	Whitey Herzog	7.00	3.50	2.00
439	Ray Narleski	5.00	2.50	1.50
440	Ed Mathews	30.00	15.00	9.00
441	Jim Marshall	4.00	2.00	1.25
442	Phil Paine	4.00	2.00	1.25
443	Billy Harrell	7.00	3.50	2.00
444	Danny Kravitz	4.00	2.00	1.25
445	Bob Smith	4.00	2.00	1.25
446	Carroll Hardy	7.00	3.50	2.00
447	Ray Monzant	4.00	2.00	1.25
448	*Charlie Lau*	5.50	2.75	1.75
449	Gene Fodge	4.00	2.00	1.25
450	Preston Ward	7.00	3.50	2.00

		NR MT	EX	VG
451	Joe Taylor	4.00	2.00	1.25
452	Roman Mejias	4.00	2.00	1.25
453	Tom Qualters	4.00	2.00	1.25
454	Harry Hanebrink	4.00	2.00	1.25
455	Hal Griggs	4.00	2.00	1.25
456	Dick Brown	4.00	2.00	1.25
457	*Milt Pappas*	5.50	2.75	1.75
458	Julio Becquer	4.00	2.00	1.25
459	Ron Blackburn	4.00	2.00	1.25
460	Chuck Essegian	4.00	2.00	1.25
461	Ed Mayer	4.00	2.00	1.25
462	Gary Geiger	7.00	3.50	2.00
463	Vito Valentinetti	4.00	2.00	1.25
464	*Curt Flood*	25.00	12.50	7.50
465	Arnie Portocarrero	4.00	2.00	1.25
466	Pete Whisenant	4.00	2.00	1.25
467	Glen Hobbie	4.00	2.00	1.25
468	Bob Schmidt	4.00	2.00	1.25
469	Don Ferrarese	4.00	2.00	1.25
470	R.C. Stevens	4.00	2.00	1.25
471	Lenny Green	4.00	2.00	1.25
472	Joe Jay	4.00	2.00	1.25
473	Bill Renna	4.00	2.00	1.25
474	Roman Semproch	4.00	2.00	1.25
475	All-Star Managers (Fred Haney, Casey Stengel)	18.00	9.00	5.50
476	Stan Musial AS	30.00	15.00	9.00
477	Bill Skowron AS	4.00	2.00	1.25
478	Johnny Temple AS	5.00	2.50	1.50
479	Nellie Fox AS	10.00	5.00	3.00
480	Eddie Mathews AS	10.00	5.00	3.00
481	Frank Malzone AS	5.00	2.50	1.50
482	Ernie Banks AS	20.00	10.00	6.00
483	Luis Aparicio AS	8.00	4.00	2.50
484	Frank Robinson AS	20.00	10.00	6.00
485	Ted Williams AS	65.00	33.00	20.00
486	Willie Mays AS	50.00	25.00	15.00
487	Mickey Mantle AS	100.00	50.00	30.00
488	Hank Aaron AS	40.00	20.00	12.00
489	Jackie Jensen AS	6.00	3.00	1.75
490	Ed Bailey AS	5.00	2.50	1.50
491	Sherm Lollar AS	5.00	2.50	1.50
492	Bob Friend AS	6.00	3.00	1.75
493	Bob Turley AS	7.00	3.50	2.00
494	Warren Spahn AS	15.00	7.50	4.50
495	Herb Score AS	7.00	3.50	2.00
----	Contest Card (All-Star Game, July 8)	15.00	7.50	4.50
----	Felt Emblems Insert Card	15.00	7.50	4.50

1959 Topps

These 2-1/2" by 3-1/2" cards have a round photograph at the center of the front with a solid-color background and white border. A facsimile autograph is found across the photo. The 572- card set marks the largest set issued to that time. Card numbers below 507 have red and green printing with the card number in white in a green box. On high number cards beginning with #507, the printing is black and red and the card number is in a black box. Specialty cards include multiple-player cards, team cards with checklists, "All-Star" cards, highlights from previous season, and 31 "Rookie Stars." There is also a card of the commissioner, Ford Frick, and one of Roy Campanella in a wheelchair. A handful of cards can be found with and without lines added to the biographies on back indicating trades or demotions;

those without the added lines are considerably more rare and valuable and are not included in the complete set price. Card numbers 199-286 can be found with either white or grey backs, with the grey stock being the less common.

		NR MT	EX	VG
Complete Set:		5000.00	2500.00	1500.
Common Player: 1-110		5.00	2.50	1.50
Common Player: 111-506		3.00	1.50	.90
Common Player: 507-572		15.00	7.50	4.50
1	Ford Frick	70.00	15.00	9.00
2	Eddie Yost	5.00	2.00	1.25
3	Don McMahon	5.00	2.50	1.50
4	Albie Pearson	5.00	2.50	1.50
5	Dick Donovan	5.00	2.50	1.50
6	Alex Grammas	5.00	2.50	1.50
7	Al Pilarcik	5.00	2.50	1.50
8	Phillies Team/Checklist 1-88	20.00	10.00	6.00
9	Paul Giel	5.00	2.50	1.50
10	Mickey Mantle	450.00	225.00	135.00
11	Billy Hunter	5.00	2.50	1.50
12	Vern Law	5.00	2.50	1.50
13	Dick Gernert	5.00	2.50	1.50
14	Pete Whisenant	5.00	2.50	1.50
15	Dick Drott	5.00	2.50	1.50
16	Joe Pignatano	5.00	2.50	1.50
17	Danny's All-Stars (Ted Kluszewski, Danny Murtaugh, Frank Thomas)		2.50	1.50
18	Jack Urban	5.00	2.50	1.50
19	Ed Bressoud	5.00	2.50	1.50
20	Duke Snider	60.00	30.00	18.00
21	Connie Johnson	5.00	2.50	1.50
22	Al Smith	5.00	2.50	1.50
23	Murry Dickson	5.00	2.50	1.50
24	Red Wilson	5.00	2.50	1.50
25	Don Hoak	6.00	3.00	1.75
26	Chuck Stobbs	5.00	2.50	1.50
27	Andy Pafko	6.00	3.00	1.75
28	Red Worthington	5.00	2.50	1.50
29	Jim Bolger	5.00	2.50	1.50
30	Nellie Fox	20.00	10.00	6.00
31	Ken Lehman	5.00	2.50	1.50
32	Don Buddin	5.00	2.50	1.50
33	Ed Fitz Gerald	5.00	2.50	1.50
34	Pitchers Beware (Al Kaline, Charlie Maxwell)	9.00	4.50	2.75
35	Ted Kluszewski	7.00	3.50	2.00
36	Hank Aguirre	5.00	2.50	1.50
37	Gene Green	5.00	2.50	1.50
38	Morrie Martin	5.00	2.50	1.50
39	Ed Bouchee	5.00	2.50	1.50
40	Warren Spahn	50.00	25.00	15.00
41	Bob Martyn	5.00	2.50	1.50
42	Murray Wall	5.00	2.50	1.50
43	Steve Bilko	5.00	2.50	1.50
44	Vito Valentinetti	5.00	2.50	1.50
45	Andy Carey	5.00	2.50	1.50
46	Bill Henry	5.00	2.50	1.50
47	Jim Finigan	5.00	2.50	1.50
48	Orioles Team/Checklist 1-88	15.00	7.50	4.50
49	Bill Hall	5.00	2.50	1.50
50	Willie Mays	160.00	80.00	50.00
51	Rip Coleman	5.00	2.50	1.50
52	Coot Veal	5.00	2.50	1.50
53	Stan Williams	5.00	2.50	1.50
54	Mel Roach	5.00	2.50	1.50
55	Tom Brewer	5.00	2.50	1.50
56	Carl Sawatski	5.00	2.50	1.50
57	Al Cicotte	5.00	2.50	1.50
58	Eddie Miksis	5.00	2.50	1.50
59	Irv Noren	5.00	2.50	1.50
60	Bob Turley	6.00	3.00	1.75
61	Dick Brown	5.00	2.50	1.50
62	Tony Taylor	5.00	2.50	1.50
63	Jim Hearn.	5.00	2.50	1.50
64	Joe DeMaestri	5.00	2.50	1.50
65	Frank Torre	5.00	2.50	1.50
66	Joe Ginsberg	5.00	2.50	1.50
67	Brooks Lawrence	5.00	2.50	1.50
68	Dick Schofield	5.00	2.50	1.50
69	Giants Team/Checklist 89-176	18.00	9.00	5.50
70	Harvey Kuenn	5.00	2.50	1.50
71	Don Bessent	5.00	2.50	1.50
72	Bill Renna	5.00	2.50	1.50
73	Ron Jackson	5.00	2.50	1.50
74	Directing the Power (Cookie Lavagetto, Jim Lemon, Roy Sievers)	6.00	3.00	1.75
75	Sam Jones	5.00	2.50	1.50
76	Bobby Richardson	15.00	7.50	4.50
77	John Goryl	5.00	2.50	1.50
78	Pedro Ramos	5.00	2.50	1.50
79	Harry Chiti	5.00	2.50	1.50
80	Minnie Minoso	5.00	2.50	1.50
81	Hal Jeffcoat	5.00	2.50	1.50
82	Bob Boyd	5.00	2.50	1.50
83	Bob Smith	5.00	2.50	1.50
84	Reno Bertoia	5.00	2.50	1.50
85	Harry Anderson	5.00	2.50	1.50
86	Bob Keegan	5.00	2.50	1.50
87	Danny O'Connell	5.00	2.50	1.50
88	Herb Score	6.00	3.00	1.75
89	Billy Gardner	5.00	2.50	1.50
90	Bill Skowron	15.00	7.50	4.50
91	Herb Moford	5.00	2.50	1.50
92	Dave Philley	5.00	2.50	1.50
93	Julio Becquer	5.00	2.50	1.50
94	W. Sox Team/Checklist 89-176	15.00	7.50	4.50
95	Carl Willey	5.00	2.50	1.50
96	Lou Berberet	5.00	2.50	1.50
97	Jerry Lynch	5.00	2.50	1.50
98	Arnie Portocarrero	5.00	2.50	1.50
99	Ted Kazanski	5.00	2.50	1.50
100	Bob Cerv	5.00	2.50	1.50
101	Alex Kellner	5.00	2.50	1.50
102	*Felipe Alou*	20.00	10.00	6.00
103	Billy Goodman	5.00	2.50	1.50
104	Del Rice	5.00	2.50	1.50
105	Lee Walls	5.00	2.50	1.50
106	Hal Woodeshick	5.00	2.50	1.50
107	Norm Larker	5.00	2.50	1.50
108	Zack Monroe	5.00	2.50	1.50
109	Bob Schmidt	5.00	2.50	1.50
110	George Witt	5.00	2.50	1.50
111	Redlegs Team/Checklist 89-176	8.00	4.00	2.50
112	Billy Consolo	3.00	1.50	.90
113	Taylor Phillips	3.00	1.50	.90
114	Earl Battey	3.25	1.75	1.00
115	Mickey Vernon	3.25	1.75	1.00
116	*Bob Allison*	7.00	3.50	2.00
117	*John Blanchard*	3.25	1.75	1.00
118	John Buzhardt	3.00	1.50	.90
119	*John Callison*	5.00	2.50	1.50
120	Chuck Coles	3.00	1.50	.90
121	Bob Conley	3.00	1.50	.90
122	Bennie Daniels	3.00	1.50	.90
123	Don Dillard	3.00	1.50	.90
124	Dan Dobbek	3.00	1.50	.90
125	*Ron Fairly*	3.50	1.75	1.00
126	Eddie Haas	3.00	1.50	.90
127	Kent Hadley	3.00	1.50	.90
128	Bob Hartman	3.00	1.50	.90
129	Frank Herrera	3.00	1.50	.90
130	Lou Jackson	3.00	1.50	.90
131	*Deron Johnson*	3.25	1.75	1.00
132	Don Lee	3.00	1.50	.90
133	*Bob Lillis*	3.25	1.75	1.00
134	Jim McDaniel	3.00	1.50	.90
135	Gene Oliver	3.00	1.50	.90
136	*Jim O'Toole*	3.25	1.75	1.00
137	Dick Ricketts	3.00	1.50	.90
138	John Romano	3.00	1.50	.90
139	Ed Sadowski	3.00	1.50	.90
140	Charlie Secrest	3.00	1.50	.90
141	Joe Shipley	3.00	1.50	.90
142	Dick Stigman	3.00	1.50	.90
143	Willie Tasby	3.00	1.50	.90
144	Jerry Walker	3.00	1.50	.90
145	Dom Zanni	3.00	1.50	.90
146	Jerry Zimmerman	3.00	1.50	.90
147	Cub's Clubbers (Ernie Banks, Dale Long, Walt Moryn)	10.00	5.00	3.00
148	Mike McCormick	3.25	1.75	1.00
149	Jim Bunning	15.00	7.50	4.50
150	Stan Musial	150.00	75.00	45.00
151	Bob Malkmus	3.00	1.50	.90
152	Johnny Klippstein	3.00	1.50	.90
153	Jim Marshall	3.00	1.50	.90
154	Ray Herbert	3.00	1.50	.90
155	Enos Slaughter	18.00	9.00	5.50
156	Ace Hurlers (Billy Pierce, Robin Roberts)	3.50	1.75	1.00
157	Felix Mantilla	3.00	1.50	.90
158	Walt Dropo	3.25	1.75	1.00
159	Bob Shaw	3.00	1.50	.90
160	Dick Groat	3.00	1.50	.90
161	Frank Baumann	3.00	1.50	.90
162	Bobby G. Smith	3.00	1.50	.90
163	Sandy Koufax	150.00	75.00	45.00
164	Johnny Groth	3.00	1.50	.90
165	Bill Bruton	3.25	1.75	1.00

		NR MT	EX	VG			NR MT	EX	VG
166	Destruction Crew (Rocky Colavito, Larry				253	Seth Morehead	3.00	1.50	.90
	Doby, Minnie Minoso)	3.25	1.75	1.00	254	Zeke Bella	3.00	1.50	.90
167	Duke Maas	3.00	1.50	.90	255	Del Ennis	3.25	1.75	1.00
168	Carroll Hardy	3.00	1.50	.90	256	Jerry Davie	3.00	1.50	.90
169	Ted Abernathy	3.00	1.50	.90	257	*Leon Wagner*	3.00	1.50	.90
170	Gene Woodling	3.25	1.75	1.00	258	Fred Kipp	3.00	1.50	.90
171	Willard Schmidt	3.00	1.50	.90	259	Jim Pisoni	3.00	1.50	.90
172	A's Team/Checklist 177-242	7.00	3.50	2.00	260	Early Wynn	15.00	7.50	4.50
173	*Bill Monbouquette*	3.25	1.75	1.00	261	Gene Stephens	3.00	1.50	.90
174	Jim Pendleton	3.00	1.50	.90	262	Hitters' Foes (Don Drysdale, Clem Labine,			
175	Dick Farrell	3.00	1.50	.90		Johnny Podres)	8.00	4.00	2.50
176	Preston Ward	3.00	1.50	.90	263	Buddy Daley	3.00	1.50	.90
177	Johnny Briggs	3.00	1.50	.90	264	Chico Carrasquel	3.00	1.50	.90
178	Ruben Amaro	3.00	1.50	.90	265	Ron Kline	3.00	1.50	.90
179	Don Rudolph	3.00	1.50	.90	266	Woody Held	3.25	1.75	1.00
180	Yogi Berra	90.00	45.00	27.00	267	John Romonosky	3.00	1.50	.90
181	Bob Porterfield	3.00	1.50	.90	268	Tito Francona	3.25	1.75	1.00
182	Milt Graff	3.00	1.50	.90	269	Jack Meyer	3.00	1.50	.90
183	Stu Miller	3.00	1.50	.90	270	Gil Hodges	20.00	10.00	6.00
184	Harvey Haddix	3.25	1.75	1.00	271	*Orlando Pena*	3.25	1.75	1.00
185	Jim Busby	3.00	1.50	.90	272	Jerry Lumpe	3.25	1.75	1.00
186	Mudcat Grant	3.25	1.75	1.00	273	Joe Jay	3.00	1.50	.90
187	Bubba Phillips	3.00	1.50	.90	274	Jerry Kindall	3.00	1.50	.90
188	Juan Pizarro	3.00	1.50	.90	275	Jack Sanford	3.00	1.50	.90
189	Neil Chrisley	3.00	1.50	.90	276	Pete Daley	3.00	1.50	.90
190	Bill Virdon	3.25	1.75	1.00	277	Turk Lown	3.00	1.50	.90
191	Russ Kemmerer	3.00	1.50	.90	278	Chuck Essegian	3.00	1.50	.90
192	Charley Beamon	3.00	1.50	.90	279	Ernie Johnson	3.00	1.50	.90
193	Sammy Taylor	3.00	1.50	.90	280	Frank Bolling	3.00	1.50	.90
194	Jim Brosnan	3.25	1.75	1.00	281	Walt Craddock	3.00	1.50	.90
195	Rip Repulski	3.00	1.50	.90	282	R.C. Stevens	3.00	1.50	.90
196	Billy Moran	3.00	1.50	.90	283	Russ Heman	3.00	1.50	.90
197	Ray Semproch	3.00	1.50	.90	284	Steve Korcheck	3.00	1.50	.90
198	Jim Davenport	3.00	1.50	.90	285	Joe Cunningham	3.25	1.75	1.00
199	Leo Kiely	3.00	1.50	.90	286	Dean Stone	3.00	1.50	.90
200	Warren Giles	3.25	1.75	1.00	287	Don Zimmer	3.25	1.75	1.00
201	Tom Acker	3.00	1.50	.90	288	Dutch Dotterer	3.00	1.50	.90
202	Roger Maris	150.00	75.00	45.00	289	Johnny Kucks	3.00	1.50	.90
203	Ozzie Virgil	3.00	1.50	.90	290	Wes Covington	3.25	1.75	1.00
204	Casey Wise	3.00	1.50	.90	291	Pitching Partners (Camilo Pascual, Pedro			
205	Don Larsen	7.00	3.50	2.00		Ramos)	3.25	1.75	1.00
206	Carl Furillo	5.00	2.50	1.50	292	Dick Williams	3.25	1.75	1.00
207	George Strickland	3.00	1.50	.90	293	Ray Moore	3.00	1.50	.90
208	Willie Jones	3.00	1.50	.90	294	Hank Foiles	3.00	1.50	.90
209	Lenny Green	3.00	1.50	.90	295	Billy Martin	15.00	7.50	4.50
210	Ed Bailey	3.00	1.50	.90	296	*Ernie Broglio*	3.25	1.75	1.00
211	Bob Blaylock	3.00	1.50	.90	297	*Jackie Brandt*	3.25	1.75	1.00
212	Fence Busters (Hank Aaron, Eddie				298	Tex Clevenger	3.00	1.50	.90
	Mathews)	55.00	28.00	16.50	299	Billy Klaus	3.00	1.50	.90
213	Jim Rivera	3.00	1.50	.90	300	Richie Ashburn	20.00	10.00	6.00
214	Marcelino Solis	3.00	1.50	.90	301	Earl Averill	3.00	1.50	.90
215	Jim Lemon	3.00	1.50	.90	302	Don Mossi	3.25	1.75	1.00
216	Andre Rodgers	3.00	1.50	.90	303	Marty Keough	3.00	1.50	.90
217	Carl Erskine	5.00	2.50	1.50	304	Cubs Team/Checklist 265-352	7.00	3.50	2.00
218	Roman Mejias	3.00	1.50	.90	305	Curt Raydon	3.00	1.50	.90
219	George Zuverink	3.00	1.50	.90	306	Jim Gilliam	5.00	2.50	1.50
220	Frank Malzone	3.25	1.75	1.00	307	Curt Barclay	3.00	1.50	.90
221	Bob Bowman	3.00	1.50	.90	308	Norm Siebern	3.50	1.75	1.00
222	Bobby Shantz	3.50	1.75	1.00	309	Sal Maglie	3.00	1.50	.90
223	Cards Team/Checklist 265-352	7.00	3.50	2.00	310	Luis Aparicio	15.00	7.50	4.50
224	*Claude Osteen*	3.00	1.50	.90	311	Norm Zauchin	3.00	1.50	.90
225	Johnny Logan	3.25	1.75	1.00	312	Don Newcombe	6.00	3.00	1.75
226	Art Ceccarelli	3.00	1.50	.90	313	Frank House	3.00	1.50	.90
227	Hal Smith	3.00	1.50	.90	314	Don Cardwell	3.00	1.50	.90
228	Don Gross	3.00	1.50	.90	315	Joe Adcock	3.00	1.50	.90
229	Vic Power	3.00	1.50	.90	316a	Ralph Lumenti (without option statement)			
230	Bill Fischer	3.00	1.50	.90			80.00	40.00	24.00
231	Ellis Burton	3.00	1.50	.90	316b	Ralph Lumenti (with option statement)			
232	Eddie Kasko	3.00	1.50	.90			3.00	1.50	.90
233	Paul Foytack	3.00	1.50	.90	317	N.L. Hitting Kings (Richie Ashburn, Willie			
234	Chuck Tanner	3.00	1.50	.90		Mays)	15.00	7.50	4.50
235	Valmy Thomas	3.00	1.50	.90	318	Rocky Bridges	3.00	1.50	.90
236	Ted Bowsfield	3.00	1.50	.90	319	Dave Hillman	3.00	1.50	.90
237	Run Preventers (Gil McDougald, Bobby				320	Bob Skinner	3.25	1.75	1.00
	Richardson, Bob Turley)	5.00	2.50	1.50	321a	Bob Giallombardo (without option			
238	Gene Baker	3.00	1.50	.90		statement)	80.00	40.00	24.00
239	Bob Trowbridge	3.00	1.50	.90	321b	Bob Giallombardo (with option statement)			
240	Hank Bauer	7.00	3.50	2.00			3.00	1.50	.90
241	Billy Muffett	3.00	1.50	.90	322a	Harry Hanebrink (without trade			
242	Ron Samford	3.00	1.50	.90		statement)	65.00	33.00	18.00
243	Marv Grissom	3.00	1.50	.90	322b	Harry Hanebrink (with trade statement)			
244	Dick Gray	3.00	1.50	.90			3.00	1.50	.90
245	Ned Garver	3.00	1.50	.90	323	Frank Sullivan	3.00	1.50	.90
246	J.W. Porter	3.00	1.50	.90	324	Don Demeter	3.00	1.50	.90
247	Don Ferrarese	3.00	1.50	.90	325	Ken Boyer	5.00	2.50	1.50
248	Red Sox Team/Checklist 177-264				326	Marv Throneberry	5.00	2.50	1.50
		8.00	4.00	2.50	327	*Gary Bell*	3.25	1.75	1.00
249	Bobby Adams	3.00	1.50	.90	328	Lou Skizas	3.00	1.50	.90
250	Billy O'Dell	3.00	1.50	.90	329	Tigers Team/Checklist 353-429	8.00	4.00	2.50
251	Cletis Boyer	6.00	3.00	1.75	330	Gus Triandos	3.25	1.75	1.00
252	Ray Boone	3.25	1.75	1.00	331	Steve Boros	3.25	1.75	1.00

#	Player	NR MT	EX	VG
332	Ray Monzant	3.00	1.50	.90
333	Harry Simpson	3.00	1.50	.90
334	Glen Hobbie	3.00	1.50	.90
335	Johnny Temple	3.00	1.50	.90
336a	Billy Loes (without trade statement)	65.00	33.00	18.00
336b	Billy Loes (with trade statement)	3.00	1.50	.90
337	George Crowe	3.00	1.50	.90
338	*George Anderson*	45.00	23.00	13.50
339	Roy Face	3.00	1.50	.90
340	Roy Sievers	3.25	1.75	1.00
341	Tom Qualters	3.00	1.50	.90
342	Ray Jablonski	3.00	1.50	.90
343	Billy Hoeft	3.00	1.50	.90
344	Russ Nixon	3.00	1.50	.90
345	Gil McDougald	8.00	4.00	2.50
346	Batter Bafflers (Tom Brewer, Dave Sisler)	3.25	1.75	1.00
347	Bob Buhl	3.25	1.75	1.00
348	Ted Lepcio	3.00	1.50	.90
349	Hoyt Wilhelm	15.00	7.50	4.50
350	Ernie Banks	75.00	38.00	23.00
351	Earl Torgeson	3.00	1.50	.90
352	Robin Roberts	15.00	7.50	4.50
353	Curt Flood	3.00	1.50	.90
354	Pete Burnside	3.00	1.50	.90
355	Jim Piersall	3.00	1.50	.90
356	Bob Mabe	3.00	1.50	.90
357	*Dick Stuart*	6.00	3.00	1.75
358	Ralph Terry	3.25	1.75	1.00
359	*Bill White*	20.00	10.00	6.00
360	Al Kaline	50.00	25.00	15.00
361	Willard Nixon	3.00	1.50	.90
362a	Dolan Nichols (without option statement)	80.00	40.00	24.00
362b	Dolan Nichols (with option statement)	3.00	1.50	.90
363	Bobby Avila	3.00	1.50	.90
364	Danny McDevitt	3.00	1.50	.90
365	Gus Bell	3.25	1.75	1.00
366	Humberto Robinson	3.00	1.50	.90
367	Cal Neeman	3.00	1.50	.90
368	Don Mueller	3.00	1.50	.90
369	Dick Tomanek	3.00	1.50	.90
370	Pete Runnels	3.25	1.75	1.00
371	Dick Brodowski	3.00	1.50	.90
372	Jim Hegan	3.00	1.50	.90
373	Herb Plews	3.00	1.50	.90
374	Art Ditmar	3.00	1.50	.90
375	Bob Nieman	3.00	1.50	.90
376	Hal Naragon	3.00	1.50	.90
377	Johnny Antonelli	3.25	1.75	1.00
378	Gail Harris	3.00	1.50	.90
379	Bob Miller	3.00	1.50	.90
380	Hank Aaron	125.00	62.00	37.00
381	Mike Baxes	3.00	1.50	.90
382	Curt Simmons	3.25	1.75	1.00
383	Words of Wisdom (Don Larsen, Casey Stengel)	5.00	2.50	1.50
384	Dave Sisler	3.00	1.50	.90
385	Sherm Lollar	3.25	1.75	1.00
386	Jim Delsing	3.00	1.50	.90
387	Don Drysdale	30.00	15.00	9.00
388	Bob Will	3.00	1.50	.90
389	Joe Nuxhall	3.25	1.75	1.00
390	Orlando Cepeda	18.00	9.00	5.50
391	Milt Pappas	3.25	1.75	1.00
392	Whitey Herzog	6.00	3.00	1.75
393	Frank Lary	3.25	1.75	1.00
394	Randy Jackson	3.00	1.50	.90
395	Elston Howard	7.00	3.50	2.00
396	Bob Rush	3.00	1.50	.90
397	Senators Team/Checklist 430-495	7.00	3.50	2.00
398	Wally Post	3.00	1.50	.90
399	Larry Jackson	3.00	1.50	.90
400	Jackie Jensen	5.00	2.50	1.50
401	Ron Blackburn	3.00	1.50	.90
402	Hector Lopez	3.00	1.50	.90
403	Clem Labine	3.25	1.75	1.00
404	Hank Sauer	3.25	1.75	1.00
405	Roy McMillan	3.00	1.50	.90
406	Solly Drake	3.00	1.50	.90
407	Moe Drabowsky	3.00	1.50	.90
408	Keystone Combo (Luis Aparicio, Nellie Fox)	7.00	3.50	2.00
409	Gus Zernial	3.25	1.75	1.00
410	Billy Pierce	3.25	1.75	1.00
411	Whitey Lockman	3.00	1.50	.90
412	Stan Lopata	3.00	1.50	.90
413	Camillo Pascual (Camilo)	3.25	1.75	1.00
414	Dale Long	3.25	1.75	1.00
415	Bill Mazeroski	3.50	1.75	1.00
416	Haywood Sullivan	3.00	1.50	.90
417	Virgil Trucks	3.00	1.50	.90
418	Gino Cimoli	3.00	1.50	.90
419	Braves Team/Checklist 353-429	8.00	4.00	2.50
420	Rocco Colavito	25.00	12.50	7.50
421	Herm Wehmeier	3.00	1.50	.90
422	Hobie Landrith	3.00	1.50	.90
423	Bob Grim	3.00	1.50	.90
424	Ken Aspromonte	3.00	1.50	.90
425	Del Crandall	3.25	1.75	1.00
426	Jerry Staley	3.00	1.50	.90
427	Charlie Neal	3.00	1.50	.90
428	Buc Hill Aces (Roy Face, Bob Friend, Ron Kline, Vern Law)	3.25	1.75	1.00
429	Bobby Thomson	3.25	1.75	1.00
430	Whitey Ford	30.00	15.00	9.00
431	Whammy Douglas	3.00	1.50	.90
432	Smoky Burgess	3.00	1.50	.90
433	Billy Harrell	3.00	1.50	.90
434	Hal Griggs	3.00	1.50	.90
435	Frank Robinson	50.00	25.00	15.00
436	Granny Hamner	3.00	1.50	.90
437	Ike Delock	3.00	1.50	.90
438	Sam Esposito	3.00	1.50	.90
439	Brooks Robinson	50.00	25.00	15.00
440	Lou Burdette	8.00	4.00	2.50
441	John Roseboro	3.25	1.75	1.00
442	Ray Narleski	3.00	1.50	.90
443	Daryl Spencer	3.00	1.50	.90
444	*Ronnie Hansen*	3.25	1.75	1.00
445	Cal McLish	3.00	1.50	.90
446	Rocky Nelson	3.00	1.50	.90
447	Bob Anderson	3.00	1.50	.90
448	Vada Pinson	5.00	2.50	1.50
449	Tom Gorman	3.00	1.50	.90
450	Ed Mathews	30.00	15.00	9.00
451	Jimmy Constable	3.00	1.50	.90
452	Chico Fernandez	3.00	1.50	.90
453	Les Moss	3.00	1.50	.90
454	Phil Clark	3.00	1.50	.90
455	Larry Doby	3.25	1.75	1.00
456	Jerry Casale	3.00	1.50	.90
457	Dodgers Team/Checklist 430-495	15.00	7.50	4.50
458	Gordon Jones	3.00	1.50	.90
459	Bill Tuttle	3.00	1.50	.90
460	Bob Friend	3.25	1.75	1.00
461	Mantle Hits 42nd Homer For Crown	35.00	17.50	10.50
462	Colavito's Great Catch Saves Game	3.00	1.50	.90
463	Kaline Becomes Youngest Bat Champ	8.00	4.00	2.50
464	Mays' Catch Makes Series History	20.00	10.00	6.00
465	Sievers Sets Homer Mark	3.25	1.75	1.00
466	Pierce All Star Starter	3.25	1.75	1.00
467	Aaron Clubs World Series Homer	15.00	7.50	4.50
468	Snider's Play Brings L.A. Victory	9.00	4.50	2.75
469	Hustler Banks Wins M.V.P. Award	8.00	4.00	2.50
470	Musial Raps Out 3,000th Hit	18.00	9.00	5.50
471	Tom Sturdivant	3.00	1.50	.90
472	Gene Freese	3.00	1.50	.90
473	Mike Fornieles	3.00	1.50	.90
474	Moe Thacker	3.00	1.50	.90
475	Jack Harshman	3.00	1.50	.90
476	Indians Team/Checklist 496-572	7.00	3.50	2.00
477	Barry Latman	3.00	1.50	.90
478	Bob Clemente	125.00	67.00	37.00
479	Lindy McDaniel	3.00	1.50	.90
480	Red Schoendienst	18.00	9.00	5.50
481	Charley Maxwell	3.00	1.50	.90
482	Russ Meyer	3.00	1.50	.90
483	Clint Courtney	3.00	1.50	.90
484	Willie Kirkland	3.00	1.50	.90
485	Ryne Duren	3.50	1.75	1.00
486	Sammy White	3.00	1.50	.90
487	Hal Brown	3.00	1.50	.90
488	Walt Moryn	3.00	1.50	.90
489	John C. Powers	3.00	1.50	.90
490	Frank Thomas	3.00	1.50	.90
491	Don Blasingame	3.00	1.50	.90
492	Gene Conley	3.25	1.75	1.00
493	Jim Landis	3.00	1.50	.90
494	Don Pavletich	3.00	1.50	.90
495	Johnny Podres	5.00	2.50	1.50
496	Wayne Terwilliger	3.00	1.50	.90
497	Hal R. Smith	3.00	1.50	.90
498	Dick Hyde	3.00	1.50	.90

		NR MT	EX	VG
499	Johnny O'Brien	3.00	1.50	.90
500	Vic Wertz	3.25	1.75	1.00
501	Bobby Tiefenauer	3.00	1.50	.90
502	Al Dark	3.25	1.75	1.00
503	Jim Owens	3.00	1.50	.90
504	Ossie Alvarez	3.00	1.50	.90
505	Tony Kubek	8.00	4.00	2.50
506	Bob Purkey	3.00	1.50	.90
507	Bob Hale	15.00	7.50	4.50
508	Art Fowler	15.00	7.50	4.50
509	*Norm Cash*	60.00	30.00	18.00
510	Yankees Team/Checklist 496-572			
		70.00	35.00	21.00
511	George Susce	15.00	7.50	4.50
512	George Altman	15.00	7.50	4.50
513	Tom Carroll	15.00	7.50	4.50
514	*Bob Gibson*	420.00	210.00	131.00
515	Harmon Killebrew	150.00	75.00	45.00
516	Mike Garcia	16.00	8.00	4.75
517	Joe Koppe	15.00	7.50	4.50
518	*Mike Cueller (Cuellar)*	15.00	7.50	4.50
519	Infield Power (Dick Gernert, Frank Malzone, Pete Runnels)			
		18.00	9.00	5.50
520	Don Elston	15.00	7.50	4.50
521	Gary Geiger	15.00	7.50	4.50
522	Gene Snyder	15.00	7.50	4.50
523	Harry Bright	15.00	7.50	4.50
524	Larry Osborne	15.00	7.50	4.50
525	Jim Coates	16.00	8.00	4.75
526	Bob Speake	15.00	7.50	4.50
527	Solly Hemus	15.00	7.50	4.50
528	Pirates Team/Checklist 496-572			
		35.00	17.50	10.50
529	*George Bamberger*	16.00	8.00	4.75
530	Wally Moon	16.00	8.00	4.75
531	Ray Webster	15.00	7.50	4.50
532	Mark Freeman	15.00	7.50	4.50
533	Darrell Johnson	16.00	8.00	4.75
534	Faye Throneberry	15.00	7.50	4.50
535	Ruben Gomez	15.00	7.50	4.50
536	Dan Kravitz	15.00	7.50	4.50
537	Rodolfo Arias	15.00	7.50	4.50
538	Chick King	15.00	7.50	4.50
539	Gary Blaylock	15.00	7.50	4.50
540	Willy Miranda	15.00	7.50	4.50
541	Bob Thurman	15.00	7.50	4.50
542	*Jim Perry*	20.00	10.00	6.00
543	Corsair Outfield Trio (Bob Clemente, Bob Skinner, Bill Virdon)			
		50.00	25.00	15.00
544	Lee Tate	15.00	7.50	4.50
545	Tom Morgan	15.00	7.50	4.50
546	Al Schroll	15.00	7.50	4.50
547	Jim Baxes	15.00	7.50	4.50
548	Elmer Singleton	15.00	7.50	4.50
549	Howie Nunn	15.00	7.50	4.50
550	Roy Campanella	125.00	62.00	37.00
551	Fred Haney AS	16.00	8.00	4.75
552	Casey Stengel AS	30.00	15.00	9.00
553	Orlando Cepeda AS	18.00	9.00	5.50
554	Bill Skowron AS	18.00	9.00	5.50
555	Bill Mazeroski AS	18.00	9.00	5.50
556	Nellie Fox AS	20.00	10.00	6.00
557	Ken Boyer AS	18.00	9.00	5.50
558	Frank Malzone AS	16.00	8.00	4.75
559	Ernie Banks AS	50.00	25.00	15.00
560	Luis Aparicio AS	20.00	10.00	6.00
561	Hank Aaron AS	125.00	62.00	37.00
562	Al Kaline AS	50.00	25.00	15.00
563	Willie Mays AS	135.00	67.00	40.00
564	Mickey Mantle AS	300.00	150.00	90.00
565	Wes Covington AS	16.00	8.00	4.75
566	Roy Sievers AS	16.00	8.00	4.75
567	Del Crandall AS	16.00	8.00	4.75
568	Gus Triandos AS	16.00	8.00	4.75
569	Bob Friend AS	16.00	8.00	4.75
570	Bob Turley AS	16.00	8.00	4.75
571	Warren Spahn AS	30.00	15.00	9.00
572	Billy Pierce AS	25.00	12.50	7.50
-----	Elect Your Favorite Rookie Insert (paper stock, September 29 date on back)	15.00	7.50	4.50
-----	Felt Pennants Insert (paper stock)			
		15.00	7.50	4.50

A player's name in italic indicates a rookie card. An (FC) indicates a player's first card for that particular card company.

1960 Topps

In 1960, Topps returned to a horizontal format (3-1/2" by 2-1/2") with a color portrait and a black and white "action" photograph on the front. The backs returned to the use of just the previous year and lifetime statistics along with a cartoon and short career summary or previous season highlights. Specialty cards in the 572-card set are multi-player cards, managers and coaches cards, and highlights of the 1959 World Series. Two groups of rookie cards are included. The first are numbers 117-148, which are the Sport Magazine rookies. The second group is called "Topps All-Star Rookies." Finally, there is a continuation of the All-Star cards to close out the set in the scarcer high numbers. Card #'s 375-440 can be found with backs printed on either white or grey cardboard, with the white stock being the less common.

		NR MT	EX	VG
Complete Set:		4000.00	2000.00	1250.
Common Player: 1-286		3.00	1.50	.90
Common Player: 287-440		3.00	1.50	.90
Common Player: 441-506		4.00	2.00	1.25
Common Player: 507-572		10.00	5.00	3.00
1	Early Wynn	40.00	20.00	12.00
2	Roman Mejias	3.25	1.75	1.00
3	Joe Adcock	3.25	1.75	1.00
4	Bob Purkey	3.00	1.50	.90
5	Wally Moon	3.00	1.50	.90
6	Lou Berberet	3.00	1.50	.90
7	Master & Mentor (Willie Mays, Bill Rigney)			
		12.00	6.00	3.50
8	Bud Daley	3.00	1.50	.90
9	Faye Throneberry	3.00	1.50	.90
10	Ernie Banks	55.00	28.00	16.50
11	Norm Siebern	3.00	1.50	.90
12	Milt Pappas	3.00	1.50	.90
13	Wally Post	3.00	1.50	.90
14	Jim Grant	3.00	1.50	.90
15	Pete Runnels	3.00	1.50	.90
16	Ernie Broglio	3.00	1.50	.90
17	Johnny Callison	3.00	1.50	.90
18	Dodgers Team/Checklist 1-88	10.00	5.00	3.00
19	Felix Mantilla	3.00	1.50	.90
20	Roy Face	3.00	1.50	.90
21	Dutch Dotterer	3.00	1.50	.90
22	Rocky Bridges	3.00	1.50	.90
23	Eddie Fisher	3.00	1.50	.90
24	Dick Gray	3.00	1.50	.90
25	Roy Sievers	4.00	2.00	1.25
26	Wayne Terwilliger	3.00	1.50	.90
27	Dick Drott	3.00	1.50	.90
28	Brooks Robinson	40.00	20.00	12.00
29	Clem Labine	3.00	1.50	.90
30	Tito Francona	3.00	1.50	.90
31	Sammy Esposito	3.00	1.50	.90
32	Sophomore Stalwarts (Jim O'Toole, Vada Pinson)			
		4.00	2.00	1.25
33	Tom Morgan	3.00	1.50	.90
34	George Anderson	2.50	1.25	.70
35	Whitey Ford	40.00	20.00	12.00
36	Russ Nixon	3.00	1.50	.90
37	Bill Bruton	3.00	1.50	.90
38	Jerry Casale	3.00	1.50	.90
39	Earl Averill	3.00	1.50	.90

		NR MT	EX	VG
40	Joe Cunningham	3.00	1.50	.90
41	Barry Latman	3.00	1.50	.90
42	Hobie Landrith	3.00	1.50	.90
43	Senators Team/Checklist 1-88	6.00	3.00	1.75
44	Bobby Locke	3.00	1.50	.90
45	Roy McMillan	3.00	1.50	.90
46	Jack Fisher	3.00	1.50	.90
47	Don Zimmer	3.25	1.75	1.00
48	Hal Smith	3.00	1.50	.90
49	Curt Raydon	3.00	1.50	.90
50	Al Kaline	50.00	25.00	15.00
51	Jim Coates	3.00	1.50	.90
52	Dave Philley	3.00	1.50	.90
53	Jackie Brandt	3.00	1.50	.90
54	Mike Fornieles	3.00	1.50	.90
55	Bill Mazeroski	3.00	1.50	.90
56	Steve Korcheck	3.00	1.50	.90
57	Win - Savers (Turk Lown, Gerry Staley)			
		3.00	1.50	.90
58	Gino Cimoli	3.00	1.50	.90
59	Juan Pizarro	3.00	1.50	.90
60	Gus Triandos	3.00	1.50	.90
61	Eddie Kasko	3.00	1.50	.90
62	Roger Craig	3.25	1.75	1.00
63	George Strickland	3.00	1.50	.90
64	Jack Meyer	3.00	1.50	.90
65	Elston Howard	6.00	3.00	1.75
66	Bob Trowbridge	3.00	1.50	.90
67	*Jose Pagan*	3.00	1.50	.90
68	Dave Hillman	3.00	1.50	.90
69	Billy Goodman	3.00	1.50	.90
70	Lou Burdette	3.25	1.75	1.00
71	Marty Keough	3.00	1.50	.90
72	Tigers Team/Checklist 89-176	10.00	5.00	3.00
73	Bob Gibson	40.00	20.00	12.00
74	Walt Moryn	3.00	1.50	.90
75	Vic Power	3.00	1.50	.90
76	Bill Fischer	3.00	1.50	.90
77	Hank Foiles	3.00	1.50	.90
78	Bob Grim	3.00	1.50	.90
79	Walt Dropo	3.00	1.50	.90
80	Johnny Antonelli	3.00	1.50	.90
81	Russ Snyder	3.00	1.50	.90
82	Ruben Gomez	3.00	1.50	.90
83	Tony Kubek	4.50	2.25	1.25
84	Hal Smith	3.00	1.50	.90
85	Frank Lary	3.00	1.50	.90
86	Dick Gernert	3.00	1.50	.90
87	John Romonosky	3.00	1.50	.90
88	John Roseboro	3.00	1.50	.90
89	Hal Brown	3.00	1.50	.90
90	Bobby Avila	3.00	1.50	.90
91	Bennie Daniels	3.00	1.50	.90
92	Whitey Herzog	3.25	1.75	1.00
93	Art Schult	3.00	1.50	.90
94	Leo Kiely	3.00	1.50	.90
95	Frank Thomas	3.00	1.50	.90
96	Ralph Terry	2.50	1.25	.70
97	Ted Lepcio	3.00	1.50	.90
98	Gordon Jones	3.00	1.50	.90
99	Lenny Green	3.00	1.50	.90
100	Nellie Fox	7.00	3.50	2.00
101	Bob Miller	3.00	1.50	.90
102	Kent Hadley	3.00	1.50	.90
103	Dick Farrell	3.00	1.50	.90
104	Dick Schofield	3.00	1.50	.90
105	Larry Sherry	3.00	1.50	.90
106	Billy Gardner	3.00	1.50	.90
107	Carl Willey	3.00	1.50	.90
108	Pete Daley	3.00	1.50	.90
109	Cletis Boyer	3.00	1.50	.90
110	Cal McLish	3.00	1.50	.90
111	Vic Wertz	3.00	1.50	.90
112	Jack Harshman	3.00	1.50	.90
113	Bob Skinner	3.00	1.50	.90
114	Ken Aspromonte	3.00	1.50	.90
115	Fork & Knuckler (Roy Face, Hoyt Wilhelm)			
		4.00	2.00	1.25
116	Jim Rivera	3.00	1.50	.90
117	Tom Borland	3.00	1.50	.90
118	Bob Bruce	3.00	1.50	.90
119	*Chico Cardenas*	3.00	1.50	.90
120	Duke Carmel	3.00	1.50	.90
121	Camilo Carreon	3.00	1.50	.90
122	Don Dillard	3.00	1.50	.90
123	Dan Dobbek	3.00	1.50	.90
124	Jim Donohue	3.00	1.50	.90
125	*Dick Ellsworth*	3.00	1.50	.90
126	*Chuck Estrada*	3.00	1.50	.90
127	Ronnie Hansen	3.00	1.50	.90
128	Bill Harris	3.00	1.50	.90

		NR MT	EX	VG
129	Bob Hartman	3.00	1.50	.90
130	Frank Herrera	3.00	1.50	.90
131	Ed Hobaugh	3.00	1.50	.90
132	*Frank Howard*	18.00	9.00	5.50
133	*Manuel Javier*	3.00	1.50	.90
134	Deron Johnson	3.00	1.50	.90
135	Ken Johnson	3.00	1.50	.90
136	*Jim Kaat*	30.00	15.00	9.00
137	Lou Klimchock	3.00	1.50	.90
138	*Art Mahaffey*	3.00	1.50	.90
139	Carl Mathias	3.00	1.50	.90
140	Julio Navarro	3.00	1.50	.90
141	Jim Proctor	3.00	1.50	.90
142	Bill Short	3.00	1.50	.90
143	Al Spangler	3.00	1.50	.90
144	Al Stieglitz	3.00	1.50	.90
145	Jim Umbricht	3.00	1.50	.90
146	Ted Wieand	3.00	1.50	.90
147	Bob Will	3.00	1.50	.90
148	*Carl Yastrzemski*	300.00	150.00	90.00
149	Bob Nieman	3.00	1.50	.90
150	Billy Pierce	3.25	1.75	1.00
151	Giants Team/Checklist 177-264	6.00	3.00	1.75
152	Gail Harris	3.00	1.50	.90
153	Bobby Thomson	3.00	1.50	.90
154	Jim Davenport	3.00	1.50	.90
155	Charlie Neal	3.00	1.50	.90
156	Art Ceccarelli	3.00	1.50	.90
157	Rocky Nelson	3.00	1.50	.90
158	Wes Covington	3.00	1.50	.90
159	Jim Piersall	3.00	1.50	.90
160	Rival All Stars (Ken Boyer, Mickey Mantle)			
		50.00	25.00	15.00
161	Ray Narleski	3.00	1.50	.90
162	Sammy Taylor	3.00	1.50	.90
163	Hector Lopez	3.00	1.50	.90
164	Reds Team/Checklist 89-176	7.00	3.50	2.00
165	Jack Sanford	3.00	1.50	.90
166	Chuck Essegian	3.00	1.50	.90
167	Valmy Thomas	3.00	1.50	.90
168	Alex Grammas	3.00	1.50	.90
169	Jake Striker	3.00	1.50	.90
170	Del Crandall	3.00	1.50	.90
171	Johnny Groth	3.00	1.50	.90
172	Willie Kirkland	3.00	1.50	.90
173	Billy Martin	10.00	5.00	3.00
174	Indians Team/Checklist 89-176	6.00	3.00	1.75
175	Pedro Ramos	3.00	1.50	.90
176	Vada Pinson	3.25	1.75	1.00
177	Johnny Kucks	3.00	1.50	.90
178	Woody Held	3.00	1.50	.90
179	Rip Coleman	3.00	1.50	.90
180	Harry Simpson	3.00	1.50	.90
181	Billy Loes	3.00	1.50	.90
182	Glen Hobbie	3.00	1.50	.90
183	Eli Grba	3.00	1.50	.90
184	Gary Geiger	3.00	1.50	.90
185	Jim Owens	3.00	1.50	.90
186	Dave Sisler	3.00	1.50	.90
187	Jay Hook	3.00	1.50	.90
188	Dick Williams	3.00	1.50	.90
189	Don McMahon	3.00	1.50	.90
190	Gene Woodling	3.00	1.50	.90
191	Johnny Klippstein	3.00	1.50	.90
192	Danny O'Connell	3.00	1.50	.90
193	Dick Hyde	3.00	1.50	.90
194	Bobby Gene Smith	3.00	1.50	.90
195	Lindy McDaniel	3.00	1.50	.90
196	Andy Carey	3.00	1.50	.90
197	Ron Kline	3.00	1.50	.90
198	Jerry Lynch	3.00	1.50	.90
199	Dick Donovan	3.00	1.50	.90
200	Willie Mays	110.00	55.00	33.00
201	Larry Osborne	3.00	1.50	.90
202	Fred Kipp	3.00	1.50	.90
203	Sammy White	3.00	1.50	.90
204	Ryne Duren	2.50	1.25	.70
205	Johnny Logan	3.00	1.50	.90
206	Claude Osteen	3.00	1.50	.90
207	Bob Boyd	3.00	1.50	.90
208	White Sox Team/Checklist 177-264			
		6.00	3.00	1.75
209	Ron Blackburn	3.00	1.50	.90
210	Harmon Killebrew	25.00	12.50	7.50
211	Taylor Phillips	3.00	1.50	.90
212	Walt Alston	6.00	3.00	1.75
213	Chuck Dressen	3.00	1.50	.90
214	Jimmie Dykes	3.00	1.50	.90
215	Bob Elliott	3.00	1.50	.90
216	Joe Gordon	3.00	1.50	.90
217	Charley Grimm	3.00	1.50	.90

		NR MT	EX	VG
218	Solly Hemus	3.00	1.50	.90
219	Fred Hutchinson	3.00	1.50	.90
220	Billy Jurges	3.00	1.50	.90
221	Cookie Lavagetto	3.00	1.50	.90
222	Al Lopez	5.00	2.50	1.50
223	Danny Murtaugh	3.00	1.50	.90
224	Paul Richards	3.00	1.50	.90
225	Bill Rigney	3.00	1.50	.90
226	Eddie Sawyer	3.00	1.50	.90
227	Casey Stengel	15.00	7.50	4.50
228	Ernie Johnson	3.00	1.50	.90
229	Joe Morgan	3.00	1.50	.90
230	Mound Magicians (Bob Buhl, Lou Burdette, Warren Spahn)	6.00	3.00	1.75
231	Hal Naragon	3.00	1.50	.90
232	Jim Busby	3.00	1.50	.90
233	Don Elston	3.00	1.50	.90
234	Don Demeter	3.00	1.50	.90
235	Gus Bell	3.00	1.50	.90
236	Dick Ricketts	3.00	1.50	.90
237	Elmer Valo	3.00	1.50	.90
238	Danny Kravitz	3.00	1.50	.90
239	Joe Shipley	3.00	1.50	.90
240	Luis Aparicio	10.00	5.00	3.00
241	Albie Pearson	3.00	1.50	.90
242	Cards Team/Checklist 265-352	6.00	3.00	1.75
243	Bubba Phillips	3.00	1.50	.90
244	Hal Griggs	3.00	1.50	.90
245	Eddie Yost	3.00	1.50	.90
246	Lee Maye	3.00	1.50	.90
247	Gil McDougald	4.50	2.25	1.25
248	Del Rice	3.00	1.50	.90
249	*Earl Wilson*	3.00	1.50	.90
250	Stan Musial	110.00	55.00	33.00
251	Bobby Malkmus	3.00	1.50	.90
252	Ray Herbert	3.00	1.50	.90
253	Eddie Bressoud	3.00	1.50	.90
254	Arnie Portocarrero	3.00	1.50	.90
255	Jim Gilliam	3.25	1.75	1.00
256	Dick Brown	3.00	1.50	.90
257	Gordy Coleman	3.00	1.50	.90
258	Dick Groat	4.00	2.00	1.25
259	George Altman	3.00	1.50	.90
260	Power Plus (Rocky Colavito, Tito Francona)	3.00	1.50	.90
261	Pete Burnside	3.00	1.50	.90
262	Hank Bauer	3.00	1.50	.90
263	Darrell Johnson	3.00	1.50	.90
264	Robin Roberts	12.00	6.00	3.50
265	Rip Repulski	3.00	1.50	.90
266	Joe Jay	3.00	1.50	.90
267	Jim Marshall	3.00	1.50	.90
268	Al Worthington	3.00	1.50	.90
269	Gene Green	3.00	1.50	.90
270	Bob Turley	3.25	1.75	1.00
271	Julio Becquer	3.00	1.50	.90
272	Fred Green	3.00	1.50	.90
273	Neil Chrisley	3.00	1.50	.90
274	Tom Acker	3.00	1.50	.90
275	Curt Flood	3.00	1.50	.90
276	Ken McBride	3.00	1.50	.90
277	Harry Bright	3.00	1.50	.90
278	Stan Williams	3.00	1.50	.90
279	Chuck Tanner	2.50	1.25	.70
280	Frank Sullivan	3.00	1.50	.90
281	Ray Boone	3.00	1.50	.90
282	Joe Nuxhall	3.00	1.50	.90
283	John Blanchard	2.75	1.50	.80
284	Don Gross	3.00	1.50	.90
285	Harry Anderson	3.00	1.50	.90
286	Ray Semproch	3.00	1.50	.90
287	Felipe Alou	2.50	1.25	.70
288	Bob Mabe	3.00	1.50	.90
289	Willie Jones	3.00	1.50	.90
290	Jerry Lumpe	3.00	1.50	.90
291	Bob Keegan	3.00	1.50	.90
292	Dodger Backstops (Joe Pignatano, John Roseboro)	3.00	1.50	.90
293	Gene Conley	3.00	1.50	.90
294	Tony Taylor	3.00	1.50	.90
295	Gil Hodges	18.00	9.00	5.50
296	Nelson Chittum	3.00	1.50	.90
297	Reno Bertoia	3.00	1.50	.90
298	George Witt	3.00	1.50	.90
299	Earl Torgeson	3.00	1.50	.90
300	Hank Aaron	125.00	67.00	37.00
301	Jerry Davie	3.00	1.50	.90
302	Phillies Team/Checklist 353-429	7.00	3.50	2.00
303	Billy O'Dell	3.00	1.50	.90
304	Joe Ginsberg	3.00	1.50	.90
305	Richie Ashburn	7.00	3.50	2.00
306	Frank Baumann	3.00	1.50	.90
307	Gene Oliver	3.00	1.50	.90
308	Dick Hall	3.00	1.50	.90
309	Bob Hale	3.00	1.50	.90
310	Frank Malzone	3.00	1.50	.90
311	Raul Sanchez	3.00	1.50	.90
312	Charlie Lau	3.00	1.50	.90
313	Turk Lown	3.00	1.50	.90
314	Chico Fernandez	3.00	1.50	.90
315	Bobby Shantz	3.25	1.75	1.00
316	*Willie McCovey*	200.00	100.00	60.00
317	Pumpsie Green	3.00	1.50	.90
318	Jim Baxes	3.00	1.50	.90
319	Joe Koppe	3.00	1.50	.90
320	Bob Allison	3.25	1.75	1.00
321	Ron Fairly	3.00	1.50	.90
322	Willie Tasby	3.00	1.50	.90
323	Johnny Romano	3.00	1.50	.90
324	Jim Perry	2.50	1.25	.70
325	Jim O'Toole	3.00	1.50	.90
326	Bob Clemente	110.00	55.00	33.00
327	*Ray Sadecki*	3.25	1.75	1.00
328	Earl Battey	3.00	1.50	.90
329	Zack Monroe	3.25	1.75	1.00
330	Harvey Kuenn	3.00	1.50	.90
331	Henry Mason	3.00	1.50	.90
332	Yankees Team/Checklist 265-352	20.00	10.00	6.00
333	Danny McDevitt	3.00	1.50	.90
334	Ted Abernathy	3.00	1.50	.90
335	Red Schoendienst	15.00	7.50	4.50
336	Ike Delock	3.00	1.50	.90
337	Cal Neeman	3.00	1.50	.90
338	Ray Monzant	3.00	1.50	.90
339	Harry Chiti	3.00	1.50	.90
340	Harvey Haddix	3.25	1.75	1.00
341	Carroll Hardy	3.00	1.50	.90
342	Casey Wise	3.00	1.50	.90
343	Sandy Koufax	110.00	55.00	33.00
344	Clint Courtney	3.00	1.50	.90
345	Don Newcombe	2.50	1.25	.70
346	J.C. Martin (photo actually Gary Peters)	3.00	1.50	.90
347	Ed Bouchee	3.00	1.50	.90
348	Barry Shetrone	3.00	1.50	.90
349	Moe Drabowsky	3.00	1.50	.90
350	Mickey Mantle	375.00	175.00	110.00
351	Don Nottebart	3.00	1.50	.90
352	Cincy Clouters (Gus Bell, Jerry Lynch, Frank Robinson)	5.00	2.50	1.50
353	Don Larsen	3.25	1.75	1.00
354	Bob Lillis	3.00	1.50	.90
355	Bill White	3.00	1.50	.90
356	Joe Amalfitano	3.00	1.50	.90
357	Al Schroll	3.00	1.50	.90
358	Joe DeMaestri	3.25	1.75	1.00
359	Buddy Gilbert	3.00	1.50	.90
360	Herb Score	2.50	1.25	.70
361	Bob Oldis	3.00	1.50	.90
362	Russ Kemmerer	3.00	1.50	.90
363	Gene Stephens	3.00	1.50	.90
364	Paul Foytack	3.00	1.50	.90
365	Minnie Minoso	3.00	1.50	.90
366	*Dallas Green*	3.25	1.75	1.00
367	Bill Tuttle	3.00	1.50	.90
368	Daryl Spencer	3.00	1.50	.90
369	Billy Hoeft	3.00	1.50	.90
370	Bill Skowron	6.00	3.00	1.75
371	Bud Byerly	3.00	1.50	.90
372	Frank House	3.00	1.50	.90
373	Don Hoak	3.00	1.50	.90
374	Bob Buhl	3.00	1.50	.90
375	Dale Long	3.00	1.50	.90
376	Johnny Briggs	3.00	1.50	.90
377	Roger Maris	120.00	60.00	36.00
378	Stu Miller	3.00	1.50	.90
379	Red Wilson	3.00	1.50	.90
380	Bob Shaw	3.00	1.50	.90
381	Braves Team/Checklist 353-429	7.00	3.50	2.00
382	Ted Bowsfield	3.00	1.50	.90
383	Leon Wagner	3.00	1.50	.90
384	Don Cardwell	3.00	1.50	.90
385	World Series Game 1 (Neal Steals Second)	4.00	2.00	1.25
386	World Series Game 2 (Neal Belts 2nd Homer)	4.00	2.00	1.25
387	World Series Game 3 (Furillo Breaks Up Game)	4.00	2.00	1.25
388	World Series Game 4 (Hodges' Winning Homer)	5.00	2.50	1.50
389	World Series Game 5 (Luis Swipes Base)	5.00	2.50	1.50

		NR MT	EX	VG
390	World Series Game 6 (Scrambling After Ball)	4.00	2.00	1.25
391	World Series Summary (The Champs Celebrate)	4.00	2.00	1.25
392	Tex Clevenger	3.00	1.50	.90
393	Smoky Burgess	2.50	1.25	.70
394	Norm Larker	3.00	1.50	.90
395	Hoyt Wilhelm	15.00	7.50	4.50
396	Steve Bilko	3.00	1.50	.90
397	Don Blasingame	3.00	1.50	.90
398	Mike Cuellar	3.25	1.75	1.00
399	Young Hill Stars (Jack Fisher, Milt Pappas, Jerry Walker)	3.25	1.75	1.00
400	Rocky Colavito	15.00	7.50	4.50
401	Bob Duliba	3.00	1.50	.90
402	Dick Stuart	3.00	1.50	.90
403	Ed Sadowski	3.00	1.50	.90
404	Bob Rush	3.00	1.50	.90
405	Bobby Richardson	6.00	3.00	1.75
406	Billy Klaus	3.00	1.50	.90
407	*Gary Peters* (photo actually J.C. Martin)	3.25	1.75	1.00
408	Carl Furillo	4.00	2.00	1.25
409	Ron Samford	3.00	1.50	.90
410	Sam Jones	3.00	1.50	.90
411	Ed Bailey	3.00	1.50	.90
412	Bob Anderson	3.00	1.50	.90
413	A's Team/Checklist 430-495	7.00	3.50	2.00
414	Don Williams	3.00	1.50	.90
415	Bob Cerv	3.00	1.50	.90
416	Humberto Robinson	3.00	1.50	.90
417	Chuck Cottier	3.00	1.50	.90
418	Don Mossi	3.00	1.50	.90
419	George Crowe	3.00	1.50	.90
420	Ed Mathews	35.00	17.50	10.50
421	Duke Maas	3.25	1.75	1.00
422	Johnny Powers	3.00	1.50	.90
423	Ed Fitz Gerald	3.00	1.50	.90
424	Pete Whisenant	3.00	1.50	.90
425	Johnny Podres	3.00	1.50	.90
426	Ron Jackson	3.00	1.50	.90
427	Al Grunwald	3.00	1.50	.90
428	Al Smith	3.00	1.50	.90
429	American League Kings (Nellie Fox, Harvey Kuenn)	3.25	1.75	1.00
430	Art Ditmar	3.00	1.50	.90
431	Andre Rodgers	3.00	1.50	.90
432	Chuck Stobbs	3.00	1.50	.90
433	Irv Noren	3.00	1.50	.90
434	Brooks Lawrence	3.00	1.50	.90
435	Gene Freese	3.00	1.50	.90
436	Marv Throneberry	3.25	1.75	1.00
437	Bob Friend	2.50	1.25	.70
438	Jim Coker	3.00	1.50	.90
439	Tom Brewer	3.00	1.50	.90
440	Jim Lemon	3.00	1.50	.90
441	Gary Bell	4.00	2.00	1.25
442	Joe Pignatano	4.00	2.00	1.25
443	Charlie Maxwell	4.00	2.00	1.25
444	Jerry Kindall	4.00	2.00	1.25
445	Warren Spahn	40.00	20.00	12.00
446	Ellis Burton	4.00	2.00	1.25
447	Ray Moore	4.00	2.00	1.25
448	*Jim Gentile*	4.00	2.00	1.25
449	Jim Brosnan	5.00	2.50	1.50
450	Orlando Cepeda	15.00	7.50	4.50
451	Curt Simmons	4.00	2.00	1.25
452	Ray Webster	4.00	2.00	1.25
453	Vern Law	4.50	2.25	1.25
454	Hal Woodeshick	4.00	2.00	1.25
455	Orioles Coaches (Harry Brecheen, Lum Harris, Eddie Robinson)	5.00	2.50	1.50
456	Red Sox Coaches (Del Baker, Billy Herman, Sal Maglie, Rudy York)	4.00	2.00	1.25
457	Cubs Coaches (Lou Klein, Charlie Root, Elvin Tappe)	5.00	2.50	1.50
458	White Sox Coaches (Ray Berres, Johnny Cooney, Tony Cuccinello, Don Gutteridge)	5.00	2.50	1.50
459	Reds Coaches (Cot Deal, Wally Moses, Reggie Otero)	5.00	2.50	1.50
460	Indians Coaches (Mel Harder, Red Kress, Bob Lemon, Jo-Jo White)	4.00	2.00	1.25
461	Tigers Coaches (Luke Appling, Tom Ferrick, Billy Hitchcock)	4.00	2.00	1.25
462	A's Coaches (Walker Cooper, Fred Fitzsimmons, Don Heffner)	5.00	2.50	1.50
463	Dodgers Coaches (Joe Becker, Bobby Bragan, Greg Mulleavy, Pete Reiser)	4.00	2.00	1.25
464	Braves Coaches (George Myatt, Andy Pafko, Bob Scheffing, Whitlow Wyatt)	5.00	2.50	1.50
465	Yankees Coaches (Frank Crosetti, Bill Dickey, Ralph Houk, Ed Lopat)	11.00	5.50	3.25
466	Phillies Coaches (Dick Carter, Andy Cohen, Ken Silvestri)	5.00	2.50	1.50
467	Pirates Coaches (Bill Burwell, Sam Narron, Frank Oceak, Mickey Vernon)	4.00	2.00	1.25
468	Cardinals Coaches (Ray Katt, Johnny Keane, Howie Pollet, Harry Walker)	5.00	2.50	1.50
469	Giants Coaches (Salty Parker, Bill Posedel, Wes Westrum)	5.00	2.50	1.50
470	Senators Coaches (Ellis Clary, Sam Mele, Bob Swift)	5.00	2.50	1.50
471	Ned Garver	4.00	2.00	1.25
472	Al Dark	4.50	2.25	1.25
473	Al Cicotte	4.00	2.00	1.25
474	Haywood Sullivan	5.00	2.50	1.50
475	Don Drysdale	30.00	15.00	9.00
476	Lou Johnson	4.00	2.00	1.25
477	Don Ferrarese	4.00	2.00	1.25
478	Frank Torre	4.00	2.00	1.25
479	Georges Maranda	4.00	2.00	1.25
480	Yogi Berra	80.00	40.00	25.00
481	Wes Stock	4.00	2.00	1.25
482	Frank Bolling	4.00	2.00	1.25
483	Camilo Pascual	5.00	2.50	1.50
484	Pirates Team/Checklist 430-495	15.00	7.50	4.50
485	Ken Boyer	4.50	2.25	1.25
486	Bobby Del Greco	4.00	2.00	1.25
487	Tom Sturdivant	4.00	2.00	1.25
488	Norm Cash	5.00	2.50	1.50
489	Steve Ridzik	4.00	2.00	1.25
490	Frank Robinson	45.00	23.00	13.50
491	Mel Roach	4.00	2.00	1.25
492	Larry Jackson	4.00	2.00	1.25
493	Duke Snider	45.00	23.00	13.50
494	Orioles Team/Checklist 496-572	7.00	3.50	2.00
495	Sherm Lollar	4.00	2.00	1.25
496	Bill Virdon	4.00	2.00	1.25
497	John Tsitouris	4.00	2.00	1.25
498	Al Pilarcik	4.00	2.00	1.25
499	Johnny James	4.00	2.00	1.25
500	Johnny Temple	4.00	2.00	1.25
501	Bob Schmidt	4.00	2.00	1.25
502	Jim Bunning	12.00	6.00	3.50
503	Don Lee	4.00	2.00	1.25
504	Seth Morehead	4.00	2.00	1.25
505	Ted Kluszewski	6.00	3.00	1.75
506	Lee Walls	4.00	2.00	1.25
507	Dick Stigman	10.00	5.00	3.00
508	Billy Consolo	10.00	5.00	3.00
509	*Tommy Davis*	25.00	12.50	7.50
510	Jerry Staley	10.00	5.00	3.00
511	Ken Walters	10.00	5.00	3.00
512	Joe Gibbon	10.00	5.00	3.00
513	Cubs Team/Checklist 496-572	25.00	12.50	7.50
514	*Steve Barber*	11.00	5.50	3.25
515	Stan Lopata	10.00	5.00	3.00
516	Marty Kutyna	10.00	5.00	3.00
517	Charley James	10.00	5.00	3.00
518	*Tony Gonzalez*	11.00	5.50	3.25
519	Ed Roebuck	10.00	5.00	3.00
520	Don Buddin	10.00	5.00	3.00
521	Mike Lee	10.00	5.00	3.00
522	Ken Hunt	11.00	5.50	3.25
523	*Clay Dalrymple*	11.00	5.50	3.25
524	Bill Henry	10.00	5.00	3.00
525	Marv Breeding	10.00	5.00	3.00
526	Paul Giel	10.00	5.00	3.00
527	Jose Valdivielso	10.00	5.00	3.00
528	Ben Johnson	10.00	5.00	3.00
529	Norm Sherry	10.00	5.00	3.00
530	Mike McCormick	11.00	5.50	3.25
531	Sandy Amoros	10.00	5.00	3.00
532	Mike Garcia	10.00	5.00	3.00
533	Lu Clinton	10.00	5.00	3.00
534	Ken MacKenzie	10.00	5.00	3.00
535	Whitey Lockman	10.00	5.00	3.00
536	Wynn Hawkins	10.00	5.00	3.00
537	Red Sox Team/Checklist 496-572	25.00	12.50	7.50
538	Frank Barnes	10.00	5.00	3.00
539	Gene Baker	10.00	5.00	3.00
540	Jerry Walker	10.00	5.00	3.00
541	Tony Curry	10.00	5.00	3.00
542	Ken Hamlin	10.00	5.00	3.00
543	Elio Chacon	10.00	5.00	3.00
544	Bill Monbouquette	11.00	5.50	3.25
545	Carl Sawatski	10.00	5.00	3.00
546	Hank Aguirre	10.00	5.00	3.00

		NR MT	EX	VG
547	*Bob Aspromonte*	11.00	5.50	3.25
548	*Don Mincher*	11.00	5.50	3.25
549	John Buzhardt	10.00	5.00	3.00
550	Jim Landis	10.00	5.00	3.00
551	Ed Rakow	10.00	5.00	3.00
552	Walt Bond	10.00	5.00	3.00
553	Bill Skowron AS	12.00	6.00	3.50
554	Willie McCovey AS	45.00	22.00	13.50
555	Nellie Fox AS	18.00	9.00	5.50
556	Charlie Neal AS	11.00	5.50	3.25
557	Frank Malzone AS	11.00	5.50	3.25
558	Eddie Mathews AS	25.00	12.50	7.50
559	Luis Aparicio AS	18.00	9.00	5.50
560	Ernie Banks AS	40.00	20.00	12.00
561	Al Kaline AS	40.00	20.00	12.00
562	Joe Cunningham AS	11.00	5.50	3.25
563	Mickey Mantle AS	250.00	125.00	75.00
564	Willie Mays AS	100.00	50.00	30.00
565	Roger Maris AS	100.00	50.00	30.00
566	Hank Aaron AS	100.00	50.00	30.00
567	Sherm Lollar AS	11.00	5.50	3.25
568	Del Crandall AS	11.00	5.50	3.25
569	Camilo Pascual AS	11.00	5.50	3.25
570	Don Drysdale AS	20.00	10.00	6.00
571	Billy Pierce AS	11.00	5.50	3.25
572	Johnny Antonelli AS	20.00	7.00	3.00
-----	Elect Your Favorite Rookie Insert (paper stock, no date on back)	15.00	7.50	4.50
-----	Hot Iron Transfer Insert (paper stock)	15.00	7.50	4.50

1960 Topps Baseball Tattoos

Probably the least popular of all Topps products among parents and teachers, the Topps Tattoos were delightful little items on the reverse of the wrappers of Topps "Tattoo Bubble Gum." The entire wrapper was 1-9/16" by 3-1/2." The happy owner simply moistened his skin and applied the back of the wrapper to the wet spot. Presto, out came a "tattoo" in color (although often blurred by running colors). The set offered 96 tattoo possibilities of which 55 were players, 16 teams, 15 action shots and 10 autographed balls. Surviving specimens are very rare today.

		NR MT	EX	VG
	Complete Set:	675.00	337.00	202.00
	Common Player:	3.00	1.50	.90
(1)	Hank Aaron	25.00	12.50	7.50
(2)	Bob Allison	5.00	2.50	1.50
(3)	John Antonelli	5.00	2.50	1.50
(4)	Richie Ashburn	7.00	3.50	2.00
(5)	Ernie Banks	15.00	7.50	4.50
(6)	Yogi Berra	18.00	9.00	5.50
(7)	Lew Burdette	6.00	3.00	1.75
(8)	Orlando Cepeda	7.00	3.50	2.00
(9)	Rocky Colavito	6.00	3.00	1.75
(10)	Joe Cunningham	3.00	1.50	.90
(11)	Buddy Daley	3.00	1.50	.90
(12)	Don Drysdale	12.00	6.00	3.50
(13)	Ryne Duren	5.00	2.50	1.50
(14)	Roy Face	5.00	2.50	1.50
(15)	Whitey Ford	15.00	7.50	4.50
(16)	Nellie Fox	7.00	3.50	2.00
(17)	Tito Francona	3.00	1.50	.90

		NR MT	EX	VG
(18)	Gene Freese	3.00	1.50	.90
(19)	Jim Gilliam	6.00	3.00	1.75
(20)	Dick Groat	6.00	3.00	1.75
(21)	Ray Herbert	3.00	1.50	.90
(22)	Glen Hobbie	3.00	1.50	.90
(23)	Jackie Jensen	6.00	3.00	1.75
(24)	Sam Jones	3.00	1.50	.90
(25)	Al Kaline	15.00	7.50	4.50
(26)	Harmon Killebrew	12.00	6.00	3.50
(27)	Harvy Kuenn (Harvey)	6.00	3.00	1.75
(28)	Frank Lary	3.00	1.50	.90
(29)	Vernon Law	5.00	2.50	1.50
(30)	Frank Malzone	3.00	1.50	.90
(31)	Mickey Mantle	75.00	37.00	22.00
(32)	Roger Maris	15.00	7.50	4.50
(33)	Ed Mathews	12.00	6.00	3.50
(34)	Willie Mays	25.00	12.50	7.50
(35)	Cal Mclish	3.00	1.50	.90
(36)	Wally Moon	5.00	2.50	1.50
(37)	Walt Moryn	3.00	1.50	.90
(38)	Don Mossi	3.00	1.50	.90
(39)	Stan Musial	25.00	12.50	7.50
(40)	Charlie Neal	3.00	1.50	.90
(41)	Don Newcombe	5.00	2.50	1.50
(42)	Milt Pappas	5.00	2.50	1.50
(43)	Camilo Pascual	5.00	2.50	1.50
(44)	Billie Pierce (Billy)	5.00	2.50	1.50
(45)	Robin Roberts	12.00	6.00	3.50
(46)	Frank Robinson	15.00	7.50	4.50
(47)	Pete Runnels	5.00	2.50	1.50
(48)	Herb Score	5.00	2.50	1.50
(49)	Warren Spahn	12.00	6.00	3.50
(50)	Johnny Temple	3.00	1.50	.90
(51)	Gus Triandos	3.00	1.50	.90
(52)	Jerry Walker	3.00	1.50	.90
(53)	Bill White	5.00	2.50	1.50
(54)	Gene Woodling	5.00	2.50	1.50
(55)	Early Wynn	12.00	6.00	3.50
(56)	Chicago Cubs Logo	3.00	1.50	.90
(57)	Cincinnati Reds Logo	3.00	1.50	.90
(58)	Los Angeles Dodgers Logo	3.00	1.50	.90
(59)	Milwaukee Braves Logo	3.00	1.50	.90
(60)	Philadelphia Phillies Logo	3.00	1.50	.90
(61)	Pittsburgh Pirates Logo	5.00	2.50	1.50
(62)	San Francisco Giants Logo	3.00	1.50	.90
(63)	St. Louis Cardinals Logo	3.00	1.50	.90
(64)	Baltimore Orioles Logo	3.00	1.50	.90
(65)	Boston Red Sox Logo	3.00	1.50	.90
(66)	Chicago White Sox Logo	3.00	1.50	.90
(67)	Cleveland Indians Logo	3.00	1.50	.90
(68)	Detroit Tigers Logo	3.00	1.50	.90
(69)	Kansas City Athletics Logo	3.00	1.50	.90
(70)	New York Yankees Logo	6.00	3.00	1.75
(71)	Washington Senators Logo	3.00	1.50	.90
(72)	Autograph (Richie Ashburn)	3.00	1.50	.90
(73)	Autograph (Rocky Colavito)	3.00	1.50	.90
(74)	Autograph (Roy Face)	3.00	1.50	.90
(75)	Autograph (Jackie Jensen)	3.00	1.50	.90
(76)	Autograph (Harmon Killebrew)	5.00	2.50	1.50
(77)	Autograph (Mickey Mantle)	25.00	12.50	7.50
(78)	Autograph (Willie Mays)	10.00	5.00	3.00
(79)	Autograph (Stan Musial)	10.00	5.00	3.00
(80)	Autograph (Billy Pierce)	3.00	1.50	.90
(81)	Autograph (Jerry Walker)	3.00	1.50	.90
(82)	Run-Down	3.00	1.50	.90
(83)	Out At First	3.00	1.50	.90
(84)	The Final Word	3.00	1.50	.90
(85)	Twisting Foul	3.00	1.50	.90
(86)	Out At Home	3.00	1.50	.90
(87)	Circus Catch	3.00	1.50	.90
(88)	Great Catch	3.00	1.50	.90
(89)	Stolen Base	3.00	1.50	.90
(90)	Grand Slam Homer	3.00	1.50	.90
(91)	Double Play	3.00	1.50	.90
(92)	Right-Handed Follow-Thru (no caption)	3.00	1.50	.90
(93)	Right-Handed High Leg Kick (no caption)	3.00	1.50	.90
(94)	Left-Handed Pitcher (no caption)	3.00	1.50	.90
(95)	Right-Handed Batter (no caption)	3.00	1.50	.90
(96)	Left-Handed Batter (no caption)	3.00	1.50	.90

1961 Topps

Except for some of the specialty cards, Topps returned to a vertical format with their 1961 cards. The set is numbered through 598, however only 587 cards were printed. No numbers 426, 587 and 588 were issued. Two cards numbered 463 exist (one a Braves team card and one a player card of Jack Fisher). Actually, the Braves team card is checklisted as #426. Designs for 1961 are basically large color portraits; the backs return to extensive statistics. A three-panel cartoon highlighting the player's career appears on the card backs. Innovations include numbered checklists, cards for statistical leaders, and 10 "Baseball Thrills" cards. The scarce high numbers are card numbers 523-589.

		NR MT	EX	VG
	Complete Set:	5500.00	2750.00	1650.
	Common Player: 1-370	2.00	1.00	.60
	Common Player: 371-522	4.00	2.00	1.25
	Common Player: 523-589	25.00	12.50	7.50
1	Dick Groat	20.00	5.00	3.00
2	Roger Maris	175.00	87.00	52.00
3	John Buzhardt	2.00	1.00	.60
4	Lenny Green	2.00	1.00	.60
5	Johnny Romano	2.00	1.00	.60
6	Ed Roebuck	2.00	1.00	.60
7	White Sox Team	4.00	2.00	1.25
8	Dick Williams	4.00	2.00	1.25
9	Bob Purkey	2.00	1.00	.60
10	Brooks Robinson	30.00	15.00	9.00
11	Curt Simmons	2.25	1.25	.70
12	Moe Thacker	2.00	1.00	.60
13	Chuck Cottier	2.00	1.00	.60
14	Don Mossi	2.25	1.25	.70
15	Willie Kirkland	2.00	1.00	.60
16	Billy Muffett	2.00	1.00	.60
17	Checklist 1-88	5.00	2.50	1.50
18	Jim Grant	2.00	1.00	.60
19	Cletis Boyer	2.25	1.25	.70
20	Robin Roberts	10.00	5.00	3.00
21	*Zorro Versalles*	4.00	2.00	1.25
22	Clem Labine	2.25	1.25	.70
23	Don Demeter	2.00	1.00	.60
24	Ken Johnson	2.00	1.00	.60
25	Red's Heavy Artillery (Gus Bell, Vada Pinson, Frank Robinson)	6.00	3.00	1.75
26	Wes Stock	2.00	1.00	.60
27	Jerry Kindall	2.00	1.00	.60
28	Hector Lopez	4.00	2.00	1.25
29	Don Nottebart	2.00	1.00	.60
30	Nellie Fox	6.00	3.00	1.75
31	Bob Schmidt	2.00	1.00	.60
32	Ray Sadecki	2.00	1.00	.60
33	Gary Geiger	2.00	1.00	.60
34	Wynn Hawkins	2.00	1.00	.60
35	*Ron Santo*	50.00	25.00	15.00
36	Jack Kralick	2.00	1.00	.60
37	Charlie Maxwell	2.00	1.00	.60
38	Bob Lillis	2.00	1.00	.60
39	Leo Posada	2.00	1.00	.60
40	Bob Turley	4.00	2.00	1.25
41	N.L. Batting Leaders (Bob Clemente, Dick Groat, Norm Larker, Willie Mays)	4.00	2.00	1.25
42	A.L. Batting Leaders (Minnie Minoso, Pete Runnels, Bill Skowron, Al Smith)	4.00	2.00	1.25
43	N.L. Home Run Leaders (Hank Aaron, Ernie Banks, Ken Boyer, Eddie Mathews)	4.00	2.00	1.25
44	A.L. Home Run Leaders (Rocky Colavito, Jim Lemon, Mickey Mantle, Roger Maris)	30.00	15.00	9.00
45	N.L. E.R.A. Leaders (Ernie Broglio, Don Drysdale, Bob Friend, Mike McCormick, Stan Williams)	3.25	1.75	1.00

		NR MT	EX	VG
46	A.L. E.R.A. Leaders (Frank Baumann, Hal Brown, Jim Bunning, Art Ditmar)	4.00	2.00	1.25
47	N.L. Pitching Leaders (Ernie Broglio, Lou Burdette, Vern Law, Warren Spahn)	3.25	1.75	1.00
48	A.L. Pitching Leaders (Bud Daley, Art Ditmar, Chuck Estrada, Frank Lary, Milt Pappas, Jim Perry)	4.00	2.00	1.25
49	N.L. Strikeout Leaders (Ernie Broglio, Don Drysdale, Sam Jones, Sandy Koufax)	4.00	2.00	1.25
50	A.L. Strikeout Leaders (Jim Bunning, Frank Lary, Pedro Ramos, Early Wynn)	5.00	2.50	1.50
51	Tigers Team	5.00	2.50	1.50
52	George Crowe	2.00	1.00	.60
53	Russ Nixon	2.00	1.00	.60
54	Earl Francis	2.00	1.00	.60
55	Jim Davenport	2.00	1.00	.60
56	Russ Kemmerer	2.00	1.00	.60
57	Marv Throneberry	4.00	2.00	1.25
58	Joe Schaffernoth	2.00	1.00	.60
59	Jim Woods	2.00	1.00	.60
60	Woodie Held	2.00	1.00	.60
61	Ron Piche	2.00	1.00	.60
62	Al Pilarcik	2.00	1.00	.60
63	Jim Kaat	9.00	4.50	2.75
64	Alex Grammas	2.00	1.00	.60
65	Ted Kluszewski	4.00	2.00	1.25
66	Bill Henry	2.00	1.00	.60
67	Ossie Virgil	2.00	1.00	.60
68	Deron Johnson	4.00	2.00	1.25
69	Earl Wilson	2.00	1.00	.60
70	Bill Virdon	4.00	2.00	1.25
71	Jerry Adair	2.25	1.25	.70
72	Stu Miller	2.00	1.00	.60
73	Al Spangler	2.00	1.00	.60
74	Joe Pignatano	2.00	1.00	.60
75	Lindy Shows Larry (Larry Jackson, Lindy McDaniel)	4.00	2.00	1.25
76	Harry Anderson	2.00	1.00	.60
77	Dick Stigman	2.00	1.00	.60
78	Lee Walls	2.00	1.00	.60
79	Joe Ginsberg	2.00	1.00	.60
80	Harmon Killebrew	25.00	12.50	7.50
81	Tracy Stallard	2.00	1.00	.60
82	Joe Christopher	2.00	1.00	.60
83	Bob Bruce	2.00	1.00	.60
84	Lee Maye	2.00	1.00	.60
85	Jerry Walker	2.00	1.00	.60
86	Dodgers Team	5.00	2.50	1.50
87	Joe Amalfitano	2.00	1.00	.60
88	Richie Ashburn	6.00	3.00	1.75
89	Billy Martin	8.00	4.00	2.50
90	Jerry Staley	2.00	1.00	.60
91	Walt Moryn	2.00	1.00	.60
92	Hal Naragon	2.00	1.00	.60
93	Tony Gonzalez	2.00	1.00	.60
94	Johnny Kucks	2.00	1.00	.60
95	Norm Cash	5.00	2.50	1.50
96	Billy O'Dell	2.00	1.00	.60
97	Jerry Lynch	2.00	1.00	.60
98a	Checklist 89-176 (word "Checklist" in red on front)	7.00	3.50	2.00
98b	Checklist 89-176 ("Checklist" in yellow, 98 on back in black)	5.00	2.50	1.50
98c	Checklist 89-176 ("Checklist" in yellow, 98 on back in white)	7.00	3.50	2.00
99	Don Buddin	2.00	1.00	.60
100	Harvey Haddix	4.00	2.00	1.25
101	Bubba Phillips	2.00	1.00	.60
102	Gene Stephens	2.00	1.00	.60
103	Ruben Amaro	2.00	1.00	.60
104	John Blanchard	4.00	2.00	1.25
105	Carl Willey	2.00	1.00	.60
106	Whitey Herzog	2.25	1.25	.70
107	Seth Morehead	2.00	1.00	.60
108	Dan Dobbek	2.00	1.00	.60
109	Johnny Podres	2.25	1.25	.70
110	Vada Pinson	5.00	2.50	1.50
111	Jack Meyer	2.00	1.00	.60
112	Chico Fernandez	2.00	1.00	.60
113	Mike Fornieles	2.00	1.00	.60
114	Hobie Landrith	2.00	1.00	.60
115	Johnny Antonelli	2.25	1.25	.70
116	Joe DeMaestri	4.00	2.00	1.25
117	Dale Long	2.25	1.25	.70
118	Chris Cannizzaro	2.00	1.00	.60
119	A's Big Armor (Hank Bauer, Jerry Lumpe, Norm Siebern)	4.00	2.00	1.25
120	Ed Mathews	30.00	15.00	9.00
121	Eli Grba	2.00	1.00	.60
122	Cubs Team	4.00	2.00	1.25
123	Billy Gardner	2.00	1.00	.60

		NR MT	EX	VG			NR MT	EX	VG
124	J.C. Martin	2.00	1.00	.60	212	Haywood Sullivan	2.25	1.25	.70
125	Steve Barber	2.00	1.00	.60	213	*Bill Stafford*	4.00	2.00	1.25
126	Dick Stuart	2.25	1.25	.70	214	Danny Murphy	2.00	1.00	.60
127	Ron Kline	2.00	1.00	.60	215	Gus Bell	2.25	1.25	.70
128	Rip Repulski	2.00	1.00	.60	216	Ted Bowsfield	2.00	1.00	.60
129	Ed Hobaugh	2.00	1.00	.60	217	Mel Roach	2.00	1.00	.60
130	Norm Larker	2.00	1.00	.60	218	Hal Brown	2.00	1.00	.60
131	Paul Richards	2.25	1.25	.70	219	Gene Mauch	4.00	2.00	1.25
132	Al Lopez	5.00	2.50	1.50	220	Al Dark	2.25	1.25	.70
133	Ralph Houk	5.00	2.50	1.50	221	Mike Higgins	2.00	1.00	.60
134	Mickey Vernon	2.25	1.25	.70	222	Jimmie Dykes	2.00	1.00	.60
135	Fred Hutchinson	2.25	1.25	.70	223	Bob Scheffing	2.00	1.00	.60
136	Walt Alston	4.00	2.00	1.25	224	Joe Gordon	2.25	1.25	.70
137	Chuck Dressen	2.25	1.25	.70	225	Bill Rigney	2.00	1.00	.60
138	Danny Murtaugh	2.25	1.25	.70	226	Harry Lavagetto	2.00	1.00	.60
139	Solly Hemus	2.00	1.00	.60	227	Juan Pizarro	2.00	1.00	.60
140	Gus Triandos	2.25	1.25	.70	228	Yankees Team	18.00	9.00	5.50
141	*Billy Williams*	125.00	62.00	37.00	229	Rudy Hernandez	2.00	1.00	.60
142	Luis Arroyo	4.00	2.00	1.25	230	Don Hoak	2.25	1.25	.70
143	Russ Snyder	2.00	1.00	.60	231	Dick Drott	2.00	1.00	.60
144	Jim Coker	2.00	1.00	.60	232	Bill White	4.00	2.00	1.25
145	Bob Buhl	2.25	1.25	.70	233	Joe Jay	2.00	1.00	.60
146	Marty Keough	2.00	1.00	.60	234	Ted Lepcio	2.00	1.00	.60
147	Ed Rakow	2.00	1.00	.60	235	Camilo Pascual	2.25	1.25	.70
148	Julian Javier	2.25	1.25	.70	236	Don Gile	2.00	1.00	.60
149	Bob Oldis	2.00	1.00	.60	237	Billy Loes	2.00	1.00	.60
150	Willie Mays	120.00	60.00	38.00	238	Jim Gilliam	4.00	2.00	1.25
151	Jim Donohue	2.00	1.00	.60	239	Dave Sisler	2.00	1.00	.60
152	Earl Torgeson	2.00	1.00	.60	240	Ron Hansen	2.00	1.00	.60
153	Don Lee	2.00	1.00	.60	241	Al Cicotte	2.00	1.00	.60
154	Bobby Del Greco	2.00	1.00	.60	242	Hal W. Smith	2.00	1.00	.60
155	Johnny Temple	2.00	1.00	.60	243	Frank Lary	2.25	1.25	.70
156	Ken Hunt	2.00	1.00	.60	244	Chico Cardenas	2.25	1.25	.70
157	Cal McLish	2.00	1.00	.60	245	Joe Adcock	4.00	2.00	1.25
158	Pete Daley	2.00	1.00	.60	246	Bob Davis	2.00	1.00	.60
159	Orioles Team	4.00	2.00	1.25	247	Billy Goodman	2.00	1.00	.60
160	Whitey Ford	35.00	17.50	10.50	248	Ed Keegan	2.00	1.00	.60
161	Sherman Jones (photo actually Eddie				249	Reds Team	4.00	2.00	1.25
	Fisher)	2.00	1.00	.60	250	Buc Hill Aces (Roy Face, Vern Law)			
162	Jay Hook	2.00	1.00	.60			4.00	2.00	1.25
163	Ed Sadowski	2.00	1.00	.60	251	Bill Bruton	2.00	1.00	.60
164	Felix Mantilla	2.00	1.00	.60	252	Bill Short	4.00	2.00	1.25
165	Gino Cimoli	2.00	1.00	.60	253	Sammy Taylor	2.00	1.00	.60
166	Danny Kravitz	2.00	1.00	.60	254	Ted Sadowski	2.00	1.00	.60
167	Giants Team	4.00	2.00	1.25	255	Vic Power	2.00	1.00	.60
168	Tommy Davis	5.00	2.50	1.50	256	Billy Hoeft	2.00	1.00	.60
169	Don Elston	2.00	1.00	.60	257	Carroll Hardy	2.00	1.00	.60
170	Al Smith	2.00	1.00	.60	258	Jack Sanford	2.00	1.00	.60
171	Paul Foytack	2.00	1.00	.60	259	John Schaive	2.00	1.00	.60
172	Don Dillard	2.00	1.00	.60	260	Don Drysdale	25.00	12.50	7.50
173	Beantown Bombers (Jackie Jensen, Frank				261	Charlie Lau	2.25	1.25	.70
	Malzone, Vic Wertz)	4.00	2.00	1.25	262	Tony Curry	2.00	1.00	.60
174	Ray Semproch	2.00	1.00	.60	263	Ken Hamlin	2.00	1.00	.60
175	Gene Freese	2.00	1.00	.60	264	Glen Hobbie	2.00	1.00	.60
176	Ken Aspromonte	2.00	1.00	.60	265	Tony Kubek	5.00	2.50	1.50
177	Don Larsen	4.00	2.00	1.25	266	Lindy McDaniel	2.00	1.00	.60
178	Bob Nieman	2.00	1.00	.60	267	Norm Siebern	2.25	1.25	.70
179	Joe Koppe	2.00	1.00	.60	268	Ike DeLock (Delock)	2.00	1.00	.60
180	Bobby Richardson	6.00	3.00	1.75	269	Harry Chiti	2.00	1.00	.60
181	Fred Green	2.00	1.00	.60	270	Bob Friend	4.00	2.00	1.25
182	Dave Nicholson	2.00	1.00	.60	271	Jim Landis	2.00	1.00	.60
183	Andre Rodgers	2.00	1.00	.60	272	Tom Morgan	2.00	1.00	.60
184	Steve Bilko	2.00	1.00	.60	273	Checklist 265-352	5.00	2.50	1.50
185	Herb Score	4.00	2.00	1.25	274	Gary Bell	2.00	1.00	.60
186	Elmer Valo	2.00	1.00	.60	275	Gene Woodling	2.25	1.25	.70
187	Billy Klaus	2.00	1.00	.60	276	Ray Rippelmeyer	2.00	1.00	.60
188	Jim Marshall	2.00	1.00	.60	277	Hank Foiles	2.00	1.00	.60
189	Checklist 177-264	5.00	2.50	1.50	278	Don McMahon	2.00	1.00	.60
190	Stan Williams	2.00	1.00	.60	279	Jose Pagan	2.00	1.00	.60
191	Mike de la Hoz	2.00	1.00	.60	280	Frank Howard	4.00	2.00	1.25
192	Dick Brown	2.00	1.00	.60	281	Frank Sullivan	2.00	1.00	.60
193	Gene Conley	2.25	1.25	.70	282	Faye Throneberry	2.00	1.00	.60
194	Gordy Coleman	2.00	1.00	.60	283	Bob Anderson	2.00	1.00	.60
195	Jerry Casale	2.00	1.00	.60	284	Dick Gernert	2.00	1.00	.60
196	Ed Bouchee	2.00	1.00	.60	285	Sherm Lollar	2.25	1.25	.70
197	Dick Hall	2.00	1.00	.60	286	George Witt	2.00	1.00	.60
198	Carl Sawatski	2.00	1.00	.60	287	Carl Yastrzemski	150.00	75.00	45.00
199	Bob Boyd	2.00	1.00	.60	288	Albie Pearson	2.00	1.00	.60
200	Warren Spahn	30.00	15.00	9.00	289	Ray Moore	2.00	1.00	.60
201	Pete Whisenant	2.00	1.00	.60	290	Stan Musial	75.00	37.00	23.00
202	Al Neiger	2.00	1.00	.60	291	Tex Clevenger	2.00	1.00	.60
203	Eddie Bressoud	2.00	1.00	.60	292	Jim Baumer	2.00	1.00	.60
204	Bob Skinner	2.25	1.25	.70	293	Tom Sturdivant	2.00	1.00	.60
205	Bill Pierce	4.00	2.00	1.25	294	Don Blasingame	2.00	1.00	.60
206	Gene Green	2.00	1.00	.60	295	Milt Pappas	2.25	1.25	.70
207	Dodger Southpaws (Sandy Koufax,				296	Wes Covington	2.00	1.00	.60
	Johnny Podres)	15.00	7.50	4.50	297	Athletics Team	4.00	2.00	1.25
208	Larry Osborne	2.00	1.00	.60	298	Jim Golden	2.00	1.00	.60
209	Ken McBride	2.00	1.00	.60	299	Clay Dalrymple	2.00	1.00	.60
210	Pete Runnels	2.25	1.25	.70	300	Mickey Mantle	400.00	200.00	125.00
211	Bob Gibson	40.00	20.00	12.00	301	Chet Nichols	2.00	1.00	.60

#	Player	NR MT	EX	VG
302	Al Heist	2.00	1.00	.60
303	Gary Peters	2.25	1.25	.70
304	Rocky Nelson	2.00	1.00	.60
305	Mike McCormick	2.25	1.25	.70
306	World Series Game 1 (Virdon Saves Game)	5.00	2.50	1.50
307	World Series Game 2 (Mantle Slams 2 Homers)	30.00	15.00	9.00
308	World Series Game 3 (Richardson Is Hero)	4.00	2.00	1.25
309	World Series Game 4 (Cimoli Is Safe In Crucial Play)	5.00	2.50	1.50
310	World Series Game 5 (Face Saves the Day)	5.00	2.50	1.50
311	World Series Game 6 (Ford Pitches Second Shutout)	5.00	2.50	1.50
312	World Series Game 7 (Mazeroski's Homer Wins It!)	5.00	2.50	1.50
313	World Series Summary (The Winners Celebrate)	5.00	2.50	1.50
314	Bob Miller	2.00	1.00	.60
315	Earl Battey	2.25	1.25	.70
316	Bobby Gene Smith	2.00	1.00	.60
317	Jim Brewer	2.25	1.25	.70
318	Danny O'Connell	2.00	1.00	.60
319	Valmy Thomas	2.00	1.00	.60
320	Lou Burdette	4.00	2.00	1.25
321	Marv Breeding	2.00	1.00	.60
322	Bill Kunkel	2.00	1.00	.60
323	Sammy Esposito	2.00	1.00	.60
324	Hank Aguirre	2.00	1.00	.60
325	Wally Moon	2.25	1.25	.70
326	Dave Hillman	2.00	1.00	.60
327	Matty Alou	4.00	2.00	1.25
328	Jim O'Toole	2.00	1.00	.60
329	Julio Becquer	2.00	1.00	.60
330	Rocky Colavito	5.00	2.50	1.50
331	Ned Garver	2.00	1.00	.60
332	Dutch Dotterer (photo actually Tommy Dotterer)	2.00	1.00	.60
333	Fritz Brickell	4.00	2.00	1.25
334	Walt Bond	2.00	1.00	.60
335	Frank Bolling	2.00	1.00	.60
336	Don Mincher	2.25	1.25	.70
337	Al's Aces (Al Lopez, Herb Score, Early Wynn)	5.00	2.50	1.50
338	Don Landrum	2.00	1.00	.60
339	Gene Baker	2.00	1.00	.60
340	Vic Wertz	2.25	1.25	.70
341	Jim Owens	2.00	1.00	.60
342	Clint Courtney	2.00	1.00	.60
343	Earl Robinson	2.00	1.00	.60
344	Sandy Koufax	85.00	42.00	26.00
345	Jim Piersall	4.00	2.00	1.25
346	Howie Nunn	2.00	1.00	.60
347	Cardinals Team	4.00	2.00	1.25
348	Steve Boros	2.00	1.00	.60
349	Danny McDevitt	4.00	2.00	1.25
350	Ernie Banks	40.00	20.00	12.00
351	Jim King	2.00	1.00	.60
352	Bob Shaw	2.00	1.00	.60
353	Howie Bedell	2.00	1.00	.60
354	Billy Harrell	2.00	1.00	.60
355	Bob Allison	2.25	1.25	.70
356	Ryne Duren	2.25	1.25	.70
357	Daryl Spencer	2.00	1.00	.60
358	Earl Averill	2.00	1.00	.60
359	Dallas Green	2.25	1.25	.70
360	Frank Robinson	30.00	15.00	9.00
361a	Checklist 353-429 ("Topps Baseball" in black on front)	5.00	2.50	1.50
361b	Checklist 353-429 ("Topps Baseball" in yellow)	6.00	3.00	1.75
362	Frank Funk	2.00	1.00	.60
363	John Roseboro	2.25	1.25	.70
364	Moe Drabowsky	2.00	1.00	.60
365	Jerry Lumpe	2.25	1.25	.70
366	Eddie Fisher	2.00	1.00	.60
367	Jim Rivera	2.00	1.00	.60
368	Bennie Daniels	2.00	1.00	.60
369	Dave Philley	2.25	1.25	.70
370	Roy Face	4.00	2.00	1.25
371	Bill Skowron	5.00	2.50	1.50
372	Bob Hendley	4.00	2.00	1.25
373	Red Sox Team	5.00	2.50	1.50
374	Paul Giel	4.00	2.00	1.25
375	Ken Boyer	4.00	2.00	1.25
376	Mike Roarke	4.00	2.00	1.25
377	Ruben Gomez	4.00	2.00	1.25
378	Wally Post	4.00	2.00	1.25
379	Bobby Shantz	4.00	2.00	1.25
380	Minnie Minoso	5.00	2.50	1.50
381	Dave Wickersham	4.00	2.00	1.25
382	Frank Thomas	4.00	2.00	1.25
383	Frisco First Liners (Mike McCormick, Billy O'Dell, Jack Sanford)	4.00	2.00	1.25
384	Chuck Essegian	4.00	2.00	1.25
385	Jim Perry	4.00	2.00	1.25
386	Joe Hicks	4.00	2.00	1.25
387	Duke Maas	4.00	2.00	1.25
388	Bob Clemente	110.00	55.00	33.00
389	Ralph Terry	5.00	2.50	1.50
390	Del Crandall	4.00	2.00	1.25
391	Winston Brown	4.00	2.00	1.25
392	Reno Bertoia	4.00	2.00	1.25
393	Batter Bafflers (Don Cardwell, Glen Hobbie)	4.00	2.00	1.25
394	Ken Walters	4.00	2.00	1.25
395	Chuck Estrada	4.00	2.00	1.25
396	Bob Aspromonte	4.00	2.00	1.25
397	Hal Woodeshick	4.00	2.00	1.25
398	Hank Bauer	4.00	2.00	1.25
399	Cliff Cook	4.00	2.00	1.25
400	Vern Law	4.00	2.00	1.25
401	Babe Ruth Hits 60th Homer	25.00	12.50	7.50
402	Larsen Pitches Perfect Game	15.00	7.50	4.50
403	Brooklyn-Boston Play 26-Inning Tie	4.00	2.00	1.25
404	Hornsby Tops N.L. With .424 Average	5.00	2.50	1.50
405	Gehrig Benched After 2,130 Games	18.00	9.00	5.50
406	Mantle Blasts 565 ft. Home Run	40.00	20.00	12.00
407	Jack Chesbro Wins 41st Game	4.00	2.00	1.25
408	Mathewson Strikes Out 267 Batters	5.00	2.50	1.50
409	Johnson Hurls 3rd Shutout in 4 Days	4.00	2.00	1.25
410	Haddix Pitches 12 Perfect Innings	4.00	2.00	1.25
411	Tony Taylor	4.00	2.00	1.25
412	Larry Sherry	4.00	2.00	1.25
413	Eddie Yost	4.00	2.00	1.25
414	Dick Donovan	4.00	2.00	1.25
415	Hank Aaron	125.00	67.00	37.00
416	Dick Howser	8.00	4.00	2.50
417	Juan Marichal	150.00	75.00	50.00
418	Ed Bailey	4.00	2.00	1.25
419	Tom Borland	4.00	2.00	1.25
420	Ernie Broglio	4.00	2.00	1.25
421	Ty Cline	4.00	2.00	1.25
422	Bud Daley	4.00	2.00	1.25
423	Charlie Neal	4.00	2.00	1.25
424	Turk Lown	4.00	2.00	1.25
425	Yogi Berra	60.00	30.00	18.00
426	Not Issued			
427	Dick Ellsworth	4.00	2.00	1.25
428	Ray Barker	4.00	2.00	1.25
429	Al Kaline	40.00	20.00	12.00
430	Bill Mazeroski	10.00	5.00	3.00
431	Chuck Stobbs	4.00	2.00	1.25
432	Coot Veal	4.00	2.00	1.25
433	Art Mahaffey	4.00	2.00	1.25
434	Tom Brewer	4.00	2.00	1.25
435	Orlando Cepeda	10.00	5.00	3.00
436	Jim Maloney	4.00	2.00	1.25
437a	Checklist 430-506 (#440 is Louis Aparicio)	6.00	3.00	1.75
437b	Checklist 430-506 (#440 is Luis Aparicio)	6.50	3.25	2.00
438	Curt Flood	4.00	2.00	1.25
439	Phil Regan	4.00	2.00	1.25
440	Luis Aparicio	12.00	6.00	3.50
441	Dick Bertell	4.00	2.00	1.25
442	Gordon Jones	4.00	2.00	1.25
443	Duke Snider	40.00	20.00	12.00
444	Joe Nuxhall	4.00	2.00	1.25
445	Frank Malzone	4.00	2.00	1.25
446	Bob "Hawk" Taylor	4.00	2.00	1.25
447	Harry Bright	4.00	2.00	1.25
448	Del Rice	4.00	2.00	1.25
449	Bobby Bolin	4.00	2.00	1.25
450	Jim Lemon	4.00	2.00	1.25
451	Power For Ernie (Ernie Broglio, Daryl Spencer, Bill White)	4.00	2.00	1.25
452	Bob Allen	4.00	2.00	1.25
453	Dick Schofield	4.00	2.00	1.25
454	Pumpsie Green	4.00	2.00	1.25
455	Early Wynn	15.00	7.50	4.50
456	Hal Bevan	4.00	2.00	1.25
457	Johnny James	4.00	2.00	1.25
458	Willie Tasby	4.00	2.00	1.25
459	Terry Fox	4.00	2.00	1.25

		NR MT	EX	VG
460	Gil Hodges	18.00	9.00	5.50
461	Smoky Burgess	4.00	2.00	1.25
462	Lou Klimchock	4.00	2.00	1.25
463a	Braves Team (should be card #426)			
		4.00	2.00	1.25
463b	Jack Fisher	4.00	2.00	1.25
464	*Leroy Thomas*	4.00	2.00	1.25
465	Roy McMillan	4.00	2.00	1.25
466	Ron Moeller	4.00	2.00	1.25
467	Indians Team	5.00	2.50	1.50
468	Johnny Callison	4.00	2.00	1.25
469	Ralph Lumenti	4.00	2.00	1.25
470	Roy Sievers	4.00	2.00	1.25
471	Phil Rizzuto MVP	12.00	6.00	3.50
472	Yogi Berra MVP	40.00	20.00	12.00
473	Bobby Shantz MVP	5.00	2.50	1.50
474	Al Rosen MVP	5.00	2.50	1.50
475	Mickey Mantle MVP	125.00	62.00	37.00
476	Jackie Jensen MVP	5.00	2.50	1.50
477	Nellie Fox MVP	4.00	2.00	1.25
478	Roger Maris MVP	40.00	20.00	12.00
479	Jim Konstanty MVP	4.00	2.00	1.25
480	Roy Campanella MVP	25.00	12.50	7.50
481	Hank Sauer MVP	4.00	2.00	1.25
482	Willie Mays MVP	40.00	20.00	12.00
483	Don Newcombe MVP	5.00	2.50	1.50
484	Hank Aaron MVP	40.00	20.00	12.00
485	Ernie Banks MVP	25.00	12.50	7.50
486	Dick Groat MVP	5.00	2.50	1.50
487	Gene Oliver	4.00	2.00	1.25
488	Joe McClain	4.00	2.00	1.25
489	Walt Dropo	4.00	2.00	1.25
490	Jim Bunning	8.00	4.00	2.50
491	Phillies Team	5.00	2.50	1.50
492	Ron Fairly	4.00	2.00	1.25
493	Don Zimmer	4.00	2.00	1.25
494	Tom Cheney	4.00	2.00	1.25
495	Elston Howard	6.00	3.00	1.75
496	Ken MacKenzie	4.00	2.00	1.25
497	Willie Jones	4.00	2.00	1.25
498	Ray Herbert	4.00	2.00	1.25
499	Chuck Schilling	4.00	2.00	1.25
500	Harvey Kuenn	5.00	2.50	1.50
501	John DeMerit	4.00	2.00	1.25
502	Clarence Coleman	4.00	2.00	1.25
503	Tito Francona	4.00	2.00	1.25
504	Billy Consolo	4.00	2.00	1.25
505	Red Schoendienst	12.00	6.00	3.50
506	*Willie Davis*	10.00	5.00	3.00
507	Pete Burnside	4.00	2.00	1.25
508	Rocky Bridges	4.00	2.00	1.25
509	Camilo Carreon	4.00	2.00	1.25
510	Art Ditmar	4.00	2.00	1.25
511	Joe Morgan	4.00	2.00	1.25
512	Bob Will	4.00	2.00	1.25
513	Jim Brosnan	4.00	2.00	1.25
514	Jake Wood	4.00	2.00	1.25
515	Jackie Brandt	4.00	2.00	1.25
516	Checklist 507-587	10.00	5.00	3.00
517	Willie McCovey	60.00	30.00	18.00
518	Andy Carey	4.00	2.00	1.25
519	Jim Pagliaroni	4.00	2.00	1.25
520	Joe Cunningham	4.00	2.00	1.25
521	Brother Battery (Larry Sherry, Norm Sherry)	4.00	2.00	1.25
522	Dick Farrell	4.00	2.00	1.25
523	Joe Gibbon	25.00	12.50	7.50
524	Johnny Logan	27.00	13.50	8.00
525	*Ron Perranoski*	27.00	13.50	8.00
526	R.C. Stevens	25.00	12.50	7.50
527	Gene Leek	25.00	12.50	7.50
528	Pedro Ramos	25.00	12.50	7.50
529	Bob Roselli	25.00	12.50	7.50
530	Bobby Malkmus	25.00	12.50	7.50
531	Jim Coates	27.00	13.50	8.00
532	Bob Hale	25.00	12.50	7.50
533	Jack Curtis	25.00	12.50	7.50
534	Eddie Kasko	25.00	12.50	7.50
535	Larry Jackson	25.00	12.50	7.50
536	Bill Tuttle	25.00	12.50	7.50
537	Bobby Locke	25.00	12.50	7.50
538	Chuck Hiller	25.00	12.50	7.50
539	Johnny Klippstein	25.00	12.50	7.50
540	Jackie Jensen	35.00	17.50	10.50
541	Roland Sheldon	27.00	13.50	8.00
542	Twins Team	60.00	30.00	18.00
543	Roger Craig	35.00	17.50	10.50
544	George Thomas	25.00	12.50	7.50
545	Hoyt Wilhelm	55.00	28.00	16.50
546	Marty Kutyna	25.00	12.50	7.50
547	Leon Wagner	27.00	13.50	8.00

		NR MT	EX	VG
548	Ted Wills	25.00	12.50	7.50
549	Hal R. Smith	25.00	12.50	7.50
550	Frank Baumann	25.00	12.50	7.50
551	George Altman	25.00	12.50	7.50
552	Jim Archer	25.00	12.50	7.50
553	Bill Fischer	25.00	12.50	7.50
554	Pirates Team	50.00	25.00	15.00
555	Sam Jones	25.00	12.50	7.50
556	Ken R. Hunt	25.00	12.50	7.50
557	Jose Valdivielso	25.00	12.50	7.50
558	Don Ferrarese	25.00	12.50	7.50
559	Jim Gentile	27.00	13.50	8.00
560	Barry Latman	25.00	12.50	7.50
561	Charley James	25.00	12.50	7.50
562	Bill Monbouquette	27.00	13.50	8.00
563	Bob Cerv	27.00	13.50	8.00
564	Don Cardwell	25.00	12.50	7.50
565	Felipe Alou	25.00	12.50	7.50
566	Paul Richards AS	25.00	12.50	7.50
567	Danny Murtaugh AS	25.00	12.50	7.50
568	Bill Skowron AS	35.00	17.50	10.50
569	Frank Herrera AS	25.00	12.50	7.50
570	Nellie Fox AS	40.00	20.00	12.00
571	Bill Mazeroski AS	35.00	17.50	10.50
572	Brooks Robinson AS	75.00	38.00	23.00
573	Ken Boyer AS	35.00	17.50	10.50
574	Luis Aparicio AS	45.00	23.00	13.50
575	Ernie Banks AS	80.00	40.00	25.00
576	Roger Maris AS	100.00	50.00	30.00
577	Hank Aaron AS	150.00	75.00	45.00
578	Mickey Mantle AS	400.00	200.00	120.00
579	Willie Mays AS	150.00	75.00	45.00
580	Al Kaline AS	90.00	45.00	27.00
581	Frank Robinson AS	80.00	40.00	25.00
582	Earl Battey AS	25.00	12.50	7.50
583	Del Crandall AS	30.00	15.00	9.00
584	Jim Perry AS	30.00	15.00	9.00
585	Bob Friend AS	30.00	15.00	9.00
586	Whitey Ford AS	90.00	45.00	27.00
587	Not Issued			
588	Not Issued			
589	Warren Spahn AS	125.00	56.00	35.00

1961 Topps Dice Game

MICKEY MANTLE
Center Field   American Lg.

One of the more obscure Topps test issues that may have never actually been issued is the 1961 Topps Dice Game. Eighteen black and white cards, each measuring 2-1/2" by 3-1/2" in size, comprise the set. Interestingly, there are no identifying marks, such as copyrights or trademarks, to indicate the set was produced by Topps. The card backs contain various baseball plays that occur when a certain pitch is called and a specific number of the dice is rolled.

		NR MT	EX	VG
Complete Set:		7500.00	3750.00	2250.
Common Player:		100.00	50.00	30.00
(1)	Earl Battey	100.00	50.00	30.00
(2)	Del Crandall	100.00	50.00	30.00
(3)	Jim Davenport	100.00	50.00	30.00
(4)	Don Drysdale	350.00	175.00	105.00
(5)	Dick Groat	150.00	75.00	45.00
(6)	Al Kaline	600.00	300.00	175.00
(7)	Tony Kubek	150.00	75.00	45.00
(8)	Mickey Mantle	2500.00	1250.00	750.00
(9)	Willie Mays	1000.00	500.00	300.00

		NR MT	EX	VG
(10)	Bill Mazeroski	150.00	75.00	45.00
(11)	Stan Musial	800.00	400.00	240.00
(12)	Camilo Pascual	100.00	50.00	30.00
(13)	Bobby Richardson	150.00	75.00	45.00
(14)	Brooks Robinson	400.00	200.00	120.00
(15)	Frank Robinson	350.00	175.00	105.00
(16)	Norm Siebern	100.00	50.00	30.00
(17)	Leon Wagner	100.00	50.00	30.00
(18)	Bill White	100.00	50.00	30.00

1961 Topps Magic Rub-Offs

Not too different in concept from the tattoos of the previous year, the Topps Magic Rub-Off was designed to leave impressions of team themes or individual players when properly applied. Measuring 2-1/16" by 3-1/16," the Magic Rub-Off was not designed specifically for application to the owner's skin. The set of 36 Rub-Offs seems to almost be a tongue-in-cheek product as the team themes were a far cry from official logos, and the players seem to have been included for their nicknames. Among the players (one representing each team) the best known and most valuable are Yogi Berra and Ernie Banks.

		NR MT	EX	VG
	Complete Set:	85.00	42.00	25.00
	Common Player:	1.00	.50	.30
(1)	Baltimore Orioles Pennant	1.00	.50	.30
(2)	Ernie "Bingo" Banks	12.00	6.00	3.50
(3)	Yogi Berra	20.00	10.00	6.00
(4)	Boston Red Sox Pennant	1.00	.50	.30
(5)	Jackie "Ozark" Brandt	1.25	.60	.40
(6)	Jim "Professor" Brosnan	1.25	.60	.40
(7)	Chicago Cubs Pennant	1.00	.50	.30
(8)	Chicago White Sox Pennant	1.00	.50	.30
(9)	Cincinnati Red Legs Pennant	1.00	.50	.30
(10)	Cleveland Indians Pennant	1.00	.50	.30
(11)	Detroit Tigers Pennant	1.25	.60	.40
(12)	Henry "Dutch" Dotterer	1.25	.60	.40
(13)	Joe "Flash" Gordon	1.50	.70	.45
(14)	Harvey "The Kitten" Haddix	1.50	.70	.45
(15)	Frank "Pancho" Hererra	1.25	.60	.40
(16)	Frank "Tower" Howard	3.50	1.75	1.00
(17)	"Sad" Sam Jones	1.25	.60	.40
(18)	Kansas City Athletics Pennant	1.00	.50	.30
(19)	Los Angeles Angels Pennant	1.00	.50	.30
(20)	Los Angeles Dodgers Pennant	1.25	.60	.40
(21)	Omar "Turk" Lown	1.25	.60	.40
(22)	Billy "The Kid" Martin	8.00	4.00	2.50
(23)	Duane "Duke" Mass (Maas)	1.25	.60	.40
(24)	Charlie "Paw Paw" Maxwell	1.25	.60	.40
(25)	Milwaukee Braves Pennant	1.00	.50	.30
(26)	Minnesota Twins Pennant	1.00	.50	.30
(27)	"Farmer" Ray Moore	1.00	.50	.30
(28)	Walt "Moose" Moryn	1.00	.50	.30
(29)	New York Yankees Pennant	2.50	1.25	.70
(30)	Philadelphia Phillies Pennant	1.00	.50	.30
(31)	Pittsburgh Pirates Pennant	1.00	.50	.30
(32)	John "Honey" Romano	1.25	.60	.40
(33)	"Pistol Pete" Runnels	1.50	.70	.45
(34)	St. Louis Cardinals Pennant	1.00	.50	.30
(35)	San Francisco Giants Pennant	1.00	.50	.30
(36)	Washington Senators Pennant	1.00	.50	.30

1961 Topps Stamps

Issued as an added insert to 1961 Topps wax packs these 1-3/8" by 1-3/16" stamps were desigend to be collected and placed in an album which could be bought for an additional 10¢. Packs of cards contained two stamps. There are 208 stamps in a complete set which depict 207 different players (Al Kaline appears twice). There are 104 players on brown stamps and 104 on green. While there are many Hall of Famers on the stamps, prices remain low because there is relatively little interest in what is a non-card set.

		NR MT	EX	VG
	Complete Set:	225.00	112.00	70.00
	Stamp Album:	35.00	17.50	10.50
	Common Player:	.40	.20	.12
(1)	Hank Aaron	10.00	5.00	3.00
(2)	Joe Adcock	.50	.25	.15
(3)	Hank Aguirre	.40	.20	.12
(4)	Bob Allison	.50	.25	.15
(5)	George Altman	.40	.20	.12
(6)	Bob Anderson	.40	.20	.12
(7)	Johnny Antonelli	.50	.25	.15
(8)	Luis Aparicio	1.50	.70	.45
(9)	Luis Arroyo	.50	.25	.15
(10)	Richie Ashburn	.80	.40	.25
(11)	Ken Aspromonte	.40	.20	.12
(12)	Ed Bailey	.40	.20	.12
(13)	Ernie Banks	6.00	3.00	1.75
(14)	Steve Barber	.40	.20	.12
(15)	Earl Battey	.50	.25	.15
(16)	Hank Bauer	.50	.25	.15
(17)	Gus Bell	.50	.25	.15
(18)	Yogi Berra	5.00	2.50	1.50
(19)	Reno Bertoia	.40	.20	.12
(20)	John Blanchard	.50	.25	.15
(21)	Don Blasingame	.40	.20	.12
(22)	Frank Bolling	.40	.20	.12
(23)	Steve Boros	.40	.20	.12
(24)	Ed Bouchee	.40	.20	.12
(25)	Bob Boyd	.40	.20	.12
(26)	Cletis Boyer	.50	.25	.15
(27)	Ken Boyer	.50	.25	.15
(28)	Jackie Brandt	.40	.20	.12
(29)	Marv Breeding	.40	.20	.12
(30)	Eddie Bressoud	.40	.20	.12
(31)	Jim Brewer	.40	.20	.12
(32)	Tom Brewer	.40	.20	.12
(33)	Jim Brosnan	.50	.25	.15
(34)	Bill Bruton	.40	.20	.12
(35)	Bob Buhl	.50	.25	.15
(36)	Jim Bunning	1.00	.50	.30
(37)	Smoky Burgess	.50	.25	.15
(38)	John Buzhardt	.40	.20	.12
(39)	Johnny Callison	.50	.25	.15
(40)	Chico Cardenas	.40	.20	.12
(41)	Andy Carey	.40	.20	.12
(42)	Jerry Casale	.40	.20	.12
(43)	Norm Cash	.50	.25	.15
(44)	Orlando Cepeda	1.25	.60	.40
(45)	Bob Cerv	.40	.20	.12
(46)	Harry Chiti	.40	.20	.12
(47)	Gene Conley	.50	.25	.15
(48)	Wes Covington	.40	.20	.12
(49)	Del Crandall	.50	.25	.15
(50)	Tony Curry	.40	.20	.12

		NR MT	EX	VG
(51)	Bud Daley	.40	.20	.12
(52)	Pete Daley	.40	.20	.12
(53)	Clay Dalrymple	.40	.20	.12
(54)	Jim Davenport	.40	.20	.12
(55)	Tommy Davis	.50	.25	.15
(56)	Bobby Del Greco	.40	.20	.12
(57)	Ike Delock	.40	.20	.12
(58)	Art Ditmar	.50	.25	.15
(59)	Dick Donovan	.40	.20	.12
(60)	Don Drysdale	6.00	3.00	1.75
(61)	Dick Ellsworth	.40	.20	.12
(62)	Don Elston	.40	.20	.12
(63)	Chuck Estrada	.40	.20	.12
(64)	Roy Face	.50	.25	.15
(65)	Dick Farrell	.40	.20	.12
(66)	Chico Fernandez	.40	.20	.12
(67)	Curt Flood	.50	.25	.15
(68)	Whitey Ford	4.00	2.00	1.25
(69)	Tito Francona	.40	.20	.12
(70)	Gene Freese	.40	.20	.12
(71)	Bob Friend	.50	.25	.15
(72)	Billy Gardner	.40	.20	.12
(73)	Ned Garver	.40	.20	.12
(74)	Gary Geiger	.40	.20	.12
(75)	Jim Gentile	.40	.20	.12
(76)	Dick Gernert	.40	.20	.12
(77)	Tony Gonzalez	.40	.20	.12
(78)	Alex Grammas	.40	.20	.12
(79)	Jim Grant	.40	.20	.12
(80)	Dick Groat	.50	.25	.15
(81)	Dick Hall	.40	.20	.12
(82)	Ron Hansen	.40	.20	.12
(83)	Bob Hartman	.40	.20	.12
(84)	Woodie Held	.40	.20	.12
(85)	Ray Herbert	.40	.20	.12
(86)	Frank Herrera	.40	.20	.12
(87)	Whitey Herzog	.50	.25	.15
(88)	Don Hoak	.50	.25	.15
(89)	Elston Howard	.80	.40	.25
(90)	Frank Howard	.50	.25	.15
(91)	Ken Hunt	.40	.20	.12
(92)	Larry Jackson	.40	.20	.12
(93)	Julian Javier	.40	.20	.12
(94)	Joe Jay	.40	.20	.12
(95)	Jackie Jensen	.50	.25	.15
(96)	Jim Kaat	1.00	.50	.30
(97a)	Al Kaline (green)	7.00	3.50	2.00
(97b)	Al Kaline (brown)	7.00	3.50	2.00
(98)	Eddie Kasko	.40	.20	.12
(99)	Russ Kemmerer	.40	.20	.12
(100)	Harmon Killebrew	5.00	2.50	1.50
(101)	Billy Klaus	.40	.20	.12
(102)	Ron Kline	.40	.20	.12
(103)	Johnny Klippstein	.40	.20	.12
(104)	Ted Kluszewski	.40	.20	.12
(105)	Tony Kubek	.80	.40	.25
(106)	Harvey Kuenn	.50	.25	.15
(107)	Jim Landis	.40	.20	.12
(108)	Hobie Landrith	.40	.20	.12
(109)	Norm Larker	.40	.20	.12
(110)	Frank Lary	.40	.20	.12
(111)	Barry Latman	.40	.20	.12
(112)	Vern Law	.50	.25	.15
(113)	Jim Lemon	.40	.20	.12
(114)	Sherm Lollar	.50	.25	.15
(115)	Dale Long	.50	.25	.15
(116)	Jerry Lumpe	.40	.20	.12
(117)	Jerry Lynch	.40	.20	.12
(118)	Art Mahaffey	.40	.20	.12
(119)	Frank Malzone	.40	.20	.12
(120)	Felix Mantilla	.40	.20	.12
(121)	Mickey Mantle	50.00	25.00	15.00
(122)	Juan Marichal	5.00	2.50	1.50
(123)	Roger Maris	12.00	6.00	3.50
(124)	Billy Martin	1.00	.50	.30
(125)	J.C. Martin	.40	.20	.12
(126)	Ed Mathews	3.00	1.50	.90
(127)	Charlie Maxwell	.40	.20	.12
(128)	Willie Mays	7.00	3.50	2.00
(129)	Bill Mazeroski	.50	.25	.15
(130)	Mike McCormick	.40	.20	.12
(131)	Willie McCovey	3.00	1.50	.90
(132)	Lindy McDaniel	.40	.20	.12
(133)	Roy McMillan	.40	.20	.12
(134)	Minnie Minoso	.50	.25	.15
(135)	Bill Monbouquette	.40	.20	.12
(136)	Wally Moon	.50	.25	.15
(137)	Stan Musial	7.00	3.50	2.00
(138)	Charlie Neal	.40	.20	.12
(139)	Rocky Nelson	.40	.20	.12
(140)	Russ Nixon	.40	.20	.12

		NR MT	EX	VG
(141)	Billy O'Dell	.40	.20	.12
(142)	Jim O'Toole	.40	.20	.12
(143)	Milt Pappas	.50	.25	.15
(144)	Camilo Pascual	.50	.25	.15
(145)	Jim Perry	.50	.25	.15
(146)	Bubba Phillips	.40	.20	.12
(147)	Bill Pierce	.50	.25	.15
(148)	Jim Piersall	.50	.25	.15
(149)	Vada Pinson	.50	.25	.15
(150)	Johnny Podres	.50	.25	.15
(151)	Wally Post	.40	.20	.12
(152)	Vic Powers (Power)	.40	.20	.12
(153)	Pedro Ramos	.40	.20	.12
(154)	Robin Roberts	1.50	.70	.45
(155)	Brooks Robinson	3.75	2.00	1.25
(156)	Frank Robinson	3.50	1.75	1.00
(157)	Ed Roebuck	.40	.20	.12
(158)	John Romano	.40	.20	.12
(159)	John Roseboro	.50	.25	.15
(160)	Pete Runnels	.50	.25	.15
(161)	Ed Sadowski	.40	.20	.12
(162)	Jack Sanford	.40	.20	.12
(163)	Ron Santo	.50	.25	.15
(164)	Ray Semproch	.40	.20	.12
(165)	Bobby Shantz	.50	.25	.15
(166)	Bob Shaw	.40	.20	.12
(167)	Larry Sherry	.40	.20	.12
(168)	Norm Siebern	.40	.20	.12
(169)	Roy Sievers	.50	.25	.15
(170)	Curt Simmons	.50	.25	.15
(171)	Dave Sisler	.40	.20	.12
(172)	Bob Skinner	.40	.20	.12
(173)	Al Smith	.40	.20	.12
(174)	Hal Smith	.40	.20	.12
(175)	Hal Smith	.40	.20	.12
(176)	Duke Snider	3.75	2.00	1.25
(177)	Warren Spahn	3.00	1.50	.90
(178)	Daryl Spencer	.40	.20	.12
(179)	Bill Stafford	.50	.25	.15
(180)	Jerry Staley	.40	.20	.12
(181)	Gene Stephens	.40	.20	.12
(182)	Chuck Stobbs	.40	.20	.12
(183)	Dick Stuart	.50	.25	.15
(184)	Willie Tasby	.40	.20	.12
(185)	Sammy Taylor	.40	.20	.12
(186)	Tony Taylor	.40	.20	.12
(187)	Johnny Temple	.40	.20	.12
(188)	Marv Throneberry	.50	.25	.15
(189)	Gus Triandos	.50	.25	.15
(190)	Bob Turley	.50	.25	.15
(191)	Bill Tuttle	.40	.20	.12
(192)	Zorro Versalles	.40	.20	.12
(193)	Bill Virdon	.50	.25	.15
(194)	Lee Walls	.40	.20	.12
(195)	Vic Wertz	.50	.25	.15
(196)	Pete Whisenant	.40	.20	.12
(197)	Bill White	.50	.25	.15
(198)	Hoyt Wilhelm	1.50	.70	.45
(199)	Bob Will	.40	.20	.12
(200)	Carl Willey	.40	.20	.12
(201)	Billy Williams	2.50	1.25	.70
(202)	Dick Williams	.50	.25	.15
(203)	Stan Williams	.40	.20	.12
(204)	Gene Woodling	.50	.25	.15
(205)	Early Wynn	2.00	1.00	.60
(206)	Carl Yastrzemski	12.00	6.00	3.50
(207)	Eddie Yost	.40	.20	.12

1962 Topps

The 1962 Topps set established another plateau for

set size with 598 cards. The 2-1/2" by 3-1/2" cards feature a photograph set against a woodgrain background. The lower righthand corner has been made to look like it is curling away. Many established specialty cards dot the set including statistical leaders, multi-player cards, team cards, checklists, World Series cards and All-Stars. Of note is that 1962 was the first year of the multi-player rookie card. There is a 9-card "In Action" subset and a 10-card run of special Babe Ruth cards. Photo variations of several cards in the 2nd Series (#'s 110-196) exist. All cards in the 2nd Series can be found with two distinct printing variations, an early printing with the cards containing a very noticeable greenish tint, having been corrected to clear photos in subsequent print runs. The complete set price in the checklist that follows does not include the higher-priced variations.

		NR MT	EX	VG
	Complete Set:	5000.00	2250.00	1350.
	Common Player: 1-370	2.00	1.00	.60
	Common Player: 371-522	4.00	2.00	1.25
	Common Player: 523-598	12.00	5.50	3.00
1	Roger Maris	225.00	45.00	27.00
2	Jim Brosnan	2.25	1.25	.70
3	Pete Runnels	2.00	1.00	.60
4	John DeMerit	2.00	.90	.50
5	Sandy Koufax	110.00	55.00	33.00
6	Marv Breeding	2.00	1.00	.60
7	Frank Thomas	2.00	.90	.50
8	Ray Herbert	2.00	1.00	.60
9	Jim Davenport	2.00	1.00	.60
10	Bob Clemente	110.00	55.00	33.00
11	Tom Morgan	2.00	1.00	.60
12	Harry Craft	2.00	1.00	.60
13	Dick Howser	2.25	1.25	.70
14	Bill White	2.00	1.00	.60
15	Dick Donovan	2.00	1.00	.60
16	Darrell Johnson	2.00	1.00	.60
17	Johnny Callison	2.25	1.25	.70
18	Managers' Dream (Mickey Mantle, Willie Mays)	100.00	50.00	30.00
19	*Ray Washburn*	2.00	1.00	.60
20	Rocky Colavito	8.00	4.00	2.50
21	Jim Kaat	5.00	2.00	1.25
22a	Checklist 1-88 (numbers 121 - 176 on back)	5.00	2.25	1.25
22b	Checklist 1-88 (numbers 33-88 on back)	4.00	1.75	1.00
23	Norm Larker	2.00	1.00	.60
24	Tigers Team	5.00	2.50	1.50
25	Ernie Banks	45.00	23.00	13.50
26	Chris Cannizzaro	2.00	.90	.50
27	Chuck Cottier	2.00	1.00	.60
28	Minnie Minoso	4.00	2.00	1.25
29	Casey Stengel	15.00	6.75	3.75
30	Ed Mathews	20.00	10.00	6.00
31	*Tom Tresh*	10.00	5.00	3.00
32	John Roseboro	2.25	1.25	.70
33	Don Larsen	2.25	1.25	.70
34	Johnny Temple	2.00	1.00	.60
35	*Don Schwall*	2.25	1.25	.70
36	Don Leppert	2.00	1.00	.60
37	Tribe Hill Trio (Barry Latman, Jim Perry, Dick Stigman)	2.25	1.25	.70
38	Gene Stephens	2.00	1.00	.60
39	Joe Koppe	2.00	1.00	.60
40	Orlando Cepeda	5.00	2.25	1.25
41	Cliff Cook	2.00	1.00	.60
42	Jim King	2.00	1.00	.60
43	Dodgers Team	5.00	2.50	1.50
44	Don Taussig	2.00	1.00	.60
45	Brooks Robinson	40.00	15.00	9.00
46	*Jack Baldschun*	2.00	1.00	.60
47	Bob Will	2.00	1.00	.60
48	Ralph Terry	4.00	2.00	1.25
49	Hal Jones	2.00	1.00	.60
50	Stan Musial	110.00	55.00	33.00
51	A.L. Batting Leaders (Norm Cash, Elston Howard, Al Kaline, Jim Piersall)	5.00	2.50	1.50
52	N.L. Batting Leaders (Ken Boyer, Bob Clemente, Wally Moon, Vada Pinson)	5.00	2.50	1.50
53	A.L. Home Run Leaders (Jim Gentile, Harmon Killebrew, Mickey Mantle, Roger Maris)	40.00	20.00	12.00
54	N.L. Home Run Leaders (Orlando Cepeda, Willie Mays, Frank Robinson)	5.00	2.50	1.50

		NR MT	EX	VG
55	A.L. E.R.A. Leaders (Dick Donovan, Don Mossi, Milt Pappas, Bill Stafford)	4.00	2.00	1.25
56	N.L. E.R.A. Leaders (Mike McCormick, Jim O'Toole, Curt Simmons, Warren Spahn)	5.00	2.50	1.50
57	A.L. Win Leaders (Steve Barber, Jim Bunning, Whitey Ford, Frank Lary)	5.00	2.50	1.50
58	N.L. Win Leaders (Joe Jay, Jim O'Toole, Warren Spahn)	5.00	2.50	1.50
59	A.L. Strikeout Leaders (Jim Bunning, Whitey Ford, Camilo Pascual, Juan Pizzaro)	5.00	2.50	1.50
60	N.L. Strikeout Leaders (Don Drysdale, Sandy Koufax, Jim O'Toole, Stan Williams)	5.00	2.50	1.50
61	Cardinals Team	4.00	2.00	1.25
62	Steve Boros	2.00	1.00	.60
63	*Tony Cloninger*	2.00	.90	.50
64	Russ Snyder	2.00	1.00	.60
65	Bobby Richardson	6.00	2.75	1.50
66	Cuno Barragon (Barragan)	2.00	1.00	.60
67	Harvey Haddix	2.25	1.25	.70
68	Ken L. Hunt	2.00	1.00	.60
69	Phil Ortega	2.00	1.00	.60
70	Harmon Killebrew	20.00	10.00	6.00
71	Dick LeMay	2.00	1.00	.60
72	Bob's Pupils (Steve Boros, Bob Scheffing, Jake Wood)	2.25	1.25	.70
73	Nellie Fox	8.00	4.00	2.50
74	Bob Lillis	2.00	1.00	.60
75	Milt Pappas	2.25	1.25	.70
76	Howie Bedell	2.00	1.00	.60
77	Tony Taylor	2.00	1.00	.60
78	Gene Green	2.00	1.00	.60
79	Ed Hobaugh	2.00	1.00	.60
80	Vada Pinson	4.00	2.00	1.25
81	Jim Pagliaroni	2.00	1.00	.60
82	Deron Johnson	2.00	1.00	.60
83	Larry Jackson	2.00	1.00	.60
84	Lenny Green	2.00	1.00	.60
85	Gil Hodges	15.00	7.50	4.50
86	*Donn Clendenon*	2.25	1.25	.70
87	Mike Roarke	2.00	1.00	.60
88	Ralph Houk	4.00	2.00	1.25
89	Barney Schultz	2.00	1.00	.60
90	Jim Piersall	2.00	.90	.50
91	J.C. Martin	2.00	1.00	.60
92	Sam Jones	2.00	1.00	.60
93	John Blanchard	2.00	.90	.50
94	Jay Hook	2.00	.90	.50
95	Don Hoak	2.25	1.25	.70
96	Eli Grba	2.00	1.00	.60
97	Tito Francona	2.00	1.00	.60
98	Checklist 89-176	4.00	1.75	1.00
99	*John Powell*	18.00	9.00	5.50
100	Warren Spahn	30.00	12.50	7.50
101	Carroll Hardy	2.00	1.00	.60
102	Al Schroll	2.00	1.00	.60
103	Don Blasingame	2.00	1.00	.60
104	Ted Savage	2.00	1.00	.60
105	Don Mossi	2.00	1.00	.60
106	Carl Sawatski	2.00	1.00	.60
107	Mike McCormick	2.00	1.00	.60
108	Willie Davis	4.00	2.00	1.25
109	Bob Shaw	2.00	1.00	.60
110	Bill Skowron	5.00	2.25	1.25
111	Dallas Green	2.25	1.25	.70
112	Hank Foiles	2.00	1.00	.60
113	White Sox Team	4.00	2.00	1.25
114	Howie Koplitz	2.00	1.00	.60
115	Bob Skinner	2.00	1.00	.60
116	Herb Score	2.00	.90	.50
117	Gary Geiger	2.00	1.00	.60
118	Julian Javier	2.00	1.00	.60
119	Danny Murphy	2.00	1.00	.60
120	Bob Purkey	2.00	1.00	.60
121	Billy Hitchcock	2.00	1.00	.60
122	Norm Bass	2.00	1.00	.60
123	Mike de la Hoz	2.00	1.00	.60
124	Bill Pleis	2.00	1.00	.60
125	Gene Woodling	2.25	1.25	.70
126	Al Cicotte	2.00	1.00	.60
127	Pride of the A's (Hank Bauer, Jerry Lumpe, Norm Siebern)	2.25	1.25	.70
128	Art Fowler	2.00	1.00	.60
129a	Lee Walls (facing left)	15.00	7.50	4.50
129b	Lee Walls (facing right)	2.00	1.00	.60
130	Frank Bolling	2.00	1.00	.60
131	*Pete Richert*	2.25	1.25	.70
132a	Angels Team (with inset photos)	10.00	4.50	2.50
132b	Angels Team (without inset photos)	5.00	2.50	1.50

		NR MT	EX	VG
133	Felipe Alou	2.25	1.25	.70
134a	Billy Hoeft (green sky in background)	15.00	7.50	4.50
134b	Billy Hoeft (blue sky in background)	2.00	1.00	.60
135	Babe As A Boy	7.00	3.25	1.75
136	Babe Joins Yanks	7.00	3.25	1.75
137	Babe and Mgr. Huggins	7.00	3.25	1.75
138	The Famous Slugger	7.00	3.25	1.75
139a	Hal Reniff (pitching)	40.00	20.00	12.00
139b	Hal Reniff (portrait)	18.00	9.00	5.50
139c	Babe Hits 60	10.00	4.00	2.50
140	Gehrig and Ruth	9.00	4.00	2.25
141	Twilight Years	7.00	3.25	1.75
142	Coaching for the Dodgers	7.00	3.25	1.75
143	Greatest Sports Hero	7.00	3.25	1.75
144	Farewell Speech	7.00	3.25	1.75
145	Barry Latman	2.00	1.00	.60
146	Don Demeter	2.00	1.00	.60
147a	Bill Kunkel (pitching)	15.00	7.50	4.50
147b	Bill Kunkel (portrait)	2.00	1.00	.60
148	Wally Post	2.00	1.00	.60
149	Bob Duliba	2.00	1.00	.60
150	Al Kaline	30.00	15.00	9.00
151	Johnny Klippstein	2.00	1.00	.60
152	Mickey Vernon	2.00	1.00	.60
153	Pumpsie Green	2.00	1.00	.60
154	Lee Thomas	2.00	1.00	.60
155	Stu Miller	2.00	1.00	.60
156	Merritt Ranew	2.00	1.00	.60
157	Wes Covington	2.00	1.00	.60
158	Braves Team	5.00	2.50	1.50
159	Hal Reniff	2.00	.90	.50
160	Dick Stuart	2.00	1.00	.60
161	Frank Baumann	2.00	1.00	.60
162	Sammy Drake	2.00	.90	.50
163	Hot Corner Guardians (Cletis Boyer, Billy Gardner)	5.00	2.50	1.50
164	Hal Naragon	2.00	1.00	.60
165	Jackie Brandt	2.00	1.00	.60
166	Don Lee	2.00	1.00	.60
167	*Tim McCarver*	30.00	12.50	7.50
168	Leo Posada	2.00	1.00	.60
169	Bob Cerv	2.00	.90	.50
170	Ron Santo	5.00	2.50	1.50
171	Dave Sisler	2.00	1.00	.60
172	Fred Hutchinson	2.00	1.00	.60
173	Chico Fernandez	2.00	1.00	.60
174a	Carl Willey (with cap)	15.00	7.50	4.50
174b	Carl Willey (no cap)	2.00	1.00	.60
175	Frank Howard	5.00	2.50	1.50
176a	Eddie Yost (batting)	15.00	7.50	4.50
176b	Eddie Yost (portrait)	2.00	1.00	.60
177	Bobby Shantz	2.25	1.25	.70
178	Camilo Carreon	2.00	1.00	.60
179	Tom Sturdivant	2.00	1.00	.60
180	Bob Allison	2.25	1.25	.70
181	Paul Brown	2.00	1.00	.60
182	Bob Nieman	2.00	1.00	.60
183	Roger Craig	5.00	2.50	1.50
184	Haywood Sullivan	2.00	1.00	.60
185	Roland Sheldon	2.00	.90	.50
186	*Mack Jones*	2.00	1.00	.60
187	Gene Conley	2.00	1.00	.60
188	Chuck Hiller	2.00	1.00	.60
189	Dick Hall	2.00	1.00	.60
190a	Wally Moon (with cap)	9.00	4.00	2.25
190b	Wally Moon (no cap)	2.25	1.25	.70
191	Jim Brewer	2.00	1.00	.60
192a	Checklist 177-264 (192 is Check List, 3)	6.00	2.75	1.50
192b	Checklist 177-264 (192 is Check List, 3)	4.00	1.75	1.00
193	Eddie Kasko	2.00	1.00	.60
194	*Dean Chance*	5.00	2.50	1.50
195	Joe Cunningham	2.00	1.00	.60
196	Terry Fox	2.00	1.00	.60
197	Daryl Spencer	2.00	1.00	.60
198	Johnny Keane	2.00	1.00	.60
199	*Gaylord Perry*	200.00	100.00	60.00
200	Mickey Mantle	450.00	225.00	135.00
201	Ike Delock	2.00	1.00	.60
202	Carl Warwick	2.00	1.00	.60
203	Jack Fisher	2.00	1.00	.60
204	Johnny Weekly	2.00	1.00	.60
205	Gene Freese	2.00	1.00	.60
206	Senators Team	4.00	2.00	1.25
207	Pete Burnside	2.00	1.00	.60
208	Billy Martin	6.00	2.75	1.50
209	*Jim Fregosi*	6.00	2.50	1.50
210	Roy Face	2.00	.90	.50
211	Midway Masters (Frank Bolling, Roy McMillan)	2.25	1.25	.70
212	Jim Owens	2.00	1.00	.60
213	Richie Ashburn	6.00	2.75	1.50
214	Dom Zanni	2.00	1.00	.60
215	Woody Held	2.00	1.00	.60
216	Ron Kline	2.00	1.00	.60
217	Walt Alston	4.00	1.75	1.00
218	*Joe Torre*	25.00	12.50	7.50
219	*Al Downing*	4.00	1.75	1.00
220	Roy Sievers	2.25	1.25	.70
221	Bill Short	2.00	1.00	.60
222	Jerry Zimmerman	2.00	1.00	.60
223	Alex Grammas	2.00	1.00	.60
224	Don Rudolph	2.00	1.00	.60
225	Frank Malzone	2.00	1.00	.60
226	Giants Team	4.00	1.75	1.00
227	Bobby Tiefenauer	2.00	1.00	.60
228	Dale Long	2.00	1.00	.60
229	Jesus McFarlane	2.00	1.00	.60
230	Camilo Pascual	2.25	1.25	.70
231	Ernie Bowman	2.00	1.00	.60
232	World Series Game 1 (Yanks Win Opener)	5.00	2.50	1.50
233	World Series Game 2 (Jay Ties It Up)	5.00	2.50	1.50
234	World Series Game 3 (Maris Wins It In The 9th)	8.00	3.50	2.00
235	World Series Game 4 (Ford Sets New Mark)	7.00	3.25	1.75
236	World Series Game 5 (Yanks Crush Reds In Finale)	5.00	2.50	1.50
237	World Series Summary (The Winners Celebrate)	5.00	2.50	1.50
238	Norm Sherry	2.00	1.00	.60
239	Cecil Butler	2.00	1.00	.60
240	George Altman	2.00	1.00	.60
241	Johnny Kucks	2.00	1.00	.60
242	Mel McGaha	2.00	1.00	.60
243	Robin Roberts	12.00	5.50	3.00
244	Don Gile	2.00	1.00	.60
245	Ron Hansen	2.00	1.00	.60
246	Art Ditmar	2.00	1.00	.60
247	Joe Pignatano	2.00	1.00	.60
248	Bob Aspromonte	2.00	1.00	.60
249	Ed Keegan	2.00	1.00	.60
250	Norm Cash	5.00	2.50	1.50
251	Yankees Team	15.00	7.50	4.50
252	Earl Francis	2.00	1.00	.60
253	Harry Chiti	2.00	1.00	.60
254	Gordon Windhorn	2.00	1.00	.60
255	Juan Pizarro	2.00	1.00	.60
256	Elio Chacon	2.00	.90	.50
257	Jack Spring	2.00	1.00	.60
258	Marty Keough	2.00	1.00	.60
259	Lou Klimchock	2.00	1.00	.60
260	Bill Pierce	2.00	.90	.50
261	George Alusik	2.00	1.00	.60
262	Bob Schmidt	2.00	1.00	.60
263	The Right Pitch (Joe Jay, Bob Purkey, Jim Turner)	2.25	1.25	.70
264	Dick Ellsworth	2.00	1.00	.60
265	Joe Adcock	2.00	.90	.60
266	John Anderson	2.00	1.00	.60
267	Dan Dobbek	2.00	1.00	.60
268	Ken McBride	2.00	1.00	.60
269	Bob Oldis	2.00	1.00	.60
270	Dick Groat	2.00	.90	.50
271	Ray Rippelmeyer	2.00	1.00	.60
272	Earl Robinson	2.00	1.00	.60
273	Gary Bell	2.00	1.00	.60
274	Sammy Taylor	2.00	1.00	.60
275	Norm Siebern	2.00	1.00	.60
276	Hal Kostad	2.00	1.00	.60
277	Checklist 265-352	4.00	1.75	1.00
278	Ken Johnson	2.00	1.00	.60
279	Hobie Landrith	2.00	.90	.50
280	Johnny Podres	4.00	2.00	1.25
281	*Jake Gibbs*	2.25	1.00	.60
282	Dave Hillman	2.00	1.00	.60
283	Charlie Smith	2.00	1.00	.60
284	Ruben Amaro	2.00	1.00	.60
285	Curt Simmons	2.00	.90	.50
286	Al Lopez	5.00	2.50	1.50
287	George Witt	2.00	1.00	.60
288	Billy Williams	30.00	15.00	9.00
289	Mike Krsnich	2.00	1.00	.60
290	Jim Gentile	2.00	1.00	.60
291	Hal Stowe	2.00	.90	.50
292	Jerry Kindall	2.00	1.00	.60
293	Bob Miller	2.00	.90	.50

		NR MT	EX	VG
294	Phillies Team	4.00	2.00	1.25
295	Vern Law	2.00	.90	.50
296	Ken Hamlin	2.00	1.00	.60
297	Ron Perranoski	2.00	1.00	.60
298	Bill Tuttle	2.00	1.00	.60
299	*Don Wert*	2.00	1.00	.60
300	Willie Mays	160.00	75.00	45.00
301	Galen Cisco	2.00	1.00	.60
302	*John Edwards*	2.00	1.00	.60
303	Frank Torre	2.00	1.00	.60
304	Dick Farrell	2.00	1.00	.60
305	Jerry Lumpe	2.00	1.00	.60
306	Redbird Rippers (Larry Jackson, Lindy McDaniel)	2.25	1.25	.70
307	Jim Grant	2.00	1.00	.60
308	Neil Chrisley	2.00	.90	.50
309	Moe Morhardt	2.00	1.00	.60
310	Whitey Ford	25.00	12.50	7.50
311	Kubek Makes The Double Play	5.00	2.50	1.50
312	Spahn Shows No-Hit Form	7.00	3.50	2.00
313	Maris Blasts 61st	20.00	10.00	6.00
314	Colavito's Power	5.00	2.50	1.50
315	Ford Tosses A Curve	6.00	2.75	1.50
316	Killebrew Sends One Into Orbit	5.00	2.25	1.25
317	Musial Plays 21st Season	12.00	5.50	3.00
318	The Switch Hitter Connects (Mickey Mantle)	50.00	25.00	15.00
319	McCormick Shows His Stuff	2.25	1.25	.70
320	Hank Aaron	125.00	62.00	37.00
321	Lee Stange	2.00	1.00	.60
322	Al Dark	2.25	1.25	.70
323	Don Landrum	2.00	1.00	.60
324	Joe McClain	2.00	1.00	.60
325	Luis Aparicio	15.00	7.50	4.50
326	Tom Parsons	2.00	1.00	.60
327	Ozzie Virgil	2.00	1.00	.60
328	Ken Walters	2.00	1.00	.60
329	Bob Bolin	2.00	1.00	.60
330	Johnny Romano	2.00	1.00	.60
331	Moe Drabowsky	2.00	1.00	.60
332	Don Buddin	2.00	1.00	.60
333	Frank Cipriani	2.00	1.00	.60
334	Red Sox Team	5.00	2.50	1.50
335	Bill Bruton	2.00	1.00	.60
336	Billy Muffett	2.00	1.00	.60
337	Jim Marshall	2.00	.90	.50
338	Billy Gardner	2.25	1.00	.60
339	Jose Valdivielso	2.00	1.00	.60
340	Don Drysdale	30.00	15.00	9.00
341	Mike Hershberger	2.00	1.00	.60
342	Ed Rakow	2.00	1.00	.60
343	Albie Pearson	2.00	1.00	.60
344	Ed Bauta	2.00	1.00	.60
345	Chuck Schilling	2.00	1.00	.60
346	Jack Kralick	2.00	1.00	.60
347	Chuck Hinton	2.00	1.00	.60
348	Larry Burright	2.00	1.00	.60
349	Paul Foytack	2.00	1.00	.60
350	Frank Robinson	50.00	25.00	15.00
351	Braves' Backstops (Del Crandall, Joe Torre)	5.00	2.50	1.50
352	Frank Sullivan	2.00	1.00	.60
353	Bill Mazeroski	5.00	2.50	1.50
354	Roman Mejias	2.00	1.00	.60
355	Steve Barber	2.00	1.00	.60
356	Tom Haller	2.25	1.25	.70
357	Jerry Walker	2.00	1.00	.60
358	Tommy Davis	4.00	2.00	1.25
359	Bobby Locke	2.00	1.00	.60
360	Yogi Berra	70.00	35.00	21.00
361	Bob Hendley	2.00	1.00	.60
362	Ty Cline	2.00	1.00	.60
363	Bob Roselli	2.00	1.00	.60
364	Ken Hunt	2.00	1.00	.60
365	Charley Neal	2.00	.90	.50
366	Phil Regan	2.00	1.00	.60
367	Checklist 353-429	4.00	1.75	1.00
368	Bob Tillman	2.00	1.00	.60
369	Ted Bowsfield	2.00	1.00	.60
370	Ken Boyer	4.00	1.75	1.00
371	Earl Battey	4.00	2.00	1.25
372	Jack Curtis	4.00	2.00	1.25
373	Al Heist	4.00	2.00	1.25
374	Gene Mauch	4.00	2.00	1.25
375	Ron Fairly	4.00	2.00	1.25
376	Bud Daley	5.00	2.50	1.50
377	Johnny Orsino	4.00	2.00	1.25
378	Bennie Daniels	4.00	2.00	1.25
379	Chuck Essegian	4.00	2.00	1.25
380	Lou Burdette	4.00	1.75	1.00
381	Chico Cardenas	4.00	2.00	1.25
382	Dick Williams	5.00	2.50	1.50
383	Ray Sadecki	4.00	2.00	1.25
384	Athletics Team	5.00	2.50	1.50
385	Early Wynn	20.00	10.00	6.00
386	Don Mincher	4.00	2.00	1.25
387	Lou Brock	200.00	100.00	60.00
388	Ryne Duren	4.00	2.00	1.25
389	Smoky Burgess	5.00	2.50	1.50
390	Orlando Cepeda AS	5.00	2.25	1.25
391	Bill Mazeroski AS	5.00	2.50	1.50
392	Ken Boyer AS	5.00	2.50	1.50
393	Roy McMillan AS	4.00	2.00	1.25
394	Hank Aaron AS	30.00	15.00	9.00
395	Willie Mays AS	30.00	15.00	9.00
396	Frank Robinson AS	12.00	5.50	3.00
397	John Roseboro AS	4.00	2.00	1.25
398	Don Drysdale AS	10.00	4.50	2.50
399	Warren Spahn AS	10.00	4.50	2.50
400	Elston Howard	7.00	3.25	1.75
401	AL & NL Homer Kings (Orlando Cepeda, Roger Maris)	25.00	10.00	6.00
402	Gino Cimoli	4.00	2.00	1.25
403	Chet Nichols	4.00	2.00	1.25
404	Tim Harkness	4.00	2.00	1.25
405	Jim Perry	5.00	2.50	1.50
406	Bob Taylor	4.00	2.00	1.25
407	Hank Aguirre	4.00	2.00	1.25
408	Gus Bell	5.00	2.50	1.50
409	Pirates Team	5.00	2.50	1.50
410	Al Smith	4.00	2.00	1.25
411	Danny O'Connell	4.00	2.00	1.25
412	Charlie James	4.00	2.00	1.25
413	Matty Alou	5.00	2.50	1.50
414	Joe Gaines	4.00	2.00	1.25
415	Bill Virdon	5.00	2.50	1.50
416	Bob Scheffing	4.00	2.00	1.25
417	Joe Azcue	4.00	2.00	1.25
418	Andy Carey	4.00	2.00	1.25
419	Bob Bruce	4.00	2.00	1.25
420	Gus Triandos	4.00	2.00	1.25
421	Ken MacKenzie	5.00	2.50	1.50
422	Steve Bilko	4.00	2.00	1.25
423	Rival League Relief Aces (Roy Face, Hoyt Wilhelm)	5.00	2.25	1.25
424	Al McBean	4.00	2.00	1.25
425	Carl Yastrzemski	225.00	100.00	60.00
426	Bob Farley	4.00	2.00	1.25
427	Jake Wood	4.00	2.00	1.25
428	Joe Hicks	4.00	2.00	1.25
429	Bill O'Dell	4.00	2.00	1.25
430	Tony Kubek	7.00	3.25	1.75
431	*Bob Rodgers*	9.00	4.50	2.75
432	Jim Pendleton	4.00	2.00	1.25
433	Jim Archer	4.00	2.00	1.25
434	Clay Dalrymple	4.00	2.00	1.25
435	Larry Sherry	4.00	2.00	1.25
436	Felix Mantilla	5.00	2.50	1.50
437	Ray Moore	4.00	2.00	1.25
438	Dick Brown	4.00	2.00	1.25
439	Jerry Buchek	4.00	2.00	1.25
440	Joe Jay	4.00	2.00	1.25
441	Checklist 430-506	5.00	2.25	1.25
442	Wes Stock	4.00	2.00	1.25
443	Del Crandall	5.00	2.50	1.50
444	Ted Wills	4.00	2.00	1.25
445	Vic Power	4.00	2.00	1.25
446	Don Elston	4.00	2.00	1.25
447	Willie Kirkland	4.00	2.00	1.25
448	Joe Gibbon	4.00	2.00	1.25
449	Jerry Adair	4.00	2.00	1.25
450	Jim O'Toole	4.00	2.00	1.25
451	*Jose Tartabull*	4.00	2.00	1.25
452	Earl Averill	4.00	2.00	1.25
453	Cal McLish	4.00	2.00	1.25
454	Floyd Robinson	4.00	2.00	1.25
455	Luis Arroyo	5.00	2.50	1.50
456	Joe Amalfitano	4.00	2.00	1.25
457	Lou Clinton	4.00	2.00	1.25
458a	Bob Buhl ("M" on cap)	4.00	2.00	1.25
458b	Bob Buhl (plain cap)	60.00	30.00	18.00
459	Ed Bailey	4.00	2.00	1.25
460	Jim Bunning	9.00	4.00	2.50
461	*Ken Hubbs*	15.00	7.50	4.50
462a	Willie Tasby ("W" on cap)	4.00	2.00	1.25
462b	Willie Tasby (plain cap)	60.00	30.00	18.00
463	Hank Bauer	5.00	2.50	1.50
464	*Al Jackson*	5.00	2.50	1.50
465	Reds Team	4.00	1.75	1.00
466	Norm Cash AS	4.00	1.75	1.00
467	Chuck Schilling AS	5.00	2.50	1.50
468	Brooks Robinson AS	12.00	5.50	3.00

		NR MT	EX	VG
469	Luis Aparicio AS	8.00	3.50	2.00
470	Al Kaline AS	18.00	7.50	4.50
471	Mickey Mantle AS	125.00	67.00	37.00
472	Rocky Colavito AS	5.00	2.25	1.25
473	Elston Howard AS	5.00	2.25	1.25
474	Frank Lary AS	5.00	2.50	1.50
475	Whitey Ford AS	10.00	4.50	2.50
476	Orioles Team	5.00	2.50	1.50
477	Andre Rodgers	4.00	2.00	1.25
478	Don Zimmer	5.00	2.50	1.50
479	*Joel Horlen*	4.00	2.00	1.25
480	Harvey Kuenn	5.00	2.50	1.50
481	Vic Wertz	4.00	2.00	1.25
482	Sam Mele	4.00	2.00	1.25
483	Don McMahon	4.00	2.00	1.25
484	Dick Schofield	4.00	2.00	1.25
485	Pedro Ramos	4.00	2.00	1.25
486	Jim Gilliam	4.00	1.75	1.00
487	Jerry Lynch	4.00	2.00	1.25
488	Hal Brown	4.00	2.00	1.25
489	Julio Gotay	4.00	2.00	1.25
490	Clete Boyer	4.00	1.75	1.00
491	Leon Wagner	4.00	2.00	1.25
492	Hal Smith	4.00	2.00	1.25
493	Danny McDevitt	4.00	2.00	1.25
494	Sammy White	4.00	2.00	1.25
495	Don Cardwell	4.00	2.00	1.25
496	Wayne Causey	4.00	2.00	1.25
497	Ed Bouchee	5.00	2.50	1.50
498	Jim Donohue	4.00	2.00	1.25
499	Zoilo Versalles	4.00	2.00	1.25
500	Duke Snider	40.00	20.00	12.00
501	Claude Osteen	4.00	2.00	1.25
502	Hector Lopez	5.00	2.50	1.50
503	Danny Murtaugh	4.00	2.00	1.25
504	Eddie Bressoud	4.00	2.00	1.25
505	Juan Marichal	35.00	17.50	10.50
506	Charley Maxwell	4.00	2.00	1.25
507	Ernie Broglio	4.00	2.00	1.25
508	Gordy Coleman	4.00	2.00	1.25
509	*Dave Giusti*	4.00	2.00	1.25
510	Jim Lemon	4.00	2.00	1.25
511	Bubba Phillips	4.00	2.00	1.25
512	Mike Fornieles	4.00	2.00	1.25
513	Whitey Herzog	4.00	1.75	1.00
514	Sherm Lollar	4.00	2.00	1.25
515	Stan Williams	4.00	2.00	1.25
516	Checklist 507-598	8.00	3.50	2.00
517	Dave Wickersham	4.00	2.00	1.25
518	Lee Maye	4.00	2.00	1.25
519	Bob Johnson	4.00	2.00	1.25
520	Bob Friend	5.00	2.50	1.50
521	Jacke Davis	4.00	2.00	1.25
522	Lindy McDaniel	4.00	2.00	1.25
523	Russ Nixon	12.00	5.50	3.00
524	Howie Nunn	12.00	5.50	3.00
525	George Thomas	12.00	5.50	3.00
526	Hal Woodeshick	12.00	5.50	3.00
527	*Dick McAuliffe*	15.00	5.00	2.75
528	Turk Lown	12.00	5.50	3.00
529	John Schaive	12.00	5.50	3.00
530	Bob Gibson	175.00	87.00	52.00
531	Bobby G. Smith	12.00	5.50	3.00
532	Dick Stigman	12.00	5.50	3.00
533	Charley Lau	13.00	5.75	3.25
534	Tony Gonzalez	12.00	5.50	3.00
535	Ed Roebuck	12.00	5.50	3.00
536	Dick Gernert	12.00	5.50	3.00
537	Indians Team	15.00	6.75	3.75
538	Jack Sanford	12.00	5.50	3.00
539	Billy Moran	12.00	5.50	3.00
540	Jim Landis	12.00	5.50	3.00
541	Don Nottebart	12.00	5.50	3.00
542	Dave Philley	12.00	5.50	3.00
543	Bob Allen	12.00	5.50	3.00
544	Willie McCovey	125.00	62.00	37.00
545	Hoyt Wilhelm	55.00	25.00	14.00
546	Moe Thacker	12.00	5.50	3.00
547	Don Ferrarese	12.00	5.50	3.00
548	Bobby Del Greco	12.00	5.50	3.00
549	Bill Rigney	12.00	5.50	3.00
550	Art Mahaffey	12.00	5.50	3.00
551	Harry Bright	12.00	5.50	3.00
552	Cubs Team	15.00	6.75	3.75
553	Jim Coates	15.00	6.75	3.75
554	Bubba Morton	12.00	5.50	3.00
555	John Buzhardt	12.00	5.50	3.00
556	Al Spangler	12.00	5.50	3.00
557	Bob Anderson	12.00	5.50	3.00
558	John Goryl	12.00	5.50	3.00
559	Mike Higgins	12.00	5.50	3.00

		NR MT	EX	VG
560	Chuck Estrada	12.00	5.50	3.00
561	Gene Oliver	12.00	5.50	3.00
562	Bill Henry	12.00	5.50	3.00
563	Ken Aspromonte	12.00	5.50	3.00
564	Bob Grim	12.00	5.50	3.00
565	Jose Pagan	12.00	5.50	3.00
566	Marty Kutyna	12.00	5.50	3.00
567	Tracy Stallard	12.00	5.50	3.00
568	Jim Golden	12.00	5.50	3.00
569	Ed Sadowski	12.00	5.50	3.00
570	Bill Stafford	15.00	6.75	3.75
571	Billy Klaus	12.00	5.50	3.00
572	Bob Miller	13.00	5.75	3.25
573	Johnny Logan	13.00	5.75	3.25
574	Dean Stone	12.00	5.50	3.00
575	Red Schoendienst	35.00	15.00	9.00
576	Russ Kemmerer	12.00	5.50	3.00
577	Dave Nicholson	12.00	5.50	3.00
578	Jim Duffalo	12.00	5.50	3.00
579	Jim Schaffer	12.00	5.50	3.00
580	Bill Monbouquette	13.00	5.75	3.25
581	Mel Roach	12.00	5.50	3.00
582	Ron Piche	12.00	5.50	3.00
583	Larry Osborne	12.00	5.50	3.00
584	Twins Team	15.00	6.75	3.75
585	Glen Hobbie	12.00	5.50	3.00
586	Sammy Esposito	12.00	5.50	3.00
587	Frank Funk	12.00	5.50	3.00
588	Birdie Tebbetts	12.00	5.50	3.00
589	Bob Turley	18.00	8.00	4.50
590	Curt Flood	18.00	8.00	4.50
591	Rookie Parade Pitchers (Sam McDowell, Ron Nischwitz, Art Quirk, *Dick Radatz*, *Ron Taylor*)	60.00	30.00	18.00
592	Rookie Parade Pitchers (Bo Belinsky, Joe Bonikowski, *Jim Bouton*, Dan Pfister, Dave Stenhouse)	45.00	20.00	11.25
593	Rookie Parade Pitchers (Craig Anderson, *Jack Hamilton*, Jack Lamabe, Bob Moorhead, *Bob Veale*)	25.00	11.25	6.25
594	Rookie Parade Catchers (Doug Camilli, *Doc Edwards*, Don Pavletich, Ken Retzer, *Bob Uecker*)	150.00	75.00	45.00
595	Rookie Parade Infielders (*Ed Charles*, Marlin Coughtry, Bob Sadowski, Felix Torres)	25.00	11.25	6.25
596	Rookie Parade Infielders (*Bernie Allen*, *Phil Linz, Joe Pepitone, Rich Rollins*)	65.00	33.00	20.00
597	Rookie Parade Infielders (Rod Kanehl, Jim McKnight, *Denis Menke*, Amado Samuel)	25.00	11.25	6.25
598	Rookie Parade Outfielders (Howie Goss, *Jim Hickman*, Manny Jimenez, Al Luplow, Ed Olivares)	65.00	33.00	20.00

1962 Topps Baseball Bucks

Issued in their own 1¢ package, the 1962 Topps "Baseball Bucks" were another in the growing list of specialty Topps items. The 96 Baseball Bucks in the set measure 4-1/8" by 1-3/4," and were designed to look vaguely like dollar bills. The center player portrait has a banner underneath with the player's name. His home park is shown on the right and there is some biographical information on the left. The back features a large denomination, with the player's league and team logo on either side.

		NR MT	EX	VG
	Complete Set:	750.00	375.00	225.00
	Common Player:	2.00	1.00	.60
(1)	Hank Aaron	30.00	15.00	9.00
(2)	Joe Adcock	3.00	1.50	.90
(3)	George Altman	2.00	1.00	.60
(4)	Jim Archer	2.00	1.00	.60
(5)	Richie Ashburn	5.00	2.50	1.50
(6)	Ernie Banks	20.00	10.00	8.00
(7)	Earl Battey	2.50	1.25	.70
(8)	Gus Bell	2.50	1.25	.70
(9)	Yogi Berra	18.00	9.00	5.50
(10)	Ken Boyer	3.00	1.50	.90
(11)	Jackie Brandt	2.00	1.00	.60
(12)	Jim Bunning	4.00	2.00	1.25
(13)	Lou Burdette	3.00	1.50	.90
(14)	Don Cardwell	2.00	1.00	.60
(15)	Norm Cash	3.00	1.50	.90
(16)	Orlando Cepeda	4.50	2.25	1.25
(17)	Bob Clemente	40.00	20.00	12.50
(18)	Rocky Colavito	3.00	1.50	.90
(19)	Chuck Cottier	2.00	1.00	.60
(20)	Roger Craig	2.50	1.25	.70
(21)	Bennie Daniels	2.00	1.00	.60
(22)	Don Demeter	2.00	1.00	.60
(23)	Don Drysdale	15.00	7.50	4.50
(24)	Chuck Estrada	2.00	1.00	.60
(25)	Dick Farrell	2.00	1.00	.60
(26)	Whitey Ford	12.00	6.00	3.50
(27)	Nellie Fox	4.00	2.00	1.25
(28)	Tito Francona	2.00	1.00	.60
(29)	Bob Friend	2.50	1.25	.70
(30)	Jim Gentile	2.00	1.00	.60
(31)	Dick Gernert	2.00	1.00	.60
(32)	Lenny Green	2.00	1.00	.60
(33)	Dick Groat	3.00	1.50	.90
(34)	Woody Held	2.00	1.00	.60
(35)	Don Hoak	2.50	1.25	.70
(36)	Gil Hodges	10.00	5.00	3.00
(37)	Frank Howard	3.00	1.50	.90
(38)	Elston Howard	4.00	2.00	1.25
(39)	Dick Howser	3.00	1.50	.90
(40)	Ken Hunt	2.00	1.00	.60
(41)	Larry Jackson	2.00	1.00	.60
(42)	Joe Jay	4.00	2.00	1.25
(43)	Al Kaline	12.00	6.00	3.50
(44)	Harmon Killebrew	12.00	6.00	3.50
(45)	Sandy Koufax	35.00	17.50	10.50
(46)	Harvey Kuenn	4.00	2.00	1.25
(47)	Jim Landis	2.00	1.00	.60
(48)	Norm Larker	2.00	1.00	.60
(49)	Frank Lary	2.00	1.00	.60
(50)	Jerry Lumpe	2.00	1.00	.60
(51)	Art Mahaffey	2.00	1.00	.60
(52)	Frank Malzone	2.00	1.00	.60
(53)	Felix Mantilla	2.50	1.25	.70
(54)	Mickey Mantle	125.00	62.00	37.00
(55)	Roger Maris	12.00	6.00	3.50
(56)	Ed Mathews	10.00	5.00	3.00
(57)	Willie Mays	35.00	17.50	10.50
(58)	Ken McBride	2.00	1.00	.60
(59)	Mike McCormick	2.00	1.00	.60
(60)	Minnie Minoso	4.00	2.00	1.25
(61)	Wally Moon	2.50	1.25	.70
(62)	Stu Miller	2.00	1.00	.60
(63)	Stan Musial	30.00	15.00	9.00
(64)	Danny O'Connell	2.00	1.00	.60
(65)	Jim O'Toole	4.00	2.00	1.25
(66)	Camilo Pascual	2.50	1.25	.70
(67)	Jim Perry	3.00	1.50	.90
(68)	Jimmy Piersall	4.00	2.00	1.25
(69)	Vada Pinson	6.00	3.00	1.75
(70)	Juan Pizarro	2.00	1.00	.60
(71)	Johnny Podres	3.00	1.50	.90
(72)	Vic Power	2.00	1.00	.60
(73)	Bob Purkey	12.00	6.00	3.50
(74)	Pedro Ramos	2.00	1.00	.60
(75)	Brooks Robinson	15.00	7.50	4.50
(76)	Floyd Robinson	2.00	1.00	.60
(77)	Frank Robinson	15.00	7.50	4.50
(78)	Johnny Romano	2.00	1.00	.60
(79)	Pete Runnels	2.50	1.25	.70
(80)	Don Schwall	2.00	1.00	.60
(81)	Bobby Shantz	3.00	1.50	.90
(82)	Norm Siebern	2.00	1.00	.60
(83)	Roy Sievers	2.50	1.25	.70
(84)	Hal (W.) Smith	2.00	1.00	.60
(85)	Warren Spahn	10.00	5.00	3.00
(86)	Dick Stuart	2.50	1.25	.70

		NR MT	EX	VG
(87)	Tony Taylor	2.00	1.00	.60
(88)	Lee Thomas	2.00	1.00	.60
(89)	Gus Triandos	2.50	1.25	.70
(90)	Leon Wagner	2.00	1.00	.60
(91)	Jerry Walker	2.00	1.00	.60
(92)	Bill White	2.50	1.25	.70
(93)	Billy Williams	9.00	4.50	2.75
(94)	Gene Woodling	2.50	1.25	.70
(95)	Early Wynn	9.00	4.50	2.75
(96)	Carl Yastrzemski	30.00	15.00	9.00

1962 Topps Stamps

An artistic improvement over the somewhat drab Topps stamps of the previous year, the 1962 stamps, 1-3/8" by 1-7/8," had color player photographs set on red or yellow backgrounds. As in 1961, they were issued in two-stamp panels as insert with Topps baseball cards. A change from 1961 was the inclusion of team emblems in the set. A complete set consists of 201 stamps; Roy Sievers was originally portrayed on the wrong team - Athletics - and was later corrected to the Phillies.

		NR MT	EX	VG
	Complete Set:	220.00	110.00	67.00
	Stamp Album:	35.00	17.50	10.50
	Common Player:	.25	.13	.08
(1)	Hank Aaron	10.00	5.00	3.00
(2)	Jerry Adair	.25	.13	.08
(3)	Joe Adcock	.35	.20	.11
(4)	Bob Allison	.30	.15	.09
(5)	Felipe Alou	.35	.20	.11
(6)	George Altman	.25	.13	.08
(7)	Joe Amalfitano	.25	.13	.08
(8)	Ruben Amaro	.25	.13	.08
(9)	Luis Aparicio	1.50	.70	.45
(10)	Jim Archer	.25	.13	.08
(11)	Bob Aspromonte	.25	.13	.08
(12)	Ed Bailey	.25	.13	.08
(13)	Jack Baldschun	.25	.13	.08
(14)	Ernie Banks	6.00	3.00	1.75
(15)	Earl Battey	.30	.15	.09
(16)	Gus Bell	.35	.20	.11
(17)	Yogi Berra	5.00	2.50	1.50
(18)	Dick Bertell	.25	.13	.08
(19)	Steve Bilko	.25	.13	.08
(20)	Frank Bolling	.25	.13	.08
(21)	Steve Boros	.25	.13	.08
(22)	Ted Bowsfield	.25	.13	.08
(23)	Clete Boyer	.35	.20	.11
(24)	Ken Boyer	.50	.25	.15
(25)	Jackie Brandt	.25	.13	.08
(26)	Bill Bruton	.25	.13	.08
(27)	Jim Bunning	1.00	.50	.30
(28)	Lou Burdette	.35	.20	.11
(29)	Smoky Burgess	.30	.15	.09
(30)	Johnny Callizon (Callison)	.30	.15	.09
(31)	Don Cardwell	.25	.13	.08
(32)	Camilo Carreon	.25	.13	.08
(33)	Norm Cash	.50	.25	.15
(34)	Orlando Cepeda	1.00	.50	.30
(35)	Bob Clemente	15.00	7.50	4.50
(36)	Ty Cline	.25	.13	.08
(37)	Rocky Colavito	.80	.40	.25
(38)	Gordon Coleman	.25	.13	.08

		NR MT	EX	VG
(39)	Chuck Cottier	.25	.13	.08
(40)	Roger Craig	.35	.20	.11
(41)	Del Crandall	.35	.20	.11
(42)	Pete Daley	.25	.13	.08
(43)	Clay Dalrymple	.25	.13	.08
(44)	Bennie Daniels	.25	.13	.08
(45)	Jim Davenport	.25	.13	.08
(46)	Don Demeter	.25	.13	.08
(47)	Dick Donovan	.25	.13	.08
(48)	Don Drysdale	7.00	3.50	2.00
(49)	John Edwards	.25	.13	.08
(50)	Dick Ellsworth	.25	.13	.08
(51)	Chuck Estrada	.25	.13	.08
(52)	Roy Face	.35	.20	.11
(53)	Ron Fairly	.30	.15	.09
(54)	Dick Farrell	.25	.13	.08
(55)	Whitey Ford	5.00	2.50	1.50
(56)	Mike Fornieles	.25	.13	.08
(57)	Nellie Fox	.80	.40	.25
(58)	Tito Francona	.25	.13	.08
(59)	Gene Freese	.25	.13	.08
(60)	Bob Friend	.35	.20	.11
(61)	Gary Geiger	.25	.13	.08
(62)	Jim Gentile	.25	.13	.08
(63)	Tony Gonzalez	.25	.13	.08
(64)	Lenny Green	.25	.13	.08
(65)	Dick Groat	.35	.20	.11
(66)	Ron Hansen	.25	.13	.08
(67)	Al Heist	.25	.13	.08
(68)	Woody Held	.25	.13	.08
(69)	Ray Herbert	.25	.13	.08
(70)	Chuck Hinton	.25	.13	.08
(71)	Don Hoak	.30	.15	.09
(72)	Glen Hobbie	.25	.13	.08
(73)	Gil Hodges	5.00	2.50	1.50
(74)	Jay Hook	.35	.20	.11
(75)	Elston Howard	.80	.40	.25
(76)	Frank Howard	.50	.25	.15
(77)	Dick Howser	.35	.20	.11
(78)	Ken Hunt	.25	.13	.08
(79)	Larry Jackson	.25	.13	.08
(80)	Julian Javier	.25	.13	.08
(81)	Joe Jay	.25	.13	.08
(82)	Bob Johnson	.25	.13	.08
(83)	Sam Jones	.25	.13	.08
(84)	Al Kaline	7.00	3.50	2.00
(85)	Eddie Kasko	.25	.13	.08
(86)	Harmon Killebrew	5.00	2.50	1.50
(87)	Sandy Koufax	10.00	5.00	3.00
(88)	Jack Kralick	.25	.13	.08
(89)	Tony Kubek	.80	.40	.25
(90)	Harvey Kuenn	.50	.25	.15
(91)	Jim Landis	.25	.13	.08
(92)	Hobie Landrith	.35	.20	.11
(93)	Frank Lary	.25	.13	.08
(94)	Barry Latman	.25	.13	.08
(95)	Jerry Lumpe	.25	.13	.08
(96)	Art Mahaffey	.25	.13	.08
(97)	Frank Malzone	.25	.13	.08
(98)	Felix Mantilla	.35	.20	.11
(99)	Mickey Mantle	45.00	22.00	13.50
(100)	Juan Marichal	2.00	1.00	.60
(101)	Roger Maris	5.00	2.50	1.50
(102)	J.C. Martin	.25	.13	.08
(103)	Ed Mathews	3.00	1.50	.90
(104)	Willie Mays	7.00	3.50	2.00
(105)	Bill Mazeroski	.50	.25	.15
(106)	Ken McBride	.25	.13	.08
(107)	Tim McCarver	.50	.25	.15
(108)	Joe McClain	.25	.13	.08
(109)	Mike McCormick	.25	.13	.08
(110)	Lindy McDaniel	.25	.13	.08
(111)	Roy McMillan	.25	.13	.08
(112)	Bob L. Miller	.35	.20	.11
(113)	Stu Miller	.25	.13	.08
(114)	Minnie Minoso	.50	.25	.15
(115)	Bill Monbouquette	.25	.13	.08
(116)	Wally Moon	.30	.15	.09
(117)	Don Mossi	.30	.15	.09
(118)	Stan Musial	7.00	3.50	2.00
(119)	Russ Nixon	.25	.13	.08
(120)	Danny O'Connell	.25	.13	.08
(121)	Jim O'Toole	.25	.13	.08
(122)	Milt Pappas	.30	.15	.09
(123)	Camilo Pascual	.30	.15	.09
(124)	Albie Pearson	.25	.13	.08
(125)	Jim Perry	.35	.20	.11
(126)	Bubba Phillips	.25	.13	.08
(127)	Jimmy Piersall	.35	.20	.11
(128)	Vada Pinson	.50	.25	.15
(129)	Juan Pizarro	.25	.13	.08

		NR MT	EX	VG
(130)	Johnny Podres	.35	.20	.11
(131)	Leo Posada	.25	.13	.08
(132)	Vic Power	.25	.13	.08
(133)	Bob Purkey	.25	.13	.08
(134)	Pedro Ramos	.25	.13	.08
(135)	Bobby Richardson	.80	.40	.25
(136)	Brooks Robinson	3.75	2.00	1.25
(137)	Floyd Robinson	.25	.13	.08
(138)	Frank Robinson	3.50	1.75	1.00
(139)	Bob Rodgers	.30	.15	.09
(140)	Johnny Romano	.25	.13	.08
(141)	John Roseboro	.30	.15	.09
(142)	Pete Runnels	.30	.15	.09
(143)	Ray Sadecki	.25	.13	.08
(144)	Ron Santo	.35	.20	.11
(145)	Chuck Schilling	.25	.13	.08
(146)	Barney Schultz	.25	.13	.08
(147)	Don Schwall	.25	.13	.08
(148)	Bobby Shantz	.35	.20	.11
(149)	Bob Shaw	.25	.13	.08
(150)	Norm Siebern	.25	.13	.08
(151a)	Roy Sievers (Kansas City)	1.00	.50	.30
(151b)	Roy Sievers (Philadelphia)	.30	.15	.09
(152)	Bill Skowron	.50	.25	.15
(153)	Hal (W.) Smith	.25	.13	.08
(154)	Duke Snider	3.75	2.00	1.25
(155)	Warren Spahn	3.00	1.50	.90
(156)	Al Spangler	.25	.13	.08
(157)	Daryl Spencer	.25	.13	.08
(158)	Gene Stephens	.25	.13	.08
(159)	Dick Stuart	.30	.15	.09
(160)	Haywood Sullivan	.25	.13	.08
(161)	Tony Taylor	.25	.13	.08
(162)	George Thomas	.25	.13	.08
(163)	Lee Thomas	.25	.13	.08
(164)	Bob Tiefenauer	.25	.13	.08
(165)	Joe Torre	.50	.25	.15
(166)	Gus Triandos	.30	.15	.09
(167)	Bill Tuttle	.25	.13	.08
(168)	Zoilo Versalles	.25	.13	.08
(169)	Bill Virdon	.35	.20	.11
(170)	Leon Wagner	.25	.13	.08
(171)	Jerry Walker	.25	.13	.08
(172)	Lee Walls	.25	.13	.08
(173)	Bill White	.30	.15	.09
(174)	Hoyt Wilhelm	1.50	.70	.45
(175)	Billy Williams	2.00	1.00	.60
(176)	Jake Wood	.25	.13	.08
(177)	Gene Woodling	.35	.20	.11
(178)	Early Wynn	2.00	1.00	.60
(179)	Carl Yastrzemski	12.00	6.00	3.50
(180)	Don Zimmer	.35	.20	.11
(181)	Baltimore Orioles Logo	.25	.13	.08
(182)	Boston Red Sox Logo	.25	.13	.08
(183)	Chicago Cubs Logo	.25	.13	.08
(184)	Chicago White Sox Logo	.25	.13	.08
(185)	Cincinnati Reds Logo	.25	.13	.08
(186)	Cleveland Indians Logo	.25	.13	.08
(187)	Detroit Tigers Logo	.25	.13	.08
(188)	Houston Colts Logo	.25	.13	.08
(189)	Kansas City Athletics Logo	.25	.13	.08
(190)	Los Angeles Angels Logo	.25	.13	.08
(191)	Los Angeles Dodgers Logo	.25	.13	.08
(192)	Milwaukee Braves Logo	.25	.13	.08
(193)	Minnesota Twins Logo	.25	.13	.08
(194)	New York Mets Logo	.35	.20	.11
(195)	New York Yankees Logo	.35	.20	.11
(196)	Philadelphia Phillies Logo	.25	.13	.08
(197)	Pittsburgh Pirates Logo	.25	.13	.08
(198)	St. Louis Cardinals Logo	.25	.13	.08
(199)	San Francisco Giants Logo	.25	.13	.08
(200)	Washington Senators Logo	.25	.13	.08

1963 Topps

Although the number of cards dropped to 576, the 1963 Topps set is among the most popular of the 1960s. A color photo dominates the 2-1/2" by 3-1/2" card, but a colored circle at the bottom carries a black and white portrait as well. A colored band gives the player's name, team and position. The backs again feature career statistics and a cartoon, career summary and brief biographical details. The set is somewhat unlike those immediately preceding it in that there are fewer specialty cards. The major groupings are statistical leaders, World Series highlights and rookies. It is one rookie which makes the set special - Pete Rose. As one of most avidly sought cards in history and a high-numbered card at that, the Rose rookie card accounts for much of the value of a complete set.

	NR MT	EX	VG
Complete Set:	5000.00	2500.00	1500.
Common Player: 1-283	1.50	.70	.45
Common Player: 284-446	3.00	1.50	.90
Common Player: 447-506	10.00	5.00	3.00
Common Player: 507-576	7.00	3.50	2.00
1	N.L. Batting Leaders (Hank Aaron, Tommy Davis, Stan Musial, Frank Robinson, Bill White) 40.00	6.00	3.50
2	A.L. Batting Leaders (Chuck Hinton, Mickey Mantle, Floyd Robinson, Pete Runnels, Norm Siebern) 25.00	12.50	7.50
3	N.L. Home Run Leaders (Hank Aaron, Ernie Banks, Orlando Cepeda, Willie Mays, Frank Robinson) 12.00	6.00	3.50
4	A.L. Home Run Leaders (Norm Cash, Rocky Colavito, Jim Gentile, Harmon Killebrew, Roger Maris, Leon Wagner) 4.00	2.00	1.25
5	N.L. E.R.A. Leaders (Don Drysdale, Bob Gibson, Sandy Koufax, Bob Purkey, Bob Shaw) 4.00	2.00	1.25
6	A.L. E.R.A. Leaders (Hank Aguirre, Dean Chance, Eddie Fisher, Whitey Ford, Robin Roberts) 3.50	1.75	1.00
7	N.L. Pitching Leaders (Don Drysdale, Joe Jay, Art Mahaffey, Billy O'Dell, Bob Purkey, Jack Sanford) 3.50	1.75	1.00
8	A.L. Pitching Leaders (Jim Bunning, Dick Donovan, Ray Herbert, Camilo Pascual, Ralph Terry) 3.00	1.50	.90
9	N.L. Strikeout Leaders (Don Drysdale, Dick Farrell, Bob Gibson, Sandy Koufax, Billy O'Dell) 4.00	2.00	1.25
10	A.L. Strikeout Leaders (Jim Bunning, Jim Kaat, Camilo Pascual, Juan Pizarro, Ralph Terry) 3.00	1.50	.90
11	Lee Walls 1.50	.70	.45
12	Steve Barber 1.50	.70	.45
13	Phillies Team 3.25	1.75	1.00
14	Pedro Ramos 1.50	.70	.45
15	Ken Hubbs 3.00	1.50	.90
16	Al Smith 1.50	.70	.45
17	Ryne Duren 1.75	.90	.50
18	Buc Blasters (Smoky Burgess, Bob Clemente, Bob Skinner, Dick Stuart) 10.00	5.00	3.00
19	Pete Burnside 1.50	.70	.45
20	Tony Kubek 7.00	3.50	2.00
21	Marty Keough 1.50	.70	.45
22	Curt Simmons 1.75	.90	.50
23	Ed Lopat 2.00	1.00	.60
24	Bob Bruce 1.50	.70	.45
25	Al Kaline 35.00	17.50	10.50
26	Ray Moore 1.50	.70	.45
27	Choo Choo Coleman 2.00	1.00	.60
28	Mike Fornieles 1.50	.70	.45
29a	1962 Rookie Stars (John Boozer, *Ray Culp, Sammy Ellis, Jesse Gonder*) 7.00	3.50	2.00
29b	1963 Rookie Stars (John Boozer, *Ray Culp, Sammy Ellis, Jesse Gonder*) 2.00	1.00	.60
30	Harvey Kuenn 1.50	.70	.45
31	Cal Koonce 1.50	.70	.45
32	Tony Gonzalez 1.50	.70	.45
33	Bo Belinsky 3.00	1.50	.90
34	Dick Schofield 1.50	.70	.45
35	John Buzhardt 1.50	.70	.45
36	Jerry Kindall 1.50	.70	.45
37	Jerry Lynch 1.50	.70	.45
38	Bud Daley 2.00	1.00	.60
39	Angels Team 3.25	1.75	1.00

		NR MT	EX	VG
40	Vic Power	1.50	.70	.45
41	Charlie Lau	1.75	.90	.50
42	Stan Williams	2.00	1.00	.60
43	Veteran Masters (Casey Stengel, Gene Woodling)	4.00	2.00	1.25
44	Terry Fox	1.50	.70	.45
45	Bob Aspromonte	1.50	.70	.45
46	*Tommie Aaron*	2.00	1.00	.60
47	Don Lock	1.50	.70	.45
48	Birdie Tebbetts	1.50	.70	.45
49	*Dal Maxvill*	2.00	1.00	.60
50	Bill Pierce	2.00	1.00	.60
51	George Alusik	1.50	.70	.45
52	Chuck Schilling	1.50	.70	.45
53	Joe Moeller	1.50	.70	.45
54a	1962 Rookie Stars (Jack Cullen, *Dave DeBusschere, Harry Fanok, Nelson Mathews*)	15.00	7.50	4.50
54b	1963 Rookie Stars (Jack Cullen, *Dave DeBusschere, Harry Fanok, Nelson Mathews*)	4.00	2.00	1.25
55	Bill Virdon	1.50	.70	.45
56	Dennis Bennett	1.50	.70	.45
57	Billy Moran	1.50	.70	.45
58	Bob Will	1.50	.70	.45
59	Craig Anderson	1.75	.90	.50
60	Elston Howard	8.00	4.00	2.50
61	Ernie Bowman	1.50	.70	.45
62	Bob Hendley	1.50	.70	.45
63	Reds Team	2.50	1.25	.70
64	Dick McAuliffe	1.75	.90	.50
65	Jackie Brandt	1.50	.70	.45
66	Mike Joyce	1.50	.70	.45
67	Ed Charles	1.50	.70	.45
68	Friendly Foes (Gil Hodges, Duke Snider)	8.00	4.00	2.50
69	Bud Zipfel	1.50	.70	.45
70	Jim O'Toole	1.50	.70	.45
71	*Bobby Wine*	1.75	.90	.50
72	Johnny Romano	1.50	.70	.45
73	Bobby Bragan	1.75	.90	.50
74	*Denver Lemaster*	1.75	.90	.50
75	Bob Allison	2.00	1.00	.60
76	Earl Wilson	1.50	.70	.45
77	Al Spangler	1.50	.70	.45
78	Marv Throneberry	3.50	1.75	1.00
79	Checklist 1-88	2.50	1.25	.70
80	Jim Gilliam	3.00	1.50	.90
81	Jimmie Schaffer	1.50	.70	.45
82	Ed Rakow	1.50	.70	.45
83	Charley James	1.50	.70	.45
84	Ron Kline	1.50	.70	.45
85	Tom Haller	1.75	.90	.50
86	Charley Maxwell	1.50	.70	.45
87	Bob Veale	1.75	.90	.50
88	Ron Hansen	1.50	.70	.45
89	Dick Stigman	1.50	.70	.45
90	Gordy Coleman	1.50	.70	.45
91	Dallas Green	1.75	.90	.50
92	Hector Lopez	2.00	1.00	.60
93	Galen Cisco	1.75	.90	.50
94	Bob Schmidt	1.50	.70	.45
95	Larry Jackson	1.50	.70	.45
96	Lou Clinton	1.50	.70	.45
97	Bob Duliba	1.50	.70	.45
98	George Thomas	1.50	.70	.45
99	Jim Umbricht	1.50	.70	.45
100	Joe Cunningham	1.75	.90	.50
101	Joe Gibbon	1.50	.70	.45
102a	Checklist 89-176 ("Checklist" in red on front)	3.00	1.50	.90
102b	Checklist 89-176 ("Checklist" in white)	8.00	4.00	2.50
103	Chuck Essegian	1.50	.70	.45
104	Lew Krausse	1.50	.70	.45
105	Ron Fairly	1.75	.90	.50
106	Bob Bolin	1.50	.70	.45
107	Jim Hickman	1.75	.90	.50
108	Hoyt Wilhelm	11.00	5.50	3.25
109	Lee Maye	1.50	.70	.45
110	Rich Rollins	1.75	.90	.50
111	Al Jackson	1.75	.90	.50
112	Dick Brown	1.50	.70	.45
113	Don Landrum (photo actally Ron Santo)	1.75	.90	.50
114	Dan Osinski	1.50	.70	.45
115	Carl Yastrzemski	100.00	50.00	30.00
116	Jim Brosnan	1.75	.90	.50
117	Jacke Davis	1.75	.90	.50
118	Sherm Lollar	1.75	.90	.50
119	Bob Lillis	1.50	.70	.45

#		NR MT	EX	VG
120	Roger Maris	65.00	32.50	19.50
121	Jim Hannan	1.50	.70	.45
122	Julio Gotay	1.50	.70	.45
123	Frank Howard	2.50	1.25	.70
124	Dick Howser	1.50	.70	.45
125	Robin Roberts	8.00	4.00	2.50
126	Bob Uecker	45.00	23.00	13.50
127	Bill Tuttle	1.50	.70	.45
128	Matty Alou	1.75	.90	.50
129	Gary Bell	1.50	.70	.45
130	Dick Groat	1.50	.70	.45
131	Senators Team	3.25	1.75	1.00
132	Jack Hamilton	1.50	.70	.45
133	Gene Freese	1.50	.70	.45
134	Bob Scheffing	1.50	.70	.45
135	Richie Ashburn	8.00	4.00	2.50
136	Ike Delock	1.50	.70	.45
137	Mack Jones	1.50	.70	.45
138	Pride of N.L. (Willie Mays, Stan Musial)	30.00	15.00	9.00
139	Earl Averill	1.50	.70	.45
140	Frank Lary	1.75	.90	.50
141	*Manny Mota*	7.00	3.50	2.00
142	World Series Game 1 (Yanks' Ford Wins Series Opener)	3.50	1.75	1.00
143	World Series Game 2 (Sanford Flashes Shutout Magic)	3.25	1.75	1.00
144	World Series Game 3 (Maris Sparks Yankee Rally)	4.00	2.00	1.25
145	World Series Game 4 (Hiller Blasts Grand Slammer)	3.25	1.75	1.00
146	World Series Game 5 (Tresh's Homer Defeats Giants)	3.00	1.50	.90
147	World Series Game 6 (Pierce Stars In 3 Hit Victory)	3.00	1.50	.90
148	World Series Game 7 (Yanks Celebrate As Terry Wins)	3.00	1.50	.90
149	Marv Breeding	1.50	.70	.45
150	Johnny Podres	3.00	1.50	.90
151	Pirates Team	3.25	1.75	1.00
152	Ron Nischwitz	1.50	.70	.45
153	Hal Smith	1.50	.70	.45
154	Walt Alston	3.00	1.50	.90
155	Bill Stafford	2.00	1.00	.60
156	Roy McMillan	1.50	.70	.45
157	*Diego Segui*	1.75	.90	.50
158	1963 Rookie Stars (Rogelio Alvarez, *Tommy Harper*, Dave Roberts, Bob Saverine)	1.75	.90	.50
159	Jim Pagliaroni	1.50	.70	.45
160	Juan Pizarro	1.50	.70	.45
161	Frank Torre	1.50	.70	.45
162	Twins Team	3.25	1.75	1.00
163	Don Larsen	2.00	1.00	.60
164	Bubba Morton	1.50	.70	.45
165	Jim Kaat	7.00	3.50	2.00
166	Johnny Keane	1.50	.70	.45
167	Jim Fregosi	1.50	.70	.45
168	Russ Nixon	1.50	.70	.45
169	1963 Rookie Stars (Dick Egan, Julio Navarro, Gaylord Perry, Tommie Sisk)	30.00	15.00	9.00
170	Joe Adcock	1.50	.70	.45
171	Steve Hamilton	1.50	.70	.45
172	Gene Oliver	1.50	.70	.45
173	Bomber's Best (Mickey Mantle, Bobby Richardson, Tom Tresh)	65.00	33.00	20.00
174	Larry Burright	1.75	.90	.50
175	Bob Buhl	1.75	.90	.50
176	Jim King	1.50	.70	.45
177	Bubba Phillips	1.50	.70	.45
178	Johnny Edwards	1.50	.70	.45
179	Ron Piche	1.50	.70	.45
180	Bill Skowron	1.50	.70	.45
181	Sammy Esposito	1.50	.70	.45
182	Albie Pearson	1.50	.70	.45
183	Joe Pepitone	4.00	2.00	1.25
184	Vern Law	2.00	1.00	.60
185	Chuck Hiller	1.50	.70	.45
186	Jerry Zimmerman	1.50	.70	.45
187	Willie Kirkland	1.50	.70	.45
188	Eddie Bressoud	1.50	.70	.45
189	Dave Giusti	1.50	.70	.45
190	Minnie Minoso	1.50	.70	.45
191	Checklist 177-264	3.00	1.50	.90
192	Clay Dalrymple	1.50	.70	.45
193	Andre Rodgers	1.50	.70	.45
194	Joe Nuxhall	1.75	.90	.50
195	Manny Jimenez	1.50	.70	.45
196	Doug Camilli	1.50	.70	.45
197	Roger Craig	3.00	1.50	.90
198	Lenny Green	1.50	.70	.45
199	Joe Amalfitano	1.50	.70	.45
200	Mickey Mantle	400.00	200.00	125.00
201	Cecil Butler	1.50	.70	.45
202	Red Sox Team	2.50	1.25	.70
203	Chico Cardenas	1.50	.70	.45
204	Don Nottebart	1.50	.70	.45
205	Luis Aparicio	10.00	5.00	3.00
206	Ray Washburn	1.50	.70	.45
207	Ken Hunt	1.50	.70	.45
208	1963 Rookie Stars (Ron Herbel, John Miller, Ron Taylor, Wally Wolf)	1.50	.70	.45
209	Hobie Landrith	1.50	.70	.45
210	Sandy Koufax	160.00	80.00	50.00
211	Fred Whitfield	1.50	.70	.45
212	Glen Hobbie	1.50	.70	.45
213	Billy Hitchcock	1.50	.70	.45
214	Orlando Pena	1.50	.70	.45
215	Bob Skinner	1.75	.90	.50
216	Gene Conley	1.75	.90	.50
217	Joe Christopher	1.75	.90	.50
218	Tiger Twirlers (Jim Bunning, Frank Lary, Don Mossi)	3.00	1.50	.90
219	Chuck Cottier	1.50	.70	.45
220	Camilo Pascual	1.75	.90	.50
221	*Cookie Rojas*	1.75	.90	.50
222	Cubs Team	3.25	1.75	1.00
223	Eddie Fisher	1.50	.70	.45
224	Mike Roarke	1.50	.70	.45
225	Joe Jay	1.50	.70	.45
226	Julian Javier	1.75	.90	.50
227	Jim Grant	1.50	.70	.45
228	1963 Rookie Stars (*Max Alvis, Bob Bailey, Ed Kranepool, Pedro Oliva*)	50.00	25.00	15.00
229	Willie Davis	1.50	.70	.45
230	Pete Runnels	1.75	.90	.50
231	Eli Grba (photo actually Ryne Duren)	1.75	.90	.50
232	Frank Malzone	1.75	.90	.50
233	Casey Stengel	15.00	7.50	4.50
234	Dave Nicholson	1.50	.70	.45
235	Billy O'Dell	1.50	.70	.45
236	Bill Bryan	1.50	.70	.45
237	Jim Coates	2.00	1.00	.60
238	Lou Johnson	1.50	.70	.45
239	Harvey Haddix	1.75	.90	.50
240	Rocky Colavito	10.00	5.00	3.00
241	Billy Smith	1.50	.70	.45
242	Power Plus (Hank Aaron, Ernie Banks)	35.00	17.50	10.50
243	Don Leppert	1.50	.70	.45
244	John Tsitouris	1.50	.70	.45
245	Gil Hodges	15.00	7.50	4.50
246	Lee Stange	1.50	.70	.45
247	Yankees Team	10.00	5.00	3.00
248	Tito Francona	1.75	.90	.50
249	Leo Burke	1.50	.70	.45
250	Stan Musial	100.00	45.00	27.00
251	Jack Lamabe	1.50	.70	.45
252	Ron Santo	3.00	1.50	.90
253	1963 Rookie Stars (Len Gabrielson, Pete Jernigan, Deacon Jones, John Wojcik)	1.50	.70	.45
254	Mike Hershberger	1.50	.70	.45
255	Bob Shaw	1.50	.70	.45
256	Jerry Lumpe	1.75	.90	.50
257	Hank Aguirre	1.50	.70	.45
258	Alvin Dark	1.75	.90	.50
259	Johnny Logan	1.75	.90	.50
260	Jim Gentile	1.75	.90	.50
261	Bob Miller	1.50	.70	.45
262	Ellis Burton	1.50	.70	.45
263	Dave Stenhouse	1.50	.70	.45
264	Phil Linz	1.50	.70	.45
265	Vada Pinson	2.50	1.25	.70
266	Bob Allen	1.50	.70	.45
267	Carl Sawatski	1.50	.70	.45
268	Don Demeter	1.50	.70	.45
269	Don Mincher	1.75	.90	.50
270	Felipe Alou	1.75	.90	.50
271	Dean Stone	1.50	.70	.45
272	Danny Murphy	1.50	.70	.45
273	Sammy Taylor	1.75	.90	.50
274	Checklist 265-352	3.00	1.50	.90
275	Ed Mathews	20.00	10.00	6.00
276	Barry Shetrone	1.50	.70	.45
277	Dick Farrell	1.50	.70	.45
278	Chico Fernandez	1.50	.70	.45
279	Wally Moon	1.75	.90	.50
280	Bob Rodgers	1.75	.90	.50
281	Tom Sturdivant	1.50	.70	.45

		NR MT	EX	VG
282	Bob Del Greco	1.50	.70	.45
283	Roy Sievers	1.75	.90	.50
284	Dave Sisler	3.00	1.50	.90
285	Dick Stuart	3.25	1.75	1.00
286	Stu Miller	3.00	1.50	.90
287	Dick Bertell	3.00	1.50	.90
288	White Sox Team	3.50	1.75	1.00
289	Hal Brown	3.50	1.75	1.00
290	Bill White	3.25	1.75	1.00
291	Don Rudolph	3.00	1.50	.90
292	Pumpsie Green	3.25	1.75	1.00
293	Bill Pleis	3.00	1.50	.90
294	Bill Rigney	3.00	1.50	.90
295	Ed Roebuck	3.00	1.50	.90
296	Doc Edwards	3.25	1.75	1.00
297	Jim Golden	3.00	1.50	.90
298	Don Dillard	3.00	1.50	.90
299	1963 Rookie Stars (Tom Butters, Bob Dustal, Dave Morehead, Dan Schneider)	3.00	1.50	.90
300	Willie Mays	160.00	80.00	50.00
301	Bill Fischer	3.00	1.50	.90
302	Whitey Herzog	3.50	1.75	1.00
303	Earl Francis	3.00	1.50	.90
304	Harry Bright	3.00	1.50	.90
305	Don Hoak	3.25	1.75	1.00
306	Star Receivers (Earl Battey, Elston Howard)	3.50	1.75	1.00
307	Chet Nichols	3.00	1.50	.90
308	Camilo Carreon	3.00	1.50	.90
309	Jim Brewer	3.00	1.50	.90
310	Tommy Davis	3.00	1.50	.90
311	Joe McClain	3.00	1.50	.90
312	Colt .45s Team	12.00	6.00	3.50
313	Ernie Broglio	3.00	1.50	.90
314	John Goryl	3.00	1.50	.90
315	Ralph Terry	3.00	1.50	.90
316	Norm Sherry	2.00	1.00	.60
317	Sam McDowell	3.00	1.50	.90
318	Gene Mauch	3.25	1.75	1.00
319	Joe Gaines	3.00	1.50	.90
320	Warren Spahn	25.00	12.50	7.50
321	Gino Cimoli	3.00	1.50	.90
322	Bob Turley	3.25	1.75	1.00
323	Bill Mazeroski	3.50	1.75	1.00
324	1963 Rookie Stars (Vic Davalillo, Phil Roof, Pete Ward, George Williams)	2.50	1.25	.70
325	Jack Sanford	3.00	1.50	.90
326	Hank Foiles	3.00	1.50	.90
327	Paul Foytack	3.00	1.50	.90
328	Dick Williams	3.50	1.75	1.00
329	Lindy McDaniel	3.00	1.50	.90
330	Chuck Hinton	3.00	1.50	.90
331	Series Foes (Bill Pierce, Bill Stafford)	3.00	1.50	.90
332	Joel Horlen	3.00	1.50	.90
333	Carl Warwick	3.00	1.50	.90
334	Wynn Hawkins	3.25	1.75	1.00
335	Leon Wagner	3.25	1.75	1.00
336	Ed Bauta	3.00	1.50	.90
337	Dodgers Team	10.00	5.00	3.00
338	Russ Kemmerer	3.00	1.50	.90
339	Ted Bowsfield	3.00	1.50	.90
340	Yogi Berra	60.00	30.00	18.00
341	Jack Baldschun	3.00	1.50	.90
342	Gene Woodling	2.50	1.25	.70
343	Johnny Pesky	3.25	1.75	1.00
344	Don Schwall	3.00	1.50	.90
345	Brooks Robinson	30.00	15.00	9.00
346	Billy Hoeft	3.00	1.50	.90
347	Joe Torre	6.00	3.00	1.75
348	Vic Wertz	3.25	1.75	1.00
349	Zoilo Versalles	3.25	1.75	1.00
350	Bob Purkey	3.00	1.50	.90
351	Al Luplow	3.00	1.50	.90
352	Ken Johnson	3.00	1.50	.90
353	Billy Williams	25.00	12.50	7.50
354	Dom Zanni	3.00	1.50	.90
355	Dean Chance	3.25	1.75	1.00
356	John Schaive	3.00	1.50	.90
357	George Altman	3.00	1.50	.90
358	Milt Pappas	3.25	1.75	1.00
359	Haywood Sullivan	3.25	1.75	1.00
360	Don Drysdale	30.00	15.00	9.00
361	Clete Boyer	3.50	1.75	1.00
362	Checklist 353-429	4.00	2.00	1.25
363	Dick Radatz	3.25	1.75	1.00
364	Howie Goss	3.00	1.50	.90
365	Jim Bunning	10.00	5.00	3.00
366	Tony Taylor	3.00	1.50	.90
367	Tony Cloninger	3.25	1.75	1.00

		NR MT	EX	VG
368	Ed Bailey	3.00	1.50	.90
369	Jim Lemon	3.00	1.50	.90
370	Dick Donovan	3.00	1.50	.90
371	Rod Kanehl	3.25	1.75	1.00
372	Don Lee	3.00	1.50	.90
373	Jim Campbell	3.00	1.50	.90
374	Claude Osteen	3.25	1.75	1.00
375	Ken Boyer	4.00	2.00	1.25
376	Johnnie Wyatt	3.00	1.50	.90
377	Orioles Team	3.50	1.75	1.00
378	Bill Henry	3.00	1.50	.90
379	Bob Anderson	3.00	1.50	.90
380	Ernie Banks	55.00	28.00	16.50
381	Frank Baumann	3.00	1.50	.90
382	Ralph Houk	3.50	1.75	1.00
383	Pete Richert	3.00	1.50	.90
384	Bob Tillman	3.00	1.50	.90
385	Art Mahaffey	3.00	1.50	.90
386	1963 Rookie Stars (John Bateman, Larry Bearnarth, Ed Kirkpatrick, Garry Roggenburk)	3.25	1.75	1.00
387	Al McBean	3.00	1.50	.90
388	Jim Davenport	3.00	1.50	.90
389	Frank Sullivan	3.00	1.50	.90
390	Hank Aaron	150.00	75.00	45.00
391	Bill Dailey	3.00	1.50	.90
392	Tribe Thumpers (Tito Francona, Johnny Romano)	3.25	1.75	1.00
393	Ken MacKenzie	3.25	1.75	1.00
394	Tim McCarver	4.00	2.00	1.25
395	Don McMahon	3.00	1.50	.90
396	Joe Koppe	3.00	1.50	.90
397	Athletics Team	3.50	1.75	1.00
398	Boog Powell	7.00	3.50	2.00
399	Dick Ellsworth	3.00	1.50	.90
400	Frank Robinson	45.00	23.00	13.50
401	Jim Bouton	10.00	5.00	3.00
402	Mickey Vernon	3.25	1.75	1.00
403	Ron Perranoski	3.25	1.75	1.00
404	Bob Oldis	3.00	1.50	.90
405	Floyd Robinson	3.00	1.50	.90
406	Howie Koplitz	3.00	1.50	.90
407	1963 Rookie Stars (Larry Elliot, Frank Kostro, Chico Ruiz, Dick Simpson)	3.00	1.50	.90
408	Billy Gardner	3.00	1.50	.90
409	Roy Face	3.50	1.75	1.00
410	Earl Battey	● 3.25	1.75	1.00
411	Jim Constable	3.00	1.50	.90
412	Dodgers' Big Three (Don Drysdale, Sandy Koufax, Johnny Podres)	30.00	15.00	9.00
413	Jerry Walker	3.00	1.50	.90
414	Ty Cline	3.00	1.50	.90
415	Bob Gibson	30.00	15.00	9.00
416	Alex Grammas	3.00	1.50	.90
417	Giants Team	3.50	1.75	1.00
418	Johnny Orsino	3.00	1.50	.90
419	Tracy Stallard	3.25	1.75	1.00
420	Bobby Richardson	10.00	5.00	3.00
421	Tom Morgan	3.00	1.50	.90
422	Fred Hutchinson	3.25	1.75	1.00
423	Ed Hobaugh	3.00	1.50	.90
424	Charley Smith	3.00	1.50	.90
425	Smoky Burgess	2.50	1.25	.70
426	Barry Latman	3.00	1.50	.90
427	Bernie Allen	3.00	1.50	.90
428	Carl Boles	3.00	1.50	.90
429	Lou Burdette	3.00	1.50	.90
430	Norm Siebern	3.25	1.75	1.00
431a	Checklist 430-506 ("Checklist" in black on front)	4.50	2.25	1.25
431b	Checklist 430-506 ("Checklist" in white)	7.00	3.50	2.00
432	Roman Mejias	3.00	1.50	.90
433	Denis Menke	3.25	1.75	1.00
434	Johnny Callison	2.50	1.25	.70
435	Woody Held	3.00	1.50	.90
436	Tim Harkness	3.25	1.75	1.00
437	Bill Bruton	3.00	1.50	.90
438	Wes Stock	3.00	1.50	.90
439	Don Zimmer	3.50	1.75	1.00
440	Juan Marichal	20.00	10.00	6.00
441	Lee Thomas	3.00	1.50	.90
442	J.C. Hartman	3.00	1.50	.90
443	Jim Piersall	3.50	1.75	1.00
444	Jim Maloney	3.25	1.75	1.00
445	Norm Cash	3.00	1.50	.90
446	Whitey Ford	35.00	17.50	10.50
447	Felix Mantilla	10.00	5.00	3.00
448	Jack Kralick	10.00	5.00	3.00
449	Jose Tartabull	10.00	5.00	3.00
450	Bob Friend	11.00	5.50	3.25

		NR MT	EX	VG
451	Indians Team	10.00	5.00	3.00
452	Barney Schultz	10.00	5.00	3.00
453	Jake Wood	10.00	5.00	3.00
454a	Art Fowler (card # on orange background)			
		10.00	5.00	3.00
454b	Art Fowler (card # on white background)			
		10.00	5.00	3.00
455	Ruben Amaro	10.00	5.00	3.00
456	Jim Coker	10.00	5.00	3.00
457	Tex Clevenger	11.00	5.50	3.25
458	Al Lopez	15.00	7.50	4.50
459	Dick LeMay	10.00	5.00	3.00
460	Del Crandall	11.00	5.50	3.25
461	Norm Bass	10.00	5.00	3.00
462	Wally Post	10.00	5.00	3.00
463	Joe Schaffernoth	10.00	5.00	3.00
464	Ken Aspromonte	10.00	5.00	3.00
465	Chuck Estrada	10.00	5.00	3.00
466	1963 Rookie Stars (*Bill Freehan*, Tony Martinez, Nate Oliver, Jerry Robinson)			
		30.00	15.00	9.00
467	Phil Ortega	10.00	5.00	3.00
468	Carroll Hardy	10.00	5.00	3.00
469	Jay Hook	11.00	5.50	3.25
470	Tom Tresh	20.00	10.00	6.00
471	Ken Retzer	10.00	5.00	3.00
472	Lou Brock	125.00	62.00	37.00
473	Mets Team	100.00	50.00	30.00
474	Jack Fisher	10.00	5.00	3.00
475	Gus Triandos	10.00	5.00	3.00
476	Frank Funk	10.00	5.00	3.00
477	Donn Clendenon	11.00	5.50	3.25
478	Paul Brown	10.00	5.00	3.00
479	*Ed Brinkman*	11.00	5.50	3.25
480	Bill Monbouquette	11.00	5.50	3.25
481	Bob Taylor	10.00	5.00	3.00
482	Felix Torres	10.00	5.00	3.00
483	Jim Owens	10.00	5.00	3.00
484	Dale Long	11.00	5.50	3.25
485	Jim Landis	10.00	5.00	3.00
486	Ray Sadecki	10.00	5.00	3.00
487	John Roseboro	11.00	5.50	3.25
488	Jerry Adair	10.00	5.00	3.00
489	Paul Toth	10.00	5.00	3.00
490	Willie McCovey	110.00	55.00	33.00
491	Harry Craft	10.00	5.00	3.00
492	Dave Wickersham	10.00	5.00	3.00
493	Walt Bond	10.00	5.00	3.00
494	Phil Regan	10.00	5.00	3.00
495	Frank Thomas	11.00	5.50	3.25
496	1963 Rookie Stars (Carl Bouldin, *Steve Dalkowski*, Fred Newman, Jack Smith)			
		11.00	5.50	3.25
497	Bennie Daniels	10.00	5.00	3.00
498	Eddie Kasko	10.00	5.00	3.00
499	J.C. Martin	10.00	5.00	3.00
500	Harmon Killebrew	125.00	62.00	37.00
501	Joe Azcue	10.00	5.00	3.00
502	Daryl Spencer	10.00	5.00	3.00
503	Braves Team	10.00	5.00	3.00
504	Bob Johnson	10.00	5.00	3.00
505	Curt Flood	12.00	6.00	3.50
506	Gene Green	11.00	5.50	3.25
507	Roland Sheldon	8.00	4.00	2.50
508	Ted Savage	7.00	3.50	2.00
509a	Checklist 507-576 (copyright centered)			
		15.00	7.50	4.50
509b	Checklist 509-576 (copyright to right)			
		12.00	6.00	3.50
510	Ken McBride	7.00	3.50	2.00
511	Charlie Neal	7.50	3.75	2.25
512	Cal McLish	7.00	3.50	2.00
513	Gary Geiger	7.00	3.50	2.00
514	Larry Osborne	7.00	3.50	2.00
515	Don Elston	7.00	3.50	2.00
516	Purnal Goldy	7.00	3.50	2.00
517	Hal Woodeshick	7.00	3.50	2.00
518	Don Blasingame	7.00	3.50	2.00
519	Claude Raymond	7.00	3.50	2.00
520	Orlando Cepeda	15.00	7.50	4.50
521	Dan Pfister	7.00	3.50	2.00
522	1963 Rookie Stars (Mel Nelson, Gary Peters, Art Quirk, Jim Roland)			
		7.50	3.75	2.25
523	Bill Kunkel	8.00	4.00	2.50
524	Cardinals Team	10.00	5.00	3.00
525	Nellie Fox	12.00	6.00	3.50
526	Dick Hall	7.00	3.50	2.00
527	Ed Sadowski	7.00	3.50	2.00
528	Carl Willey	7.50	3.75	2.25
529	Wes Covington	7.00	3.50	2.00
530	Don Mossi	7.50	3.75	2.25

		NR MT	EX	VG
531	Sam Mele	7.00	3.50	2.00
532	Steve Boros	7.00	3.50	2.00
533	Bobby Shantz	8.00	4.00	2.50
534	Ken Walters	7.00	3.50	2.00
535	Jim Perry	8.00	4.00	2.50
536	Norm Larker	7.00	3.50	2.00
537	1963 Rookie Stars (Pedro Gonzalez, Ken McMullen, Pete Rose, Al Weis)			
		600.00	300.00	175.00
538	George Brunet	7.00	3.50	2.00
539	Wayne Causey	7.00	3.50	2.00
540	Bob Clemente	225.00	112.00	67.00
541	Ron Moeller	7.00	3.50	2.00
542	Lou Klimchock	7.00	3.50	2.00
543	Russ Snyder	7.00	3.50	2.00
544	1963 Rookie Stars (Duke Carmel, Bill Haas, Dick Phillips, *Rusty Staub*)			
		30.00	15.00	9.00
545	Jose Pagan	7.00	3.50	2.00
546	Hal Reniff	8.00	4.00	2.50
547	Gus Bell	7.50	3.75	2.25
548	Tom Satriano	7.00	3.50	2.00
549	1963 Rookie Stars (*Marcelino Lopez*, Pete Lovrich, Elmo Plaskett, Paul Ratliff)			
		7.50	3.75	2.25
550	Duke Snider	50.00	25.00	15.00
551	Billy Klaus	7.00	3.50	2.00
552	Tigers Team	20.00	10.00	6.00
553	1963 Rookie Stars (Brock Davis, Jim Gosger, John Herrnstein, *Willie Stargell*)			
		200.00	100.00	60.00
554	Hank Fischer	7.00	3.50	2.00
555	John Blanchard	8.00	4.00	2.50
556	Al Worthington	7.00	3.50	2.00
557	Cuno Barragan	7.00	3.50	2.00
558	1963 Rookie Stars (Bill Faul, *Ron Hunt*, Bob Lipski, Al Moran)			
		8.00	4.00	2.50
559	Danny Murtaugh	7.50	3.75	2.25
560	Ray Herbert	7.00	3.50	2.00
561	Mike de la Hoz	7.00	3.50	2.00
562	1963 Rookie Stars (Randy Cardinal, *Dave McNally*, Don Rowe, Ken Rowe)			
		15.00	7.50	4.50
563	Mike McCormick	7.50	3.75	2.25
564	George Banks	7.00	3.50	2.00
565	Larry Sherry	7.00	3.50	2.00
566	Cliff Cook	7.50	3.75	2.25
567	Jim Duffalo	7.00	3.50	2.00
568	Bob Sadowski	7.00	3.50	2.00
569	Luis Arroyo	8.00	4.00	2.50
570	Frank Bolling	7.00	3.50	2.00
571	Johnny Klippstein	7.00	3.50	2.00
572	Jack Spring	7.00	3.50	2.00
573	Coot Veal	7.00	3.50	2.00
574	Hal Kolstad	7.00	3.50	2.00
575	Don Cardwell	7.50	3.75	2.25
576	Johnny Temple	10.00	5.00	3.00

1963 Topps Peel-Offs

BOB CLEMENTE
PITTS. PIRATES   OUTFIELD

Measuring 1-1/4" by 2-3/4," Topps Peel-Offs were an insert with 1963 Topps baseball cards. There are 46 players in the unnumbered set, each pictured in a color photo inside an oval with the player's name, team and position in a band below. The back of the Peel-Off is removable, leaving a sticky surface that made the Peel-Off a popular decorative item among youngsters of the day. Naturally, that makes them quite scarce today, but as a non-card Topps issue, demand is not particularly strong.

		NR MT	EX	VG
	Complete Set:	175.00	87.00	52.00
	Common Player:	1.00	.50	.30
(1)	Hank Aaron	10.00	5.00	3.00
(2)	Luis Aparicio	3.00	1.50	.90
(3)	Richie Ashburn	2.00	1.00	.60
(4)	Bob Aspromonte	1.00	.50	.30
(5)	Ernie Banks	5.00	2.50	1.50
(6)	Ken Boyer	1.50	.70	.45
(7)	Jim Bunning	1.75	.90	.50
(8)	Johnny Callison	1.25	.60	.40
(9)	Orlando Cepeda	1.75	.90	.50
(10)	Bob Clemente	8.00	4.00	2.50
(11)	Rocky Colavito	1.75	.90	.50
(12)	Tommy Davis	1.50	.70	.45
(13)	Dick Donovan	1.00	.50	.30
(14)	Don Drysdale	4.00	2.00	1.25
(15)	Dick Farrell	1.00	.50	.30
(16)	Jim Gentile	1.00	.50	.30
(17)	Ray Herbert	1.00	.50	.30
(18)	Chuck Hinton	1.00	.50	.30
(19)	Ken Hubbs	1.50	.70	.45
(20)	Al Jackson	1.00	.50	.30
(21)	Al Kaline	5.00	2.50	1.50
(22)	Harmon Killebrew	5.00	2.50	1.50
(23)	Sandy Koufax	8.00	4.00	2.50
(24)	Jerry Lumpe	1.00	.50	.30
(25)	Art Mahaffey	1.00	.50	.30
(26)	Mickey Mantle	50.00	25.00	15.00
(27)	Willie Mays	10.00	5.00	3.00
(28)	Bill Mazeroski	1.50	.70	.45
(29)	Bill Monbouquette	1.00	.50	.30
(30)	Stan Musial	10.00	5.00	3.00
(31)	Camilo Pascual	1.25	.60	.40
(32)	Bob Purkey	1.00	.50	.30
(33)	Bobby Richardson	1.75	.90	.50
(34)	Brooks Robinson	6.00	3.00	1.75
(35)	Floyd Robinson	1.00	.50	.30
(36)	Frank Robinson	5.00	2.50	1.50
(37)	Bob Rodgers	1.00	.50	.30
(38)	Johnny Romano	1.00	.50	.30
(39)	Jack Sanford	1.00	.50	.30
(40)	Norm Siebern	1.00	.50	.30
(41)	Warren Spahn	5.00	2.50	1.50
(42)	Dave Stenhouse	1.00	.50	.30
(43)	Ralph Terry	1.25	.60	.40
(44)	Lee Thomas	1.00	.50	.30
(45)	Bill White	1.25	.60	.40
(46)	Carl Yastrzemski	12.00	6.00	3.50

1964 Topps

The 1964 Topps set is a 587-card issue of 2-1/2"
by 3-1/2" cards which is considered by many as
being among the company's best efforts. Card fronts
feature a large color photo which blends into a top
panel which contains the team name, while a panel
below the picture carries the player's name and
position. An interesting innovation on the back is a
baseball quiz question which required the rubbing of a
white panel to reveal the answer. As in 1963,
specialty cards remained modest in number with a
12-card set of statistical leaders, a few multi-player
cards, rookies and World Series highlights. An
interesting card is an "In Memoriam" card for Ken
Hubbs who was killed in an airplane crash.

		NR MT	EX	VG
	Complete Set:	3000.00	1500.00	900.00
	Common Player: 1-370	2.00	1.00	.60
	Common Player: 371-522	3.00	1.50	.90
	Common Player: 523-587	7.00	3.50	2.00
1	N.L. E.R.A. Leaders (Dick Ellsworth, Bob Friend, Sandy Koufax)	10.00	3.00	1.50
2	A.L. E.R.A. Leaders (Camilo Pascual, Gary Peters, Juan Pizarro)	3.00	1.50	.90
3	N.L. Pitching Leaders (Sandy Koufax, Jim Maloney, Juan Marichal, Warren Spahn)	7.00	3.50	2.00
4a	A.L. Pitching Leaders (Jim Bouton, Whitey Ford, Camilo Pascual) (apostrophe after "Pitching" on back)	7.00	3.50	2.00
4b	A.L. Pitching Leaders (Jim Bouton, Whitey Ford, Camilo Pascual) (no apostrophe)	3.50	1.75	1.00
5	N.L. Strikeout Leaders (Don Drysdale, Sandy Koufax, Jim Maloney)	7.00	3.50	2.00
6	A.L. Strikeout Leaders (Jim Bunning, Camilo Pascual, Dick Stigman)	3.00	1.50	.90
7	N.L. Batting Leaders (Hank Aaron, Bob Clemente, Tommy Davis, Dick Groat)	7.00	3.50	2.00
8	A.L. Batting Leaders (Al Kaline, Rich Rollins, Carl Yastrzemski)	7.00	3.50	2.00
9	N.L. Home Run Leaders (Hank Aaron, Orlando Cepeda, Willie Mays, Willie McCovey)	7.00	3.50	2.00
10	A.L. Home Run Leaders (Bob Allison, Harmon Killebrew, Dick Stuart)	3.50	1.75	1.00
11	N.L. R.B.I. Leaders (Hank Aaron, Ken Boyer, Bill White)	7.50	3.75	2.25
12	A.L. R.B.I. Leaders (Al Kaline, Harmon Killebrew, Dick Stuart)	7.50	3.75	2.25
13	Hoyt Wilhelm	8.00	4.00	2.50
14	Dodgers Rookies (Dick Nen, Nick Willhite)	2.00	1.00	.60
15	Zoilo Versalles	2.00	1.00	.60
16	John Boozer	2.00	1.00	.60
17	Willie Kirkland	2.00	1.00	.60
18	Billy O'Dell	2.00	1.00	.60
19	Don Wert	2.00	1.00	.60
20	Bob Friend	3.75	2.00	1.25
21	Yogi Berra	40.00	20.00	12.00
22	Jerry Adair	2.00	1.00	.60
23	Chris Zachary	2.00	1.00	.60
24	Carl Sawatski	2.00	1.00	.60
25	Bill Monbouquette	2.00	1.00	.60
26	Gino Cimoli	2.00	1.00	.60
27	Mets Team	3.50	1.75	1.00
28	Claude Osteen	2.00	1.00	.60
29	Lou Brock	35.00	17.50	10.50
30	Ron Perranoski	2.00	1.00	.60
31	Dave Nicholson	2.00	1.00	.60
32	Dean Chance	3.75	2.00	1.25
33	Reds Rookies (Sammy Ellis, Mel Queen)	2.00	1.00	.60
34	Jim Perry	3.75	2.00	1.25
35	Ed Mathews	20.00	10.00	6.00
36	Hal Reniff	3.00	1.50	.90
37	Smoky Burgess	3.75	2.00	1.25
38	*Jim Wynn*	3.25	1.75	1.00
39	Hank Aguirre	2.00	1.00	.60
40	Dick Groat	3.25	1.75	1.00
41	Friendly Foes (Willie McCovey, Leon Wagner)	3.00	1.50	.90
42	Moe Drabowsky	2.00	1.00	.60
43	Roy Sievers	2.25	1.25	.70
44	Duke Carmel	2.00	1.00	.60
45	Milt Pappas	2.25	1.25	.70
46	·Ed Brinkman	2.00	1.00	.60
47	Giants Rookies (*Jesus Alou*, Ron Herbel)	3.75	2.00	1.25
48	Bob Perry	2.00	1.00	.60
49	Bill Henry	2.00	1.00	.60
50	Mickey Mantle	300.00	150.00	90.00
51	Pete Richert	2.00	1.00	.60
52	Chuck Hinton	2.00	1.00	.60
53	Denis Menke	2.00	1.00	.60
54	Sam Mele	2.00	1.00	.60
55	Ernie Banks	35.00	17.50	10.50
56	Hal Brown	2.00	1.00	.60
57	Tim Harkness	2.00	1.00	.60
58	Don Demeter	2.00	1.00	.60
59	Ernie Broglio	2.00	1.00	.60
60	Frank Malzone	2.00	1.00	.60
61	Angel Backstops (Bob Rodgers, Ed Sadowski)	2.00	1.00	.60
62	Ted Savage	2.00	1.00	.60
63	Johnny Orsino	2.00	1.00	.60

		NR MT	EX	VG
64	Ted Abernathy	2.00	1.00	.60
65	Felipe Alou	3.75	2.00	1.25
66	Eddie Fisher	2.00	1.00	.60
67	Tigers Team	3.50	1.75	1.00
68	Willie Davis	3.25	1.75	1.00
69	Clete Boyer	3.25	1.75	1.00
70	Joe Torre	2.50	1.25	.70
71	Jack Spring	2.00	1.00	.60
72	Chico Cardenas	2.00	1.00	.60
73	*Jimmie Hall*	2.00	1.00	.60
74	Pirates Rookies (Tom Butters, Bob Priddy)	2.00	1.00	.60
75	Wayne Causey	2.00	1.00	.60
76	Checklist 1-88	3.00	1.50	.90
77	Jerry Walker	2.00	1.00	.60
78	Merritt Ranew	2.00	1.00	.60
79	Bob Heffner	2.00	1.00	.60
80	Vada Pinson	2.50	1.25	.70
81	All-Star Vets (Nellie Fox, Harmon Killebrew)	7.00	3.50	2.00
82	Jim Davenport	2.00	1.00	.60
83	Gus Triandos	2.00	1.00	.60
84	Carl Willey	2.00	1.00	.60
85	Pete Ward	2.00	1.00	.60
86	Al Downing	3.25	1.75	1.00
87	Cardinals Team	7.00	3.50	2.00
88	John Roseboro	2.00	1.00	.60
89	Boog Powell	2.50	1.25	.70
90	Earl Battey	2.00	1.00	.60
91	Bob Bailey	2.00	1.00	.60
92	Steve Ridzik	2.00	1.00	.60
93	Gary Geiger	2.00	1.00	.60
94	Braves Rookies (Jim Britton, Larry Maxie)	2.00	1.00	.60
95	George Altman	2.00	1.00	.60
96	Bob Buhl	2.00	1.00	.60
97	Jim Fregosi	3.75	2.00	1.25
98	Bill Bruton	2.00	1.00	.60
99	Al Stanek	2.00	1.00	.60
100	Elston Howard	7.00	3.50	2.00
101	Walt Alston	3.00	1.50	.90
102	Checklist 89-176	3.00	1.50	.90
103	Curt Flood	3.00	1.50	.90
104	Art Mahaffey	2.00	1.00	.60
105	Woody Held	2.00	1.00	.60
106	Joe Nuxhall	2.00	1.00	.60
107	White Sox Rookies (Bruce Howard, Frank Kreutzer)	2.00	1.00	.60
108	John Wyatt	2.00	1.00	.60
109	Rusty Staub	9.00	4.50	2.75
110	Albie Pearson	2.00	1.00	.60
111	Don Elston	2.00	1.00	.60
112	Bob Tillman	2.00	1.00	.60
113	Grover Powell	2.00	1.00	.60
114	Don Lock	2.00	1.00	.60
115	Frank Bolling	2.00	1.00	.60
116	Twins Rookies (Tony Oliva, Jay Ward)	8.00	4.00	2.50
117	Earl Francis	2.00	1.00	.60
118	John Blanchard	3.00	1.50	.90
119	Gary Kolb	2.00	1.00	.60
120	Don Drysdale	18.00	9.00	5.50
121	Pete Runnels	2.00	1.00	.60
122	Don McMahon	2.00	1.00	.60
123	Jose Pagan	2.00	1.00	.60
124	Orlando Pena	2.00	1.00	.60
125	Pete Rose	150.00	75.00	45.00
126	Russ Snyder	2.00	1.00	.60
127	Angels Rookies (Aubrey Gatewood, Dick Simpson)	2.00	1.00	.60
128	*Mickey Lolich*	12.00	6.00	3.50
129	Amado Samuel	2.00	1.00	.60
130	Gary Peters	2.00	1.00	.60
131	Steve Boros	2.00	1.00	.60
132	Braves Team	3.75	2.00	1.25
133	Jim Grant	2.00	1.00	.60
134	Don Zimmer	3.25	1.75	1.00
135	Johnny Callison	3.25	1.75	1.00
136	World Series Game 1 (Koufax Strikes Out 15)	10.00	5.00	3.00
137	World Series Game 2 (Davis Sparks Rally)	2.50	1.25	.70
138	World Series Game 3 (L.A. Takes 3rd Straight)	2.50	1.25	.70
139	World Series Game 4 (Sealing Yanks' Doom)	2.50	1.25	.70
140	World Series Summary (The Dodgers Celebrate)	2.50	1.25	.70
141	Danny Murtaugh	2.00	1.00	.60
142	John Bateman	2.00	1.00	.60
143	Bubba Phillips	2.00	1.00	.60
144	Al Worthington	2.00	1.00	.60
145	Norm Siebern	2.00	1.00	.60
146	Indians Rookies (Bob Chance, *Tommy John*)	72.00	36.00	20.60
147	Ray Sadecki	2.00	1.00	.60
148	J.C. Martin	2.00	1.00	.60
149	Paul Foytack	2.00	1.00	.60
150	Willie Mays	90.00	45.00	27.00
151	Athletics Team	3.75	2.00	1.25
152	Denver Lemaster	2.00	1.00	.60
153	Dick Williams	3.25	1.75	1.00
154	Dick Tracewski	2.00	1.00	.60
155	Duke Snider	25.00	12.50	7.50
156	Bill Dailey	2.00	1.00	.60
157	Gene Mauch	2.25	1.25	.70
158	Ken Johnson	2.00	1.00	.60
159	Charlie Dees	2.00	1.00	.60
160	Ken Boyer	7.00	3.50	2.00
161	Dave McNally	3.75	2.00	1.25
162	Hitting Area (Vada Pinson, Dick Sisler)	2.00	1.00	.60
163	Donn Clendenon	3.00	1.50	.90
164	Bud Daley	3.00	1.50	.90
165	Jerry Lumpe	2.00	1.00	.60
166	Marty Keough	2.00	1.00	.60
167	Senators Rookies (Mike Brumley, *Lou Piniella*)	30.00	15.00	9.00
168	Al Weis	2.00	1.00	.60
169	Del Crandall	3.75	2.00	1.25
170	Dick Radatz	2.00	1.00	.60
171	Ty Cline	2.00	1.00	.60
172	Indians Team	3.75	2.00	1.25
173	Ryne Duren	2.25	1.25	.70
174	Doc Edwards	2.00	1.00	.60
175	Billy Williams	12.00	6.00	3.50
176	Tracy Stallard	2.00	1.00	.60
177	Harmon Killebrew	20.00	10.00	6.00
178	Hank Bauer	2.25	1.25	.70
179	Carl Warwick	2.00	1.00	.60
180	Tommy Davis	3.25	1.75	1.00
181	Dave Wickersham	2.00	1.00	.60
182	Sox Sockers (Chuck Schilling, Carl Yastrzemski)	10.00	5.00	3.00
183	Ron Taylor	2.00	1.00	.60
184	Al Luplow	2.00	1.00	.60
185	Jim O'Toole	2.00	1.00	.60
186	Roman Mejias	2.00	1.00	.60
187	Ed Roebuck	2.00	1.00	.60
188	Checklist 177-264	3.00	1.50	.90
189	Bob Hendley	2.00	1.00	.60
190	Bobby Richardson	7.50	3.75	2.25
191	Clay Dalrymple	2.00	1.00	.60
192	Cubs Rookies (John Boccabella, Billy Cowan)	2.00	1.00	.60
193	Jerry Lynch	2.00	1.00	.60
194	John Goryl	2.00	1.00	.60
195	Floyd Robinson	2.00	1.00	.60
196	Jim Gentile	2.00	1.00	.60
197	Frank Lary	2.00	1.00	.60
198	Len Gabrielson	2.00	1.00	.60
199	Joe Azcue	2.00	1.00	.60
200	Sandy Koufax	100.00	50.00	30.00
201	Orioles Rookies (Sam Bowens, *Wally Bunker*)	2.00	1.00	.60
202	Galen Cisco	2.00	1.00	.60
203	John Kennedy	2.00	1.00	.60
204	Matty Alou	2.25	1.25	.70
205	Nellie Fox	7.00	3.50	2.00
206	Steve Hamilton	3.00	1.50	.90
207	Fred Hutchinson	2.00	1.00	.60
208	Wes Covington	2.00	1.00	.60
209	Bob Allen	2.00	1.00	.60
210	Carl Yastrzemski	80.00	40.00	25.00
211	Jim Coker	2.00	1.00	.60
212	Pete Lovrich	2.00	1.00	.60
213	Angels Team	3.75	2.00	1.25
214	Ken McMullen	2.00	1.00	.60
215	Ray Herbert	2.00	1.00	.60
216	Mike de la Hoz	2.00	1.00	.60
217	Jim King	2.00	1.00	.60
218	Hank Fischer	2.00	1.00	.60
219	Young Aces (Jim Bouton, Al Downing)	3.00	1.50	.90
220	Dick Ellsworth	2.00	1.00	.60
221	Bob Saverine	2.00	1.00	.60
222	Bill Pierce	2.25	1.25	.70
223	George Banks	2.00	1.00	.60
224	Tommie Sisk	2.00	1.00	.60
225	Roger Maris	60.00	30.00	18.00
226	Colts Rookies (*Gerald Grote*, Larry Yellen)	3.75	2.00	1.25

		NR MT	EX	VG
227	Barry Latman	2.00	1.00	.60
228	Felix Mantilla	2.00	1.00	.60
229	Charley Lau	2.00	1.00	.60
230	Brooks Robinson	30.00	15.00	9.00
231	Dick Calmus	2.00	1.00	.60
232	Al Lopez	3.00	1.50	.90
233	Hal Smith	2.00	1.00	.60
234	Gary Bell	2.00	1.00	.60
235	Ron Hunt	2.00	1.00	.60
236	Bill Faul	2.00	1.00	.60
237	Cubs Team	3.75	2.00	1.25
238	Roy McMillan	2.00	1.00	.60
239	Herm Starrette	2.00	1.00	.60
240	Bill White	3.25	1.75	1.00
241	Jim Owens	2.00	1.00	.60
242	Harvey Kuenn	3.25	1.75	1.00
243	Phillies Rookies (Richie Allen, John Herrnstein)	10.00	5.00	3.00
244	Tony LaRussa	20.00	10.00	6.00
245	Dick Stigman	2.00	1.00	.60
246	Manny Mota	3.75	2.00	1.25
247	Dave DeBusschere	3.00	1.50	.90
248	Johnny Pesky	2.00	1.00	.60
249	Doug Camilli	2.00	1.00	.60
250	Al Kaline	30.00	15.00	9.00
251	Choo Choo Coleman	2.00	1.00	.60
252	Ken Aspromonte	2.00	1.00	.60
253	Wally Post	2.00	1.00	.60
254	Don Hoak	2.00	1.00	.60
255	Lee Thomas	2.00	1.00	.60
256	Johnny Weekly	2.00	1.00	.60
257	Giants Team	3.75	2.00	1.25
258	Garry Roggenburk	2.00	1.00	.60
259	Harry Bright	3.00	1.50	.90
260	Frank Robinson	25.00	12.50	7.50
261	Jim Hannan	2.00	1.00	.60
262	Cardinals Rookie Stars (Harry Fanok, Mike Shannon)	3.25	1.75	1.00
263	Chuck Estrada	2.00	1.00	.60
264	Jim Landis	2.00	1.00	.60
265	Jim Bunning	7.00	3.50	2.00
266	Gene Freese	2.00	1.00	.60
267	Wilbur Wood	3.25	1.75	1.00
268	Bill's Got It (Danny Murtaugh, Bill Virdon)	2.25	1.25	.70
269	Ellis Burton	2.00	1.00	.60
270	Rich Rollins	2.00	1.00	.60
271	Bob Sadowski	2.00	1.00	.60
272	Jake Wood	2.00	1.00	.60
273	Mel Nelson	2.00	1.00	.60
274	Checklist 265-352	3.00	1.50	.90
275	John Tsitouris	2.00	1.00	.60
276	Jose Tartabull	2.00	1.00	.60
277	Ken Retzer	2.00	1.00	.60
278	Bobby Shantz	3.25	1.75	1.00
279	Joe Koppe	2.00	1.00	.60
280	Juan Marichal	10.00	5.00	3.00
281	Yankees Rookies (Jake Gibbs, Tom Metcalf)	3.00	1.50	.90
282	Bob Bruce	2.00	1.00	.60
283	Tommy McCraw	2.00	1.00	.60
284	Dick Schofield	2.00	1.00	.60
285	Robin Roberts	10.00	5.00	3.00
286	Don Landrum	2.00	1.00	.60
287	Red Sox Rookies (Tony Conigliaro, Bill Spanswick)	30.00	15.00	9.00
288	Al Moran	2.00	1.00	.60
289	Frank Funk	2.00	1.00	.60
290	Bob Allison	2.25	1.25	.70
291	Phil Ortega	2.00	1.00	.60
292	Mike Roarke	2.00	1.00	.60
293	Phillies Team	3.75	2.00	1.25
294	Ken Hunt	2.00	1.00	.60
295	Roger Craig	3.25	1.75	1.00
296	Ed Kirkpatrick	2.00	1.00	.60
297	Ken MacKenzie	2.00	1.00	.60
298	Harry Craft	2.00	1.00	.60
299	Bill Stafford	3.00	1.50	.90
300	Hank Aaron	100.00	50.00	30.00
301	Larry Brown	2.00	1.00	.60
302	Dan Pfister	2.00	1.00	.60
303	Jim Campbell	2.00	1.00	.60
304	Bob Johnson	2.00	1.00	.60
305	Jack Lamabe	2.00	1.00	.60
306	Giant Gunners (Orlando Cepeda, Willie Mays)	18.00	9.00	5.50
307	Joe Gibbon	2.00	1.00	.60
308	Gene Stephens	2.00	1.00	.60
309	Paul Toth	2.00	1.00	.60
310	Jim Gilliam	3.00	1.50	.90
311	Tom Brown	2.00	1.00	.60
312	Tigers Rookies (Fritz Fisher, Fred Gladding)	2.00	1.00	.60
313	Chuck Hiller	2.00	1.00	.60
314	Jerry Buchek	2.00	1.00	.60
315	Bo Belinsky	2.25	1.25	.70
316	Gene Oliver	2.00	1.00	.60
317	Al Smith	2.00	1.00	.60
318	Twins Team	3.75	2.00	1.25
319	Paul Brown	2.00	1.00	.60
320	Rocky Colavito	3.00	1.50	.90
321	Bob Lillis	2.00	1.00	.60
322	George Brunet	2.00	1.00	.60
323	John Buzhardt	2.00	1.00	.60
324	Casey Stengel	15.00	7.50	4.50
325	Hector Lopez	3.00	1.50	.90
326	Ron Brand	2.00	1.00	.60
327	Don Blasingame	2.00	1.00	.60
328	Bob Shaw	2.00	1.00	.60
329	Russ Nixon	2.00	1.00	.60
330	Tommy Harper	2.00	1.00	.60
331	A.L. Bombers (Norm Cash, Al Kaline, Mickey Mantle, Roger Maris)	90.00	45.00	27.00
332	Ray Washburn	2.00	1.00	.60
333	Billy Moran	2.00	1.00	.60
334	Lew Krausse	2.00	1.00	.60
335	Don Mossi	2.00	1.00	.60
336	Andre Rodgers	2.00	1.00	.60
337	Dodgers Rookies (Al Ferrara, Jeff Torborg)	2.00	1.00	.60
338	Jack Kralick	2.00	1.00	.60
339	Walt Bond	2.00	1.00	.60
340	Joe Cunningham	2.00	1.00	.60
341	Jim Roland	2.00	1.00	.60
342	Willie Stargell	40.00	20.00	12.00
343	Senators Team	3.75	2.00	1.25
344	Phil Linz	3.00	1.50	.90
345	Frank Thomas	2.00	1.00	.60
346	Joe Jay	2.00	1.00	.60
347	Bobby Wine	2.00	1.00	.60
348	Ed Lopat	2.25	1.25	.70
349	Art Fowler	2.00	1.00	.60
350	Willie McCovey	20.00	10.00	6.00
351	Dan Schneider	2.00	1.00	.60
352	Eddie Bressoud	2.00	1.00	.60
353	Wally Moon	2.25	1.25	.70
354	Dave Giusti	2.00	1.00	.60
355	Vic Power	2.00	1.00	.60
356	Reds Rookies (Bill McCool, Chico Ruiz)	2.00	1.00	.60
357	Charley James	2.00	1.00	.60
358	Ron Kline	2.00	1.00	.60
359	Jim Schaffer	2.00	1.00	.60
360	Joe Pepitone	2.50	1.25	.70
361	Jay Hook	2.00	1.00	.60
362	Checklist 353-429	3.00	1.50	.90
363	Dick McAuliffe	2.00	1.00	.60
364	Joe Gaines	2.00	1.00	.60
365	Cal McLish	2.00	1.00	.60
366	Nelson Mathews	2.00	1.00	.60
367	Fred Whitfield	2.00	1.00	.60
368	White Sox Rookies (Fritz Ackley, Don Buford)	2.25	1.25	.70
369	Jerry Zimmerman	2.00	1.00	.60
370	Hal Woodeshick	2.00	1.00	.60
371	Frank Howard	3.00	1.50	.90
372	Howie Koplitz	3.00	1.50	.90
373	Pirates Team	3.00	1.50	.90
374	Bobby Bolin	3.00	1.50	.90
375	Ron Santo	2.50	1.25	.70
376	Dave Morehead	3.00	1.50	.90
377	Bob Skinner	3.00	1.50	.90
378	Braves Rookies (Jack Smith, Woody Woodward)	3.75	2.00	1.25
379	Tony Gonzalez	3.00	1.50	.90
380	Whitey Ford	30.00	15.00	9.00
381	Bob Taylor	3.75	2.00	1.25
382	Wes Stock	3.00	1.50	.90
383	Bill Rigney	3.00	1.50	.90
384	Ron Hansen	3.00	1.50	.90
385	Curt Simmons	3.75	2.00	1.25
386	Lenny Green	3.00	1.50	.90
387	Terry Fox	3.00	1.50	.90
388	Athletics Rookies (John O'Donoghue, George Williams)	3.00	1.50	.90
389	Jim Umbricht	3.00	1.50	.90
390	Orlando Cepeda	9.00	4.50	2.75
391	Sam McDowell	3.75	2.00	1.25
392	Jim Pagliaroni	3.00	1.50	.90
393	Casey Teaches (Ed Kranepool, Casey Stengel)	7.00	3.50	2.00
394	Bob Miller	3.00	1.50	.90

		NR MT	EX	VG
395	Tom Tresh	3.00	1.50	.90
396	Dennis Bennett	3.00	1.50	.90
397	Chuck Cottier	3.00	1.50	.90
398	Mets Rookies (Bill Haas, Dick Smith)	3.75	2.00	1.25
399	Jackie Brandt	3.00	1.50	.90
400	Warren Spahn	25.00	12.50	7.50
401	Charlie Maxwell	3.00	1.50	.90
402	Tom Sturdivant	3.00	1.50	.90
403	Reds Team	3.50	1.75	1.00
404	Tony Martinez	3.00	1.50	.90
405	Ken McBride	3.00	1.50	.90
406	Al Spangler	3.00	1.50	.90
407	Bill Freehan	3.00	1.50	.90
408	Cubs Rookies (Fred Burdette, Jim Stewart)	3.00	1.50	.90
409	Bill Fischer	3.00	1.50	.90
410	Dick Stuart	3.75	2.00	1.25
411	Lee Walls	3.00	1.50	.90
412	Ray Culp	3.00	1.50	.90
413	Johnny Keane	3.00	1.50	.90
414	Jack Sanford	3.00	1.50	.90
415	Tony Kubek	7.00	3.50	2.00
416	Lee Maye	3.00	1.50	.90
417	Don Cardwell	3.00	1.50	.90
418	Orioles Rookies (Darold Knowles, Les Narum)	3.75	2.00	1.25
419	Ken Harrelson	7.00	3.50	2.00
420	Jim Maloney	3.75	2.00	1.25
421	Camilo Carreon	3.00	1.50	.90
422	Jack Fisher	3.75	2.00	1.25
423	Tops In NL (Hank Aaron, Willie Mays)	100.00	50.00	30.00
424	Dick Bertell	3.00	1.50	.90
425	Norm Cash	2.50	1.25	.70
426	Bob Rodgers	3.75	2.00	1.25
427	Don Rudolph	3.00	1.50	.90
428	Red Sox Rookies (Archie Skeen, Pete Smith)	3.00	1.50	.90
429	Tim McCarver	3.00	1.50	.90
430	Juan Pizarro	3.00	1.50	.90
431	George Alusik	3.00	1.50	.90
432	Ruben Amaro	3.00	1.50	.90
433	Yankees Team	10.00	5.00	3.00
434	Don Nottebart	3.00	1.50	.90
435	Vic Davalillo	3.00	1.50	.90
436	Charlie Neal	3.00	1.50	.90
437	Ed Bailey	3.00	1.50	.90
438	Checklist 430-506	7.00	3.50	2.00
439	Harvey Haddix	3.25	1.75	1.00
440	Bob Clemente	125.00	62.00	37.00
441	Bob Duliba	3.00	1.50	.90
442	Pumpsie Green	3.75	2.00	1.25
443	Chuck Dressen	3.75	2.00	1.25
444	Larry Jackson	3.00	1.50	.90
445	Bill Skowron	2.50	1.25	.70
446	Julian Javier	3.75	2.00	1.25
447	Ted Bowsfield	3.00	1.50	.90
448	Cookie Rojas	3.75	2.00	1.25
449	Deron Johnson	3.00	1.50	.90
450	Steve Barber	3.00	1.50	.90
451	Joe Amalfitano	3.00	1.50	.90
452	Giants Rookies (Gil Garrido, Jim Hart)	3.75	2.00	1.25
453	Frank Baumann	3.00	1.50	.90
454	Tommie Aaron	3.75	2.00	1.25
455	Bernie Allen	3.00	1.50	.90
456	Dodgers Rookies (Wes Parker, John Werhas)	3.00	1.50	.90
457	Jesse Gonder	3.75	2.00	1.25
458	Ralph Terry	3.00	1.50	.90
459	Red Sox Rookies (Pete Charton, Dalton Jones)	3.00	1.50	.90
460	Bob Gibson	25.00	12.50	7.50
461	George Thomas	3.00	1.50	.90
462	Birdie Tebbetts	3.00	1.50	.90
463	Don Leppert	3.00	1.50	.90
464	Dallas Green	3.75	2.00	1.25
465	Mike Hershberger	3.00	1.50	.90
466	Athletics Rookies (Dick Green, Aurelio Monteagudo)	3.75	2.00	1.25
467	Bob Aspromonte	3.00	1.50	.90
468	Gaylord Perry	45.00	23.00	13.50
469	Cubs Rookies (Fred Norman, Sterling Slaughter)	3.00	1.50	.90
470	Jim Bouton	3.00	1.50	.90
471	Gates Brown	3.75	2.00	1.25
472	Vern Law	3.25	1.75	1.00
473	Orioles Team	3.00	1.50	.90
474	Larry Sherry	3.00	1.50	.90
475	Ed Charles	3.00	1.50	.90

		NR MT	EX	VG
476	Braves Rookies (Rico Carty, Dick Kelley)	7.00	3.50	2.00
477	Mike Joyce	2.25	1.25	.70
478	Dick Howser	3.00	1.50	.90
479	Cardinals Rookies (Dave Bakenhaster, Johnny Lewis)	3.00	1.50	.90
480	Bob Purkey	3.00	1.50	.90
481	Chuck Schilling	3.00	1.50	.90
482	Phillies Rookies (John Briggs, Danny Cater)	3.75	2.00	1.25
483	Fred Valentine	3.00	1.50	.90
484	Bill Pleis	3.00	1.50	.90
485	Tom Haller	3.75	2.00	1.25
486	Bob Kennedy	3.00	1.50	.90
487	Mike McCormick	3.75	2.00	1.25
488	Yankees Rookies (Bob Meyer, Pete Mikkelsen)	3.25	1.75	1.00
489	Julio Navarro	3.00	1.50	.90
490	Ron Fairly	3.25	1.75	1.00
491	Ed Rakow	3.00	1.50	.90
492	Colts Rookies (Jim Beauchamp, Mike White)	3.00	1.50	.90
493	Don Lee	3.00	1.50	.90
494	Al Jackson	3.75	2.00	1.25
495	Bill Virdon	3.00	1.50	.90
496	White Sox Team	3.00	1.50	.90
497	Jeoff Long	3.00	1.50	.90
498	Dave Stenhouse	3.00	1.50	.90
499	Indians Rookies (Chico Salmon, Gordon Seyfried)	3.00	1.50	.90
500	Camilo Pascual	3.75	2.00	1.25
501	Bob Veale	3.75	2.00	1.25
502	Angels Rookies (Bobby Knoop, Bob Lee)	3.75	2.00	1.25
503	Earl Wilson	3.00	1.50	.90
504	Claude Raymond	3.00	1.50	.90
505	Stan Williams	3.25	1.75	1.00
506	Bobby Bragan	3.75	2.00	1.25
507	John Edwards	3.00	1.50	.90
508	Diego Segui	3.00	1.50	.90
509	Pirates Rookies (Gene Alley, Orlando McFarlane)	3.75	2.00	1.25
510	Lindy McDaniel	3.00	1.50	.90
511	Lou Jackson	3.00	1.50	.90
512	Tigers Rookies (Willie Horton, Joe Sparma)	7.00	3.50	2.00
513	Don Larsen	3.25	1.75	1.00
514	Jim Hickman	3.75	2.00	1.25
515	Johnny Romano	3.00	1.50	.90
516	Twins Rookies (Jerry Arrigo, Dwight Siebler)	3.00	1.50	.90
517a	Checklist 507-587 (wrong numbering on back)	7.00	3.50	2.00
517b	Checklist 507-587 (correct numbering on back)	7.50	3.75	2.25
518	Carl Bouldin	3.00	1.50	.90
519	Charlie Smith	3.75	2.00	1.25
520	Jack Baldschun	3.00	1.50	.90
521	Tom Satriano	3.00	1.50	.90
522	Bobby Tiefenauer	3.00	1.50	.90
523	Lou Burdette	9.00	4.50	2.75
524	Reds Rookies (Jim Dickson, Bobby Klaus)	7.00	3.50	2.00
525	Al McBean	7.00	3.50	2.00
526	Lou Clinton	7.00	3.50	2.00
527	Larry Bearnarth	7.50	3.75	2.25
528	Athletics Rookies (Dave Duncan, Tom Reynolds)	7.50	3.75	2.25
529	Al Dark	7.50	3.75	2.25
530	Leon Wagner	7.50	3.75	2.25
531	Dodgers Team	8.00	4.00	2.50
532	Twins Rookies (Bud Bloomfield, Joe Nossek)	7.00	3.50	2.00
533	Johnny Klippstein	7.00	3.50	2.00
534	Gus Bell	7.50	3.75	2.25
535	Phil Regan	7.00	3.50	2.00
536	Mets Rookies (Larry Elliot, John Stephenson)	7.50	3.75	2.25
537	Dan Osinski	7.00	3.50	2.00
538	Minnie Minoso	8.00	4.00	2.50
539	Roy Face	7.00	3.50	2.00
540	Luis Aparicio	15.00	7.50	4.50
541	Braves Rookies (Phil Niekro, Phil Roof)	225.00	112.00	65.00
542	Don Mincher	7.50	3.75	2.25
543	Bob Uecker	70.00	35.00	21.00
544	Colts Rookies (Steve Hertz, Joe Hoerner)	7.00	3.50	2.00
545	Max Alvis	7.50	3.75	2.25
546	Joe Christopher	7.50	3.75	2.25
547	Gil Hodges	12.00	6.00	3.50

		NR MT	EX	VG
548	N.L. Rookies (Wayne Schurr, Paul			
	Speckenbach)	7.00	3.50	2.00
549	Joe Moeller	7.00	3.50	2.00
550	Ken Hubbs	20.00	10.00	6.00
551	Billy Hoeft	7.00	3.50	2.00
552	Indians Rookies (Tom Kelley, *Sonny*			
	Siebert)	7.50	3.75	2.25
553	Jim Brewer	7.00	3.50	2.00
554	Hank Foiles	7.00	3.50	2.00
555	Lee Stange	7.00	3.50	2.00
556	Mets Rookies (Steve Dillon, Ron Locke)			
		7.50	3.75	2.25
557	Leo Burke	7.00	3.50	2.00
558	Don Schwall	7.00	3.50	2.00
559	Dick Phillips	7.00	3.50	2.00
560	Dick Farrell	7.00	3.50	2.00
561	Phillies Rookies (Dave Bennett, *Rick Wise*)			
		7.50	3.75	2.25
562	Pedro Ramos	7.00	3.50	2.00
563	Dal Maxvill	7.50	3.75	2.25
564	A.L. Rookies (Joe McCabe, Jerry			
	McNertney)	7.00	3.50	2.00
565	Stu Miller	7.00	3.50	2.00
566	Ed Kranepool	7.00	3.50	2.00
567	Jim Kaat	12.00	6.00	3.50
568	N.L. Rookies (Phil Gagliano, Cap			
	Peterson)	7.00	3.50	2.00
569	Fred Newman	7.00	3.50	2.00
570	Bill Mazeroski	8.00	4.00	2.50
571	Gene Conley	3.50	1.75	1.00
572	A.L. Rookies (Dick Egan, Dave Gray)			
		7.00	3.50	2.00
573	Jim Duffalo	7.00	3.50	2.00
574	Manny Jimenez	7.00	3.50	2.00
575	Tony Cloninger	7.50	3.75	2.25
576	Mets Rookies (Jerry Hinsley, Bill			
	Wakefield)	7.50	3.75	2.25
577	Gordy Coleman	7.00	3.50	2.00
578	Glen Hobbie	7.00	3.50	2.00
579	Red Sox Team	15.00	7.50	4.50
580	Johnny Podres	9.00	4.50	2.75
581	Yankees Rookies (Pedro Gonzalez, Archie			
	Moore)	7.00	3.50	2.00
582	Rod Kanehl	7.50	3.75	2.25
583	Tito Francona	7.50	3.75	2.25
584	Joel Horlen	7.00	3.50	2.00
585	Tony Taylor	7.00	3.50	2.00
586	Jim Piersall	9.00	4.50	2.75
587	Bennie Daniels	8.00	2.50	1.25

1964 Topps Coins

The 164 metal coins in this set were issued by Topps as inserts in the company's baseball card wax packs. The series is divided into two principal types, 120 "regular" coins and 44 All-Star coins. The 1-1/2" diameter coins feature a full-color background for the player photos in the "regular" series, while the players in the All-Star series are featured against plain red or blue backgrounds. There are two variations each of the Mantle, Causey and Hinton coins among the All-Star subset.

	NR MT	EX	VG
Complete Set:	700.00	350.00	210.00
Common Player:	1.00	.50	.30

		NR MT	EX	VG
1	Don Zimmer	1.00	.50	.30
2	Jim Wynn	1.00	.50	.30
3	Johnny Orsino	1.00	.50	.30
4	Jim Bouton	1.25	.60	.40
5	Dick Groat	1.25	.60	.40
6	Leon Wagner	1.00	.50	.30
7	Frank Malzone	1.00	.50	.30
8	Steve Barber	1.00	.50	.30
9	Johnny Romano	1.00	.50	.30
10	Tom Tresh	1.25	.60	.40
11	Felipe Alou	1.00	.50	.30
12	Dick Stuart	1.00	.50	.30
13	Claude Osteen	1.00	.50	.30
14	Juan Pizarro	1.00	.50	.30
15	Donn Clendenon	1.00	.50	.30
16	Jimmie Hall	1.00	.50	.30
17	Larry Jackson	1.00	.50	.30
18	Brooks Robinson	12.00	6.00	3.50
19	Bob Allison	1.00	.50	.30
20	Ed Roebuck	1.00	.50	.30
21	Pete Ward	1.00	.50	.30
22	Willie McCovey	8.00	4.00	2.50
23	Elston Howard	1.50	.70	.45
24	Diego Segui	1.00	.50	.30
25	Ken Boyer	1.50	.70	.45
26	Carl Yastrzemski	20.00	10.00	6.00
27	Bill Mazeroski	1.50	.70	.45
28	Jerry Lumpe	1.00	.50	.30
29	Woody Held	1.00	.50	.30
30	Dick Radatz	1.00	.50	.30
31	Luis Aparicio	5.00	2.50	1.50
32	Dave Nicholson	1.00	.50	.30
33	Ed Mathews	8.00	4.00	2.50
34	Don Drysdale	10.00	5.00	3.00
35	Ray Culp	1.00	.50	.30
36	Juan Marichal	8.00	4.00	2.50
37	Frank Robinson	8.00	4.00	2.50
38	Chuck Hinton	1.00	.50	.30
39	Floyd Robinson	1.00	.50	.30
40	Tommy Harper	1.00	.50	.30
41	Ron Hansen	1.00	.50	.30
42	Ernie Banks	10.00	5.00	3.00
43	Jesse Gonder	1.00	.50	.30
44	Billy Williams	7.00	3.50	2.00
45	Vada Pinson	1.50	.70	.45
46	Rocky Colavito	1.50	.70	.45
47	Bill Monbouquette	1.00	.50	.30
48	Max Alvis	1.00	.50	.30
49	Norm Siebern	1.00	.50	.30
50	John Callison	1.00	.50	.30
51	Rich Rollins	1.00	.50	.30
52	Ken McBride	1.00	.50	.30
53	Don Lock	1.00	.50	.30
54	Ron Fairly	1.00	.50	.30
55	Bob Clemente	20.00	10.00	6.00
56	Dick Ellsworth	1.00	.50	.30
57	Tommy Davis	1.25	.60	.40
58	Tony Gonzalez	1.00	.50	.30
59	Bob Gibson	10.00	5.00	3.00
60	Jim Maloney	1.00	.50	.30
61	Frank Howard	1.50	.70	.45
62	Jim Pagliaroni	1.00	.50	.30
63	Orlando Cepeda	2.00	1.00	.60
64	Ron Perranoski	1.00	.50	.30
65	Curt Flood	1.25	.60	.40
66	Al McBean	1.00	.50	.30
67	Dean Chance	1.00	.50	.30
68	Ron Santo	1.25	.60	.40
69	Jack Baldschun	1.00	.50	.30
70	Milt Pappas	1.00	.50	.30
71	Gary Peters	1.00	.50	.30
72	Bobby Richardson	1.50	.70	.45
73	Lee Thomas	1.00	.50	.30
74	Hank Aguirre	1.00	.50	.30
75	Carl Willey	1.00	.50	.30
76	Camilo Pascual	1.00	.50	.30
77	Bob Friend	1.00	.50	.30
78	Bill White	1.00	.50	.30
79	Norm Cash	1.25	.60	.40
80	Willie Mays	18.00	9.00	5.50
81	Duke Carmel	1.00	.50	.30
82	Pete Rose	25.00	12.50	7.50
83	Hank Aaron	20.00	10.00	6.00
84	Bob Aspromonte	1.00	.50	.30
85	Jim O'Toole	1.00	.50	.30
86	Vic Davalillo	1.00	.50	.30
87	Bill Freehan	1.00	.50	.30
88	Warren Spahn	8.00	4.00	2.50
89	Ron Hunt	1.00	.50	.30
90	Denis Menke	1.00	.50	.30
91	Turk Farrell	1.00	.50	.30

		NR MT	EX	VG
92	Jim Hickman	1.00	.50	.30
93	Jim Bunning	2.00	1.00	.60
94	Bob Hendley	1.00	.50	.30
95	Ernie Broglio	1.00	.50	.30
96	Rusty Staub	1.50	.70	.45
97	Lou Brock	8.00	4.00	2.50
98	Jim Fregosi	1.00	.50	.30
99	Jim Grant	1.00	.50	.30
100	Al Kaline	15.00	7.50	4.50
101	Earl Battey	1.00	.50	.30
102	Wayne Causey	1.00	.50	.30
103	Chuck Schilling	1.00	.50	.30
104	Boog Powell	1.50	.70	.45
105	Dave Wickersham	1.00	.50	.30
106	Sandy Koufax	15.00	7.50	4.50
107	John Bateman	1.00	.50	.30
108	Ed Brinkman	1.00	.50	.30
109	Al Downing	1.00	.50	.30
110	Joe Azcue	1.00	.50	.30
111	Albie Pearson	1.00	.50	.30
112	Harmon Killebrew	10.00	5.00	3.00
113	Tony Taylor	1.00	.50	.30
114	Alvin Jackson	1.00	.50	.30
115	Billy O'Dell	1.00	.50	.30
116	Don Demeter	1.00	.50	.30
117	Ed Charles	1.00	.50	.30
118	Joe Torre	1.50	.70	.45
119	Don Nottebart	1.00	.50	.30
120	Mickey Mantle	40.00	20.00	12.00
121	Joe Pepitone	1.25	.60	.40
122	Dick Stuart	1.00	.50	.30
123	Bobby Richardson	1.50	.70	.45
124	Jerry Lumpe	1.00	.50	.30
125	Brooks Robinson	10.00	5.00	3.00
126	Frank Malzone	1.00	.50	.30
127	Luis Aparicio	5.00	2.50	1.50
128	Jim Fregosi	1.00	.50	.30
129	Al Kaline	15.00	7.50	4.50
130	Leon Wagner	1.00	.50	.30
131a	Mickey Mantle (batting lefthanded)	45.00	23.00	13.50
131b	Mickey Mantle (batting righthanded)	45.00	23.00	13.50
132	Albie Pearson	1.00	.50	.30
133	Harmon Killebrew	10.00	5.00	3.00
134	Carl Yastrzemski	20.00	10.00	6.00
135	Elston Howard	1.50	.70	.45
136	Earl Battey	1.00	.50	.30
137	Camilo Pascual	1.00	.50	.30
138	Jim Bouton	1.25	.60	.40
139	Whitey Ford	8.00	4.00	2.50
140	Gary Peters	1.00	.50	.30
141	Bill White	1.00	.50	.30
142	Orlando Cepeda	2.00	1.00	.60
143	Bill Mazeroski	1.50	.70	.45
144	Tony Taylor	1.00	.50	.30
145	Ken Boyer	1.50	.70	.45
146	Ron Santo	1.25	.60	.40
147	Dick Groat	1.25	.60	.40
148	Roy McMillan	1.00	.50	.30
149	Hank Aaron	18.00	9.00	4.50
150	Bob Clemente	20.00	10.00	6.00
151	Willie Mays	18.00	9.00	5.50
152	Vada Pinson	1.50	.70	.45
153	Tommy Davis	1.25	.60	.40
154	Frank Robinson	8.00	4.00	2.50
155	Joe Torre	1.50	.70	.45
156	Tim McCarver	1.25	.60	.40
157	Juan Marichal	7.00	3.50	2.00
158	Jim Maloney	1.00	.50	.30
159	Sandy Koufax	15.00	7.50	4.50
160	Warren Spahn	8.00	4.00	2.50
161a	Wayne Causey (N.L. on back)	15.00	7.50	4.50
161b	Wayne Causey (A.L. on back)	1.00	.50	.30
162a	Chuck Hinton (N.L. on back)	15.00	7.50	4.50
162b	Chuck Hinton (A.L. on back)	1.00	.50	.30
163	Bob Aspromonte	1.00	.50	.30
164	Ron Hunt	1.00	.50	.30

1964 Topps Giants

Measuring 3-1/8" by 5-1/4" the Topps Giants were the company's first postcard-size issue. The cards feature large color photographs surrounded by white borders with a white baseball containing the player's name, position and team. Card backs carry another photo of the player surrounded by a newspaper-style

explanation of the depicted career highlight. The 60-card set contains primarily stars which means it's an excellent place to find inexpensive cards of Hall of Famers. The '64 Giants were not printed in equal quantity and seven of the cards, including Sandy Koufax and Willie Mays, are significantly scarcer than the remainder of the set.

		NR MT	EX	VG
Complete Set:		110.00	55.00	33.00
Common Player:		.12	.06	.04
1	Gary Peters	.12	.06	.04
2	Ken Johnson	.12	.06	.04
3	Sandy Koufax	18.00	9.00	5.50
4	Bob Bailey	.12	.06	.04
5	Milt Pappas	.25	.13	.08
6	Ron Hunt	.12	.06	.04
7	Whitey Ford	1.75	.90	.50
8	Roy McMillan	.12	.06	.04
9	Rocky Colavito	.40	.20	.12
10	Jim Bunning	.50	.25	.15
11	Bob Clemente	5.00	2.50	1.50
12	Al Kaline	3.00	1.50	.90
13	Nellie Fox	.60	.30	.20
14	Tony Gonzalez	.12	.06	.04
15	Jim Gentile	.12	.06	.04
16	Dean Chance	.12	.06	.04
17	Dick Ellsworth	.12	.06	.04
18	Jim Fregosi	.25	.13	.08
19	Dick Groat	.40	.20	.12
20	Chuck Hinton	.12	.06	.04
21	Elston Howard	.50	.25	.15
22	Dick Farrell	.12	.06	.04
23	Albie Pearson	.12	.06	.04
24	Frank Howard	.50	.25	.15
25	Mickey Mantle	18.00	9.00	5.50
26	Joe Torre	.40	.20	.12
27	Ed Brinkman	.12	.06	.04
28	Bob Friend	4.00	2.00	1.25
29	Frank Robinson	1.75	.90	.50
30	Bill Freehan	.25	.13	.08
31	Warren Spahn	1.25	.60	.40
32	Camilo Pascual	.12	.06	.04
33	Pete Ward	.12	.06	.04
34	Jim Maloney	.12	.06	.04
35	Dave Wickersham	.12	.06	.04
36	Johnny Callison	.25	.13	.08
37	Juan Marichal	3.00	1.50	.90
38	Harmon Killebrew	3.00	1.50	.90
39	Luis Aparicio	1.25	.60	.40
40	Dick Radatz	.12	.06	.04
41	Bob Gibson	3.00	1.50	.90
42	Dick Stuart	4.00	2.00	1.25
43	Tommy Davis	.40	.20	.12
44	Tony Oliva	.50	.25	.15
45	Wayne Causey	4.00	2.00	1.25
46	Max Alvis	.12	.06	.04
47	Galen Cisco	4.00	2.00	1.25
48	Carl Yastrzemski	3.00	1.50	.90
49	Hank Aaron	5.00	2.50	1.50
50	Brooks Robinson	3.00	1.50	.90
51	Willie Mays	18.00	9.00	5.50
52	Billy Williams	1.25	.60	.40
53	Juan Pizarro	.12	.06	.04
54	Leon Wagner	.12	.06	.04
55	Orlando Cepeda	.70	.35	.20
56	Vada Pinson	.50	.25	.15
57	Ken Boyer	.60	.30	.20
58	Ron Santo	.40	.20	.12

		NR MT	EX	VG
59	John Romano	.12	.06	.04
60	Bill Skowron	4.00	2.00	1.25

1964 Topps Photo Tatoos

Apparently not content to leave the skin of American children without adornment, Topps jumped back into the tattoo field in 1964 with the release of a new series. Measuring 1-9/16" by 3-1/2," there were 75 tattoos in a complete set. The picture side for the 20 team tattoos gives the team logo and name. For the player tattoos, the picture side has the player's face, name and team.

		NR MT	EX	VG
Complete Set:		600.00	300.00	180.00
Common Player:		3.00	1.50	.90
(1)	Hank Aaron	40.00	20.00	12.50
(2)	H. Aguirre	3.00	1.50	.90
(3)	Max Alvis	3.00	1.50	.90
(4)	Ernie Banks	25.00	12.50	7.50
(5)	S. Barber	3.00	1.50	.90
(6)	K. Boyer	5.00	2.50	1.50
(7)	J. Callison	4.00	2.00	1.25
(8)	Norm Cash	5.00	2.50	1.50
(9)	W. Causey	3.00	1.50	.90
(10)	O. Cepeda	7.00	3.50	2.00
(11)	R. Colavito	7.00	3.50	2.00
(12)	Ray Culp	3.00	1.50	.90
(13)	Davalillo	3.00	1.50	.90
(14)	Drabowsky	3.00	1.50	.90
(15)	Ellsworth	3.00	1.50	.90
(16)	Curt Flood	5.00	2.50	1.50
(17)	B. Freehan	4.00	2.00	1.25
(18)	J. Fregosi	4.00	2.00	1.25
(19)	Bob Friend	4.00	2.00	1.25
(20)	D. Groat	4.00	2.00	1.25
(21)	Woody Held	3.00	1.50	.90
(22)	F. Howard	5.00	2.50	1.50
(23)	Al Jackson	3.00	1.50	.90
(24)	L. Jackson	3.00	1.50	.90
(25)	K. Johnson	3.00	1.50	.90
(26)	Al Kaline	25.00	12.50	7.50
(27a)	Killebrew (green background)	25.00	12.50	7.50
(27b)	Killebrew (red background)	25.00	12.50	7.50
(28)	S. Koufax	35.00	17.50	10.50
(29)	Lock	3.00	1.50	.90
(30)	F. Malzone	3.00	1.50	.90
(31)	M. Mantle	100.00	45.00	27.00
(32)	E. Mathews	15.00	7.50	4.50
(33a)	Willie Mays (yellow background encompasses entire head)	40.00	20.00	12.50
(33b)	Willie Mays (yellow background covers one-half of head)	40.00	20.00	12.50
(34)	Mazeroski	5.00	2.50	1.50
(35)	K. McBride	3.00	1.50	.90
(36)	Monbouquette	3.00	1.50	.90
(37)	Nicholson	3.00	1.50	.90
(38)	C. Osteen	4.00	2.00	1.25
(39)	M. Pappas	4.00	2.00	1.25
(40)	C. Pascual	4.00	2.00	1.25
(41)	A. Pearson	3.00	1.50	.90
(42)	Perranoski	3.00	1.50	.90
(43)	G. Peters	3.00	1.50	.90
(44)	B. Powell	5.00	2.50	1.50
(45)	F. Robinson	20.00	10.00	6.00
(46)	J. Romano	3.00	1.50	.90
(47)	N. Siebern	3.00	1.50	.90
(48)	W. Spahn	15.00	7.50	4.50
(49)	D. Stuart	4.00	2.00	1.25
(50)	Lee Thomas	3.00	1.50	.90
(51)	Joe Torre	5.00	2.50	1.50
(52)	Pete Ward	3.00	1.50	.90
(53)	C. Willey	3.00	1.50	.90
(54)	B. Williams	25.00	12.50	7.50
(55)	Yastrzemski	50.00	25.00	15.00
(56)	Baltimore Orioles Logo	3.00	1.50	.90
(57)	Boston Red Sox Logo	3.00	1.50	.90
(58)	Chicago Cubs Logo	3.00	1.50	.90
(59)	Chicago White Sox Logo	3.00	1.50	.90
(60)	Cincinnati Reds Logo	3.00	1.50	.90
(61)	Cleveland Indians Logo	3.00	1.50	.90
(62)	Detroit Tigers Logo	2.50	1.25	.70
(63)	Houston Colts Logo	3.00	1.50	.90
(64)	Kansas City Athletics Logo	3.00	1.50	.90
(65)	Los Angeles Angels Logo	3.00	1.50	.90
(66)	Los Angeles Dodgers Logo	2.50	1.25	.70
(67)	Milwaukee Braves Logo	3.00	1.50	.90
(68)	Minnesota Twins Logo	3.00	1.50	.90
(69)	New York Mets Logo	2.50	1.25	.70
(70)	New York Yankees Logo	4.00	2.00	1.25
(71)	Philadelphia Phillies Logo	3.00	1.50	.90
(72)	Pittsburgh Pirates Logo	3.00	1.50	.90
(73)	St. Louis Cardinals Logo	2.50	1.25	.70
(74)	San Francisco Giants Logo	3.00	1.50	.90
(75)	Washington Senators Logo	3.00	1.50	.90

1964 Topps Stand-Ups

These 2-1/2" by 3-1/2" cards were the first since the All-Star sets of 1951 to be die-cut. This made it possible for a folded card to stand on display. The 77-cards in the set feature color photographs of the player with yellow and green backgrounds. Directions for folding are on the yellow top background, and when folded only the green background remains. Of the 77 cards, 55 were double-printed while 22 were single-printed, making them twice as scarce. Included in the single-printed group are Warren Spahn, Don Drysdale, Juan Marichal, Willie McCovey and Carl Yastrzemski.

		NR MT	EX	VG
Complete Set:		2400.00	1200.00	720.00
Common Player:		3.50	1.75	1.00
(1)	Hank Aaron	110.00	55.00	33.00
(2)	Hank Aguirre	3.50	1.75	1.00
(3)	George Altman	3.50	1.75	1.00
(4)	Max Alvis	3.50	1.75	1.00
(5)	Bob Aspromonte	3.50	1.75	1.00
(6)	Jack Baldschun	20.00	10.00	6.00
(7)	Ernie Banks	40.00	20.00	12.00
(8)	Steve Barber	3.50	1.75	1.00
(9)	Earl Battey	3.50	1.75	1.00
(10)	Ken Boyer	6.00	3.00	1.75
(11)	Ernie Broglio	3.50	1.75	1.00
(12)	Johnny Callison	4.00	2.00	1.25
(13)	Norm Cash	25.00	12.50	7.50
(14)	Wayne Causey	3.50	1.75	1.00
(15)	Orlando Cepeda	8.00	4.00	2.50
(16)	Ed Charles	3.50	1.75	1.00
(17)	Bob Clemente	55.00	27.00	16.50
(18)	Donn Clendenon	20.00	10.00	6.00

Carl Yastrzemski / Boston Red Sox / Outfield

		NR MT	EX	VG
(19)	Rocky Colavito	6.00	3.00	1.75
(20)	Ray Culp	20.00	10.00	6.00
(21)	Tommy Davis	6.00	3.00	1.75
(22)	Don Drysdale	125.00	62.00	37.00
(23)	Dick Ellsworth	3.50	1.75	1.00
(24)	Dick Farrell	3.50	1.75	1.00
(25)	Jim Fregosi	4.00	2.00	1.25
(26)	Bob Friend	4.00	2.00	1.25
(27)	Jim Gentile	3.50	1.75	1.00
(28)	Jesse Gonder	20.00	10.00	6.00
(29)	Tony Gonzalez	20.00	10.00	6.00
(30)	Dick Groat	6.00	3.00	1.75
(31)	Woody Held	3.50	1.75	1.00
(32)	Chuck Hinton	3.50	1.75	1.00
(33)	Elston Howard	7.00	3.50	2.00
(34)	Frank Howard	25.00	12.50	7.50
(35)	Ron Hunt	3.50	1.75	1.00
(36)	Al Jackson	3.50	1.75	1.00
(37)	Ken Johnson	3.50	1.75	1.00
(38)	Al Kaline	40.00	20.00	12.00
(39)	Harmon Killebrew	40.00	20.00	12.00
(40)	Sandy Koufax	40.00	20.00	12.00
(41)	Don Lock	20.00	10.00	6.00
(42)	Jerry Lumpe	20.00	10.00	6.00
(43)	Jim Maloney	3.50	1.75	1.00
(44)	Frank Malzone	3.50	1.75	1.00
(45)	Mickey Mantle	400.00	200.00	120.00
(46)	Juan Marichal	125.00	62.00	37.00
(47)	Ed Mathews	125.00	62.00	37.00
(48)	Willie Mays	110.00	55.00	33.00
(49)	Bill Mazeroski	6.00	3.00	1.75
(50)	Ken McBride	3.50	1.75	1.00
(51)	Willie McCovey	125.00	62.00	37.00
(52)	Claude Osteen	3.50	1.75	1.00
(53)	Jim O'Toole	3.50	1.75	1.00
(54)	Camilo Pascual	3.50	1.75	1.00
(55)	Albie Pearson	20.00	10.00	6.00
(56)	Gary Peters	3.50	1.75	1.00
(57)	Vada Pinson	6.00	3.00	1.75
(58)	Juan Pizarro	3.50	1.75	1.00
(59)	Boog Powell	6.00	3.00	1.75
(60)	Bobby Richardson	7.00	3.50	2.00
(61)	Brooks Robinson	50.00	25.00	15.00
(62)	Floyd Robinson	3.50	1.75	1.00
(63)	Frank Robinson	40.00	20.00	12.00
(64)	Ed Roebuck	20.00	10.00	6.00
(65)	Rich Rollins	3.50	1.75	1.00
(66)	Johnny Romano	3.50	1.75	1.00
(67)	Ron Santo	25.00	12.50	7.50
(68)	Norm Siebern	3.50	1.75	1.00
(69)	Warren Spahn	125.00	62.00	37.00
(70)	Dick Stuart	20.00	10.00	6.00
(71)	Lee Thomas	3.50	1.75	1.00
(72)	Joe Torre	7.00	3.50	2.00
(73)	Pete Ward	3.50	1.75	1.00
(74)	Bill White	20.00	10.00	6.00
(75)	Billy Williams	125.00	62.00	37.00
(76)	Hal Woodeshick	20.00	10.00	6.00
(77)	Carl Yastrzemski	400.00	200.00	120.00

1965 Topps

OUTFIELD
ROGER MARIS
YANKEES

The 1965 Topps set features a large color photograph of the player which was surrounded by a colored, round-cornered frame and a white border. The bottom of the 2-1/2" by 3-1/2" cards include a pennant with a color team logo and name over the left side of a rectangle which features the player's name and position. Backs feature statistics and, if

space allowed, a cartoon and headline about the player. There are no multi-player cards in the 1965 set other than the usual team cards and World Series highlights. Rookie cards include team, as well as league groupings from two to four players per card. Also present in the 598-card set are statistical leaders.

		NR MT	EX	VG
Complete Set:		3500.00	1750.00	1050.
Common Player: 1-198		2.00	1.00	.60
Common Player: 199-446		2.00	1.00	.60
Common Player: 447-522		2.00	1.00	.60
Common Player: 523-598		5.00	2.50	1.50
1	A.L. Batting Leaders (Elston Howard, Tony Oliva, Brooks Robinson)	10.00	4.00	2.50
2	N.L. Batting Leaders (Hank Aaron, Rico Carty, Bob Clemente)	5.00	2.50	1.50
3	A.L. Home Run Leaders (Harmon Killebrew, Mickey Mantle, Boog Powell)	20.00	10.00	6.00
4	N.L. Home Run Leaders (Johnny Callison, Orlando Cepeda, Jim Hart, Willie Mays, Billy Williams)	6.00	3.00	1.75
5	A.L. RBI Leaders (Harmon Killebrew, Mickey Mantle, Brooks Robinson, Dick Stuart)	20.00	10.00	6.00
6	N.L. RBI Leaders (Ken Boyer, Willie Mays, Ron Santo)	6.00	3.00	1.75
7	A.L. ERA Leaders (Dean Chance, Joel Horlen)	5.00	2.50	1.50
8	N.L. ERA Leaders (Don Drysdale, Sandy Koufax)	6.00	3.00	1.75
9	A.L. Pitching Leaders (Wally Bunker, Dean Chance, Gary Peters, Juan Pizarro, Dave Wickersham)	5.00	2.50	1.50
10	N.L. Pitching Leaders (Larry Jackson, Juan Marichal, Ray Sadecki)	3.50	1.75	1.00
11	A.L. Strikeout Leaders (Dean Chance, Al Downing, Camilo Pascual)	5.00	2.50	1.50
12	N.L. Strikeout Leaders (Don Drysdale, Bob Gibson, Bob Veale)	3.50	1.75	1.00
13	Pedro Ramos	2.00	1.00	.60
14	Len Gabrielson	2.00	1.00	.60
15	Robin Roberts	8.00	4.00	2.50
16	Astros Rookies (Sonny Jackson, Joe Morgan)	175.00	87.00	52.00
17	Johnny Romano	2.00	1.00	.60
18	Bill McCool	2.00	1.00	.60
19	Gates Brown	2.00	1.00	.60
20	Jim Bunning	5.00	2.50	1.50
21	Don Blasingame	2.00	1.00	.60
22	Charlie Smith	2.00	1.00	.60
23	Bob Tiefenauer	2.00	1.00	.60
24	Twins Team	5.00	2.50	1.50
25	Al McBean	2.00	1.00	.60
26	Bobby Knoop	2.00	1.00	.60
27	Dick Bertell	2.00	1.00	.60
28	Barney Schultz	2.00	1.00	.60
29	Felix Mantilla	2.00	1.00	.60
30	Jim Bouton	5.00	2.50	1.50
31	Mike White	2.00	1.00	.60
32	Herman Franks	2.00	1.00	.60
33	Jackie Brandt	2.00	1.00	.60
34	Cal Koonce	2.00	1.00	.60
35	Ed Charles	2.00	1.00	.60
36	Bobby Wine	2.00	1.00	.60
37	Fred Gladding	2.00	1.00	.60
38	Jim King	2.00	1.00	.60
39	Gerry Arrigo	2.00	1.00	.60
40	Frank Howard	5.00	2.50	1.50
41	White Sox Rookies (Bruce Howard, Marv Staehle)	2.00	1.00	.60
42	Earl Wilson	2.00	1.00	.60
43	Mike Shannon	2.00	1.00	.60
44	Wade Blasingame	2.00	1.00	.60
45	Roy McMillan	2.00	1.00	.60
46	Bob Lee	2.00	1.00	.60
47	Tommy Harper	2.00	1.00	.60
48	Claude Raymond	2.00	1.00	.60
49	Orioles Rookies (Curt Blefary, John Miller)	2.00	1.00	.60
50	Juan Marichal	10.00	5.00	3.00
51	Billy Bryan	2.00	1.00	.60
52	Ed Roebuck	2.00	1.00	.60
53	Dick McAuliffe	2.00	1.00	.60
54	Joe Gibbon	2.00	1.00	.60
55	Tony Conigliaro	7.00	3.50	2.00
56	Ron Kline	2.00	1.00	.60

No.	Player	NR MT	EX	VG
57	Cardinals Team	2.25	1.25	.70
58	Fred Talbot	2.00	1.00	.60
59	Nate Oliver	2.00	1.00	.60
60	Jim O'Toole	2.00	1.00	.60
61	Chris Cannizzaro	2.00	1.00	.60
62	Jim Katt (Kaat)	5.00	2.50	1.50
63	Ty Cline	2.00	1.00	.60
64	Lou Burdette	2.00	1.00	.60
65	Tony Kubek	6.00	3.00	1.75
66	Bill Rigney	2.00	1.00	.60
67	Harvey Haddix	2.00	1.00	.60
68	Del Crandall	2.00	1.00	.60
69	Bill Virdon	2.00	1.00	.60
70	Bill Skowron	2.00	1.00	.60
71	John O'Donoghue	2.00	1.00	.60
72	Tony Gonzalez	2.00	1.00	.60
73	Dennis Ribant	2.00	1.00	.60
74	Red Sox Rookies (*Rico Petrocelli*, Jerry Stephenson)	5.00	2.50	1.50
75	Deron Johnson	2.00	1.00	.60
76	Sam McDowell	2.00	1.00	.60
77	Doug Camilli	2.00	1.00	.60
78	Dal Maxvill	2.00	1.00	.60
79a	Checklist 1-88 (61 is C. Cannizzaro)	2.00	1.00	.60
79b	Checklist 1-88 (61 is Cannizzaro)	5.00	2.50	1.50
80	Turk Farrell	2.00	1.00	.60
81	Don Buford	2.00	1.00	.60
82	Braves Rookies (*Santos Alomar*, John Braun)	2.00	1.00	.60
83	George Thomas	2.00	1.00	.60
84	Ron Herbel	2.00	1.00	.60
85	Willie Smith	2.00	1.00	.60
86	Les Narum	2.00	1.00	.60
87	Nelson Mathews	2.00	1.00	.60
88	Jack Lamabe	2.00	1.00	.60
89	Mike Hershberger	2.00	1.00	.60
90	Rich Rollins	2.00	1.00	.60
91	Cubs Team	2.25	1.25	.70
92	Dick Howser	2.00	1.00	.60
93	Jack Fisher	2.00	1.00	.60
94	Charlie Lau	2.00	1.00	.60
95	Bill Mazeroski	5.00	2.50	1.50
96	Sonny Siebert	2.00	1.00	.60
97	Pedro Gonzalez	2.00	1.00	.60
98	Bob Miller	2.00	1.00	.60
99	Gil Hodges	6.00	3.00	1.75
100	Ken Boyer	5.00	2.50	1.50
101	Fred Newman	2.00	1.00	.60
102	Steve Boros	2.00	1.00	.60
103	Harvey Kuenn	2.00	1.00	.60
104	Checklist 89-176	2.00	1.00	.60
105	Chico Salmon	2.00	1.00	.60
106	Gene Oliver	2.00	1.00	.60
107	Phillies Rookies (*Pat Corrales*, Costen Shockley)	2.00	1.00	.60
108	Don Mincher	2.00	1.00	.60
109	Walt Bond	2.00	1.00	.60
110	Ron Santo	2.25	1.25	.70
111	Lee Thomas	2.00	1.00	.60
112	Derrell Griffith	2.00	1.00	.60
113	Steve Barber	2.00	1.00	.60
114	Jim Hickman	2.00	1.00	.60
115	Bobby Richardson	6.00	3.00	1.75
116	Cardinals Rookies (Dave Dowling, *Bob Tolan*)	2.00	1.00	.60
117	Wes Stock	2.00	1.00	.60
118	Hal Lanier	2.25	1.25	.70
119	John Kennedy	2.00	1.00	.60
120	Frank Robinson	25.00	12.50	7.50
121	Gene Alley	2.00	1.00	.60
122	Bill Pleis	2.00	1.00	.60
123	Frank Thomas	2.00	1.00	.60
124	Tom Satriano	2.00	1.00	.60
125	Juan Pizarro	2.00	1.00	.60
126	Dodgers Team	5.00	2.50	1.50
127	Frank Lary	2.00	1.00	.60
128	Vic Davalillo	2.00	1.00	.60
129	Bennie Daniels	2.00	1.00	.60
130	Al Kaline	25.00	12.50	7.50
131	Johnny Keane	2.25	1.25	.70
132	World Series Game 1 (Cards Take Opener)	5.00	2.50	1.50
133	World Series Game 2 (Stottlemyre Wins)	2.00	1.00	.60
134	World Series Game 3 (Mantle's Clutch HR)	25.00	12.50	7.50
135	World Series Game 4 (Boyer's Grand Slam)	5.00	2.50	1.50
136	World Series Game 5 (10th Inning Triumph)	5.00	2.50	1.50
137	World Series Game 6 (Bouton Wins Again)	2.00	1.00	.60
138	World Series Game 7 (Gibson Wins Finale)	3.50	1.75	1.00
139	World Series Summary (The Cards Celebrate)	5.00	2.50	1.50
140	Dean Chance	2.00	1.00	.60
141	Charlie James	2.00	1.00	.60
142	Bill Monbouquette	2.00	1.00	.60
143	Pirates Rookies (John Gelnar, Jerry May)	2.00	1.00	.60
144	Ed Kranepool	2.00	1.00	.60
145	*Luis Tiant*	10.00	5.00	3.00
146	Ron Hansen	2.00	1.00	.60
147	Dennis Bennett	2.00	1.00	.60
148	Willie Kirkland	2.00	1.00	.60
149	Wayne Schurr	2.00	1.00	.60
150	Brooks Robinson	25.00	12.50	7.50
151	Athletics Team	2.25	1.25	.70
152	Phil Ortega	2.00	1.00	.60
153	Norm Cash	2.00	1.00	.60
154	Bob Humphreys	2.00	1.00	.60
155	Roger Maris	60.00	30.00	18.00
156	Bob Sadowski	2.00	1.00	.60
157	Zoilo Versalles	2.25	1.25	.70
158	Dick Sisler	2.00	1.00	.60
159	Jim Duffalo	2.00	1.00	.60
160	Bob Clemente	85.00	42.00	26.00
161	Frank Baumann	2.00	1.00	.60
162	Russ Nixon	2.00	1.00	.60
163	John Briggs	2.00	1.00	.60
164	Al Spangler	2.00	1.00	.60
165	Dick Ellsworth	2.00	1.00	.60
166	Indians Rookies (*Tommie Agee*, George Culver)	2.25	1.25	.70
167	Bill Wakefield	2.00	1.00	.60
168	Dick Green	2.00	1.00	.60
169	Dave Vineyard	2.00	1.00	.60
170	Hank Aaron	95.00	47.50	28.50
171	Jim Roland	2.00	1.00	.60
172	Jim Piersall	2.25	1.25	.70
173	Tigers Team	3.25	1.75	1.00
174	Joe Jay	2.00	1.00	.60
175	Bob Aspromonte	2.00	1.00	.60
176	Willie McCovey	20.00	10.00	6.00
177	Pete Mikkelsen	2.00	1.00	.60
178	Dalton Jones	2.00	1.00	.60
179	Hal Woodeshick	2.00	1.00	.60
180	Bob Allison	2.00	1.00	.60
181	Senators Rookies (Don Loun, Joe McCabe)	2.00	1.00	.60
182	Mike de la Hoz	2.00	1.00	.60
183	Dave Nicholson	2.00	1.00	.60
184	John Boozer	2.00	1.00	.60
185	Max Alvis	2.00	1.00	.60
186	Billy Cowan	2.00	1.00	.60
187	Casey Stengel	18.00	9.00	5.00
188	Sam Bowens	2.00	1.00	.60
189	Checklist 177-264	2.00	1.00	.60
190	Bill White	2.00	1.00	.60
191	Phil Regan	2.00	1.00	.60
192	Jim Coker	2.00	1.00	.60
193	Gaylord Perry	20.00	10.00	6.00
194	Angels Rookies (Bill Kelso, *Rick Reichardt*)	2.00	1.00	.60
195	Bob Veale	2.00	1.00	.60
196	Ron Fairly	2.00	1.00	.60
197	Diego Segui	2.00	1.00	.60
198	Smoky Burgess	2.00	1.00	.60
199	Bob Heffner	2.00	1.00	.60
200	Joe Torre	5.00	2.50	1.50
201	Twins Rookies (*Cesar Tovar*, Sandy Valdespino)	2.00	1.00	.60
202	Leo Burke	2.00	1.00	.60
203	Dallas Green	2.00	1.00	.60
204	Russ Snyder	2.00	1.00	.60
205	Warren Spahn	20.00	10.00	6.00
206	Willie Horton	2.00	1.00	.60
207	Pete Rose	135.00	67.00	37.00
208	Tommy John	10.00	5.00	3.00
209	Pirates Team	5.00	2.50	1.50
210	Jim Fregosi	2.25	1.25	.70
211	Steve Ridzik	2.00	1.00	.60
212	Ron Brand	2.00	1.00	.60
213	Jim Davenport	2.00	1.00	.60
214	Bob Purkey	2.00	1.00	.60
215	Pete Ward	2.00	1.00	.60
216	Al Worthington	2.00	1.00	.60
217	Walt Alston	3.50	1.75	1.00
218	Dick Schofield	2.00	1.00	.60
219	Bob Meyer	2.00	1.00	.60

#	Player	NR MT	EX	VG
220	Billy Williams	10.00	5.00	3.00
221	John Tsitouris	2.00	1.00	.60
222	Bob Tillman	2.00	1.00	.60
223	Dan Osinski	2.00	1.00	.60
224	Bob Chance	2.00	1.00	.60
225	Bo Belinsky	2.00	1.00	.60
226	Yankees Rookies (Jake Gibbs, Elvio Jimenez)	2.25	1.25	.70
227	Bobby Klaus	2.00	1.00	.60
228	Jack Sanford	2.00	1.00	.60
229	Lou Clinton	2.00	1.00	.60
230	Ray Sadecki	2.00	1.00	.60
231	Jerry Adair	2.00	1.00	.60
232	*Steve Blass*	2.00	1.00	.60
233	Don Zimmer	2.25	1.25	.70
234	White Sox Team	5.00	2.50	1.50
235	Chuck Hinton	2.00	1.00	.60
236	*Dennis McLain*	20.00	10.00	6.00
237	Bernie Allen	2.00	1.00	.60
238	Joe Moeller	2.00	1.00	.60
239	Doc Edwards	2.00	1.00	.60
240	Bob Bruce	2.00	1.00	.60
241	Mack Jones	2.00	1.00	.60
242	George Brunet	2.00	1.00	.60
243	Reds Rookies (Ted Davidson, *Tommy Helms*)	2.00	1.00	.60
244	Lindy McDaniel	2.00	1.00	.60
245	Joe Pepitone	2.00	1.00	.60
246	Tom Butters	2.00	1.00	.60
247	Wally Moon	2.00	1.00	.60
248	Gus Triandos	2.00	1.00	.60
249	Dave McNally	2.00	1.00	.60
250	Willie Mays	110.00	55.00	33.00
251	Billy Herman	2.00	1.00	.60
252	Pete Richert	2.00	1.00	.60
253	Danny Cater	2.00	1.00	.60
254	Roland Sheldon	2.25	1.25	.70
255	Camilo Pascual	2.00	1.00	.60
256	Tito Francona	2.00	1.00	.60
257	Jim Wynn	2.00	1.00	.60
258	Larry Bearnarth	2.00	1.00	.60
259	Tigers Rookies (*Jim Northrup, Ray Oyler*)	2.00	1.00	.60
260	Don Drysdale	18.00	9.00	5.50
261	Duke Carmel	2.25	1.25	.70
262	Bud Daley	2.00	1.00	.60
263	Marty Keough	2.00	1.00	.60
264	Bob Buhl	2.00	1.00	.60
265	Jim Pagliaroni	2.00	1.00	.60
266	*Bert Campaneris*	5.00	2.50	1.50
267	Senators Team	5.00	2.50	1.50
268	Ken McBride	2.00	1.00	.60
269	Frank Bolling	2.00	1.00	.60
270	Milt Pappas	2.00	1.00	.60
271	Don Wert	2.00	1.00	.60
272	Chuck Schilling	2.00	1.00	.60
273	Checklist 265-352	3.25	1.75	1.00
274	Lum Harris	2.00	1.00	.60
275	Dick Groat	3.25	1.75	1.00
276	Hoyt Wilhelm	8.00	4.00	2.50
277	Johnny Lewis	2.00	1.00	.60
278	Ken Retzer	2.00	1.00	.60
279	Dick Tracewski	2.00	1.00	.60
280	Dick Stuart	2.00	1.00	.60
281	Bill Stafford	2.25	1.25	.70
282	Giants Rookies (Dick Estelle, *Masanori Murakami*)	2.00	1.00	.60
283	Fred Whitfield	2.00	1.00	.60
284	Nick Willhite	2.00	1.00	.60
285	Ron Hunt	2.00	1.00	.60
286	Athletics Rookies (Jim Dickson, Aurelio Monteagudo)	2.00	1.00	.60
287	Gary Kolb	2.00	1.00	.60
288	Jack Hamilton	2.00	1.00	.60
289	Gordy Coleman	2.00	1.00	.60
290	Wally Bunker	2.00	1.00	.60
291	Jerry Lynch	2.00	1.00	.60
292	Larry Yellen	2.00	1.00	.60
293	Angels Team	5.00	2.50	1.50
294	Tim McCarver	2.75	1.50	.80
295	Dick Radatz	2.00	1.00	.60
296	Tony Taylor	2.00	1.00	.60
297	Dave DeBusschere	3.50	1.75	1.00
298	Jim Stewart	2.00	1.00	.60
299	Jerry Zimmerman	2.00	1.00	.60
300	Sandy Koufax	130.00	65.00	37.00
301	Birdie Tebbetts	2.00	1.00	.60
302	Al Stanek	2.00	1.00	.60
303	Johnny Orsino	2.00	1.00	.60
304	Dave Stenhouse	2.00	1.00	.60
305	Rico Carty	2.25	1.25	.70
306	Bubba Phillips	2.00	1.00	.60
307	Barry Latman	2.00	1.00	.60
308	Mets Rookies (*Cleon Jones*, Tom Parsons)	2.00	1.00	.60
309	Steve Hamilton	2.25	1.25	.70
310	Johnny Callison	2.00	1.00	.60
311	Orlando Pena	2.00	1.00	.60
312	Joe Nuxhall	2.00	1.00	.60
313	Jimmie Schaffer	2.00	1.00	.60
314	Sterling Slaughter	2.00	1.00	.60
315	Frank Malzone	2.00	1.00	.60
316	Reds Team	2.75	1.50	.80
317	Don McMahon	2.00	1.00	.60
318	Matty Alou	2.00	1.00	.60
319	Ken McMullen	2.00	1.00	.60
320	Bob Gibson	30.00	15.00	9.00
321	Rusty Staub	5.00	2.50	1.50
322	Rick Wise	2.00	1.00	.60
323	Hank Bauer	2.00	1.00	.60
324	Bobby Locke	2.00	1.00	.60
325	Donn Clendenon	2.00	1.00	.60
326	Dwight Siebler	2.00	1.00	.60
327	Denis Menke	2.00	1.00	.60
328	Eddie Fisher	2.00	1.00	.60
329	Hawk Taylor	2.00	1.00	.60
330	Whitey Ford	20.00	10.00	6.00
331	Dodgers Rookies (Al Ferrara, John Purdin)	2.00	1.00	.60
332	Ted Abernathy	2.00	1.00	.60
333	Tommie Reynolds	2.00	1.00	.60
334	Vic Roznovsky	2.00	1.00	.60
335	Mickey Lolich	3.50	1.75	1.00
336	Woody Held	2.00	1.00	.60
337	Mike Cuellar	2.25	1.25	.70
338	Phillies Team	5.00	2.50	1.50
339	Ryne Duren	2.00	1.00	.60
340	Tony Oliva	3.50	1.75	1.00
341	Bobby Bolin	2.00	1.00	.60
342	Bob Rodgers	2.00	1.00	.60
343	Mike McCormick	2.00	1.00	.60
344	Wes Parker	2.00	1.00	.60
345	Floyd Robinson	2.00	1.00	.60
346	Bobby Bragan	2.00	1.00	.60
347	Roy Face	2.25	1.25	.70
348	George Banks	2.00	1.00	.60
349	Larry Miller	2.00	1.00	.60
350	Mickey Mantle	450.00	225.00	135.00
351	Jim Perry	2.00	1.00	.60
352	*Alex Johnson*	2.00	1.00	.60
353	Jerry Lumpe	2.00	1.00	.60
354	Cubs Rookies (Billy Ott, Jack Warner)	2.00	1.00	.60
355	Vada Pinson	5.00	2.50	1.50
356	Bill Spanswick	2.00	1.00	.60
357	Carl Warwick	2.00	1.00	.60
358	Albie Pearson	2.00	1.00	.60
359	Ken Johnson	2.00	1.00	.60
360	Orlando Cepeda	6.00	3.00	1.75
361	Checklist 353-429	3.25	1.75	1.00
362	Don Schwall	2.00	1.00	.60
363	Bob Johnson	2.00	1.00	.60
364	Galen Cisco	2.00	1.00	.60
365	Jim Gentile	2.00	1.00	.60
366	Dan Schneider	2.00	1.00	.60
367	Leon Wagner	2.00	1.00	.60
368	White Sox Rookies (Ken Berry, Joel Gibson)	2.00	1.00	.60
369	Phil Linz	2.25	1.25	.70
370	Tommy Davis	2.25	1.25	.70
371	Frank Kreutzer	2.00	1.00	.60
372	Clay Dalrymple	2.00	1.00	.60
373	Curt Simmons	2.00	1.00	.60
374	Angels Rookies (*Jose Cardenal*, Dick Simpson)	2.00	1.00	.60
375	Dave Wickersham	2.00	1.00	.60
376	Jim Landis	2.00	1.00	.60
377	Willie Stargell	25.00	12.50	7.50
378	Chuck Estrada	2.00	1.00	.60
379	Giants Team	5.00	2.50	1.50
380	Rocky Colavito	2.00	1.00	.60
381	Al Jackson	2.00	1.00	.60
382	J.C. Martin	2.00	1.00	.60
383	Felipe Alou	2.00	1.00	.60
384	Johnny Klippstein	2.00	1.00	.60
385	Carl Yastrzemski	70.00	35.00	21.00
386	Cubs Rookies (Paul Jaeckel, Fred Norman)	2.00	1.00	.60
387	Johnny Podres	2.00	1.00	.60
388	John Blanchard	2.25	1.25	.70
389	Don Larsen	2.00	1.00	.60
390	Bill Freehan	2.00	1.00	.60

#	Player	NR MT	EX	VG
391	Mel McGaha	2.00	1.00	.60
392	Bob Friend	2.25	1.25	.70
393	Ed Kirkpatrick	2.00	1.00	.60
394	Jim Hannan	2.00	1.00	.60
395	Jim Hart	2.00	1.00	.60
396	Frank Bertaina	2.00	1.00	.60
397	Jerry Buchek	2.00	1.00	.60
398	Reds Rookies (Dan Neville, *Art Shamsky*)	2.00	1.00	.60
399	Ray Herbert	2.00	1.00	.60
400	Harmon Killebrew	25.00	12.50	7.50
401	Carl Willey	2.00	1.00	.60
402	Joe Amalfitano	2.00	1.00	.60
403	Red Sox Team	2.00	1.00	.60
404	Stan Williams	2.00	1.00	.60
405	John Roseboro	2.00	1.00	.60
406	Ralph Terry	2.00	1.00	.60
407	Lee Maye	2.00	1.00	.60
408	Larry Sherry	2.00	1.00	.60
409	Astros Rookies (Jim Beauchamp, *Larry Dierker*)	2.00	1.00	.60
410	Luis Aparicio	9.00	4.50	2.75
411	Roger Craig	2.00	1.00	.60
412	Bob Bailey	2.00	1.00	.60
413	Hal Reniff	2.25	1.25	.70
414	Al Lopez	2.00	1.00	.60
415	Curt Flood	2.25	1.25	.70
416	Jim Brewer	2.00	1.00	.60
417	Ed Brinkman	2.00	1.00	.60
418	Johnny Edwards	2.00	1.00	.60
419	Ruben Amaro	2.00	1.00	.60
420	Larry Jackson	2.00	1.00	.60
421	Twins Rookies (Gary Dotter, Jay Ward)	2.00	1.00	.60
422	Aubrey Gatewood	2.00	1.00	.60
423	Jesse Gonder	2.00	1.00	.60
424	Gary Bell	2.00	1.00	.60
425	Wayne Causey	2.00	1.00	.60
426	Braves Team	5.00	2.50	1.50
427	Bob Saverine	2.00	1.00	.60
428	Bob Shaw	2.00	1.00	.60
429	Don Demeter	2.00	1.00	.60
430	Gary Peters	2.00	1.00	.60
431	Cardinals Rookies (*Nelson Briles*, Wayne Spiezio)	2.00	1.00	.60
432	Jim Grant	2.00	1.00	.60
433	John Bateman	2.00	1.00	.60
434	Dave Morehead	2.00	1.00	.60
435	Willie Davis	2.25	1.25	.70
436	Don Elston	2.00	1.00	.60
437	Chico Cardenas	2.00	1.00	.60
438	Harry Walker	2.00	1.00	.60
439	Moe Drabowsky	2.00	1.00	.60
440	Tom Tresh	5.00	2.50	1.50
441	Denver Lemaster	2.00	1.00	.60
442	Vic Power	2.00	1.00	.60
443	Checklist 430-506	3.25	1.75	1.00
444	Bob Hendley	2.00	1.00	.60
445	Don Lock	2.00	1.00	.60
446	Art Mahaffey	2.00	1.00	.60
447	Julian Javier	2.00	1.00	.60
448	Lee Stange	2.00	1.00	.60
449	Mets Rookies (Jerry Hinsley, Gary Kroll)	2.25	1.25	.70
450	Elston Howard	5.00	2.50	1.50
451	Jim Owens	2.00	1.00	.60
452	Gary Geiger	2.00	1.00	.60
453	Dodgers Rookies (*Willie Crawford*, John Werhas)	2.25	1.25	.70
454	Ed Rakow	2.00	1.00	.60
455	Norm Siebern	2.25	1.25	.70
456	Bill Henry	2.00	1.00	.60
457	Bob Kennedy	2.00	1.00	.60
458	John Buzhardt	2.00	1.00	.60
459	Frank Kostro	2.00	1.00	.60
460	Richie Allen	10.00	5.00	3.00
461	Braves Rookies (*Clay Carroll*, Phil Niekro)	50.00	25.00	15.00
462	Lew Krausse (photo actually Pete Lovrich)	2.00	1.00	.60
463	Manny Mota	2.25	1.25	.70
464	Ron Piche	2.00	1.00	.60
465	Tom Haller	2.00	1.00	.60
466	Senators Rookies (Pete Craig, Dick Nen)	2.00	1.00	.60
467	Ray Washburn	2.00	1.00	.60
468	Larry Brown	2.00	1.00	.60
469	Don Nottebart	2.00	1.00	.60
470	Yogi Berra	50.00	30.00	15.00
471	Billy Hoeft	2.00	1.00	.60
472	Don Pavletich	2.00	1.00	.60
473	Orioles Rookies (*Paul Blair, Dave Johnson*)	15.00	7.50	4.50
474	Cookie Rojas	2.00	1.00	.60
475	Clete Boyer	2.00	1.00	.60
476	Billy O'Dell	2.00	1.00	.60
477	Cardinals Rookies (Fritz Ackley, *Steve Carlton*)	525.00	260.00	165.00
478	Wilbur Wood	2.00	1.00	.60
479	Ken Harrelson	5.00	2.50	1.50
480	Joel Horlen	2.00	1.00	.60
481	Indians Team	2.00	1.00	.60
482	Bob Priddy	2.00	1.00	.60
483	George Smith	2.00	1.00	.60
484	Ron Perranoski	2.25	1.25	.70
485	Nellie Fox	6.00	3.00	1.75
486	Angels Rookies (Tom Egan, Pat Rogan)	2.00	1.00	.60
487	Woody Woodward	2.25	1.25	.70
488	Ted Wills	2.00	1.00	.60
489	Gene Mauch	2.25	1.25	.70
490	Earl Battey	2.25	1.25	.70
491	Tracy Stallard	2.00	1.00	.60
492	Gene Freese	2.00	1.00	.60
493	Tigers Rookies (Bruce Brubaker, Bill Roman)	2.00	1.00	.60
494	Jay Ritchie	2.00	1.00	.60
495	Joe Christopher	2.25	1.25	.70
496	Joe Cunningham	2.00	1.00	.60
497	Giants Rookies (*Ken Henderson*, Jack Hiatt)	2.25	1.25	.70
498	Gene Stephens	2.00	1.00	.60
499	Stu Miller	2.00	1.00	.60
500	Ed Mathews	30.00	15.00	9.00
501	Indians Rookies (Ralph Gagliano, Jim Rittwage)	2.00	1.00	.60
502	Don Cardwell	2.00	1.00	.60
503	Phil Gagliano	2.00	1.00	.60
504	Jerry Grote	2.25	1.25	.70
505	Ray Culp	2.00	1.00	.60
506	Sam Mele	2.00	1.00	.60
507	Sammy Ellis	2.00	1.00	.60
508a	Checklist 507-598 (large print on front)	6.00	3.00	1.75
508b	Checklist 507-598 (small print on front)	5.00	2.50	1.50
509	Red Sox Rookies (Bob Guindon, Gerry Vezendy)	2.00	1.00	.60
510	Ernie Banks	75.00	38.00	23.00
511	Ron Locke	2.25	1.25	.70
512	Cap Peterson	2.00	1.00	.60
513	Yankees Team	10.00	5.00	3.00
514	Joe Azcue	2.00	1.00	.60
515	Vern Law	2.00	1.00	.60
516	Al Weis	2.00	1.00	.60
517	Angels Rookies (Paul Schaal, Jack Warner)	2.00	1.00	.60
518	Ken Rowe	2.00	1.00	.60
519	Bob Uecker	45.00	22.00	13.50
520	Tony Cloninger	2.25	1.25	.70
521	Phillies Rookies (Dave Bennett, Morrie Stevens)	2.00	1.00	.60
522	Hank Aguirre	2.00	1.00	.60
523	Mike Brumley	5.00	2.50	1.50
524	Dave Giusti	5.00	2.50	1.50
525	Eddie Bressoud	5.00	2.50	1.50
526	Athletics Rookies (*Jim Hunter, Rene Lachemann, Skip Lockwood, Johnny Odom*)	150.00	75.00	45.00
527	Jeff Torborg	6.00	3.00	1.75
528	George Altman	5.00	2.50	1.50
529	Jerry Fosnow	5.00	2.50	1.50
530	Jim Maloney	6.00	3.00	1.75
531	Chuck Hiller	5.00	2.50	1.50
532	Hector Lopez	5.00	2.50	1.50
533	Mets Rookies (Jim Bethke, *Tug McGraw*, Dan Napolean, *Ron Swoboda*)	20.00	10.00	6.00
534	John Herrnstein	5.00	2.50	1.50
535	Jack Kralick	5.00	2.50	1.50
536	Andre Rodgers	5.00	2.50	1.50
537	Angels Rookies (Marcelino Lopez, *Rudy May*, Phil Roof)	5.00	2.50	1.50
538	Chuck Dressen	6.00	3.00	1.75
539	Herm Starrette	5.00	2.50	1.50
540	Lou Brock	50.00	25.00	15.00
541	White Sox Rookies (Greg Bollo, Bob Locker)	5.00	2.50	1.50
542	Lou Klimchock	5.00	2.50	1.50
543	Ed Connolly	5.00	2.50	1.50
544	Howie Reed	5.00	2.50	1.50
545	Jesus Alou	6.00	3.00	1.75
546	Indians Rookies (Ray Barker, Bill Davis, Mike Hedlund, Floyd Weaver)	5.00	2.50	1.50

		NR MT	EX	VG
547	Jake Wood	5.00	2.50	1.50
548	Dick Stigman	5.00	2.50	1.50
549	Cubs Rookies (*Glenn Beckert*, Roberto Pena)	5.00	2.50	1.50
550	*Mel Stottlemyre*	25.00	12.50	7.50
551	Mets Team	15.00	7.50	4.50
552	Julio Gotay	5.00	2.50	1.50
553	Astros Rookies (Dan Coombs, Jack McClure, Gene Ratliff)	5.00	2.50	1.50
554	Chico Ruiz	5.00	2.50	1.50
555	Jack Baldschun	5.00	2.50	1.50
556	Red Schoendienst	10.00	5.00	3.00
557	Jose Santiago	5.00	2.50	1.50
558	Tommie Sisk	5.00	2.50	1.50
559	Ed Bailey	5.00	2.50	1.50
560	Boog Powell	12.00	6.00	3.50
561	Dodgers Rookies (Dennis Daboll, *Mike Kekich, Jim Lefebvre*, Hector Valle)	12.00	6.00	3.50
562	Billy Moran	5.00	2.50	1.50
563	Julio Navarro	5.00	2.50	1.50
564	Mel Nelson	5.00	2.50	1.50
565	Ernie Broglio	5.00	2.50	1.50
566	Yankees Rookies (Gil Blanco, Art Lopez, Ross Moschitto)	5.00	2.50	1.50
567	Tommie Aaron	6.00	3.00	1.75
568	Ron Taylor	5.00	2.50	1.50
569	Gino Cimoli	5.00	2.50	1.50
570	Claude Osteen	6.00	3.00	1.75
571	Ossie Virgil	5.00	2.50	1.50
572	Orioles Team	10.00	5.00	3.00
573	Red Sox Rookies (*Jim Lonborg*, Gerry Moses, Mike Ryan, Bill Schlesinger)	10.00	5.00	3.00
574	Roy Sievers	6.00	3.00	1.75
575	Jose Pagan	5.00	2.50	1.50
576	Terry Fox	5.00	2.50	1.50
577	A.L. Rookies (Jim Buschhorn, Darold Knowles, Richie Scheinblum)	5.00	2.50	1.50
578	Camilo Carreon	5.00	2.50	1.50
579	Dick Smith	5.00	2.50	1.50
580	Jimmie Hall	5.00	2.50	1.50
581	N.L. Rookies (Kevin Collins, *Tony Perez*, Dave Ricketts)	175.00	87.00	52.00
582	Bob Schmidt	5.00	2.50	1.50
583	Wes Covington	5.00	2.50	1.50
584	Harry Bright	5.00	2.50	1.50
585	Hank Fischer	5.00	2.50	1.50
586	Tommy McCraw	5.00	2.50	1.50
587	Joe Sparma	5.00	2.50	1.50
588	Lenny Green	5.00	2.50	1.50
589	Giants Rookies (Frank Linzy, Bob Schroder)	5.00	2.50	1.50
590	Johnnie Wyatt	5.00	2.50	1.50
591	Bob Skinner	6.00	3.00	1.75
592	Frank Bork	5.00	2.50	1.50
593	Tigers Rookies (Jackie Moore, John Sullivan)	5.00	2.50	1.50
594	Joe Gaines	5.00	2.50	1.50
595	Don Lee	5.00	2.50	1.50
596	Don Landrum	5.00	2.50	1.50
597	Twins Rookies (Joe Nossek, Dick Reese, John Sevcik)	6.00	3.00	1.75
598	Al Downing	10.00	3.00	1.75

1965 Topps Embossed

Inserted in regular packs, the 2-1/8" by 3-1/2" Topps Embossed cards are one of the more fascinating issues of the company. The fronts feature an embossed profile portrait on gold foil-like cardboard (some collectors report finding the cards with silver cardboard). The player's name, team and position are below the portrait - which is good, because most of the embossed portraits are otherwise unrecognizeable. There is a gold border with American players framed in blue and National Leaguers in red. The set contains 72 cards divided equally bwetween the leagues. The set provides an inexpensive way to add some interesting cards to a collection. Being special cards, many stars appear in the set.

		NR MT	EX	VG
Complete Set:		100.00	50.00	30.00
Common Player:		.50	.25	.15
1	Carl Yastrzemski	5.00	2.50	1.50
2	Ron Fairly	.50	.25	.15
3	Max Alvis	.50	.25	.15
4	Jim Ray Hart	.50	.25	.15
5	Bill Skowron	.60	.30	.20
6	Ed Kranepool	.50	.25	.15
7	Tim McCarver	.60	.30	.20
8	Sandy Koufax	5.00	2.50	1.50
9	Donn Clendenon	.50	.25	.15
10	John Romano	.50	.25	.15
11	Mickey Mantle	15.00	7.50	4.50
12	Joe Torre	.70	.35	.20
13	Al Kaline	5.00	2.50	1.50
14	Al McBean	.50	.25	.15
15	Don Drysdale	1.50	.70	.45
16	Brooks Robinson	2.00	1.00	.60
17	Jim Bunning	1.00	.50	.30
18	Gary Peters	.50	.25	.15
19	Bob Clemente	5.00	2.50	1.50
20	Milt Pappas	.50	.25	.15
21	Wayne Causey	.50	.25	.15
22	Frank Robinson	2.00	1.00	.60
23	Bill Mazeroski	.60	.30	.20
24	Diego Segui	.50	.25	.15
25	Jim Bouton	.60	.30	.20
26	Ed Mathews	1.50	.70	.45
27	Willie Mays	6.00	3.00	1.75
28	Ron Santo	.60	.30	.20
29	Boog Powell	.60	.30	.20
30	Ken McBride	.50	.25	.15
31	Leon Wagner	.50	.25	.15
32	John Callison	.50	.25	.15
33	Zoilo Versalles	.50	.25	.15
34	Jack Baldschun	.50	.25	.15
35	Ron Hunt	.50	.25	.15
36	Richie Allen	.70	.35	.20
37	Frank Malzone	.50	.25	.15
38	Bob Allison	.50	.25	.15
39	Jim Fregosi	.60	.30	.20
40	Billy Williams	1.50	.70	.45
41	Bill Freehan	.50	.25	.15
42	Vada Pinson	.70	.35	.20
43	Bill White	.50	.25	.15
44	Roy McMillan	.50	.25	.15
45	Orlando Cepeda	1.00	.50	.30
46	Rocky Colavito	.70	.35	.20
47	Ken Boyer	.70	.35	.20
48	Dick Radatz	.50	.25	.15
49	Tommy Davis	.60	.30	.20
50	Walt Bond	.50	.25	.15
51	John Orsino	.50	.25	.15
52	Joe Christopher	.50	.25	.15
53	Al Spangler	.50	.25	.15
54	Jim King	.50	.25	.15
55	Mickey Lolich	.70	.35	.20
56	Harmon Killebrew	2.00	1.00	.60
57	Bob Shaw	.50	.25	.15
58	Ernie Banks	4.00	2.00	1.25
59	Hank Aaron	5.00	2.50	1.50
60	Chuck Hinton	.50	.25	.15
61	Bob Aspromonte	.50	.25	.15
62	Lee Maye	.50	.25	.15
63	Joe Cunningham	.50	.25	.15
64	Pete Ward	.50	.25	.15
65	Bobby Richardson	1.00	.50	.30
66	Dean Chance	.50	.25	.15
67	Dick Ellsworth	.50	.25	.15
68	Jim Maloney	.50	.25	.15
69	Bob Gibson	1.50	.70	.45
70	Earl Battey	.50	.25	.15
71	Tony Kubek	1.00	.50	.30
72	Jack Kralick	.50	.25	.15

1965 Topps Transfers

Issued as strips of three players each as inserts in 1965, the Topps Transfers were 2" by 3" portraits of players. The transfers have blue or red bands at the top and bottom with the team name and position in the top band and the player's name in the bottom. As is so often the case, the superstars in the transfer set can be quite expensive, but like many of Topps non-card products, the transfers are neither terribly expensive or popular today.

		NR MT	EX	VG
Complete Set:		225.00	112.00	67.00
Common Player:		.60	.30	.20
(1)	Hank Aaron	15.00	7.50	4.50
(2)	Richie Allen	.80	.40	.25
(3)	Bob Allison	.70	.35	.20
(4)	Max Alvis	.60	.30	.20
(5)	Luis Aparicio	2.50	1.25	.70
(6)	Bob Aspromonte	.60	.30	.20
(7)	Walt Bond	.60	.30	.20
(8)	Jim Bouton	.80	.40	.25
(9)	Ken Boyer	.80	.40	.25
(10)	Jim Bunning	1.00	.50	.30
(11)	John Callison	.70	.35	.20
(12)	Rico Carty	.70	.35	.20
(13)	Wayne Causey	.60	.30	.20
(14)	Orlando Cepeda	1.00	.50	.30
(15)	Bob Chance	.60	.30	.20
(16)	Dean Chance	.60	.30	.20
(17)	Joe Christopher	.60	.30	.20
(18)	Bob Clemente	15.00	7.50	4.50
(19)	Rocky Colavito	.80	.40	.25
(20)	Tony Conigliaro	.70	.35	.20
(21)	Tommy Davis	.80	.40	.25
(22)	Don Drysdale	4.00	2.00	1.25
(23)	Bill Freehan	.70	.35	.20
(24)	Jim Fregosi	.70	.35	.20
(25)	Bob Gibson	4.00	2.00	1.25
(26)	Dick Groat	.70	.35	.20
(27)	Tom Haller	.60	.30	.20
(28)	Chuck Hinton	.60	.30	.20
(29)	Elston Howard	1.00	.50	.30
(30)	Ron Hunt	.60	.30	.20
(31)	Al Jackson	.60	.30	.20
(32)	Al Kaline	5.00	2.50	1.50
(33)	Harmon Killebrew	5.00	2.50	1.50
(34)	Jim King	.60	.30	.20
(35)	Ron Kline	.60	.30	.20
(36)	Bobby Knoop	.60	.30	.20
(37)	Sandy Koufax	10.00	5.00	3.00
(38)	Ed Kranepool	.60	.30	.20
(39)	Jim Maloney	.60	.30	.20
(40)	Mickey Mantle	60.00	30.00	18.00
(41)	Juan Marichal	4.00	2.00	1.25
(42)	Lee Maye	.60	.30	.20
(43)	Willie Mays	15.00	7.50	4.50
(44)	Bill Mazeroski	.80	.40	.25
(45)	Tony Oliva	.80	.40	.25
(46)	Jim O'Toole	.60	.30	.20
(47)	Milt Pappas	.70	.35	.20
(48)	Camilo Pascual	.70	.35	.20
(49)	Gary Peters	.60	.30	.20
(50)	Vada Pinson	.80	.40	.25
(51)	Juan Pizarro	.60	.30	.20
(52)	Boog Powell	.80	.40	.25
(53)	Dick Radatz	.60	.30	.20

		NR MT	EX	VG
(54)	Bobby Richardson	1.00	.50	.30
(55)	Brooks Robinson	6.00	3.00	1.75
(56)	Frank Robinson	5.00	2.50	1.50
(57)	Bob Rodgers	.70	.35	.20
(58)	John Roseboro	.70	.35	.20
(59)	Ron Santo	.80	.40	.25
(60)	Diego Segui	.60	.30	.20
(61)	Bill Skowron	.70	.35	.20
(62)	Al Spangler	.60	.30	.20
(63)	Dick Stuart	.70	.35	.20
(64)	Luis Tiant	.80	.40	.25
(65)	Joe Torre	.80	.40	.25
(66)	Bob Veale	.60	.30	.20
(67)	Leon Wagner	.60	.30	.20
(68)	Pete Ward	.60	.30	.20
(69)	Bill White	.70	.35	.20
(70)	Dave Wickersham	.60	.30	.20
(71)	Billy Williams	3.00	1.50	.90
(72)	Carl Yastrzemski	25.00	12.50	7.50

1966 Topps

In 1966, Topps produced another 598-card set. The 2-1/2" by 3-1/2" cards feature the almost traditional color photograph with a diagonal strip in the upper left-hand corner carrying the team name. A band at the bottom carries the player's name and position. Multi-player cards returned in 1966 after having had a year's hiatus. The statistical leader cards feature the categorical leader and two runners-up. Most team managers have cards as well. The 1966 set features a handful of cards found with without a notice of the player's sale or trade to another team. Cards without the notice bring higher prices not included in the complete set prices below.

		NR MT	EX	VG
Complete Set:		4500.00	2250.00	1350.
Common Player: 1-110		1.00	.50	.30
Common Player: 111-446		1.25	.60	.40
Common Player: 447-522		5.00	2.50	1.50
Common Player Singleprint: 523-598		20.00	10.00	6.00
Common Player: 523-598		15.00	7.50	4.50
1	Willie Mays	155.00	60.00	30.00
2	Ted Abernathy	1.25	.60	.40
3	Sam Mele	1.00	.50	.30
4	Ray Culp	1.00	.50	.30
5	Jim Fregosi	1.50	.70	.45
6	Chuck Schilling	1.00	.50	.30
7	Tracy Stallard	1.00	.50	.30
8	Floyd Robinson	1.00	.50	.30
9	Clete Boyer	5.00	2.50	1.50
10	Tony Cloninger	1.25	.60	.40
11	Senators Rookies (Brant Alyea, Pete Craig)	1.00	.50	.30
12	John Tsitouris	1.00	.50	.30
13	Lou Johnson	1.00	.50	.30
14	Norm Siebern	1.25	.60	.40
15	Vern Law	1.50	.70	.45
16	Larry Brown	1.25	.60	.40
17	Johnny Stephenson	1.25	.60	.40
18	Roland Sheldon	1.00	.50	.30
19	Giants Team	5.00	2.50	1.50
20	Willie Horton	1.25	.60	.40
21	Don Nottebart	1.00	.50	.30

#	Player	NR MT	EX	VG
22	Joe Nossek	1.00	.50	.30
23	Jack Sanford	1.00	.50	.30
24	*Don Kessinger*	1.25	.60	.40
25	Pete Ward	1.00	.50	.30
26	Ray Sadecki	1.00	.50	.30
27	Orioles Rookies (*Andy Etchebarren, Darold Knowles*)	1.25	.60	.40
28	Phil Niekro	12.00	6.00	3.50
29	Mike Brumley	1.00	.50	.30
30	Pete Rose	60.00	30.00	18.00
31	Jack Cullen	1.25	.60	.40
32	Adolfo Phillips	1.00	.50	.30
33	Jim Pagliaroni	1.00	.50	.30
34	Checklist 1-88	5.00	2.50	1.50
35	Ron Swoboda	1.25	.60	.40
36	Jim Hunter	30.00	15.00	9.00
37	Billy Herman	5.00	2.50	1.50
38	Ron Nischwitz	1.00	.50	.30
39	Ken Henderson	1.00	.50	.30
40	Jim Grant	1.00	.50	.30
41	Don LeJohn	1.00	.50	.30
42	Aubrey Gatewood	1.00	.50	.30
43	Don Landrum	1.00	.50	.30
44	Indians Rookies (Bill Davis, Tom Kelley)	1.00	.50	.30
45	Jim Gentile	1.25	.60	.40
46	Howie Koplitz	1.00	.50	.30
47	J.C. Martin	1.00	.50	.30
48	Paul Blair	1.25	.60	.40
49	Woody Woodward	1.25	.60	.40
50	Mickey Mantle	200.00	100.00	60.00
51	Gordon Richardson	1.25	.60	.40
52	Power Plus (Johnny Callison, Wes Covington)	1.50	.70	.45
53	Bob Duliba	1.00	.50	.30
54	Jose Pagan	1.00	.50	.30
55	Ken Harrelson	5.00	2.50	1.50
56	Sandy Valdespino	1.00	.50	.30
57	Jim Lefebvre	1.25	.60	.40
58	Dave Wickersham	1.00	.50	.30
59	Reds Team	2.25	1.25	.70
60	Curt Flood	5.00	2.50	1.50
61	Bob Bolin	1.00	.50	.30
62a	Merritt Ranew (no sold statement)	15.00	7.50	4.50
62b	Merritt Ranew (with sold statement)	1.00	.50	.30
63	Jim Stewart	1.00	.50	.30
64	Bob Bruce	1.00	.50	.30
65	Leon Wagner	1.25	.60	.40
66	Al Weis	1.00	.50	.30
67	Mets Rookies (Cleon Jones, Dick Selma)	1.25	.60	.40
68	Hal Reniff	1.25	.60	.40
69	Ken Hamlin	1.00	.50	.30
70	Carl Yastrzemski	50.00	25.00	15.00
71	Frank Carpin	1.00	.50	.30
72	Tony Perez	35.00	17.50	10.50
73	Jerry Zimmerman	1.00	.50	.30
74	Don Mossi	1.25	.60	.40
75	Tommy Davis	5.00	2.50	1.50
76	Red Schoendienst	4.00	2.00	1.50
77	Johnny Orsino	1.00	.50	.30
78	Frank Linzy	1.00	.50	.30
79	Joe Pepitone	5.00	2.50	1.50
80	Richie Allen	2.50	1.25	.70
81	Ray Oyler	1.00	.50	.30
82	Bob Hendley	1.00	.50	.30
83	Albie Pearson	1.00	.50	.30
84	Braves Rookies (Jim Beauchamp, Dick Kelley)	1.00	.50	.30
85	Eddie Fisher	1.00	.50	.30
86	John Bateman	1.00	.50	.30
87	Dan Napoleon	1.25	.60	.40
88	Fred Whitfield	1.00	.50	.30
89	Ted Davidson	1.00	.50	.30
90	Luis Aparicio	9.00	4.50	2.75
91a	Bob Uecker (no trade statement)	80.00	40.00	25.00
91b	Bob Uecker (with trade statement)	20.00	10.00	6.00
92	Yankees Team	5.00	2.50	1.50
93	Jim Lonborg	1.50	.70	.45
94	Matty Alou	1.50	.70	.45
95	Pete Richert	1.00	.50	.30
96	Felipe Alou	1.50	.70	.45
97	Jim Merritt	1.00	.50	.30
98	Don Demeter	1.00	.50	.30
99	Buc Belters (Donn Clendenon, Willie Stargell)	5.00	2.50	1.50
100	Sandy Koufax	110.00	55.00	33.00
101a	Checklist 89-176 (115 is Spahn)	7.00	3.50	2.00
101b	Checklist 89-176 (115 is Henry)	3.00	1.50	.90
102	Ed Kirkpatrick	1.00	.50	.30
103a	Dick Groat (no trade statement)	20.00	10.00	6.00
103b	Dick Groat (with trade statement)	5.00	2.50	1.50
104a	Alex Johnson (no trade statement)	15.00	7.50	4.50
104b	Alex Johnson (with trade statement)	1.25	.60	.40
105	Milt Pappas	1.25	.60	.40
106	Rusty Staub	2.50	1.25	.70
107	Athletics Rookies (Larry Stahl, Ron Tompkins)	1.00	.50	.30
108	Bobby Klaus	1.25	.60	.40
109	Ralph Terry	1.25	.60	.40
110	Ernie Banks	30.00	15.00	9.00
111	Gary Peters	1.25	.60	.40
112	Manny Mota	1.25	.60	.40
113	Hank Aguirre	1.25	.60	.40
114	Jim Gosger	1.25	.60	.40
115	Bill Henry	1.25	.60	.40
116	Walt Alston	2.50	1.25	.70
117	Jake Gibbs	1.50	.70	.45
118	Mike McCormick	1.25	.60	.40
119	Art Shamsky	1.25	.60	.40
120	Harmon Killebrew	15.00	7.50	4.50
121	Ray Herbert	1.25	.60	.40
122	Joe Gaines	1.25	.60	.40
123	Pirates Rookies (Frank Bork, Jerry May)	1.25	.60	.40
124	Tug McGraw	3.00	1.50	.90
125	Lou Brock	20.00	10.00	6.00
126	*Jim Palmer*	225.00	112.00	67.00
127	Ken Berry	1.25	.60	.40
128	Jim Landis	1.25	.60	.40
129	Jack Kralick	1.25	.60	.40
130	Joe Torre	2.25	1.25	.70
131	Angels Team	2.25	1.25	.70
132	Orlando Cepeda	5.00	2.50	1.50
133	Don McMahon	1.25	.60	.40
134	Wes Parker	1.25	.60	.40
135	Dave Morehead	1.25	.60	.40
136	Woody Held	1.25	.60	.40
137	Pat Corrales	1.50	.70	.45
138	Roger Repoz	1.50	.70	.45
139	Cubs Rookies (Byron Browne, Don Young)	1.25	.60	.40
140	Jim Maloney	1.25	.60	.40
141	Tom McCraw	1.25	.60	.40
142	Don Dennis	1.25	.60	.40
143	Jose Tartabull	1.25	.60	.40
144	Don Schwall	1.25	.60	.40
145	Bill Freehan	1.25	.60	.40
146	George Altman	1.25	.60	.40
147	Lum Harris	1.25	.60	.40
148	Bob Johnson	1.25	.60	.40
149	Dick Nen	1.25	.60	.40
150	Rocky Colavito	2.50	1.25	.70
151	Gary Wagner	1.25	.60	.40
152	Frank Malzone	1.25	.60	.40
153	Rico Carty	5.00	2.50	1.50
154	Chuck Hiller	1.25	.60	.40
155	Marcelino Lopez	1.25	.60	.40
156	DP Combo (Hal Lanier, Dick Schofield)	1.50	.70	.45
157	Rene Lachemann	1.25	.60	.40
158	Jim Brewer	1.25	.60	.40
159	Chico Ruiz	1.25	.60	.40
160	Whitey Ford	25.00	12.50	7.50
161	Jerry Lumpe	1.25	.60	.40
162	Lee Maye	1.25	.60	.40
163	Tito Francona	1.25	.60	.40
164	White Sox Rookies (Tommie Agee, Marv Staehle)	1.25	.60	.40
165	Don Lock	1.25	.60	.40
166	Chris Krug	1.25	.60	.40
167	Boog Powell	2.50	1.25	.70
168	Dan Osinski	1.25	.60	.40
169	Duke Sims	1.25	.60	.40
170	Cookie Rojas	1.25	.60	.40
171	Nick Willhite	1.25	.60	.40
172	Mets Team	3.00	1.50	.90
173	Al Spangler	1.25	.60	.40
174	Ron Taylor	1.25	.60	.40
175	Bert Campaneris	5.00	2.50	1.50
176	Jim Davenport	1.25	.60	.40
177	Hector Lopez	1.50	.70	.45
178	Bob Tillman	1.25	.60	.40
179	Cardinals Rookies (Dennis Aust, Bob Tolan)	1.25	.60	.40
180	Vada Pinson	2.50	1.25	.70

		NR MT	EX	VG
181	Al Worthington	1.25	.60	.40
182	Jerry Lynch	1.25	.60	.40
183a	Checklist 177-264 (large print on front)			
		2.50	1.25	.70
183b	Checklist 177-264 (small print on front)			
		6.00	3.00	1.75
184	Denis Menke	1.25	.60	.40
185	Bob Buhl	1.25	.60	.40
186	Ruben Amaro	1.50	.70	.45
187	Chuck Dressen	1.25	.60	.40
188	Al Luplow	1.25	.60	.40
189	John Roseboro	1.25	.60	.40
190	Jimmie Hall	1.25	.60	.40
191	Darrell Sutherland	1.25	.60	.40
192	Vic Power	1.25	.60	.40
193	Dave McNally	1.50	.70	.45
194	Senators Team	2.25	1.25	.70
195	Joe Morgan	40.00	20.00	12.00
196	Don Pavletich	1.25	.60	.40
197	Sonny Siebert	1.25	.60	.40
198	*Mickey Stanley*	1.50	.70	.45
199	Chisox Clubbers (Floyd Robinson, Johnny Romano, Bill Skowron)	1.50	.70	.45
200	Ed Mathews	15.00	7.50	4.50
201	Jim Dickson	1.25	.60	.40
202	Clay Dalrymple	1.25	.60	.40
203	Jose Santiago	1.25	.60	.40
204	Cubs Team	2.25	1.25	.70
205	Tom Tresh	5.00	2.50	1.50
206	Alvin Jackson	1.25	.60	.40
207	Frank Quilici	1.25	.60	.40
208	Bob Miller	1.25	.60	.40
209	Tigers Rookies (Fritz Fisher, *John Hiller*)	1.25	.60	.40
210	Bill Mazeroski	2.50	1.25	.70
211	Frank Kreutzer	1.25	.60	.40
212	Ed Kranepool	1.50	.70	.45
213	Fred Newman	1.25	.60	.40
214	Tommy Harper	1.25	.60	.40
215	N.L. Batting Leaders (Hank Aaron, Bob Clemente, Willie Mays)	10.00	5.00	3.00
216	A.L. Batting Leaders (Vic Davalillo, Tony Oliva, Carl Yastrzemski)	6.00	3.00	1.75
217	N.L. Home Run Leaders (Willie Mays, Willie McCovey, Billy Williams)	5.00	2.50	1.50
218	A.L. Home Run Leaders (Norm Cash, Tony Conigliaro, Willie Horton)	2.50	1.25	.70
219	N.L. RBI Leaders (Deron Johnson, Willie Mays, Frank Robinson)	6.00	3.00	1.75
220	A.L. RBI Leaders (Rocky Colavito, Willie Horton, Tony Oliva)	2.50	1.25	.70
221	N.L. ERA Leaders (Sandy Koufax, Vern Law, Juan Marichal)	6.00	3.00	1.75
222	A.L. ERA Leaders (Eddie Fisher, Sam McDowell, Sonny Siebert)	2.50	1.25	.70
223	N.L. Pitching Leaders (Tony Cloninger, Don Drysdale, Sandy Koufax)	6.00	3.00	1.75
224	A.L. Pitching Leaders (Jim Grant, Jim Kaat, Mel Stottlemyre)	3.00	1.50	.90
225	N.L. Strikeout Leaders (Bob Gibson, Sandy Koufax, Bob Veale)	6.00	3.00	1.75
226	A.L. Strikeout Leaders (Mickey Lolich, Sam McDowell, Denny McLain, Sonny Siebert)	2.50	1.25	.70
227	Russ Nixon	1.25	.60	.40
228	Larry Dierker	1.25	.60	.40
229	Hank Bauer	1.25	.60	.40
230	Johnny Callison	1.25	.60	.40
231	Floyd Weaver	1.25	.60	.40
232	Glenn Beckert	1.50	.70	.45
233	Dom Zanni	1.25	.60	.40
234	Yankees Rookies (Rich Beck, *Roy White*)	5.00	2.50	1.50
235	Don Cardwell	1.25	.60	.40
236	Mike Hershberger	1.25	.60	.40
237	Billy O'Dell	1.25	.60	.40
238	Dodgers Team	5.00	2.50	1.50
239	Orlando Pena	1.25	.60	.40
240	Earl Battey	1.25	.60	.40
241	Dennis Ribant	1.25	.60	.40
242	Jesus Alou	1.25	.60	.40
243	Nelson Briles	1.25	.60	.40
244	Astros Rookies (Chuck Harrison, Sonny Jackson)	1.25	.60	.40
245	John Buzhardt	1.25	.60	.40
246	Ed Bailey	1.25	.60	.40
247	Carl Warwick	1.25	.60	.40
248	Pete Mikkelsen	1.25	.60	.40
249	Bill Rigney	1.25	.60	.40
250	Sam Ellis	1.25	.60	.40
251	Ed Brinkman	1.25	.60	.40
252	Denver Lemaster	1.25	.60	.40
253	Don Wert	1.25	.60	.40
254	Phillies Rookies (*Ferguson Jenkins*, Bill Sorrell)	150.00	75.00	45.00
255	Willie Stargell	18.00	9.00	5.50
256	Lew Krausse	1.25	.60	.40
257	Jeff Torborg	1.25	.60	.40
258	Dave Giusti	1.25	.60	.40
259	Red Sox Team	2.50	1.25	.70
260	Bob Shaw	1.25	.60	.40
261	Ron Hansen	1.25	.60	.40
262	Jack Hamilton	1.25	.60	.40
263	Tom Egan	1.25	.60	.40
264	Twins Rookies (Andy Kosco, Ted Uhlaender)	1.25	.60	.40
265	Stu Miller	1.25	.60	.40
266	Pedro Gonzalez	1.25	.60	.40
267	Joe Sparma	1.25	.60	.40
268	John Blanchard	1.25	.60	.40
269	Don Heffner	1.25	.60	.40
270	Claude Osteen	1.25	.60	.40
271	Hal Lanier	1.50	.70	.45
272	Jack Baldschun	1.25	.60	.40
273	Astro Aces (Bob Aspromonte, Rusty Staub)	5.00	2.50	1.50
274	Buster Narum	1.25	.60	.40
275	Tim McCarver	2.50	1.25	.70
276	Jim Bouton	2.50	1.25	.70
277	George Thomas	1.25	.60	.40
278	Calvin Koonce	1.25	.60	.40
279a	Checklist 265-352 (player's cap black)	6.00	3.00	1.75
279b	Checklist 265-352 (player's cap red)	3.00	1.50	.90
280	Bobby Knoop	1.25	.60	.40
281	Bruce Howard	1.25	.60	.40
282	Johnny Lewis	1.25	.60	.40
283	Jim Perry	1.50	.70	.45
284	Bobby Wine	1.25	.60	.40
285	Luis Tiant	2.50	1.25	.70
286	Gary Geiger	1.25	.60	.40
287	Jack Aker	1.25	.60	.40
288	Dodgers Rookies (*Bill Singer, Don Sutton*)	125.00	56.00	35.00
289	Larry Sherry	1.25	.60	.40
290	Ron Santo	5.00	2.50	1.50
291	Moe Drabowsky	1.25	.60	.40
292	Jim Coker	1.25	.60	.40
293	Mike Shannon	1.25	.60	.40
294	Steve Ridzik	1.25	.60	.40
295	Jim Hart	1.25	.60	.40
296	Johnny Keane	1.25	.60	.40
297	Jim Owens	1.25	.60	.40
298	Rico Petrocelli	1.25	.60	.40
299	Lou Burdette	5.00	2.50	1.50
300	Bob Clemente	110.00	55.00	33.00
301	Greg Bollo	1.25	.60	.40
302	Ernie Bowman	1.25	.60	.40
303	Indians Team	2.25	1.25	.70
304	John Herrnstein	1.25	.60	.40
305	Camilo Pascual	1.25	.60	.40
306	Ty Cline	1.25	.60	.40
307	Clay Carroll	1.25	.60	.40
308	Tom Haller	1.25	.60	.40
309	Diego Segui	1.25	.60	.40
310	Frank Robinson	35.00	17.50	10.50
311	Reds Rookies (Tommy Helms, Dick Simpson)	1.25	.60	.40
312	Bob Saverine	1.25	.60	.40
313	Chris Zachary	1.25	.60	.40
314	Hector Valle	1.25	.60	.40
315	Norm Cash	5.00	2.50	1.50
316	Jack Fisher	1.25	.60	.40
317	Dalton Jones	1.25	.60	.40
318	Harry Walker	1.25	.60	.40
319	Gene Freese	1.25	.60	.40
320	Bob Gibson	20.00	10.00	6.00
321	Rick Reichardt	1.25	.60	.40
322	Bill Faul	1.25	.60	.40
323	Ray Barker	1.50	.70	.45
324	John Boozer	1.25	.60	.40
325	Vic Davalillo	1.25	.60	.40
326	Braves Team	2.25	1.25	.70
327	Bernie Allen	1.25	.60	.40
328	Jerry Grote	1.25	.60	.40
329	Pete Charton	1.25	.60	.40
330	Ron Fairly	1.25	.60	.40
331	Ron Herbel	1.25	.60	.40
332	Billy Bryan	1.25	.60	.40
333	Senators Rookies (*Joe Coleman*, Jim French)	1.25	.60	.40

#	Name	NR MT	EX	VG
334	Marty Keough	1.25	.60	.40
335	Juan Pizarro	1.25	.60	.40
336	Gene Alley	1.25	.60	.40
337	Fred Gladding	1.25	.60	.40
338	Dal Maxvill	1.25	.60	.40
339	Del Crandall	1.50	.70	.45
340	Dean Chance	1.25	.60	.40
341	Wes Westrum	1.25	.60	.40
342	Bob Humphreys	1.25	.60	.40
343	Joe Christopher	1.25	.60	.40
344	Steve Blass	1.25	.60	.40
345	Bob Allison	1.50	.70	.45
346	Mike de la Hoz	1.25	.60	.40
347	Phil Regan	1.25	.60	.40
348	Orioles Team	5.00	2.50	1.50
349	Cap Peterson	1.25	.60	.40
350	Mel Stottlemyre	3.00	1.50	.90
351	Fred Valentine	1.25	.60	.40
352	Bob Aspromonte	1.25	.60	.40
353	Al McBean	1.25	.60	.40
354	Smoky Burgess	1.50	.70	.45
355	Wade Blasingame	1.25	.60	.40
356	Red Sox Rookies (Owen Johnson, Ken Sanders)	1.25	.60	.40
357	Gerry Arrigo	1.25	.60	.40
358	Charlie Smith	1.25	.60	.40
359	Johnny Briggs	1.25	.60	.40
360	Ron Hunt	1.25	.60	.40
361	Tom Satriano	1.25	.60	.40
362	Gates Brown	1.25	.60	.40
363	Checklist 353-429	3.00	1.50	.90
364	Nate Oliver	1.25	.60	.40
365	Roger Maris	60.00	30.00	18.00
366	Wayne Causey	1.25	.60	.40
367	Mel Nelson	1.25	.60	.40
368	Charlie Lau	1.25	.60	.40
369	Jim King	1.25	.60	.40
370	Chico Cardenas	1.25	.60	.40
371	Lee Stange	1.25	.60	.40
372	Harvey Kuenn	5.00	2.50	1.50
373	Giants Rookies (Dick Estelle, Jack Hiatt)	1.25	.60	.40
374	Bob Locker	1.25	.60	.40
375	Donn Clendenon	1.25	.60	.40
376	Paul Schaal	1.25	.60	.40
377	Turk Farrell	1.25	.60	.40
378	Dick Tracewski	1.25	.60	.40
379	Cardinals Team	2.25	1.25	.70
380	Tony Conigliaro	5.00	2.50	1.50
381	Hank Fischer	1.25	.60	.40
382	Phil Roof	1.25	.60	.40
383	Jackie Brandt	1.25	.60	.40
384	Al Downing	5.00	2.50	1.50
385	Ken Boyer	2.50	1.25	.70
386	Gil Hodges	6.00	3.00	1.75
387	Howie Reed	1.25	.60	.40
388	Don Mincher	1.25	.60	.40
389	Jim O'Toole	1.25	.60	.40
390	Brooks Robinson	30.00	15.00	9.00
391	Chuck Hinton	1.25	.60	.40
392	Cubs Rookies (Bill Hands, Randy Hundley)	1.25	.60	.40
393	George Brunet	1.25	.60	.40
394	Ron Brand	1.25	.60	.40
395	Len Gabrielson	1.25	.60	.40
396	Jerry Stephenson	1.25	.60	.40
397	Bill White	1.50	.70	.45
398	Danny Cater	1.25	.60	.40
399	Ray Washburn	1.25	.60	.40
400	Zoilo Versalles	1.25	.60	.40
401	Ken McMullen	1.25	.60	.40
402	Jim Hickman	1.25	.60	.40
403	Fred Talbot	1.25	.60	.40
404	Pirates Team	2.25	1.25	.70
405	Elston Howard	6.00	3.00	1.75
406	Joe Jay	1.25	.60	.40
407	John Kennedy	1.25	.60	.40
408	Lee Thomas	1.25	.60	.40
409	Billy Hoeft	1.25	.60	.40
410	Al Kaline	25.00	12.50	7.50
411	Gene Mauch	1.25	.60	.40
412	Sam Bowens	1.25	.60	.40
413	John Romano	1.25	.60	.40
414	Dan Coombs	1.25	.60	.40
415	Max Alvis	1.25	.60	.40
416	Phil Ortega	1.25	.60	.40
417	Angels Rookies (Jim McGlothlin, Ed Sukla)	1.25	.60	.40
418	Phil Gagliano	1.25	.60	.40
419	Mike Ryan	1.25	.60	.40
420	Juan Marichal	8.00	4.00	2.50
421	Roy McMillan	1.25	.60	.40
422	Ed Charles	1.25	.60	.40
423	Ernie Broglio	1.25	.60	.40
424	Reds Rookies (Lee May, Darrell Osteen)	2.25	1.25	.70
425	Bob Veale	1.25	.60	.40
426	White Sox Team	2.25	1.25	.70
427	John Miller	1.25	.60	.40
428	Sandy Alomar	1.25	.60	.40
429	Bill Monbouquette	1.25	.60	.40
430	Don Drysdale	15.00	7.50	4.50
431	Walt Bond	1.25	.60	.40
432	Bob Heffner	1.25	.60	.40
433	Alvin Dark	1.25	.60	.40
434	Willie Kirkland	1.25	.60	.40
435	Jim Bunning	6.00	3.00	1.75
436	Julian Javier	1.25	.60	.40
437	Al Stanek	1.25	.60	.40
438	Willie Smith	1.25	.60	.40
439	Pedro Ramos	1.50	.70	.45
440	Deron Johnson	1.25	.60	.40
441	Tommie Sisk	1.25	.60	.40
442	Orioles Rookies (Ed Barnowski, Eddie Watt)	1.25	.60	.40
443	Bill Wakefield	1.25	.60	.40
444a	Checklist 430-506 (456 is R. Sox Rookies)	3.00	1.50	.90
444b	Checklist 430-506 (456 is Red Sox Rookies)	5.00	2.50	1.50
445	Jim Kaat	6.00	3.00	1.75
446	Mack Jones	1.25	.60	.40
447	Dick Ellsworth (photo actually Ken Hubbs)	5.00	2.50	1.50
448	Eddie Stanky	6.00	3.00	1.75
449	Joe Moeller	5.00	2.50	1.50
450	Tony Oliva	7.00	3.50	2.00
451	Barry Latman	5.00	2.50	1.50
452	Joe Azcue	5.00	2.50	1.50
453	Ron Kline	5.00	2.50	1.50
454	Jerry Buchek	5.00	2.50	1.50
455	Mickey Lolich	6.00	3.00	1.75
456	Red Sox Rookies (Darrell Brandon, Joe Foy)	5.00	2.50	1.50
457	Joe Gibbon	5.00	2.50	1.50
458	Manny Jiminez (Jimenez)	5.00	2.50	1.50
459	Bill McCool	5.00	2.50	1.50
460	Curt Blefary	5.00	2.50	1.50
461	Roy Face	6.00	3.00	1.75
462	Bob Rodgers	2.50	1.25	.70
463	Phillies Team	6.00	3.00	1.75
464	Larry Bearnarth	6.00	3.00	1.75
465	Don Buford	6.00	3.00	1.75
466	Ken Johnson	5.00	2.50	1.50
467	Vic Roznovsky	5.00	2.50	1.50
468	Johnny Podres	6.00	3.00	1.75
469	Yankees Rookies (Bobby Murcer, Dooley Womack)	20.00	10.00	6.00
470	Sam McDowell	6.00	3.00	1.75
471	Bob Skinner	5.00	2.50	1.50
472	Terry Fox	5.00	2.50	1.50
473	Rich Rollins	5.00	2.50	1.50
474	Dick Schofield	5.00	2.50	1.50
475	Dick Radatz	6.00	3.00	1.75
476	Bobby Bragan	6.00	3.00	1.75
477	Steve Barber	5.00	2.50	1.50
478	Tony Gonzalez	5.00	2.50	1.50
479	Jim Hannan	5.00	2.50	1.50
480	Dick Stuart	6.00	3.00	1.75
481	Bob Lee	5.00	2.50	1.50
482	Cubs Rookies (John Boccabella, Dave Dowling)	5.00	2.50	1.50
483	Joe Nuxhall	6.00	3.00	1.75
484	Wes Covington	5.00	2.50	1.50
485	Bob Bailey	5.00	2.50	1.50
486	Tommy John	15.00	7.50	4.50
487	Al Ferrara	5.00	2.50	1.50
488	George Banks	5.00	2.50	1.50
489	Curt Simmons	6.00	3.00	1.75
490	Bobby Richardson	12.00	6.00	3.50
491	Dennis Bennett	5.00	2.50	1.50
492	Athletics Team	5.00	2.50	1.50
493	Johnny Klippstein	5.00	2.50	1.50
494	Gordon Coleman	5.00	2.50	1.50
495	Dick McAuliffe	6.00	3.00	1.75
496	Lindy McDaniel	5.00	2.50	1.50
497	Chris Cannizzaro	5.00	2.50	1.50
498	Pirates Rookies (Woody Fryman, Luke Walker)	6.00	3.00	1.75
499	Wally Bunker	5.00	2.50	1.50
500	Hank Aaron	110.00	55.00	33.00
501	John O'Donoghue	5.00	2.50	1.50

		NR MT	EX	VG
502	Lenny Green	5.00	2.50	1.50
503	Steve Hamilton	6.00	3.00	1.75
504	Grady Hatton	5.00	2.50	1.50
505	Jose Cardenal	5.00	2.50	1.50
506	Bo Belinsky	6.00	3.00	1.75
507	John Edwards	5.00	2.50	1.50
508	*Steve Hargan*	6.00	3.00	1.75
509	Jake Wood	5.00	2.50	1.50
510	Hoyt Wilhelm	15.00	7.50	4.50
511	Giants Rookies (Bob Barton, *Tito Fuentes*)			
		6.00	3.00	1.75
512	Dick Stigman	5.00	2.50	1.50
513	Camilo Carreon	5.00	2.50	1.50
514	Hal Woodeshick	5.00	2.50	1.50
515	Frank Howard	7.00	3.50	2.00
516	Eddie Bressoud	5.00	2.50	1.50
517a	Checklist 507-598 (529 is W. Sox Rookies)			
		9.00	4.50	2.75
517b	Checklist 506-598 (529 is White Sox Rookies)			
		10.00	5.00	3.00
518	Braves Rookies (Herb Hippauf, Arnie Umbach)			
		5.00	2.50	1.50
519	Bob Friend	6.00	3.00	1.75
520	Jim Wynn	6.00	3.00	1.75
521	John Wyatt	5.00	2.50	1.50
522	Phil Linz	5.00	2.50	1.50
523	Bob Sadowski	15.00	7.50	4.50
524	Giants Rookies (Ollie Brown, Don Mason)			
		20.00	10.00	6.00
525	Gary Bell	15.00	7.50	4.50
526	Twins Team	70.00	35.00	20.00
527	Julio Navarro	15.00	7.50	4.50
528	Jesse Gonder	20.00	10.00	6.00
529	White Sox Rookies (*Lee Elia*, Dennis Higgins, Bill Voss)			
		18.00	9.00	5.50
530	Robin Roberts	35.00	17.50	10.50
531	Joe Cunningham	15.00	7.50	4.50
532	Aurelio Monteagudo	15.00	7.50	4.50
533	Jerry Adair	15.00	7.50	4.50
534	Mets Rookies (Dave Eilers, Rob Gardner)			
		18.00	9.00	5.50
535	Willie Davis	35.00	17.50	10.50
536	Dick Egan	15.00	7.50	4.50
537	Herman Franks	15.00	7.50	4.50
538	Bob Allen	15.00	7.50	4.50
539	Astros Rookies (Bill Heath, Carroll Sembera)			
		15.00	7.50	4.50
540	Denny McLain	35.00	17.50	10.50
541	Gene Oliver	15.00	7.50	4.50
542	George Smith	15.00	7.50	4.50
543	Roger Craig	35.00	17.50	10.50
544	Cardinals Rookies (Joe Hoerner, George Kernek, Jimmy Williams)			
		20.00	10.00	6.00
545	Dick Green	20.00	10.00	6.00
546	Dwight Siebler	15.00	7.50	4.50
547	*Horace Clarke*	20.00	10.00	6.00
548	Gary Kroll	20.00	10.00	6.00
549	Senators Rookies (Al Closter, Casey Cox)			
		15.00	7.50	4.50
550	Willie McCovey	125.00	62.00	37.00
551	Bob Purkey	20.00	10.00	6.00
552	Birdie Tebbetts	15.00	7.50	4.50
553	Major League Rookies (Pat Garrett, Jackie Warner)			
		15.00	7.50	4.50
554	Jim Northrup	18.00	9.00	5.50
555	Ron Perranoski	18.00	9.00	5.50
556	Mel Queen	20.00	10.00	6.00
557	Felix Mantilla	15.00	7.50	4.50
558	Red Sox Rookies (Guido Grilli, Pete Magrini, *George Scott*)			
		20.00	10.00	6.00
559	Roberto Pena	15.00	7.50	4.50
560	Joel Horlen	15.00	7.50	4.50
561	Choo Choo Coleman	20.00	10.00	6.00
562	Russ Snyder	15.00	7.50	4.50
563	Twins Rookies (Pete Cimino, Cesar Tovar)			
		18.00	9.00	5.50
564	Bob Chance	15.00	7.50	4.50
565	Jimmy Piersall	35.00	17.50	10.50
566	Mike Cuellar	18.00	9.00	5.50
567	Dick Howser	20.00	10.00	6.00
568	Athletics Rookies (Paul Lindblad, Ron Stone)			
		15.00	7.50	4.50
569	Orlando McFarlane	15.00	7.50	4.50
570	Art Mahaffey	20.00	10.00	6.00
571	Dave Roberts	15.00	7.50	4.50
572	Bob Priddy	15.00	7.50	4.50
573	Derrell Griffith	15.00	7.50	4.50
574	Mets Rookies (Bill Hepler, Bill Murphy)			
		18.00	9.00	5.50
575	Earl Wilson	15.00	7.50	4.50
576	Dave Nicholson	20.00	10.00	6.00
577	Jack Lamabe	15.00	7.50	4.50
578	Chi Chi Olivo	15.00	7.50	4.50
579	Orioles Rookies (Frank Bertaina, Gene Brabender, Dave Johnson)			
		20.00	10.00	6.00
580	Billy Williams	100.00	50.00	30.00
581	Tony Martinez	15.00	7.50	4.50
582	Garry Roggenburk	15.00	7.50	4.50
583	Tigers Team	150.00	75.00	52.00
584	Yankees Rookies (Frank Fernandez, *Fritz Peterson*)			
		18.00	9.00	5.50
585	Tony Taylor	15.00	7.50	4.50
586	Claude Raymond	15.00	7.50	4.50
587	Dick Bertell	15.00	7.50	4.50
588	Athletics Rookies (Chuck Dobson, Ken Suarez)			
		15.00	7.50	4.50
589	Lou Klimchock	18.00	9.00	5.50
590	Bill Skowron	35.00	17.50	10.50
591	N.L. Rookies (*Grant Jackson*, Bart Shirley)			
		20.00	10.00	6.00
592	Andre Rodgers	15.00	7.50	4.50
593	Doug Camilli	20.00	10.00	6.00
594	Chico Salmon	15.00	7.50	4.50
595	Larry Jackson	15.00	7.50	4.50
596	Astros Rookies (*Nate Colbert*, Greg Sims)			
		18.00	9.00	5.50
597	John Sullivan	15.00	7.50	4.50
598	Gaylord Perry	310.00	155.00	93.00

1966 Topps Rub-Offs

Returning to a concept last tried in 1961, Topps tried an expanded version of Rub-Offs in 1966. Measuring 2-1/16" by 3," the Rub-Offs are in vertical format for the 100 players and horizontal for the 20 team pennants. The player Rub-Offs feature a color photo.

		NR MT	EX	VG
Complete Set:		225.00	112.00	67.00
Common Player:		.60	.30	.20
(1)	Hank Aaron	8.00	4.00	2.50
(2)	Jerry Adair	.60	.30	.20
(3)	Richie Allen	1.00	.50	.30
(4)	Jesus Alou	.60	.30	.20
(5)	Max Alvis	.60	.30	.20
(6)	Bob Aspromonte	.60	.30	.20
(7)	Ernie Banks	3.50	1.75	1.00
(8)	Earl Battey	.70	.35	.20
(9)	Curt Blefary	.60	.30	.20
(10)	Ken Boyer	1.00	.50	.30
(11)	Bob Bruce	.60	.30	.20
(12)	Jim Bunning	1.50	.70	.45
(13)	Johnny Callison	.70	.35	.20
(14)	Bert Campaneris	.70	.35	.20
(15)	Jose Cardenal	.60	.30	.20
(16)	Dean Chance	.60	.30	.20
(17)	Ed Charles	.60	.30	.20
(18)	Bob Clemente	7.00	3.50	2.00
(19)	Tony Cloninger	.60	.30	.20
(20)	Rocky Colavito	1.00	.50	.30
(21)	Tony Conigliaro	1.00	.50	.30
(22)	Vic Davalillo	.60	.30	.20
(23)	Willie Davis	.70	.35	.20
(24)	Don Drysdale	3.00	1.50	.90
(25)	Sammy Ellis	.60	.30	.20
(26)	Dick Ellsworth	.60	.30	.20
(27)	Ron Fairly	.70	.35	.20

		NR MT	EX	VG
(28)	Dick Farrell	.60	.30	.20
(29)	Eddie Fisher	.60	.30	.20
(30)	Jack Fisher	.60	.30	.20
(31)	Curt Flood	.70	.35	.20
(32)	Whitey Ford	3.50	1.75	1.00
(33)	Bill Freehan	.70	.35	.20
(34)	Jim Fregosi	.70	.35	.20
(35)	Bob Gibson	3.00	1.50	.90
(36)	Jim Grant	.60	.30	.20
(37)	Jimmie Hall	.60	.30	.20
(38)	Ken Harrelson	.70	.35	.20
(39)	Jim Hart	.60	.30	.20
(40)	Joel Horlen	.60	.30	.20
(41)	Willie Horton	.70	.35	.20
(42)	Frank Howard	1.00	.50	.30
(43)	Deron Johnson	.60	.30	.20
(44)	Al Kaline	4.00	2.00	1.25
(45)	Harmon Killebrew	4.00	2.00	1.25
(46)	Bobby Knoop	.60	.30	.20
(47)	Sandy Koufax	7.00	3.50	2.00
(48)	Ed Kranepool	.60	.30	.20
(49)	Gary Kroll	.60	.30	.20
(50)	Don Landrum	.60	.30	.20
(51)	Vernon Law	.70	.35	.20
(52)	Johnny Lewis	.60	.30	.20
(53)	Don Lock	.60	.30	.20
(54)	Mickey Lolich	1.00	.50	.30
(55)	Jim Maloney	.60	.30	.20
(56)	Felix Mantilla	.60	.30	.20
(57)	Mickey Mantle	40.00	20.00	12.00
(58)	Juan Marichal	3.00	1.50	.90
(59)	Ed Mathews	3.00	1.50	.90
(60)	Willie Mays	8.00	4.00	2.50
(61)	Bill Mazeroski	1.00	.50	.30
(62)	Dick McAuliffe	.60	.30	.20
(63)	Tim McCarver	.70	.35	.20
(64)	Willie McCovey	3.00	1.50	.90
(65)	Sammy McDowell	.70	.35	.20
(66)	Ken McMullen	.60	.30	.20
(67)	Denis Menke	.60	.30	.20
(68)	Bill Monbouquette	.60	.30	.20
(69)	Joe Morgan	2.00	1.00	.60
(70)	Fred Newman	.60	.30	.20
(71)	John O'Donoghue	.60	.30	.20
(72)	Tony Oliva	1.00	.50	.30
(73)	Johnny Orsino	.60	.30	.20
(74)	Phil Ortega	.60	.30	.20
(75)	Milt Pappas	.70	.35	.20
(76)	Dick Radatz	.60	.30	.20
(77)	Bobby Richardson	1.50	.70	.45
(78)	Pete Richert	.60	.30	.20
(79)	Brooks Robinson	4.00	2.00	1.25
(80)	Floyd Robinson	.60	.30	.20
(81)	Frank Robinson	3.50	1.75	1.00
(82)	Cookie Rojas	.60	.30	.20
(83)	Pete Rose	20.00	10.00	6.00
(84)	John Roseboro	.60	.30	.20
(85)	Ron Santo	1.00	.50	.30
(86)	Bill Skowron	.70	.35	.20
(87)	Willie Stargell	3.00	1.50	.90
(88)	Mel Stottlemyre	.70	.35	.20
(89)	Dick Stuart	.60	.30	.20
(90)	Ron Swoboda	.60	.30	.20
(91)	Fred Talbot	.60	.30	.20
(92)	Ralph Terry	.60	.30	.20
(93)	Joe Torre	1.00	.50	.30
(94)	Tom Tresh	.70	.35	.20
(95)	Bob Veale	.60	.30	.20
(96)	Pete Ward	.60	.30	.20
(97)	Bill White	.70	.35	.20
(98)	Billy Williams	2.00	1.00	.60
(99)	Jim Wynn	.70	.35	.20
(100)	Carl Yastrzemski	12.00	6.00	3.50
(101)	Angels Pennant	.60	.30	.20
(102)	Astros Pennant	.60	.30	.20
(103)	Athletics Pennant	.60	.30	.20
(104)	Braves Pennant	.60	.30	.20
(105)	Cards Pennant	.60	.30	.20
(106)	Cubs Pennant	.60	.30	.20
(107)	Dodgers Pennant	.60	.30	.20
(108)	Giants Pennant	.60	.30	.20
(109)	Indians Pennant	.60	.30	.20
(110)	Mets Pennant	.60	.30	.20
(111)	Orioles Pennant	.60	.30	.20
(112)	Phillies Pennant	.60	.30	.20
(113)	Pirates Pennant	.60	.30	.20
(114)	Red Sox Pennant	.60	.30	.20
(115)	Reds Pennant	.60	.30	.20
(116)	Senators Pennant	.60	.30	.20
(117)	Tigers Pennant	.60	.30	.20
(118)	Twins Pennant	.60	.30	.20

		NR MT	EX	VG
(119)	White Sox Pennant	.60	.30	.20
(120)	Yankees Pennant	.60	.30	.20

1967 Topps

This 609-card set of 2-1/2" by 3-1/2" cards marked the largest set up to that time for Topps. Card fronts feature large color photographs bordered by white. The player's name and position are printed at the top with the team at the bottom. Across the front of the card with the exception of #254 (Milt Pappas) there is a facsimile autograph. The backs were the first to be done vertically, although they continued to carry familiar statistical and biographical information. The only subsets are statistical leaders and World Series highlights. Rookie cards are done by team or league with two players per card. The high numbers (#'s 534-609) in '67 are quite scarce, and while it is known that some are even scarcer, by virtue of having been short-printed in relation to the rest of the series, there is no general agreement on which cards are involved.

		NR MT	EX	VG
Complete Set:		5000.00	2500.00	1500.
Common Player: 1-110		1.00	.50	.30
Common Player: 111-370		1.50	.70	.45
Common Player: 371-457		1.25	.60	.40
Common Player: 458-533		5.00	2.50	1.50
Common Player: 534-609		12.00	6.00	3.50
1	The Champs (Hank Bauer, Brooks Robinson, Frank Robinson)	20.00	9.00	5.50
2	Jack Hamilton	1.25	.60	.40
3	Duke Sims	1.00	.50	.30
4	Hal Lanier	1.25	.60	.40
5	Whitey Ford	20.00	10.00	6.00
6	Dick Simpson	1.00	.50	.30
7	Don McMahon	1.00	.50	.30
8	Chuck Harrison	1.00	.50	.30
9	Ron Hansen	1.00	.50	.30
10	Matty Alou	1.25	.60	.40
11	Barry Moore	1.00	.50	.30
12	Dodgers Rookies (Jimmy Campanis, Bill Singer)	1.50	.70	.45
13	Joe Sparma	1.00	.50	.30
14	Phil Linz	1.00	.50	.30
15	Earl Battey	1.50	.70	.45
16	Bill Hands	1.00	.50	.30
17	Jim Gosger	1.00	.50	.30
18	Gene Oliver	1.00	.50	.30
19	Jim McGlothlin	1.00	.50	.30
20	Orlando Cepeda	10.00	5.00	3.00
21	Dave Bristol	1.00	.50	.30
22	Gene Brabender	1.00	.50	.30
23	Larry Elliot	1.50	.70	.45
24	Bob Allen	1.00	.50	.30
25	Elston Howard	5.00	2.50	1.50
26a	Bob Priddy (no trade statement)	15.00	7.50	4.50
26b	Bob Priddy (with trade statement)	1.00	.50	.30
27	Bob Saverine	1.00	.50	.30
28	Barry Latman	1.00	.50	.30
29	Tommy McCraw	1.00	.50	.30
30	Al Kaline	20.00	10.00	6.00

#	Player	NR MT	EX	VG
31	Jim Brewer	1.00	.50	.30
32	Bob Bailey	1.00	.50	.30
33	Athletics Rookies (Sal Bando, Randy Schwartz)	1.75	.90	.50
34	Pete Cimino	1.00	.50	.30
35	Rico Carty	1.25	.60	.40
36	Bob Tillman	1.00	.50	.30
37	Rick Wise	1.50	.70	.45
38	Bob Johnson	1.00	.50	.30
39	Curt Simmons	1.25	.60	.40
40	Rick Reichardt	1.00	.50	.30
41	Joe Hoerner	1.00	.50	.30
42	Mets Team	5.00	2.50	1.50
43	Chico Salmon	1.00	.50	.30
44	Joe Nuxhall	1.25	.60	.40
45	Roger Maris	50.00	25.00	15.00
46	Lindy McDaniel	1.00	.50	.30
47	Ken McMullen	1.00	.50	.30
48	Bill Freehan	1.25	.60	.40
49	Roy Face	1.50	.70	.45
50	Tony Oliva	4.00	2.00	1.25
51	Astros Rookies (Dave Adlesh, Wes Bales)	1.00	.50	.30
52	Dennis Higgins	1.00	.50	.30
53	Clay Dalrymple	1.00	.50	.30
54	Dick Green	1.00	.50	.30
55	Don Drysdale	12.00	6.00	3.50
56	Jose Tartabull	1.00	.50	.30
57	Pat Jarvis	1.50	.70	.45
58	Paul Schaal	1.00	.50	.30
59	Ralph Terry	1.25	.60	.40
60	Luis Aparicio	5.00	2.50	1.50
61	Gordy Coleman	1.00	.50	.30
62	Checklist 1-109 (Frank Robinson)	5.00	2.50	1.50
63	Cards' Clubbers (Lou Brock, Curt Flood)	13.00	6.50	4.00
64	Fred Valentine	1.00	.50	.30
65	Tom Haller	1.50	.70	.45
66	Manny Mota	1.25	.60	.40
67	Ken Berry	1.00	.50	.30
68	Bob Buhl	1.50	.70	.45
69	Vic Davalillo	1.50	.70	.45
70	Ron Santo	1.75	.90	.50
71	Camilo Pascual	1.50	.70	.45
72	Tigers Rookies (George Korince, John Matchick)	1.00	.50	.30
73	Rusty Staub	2.50	1.25	.70
74	Wes Stock	1.00	.50	.30
75	George Scott	1.25	.60	.40
76	Jim Barbieri	1.00	.50	.30
77	Dooley Womack	1.25	.60	.40
78	Pat Corrales	1.25	.60	.40
79	Bubba Morton	1.00	.50	.30
80	Jim Maloney	1.50	.70	.45
81	Eddie Stanky	1.50	.70	.45
82	Steve Barber	1.00	.50	.30
83	Ollie Brown	1.00	.50	.30
84	Tommie Sisk	1.00	.50	.30
85	Johnny Callison	1.25	.60	.40
86a	Mike McCormick (no trade statement)	15.00	7.50	4.50
86b	Mike McCormick (with trade statement)	1.50	.70	.45
87	George Altman	1.00	.50	.30
88	Mickey Lolich	2.25	1.25	.70
89	Felix Millan	1.25	.60	.40
90	Jim Nash	1.00	.50	.30
91	Johnny Lewis	1.50	.70	.45
92	Ray Washburn	1.00	.50	.30
93	Yankees Rookies (Stan Bahnsen, Bobby Murcer)	2.50	1.25	.70
94	Ron Fairly	1.25	.60	.40
95	Sonny Siebert	1.50	.70	.45
96	Art Shamsky	1.00	.50	.30
97	Mike Cuellar	1.25	.60	.40
98	Rich Rollins	1.00	.50	.30
99	Lee Stange	1.00	.50	.30
100	Frank Robinson	20.00	10.00	6.00
101	Ken Johnson	1.00	.50	.30
102	Phillies Team	2.00	1.00	.60
103a	Checklist 110-196 (Mickey Mantle) (170 is D McAuliffe)	15.00	7.50	4.50
103b	Checklist 110-196 (Mickey Mantle) (170 is D. McAuliffe)	12.00	6.00	3.50
104	Minnie Rojas	1.00	.50	.30
105	Ken Boyer	2.00	1.00	.60
106	Randy Hundley	1.50	.70	.45
107	Joel Horlen	1.00	.50	.30
108	Alex Johnson	1.00	.50	.30
109	Tribe Thumpers (Rocky Colavito, Leon Wagner)	1.50	.70	.45
110	Jack Aker	1.00	.50	.30
111	John Kennedy	1.50	.70	.45
112	Dave Wickersham	1.50	.70	.45
113	Dave Nicholson	1.50	.70	.45
114	Jack Baldschun	1.50	.70	.45
115	Paul Casanova	1.50	.70	.45
116	Herman Franks	1.50	.70	.45
117	Darrell Brandon	1.50	.70	.45
118	Bernie Allen	1.50	.70	.45
119	Wade Blasingame	1.50	.70	.45
120	Floyd Robinson	1.50	.70	.45
121	Ed Bressoud	1.25	.60	.40
122	George Brunet	1.50	.70	.45
123	Pirates Rookies (Jim Price, Luke Walker)	1.50	.70	.45
124	Jim Stewart	1.50	.70	.45
125	Moe Drabowsky	1.50	.70	.45
126	Tony Taylor	1.50	.70	.45
127	John O'Donoghue	1.50	.70	.45
128	Ed Spiezio	1.50	.70	.45
129	Phil Roof	1.50	.70	.45
130	Phil Regan	1.50	.70	.45
131	Yankees Team	5.00	2.50	1.50
132	Ozzie Virgil	1.50	.70	.45
133	Ron Kline	1.50	.70	.45
134	Gates Brown	1.50	.70	.45
135	Deron Johnson	1.50	.70	.45
136	Carroll Sembera	1.50	.70	.45
137	Twins Rookies (Ron Clark, Jim Ollom)	1.50	.70	.45
138	Dick Kelley	1.50	.70	.45
139	Dalton Jones	1.50	.70	.45
140	Willie Stargell	20.00	10.00	6.00
141	John Miller	1.50	.70	.45
142	Jackie Brandt	1.50	.70	.45
143	Sox Sockers (Don Buford, Pete Ward)	1.25	.60	.40
144	Bill Hepler	1.25	.60	.40
145	Larry Brown	1.50	.70	.45
146	Steve Carlton	125.00	62.00	37.00
147	Tom Egan	1.50	.70	.45
148	Adolfo Phillips	1.50	.70	.45
149	Joe Moeller	1.50	.70	.45
150	Mickey Mantle	200.00	80.00	50.00
151	World Series Game 1 (Moe Mows Down 11)	2.00	1.00	.60
152	World Series Game 2 (Palmer Blanks Dodgers)	3.50	1.75	1.00
153	World Series Game 3 (Blair's Homer Defeats L.A.)	2.00	1.00	.60
154	World Series Game 4 (Orioles Win 4th Straight)	2.00	1.00	.60
155	World Series Summary (The Winners Celebrate)	2.00	1.00	.60
156	Ron Herbel	1.50	.70	.45
157	Danny Cater	1.50	.70	.45
158	Jimmy Coker	1.50	.70	.45
159	Bruce Howard	1.50	.70	.45
160	Willie Davis	1.50	.70	.45
161	Dick Williams	1.50	.70	.45
162	Billy O'Dell	1.50	.70	.45
163	Vic Roznovsky	1.50	.70	.45
164	Dwight Siebler	1.50	.70	.45
165	Cleon Jones	1.25	.60	.40
166	Ed Mathews	12.00	6.00	3.50
167	Senators Rookies (Joe Coleman, Tim Cullen)	1.25	.60	.40
168	Ray Culp	1.50	.70	.45
169	Horace Clarke	1.25	.60	.40
170	Dick McAuliffe	1.25	.60	.40
171	Calvin Koonce	1.50	.70	.45
172	Bill Heath	1.50	.70	.45
173	Cardinals Team	2.00	1.00	.60
174	Dick Radatz	1.25	.60	.40
175	Bobby Knoop	1.50	.70	.45
176	Sammy Ellis	1.50	.70	.45
177	Tito Fuentes	1.50	.70	.45
178	John Buzhardt	1.50	.70	.45
179	Braves Rookies (Cecil Upshaw, Chas. Vaughn)	1.50	.70	.45
180	Curt Blefary	1.50	.70	.45
181	Terry Fox	1.50	.70	.45
182	Ed Charles	1.50	.70	.45
183	Jim Pagliaroni	1.50	.70	.45
184	George Thomas	1.50	.70	.45
185	Ken Holtzman	2.75	1.50	.80
186	Mets Maulers (Ed Kranepool, Ron Swoboda)	1.50	.70	.45
187	Pedro Ramos	1.50	.70	.45
188	Ken Harrelson	1.50	.70	.45
189	Chuck Hinton	1.50	.70	.45

#	Player	NR MT	EX	VG
190	Turk Farrell	1.50	.70	.45
191a	Checklist 197-283 (Willie Mays) (214 is Dick Kelley)	12.00	6.00	3.50
191b	Checklist 197-283 (Willie Mays) (214 is Tom Kelley)	12.00	6.00	3.50
192	Fred Gladding	1.50	.70	.45
193	Jose Cardenal	1.25	.60	.40
194	Bob Allison	1.50	.70	.45
195	Al Jackson	1.50	.70	.45
196	Johnny Romano	1.50	.70	.45
197	Ron Perranoski	1.25	.60	.40
198	Chuck Hiller	1.25	.60	.40
199	Billy Hitchcock	1.50	.70	.45
200	Willie Mays	90.00	45.00	27.00
201	Hal Reniff	1.25	.60	.40
202	Johnny Edwards	1.50	.70	.45
203	Al McBean	1.50	.70	.45
204	Orioles Rookies (*Mike Epstein*, Tom Phoebus)	1.50	.70	.45
205	Dick Groat	1.50	.70	.45
206	Dennis Bennett	1.50	.70	.45
207	John Orsino	1.50	.70	.45
208	Jack Lamabe	1.50	.70	.45
209	Joe Nossek	1.50	.70	.45
210	Bob Gibson	18.00	9.00	5.50
211	Twins Team	2.00	1.00	.60
212	Chris Zachary	1.50	.70	.45
213	*Jay Johnstone*	1.75	.90	.50
214	Tom Kelley	1.50	.70	.45
215	Ernie Banks	20.00	10.00	6.00
216	Bengal Belters (Norm Cash, Al Kaline)	5.00	2.50	1.50
217	Rob Gardner	1.25	.60	.40
218	Wes Parker	1.25	.60	.40
219	Clay Carroll	1.25	.60	.40
220	Jim Hart	1.25	.60	.40
221	Woody Fryman	1.25	.60	.40
222	Reds Rookies (Lee May, Darrell Osteen)	1.25	.60	.40
223	Mike Ryan	1.50	.70	.45
224	Walt Bond	1.50	.70	.45
225	Mel Stottlemyre	2.25	1.25	.70
226	Julian Javier	1.25	.60	.40
227	Paul Lindblad	1.50	.70	.45
228	Gil Hodges	5.00	2.50	1.50
229	Larry Jackson	1.50	.70	.45
230	Boog Powell	2.50	1.25	.70
231	John Bateman	1.50	.70	.45
232	Don Buford	1.25	.60	.40
233	A.L. ERA Leaders (Steve Hargan, Joel Horlen, Gary Peters)	2.00	1.00	.60
234	N.L. ERA Leaders (Mike Cuellar, Sandy Koufax, Juan Marichal)	12.00	6.00	3.50
235	A.L. Pitching Leaders (Jim Kaat, Denny McLain, Earl Wilson)	2.50	1.25	.70
236	N.L. Pitching Leaders (Bob Gibson, Sandy Koufax, Juan Marichal, Gaylord Perry)	12.00	6.00	3.50
237	A.L. Strikeout Leaders (Jim Kaat, Sam McDowell, Earl Wilson)	2.50	1.25	.70
238	N.L. Strikeout Leaders (Jim Bunning, Sandy Koufax, Bob Veale)	12.00	6.00	3.50
239	AL 1966 Batting Leaders (Al Kaline, Tony Oliva, Frank Robinson)	12.00	6.00	3.50
240	N.L. Batting Leaders (Felipe Alou, Matty Alou, Rico Carty)	2.00	1.00	.60
241	A.L. RBI Leaders (Harmon Killebrew, Boog Powell, Frank Robinson)	3.50	1.75	1.00
242	N.L. RBI Leaders (Hank Aaron, Richie Allen, Bob Clemente)	12.00	6.00	3.50
243	A.L. Home Run Leaders (Harmon Killebrew, Boog Powell, Frank Robinson)	3.50	1.75	1.00
244	N.L. Home Run Leaders (Hank Aaron, Richie Allen, Willie Mays)	12.00	6.00	3.50
245	Curt Flood	2.50	1.25	.70
246	Jim Perry	1.25	.60	.40
247	Jerry Lumpe	1.25	.60	.40
248	Gene Mauch	1.25	.60	.40
249	Nick Willhite	1.50	.70	.45
250	Hank Aaron	100.00	50.00	30.00
251	Woody Held	1.50	.70	.45
252	Bob Bolin	1.50	.70	.45
253	Indians Rookies (Bill Davis, Gus Gil)	1.50	.70	.45
254	Milt Pappas	1.25	.60	.40
255	Frank Howard	2.50	1.25	.70
256	Bob Hendley	1.50	.70	.45
257	Charley Smith	1.25	.60	.40
258	Lee Maye	1.50	.70	.45
259	Don Dennis	1.50	.70	.45
260	Jim Lefebvre	1.25	.60	.40
261	John Wyatt	1.50	.70	.45
262	Athletics Team	2.00	1.00	.60
263	Hank Aguirre	1.50	.70	.45
264	Ron Swoboda	1.25	.60	.40
265	Lou Burdette	2.50	1.25	.70
266	Pitt Power (Donn Clendenon, Willie Stargell)	3.50	1.75	1.00
267	Don Schwall	1.50	.70	.45
268	John Briggs	1.50	.70	.45
269	Don Nottebart	1.50	.70	.45
270	Zoilo Versalles	1.25	.60	.40
271	Eddie Watt	1.50	.70	.45
272	Cubs Rookies (Bill Connors, Dave Dowling)	1.50	.70	.45
273	Dick Lines	1.50	.70	.45
274	Bob Aspromonte	1.50	.70	.45
275	Fred Whitfield	1.50	.70	.45
276	Bruce Brubaker	1.50	.70	.45
277	Steve Whitaker	1.25	.60	.40
278	Checklist 284-370 (Jim Kaat)	5.00	2.50	1.50
279	Frank Linzy	1.50	.70	.45
280	Tony Conigliaro	2.00	1.00	.60
281	Bob Rodgers	1.50	.70	.45
282	Johnny Odom	1.25	.60	.40
283	Gene Alley	1.25	.60	.40
284	Johnny Podres	5.00	2.50	1.50
285	Lou Brock	20.00	10.00	6.00
286	Wayne Causey	1.50	.70	.45
287	Mets Rookies (Greg Goossen, Bart Shirley)	1.25	.60	.40
288	Denver Lemaster	1.50	.70	.45
289	Tom Tresh	1.75	.90	.50
290	Bill White	1.25	.60	.40
291	Jim Hannan	1.50	.70	.45
292	Don Pavletich	1.50	.70	.45
293	Ed Kirkpatrick	1.50	.70	.45
294	Walt Alston	3.25	1.75	1.00
295	Sam McDowell	1.25	.60	.40
296	Glenn Beckert	1.25	.60	.40
297	Dave Morehead	1.50	.70	.45
298	Ron Davis	1.50	.70	.45
299	Norm Siebern	1.25	.60	.40
300	Jim Kaat	13.00	6.50	4.00
301	Jesse Gonder	1.50	.70	.45
302	Orioles Team	2.00	1.00	.60
303	Gil Blanco	1.50	.70	.45
304	Phil Gagliano	1.50	.70	.45
305	Earl Wilson	1.50	.70	.45
306	*Bud Harrelson*	1.75	.90	.50
307	Jim Beauchamp	1.50	.70	.45
308	Al Downing	1.50	.70	.45
309	Hurlers Beware (Richie Allen, Johnny Callison)	2.00	1.00	.60
310	Gary Peters	1.25	.60	.40
311	Ed Brinkman	1.25	.60	.40
312	Don Mincher	1.25	.60	.40
313	Bob Lee	1.50	.70	.45
314	Red Sox Rookies (*Mike Andrews, Reggie Smith*)	5.00	2.50	1.50
315	Billy Williams	12.00	6.00	3.50
316	Jack Kralick	1.50	.70	.45
317	Cesar Tovar	1.50	.70	.45
318	Dave Giusti	1.50	.70	.45
319	Paul Blair	1.25	.60	.40
320	Gaylord Perry	15.00	7.50	4.50
321	Mayo Smith	1.50	.70	.45
322	Jose Pagan	1.50	.70	.45
323	Mike Hershberger	1.50	.70	.45
324	Hal Woodeshick	1.50	.70	.45
325	Chico Cardenas	1.50	.70	.45
326	Bob Uecker	20.00	10.00	6.00
327	Angels Team	2.00	1.00	.60
328	Clete Boyer	1.50	.70	.45
329	Charlie Lau	1.25	.60	.40
330	Claude Osteen	1.25	.60	.40
331	Joe Foy	1.50	.70	.45
332	Jesus Alou	1.50	.70	.45
333	Ferguson Jenkins	25.00	12.50	7.50
334	Twin Terrors (Bob Allison, Harmon Killebrew)	3.50	1.75	1.00
335	Bob Veale	1.25	.60	.40
336	Joe Azcue	1.50	.70	.45
337	Joe Morgan	25.00	12.50	7.50
338	Bob Locker	1.50	.70	.45
339	Chico Ruiz	1.50	.70	.45
340	Joe Pepitone	2.00	1.00	.60
341	Giants Rookies (*Dick Dietz*, Bill Sorrell)	1.25	.60	.40
342	Hank Fischer	1.50	.70	.45
343	Tom Satriano	1.50	.70	.45

	NR MT	EX	VG
344 Ossie Chavarria	1.50	.70	.45
345 Stu Miller	1.50	.70	.45
346 Jim Hickman	1.25	.60	.40
347 Grady Hatton	1.50	.70	.45
348 Tug McGraw	2.25	1.25	.70
349 Bob Chance	1.50	.70	.45
350 Joe Torre	2.00	1.00	.60
351 Vern Law	1.50	.70	.45
352 Ray Oyler	1.50	.70	.45
353 Bill McCool	1.50	.70	.45
354 Cubs Team	2.00	1.00	.60
355 Carl Yastrzemski	75.00	37.50	23.50
356 Larry Jaster	1.50	.70	.45
357 Bill Skowron	1.50	.70	.45
358 Ruben Amaro	1.25	.60	.40
359 Dick Ellsworth	1.50	.70	.45
360 Leon Wagner	1.25	.60	.40
361 Checklist 371-457 (Bob Clemente)	13.00	6.50	4.00
362 Darold Knowles	1.50	.70	.45
363 Dave Johnson	2.00	1.00	.60
364 Claude Raymond	1.50	.70	.45
365 John Roseboro	1.25	.60	.40
366 Andy Kosco	1.50	.70	.45
367 Angels Rookies (Bill Kelso, Don Wallace)	1.50	.70	.45
368 Jack Hiatt	1.50	.70	.45
369 Jim Hunter	18.00	9.00	5.50
370 Tommy Davis	1.50	.70	.45
371 Jim Lonborg	1.50	.70	.45
372 Mike de la Hoz	1.25	.60	.40
373 White Sox Rookies (Duane Josephson, Fred Klages)	1.25	.60	.40
374 Mel Queen	1.25	.60	.40
375 Jake Gibbs	1.25	.60	.40
376 Don Lock	1.25	.60	.40
377 Luis Tiant	2.25	1.25	.70
378 Tigers Team	5.00	2.50	1.50
379 Jerry May	1.25	.60	.40
380 Dean Chance	1.50	.70	.45
381 Dick Schofield	1.25	.60	.40
382 Dave McNally	1.25	.60	.40
383 Ken Henderson	1.25	.60	.40
384 Cardinals Rookies (Jim Cosman, Dick Hughes)	1.25	.60	.40
385 Jim Fregosi	1.50	.70	.45
386 Dick Selma	1.50	.70	.45
387 Cap Peterson	1.25	.60	.40
388 Arnold Earley	1.25	.60	.40
389 Al Dark	1.50	.70	.45
390 Jim Wynn	1.25	.60	.40
391 Wilbur Wood	1.50	.70	.45
392 Tommy Harper	1.50	.70	.45
393 Jim Bouton	2.25	1.25	.70
394 Jake Wood	1.25	.60	.40
395 Chris Short	1.25	.60	.40
396 Atlanta Aces (Tony Cloninger, Denis Menke)	1.25	.60	.40
397 Willie Smith	1.25	.60	.40
398 Jeff Torborg	1.50	.70	.45
399 Al Worthington	1.25	.60	.40
400 Bob Clemente	85.00	42.00	26.00
401 Jim Coates	1.25	.60	.40
402 Phillies Rookies (Grant Jackson, Billy Wilson)	1.25	.60	.40
403 Dick Nen	1.25	.60	.40
404 Nelson Briles	1.50	.70	.45
405 Russ Snyder	1.25	.60	.40
406 Lee Elia	1.50	.70	.45
407 Reds Team	2.50	1.25	.70
408 Jim Northrup	1.50	.70	.45
409 Ray Sadecki	1.25	.60	.40
410 Lou Johnson	1.25	.60	.40
411 Dick Howser	1.50	.70	.45
412 Astros Rookies (Norm Miller, Doug Rader)	1.25	.60	.40
413 Jerry Grote	1.50	.70	.45
414 Casey Cox	1.25	.60	.40
415 Sonny Jackson	1.25	.60	.40
416 Roger Repoz	1.25	.60	.40
417 Bob Bruce	1.25	.60	.40
418 Sam Mele	1.25	.60	.40
419 Don Kessinger	1.50	.70	.45
420 Denny McLain	5.00	2.50	1.50
421 Dal Maxvill	1.50	.70	.45
422 Hoyt Wilhelm	15.00	7.50	4.50
423 Fence Busters (Willie Mays, Willie McCovey)	20.00	10.00	6.00
424 Pedro Gonzalez	1.25	.60	.40
425 Pete Mikkelsen	1.25	.60	.40
426 Lou Clinton	1.25	.60	.40
427 Ruben Gomez	1.25	.60	.40
428 Dodgers Rookies (Tom Hutton, Gene Michael)	1.25	.60	.40
429 Garry Roggenburk	1.25	.60	.40
430 Pete Rose	75.00	38.00	23.00
431 Ted Uhlaender	1.25	.60	.40
432 Jimmie Hall	1.25	.60	.40
433 Al Luplow	1.50	.70	.45
434 Eddie Fisher	1.25	.60	.40
435 Mack Jones	1.25	.60	.40
436 Pete Ward	1.25	.60	.40
437 Senators Team	2.25	1.25	.70
438 Chuck Dobson	1.25	.60	.40
439 Byron Browne	1.25	.60	.40
440 Steve Hargan	1.25	.60	.40
441 Jim Davenport	1.25	.60	.40
442 Yankees Rookies (Bill Robinson, Joe Verbanic)	1.50	.70	.45
443 Tito Francona	1.50	.70	.45
444 George Smith	1.25	.60	.40
445 Don Sutton	30.00	15.00	9.00
446 Russ Nixon	1.25	.60	.40
447 Bo Belinsky	1.25	.60	.40
448 Harry Walker	1.50	.70	.45
449 Orlando Pena	1.25	.60	.40
450 Richie Allen	5.00	2.50	1.50
451 Fred Newman	1.25	.60	.40
452 Ed Kranepool	1.25	.60	.40
453 Aurelio Monteagudo	1.25	.60	.40
454a Checklist 458-533 (Juan Marichal) (left ear shows)	12.00	6.00	3.50
454b Checklist 458-533 (Juan Marichal) (no left ear)	12.00	6.00	3.50
455 Tommie Agee	1.50	.70	.45
456 Phil Niekro	12.00	6.00	3.50
457 Andy Etchebarren	1.25	.60	.40
458 Lee Thomas	5.00	2.50	1.50
459 Senators Rookies (Dick Bosman, Pete Craig)	12.00	6.00	3.50
460 Harmon Killebrew	50.00	25.00	15.00
461 Bob Miller	5.00	2.50	1.50
462 Bob Barton	5.00	2.50	1.50
463 Tribe Hill Aces (Sam McDowell, Sonny Siebert)	12.00	6.00	3.50
464 Dan Coombs	5.00	2.50	1.50
465 Willie Horton	12.00	6.00	3.50
466 Bobby Wine	5.00	2.50	1.50
467 Jim O'Toole	5.00	2.50	1.50
468 Ralph Houk	13.00	6.50	4.00
469 Len Gabrielson	5.00	2.50	1.50
470 Bob Shaw	5.00	2.50	1.50
471 Rene Lachemann	5.00	2.50	1.50
472 Pirates Rookies (John Gelnar, George Spriggs)	5.00	2.50	1.50
473 Jose Santiago	5.00	2.50	1.50
474 Bob Tolan	12.00	6.00	3.50
475 Jim Palmer	100.00	50.00	30.00
476 Tony Perez	70.00	35.00	20.00
477 Braves Team	5.50	2.75	1.75
478 Bob Humphreys	5.00	2.50	1.50
479 Gary Bell	5.00	2.50	1.50
480 Willie McCovey	30.00	15.00	9.00
481 Leo Durocher	13.00	6.50	4.00
482 Bill Monbouquette	12.00	6.00	3.50
483 Jim Landis	5.00	2.50	1.50
484 Jerry Adair	5.00	2.50	1.50
485 Tim McCarver	13.00	6.50	4.00
486 Twins Rookies (Rich Reese, Bill Whitby)	5.00	2.50	1.50
487 Tom Reynolds	5.00	2.50	1.50
488 Gerry Arrigo	5.00	2.50	1.50
489 Doug Clemens	5.00	2.50	1.50
490 Tony Cloninger	12.00	6.00	3.50
491 Sam Bowens	5.00	2.50	1.50
492 Pirates Team	5.50	2.75	1.75
493 Phil Ortega	5.00	2.50	1.50
494 Bill Rigney	5.00	2.50	1.50
495 Fritz Peterson	12.00	6.00	3.50
496 Orlando McFarlane	5.00	2.50	1.50
497 Ron Campbell	5.00	2.50	1.50
498 Larry Dierker	12.00	6.00	3.50
499 Indians Rookies (George Culver, Jose Vidal)	5.00	2.50	1.50
500 Juan Marichal	20.00	10.00	6.00
501 Jerry Zimmerman	5.00	2.50	1.50
502 Derrell Griffith	5.00	2.50	1.50
503 Dodgers Team	13.00	6.50	4.00
504 Orlando Martinez	5.00	2.50	1.50
505 Tommy Helms	5.00	2.50	1.50
506 Smoky Burgess	12.00	6.00	3.50
507 Orioles Rookies (Ed Barnowski, Larry Haney)	5.00	2.50	1.50

		NR MT	EX	VG
508	Dick Hall	5.00	2.50	1.50
509	Jim King	5.00	2.50	1.50
510	Bill Mazeroski	13.00	6.50	4.00
511	Don Wert	5.00	2.50	1.50
512	Red Schoendienst	15.00	7.50	4.50
513	Marcelino Lopez	5.00	2.50	1.50
514	John Werhas	5.00	2.50	1.50
515	Bert Campaneris	12.00	6.00	3.50
516	Giants Team	5.50	2.75	1.75
517	Fred Talbot	12.00	6.00	3.50
518	Denis Menke	5.00	2.50	1.50
519	Ted Davidson	5.00	2.50	1.50
520	Max Alvis	5.00	2.50	1.50
521	Bird Bombers (Curt Blefary, Boog Powell)			
		13.00	6.50	4.00
522	John Stephenson	5.00	2.50	1.50
523	Jim Merritt	5.00	2.50	1.50
524	Felix Mantilla	5.00	2.50	1.50
525	Ron Hunt	12.00	6.00	3.50
526	Tigers Rookies (Pat Dobson, George Korince)			
		12.00	6.00	3.50
527	Dennis Ribant	5.00	2.50	1.50
528	Rico Petrocelli	12.00	6.00	3.50
529	Gary Wagner	5.00	2.50	1.50
530	Felipe Alou	12.00	6.00	3.50
531	Checklist 534-609 (Brooks Robinson)			
		12.00	6.00	3.50
532	Jim Hicks	5.00	2.50	1.50
533	Jack Fisher	5.00	2.50	1.50
534	Hank Bauer	15.00	7.50	4.50
535	Donn Clendenon	12.00	6.00	3.50
536	Cubs Rookies (Joe Niekro, Paul Popovich)			
		30.00	15.00	9.00
537	Chuck Estrada	12.00	6.00	3.50
538	J.C. Martin	15.00	7.50	4.50
539	Dick Egan	12.00	6.00	3.50
540	Norm Cash	35.00	17.50	10.50
541	Joe Gibbon	15.00	7.50	4.50
542	Athletics Rookies (Rick Monday, Tony Pierce)			
		12.00	6.00	3.50
543	Dan Schneider	15.00	7.50	4.50
544	Indians Team	12.00	6.00	3.50
545	Jim Grant	15.00	7.50	4.50
546	Woody Woodward	15.00	7.50	4.50
547	Red Sox Rookies (Russ Gibson, Bill Rohr)			
		15.00	7.50	4.50
548	Tony Gonzalez	12.00	6.00	3.50
549	Jack Sanford	12.00	6.00	3.50
550	Vada Pinson	12.00	6.00	3.50
551	Doug Camilli	12.00	6.00	3.50
552	Ted Savage	12.00	6.00	3.50
553	Yankees Rookies (Mike Hegan, Thad Tillotson)			
		18.00	9.00	5.50
554	Andre Rodgers	12.00	6.00	3.50
555	Don Cardwell	15.00	7.50	4.50
556	Al Weis	12.00	6.00	3.50
557	Al Ferrara	12.00	6.00	3.50
558	Orioles Rookies (Mark Belanger, Bill Dillman)			
		40.00	20.00	12.00
559	Dick Tracewski	12.00	6.00	3.50
560	Jim Bunning	50.00	25.00	15.00
561	Sandy Alomar	15.00	7.50	4.50
562	Steve Blass	12.00	6.00	3.50
563	Joe Adcock	20.00	10.00	6.00
564	Astros Rookies (Alonzo Harris, Aaron Pointer)			
		15.00	7.50	4.50
565	Lew Krausse	15.00	7.50	4.50
566	Gary Geiger	12.00	6.00	3.50
567	Steve Hamilton	15.00	7.50	4.50
568	John Sullivan	15.00	7.50	4.50
569	A.L. Rookies (Hank Allen, Rod Carew)			
		500.00	250.00	150.00
570	Maury Wills	80.00	40.00	25.00
571	Larry Sherry	12.00	6.00	3.50
572	Don Demeter	12.00	6.00	3.50
573	White Sox Team	18.00	9.00	5.50
574	Jerry Buchek	12.00	6.00	3.50
575	Dave Boswell	12.00	6.00	3.50
576	N.L. Rookies (Norm Gigon, Ramon Hernandez)			
		18.00	9.00	5.50
577	Bill Short	15.00	7.50	4.50
578	John Boccabella	15.00	7.50	4.50
579	Bill Henry	15.00	7.50	4.50
580	Rocky Colavito	75.00	38.00	23.00
581	Mets Rookies (Bill Denehy, Tom Seaver)			
		1200.00	600.00	350.00
582	Jim Owens	12.00	6.00	3.50
583	Ray Barker	15.00	7.50	4.50
584	Jim Piersall	20.00	10.00	6.00
585	Wally Bunker	15.00	7.50	4.50
586	Manny Jimenez	15.00	7.50	4.50

		NR MT	EX	VG
587	N.L. Rookies (Don Shaw, Gary Sutherland)			
		18.00	9.00	5.50
588	Johnny Klippstein	12.00	6.00	3.50
589	Dave Ricketts	12.00	6.00	3.50
590	Pete Richert	15.00	7.50	4.50
591	Ty Cline	12.00	6.00	3.50
592	N.L. Rookies (Jim Shellenback, Ron Willis)			
		13.00	6.50	4.00
593	Wes Westrum	15.00	7.50	4.50
594	Dan Osinski	15.00	7.50	4.50
595	Cookie Rojas	12.00	6.00	3.50
596	Galen Cisco	12.00	6.00	3.50
597	Ted Abernathy	12.00	6.00	3.50
598	White Sox Rookies (Ed Stroud, Walt Williams)			
		13.00	6.50	4.00
599	Bob Duliba	12.00	6.00	3.50
600	Brooks Robinson	225.00	112.00	67.00
601	Bill Bryan	15.00	7.50	4.50
602	Juan Pizarro	15.00	7.50	4.50
603	Athletics Rookies (Tim Talton, Ramon Webster)			
		15.00	7.50	4.50
604	Red Sox Team	100.00	50.00	30.00
605	Mike Shannon	40.00	20.00	12.00
606	Ron Taylor	15.00	7.50	4.50
607	Mickey Stanley	12.00	6.00	3.50
608	Cubs Rookies (Rich Nye, John Upham)			
		12.00	6.00	3.50
609	Tommy John	125.00	62.00	37.00

1967 Topps Pin-Ups

The 5" by 7" "All Star Pin-ups" were inserts to regular 1967 Topps baseball cards. They feature a full color picture with the player's name, position and team in a circle on the lower left side of the front. The numbered set consists of 32 players (generally big names). Even so, they are rather inexpensive. Because the large paper pin-ups had to be folded several times to fit into the wax packs, they are almost never found in true "Mint" condition.

		NR MT	EX	VG
	Complete Set:	60.00	30.00	18.00
	Common Player:	.25	.13	.08
1	Boog Powell	.40	.20	.12
2	Bert Campaneris	.30	.15	.09
3	Brooks Robinson	3.00	1.50	.90
4	Tommie Agee	.25	.13	.08
5	Carl Yastrzemski	3.50	1.75	1.00
6	Mickey Mantle	12.00	6.00	3.50
7	Frank Howard	.50	.25	.15
8	Sam McDowell	.25	.13	.08
9	Orlando Cepeda	.60	.30	.20
10	Chico Cardenas	.25	.13	.08
11	Bob Clemente	5.00	2.50	1.50
12	Willie Mays	5.00	2.50	1.50
13	Cleon Jones	.25	.13	.08
14	John Callison	.25	.13	.08
15	Hank Aaron	5.00	2.50	1.50
16	Don Drysdale	3.00	1.50	.90
17	Bobby Knoop	.25	.13	.08
18	Tony Oliva	.50	.25	.15
19	Frank Robinson	2.00	1.00	.60
20	Denny McLain	.50	.25	.15
21	Al Kaline	5.00	2.50	1.50
22	Joe Pepitone	.40	.20	.12
23	Harmon Killebrew	5.00	2.50	1.50

		NR MT	EX	VG
24	Leon Wagner	.25	.13	.08
25	Joe Morgan	5.00	2.50	1.50
26	Ron Santo	.40	.20	.12
27	Joe Torre	.60	.30	.20
28	Juan Marichal	2.00	1.00	.60
29	Matty Alou	.25	.13	.08
30	Felipe Alou	.25	.13	.08
31	Ron Hunt	.25	.13	.08
32	Willie McCovey	2.00	1.00	.60

1967 Topps Stand-Ups

Never actually issued, no more than a handful of each of these rare test issues has made their way into the hobby market. Designed so that the color photo of the player's head could be popped out of the black background, and the top folded over to create a stand-up display, examples of these 3-1/8" by 5-1/4" cards can be found either die-cut around the portrait or without the cutting. Blank-backed, there are 24 cards in the set, numbered on the front at bottom left. The cards are popular with advanced superstar collectors.

		NR MT	EX	VG
Complete Set:		6750.00	3375.00	2025.
Common Player:		65.00	32.00	19.50
1	Pete Rose	700.00	350.00	210.00
2	Gary Peters	65.00	32.00	19.50
3	Frank Robinson	200.00	100.00	60.00
4	Jim Lonborg	65.00	32.00	19.50
5	Ron Swoboda	65.00	32.00	19.50
6	Harmon Killebrew	200.00	100.00	60.00
7	Bob Clemente	800.00	400.00	240.00
8	Mickey Mantle	1500.00	750.00	450.00
9	Jim Fregosi	75.00	37.00	22.00
10	Al Kaline	300.00	150.00	90.00
11	Don Drysdale	250.00	125.00	75.00
12	Dean Chance	65.00	32.00	19.50
13	Orlando Cepeda	75.00	37.00	22.00
14	Tim McCarver	75.00	37.00	22.00
15	Frank Howard	75.00	37.00	22.00
16	Max Alvis	65.00	32.00	19.50
17	Rusty Staub	75.00	37.00	22.00
18	Richie Allen	75.00	37.00	22.00
19	Willie Mays	600.00	300.00	175.00
20	Hank Aaron	600.00	300.00	175.00
21	Carl Yastrzemski	600.00	300.00	180.00
22	Ron Santo	75.00	37.00	22.00
23	Jim Hunter	200.00	100.00	60.00
24	Jim Wynn	65.00	32.00	19.50

1967 Topps Stickers Pirates

Considered a "test" issue, this 33-sticker set of 2-1/2" by 3-1/2" stickers is very similar to the Red Sox stickers which were produced the same year. Player stickers have a color picture (often just the player's head) and the player's name in large "comic book" letters. Besides the players, there are other topics such as "I Love the Pirates," "Bob Clemente for Mayor," and a number of similar sentiments. The

stickers have blank backs and are rather scarce.

		NR MT	EX	VG
Complete Set:		250.00	125.00	75.00
Common Player:		3.00	1.50	.90
1	Gene Alley	5.00	2.50	1.50
2	Matty Alou	7.00	3.50	2.00
3	Dennis Ribant	3.00	1.50	.90
4	Steve Blass	5.00	2.50	1.50
5	Juan Pizarro	3.00	1.50	.90
6	Bob Clemente	75.00	38.00	23.00
7	Donn Clendenon	5.00	2.50	1.50
8	Roy Face	7.00	3.50	2.00
9	Woody Fryman	3.00	1.50	.90
10	Jesse Gonder	3.00	1.50	.90
11	Vern Law	7.00	3.50	2.00
12	Al McBean	3.00	1.50	.90
13	Jerry May	3.00	1.50	.90
14	Bill Mazeroski	12.00	6.00	3.50
15	Pete Mikkelsen	3.00	1.50	.90
16	Manny Mota	5.00	2.50	1.50
17	Billy O'Dell	3.00	1.50	.90
18	Jose Pagan	3.00	1.50	.90
19	Jim Pagliaroni	3.00	1.50	.90
20	Johnny Pesky	3.00	1.50	.90
21	Tommie Sisk	3.00	1.50	.90
22	Willie Stargell	40.00	20.00	12.50
23	Bob Veale	5.00	2.50	1.50
24	Harry Walker	3.00	1.50	.90
25	I Love The Pirates	3.00	1.50	.90
26	Let's Go Pirates	3.00	1.50	.90
27	Bob Clemente For Mayor	35.00	17.50	10.50
28	National League Batting Champion (Matty Alou)	4.00	2.00	1.25
29	Happiness Is A Pirate Win	3.00	1.50	.90
30	Donn Clendenon Is My Hero	4.00	2.00	1.25
31	Pirates' Home Run Champion (Willie Stargell)	15.00	7.50	4.50
32	Pirates Logo	3.00	1.50	.90
33	Pirates Pennant	3.00	1.50	.90

1967 Topps Stickers Red Sox

Like the 1967 Pirates Stickers, the Red Sox Stickers were part of the same test procedure. The Red Sox Stickers have the same 2-1/2" by 3-1/2" dimensions, color picture and large player's name on the front. A set is complete at 33 stickers. The majority are players, but themes such as "Let's Go Red Sox" are also included.

		NR MT	EX	VG
	Complete Set:	225.00	112.00	67.00
	Common Player:	3.00	1.50	.90
1	Dennis Bennett	3.00	1.50	.90
2	Darrell Brandon	3.00	1.50	.90
3	Tony Conigliaro	15.00	7.50	4.50
4	Don Demeter	3.00	1.50	.90
5	Hank Fischer	3.00	1.50	.90
6	Joe Foy	3.00	1.50	.90
7	Mike Andrews	3.00	1.50	.90
8	Dalton Jones	3.00	1.50	.90
9	Jim Lonborg	9.00	4.50	2.75
10	Don McMahon	3.00	1.50	.90
11	Dave Morehead	3.00	1.50	.90
12	George Smith	3.00	1.50	.90
13	Rico Petrocelli	6.00	3.00	1.75
14	Mike Ryan	3.00	1.50	.90
15	Jose Santiago	3.00	1.50	.90
16	George Scott	6.00	3.00	1.75
17	Sal Maglie	5.00	2.50	1.50
18	Reggie Smith	10.00	5.00	3.00
19	Lee Stange	3.00	1.50	.90
20	Jerry Stephenson	3.00	1.50	.90
21	Jose Tartabull	3.00	1.50	.90
22	George Thomas	3.00	1.50	.90
23	Bob Tillman	3.00	1.50	.90
24	Johnnie Wyatt	3.00	1.50	.90
25	Carl Yastrzemski	75.00	37.00	22.00
26	Dick Williams	6.00	3.00	1.75
27	I Love The Red Sox	3.00	1.50	.90
28	Let's Go Red Sox	3.00	1.50	.90
29	Carl Yastrzemski For Mayor	35.00	17.50	10.50
30	Tony Conigliaro Is My Hero	7.00	3.50	2.00
31	Happiness Is A Boston Win	3.00	1.50	.90
32	Red Sox Logo	3.00	1.50	.90
33	Red Sox Pennant	3.00	1.50	.90

1968 Topps

In 1968, Topps returned to a 598-card set of 2-1/2" by 3-1/2" cards. It is not, however, more of the same by way of appearance as the cards feature a color photograph on a background of what appears to be a burlap fabric. The player's name is below the photo but on the unusual background. A colored circle on the lower right carries the team and position. Backs were also changed. While retaining the vertical format introduced the previous year, with stats in the middle and cartoon at the bottom. The set features many of the old favorite subsets, including statistical leaders, World Series highlights, multi-player cards, checklists, rookie cards and the return of All-Star cards.

		NR MT	EX	VG
	Complete Set:	3200.00	1600.00	950.00
	Common Player: 1-533	1.00	.50	.30
	Common Player: 534-598	2.50	1.25	.70
1	N.L. Batting Leaders (Matty Alou, Bob Clemente, Tony Gonzalez)	15.00	7.50	4.50
2	A.L. Batting Leaders (Al Kaline, Frank Robinson, Carl Yastrzemski)	4.00	2.00	1.25
3	N.L. RBI Leaders (Hank Aaron, Orlando Cepeda, Bob Clemente)	4.00	2.00	1.25
4	A.L. RBI Leaders (Harmon Killebrew, Frank Robinson, Carl Yastrzemski)	4.00	2.00	1.25
5	N.L. Home Run Leaders (Hank Aaron, Willie McCovey, Ron Santo, Jim Wynn)	4.00	2.00	1.25
6	A.L. Home Run Leaders (Frank Howard, Harmon Killebrew, Carl Yastrzemski)	4.00	2.00	1.25
7	N.L. ERA Leaders (Jim Bunning, Phil Niekro, Chris Short)	2.50	1.25	.70
8	A.L. ERA Leaders (Joe Horlen, Gary Peters, Sonny Siebert)	2.50	1.25	.70
9	N.L. Pitching Leaders (Jim Bunning, Ferguson Jenkins, Mike McCormick, Claude Osteen)	2.50	1.25	.70
10a	A.L. Pitching Leaders (Dean Chance, Jim Lonborg, Earl Wilson) ("Lonberg" on back)	3.50	1.75	1.00
10b	A.L. Pitching Leaders (Dean Chance, Jim Lonborg, Earl Wilson) ("Lonborg" on back)	2.50	1.25	.70
11	N.L. Strikeout Leaders (Jim Bunning, Ferguson Jenkins, Gaylord Perry)	3.00	1.50	.90
12	A.L. Strikeout Leaders (Dean Chance, Jim Lonborg, Sam McDowell)	2.50	1.25	.70
13	Chuck Hartenstein	1.00	.50	.30
14	Jerry McNertney	1.00	.50	.30
15	Ron Hunt	1.00	.50	.30
16	Indians Rookies (Lou Piniella, Richie Scheinblum)	3.50	1.75	1.00
17	Dick Hall	1.00	.50	.30
18	Mike Hershberger	1.00	.50	.30
19	Juan Pizarro	1.00	.50	.30
20	Brooks Robinson	20.00	10.00	6.00
21	Ron Davis	1.00	.50	.30
22	Pat Dobson	1.00	.50	.30
23	Chico Cardenas	1.00	.50	.30
24	Bobby Locke	1.00	.50	.30
25	Julian Javier	1.00	.50	.30
26	Darrell Brandon	1.00	.50	.30
27	Gil Hodges	6.00	3.00	1.75
28	Ted Uhlaender	1.00	.50	.30
29	Joe Verbanic	1.00	.50	.30
30	Joe Torre	3.00	1.50	.90
31	Ed Stroud	1.00	.50	.30
32	Joe Gibbon	1.00	.50	.30
33	Pete Ward	1.00	.50	.30
34	Al Ferrara	1.00	.50	.30
35	Steve Hargan	1.00	.50	.30
36	Pirates Rookies (Bob Moose, *Bob Robertson*)	1.00	.50	.30
37	Billy Williams	7.00	3.50	2.00
38	Tony Pierce	1.00	.50	.30
39	Cookie Rojas	1.00	.50	.30
40	Denny McLain	3.75	2.00	1.25
41	Julio Gotay	1.00	.50	.30
42	Larry Haney	1.00	.50	.30
43	Gary Bell	1.00	.50	.30
44	Frank Kostro	1.00	.50	.30
45	Tom Seaver	225.00	112.00	67.00
46	Dave Ricketts	1.00	.50	.30
47	Ralph Houk	3.00	1.50	.90
48	Ted Davidson	1.00	.50	.30
49a	Ed Brinkman (yellow team letters)	60.00	30.00	18.00
49b	Ed Brinkman (white team letters)	1.00	.50	.30
50	Willie Mays	65.00	33.00	21.00
51	Bob Locker	1.00	.50	.30
52	Hawk Taylor	1.00	.50	.30
53	Gene Alley	1.00	.50	.30
54	Stan Williams	1.00	.50	.30
55	Felipe Alou	2.50	1.25	.70
56	Orioles Rookies (Dave Leonhard, Dave May)	1.00	.50	.30
57	Dan Schneider	1.00	.50	.30
58	Ed Mathews	10.00	5.00	3.00
59	Don Lock	1.00	.50	.30
60	Ken Holtzman	2.50	1.25	.70
61	Reggie Smith	2.50	1.25	.70
62	Chuck Dobson	1.00	.50	.30
63	Dick Kenworthy	1.00	.50	.30
64	Jim Merritt	1.00	.50	.30
65	John Roseboro	1.00	.50	.30
66a	Casey Cox (yellow team letters)	60.00	30.00	18.00
66b	Casey Cox (white team letters)	1.00	.50	.30
67	Checklist 1-109 (Jim Kaat)	3.00	1.50	.90
68	Ron Willis	1.00	.50	.30
69	Tom Tresh	3.00	1.50	.90
70	Bob Veale	1.00	.50	.30
71	Vern Fuller	1.00	.50	.30
72	Tommy John	5.00	2.50	1.25

		NR MT	EX	VG
73	Jim Hart	1.00	.50	.30
74	Milt Pappas	1.00	.50	.30
75	Don Mincher	1.00	.50	.30
76	Braves Rookies (Jim Britton, *Ron Reed*)	2.50	1.25	.70
77	*Don Wilson*	1.00	.50	.30
78	Jim Northrup	1.00	.50	.30
79	Ted Kubiak	1.00	.50	.30
80	Rod Carew	150.00	75.00	45.00
81	Larry Jackson	1.00	.50	.30
82	Sam Bowens	1.00	.50	.30
83	John Stephenson	1.00	.50	.30
84	Bob Tolan	1.00	.50	.30
85	Gaylord Perry	15.00	7.50	4.50
86	Willie Stargell	10.00	5.00	3.00
87	Dick Williams	2.50	1.25	.70
88	Phil Regan	1.00	.50	.30
89	Jake Gibbs	1.00	.50	.30
90	Vada Pinson	3.00	1.50	.90
91	Jim Ollom	1.00	.50	.30
92	Ed Kranepool	1.00	.50	.30
93	Tony Cloninger	1.00	.50	.30
94	Lee Maye	1.00	.50	.30
95	Bob Aspromonte	1.00	.50	.30
96	Senators Rookies (Frank Coggins, Dick Nold)	1.00	.50	.30
97	Tom Phoebus	1.00	.50	.30
98	Gary Sutherland	1.00	.50	.30
99	Rocky Colavito	2.25	1.25	.70
100	Bob Gibson	20.00	10.00	6.00
101	Glenn Beckert	1.00	.50	.30
102	Jose Cardenal	1.00	.50	.30
103	Don Sutton	8.00	4.00	2.50
104	Dick Dietz	1.00	.50	.30
105	Al Downing	2.50	1.25	.70
106	Dalton Jones	1.00	.50	.30
107	Checklist 110-196 (Juan Marichal)	3.50	1.75	1.00
108	Don Pavletich	1.00	.50	.30
109	Bert Campaneris	2.50	1.25	.70
110	Hank Aaron	80.00	40.00	25.00
111	Rich Reese	1.00	.50	.30
112	Woody Fryman	1.00	.50	.30
113	Tigers Rookies (Tom Matchick, Daryl Patterson)	1.00	.50	.30
114	Ron Swoboda	1.00	.50	.30
115	Sam McDowell	1.00	.50	.30
116	Ken McMullen	1.00	.50	.30
117	Larry Jaster	1.00	.50	.30
118	Mark Belanger	2.50	1.25	.70
119	Ted Savage	1.00	.50	.30
120	Mel Stottlemyre	3.00	1.50	.90
121	Jimmie Hall	1.00	.50	.30
122	Gene Mauch	1.00	.50	.30
123	Jose Santiago	1.00	.50	.30
124	Nate Oliver	1.00	.50	.30
125	Joe Horlen	1.00	.50	.30
126	Bobby Etheridge	1.00	.50	.30
127	Paul Lindblad	1.00	.50	.30
128	Astros Rookies (Tom Dukes, Alonzo Harris)	1.00	.50	.30
129	Mickey Stanley	1.00	.50	.30
130	Tony Perez	6.00	3.00	1.75
131	Frank Bertaina	1.00	.50	.30
132	Bud Harrelson	2.50	1.25	.70
133	Fred Whitfield	1.00	.50	.30
134	Pat Jarvis	1.00	.50	.30
135	Paul Blair	1.00	.50	.30
136	Randy Hundley	1.00	.50	.30
137	Twins Team	3.00	1.50	.90
138	Ruben Amaro	1.00	.50	.30
139	Chris Short	1.00	.50	.30
140	Tony Conigliaro	2.50	1.25	.70
141	Dal Maxvill	1.00	.50	.30
142	White Sox Rookies (Buddy Bradford, Bill Voss)	1.00	.50	.30
143	Pete Cimino	1.00	.50	.30
144	Joe Morgan	15.00	7.50	4.50
145	Don Drysdale	8.00	4.00	2.50
146	Sal Bando	2.50	1.25	.70
147	Frank Linzy	1.00	.50	.30
148	Dave Bristol	1.00	.50	.30
149	Bob Saverine	1.00	.50	.30
150	Bob Clemente	65.00	33.00	21.00
151	World Series Game 1 (Brock Socks 4-Hits In Opener)	3.50	1.75	1.00
152	World Series Game 2 (Yaz Smashes Two Homers)	5.00	2.50	1.50
153	World Series Game 3 (Briles Cools Off Boston)	3.00	1.50	.90
154	World Series Game 4 (Gibson Hurls Shutout!)	3.50	1.75	1.00
155	World Series Game 5 (Lonborg Wins Again!)	2.50	1.25	.70
156	World Series Game 6 (Petrocelli Socks Two Homers)	2.50	1.25	.70
157	World Series Game 7 (St. Louis Wins It!)	3.00	1.50	.90
158	World Series Summary (The Cardinals Celebrate!)	3.00	1.50	.90
159	Don Kessinger	1.00	.50	.30
160	Earl Wilson	1.00	.50	.30
161	Norm Miller	1.00	.50	.30
162	Cardinals Rookies (Hal Gilson, *Mike Torrez*)	2.50	1.25	.70
163	Gene Brabender	1.00	.50	.30
164	Ramon Webster	1.00	.50	.30
165	Tony Oliva	2.50	1.25	.70
166	Claude Raymond	1.00	.50	.30
167	Elston Howard	3.00	1.50	.90
168	Dodgers Team	2.50	1.25	.70
169	Bob Bolin	1.00	.50	.30
170	Jim Fregosi	2.50	1.25	.70
171	Don Nottebart	1.00	.50	.30
172	Walt Williams	1.00	.50	.30
173	John Boozer	1.00	.50	.30
174	Bob Tillman	1.00	.50	.30
175	Maury Wills	3.50	1.75	1.00
176	Bob Allen	1.00	.50	.30
177	Mets Rookies (*Jerry Koosman, Nolan Ryan*)	1500.00	750.00	450.00
178	Don Wert	1.00	.50	.30
179	Bill Stoneman	1.00	.50	.30
180	Curt Flood	2.50	1.25	.70
181	Jerry Zimmerman	1.00	.50	.30
182	Dave Giusti	1.00	.50	.30
183	Bob Kennedy	1.00	.50	.30
184	Lou Johnson	1.00	.50	.30
185	Tom Haller	1.00	.50	.30
186	Eddie Watt	1.00	.50	.30
187	Sonny Jackson	1.00	.50	.30
188	Cap Peterson	1.00	.50	.30
189	Bill Landis	1.00	.50	.30
190	Bill White	2.50	1.25	.70
191	Dan Frisella	1.00	.50	.30
192a	Checklist 197-283 (Carl Yastrzemski) ("To increase the..." on back)	4.50	2.25	1.25
192b	Checklist 197-283 (Carl Yastrzemski) ("To increase your..." on back)	6.00	3.00	1.75
193	Jack Hamilton	1.00	.50	.30
194	Don Buford	1.00	.50	.30
195	Joe Pepitone	3.00	1.50	.90
196	Gary Nolan	1.00	.50	.30
197	Larry Brown	1.00	.50	.30
198	Roy Face	2.50	1.25	.70
199	A's Rookies (Darrell Osteen, Roberto Rodriguez)	1.00	.50	.30
200	Orlando Cepeda	4.00	2.00	1.25
201	*Mike Marshall*	3.00	1.50	.90
202	Adolfo Phillips	1.00	.50	.30
203	Dick Kelley	1.00	.50	.30
204	Andy Etchebarren	1.00	.50	.30
205	Juan Marichal	8.00	4.00	2.50
206	Cal Ermer	1.00	.50	.30
207	Carroll Sembera	1.00	.50	.30
208	Willie Davis	2.50	1.25	.70
209	Tim Cullen	1.00	.50	.30
210	Gary Peters	1.00	.50	.30
211	J.C. Martin	1.00	.50	.30
212	Dave Morehead	1.00	.50	.30
213	Chico Ruiz	1.00	.50	.30
214	Yankees Rookies (Stan Bahnsen, Frank Fernandez)	2.50	1.25	.70
215	Jim Bunning	4.50	2.25	1.25
216	Bubba Morton	1.00	.50	.30
217	Turk Farrell	1.00	.50	.30
218	Ken Suarez	1.00	.50	.30
219	Rob Gardner	1.00	.50	.30
220	Harmon Killebrew	12.00	6.00	3.50
221	Braves Team	3.00	1.50	.90
222	Jim Hardin	1.00	.50	.30
223	Ollie Brown	1.00	.50	.30
224	Jack Aker	1.00	.50	.30
225	Richie Allen	2.25	1.25	.70
226	Jimmie Price	1.00	.50	.30
227	Joe Hoerner	1.00	.50	.30
228	Dodgers Rookies (*Jack Billingham*, Jim Fairey)	.80	.40	.25
229	Fred Klages	1.00	.50	.30
230	Pete Rose	40.00	20.00	12.00
231	Dave Baldwin	1.00	.50	.30
232	Denis Menke	1.00	.50	.30
233	George Scott	1.00	.50	.30

		NR MT	EX	VG
234	Bill Monbouquette	1.00	.50	.30
235	Ron Santo	2.50	1.25	.70
236	Tug McGraw	3.00	1.50	.90
237	Alvin Dark	1.00	.50	.30
238	Tom Satriano	1.00	.50	.30
239	Bill Henry	1.00	.50	.30
240	Al Kaline	20.00	10.00	6.00
241	Felix Millan	1.00	.50	.30
242	Moe Drabowsky	1.00	.50	.30
243	Rich Rollins	1.00	.50	.30
244	John Donaldson	1.00	.50	.30
245	Tony Gonzalez	1.00	.50	.30
246	Fritz Peterson	2.50	1.25	.70
247	Red Rookies (*Johnny Bench*, Ron Tompkins)	300.00	150.00	90.00
248	Fred Valentine	1.00	.50	.30
249	Bill Singer	.80	.40	.25
250	Carl Yastrzemski	30.00	15.00	9.00
251	*Manny Sanguillen*	2.50	1.25	.70
252	Angels Team	3.00	1.50	.90
253	Dick Hughes	1.00	.50	.30
254	Cleon Jones	1.00	.50	.30
255	Dean Chance	1.00	.50	.30
256	Norm Cash	3.00	1.50	.90
257	Phil Niekro	5.00	2.50	1.50
258	Cubs Rookies (Jose Arcia, Bill Schlesinger)	1.00	.50	.30
259	Ken Boyer	3.00	1.50	.90
260	Jim Wynn	1.00	.50	.30
261	Dave Duncan	1.00	.50	.30
262	Rick Wise	1.00	.50	.30
263	Horace Clarke	1.00	.50	.30
264	Ted Abernathy	1.00	.50	.30
265	Tommy Davis	2.50	1.25	.70
266	Paul Popovich	1.00	.50	.30
267	Herman Franks	1.00	.50	.30
268	Bob Humphreys	1.00	.50	.30
269	Bob Tiefenauer	1.00	.50	.30
270	Matty Alou	2.50	1.25	.70
271	Bobby Knoop	1.00	.50	.30
272	Ray Culp	1.00	.50	.30
273	Dave Johnson	3.00	1.50	.90
274	Mike Cuellar	1.00	.50	.30
275	Tim McCarver	3.00	1.50	.90
276	Jim Roland	1.00	.50	.30
277	Jerry Buchek	1.00	.50	.30
278a	Checklist 284-370 (Orlando Cepeda) (copyright at right)	3.00	1.50	.90
278b	Checklist 284-370 (Orlando Cepeda) (copyright at left)	5.00	2.50	1.50
279	Bill Hands	1.00	.50	.30
280	Mickey Mantle	200.00	100.00	60.00
281	Jim Campanis	1.00	.50	.30
282	Rick Monday	2.50	1.25	.70
283	Mel Queen	1.00	.50	.30
284	John Briggs	1.00	.50	.30
285	Dick McAuliffe	.80	.40	.25
286	Cecil Upshaw	1.00	.50	.30
287	White Sox Rookies (Mickey Abarbanel, Cisco Carlos)	1.00	.50	.30
288	Dave Wickersham	1.00	.50	.30
289	Woody Held	1.00	.50	.30
290	Willie McCovey	10.00	5.00	3.00
291	Dick Lines	1.00	.50	.30
292	Art Shamsky	.80	.40	.25
293	Bruce Howard	1.00	.50	.30
294	Red Schoendienst	2.50	1.25	.70
295	Sonny Siebert	1.00	.50	.30
296	Byron Browne	1.00	.50	.30
297	Russ Gibson	1.00	.50	.30
298	Jim Brewer	1.00	.50	.30
299	Gene Michael	2.50	1.25	.70
300	Rusty Staub	3.00	1.50	.90
301	Twins Rookies (George Mitterwald, Rick Renick)	1.00	.50	.30
302	Gerry Arrigo	1.00	.50	.30
303	Dick Green	1.00	.50	.30
304	Sandy Valdespino	1.00	.50	.30
305	Minnie Rojas	1.00	.50	.30
306	Mike Ryan	1.00	.50	.30
307	John Hiller	1.00	.50	.30
308	Pirates Team	3.00	1.50	.90
309	Ken Henderson	1.00	.50	.30
310	Luis Aparicio	5.00	2.50	1.50
311	Jack Lamabe	1.00	.50	.30
312	Curt Blefary	1.00	.50	.30
313	Al Weis	1.00	.50	.30
314	Red Sox Rookies (Bill Rohr, George Spriggs)	1.00	.50	.30
315	Zoilo Versalles	1.00	.50	.30
316	Steve Barber	1.00	.50	.30

		NR MT	EX	VG
317	Ron Brand	1.00	.50	.30
318	Chico Salmon	1.00	.50	.30
319	George Culver	1.00	.50	.30
320	Frank Howard	3.00	1.50	.90
321	Leo Durocher	2.25	1.25	.70
322	Dave Boswell	1.00	.50	.30
323	Deron Johnson	1.00	.50	.30
324	Jim Nash	1.00	.50	.30
325	Manny Mota	1.00	.50	.30
326	Dennis Ribant	1.00	.50	.30
327	Tony Taylor	1.00	.50	.30
328	Angels Rookies (Chuck Vinson, Jim Weaver)	1.00	.50	.30
329	Duane Josephson	1.00	.50	.30
330	Roger Maris	40.00	20.00	12.00
331	Dan Osinski	1.00	.50	.30
332	Doug Rader	1.00	.50	.30
333	Ron Herbel	1.00	.50	.30
334	Orioles Team	3.00	1.50	.90
335	Bob Allison	2.50	1.25	.70
336	John Purdin	1.00	.50	.30
337	Bill Robinson	1.00	.50	.30
338	Bob Johnson	1.00	.50	.30
339	Rich Nye	1.00	.50	.30
340	Max Alvis	1.00	.50	.30
341	Jim Lemon	1.00	.50	.30
342	Ken Johnson	1.00	.50	.30
343	Jim Gosger	1.00	.50	.30
344	Donn Clendenon	1.00	.50	.30
345	Bob Hendley	1.00	.50	.30
346	Jerry Adair	1.00	.50	.30
347	George Brunet	1.00	.50	.30
348	Phillies Rookies (Larry Colton, Dick Thoenen)	1.00	.50	.30
349	Ed Spiezio	1.00	.50	.30
350	Hoyt Wilhelm	6.00	3.00	1.75
351	Bob Barton	1.00	.50	.30
352	Jackie Hernandez	1.00	.50	.30
353	Mack Jones	1.00	.50	.30
354	Pete Richert	1.00	.50	.30
355	Ernie Banks	25.00	12.50	7.50
356	Checklist 371-457 (Ken Holtzman)	2.50	1.25	.70
357	Len Gabrielson	1.00	.50	.30
358	Mike Epstein	1.00	.50	.30
359	Joe Moeller	1.00	.50	.30
360	Willie Horton	1.00	.50	.30
361	Harmon Killebrew AS	5.00	2.50	1.50
362	Orlando Cepeda AS	2.75	1.50	.80
363	Rod Carew AS	12.00	6.00	3.50
364	Joe Morgan AS	3.00	1.50	.90
365	Brooks Robinson AS	6.00	3.00	1.75
366	Ron Santo AS	3.00	1.50	.90
367	Jim Fregosi AS	2.50	1.25	.70
368	Gene Alley AS	2.50	1.25	.70
369	Carl Yastrzemski AS	15.00	7.50	4.50
370	Hank Aaron AS	15.00	7.50	4.50
371	Tony Oliva AS	3.00	1.50	.90
372	Lou Brock AS	6.00	3.00	1.75
373	Frank Robinson AS	8.00	4.00	2.50
374	Bob Clemente AS	15.00	7.50	4.50
375	Bill Freehan AS	2.50	1.25	.70
376	Tim McCarver AS	2.50	1.25	.70
377	Joe Horlen AS	2.50	1.25	.70
378	Bob Gibson AS	7.00	3.50	2.00
379	Gary Peters AS	2.50	1.25	.70
380	Ken Holtzman AS	2.50	1.25	.70
381	Boog Powell	2.50	1.25	.70
382	Ramon Hernandez	1.00	.50	.30
383	Steve Whitaker	1.00	.50	.30
384	Reds Rookies (Bill Henry, *Hal McRae*)	12.00	6.00	3.50
385	Jim Hunter	10.00	5.00	3.00
386	Greg Goossen	1.00	.50	.30
387	Joe Foy	1.00	.50	.30
388	Ray Washburn	1.00	.50	.30
389	Jay Johnstone	1.00	.50	.30
390	Bill Mazeroski	3.00	1.50	.90
391	Bob Priddy	1.00	.50	.30
392	Grady Hatton	1.00	.50	.30
393	Jim Perry	2.50	1.25	.70
394	Tommie Aaron	1.00	.50	.30
395	Camilo Pascual	1.00	.50	.30
396	Bobby Wine	1.00	.50	.30
397	Vic Davalillo	1.00	.50	.30
398	Jim Grant	1.00	.50	.30
399	Ray Oyler	1.00	.50	.30
400a	Mike McCormick (white team letters)	40.00	20.00	12.00
400b	Mike McCormick (yellow team letters)	1.00	.50	.30

		NR MT	EX	VG
401	Mets Team	3.25	1.75	1.00
402	Mike Hegan	2.50	1.25	.70
403	John Buzhardt	1.00	.50	.30
404	Floyd Robinson	1.00	.50	.30
405	Tommy Helms	1.00	.50	.30
406	Dick Ellsworth	1.00	.50	.30
407	Gary Kolb	1.00	.50	.30
408	Steve Carlton	50.00	25.00	15.00
409	Orioles Rookies (Frank Peters, Ron Stone)	1.00	.50	.30
410	Ferguson Jenkins	18.00	9.00	5.50
411	Ron Hansen	1.00	.50	.30
412	Clay Carroll	1.00	.50	.30
413	Tommy McCraw	1.00	.50	.30
414	Mickey Lolich	2.75	1.50	.80
415	Johnny Callison	2.50	1.25	.70
416	Bill Rigney	1.00	.50	.30
417	Willie Crawford	1.00	.50	.30
418	Eddie Fisher	1.00	.50	.30
419	Jack Hiatt	1.00	.50	.30
420	Cesar Tovar	1.00	.50	.30
421	Ron Taylor	1.00	.50	.30
422	Rene Lachemann	1.00	.50	.30
423	Fred Gladding	1.00	.50	.30
424	White Sox Team	3.00	1.50	.90
425	Jim Maloney	1.00	.50	.30
426	Hank Allen	1.00	.50	.30
427	Dick Calmus	1.00	.50	.30
428	Vic Roznovsky	1.00	.50	.30
429	Tommie Sisk	1.00	.50	.30
430	Rico Petrocelli	1.00	.50	.30
431	Dooley Womack	1.00	.50	.30
432	Indians Rookies (Bill Davis, Jose Vidal)	1.00	.50	.30
433	Bob Rodgers	1.00	.50	.30
434	Ricardo Joseph	1.00	.50	.30
435	Ron Perranoski	1.00	.50	.30
436	Hal Lanier	1.00	.50	.30
437	Don Cardwell	1.00	.50	.30
438	Lee Thomas	1.00	.50	.30
439	Luman Harris	1.00	.50	.30
440	Claude Osteen	1.00	.50	.30
441	Alex Johnson	1.00	.50	.30
442	Dick Bosman	1.00	.50	.30
443	Joe Azcue	1.00	.50	.30
444	Jack Fisher	1.00	.50	.30
445	Mike Shannon	1.00	.50	.30
446	Ron Kline	1.00	.50	.30
447	Tigers Rookies (George Korince, Fred Lasher)	1.00	.50	.30
448	Gary Wagner	1.00	.50	.30
449	Gene Oliver	1.00	.50	.30
450	Jim Kaat	6.00	3.00	1.75
451	Al Spangler	1.00	.50	.30
452	Jesus Alou	1.00	.50	.30
453	Sammy Ellis	1.00	.50	.30
454	Checklist 458-533 (Frank Robinson)	4.00	2.00	1.25
455	Rico Carty	2.50	1.25	.70
456	John O'Donoghue	1.00	.50	.30
457	Jim Lefebvre	1.00	.50	.30
458	Lew Krausse	1.00	.50	.30
459	Dick Simpson	1.00	.50	.30
460	Jim Lonborg	2.50	1.25	.70
461	Chuck Hiller	1.00	.50	.30
462	Barry Moore	1.00	.50	.30
463	Jimmie Schaffer	1.00	.50	.30
464	Don McMahon	1.00	.50	.30
465	Tommie Agee	1.00	.50	.30
466	Bill Dillman	1.00	.50	.30
467	Dick Howser	2.50	1.25	.70
468	Larry Sherry	1.00	.50	.30
469	Ty Cline	1.00	.50	.30
470	Bill Freehan	2.50	1.25	.70
471	Orlando Pena	1.00	.50	.30
472	Walt Alston	2.50	1.25	.70
473	Al Worthington	1.00	.50	.30
474	Paul Schaal	1.00	.50	.30
475	Joe Niekro	2.25	1.25	.70
476	Woody Woodward	1.00	.50	.30
477	Phillies Team	3.00	1.50	.90
478	Dave McNally	2.50	1.25	.70
479	Phil Gagliano	1.00	.50	.30
480	Manager's Dream (Chico Cardenas, Bob Clemente, Tony Oliva)	25.00	12.50	7.50
481	John Wyatt	1.00	.50	.30
482	Jose Pagan	1.00	.50	.30
483	Darold Knowles	1.00	.50	.30
484	Phil Roof	1.00	.50	.30
485	Ken Berry	1.00	.50	.30
486	Cal Koonce	1.00	.50	.30
487	Lee May	2.50	1.25	.70
488	Dick Tracewski	1.00	.50	.30
489	Wally Bunker	1.00	.50	.30
490	Super Stars (Harmon Killebrew, Mickey Mantle, Willie Mays)	100.00	50.00	30.00
491	Denny Lemaster	1.00	.50	.30
492	Jeff Torborg	1.00	.50	.30
493	Jim McGlothlin	1.00	.50	.30
494	Ray Sadecki	1.00	.50	.30
495	Leon Wagner	1.00	.50	.30
496	Steve Hamilton	1.00	.50	.30
497	Cards Team	3.50	1.75	1.00
498	Bill Bryan	1.00	.50	.30
499	Steve Blass	1.00	.50	.30
500	Frank Robinson	20.00	10.00	6.00
501	John Odom	1.00	.50	.30
502	Mike Andrews	1.00	.50	.30
503	Al Jackson	1.00	.50	.30
504	Russ Snyder	1.00	.50	.30
505	Joe Sparma	1.00	.50	.30
506	Clarence Jones	1.00	.50	.30
507	Wade Blasingame	1.00	.50	.30
508	Duke Sims	1.00	.50	.30
509	Dennis Higgins	1.00	.50	.30
510	Ron Fairly	1.00	.50	.30
511	Bill Kelso	1.00	.50	.30
512	Grant Jackson	1.00	.50	.30
513	Hank Bauer	1.00	.50	.30
514	Al McBean	1.00	.50	.30
515	Russ Nixon	1.00	.50	.30
516	Pete Mikkelsen	1.00	.50	.30
517	Diego Segui	1.00	.50	.30
518a	Checklist 534-598 (Clete Boyer) (539 is Maj. L. Rookies)	3.00	1.50	.90
518b	Checklist 534-598 (Clete Boyer) (539 is Amer. L. Rookies)	5.00	2.50	1.50
519	Jerry Stephenson	1.00	.50	.30
520	Lou Brock	20.00	10.00	6.00
521	Don Shaw	1.00	.50	.30
522	Wayne Causey	1.00	.50	.30
523	John Tsitouris	1.00	.50	.30
524	Andy Kosco	1.00	.50	.30
525	Jim Davenport	1.00	.50	.30
526	Bill Denehy	1.00	.50	.30
527	Tito Francona	1.00	.50	.30
528	Tigers Team	60.00	30.00	18.00
529	Bruce Von Hoff	1.00	.50	.30
530	Bird Belters (Brooks Robinson, Frank Robinson)	10.00	5.00	3.00
531	Chuck Hinton	1.00	.50	.30
532	Luis Tiant	3.00	1.50	.90
533	Wes Parker	1.00	.50	.30
534	Bob Miller	2.50	1.25	.70
535	Danny Cater	2.50	1.25	.70
536	Bill Short	2.50	1.25	.70
537	Norm Siebern	2.50	1.25	.70
538	Manny Jimenez	2.50	1.25	.70
539	Major League Rookies (Mike Ferraro, Jim Ray)	2.50	1.25	.70
540	Nelson Briles	2.50	1.25	.70
541	Sandy Alomar	2.50	1.25	.70
542	John Boccabella	2.50	1.25	.70
543	Bob Lee	2.50	1.25	.70
544	Mayo Smith	2.50	1.25	.70
545	Lindy McDaniel	2.50	1.25	.70
546	Roy White	2.50	1.25	.70
547	Dan Coombs	2.50	1.25	.70
548	Bernie Allen	2.50	1.25	.70
549	Orioles Rookies (Curt Motton, Roger Nelson)	2.50	1.25	.70
550	Clete Boyer	2.50	1.25	.70
551	Darrell Sutherland	2.50	1.25	.70
552	Ed Kirkpatrick	2.50	1.25	.70
553	Hank Aguirre	2.50	1.25	.70
554	A's Team	3.00	1.50	.90
555	Jose Tartabull	2.50	1.25	.70
556	Dick Selma	2.50	1.25	.70
557	Frank Quilici	2.50	1.25	.70
558	John Edwards	2.50	1.25	.70
559	Pirates Rookies (Carl Taylor, Luke Walker)	2.50	1.25	.70
560	Paul Casanova	2.50	1.25	.70
561	Lee Elia	2.50	1.25	.70
562	Jim Bouton	2.50	1.25	.70
563	Ed Charles	2.50	1.25	.70
564	Eddie Stanky	2.50	1.25	.70
565	Larry Dierker	2.50	1.25	.70
566	Ken Harrelson	3.00	1.50	.90
567	Clay Dalrymple	2.50	1.25	.70
568	Willie Smith	2.50	1.25	.70
569	N.L. Rookies (Ivan Murrell, Les Rohr)	2.50	1.25	.70

		NR MT	EX	VG
570	Rick Reichardt	2.50	1.25	.70
571	Tony LaRussa	3.00	1.50	.90
572	Don Bosch	2.50	1.25	.70
573	Joe Coleman	2.50	1.25	.70
574	Reds Team	3.00	1.50	.90
575	Jim Palmer	60.00	30.00	18.00
576	Dave Adlesh	2.50	1.25	.70
577	Fred Talbot	2.50	1.25	.70
578	Orlando Martinez	2.50	1.25	.70
579	N.L. Rookies (Larry Hisle, Mike Lum)			
		3.00	1.50	.90
580	Bob Bailey	2.50	1.25	.70
581	Garry Roggenburk	2.50	1.25	.70
582	Jerry Grote	2.50	1.25	.70
583	Gates Brown	2.50	1.25	.70
584	Larry Shepard	2.50	1.25	.70
585	Wilbur Wood	2.50	1.25	.70
586	Jim Pagliaroni	2.50	1.25	.70
587	Roger Repoz	2.50	1.25	.70
588	Dick Schofield	2.50	1.25	.70
589	Twins Rookies (Ron Clark, Moe Ogier)			
		2.50	1.25	.70
590	Tommy Harper	2.50	1.25	.70
591	Dick Nen	2.50	1.25	.70
592	John Bateman	2.50	1.25	.70
593	Lee Stange	2.50	1.25	.70
594	Phil Linz	2.50	1.25	.70
595	Phil Ortega	2.50	1.25	.70
596	Charlie Smith	2.50	1.25	.70
597	Bill McCool	2.50	1.25	.70
598	Jerry May	3.00	1.50	.90

1968 Topps
Action All-Star Stickers

Still another of the many Topps test issues of the late 1960s, the Action All-Star stickers were sold in a strip of three, with bubblegum, for 10¢. The strip is comprised of three 3-1/4" by 5-1/4" panels, perforated at the joints for separation. The central panel which is numbered, contains a large color picture of a star player. The top and bottom panels contains smaller pictures of three players each. While there are 16 numbered center panels, only 12 of them are different; panels 13-16 show players previously used. Similarly, the triple-player panels at top and bottom of stickers 13-16 repeat panels from #'s 1-4. Prices below are for stickers which have all three panels still joined. Individual panels are priced signicantly lower.

		NR MT	EX	VG
	Complete Set:	1300.00	650.00	390.00
	Common Player:	18.00	9.00	5.50
1	Orlando Cepeda, Joe Horlen, Al Kaline, Bill Mazeroski, Claude Osteen, Mel Stottlemyre, Carl Yastrzemski	100.00	50.00	30.00
2	Don Drysdale, Harmon Killebrew, Mike McCormick, Tom Phoebus, George Scott, Ron Swoboda, Pete Ward	30.00	15.00	9.00
3	Hank Aaron, Paul Casanova, Jim Maloney, Joe Pepitone, Rick Reichardt, Frank Robinson, Tom Seaver	35.00	17.50	10.50

		NR MT	EX	VG
4	Bob Aspromonte, Johnny Callison, Dean Chance, Jim Lefebvre, Jim Lonborg, Frank Robinson, Ron Santo	25.00	12.50	7.50
5	Bert Campaneris, Al Downing, Willie Horton, Ed Kranepool, Willie Mays, Pete Rose, Ron Santo	200.00	100.00	60.00
6	Max Alvis, Ernie Banks, Al Kaline, Tim McCarver, Rusty Staub, Walt Williams, Carl Yastrzemski	70.00	35.00	21.00
7	Rod Carew, Tony Gonzalez, Steve Hargan, Mickey Mantle, Willie McCovey, Rick Monday, Billy Williams	300.00	150.00	90.00
8	Clete Boyer, Jim Bunning, Tony Conigliaro, Mike Cuellar, Joe Horlen, Ken McMullen, Don Mincher	18.00	9.00	5.50
9	Orlando Cepeda, Bob Clemente, Jim Fregosi, Harmon Killebrew, Willie Mays, Chris Short, Earl Wilson	40.00	20.00	12.00
10	Hank Aaron, Bob Gibson, Bud Harrelson, Jim Hunter, Mickey Mantle, Gary Peters, Vada Pinson	100.00	50.00	30.00
11	Don Drysdale, Bill Freehan, Frank Howard, Ferguson Jenkins, Tony Oliva, Bob Veale, Jim Wynn	30.00	15.00	9.00
12	Richie Allen, Bob Clemente, Sam McDowell, Jim McGlothlin, Tony Perez, Brooks Robinson, Joe Torre	100.00	50.00	30.00
13	Dean Chance, Don Drysdale, Jim Lefebvre, Tom Phoebus, Frank Robinson, George Scott, Carl Yastrzemski	100.00	50.00	30.00
14	Paul Casanova, Orlando Cepeda, Joe Horlen, Harmon Killebrew, Bill Mazeroski, Rick Reichardt, Tom Seaver	35.00	17.50	10.50
15	Bob Aspromonte, Johnny Callison, Jim Lonborg, Mike McCormick, Frank Robinson, Ron Swoboda, Pete Ward	30.00	15.00	9.00
16	Hank Aaron, Al Kaline, Jim Maloney, Claude Osteen, Joe Pepitone, Ron Santo, Mel Stottlemyre	30.00	15.00	9.00

1968 Topps Discs

One of the scarcest of all Topps collectibles, this 28-player set was apparently a never-completed test issue. These full-color, cardboard discs, which measure approximately 2-1/8" in diameter, were apparently intended to be made into a "pin" set, but for some reason, production was never completed and no actual "pins" are known to exist. Uncut sheets of the player discs have been found, however. The discs include a player portrait photo with the name beneath and the city and team nickname along the sides. The set includes eight Hall of Famers.

		NR MT	EX	VG
	Complete Set:	3500.00	1750.00	1050.
	Common Player:	35.00	17.50	10.50
(1)	Hank Aaron	250.00	125.00	75.00
(2)	Richie Allen	60.00	30.00	18.00
(3)	Gene Alley	35.00	17.50	10.50
(4)	Rod Carew	300.00	150.00	90.00
(5)	Orlando Cepeda	60.00	30.00	18.00
(6)	Dean Chance	35.00	17.50	10.50
(7)	Bob Clemente	350.00	175.00	100.00
(8)	Tommy Davis	35.00	17.50	10.50
(9)	Bill Freehan	35.00	17.50	10.50
(10)	Jim Fregosi	35.00	17.50	10.50
(11)	Steve Hargan	35.00	17.50	10.50
(12)	Frank Howard	60.00	30.00	18.00
(13)	Al Kaline	200.00	100.00	60.00

		NR MT	EX	VG
(14)	Harmon Killebrew	150.00	75.00	45.00
(15)	Mickey Mantle	600.00	300.00	175.00
(16)	Willie Mays	300.00	150.00	90.00
(17)	Mike McCormick	35.00	17.50	10.50
(18)	Rick Monday	35.00	17.50	10.50
(19)	Claude Osteen	35.00	17.50	10.50
(20)	Gary Peters	35.00	17.50	10.50
(21)	Brooks Robinson	200.00	100.00	60.00
(22)	Frank Robinson	150.00	75.00	45.00
(23)	Pete Rose	400.00	200.00	125.00
(24)	Ron Santo	60.00	30.00	18.00
(25)	Rusty Staub	60.00	30.00	18.00
(26)	Joe Torre	60.00	30.00	18.00
(27)	Carl Yastrzemski	150.00	75.00	45.00
(28)	Bob Veale	35.00	17.50	10.50

1968 Topps Game

A throwback to the Red and Blue Back sets of 1951, the 33-cards in the 1968 Topps Game set, inserted into packs of regular '68 Topps cards or purchases as a complete boxed set, enable the owner to play a game of baseball based on the game situations on each card. Also on the 2-1/4" by 3-1/4" cards were a color photograph of a player and his facsimile autograph. One redeeming social value of the set (assuming you're not mesmerized by the game) is that it affords an inexpensive way to get big-name cards as the set is loaded with stars, but not at all popular with collectors.

		NR MT	EX	VG
Complete Set:		70.00	35.00	21.00
Common Player:		.30	.15	.09
1	Mateo Alou	.50	.25	.15
2	Mickey Mantle	15.00	7.50	4.50
3	Carl Yastrzemski	3.25	1.75	1.00
4	Henry Aaron	3.00	1.50	.90
5	Harmon Killebrew	1.75	.90	.50
6	Roberto Clemente	3.00	1.50	.90
7	Frank Robinson	1.75	.90	.50
8	Willie Mays	3.00	1.50	.90
9	Brooks Robinson	2.00	1.00	.60
10	Tommy Davis	.50	.25	.15
11	Bill Freehan	.50	.25	.15
12	Claude Osteen	.40	.20	.12
13	Gary Peters	.30	.15	.09
14	Jim Lonborg	.40	.20	.12
15	Steve Hargan	.30	.15	.09
16	Dean Chance	.40	.20	.12
17	Mike McCormick	.30	.15	.09
18	Tim McCarver	.60	.30	.20
19	Ron Santo	.60	.30	.20
20	Tony Gonzalez	.30	.15	.09
21	Frank Howard	.70	.35	.20
22	George Scott	.40	.20	.12
23	Rich Allen	.70	.35	.20
24	Jim Wynn	.40	.20	.12
25	Gene Alley	.40	.20	.12
26	Rick Monday	.40	.20	.12
27	Al Kaline	2.00	1.00	.60
28	Rusty Staub	.70	.35	.20
29	Rod Carew	2.75	1.50	.80
30	Pete Rose	7.50	3.75	2.25
31	Joe Torre	.70	.35	.20
32	Orlando Cepeda	1.00	.50	.30
33	Jim Fregosi	.50	.25	.15

1968 Topps Plaks

Among the scarcest of the Topps test issues of the late 1960s, the "All Star Baseball Plaks" were plastic busts of two dozen stars of the era which came packaged like model airplane parts. The busts had to be snapped off a sprue and could be inserted into a base which carried the player's name. Packed with the plastic plaks was one of two checklist cards which featured six color photos per side. The 2-1/8" by 4" checklist cards are popular with superstar collectors and are considerably easier to find today than the actual plaks.

		NR MT	EX	VG
Complete Set:		2300.00	1150.00	690.00
Common Player:		20.00	10.00	6.00
1	Max Alvis	20.00	10.00	6.00
2	Frank Howard	30.00	15.00	9.00
3	Dean Chance	20.00	10.00	6.00
4	Jim Hunter	50.00	25.00	15.00
5	Jim Fregosi	25.00	12.50	7.50
6	Al Kaline	60.00	30.00	18.00
7	Harmon Killebrew	60.00	30.00	18.00
8	Gary Peters	20.00	10.00	6.00
9	Jim Lonborg	20.00	10.00	6.00
10	Frank Robinson	60.00	30.00	18.00
11	Mickey Mantle	800.00	400.00	240.00
12	Carl Yastrzemski	175.00	87.00	52.00
13	Hank Aaron	100.00	50.00	30.00
14	Bob Clemente	100.00	50.00	30.00
15	Richie Allen	30.00	15.00	9.00
16	Tommy Davis	25.00	12.50	7.50
17	Orlando Cepeda	30.00	15.00	9.00
18	Don Drysdale	50.00	25.00	15.00
19	Willie Mays	100.00	50.00	30.00
20	Rusty Staub	30.00	15.00	9.00
21	Tim McCarver	30.00	15.00	9.00
22	Pete Rose	250.00	125.00	75.00
23	Ron Santo	30.00	15.00	9.00
24	Jim Wynn	20.00	10.00	6.00
----	Checklist Card 1-12	250.00	125.00	75.00
----	Checklist Card 13-24	250.00	125.00	75.00

1968 Topps Posters

Yet another innovation from the creative minds at Topps appeared in 1968; a set of color player posters. Measuring 9-3/4" by 18-1/8," each poster was sold separately with its own piece of gum, rather than as an insert. The posters feature a large color photograph with a star at the bottom containing the player's name, position and team. There are 24 different posters which were folded numerous times to fit into the package they were sold in.

		NR MT	EX	VG
Complete Set:		325.00	162.00	97.00
Common Player:		3.00	1.50	.90
1	Dean Chance	3.00	1.50	.90
2	Max Alvis	3.00	1.50	.90
3	Frank Howard	8.00	4.00	2.50
4	Jim Fregosi	7.00	3.50	2.00
5	Jim Hunter	12.00	6.00	3.50
6	Bob Clemente	25.00	12.50	7.50
7	Don Drysdale	12.00	6.00	3.50
8	Jim Wynn	3.00	1.50	.90
9	Al Kaline	25.00	12.50	7.50
10	Harmon Killebrew	20.00	10.00	6.00
11	Jim Lonborg	3.00	1.50	.90
12	Orlando Cepeda	8.00	4.00	2.50
13	Gary Peters	3.00	1.50	.90
14	Hank Aaron	25.00	12.50	7.50
15	Richie Allen	8.00	4.00	2.50
16	Carl Yastrzemski	20.00	10.00	6.00
17	Ron Swoboda	3.00	1.50	.90
18	Mickey Mantle	50.00	25.00	15.00
19	Tim McCarver	7.00	3.50	2.00
20	Willie Mays	25.00	12.50	7.50
21	Ron Santo	7.00	3.50	2.00
22	Rusty Staub	7.00	3.50	2.00
23	Pete Rose	40.00	20.00	12.00
24	Frank Robinson	15.00	7.50	4.50

1968 Topps 3-D

These are very rare pioneer issues on the part of Topps. The cards measure 2-1/4" by 3-1/2" and were specially printed to simulate a three-dimensional effect. Backgrounds are a purposely blurred stadium scene, in front of which was a normally sharp color player photograph. The outer layer is a thin coating of ribbed plastic. The special process gives the picture the illusion of depth when the card is moved or tilted. As this was done two years before Kellogg's began its 3-D cards, this 12-card test issue really was breaking new ground. Unfortunately, production and distribution were limited making the cards very tough to find.

		NR MT	EX	VG
Complete Set:		9000.00	4500.00	2500.
Common Player:		350.00	175.00	105.00
(1)	Bob Clemente	2500.00	1250.00	750.00
(2)	Willie Davis	400.00	200.00	125.00
(3)	Ron Fairly	400.00	200.00	125.00
(4)	Curt Flood	400.00	200.00	125.00
(5)	Jim Lonborg	400.00	200.00	125.00
(6)	Jim Maloney	350.00	175.00	105.00
(7)	Tony Perez	600.00	300.00	175.00

		NR MT	EX	VG
(8)	Boog Powell	500.00	250.00	150.00
(9)	Bill Robinson	350.00	175.00	105.00
(10)	Rusty Staub	450.00	230.00	135.00
(11)	Mel Stottlemyre	400.00	200.00	120.00
(12)	Ron Swoboda	350.00	175.00	105.00

1969 Topps

The 1969 Topps set broke yet another record for quantity as the issue is officially a whopping 664 cards. With substantial numbers of variations, the number of possible cards runs closer to 700. The design of the 2-1/2" by 3-1/2" cards in the set feature a color photo with the team name printed in block letters underneath. A circle contains the player's name and position. Card backs returned to a horizontal format. Despite the size of the set, it contains no teamcards. It does, however, have multi-player cards, All-Stars, statistical leaders, and World Series highlights. Most significant among the varieties are white and yellow letter cards from the run of #'s 440-511. The complete set prices below do not include the scarcer and more expensive "white letter" variations.

		NR MT	EX	VG
Complete Set:		2500.00	1250.00	750.00
Common Player: 1-218		1.00	.50	.30
Common Player: 219-327		1.50	.70	.45
Common Player: 328-512		1.00	.50	.30
Common Player: 513-664		1.00	.50	.30
1	A.L. Batting Leaders (Danny Cater, Tony Oliva, Carl Yastrzemski)	10.00	5.00	3.00
2	N.L. Batting Leaders (Felipe Alou, Matty Alou, Pete Rose)	4.00	2.00	1.25
3	A.L. RBI Leaders (Ken Harrelson, Frank Howard, Jim Northrup)	2.00	1.00	.60
4	N.L. RBI Leaders (Willie McCovey, Ron Santo, Billy Williams)	3.50	1.75	1.00
5	A.L. Home Run Leaders (Ken Harrelson, Willie Horton, Frank Howard)	2.00	1.00	.60
6	N.L. Home Run Leaders (Richie Allen, Ernie Banks, Willie McCovey)	3.50	1.75	1.00
7	A.L. ERA Leaders (Sam McDowell, Dave McNally, Luis Tiant)	2.00	1.00	.60
8	N.L. ERA Leaders (Bobby Bolin, Bob Gibson, Bob Veale)	3.00	1.50	.90
9	A.L. Pitching Leaders (Denny McLain, Dave McNally, Mel Stottlemyre, Luis Tiant)	2.00	1.00	.60
10	N.L. Pitching Leaders (Bob Gibson, Fergie Jenkins, Juan Marichal)	3.50	1.75	1.00
11	A.L. Strikeout Leaders (Sam McDowell, Denny McLain, Luis Tiant)	2.00	1.00	.60
12	N.L. Strikeout Leaders (Bob Gibson, Fergie Jenkins, Bill Singer)	3.00	1.50	.90
13	Mickey Stanley	1.00	.50	.30
14	Al McBean	1.00	.50	.30
15	Boog Powell	2.50	1.25	.70
16	Giants Rookies (Cesar Gutierrez, Rich Robertson)	1.00	.50	.30
17	Mike Marshall	1.50	.70	.45
18	Dick Schofield	1.00	.50	.30
19	Ken Suarez	1.00	.50	.30
20	Ernie Banks	20.00	10.00	6.00
21	Jose Santiago	1.00	.50	.30

		NR MT	EX	VG
22	Jesus Alou	1.00	.50	.30
23	Lew Krausse	1.00	.50	.30
24	Walt Alston	3.00	1.50	.90
25	Roy White	1.50	.70	.45
26	Clay Carroll	1.00	.50	.30
27	Bernie Allen	1.00	.50	.30
28	Mike Ryan	1.00	.50	.30
29	Dave Morehead	1.00	.50	.30
30	Bob Allison	1.00	.50	.30
31	Mets Rookies (Gary Gentry, Amos Otis)			
		1.50	.70	.45
32	Sammy Ellis	1.00	.50	.30
33	Wayne Causey	1.00	.50	.30
34	Gary Peters	1.00	.50	.30
35	Joe Morgan	12.00	6.00	3.50
36	Luke Walker	1.00	.50	.30
37	Curt Motton	1.00	.50	.30
38	Zoilo Versalles	1.00	.50	.30
39	Dick Hughes	1.00	.50	.30
40	Mayo Smith	1.00	.50	.30
41	Bob Barton	1.00	.50	.30
42	Tommy Harper	1.00	.50	.30
43	Joe Niekro	1.50	.70	.45
44	Danny Cater	1.00	.50	.30
45	Maury Wills	2.50	1.25	.70
46	Fritz Peterson	1.00	.50	.30
47a	Paul Popovich (emblem visible thru airbrush)	4.00	2.00	1.25
47b	Paul Popovich (helmet emblem completely airbrushed)	1.00	.50	.30
48	Brant Alyea	1.00	.50	.30
49a	Royals Rookies (Steve Jones, Eliseo Rodriquez) (Rodriquez on front)	6.00	3.00	1.75
49b	Royals Rookies (Steve Jones, Eliseo Rodriquez) (Rodriquez on front)	1.00	.50	.30
50	Bob Clemente	55.00	28.00	16.50
51	Woody Fryman	1.00	.50	.30
52	Mike Andrews	1.00	.50	.30
53	Sonny Jackson	1.00	.50	.30
54	Cisco Carlos	1.00	.50	.30
55	Jerry Grote	1.00	.50	.30
56	Rich Reese	1.00	.50	.30
57	Checklist 1-109 (Denny McLain)	3.00	1.50	.90
58	Fred Gladding	1.00	.50	.30
59	Jay Johnstone	1.00	.50	.30
60	Nelson Briles	1.00	.50	.30
61	Jimmie Hall	1.00	.50	.30
62	Chico Salmon	1.25	.60	.40
63	Jim Hickman	1.00	.50	.30
64	Bill Monbouquette	1.00	.50	.30
65	Willie Davis	1.00	.50	.30
66	Orioles Rookies (Mike Adamson, Merv Rettenmund)	1.00	.50	.30
67	Bill Stoneman	1.00	.50	.30
68	Dave Duncan	1.00	.50	.30
69	Steve Hamilton	1.00	.50	.30
70	Tommy Helms	1.00	.50	.30
71	Steve Whitaker	1.00	.50	.30
72	Ron Taylor	1.00	.50	.30
73	Johnny Briggs	1.00	.50	.30
74	Preston Gomez	1.00	.50	.30
75	Luis Aparicio	5.00	2.50	1.50
76	Norm Miller	1.00	.50	.30
77a	Ron Perranoski (LA visible thru airbrush)	4.50	2.25	1.25
77b	Ron Perranoski (cap emblem completely airbrushed)	1.00	.50	.30
78	Tom Satriano	1.00	.50	.30
79	Milt Pappas	1.00	.50	.30
80	Norm Cash	1.75	.90	.50
81	Mel Queen	1.00	.50	.30
82	Pirates Rookies (Rich Hebner, Al Oliver)	12.00	6.00	3.50
83	Mike Ferraro	1.25	.60	.40
84	Bob Humphreys	1.00	.50	.30
85	Lou Brock	18.00	9.00	5.50
86	Pete Richert	1.00	.50	.30
87	Horace Clarke	1.00	.50	.30
88	Rich Nye	1.00	.50	.30
89	Russ Gibson	1.00	.50	.30
90	Jerry Koosman	2.50	1.25	.70
91	Al Dark	1.00	.50	.30
92	Jack Billingham	1.00	.50	.30
93	Joe Foy	1.00	.50	.30
94	Hank Aguirre	1.00	.50	.30
95	Johnny Bench	150.00	75.00	50.00
96	Denver Lemaster	1.00	.50	.30
97	Buddy Bradford	1.00	.50	.30
98	Dave Giusti	1.00	.50	.30
99a	Twins Rookies (Danny Morris, Graig Nettles) (black loop above "Twins")	20.00	10.00	6.00
99b	Twins Rookies (Danny Morris, Graig Nettles) (no black loop)	12.00	6.00	3.50
100	Hank Aaron	60.00	30.00	18.00
101	Daryl Patterson	1.00	.50	.30
102	Jim Davenport	1.00	.50	.30
103	Roger Repoz	1.00	.50	.30
104	Steve Blass	1.00	.50	.30
105	Rick Monday	1.25	.60	.40
106	Jim Hannan	1.00	.50	.30
107a	Checklist 110-218 (Bob Gibson) (161 is Jim Purdin)	3.00	1.50	.90
107b	Checklist 110-218 (Bob Gibson) (161 is John Purdin)	6.00	3.00	1.75
108	Tony Taylor	1.00	.50	.30
109	Jim Lonborg	1.25	.60	.40
110	Mike Shannon	1.00	.50	.30
111	Johnny Morris	1.25	.60	.40
112	J.C. Martin	1.00	.50	.30
113	Dave May	1.00	.50	.30
114	Yankees Rookies (Alan Closter, John Cumberland)	1.00	.50	.30
115	Bill Hands	1.00	.50	.30
116	Chuck Harrison	1.00	.50	.30
117	Jim Fairey	1.00	.50	.30
118	Stan Williams	1.00	.50	.30
119	Doug Rader	1.00	.50	.30
120	Pete Rose	35.00	17.50	10.50
121	Joe Grzenda	1.00	.50	.30
122	Ron Fairly	1.25	.60	.40
123	Wilbur Wood	1.25	.60	.40
124	Hank Bauer	1.25	.60	.40
125	Ray Sadecki	1.00	.50	.30
126	Dick Tracewski	1.00	.50	.30
127	Kevin Collins	1.00	.50	.30
128	Tommie Aaron	1.00	.50	.30
129	Bill McCool	1.00	.50	.30
130	Carl Yastrzemski	30.00	15.00	9.00
131	Chris Cannizzaro	1.00	.50	.30
132	Dave Baldwin	1.00	.50	.30
133	Johnny Callison	1.00	.50	.30
134	Jim Weaver	1.00	.50	.30
135	Tommy Davis	1.50	.70	.45
136	Cards Rookies (Steve Huntz, Mike Torrez)	1.00	.50	.30
137	Wally Bunker	1.00	.50	.30
138	John Bateman	1.00	.50	.30
139	Andy Kosco	1.00	.50	.30
140	Jim Lefebvre	1.00	.50	.30
141	Bill Dillman	1.00	.50	.30
142	Woody Woodward	1.00	.50	.30
143	Joe Nossek	1.00	.50	.30
144	Bob Hendley	1.00	.50	.30
145	Max Alvis	1.00	.50	.30
146	Jim Perry	1.00	.50	.30
147	Leo Durocher	2.25	1.25	.70
148	Lee Stange	1.00	.50	.30
149	Ollie Brown	1.00	.50	.30
150	Denny McLain	3.00	1.50	.90
151a	Clay Dalrymple (Phillies)	7.00	3.50	2.00
151b	Clay Dalrymple (Orioles)	1.00	.50	.30
152	Tommie Sisk	1.00	.50	.30
153	Ed Brinkman	1.00	.50	.30
154	Jim Britton	1.00	.50	.30
155	Pete Ward	1.00	.50	.30
156	Astros Rookies (Hal Gilson, Leon McFadden)	1.00	.50	.30
157	Bob Rodgers	1.00	.50	.30
158	Joe Gibbon	1.00	.50	.30
159	Jerry Adair	1.00	.50	.30
160	Vada Pinson	2.00	1.00	.60
161	John Purdin	1.00	.50	.30
162	World Series Game 1 (Gibson Fans 17; Sets New Record)	3.50	1.75	1.00
163	World Series Game 2 (Tiger Homers Deck The Cards)	2.50	1.25	.70
164	World Series Game 3 (McCarver's Homer Puts St. Louis Ahead)	2.50	1.25	.70
165	World Series Game 4 (Brock's Lead-Off Homer Starts Cards' Romp)	3.50	1.75	1.00
166	World Series Game 5 (Kaline's Key Hit Sparks Tiger Rally)	3.50	1.75	1.00
167	World Series Game 6 (Tiger 10-Run Inning Ties Mark)	2.50	1.25	.70
168	World Series Game 7 (Lolich Series Hero, Outduels Gibson)	2.75	1.50	.80
169	World Series Summary (Tigers Celebrate Their Victory)	2.50	1.25	.70
170	Frank Howard	2.00	1.00	.60
171	Glenn Beckert	1.25	.60	.40
172	Jerry Stephenson	1.00	.50	.30
173	White Sox Rookies (Bob Christian, Gerry Nyman)	1.00	.50	.30

		NR MT	EX	VG
174	Grant Jackson	1.00	.50	.30
175	Jim Bunning	4.00	2.00	1.25
176	Joe Azcue	1.00	.50	.30
177	Ron Reed	1.00	.50	.30
178	Ray Oyler	1.25	.60	.40
179	Don Pavletich	1.00	.50	.30
180	Willie Horton	1.25	.60	.40
181	Mel Nelson	1.00	.50	.30
182	Bill Rigney	1.00	.50	.30
183	Don Shaw	1.00	.50	.30
184	Roberto Pena	1.00	.50	.30
185	Tom Phoebus	1.00	.50	.30
186	John Edwards	1.00	.50	.30
187	Leon Wagner	1.00	.50	.30
188	Rick Wise	1.00	.50	.30
189	Red Sox Rookies (Joe Lahoud, John Thibdeau)	1.00	.50	.30
190	Willie Mays	65.00	33.00	21.00
191	Lindy McDaniel	1.00	.50	.30
192	Jose Pagan	1.00	.50	.30
193	Don Cardwell	1.00	.50	.30
194	Ted Uhlaender	1.00	.50	.30
195	John Odom	1.00	.50	.30
196	Lum Harris	1.00	.50	.30
197	Dick Selma	1.00	.50	.30
198	Willie Smith	1.00	.50	.30
199	Jim French	1.00	.50	.30
200	Bob Gibson	12.00	6.00	3.50
201	Russ Snyder	1.00	.50	.30
202	Don Wilson	1.00	.50	.30
203	Dave Johnson	1.50	.70	.45
204	Jack Hiatt	1.00	.50	.30
205	Rick Reichardt	1.00	.50	.30
206	Phillies Rookies (Larry Hisle, Barry Lersch)	1.25	.60	.40
207	Roy Face	1.50	.70	.45
208a	Donn Clendenon (Expos)	7.00	3.50	2.00
208b	Donn Clendenon (Houston)	1.00	.50	.30
209	Larry Haney (photo reversed)	1.25	.60	.40
210	Felix Millan	1.00	.50	.30
211	Galen Cisco	1.00	.50	.30
212	Tom Tresh	1.50	.70	.45
213	Gerry Arrigo	1.00	.50	.30
214	Checklist 219-327	2.50	1.25	.70
215	Rico Petrocelli	1.25	.60	.40
216	Don Sutton	5.00	2.50	1.50
217	John Donaldson	1.00	.50	.30
218	John Roseboro	1.00	.50	.30
219	*Freddie Patek*	2.00	1.00	.60
220	Sam McDowell	1.50	.70	.45
221	Art Shamsky	1.50	.70	.45
222	Duane Josephson	1.50	.70	.45
223	Tom Dukes	1.50	.70	.45
224	Angels Rookies (Bill Harrelson, Steve Kealey)	1.50	.70	.45
225	Don Kessinger	1.50	.70	.45
226	Bruce Howard	1.50	.70	.45
227	Frank Johnson	1.50	.70	.45
228	Dave Leonhard	1.50	.70	.45
229	Don Lock	1.50	.70	.45
230	Rusty Staub	2.50	1.25	.70
231	Pat Dobson	1.50	.70	.45
232	Dave Ricketts	1.50	.70	.45
233	Steve Barber	1.50	.70	.45
234	Dave Bristol	1.50	.70	.45
235	Jim Hunter	10.00	5.00	3.00
236	Manny Mota	1.50	.70	.45
237	*Bobby Cox*	1.50	.70	.45
238	Ken Johnson	1.50	.70	.45
239	Bob Taylor	1.50	.70	.45
240	Ken Harrelson	2.00	1.00	.60
241	Jim Brewer	1.50	.70	.45
242	Frank Kostro	1.50	.70	.45
243	Ron Kline	1.50	.70	.45
244	Indians Rookies *(Ray Fosse, George Woodson)*	1.50	.70	.45
245	Ed Charles	1.50	.70	.45
246	Joe Coleman	1.50	.70	.45
247	Gene Oliver	1.50	.70	.45
248	Bob Priddy	1.50	.70	.45
249	Ed Spiezio	1.50	.70	.45
250	Frank Robinson	20.00	10.00	6.00
251	Ron Herbel	1.50	.70	.45
252	Chuck Cottier	1.50	.70	.45
253	Jerry Johnson	1.50	.70	.30
254	Joe Schultz	1.50	.70	.30
255	Steve Carlton	50.00	25.00	15.00
256	Gates Brown	1.50	.70	.30
257	Jim Ray	1.50	.70	.30
258	Jackie Hernandez	1.50	.70	.30
259	Bill Short	1.50	.70	.30
260	*Reggie Jackson*	650.00	325.00	185.00
261	Bob Johnson	1.50	.70	.30
262	Mike Kekich	1.50	.70	.30
263	Jerry May	1.50	.70	.30
264	Bill Landis	1.50	.70	.30
265	Chico Cardenas	1.50	.70	.30
266	Dodgers Rookies (Alan Foster, Tom Hutton)	1.50	.70	.30
267	Vicente Romo	1.50	.70	.30
268	Al Spangler	1.50	.70	.30
269	Al Weis	1.50	.70	.30
270	Mickey Lolich	3.50	1.75	1.00
271	Larry Stahl	1.50	.70	.30
272	Ed Stroud	1.50	.70	.30
273	Ron Willis	1.50	.70	.30
274	Clyde King	1.50	.70	.30
275	Vic Davalillo	1.50	.70	.30
276	Gary Wagner	1.50	.70	.30
277	*Rod Hendricks*	1.50	.70	.30
278	Gary Geiger	1.50	.70	.30
279	Roger Nelson	1.50	.70	.30
280	Alex Johnson	1.50	.70	.30
281	Ted Kubiak	1.50	.70	.30
282	Pat Jarvis	1.50	.70	.30
283	Sandy Alomar	1.50	.70	.30
284	Expos Rookies (Jerry Robertson, Mike Wegener)	1.50	.70	.30
285	Don Mincher	1.50	.70	.30
286	*Dock Ellis*	1.50	.70	.30
287	Jose Tartabull	1.50	.70	.30
288	Ken Holtzman	1.50	.70	.30
289	Bart Shirley	1.50	.70	.30
290	Jim Kaat	4.50	2.25	1.25
291	Vern Fuller	1.50	.70	.30
292	Al Downing	1.50	.70	.45
293	Dick Dietz	1.50	.70	.30
294	Jim Lemon	1.50	.70	.30
295	Tony Perez	10.00	5.00	3.00
296	*Andy Messersmith*	1.50	.70	.45
297	Deron Johnson	1.50	.70	.30
298	Dave Nicholson	1.50	.70	.30
299	Mark Belanger	1.50	.70	.30
300	Felipe Alou	1.50	.70	.45
301	Darrell Brandon	1.50	.70	.30
302	Jim Pagliaroni	1.50	.70	.30
303	Cal Koonce	1.50	.70	.30
304	Padres Rookies (Bill Davis, *Clarence Gaston*)	8.00	4.00	2.50
305	Dick McAuliffe	1.50	.70	.30
306	Jim Grant	1.50	.70	.30
307	Gary Kolb	1.50	.70	.30
308	Wade Blasingame	1.50	.70	.30
309	Walt Williams	1.50	.70	.30
310	Tom Haller	1.50	.70	.30
311	*Sparky Lyle*	12.00	6.00	3.50
312	Lee Elia	1.50	.70	.30
313	Bill Robinson	1.50	.70	.30
314	Checklist 328-425 (Don Drysdale)	3.50	1.75	1.00
315	Eddie Fisher	1.50	.70	.30
316	Hal Lanier	1.50	.70	.30
317	Bruce Look	1.50	.70	.30
318	Jack Fisher	1.50	.70	.30
319	Ken McMullen	1.50	.70	.30
320	Dal Maxvill	1.50	.70	.30
321	Jim McAndrew	1.50	.70	.30
322	Jose Vidal	1.50	.70	.30
323	Larry Miller	1.50	.70	.30
324	Tigers Rookies (Les Cain, Dave Campbell)	1.50	.70	.30
325	Jose Cardenal	1.50	.70	.30
326	Gary Sutherland	1.50	.70	.30
327	Willie Crawford	1.50	.70	.30
328	Joe Horlen	1.00	.50	.30
329	Rick Joseph	1.00	.50	.30
330	Tony Conigliaro	1.50	.70	.45
331	Braves Rookies (Gil Garrido, *Tom House*)	1.00	.50	.30
332	Fred Talbot	1.25	.60	.40
333	Ivan Murrell	1.00	.50	.30
334	Phil Roof	1.00	.50	.30
335	Bill Mazeroski	1.75	.90	.50
336	Jim Roland	1.00	.50	.30
337	Marty Martinez	1.00	.50	.30
338	*Del Unser*	1.00	.50	.30
339	Reds Rookies (Steve Mingori, Jose Pena)	1.00	.50	.30
340	Dave McNally	1.25	.60	.40
341	Dave Adlesh	1.00	.50	.30
342	Bubba Morton	1.00	.50	.30
343	Dan Frisella	1.00	.50	.30
344	Tom Matchick	1.00	.50	.30

		NR MT	EX	VG
345	Frank Linzy	1.00	.50	.30
346	Wayne Comer	1.25	.60	.40
347	Randy Hundley	1.00	.50	.30
348	Steve Hargan	1.00	.50	.30
349	Dick Williams	1.25	.60	.40
350	Richie Allen	2.00	1.00	.60
351	Carroll Sembera	1.00	.50	.30
352	Paul Schaal	1.00	.50	.30
353	Jeff Torborg	1.00	.50	.30
354	Nate Oliver	1.25	.60	.40
355	Phil Niekro	7.00	3.50	2.00
356	Frank Quilici	1.00	.50	.30
357	Carl Taylor	1.00	.50	.30
358	Athletics Rookies (George Lauzerique, Roberto Rodriguez)	1.00	.50	.30
359	Dick Kelley	1.00	.50	.30
360	Jim Wynn	1.25	.60	.40
361	Gary Holman	1.00	.50	.30
362	Jim Maloney	1.00	.50	.30
363	Russ Nixon	1.00	.50	.30
364	Tommie Agee	1.25	.60	.40
365	Jim Fregosi	1.00	.50	.30
366	Bo Belinsky	1.00	.50	.30
367	Lou Johnson	1.00	.50	.30
368	Vic Roznovsky	1.00	.50	.30
369	Bob Skinner	1.00	.50	.30
370	Juan Marichal	7.00	3.50	2.00
371	Sal Bando	1.25	.60	.40
372	Adolfo Phillips	1.00	.50	.30
373	Fred Lasher	1.00	.50	.30
374	Bob Tillman	1.00	.50	.30
375	Harmon Killebrew	20.00	10.00	6.00
376	Royals Rookies (Mike Fiore, *Jim Rooker*)	1.00	.50	.30
377	Gary Bell	1.25	.60	.40
378	Jose Herrera	1.00	.50	.30
379	Ken Boyer	1.75	.90	.50
380	Stan Bahnsen	1.25	.60	.40
381	Ed Kranepool	1.25	.60	.40
382	Pat Corrales	1.25	.60	.40
383	Casey Cox	1.00	.50	.30
384	Larry Shepard	1.00	.50	.30
385	Orlando Cepeda	3.50	1.75	1.00
386	Jim McGlothlin	1.00	.50	.30
387	Bobby Klaus	1.00	.50	.30
388	Tom McCraw	1.00	.50	.30
389	Dan Coombs	1.00	.50	.30
390	Bill Freehan	1.00	.50	.30
391	Ray Culp	1.00	.50	.30
392	Bob Burda	1.00	.50	.30
393	Gene Brabender	1.00	.50	.30
394	Pilots Rookies (Lou Piniella, Marv Staehle)	3.00	1.50	.90
395	Chris Short	1.00	.50	.30
396	Jim Campanis	1.00	.50	.30
397	Chuck Dobson	1.00	.50	.30
398	Tito Francona	1.00	.50	.30
399	Bob Bailey	1.00	.50	.30
400	Don Drysdale	8.00	4.00	2.50
401	Jake Gibbs	1.25	.60	.40
402	Ken Boswell	1.00	.50	.30
403	Bob Miller	1.00	.50	.30
404	Cubs Rookies (Vic LaRose, Gary Ross)	1.00	.50	.30
405	Lee May	1.00	.50	.30
406	Phil Ortega	1.00	.50	.30
407	Tom Egan	1.00	.50	.30
408	Nate Colbert	1.00	.50	.30
409	Bob Moose	1.00	.50	.30
410	Al Kaline	15.00	7.50	4.50
411	Larry Dierker	1.00	.50	.30
412	Checklist 426-512 (Mickey Mantle)	7.00	3.50	2.00
413	Roland Sheldon	1.25	.60	.40
414	Duke Sims	1.00	.50	.30
415	Ray Washburn	1.00	.50	.30
416	Willie McCovey AS	3.50	1.75	1.00
417	Ken Harrelson AS	1.00	.50	.30
418	Tommy Helms AS	1.00	.50	.30
419	Rod Carew AS	10.00	7.50	4.50
420	Ron Santo AS	1.00	.50	.30
421	Brooks Robinson AS	4.00	2.00	1.25
422	Don Kessinger AS	1.00	.50	.30
423	Bert Campaneris AS	1.25	.60	.40
424	Pete Rose AS	12.00	6.00	3.50
425	Carl Yastrzemski AS	6.00	3.00	1.75
426	Curt Flood AS	1.00	.50	.30
427	Tony Oliva AS	1.50	.70	.45
428	Lou Brock AS	5.00	2.50	1.50
429	Willie Horton AS	1.25	.60	.40
430	Johnny Bench AS	12.00	6.00	3.50
431	Bill Freehan AS	1.00	.50	.30
432	Bob Gibson AS	5.00	2.50	1.50
433	Denny McLain AS	1.50	.70	.45
434	Jerry Koosman AS	1.00	.50	.30
435	Sam McDowell AS	1.25	.60	.40
436	Gene Alley	1.00	.50	.30
437	Luis Alcaraz	1.00	.50	.30
438	Gary Waslewski	1.00	.50	.30
439	White Sox Rookies (Ed Herrmann, Dan Lazar)	1.00	.50	.30
440a	Willie McCovey (last name in white)	90.00	45.00	27.00
440b	Willie McCovey (last name in yellow)	18.00	9.00	5.50
441a	Dennis Higgins (last name in white)	10.00	5.00	3.00
441b	Dennis Higgins (last name in yellow)	1.00	.50	.30
442	Ty Cline	1.00	.50	.30
443	Don Wert	1.00	.50	.30
444a	Joe Moeller (last name in white)	10.00	5.00	3.00
444b	Joe Moeller (last name in yellow)	1.00	.50	.30
445	Bobby Knoop	1.00	.50	.30
446	Claude Raymond	1.00	.50	.30
447a	Ralph Houk (last name in white)	15.00	7.50	4.50
447b	Ralph Houk (last name in yellow)	1.50	.70	.45
448	Bob Tolan	1.00	.50	.30
449	Paul Lindblad	1.00	.50	.30
450	Billy Williams	6.00	3.00	1.75
451a	Rich Rollins (first name in white)	10.00	5.00	3.00
451b	Rich Rollins (first name in yellow)	1.25	.60	.40
452a	Al Ferrara (first name in white)	10.00	5.00	3.00
452b	Al Ferrara (first name in yellow)	1.00	.50	.30
453	Mike Cuellar	1.25	.60	.40
454a	Phillies Rookies (Larry Colton, *Don Money*) (names in white)	10.00	5.00	3.00
454b	Phillies Rookies (Larry Colton, *Don Money*) (names in yellow)	1.25	.60	.40
455	Sonny Siebert	1.00	.50	.30
456	Bud Harrelson	1.00	.50	.30
457	Dalton Jones	1.00	.50	.30
458	Curt Blefary	1.00	.50	.30
459	Dave Boswell	1.00	.50	.30
460	Joe Torre	1.75	.90	.50
461a	Mike Epstein (last name in white)	10.00	5.00	3.00
461b	Mike Epstein (last name in yellow)	1.00	.50	.30
462	Red Schoendienst	1.50	.70	.45
463	Dennis Ribant	1.00	.50	.30
464a	Dave Marshall (last name in white)	10.00	5.00	3.00
464b	Dave Marshall (last name in yellow)	1.00	.50	.30
465	Tommy John	4.50	2.25	1.25
466	John Boccabella	1.00	.50	.30
467	Tom Reynolds	1.00	.50	.30
468a	Pirates Rookies (Bruce Dal Canton, Bob Robertson) (names in white)	10.00	5.00	3.00
468b	Pirates Rookies (Bruce Dal Canton, Bob Robertson) (names in yellow)	1.00	.50	.30
469	Chico Ruiz	1.00	.50	.30
470a	Mel Stottlemyre (last name in white)	15.00	7.50	4.50
470b	Mel Stottlemyre (last name in yellow)	1.50	.70	.45
471a	Ted Savage (last name in white)	10.00	5.00	3.00
471b	Ted Savage (last name in yellow)	1.00	.50	.30
472	Jim Price	1.00	.50	.30
473a	Jose Arcia (first name in white)	10.00	5.00	3.00
473b	Jose Arcia (first name in yellow)	1.00	.50	.30
474	Tom Murphy	1.00	.50	.30
475	Tim McCarver	1.50	.70	.45
476a	Red Sox Rookies (*Ken Brett*, Gerry Moses) (names in white)	10.00	5.00	3.00
476b	Red Sox Rookies (*Ken Brett*, Gerry Moses) (names in yellow)	1.00	.50	.30
477	Jeff James	1.00	.50	.30
478	Don Buford	1.00	.50	.30
479	Richie Scheinblum	1.00	.50	.30
480	Tom Seaver	160.00	80.00	52.00
481	*Bill Melton*	1.25	.60	.40
482a	Jim Gosger (first name in white)	10.00	5.00	3.00
482b	Jim Gosger (first name in yellow)	1.25	.60	.40
483	Ted Abernathy	1.00	.50	.30
484	Joe Gordon	1.00	.50	.30
485a	Gaylord Perry (last name in white)	75.00	38.00	23.00
485b	Gaylord Perry (last name in yellow)	10.00	5.00	3.00
486a	Paul Casanova (last name in white)	10.00	5.00	3.00

	NR MT	EX	VG
486b Paul Casanova (last name in yellow)			
	1.00	.50	.30
487 Denis Menke	1.00	.50	.30
488 Joe Sparma	1.00	.50	.30
489 Clete Boyer	1.25	.60	.40
490 Matty Alou	1.00	.50	.30
491a Twins Rookies (Jerry Crider, George			
Mitterwald) (names in white)	10.00	5.00	3.00
491b Twins Rookies (Jerry Crider, George			
Mitterwald) (names in yellow)	1.00	.50	.30
492 Tony Cloninger	1.00	.50	.30
493a Wes Parker (last name in white)	10.00	5.00	3.00
493b Wes Parker (last name in yellow)	1.00	.50	.30
494 Ken Berry	1.00	.50	.30
495 Bert Campaneris	1.50	.70	.45
496 Larry Jaster	1.00	.50	.30
497 Julian Javier	1.00	.50	.30
498 Juan Pizarro	1.00	.50	.30
499 Astros Rookies (Don Bryant, Steve Shea)			
	1.00	.50	.30
500a Mickey Mantle (last name in white)			
	475.00	190.00	119.00
500b Mickey Mantle (last name in yellow)			
	175.00	87.00	52.00
501a Tony Gonzalez (first name in white)			
	10.00	5.00	3.00
501b Tony Gonzalez (first name in yellow)			
	1.00	.50	.30
502 Minnie Rojas	1.00	.50	.30
503 Larry Brown	1.00	.50	.30
504 Checklist 513-588 (Brooks Robinson)			
	4.00	2.00	1.25
505a Bobby Bolin (last name in white)	10.00	5.00	3.00
505b Bobby Bolin (last name in yellow)	1.00	.50	.30
506 Paul Blair	1.00	.50	.30
507 Cookie Rojas	1.00	.50	.30
508 Moe Drabowsky	1.00	.50	.30
509 Manny Sanguillen	1.00	.50	.30
510 Rod Carew	60.00	30.00	18.00
511a Diego Segui (first name in white)	10.00	5.00	3.00
511b Diego Segui (first name in yellow)	1.25	.60	.40
512 Cleon Jones	1.25	.60	.40
513 Camilo Pascual	1.00	.50	.30
514 Mike Lum	1.00	.50	.30
515 Dick Green	1.00	.50	.30
516 Earl Weaver	5.00	2.50	1.50
517 Mike McCormick	1.25	.60	.40
518 Fred Whitfield	1.00	.50	.30
519 Yankees Rookies (Len Boehmer, Gerry			
Kenney)	1.00	.50	.30
520 Bob Veale	1.25	.60	.40
521 George Thomas	1.00	.50	.30
522 Joe Hoerner	1.00	.50	.30
523 Bob Chance	1.00	.50	.30
524 Expos Rookies (Jose Laboy, Floyd Wicker)			
	1.00	.50	.30
525 Earl Wilson	1.00	.50	.30
526 Hector Torres	1.00	.50	.30
527 Al Lopez	3.00	1.50	.90
528 Claude Osteen	1.00	.50	.30
529 Ed Kirkpatrick	1.00	.50	.30
530 Cesar Tovar	1.00	.50	.30
531 Dick Farrell	1.00	.50	.30
532 Bird Hill Aces (Mike Cuellar, Jim Hardin,			
Dave McNally, Tom Phoebus)	1.50	.70	.45
533 Nolan Ryan	500.00	250.00	150.00
534 Jerry McNertney	1.00	.50	.30
535 Phil Regan	1.00	.50	.30
536 Padres Rookies (Danny Breeden, Dave			
Roberts)	1.25	.60	.40
537 Mike Paul	1.00	.50	.30
538 Charlie Smith	1.00	.50	.30
539 Ted Shows How (Mike Epstein, Ted			
Williams)	3.25	1.75	1.00
540 Curt Flood	1.50	.70	.45
541 Joe Verbanic	1.00	.50	.30
542 Bob Aspromonte	1.00	.50	.30
543 Fred Newman	1.00	.50	.30
544 Tigers Rookies (Mike Kilkenny, Ron			
Woods)	1.00	.50	.30
545 Willie Stargell	10.00	5.00	3.00
546 Jim Nash	1.00	.50	.30
547 Billy Martin	5.00	2.50	1.50
548 Bob Locker	1.00	.50	.30
549 Ron Brand	1.00	.50	.30
550 Brooks Robinson	15.00	7.50	4.50
551 Wayne Granger	1.00	.50	.30
552 Dodgers Rookies (Ted Sizemore, Bill			
Sudakis)	1.25	.60	.40
553 Ron Davis	1.00	.50	.30
554 Frank Bertaina	1.00	.50	.30

	NR MT	EX	VG
555 Jim Hart	1.25	.60	.40
556 A's Stars (Sal Bando, Bert Campaneris,			
Danny Cater)	1.50	.70	.45
557 Frank Fernandez	1.00	.50	.30
558 Tom Burgmeier	1.25	.60	.40
559 Cards Rookies (Joe Hague, Jim Hicks)			
	1.00	.50	.30
560 Luis Tiant	1.50	.70	.45
561 Ron Clark	1.00	.50	.30
562 Bob Watson	1.00	.50	.30
563 Marty Pattin	1.00	.50	.30
564 Gil Hodges	6.00	3.00	1.75
565 Hoyt Wilhelm	6.00	3.00	1.75
566 Ron Hansen	1.00	.50	.30
567 Pirates Rookies (Elvio Jimenez, Jim			
Shellenback)	1.00	.50	.30
568 Cecil Upshaw	1.00	.50	.30
569 Billy Harris	1.00	.50	.30
570 Ron Santo	1.75	.90	.50
571 Cap Peterson	1.00	.50	.30
572 Giants Heroes (Juan Marichal, Willie			
McCovey)	7.00	3.50	2.00
573 Jim Palmer	40.00	20.00	12.00
574 George Scott	1.00	.50	.30
575 Bill Singer	1.25	.60	.40
576 Phillies Rookies (Ron Stone, Bill Wilson)			
	1.00	.50	.30
577 Mike Hegan	1.00	.50	.30
578 Don Bosch	1.00	.50	.30
579 Dave Nelson	1.25	.60	.40
580 Jim Northrup	1.25	.60	.40
581 Gary Nolan	1.00	.50	.30
582a Checklist 589-664 (Tony Oliva) (red circle			
on back)	3.50	1.75	1.00
582b Checklist 589-664 (Tony Oliva) (white			
circle on back)	2.50	1.25	.70
583 Clyde Wright	1.25	.60	.40
584 Don Mason	1.00	.50	.30
585 Ron Swoboda	1.00	.50	.30
586 Tim Cullen	1.00	.50	.30
587 Joe Rudi	1.75	.90	.50
588 Bill White	1.00	.50	.30
589 Joe Pepitone	2.00	1.00	.60
590 Rico Carty	1.00	.50	.30
591 Mike Hedlund	1.00	.50	.30
592 Padres Rookies (Rafael Robles, Al			
Santorini)	1.00	.50	.30
593 Don Nottebart	1.00	.50	.30
594 Dooley Womack	1.00	.50	.30
595 Lee Maye	1.00	.50	.30
596 Chuck Hartenstein	1.00	.50	.30
597 A.L. Rookies (Larry Burchart, Rollie			
Fingers, Bob Floyd)	150.00	75.00	50.00
598 Ruben Amaro	1.00	.50	.30
599 John Boozer	1.00	.50	.30
600 Tony Oliva	4.00	2.00	1.25
601 Tug McGraw	2.00	1.00	.60
602 Cubs Rookies (Alec Distaso, Jim Qualls,			
Don Young)	1.00	.50	.30
603 Joe Keough	1.00	.50	.30
604 Bobby Etheridge	1.00	.50	.30
605 Dick Ellsworth	1.00	.50	.30
606 Gene Mauch	1.00	.50	.30
607 Dick Bosman	1.00	.50	.30
608 Dick Simpson	1.00	.50	.30
609 Phil Gagliano	1.00	.50	.30
610 Jim Hardin	1.00	.50	.30
611 Braves Rookies (Bob Didier, Walt Hriniak,			
Gary Neibauer)	1.00	.50	.30
612 Jack Aker	1.00	.50	.30
613 Jim Beauchamp	1.00	.50	.30
614 Astros Rookies (Tom Griffin, Skip Guinn)			
	1.00	.50	.30
615 Len Gabrielson	1.00	.50	.30
616 Don McMahon	1.00	.50	.30
617 Jesse Gonder	1.00	.50	.30
618 Ramon Webster	1.00	.50	.30
619 Royals Rookies (Bill Butler, Pat Kelly,			
Juan Rios)	1.25	.60	.40
620 Dean Chance	1.25	.60	.40
621 Bill Voss	1.00	.50	.30
622 Dan Osinski	1.00	.50	.30
623 Hank Allen	1.00	.50	.30
624 N.L. Rookies (Darrel Chaney, Duffy Dyer,			
Terry Harmon)	1.25	.60	.40
625 Mack Jones	1.00	.50	.30
626 Gene Michael	1.00	.50	.30
627 George Stone	1.00	.50	.30
628 Red Sox Rookies (Bill Conigliaro, Syd			
O'Brien, Fred Wenz)	1.00	.50	.30
629 Jack Hamilton	1.00	.50	.30

		NR MT	EX	VG
630	*Bobby Bonds*	35.00	17.50	10.50
631	John Kennedy	1.00	.50	.30
632	Jon Warden	1.00	.50	.30
633	Harry Walker	1.25	.60	.40
634	Andy Etchebarren	1.00	.50	.30
635	George Culver	1.00	.50	.30
636	Woodie Held	1.00	.50	.30
637	Padres Rookies (Jerry DaVanon, *Clay Kirby*, Frank Reberger)	1.25	.60	.40
638	Ed Sprague	1.00	.50	.30
639	Barry Moore	1.00	.50	.30
640	Fergie Jenkins	18.00	9.00	5.50
641	N.L. Rookies (Bobby Darwin, Tommy Dean, John Miller)	1.00	.50	.30
642	John Hiller	1.25	.60	.40
643	Billy Cowan	1.00	.50	.30
644	Chuck Hinton	1.00	.50	.30
645	George Brunet	1.00	.50	.30
646	Expos Rookies (Dan McGinn, *Carl Morton*)	1.00	.50	.30
647	Dave Wickersham	1.00	.50	.30
648	Bobby Wine	1.00	.50	.30
649	Al Jackson	1.00	.50	.30
650	Ted Williams	10.00	5.00	3.00
651	Gus Gil	1.00	.50	.30
652	Eddie Watt	1.00	.50	.30
653	*Aurelio Rodriguez* (photo actually batboy Leonard Garcia)	1.50	.70	.45
654	White Sox Rookies (*Carlos May*, Rich Morales, Don Secrist)	1.00	.50	.30
655	Mike Hershberger	1.00	.50	.30
656	Dan Schneider	1.00	.50	.30
657	Bobby Murcer	2.25	1.25	.70
658	A.L. Rookies (Bill Burbach, Tom Hall, Jim Miles)	1.00	.50	.30
659	Johnny Podres	1.75	.90	.50
660	Reggie Smith	1.75	.90	.50
661	Jim Merritt	1.00	.50	.30
662	Royals Rookies (Dick Drago, Bob Oliver, George Spriggs)	1.25	.60	.40
663	Dick Radatz	1.00	.50	.30
664	Ron Hunt	2.00	.50	.25

1969 Topps Decals

Designed as an insert for 1969 regular issue card packs, these decals are virtually identical in format to the '69 cards. The 48 decals in the set measure 1" by 2-1/2," although they are mounted on white paper backing which measures 1-3/4" by 2-1/8."

		NR MT	EX	VG
Complete Set:		350.00	175.00	105.00
Common Player:		4.00	2.00	1.25
(1)	Hank Aaron	40.00	20.00	12.00
(2)	Richie Allen	4.00	2.00	1.25
(3)	Felipe Alou	4.00	2.00	1.25
(4)	Matty Alou	4.00	2.00	1.25
(5)	Luis Aparicio	4.50	2.25	1.25
(6)	Bob Clemente	50.00	25.00	15.00
(7)	Donn Clendenon	4.00	2.00	1.25
(8)	Tommy Davis	4.00	2.00	1.25
(9)	Don Drysdale	7.00	3.50	2.00
(10)	Joe Foy	4.00	2.00	1.25
(11)	Jim Fregosi	4.00	2.00	1.25
(12)	Bob Gibson	7.00	3.50	2.00
(13)	Tony Gonzalez	4.00	2.00	1.25
(14)	Tom Haller	4.00	2.00	1.25
(15)	Ken Harrelson	4.00	2.00	1.25
(16)	Tommy Helms	4.00	2.00	1.25
(17)	Willie Horton	4.00	2.00	1.25
(18)	Frank Howard	4.00	2.00	1.25
(19)	Reggie Jackson	100.00	50.00	30.00
(20)	Fergie Jenkins	6.00	3.00	1.75
(21)	Harmon Killebrew	6.00	3.00	1.75
(22)	Jerry Koosman	4.00	2.00	1.25
(23)	Mickey Mantle	75.00	38.00	23.00
(24)	Willie Mays	35.00	17.50	10.50
(25)	Tim McCarver	4.00	2.00	1.25
(26)	Willie McCovey	7.00	3.50	2.00
(27)	Sam McDowell	4.00	2.00	1.25
(28)	Denny McLain	4.00	2.00	1.25
(29)	Dave McNally	4.00	2.00	1.25
(30)	Don Mincher	4.00	2.00	1.25
(31)	Rick Monday	4.00	2.00	1.25
(32)	Tony Oliva	4.00	2.00	1.25
(33)	Camilo Pascual	4.00	2.00	1.25
(34)	Rick Reichardt	4.00	2.00	1.25
(35)	Pete Rose	25.00	12.50	7.50
(36)	Frank Robinson	7.00	3.50	2.00
(37)	Ron Santo	4.00	2.00	1.25
(38)	Dick Selma	4.00	2.00	1.25
(39)	Tom Seaver	50.00	25.00	15.00
(40)	Chris Short	4.00	2.00	1.25
(41)	Rusty Staub	4.00	2.00	1.25
(42)	Mel Stottlemyre	4.00	2.00	1.25
(43)	Luis Tiant	4.00	2.00	1.25
(44)	Pete Ward	4.00	2.00	1.25
(45)	Hoyt Wilhelm	6.00	3.00	1.75
(46)	Maury Wills	4.00	2.00	1.25
(47)	Jim Wynn	4.00	2.00	1.25
(48)	Carl Yastrzemski	30.00	15.00	9.00

1969 Topps Deckle Edge

PETE ROSE
No. 21 of 33 photos

These 2-1/4" by 3-1/4" inch cards take their name from their interesting borders which have a scalloped effect. The fronts have a black and white picture of the player along with a blue facsimile autograph. Backs have the player's name and the card number in light blue ink in a small box at the bottom of the card. Technically, there are only 33 numbered cards, but there are actually 35 possible players; both Jim Wynn and Hoyt Wilhelm cards are found as #11 while cards of Joe Foy and Rusty Staub can be found as #22. Many of the players in the set are stars.

		NR MT	EX	VG
Complete Set:		100.00	50.00	30.00
Common Player:		1.00	.50	.30
1	Brooks Robinson	15.00	7.50	4.50
2	Boog Powell	1.00	.50	.30
3	Ken Harrelson	1.00	.50	.30
4	Carl Yastrzemski	15.00	7.50	4.50
5	Jim Fregosi	1.00	.50	.30
6	Luis Aparicio	1.25	.60	.40
7	Luis Tiant	1.00	.50	.30
8	Denny McLain	1.00	.50	.30
9	Willie Horton	1.00	.50	.30
10	Bill Freehan	1.00	.50	.30
11a	Hoyt Wilhelm	10.00	5.00	3.00
11b	Jim Wynn	10.00	5.00	3.00
12	Rod Carew	15.00	7.50	4.50

		NR MT	EX	VG
13	Mel Stottlemyre	1.00	.50	.30
14	Rick Monday	1.00	.50	.30
15	Tommy Davis	1.00	.50	.30
16	Frank Howard	1.00	.50	.30
17	Felipe Alou	1.00	.50	.30
18	Don Kessinger	1.00	.50	.30
19	Ron Santo	1.00	.50	.30
20	Tommy Helms	1.00	.50	.30
21	Pete Rose	10.00	5.00	3.00
22a	Rusty Staub	2.25	1.25	.70
22b	Joe Foy	7.00	3.50	2.00
23	Tom Haller	1.00	.50	.30
24	Maury Wills	1.00	.50	.30
25	Jerry Koosman	1.00	.50	.30
26	Richie Allen	1.00	.50	.30
27	Bob Clemente	15.00	7.50	4.50
28	Curt Flood	1.00	.50	.30
29	Bob Gibson	10.00	5.00	3.00
30	Al Ferrara	1.00	.50	.30
31	Willie McCovey	10.00	5.00	3.00
32	Juan Marichal	7.00	3.50	2.00
33	Willie Mays, Willie Mays	15.00	7.50	4.50

1969 Topps
4-On-1 Mini Stickers

Another in the long line of Topps test issues, the 4-on-1s are 2-1/2" by 3-1/2" cards with blank backs featuring a quartet of miniature stickers in the design of the same cards from the 1969 Topps regular set. There are 25 different cards, for a total of 100 different stickers. As they are not common, Mint cards bring fairly strong prices on today's market. As the set was drawn from the 3rd Series of the regular cards, it includes some rookie stickers and World Series highlight stickers.

	NR MT	EX	VG
Complete Set:	950.00	475.00	285.00
Common Player:	15.00	7.50	4.50
(1) Jerry Adair, Willie Mays, Johnny Morris, Don Wilson	100.00	50.00	30.00
(2) Tommie Aaron, Jim Britton, Donn Clendenon, Woody Woodward	15.00	7.50	4.50
(3) World Series Game 4, Tommy Davis, Don Pavletich, Vada Pinson	20.00	10.00	6.00
(4) Max Alvis, Glenn Beckert, Ron Fairly, Rick Wise	15.00	7.50	4.50
(5) Johnny Callison, Jim French, Lum Harris, Dick Selma	15.00	7.50	4.50
(6) World Series Game 3, Bob Gibson, Larry Haney, Rick Reichardt	40.00	20.00	12.00
(7) Houston Rookie Stars, Wally Bunker, Don Cardwell, Joe Gibbon	15.00	7.50	4.50
(8) Ollie Brown, Jim Bunning, Andy Kosco, Ron Reed	20.00	10.00	6.00
(9) Bill Dillman, Jim Lefebvre, John Purdin, John Roseboro	15.00	7.50	4.50
(10) Bill Hands, Chuck Harrison, Lindy McDaniel, Felix Millan	15.00	7.50	4.50
(11) Jack Hiatt, Dave Johnson, Mel Nelson, Tommie Sisk	18.00	9.00	5.50
(12) Clay Dalrymple, Leo Durocher, John Odom, Wilbur Wood	18.00	9.00	5.50
(13) Hank Bauer, Kevin Collins, Ray Oyler, Russ Snyder	15.00	7.50	4.50

	NR MT	EX	VG
(14) Red Sox Rookie Stars, World Series Game 7, Gerry Arrigo, Jim Perry	18.00	9.00	5.50
(15) World Series Game 2, Bill McCool, Roberto Pena, Doug Rader	15.00	7.50	4.50
(16) Ed Brinkman, Roy Face, Willie Horton, Bob Rodgers	18.00	9.00	5.50
(17) Dave Baldwin, J.C. Martin, Dave May, Ray Sadecki	15.00	7.50	4.50
(18) World Series Game 1, Jose Pagan, Tom Phoebus, Mike Shannon	15.00	7.50	4.50
(19) Pete Rose, Lee Stange, Don Sutton, Ted Uhlaender	275.00	137.00	82.00
(20) Joe Grzenda, Frank Howard, Dick Tracewski, Jim Weaver	20.00	10.00	6.00
(21) White Sox Rookie Stars, Joe Azcue, Grant Jackson, Denny McLain	20.00	10.00	6.00
(22) John Edwards, Jim Fairey, Phillies Rookies, Stan Williams	15.00	7.50	4.50
(23) World Series Summary, John Bateman, Willie Smith, Leon Wagner	15.00	7.50	4.50
(24) World Series Game 5, Yankees Rookies, Chris Cannizzaro, Bob Hendley	15.00	7.50	4.50
(25) Cardinals Rookie Stars, Joe Nossek, Rico Petrocelli, Carl Yastrzemski	175.00	87.00	52.00

1969 Topps Stamps

Topps continued to refine its efforts at baseball stamps in 1969 with the release of 240 player stamps, each measuring 1" by 1-7/16." Each stamp jsd s color photo along with the player's name, position and team. Unlike prior stamp issues, the 1969 stamps have 24 separate albums (one per team). The stamps were issued in strips of 12.

	NR MT	EX	VG
Complete Sheet Set:	250.00	125.00	75.00
Common Sheet:	1.25	.60	.40
Complete Stamp Album Set:	14.00	7.00	4.25
Single Stamp Album:	.50	.25	.15
(1) Tommie Agee, Sandy Alomar, Jose Cardenal, Dean Chance, Joe Foy, Jim Grant, Don Kessinger, Mickey Mantle, Jerry May, Bob Rodgers, Cookie Rojas, Gary Sutherland	18.00	9.00	5.50
(2) Jesus Alou, Mike Andrews, Larry Brown, Moe Drabowsky, Alex Johnson, Lew Krausse, Jim Lefebvre, Dal Maxvill, John Odom, Claude Osteen, Rick Reichardt, Luis Tiant	1.50	.70	.45
(3) Hank Aaron, Matty Alou, Max Alvis, Nelson Briles, Eddie Fisher, Bud Harrelson, Willie Horton, Randy Hundley, Larry Jaster, Jim Kaat, Gary Peters, Pete Ward	7.00	3.50	2.00
(4) Don Buford, John Callison, Tommy Davis, Jackie Hernandez, Fergie Jenkins, Lee May, Denny McLain, Bob Oliver, Roberto Pena, Tony Perez, Joe Torre, Tom Tresh	3.00	1.50	.90
(5) Jim Bunning, Dean Chance, Joe Foy, Sonny Jackson, Don Kessinger, Rick Monday, Gaylord Perry, Roger Repoz, Cookie Rojas, Mel Stottlemyre, Leon Wagner, Jim Wynn	3.00	1.50	.90
(6) Felipe Alou, Gerry Arrigo, Bob Aspromonte, Gary Bell, Clay Dalrymple, Jim Fregosi, Tony Gonzalez, Duane Josephson, Dick McAuliffe, Tony Oliva, Brooks Robinson, Willie Stargell	6.00	3.00	1.75

(7)   Steve Barber, Donn Clendenon, Joe
Coleman, Vic Davalillo, Russ Gibson, Jerry
Grote, Tom Haller, Andy Kosco, Willie
McCovey, Don Mincher, Joe Morgan, Don
Wilson   4.00   2.00   1.25
(8)   George Brunet, Don Buford, John
Callison, Danny Cater, Tommy Davis, Willie
Davis, John Edwards, Jim Hart, Mickey
Lolich, Willie Mays, Roberto Pena, Mickey
Stanley   7.00   3.50   2.00
(9)   Ernie Banks, Glenn Beckert, Ken Berry,
Horace Clarke, Bob Clemente, Larry Dierker,
Len Gabrielson, Jake Gibbs, Jerry Koosman,
Sam McDowell, Tom Satriano, Bill Singer
                                          3.50   1.75   1.00
(10) Gene Alley, Lou Brock, Larry Brown, Moe
Drabowsky, Frank Howard, Tommie John,
Roger Nelson, Claude Osteen, Phil Regan,
Rick Reichardt, Tony Taylor, Roy White
                                          4.00   2.00   1.25
(11) Bob Allison, John Bateman, Don Drysdale,
Dave Johnson, Harmon Killebrew, Jim
Maloney, Bill Mazeroski, Gerry McNertney,
Ron Perranoski, Rico Petrocelli, Pete Rose,
Billy Williams   18.00   9.00   5.50
(12) Bernie Allen, Jose Arcia, Stan Bahnsen,
Sal Bando, Jim Davenport, Tito Francona,
Dick Green, Ron Hunt, Mack Jones, Vada
Pinson, George Scott, Don Wert   1.50   .70   .45
(13) Gerry Arrigo, Bob Aspromonte, Joe
Azcue, Curt Blefary, Orlando Cepeda, Bill
Freehan, Jim Fregosi, Dave Giusti, Duane
Josephson, Tim McCarver, Jose Santiago,
Bob Tolan   2.00   1.00   .60
(14) Jerry Adair, Johnny Bench, Clete Boyer,
John Briggs, Bert Campaneris, Woody
Fryman, Ron Kline, Bobby Knoop, Ken
McMullen, Adolfo Phillips, John Roseboro,
Tom Seaver   7.00   3.50   2.00
(15) Norm Cash, Ron Fairly, Bob Gibson, Bill
Hands, Cleon Jones, Al Kaline, Paul Schaal,
Mike Shannon, Duke Sims, Reggie Smith,
Steve Whitaker, Carl Yastrzemski   12.00   6.00   3.50
(16) Steve Barber, Paul Casanova, Dick Dietz,
Russ Gibson, Jerry Grote, Tom Haller, Ed
Kranepool, Juan Marichal, Denis Menke, Jim
Nash, Bill Robinson, Frank Robinson   4.00   2.00   1.25
(17) Bobby Bolin, Ollie Brown, Rod Carew,
Mike Epstein, Bud Harrelson, Larry Jaster,
Dave McNally, Willie Norton, Milt Pappas,
Gary Peters, Paul Popovich, Stan Williams
                                          6.00   3.00   1.75
(18) Ted Abernathy, Bob Allison, Ed Brinkman,
Don Drysdale, Jim Hardin, Julian Javier, Hal
Lanier, Jim McGlothlin, Ron Perranoski, Rich
Rollins, Ron Santo, Billy Williams   3.00   1.50   .90
(19) Richie Allen, Luis Aparicio, Wally Bunker,
Curt Flood, Ken Harrelson, Jim Hunter,
Denver Lemaster, Felix Millan, Jim Northrop
(Northrup), Art Shamsky, Larry Stahl, Ted
Uhlaender   3.00   1.50   .90
(20) Bob Bailey, Johnny Bench, Woody
Fryman, Jim Hannan, Ron Kline, Al McBean,
Camilo Pascual, Joe Pepitone, Doug Rader,
Ron Reed, John Roseboro, Sonny Siebert
                                          3.00   1.50   .90
(21) Jack Aker, Tommy Harper, Tommy
Helms, Dennis Higgins, Jim Hunter, Don
Lock, Lee Maye, Felix Millan, Jim Northrop
(Northrup), Larry Stahl, Don Sutton, Zoilo
Versalles   3.00   1.50   .90
(22) Norm Cash, Ed Charles, Joe Horlen, Pat
Jarvis, Jim Lonborg, Manny Mota, Boog
Powell, Dick Selma, Mike Shannon, Duke
Sims, Steve Whitaker, Hoyt Wilhelm   3.00   1.50   .90
(23) Bernie Allen, Ray Culp, Al Ferrara, Tito
Francona, Dick Green, Ron Hunt, Ray Oyler,
Tom Phoebus, Rusty Staub, Bob Veale,
Maury Wills, Wilbur Wood   2.00   1.00   .60
(24) Ernie Banks, Mark Belanger, Steve Blass,
Horace Clarke, Bob Clemente, Larry Dierker,
Dave Duncan, Chico Salmon, Chris Short,
Ron Swoboda, Cesar Tovar, Rick Wise
                                          3.50   1.75   1.00

**NOTE: A card number in parentheses ( )
indicates the set is unnumbered.**

1969 Topps Super

These 2-1/4" by 3-1/4" cards are not the bigger
"Super" cards which would be seen in following years.
Rather, what enabled Topps to dub them "Super
Baseball Cards" is their high-gloss finish which
enhances the bright color photograph used on their
fronts. The only other design element on the front is
a facsimile autograph. The backs contain a box at the
the bottom which carries the player's name, team,
position, a copyright line and the card number.
Another unusual feature is that the cards have
rounded corners. The 66-card set saw limited
production, meaning supplies are tight today.
Considering the quality of the cards and the fact that
many big names are represented, it's easy to
understand why the set is quite expensive and
desirable.

		NR MT	EX	VG
	Complete Set:	6000.00	3000.00	1800.
	Common Player:	25.00	12.50	7.50
1	Dave McNally	25.00	12.50	7.50
2	Frank Robinson	350.00	175.00	105.00
3	Brooks Robinson	350.00	175.00	105.00
4	Ken Harrelson	25.00	12.50	7.50
5	Carl Yastrzemski	700.00	350.00	210.00
6	Ray Culp	25.00	12.50	7.50
7	James Fregosi	25.00	12.50	7.50
8	Rick Reichardt	25.00	12.50	7.50
9	V. Davalillo	25.00	12.50	7.50
10	Luis Aparicio	35.00	17.50	10.50
11	Pete Ward	25.00	12.50	7.50
12	Joe Horlen	25.00	12.50	7.50
13	Luis Tiant	25.00	12.50	7.50
14	Sam McDowell	25.00	12.50	7.50
15	Jose Cardenal	25.00	12.50	7.50
16	Willie Horton	25.00	12.50	7.50
17	Denny McLain	25.00	12.50	7.50
18	Bill Freehan	25.00	12.50	7.50
19	Harmon Killebrew	275.00	137.00	82.00
20	Tony Oliva	25.00	12.50	7.50
21	Dean Chance	25.00	12.50	7.50
22	Joe Foy	25.00	12.50	7.50
23	Roger Nelson	25.00	12.50	7.50
24	Mickey Mantle	1500.00	750.00	450.00
25	Mel Stottlemyre	25.00	12.50	7.50
26	Roy White	25.00	12.50	7.50
27	Rick Monday	25.00	12.50	7.50
28	Reginald Jackson	750.00	375.00	225.00
29	Dagoberto Campaneris	25.00	12.50	7.50
30	Frank Howard	25.00	12.50	7.50
31	Camilo Pascual	25.00	12.50	7.50
32	Tommy Davis	25.00	12.50	7.50
33	Don Mincher	25.00	12.50	7.50
34	Henry Aaron	500.00	250.00	150.00
35	Felipe Rojas Alou	25.00	12.50	7.50
36	Joseph Torre	25.00	12.50	7.50
37	Fergie Jenkins	25.00	12.50	7.50
38	Ronald Santo	25.00	12.50	7.50
39	Billy Williams	40.00	20.00	12.00
40	Tommy Helms	25.00	12.50	7.50
41	Pete Rose	500.00	250.00	150.00
42	Joe Morgan	275.00	137.00	82.00
43	Jim Wynn	25.00	12.50	7.50
44	Curt Blefary	25.00	12.50	7.50
45	Willie Davis	25.00	12.50	7.50

		NR MT	EX	VG
46	Donald Drysdale	275.00	137.00	82.00
47	Tom Haller	25.00	12.50	7.50
48	Rusty Staub	25.00	12.50	7.50
49	Maurice Wills	25.00	12.50	7.50
50	Cleon Jones	25.00	12.50	7.50
51	Jerry Koosman	25.00	12.50	7.50
52	Tom Seaver	700.00	350.00	210.00
53	Rich Allen	25.00	12.50	7.50
54	Chris Short	25.00	12.50	7.50
55	Cookie Rojas	25.00	12.50	7.50
56	Mateo Alou	25.00	12.50	7.50
57	Steve Blass	25.00	12.50	7.50
58	Roberto Clemente	700.00	350.00	210.00
59	Curt Flood	25.00	12.50	7.50
60	Robert Gibson	90.00	45.00	27.00
61	Tim McCarver	25.00	12.50	7.50
62	Dick Selma	25.00	12.50	7.50
63	Ollie Brown	25.00	12.50	7.50
64	Juan Marichal	90.00	45.00	27.00
65	Willie Mays	500.00	250.00	150.00
66	Willie McCovey	90.00	45.00	27.00

1969 Topps Team Posters

Picking up where the 1968 posters left off, the 1969 poster is larger at about 12" by 20." The posters, 24 in number like the previous year, are very different in style. Each has a team focus with a large pennant carrying the team name, along with nine or ten photos of players. Each of the photos carries a name and a facsimile autograph. Unfortunately, the bigger size of 1969 posters meant they had to be folded to fit in their packages as was the case in 1968. That means that collectors today will have a tough job finding them without fairly heavy creases from the folding.

		NR MT	EX	VG
Complete Set:		900.00	450.00	270.00
Common Poster:		17.00	8.50	5.00
1	Detroit Tigers (Norm Cash, Bill Freehan, Willie Horton, Al Kaline, Mickey Lolich, Dick McAuliffe, Denny McLain, Jim Northrup, Mickey Stanley, Don Wert, Earl Wilson)	40.00	20.00	12.00
2	Atlanta Braves (Hank Aaron, Felipe Alou, Clete Boyer, Rico Carty, Tito Francona, Sonny Jackson, Pat Jarvis, Felix Millan, Phil Niekro, Milt Pappas, Joe Torre)	40.00	20.00	12.00
3	Boston Red Sox (Mike Andrews, Tony Conigliaro, Ray Culp, Russ Gibson, Ken Harrelson, Jim Lonborg, Rico Petrocelli, Jose Santiago, George Scott, Reggie Smith, Carl Yastrzemski)	60.00	30.00	18.00
4	Chicago Cubs (Ernie Banks, Glenn Beckert, Bill Hands, Jim Hickman, Ken Holtzman, Randy Hundley, Fergie Jenkins, Don Kessinger, Adolfo Phillips, Ron Santo, Billy Williams)	35.00	17.50	10.50
5	Baltimore Orioles (Mark Belanger, Paul Blair, Don Buford, Andy Etchebarren, Jim Hardin, Dave Johnson, Dave McNally, Tom Phoebus, Boog Powell, Brooks Robinson, Frank Robinson)	50.00	25.00	15.00
6	Houston Astros (Curt Blefary, Donn Clendenon, Larry Dierker, John Edwards, Denny Lemaster, Denis Menke, Norm Miller, Joe Morgan, Doug Rader, Don Wilson, Jim Wynn)	17.00	8.50	5.00
7	Kansas City Royals (Jerry Adair, Wally Bunker, Mike Fiore, Joe Foy, Jackie Hernandez, Pat Kelly, Dave Morehead, Roger Nelson, Dave Nicholson, Eliseo Rodriguez, Steve Whitaker)	17.00	8.50	5.00
8	Philadelphia Phillies (Richie Allen, Johnny Callison, Woody Fryman, Larry Hisle, Don Money, Cookie Rojas, Mike Ryan, Chris Short, Tony Taylor, Bill White, Rick Wise)	17.00	8.50	5.00
9	Seattle Pilots (Jack Aker, Steve Barber, Gary Bell, Tommy Davis, Jim Gosger, Tommy Harper, Gerry McNertney, Don Mincher, Ray Oyler, Rich Rollins, Chico Salmon)	35.00	17.50	10.50
10	Montreal Expos (Bob Bailey, John Bateman, Jack Billingham, Jim Grant, Larry Jaster, Mack Jones, Manny Mota, Rusty Staub, Gary Sutherland, Jim Williams, Maury Wills)	17.00	8.50	5.00
11	Chicago White Sox (Sandy Alomar, Luis Aparicio, Ken Berry, Buddy Bradford, Joe Horlen, Tommy John, Duane Josephson, Tom McCraw, Bill Melton, Pete Ward, Wilbur Wood)	17.00	8.50	5.00
12	San Diego Padres (Jose Arcia, Danny Breeden, Ollie Brown, Bill Davis, Ron Davis, Tony Gonzalez, Dick Kelley, Al McBean, Roberto Pena, Dick Selma, Ed Spiezio)	17.00	8.50	5.00
13	Cleveland Indians (Max Alvis, Joe Azcue, Jose Cardenal, Vern Fuller, Lou Johnson, Sam McDowell, Sonny Siebert, Duke Sims, Russ Snyder, Luis Tiant, Zoilo Versalles)	17.00	8.50	5.00
14	San Francisco Giants (Bobby Bolin, Jim Davenport, Dick Dietz, Jim Hart, Ron Hunt, Hal Lanier, Juan Marichal, Willie Mays, Willie McCovey, Gaylord Perry, Charlie Smith)	40.00	20.00	12.00
15	Minnesota Twins (Bob Allison, Chico Cardenas, Rod Carew, Dean Chance, Jim Kaat, Harmon Killebrew, Tony Oliva, Jim Perry, John Roseboro, Cesar Tovar, Ted Uhlaender)	40.00	20.00	12.00
16	Pittsburgh Pirates (Gene Alley, Matty Alou, Steve Blass, Jim Bunning, Bob Clemente, Rich Hebner, Jerry May, Bill Mazeroski, Bob Robertson, Willie Stargell, Bob Veale)	40.00	20.00	12.00
17	California Angels (Ruben Amaro, George Brunet, Bob Chance, Vic Davalillo, Jim Fregosi, Bobby Knoop, Jim McGlothlin, Rick Reichardt, Roger Repoz, Bob Rodgers, Hoyt Wilhelm)	20.00	10.00	6.00
18	St. Louis Cardinals (Nelson Briles, Lou Brock, Orlando Cepeda, Curt Flood, Bob Gibson, Julian Javier, Dal Maxvill, Tim McCarver, Vada Pinson, Mike Shannon, Ray Washburn)	35.00	17.50	10.50
19	New York Yankees (Stan Bahnsen, Horace Clarke, Bobby Cox, Jake Gibbs, Mickey Mantle, Joe Pepitone, Fritz Peterson, Bill Robinson, Mel Stottlemyre, Tom Tresh, Roy White)	90.00	45.00	27.00
20	Cincinnati Reds (Gerry Arrigo, Johnny Bench, Tommy Helms, Alex Johnson, Jim Maloney, Lee May, Gary Nolan, Tony Perez, Pete Rose, Bob Tolan, Woody Woodward)	90.00	45.00	27.00
21	Oakland Athletics (Sal Bando, Bert Campaneris, Danny Cater, Dick Green, Mike Hershberger, Jim Hunter, Reggie Jackson, Rick Monday, Jim Nash, John Odom, Jim Pagliaroni)	60.00	30.00	18.00
22	Los Angeles Dodgers (Willie Crawford, Willie Davis, Don Drysdale, Ron Fairly, Tom Haller, Andy Kosco, Jim Lefebvre, Claude Osteen, Paul Popovich, Bill Singer, Bill Sudakis)	35.00	17.50	10.50
23	Washington Senators (Bernie Allen, Brant Alyea, Ed Brinkman, Paul Casanova, Joe Coleman, Mike Epstein, Jim Hannan, Frank Howard, Ken McMullen, Camilo Pascual, Del Unser)	17.00	8.50	5.00
24	New York Mets (Tommie Agee, Ken Boswell, Ed Charles, Jerry Grote, Bud Harrelson, Cleon Jones, Jerry Koosman, Ed Kranepool, Jim McAndrew, Tom Seaver, Ron Swoboda)	100.00	50.00	30.00

1970 Topps

Topps established another set size record by coming out with 720 cards in 1970. The 2-1/2" by 3-1/2" cards have a color photo with a thin white frame. The photo have the player's team overprinted at the top, while the player's name in script and his position are at the bottom. A gray border surrounds the front. Card backs follows the normal design pattern, although they are more readable than some issues of the past. Team cards returned and were joined with many of the usual specialty cards. The World Series highlights were joined by cards with playoff highlights. Statistical leaders and All-Stars are also included in the set. High-numbered cards provide the most expensive cards in the set.

		NR MT	EX	VG
	Complete Set:	2000.00	1000.00	600.00
	Common Player: 1-546	.80	.40	.25
	Common Player: 547-633	1.50	.70	.45
	Common Player: 634-720	3.00	1.50	.90
1	World Champions (Mets Team)	10.00	3.00	1.00
2	Diego Segui	1.00	.50	.30
3	Darrel Chaney	.80	.40	.25
4	Tom Egan	.80	.40	.25
5	Wes Parker	.90	.45	.25
6	Grant Jackson	.80	.40	.25
7	Indians Rookies (Gary Boyd, Russ Nagelson)	.80	.40	.25
8	Jose Martinez	.80	.40	.25
9	Checklist 1-132	3.50	1.75	1.00
10	Carl Yastrzemski	30.00	15.00	9.00
11	Nate Colbert	.80	.40	.25
12	John Hiller	.90	.45	.25
13	Jack Hiatt	.80	.40	.25
14	Hank Allen	.80	.40	.25
15	Larry Dierker	.90	.45	.25
16	Charlie Metro	.80	.40	.25
17	Hoyt Wilhelm	4.00	2.00	1.25
18	Carlos May	.80	.40	.25
19	John Boccabella	.80	.40	.25
20	Dave McNally	1.00	.50	.30
21	Athletics Rookies (*Vida Blue*, Gene Tenace)	6.00	3.00	1.75
22	Ray Washburn	.80	.40	.25
23	Bill Robinson	.80	.40	.25
24	Dick Selma	.80	.40	.25
25	Cesar Tovar	.80	.40	.25
26	Tug McGraw	1.75	.90	.50
27	Chuck Hinton	.80	.40	.25
28	Billy Wilson	.80	.40	.25
29	Sandy Alomar	.80	.40	.25
30	Matty Alou	1.50	.70	.45
31	Marty Pattin	.80	.40	.25
32	Harry Walker	.90	.45	.25
33	Don Wert	.80	.40	.25
34	Willie Crawford	.80	.40	.25
35	Joe Horlen	.80	.40	.25
36	Reds Rookies (Danny Breeden, *Bernie Carbo*)	.80	.40	.25
37	Dick Drago	.80	.40	.25
38	Mack Jones	.80	.40	.25
39	Mike Nagy	.80	.40	.25
40	Rich Allen	3.00	1.50	.90
41	George Lauzerique	.80	.40	.25
42	Tito Fuentes	.80	.40	.25
43	Jack Aker	.80	.40	.25

		NR MT	EX	VG
44	Roberto Pena	.80	.40	.25
45	Dave Johnson	1.50	.70	.45
46	Ken Rudolph	.80	.40	.25
47	Bob Miller	.80	.40	.25
48	Gill Garrido (Gil)	.80	.40	.25
49	Tim Cullen	.80	.40	.25
50	Tommie Agee	.90	.45	.25
51	Bob Christian	.80	.40	.25
52	Bruce Dal Canton	.80	.40	.25
53	John Kennedy	.80	.40	.25
54	Jeff Torborg	.90	.45	.25
55	John Odom	.90	.45	.25
56	Phillies Rookies (Joe Lis, Scott Reid)	.80	.40	.25
57	Pat Kelly	.80	.40	.25
58	Dave Marshall	.80	.40	.25
59	Dick Ellsworth	.80	.40	.25
60	Jim Wynn	1.00	.50	.30
61	N.L. Batting Leaders (Bob Clemente, Cleon Jones, Pete Rose)	5.00	2.50	1.50
62	A.L. Batting Leaders (Rod Carew, Tony Oliva, Reggie Smith)	3.50	1.75	1.00
63	N.L. RBI Leaders (Willie McCovey, Tony Perez, Ron Santo)	3.50	1.75	1.00
64	A.L. RBI Leaders (Reggie Jackson, Harmon Killebrew, Boog Powell)	3.50	1.75	1.00
65	N.L. Home Run Leaders (Hank Aaron, Lee May, Willie McCovey)	3.00	1.50	.90
66	A.L. Home Run Leaders (Frank Howard, Reggie Jackson, Harmon Killebrew)	3.50	1.75	1.00
67	N.L. ERA Leaders (Steve Carlton, Bob Gibson, Juan Marichal)	3.00	1.50	.90
68	A.L. ERA Leaders (Dick Bosman, Mike Cuellar, Jim Palmer)	3.00	1.50	.90
69	N.L. Pitching Leaders (Fergie Jenkins, Juan Marichal, Phil Niekro, Tom Seaver)	3.50	1.75	1.00
70	A.L. Pitching Leaders (Dave Boswell, Mike Cuellar, Dennis McLain, Dave McNally, Jim Perry, Mel Stottlemyre)	3.00	1.50	.90
71	N.L. Strikeout Leaders (Bob Gibson, Fergie Jenkins, Bill Singer)	3.50	1.75	1.00
72	A.L. Strikeout Leaders (Mickey Lolich, Sam McDowell, Andy Messersmith)	3.00	1.50	.90
73	Wayne Granger	.80	.40	.25
74	Angels Rookies (Greg Washburn, Wally Wolf)	.80	.40	.25
75	Jim Kaat	3.00	1.50	.90
76	Carl Taylor	.80	.40	.25
77	Frank Linzy	.80	.40	.25
78	Joe Lahoud	.80	.40	.25
79	Clay Kirby	.80	.40	.25
80	Don Kessinger	.90	.45	.25
81	Dave May	.80	.40	.25
82	Frank Fernandez	.80	.40	.25
83	Don Cardwell	.80	.40	.25
84	Paul Casanova	.80	.40	.25
85	Max Alvis	.80	.40	.25
86	Lum Harris	.80	.40	.25
87	Steve Renko	.80	.40	.25
88	Pilots Rookies (Dick Baney, Miguel Fuentes)	.80	.40	.25
89	Juan Rios	.80	.40	.25
90	Tim McCarver	1.50	.70	.45
91	Rich Morales	.80	.40	.25
92	George Culver	.80	.40	.25
93	Rick Renick	.80	.40	.25
94	Fred Patek	.90	.45	.25
95	Earl Wilson	.80	.40	.25
96	Cards Rookies (Leron Lee, *Jerry Reuss*)	3.00	1.50	.90
97	Joe Moeller	.80	.40	.25
98	Gates Brown	.80	.40	.25
99	Bobby Pfeil	.80	.40	.25
100	Mel Stottlemyre	1.50	.70	.45
101	Bobby Floyd	.80	.40	.25
102	Joe Rudi	1.50	.70	.45
103	Frank Reberger	.80	.40	.25
104	Gerry Moses	.80	.40	.25
105	Tony Gonzalez	.80	.40	.25
106	Darold Knowles	.80	.40	.25
107	Bobby Etheridge	.80	.40	.25
108	Tom Burgmeier	.90	.45	.25
109	Expos Rookies (Garry Jestadt, Carl Morton)	.90	.45	.25
110	Bob Moose	.80	.40	.25
111	Mike Hegan	.80	.40	.25
112	Dave Nelson	.80	.40	.25
113	Jim Ray	.80	.40	.25
114	Gene Michael	1.00	.50	.30
115	Alex Johnson	.90	.45	.25
116	Sparky Lyle	1.50	.70	.45

		NR MT	EX	VG
117	Don Young	.80	.40	.25
118	George Mitterwald	.80	.40	.25
119	Chuck Taylor	.80	.40	.25
120	Sal Bando	1.50	.70	.45
121	Orioles Rookies (Fred Beene, *Terry Crowley*)	.90	.45	.25
122	George Stone	.80	.40	.25
123	Don Gutteridge	.80	.40	.25
124	Larry Jaster	.80	.40	.25
125	Deron Johnson	.80	.40	.25
126	Marty Martinez	.80	.40	.25
127	Joe Coleman	.90	.45	.25
128a	Checklist 133-263 (226 is R Perranoski)	3.00	1.50	.90
128b	Checklist 133-263 (226 is R. Perranoski)	3.50	1.75	1.00
129	Jimmie Price	.80	.40	.25
130	Ollie Brown	.80	.40	.25
131	Dodgers Rookies (Ray Lamb, Bob Stinson)	.80	.40	.25
132	Jim McGlothlin	.80	.40	.25
133	Clay Carroll	.90	.45	.25
134	Danny Walton	.80	.40	.25
135	Dick Dietz	.80	.40	.25
136	Steve Hargan	.80	.40	.25
137	Art Shamsky	.80	.40	.25
138	Joe Foy	.80	.40	.25
139	Rich Nye	.80	.40	.25
140	Reggie Jackson	175.00	87.00	52.00
141	Pirates Rookies (*Dave Cash*, Johnny Jeter)	.80	.40	.25
142	Fritz Peterson	.80	.40	.25
143	Phil Gagliano	.80	.40	.25
144	Ray Culp	.80	.40	.25
145	Rico Carty	1.50	.70	.45
146	Danny Murphy	.80	.40	.25
147	Angel Hermoso	.80	.40	.25
148	Earl Weaver	1.75	.90	.50
149	Billy Champion	.80	.40	.25
150	Harmon Killebrew	7.00	3.50	2.00
151	Dave Roberts	.80	.40	.25
152	Ike Brown	.80	.40	.25
153	Gary Gentry	.80	.40	.25
154	Senators Rookies (Jan Dukes, Jim Miles)	.80	.40	.25
155	Denis Menke	.80	.40	.25
156	Eddie Fisher	.80	.40	.25
157	Manny Mota	.80	.40	.25
158	Jerry McNertney	.80	.40	.25
159	Tommy Helms	.90	.45	.25
160	Phil Niekro	3.50	1.75	1.00
161	Richie Scheinblum	.80	.40	.25
162	Jerry Johnson	.80	.40	.25
163	Syd O'Brien	.80	.40	.25
164	Ty Cline	.80	.40	.25
165	Ed Kirkpatrick	.80	.40	.25
166	Al Oliver	3.00	1.50	.90
167	Bill Burbach	.80	.40	.25
168	Dave Watkins	.80	.40	.25
169	Tom Hall	.80	.40	.25
170	Billy Williams	6.00	3.00	1.75
171	Jim Nash	.80	.40	.25
172	Braves Rookies (*Ralph Garr*, Garry Hill)	1.50	.70	.45
173	Jim Hicks	.80	.40	.25
174	Ted Sizemore	.80	.40	.25
175	Dick Bosman	.80	.40	.25
176	Jim Hart	.90	.45	.25
177	Jim Northrup	.90	.45	.25
178	Denny Lemaster	.80	.40	.25
179	Ivan Murrell	.80	.40	.25
180	Tommy John	4.00	2.00	1.25
181	Sparky Anderson	1.75	.90	.50
182	Dick Hall	.80	.40	.25
183	Jerry Grote	.90	.45	.25
184	Ray Fosse	.90	.45	.25
185	Don Mincher	.80	.40	.25
186	Rick Joseph	.80	.40	.25
187	Mike Hedlund	.80	.40	.25
188	Manny Sanguillen	.90	.45	.25
189	Yankees Rookies (Dave McDonald, *Thurman Munson*)	90.00	45.00	27.00
190	Joe Torre	1.75	.90	.50
191	Vicente Romo	.80	.40	.25
192	Jim Qualls	.80	.40	.25
193	Mike Wegener	.80	.40	.25
194	Chuck Manuel	.80	.40	.25
195	N.L. Playoff Game 1 (Seaver Wins Opener!)	4.00	2.00	1.25
196	N.L. Playoff Game 2 (Mets Show Muscle!)	3.50	1.75	1.00

		NR MT	EX	VG
197	N.L. Playoff Game 3 (Ryan Saves The Day!)	6.00	3.00	1.75
198	N.L. Playoffs Summary (We're Number One!)	3.50	1.75	1.00
199	A.L. Playoff Game 1 (Orioles Win A Squeaker!)	3.00	1.50	.90
200	A.L. Playoff Game 2 (Powell Scores Winning Run!)	3.50	1.75	1.00
201	A.L. Playoff Game 3 (Birds Wrap It Up!)	3.00	1.50	.90
202	A.L. Playoffs Summary (Sweep Twins In Three!)	3.00	1.50	.90
203	Rudy May	.90	.45	.25
204	Len Gabrielson	.80	.40	.25
205	Bert Campaneris	1.50	.70	.45
206	Clete Boyer	.90	.45	.25
207	Tigers Rookies (Norman McRae, Bob Reed)	.80	.40	.25
208	Fred Gladding	.80	.40	.25
209	Ken Suarez	.80	.40	.25
210	Juan Marichal	8.00	4.00	2.50
211	Ted Williams	7.00	3.50	2.00
212	Al Santorini	.80	.40	.25
213	Andy Etchebarren	.80	.40	.25
214	Ken Boswell	.80	.40	.25
215	Reggie Smith	1.00	.50	.30
216	Chuck Hartenstein	.80	.40	.25
217	Ron Hansen	.80	.40	.25
218	Ron Stone	.80	.40	.25
219	Jerry Kenney	.80	.40	.25
220	Steve Carlton	35.00	17.50	10.50
221	Ron Brand	.80	.40	.25
222	Jim Rooker	.80	.40	.25
223	Nate Oliver	.80	.40	.25
224	Steve Barber	.80	.40	.25
225	Lee May	1.00	.50	.30
226	Ron Perranoski	.90	.45	.25
227	Astros Rookies (*John Mayberry*, Bob Watkins)	1.50	.70	.45
228	Aurelio Rodriguez	.90	.45	.25
229	Rich Robertson	.80	.40	.25
230	Brooks Robinson	12.00	6.00	3.50
231	Luis Tiant	1.75	.90	.50
232	Bob Didier	.80	.40	.25
233	Lew Krausse	.80	.40	.25
234	Tommy Dean	.80	.40	.25
235	Mike Epstein	.90	.45	.25
236	Bob Veale	.90	.45	.25
237	Russ Gibson	.80	.40	.25
238	Jose Laboy	.80	.40	.25
239	Ken Berry	.80	.40	.25
240	Fergie Jenkins	10.00	5.00	3.00
241	Royals Rookies (Al Fitzmorris, Scott Northey)	.80	.40	.25
242	Walter Alston	3.50	1.75	1.00
243	Joe Sparma	.80	.40	.25
244a	Checklist 264-372 (red bat on front)	3.00	1.50	.90
244b	Checklist 264-372 (brown bat on front)	3.50	1.75	1.00
245	Leo Cardenas	.80	.40	.25
246	Jim McAndrew	.80	.40	.25
247	Lou Klimchock	.80	.40	.25
248	Jesus Alou	.90	.45	.25
249	Bob Locker	.80	.40	.25
250	Willie McCovey	8.00	4.00	2.50
251	Dick Schofield	.80	.40	.25
252	Lowell Palmer	.80	.40	.25
253	Ron Woods	.80	.40	.25
254	Camilo Pascual	.80	.40	.25
255	*Jim Spencer*	.80	.40	.25
256	Vic Davalillo	.90	.45	.25
257	Dennis Higgins	.80	.40	.25
258	Paul Popovich	.80	.40	.25
259	Tommie Reynolds	.80	.40	.25
260	Claude Osteen	.80	.40	.25
261	Curt Motton	.80	.40	.25
262	Padres Rookies (Jerry Morales, Jim Williams)	.80	.40	.25
263	Duane Josephson	.80	.40	.25
264	Rich Hebner	.90	.45	.25
265	Randy Hundley	.80	.40	.25
266	Wally Bunker	.80	.40	.25
267	Twins Rookies (Herman Hill, Paul Ratliff)	.80	.40	.25
268	Claude Raymond	.80	.40	.25
269	Cesar Gutierrez	.80	.40	.25
270	Chris Short	.90	.45	.25
271	Greg Goossen	.80	.40	.25
272	Hector Torres	.80	.40	.25
273	Ralph Houk	1.50	.70	.45

#	Player	NR MT	EX	VG
274	Gerry Arrigo	.80	.40	.25
275	Duke Sims	.80	.40	.25
276	Ron Hunt	.90	.45	.25
277	Paul Doyle	.80	.40	.25
278	Tommie Aaron	.80	.40	.25
279	*Bill Lee*	.80	.40	.25
280	Donn Clendenon	.90	.45	.25
281	Casey Cox	.80	.40	.25
282	Steve Huntz	.80	.40	.25
283	Angel Bravo	.80	.40	.25
284	Jack Baldschun	.80	.40	.25
285	Paul Blair	.90	.45	.25
286	Dodgers Rookies (*Bill Buckner*, Jack Jenkins)	6.00	3.00	1.75
287	Fred Talbot	.80	.40	.25
288	Larry Hisle	.90	.45	.25
289	Gene Brabender	.80	.40	.25
290	Rod Carew	60.00	30.00	18.00
291	Leo Durocher	1.75	.90	.50
292	Eddie Leon	.80	.40	.25
293	Bob Bailey	.80	.40	.25
294	Jose Azcue	.80	.40	.25
295	Cecil Upshaw	.80	.40	.25
296	Woody Woodward	.90	.45	.25
297	Curt Blefary	.80	.40	.25
298	Ken Henderson	.80	.40	.25
299	Buddy Bradford	.80	.40	.25
300	Tom Seaver	110.00	55.00	33.00
301	Chico Salmon	.80	.40	.25
302	Jeff James	.80	.40	.25
303	Brant Alyea	.80	.40	.25
304	*Bill Russell*	3.00	1.50	.90
305	World Series Game 1 (Buford Belts Leadoff Homer!)	3.50	1.75	1.00
306	World Series Game 2 (Clendenon's Homer Breaks Ice!)	3.50	1.75	1.00
307	World Series Game 3 (Agee's Catch Saves The Day!)	3.50	1.75	1.00
308	World Series Game 4 (Martin's Bunt Ends Deadlock!)	3.50	1.75	1.00
309	World Series Game 5 (Koosman Shuts The Door!)	3.50	1.75	1.00
310	World Series Summary (Mets Whoop It Up!)	3.50	1.75	1.00
311	Dick Green	.80	.40	.25
312	Mike Torrez	.90	.45	.25
313	Mayo Smith	.80	.40	.25
314	Bill McCool	.80	.40	.25
315	Luis Aparicio	4.50	2.25	1.25
316	Skip Guinn	.80	.40	.25
317	Red Sox Rookies (Luis Alvarado, Billy Conigliaro)	.90	.45	.25
318	Willie Smith	.80	.40	.25
319	Clayton Dalrymple	.80	.40	.25
320	Jim Maloney	.90	.45	.25
321	Lou Piniella	3.00	1.50	.90
322	Luke Walker	.80	.40	.25
323	Wayne Comer	.80	.40	.25
324	Tony Taylor	.80	.40	.25
325	Dave Boswell	.80	.40	.25
326	Bill Voss	.80	.40	.25
327	Hal King	.80	.40	.25
328	George Brunet	.80	.40	.25
329	Chris Cannizzaro	.80	.40	.25
330	Lou Brock	8.00	4.00	2.50
331	Chuck Dobson	.80	.40	.25
332	Bobby Wine	.80	.40	.25
333	Bobby Murcer	1.75	.90	.50
334	Phil Regan	.80	.40	.25
335	Bill Freehan	.90	.45	.25
336	Del Unser	.80	.40	.25
337	Mike McCormick	.90	.45	.25
338	Paul Schaal	.80	.40	.25
339	Johnny Edwards	.80	.40	.25
340	Tony Conigliaro	1.75	.90	.50
341	Bill Sudakis	.80	.40	.25
342	Wilbur Wood	.90	.45	.25
343a	Checklist 373-459 (red bat on front)	3.50	1.75	1.00
343b	Checklist 373-459 (brown bat on front)	3.00	1.50	.90
344	Marcelino Lopez	.80	.40	.25
345	Al Ferrara	.80	.40	.25
346	Red Schoendienst	1.75	.90	.50
347	Russ Snyder	.80	.40	.25
348	Mets Rookies (Jesse Hudson, Mike Jorgensen)	.90	.45	.25
349	Steve Hamilton	.80	.40	.25
350	Roberto Clemente	50.00	25.00	15.00
351	Tom Murphy	.80	.40	.25
352	Bob Barton	.80	.40	.25
353	Stan Williams	.80	.40	.25
354	Amos Otis	.80	.40	.25
355	Doug Rader	.80	.40	.25
356	Fred Lasher	.80	.40	.25
357	Bob Burda	.80	.40	.25
358	*Pedro Borbon*	.90	.45	.25
359	Phil Roof	.80	.40	.25
360	Curt Flood	1.50	.70	.45
361	Ray Jarvis	.80	.40	.25
362	Joe Hague	.80	.40	.25
363	Tom Shopay	.80	.40	.25
364	Dan McGinn	.80	.40	.25
365	Zoilo Versalles	.90	.45	.25
366	Barry Moore	.80	.40	.25
367	Mike Lum	.80	.40	.25
368	Ed Herrmann	.80	.40	.25
369	Alan Foster	.80	.40	.25
370	Tommy Harper	.70	.35	.20
371	Rod Gaspar	.80	.40	.25
372	Dave Giusti	.80	.40	.25
373	Roy White	1.50	.70	.45
374	Tommie Sisk	.80	.40	.25
375	Johnny Callison	1.50	.70	.45
376	Lefty Phillips	.80	.40	.25
377	Bill Butler	.80	.40	.25
378	Jim Davenport	.80	.40	.25
379	Tom Tischinski	.80	.40	.25
380	Tony Perez	3.00	1.50	.90
381	Athletics Rookies (Bobby Brooks, Mike Olivo)	.80	.40	.25
382	Jack DiLauro	.80	.40	.25
383	Mickey Stanley	.90	.45	.25
384	Gary Neibauer	.80	.40	.25
385	George Scott	.90	.45	.25
386	Bill Dillman	.80	.40	.25
387	Orioles Team	3.00	1.50	.90
388	Byron Browne	.80	.40	.25
389	Jim Shellenback	.80	.40	.25
390	Willie Davis	1.50	.70	.45
391	Larry Brown	.80	.40	.25
392	Walt Hriniak	.80	.40	.25
393	John Gelnar	.80	.40	.25
394	Gil Hodges	4.00	2.00	1.25
395	Walt Williams	.80	.40	.25
396	Steve Blass	.90	.45	.25
397	Roger Repoz	.80	.40	.25
398	Bill Stoneman	.80	.40	.25
399	Yankees Team	3.00	1.50	.90
400	Denny McLain	3.00	1.50	.90
401	Giants Rookies (John Harrell, Bernie Williams)	.80	.40	.25
402	Ellie Rodriguez	.80	.40	.25
403	Jim Bunning	3.25	1.75	1.00
404	Rich Reese	.80	.40	.25
405	Bill Hands	.80	.40	.25
406	Mike Andrews	.80	.40	.25
407	Bob Watson	.90	.45	.25
408	Paul Lindblad	.80	.40	.25
409	Bob Tolan	.90	.45	.25
410	Boog Powell	3.00	1.50	.90
411	Dodgers Team	3.00	1.50	.90
412	Larry Burchart	.80	.40	.25
413	Sonny Jackson	.80	.40	.25
414	Paul Edmondson	.80	.40	.25
415	Julian Javier	.80	.40	.25
416	Joe Verbanic	.80	.40	.25
417	John Bateman	.80	.40	.25
418	John Donaldson	.80	.40	.25
419	Ron Taylor	.80	.40	.25
420	Ken McMullen	.80	.40	.25
421	Pat Dobson	.90	.45	.25
422	Royals Team	1.75	.90	.50
423	Jerry May	.80	.40	.25
424	Mike Kilkenny	.80	.40	.25
425	Bobby Bonds	1.75	.90	.50
426	Bill Rigney	.80	.40	.25
427	Fred Norman	.80	.40	.25
428	Don Buford	.90	.45	.25
429	Cubs Rookies (Randy Bobb, Jim Cosman)	.80	.40	.25
430	Andy Messersmith	.80	.40	.25
431	Ron Swoboda	.90	.45	.25
432a	Checklist 460-546 ("Baseball" on front in yellow)	4.00	2.00	1.25
432b	Checklist 460-546 ("Baseball" on front in white)	3.50	1.75	1.00
433	Ron Bryant	.80	.40	.25
434	Felipe Alou	.70	.35	.20
435	Nelson Briles	.80	.40	.25
436	Phillies Team	1.75	.90	.50
437	Danny Cater	.80	.40	.25

		NR MT	EX	VG
438	Pat Jarvis	.80	.40	.25
439	Lee Maye	.80	.40	.25
440	Bill Mazeroski	1.50	.70	.45
441	John O'Donoghue	.80	.40	.25
442	Gene Mauch	.70	.35	.20
443	Al Jackson	.80	.40	.25
444	White Sox Rookies (Bill Farmer, John			
	Matias)	.80	.40	.25
445	Vada Pinson	1.75	.90	.50
446	*Billy Grabarkewitz*	.90	.45	.25
447	Lee Stange	.80	.40	.25
448	Astros Team	1.75	.90	.50
449	Jim Palmer	25.00	12.50	7.50
450	Willie McCovey AS	3.50	1.75	1.00
451	Boog Powell AS	1.50	.70	.45
452	Felix Millan AS	.80	.40	.25
453	Rod Carew AS	4.00	2.00	1.25
454	Ron Santo AS	1.50	.70	.45
455	Brooks Robinson AS	3.50	1.75	1.00
456	Don Kessinger AS	.80	.40	.25
457	Rico Petrocelli AS	.80	.40	.25
458	Pete Rose AS	8.00	4.00	2.50
459	Reggie Jackson AS	20.00	10.00	6.00
460	Matty Alou AS	.70	.35	.20
461	Carl Yastrzemski AS	8.00	4.00	2.50
462	Hank Aaron AS	12.00	6.00	3.50
463	Frank Robinson AS	8.00	4.00	2.50
464	Johnny Bench AS	10.00	5.00	3.00
465	Bill Freehan AS	.80	.40	.25
466	Juan Marichal AS	4.00	2.00	1.25
467	Denny McLain AS	1.50	.70	.45
468	Jerry Koosman AS	1.00	.50	.30
469	Sam McDowell AS	1.00	.50	.30
470	Willie Stargell	7.00	3.50	2.00
471	Chris Zachary	.80	.40	.25
472	Braves Team	1.75	.90	.50
473	Don Bryant	.80	.40	.25
474	Dick Kelley	.80	.40	.25
475	Dick McAuliffe	.90	.45	.25
476	Don Shaw	.80	.40	.25
477	Orioles Rookies (Roger Freed, Al			
	Severinsen)	.80	.40	.25
478	Bob Heise	.80	.40	.25
479	Dick Woodson	.80	.40	.25
480	Glenn Beckert	.90	.45	.25
481	Jose Tartabull	.80	.40	.25
482	Tom Hilgendorf	.80	.40	.25
483	Gail Hopkins	.80	.40	.25
484	Gary Nolan	.80	.40	.25
485	Jay Johnstone	.80	.40	.25
486	Terry Harmon	.80	.40	.25
487	Cisco Carlos	.80	.40	.25
488	J.C. Martin	.80	.40	.25
489	Eddie Kasko	.80	.40	.25
490	Bill Singer	.90	.45	.25
491	Graig Nettles	4.00	2.00	1.25
492	Astros Rookies (Keith Lampard, Scipio			
	Spinks)	.80	.40	.25
493	Lindy McDaniel	.80	.40	.25
494	Larry Stahl	.80	.40	.25
495	Dave Morehead	.80	.40	.25
496	Steve Whitaker	.80	.40	.25
497	Eddie Watt	.80	.40	.25
498	Al Weis	.80	.40	.25
499	Skip Lockwood	.80	.40	.25
500	Hank Aaron	55.00	28.00	16.50
501	White Sox Team	1.75	.90	.50
502	Rollie Fingers	35.00	17.50	9.60
503	Dal Maxvill	.90	.45	.25
504	Don Pavletich	.80	.40	.25
505	Ken Holtzman	.90	.45	.25
506	Ed Stroud	.80	.40	.25
507	Pat Corrales	.80	.40	.25
508	Joe Niekro	.70	.35	.20
509	Expos Team	1.75	.90	.50
510	Tony Oliva	3.50	1.75	1.00
511	Joe Hoerner	.80	.40	.25
512	Billy Harris	.80	.40	.25
513	Preston Gomez	.80	.40	.25
514	Steve Hovley	.80	.40	.25
515	Don Wilson	.80	.40	.25
516	Yankees Rookies (John Ellis, Jim Lyttle)			
		.80	.40	.25
517	Joe Gibbon	.80	.40	.25
518	Bill Melton	.90	.45	.25
519	Don McMahon	.80	.40	.25
520	Willie Horton	.70	.35	.20
521	Cal Koonce	.80	.40	.25
522	Angels Team	1.75	.90	.50
523	Jose Pena	.80	.40	.25
524	Alvin Dark	1.00	.50	.30

		NR MT	EX	VG
525	Jerry Adair	.80	.40	.25
526	Ron Herbel	.80	.40	.25
527	Don Bosch	.80	.40	.25
528	Elrod Hendricks	.80	.40	.25
529	Bob Aspromonte	.80	.40	.25
530	Bob Gibson	10.00	5.00	3.00
531	Ron Clark	.80	.40	.25
532	Danny Murtaugh	.80	.40	.25
533	Buzz Stephen	.80	.40	.25
534	Twins Team	3.00	1.50	.90
535	Andy Kosco	.80	.40	.25
536	Mike Kekich	.80	.40	.25
537	Joe Morgan	10.00	5.00	3.00
538	Bob Humphreys	.80	.40	.25
539	Phillies Rookies (*Larry Bowa*, Dennis			
	Doyle)	3.00	1.50	.90
540	Gary Peters	.90	.45	.25
541	Bill Heath	.80	.40	.25
542a	Checklist 547-633 (grey bat on front)			
		3.50	1.75	1.00
542b	Checklist 547-633 (brown bat on front)			
		3.50	1.75	1.00
543	Clyde Wright	.80	.40	.25
544	Reds Team	1.75	.90	.50
545	Ken Harrelson	1.75	.90	.50
546	Ron Reed	.90	.45	.25
547	Rick Monday	1.50	.70	.45
548	Howie Reed	1.50	.70	.45
549	Cardinals Team	3.50	1.75	1.00
550	Frank Howard	3.50	1.75	1.00
551	Dock Ellis	1.50	.70	.45
552	Royals Rookies (Don O'Riley, Dennis			
	Paepke, Fred Rico)	1.50	.70	.45
553	Jim Lefebvre	1.50	.70	.45
554	Tom Timmermann	1.50	.70	.45
555	Orlando Cepeda	3.50	1.75	1.00
556	Dave Bristol	1.50	.70	.45
557	Ed Kranepool	1.50	.70	.45
558	Vern Fuller	1.50	.70	.45
559	Tommy Davis	1.75	.90	.50
560	Gaylord Perry	10.00	5.00	3.00
561	Tom McCraw	1.50	.70	.45
562	Ted Abernathy	1.50	.70	.45
563	Red Sox Team	3.00	1.50	.90
564	Johnny Briggs	1.50	.70	.45
565	Jim Hunter	7.00	3.50	2.00
566	Gene Alley	1.50	.70	.45
567	Bob Oliver	1.50	.70	.45
568	Stan Bahnsen	1.50	.70	.45
569	Cookie Rojas	1.50	.70	.45
570	Jim Fregosi	1.50	.70	.45
571	Jim Brewer	1.50	.70	.45
572	Frank Quilici	1.50	.70	.45
573	Padres Rookies (Mike Corkins, Rafael			
	Robles, Ron Slocum)	1.50	.70	.45
574	Bobby Bolin	1.50	.70	.45
575	Cleon Jones	1.50	.70	.45
576	Milt Pappas	1.50	.70	.45
577	Bernie Allen	1.50	.70	.45
578	Tom Griffin	1.50	.70	.45
579	Tigers Team	3.50	1.75	1.00
580	Pete Rose	70.00	35.00	20.00
581	Tom Satriano	1.50	.70	.45
582	Mike Paul	1.50	.70	.45
583	Hal Lanier	1.50	.70	.45
584	Al Downing	1.50	.70	.45
585	Rusty Staub	3.00	1.50	.90
586	Rickey Clark	1.50	.70	.45
587	Jose Arcia	1.50	.70	.45
588a	Checklist 634-720 (666 is Adolpho			
	Phillips)	4.50	2.25	1.25
588b	Checklist 634-720 (666 is Adolfo Phillips)			
		3.00	1.50	.90
589	Joe Keough	1.50	.70	.45
590	Mike Cuellar	1.50	.70	.45
591	Mike Ryan	1.50	.70	.45
592	Daryl Patterson	1.50	.70	.45
593	Cubs Team	3.50	1.75	1.00
594	Jake Gibbs	1.50	.70	.45
595	Maury Wills	3.50	1.75	1.00
596	Mike Hershberger	1.50	.70	.45
597	Sonny Siebert	1.50	.70	.45
598	Joe Pepitone	1.75	.90	.50
599	Senators Rookies (Gene Martin, Dick			
	Stelmaszek, Dick Such)	1.50	.70	.45
600	Willie Mays	80.00	40.00	25.00
601	Pete Richert	1.50	.70	.45
602	Ted Savage	1.50	.70	.45
603	Ray Oyler	1.50	.70	.45
604	Clarence Gaston	1.50	.70	.45
605	Rick Wise	1.50	.70	.45

		NR MT	EX	VG
606	Chico Ruiz	1.50	.70	.45
607	Gary Waslewski	1.50	.70	.45
608	Pirates Team	3.50	1.75	1.00
609	*Buck Martinez*	1.50	.70	.45
610	Jerry Koosman	1.75	.90	.50
611	Norm Cash	3.00	1.50	.90
612	Jim Hickman	1.50	.70	.45
613	Dave Baldwin	1.50	.70	.45
614	Mike Shannon	1.50	.70	.45
615	Mark Belanger	1.50	.70	.45
616	Jim Merritt	1.50	.70	.45
617	Jim French	1.50	.70	.45
618	Billy Wynne	1.50	.70	.45
619	Norm Miller	1.50	.70	.45
620	Jim Perry	1.50	.70	.45
621	Braves Rookies (*Darrell Evans*, Rick Kester, Mike McQueen)	20.00	10.00	6.00
622	Don Sutton	7.00	3.50	2.00
623	Horace Clarke	1.50	.70	.45
624	Clyde King	1.50	.70	.45
625	Dean Chance	1.50	.70	.45
626	Dave Ricketts	1.50	.70	.45
627	Gary Wagner	1.50	.70	.45
628	Wayne Garrett	1.50	.70	.45
629	Merv Rettenmund	1.50	.70	.45
630	Ernie Banks	30.00	15.00	9.00
631	Athletics Team	3.50	1.75	1.00
632	Gary Sutherland	1.50	.70	.45
633	Roger Nelson	1.50	.70	.45
634	Bud Harrelson	3.50	1.75	1.00
635	Bob Allison	3.50	1.75	1.00
636	Jim Stewart	3.00	1.50	.90
637	Indians Team	3.00	1.50	.90
638	Frank Bertaina	3.00	1.50	.90
639	Dave Campbell	3.00	1.50	.90
640	Al Kaline	50.00	25.00	15.00
641	Al McBean	3.00	1.50	.90
642	Angels Rookies (Greg Garrett, Gordon Lund, Jarvis Tatum)	3.00	1.50	.90
643	Jose Pagan	3.00	1.50	.90
644	Gerry Nyman	3.00	1.50	.90
645	Don Money	3.00	1.50	.90
646	Jim Britton	3.00	1.50	.90
647	Tom Matchick	3.00	1.50	.90
648	Larry Haney	3.00	1.50	.90
649	Jimmie Hall	3.00	1.50	.90
650	Sam McDowell	3.50	1.75	1.00
651	Jim Gosger	3.00	1.50	.90
652	Rich Rollins	3.50	1.75	1.00
653	Moe Drabowsky	3.00	1.50	.90
654	N.L. Rookies (Boots Day, *Oscar Gamble*, Angel Mangual)	3.50	1.75	1.00
655	John Roseboro	3.50	1.75	1.00
656	Jim Hardin	3.00	1.50	.90
657	Padres Team	4.00	2.00	1.25
658	Ken Tatum	3.00	1.50	.90
659	Pete Ward	3.50	1.75	1.00
660	Johnny Bench	150.00	75.00	45.00
661	Jerry Robertson	3.00	1.50	.90
662	Frank Lucchesi	3.00	1.50	.90
663	Tito Francona	3.50	1.75	1.00
664	Bob Robertson	3.00	1.50	.90
665	Jim Lonborg	3.50	1.75	1.00
666	Adolfo Phillips	3.00	1.50	.90
667	Bob Meyer	3.50	1.75	1.00
668	Bob Tillman	3.00	1.50	.90
669	White Sox Rookies (Bart Johnson, Dan Lazar, Mickey Scott)	3.00	1.50	.90
670	Ron Santo	3.25	1.75	1.00
671	Jim Campanis	3.00	1.50	.90
672	Leon McFadden	3.00	1.50	.90
673	Ted Uhlaender	3.00	1.50	.90
674	Dave Leonhard	3.00	1.50	.90
675	Jose Cardenal	3.50	1.75	1.00
676	Senators Team	3.25	1.75	1.00
677	Woodie Fryman	3.50	1.75	1.00
678	Dave Duncan	3.00	1.50	.90
679	Ray Sadecki	3.00	1.50	.90
680	Rico Petrocelli	3.50	1.75	1.00
681	Bob Garibaldi	3.00	1.50	.90
682	Dalton Jones	3.00	1.50	.90
683	Reds Rookies (Vern Geishert, Hal McRae, Wayne Simpson)	4.00	2.00	1.25
684	Jack Fisher	3.00	1.50	.90
685	Tom Haller	3.50	1.75	1.00
686	Jackie Hernandez	3.00	1.50	.90
687	Bob Priddy	3.00	1.50	.90
688	Ted Kubiak	3.50	1.75	1.00
689	Frank Tepedino	3.50	1.75	1.00
690	Ron Fairly	3.50	1.75	1.00
691	Joe Grzenda	3.00	1.50	.90

		NR MT	EX	VG
692	Duffy Dyer	3.00	1.50	.90
693	Bob Johnson	3.00	1.50	.90
694	Gary Ross	3.00	1.50	.90
695	Bobby Knoop	3.00	1.50	.90
696	Giants Team	3.25	1.75	1.00
697	Jim Hannan	3.00	1.50	.90
698	Tom Tresh	4.00	2.00	1.25
699	Hank Aguirre	3.00	1.50	.90
700	Frank Robinson	50.00	25.00	15.00
701	Jack Billingham	3.00	1.50	.90
702	A.L. Rookies (Bob Johnson, Ron Klimkowski, Bill Zepp)	3.50	1.75	1.00
703	Lou Marone	3.00	1.50	.90
704	Frank Baker	3.00	1.50	.90
705	Tony Cloninger	3.50	1.75	1.00
706	John McNamara	3.50	1.75	1.00
707	Kevin Collins	3.00	1.50	.90
708	Jose Santiago	3.00	1.50	.90
709	Mike Fiore	3.00	1.50	.90
710	Felix Millan	3.00	1.50	.90
711	Ed Brinkman	3.50	1.75	1.00
712	Nolan Ryan	500.00	250.00	150.00
713	Pilots Team	15.00	7.50	4.50
714	Al Spangler	3.00	1.50	.90
715	Mickey Lolich	5.00	2.50	1.50
716	Cards Rookies (Sal Campisi, *Reggie Cleveland*, Santiago Guzman)	3.50	1.75	1.00
717	Tom Phoebus	3.00	1.50	.90
718	Ed Spiezio	3.00	1.50	.90
719	Jim Roland	3.50	1.75	1.00
720	Rick Reichardt	4.00	1.00	.50

1970 Topps Candy Lids

The 1970 Topps Candy Lids are a test issue that was utilized again in 1973. The set is made up of 24 lids that measure 1-7/8" in diameter and were the tops of small 1.1 oz. tubs of "Baseball Stars Candy." Unlike the 1973 versions, the 1970 lids have no border surrounding the full-color photos. Frank Howard, Tom Seaver and Carl Yastrzemski photos are found on the bottom (inside) of the candy lid.

		NR MT	EX	VG
Complete Set:		2000.00	1000.00	600.00
Common Player:		30.00	15.00	9.00
(1)	Hank Aaron	200.00	100.00	60.00
(2)	Rich Allen	50.00	25.00	15.00
(3)	Luis Aparicio	80.00	40.00	24.00
(4)	Johnny Bench	200.00	100.00	60.00
(5)	Ollie Brown	30.00	15.00	9.00
(6)	Willie Davis	30.00	15.00	9.00
(7)	Jim Fregosi	30.00	15.00	9.00
(8)	Mike Hegan	30.00	15.00	9.00
(9)	Frank Howard	50.00	25.00	15.00
(10)	Reggie Jackson	200.00	100.00	60.00
(11)	Fergie Jenkins	60.00	30.00	18.00
(12)	Harmon Killebrew	100.00	50.00	30.00
(13)	Juan Marichal	100.00	50.00	30.00
(14)	Bill Mazeroski	50.00	25.00	15.00
(15)	Tim McCarver	50.00	25.00	15.00
(16)	Sam McDowell	30.00	15.00	9.00
(17)	Denny McLain	50.00	25.00	15.00
(18)	Lou Piniella	50.00	25.00	15.00
(19)	Frank Robinson	100.00	50.00	30.00
(20)	Tom Seaver	175.00	87.00	52.00
(21)	Rusty Staub	50.00	25.00	15.00

		NR MT	EX	VG
(22)	Mel Stottlemyre	50.00	25.00	15.00
(23)	Jim Wynn	30.00	15.00	9.00
(24)	Carl Yastrzemski	150.00	75.00	45.00

1970 Topps Posters

Helping to ease a price increase, Topps included extremely fragile 8-11/16" by 9-5/8" posters in packs of regular cards. The posters feature color portraits and a smaller black and white "action" pose as well as the player's name, team and position at the top. Although there are Hall of Famers in the 24-poster set, all the top names are not represented. Once again, due to folding, heavy creases are a fact of life for today's collector.

		NR MT	EX	VG
Complete Set:		30.00	15.00	9.00
Common Player:		.40	.20	.12
1	Joe Horlen	.40	.20	.12
2	Phil Niekro	1.50	.70	.45
3	Willie Davis	.50	.25	.15
4	Lou Brock	2.00	1.00	.60
5	Ron Santo	.60	.30	.20
6	Ken Harrelson	.50	.25	.15
7	Willie McCovey	2.00	1.00	.60
8	Rick Wise	.40	.20	.12
9	Andy Messersmith	.40	.20	.12
10	Ron Fairly	.50	.25	.15
11	Johnny Bench	3.25	1.75	1.00
12	Frank Robinson	2.50	1.25	.70
13	Tommie Agee	.40	.20	.12
14	Roy White	.50	.25	.15
15	Larry Dierker	.40	.20	.12
16	Rod Carew	3.00	1.50	.90
17	Don Mincher	.40	.20	.12
18	Ollie Brown	.40	.20	.12
19	Ed Kirkpatrick	.40	.20	.12
20	Reggie Smith	.50	.25	.15
21	Bob Clemente	5.00	2.50	1.50
22	Frank Howard	.60	.30	.20
23	Bert Campaneris	.50	.25	.15
24	Denny McLain	.60	.30	.20

1970 Topps Scratch-Offs

Needing inserts, and having not given up on the idea of a game which could be played with baseball cards, Topps provided a new game - the baseball scratch-off. The set consists of 24 cards. Unfolded, they measure 3-3/8" by 5," and reveal a baseball game of sorts which was played by rubbing the black ink off playing squares which then determined the "action." Fronts of the cards have a player picture as "captain," while backs have instructions and a scoreboard. Inserts with white centers are from 1970 while those with red centers are from 1971.

		NR MT	EX	VG
Complete Set:		20.00	10.00	6.00
Common Player:		.30	.15	.09
(1)	Hank Aaron	2.00	1.00	.60
(2)	Rich Allen	.50	.25	.15
(3)	Luis Aparicio	1.00	.50	.30
(4)	Sal Bando	.30	.15	.09
(5)	Glenn Beckert	.30	.15	.09
(6)	Dick Bosman	.30	.15	.09
(7)	Nate Colbert	.30	.15	.09
(8)	Mike Hegan	.30	.15	.09
(9)	Mack Jones	.30	.15	.09
(10)	Al Kaline	1.50	.70	.45
(11)	Harmon Killebrew	1.50	.70	.45
(12)	Juan Marichal	1.25	.60	.40
(13)	Tim McCarver	.40	.20	.12
(14)	Sam McDowell	.30	.15	.09
(15)	Claude Osteen	.30	.15	.09
(16)	Tony Perez	.60	.30	.20
(17)	Lou Piniella	.40	.20	.12
(18)	Boog Powell	.50	.25	.15
(19)	Tom Seaver	2.00	1.00	.60
(20)	Jim Spencer	.30	.15	.09
(21)	Willie Stargell	1.25	.60	.40
(22)	Mel Stottlemyre	.30	.15	.09
(23)	Jim Wynn	.30	.15	.09
(24)	Carl Yastrzemski	2.25	1.25	.70

1970 Topps Story Booklets

Measuring 2-1/2" by 3-7/16," the Topps Story Booklet was a 1970 regular pack insert. The booklet feature a photo, title and booklet number on the "cover." Inside are six pages of comic book story. The backs give a checklist of other available booklets. Not every star had a booklet as the set is only 24 in number.

		NR MT	EX	VG
Complete Set:		30.00	15.00	9.00
Common Player:		.30	.15	.09
1	Mike Cuellar	.40	.20	.12
2	Rico Petrocelli	.40	.20	.12
3	Jay Johnstone	.40	.20	.12
4	Walt Williams	.30	.15	.09
5	Vada Pinson	.50	.25	.15
6	Bill Freehan	.40	.20	.12
7	Wally Bunker	.30	.15	.09
8	Tony Oliva	.50	.25	.15
9	Bobby Murcer	.40	.20	.12
10	Reggie Jackson	5.00	2.50	1.50
11	Tommy Harper	.30	.15	.09

		NR MT	EX	VG
12	Mike Epstein	.30	.15	.09
13	Orlando Cepeda	.90	.45	.25
14	Ernie Banks	3.00	1.50	.90
15	Pete Rose	8.00	4.00	2.50
16	Denis Menke	.30	.15	.09
17	Bill Singer	.30	.15	.09
18	Rusty Staub	.50	.25	.15
19	Cleon Jones	.30	.15	.09
20	Deron Johnson	.30	.15	.09
21	Bob Moose	.30	.15	.09
22	Bob Gibson	4.00	2.00	1.25
23	Al Ferrara	.30	.15	.09
24	Willie Mays	7.00	3.50	2.00

		NR MT	EX	VG
34	Pete Rose	25.00	12.50	7.50
35	Jim Wynn	1.00	.50	.30
36	Ollie Brown	3.00	1.50	.90
37	Frank Robinson	18.00	9.00	5.50
38	John "Boog" Powell	60.00	30.00	18.00
39	Willie Davis	3.50	1.75	1.00
40	Billy Williams	12.00	6.00	3.50
41	Rusty Staub	1.25	.60	.40
42	Tommie Agee	.90	.45	.25

1970 Topps Super

Representing a refinement of the concept begun in 1969, the 1970 Topps Supers had a new 3-1/8" by 5-1/4" postcard size. Printed on heavy stock with rounded corners, card fronts feature a borderless color photograph and facsimile autograph. Card backs are simply an enlarged back from the player's regular 1970 Topps card. The Topps Supers set numbers 42 cards. Probably due to the press sheet configuration eight of the 42 had smaller printings. The most elusive is card #38 (Boog Powell). The set was more widely produced than was the case in 1969, meaning collectors stand a much better chance of affording it.

		NR MT	EX	VG
Complete Set:		250.00	125.00	75.00
Common Player:		.75	.40	.25
1	Claude Osteen	3.00	1.50	.90
2	Sal Bando	3.50	1.75	1.00
3	Luis Aparicio	2.50	1.25	.70
4	Harmon Killebrew	4.00	2.00	1.25
5	Tom Seaver	25.00	12.50	7.50
6	Larry Dierker	.90	.45	.25
7	Bill Freehan	1.00	.50	.30
8	Johnny Bench	15.00	7.50	4.50
9	Tommy Harper	.90	.45	.25
10	Sam McDowell	1.00	.50	.30
11	Louis Brock	4.00	2.00	1.25
12	Roberto Clemente	15.00	7.50	4.50
13	Willie McCovey	4.00	2.00	1.25
14	Rico Petrocelli	.90	.45	.25
15	Philip Niekro	2.25	1.25	.70
16	Frank Howard	1.50	.70	.45
17	Denny McLain	1.25	.60	.40
18	Willie Mays	15.00	7.50	4.50
19	Wilver Stargell	3.50	1.75	1.00
20	Joe Horlen	.90	.45	.25
21	Ronald Santo	1.00	.50	.30
22	Dick Bosman	.90	.45	.25
23	Tim McCarver	1.00	.50	.30
24	Henry Aaron	15.00	7.50	4.50
25	Andy Messersmith	.90	.45	.25
26	Tony Oliva	1.25	.60	.40
27	Mel Stottlemyre	1.00	.50	.30
28	Reginald M. Jackson	18.00	9.00	5.50
29	Carl Yastrzemski	12.00	6.00	3.50
30	James Fregosi	1.00	.50	.30
31	Vada Pinson	1.25	.60	.40
32	Lou Piniella	1.25	.60	.40
33	Robert Gibson	4.00	2.00	1.25

1971 Topps Baseball Tattoos

Topps once again produced baseball tattoos in 1971. This time, the tattoos came in a variety of sizes, shapes and themes. The sheets of tattoos measure 3-1/2" by 14-1/4." Each sheet contains an assortment of tattoos in two sizes, 1-3/4" by 2-3/8," or 1-3/16" by 1-3/4." There are players, facsimile autographed baseballs, team pennants and assorted baseball cartoon figures carried on the 16 different sheets. Listings below are for complete sheets; with the exception of the biggest-name stars, individual tattoos have little or no collector value.

		NR MT	EX	VG
Complete Sheet Set:		175.00	87.00	52.00
Common Sheet:		4.00	2.00	1.25
1	Brooks Robinson Autograph, Montreal Expos Pennant, San Francisco Giants Pennant, Sal Bando, Dick Bosman, Nate Colbert, Cleon Jones, Juan Marichal, B. Robinson	10.00	5.00	3.00
2	Boston Red Sox Pennant, Carl Yastrzemski Autograph, New York Mets Pennant, Glenn Beckert, Tommy Harper, Ken Henderson, Fritz Peterson, Bob Robertson, C. Yastrzemski	18.00	9.00	5.50
3	Jim Fregosi Autograph, New York Yankees Pennant, Philadelphia Phillies Pennant ector value., Orlando Cepeda, Jim Fregosi, Randy Hundley, Reggie Jackson, Jerry Koosman, Jim Palmer	15.00	7.50	4.50
4	Kansas City Royals Pennant, Oakland Athletics Pennant, Sam McDowell Autograph, Dick Dietz, C. Gaston, Dave Johnson, Sam McDowell, Gary Nolan, Amos Otis	3.50	1.75	1.00
5	Al Kaline Autograph, Atlanta Braves Pennant, L.A. Dodgers Pennant, B. Grabarkewitz, Al Kaline, Lee May, Tom Murphy, Vada Pinson, M. Sanguillen	10.00	5.00	3.00
6	Chicago Cubs Pennant, Cincinnati Reds Pennant, Harmon Killebrew Autograph, Luis Aparicio, Paul Blair, C. Cannizzaro, D. Clendenon, Larry Dieker, H. Killebrew	10.00	5.00	3.00
7	Boog Powell Autograph, Cleveland Indians Pennant, Milwaukee Brewers Pennant, Rich Allen, B. Campaneris, Don Money, Boog Powell, Ted Savage, Rusty Staub	5.00	2.50	1.50
8	Chicago White Sox Pennant, Frank Howard Autograph, San Diego Padres Pennant, Leo Cardenas, Bill Hands, Frank Howard, Wes Parker, Reggie Smith, W. Stargell	5.00	2.50	1.50
9	Detroit Tigers Pennant, Henry Aaron Autograph, Hank Aaron, Tommy Agee, Jim Hunter, Dick McAuliffe, Tony Perez, Lou Piniella	15.00	7.50	4.50

		NR MT	EX	VG
10	Baltimore Orioles Pennant, Fergie Jenkins Autograph, R. Clemente, T. Conigliaro, Fergie Jenkins, T. Munson, Gary Peters, Joe Torre	12.00	6.00	3.50
11	Johnny Bench Autograph, Washington Senators Pennant, Johnny Bench, Rico Carty, B. Mazeroski, Bob Oliver, R. Petrocelli, F. Robinson	10.00	5.00	3.00
12	Billy Williams Autograph, Houston Astros Pennant, Bill Freehan, Dave McNally, Felix Millan, M. Stottlemyre, Bob Tolan, Billy Williams	6.00	3.00	1.75
13	Pittsburgh Pirates Pennant, Willie McCovey Autograph, Ray Culp, Bud Harrelson, Mickey Lolich, W. McCovey, Ron Santo, Roy White	9.00	4.50	2.75
14	Minnesota Twins Pennant, Tom Seaver Autograph, Bill Melton, Jim Perry, Pete Rose, Tom Seaver, Maury Wills, Clyde Wright	25.00	12.50	7.50
15	Robert Gibson Autograph, St. Louis Cardinals Pennant, Rod Carew, Bob Gibson, Alex Johnson, Don Kessinger, Jim Merritt, Rick Monday	9.00	4.50	2.75
16	California Angels Pennant, Willie Mays Autograph, Larry Bowa, Mike Cuellar, Ray Fosse, Willie Mays, Carl Morton, Tony Oliva	15.00	7.50	4.50

1971 Topps

In 1971, Topps again increased the size of its set to 752 cards. These well-liked cards, measuring 2-1/2" by 3-1/2," feature a large color photo which has a thin white frame. Above the picture, in the card's overall black border, is the player's name, team and position. A facsimile autograph completes the front. Backs feature a major change as a black and white "snapshot" of the player appears. Abbreviated statistics, a line giving the player's first pro and major league games and a short biography complete the back of these innovative cards. Specialty cards in this issue are limited. There are statistical leaders as well as World Series and playoff highlights. High numbered cards #644-752 are scarce.

		NR MT	EX	VG
	Complete Set:	2200.00	1100.00	650.00
	Common Player: 1-523	.70	.35	.20
	Common Player: 524-643	1.75	.90	.50
	Common Player: 644-752	3.00	1.50	.90
1	World Champions (Orioles Team)	12.00	6.00	3.50
2	Dock Ellis	.80	.40	.25
3	Dick McAuliffe	.80	.40	.25
4	Vic Davalillo	.80	.40	.25
5	Thurman Munson	30.00	15.00	9.00
6	Ed Spiezio	.70	.35	.20
7	Jim Holt	.70	.35	.20
8	Mike McQueen	.70	.35	.20
9	George Scott	.80	.40	.25
10	Claude Osteen	.80	.40	.25
11	*Elliott Maddox*	.80	.40	.25
12	Johnny Callison	2.00	1.00	.60
13	White Sox Rookies (Charlie Brinkman, Dick Moloney)	.70	.35	.20

		NR MT	EX	VG
14	*Dave Concepcion*	20.00	10.00	6.00
15	Andy Messersmith	.80	.40	.25
16	*Ken Singleton*	2.25	1.25	.70
17	Billy Sorrell	.70	.35	.20
18	Norm Miller	.70	.35	.20
19	Skip Pitlock	.70	.35	.20
20	Reggie Jackson	90.00	45.00	27.00
21	Dan McGinn	.70	.35	.20
22	Phil Roof	.70	.35	.20
23	Oscar Gamble	.80	.40	.25
24	Rich Hand	.70	.35	.20
25	Clarence Gaston	.70	.35	.20
26	*Bert Blyleven*	50.00	25.00	15.00
27	Pirates Rookies (Fred Cambria, Gene Clines)	.70	.35	.20
28	Ron Klimkowski	.80	.40	.25
29	Don Buford	.80	.40	.25
30	Phil Niekro	3.25	1.75	1.00
31	Eddie Kasko	.70	.35	.20
32	Jerry DaVanon	.70	.35	.20
33	Del Unser	.70	.35	.20
34	Sandy Vance	.70	.35	.20
35	Lou Piniella	1.25	.60	.40
36	Dean Chance	.80	.40	.25
37	Rich McKinney	.70	.35	.20
38	*Jim Colborn*	.80	.40	.25
39	Tigers Rookies (Gene Lamont, *Lerrin LaGrow*)	.80	.40	.25
40	Lee May	2.00	1.00	.60
41	Rick Austin	.70	.35	.20
42	Boots Day	.70	.35	.20
43	Steve Kealey	.70	.35	.20
44	Johnny Edwards	.70	.35	.20
45	Jim Hunter	5.00	2.50	1.50
46	Dave Campbell	.70	.35	.20
47	Johnny Jeter	.70	.35	.20
48	Dave Baldwin	.70	.35	.20
49	Don Money	.80	.40	.25
50	Willie McCovey	7.00	3.50	2.00
51	Steve Kline	.80	.40	.25
52	Braves Rookies (Oscar Brown, *Earl Williams*)	.80	.40	.25
53	Paul Blair	.80	.40	.25
54	Checklist 1-132	3.25	1.75	1.00
55	Steve Carlton	30.00	15.00	9.00
56	Duane Josephson	.70	.35	.20
57	Von Joshua	.70	.35	.20
58	Bill Lee	.80	.40	.25
59	Gene Mauch	2.00	1.00	.60
60	Dick Bosman	.70	.35	.20
61	A.L. Batting Leaders (Alex Johnson, Tony Oliva, Carl Yastrzemski)	3.00	1.50	.90
62	N.L. Batting Leaders (Rico Carty, Manny Sanguillen, Joe Torre)	1.25	.60	.40
63	A.L. RBI Leaders (Tony Conigliaro, Frank Howard, Boog Powell)	1.25	.60	.40
64	N.L. RBI Leaders (Johnny Bench, Tony Perez, Billy Williams)	3.00	1.50	.90
65	A.L. Home Run Leaders (Frank Howard, Harmon Killebrew, Carl Yastrzemski)	3.00	1.50	.90
66	N.L. Home Run Leaders (Johnny Bench, Tony Perez, Billy Williams)	3.00	1.50	.90
67	A.L. ERA Leaders (Jim Palmer, Diego Segui, Clyde Wright)	1.25	.60	.40
68	N.L. ERA Leaders (Tom Seaver, Wayne Simpson, Luke Walker)	1.50	.70	.45
69	A.L. Pitching Leaders (Mike Cuellar, Dave McNally, Jim Perry)	1.25	.60	.40
70	N.L. Pitching Leaders (Bob Gibson, Fergie Jenkins, Gaylord Perry)	2.00	1.00	.60
71	A.L. Strikeout Leaders (Bob Johnson, Mickey Lolich, Sam McDowell)	1.25	.60	.40
72	N.L. Strikeout Leaders (Bob Gibson, Fergie Jenkins, Tom Seaver)	3.00	1.50	.90
73	George Brunet	.70	.35	.20
74	Twins Rookies (Pete Hamm, Jim Nettles)	.70	.35	.20
75	Gary Nolan	.70	.35	.20
76	Ted Savage	.70	.35	.20
77	Mike Compton	.70	.35	.20
78	Jim Spencer	.80	.40	.25
79	Wade Blasingame	.70	.35	.20
80	Bill Melton	.80	.40	.25
81	Felix Millan	.70	.35	.20
82	Casey Cox	.70	.35	.20
83	Mets Rookies (Randy Bobb, *Tim Foli*)	.80	.40	.25
84	Marcel Lachemann	.70	.35	.20
85	Billy Grabarkewitz	.70	.35	.20
86	Mike Kilkenny	.70	.35	.20
87	Jack Heidemann	.70	.35	.20

		NR MT	EX	VG
88	Hal King	.70	.35	.20
89	Ken Brett	.70	.35	.20
90	Joe Pepitone	.70	.35	.20
91	Bob Lemon	1.25	.60	.40
92	Fred Wenz	.70	.35	.20
93	Senators Rookies (Norm McRae, Denny Riddleberger)	.70	.35	.20
94	Don Hahn	.70	.35	.20
95	Luis Tiant	1.50	.70	.45
96	Joe Hague	.70	.35	.20
97	Floyd Wicker	.70	.35	.20
98	Joe Decker	.70	.35	.20
99	Mark Belanger	.80	.40	.25
100	Pete Rose	40.00	20.00	12.00
101	Les Cain	.70	.35	.20
102	Astros Rookies (*Ken Forsch*, Larry Howard)	.80	.40	.25
103	Rich Severson	.70	.35	.20
104	Dan Frisella	.70	.35	.20
105	Tony Conigliaro	1.25	.60	.40
106	Tom Dukes	.70	.35	.20
107	Roy Foster	.70	.35	.20
108	John Cumberland	.70	.35	.20
109	Steve Hovley	.70	.35	.20
110	Bill Mazeroski	1.25	.60	.40
111	Yankees Rookies (Loyd Colson, Bobby Mitchell)	.80	.40	.25
112	Manny Mota	2.00	1.00	.60
113	Jerry Crider	.70	.35	.20
114	Billy Conigliaro	.80	.40	.25
115	Donn Clendenon	.80	.40	.25
116	Ken Sanders	.70	.35	.20
117	*Ted Simmons*	20.00	10.00	6.00
118	Cookie Rojas	.70	.35	.20
119	Frank Lucchesi	.70	.35	.20
120	Willie Horton	2.00	1.00	.60
121	1971 Rookie Stars (Jim Dunegan, Roe Skidmore)	.70	.35	.20
122	Eddie Watt	.70	.35	.20
123a	Checklist 133-263 (card # on right, orange helmet)	3.25	1.75	1.00
123b	Checklist 133-263 (card # on right, red helmet)	3.25	1.75	1.00
123c	Checklist 133-263 (card # centered)	3.50	1.75	1.00
124	*Don Gullett*	.70	.35	.20
125	Ray Fosse	.70	.35	.20
126	Danny Coombs	.70	.35	.20
127	*Danny Thompson*	.80	.40	.25
128	Frank Johnson	.70	.35	.20
129	Aurelio Monteagudo	.70	.35	.20
130	Denis Menke	.70	.35	.20
131	Curt Blefary	.80	.40	.25
132	Jose Laboy	.70	.35	.20
133	Mickey Lolich	1.25	.60	.40
134	Jose Arcia	.70	.35	.20
135	Rick Monday	.80	.40	.25
136	Duffy Dyer	.70	.35	.20
137	Marcelino Lopez	.70	.35	.20
138	Phillies Rookies (Joe Lis, *Willie Montanez*)	.80	.40	.25
139	Paul Casanova	.70	.35	.20
140	Gaylord Perry	8.00	4.00	2.50
141	Frank Quilici	.70	.35	.20
142	Mack Jones	.70	.35	.20
143	Steve Blass	.80	.40	.25
144	Jackie Hernandez	.70	.35	.20
145	Bill Singer	.80	.40	.25
146	Ralph Houk	1.75	.90	.50
147	Bob Priddy	.70	.35	.20
148	John Mayberry	.80	.40	.25
149	Mike Hershberger	.70	.35	.20
150	Sam McDowell	.70	.35	.20
151	Tommy Davis	.70	.35	.20
152	Angels Rookies (Lloyd Allen, Winston Llenas)	.70	.35	.20
153	Gary Ross	.70	.35	.20
154	Cesar Gutierrez	.70	.35	.20
155	Ken Henderson	.70	.35	.20
156	Bart Johnson	.70	.35	.20
157	Bob Bailey	.70	.35	.20
158	Jerry Reuss	2.00	1.00	.60
159	Jarvis Tatum	.70	.35	.20
160	Tom Seaver	65.00	33.00	21.00
161	Coins Checklist	3.25	1.75	1.00
162	Jack Billingham	.70	.35	.20
163	Buck Martinez	.70	.35	.20
164	Reds Rookies (Frank Duffy, *Milt Wilcox*)	2.00	1.00	.60
165	Cesar Tovar	.70	.35	.20
166	Joe Hoerner	.70	.35	.20
167	Tom Grieve	.70	.35	.20
168	Bruce Dal Canton	.70	.35	.20
169	Ed Herrmann	.70	.35	.20
170	Mike Cuellar	2.00	1.00	.60
171	Bobby Wine	.70	.35	.20
172	Duke Sims	.70	.35	.20
173	Gil Garrido	.70	.35	.20
174	*Dave LaRoche*	.80	.40	.25
175	Jim Hickman	.80	.40	.25
176	Red Sox Rookies (Doug Griffin, Bob Montgomery)	.70	.35	.20
177	Hal McRae	.70	.35	.20
178	Dave Duncan	.70	.35	.20
179	Mike Corkins	.70	.35	.20
180	Al Kaline	18.00	9.00	5.50
181	Hal Lanier	2.00	1.00	.60
182	Al Downing	.80	.40	.25
183	Gil Hodges	4.00	2.00	1.25
184	Stan Bahnsen	.80	.40	.25
185	Julian Javier	.80	.40	.25
186	Bob Spence	.70	.35	.20
187	Ted Abernathy	.70	.35	.20
188	Dodgers Rookies (Mike Strahler, *Bob Valentine*)	2.25	1.25	.70
189	George Mitterwald	.70	.35	.20
190	Bob Tolan	.80	.40	.25
191	Mike Andrews	.70	.35	.20
192	Billy Wilson	.70	.35	.20
193	*Bob Grich*	2.25	1.25	.70
194	Mike Lum	.70	.35	.20
195	A.L. Playoff Game 1 (Powell Muscles Twins!)	1.25	.60	.40
196	A.L. Playoff Game 2 (McNally Makes It Two Straight!)	1.25	.60	.40
197	A.L. Playoff Game 3 (Palmer Mows 'Em Down!)	2.25	1.25	.70
198	A.L. Playoffs Summary (A Team Effort!)	1.25	.60	.40
199	N.L. Playoff Game 1 (Cline Pinch-Triple Decides It!)	1.25	.60	.40
200	N.L. Playoff Game 2 (Tolan Scores For Third Time!)	1.25	.60	.40
201	N.L. Playoff Game 3 (Cline Scores Winning Run!)	1.25	.60	.40
202	N.L. Playoffs Summary (World Series Bound!)	1.25	.60	.40
203	*Larry Gura*	.70	.35	.20
204	Brewers Rookies (George Kopacz, Bernie Smith)	.70	.35	.20
205	Gerry Moses	.70	.35	.20
206a	Checklist 264-393 (orange helmet)	3.25	1.75	1.00
206b	Checklist 264-393 (red helmet)	3.25	1.75	1.00
207	Alan Foster	.70	.35	.20
208	Billy Martin	2.25	1.25	.70
209	Steve Renko	.70	.35	.20
210	Rod Carew	52.00	26.00	15.50
211	Phil Hennigan	.70	.35	.20
212	Rich Hebner	.80	.40	.25
213	Frank Baker	.80	.40	.25
214	Al Ferrara	.70	.35	.20
215	Diego Segui	.70	.35	.20
216	Cards Rookies (Reggie Cleveland, Luis Melendez)	.70	.35	.20
217	Ed Stroud	.70	.35	.20
218	Tony Cloninger	.80	.40	.25
219	Elrod Hendricks	.70	.35	.20
220	Ron Santo	1.75	.90	.50
221	Dave Morehead	.70	.35	.20
222	Bob Watson	.80	.40	.25
223	Cecil Upshaw	.70	.35	.20
224	Alan Gallagher	.70	.35	.20
225	Gary Peters	.80	.40	.25
226	Bill Russell	2.00	1.00	.60
227	Floyd Weaver	.70	.35	.20
228	Wayne Garrett	.70	.35	.20
229	Jim Hannan	.70	.35	.20
230	Willie Stargell	8.00	4.00	2.50
231	Indians Rookies (Vince Colbert, *John Lowenstein*)	.80	.40	.25
232	John Strohmayer	.70	.35	.20
233	Larry Bowa	2.25	1.25	.70
234	Jim Lyttle	.80	.40	.25
235	Nate Colbert	.70	.35	.20
236	Bob Humphreys	.70	.35	.20
237	*Cesar Cedeno*	1.50	.70	.45
238	Chuck Dobson	.70	.35	.20
239	Red Schoendienst	2.00	1.00	.60
240	Clyde Wright	.70	.35	.20
241	Dave Nelson	.70	.35	.20
242	Jim Ray	.70	.35	.20

#	Player	NR MT	EX	VG
243	Carlos May	.80	.40	.25
244	Bob Tillman	.70	.35	.20
245	Jim Kaat	3.25	1.75	1.00
246	Tony Taylor	.70	.35	.20
247	Royals Rookies (Jerry Cram, Paul Splittorff)	.70	.35	.20
248	Hoyt Wilhelm	3.75	2.00	1.25
249	Chico Salmon	.70	.35	.20
250	Johnny Bench	45.00	23.00	13.50
251	Frank Reberger	.70	.35	.20
252	Eddie Leon	.70	.35	.20
253	Bill Sudakis	.70	.35	.20
254	Cal Koonce	.70	.35	.20
255	Bob Robertson	.70	.35	.20
256	Tony Gonzalez	.70	.35	.20
257	Nelson Briles	.70	.35	.20
258	Dick Green	.70	.35	.20
259	Dave Marshall	.70	.35	.20
260	Tommy Harper	.80	.40	.25
261	Darold Knowles	.70	.35	.20
262	Padres Rookies (Dave Robinson, Jim Williams)	.70	.35	.20
263	John Ellis	.80	.40	.25
264	Joe Morgan	10.00	5.00	3.00
265	Jim Northrup	.80	.40	.25
266	Bill Stoneman	.70	.35	.20
267	Rich Morales	.70	.35	.20
268	Phillies Team	1.25	.60	.40
269	Gail Hopkins	.70	.35	.20
270	Rico Carty	.70	.35	.20
271	Bill Zepp	.70	.35	.20
272	Tommy Helms	.80	.40	.25
273	Pete Richert	.70	.35	.20
274	Ron Slocum	.70	.35	.20
275	Vada Pinson	1.25	.60	.40
276	Giants Rookies (Mike Davison, *George Foster*)	6.00	3.00	1.75
277	Gary Waslewski	.80	.40	.25
278	Jerry Grote	.80	.40	.25
279	Lefty Phillips	.70	.35	.20
280	Fergie Jenkins	12.00	6.00	3.50
281	Danny Walton	.70	.35	.20
282	Jose Pagan	.70	.35	.20
283	Dick Such	.70	.35	.20
284	Jim Gosger	.70	.35	.20
285	Sal Bando	2.00	1.00	.60
286	Jerry McNertney	.70	.35	.20
287	Mike Fiore	.70	.35	.20
288	Joe Moeller	.70	.35	.20
289	White Sox Team	1.25	.60	.40
290	Tony Oliva	1.50	.70	.45
291	George Culver	.70	.35	.20
292	Jay Johnstone	2.00	1.00	.60
293	Pat Corrales	.80	.40	.25
294	Steve Dunning	.70	.35	.20
295	Bobby Bonds	1.25	.60	.40
296	Tom Timmermann	.70	.35	.20
297	Johnny Briggs	.70	.35	.20
298	Jim Nelson	.70	.35	.20
299	Ed Kirkpatrick	.70	.35	.20
300	Brooks Robinson	12.00	6.00	3.50
301	Earl Wilson	.70	.35	.20
302	Phil Gagliano	.70	.35	.20
303	Lindy McDaniel	.80	.40	.25
304	Ron Brand	.70	.35	.20
305	Reggie Smith	2.00	1.00	.60
306	Jim Nash	.70	.35	.20
307	Don Wert	.70	.35	.20
308	Cards Team	1.25	.60	.40
309	Dick Ellsworth	.70	.35	.20
310	Tommie Agee	.80	.40	.25
311	Lee Stange	.70	.35	.20
312	Harry Walker	.80	.40	.25
313	Tom Hall	.70	.35	.20
314	Jeff Torborg	.80	.40	.25
315	Ron Fairly	.80	.40	.25
316	Fred Scherman	.70	.35	.20
317	Athletics Rookies (Jim Driscoll, Angel Mangual)	.70	.35	.20
318	Rudy May	.80	.40	.25
319	Ty Cline	.70	.35	.20
320	Dave McNally	.80	.40	.25
321	Tom Matchick	.70	.35	.20
322	Jim Beauchamp	.70	.35	.20
323	Billy Champion	.70	.35	.20
324	Graig Nettles	3.25	1.75	1.00
325	Juan Marichal	5.00	2.50	1.50
326	Richie Scheinblum	.70	.35	.20
327	World Series Game 1 (Powell Homers To Opposite Field!)	1.25	.60	.40
328	World Series Game 2 (Buford Goes 2-For 4!)	1.25	.60	.40
329	World Series Game 3 (F. Robinson Shows Muscle!)	2.00	1.00	.60
330	World Series Game 4 (Reds Stay Alive!)	1.25	.60	.40
331	World Series Game 5 (B. Robinson Commits Robbery!)	2.00	1.00	.60
332	World Series Summary (Clinching Performance!)	1.25	.60	.40
333	Clay Kirby	.70	.35	.20
334	Roberto Pena	.70	.35	.20
335	Jerry Koosman	2.00	1.00	.60
336	Tigers Team	2.25	1.25	.70
337	Jesus Alou	.80	.40	.25
338	Gene Tenace	.80	.40	.25
339	Wayne Simpson	.70	.35	.20
340	Rico Petrocelli	.80	.40	.25
341	*Steve Garvey*	70.00	35.00	21.00
342	Frank Tepedino	.80	.40	.25
343	Pirates Rookies (Ed Acosta, *Milt May*)	.80	.40	.25
344	Ellie Rodriguez	.70	.35	.20
345	Joe Horlen	.70	.35	.20
346	Lum Harris	.70	.35	.20
347	Ted Uhlaender	.70	.35	.20
348	Fred Norman	.70	.35	.20
349	Rich Reese	.70	.35	.20
350	Billy Williams	4.50	2.25	1.25
351	Jim Shellenback	.70	.35	.20
352	Denny Doyle	.70	.35	.20
353	Carl Taylor	.70	.35	.20
354	Don McMahon	.70	.35	.20
355	Bud Harrelson	.80	.40	.25
356	Bob Locker	.70	.35	.20
357	Reds Team	1.25	.60	.40
358	Danny Cater	.80	.40	.25
359	Ron Reed	.80	.40	.25
360	Jim Fregosi	1.75	.90	.50
361	Don Sutton	3.50	1.75	1.00
362	Orioles Rookies (Mike Adamson, Roger Freed)	.70	.35	.20
363	Mike Nagy	.70	.35	.20
364	Tommy Dean	.70	.35	.20
365	Bob Johnson	.70	.35	.20
366	Ron Stone	.70	.35	.20
367	Dalton Jones	.70	.35	.20
368	Bob Veale	.80	.40	.25
369a	Checklist 394-523 (orange helmet)	3.25	1.75	1.00
369b	Checklist 394-523 (red helmet, black line above ear)	3.25	1.75	1.00
369c	Checklist 394-523 (red helmet, no line)	3.25	1.75	1.00
370	Joe Torre	3.00	1.50	.90
371	Jack Hiatt	.70	.35	.20
372	Lew Krausse	.70	.35	.20
373	Tom McCraw	.70	.35	.20
374	Clete Boyer	.80	.40	.25
375	Steve Hargan	.70	.35	.20
376	Expos Rookies (Clyde Mashore, Ernie McAnally)	.70	.35	.20
377	Greg Garrett	.70	.35	.20
378	Tito Fuentes	.70	.35	.20
379	Wayne Granger	.70	.35	.20
380	Ted Williams	5.00	2.50	1.50
381	Fred Gladding	.70	.35	.20
382	Jake Gibbs	.80	.40	.25
383	Rod Gaspar	.70	.35	.20
384	Rollie Fingers	10.00	5.00	3.00
385	Maury Wills	1.25	.60	.40
386	Red Sox Team	1.50	.70	.45
387	Ron Herbel	.70	.35	.20
388	Al Oliver	2.25	1.25	.70
389	Ed Brinkman	.80	.40	.25
390	Glenn Beckert	.80	.40	.25
391	Twins Rookies (Steve Brye, Cotton Nash)	.70	.35	.20
392	Grant Jackson	.70	.35	.20
393	Merv Rettenmund	.80	.40	.25
394	Clay Carroll	.80	.40	.25
395	Roy White	.70	.35	.20
396	Dick Schofield	.70	.35	.20
397	Alvin Dark	.80	.40	.25
398	Howie Reed	.70	.35	.20
399	Jim French	.70	.35	.20
400	Hank Aaron	40.00	20.00	12.00
401	Tom Murphy	.70	.35	.20
402	Dodgers Team	1.50	.70	.45
403	Joe Coleman	.80	.40	.25
404	Astros Rookies (Buddy Harris, Roger Metzger)	.70	.35	.20
405	Leo Cardenas	.70	.35	.20

		NR MT	EX	VG
406	Ray Sadecki	.70	.35	.20
407	Joe Rudi	2.00	1.00	.60
408	Rafael Robles	.70	.35	.20
409	Don Pavletich	.70	.35	.20
410	Ken Holtzman	.80	.40	.25
411	George Spriggs	.70	.35	.20
412	Jerry Johnson	.70	.35	.20
413	Pat Kelly	.70	.35	.20
414	Woodie Fryman	.80	.40	.25
415	Mike Hegan	.70	.35	.20
416	Gene Alley	.80	.40	.25
417	Dick Hall	.70	.35	.20
418	Adolfo Phillips	.70	.35	.20
419	Ron Hansen	.80	.40	.25
420	Jim Merritt	.70	.35	.20
421	John Stephenson	.70	.35	.20
422	Frank Bertaina	.70	.35	.20
423	Tigers Rookies (Tim Marting, Dennis Saunders)	.70	.35	.20
424	Roberto Rodriquez (Rodriguez)	.70	.35	.20
425	Doug Rader	.70	.35	.20
426	Chris Cannizzaro	.70	.35	.20
427	Bernie Allen	.70	.35	.20
428	Jim McAndrew	.70	.35	.20
429	Chuck Hinton	.70	.35	.20
430	Wes Parker	.80	.40	.25
431	Tom Burgmeier	.70	.35	.20
432	Bob Didier	.70	.35	.20
433	Skip Lockwood	.70	.35	.20
434	Gary Sutherland	.70	.35	.20
435	Jose Cardenal	.80	.40	.25
436	Wilbur Wood	.80	.40	.25
437	Danny Murtaugh	.80	.40	.25
438	Mike McCormick	.80	.40	.25
439	Phillies Rookies (Greg Luzinski, Scott Reid)	2.00	1.00	.60
440	Bert Campaneris	.70	.35	.20
441	Milt Pappas	.80	.40	.25
442	Angels Team	1.25	.60	.40
443	Rich Robertson	.70	.35	.20
444	Jimmie Price	.70	.35	.20
445	Art Shamsky	.70	.35	.20
446	Bobby Bolin	.70	.35	.20
447	Cesar Geronimo	2.00	1.00	.60
448	Dave Roberts	.70	.35	.20
449	Brant Alyea	.70	.35	.20
450	Bob Gibson	10.00	5.00	3.00
451	Joe Keough	.70	.35	.20
452	John Boccabella	.70	.35	.20
453	Terry Crowley	.70	.35	.20
454	Mike Paul	.70	.35	.20
455	Don Kessinger	.80	.40	.25
456	Bob Meyer	.70	.35	.20
457	Willie Smith	.70	.35	.20
458	White Sox Rookies (Dave Lemonds, Ron Lolich)	.70	.35	.20
459	Jim Lefebvre	.80	.40	.25
460	Fritz Peterson	.80	.40	.25
461	Jim Hart	.80	.40	.25
462	Senators Team	1.50	.70	.45
463	Tom Kelley	.70	.35	.20
464	Aurelio Rodriguez	.80	.40	.25
465	Tim McCarver	1.75	.90	.50
466	Ken Berry	.70	.35	.20
467	Al Santorini	.70	.35	.20
468	Frank Fernandez	.70	.35	.20
469	Bob Aspromonte	.70	.35	.20
470	Bob Oliver	.70	.35	.20
471	Tom Griffin	.70	.35	.20
472	Ken Rudolph	.70	.35	.20
473	Gary Wagner	.70	.35	.20
474	Jim Fairey	.70	.35	.20
475	Ron Perranoski	.80	.40	.25
476	Dal Maxvill	.80	.40	.25
477	Earl Weaver	2.00	1.00	.60
478	Bernie Carbo	.80	.40	.25
479	Dennis Higgins	.70	.35	.20
480	Manny Sanguillen	.80	.40	.25
481	Daryl Patterson	.70	.35	.20
482	Padres Team	1.25	.60	.40
483	Gene Michael	.80	.40	.25
484	Don Wilson	.70	.35	.20
485	Ken McMullen	.70	.35	.20
486	Steve Huntz	.70	.35	.20
487	Paul Schaal	.70	.35	.20
488	Jerry Stephenson	.70	.35	.20
489	Luis Alvarado	.70	.35	.20
490	Deron Johnson	.70	.35	.20
491	Jim Hardin	.70	.35	.20
492	Ken Boswell	.70	.35	.20
493	Dave May	.70	.35	.20

		NR MT	EX	VG
494	Braves Rookies (Ralph Garr, Rick Kester)	.80	.40	.25
495	Felipe Alou	2.00	1.00	.60
496	Woody Woodward	.80	.40	.25
497	Horacio Pina	.70	.35	.20
498	John Kennedy	.70	.35	.20
499	Checklist 524-643	3.25	1.75	1.00
500	Jim Perry	2.00	1.00	.60
501	Andy Etchebarren	.70	.35	.20
502	Cubs Team	1.25	.60	.40
503	Gates Brown	.70	.35	.20
504	Ken Wright	.70	.35	.20
505	Ollie Brown	.70	.35	.20
506	Bobby Knoop	.70	.35	.20
507	George Stone	.70	.35	.20
508	Roger Repoz	.70	.35	.20
509	Jim Grant	.70	.35	.20
510	Ken Harrelson	1.25	.60	.40
511	Chris Short	.80	.40	.25
512	Red Sox Rookies (Mike Garman, Dick Mills)	.70	.35	.20
513	Nolan Ryan	250.00	125.00	75.00
514	Ron Woods	.80	.40	.25
515	Carl Morton	.70	.35	.20
516	Ted Kubiak	.70	.35	.20
517	Charlie Fox	.70	.35	.20
518	Joe Grzenda	.70	.35	.20
519	Willie Crawford	.70	.35	.20
520	Tommy John	3.00	1.50	.90
521	Leron Lee	.70	.35	.20
522	Twins Team	1.25	.60	.40
523	John Odom	.80	.40	.25
524	Mickey Stanley	2.00	1.00	.60
525	Ernie Banks	30.00	15.00	9.00
526	Ray Jarvis	1.75	.90	.50
527	Cleon Jones	2.00	1.00	.60
528	Wally Bunker	1.75	.90	.50
529	N.L. Rookies (Bill Buckner, Enzo Hernandez, Marty Perez)	4.00	2.00	1.25
530	Carl Yastrzemski	40.00	20.00	12.00
531	Mike Torrez	2.00	1.00	.60
532	Bill Rigney	1.75	.90	.50
533	Mike Ryan	1.75	.90	.50
534	Luke Walker	1.75	.90	.50
535	Curt Flood	2.25	1.25	.70
536	Claude Raymond	1.75	.90	.50
537	Tom Egan	1.75	.90	.50
538	Angel Bravo	1.75	.90	.50
539	Larry Brown	1.75	.90	.50
540	Larry Dierker	2.00	1.00	.60
541	Bob Burda	1.75	.90	.50
542	Bob Miller	1.75	.90	.50
543	Yankees Team	3.50	1.75	1.00
544	Vida Blue	3.25	1.75	1.00
545	Dick Dietz	1.75	.90	.50
546	John Matias	1.75	.90	.50
547	Pat Dobson	2.00	1.00	.60
548	Don Mason	1.75	.90	.50
549	Jim Brewer	1.75	.90	.50
550	Harmon Killebrew	15.00	7.50	4.50
551	Frank Linzy	1.75	.90	.50
552	Buddy Bradford	1.75	.90	.50
553	Kevin Collins	1.75	.90	.50
554	Lowell Palmer	1.75	.90	.50
555	Walt Williams	1.75	.90	.50
556	Jim McGlothlin	1.75	.90	.50
557	Tom Satriano	1.75	.90	.50
558	Hector Torres	1.75	.90	.50
559	A.L. Rookies (Terry Cox, Bill Gogolewski, Gary Jones)	2.00	1.00	.60
560	Rusty Staub	3.00	1.50	.90
561	Syd O'Brien	1.75	.90	.50
562	Dave Giusti	1.75	.90	.50
563	Giants Team	2.00	1.00	.60
564	Al Fitzmorris	1.75	.90	.50
565	Jim Wynn	2.00	1.00	.60
566	Tim Cullen	1.75	.90	.50
567	Walt Alston	3.25	1.75	1.00
568	Sal Campisi	1.75	.90	.50
569	Ivan Murrell	1.75	.90	.50
570	Jim Palmer	30.00	15.00	9.00
571	Ted Sizemore	1.75	.90	.50
572	Jerry Kenney	2.00	1.00	.60
573	Ed Kranepool	2.00	1.00	.60
574	Jim Bunning	4.00	2.00	1.25
575	Bill Freehan	2.00	1.00	.60
576	Cubs Rookies (Brock Davis, Adrian Garrett, Garry Jestadt)	1.75	.90	.50
577	Jim Lonborg	2.00	1.00	.60
578	Ron Hunt	2.00	1.00	.60
579	Marty Pattin	1.75	.90	.50

		NR MT	EX	VG
580	Tony Perez	6.00	3.00	1.75
581	Roger Nelson	1.75	.90	.50
582	Dave Cash	1.75	.90	.50
583	Ron Cook	1.75	.90	.50
584	Indians Team	2.00	1.00	.60
585	Willie Davis	3.00	1.50	.90
586	Dick Woodson	1.75	.90	.50
587	Sonny Jackson	1.75	.90	.50
588	Tom Bradley	1.75	.90	.50
589	Bob Barton	1.75	.90	.50
590	Alex Johnson	1.75	.90	.50
591	Jackie Brown	1.75	.90	.50
592	Randy Hundley	1.75	.90	.50
593	Jack Aker	2.00	1.00	.60
594	Cards Rookies (Bob Chlupsa, Al Hrabosky, Bob Stinson)	3.00	1.50	.90
595	Dave Johnson	2.25	1.25	.70
596	Mike Jorgensen	1.75	.90	.50
597	Ken Suarez	1.75	.90	.50
598	Rick Wise	2.00	1.00	.60
599	Norm Cash	2.00	1.00	.60
600	Willie Mays	80.00	40.00	25.00
601	Ken Tatum	1.75	.90	.50
602	Marty Martinez	1.75	.90	.50
603	Pirates Team	3.00	1.50	.90
604	John Gelnar	1.75	.90	.50
605	Orlando Cepeda	3.25	1.75	1.00
606	Chuck Taylor	1.75	.90	.50
607	Paul Ratliff	1.75	.90	.50
608	Mike Wegener	1.75	.90	.50
609	Leo Durocher	3.00	1.50	.90
610	Amos Otis	2.00	1.00	.60
611	Tom Phoebus	1.75	.90	.50
612	Indians Rookies (Lou Camilli, Ted Ford, Steve Mingori)	1.75	.90	.50
613	Pedro Borbon	2.00	1.00	.60
614	Billy Cowan	1.75	.90	.50
615	Mel Stottlemyre	2.25	1.25	.70
616	Larry Hisle	2.00	1.00	.60
617	Clay Dalrymple	1.75	.90	.50
618	Tug McGraw	3.00	1.50	.90
619a	Checklist 644-752 (no copyright on back)	4.50	2.25	1.25
619b	Checklist 644-752 (with copyright, no wavy line on helmet brim)	3.00	1.50	.90
619c	Checklist 644-752 (with copyright, wavy line on helmet brim)	3.00	1.50	.90
620	Frank Howard	3.00	1.50	.90
621	Ron Bryant	1.75	.90	.50
622	Joe Lahoud	1.75	.90	.50
623	Pat Jarvis	1.75	.90	.50
624	Athletics Team	2.00	1.00	.60
625	Lou Brock	25.00	12.50	7.50
626	Freddie Patek	2.00	1.00	.60
627	Steve Hamilton	1.75	.90	.50
628	John Bateman	1.75	.90	.50
629	John Hiller	2.00	1.00	.60
630	Roberto Clemente	65.00	33.00	21.00
631	Eddie Fisher	1.75	.90	.50
632	Darrel Chaney	1.75	.90	.50
633	A.L. Rookies (Bobby Brooks, Pete Koegel, Scott Northey)	1.75	.90	.50
634	Phil Regan	1.75	.90	.50
635	Bobby Murcer	2.00	1.00	.60
636	Denny Lemaster	1.75	.90	.50
637	Dave Bristol	1.75	.90	.50
638	Stan Williams	1.75	.90	.50
639	Tom Haller	2.00	1.00	.60
640	Frank Robinson	35.00	17.50	10.50
641	Mets Team	8.00	4.00	2.50
642	Jim Roland	1.75	.90	.50
643	Rick Reichardt	1.75	.90	.50
644	Jim Stewart	3.00	1.50	.90
645	Jim Maloney	3.25	1.75	1.00
646	Bobby Floyd	3.00	1.50	.90
647	Juan Pizarro	3.00	1.50	.90
648	Mets Rookies (Rich Folkers, Ted Martinez, Jon Matlack)	3.50	1.75	1.00
649	Sparky Lyle	3.00	1.50	.90
650	Rich Allen	9.00	4.50	2.75
651	Jerry Robertson	3.00	1.50	.90
652	Braves Team	3.25	1.75	1.00
653	Russ Snyder	3.00	1.50	.90
654	Don Shaw	3.00	1.50	.90
655	Mike Epstein	3.25	1.75	1.00
656	Gerry Nyman	3.00	1.50	.90
657	Jose Azcue	3.00	1.50	.90
658	Paul Lindblad	3.00	1.50	.90
659	Byron Browne	3.00	1.50	.90
660	Ray Culp	3.00	1.50	.90
661	Chuck Tanner	3.00	1.50	.90

		NR MT	EX	VG
662	Mike Hedlund	3.00	1.50	.90
663	Marv Staehle	3.00	1.50	.90
664	Major League Rookies (Archie Reynolds, Bob Reynolds, Ken Reynolds)	3.00	1.50	.90
665	Ron Swoboda	3.00	1.50	.90
666	Gene Brabender	3.00	1.50	.90
667	Pete Ward	3.25	1.75	1.00
668	Gary Neibauer	3.00	1.50	.90
669	Ike Brown	3.00	1.50	.90
670	Bill Hands	3.00	1.50	.90
671	Bill Voss	3.00	1.50	.90
672	Ed Crosby	3.00	1.50	.90
673	Gerry Janeski	3.00	1.50	.90
674	Expos Team	3.25	1.75	1.00
675	Dave Boswell	3.00	1.50	.90
676	Tommie Reynolds	3.00	1.50	.90
677	Jack DiLauro	3.00	1.50	.90
678	George Thomas	3.00	1.50	.90
679	Don O'Riley	3.00	1.50	.90
680	Don Mincher	3.25	1.75	1.00
681	Bill Butler	3.00	1.50	.90
682	Terry Harmon	3.00	1.50	.90
683	Bill Burbach	3.25	1.75	1.00
684	Curt Motton	3.00	1.50	.90
685	Moe Drabowsky	3.00	1.50	.90
686	Chico Ruiz	3.00	1.50	.90
687	Ron Taylor	3.00	1.50	.90
688	Sparky Anderson	3.50	1.75	1.00
689	Frank Baker	3.00	1.50	.90
690	Bob Moose	3.00	1.50	.90
691	Bob Heise	3.00	1.50	.90
692	A.L. Rookies (Hal Haydel, Rogelio Moret, Wayne Twitchell)	3.00	1.50	.90
693	Jose Pena	3.00	1.50	.90
694	Rick Renick	3.00	1.50	.90
695	Joe Niekro	3.25	1.75	1.00
696	Jerry Morales	3.00	1.50	.90
697	Rickey Clark	3.00	1.50	.90
698	Brewers Team	3.50	1.75	1.00
699	Jim Britton	3.00	1.50	.90
700	Boog Powell	4.00	2.00	1.25
701	Bob Garibaldi	3.00	1.50	.90
702	Milt Ramirez	3.00	1.50	.90
703	Mike Kekich	3.25	1.75	1.00
704	J.C. Martin	3.00	1.50	.90
705	Dick Selma	3.00	1.50	.90
706	Joe Foy	3.00	1.50	.90
707	Fred Lasher	3.00	1.50	.90
708	Russ Nagelson	3.00	1.50	.90
709	Major League Rookies (Dusty Baker, Don Baylor, Tom Paciorek)	50.00	25.00	15.00
710	Sonny Siebert	3.00	1.50	.90
711	Larry Stahl	3.00	1.50	.90
712	Jose Martinez	3.00	1.50	.90
713	Mike Marshall	3.50	1.75	1.00
714	Dick Williams	3.50	1.75	1.00
715	Horace Clarke	3.25	1.75	1.00
716	Dave Leonhard	3.00	1.50	.90
717	Tommie Aaron	3.25	1.75	1.00
718	Billy Wynne	3.00	1.50	.90
719	Jerry May	3.00	1.50	.90
720	Matty Alou	3.50	1.75	1.00
721	John Morris	3.00	1.50	.90
722	Astros Team	3.25	1.75	1.00
723	Vicente Romo	3.00	1.50	.90
724	Tom Tischinski	3.00	1.50	.90
725	Gary Gentry	3.00	1.50	.90
726	Paul Popovich	3.00	1.50	.90
727	Ray Lamb	3.00	1.50	.90
728	N.L. Rookies (Keith Lampard, Wayne Redmond, Bernie Williams)	3.00	1.50	.90
729	Dick Billings	3.00	1.50	.90
730	Jim Rooker	3.00	1.50	.90
731	Jim Qualls	3.00	1.50	.90
732	Bob Reed	3.00	1.50	.90
733	Lee Maye	3.00	1.50	.90
734	Rob Gardner	3.25	1.75	1.00
735	Mike Shannon	3.25	1.75	1.00
736	Mel Queen	3.00	1.50	.90
737	Preston Gomez	3.00	1.50	.90
738	Russ Gibson	3.00	1.50	.90
739	Barry Lersch	3.00	1.50	.90
740	Luis Aparicio	15.00	7.50	4.50
741	Skip Guinn	3.00	1.50	.90
742	Royals Team	3.25	1.75	1.00
743	John O'Donoghue	3.00	1.50	.90
744	Chuck Manuel	3.00	1.50	.90
745	Sandy Alomar	3.00	1.50	.90
746	Andy Kosco	3.00	1.50	.90
747	N.L. Rookies (Balor Moore, Al Severinsen, Scipio Spinks)	3.00	1.50	.90

		NR MT	EX	VG
748	John Purdin	3.00	1.50	.90
749	Ken Szotkiewicz	3.00	1.50	.90
750	Denny McLain	10.00	5.00	3.00
751	Al Weis	3.25	1.75	1.00
752	Dick Drago	3.75	1.25	.70

1971 Topps Coins

Measuring 1-1/2" in diameter, the latest edition of the Topps coins was a 153-piece set. The coins feature a color photograph surrounded by a colored band on the front. The band carries the player's name, team, position and several stars. Backs have a short biography, the coin number and encouragement to collect the entire set. Back colors differ, with #'s 1-51 having a brass back, #'s 52-102 chrome backs, and the rest have blue backs. Most of the stars of the period are included in the set.

		NR MT	EX	VG
Complete Set:		400.00	200.00	120.00
Common Player:		.90	.45	.25
1	Clarence Gaston	.90	.45	.25
2	Dave Johnson	1.25	.60	.40
3	Jim Bunning	2.00	1.00	.60
4	Jim Spencer	.90	.45	.25
5	Felix Millan	.90	.45	.25
6	Gerry Moses	.90	.45	.25
7	Fergie Jenkins	2.00	1.00	.60
8	Felipe Alou	1.00	.50	.30
9	Jim McGlothlin	.90	.45	.25
10	Dick McAuliffe	.90	.45	.25
11	Joe Torre	1.50	.70	.45
12	Jim Perry	1.25	.60	.40
13	Bobby Bonds	1.25	.60	.40
14	Danny Cater	.90	.45	.25
15	Bill Mazeroski	1.50	.70	.45
16	Luis Aparicio	5.00	2.50	1.50
17	Doug Rader	.90	.45	.25
18	Vada Pinson	1.50	.70	.45
19	John Bateman	.90	.45	.25
20	Lew Krausse	.90	.45	.25
21	Billy Grabarkewitz	.90	.45	.25
22	Frank Howard	1.50	.70	.45
23	Jerry Koosman	1.25	.60	.40
24	Rod Carew	8.00	4.00	2.50
25	Al Ferrara	.90	.45	.25
26	Dave McNally	1.00	.50	.30
27	Jim Hickman	.90	.45	.25
28	Sandy Alomar	.90	.45	.25
29	Lee May	1.00	.50	.30
30	Rico Petrocelli	1.00	.50	.30
31	Don Money	.90	.45	.25
32	Jim Rooker	.90	.45	.25
33	Dick Dietz	.90	.45	.25
34	Roy White	1.00	.50	.30
35	Carl Morton	.90	.45	.25
36	Walt Williams	.90	.45	.25
37	Phil Niekro	3.25	1.75	1.00
38	Bill Freehan	1.00	.50	.30
39	Julian Javier	.90	.45	.25
40	Rick Monday	1.00	.50	.30
41	Don Wilson	.90	.45	.25
42	Ray Fosse	.90	.45	.25
43	Art Shamsky	.90	.45	.25
44	Ted Savage	.90	.45	.25

		NR MT	EX	VG
45	Claude Osteen	1.00	.50	.30
46	Ed Brinkman	.90	.45	.25
47	Matty Alou	1.00	.50	.30
48	Bob Oliver	.90	.45	.25
49	Danny Coombs	.90	.45	.25
50	Frank Robinson	7.00	3.50	2.00
51	Randy Hundley	.90	.45	.25
52	Cesar Tovar	.90	.45	.25
53	Wayne Simpson	.90	.45	.25
54	Bobby Murcer	1.25	.60	.40
55	Tony Taylor	.90	.45	.25
56	Tommy John	2.50	1.25	.70
57	Willie McCovey	7.00	3.50	2.00
58	Carl Yastrzemski	15.00	7.50	4.50
59	Bob Bailey	.90	.45	.25
60	Clyde Wright	.90	.45	.25
61	Orlando Cepeda	2.00	1.00	.60
62	Al Kaline	7.00	3.50	2.00
63	Bob Gibson	7.00	3.50	2.00
64	Bert Campaneris	1.25	.60	.40
65	Ted Sizemore	.90	.45	.25
66	Duke Sims	.90	.45	.25
67	Bud Harrelson	.90	.45	.25
68	Jerry McNertney	.90	.45	.25
69	Jim Wynn	1.00	.50	.30
70	Dick Bosman	.90	.45	.25
71	Roberto Clemente	15.00	7.50	4.50
72	Rich Reese	.90	.45	.25
73	Gaylord Perry	4.00	2.00	1.25
74	Boog Powell	1.50	.70	.45
75	Billy Williams	5.00	2.50	1.50
76	Bill Melton	.90	.45	.25
77	Nate Colbert	.90	.45	.25
78	Reggie Smith	1.25	.60	.40
79	Deron Johnson	.90	.45	.25
80	Jim Hunter	5.00	2.50	1.50
81	Bob Tolan	.90	.45	.25
82	Jim Northrup	.90	.45	.25
83	Ron Fairly	1.00	.50	.30
84	Alex Johnson	.90	.45	.25
85	Pat Jarvis	.90	.45	.25
86	Sam McDowell	1.00	.50	.30
87	Lou Brock	7.00	3.50	2.00
88	Danny Walton	.90	.45	.25
89	Denis Menke	.90	.45	.25
90	Jim Palmer	7.00	3.50	2.00
91	Tommie Agee	.90	.45	.25
92	Duane Josephson	.90	.45	.25
93	Willie Davis	1.00	.50	.30
94	Mel Stottlemyre	1.00	.50	.30
95	Ron Santo	1.25	.60	.40
96	Amos Otis	1.00	.50	.30
97	Ken Henderson	.90	.45	.25
98	George Scott	1.00	.50	.30
99	Dock Ellis	.90	.45	.25
100	Harmon Killebrew	7.00	3.50	2.00
101	Pete Rose	30.00	15.00	9.00
102	Rick Reichardt	.90	.45	.25
103	Cleon Jones	.90	.45	.25
104	Ron Perranoski	.90	.45	.25
105	Tony Perez	2.50	1.25	.70
106	Mickey Lolich	1.25	.60	.40
107	Tim McCarver	1.25	.60	.40
108	Reggie Jackson	12.00	6.00	3.50
109	Chris Cannizzaro	.90	.45	.25
110	Steve Hargan	.90	.45	.25
111	Rusty Staub	2.50	1.25	.70
112	Andy Messersmith	1.00	.50	.30
113	Rico Carty	1.25	.60	.40
114	Brooks Robinson	7.00	3.50	2.00
115	Steve Carlton	7.00	3.50	2.00
116	Mike Hegan	.90	.45	.25
117	Joe Morgan	4.50	2.25	1.25
118	Thurman Munson	5.00	2.50	1.50
119	Don Kessinger	1.00	.50	.30
120	Joe Horlen	.90	.45	.25
121	Wes Parker	1.00	.50	.30
122	Sonny Siebert	.90	.45	.25
123	Willie Stargell	5.00	2.50	1.50
124	Ellie Rodriguez	.90	.45	.25
125	Juan Marichal	5.00	2.50	1.50
126	Mike Epstein	.90	.45	.25
127	Tom Seaver	8.00	4.00	2.50
128	Tony Oliva	2.50	1.25	.70
129	Jim Merritt	.90	.45	.25
130	Willie Horton	1.00	.50	.30
131	Rick Wise	.90	.45	.25
132	Sal Bando	1.00	.50	.30
133	Ollie Brown	.90	.45	.25
134	Ken Harrelson	1.00	.50	.30
135	Mack Jones	.90	.45	.25

		NR MT	EX	VG
136	Jim Fregosi	1.00	.50	.30
137	Hank Aaron	15.00	7.50	4.50
138	Fritz Peterson	.90	.45	.25
139	Joe Hague	.90	.45	.25
140	Tommy Harper	.90	.45	.25
141	Larry Dierker	.90	.45	.25
142	Tony Conigliaro	1.50	.70	.45
143	Glenn Beckert	1.00	.50	.30
144	Carlos May	.90	.45	.25
145	Don Sutton	3.25	1.75	1.00
146	Paul Casanova	.90	.45	.25
147	Bob Moose	.90	.45	.25
148	Leo Cardenas	.90	.45	.25
149	Johnny Bench	8.00	4.00	2.50
150	Mike Cuellar	1.00	.50	.30
151	Donn Clendenon	.90	.45	.25
152	Lou Piniella	1.25	.60	.40
153	Willie Mays	15.00	7.50	4.50

1971 Topps Greatest Moments

This 55-card set features a great moment from the careers of top players at the time. The front of the 2-1/2" by 4-3/4" cards features a portrait photo of the player at the left and deckle-edge action photo at the right. There is a small headline on the white border of the action photo. The player's name and "One of Baseball's Greatest Moments" along with a black border complete the front. The back features a detail from the front photo and the story of the event. The newspaper style presentation includes the name of real newspapers. Relatively scarce, virtually every card in this set is a star or at least an above-average player.

		NR MT	EX	VG
Complete Set:		1650.00	825.00	495.00
Common Player:		4.00	2.00	1.25
1	Thurman Munson	60.00	30.00	18.00
2	Hoyt Wilhelm	30.00	15.00	9.00
3	Rico Carty	15.00	7.50	4.50
4	Carl Morton	4.00	2.00	1.25
5	Sal Bando	5.00	2.50	1.50
6	Bert Campaneris	5.00	2.50	1.50
7	Jim Kaat	20.00	10.00	6.00
8	Harmon Killebrew	60.00	30.00	18.00
9	Brooks Robinson	75.00	37.00	22.00
10	Jim Perry	15.00	7.50	4.50
11	Tony Oliva	20.00	10.00	6.00
12	Vada Pinson	20.00	10.00	6.00
13	Johnny Bench	175.00	87.00	52.00
14	Tony Perez	25.00	12.50	7.50
15	Pete Rose	90.00	45.00	27.00
16	Jim Fregosi	4.00	2.00	1.25
17	Alex Johnson	4.00	2.00	1.25
18	Clyde Wright	4.00	2.00	1.25
19	Al Kaline	25.00	12.50	7.50
20	Denny McLain	20.00	10.00	6.00
21	Jim Northrup	15.00	7.50	4.50
22	Bill Freehan	15.00	7.50	4.50
23	Mickey Lolich	20.00	10.00	6.00
24	Bob Gibson	18.00	9.00	5.50
25	Tim McCarver	5.00	2.50	1.50
26	Orlando Cepeda	7.00	3.50	2.00
27	Lou Brock	18.00	9.00	5.50
28	Nate Colbert	4.00	2.00	1.25
29	Maury Wills	20.00	10.00	6.00

		NR MT	EX	VG
30	Wes Parker	15.00	7.50	4.50
31	Jim Wynn	15.00	7.50	4.50
32	Larry Dierker	15.00	7.50	4.50
33	Bill Melton	15.00	7.50	4.50
34	Joe Morgan	40.00	20.00	12.00
35	Rusty Staub	20.00	10.00	6.00
36	Ernie Banks	25.00	12.50	7.50
37	Billy Williams	50.00	25.00	15.00
38	Lou Piniella	20.00	10.00	6.00
39	Rico Petrocelli	4.00	2.00	1.25
40	Carl Yastrzemski	60.00	30.00	18.00
41	Willie Mays	45.00	22.00	13.50
42	Tommy Harper	15.00	7.50	4.50
43	Jim Bunning	7.00	3.50	2.00
44	Fritz Peterson	15.00	7.50	4.50
45	Roy White	15.00	7.50	4.50
46	Bobby Murcer	15.00	7.50	4.50
47	Reggie Jackson	250.00	125.00	75.00
48	Frank Howard	20.00	10.00	6.00
49	Dick Bosman	15.00	7.50	4.50
50	Sam McDowell	4.00	2.00	1.25
51	Luis Aparicio	12.00	6.00	3.50
52	Willie McCovey	15.00	7.50	4.50
53	Joe Pepitone	15.00	7.50	4.50
54	Jerry Grote	15.00	7.50	4.50
55	Bud Harrelson	15.00	7.50	4.50

1971 Topps Super

Topps continued to produce its special oversized cards in 1971. The cards, measuring 3-1/8" by 5-1/4," carry a large color photograph with a facsimile autograph on the front. Backs are basically enlargements of the player's regular Topps card. The set size was enlarged to 63 cards in 1971, so there are no short-printed cards as in 1970. Again, Topps included almost every major star who was active at the time, so the set of oversized cards with rounded corners remains an interesting source for those seeking the big names of the era.

		NR MT	EX	VG
Complete Set:		200.00	100.00	60.00
Common Player:		.80	.40	.25
1	Reggie Smith	1.00	.50	.30
2	Gaylord Perry	3.00	1.50	.90
3	Ted Savage	.80	.40	.25
4	Donn Clendenon	.80	.40	.25
5	John "Boog" Powell	1.25	.60	.40
6	Tony Perez	1.75	.90	.50
7	Dick Bosman	.80	.40	.25
8	Alex Johnson	.80	.40	.25
9	Rusty Staub	1.25	.60	.40
10	Mel Stottlemyre	1.00	.50	.30
11	Tony Oliva	1.50	.70	.45
12	Bill Freehan	1.00	.50	.30
13	Fritz Peterson	.80	.40	.25
14	Wes Parker	.80	.40	.25
15	Cesar Cedeno	1.25	.60	.40
16	Sam McDowell	1.00	.50	.30
17	Frank Howard	1.50	.70	.45
18	Dave McNally	1.00	.50	.30
19	Rico Petrocelli	.80	.40	.25
20	Pete Rose	25.00	12.50	7.50
21	Luke Walker	.80	.40	.25

		NR MT	EX	VG
22	Nate Colbert	.80	.40	.25
23	Luis Aparicio	2.50	1.25	.70
24	Jim Perry	1.00	.50	.30
25	Louis Brock	4.50	2.25	1.25
26	Roy White	1.00	.50	.30
27	Claude Osteen	.80	.40	.25
28	Carl W. Morton	.80	.40	.25
29	Ricardo A. Jacabo Carty	1.00	.50	.30
30	Larry Dierker	.80	.40	.25
31	Dagoberto Campaneris	1.00	.50	.30
32	Johnny Bench	8.00	4.00	2.50
33	Felix Millan	.80	.40	.25
34	Tim McCarver	1.25	.60	.40
35	Ronald Santo	1.25	.60	.40
36	Tommie Agee	.80	.40	.25
37	Roberto Clemente	10.00	5.00	3.00
38	Reggie Jackson	15.00	7.50	4.50
39	Clyde Wright	.80	.40	.25
40	Rich Allen	1.50	.70	.45
41	Curt Flood	1.25	.60	.40
42	Fergie Jenkins	1.75	.90	.50
43	Willie Stargell	3.00	1.50	.90
44	Henry Aaron	10.00	5.00	3.00
45	Amos Otis	1.00	.50	.30
46	Willie McCovey	4.50	2.25	1.25
47	William Melton	.80	.40	.25
48	Robert Gibson	3.50	1.75	1.00
49	Carl Yastrzemski	15.00	7.50	4.50
50	Glenn Beckert	1.00	.50	.30
51	Ray Fosse	.80	.40	.25
52	Clarence Gaston	.80	.40	.25
53	Tom Seaver	8.00	4.00	2.50
54	Al Kaline	6.00	3.00	1.75
55	Jim Northrup	.80	.40	.25
56	Willie Mays	10.00	5.00	3.00
57	Sal Bando	1.00	.50	.30
58	Deron Johnson	.80	.40	.25
59	Brooks Robinson	7.00	3.50	2.00
60	Harmon Killebrew	6.00	3.00	1.75
61	Joseph Torre	1.75	.90	.50
62	Lou Piniella	1.25	.60	.40
63	Tommy Harper	.80	.40	.25

1972 Topps

The largest Topps issue of its time appeared in 1972, with the set size reaching the 787 mark. The 2-1/2" by 3-1/2" cards are something special as well. Their fronts have a color photo which is shaped into an arch and surrounded by two different color borders, all of which is inside the overall white border. The player's name is in a white panel below the picture while the team name is above the picture in what might best be described as "superhero" type in a variety of colors. No mention of the player's position appears on the front. Cards backs are tame by comparison, featuring statistics and a trivia question. The set features a record number of specialty card including more than six dozen "In Action" (shown as "IA" in checklists below) cards featuring action shots of popular players. There are the usual statistical leaders, playoff and World Series highlights. Other innovations are 16 "Boyhood Photo" cards which depict scrapbook black and white photos of 1972's top players, and a group of cards depicting the trophies which comprise baseball's major awards. Finally, a group of seven "Traded"

cards was included which feature a large "Traded" across the front of the card.

		NR MT	EX	VG
Complete Set:		2000.00	1000.00	600.00
Common Player: 1-394		.40	.20	.12
Common Player: 395-525		.40	.20	.12
Common Player: 526-656		1.00	.50	.30
Common Player: 657-787		3.00	1.50	.90
1	World Champions (Pirates Team)	6.00	3.00	1.75
2	Ray Culp	.40	.20	.12
3	Bob Tolan	.40	.20	.12
4	Checklist 1-132	3.00	1.50	.90
5	John Bateman	.40	.20	.12
6	Fred Scherman	.40	.20	.12
7	Enzo Hernandez	.40	.20	.12
8	Ron Swoboda	.40	.20	.12
9	Stan Williams	.40	.20	.12
10	Amos Otis	.60	.30	.20
11	Bobby Valentine	.80	.40	.25
12	Jose Cardenal	.40	.20	.12
13	Joe Grzenda	.40	.20	.12
14	Phillies Rookiess (Mike Anderson, Pete Koegel, Wayne Twitchell)	.40	.20	.12
15	Walt Williams	.40	.20	.12
16	Mike Jorgensen	.40	.20	.12
17	Dave Duncan	.40	.20	.12
18a	Juan Pizarro (green under "C" and "S")	3.50	1.75	1.00
18b	Juan Pizarro (yellow under "C" and "S")	.40	.20	.12
19	Billy Cowan	.40	.20	.12
20	Don Wilson	.40	.20	.12
21	Braves Team	1.25	.60	.40
22	Rob Gardner	.40	.20	.12
23	Ted Kubiak	.40	.20	.12
24	Ted Ford	.40	.20	.12
25	Bill Singer	.40	.20	.12
26	Andy Etchebarren	.40	.20	.12
27	Bob Johnson	.40	.20	.12
28	Twins Rookies (Steve Brye, Bob Gebhard, Hal Haydel)	.40	.20	.12
29a	Bill Bonham (green under "C" and "S")	3.50	1.75	1.00
29b	Bill Bonham (yellow under "C" and "S")	.40	.20	.12
30	Rico Petrocelli	.70	.35	.20
31	Cleon Jones	.40	.20	.12
32	Cleon Jones IA	.40	.20	.12
33	Billy Martin	3.00	1.50	.90
34	Billy Martin IA	1.00	.50	.30
35	Jerry Johnson	.40	.20	.12
36	Jerry Johnson IA	.40	.20	.12
37	Carl Yastrzemski	15.00	7.50	4.50
38	Carl Yastrzemski IA	8.00	4.00	2.50
39	Bob Barton	.40	.20	.12
40	Bob Barton IA	.40	.20	.12
41	Tommy Davis	.80	.40	.25
42	Tommy Davis IA	.40	.20	.12
43	Rick Wise	.40	.20	.12
44	Rick Wise IA	.40	.20	.12
45a	Glenn Beckert (green under "C" and "S")	3.50	1.75	1.00
45b	Glenn Beckert (yellow under "C" and "S")	.60	.30	.20
46	Glenn Beckert IA	.40	.20	.12
47	John Ellis	.40	.20	.12
48	John Ellis IA	.40	.20	.12
49	Willie Mays	25.00	12.50	7.50
50	Willie Mays IA	10.00	5.00	3.00
51	Harmon Killebrew	5.00	2.50	1.50
52	Harmon Killebrew IA	2.00	1.00	.60
53	Bud Harrelson	.60	.30	.20
54	Bud Harrelson IA	.40	.20	.12
55	Clyde Wright	.40	.20	.12
56	Rich Chiles	.40	.20	.12
57	Bob Oliver	.40	.20	.12
58	Ernie McAnally	.40	.20	.12
59	*Fred Stanley*	.60	.30	.20
60	Manny Sanguillen	.40	.20	.12
61	Cubs Rookies (Gene Hiser, *Burt Hooton*, Earl Stephenson)	1.00	.50	.30
62	Angel Mangual	.40	.20	.12
63	Duke Sims	.40	.20	.12
64	Pete Broberg	.40	.20	.12
65	Cesar Cedeno	1.00	.50	.30
66	Ray Corbin	.40	.20	.12
67	Red Schoendienst	1.00	.50	.30
68	Jim York	.40	.20	.12
69	Roger Freed	.40	.20	.12
70	Mike Cuellar	.70	.35	.20

#	Player	NR MT	EX	VG
71	Angels Team	1.25	.60	.40
72	*Bruce Kison*	1.00	.50	.30
73	Steve Huntz	.40	.20	.12
74	Cecil Upshaw	.40	.20	.12
75	Bert Campaneris	.80	.40	.25
76	Don Carrithers	.40	.20	.12
77	Ron Theobald	.40	.20	.12
78	Steve Arlin	.40	.20	.12
79	Red Sox Rookies (Cecil Cooper, Carlton *Fisk*, Mike Garman)	135.00	67.00	37.00
80	Tony Perez	3.00	1.50	.90
81	Mike Hedlund	.40	.20	.12
82	Ron Woods	.40	.20	.12
83	Dalton Jones	.40	.20	.12
84	Vince Colbert	.40	.20	.12
85	N.L. Batting Leaders (Glenn Beckert, Ralph Garr, Joe Torre)	1.25	.60	.40
86	A.L. Batting Leaders (Bobby Murcer, Tony Oliva, Merv Rettenmund)	1.25	.60	.40
87	N.L. RBI Leaders (Hank Aaron, Willie Stargell, Joe Torre)	3.00	1.50	.90
88	A.L. RBI Leaders (Harmon Killebrew, Frank Robinson, Reggie Smith)	3.00	1.50	.90
89	N.L. Home Run Leaders (Hank Aaron, Lee May, Willie Stargell)	3.00	1.50	.90
90	A.L. Home Run Leaders (Norm Cash, Reggie Jackson, Bill Melton)	1.75	.90	.50
91	N.L. ERA Leaders (Dave Roberts, Tom Seaver, Don Wilson)	1.75	.90	.50
92	A.L. ERA Leaders (Vida Blue, Jim Palmer, Wilbur Wood)	1.50	.70	.45
93	N.L. Pitching Leaders (Steve Carlton, Al Downing, Fergie Jenkins, Tom Seaver)	2.00	1.00	.60
94	A.L. Pitching Leaders (Vida Blue, Mickey Lolich, Wilbur Wood)	1.25	.60	.40
95	N.L. Strikeout Leaders (Fergie Jenkins, Tom Seaver, Bill Stoneman)	1.75	.90	.50
96	A.L. Strikeout Leaders (Vida Blue, Joe Coleman, Mickey Lolich)	1.25	.60	.40
97	Tom Kelley	.40	.20	.12
98	Chuck Tanner	.70	.35	.20
99	*Ross Grimsley*	.80	.40	.25
100	Frank Robinson	5.00	2.50	1.50
101	Astros Rookies (Ray Busse, Bill Grief, *J.R. Richard*)	1.00	.50	.30
102	Lloyd Allen	.40	.20	.12
103	Checklist 133-263	3.00	1.50	.90
104	*Toby Harrah*	1.00	.50	.30
105	Gary Gentry	.40	.20	.12
106	Brewers Team	1.25	.60	.40
107	*Jose Cruz*	1.75	.90	.50
108	Gary Waslewski	.40	.20	.12
109	Jerry May	.40	.20	.12
110	Ron Hunt	.40	.20	.12
111	Jim Grant	.40	.20	.12
112	Greg Luzinski	1.00	.50	.30
113	Rogelio Moret	.40	.20	.12
114	Bill Buckner	1.25	.60	.40
115	Jim Fregosi	1.00	.50	.30
116	*Ed Farmer*	.40	.20	.12
117a	Cleo James (green under "C" and "S")	3.50	1.75	1.00
117b	Cleo James (yellow under "C" and "S")	.40	.20	.12
118	Skip Lockwood	.40	.20	.12
119	Marty Perez	.40	.20	.12
120	Bill Freehan	.80	.40	.25
121	Ed Sprague	.40	.20	.12
122	Larry Biittner	.40	.20	.12
123	Ed Acosta	.40	.20	.12
124	Yankees (Alan Closter, Roger Hambright, Rusty Torres)	.40	.20	.12
125	Dave Cash	.40	.20	.12
126	Bart Johnson	.40	.20	.12
127	Duffy Dyer	.40	.20	.12
128	Eddie Watt	.40	.20	.12
129	Charlie Fox	.40	.20	.12
130	Bob Gibson	5.00	2.50	1.50
131	Jim Nettles	.40	.20	.12
132	Joe Morgan	5.00	2.50	1.50
133	Joe Keough	.40	.20	.12
134	Carl Morton	.40	.20	.12
135	Vada Pinson	1.00	.50	.30
136	Darrel Chaney	.40	.20	.12
137	Dick Williams	.70	.35	.20
138	Mike Kekich	.40	.20	.12
139	Tim McCarver	1.00	.50	.30
140	Pat Dobson	.40	.20	.12
141	Mets Rookies (Buzz Capra, Jon Matlack, Leroy Stanton)	.60	.30	.20
142	*Chris Chambliss*	1.25	.60	.40
143	Garry Jestadt	.40	.20	.12
144	Marty Pattin	.40	.20	.12
145	Don Kessinger	.60	.30	.20
146	Steve Kealey	.40	.20	.12
147	*Dave Kingman*	6.00	3.00	1.75
148	Dick Billings	.40	.20	.12
149	Gary Neibauer	.40	.20	.12
150	Norm Cash	1.00	.50	.30
151	Jim Brewer	.40	.20	.12
152	Gene Clines	.40	.20	.12
153	Rick Auerbach	.40	.20	.12
154	Ted Simmons	2.00	1.00	.60
155	Larry Dierker	.40	.20	.12
156	Twins Team	1.25	.60	.40
157	Don Gullett	.60	.30	.20
158	Jerry Kenney	.40	.20	.12
159	John Boccabella	.40	.20	.12
160	Andy Messersmith	.60	.30	.20
161	Brock Davis	.40	.20	.12
162	Brewers Rookies (Jerry Bell, *Darrell Porter*, Bob Reynolds) (Bell & Porter photos transposed)	1.00	.50	.30
163	Tug McGraw	1.00	.50	.30
164	Tug McGraw IA	.60	.30	.20
165	*Chris Speier*	1.00	.50	.30
166	Chris Speier IA	.60	.30	.20
167	Deron Johnson	.40	.20	.12
168	Deron Johnson IA	.40	.20	.12
169	Vida Blue	1.00	.50	.30
170	Vida Blue IA	.60	.30	.20
171	Darrell Evans	1.50	.70	.45
172	Darrell Evans IA	1.00	.50	.30
173	Clay Kirby	.40	.20	.12
174	Clay Kirby IA	.40	.20	.12
175	Tom Haller	.40	.20	.12
176	Tom Haller IA	.40	.20	.12
177	Paul Schaal	.40	.20	.12
178	Paul Schaal IA	.40	.20	.12
179	Dock Ellis	.40	.20	.12
180	Dock Ellis IA	.40	.20	.12
181	Ed Kranepool	.60	.30	.20
182	Ed Kranepool IA	.40	.20	.12
183	Bill Melton	.40	.20	.12
184	Bill Melton IA	.40	.20	.12
185	Ron Bryant	.40	.20	.12
186	Ron Bryant IA	.40	.20	.12
187	Gates Brown	.40	.20	.12
188	Frank Lucchesi	.40	.20	.12
189	Gene Tenace	.60	.30	.20
190	Dave Giusti	.40	.20	.12
191	*Jeff Burroughs*	1.00	.50	.30
192	Cubs Team	1.25	.60	.40
193	*Kurt Bevacqua*	.60	.30	.20
194	Fred Norman	.40	.20	.12
195	Orlando Cepeda	2.00	1.00	.60
196	Mel Queen	.40	.20	.12
197	Johnny Briggs	.40	.20	.12
198	Dodgers Rookies (*Charlie Hough*, Bob O'Brien, Mike Strahler)	3.00	1.50	.90
199	Mike Fiore	.40	.20	.12
200	Lou Brock	6.00	3.00	1.75
201	Phil Roof	.40	.20	.12
202	Scipio Spinks	.40	.20	.12
203	*Ron Blomberg*	.70	.35	.20
204	Tommy Helms	.40	.20	.12
205	Dick Drago	.40	.20	.12
206	Dal Maxvill	.40	.20	.12
207	Tom Egan	.40	.20	.12
208	Milt Pappas	.60	.30	.20
209	Joe Rudi	.80	.40	.25
210	Denny McLain	1.25	.60	.40
211	Gary Sutherland	.40	.20	.12
212	Grant Jackson	.40	.20	.12
213	Angels Rookies (Art Kusnyer, Billy Parker, Tom Silverio)	.40	.20	.12
214	Mike McQueen	.40	.20	.12
215	Alex Johnson	.40	.20	.12
216	Joe Niekro	.70	.35	.20
217	Roger Metzger	.40	.20	.12
218	Eddie Kasko	.40	.20	.12
219	*Rennie Stennett*	.60	.30	.20
220	Jim Perry	.80	.40	.25
221	N.L. Playoffs (Bucs Champs!)	1.25	.60	.40
222	A.L. Playoffs (Orioles Champs!)	1.25	.60	.40
223	World Series Game 1	1.25	.60	.40
224	World Series Game 2	1.25	.60	.40
225	World Series Game 3	1.25	.60	.40
226	World Series Game 4	1.50	.70	.45
227	World Series Game 5	1.25	.60	.40
228	World Series Game 6	1.25	.60	.40

		NR MT	EX	VG
229	World Series Game 7	1.25	.60	.40
230	World Series Summary (Series Celebration)	1.25	.60	.40
231	Casey Cox	.40	.20	.12
232	Giants Rookies (Chris Arnold, Jim Barr, Dave Rader)	.40	.20	.12
233	Jay Johnstone	.60	.30	.20
234	Ron Taylor	.40	.20	.12
235	Merv Rettenmund	.40	.20	.12
236	Jim McGlothlin	.40	.20	.12
237	Yankees Team	1.25	.60	.40
238	Leron Lee	.40	.20	.12
239	Tom Timmermann	.40	.20	.12
240	Rich Allen	1.75	.90	.50
241	Rollie Fingers	10.00	5.00	3.00
242	Don Mincher	.40	.20	.12
243	Frank Linzy	.40	.20	.12
244	Steve Braun	.40	.20	.12
245	Tommie Agee	.40	.20	.12
246	Tom Burgmeier	.40	.20	.12
247	Milt May	.40	.20	.12
248	Tom Bradley	.40	.20	.12
249	Harry Walker	.40	.20	.12
250	Boog Powell	1.25	.60	.40
251a	Checklist 264-394 (small print on front)	3.00	1.50	.90
251b	Checklist 264-394 (large print on front)	3.00	1.50	.90
252	Ken Reynolds	.40	.20	.12
253	Sandy Alomar	.40	.20	.12
254	Boots Day	.40	.20	.12
255	Jim Lonborg	.60	.30	.20
256	George Foster	1.50	.70	.45
257	Tigers Rookies (Jim Foor, Tim Hosley, Paul Jata)	.40	.20	.12
258	Randy Hundley	.40	.20	.12
259	Sparky Lyle	1.00	.50	.30
260	Ralph Garr	.60	.30	.20
261	Steve Mingori	.40	.20	.12
262	Padres Team	1.25	.60	.40
263	Felipe Alou	.70	.35	.20
264	Tommy John	2.00	1.00	.60
265	Wes Parker	.40	.20	.12
266	Bobby Bolin	.40	.20	.12
267	Dave Concepcion	1.75	.90	.50
268	A's Rookies (Dwain Anderson, Chris Floethe)	.40	.20	.12
269	Don Hahn	.40	.20	.12
270	Jim Palmer	12.00	6.00	3.50
271	Ken Rudolph	.40	.20	.12
272	*Mickey Rivers*	1.00	.50	.30
273	Bobby Floyd	.40	.20	.12
274	Al Severinsen	.40	.20	.12
275	Cesar Tovar	.40	.20	.12
276	Gene Mauch	.70	.35	.20
277	Elliott Maddox	.40	.20	.12
278	Dennis Higgins	.40	.20	.12
279	Larry Brown	.40	.20	.12
280	Willie McCovey	4.00	2.00	1.25
281	Bill Parsons	.40	.20	.12
282	Astros Team	1.25	.60	.40
283	Darrell Brandon	.40	.20	.12
284	Ike Brown	.40	.20	.12
285	Gaylord Perry	6.00	3.00	1.75
286	Gene Alley	.40	.20	.12
287	Jim Hardin	.40	.20	.12
288	Johnny Jeter	.40	.20	.12
289	Syd O'Brien	.40	.20	.12
290	Sonny Siebert	.40	.20	.12
291	Hal McRae	.80	.40	.25
292	Hal McRae IA	.40	.20	.12
293	Danny Frisella	.40	.20	.12
294	Danny Frisella IA	.40	.20	.12
295	Dick Dietz	.40	.20	.12
296	Dick Dietz IA	.40	.20	.12
297	Claude Osteen	.60	.30	.20
298	Claude Osteen IA	.40	.20	.12
299	Hank Aaron	30.00	15.00	9.00
300	Hank Aaron IA	15.00	7.50	4.50
301	George Mitterwald	.40	.20	.12
302	George Mitterwald IA	.40	.20	.12
303	Joe Pepitone	.70	.35	.20
304	Joe Pepitone IA	.40	.20	.12
305	Ken Boswell	.40	.20	.12
306	Ken Boswell IA	.40	.20	.12
307	Steve Renko	.40	.20	.12
308	Steve Renko IA	.40	.20	.12
309	Roberto Clemente	35.00	17.50	10.50
310	Roberto Clemente IA	15.00	7.50	4.50
311	Clay Carroll	.40	.20	.12
312	Clay Carroll IA	.40	.20	.12
313	Luis Aparicio	4.00	2.00	1.25
314	Luis Aparicio IA	2.00	1.00	.60
315	Paul Splittorff	.40	.20	.12
316	Cardinals Rookies (*Jim Bibby*, Santiago Guzman, Jorge Roque)	.70	.35	.20
317	Rich Hand	.40	.20	.12
318	Sonny Jackson	.40	.20	.12
319	Aurelio Rodriguez	.40	.20	.12
320	Steve Blass	.40	.20	.12
321	Joe Lahoud	.40	.20	.12
322	Jose Pena	.40	.20	.12
323	Earl Weaver	1.00	.50	.30
324	Mike Ryan	.40	.20	.12
325	Mel Stottlemyre	1.00	.50	.30
326	Pat Kelly	.40	.20	.12
327	*Steve Stone*	1.00	.50	.30
328	Red Sox Team	1.00	.50	.30
329	Roy Foster	.40	.20	.12
330	Jim Hunter	3.50	1.75	1.00
331	Stan Swanson	.40	.20	.12
332	Buck Martinez	.40	.20	.12
333	Steve Barber	.40	.20	.12
334	Rangers Rookies (Bill Fahey, Jim Mason, Tom Ragland)	.40	.20	.12
335	Bill Hands	.40	.20	.12
336	Marty Martinez	.40	.20	.12
337	Mike Kilkenny	.40	.20	.12
338	Bob Grich	1.00	.50	.30
339	Ron Cook	.40	.20	.12
340	Roy White	1.00	.50	.30
341	Boyhood Photo (Joe Torre)	.70	.35	.20
342	Boyhood Photo (Wilbur Wood)	.60	.30	.20
343	Boyhood Photo (Willie Stargell)	1.50	.70	.45
344	Boyhood Photo (Dave McNally)	.60	.30	.20
345	Boyhood Photo (Rick Wise)	.40	.20	.12
346	Boyhood Photo (Jim Fregosi)	.60	.30	.20
347	Boyhood Photo (Tom Seaver)	4.00	2.00	1.25
348	Boyhood Photo (Sal Bando)	.60	.30	.20
349	Al Fitzmorris	.40	.20	.12
350	Frank Howard	1.25	.60	.40
351	Braves Rookies (Jimmy Britton, Tom House, Rick Kester)	.40	.20	.12
352	Dave LaRoche	.40	.20	.12
353	Art Shamsky	.40	.20	.12
354	Tom Murphy	.40	.20	.12
355	Bob Watson	.40	.20	.12
356	Gerry Moses	.40	.20	.12
357	Woodie Fryman	.40	.20	.12
358	Sparky Anderson	1.00	.50	.30
359	Don Pavletich	.40	.20	.12
360	Dave Roberts	.40	.20	.12
361	Mike Andrews	.40	.20	.12
362	Mets Team	1.25	.60	.40
363	Ron Klimkowski	.40	.20	.12
364	Johnny Callison	.70	.35	.20
365	Dick Bosman	.40	.20	.12
366	Jimmy Rosario	.40	.20	.12
367	Ron Perranoski	.40	.20	.12
368	Danny Thompson	.40	.20	.12
369	Jim Lefebvre	.40	.20	.12
370	Don Buford	.40	.20	.12
371	Denny Lemaster	.40	.20	.12
372	Royals Rookies (Lance Clemons, Monty Montgomery)	.40	.20	.12
373	John Mayberry	.60	.30	.20
374	Jack Heidemann	.40	.20	.12
375	Reggie Cleveland	.40	.20	.12
376	Andy Kosco	.40	.20	.12
377	Terry Harmon	.40	.20	.12
378	Checklist 395-525	3.00	1.50	.90
379	Ken Berry	.40	.20	.12
380	Earl Williams	.40	.20	.12
381	White Sox Team	1.25	.60	.40
382	Joe Gibbon	.40	.20	.12
383	Brant Alyea	.40	.20	.12
384	Dave Campbell	.40	.20	.12
385	Mickey Stanley	.40	.20	.12
386	Jim Colborn	.40	.20	.12
387	Horace Clarke	.40	.20	.12
388	Charlie Williams	.40	.20	.12
389	Bill Rigney	.40	.20	.12
390	Willie Davis	.70	.35	.20
391	Ken Sanders	.40	.20	.12
392	Pirates Rookies (Fred Cambria, *Richie Zisk*)	1.00	.50	.30
393	Curt Motton	.40	.20	.12
394	Ken Forsch	.40	.20	.12
395	Matty Alou	.80	.40	.25
396	Paul Lindblad	.40	.20	.12
397	Phillies Team	1.25	.60	.40
398	Larry Hisle	.60	.30	.20

		NR MT	EX	VG
399	Milt Wilcox	.60	.30	.20
400	Tony Oliva	1.50	.70	.45
401	Jim Nash	.40	.20	.12
402	Bobby Heise	.40	.20	.12
403	John Cumberland	.40	.20	.12
404	Jeff Torborg	.60	.30	.20
405	Ron Fairly	.70	.35	.20
406	*George Hendrick*	1.50	.70	.45
407	Chuck Taylor	.40	.20	.12
408	Jim Northrup	.60	.30	.20
409	Frank Baker	.60	.30	.20
410	Fergie Jenkins	6.00	3.00	1.75
411	Bob Montgomery	.40	.20	.12
412	Dick Kelley	.40	.20	.12
413	White Sox Rookies (Don Eddy, Dave Lemonds)	.40	.20	.12
414	Bob Miller	.40	.20	.12
415	Cookie Rojas	.40	.20	.12
416	Johnny Edwards	.40	.20	.12
417	Tom Hall	.40	.20	.12
418	Tom Shopay	.40	.20	.12
419	Jim Spencer	.40	.20	.12
420	Steve Carlton	20.00	10.00	6.00
421	Ellie Rodriguez	.40	.20	.12
422	Ray Lamb	.40	.20	.12
423	Oscar Gamble	.60	.30	.20
424	Bill Gogolewski	.40	.20	.12
425	Ken Singleton	1.00	.50	.30
426	Ken Singleton IA	.60	.30	.20
427	Tito Fuentes	.40	.20	.12
428	Tito Fuentes IA	.40	.20	.12
429	Bob Robertson	.40	.20	.12
430	Bob Robertson IA	.40	.20	.12
431	Clarence Gaston	.40	.20	.12
432	Clarence Gaston IA	.40	.20	.12
433	Johnny Bench	35.00	17.50	10.50
434	Johnny Bench IA	18.00	9.00	5.50
435	Reggie Jackson	38.00	19.00	11.40
436	Reggie Jackson IA	20.00	10.00	6.00
437	Maury Wills	1.50	.70	.45
438	Maury Wills IA	1.00	.50	.30
439	Billy Williams	4.00	2.00	1.25
440	Billy Williams IA	2.00	1.00	.60
441	Thurman Munson	15.00	7.50	4.50
442	Thurman Munson IA	10.00	5.00	3.00
443	Ken Henderson	.40	.20	.12
444	Ken Henderson IA	.40	.20	.12
445	Tom Seaver	30.00	15.00	9.00
446	Tom Seaver IA	10.00	5.00	3.00
447	Willie Stargell	4.00	2.00	1.25
448	Willie Stargell IA	2.00	1.00	.60
449	Bob Lemon	1.50	.70	.45
450	Mickey Lolich	1.25	.60	.40
451	Tony LaRussa	.80	.40	.25
452	Ed Herrmann	.40	.20	.12
453	Barry Lersch	.40	.20	.12
454	A's Team	2.00	1.00	.60
455	Tommy Harper	.60	.30	.20
456	Mark Belanger	.60	.30	.20
457	Padres Rookies (Darcy Fast, Mike Ivie, *Derrel Thomas*)	.60	.30	.20
458	Aurelio Monteagudo	.40	.20	.12
459	Rick Renick	.40	.20	.12
460	Al Downing	.60	.30	.20
461	Tim Cullen	.40	.20	.12
462	Rickey Clark	.40	.20	.12
463	Bernie Carbo	.40	.20	.12
464	Jim Roland	.40	.20	.12
465	Gil Hodges	3.00	1.50	.90
466	Norm Miller	.40	.20	.12
467	Steve Kline	.60	.30	.20
468	Richie Scheinblum	.40	.20	.12
469	Ron Herbel	.40	.20	.12
470	Ray Fosse	.40	.20	.12
471	Luke Walker	.40	.20	.12
472	Phil Gagliano	.40	.20	.12
473	Dan McGinn	.40	.20	.12
474	Orioles Rookies (Don Baylor, Roric Harrison, Johnny Oates)	6.00	3.00	1.75
475	Gary Nolan	.40	.20	.12
476	Lee Richard	.40	.20	.12
477	Tom Phoebus	.40	.20	.12
478a	Checklist 526-656 (small print on front)	3.00	1.50	.90
478b	Checklist 526-656 (large printing on front)	3.00	1.50	.90
479	Don Shaw	.40	.20	.12
480	Lee May	.80	.40	.25
481	Billy Conigliaro	.40	.20	.12
482	Joe Hoerner	.40	.20	.12
483	Ken Suarez	.40	.20	.12

		NR MT	EX	VG
484	Lum Harris	.40	.20	.12
485	Phil Regan	.40	.20	.12
486	John Lowenstein	.40	.20	.12
487	Tigers Team	1.50	.70	.45
488	Mike Nagy	.40	.20	.12
489	Expos Rookies (Terry Humphrey, Keith Lampard)	.40	.20	.12
490	Dave McNally	.70	.35	.20
491	Boyhood Photo (Lou Piniella)	.80	.40	.25
492	Boyhood Photo (Mel Stottlemyre)	.60	.30	.20
493	Boyhood Photo (Bob Bailey)	.40	.20	.12
494	Boyhood Photo (Willie Horton)	.60	.30	.20
495	Boyhood Photo (Bill Melton)	.40	.20	.12
496	Boyhood Photo (Bud Harrelson)	.60	.30	.20
497	Boyhood Photo (Jim Perry)	.60	.30	.20
498	Boyhood Photo (Brooks Robinson)	2.00	1.00	.60
499	Vicente Romo	.40	.20	.12
500	Joe Torre	1.25	.60	.40
501	Pete Hamm	.40	.20	.12
502	Jackie Hernandez	.40	.20	.12
503	Gary Peters	.40	.20	.12
504	Ed Spiezio	.40	.20	.12
505	Mike Marshall	.70	.35	.20
506	Indians Rookies (Terry Ley, Jim Moyer, *Dick Tidrow*)	.80	.40	.25
507	Fred Gladding	.40	.20	.12
508	Ellie Hendricks	.40	.20	.12
509	Don McMahon	.40	.20	.12
510	Ted Williams	6.00	3.00	1.75
511	Tony Taylor	.40	.20	.12
512	Paul Popovich	.40	.20	.12
513	Lindy McDaniel	.60	.30	.20
514	Ted Sizemore	.40	.20	.12
515	Bert Blyleven	10.00	5.00	3.00
516	Oscar Brown	.40	.20	.12
517	Ken Brett	.60	.30	.20
518	Wayne Garrett	.40	.20	.12
519	Ted Abernathy	.40	.20	.12
520	Larry Bowa	1.25	.60	.40
521	Alan Foster	.40	.20	.12
522	Dodgers Team	1.25	.60	.40
523	Chuck Dobson	.40	.20	.12
524	Reds Rookies (Ed Armbrister, Mel Behney)	.40	.20	.12
525	Carlos May	.60	.30	.20
526	Bob Bailey	1.00	.50	.30
527	Dave Leonhard	1.00	.50	.30
528	Ron Stone	1.00	.50	.30
529	Dave Nelson	1.00	.50	.30
530	Don Sutton	4.00	2.00	1.25
531	Freddie Patek	1.00	.50	.30
532	Fred Kendall	1.00	.50	.30
533	Ralph Houk	1.25	.60	.40
534	Jim Hickman	1.00	.50	.30
535	Ed Brinkman	1.00	.50	.30
536	Doug Rader	1.00	.50	.30
537	Bob Locker	1.00	.50	.30
538	Charlie Sands	1.00	.50	.30
539	*Terry Forster*	2.00	1.00	.60
540	Felix Millan	1.00	.50	.30
541	Roger Repoz	1.00	.50	.30
542	Jack Billingham	1.00	.50	.30
543	Duane Josephson	1.00	.50	.30
544	Ted Martinez	1.00	.50	.30
545	Wayne Granger	1.00	.50	.30
546	Joe Hague	1.00	.50	.30
547	Indians Team	1.50	.70	.45
548	Frank Reberger	1.00	.50	.30
549	Dave May	1.00	.50	.30
550	Brooks Robinson	20.00	10.00	6.00
551	Ollie Brown	1.00	.50	.30
552	Ollie Brown IA	1.00	.50	.30
553	Wilbur Wood	1.25	.60	.40
554	Wilbur Wood IA	1.00	.50	.30
555	Ron Santo	1.50	.70	.45
556	Ron Santo IA	1.00	.50	.30
557	John Odom	1.00	.50	.30
558	John Odom IA	1.00	.50	.30
559	Pete Rose	40.00	20.00	12.00
560	Pete Rose IA	20.00	10.00	6.00
561	Leo Cardenas	1.00	.50	.30
562	Leo Cardenas IA	1.00	.50	.30
563	Ray Sadecki	1.00	.50	.30
564	Ray Sadecki IA	1.00	.50	.30
565	Reggie Smith	1.25	.60	.40
566	Reggie Smith IA	1.00	.50	.30
567	Juan Marichal	6.00	3.00	1.75
568	Juan Marichal IA	3.00	1.50	.90
569	Ed Kirkpatrick	1.00	.50	.30
570	Ed Kirkpatrick IA	1.00	.50	.30

#	Name	NR MT	EX	VG
571	Nate Colbert	1.00	.50	.30
572	Nate Colbert IA	1.00	.50	.30
573	Fritz Peterson	1.00	.50	.30
574	Fritz Peterson IA	1.00	.50	.30
575	Al Oliver	2.00	1.00	.60
576	Leo Durocher	1.25	.60	.40
577	Mike Paul	1.00	.50	.30
578	Billy Grabarkewitz	1.00	.50	.30
579	*Doyle Alexander*	3.25	1.75	1.00
580	Lou Piniella	2.50	1.25	.70
581	Wade Blasingame	1.00	.50	.30
582	Expos Team	3.00	1.50	.90
583	Darold Knowles	1.00	.50	.30
584	Jerry McNertney	1.00	.50	.30
585	George Scott	1.00	.50	.30
586	Denis Menke	1.00	.50	.30
587	Billy Wilson	1.00	.50	.30
588	Jim Holt	1.00	.50	.30
589	Hal Lanier	1.00	.50	.30
590	Graig Nettles	3.25	1.75	1.00
591	Paul Casanova	1.00	.50	.30
592	Lew Krausse	1.00	.50	.30
593	Rich Morales	1.00	.50	.30
594	Jim Beauchamp	1.00	.50	.30
595	Nolan Ryan	225.00	112.00	67.00
596	Manny Mota	1.25	.60	.40
597	Jim Magnuson	1.00	.50	.30
598	Hal King	1.00	.50	.30
599	Billy Champion	1.00	.50	.30
600	Al Kaline	12.00	6.00	3.50
601	George Stone	1.00	.50	.30
602	Dave Bristol	1.00	.50	.30
603	Jim Ray	1.00	.50	.30
604a	Checklist 657-787 (copyright on right)			
		3.50	1.75	1.00
604b	Checklist 657-787 (copyright on left)			
		5.00	2.50	1.50
605	Nelson Briles	1.00	.50	.30
606	Luis Melendez	1.00	.50	.30
607	Frank Duffy	1.00	.50	.30
608	Mike Corkins	1.00	.50	.30
609	Tom Grieve	1.00	.50	.30
610	Bill Stoneman	1.00	.50	.30
611	Rich Reese	1.00	.50	.30
612	Joe Decker	1.00	.50	.30
613	Mike Ferraro	1.00	.50	.30
614	Ted Uhlaender	1.00	.50	.30
615	Steve Hargan	1.00	.50	.30
616	*Joe Ferguson*	1.00	.50	.30
617	Royals Team	3.00	1.50	.90
618	Rich Robertson	1.00	.50	.30
619	Rich McKinney	1.00	.50	.30
620	Phil Niekro	4.50	2.25	1.25
621	Commissioners Award	1.25	.60	.40
622	MVP Award	1.25	.60	.40
623	Cy Young Award	1.25	.60	.40
624	Minor League Player Of The Year Award			
		1.25	.60	.40
625	Rookie Of The Year Award	1.25	.60	.40
626	Babe Ruth Award	1.00	.50	.30
627	Moe Drabowsky	1.00	.50	.30
628	Terry Crowley	1.00	.50	.30
629	Paul Doyle	1.00	.50	.30
630	Rich Hebner	1.00	.50	.30
631	John Strohmayer	1.00	.50	.30
632	Mike Hegan	1.00	.50	.30
633	Jack Hiatt	1.00	.50	.30
634	Dick Woodson	1.00	.50	.30
635	Don Money	1.00	.50	.30
636	Bill Lee	1.25	.60	.40
637	Preston Gomez	1.00	.50	.30
638	Ken Wright	1.00	.50	.30
639	J.C. Martin	1.00	.50	.30
640	Joe Coleman	1.00	.50	.30
641	Mike Lum	1.00	.50	.30
642	Denny Riddleberger	1.00	.50	.30
643	Russ Gibson	1.00	.50	.30
644	Bernie Allen	1.00	.50	.30
645	Jim Maloney	1.00	.50	.30
646	Chico Salmon	1.00	.50	.30
647	Bob Moose	1.00	.50	.30
648	Jim Lyttle	1.00	.50	.30
649	Pete Richert	1.00	.50	.30
650	Sal Bando	1.00	.50	.30
651	Reds Team	2.00	1.00	.60
652	Marcelino Lopez	1.00	.50	.30
653	Jim Fairey	1.00	.50	.30
654	Horacio Pina	1.00	.50	.30
655	Jerry Grote	1.00	.50	.30
656	Rudy May	1.00	.50	.30
657	Bobby Wine	3.00	1.50	.90
658	Steve Dunning	3.00	1.50	.90
659	Bob Aspromonte	3.00	1.50	.90
660	Paul Blair	3.25	1.75	1.00
661	Bill Virdon	3.25	1.75	1.00
662	Stan Bahnsen	3.25	1.75	1.00
663	Fran Healy	3.00	1.50	.90
664	Bobby Knoop	3.00	1.50	.90
665	Chris Short	3.25	1.75	1.00
666	Hector Torres	3.00	1.50	.90
667	Ray Newman	3.00	1.50	.90
668	Rangers Team	3.25	1.75	1.00
669	Willie Crawford	3.00	1.50	.90
670	Ken Holtzman	3.50	1.75	1.00
671	Donn Clendenon	3.25	1.75	1.00
672	Archie Reynolds	3.00	1.50	.90
673	Dave Marshall	3.00	1.50	.90
674	John Kennedy	3.00	1.50	.90
675	Pat Jarvis	3.00	1.50	.90
676	Danny Cater	3.00	1.50	.90
677	Ivan Murrell	3.00	1.50	.90
678	Steve Luebber	3.00	1.50	.90
679	Astros Rookies (Bob Fenwick, Bob Stinson)	3.00	1.50	.90
680	Dave Johnson	3.50	1.75	1.00
681	Bobby Pfeil	3.00	1.50	.90
682	Mike McCormick	3.25	1.75	1.00
683	Steve Hovley	3.00	1.50	.90
684	Hal Breeden	3.00	1.50	.90
685	Joe Horlen	3.00	1.50	.90
686	Steve Garvey	70.00	35.00	20.00
687	Del Unser	3.00	1.50	.90
688	Cardinals Team	3.25	1.75	1.00
689	Eddie Fisher	3.00	1.50	.90
690	Willie Montanez	3.25	1.75	1.00
691	Curt Blefary	3.00	1.50	.90
692	Curt Blefary IA	3.00	1.50	.90
693	Alan Gallagher	3.00	1.50	.90
694	Alan Gallagher IA	3.00	1.50	.90
695	Rod Carew	100.00	50.00	30.00
696	Rod Carew IA	40.00	20.00	12.00
697	Jerry Koosman	4.50	2.25	1.25
698	Jerry Koosman IA	3.25	1.75	1.00
699	Bobby Murcer	4.00	2.00	1.25
700	Bobby Murcer IA	3.25	1.75	1.00
701	Jose Pagan	3.00	1.50	.90
702	Jose Pagan IA	3.00	1.50	.90
703	Doug Griffin	3.00	1.50	.90
704	Doug Griffin IA	3.00	1.50	.90
705	Pat Corrales	3.25	1.75	1.00
706	Pat Corrales IA	3.00	1.50	.90
707	Tim Foli	3.00	1.50	.90
708	Tim Foli IA	3.00	1.50	.90
709	Jim Kaat	9.00	4.50	2.75
710	Jim Kaat IA	5.00	2.50	1.50
711	Bobby Bonds	12.00	6.00	3.50
712	Bobby Bonds IA	6.00	3.00	1.75
713	Gene Michael	3.25	1.75	1.00
714	Gene Michael IA	3.25	1.75	1.00
715	Mike Epstein	3.25	1.75	1.00
716	Jesus Alou	3.25	1.75	1.00
717	Bruce Dal Canton	3.00	1.50	.90
718	Del Rice	3.00	1.50	.90
719	Cesar Geronimo	3.25	1.75	1.00
720	Sam McDowell	3.00	1.50	.90
721	Eddie Leon	3.00	1.50	.90
722	Bill Sudakis	3.00	1.50	.90
723	Al Santorini	3.00	1.50	.90
724	A.L. Rookies (John Curtis, Rich Hinton, Mickey Scott)	3.25	1.75	1.00
725	Dick McAuliffe	3.25	1.75	1.00
726	Dick Selma	3.00	1.50	.90
727	Jose Laboy	3.00	1.50	.90
728	Gail Hopkins	3.00	1.50	.90
729	Bob Veale	3.25	1.75	1.00
730	Rick Monday	3.50	1.75	1.00
731	Orioles Team	3.25	1.75	1.00
732	George Culver	3.00	1.50	.90
733	Jim Hart	3.25	1.75	1.00
734	Bob Burda	3.00	1.50	.90
735	Diego Segui	3.00	1.50	.90
736	Bill Russell	3.00	1.50	.90
737	*Lenny Randle*	3.25	1.75	1.00
738	Jim Merritt	3.00	1.50	.90
739	Don Mason	3.00	1.50	.90
740	Rico Carty	3.25	1.75	1.00
741	Major League Rookies (Tom Hutton, *Rick Miller*, John Milner)	3.25	1.75	1.00
742	Jim Rooker	3.00	1.50	.90
743	Cesar Gutierrez	3.00	1.50	.90
744	*Jim Slaton*	3.25	1.75	1.00
745	Julian Javier	3.00	1.50	.90

		NR MT	EX	VG
746	Lowell Palmer	3.00	1.50	.90
747	Jim Stewart	3.00	1.50	.90
748	Phil Hennigan	3.00	1.50	.90
749	Walter Alston	5.00	2.50	1.50
750	Willie Horton	3.50	1.75	1.00
751	Steve Carlton Traded	50.00	25.00	15.00
752	Joe Morgan Traded	40.00	20.00	12.00
753	Denny McLain Traded	8.00	4.00	2.50
754	Frank Robinson Traded	35.00	17.50	10.50
755	Jim Fregosi Traded	3.50	1.75	1.00
756	Rick Wise Traded	3.25	1.75	1.00
757	Jose Cardenal Traded	3.25	1.75	1.00
758	Gil Garrido	3.00	1.50	.90
759	Chris Cannizzaro	3.00	1.50	.90
760	Bill Mazeroski	6.00	3.00	1.75
761	Major League Rookies (Ron Cey, Ben			
	Oglivie, Bernie Williams)	18.00	9.00	5.50
762	Wayne Simpson	3.00	1.50	.90
763	Ron Hansen	3.00	1.50	.90
764	Dusty Baker	6.00	3.00	1.75
765	Ken McMullen	3.00	1.50	.90
766	Steve Hamilton	3.00	1.50	.90
767	Tom McCraw	3.00	1.50	.90
768	Denny Doyle	3.00	1.50	.90
769	Jack Aker	3.25	1.75	1.00
770	Jim Wynn	3.50	1.75	1.00
771	Giants Team	3.25	1.75	1.00
772	Ken Tatum	3.00	1.50	.90
773	Ron Brand	3.00	1.50	.90
774	Luis Alvarado	3.00	1.50	.90
775	Jerry Reuss	3.50	1.75	1.00
776	Bill Voss	3.00	1.50	.90
777	Hoyt Wilhelm	18.00	9.00	5.50
778	Twins Rookies (Vic Albury, Rick Dempsey,			
	Jim Strickland)	3.25	1.75	1.00
779	Tony Cloninger	3.25	1.75	1.00
780	Dick Green	3.00	1.50	.90
781	Jim McAndrew	3.00	1.50	.90
782	Larry Stahl	3.00	1.50	.90
783	Les Cain	3.00	1.50	.90
784	Ken Aspromonte	3.00	1.50	.90
785	Vic Davalillo	3.00	1.50	.90
786	Chuck Brinkman	3.25	1.75	1.00
787	Ron Reed	4.50	1.25	.70

1972 Topps Cloth Stickers

HANK AARON

Despite the fact they were never actually issued, examples of this test issue can readily be found within the hobby. The set of 33 contains stickers with designs identical to cards found in three contiguous rows of a regular Topps card sheet that year; thus the inclusion of a meaningless checklist card. Sometimes found in complete 33-sticker strips, individual stickers nominally measure 2-1/2" by 3-1/2," though dimensions vary according to the care with which they were cut. Stickers are unnumbered and blank-backed, and do not contain glue.

		NR MT	EX	VG
Complete Set:		200.00	100.00	60.00
Common Player:		3.00	1.50	.90
(1)	Hank Aaron	50.00	25.00	15.00
(2)	Luis Aparicio IA	10.00	5.00	3.00
(3)	Ike Brown	3.00	1.50	.90
(4)	Johnny Callison	5.00	2.50	1.50

		NR MT	EX	VG
(5)	Checklist 264-319	3.00	1.50	.90
(6)	Roberto Clemente IA	25.00	12.50	7.50
(7)	Dave Concepcion	8.00	4.00	2.50
(8)	Ron Cook	3.00	1.50	.90
(9)	Willie Davis	5.00	2.50	1.50
(10)	Al Fitzmorris	3.00	1.50	.90
(11)	Bobby Floyd	3.00	1.50	.90
(12)	Roy Foster	3.00	1.50	.90
(13)	Jim Fregosi Boyhood Photo	4.00	2.00	1.25
(14)	Danny Frisella IA	3.00	1.50	.90
(15)	Woody Fryman	3.50	1.75	1.00
(16)	Terry Harmon	3.00	1.50	.90
(17)	Frank Howard	7.00	3.50	2.00
(18)	Ron Klimkowski	3.00	1.50	.90
(19)	Joe Lahoud	3.00	1.50	.90
(20)	Jim Lefebvre	3.50	1.75	1.00
(21)	Elliott Maddox	3.00	1.50	.90
(22)	Marty Martinez	3.00	1.50	.90
(23)	Willie McCovey	25.00	12.50	7.50
(24)	Hal McRae	6.00	3.00	1.75
(25)	Syd O'Brien	3.00	1.50	.90
(26)	Red Sox Team	4.00	2.00	1.25
(27)	Aurelio Rodriguez	3.50	1.75	1.00
(28)	Al Severinsen	3.00	1.50	.90
(29)	Art Shamsky	3.00	1.50	.90
(30)	Steve Stone	4.00	2.00	1.25
(31)	Stan Swanson	3.00	1.50	.90
(32)	Bob Watson	3.50	1.75	1.00
(33)	Roy White	6.00	3.00	1.75

1972 Topps Posters

Issued as a separate set, rather than as a wax pack insert, the twenty-four 9-7/16" by 18" posters of 1972 feature a borderless full-color picture on the front with the player's name, team and position. Printed on very thin paper, the posters, as happened with earlier issues, were folded for packaging, causing large creases which cannot be removed. Even so, they are good display items for they feature many of stars of the period.

		NR MT	EX	VG
Complete Set:		300.00	150.00	90.00
Common Player:		5.00	2.50	1.50
1	Dave McNally	5.00	2.50	1.50
2	Carl Yastrzemski	30.00	15.00	9.00
3	Bill Melton	5.00	2.50	1.50
4	Ray Fosse	5.00	2.50	1.50
5	Mickey Lolich	6.00	3.00	1.75
6	Amos Otis	5.00	2.50	1.50
7	Tony Oliva	6.00	3.00	1.75
8	Vida Blue	6.00	3.00	1.75
9	Hank Aaron	20.00	10.00	6.00
10	Fergie Jenkins	8.00	4.00	2.50
11	Pete Rose	50.00	25.00	15.00
12	Willie Davis	6.00	3.00	1.75
13	Tom Seaver	20.00	10.00	6.00
14	Rick Wise	5.00	2.50	1.50
15	Willie Stargell	12.00	6.00	3.50
16	Joe Torre	7.00	3.50	2.00
17	Willie Mays	20.00	10.00	6.00
18	Andy Messersmith	5.00	2.50	1.50
19	Wilbur Wood	5.00	2.50	1.50
20	Harmon Killebrew	15.00	7.50	4.50
21	Billy Williams	12.00	6.00	3.50
22	Bud Harrelson	5.00	2.50	1.50

		NR MT	EX	VG
23	Roberto Clemente	20.00	10.00	6.00
24	Willie McCovey	15.00	7.50	4.50

1973 Topps

Topps cut back to 660 cards in 1973. The set is interesting for it marks the last time cards were issued by series, a procedure which had produced many a scarce high number card over the years. These 2-1/2" by 3-1/2" cards have a color photo, accented by a silhouette of a player on the front, indicative of his position. Card backs are vertical for the first time since 1968, with the usual statistical and biographical information. Specialty cards begin with card number 1, which depicted Ruth, Mays and Aaron as the all-time home run leaders. It was followed by statistical leaders, although there also were additional all-time leader cards. Also present are playoff and World Series highlights. From the age-and-youth department, the 1973 Topps set has coaches and managers as well as more "Boyhood Photos."

		NR MT	EX	VG
	Complete Set:	1200.00	600.00	350.00
	Common Player: 1-396	.40	.20	.12
	Common Player: 397-528	.70	.35	.20
	Common Player: 529-660	2.00	1.00	.60
1	All Time Home Run Leaders (Hank Aaron, Willie Mays, Babe Ruth)	30.00	22.50	12.50
2	Rich Hebner	.50	.25	.15
3	Jim Lonborg	.70	.35	.20
4	John Milner	.40	.20	.12
5	Ed Brinkman	.50	.25	.15
6	Mac Scarce	.40	.20	.12
7	Rangers Team	1.25	.60	.40
8	Tom Hall	.40	.20	.12
9	Johnny Oates	.40	.20	.12
10	Don Sutton	2.00	1.00	.60
11	Chris Chambliss	.90	.45	.25
12a	Padres Mgr./Coaches (Dave Garcia, Johnny Podres, Bob Skinner, Whitey Wietelmann, Don Zimmer) (Coaches background brown)	.70	.35	.20
12b	Padres Mgr./Coaches (Dave Garcia, Johnny Podres, Bob Skinner, Whitey Wietelmann, Don Zimmer) (Coaches background orange)	.70	.35	.20
13	George Hendrick	.90	.45	.25
14	Sonny Siebert	.40	.20	.12
15	Ralph Garr	.50	.25	.15
16	Steve Braun	.40	.20	.12
17	Fred Gladding	.40	.20	.12
18	Leroy Stanton	.40	.20	.12
19	Tim Foli	.40	.20	.12
20a	Stan Bahnsen (small gap in left border)	.70	.35	.20
20b	Stan Bahnsen (no gap)	.40	.20	.12
21	Randy Hundley	.40	.20	.12
22	Ted Abernathy	.40	.20	.12
23	Dave Kingman	2.00	1.00	.60
24	Al Santorini	.40	.20	.12
25	Roy White	.70	.35	.20
26	Pirates Team	1.25	.60	.40
27	Bill Gogolewski	.40	.20	.12
28	Hal McRae	.70	.35	.20

		NR MT	EX	VG
29	Tony Taylor	.40	.20	.12
30	Tug McGraw	.80	.40	.25
31	*Buddy Bell*	4.00	2.00	1.25
32	Fred Norman	.40	.20	.12
33	Jim Breazeale	.40	.20	.12
34	Pat Dobson	.50	.25	.15
35	Willie Davis	.70	.35	.20
36	Steve Barber	.40	.20	.12
37	Bill Robinson	.40	.20	.12
38	Mike Epstein	.50	.25	.15
39	Dave Roberts	.40	.20	.12
40	Reggie Smith	.70	.35	.20
41	Tom Walker	.40	.20	.12
42	Mike Andrews	.40	.20	.12
43	*Randy Moffitt*	.50	.25	.15
44	Rick Monday	.70	.35	.20
45	Ellie Rodriguez (photo actually Paul Ratliff)	.40	.20	.12
46	Lindy McDaniel	.50	.25	.15
47	Luis Melendez	.40	.20	.12
48	Paul Splittorff	.50	.25	.15
49a	Twins Mgr./Coaches (Vern Morgan, Frank Quilici, Bob Rodgers, Ralph Rowe, Al Worthington) (Coaches background brown)	.70	.35	.20
49b	Twins Mgr./Coaches (Vern Morgan, Frank Quilici, Bob Rodgers, Ralph Rowe, Al Worthington) (Coaches background orange)	.50	.25	.15
50	Roberto Clemente	30.00	15.00	9.00
51	Chuck Seelbach	.40	.20	.12
52	Denis Menke	.40	.20	.12
53	Steve Dunning	.40	.20	.12
54	Checklist 1-132	2.00	1.00	.60
55	Jon Matlack	.70	.35	.20
56	Merv Rettenmund	.50	.25	.15
57	Derrel Thomas	.40	.20	.12
58	Mike Paul	.40	.20	.12
59	*Steve Yeager*	.80	.40	.25
60	Ken Holtzman	.70	.35	.20
61	Batting Leaders (Rod Carew, Billy Williams)	2.25	1.25	.70
62	Home Run Leaders (Dick Allen, Johnny Bench)	2.25	1.25	.70
63	Runs Batted In Leaders (Dick Allen, Johnny Bench)	2.25	1.25	.70
64	Stolen Base Leaders (Lou Brock, Bert Campaneris)	2.00	1.00	.60
65	Earned Run Average Leaders (Steve Carlton, Luis Tiant)	2.00	1.00	.60
66	Victory Leaders (Steve Carlton, Gaylord Perry, Wilbur Wood)	2.00	1.00	.60
67	Strikeout Leaders (Steve Carlton, Nolan Ryan)	8.00	4.00	2.50
68	Leading Firemen (Clay Carroll, Sparky Lyle)	1.00	.50	.30
69	Phil Gagliano	.40	.20	.12
70	Milt Pappas	.70	.35	.20
71	Johnny Briggs	.40	.20	.12
72	Ron Reed	.50	.25	.15
73	Ed Herrmann	.40	.20	.12
74	Billy Champion	.40	.20	.12
75	Vada Pinson	1.00	.50	.30
76	Doug Rader	.40	.20	.12
77	Mike Torrez	.50	.25	.15
78	Richie Scheinblum	.40	.20	.12
79	Jim Willoughby	.40	.20	.12
80	Tony Oliva	1.00	.50	.30
81a	Cubs Mgr./Coaches (Hank Aguirre, Ernie Banks, Larry Jansen, Whitey Lockman, Pete Reiser) (trees in Coaches background)	.90	.45	.25
81b	Cubs Mgr./Coaches (Hank Aguirre, Ernie Banks, Larry Jansen, Whitey Lockman, Pete Reiser) (orange, solid background)	.70	.35	.20
82	Fritz Peterson	.50	.25	.15
83	Leron Lee	.40	.20	.12
84	Rollie Fingers	7.00	3.50	2.00
85	Ted Simmons	2.00	1.00	.60
86	Tom McCraw	.40	.20	.12
87	Ken Boswell	.40	.20	.12
88	Mickey Stanley	.50	.25	.15
89	Jack Billingham	.40	.20	.12
90	Brooks Robinson	5.00	2.50	1.50
91	Dodgers Team	2.25	1.25	.70
92	Jerry Bell	.40	.20	.12
93	Jesus Alou	.50	.25	.15
94	Dick Billings	.40	.20	.12
95	Steve Blass	.50	.25	.15
96	Doug Griffin	.40	.20	.12
97	Willie Montanez	.50	.25	.15
98	Dick Woodson	.40	.20	.12
99	Carl Taylor	.40	.20	.12

#	Player	NR MT	EX	VG
100	Hank Aaron	20.00	10.00	6.00
101	Ken Henderson	.40	.20	.12
102	Rudy May	.50	.25	.15
103	Celerino Sanchez	.50	.25	.15
104	Reggie Cleveland	.40	.20	.12
105	Carlos May	.50	.25	.15
106	Terry Humphrey	.40	.20	.12
107	Phil Hennigan	.40	.20	.12
108	Bill Russell	.70	.35	.20
109	Doyle Alexander	2.25	1.25	.70
110	Bob Watson	.50	.25	.15
111	Dave Nelson	.40	.20	.12
112	Gary Ross	.40	.20	.12
113	Jerry Grote	.50	.25	.15
114	Lynn McGlothen	.40	.20	.12
115	Ron Santo	1.00	.50	.30
116a	Yankees Mgr./Coaches (Jim Hegan, Ralph Houk, Elston Howard, Dick Howser, Jim Turner) (Coaches background brown)	2.25	1.25	.70
116b	Yankees Mgr./Coaches (Jim Hegan, Ralph Houk, Elston Howard, Dick Howser, Jim Turner) (Coaches background orange)	.90	.45	.25
117	Ramon Hernandez	.40	.20	.12
118	John Mayberry	.70	.35	.20
119	Larry Bowa	1.00	.50	.30
120	Joe Coleman	.50	.25	.15
121	Dave Rader	.40	.20	.12
122	Jim Strickland	.40	.20	.12
123	Sandy Alomar	.40	.20	.12
124	Jim Hardin	.40	.20	.12
125	Ron Fairly	.70	.35	.20
126	Jim Brewer	.40	.20	.12
127	Brewers Team	1.25	.60	.40
128	Ted Sizemore	.40	.20	.12
129	Terry Forster	.70	.35	.20
130	Pete Rose	20.00	10.00	6.00
131a	Red Sox Mgr./Coaches (Doug Camilli, Eddie Kasko, Don Lenhardt, Eddie Popowski, Lee Stange) (Coaches background brown)	.70	.35	.20
131b	Red Sox Mgr./Coaches (Doug Camilli, Eddie Kasko, Don Lenhardt, Eddie Popowski, Lee Stange) (Coaches background orange)	.50	.25	.15
132	Matty Alou	.80	.40	.25
133	Dave Roberts	.40	.20	.12
134	Milt Wilcox	.50	.25	.15
135	Lee May	.70	.35	.20
136a	Orioles Mgr./Coaches (George Bamberger, Jim Frey, Billy Hunter, George Staller, Earl Weaver) (Coaches background brown)	2.25	1.25	.70
136b	Orioles Mgr./Coaches (George Bamberger, Jim Frey, Billy Hunter, George Staller, Earl Weaver) (Coaches background orange)	.90	.45	.25
137	Jim Beauchamp	.40	.20	.12
138	Horacio Pina	.40	.20	.12
139	Carmen Fanzone	.40	.20	.12
140	Lou Piniella	1.00	.50	.30
141	Bruce Kison	.50	.25	.15
142	Thurman Munson	10.00	5.00	3.00
143	John Curtis	.40	.20	.12
144	Marty Perez	.40	.20	.12
145	Bobby Bonds	.90	.45	.25
146	Woodie Fryman	.50	.25	.15
147	Mike Anderson	.40	.20	.12
148	*Dave Goltz*	.80	.40	.25
149	Ron Hunt	.50	.25	.15
150	Wilbur Wood	.70	.35	.20
151	Wes Parker	.50	.25	.15
152	Dave May	.40	.20	.12
153	Al Hrabosky	.70	.35	.20
154	Jeff Torborg	.50	.25	.15
155	Sal Bando	.90	.45	.25
156	Cesar Geronimo	.50	.25	.15
157	Denny Riddleberger	.40	.20	.12
158	Astros Team	1.25	.60	.40
159	Clarence Gaston	.40	.20	.12
160	Jim Palmer	10.00	5.00	3.00
161	Ted Martinez	.40	.20	.12
162	Pete Broberg	.40	.20	.12
163	Vic Davalillo	.50	.25	.15
164	Monty Montgomery	.40	.20	.12
165	Luis Aparicio	2.75	1.50	.80
166	Terry Harmon	.40	.20	.12
167	Steve Stone	.70	.35	.20
168	Jim Northrup	.50	.25	.15
169	Ron Schueler	.40	.20	.12
170	Harmon Killebrew	5.00	2.50	1.50
171	Bernie Carbo	.40	.20	.12
172	Steve Kline	.50	.25	.15
173	Hal Breeden	.40	.20	.12
174	*Rich Gossage*	18.00	9.00	5.50
175	Frank Robinson	5.00	2.50	1.50
176	Chuck Taylor	.40	.20	.12
177	Bill Plummer	.40	.20	.12
178	Don Rose	.40	.20	.12
179a	A's Mgr./Coaches (Jerry Adair, Vern Hoscheit, Irv Noren, Wes Stock, Dick Williams) (Coaches background brown)	1.00	.50	.30
179b	A's Mgr./Coaches (Jerry Adair, Vern Hoscheit, Irv Noren, Wes Stock, Dick Williams) (Coaches background orange)	.70	.35	.20
180	Fergie Jenkins	4.00	2.00	1.25
181	Jack Brohamer	.40	.20	.12
182	*Mike Caldwell*	.70	.35	.20
183	Don Buford	.50	.25	.15
184	Jerry Koosman	.70	.35	.20
185	Jim Wynn	.70	.35	.20
186	Bill Fahey	.40	.20	.12
187	Luke Walker	.40	.20	.12
188	Cookie Rojas	.40	.20	.12
189	Greg Luzinski	.90	.45	.25
190	Bob Gibson	5.00	2.50	1.50
191	Tigers Team	2.00	1.00	.60
192	Pat Jarvis	.40	.20	.12
193	Carlton Fisk	45.00	23.00	13.50
194	*Jorge Orta*	.70	.35	.20
195	Clay Carroll	.50	.25	.15
196	Ken McMullen	.40	.20	.12
197	Ed Goodson	.40	.20	.12
198	Horace Clarke	.50	.25	.15
199	Bert Blyleven	4.00	3.00	1.50
200	Billy Williams	2.75	1.50	.80
201	A.L. Playoffs (Hendrick Scores Winning Run.)	2.25	1.25	.70
202	N.L. Playoffs (Foster's Run Decides It.)	2.25	1.25	.70
203	World Series Game 1 (Tenace The Menace.)	2.25	1.25	.70
204	World Series Game 2 (A's Make It Two Straight.)	2.25	1.25	.70
205	World Series Game 3 (Reds Win Squeeker.)	2.25	1.25	.70
206	World Series Game 4 (Tenace Singles In Ninth.)	2.25	1.25	.70
207	World Series Game 5 (Odom Out At Plate.)	2.25	1.25	.70
208	World Series Game 6 (Reds' Slugging Ties Series.)	2.25	1.25	.70
209	World Series Game 7 (Campy Starts Winning Rally.)	2.25	1.25	.70
210	World Series Summary (World Champions.)	2.25	1.25	.70
211	Balor Moore	.40	.20	.12
212	Joe Lahoud	.40	.20	.12
213	Steve Garvey	15.00	7.50	4.50
214	Dave Hamilton	.40	.20	.12
215	Dusty Baker	.70	.35	.20
216	Toby Harrah	.70	.35	.20
217	Don Wilson	.40	.20	.12
218	Aurelio Rodriguez	.50	.25	.15
219	Cardinals Team	1.25	.60	.40
220	Nolan Ryan	85.00	43.00	27.00
221	Fred Kendall	.40	.20	.12
222	Rob Gardner	.40	.20	.12
223	Bud Harrelson	.50	.25	.15
224	Bill Lee	.50	.25	.15
225	Al Oliver	2.00	1.00	.60
226	Ray Fosse	.40	.20	.12
227	Wayne Twitchell	.40	.20	.12
228	Bobby Darwin	.40	.20	.12
229	Roric Harrison	.40	.20	.12
230	Joe Morgan	5.00	2.50	1.50
231	Bill Parsons	.40	.20	.12
232	Ken Singleton	.70	.35	.20
233	Ed Kirkpatrick	.40	.20	.12
234	*Bill North*	.70	.35	.20
235	Jim Hunter	4.00	2.00	1.25
236	Tito Fuentes	.40	.20	.12
237a	Braves Mgr./Coaches (Lew Burdette, Jim Busby, Roy Hartsfield, Eddie Mathews, Ken Silvestri) (Coaches background brown)	2.00	1.00	.60
237b	Braves Mgr./Coaches (Lew Burdette, Jim Busby, Roy Hartsfield, Eddie Mathews, Ken Silvestri) (Coaches background orange)	2.25	1.25	.70

		NR MT	EX	VG
238	Tony Muser	.40	.20	.12
239	Pete Richert	.40	.20	.12
240	Bobby Murcer	.80	.40	.25
241	Dwain Anderson	.40	.20	.12
242	George Culver	.40	.20	.12
243	Angels Team	1.25	.60	.40
244	Ed Acosta	.40	.20	.12
245	Carl Yastrzemski	15.00	7.50	4.50
246	Ken Sanders	.40	.20	.12
247	Del Unser	.40	.20	.12
248	Jerry Johnson	.40	.20	.12
249	Larry Biittner	.40	.20	.12
250	Manny Sanguillen	.50	.25	.15
251	Roger Nelson	.40	.20	.12
252a	Giants Mgr./Coaches (Joe Amalfitano, Charlie Fox, Andy Gilbert, Don McMahon, John McNamara) (Coaches background brown)	.70	.35	.20
252b	Giants Mgr./Coaches (Joe Amalfitano, Charlie Fox, Andy Gilbert, Don McMahon, John McNamara) (Coaches background orange)	.50	.25	.15
253	Mark Belanger	.50	.25	.15
254	Bill Stoneman	.40	.20	.12
255	Reggie Jackson	32.00	16.00	9.60
256	Chris Zachary	.40	.20	.12
257a	Mets Mgr./Coaches (Yogi Berra, Roy McMillan, Joe Pignatano, Rube Walker, Eddie Yost) (Coaches background brown)	2.25	1.25	.70
257b	Mets Mgr./Coaches (Yogi Berra, Roy McMillan, Joe Pignatano, Rube Walker, Eddie Yost) (Coaches background orange)	2.00	1.00	.60
258	Tommy John	2.25	1.25	.70
259	Jim Holt	.40	.20	.12
260	Gary Nolan	.40	.20	.12
261	Pat Kelly	.40	.20	.12
262	Jack Aker	.40	.20	.12
263	George Scott	.50	.25	.15
264	Checklist 133-264	2.00	1.00	.60
265	Gene Michael	.70	.35	.20
266	Mike Lum	.40	.20	.12
267	Lloyd Allen	.40	.20	.12
268	Jerry Morales	.40	.20	.12
269	Tim McCarver	.90	.45	.25
270	Luis Tiant	1.00	.50	.30
271	Tom Hutton	.40	.20	.12
272	Ed Farmer	.40	.20	.12
273	Chris Speier	.50	.25	.15
274	Darold Knowles	.40	.20	.12
275	Tony Perez	2.00	1.00	.60
276	Joe Lovitto	.40	.20	.12
277	Bob Miller	.40	.20	.12
278	Orioles Team	1.25	.60	.40
279	Mike Strahler	.40	.20	.12
280	Al Kaline	6.00	3.00	1.75
281	Mike Jorgensen	.40	.20	.12
282	Steve Hovley	.40	.20	.12
283	Ray Sadecki	.40	.20	.12
284	Glenn Borgmann	.40	.20	.12
285	Don Kessinger	.50	.25	.15
286	Frank Linzy	.40	.20	.12
287	Eddie Leon	.40	.20	.12
288	Gary Gentry	.40	.20	.12
289	Bob Oliver	.40	.20	.12
290	Cesar Cedeno	.70	.35	.20
291	Rogelio Moret	.40	.20	.12
292	Jose Cruz	1.00	.50	.30
293	Bernie Allen	.50	.25	.15
294	Steve Arlin	.40	.20	.12
295	Bert Campaneris	.80	.40	.25
296	Reds Mgr./Coaches (Sparky Anderson, Alex Grammas, Ted Kluszewski, George Scherger, Larry Shepard)	.90	.45	.25
297	Walt Williams	.40	.20	.12
298	Ron Bryant	.40	.20	.12
299	Ted Ford	.40	.20	.12
300	Steve Carlton	15.00	7.50	4.50
301	Billy Grabarkewitz	.40	.20	.12
302	Terry Crowley	.40	.20	.12
303	Nelson Briles	.40	.20	.12
304	Duke Sims	.40	.20	.12
305	Willie Mays	30.00	15.00	9.00
306	Tom Burgmeier	.40	.20	.12
307	Boots Day	.40	.20	.12
308	Skip Lockwood	.40	.20	.12
309	Paul Popovich	.40	.20	.12
310	Dick Allen	1.00	.50	.30
311	Joe Decker	.40	.20	.12
312	Oscar Brown	.40	.20	.12
313	Jim Ray	.40	.20	.12
314	Ron Swoboda	.50	.25	.15
315	John Odom	.50	.25	.15
316	Padres Team	1.25	.60	.40
317	Danny Cater	.40	.20	.12
318	Jim McGlothlin	.40	.20	.12
319	Jim Spencer	.40	.20	.12
320	Lou Brock	6.00	3.00	1.75
321	Rich Hinton	.40	.20	.12
322	*Garry Maddox*	1.00	.50	.30
323	Tigers Mgr./Coaches (Art Fowler, Billy Martin, Joe Schultz, Charlie Silvera, Dick Tracewski)	2.25	1.25	.70
324	Al Downing	.50	.25	.15
325	Boog Powell	2.25	1.25	.70
326	Darrell Brandon	.40	.20	.12
327	John Lowenstein	.40	.20	.12
328	Bill Bonham	.40	.20	.12
329	Ed Kranepool	.50	.25	.15
330	Rod Carew	18.00	9.00	5.50
331	Carl Morton	.40	.20	.12
332	*John Felske*	.50	.25	.15
333	Gene Clines	.40	.20	.12
334	Freddie Patek	.40	.20	.12
335	Bob Tolan	.50	.25	.15
336	Tom Bradley	.40	.20	.12
337	Dave Duncan	.40	.20	.12
338	Checklist 265-396	2.00	1.00	.60
339	Dick Tidrow	.50	.25	.15
340	Nate Colbert	.50	.25	.15
341	Boyhood Photo (Jim Palmer)	2.00	1.00	.60
342	Boyhood Photo (Sam McDowell)	.70	.35	.20
343	Boyhood Photo (Bobby Murcer)	.70	.35	.20
344	Boyhood Photo (Jim Hunter)	2.00	1.00	.60
345	Boyhood Photo (Chris Speier)	.50	.25	.15
346	Boyhood Photo (Gaylord Perry)	2.00	1.00	.60
347	Royals Team	1.25	.60	.40
348	Rennie Stennett	.50	.25	.15
349	Dick McAuliffe	.50	.25	.15
350	Tom Seaver	28.00	14.00	8.00
351	Jimmy Stewart	.40	.20	.12
352	*Don Stanhouse*	.70	.35	.20
353	Steve Brye	.40	.20	.12
354	Billy Parker	.40	.20	.12
355	Mike Marshall	.70	.35	.20
356	White Sox Mgr./Coaches (Joe Lonnett, Jim Mahoney, Al Monchak, Johnny Sain, Chuck Tanner)	.70	.35	.20
357	Ross Grimsley	.50	.25	.15
358	Jim Nettles	.40	.20	.12
359	Cecil Upshaw	.40	.20	.12
360	Joe Rudi (photo actually Gene Tenace)	.70	.35	.20
361	Fran Healy	.40	.20	.12
362	Eddie Watt	.40	.20	.12
363	Jackie Hernandez	.40	.20	.12
364	Rick Wise	.50	.25	.15
365	Rico Petrocelli	.70	.35	.20
366	Brock Davis	.40	.20	.12
367	Burt Hooton	.70	.35	.20
368	Bill Buckner	.90	.45	.25
369	Lerrin LaGrow	.40	.20	.12
370	Willie Stargell	5.00	2.50	1.50
371	Mike Kekich	.50	.25	.15
372	Oscar Gamble	.50	.25	.15
373	Clyde Wright	.40	.20	.12
374	Darrell Evans	.90	.45	.25
375	Larry Dierker	.50	.25	.15
376	Frank Duffy	.40	.20	.12
377	Expos Mgr./Coaches (Dave Bristol, Larry Doby, Gene Mauch, Cal McLish, Jerry Zimmerman)	.70	.35	.20
378	Lenny Randle	.40	.20	.12
379	Cy Acosta	.40	.20	.12
380	Johnny Bench	25.00	12.50	7.50
381	Vicente Romo	.40	.20	.12
382	Mike Hegan	.40	.20	.12
383	Diego Segui	.40	.20	.12
384	Don Baylor	2.25	1.25	.70
385	Jim Perry	.70	.35	.20
386	Don Money	.50	.25	.15
387	Jim Barr	.40	.20	.12
388	Ben Oglivie	.70	.35	.20
389	Mets Team	2.00	1.00	.60
390	Mickey Lolich	.90	.45	.25
391	*Lee Lacy*	1.00	.50	.30
392	Dick Drago	.40	.20	.12
393	Jose Cardenal	.50	.25	.15
394	Sparky Lyle	.90	.45	.25
395	Roger Metzger	.40	.20	.12
396	Grant Jackson	.40	.20	.12
397	Dave Cash	.70	.35	.20
398	Rich Hand	.70	.35	.20

		NR MT	EX	VG
399	George Foster	2.25	1.25	.70
400	Gaylord Perry	6.00	3.00	1.75
401	Clyde Mashore	.70	.35	.20
402	Jack Hiatt	.70	.35	.20
403	Sonny Jackson	.70	.35	.20
404	Chuck Brinkman	.70	.35	.20
405	Cesar Tovar	.70	.35	.20
406	Paul Lindblad	.70	.35	.20
407	Felix Millan	.70	.35	.20
408	Jim Colborn	.70	.35	.20
409	Ivan Murrell	.70	.35	.20
410	Willie McCovey	5.00	2.50	1.50
411	Ray Corbin	.70	.35	.20
412	Manny Mota	.80	.40	.25
413	Tom Timmermann	.70	.35	.20
414	Ken Rudolph	.70	.35	.20
415	Marty Pattin	.70	.35	.20
416	Paul Schaal	.70	.35	.20
417	Scipio Spinks	.70	.35	.20
418	Bobby Grich	.80	.40	.25
419	Casey Cox	.70	.35	.20
420	Tommie Agee	.70	.35	.20
421	Angels Mgr./Coaches (Tom Morgan, Salty Parker, Jimmie Reese, John Roseboro, Bobby Winkles)	.70	.35	.20
422	Bob Robertson	.70	.35	.20
423	Johnny Jeter	.70	.35	.20
424	Denny Doyle	.70	.35	.20
425	Alex Johnson	.70	.35	.20
426	Dave LaRoche	.70	.35	.20
427	Rick Auerbach	.70	.35	.20
428	Wayne Simpson	.70	.35	.20
429	Jim Fairey	.70	.35	.20
430	Vida Blue	1.00	.50	.30
431	Gerry Moses	.70	.35	.20
432	Dan Frisella	.70	.35	.20
433	Willie Horton	.80	.40	.25
434	Giants Team	2.25	1.25	.70
435	Rico Carty	.80	.40	.25
436	Jim McAndrew	.70	.35	.20
437	John Kennedy	.70	.35	.20
438	Enzo Hernandez	.70	.35	.20
439	Eddie Fisher	.70	.35	.20
440	Glenn Beckert	.70	.35	.20
441	Gail Hopkins	.70	.35	.20
442	Dick Dietz	.70	.35	.20
443	Danny Thompson	.70	.35	.20
444	Ken Brett	.70	.35	.20
445	Ken Berry	.70	.35	.20
446	Jerry Reuss	.80	.40	.25
447	Joe Hague	.70	.35	.20
448	John Hiller	.70	.35	.20
449a	Indians Mgr./Coaches (Ken Aspromonte, Rocky Colavito, Joe Lutz, Warren Spahn) (Spahn's ear pointed)	.70	.35	.20
449b	Indians Mgr./Coaches (Ken Aspromonte, Rocky Colavito, Joe Lutz, Warren Spahn) (Spahn's ear round)	1.00	.50	.30
450	Joe Torre	2.25	1.25	.70
451	John Vukovich	.70	.35	.20
452	Paul Casanova	.70	.35	.20
453	Checklist 397-528	2.25	1.25	.70
454	Tom Haller	.70	.35	.20
455	Bill Melton	.70	.35	.20
456	Dick Green	.70	.35	.20
457	John Strohmayer	.70	.35	.20
458	Jim Mason	.70	.35	.20
459	Jimmy Howarth	.70	.35	.20
460	Bill Freehan	.80	.40	.25
461	Mike Corkins	.70	.35	.20
462	Ron Blomberg	.70	.35	.20
463	Ken Tatum	.70	.35	.20
464	Cubs Team	2.25	1.25	.70
465	Dave Giusti	.70	.35	.20
466	Jose Arcia	.70	.35	.20
467	Mike Ryan	.70	.35	.20
468	Tom Griffin	.70	.35	.20
469	Dan Monzon	.70	.35	.20
470	Mike Cuellar	.80	.40	.25
471	Hit Leader (Ty Cobb)	4.00	2.00	1.25
472	Grand Slam Leader (Lou Gehrig)	4.00	2.00	1.25
473	Total Base Leader (Hank Aaron)	4.00	2.00	1.25
474	R.B.I. Leader (Babe Ruth)	8.00	4.00	2.50
475	Batting Leader (Ty Cobb)	4.00	2.00	1.25
476	Shutout Leader (Walter Johnson)	2.00	1.00	.60
477	Victory Leader (Cy Young)	2.00	1.00	.60
478	Strikeout Leader (Walter Johnson)	2.00	1.00	.60
479	Hal Lanier	.80	.40	.25
480	Juan Marichal	4.00	2.00	1.25
481	White Sox Team	2.00	1.00	.60
482	*Rick Reuschel*	4.00	2.00	1.25
483	Dal Maxvill	.70	.35	.20
484	Ernie McAnally	.70	.35	.20
485	Norm Cash	1.00	.50	.30
486a	Phillies Mgr./Coaches (Carroll Berringer, Billy DeMars, Danny Ozark, Ray Rippelmeyer, Bobby Wine) (Coaches background brown red)	.90	.45	.25
486b	Phillies Mgr./Coaches (Carroll Beringer, Billy DeMars, Danny Ozark, Ray Rippelmeyer, Bobby Wine) (Coaches background orange)	.70	.35	.20
487	Bruce Dal Canton	.70	.35	.20
488	Dave Campbell	.70	.35	.20
489	Jeff Burroughs	.80	.40	.25
490	Claude Osteen	.80	.40	.25
491	Bob Montgomery	.70	.35	.20
492	Pedro Borbon	.70	.35	.20
493	Duffy Dyer	.70	.35	.20
494	Rich Morales	.70	.35	.20
495	Tommy Helms	.70	.35	.20
496	Ray Lamb	.70	.35	.20
497	Cardinals Mgr./Coaches (Vern Benson, George Kissell, Red Schoendienst, Barney Schultz)	1.25	.60	.40
498	Graig Nettles	2.50	1.25	.70
499	Bob Moose	.70	.35	.20
500	A's Team	2.25	1.25	.70
501	Larry Gura	.70	.35	.20
502	Bobby Valentine	.80	.40	.25
503	Phil Niekro	5.00	2.50	1.50
504	Earl Williams	.70	.35	.20
505	Bob Bailey	.70	.35	.20
506	Bart Johnson	.70	.35	.20
507	Darrel Chaney	.70	.35	.20
508	Gates Brown	.70	.35	.20
509	Jim Nash	.70	.35	.20
510	Amos Otis	.80	.40	.25
511	Sam McDowell	.80	.40	.25
512	Dalton Jones	.70	.35	.20
513	Dave Marshall	.70	.35	.20
514	Jerry Kenney	.70	.35	.20
515	Andy Messersmith	.70	.35	.20
516	Danny Walton	.70	.35	.20
517a	Pirates Mgr./Coaches (Don Leppert, Bill Mazeroski, Dave Ricketts, Bill Virdon, Mel Wright) (Coaches background brown)	2.25	1.25	.70
517b	Pirates Mgr./Coaches (Don Leppert, Bill Mazeroski, Dave Ricketts, Bill Virdon, Mel Wright) (Coaches background orange)	.70	.35	.20
518	Bob Veale	.70	.35	.20
519	John Edwards	.70	.35	.20
520	Mel Stottlemyre	.80	.40	.25
521	Braves Team	2.25	1.25	.70
522	Leo Cardenas	.70	.35	.20
523	Wayne Granger	.70	.35	.20
524	Gene Tenace	.70	.35	.20
525	Jim Fregosi	.90	.45	.25
526	Ollie Brown	.70	.35	.20
527	Dan McGinn	.70	.35	.20
528	Paul Blair	.70	.35	.20
529	Milt May	2.00	1.00	.60
530	Jim Kaat	4.00	2.00	1.25
531	Ron Woods	2.00	1.00	.60
532	Steve Mingori	2.00	1.00	.60
533	Larry Stahl	2.00	1.00	.60
534	Dave Lemonds	2.00	1.00	.60
535	John Callison	2.25	1.25	.70
536	Phillies Team	2.50	1.25	.70
537	Bill Slayback	2.00	1.00	.60
538	Jim Hart	2.25	1.25	.70
539	Tom Murphy	2.00	1.00	.60
540	Cleon Jones	2.25	1.25	.70
541	Bob Bolin	2.00	1.00	.60
542	Pat Corrales	2.25	1.25	.70
543	Alan Foster	2.00	1.00	.60
544	Von Joshua	2.00	1.00	.60
545	Orlando Cepeda	4.00	2.00	1.25
546	Jim York	2.00	1.00	.60
547	Bobby Heise	2.00	1.00	.60
548	Don Durham	2.00	1.00	.60
549	Rangers Mgr./Coaches (Chuck Estrada, Whitey Herzog, Chuck Hiller, Jackie Moore)	2.00	1.00	.60
550	Dave Johnson	2.75	1.50	.80
551	Mike Kilkenny	2.00	1.00	.60
552	J.C. Martin	2.00	1.00	.60
553	Mickey Scott	2.00	1.00	.60
554	Dave Concepcion	2.50	1.25	.70
555	Bill Hands	2.00	1.00	.60

		NR MT	EX	VG
556	Yankees Team	6.00	3.00	1.75
557	Bernie Williams	2.00	1.00	.60
558	Jerry May	2.00	1.00	.60
559	Barry Lersch	2.00	1.00	.60
560	Frank Howard	2.25	1.25	.70
561	Jim Geddes	2.00	1.00	.60
562	Wayne Garrett	2.00	1.00	.60
563	Larry Haney	2.00	1.00	.60
564	Mike Thompson	2.00	1.00	.60
565	Jim Hickman	2.25	1.25	.70
566	Lew Krausse	2.00	1.00	.60
567	Bob Fenwick	2.00	1.00	.60
568	Ray Newman	2.00	1.00	.60
569	Dodgers Mgr./Coaches (Red Adams, Walt Alston, Monty Basgall, Jim Gilliam, Tom Lasorda)	3.00	1.50	.90
570	Bill Singer	2.25	1.25	.70
571	Rusty Torres	2.00	1.00	.60
572	Gary Sutherland	2.00	1.00	.60
573	Fred Beene	2.25	1.25	.70
574	Bob Didier	2.00	1.00	.60
575	Dock Ellis	2.25	1.25	.70
576	Expos Team	2.50	1.25	.70
577	*Eric Soderholm*	2.25	1.25	.70
578	Ken Wright	2.00	1.00	.60
579	Tom Grieve	2.00	1.00	.60
580	Joe Pepitone	2.00	1.00	.60
581	Steve Kealey	2.00	1.00	.60
582	Darrell Porter	2.25	1.25	.70
583	Bill Greif	2.00	1.00	.60
584	Chris Arnold	2.00	1.00	.60
585	Joe Niekro	2.00	1.00	.60
586	Bill Sudakis	2.25	1.25	.70
587	Rich McKinney	2.00	1.00	.60
588	Checklist 529-660	20.00	10.00	6.00
589	Ken Forsch	2.25	1.25	.70
590	Deron Johnson	2.00	1.00	.60
591	Mike Hedlund	2.00	1.00	.60
592	John Boccabella	2.00	1.00	.60
593	Royals Mgr./Coaches (Galen Cisco, Harry Dunlop, Charlie Lau, Jack McKeon)	2.25	1.25	.70
594	Vic Harris	2.00	1.00	.60
595	Don Gullett	2.25	1.25	.70
596	Red Sox Team	2.75	1.50	.80
597	Mickey Rivers	2.25	1.25	.70
598	Phil Roof	2.00	1.00	.60
599	Ed Crosby	2.00	1.00	.60
600	Dave McNally	2.25	1.25	.70
601	Rookie Catchers (George Pena, Sergio Robles, Rick Stelmaszek)	2.00	1.00	.60
602	Rookie Pitchers (Mel Behney, Ralph Garcia, *Doug Rau*)	2.25	1.25	.70
603	Rookie Third Basemen (Terry Hughes, Bill McNulty, *Ken Reitz*)	2.25	1.25	.70
604	Rookie Pitchers (Jesse Jefferson, Dennis O'Toole, Bob Strampe)	2.00	1.00	.60
605	Rookie First Basemen (Pat Bourque, *Enos Cabell*, Gonzalo Marquez)	2.25	1.25	.70
606	Rookie Outfielders (*Gary Matthews*, Tom Paciorek, Jorge Roque)	2.25	1.25	.70
607	Rookie Shortstops (Ray Busse, Pepe Frias, Mario Guerrero)	2.00	1.00	.60
608	Rookie Pitchers (*Steve Busby*, Dick Colpaert, *George Medich*)	2.25	1.25	.70
609	Rookie Second Basemen (Larvell Blanks, Pedro Garcia, *Dave Lopes*)	4.00	2.00	1.25
610	Rookie Pitchers (Jimmy Freeman, Charlie Hough, Hank Webb)	2.25	1.25	.70
611	Rookie Outfielders (Rich Coggins, Jim Wohlford, Richie Zisk)	2.25	1.25	.70
612	Rookie Pitchers (Steve Lawson, Bob Reynolds, Brent Strom)	2.00	1.00	.60
613	Rookie Catchers (*Bob Boone*, Mike Ivie, Skip Jutze)	35.00	17.50	10.50
614	Rookie Outfielders (*Alonza Bumbry*, *Dwight Evans*, Charlie Spikes)	60.00	30.00	18.00
615	Rookie Third Basemen (Ron Cey, John Hilton, *Mike Schmidt*)	450.00	225.00	135.00
616	Rookie Pitchers (Norm Angelini, Steve Blateric, Mike Garman)	2.25	1.25	.70
617	Rich Chiles	2.00	1.00	.60
618	Andy Etchebarren	2.00	1.00	.60
619	Billy Wilson	2.00	1.00	.60
620	Tommy Harper	2.25	1.25	.70
621	Joe Ferguson	2.00	1.00	.60
622	Larry Hisle	2.25	1.25	.70
623	Steve Renko	2.00	1.00	.60
624	Astros Mgr./Coaches (Leo Durocher, Preston Gomez, Grady Hatton, Hub Kittle, Jim Owens)	2.25	1.25	.70
625	Angel Mangual	2.00	1.00	.60

		NR MT	EX	VG
626	Bob Barton	2.00	1.00	.60
627	Luis Alvarado	2.00	1.00	.60
628	Jim Slaton	2.25	1.25	.70
629	Indians Team	2.50	1.25	.70
630	Denny McLain	3.00	1.50	.90
631	Tom Matchick	2.00	1.00	.60
632	Dick Selma	2.00	1.00	.60
633	Ike Brown	2.00	1.00	.60
634	Alan Closter	2.25	1.25	.70
635	Gene Alley	2.25	1.25	.70
636	Rick Clark	2.00	1.00	.60
637	Norm Niller	2.00	1.00	.60
638	Ken Reynolds	2.00	1.00	.60
639	Willie Crawford	2.00	1.00	.60
640	Dick Bosman	2.00	1.00	.60
641	Reds Team	2.75	1.50	.80
642	Jose Laboy	2.00	1.00	.60
643	Al Fitzmorris	2.00	1.00	.60
644	Jack Heidemann	2.00	1.00	.60
645	Bob Locker	2.00	1.00	.60
646	Brewers Mgr./Coaches (Del Crandall, Harvey Kuenn, Joe Nossek, Bob Shaw, Jim Walton)	2.25	1.25	.70
647	George Stone	2.00	1.00	.60
648	Tom Egan	2.00	1.00	.60
649	Rich Folkers	2.00	1.00	.60
650	Felipe Alou	2.25	1.25	.70
651	Don Carrithers	2.00	1.00	.60
652	Ted Kubiak	2.00	1.00	.60
653	Joe Hoerner	2.00	1.00	.60
654	Twins Team	2.50	1.25	.70
655	Clay Kirby	2.00	1.00	.60
656	John Ellis	2.00	1.00	.60
657	Bob Johnson	2.00	1.00	.60
658	Elliott Maddox	2.25	1.25	.70
659	Jose Pagan	2.25	1.25	.70
660	Fred Scherman	2.25	.70	.45

1973 Topps Candy Lids

A bit out of the ordinary, the Topps Candy Lids were the top of a product called "Baseball Stars Bubble Gum." The bottom (inside) of the lids carry a color photo of a player with a ribbon which contains the name, position and team. The lids are 1-7/8" in diameter. A total of 55 different lids were made, featuring most of the stars of the day.

		NR MT	EX	VG
Complete Set:		450.00	225.00	135.00
Common Player:		2.00	1.00	.60
(1)	Hank Aaron	30.00	15.00	9.00
(2)	Dick Allen	4.00	2.00	1.25
(3)	Dusty Baker	2.00	1.00	.60
(4)	Sal Bando	3.00	1.50	.90
(5)	Johnny Bench	20.00	10.00	6.00
(6)	Bobby Bonds	3.00	1.50	.90
(7)	Dick Bosman	2.00	1.00	.60
(8)	Lou Brock	15.00	7.50	4.50
(9)	Rod Carew	20.00	10.00	6.00
(10)	Steve Carlton	20.00	10.00	6.00
(11)	Nate Colbert	2.00	1.00	.60
(12)	Willie Davis	3.00	1.50	.90
(13)	Larry Dierker	2.00	1.00	.60
(14)	Mike Epstein	2.00	1.00	.60
(15)	Carlton Fisk	7.00	3.50	2.00
(16)	Tim Foli	2.00	1.00	.60

		NR MT	EX	VG
(17)	Ray Fosse	2.00	1.00	.60
(18)	Bill Freehan	3.00	1.50	.90
(19)	Bob Gibson	15.00	7.50	4.50
(20)	Bud Harrelson	2.00	1.00	.60
(21)	Jim Hunter	12.00	6.00	3.50
(22)	Reggie Jackson	25.00	12.50	7.50
(23)	Fergie Jenkins	7.00	3.50	2.00
(24)	Al Kaline	15.00	7.50	4.50
(25)	Harmon Killebrew	15.00	7.50	4.50
(26)	Clay Kirby	2.00	1.00	.60
(27)	Mickey Lolich	4.00	2.00	1.25
(28)	Greg Luzinski	3.00	1.50	.90
(29)	Mike Marshall	2.00	1.00	.60
(30)	Lee May	2.00	1.00	.60
(31)	John Mayberry	2.00	1.00	.60
(32)	Willie Mays	30.00	15.00	9.00
(33)	Willie McCovey	15.00	7.50	4.50
(34)	Thurman Munson	15.00	7.50	4.50
(35)	Bobby Murcer	3.00	1.50	.90
(36)	Gary Nolan	2.00	1.00	.60
(37)	Amos Otis	2.00	1.00	.60
(38)	Jim Palmer	12.00	6.00	3.50
(39)	Gaylord Perry	12.00	6.00	3.50
(40)	Lou Piniella	3.00	1.50	.90
(41)	Brooks Robinson	18.00	9.00	5.50
(42)	Frank Robinson	15.00	7.50	4.50
(43)	Ellie Rodriguez	2.00	1.00	.60
(44)	Pete Rose	65.00	32.00	19.50
(45)	Nolan Ryan	18.00	9.00	5.50
(46)	Manny Sanguillen	2.00	1.00	.60
(47)	George Scott	2.00	1.00	.60
(48)	Tom Seaver	20.00	10.00	6.00
(49)	Chris Speier	2.00	1.00	.60
(50)	Willie Stargell	15.00	7.50	4.50
(51)	Don Sutton	12.00	6.00	3.50
(52)	Joe Torre	4.00	2.00	1.25
(53)	Billy Williams	12.00	6.00	3.50
(54)	Wilbur Wood	2.00	1.00	.60
(55)	Carl Yastrzemski	25.00	12.50	7.50

1973 Topps Comics

Strictly a test issue, if ever publicly distributed at all (most are found without any folding which would have occurred had they actually been used to wrap a piece of bubblegum), the 24 players in the 1973 Topps Comics issue appear on 4-5/8" by 3-7/16" waxed paper wrappers. The inside of the wrapper combines a color photo and facsimile autograph with a comic-style presentation of the player's career highlights. The Comics share a checklist with the 1973 Topps Pin-Ups, virtually all star players.

		NR MT	EX	VG
Complete Set:		3000.00	1500.00	900.00
Common Player:		70.00	35.00	21.00
(1)	Hank Aaron	200.00	100.00	60.00
(2)	Dick Allen	80.00	40.00	24.00
(3)	Johnny Bench	150.00	75.00	45.00
(4)	Steve Carlton	125.00	62.00	37.00
(5)	Nate Colbert	70.00	35.00	21.00
(6)	Willie Davis	80.00	40.00	24.00
(7)	Mike Epstein	70.00	35.00	21.00
(8)	Reggie Jackson	200.00	100.00	60.00
(9)	Harmon Killebrew	125.00	62.00	37.00
(10)	Mickey Lolich	80.00	40.00	24.00

		NR MT	EX	VG
(11)	Mike Marshall	70.00	35.00	21.00
(12)	Lee May	70.00	35.00	21.00
(13)	Willie McCovey	125.00	62.00	37.00
(14)	Bobby Murcer	80.00	40.00	24.00
(15)	Gaylord Perry	100.00	50.00	30.00
(16)	Lou Piniella	80.00	40.00	24.00
(17)	Brooks Robinson	125.00	62.00	37.00
(18)	Nolan Ryan	125.00	62.00	37.00
(19)	George Scott	70.00	35.00	21.00
(20)	Tom Seaver	150.00	75.00	45.00
(21)	Willie Stargell	100.00	50.00	30.00
(22)	Joe Torre	80.00	40.00	24.00
(23)	Billy Williams	100.00	50.00	30.00
(24)	Carl Yastrzemski	250.00	125.00	75.00

1973 Topps Pin-Ups

Another test issue of 1973, the 24 Topps Pin-Ups include the same basic format and the same checklist of star-caliber players as the Comics test issue of the same year. The 3-7/16" by 4-5/8" Pin-Ups are actually the inside of a wrapper for a piece of bubblegum. The color player photo features a decorative lozenge inserted at bottom with the player's name, team and position. There is also a facsimile autograph. Curiously, neither the Pin-Ups nor the Comics of 1973 bear team logos on the players' caps.

		NR MT	EX	VG
Complete Set:		1250.00	625.00	375.00
Common Player:		30.00	15.00	9.00
(1)	Hank Aaron	90.00	45.00	27.00
(2)	Dick Allen	35.00	17.50	10.50
(3)	Johnny Bench	70.00	35.00	21.00
(4)	Steve Carlton	60.00	30.00	18.00
(5)	Nate Colbert	30.00	15.00	9.00
(6)	Willie Davis	35.00	17.50	10.50
(7)	Mike Epstein	30.00	15.00	9.00
(8)	Reggie Jackson	90.00	45.00	27.00
(9)	Harmon Killebrew	50.00	25.00	15.00
(10)	Mickey Lolich	35.00	17.50	10.50
(11)	Mike Marshall	30.00	15.00	9.00
(12)	Lee May	30.00	15.00	9.00
(13)	Willie McCovey	50.00	25.00	15.00
(14)	Bobby Murcer	35.00	17.50	10.50
(15)	Gaylord Perry	45.00	22.00	13.50
(16)	Lou Piniella	35.00	17.50	10.50
(17)	Brooks Robinson	55.00	27.00	16.50
(18)	Nolan Ryan	55.00	27.00	16.50
(19)	George Scott	30.00	15.00	9.00
(20)	Tom Seaver	75.00	37.00	22.00
(21)	Willie Stargell	45.00	22.00	13.50
(22)	Joe Torre	35.00	17.50	10.50
(23)	Billy Williams	45.00	22.00	13.50
(24)	Carl Yastrzemski	110.00	55.00	33.00

1973 Topps Team Checklists

This is a 24-card unnumbered set of 2-1/2" by 3-1/2" cards that is generally believed to have been included with the high-numbered series in 1973, while also being made available in a mail-in offer. The front of the cards have the team name at the top and a white panel with various facsimile autographs takes up the rest of the space except for a blue border. Backs feature the team name and checklist. Relatively scarce, these somewhat mysterious cards are not included by many in their collections despite their obvious relationship to the regular set.

		NR MT	EX	VG
	Complete Set:	75.00	37.00	22.00
	Common Checklist:	3.00	1.50	.90
(1)	Atlanta Braves	3.00	1.50	.90
(2)	Baltimore Orioles	3.00	1.50	.90
(3)	Boston Red Sox	3.00	1.50	.90
(4)	California Angels	3.00	1.50	.90
(5)	Chicago Cubs	3.00	1.50	.90
(6)	Chicago White Sox	3.00	1.50	.90
(7)	Cincinnati Reds	3.00	1.50	.90
(8)	Cleveland Indians	3.00	1.50	.90
(9)	Detroit Tigers	3.50	1.75	1.00
(10)	Houston Astros	3.00	1.50	.90
(11)	Kansas City Royals	3.00	1.50	.90
(12)	Los Angeles Dodgers	3.00	1.50	.90
(13)	Milwaukee Brewers	3.00	1.50	.90
(14)	Minnesota Twins	3.00	1.50	.90
(15)	Montreal Expos	3.00	1.50	.90
(16)	New York Mets	3.50	1.75	1.00
(17)	New York Yankees	3.50	1.75	1.00
(18)	Oakland A's	3.50	1.75	1.00
(19)	Philadelphia Phillies	3.00	1.50	.90
(20)	Pittsburgh Pirates	3.00	1.50	.90
(21)	St. Louis Cardinals	3.00	1.50	.90
(22)	San Diego Padres	3.00	1.50	.90
(23)	San Francisco Giants	3.00	1.50	.90
(24)	Texas Rangers	3.00	1.50	.90

1974 Topps

Issued all at once at the beginning of the year, rather than by series throughout the baseball season as had been done since 1952, this 660-card '74 Topps set features a famous group of error cards. At the time the cards were printed, it was uncertain whether the San Diego Padres would move to Washington, D.C., and by the time a decision was made some Padres cards had appeared with a "Washington, Nat'l League" designation on the front. A total of 15 cards were affected, and those with the

Washington designation bring prices well in excess of regular cards of the same players (the Washington variations are not included in the complete set prices quoted below). The 2-1/2" by 3-1/2" cards feature color photos (frequently game-action shots) along with the player's name, team and position. Specialty cards abound, starting with a Hank Aaron tribute and running through the usual managers, statistical leaders, playoff and World Series highlights, multi-player rookie cards and All-Stars.

		NR MT	EX	VG
	Complete Set:	650.00	325.00	200.00
	Common Player:	.30	.15	.09
1	Hank Aaron	30.00	15.00	9.00
2	Aaron Special 1954-57	3.00	1.50	.90
3	Aaron Special 1958-61	3.00	1.50	.90
4	Aaron Special 1962-65	3.00	1.50	.90
5	Aaron Special 1966-69	3.00	1.50	.90
6	Aaron Special 1970-73	3.00	1.50	.90
7	Jim Hunter	4.00	2.00	1.25
8	George Theodore	.30	.15	.09
9	Mickey Lolich	.60	.30	.20
10	Johnny Bench	15.00	7.50	4.50
11	Jim Bibby	.30	.15	.09
12	Dave May	.30	.15	.09
13	Tom Hilgendorf	.30	.15	.09
14	Paul Popovich	.30	.15	.09
15	Joe Torre	.80	.40	.25
16	Orioles Team	.80	.40	.25
17	Doug Bird	.30	.15	.09
18	Gary Thomasson	.30	.15	.09
19	Gerry Moses	.30	.15	.09
20	Nolan Ryan	65.00	33.00	20.00
21	Bob Gallagher	.30	.15	.09
22	Cy Acosta	.30	.15	.09
23	Craig Robinson	.30	.15	.09
24	John Hiller	.30	.15	.09
25	Ken Singleton	.30	.15	.09
26	*Bill Campbell*	.40	.20	.12
27	George Scott	.30	.15	.09
28	Manny Sanguillen	.30	.15	.09
29	Phil Niekro	2.00	1.00	.60
30	Bobby Bonds	.50	.25	.15
31	Astros Mgr./Coaches (Roger Craig, Preston Gomez, Grady Hatton, Hub Kittle, Bob Lillis)	.30	.15	.09
32a	John Grubb (Washington)	3.50	1.75	1.00
32b	John Grubb (San Diego)	.30	.15	.09
33	Don Newhauser	.30	.15	.09
34	Andy Kosco	.30	.15	.09
35	Gaylord Perry	4.00	2.00	1.25
36	Cardinals Team	.80	.40	.25
37	Dave Sells	.30	.15	.09
38	Don Kessinger	.30	.15	.09
39	Ken Suarez	.30	.15	.09
40	Jim Palmer	9.00	4.50	2.75
41	Bobby Floyd	.30	.15	.09
42	Claude Osteen	.30	.15	.09
43	Jim Wynn	.30	.15	.09
44	Mel Stottlemyre	.40	.20	.12
45	Dave Johnson	.70	.35	.20
46	Pat Kelly	.30	.15	.09
47	*Dick Ruthven*	.30	.15	.09
48	Dick Sharon	.30	.15	.09
49	Steve Renko	.30	.15	.09
50	Rod Carew	12.00	6.00	3.50
51	Bobby Heise	.30	.15	.09
52	Al Oliver	1.00	.50	.30
53a	Fred Kendall (Washington)	3.50	1.75	1.00
53b	Fred Kendall (San Diego)	.30	.15	.09
54	*Elias Sosa*	.30	.15	.09
55	Frank Robinson	5.00	2.50	1.50
56	Mets Team	1.00	.50	.30
57	Darold Knowles	.30	.15	.09
58	Charlie Spikes	.30	.15	.09
59	Ross Grimsley	.30	.15	.09
60	Lou Brock	5.00	2.50	1.50
61	Luis Aparicio	2.50	1.25	.70
62	Bob Locker	.30	.15	.09
63	Bill Sudakis	.30	.15	.09
64	Doug Rau	.30	.15	.09
65	Amos Otis	.30	.15	.09
66	Sparky Lyle	.50	.25	.15
67	Tommy Helms	.30	.15	.09
68	Grant Jackson	.30	.15	.09
69	Del Unser	.30	.15	.09
70	Dick Allen	.80	.40	.25

		NR MT	EX	VG				NR MT	EX	VG
71	Danny Frisella	.30	.15	.09		150	John Mayberry	.30	.15	.09
72	Aurleio Rodriguez	.30	.15	.09		151	Diego Segui	.30	.15	.09
73	Mike Marshall	.70	.35	.20		152	Oscar Gamble	.30	.15	.09
74	Twins Team	.80	.40	.25		153	Jon Matlack	.30	.15	.09
75	Jim Colborn	.30	.15	.09		154	Astros Team	.80	.40	.25
76	Mickey Rivers	.30	.15	.09		155	Bert Campaneris	.40	.20	.12
77a	Rich Troedson (Washington)	3.50	1.75	1.00		156	Randy Moffitt	.30	.15	.09
77b	Rich Troedson (San Diego)	.30	.15	.09		157	Vic Harris	.30	.15	.09
78	Giants Mgr./Coaches (Joe Amalfitano, Charlie Fox, Andy Gilbert, Don McMahon, John McNamara)	.30	.15	.09		158	Jack Billingham	.30	.15	.09
						159	Jim Ray Hart	.30	.15	.09
79	Gene Tenace	.30	.15	.09		160	Brooks Robinson	3.50	1.75	1.00
80	Tom Seaver	22.00	11.00	6.50		161	*Ray Burris*	.40	.20	.12
81	Frank Duffy	.30	.15	.09		162	Bill Freehan	.40	.20	.12
82	Dave Giusti	.30	.15	.09		163	Ken Berry	.30	.15	.09
83	Orlando Cepeda	1.00	.50	.30		164	Tom House	.30	.15	.09
84	Rick Wise	.30	.15	.09		165	Willie Davis	.40	.20	.12
85	Joe Morgan	5.00	2.50	1.50		166	Royals Mgr./Coaches (Galen Cisco, Harry Dunlop, Charlie Lau, Jack McKeon)	.30	.15	.09
86	Joe Ferguson	.30	.15	.09						
87	Fergie Jenkins	4.00	2.00	1.25		167	Luis Tiant	.50	.25	.15
88	Freddie Patek	.30	.15	.09		168	Danny Thompson	.30	.15	.09
89	Jackie Brown	.30	.15	.09		169	*Steve Rogers*	.70	.35	.20
90	Bobby Murcer	.40	.20	.12		170	Bill Melton	.30	.15	.09
91	Ken Forsch	.30	.15	.09		171	Eduardo Rodriguez	.30	.15	.09
92	Paul Blair	.30	.15	.09		172	Gene Clines	.30	.15	.09
93	Rod Gilbreath	.30	.15	.09		173a	*Randy Jones* (Washington)	6.00	3.00	1.75
94	Tigers Team	.90	.45	.25		173b	*Randy Jones* (San Diego)	.40	.20	.12
95	Steve Carlton	10.00	5.00	3.00		174	Bill Robinson	.30	.15	.09
96	*Jerry Hairston*	.40	.20	.12		175	Reggie Cleveland	.30	.15	.09
97	Bob Bailey	.30	.15	.09		176	John Lowenstein	.30	.15	.09
98	Bert Blyleven	1.00	.50	.30		177	Dave Roberts	.30	.15	.09
99	Brewers Mgr./Coaches (Del Crandall, Harvey Kuenn, Joe Nossek, Jim Walton, Al Widmar)	.30	.15	.09		178	Garry Maddox	.40	.20	.12
						179	Mets Mgr./Coaches (Yogi Berra, Roy McMillan, Joe Pignatano, Rube Walker, Eddie Yost)	1.25	.60	.40
100	Willie Stargell	4.00	2.00	1.25						
101	Bobby Valentine	.30	.15	.09		180	Ken Holtzman	.30	.15	.09
102a	Bill Greif (Washington)	3.50	1.75	1.00		181	Cesar Geronimo	.30	.15	.09
102b	Bill Greif (San Diego)	.30	.15	.09		182	Lindy McDaniel	.30	.15	.09
103	Sal Bando	.40	.20	.12		183	Johnny Oates	.30	.15	.09
104	Ron Bryant	.30	.15	.09		184	Rangers Team	.80	.40	.25
105	Carlton Fisk	22.00	11.00	6.50		185	Jose Cardenal	.30	.15	.09
106	Harry Parker	.30	.15	.09		186	Fred Scherman	.30	.15	.09
107	Alex Johnson	.30	.15	.09		187	Don Baylor	.70	.35	.20
108	Al Hrabosky	.30	.15	.09		188	Rudy Meoli	.30	.15	.09
109	Bob Grich	.40	.20	.12		189	Jim Brewer	.30	.15	.09
110	Billy Williams	3.00	1.50	.90		190	Tony Oliva	.80	.40	.25
111	Clay Carroll	.30	.15	.09		191	Al Fitzmorris	.30	.15	.09
112	Dave Lopes	.40	.20	.12		192	Mario Guerrero	.30	.15	.09
113	Dick Drago	.30	.15	.09		193	Tom Walker	.30	.15	.09
114	Angels Team	.80	.40	.25		194	Darrell Porter	.30	.15	.09
115	Willie Horton	.30	.15	.09		195	Carlos May	.30	.15	.09
116	Jerry Reuss	.30	.15	.09		196	Jim Fregosi	.40	.20	.12
117	Ron Blomberg	.30	.15	.09		197a	Vicente Romo (Washington)	3.50	1.75	1.00
118	Bill Lee	.30	.15	.09		197b	Vicente Romo (San Diego)	.30	.15	.09
119	Phillies Mgr./Coaches (Carroll Beringer, Bill DeMars, Danny Ozark, Ray Ripplemeyer, Bobby Wine)	.30	.15	.09		198	Dave Cash	.30	.15	.09
						199	Mike Kekich	.30	.15	.09
						200	Cesar Cedeno	.40	.20	.12
120	Wilbur Wood	.30	.15	.09		201	Batting Leaders (Rod Carew, Pete Rose)	4.00	2.00	1.25
121	Larry Lintz	.30	.15	.09						
122	Jim Holt	.30	.15	.09		202	Home Run Leaders (Reggie Jackson, Willie Stargell)	2.00	1.00	.60
123	Nelson Briles	.30	.15	.09						
124	Bob Coluccio	.30	.15	.09		203	Runs Batted In Leaders (Reggie Jackson, Willie Stargell)	2.00	1.00	.60
125a	Nate Colbert (Washington)	3.50	1.75	1.00						
125b	Nate Colbert (San Diego)	.30	.15	.09		204	Stolen Base Leaders (Lou Brock, Tommy Harper)	1.25	.60	.40
126	Checklist 1-132	1.50	.70	.45						
127	Tom Paciorek	.30	.15	.09		205	Victory Leaders (Ron Bryant, Wilbur Wood)	.50	.25	.15
128	John Ellis	.30	.15	.09						
129	Chris Speier	.30	.15	.09		206	Earned Run Average Leaders (Jim Palmer, Tom Seaver)	2.00	1.00	.60
130	Reggie Jackson	25.00	12.50	7.50						
131	Bob Boone	2.00	1.00	.60		207	Strikeout Leaders (Nolan Ryan, Tom Seaver)	7.00	3.50	2.00
132	Felix Millan	.30	.15	.09						
133	*David Clyde*	.30	.15	.09		208	Leading Firemen (John Hiller, Mike Marshall)	.50	.25	.15
134	Denis Menke	.30	.15	.09						
135	Roy White	.40	.20	.12		209	Ted Sizemore	.30	.15	.09
136	Rick Reuschel	.80	.40	.25		210	Bill Singer	.30	.15	.09
137	Al Bumbry	.30	.15	.09		211	Cubs Team	.80	.40	.25
138	Ed Brinkman	.30	.15	.09		212	Rollie Fingers	5.00	2.50	1.50
139	Aurelio Monteagudo	.30	.15	.09		213	Dave Rader	.30	.15	.09
140	Darrell Evans	.60	.30	.20		214	Billy Grabarkewitz	.30	.15	.09
141	Pat Bourque	.30	.15	.09		215	Al Kaline	5.00	2.50	1.50
142	Pedro Garcia	.30	.15	.09		216	Ray Sadecki	.30	.15	.09
143	Dick Woodson	.30	.15	.09		217	Tim Foli	.30	.15	.09
144	Dodgers Mgr./Coaches (Red Adams, Walter Alston, Monty Basgall, Jim Gilliam, Tom Lasorda)	1.25	.60	.40		218	Johnny Briggs	.30	.15	.09
						219	Doug Griffin	.30	.15	.09
						220	Don Sutton	2.00	1.00	.60
145	Dock Ellis	.30	.15	.09		221	White Sox Mgr./Coaches (Joe Lonnett, Jim Mahoney, Alex Monchak, Johnny Sain, Chuck Tanner)	.30	.15	.09
146	Ron Fairly	.30	.15	.09						
147	Bart Johnson	.30	.15	.09						
148a	Dave Hilton (Washington)	3.50	1.75	1.00		222	Ramon Hernandez	.30	.15	.09
148b	Dave Hilton (San Diego)	.30	.15	.09		223	Jeff Burroughs	.50	.25	.15
149	Mac Scarce	.30	.15	.09		224	Roger Metzger	.30	.15	.09
						225	Paul Splittorff	.30	.15	.09

No.	Player	NR MT	EX	VG
226a	Washington Nat'l. Team	6.00	3.00	1.75
226b	Padres Team	1.00	.50	.30
227	Mike Lum	.30	.15	.09
228	Ted Kubiak	.30	.15	.09
229	Fritz Peterson	.30	.15	.09
230	Tony Perez	1.25	.60	.40
231	Dick Tidrow	.30	.15	.09
232	Steve Brye	.30	.15	.09
233	Jim Barr	.30	.15	.09
234	John Milner	.30	.15	.09
235	Dave McNally	.30	.15	.09
236	Cardinals Mgr./Coaches (Vern Benson, George Kissell, Johnny Lewis, Red Schoendienst, Barney Schultz)	.40	.20	.12
237	Ken Brett	.30	.15	.09
238	Fran Healy	.30	.15	.09
239	Bill Russell	.30	.15	.09
240	Joe Coleman	.30	.15	.09
241a	Glenn Beckert (Washington)	4.00	2.00	1.25
241b	Glenn Beckert (San Diego)	.30	.15	.09
242	Bill Gogolewski	.30	.15	.09
243	Bob Oliver	.30	.15	.09
244	Carl Morton	.30	.15	.09
245	Cleon Jones	.30	.15	.09
246	A's Team	1.25	.60	.40
247	Rick Miller	.30	.15	.09
248	Tom Hall	.30	.15	.09
249	George Mitterwald	.30	.15	.09
250a	Willie McCovey (Washington)	25.00	12.50	7.50
250b	Willie McCovey (San Diego)	5.00	2.50	1.50
251	Graig Nettles	1.50	.70	.45
252	*Dave Parker*	30.00	15.00	9.00
253	John Boccabella	.30	.15	.09
254	Stan Bahnsen	.30	.15	.09
255	Larry Bowa	.40	.20	.12
256	Tom Griffin	.30	.15	.09
257	Buddy Bell	1.25	.60	.40
258	Jerry Morales	.30	.15	.09
259	Bob Reynolds	.30	.15	.09
260	Ted Simmons	.80	.40	.25
261	Jerry Bell	.30	.15	.09
262	Ed Kirkpatrick	.30	.15	.09
263	Checklist 133-264	1.50	.70	.45
264	Joe Rudi	.40	.20	.12
265	Tug McGraw	.60	.30	.20
266	Jim Northrup	.30	.15	.09
267	Andy Messersmith	.30	.15	.09
268	Tom Grieve	.30	.15	.09
269	Bob Johnson	.30	.15	.09
270	Ron Santo	.50	.25	.15
271	Bill Hands	.30	.15	.09
272	Paul Casanova	.30	.15	.09
273	Checklist 265-396	1.50	.70	.45
274	Fred Beene	.30	.15	.09
275	Ron Hunt	.30	.15	.09
276	Angels Mgr./Coaches (Tom Morgan, Salty Parker, Jimmie Reese, John Roseboro, Bobby Winkles)	.30	.15	.09
277	Gary Nolan	.30	.15	.09
278	Cookie Rojas	.30	.15	.09
279	Jim Crawford	.30	.15	.09
280	Carl Yastrzemski	15.00	7.50	4.50
281	Giants Team	.80	.40	.25
282	Doyle Alexander	.40	.20	.12
283	Mike Schmidt	75.00	38.00	23.00
284	Dave Duncan	.30	.15	.09
285	Reggie Smith	.40	.20	.12
286	Tony Muser	.30	.15	.09
287	Clay Kirby	.30	.15	.09
288	*Gorman Thomas*	2.00	1.00	.60
289	Rick Auerbach	.30	.15	.09
290	Vida Blue	.60	.30	.20
291	Don Hahn	.30	.15	.09
292	Chuck Seelbach	.30	.15	.09
293	Milt May	.30	.15	.09
294	Steve Foucault	.30	.15	.09
295	Rick Monday	.30	.15	.09
296	Ray Corbin	.30	.15	.09
297	Hal Breeden	.30	.15	.09
298	Roric Harrison	.30	.15	.09
299	Gene Michael	.30	.15	.09
300	Pete Rose	15.00	7.50	4.50
301	Bob Montgomery	.30	.15	.09
302	Rudy May	.30	.15	.09
303	George Hendrick	.30	.15	.09
304	Don Wilson	.30	.15	.09
305	Tito Fuentes	.30	.15	.09
306	Orioles Mgr./Coaches (George Bamberger, Jim Frey, Billy Hunter, George Staller, Earl Weaver)	.70	.35	.20
307	Luis Melendez	.30	.15	.09
308	Bruce Dal Canton	.30	.15	.09
309a	Dave Roberts (Washington)	3.50	1.75	1.00
309b	Dave Roberts (San Diego)	.30	.15	.09
310	Terry Forster	.30	.15	.09
311	Jerry Grote	.30	.15	.09
312	Deron Johnson	.30	.15	.09
313	Berry Lersch	.30	.15	.09
314	Brewers Team	.80	.40	.25
315	Ron Cey	.60	.30	.20
316	Jim Perry	.40	.20	.12
317	Richie Zisk	.30	.15	.09
318	Jim Merritt	.30	.15	.09
319	Randy Hundley	.30	.15	.09
320	Dusty Baker	.40	.20	.12
321	Steve Braun	.30	.15	.09
322	Ernie McAnally	.30	.15	.09
323	Richie Scheinblum	.30	.15	.09
324	Steve Kline	.30	.15	.09
325	Tommy Harper	.30	.15	.09
326	Reds Mgr./Coaches (Sparky Anderson, Alex Grammas, Ted Kluszewski, George Scherger, Larry Shepard)	.50	.25	.15
327	Tom Timmermann	.30	.15	.09
328	Skip Jutze	.30	.15	.09
329	Mark Belanger	.30	.15	.09
330	Juan Marichal	2.75	1.50	.80
331	All Star Catchers (Johnny Bench, Carlton Fisk)	2.00	1.00	.60
332	All Star First Basemen (Hank Aaron, Dick Allen)	2.00	1.00	.60
333	All Star Second Basemen (Rod Carew, Joe Morgan)	2.00	1.00	.60
334	All Star Third Basemen (Brooks Robinson, Ron Santo)	1.25	.60	.40
335	All Star Shortstops (Bert Campaneris, Chris Speier)	.40	.20	.12
336	All Star Left Fielders (Bobby Murcer, Pete Rose)	2.50	1.25	.70
337	All Star Center Fielders (Cesar Cedeno, Amos Otis)	.40	.20	.12
338	All Star Right Fielders (Reggie Jackson, Billy Williams)	2.00	1.00	.60
339	All Star Pitchers (Jim Hunter, Rick Wise)	.80	.40	.25
340	Thurman Munson	8.00	4.00	2.50
341	*Dan Driessen*	.80	.40	.25
342	Jim Lonborg	.30	.15	.09
343	Royals Team	.80	.40	.25
344	Mike Caldwell	.30	.15	.09
345	Bill North	.30	.15	.09
346	Ron Reed	.30	.15	.09
347	Sandy Alomar	.30	.15	.09
348	Pete Richert	.30	.15	.09
349	John Vukovich	.30	.15	.09
350	Bob Gibson	6.00	3.00	1.75
351	Dwight Evans	15.00	7.50	4.50
352	Bill Stoneman	.30	.15	.09
353	Rich Coggins	.30	.15	.09
354	Cubs Mgr./Coaches (Hank Aguirre, Whitey Lockman, Jim Marshall, J.C. Martin, Al Spangler)	.30	.15	.09
355	Dave Nelson	.30	.15	.09
356	Jerry Koosman	.40	.20	.12
357	Buddy Bradford	.30	.15	.09
358	Dal Maxvill	.30	.15	.09
359	Brent Strom	.30	.15	.09
360	Greg Luzinski	.70	.35	.20
361	Don Carrithers	.30	.15	.09
362	Hal King	.30	.15	.09
363	Yankees Team	1.25	.60	.40
364a	Clarence Gaston (Washington)	3.50	1.75	1.00
364b	Clarence Gaston (San Diego)	.30	.15	.09
365	Steve Busby	.30	.15	.09
366	Larry Hisle	.30	.15	.09
367	Norm Cash	.50	.25	.15
368	Manny Mota	.40	.20	.12
369	Paul Lindblad	.30	.15	.09
370	Bob Watson	.30	.15	.09
371	Jim Slaton	.30	.15	.09
372	Ken Reitz	.30	.15	.09
373	John Curtis	.30	.15	.09
374	Marty Perez	.30	.15	.09
375	Earl Williams	.30	.15	.09
376	Jorge Orta	.30	.15	.09
377	Ron Woods	.30	.15	.09
378	Burt Hooton	.30	.15	.09
379	Rangers Mgr./Coaches (Art Fowler, Frank Lucchesi, Billy Martin, Jackie Moore, Charlie Silvera)	.80	.40	.25
380	Bud Harrelson	.30	.15	.09
381	Charlie Sands	.30	.15	.09

#		NR MT	EX	VG
382	Bob Moose	.30	.15	.09
383	Phillies Team	.80	.40	.25
384	Chris Chambliss	.40	.20	.12
385	Don Gullett	.30	.15	.09
386	Gary Matthews	.60	.30	.20
387a	Rich Morales (Washington)	3.50	1.75	1.00
387b	Rich Morales (San Diego)	.30	.15	.09
388	Phil Roof	.30	.15	.09
389	Gates Brown	.30	.15	.09
390	Lou Piniella	.70	.35	.20
391	Billy Champion	.30	.15	.09
392	Dick Green	.30	.15	.09
393	Orlando Pena	.30	.15	.09
394	Ken Henderson	.30	.15	.09
395	Doug Rader	.30	.15	.09
396	Tommy Davis	.40	.20	.12
397	George Stone	.30	.15	.09
398	Duke Sims	.30	.15	.09
399	Mike Paul	.30	.15	.09
400	Harmon Killebrew	4.00	2.00	1.25
401	Elliott Maddox	.30	.15	.09
402	Jim Rooker	.30	.15	.09
403	Red Sox Mgr./Coaches (Don Bryant, Darrell Johnson, Eddie Popowski, Lee Stange, Don Zimmer)	.30	.15	.09
404	Jim Howarth	.30	.15	.09
405	Ellie Rodriguez	.30	.15	.09
406	Steve Arlin	.30	.15	.09
407	Jim Wohlford	.30	.15	.09
408	Charlie Hough	.40	.20	.12
409	Ike Brown	.30	.15	.09
410	Pedro Borbon	.30	.15	.09
411	Frank Baker	.30	.15	.09
412	Chuck Taylor	.30	.15	.09
413	Don Money	.30	.15	.09
414	Checklist 397-528	1.50	.70	.45
415	Gary Gentry	.30	.15	.09
416	White Sox Team	.80	.40	.25
417	Rich Folkers	.30	.15	.09
418	Walt Williams	.30	.15	.09
419	Wayne Twitchell	.30	.15	.09
420	Ray Fosse	.30	.15	.09
421	Dan Fife	.30	.15	.09
422	Gonzalo Marquez	.30	.15	.09
423	Fred Stanley	.30	.15	.09
424	Jim Beauchamp	.30	.15	.09
425	Pete Broberg	.30	.15	.09
426	Rennie Stennett	.30	.15	.09
427	Bobby Bolin	.30	.15	.09
428	Gary Sutherland	.30	.15	.09
429	Dick Lange	.30	.15	.09
430	Matty Alou	.40	.20	.12
431	*Gene Garber*	.50	.25	.15
432	Chris Arnold	.30	.15	.09
433	Lerrin LaGrow	.30	.15	.09
434	Ken McMullen	.30	.15	.09
435	Dave Concepcion	.70	.35	.20
436	Don Hood	.30	.15	.09
437	Jim Lyttle	.30	.15	.09
438	Ed Herrmann	.30	.15	.09
439	Norm Miller	.30	.15	.09
440	Jim Kaat	1.25	.60	.40
441	Tom Ragland	.30	.15	.09
442	Alan Foster	.30	.15	.09
443	Tom Hutton	.30	.15	.09
444	Vic Davalillo	.30	.15	.09
445	George Medich	.30	.15	.09
446	Len Randle	.30	.15	.09
447	Twins Mgr./Coaches (Vern Morgan, Frank Quilici, Bob Rodgers, Ralph Rowe)	.30	.15	.09
448	Ron Hodges	.30	.15	.09
449	Tom McCraw	.30	.15	.09
450	Rich Hebner	.30	.15	.09
451	Tommy John	1.50	.70	.45
452	Gene Hiser	.30	.15	.09
453	Balor Moore	.30	.15	.09
454	Kurt Bevacqua	.30	.15	.09
455	Tom Bradley	.30	.15	.09
456	*Dave Winfield*	150.00	75.00	45.00
457	Chuck Goggin	.30	.15	.09
458	Jim Ray	.30	.15	.09
459	Reds Team	.90	.45	.25
460	Boog Powell	.90	.45	.25
461	John Odom	.30	.15	.09
462	Luis Alvarado	.30	.15	.09
463	Pat Dobson	.30	.15	.09
464	Jose Cruz	.80	.40	.25
465	Dick Bosman	.30	.15	.09
466	Dick Billings	.30	.15	.09
467	Winston Llenas	.30	.15	.09
468	Pepe Frias	.30	.15	.09
469	Joe Decker	.30	.15	.09
470	A.L. Playoffs	4.00	2.00	1.25
471	N.L. Playoffs	.80	.40	.25
472	World Series Game 1	.80	.40	.25
473	World Series Game 2	4.00	2.00	1.25
474	World Series Game 3	.80	.40	.25
475	World Series Game 4	.80	.40	.25
476	World Series Game 5	.80	.40	.25
477	World Series Game 6	4.00	2.00	1.25
478	World Series Game 7	.80	.40	.25
479	World Series Summary	.80	.40	.25
480	Willie Crawford	.30	.15	.09
481	Jerry Terrell	.30	.15	.09
482	Bob Didier	.30	.15	.09
483	Braves Team	.80	.40	.25
484	Carmen Fanzone	.30	.15	.09
485	Felipe Alou	.40	.20	.12
486	Steve Stone	.40	.20	.12
487	Ted Martinez	.30	.15	.09
488	Andy Etchebarren	.30	.15	.09
489	Pirates Mgr./Coaches (Don Leppert, Bill Mazeroski, Danny Murtaugh, Don Osborn, Bob Skinner)	.30	.15	.09
490	Vada Pinson	.70	.35	.20
491	Roger Nelson	.30	.15	.09
492	Mike Rogodzinski	.30	.15	.09
493	Joe Hoerner	.30	.15	.09
494	Ed Goodson	.30	.15	.09
495	Dick McAuliffe	.30	.15	.09
496	Tom Murphy	.30	.15	.09
497	Bobby Mitchell	.30	.15	.09
498	Pat Corrales	.40	.20	.12
499	Rusty Torres	.30	.15	.09
500	Lee May	.40	.20	.12
501	Eddie Leon	.30	.15	.09
502	Dave LaRoche	.30	.15	.09
503	Eric Soderholm	.30	.15	.09
504	Joe Niekro	.40	.20	.12
505	Bill Buckner	.50	.25	.15
506	Ed Farmer	.30	.15	.09
507	Larry Stahl	.30	.15	.09
508	Expos Team	.80	.40	.25
509	Jesse Jefferson	.30	.15	.09
510	Wayne Garrett	.30	.15	.09
511	Toby Harrah	.30	.15	.09
512	Joe Lahoud	.30	.15	.09
513	Jim Campanis	.30	.15	.09
514	Paul Schaal	.30	.15	.09
515	Willie Montanez	.30	.15	.09
516	Horacio Pina	.30	.15	.09
517	Mike Hegan	.30	.15	.09
518	Derrel Thomas	.30	.15	.09
519	Bill Sharp	.30	.15	.09
520	Tim McCarver	.60	.30	.20
521	Indians Mgr./Coaches (Ken Aspromonte, Clay Bryant, Tony Pacheco)	.30	.15	.09
522	J.R. Richard	.30	.15	.09
523	Cecil Cooper	1.50	.70	.45
524	Bill Plummer	.30	.15	.09
525	Clyde Wright	.30	.15	.09
526	Frank Tepedino	.30	.15	.09
527	Bobby Darwin	.30	.15	.09
528	Bill Bonham	.30	.15	.09
529	Horace Clarke	.30	.15	.09
530	Mickey Stanley	.30	.15	.09
531	Expos Mgr./Coaches (Dave Bristol, Larry Doby, Gene Mauch, Cal McLish, Jerry Zimmerman)	.40	.20	.12
532	Skip Lockwood	.30	.15	.09
533	Mike Phillips	.30	.15	.09
534	Eddie Watt	.30	.15	.09
535	Bob Tolan	.30	.15	.09
536	Duffy Dyer	.30	.15	.09
537	Steve Mingori	.30	.15	.09
538	Cesar Tovar	.30	.15	.09
539	Lloyd Allen	.30	.15	.09
540	Bob Robertson	.30	.15	.09
541	Indians Team	.80	.40	.25
542	Rich Gossage	4.00	2.00	1.25
543	Danny Cater	.30	.15	.09
544	Ron Schueler	.30	.15	.09
545	Billy Conigliaro	.30	.15	.09
546	Mike Corkins	.30	.15	.09
547	Glenn Borgmann	.30	.15	.09
548	Sonny Siebert	.30	.15	.09
549	Mike Jorgensen	.30	.15	.09
550	Sam McDowell	.40	.20	.12
551	Von Joshua	.30	.15	.09
552	Denny Doyle	.30	.15	.09
553	Jim Willoughby	.30	.15	.09
554	Tim Johnson	.30	.15	.09

		NR MT	EX	VG
555	Woodie Fryman	.30	.15	.09
556	Dave Campbell	.30	.15	.09
557	Jim McGlothlin	.30	.15	.09
558	Bill Fahey	.30	.15	.09
559	Darrel Chaney	.30	.15	.09
560	Mike Cuellar	.40	.20	.12
561	Ed Kranepool	.30	.15	.09
562	Jack Aker	.30	.15	.09
563	Hal McRae	.40	.20	.12
564	Mike Ryan	.30	.15	.09
565	Milt Wilcox	.30	.15	.09
566	Jackie Hernandez	.30	.15	.09
567	Red Sox Team	.90	.45	.25
568	Mike Torrez	.30	.15	.09
569	Rick Dempsey	.40	.20	.12
570	Ralph Garr	.30	.15	.09
571	Rich Hand	.30	.15	.09
572	Enzo Hernandez	.30	.15	.09
573	Mike Adams	.30	.15	.09
574	Bill Parsons	.30	.15	.09
575	Steve Garvey	12.00	6.00	3.50
576	Scipio Spinks	.30	.15	.09
577	Mike Sadek	.30	.15	.09
578	Ralph Houk	.40	.20	.12
579	Cecil Upshaw	.30	.15	.09
580	Jim Spencer	.30	.15	.09
581	Fred Norman	.30	.15	.09
582	*Bucky Dent*	.90	.45	.25
583	Marty Pattin	.30	.15	.09
584	Ken Rudolph	.30	.15	.09
585	Merv Rettenmund	.30	.15	.09
586	Jack Brohamer	.30	.15	.09
587	*Larry Christenson*	.30	.15	.09
588	Hal Lanier	.40	.20	.12
589	Boots Day	.30	.15	.09
590	Rogelio Moret	.30	.15	.09
591	Sonny Jackson	.30	.15	.09
592	Ed Bane	.30	.15	.09
593	Steve Yeager	.30	.15	.09
594	Leroy Stanton	.30	.15	.09
595	Steve Blass	.30	.15	.09
596	Rookie Pitchers (*Wayne Garland*, Fred Holdsworth, *Mark Littell*, Dick Pole)	.30	.15	.09
597	Rookie Shortstops (Dave Chalk, John Gamble, Pete Mackanin, *Manny Trillo*)	.80	.40	.25
598	Rookie Outfielders (Dave Augustine, *Ken Griffey*, Steve Ontiveros, Jim Tyrone)	20.00	10.00	6.00
599a	Rookie Pitchers (Ron Diorio, Dave Freisleben, Frank Riccelli, Greg Shanahan) (Freisleben- Washington)	.80	.40	.25
599b	Rookie Pitchers (Ron Diorio, Dave Freisleben, Frank Riccelli, Greg Shanahan) (Freisleben- San Diego large print)	3.50	1.75	1.00
599c	Rookie Pitchers (Ron Diorio, Dave Freisleben, Frank Riccelli, Greg Shanahan) (Freisleben- San Diego small print)	6.00	3.00	1.75
600	Rookie Infielders (Ron Cash, Jim Cox, *Bill Madlock*, Reggie Sanders)	5.00	2.50	1.50
601	Rookie Outfielders (Ed Armbrister, Rich Bladt, *Brian Downing*, Bake McBride)	5.00	2.50	1.50
602	Rookie Pitchers (Glenn Abbott, Rick Henninger, Craig Swan, Dan Vossler)	.30	.15	.09
603	Rookie Catchers (Barry Foote, Tom Lundstedt, *Charlie Moore*, Sergio Robles)	.30	.15	.09
604	Rookie Infielders (Terry Hughes, John Knox, *Andy Thornton, Frank White*)	5.00	2.50	1.50
605	Rookie Pitchers (Vic Albury, Ken Frailing, Kevin Kobel, *Frank Tanana*)	2.00	1.00	.60
606	Rookie Outfielders (Jim Fuller, Wilbur Howard, Tommy Smith, Otto Velez)	.30	.15	.09
607	Rookie Shortstops (Leo Foster, Tom Heintzelman, Dave Rosello, *Frank Taveras*)	.30	.15	.09
608a	Rookie Pitchers (Bob Apodaco, Dick Baney, John D'Acquisto, Mike Wallace)	2.00	1.00	.60
608b	Rookie Pitchers (Bob Apodaco, Dick Baney, John D'Acquisto, Mike Wallace)	.30	.15	.09
609	Rico Petrocelli	.30	.15	.09
610	Dave Kingman	.90	.45	.25
611	Rick Stelmaszek	.30	.15	.09
612	Luke Walker	.30	.15	.09
613	Dan Monzon	.30	.15	.09
614	Adrian Devine	.30	.15	.09
615	Johnny Jeter	.30	.15	.09
616	Larry Gura	.30	.15	.09
617	Ted Ford	.30	.15	.09
618	Jim Mason	.30	.15	.09
619	Mike Anderson	.30	.15	.09

		NR MT	EX	VG
620	Al Downing	.30	.15	.09
621	Bernie Carbo	.30	.15	.09
622	Phil Gagliano	.30	.15	.09
623	Celerino Sanchez	.30	.15	.09
624	Bob Miller	.30	.15	.09
625	Ollie Brown	.30	.15	.09
626	Pirates Team	.80	.40	.25
627	Carl Taylor	.30	.15	.09
628	Ivan Murrell	.30	.15	.09
629	Rusty Staub	.70	.35	.20
630	Tommie Agee	.30	.15	.09
631	Steve Barber	.30	.15	.09
632	George Culver	.30	.15	.09
633	Dave Hamilton	.30	.15	.09
634	Braves Mgr./Coaches (Jim Busby, Eddie Mathews, Connie Ryan, Ken Silvestri, Herm Starrette)	.90	.45	.25
635	John Edwards	.30	.15	.09
636	Dave Goltz	.30	.15	.09
637	Checklist 529-660	1.50	.70	.45
638	Ken Sanders	.30	.15	.09
639	Joe Lovitto	.30	.15	.09
640	Milt Pappas	.40	.20	.12
641	Chuck Brinkman	.30	.15	.09
642	Terry Harmon	.30	.15	.09
643	Dodgers Team	.90	.45	.25
644	Wayne Granger	.30	.15	.09
645	Ken Boswell	.30	.15	.09
646	George Foster	1.25	.60	.40
647	*Juan Beniquez*	.70	.35	.20
648	Terry Crowley	.30	.15	.09
649	Fernando Gonzalez	.30	.15	.09
650	Mike Epstein	.30	.15	.09
651	Leron Lee	.30	.15	.09
652	Gail Hopkins	.30	.15	.09
653	Bob Stinson	.30	.15	.09
654a	Jesus Alou (no position listed)	5.00	2.50	1.50
654b	Jesus Alou (Outfield)	.40	.20	.12
655	Mike Tyson	.30	.15	.09
656	Adrian Garrett	.30	.15	.09
657	Jim Shellenback	.30	.15	.09
658	Lee Lacy	.30	.15	.09
659	Joe Lis	.30	.15	.09
660	Larry Dierker	.50	.15	.09

1974 Topps Deckle Edge

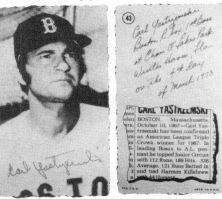

These borderless 2-7/8" by 5" cards feature a black and white photograph with a facsimile autograph on the front. The backs have in handwritten script the player's name, team, position and the date and location of the picture. Below is a mock newspaper clipping providing a detail from the player's career. The cards take their names from their specially cut edges which give them a scalloped appearance. The 72-card set was a test issue and received rather limited distribution.

		NR MT	EX	VG
Complete Set:		2000.00	1000.00	600.00
Common Player:		10.00	5.00	3.00
1	Amos Otis	10.00	5.00	3.00
2	Darrell Evans	15.00	7.50	4.50

		NR MT	EX	VG
3	Robert Gibson	50.00	25.00	15.00
4	David Nelson	10.00	5.00	3.00
5	Steven N. Carlton	80.00	40.00	25.00
6	Jim "Catfish" Hunter	40.00	20.00	12.00
7	Thurman Munson	50.00	25.00	15.00
8	Bob Grich	15.00	7.50	4.50
9	Tom Seaver	100.00	50.00	30.00
10	Ted L. Simmons	20.00	10.00	6.00
11	Robert J. Valentine	10.00	5.00	3.00
12	Don Sutton	25.00	12.50	7.50
13	Wilbur Wood	10.00	5.00	3.00
14	Douglas Lee Rader	10.00	5.00	3.00
15	Chris Chambliss	10.00	5.00	3.00
16	Pete Rose	200.00	100.00	60.00
17	John F. Hiller	10.00	5.00	3.00
18	Burt Hooton	10.00	5.00	3.00
19	Tim Foli	10.00	5.00	3.00
20	Louis Brock	60.00	30.00	20.00
21	Ron Bryant	10.00	5.00	3.00
22	Manuel Sanguillen	10.00	5.00	3.00
23	Bobby Tolan	10.00	5.00	3.00
24	Greg Luzinski	15.00	7.50	4.50
25	Brooks Robinson	60.00	30.00	18.00
26	Felix Millan	10.00	5.00	3.00
27	Luis Tiant	15.00	7.50	4.50
28	Willie McCovey	60.00	30.00	20.00
29	Chris Speier	10.00	5.00	3.00
30	George Scott	10.00	5.00	3.00
31	Willie Stargell	50.00	25.00	15.00
32	Rod Carew	100.00	50.00	30.00
33	Leslie Charles Spikes	10.00	5.00	3.00
34	Nate Colbert	10.00	5.00	3.00
35	Richie Hebner	10.00	5.00	3.00
36	Bobby Lee Bonds	15.00	7.50	4.50
37	Buddy Bell	15.00	7.50	4.50
38	Claude Osteen	10.00	5.00	3.00
39	Richard A. Allen	15.00	7.50	4.50
40	Bill Russell	10.00	5.00	3.00
41	Nolan Ryan	175.00	87.00	52.00
42	Willie Davis	15.00	7.50	4.50
43	Carl Yastrzemski	125.00	62.00	37.00
44	Jonathon T. Matlack	10.00	5.00	3.00
45	Jim Palmer	30.00	15.00	9.00
46	Dagoberto Campaneris	15.00	7.50	4.50
47	Bert Blyleven	20.00	10.00	6.00
48	Jeff Burroughs	10.00	5.00	3.00
49	James W. Colborn	10.00	5.00	3.00
50	Dave Johnson	15.00	7.50	4.50
51	John Mayberry	10.00	5.00	3.00
52	Don Kessinger	10.00	5.00	3.00
53	Joseph H. Coleman	10.00	5.00	3.00
54	Tony Perez	20.00	10.00	6.00
55	Jose Cardenal	10.00	5.00	3.00
56	Paul Splittorff	10.00	5.00	3.00
57	Henry Aaron	150.00	75.00	45.00
58	David May	10.00	5.00	3.00
59	Fergie Jenkins	30.00	15.00	9.00
60	Ron Blomberg	10.00	5.00	3.00
61	Reggie Jackson	150.00	75.00	45.00
62	Tony Oliva	15.00	7.50	4.50
63	Bobby Ray Murcer	15.00	7.50	4.50
64	Carlton Fisk	20.00	10.00	6.00
65	Stephen Rogers	10.00	5.00	3.00
66	Frank Robinson	40.00	20.00	12.00
67	Joe Ferguson	10.00	5.00	3.00
68	Bill Melton	10.00	5.00	3.00
69	Robert Watson	10.00	5.00	3.00
70	Larry Bowa	15.00	7.50	4.50
71	Johnny Bench	90.00	45.00	27.00
72	Willie Horton	10.00	5.00	3.00

1974 Topps Puzzles

One of many test issues by Topps in the mid-1970s, the 12-player jigsaw puzzle set was an innovation which never caught on with collectors. The 40-piece puzzles (4-3/4" by 7-1/2") feature color photos with a decorative lozenge at bottom naming the player, team and position. The puzzles came in individual wrappers.

		NR MT	EX	VG
Complete Set:		600.00	300.00	200.00
Common Player:		12.00	6.00	3.50
(1)	Hank Aaron	80.00	40.00	25.00
(2)	Dick Allen	12.00	6.00	3.50
(3)	Johnny Bench	75.00	38.00	23.00
(4)	Bobby Bonds	12.00	6.00	3.50
(5)	Bob Gibson	35.00	17.50	10.50
(6)	Reggie Jackson	60.00	30.00	18.00
(7)	Bobby Murcer	12.00	6.00	3.50
(8)	Jim Palmer	50.00	25.00	15.00
(9)	Nolan Ryan	80.00	40.00	24.00
(10)	Tom Seaver	80.00	40.00	24.00
(11)	Willie Stargell	30.00	15.00	9.00
(12)	Carl Yastrzemski	70.00	35.00	21.00

1974 Topps Stamps

Topps continued to market baseball stamps in 1974 through the release of 240 unnumbered stamps featuring color player portraits. The player's name, team and position are found in an oval at the bottom of the 1" by 1-1/2" stamps. The stamps, sold separately rather than issued as an insert, came in strips of six which were then pasted in an appropriate team album designed to hold 10 stamps.

		NR MT	EX	VG
Complete Sheet Set:		100.00	50.00	30.00
Common Sheet:		1.00	.50	.30
Complete Stamp Album Set:		75.00	37.00	22.00
Single Stamp Album:		2.50	1.25	.70

(1) Hank Aaron, Luis Aparicio, Bob Bailey, Johnny Bench, Ron Blomberg, Bob Boone, Lou Brock, Bud Harrelson, Randy Jones, Dave Rader, Nolan Ryan, Joe Torre — 6.00 3.00 1.75

(2) Buddy Bell, Steve Braun, Jerry Grote, Tommy Helms, Bill Lee, Mike Lum, Dave May, Brooks Robinson, Bill Russell, Del Unser, Wilbur Wood, Carl Yastrzemski — 10.00 5.00 3.00

(3) Jerry Bell, Jerry Bell, Jim Colborn, Toby Harrah, Ken Henderson, John Hiller, Randy Hundley, Don Kessinger, Jerry Koosman, Dave Lopes, Felix Millan, Thurman Munson, Ted Simmons — 3.50 1.75 1.00

(4) Jerry Bell, Bill Buckner, Jim Colborn, Ken Henderson, Don Kessinger, Felix Millan, George Mitterwald, Dave Roberts, Ted Simmons, Jim Slaton, Charlie Spikes, Paul Splittorff — 1.00 .50 .30

(5) Glenn Beckert, Jim Bibby, Bill Buckner, Jim Lonborg, George Mitterwald, Dave Parker, Dave Roberts, Jim Slaton, Reggie Smith, Charlie Spikes, Paul Splittorff, Bob Watson — 3.50 1.75 1.00

(6) Paul Blair, Bobby Bonds, Ed Brinkman, Norm Cash, Mike Epstein, Tommy Harper, Mike Marshall, Phil Niekro, Cookie Rojas, George Scott, Mel Stottlemyre, Jim Wynn — 3.50 1.75 1.00

		NR MT	EX	VG
(7)	Jack Billingham, Reggie Cleveland, Bobby Darwin, Dave Duncan, Tim Foli, Ed Goodson, Cleon Jones, Mickey Lolich, George Medich, John Milner, Rick Monday, Bobby Murcer	1.00	.50	.30
(8)	Steve Carlton, Orlando Cepeda, Joe Decker, Reggie Jackson, Dave Johnson, John Mayberry, Bill Melton, Roger Metzger, Dave Nelson, Jerry Reuss, Jim Spencer, Bobby Valentine	6.00	3.00	1.75
(9)	Dan Driessen, Pedro Garcia, Grant Jackson, Al Kaline, Clay Kirby, Carlos May, Willie Montanez, Rogelio Moret, Jim Palmer, Doug Rader, J. R. Richard, Frank Robinson	3.50	1.75	1.00
(10)	Pedro Garcia, Ralph Garr, Wayne Garrett, Ron Hunt, Al Kaline, Fred Kendall, Carlos May, Jim Palmer, Doug Rader, Frank Robinson, Rick Wise, Richie Zisk	3.50	1.75	1.00
(11)	Dusty Baker, Larry Bowa, Steve Busby, Chris Chambliss, Dock Ellis, Cesar Geronimo, Fran Healy, Deron Johnson, Jorge Orta, Joe Rudi, Mickey Stanley, Rennie Stennett	3.50	1.75	1.00
(12)	Bob Coluccio, Ray Corbin, John Ellis, Oscar Gamble, Dave Giusti, Bill Greif, Alex Johnson, Mike Jorgensen, Andy Messersmith, Elias Sosa, Willie Stargell	3.50	1.75	1.00
(13)	Ron Bryant, Nate Colbert, Jose Cruz, Dan Driessen, Billy Grabarkewitz, Don Gullett, Willie Horton, Grant Jackson, Clay Kirby, Willie Montanez, Rogelio Moret, J. R. Richard	1.00	.50	.30
(14)	Carlton Fisk, Bill Freehan, Bobby Grich, Vic Harris, George Hendrick, Ed Herrmann, Jim Holt, Ken Holtzman, Fergie Jenkins, Lou Piniella, Steve Rogers, Ken Singleton	3.50	1.75	1.00
(15)	Stan Bahnsen, Sal Bando, Mark Belanger, David Clyde, Willie Crawford, Burt Hooton, Jon Matlack, Tim McCarver, Joe Morgan, Gene Tenace, Dick Tidrow, Dave Winfield	5.00	2.50	1.50
(16)	Hank Aaron, Stan Bahnsen, Bob Bailey, Johnny Bench, Bob Boone, Joe Matlack, Tim McCarver, Joe Morgan, Dave Rader, Gene Tenace, Dick Tidrow, Joe Torre	5.00	2.50	1.50
(17)	John Boccabella, Frank Duffy, Darrell Evans, Sparky Lyle, Lee May, Don Money, Bill North, Ted Sizemore, Chris Speier, Wayne Twitchell, Billy Williams, Earl Williams	1.00	.50	.30
(18)	John Boccabella, Bobby Darwin, Frank Duffy, Dave Duncan, Tim Foli, Cleon Jones, Mickey Lolich, Sparky Lyle, Lee May, Rick Monday, Bill North, Billy Williams	1.00	.50	.30
(19)	Don Baylor, Vida Blue, Tom Bradley, Jose Cardenal, Ron Cey, Greg Luzinski, Johnny Oates, Tony Oliva, Al Oliver, Tony Perez, Darrell Porter, Roy White	3.50	1.75	1.00
(20)	Pedro Borbon, Rod Carew, Roric Harrison, Jim Hunter, Ed Kirkpatrick, Garry Maddox, Gene Michael, Rick Miller, Claude Osteen, Amos Otis, Rich Reuschel, Mike Tyson	5.00	2.50	1.50
(21)	Sandy Alomar, Bert Campaneris, Tommy Davis, Joe Ferguson, Tito Fuentes, Jerry Morales, Carl Morton, Gaylord Perry, Vada Pinson, Dave Roberts, Ellie Rodriguez	3.50	1.75	1.00
(22)	Dick Allen, Jeff Burroughs, Joe Coleman, Terry Forster, Bob Gibson, Harmon Killebrew, Tug McGraw, Bob Oliver, Steve Renko, Pete Rose, Luis Tiant, Otto Velez	13.00	6.50	4.00
(23)	Johnny Briggs, Willie Davis, Jim Fregosi, Rich Hebner, Pat Kelly, Dave Kingman, Willie McCovey, Graig Nettles, Freddie Patek, Marty Pattin, Manny Sanguillen, Richie Scheinblum	5.00	2.50	1.50
(24)	Bert Blyleven, Nelson Briles, Cesar Cedeno, Ron Fairly, Johnny Grubb, Dave McNally, Aurelio Rodriguez, Ron Santo, Tom Seaver, Bill Singer, Bill Sudakis, Don Sutton	6.00	3.00	1.75

**NOTE: A card number in parentheses ( )
indicates the set is unnumbered.**

1974 Topps Team Checklists

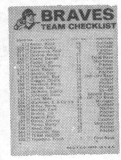

This set is a repeat of the 1973 mystery set in the form of 24 unnumbered 2-1/2" by 3-1/2" checklist cards. As with the 1973 set, the 1974s feature a team name on the front at the top with a white panel and a number of facsimile autographs below. Backs feature the team name and a checklist. The big difference between the 1973 and 1974 checklists is that the 1973s have blue borders while the 1974s have a red border. The 1974s were inserted into packages of the regular issue Topps cards.

		NR MT	EX	VG
Complete Set:		12.00	6.00	3.50
Common Checklist:		.50	.25	.15
(1)	Atlanta Braves	.50	.25	.15
(2)	Baltimore Orioles	.50	.25	.15
(3)	Boston Red Sox	.50	.25	.15
(4)	California Angels	.50	.25	.15
(5)	Chicago Cubs	.50	.25	.15
(6)	Chicago White Sox	.50	.25	.15
(7)	Cincinnati Reds	.50	.25	.15
(8)	Cleveland Indians	.50	.25	.15
(9)	Detroit Tigers	.50	.25	.15
(10)	Houston Astros	.50	.25	.15
(11)	Kansas City Royals	.50	.25	.15
(12)	Los Angeles Dodgers	.50	.25	.15
(13)	Milwaukee Brewers	.50	.25	.15
(14)	Minnesota Twins	.50	.25	.15
(15)	Montreal Expos	.50	.25	.15
(16)	New York Mets	.50	.25	.15
(17)	New York Yankees	.50	.25	.15
(18)	Oakland A's	.50	.25	.15
(19)	Philadelphia Phillies	.50	.25	.15
(20)	Pittsburgh Pirates	.50	.25	.15
(21)	St. Louis Cardinals	.50	.25	.15
(22)	San Diego Padres	.50	.25	.15
(23)	San Francisco Giants	.50	.25	.15
(24)	Texas Rangers	.50	.25	.15

1974 Topps Traded

Appearing late in the season, these 2-1/2" by 3-1/2" cards are basically the same as the regular issue Topps cards. The major change was that a big red panel with the word "Traded" was added below the player photo. Backs feature a "Baseball News" newspaper which contains the details of the trade. Card numbers correspond to the player's regular card number in 1974 except that the suffix "T" is added after the number. The set consists of 43 player cards and a checklist. In most cases, Topps did not obtain pictures of the players in their new uniforms. Instead the Topps artists simply provided the needed changes to existing photos.

		NR MT	EX	VG
Complete Set:		8.00	4.00	2.50
Common Player:		.12	.06	.04
23T	Craig Robinson	.12	.06	.04
42T	Claude Osteen	.15	.08	.05
43T	Jim Wynn	.20	.10	.06
51T	Bobby Heise	.12	.06	.04
59T	Ross Grimsley	.15	.08	.05
62T	Bob Locker	.12	.06	.04
63T	Bill Sudakis	.12	.06	.04
73T	Mike Marshall	.20	.10	.06
123T	Nelson Briles	.12	.06	.04
139T	Aurelio Monteagudo	.12	.06	.04
151T	Diego Segui	.12	.06	.04
165T	Willie Davis	.20	.10	.06
175T	Reggie Cleveland	.12	.06	.04
182T	Lindy McDaniel	.12	.06	.04
186T	Fred Scherman	.12	.06	.04
249T	George Mitterwald	.12	.06	.04
262T	Ed Kirkpatrick	.12	.06	.04
269T	Bob Johnson	.12	.06	.04
270T	Ron Santo	.30	.15	.09
313T	Barry Lersch	.12	.06	.04
319T	Randy Hundley	.12	.06	.04
330T	Juan Marichal	1.50	.70	.45
348T	Pete Richert	.12	.06	.04
373T	John Curtis	.12	.06	.04
390T	Lou Piniella	.50	.25	.15
428T	Gary Sutherland	.12	.06	.04
454T	Kurt Bevacqua	.12	.06	.04
458T	Jim Ray	.12	.06	.04
485T	Felipe Alou	.20	.10	.06
486T	Steve Stone	.20	.10	.06
496T	Tom Murphy	.12	.06	.04
516T	Horacio Pina	.12	.06	.04
534T	Eddie Watt	.12	.06	.04
538T	Cesar Tovar	.12	.06	.04
544T	Ron Schueler	.12	.06	.04
579T	Cecil Upshaw	.12	.06	.04
585T	Merv Rettenmund	.15	.08	.05
612T	Luke Walker	.12	.06	.04
616T	Larry Gura	.15	.08	.05
618T	Jim Mason	.12	.06	.04
630T	Tommie Agee	.15	.08	.05
648T	Terry Crowley	.12	.06	.04
649T	Fernando Gonzalez	.12	.06	.04
-----	Traded Checklist	.70	.35	.20

1975 Topps

This year Topps produced another 660-card set, one which collectors either seem to like or despise. The 2-1/2" by 3-1/2" cards have a color photo which is framed by a round-cornered white frame. Around that is an eye-catching two-color border in bright colors. The team name appears at the top in bright

letters while the player name is at the bottom and his position a baseball at the lower right. A facsimile autograph runs across the picture. The card backs are vertical feature normal statistical and biographical information along with a trivia quiz. Specialty cards include a new 24-card series on MVP winners going back to 1951. Other specialty cards include statistical leaders and post-season highlights. The real highlight of the set, however, are the rookie cards which include their numbers such names as George Brett, Gary Carter, Robin Yount, Jim Rice, Keith Hernandez and Fred Lynn. While the set was released at one time, card numbers 1-132 were printed in somewhat shorter supply than the remainder of the issue.

		NR MT	EX	VG
Complete Set:		900.00	450.00	275.00
Common Player: 1-132		.35	.20	.11
Common Player: 133-660		.30	.15	.09
Complete Mini Set:		1000.00	500.00	300.00
Common Mini Player:		.40	.20	.12
1	'74 Highlights (Hank Aaron)	30.00	15.00	9.00
2	'74 Highlights (Lou Brock)	2.00	1.00	.60
3	'74 Highlights (Bob Gibson)	1.75	.90	.50
4	'74 Highlights (Al Kaline)	1.75	.90	.50
5	'74 Highlights (Nolan Ryan)	12.00	6.00	3.50
6	'74 Highlights (Mike Marshall)	.40	.20	.12
7	'74 Highlights (Dick Bosman, Steve Busby, Nolan Ryan)	1.00	.50	.30
8	Rogelio Moret	.35	.20	.11
9	Frank Tepedino	.35	.20	.11
10	Willie Davis	.35	.20	.11
11	Bill Melton	.35	.20	.11
12	David Clyde	.35	.20	.11
13	Gene Locklear	.35	.20	.11
14	Milt Wilcox	.35	.20	.11
15	Jose Cardenal	.35	.20	.11
16	Frank Tanana	.40	.20	.12
17	Dave Concepcion	.60	.30	.20
18	Tigers Team (Ralph Houk)	.90	.45	.25
19	Jerry Koosman	.40	.20	.12
20	Thurman Munson	7.00	3.50	2.00
21	Rollie Fingers	5.00	2.50	1.50
22	Dave Cash	.35	.20	.11
23	Bill Russell	.35	.20	.11
24	Al Fitzmorris	.35	.20	.11
25	Lee May	.40	.20	.12
26	Dave McNally	.35	.20	.11
27	Ken Reitz	.35	.20	.11
28	Tom Murphy	.35	.20	.11
29	Dave Parker	9.00	4.50	2.75
30	Bert Blyleven	1.00	.50	.30
31	Dave Rader	.35	.20	.11
32	Reggie Cleveland	.35	.20	.11
33	Dusty Baker	.40	.20	.12
34	Steve Renko	.35	.20	.11
35	Ron Santo	.50	.25	.15
36	Joe Lovitto	.35	.20	.11
37	Dave Freisleben	.35	.20	.11
38	Buddy Bell	.80	.40	.25
39	Andy Thornton	.70	.35	.20
40	Bill Singer	.35	.20	.11
41	Cesar Geronimo	.35	.20	.11
42	Joe Coleman	.35	.20	.11
43	Cleon Jones	.35	.20	.11
44	Pat Dobson	.35	.20	.11
45	Joe Rudi	.40	.20	.12
46	Phillies Team (Danny Ozark)	.80	.40	.25
47	Tommy John	1.25	.60	.40
48	Freddie Patek	.35	.20	.11
49	Larry Dierker	.35	.20	.11
50	Brooks Robinson	5.00	2.50	1.50
51	*Bob Forsch*	.80	.40	.25
52	Darrell Porter	.35	.20	.11
53	Dave Giusti	.35	.20	.11
54	Eric Soderholm	.35	.20	.11
55	Bobby Bonds	.50	.25	.15
56	Rick Wise	.35	.20	.11
57	Dave Johnson	.80	.40	.25
58	Chuck Taylor	.35	.20	.11
59	Ken Henderson	.35	.20	.11
60	Fergie Jenkins	4.00	2.00	1.25
61	Dave Winfield	50.00	25.00	15.00
62	Fritz Peterson	.35	.20	.11
63	Steve Swisher	.35	.20	.11
64	Dave Chalk	.35	.20	.11
65	Don Gullett	.35	.20	.11

		NR MT	EX	VG
66	Willie Horton	.35	.20	.11
67	Tug McGraw	.50	.25	.15
68	Ron Blomberg	.35	.20	.11
69	John Odom	.35	.20	.11
70	Mike Schmidt	70.00	35.00	21.00
71	Charlie Hough	.35	.20	.11
72	Royals Team (Jack McKeon)	.80	.40	.25
73	J.R. Richard	.35	.20	.11
74	Mark Belanger	.35	.20	.11
75	Ted Simmons	.70	.35	.20
76	Ed Sprague	.35	.20	.11
77	Richie Zisk	.35	.20	.11
78	Ray Corbin	.40	.20	.12
79	Gary Matthews	.40	.20	.12
80	Carlton Fisk	20.00	10.00	6.00
81	Ron Reed	.35	.20	.11
82	Pat Kelly	.35	.20	.11
83	Jim Merritt	.35	.20	.11
84	Enzo Hernandez	.35	.20	.11
85	Bill Bonham	.35	.20	.11
86	Joe Lis	.35	.20	.11
87	George Foster	1.25	.60	.40
88	Tom Egan	.35	.20	.11
89	Jim Ray	.35	.20	.11
90	Rusty Staub	.60	.30	.20
91	Dick Green	.35	.20	.11
92	Cecil Upshaw	.35	.20	.11
93	Dave Lopes	.40	.20	.12
94	Jim Lonborg	.35	.20	.11
95	John Mayberry	.35	.20	.11
96	Mike Cosgrove	.35	.20	.11
97	Earl Williams	.35	.20	.11
98	Rich Folkers	.35	.20	.11
99	Mike Hegan	.35	.20	.11
100	Willie Stargell	2.50	1.25	.70
101	Expos Team (Gene Mauch)	.80	.40	.25
102	Joe Decker	.35	.20	.11
103	Rick Miller	.35	.20	.11
104	Bill Madlock	1.25	.60	.40
105	Buzz Capra	.35	.20	.11
106	*Mike Hargrove*	.40	.20	.12
107	Jim Barr	.35	.20	.11
108	Tom Hall	.35	.20	.11
109	George Hendrick	.35	.20	.11
110	Wilbur Wood	.35	.20	.11
111	Wayne Garrett	.35	.20	.11
112	Larry Hardy	.35	.20	.11
113	Elliott Maddox	.35	.20	.11
114	Dick Lange	.35	.20	.11
115	Joe Ferguson	.35	.20	.11
116	Lerrin LaGrow	.35	.20	.11
117	Orioles Team (Earl Weaver)	.90	.45	.25
118	Mike Anderson	.35	.20	.11
119	Tommy Helms	.35	.20	.11
120	Steve Busby (photo actually Fran Healy)	.35	.20	.11
121	Bill North	.35	.20	.11
122	Al Hrabosky	.35	.20	.11
123	Johnny Briggs	.40	.20	.12
124	Jerry Reuss	.40	.20	.12
125	Ken Singleton	1.50	.70	.45
126	Checklist 1-132	.35	.20	.11
127	Glen Borgmann	.35	.20	.11
128	Bill Lee	.35	.20	.11
129	Rick Monday	2.00	1.00	.60
130	Phil Niekro	.35	.20	.11
131	Toby Harrah	.35	.20	.11
132	Randy Moffitt	.35	.20	.11
133	Dan Driessen	.30	.15	.09
134	Ron Hodges	.30	.15	.09
135	Charlie Spikes	.30	.15	.09
136	Jim Mason	.35	.20	.11
137	Terry Forster	.30	.15	.09
138	Del Unser	.30	.15	.09
139	Horacio Pina	7.00	3.50	2.00
140	Steve Garvey	.30	.15	.09
141	Mickey Stanley	.30	.15	.09
142	Bob Reynolds	.40	.20	.12
143	*Cliff Johnson*	.30	.15	.09
144	Jim Wohlford	.35	.20	.11
145	Ken Holtzman	.80	.40	.25
146	Padres Team (John McNamara)	.30	.15	.09
147	Pedro Garcia	.30	.15	.09
148	Jim Rooker	.30	.15	.09
149	Tim Foli	4.00	2.00	1.25
150	Bob Gibson	.30	.15	.09
151	Steve Brye	.30	.15	.09
152	Mario Guerrero	.40	.20	.12
153	Rick Reuschel	.30	.15	.09
154	Mike Lum	.30	.15	.09
155	Jim Bibby			
156	Dave Kingman	.90	.45	.25
157	Pedro Borbon	.30	.15	.09
158	Jerry Grote	.30	.15	.09
159	Steve Arlin	.30	.15	.09
160	Graig Nettles	1.50	.70	.45
161	Stan Bahnsen	.30	.15	.09
162	Willie Montanez	.30	.15	.09
163	Jim Brewer	.30	.15	.09
164	Mickey Rivers	.30	.15	.09
165	Doug Rader	.30	.15	.09
166	Woodie Fryman	.30	.15	.09
167	Rich Coggins	.30	.15	.09
168	Bill Greif	.30	.15	.09
169	Cookie Rojas	.30	.15	.09
170	Bert Campaneris	.40	.20	.12
171	Ed Kirkpatrick	.30	.15	.09
172	Red Sox Team (Darrell Johnson)	1.25	.60	.40
173	Steve Rogers	.35	.20	.11
174	Bake McBride	.30	.15	.09
175	Don Money	.30	.15	.09
176	Burt Hooton	.35	.20	.11
177	Vic Correll	.30	.15	.09
178	Cesar Tovar	.30	.15	.09
179	Tom Bradley	.30	.15	.09
180	Joe Morgan	6.00	3.00	1.75
181	Fred Beene	.30	.15	.09
182	Don Hahn	.30	.15	.09
183	Mel Stottlemyre	.40	.20	.12
184	Jorge Orta	.30	.15	.09
185	Steve Carlton	10.00	5.00	3.00
186	Willie Crawford	.30	.15	.09
187	Denny Doyle	.30	.15	.09
188	Tom Griffin	.30	.15	.09
189	1951 - MVPs (Larry (Yogi) Berra, Roy Campanella)	1.50	.70	.45
190	1952 - MVPs (Hank Sauer, Bobby Shantz)	.40	.20	.12
191	1953 - MVPs (Roy Campanella, Al Rosen)	.90	.45	.25
192	1954 - MVPs (Yogi Berra, Willie Mays)	1.50	.70	.45
193	1955 - MVPs (Yogi Berra, Roy Campanella)	1.50	.70	.45
194	1956 - MVPs (Mickey Mantle, Don Newcombe)	12.00	6.00	3.50
195	1957 - MVPs (Hank Aaron, Mickey Mantle)	12.00	6.00	3.50
196	1958 - MVPs (Ernie Banks, Jackie Jensen)	.90	.45	.25
197	1959 - MVPs (Ernie Banks, Nellie Fox)	.90	.45	.25
198	1960 - MVPs (Dick Groat, Roger Maris)	1.25	.60	.40
199	1961 - MVPs (Roger Maris, Frank Robinson)	1.50	.70	.45
200	1962 - MVPs (Mickey Mantle, Maury Wills)	12.00	6.00	3.50
201	1963 - MVPs (Elston Howard, Sandy Koufax)	1.50	.70	.45
202	1964 - MVPs (Ken Boyer, Brooks Robinson)	1.25	.60	.40
203	1965 - MVPs (Willie Mays, Zoilo Versalles)	1.25	.60	.40
204	1966 - MVPs (Bob Clemente, Frank Robinson)	1.50	.70	.45
205	1967 - MVPs (Orlando Cepeda, Carl Yastrzemski)	1.25	.60	.40
206	1968 - MVPs (Bob Gibson, Denny McLain)	1.25	.60	.40
207	1969 - MVPs (Harmon Killebrew, Willie McCovey)	1.50	.70	.45
208	1970 - MVPs (Johnny Bench, Boog Powell)	1.25	.60	.40
209	1971 - MVPs (Vida Blue, Joe Torre)	.50	.25	.15
210	1972 - MVPs (Rich Allen, Johnny Bench)	1.25	.60	.40
211	1973 - MVPs (Reggie Jackson, Pete Rose)	4.00	2.00	1.25
212	1974 - MVPs (Jeff Burroughs, Steve Garvey)	.90	.45	.25
213	Oscar Gamble	.30	.15	.09
214	Harry Parker	.30	.15	.09
215	Bobby Valentine	.35	.20	.11
216	Giants Team (Wes Westrum)	.80	.40	.25
217	Lou Piniella	.70	.35	.20
218	Jerry Johnson	.30	.15	.09
219	Ed Herrmann	.30	.15	.09
220	Don Sutton	2.00	1.00	.60
221	Aurelio Rodriguez (Rodriquez)	.30	.15	.09
222	Dan Spillner	.30	.15	.09
223	*Robin Yount*	250.00	125.00	75.00

#	Player	NR MT	EX	VG
224	Ramon Hernandez	.30	.15	.09
225	Bob Grich	.40	.20	.12
226	Bill Campbell	.30	.15	.09
227	Bob Watson	.30	.15	.09
228	*George Brett*	250.00	125.00	75.00
229	Barry Foote	.30	.15	.09
230	Jim Hunter	2.00	1.00	.60
231	Mike Tyson	.30	.15	.09
232	Diego Segui	.30	.15	.09
233	Billy Grabarkewitz	.30	.15	.09
234	Tom Grieve	.30	.15	.09
235	Jack Billingham	.30	.15	.09
236	Angels Team (Dick Williams)	.80	.40	.25
237	Carl Morton	.30	.15	.09
238	Dave Duncan	.30	.15	.09
239	George Stone	.30	.15	.09
240	Garry Maddox	.30	.15	.09
241	Dick Tidrow	.30	.15	.09
242	Jay Johnstone	.30	.15	.09
243	Jim Kaat	1.25	.60	.40
244	Bill Buckner	.50	.25	.15
245	Mickey Lolich	.50	.25	.15
246	Cardinals Team (Red Schoendienst)	.80	.40	.25
247	Enos Cabell	.30	.15	.09
248	Randy Jones	.30	.15	.09
249	Danny Thompson	.30	.15	.09
250	Ken Brett	.30	.15	.09
251	Fran Healy	.30	.15	.09
252	Fred Scherman	.30	.15	.09
253	Jesus Alou	.30	.15	.09
254	Mike Torrez	.30	.15	.09
255	Dwight Evans	6.00	3.00	1.75
256	Billy Champion	.30	.15	.09
257	Checklist 133-264	1.50	.70	.45
258	Dave LaRoche	.30	.15	.09
259	Len Randle	.30	.15	.09
260	Johnny Bench	12.00	6.00	3.50
261	Andy Hassler	.30	.15	.09
262	Rowland Office	.30	.15	.09
263	Jim Perry	.40	.20	.12
264	John Milner	.30	.15	.09
265	Ron Bryant	.30	.15	.09
266	Sandy Alomar	.30	.15	.09
267	Dick Ruthven	.30	.15	.09
268	Hal McRae	.40	.20	.12
269	Doug Rau	.30	.15	.09
270	Ron Fairly	.35	.20	.11
271	Jerry Moses	.30	.15	.09
272	Lynn McGlothen	.30	.15	.09
273	Steve Braun	.30	.15	.09
274	Vicente Romo	.30	.15	.09
275	Paul Blair	.30	.15	.09
276	White Sox Team (Chuck Tanner)	.80	.40	.25
277	Frank Taveras	.30	.15	.09
278	Paul Lindblad	.30	.15	.09
279	Milt May	.30	.15	.09
280	Carl Yastrzemski	12.00	6.00	3.50
281	Jim Slaton	.30	.15	.09
282	Jerry Morales	.30	.15	.09
283	Steve Foucault	.30	.15	.09
284	Ken Griffey	.70	.35	.20
285	Ellie Rodriguez	.30	.15	.09
286	Mike Jorgensen	.30	.15	.09
287	Roric Harrison	.30	.15	.09
288	Bruce Ellingsen	.30	.15	.09
289	Ken Rudolph	.30	.15	.09
290	Jon Matlack	.30	.15	.09
291	Bill Sudakis	.30	.15	.09
292	Ron Schueler	.30	.15	.09
293	Dick Sharon	.30	.15	.09
294	*Geoff Zahn*	.40	.20	.12
295	Vada Pinson	.60	.30	.20
296	Alan Foster	.30	.15	.09
297	Craig Kusick	.30	.15	.09
298	Johnny Grubb	.30	.15	.09
299	Bucky Dent	.40	.20	.12
300	Reggie Jackson	22.00	11.00	6.60
301	Dave Roberts	.30	.15	.09
302	*Rick Burleson*	.50	.25	.15
303	Grant Jackson	.30	.15	.09
304	Pirates Team (Danny Murtaugh)	.80	.40	.25
305	Jim Colborn	.30	.15	.09
306	Batting Leaders (Rod Carew, Ralph Garr)	.80	.40	.25
307	Home Run Leaders (Dick Allen, Mike Schmidt)	.90	.45	.25
308	Runs Batted In Leaders (Johnny Bench, Jeff Burroughs)	.90	.45	.25
309	Stolen Base Leaders (Lou Brock, Bill North)	.80	.40	.25
310	Victory Leaders (Jim Hunter, Fergie Jenkins, Andy Messersmith, Phil Niekro)	.80	.40	.25
311	Earned Run Average Leaders (Buzz Capra, Jim Hunter)	.50	.25	.15
312	Strikeout Leaders (Steve Carlton, Nolan Ryan)	4.00	2.00	1.25
313	Leading Firemen (Terry Forster, Mike Marshall)	.50	.25	.15
314	Buck Martinez	.30	.15	.09
315	Don Kessinger	.30	.15	.09
316	Jackie Brown	.30	.15	.09
317	Joe Lahoud	.30	.15	.09
318	Ernie McAnally	.30	.15	.09
319	Johnny Oates	.30	.15	.09
320	Pete Rose	18.00	9.00	5.50
321	Rudy May	.30	.15	.09
322	Ed Goodson	.30	.15	.09
323	Fred Holdsworth	.30	.15	.09
324	Ed Kranepool	.35	.20	.11
325	Tony Oliva	.80	.40	.25
326	Wayne Twitchell	.30	.15	.09
327	Jerry Hairston	.30	.15	.09
328	Sonny Siebert	.30	.15	.09
329	Ted Kubiak	.30	.15	.09
330	Mike Marshall	.35	.20	.11
331	Indians Team (Frank Robinson)	.90	.45	.25
332	Fred Kendall	.30	.15	.09
333	Dick Drago	.30	.15	.09
334	*Greg Gross*	.35	.20	.11
335	Jim Palmer	10.00	5.00	3.00
336	Rennie Stennett	.30	.15	.09
337	Kevin Kobel	.30	.15	.09
338	Rick Stelmaszek	.30	.15	.09
339	Jim Fregosi	.40	.20	.12
340	Paul Splittorff	.30	.15	.09
341	Hal Breeden	.30	.15	.09
342	Leroy Stanton	.30	.15	.09
343	Danny Frisella	.30	.15	.09
344	Ben Oglivie	.35	.20	.11
345	Clay Carroll	.30	.15	.09
346	Bobby Darwin	.30	.15	.09
347	Mike Caldwell	.30	.15	.09
348	Tony Muser	.30	.15	.09
349	Ray Sadecki	.30	.15	.09
350	Bobby Murcer	.40	.20	.12
351	Bob Boone	.40	.20	.12
352	Darold Knowles	.30	.15	.09
353	Luis Melendez	.30	.15	.09
354	Dick Bosman	.30	.15	.09
355	Chris Cannizzaro	.30	.15	.09
356	Rico Petrocelli	.35	.20	.11
357	Ken Forsch	.30	.15	.09
358	Al Bumbry	.30	.15	.09
359	Paul Popovich	.30	.15	.09
360	George Scott	.35	.20	.11
361	Dodgers Team (Walter Alston)	1.00	.50	.30
362	Steve Hargan	.30	.15	.09
363	Carmen Fanzone	.30	.15	.09
364	Doug Bird	.30	.15	.09
365	Bob Bailey	.30	.15	.09
366	Ken Sanders	.30	.15	.09
367	Craig Robinson	.30	.15	.09
368	Vic Albury	.30	.15	.09
369	Merv Rettenmund	.30	.15	.09
370	Tom Seaver	20.00	10.00	6.00
371	Gates Brown	.30	.15	.09
372	John D'Acquisto	.30	.15	.09
373	Bill Sharp	.30	.15	.09
374	Eddie Watt	.30	.15	.09
375	Roy White	.40	.20	.12
376	Steve Yeager	.30	.15	.09
377	Tom Hilgendorf	.30	.15	.09
378	Derrel Thomas	.30	.15	.09
379	Bernie Carbo	.30	.15	.09
380	Sal Bando	.40	.20	.12
381	John Curtis	.30	.15	.09
382	Don Baylor	.60	.30	.20
383	Jim York	.30	.15	.09
384	Brewers Team (Del Crandall)	.80	.40	.25
385	Dock Ellis	.30	.15	.09
386	Checklist 265-396	1.50	.70	.45
387	Jim Spencer	.30	.15	.09
388	Steve Stone	.35	.20	.11
389	Tony Solaita	.30	.15	.09
390	Ron Cey	.40	.20	.12
391	Don DeMola	.30	.15	.09
392	Bruce Bochte	.40	.20	.12
393	Gary Gentry	.30	.15	.09
394	Larvell Blanks	.30	.15	.09
395	Bud Harrelson	.30	.15	.09

#	Player	NR MT	EX	VG
396	Fred Norman	.30	.15	.09
397	Bill Freehan	.40	.20	.12
398	Elias Sosa	.30	.15	.09
399	Terry Harmon	.30	.15	.09
400	Dick Allen	.80	.40	.25
401	Mike Wallace	.30	.15	.09
402	Bob Tolan	.30	.15	.09
403	Tom Buskey	.30	.15	.09
404	Ted Sizemore	.30	.15	.09
405	John Montague	.30	.15	.09
406	Bob Gallagher	.30	.15	.09
407	Herb Washington	.35	.20	.11
408	Clyde Wright	.30	.15	.09
409	Bob Robertson	.30	.15	.09
410	Mike Cueller (Cuellar)	.40	.20	.12
411	George Mitterwald	.30	.15	.09
412	Bill Hands	.30	.15	.09
413	Marty Pattin	.30	.15	.09
414	Manny Mota	.35	.20	.11
415	John Hiller	.30	.15	.09
416	Larry Lintz	.30	.15	.09
417	Skip Lockwood	.30	.15	.09
418	Leo Foster	.30	.15	.09
419	Dave Goltz	.30	.15	.09
420	Larry Bowa	.40	.20	.12
421	Mets Team (Yogi Berra)	1.00	.50	.30
422	Brian Downing	.35	.20	.11
423	Clay Kirby	.30	.15	.09
424	John Lowenstein	.30	.15	.09
425	Tito Fuentes	.30	.15	.09
426	George Medich	.30	.15	.09
427	Clarence Gaston	.30	.15	.09
428	Dave Hamilton	.30	.15	.09
429	Jim Dwyer	.35	.20	.11
430	Luis Tiant	.50	.25	.15
431	Rod Gilbreath	.30	.15	.09
432	Ken Berry	.30	.15	.09
433	Larry Demery	.30	.15	.09
434	Bob Locker	.30	.15	.09
435	Dave Nelson	.30	.15	.09
436	Ken Frailing	.30	.15	.09
437	Al Cowens	.40	.20	.12
438	Don Carrithers	.30	.15	.09
439	Ed Brinkman	.30	.15	.09
440	Andy Messersmith	.35	.20	.11
441	Bobby Heise	.30	.15	.09
442	Maximino Leon	.30	.15	.09
443	Twins Team (Frank Quilici)	.80	.40	.25
444	Gene Garber	.30	.15	.09
445	Felix Millan	.30	.15	.09
446	Bart Johnson	.30	.15	.09
447	Terry Crowley	.30	.15	.09
448	Frank Duffy	.30	.15	.09
449	Charlie Williams	.30	.15	.09
450	Willie McCovey	3.00	1.50	.90
451	Rick Dempsey	.40	.20	.12
452	Angel Mangual	.30	.15	.09
453	Claude Osteen	.35	.20	.11
454	Doug Griffin	.30	.15	.09
455	Don Wilson	.30	.15	.09
456	Bob Coluccio	.30	.15	.09
457	Mario Mendoza	.30	.15	.09
458	Ross Grimsley	.30	.15	.09
459	A.L. Championships	.80	.40	.25
460	N.L. Championships	.80	.40	.25
461	World Series Game 1	2.00	1.00	.60
462	World Series Game 2	.80	.40	.25
463	World Series Game 3	1.00	.50	.30
464	World Series Game 4	.80	.40	.25
465	World Series Game 5	.80	.40	.25
466	World Series Summary	.80	.40	.25
467	Ed Halicki	.30	.15	.09
468	Bobby Mitchell	.30	.15	.09
469	Tom Dettore	.30	.15	.09
470	Jeff Burroughs	.35	.20	.11
471	Bob Stinson	.30	.15	.09
472	Bruce Dal Canton	.30	.15	.09
473	Ken McMullen	.30	.15	.09
474	Luke Walker	.30	.15	.09
475	Darrell Evans	.60	.30	.20
476	Ed Figueroa	.35	.20	.11
477	Tom Hutton	.30	.15	.09
478	Tom Burgmeier	.30	.15	.09
479	Ken Boswell	.30	.15	.09
480	Carlos May	.30	.15	.09
481	Will McEnaney	.35	.20	.11
482	Tom McCraw	.30	.15	.09
483	Steve Ontiveros	.30	.15	.09
484	Glenn Beckert	.35	.20	.11
485	Sparky Lyle	.40	.20	.12
486	Ray Fosse	.30	.15	.09
487	Astros Team (Preston Gomez)	.80	.40	.25
488	Bill Travers	.30	.15	.09
489	Cecil Cooper	1.00	.50	.30
490	Reggie Smith	.35	.20	.11
491	Doyle Alexander	.40	.20	.12
492	Rich Hebner	.30	.15	.09
493	Don Stanhouse	.30	.15	.09
494	Pete LaCock	.30	.15	.09
495	Nelson Briles	.30	.15	.09
496	Pepe Frias	.30	.15	.09
497	Jim Nettles	.30	.15	.09
498	Al Downing	.30	.15	.09
499	Marty Perez	.30	.15	.09
500	Nolan Ryan	65.00	33.00	20.00
501	Bill Robinson	.30	.15	.09
502	Pat Bourque	.30	.15	.09
503	Fred Stanley	.30	.15	.09
504	Buddy Bradford	.30	.15	.09
505	Chris Speier	.30	.15	.09
506	Leron Lee	.30	.15	.09
507	Tom Carroll	.30	.15	.09
508	Bob Hansen	.30	.15	.09
509	Dave Hilton	.30	.15	.09
510	Vida Blue	.50	.25	.15
511	Rangers Team (Billy Martin)	.90	.45	.25
512	Larry Milbourne	.30	.15	.09
513	Dick Pole	.30	.15	.09
514	Jose Cruz	.50	.25	.15
515	Manny Sanguillen	.30	.15	.09
516	Don Hood	.30	.15	.09
517	Checklist 397-528	1.25	.60	.40
518	Leo Cardenas	.30	.15	.09
519	Jim Todd	.30	.15	.09
520	Amos Otis	.35	.20	.11
521	Dennis Blair	.30	.15	.09
522	Gary Sutherland	.30	.15	.09
523	Tom Paciorek	.30	.15	.09
524	John Doherty	.30	.15	.09
525	Tom House	.30	.15	.09
526	Larry Hisle	.30	.15	.09
527	Mac Scarce	.30	.15	.09
528	Eddie Leon	.30	.15	.09
529	Gary Thomasson	.30	.15	.09
530	Gaylord Perry	3.00	1.50	.90
531	Reds Team (Sparky Anderson)	.90	.45	.25
532	Gorman Thomas	.60	.30	.20
533	Rudy Meoli	.30	.15	.09
534	Alex Johnson	.30	.15	.09
535	Gene Tenace	.30	.15	.09
536	Bob Moose	.30	.15	.09
537	Tommy Harper	.30	.15	.09
538	Duffy Dyer	.30	.15	.09
539	Jesse Jefferson	.30	.15	.09
540	Lou Brock	4.00	2.00	1.25
541	Roger Metzger	.30	.15	.09
542	Pete Broberg	.30	.15	.09
543	Larry Biittner	.30	.15	.09
544	Steve Mingori	.30	.15	.09
545	Billy Williams	3.00	1.50	.90
546	John Knox	.30	.15	.09
547	Von Joshua	.30	.15	.09
548	Charlie Sands	.30	.15	.09
549	Bill Butler	.30	.15	.09
550	Ralph Garr	.30	.15	.09
551	Larry Christenson	.30	.15	.09
552	Jack Brohamer	.30	.15	.09
553	John Boccabella	.30	.15	.09
554	Rich Gossage	1.50	.70	.45
555	Al Oliver	.80	.40	.25
556	Tim Johnson	.30	.15	.09
557	Larry Gura	.30	.15	.09
558	Dave Roberts	.30	.15	.09
559	Bob Montgomery	.30	.15	.09
560	Tony Perez	3.00	1.50	.90
561	A's Team (Alvin Dark)	.90	.45	.25
562	Gary Nolan	.30	.15	.09
563	Wilbur Howard	.30	.15	.09
564	Tommy Davis	.40	.20	.12
565	Joe Torre	.70	.35	.20
566	Ray Burris	.30	.15	.09
567	Jim Sundberg	.70	.35	.20
568	Dale Murray	.30	.15	.09
569	Frank White	.40	.20	.12
570	Jim Wynn	.35	.20	.11
571	Dave Lemanczyk	.30	.15	.09
572	Roger Nelson	.30	.15	.09
573	Orlando Pena	.30	.15	.09
574	Tony Taylor	.30	.15	.09
575	Gene Clines	.30	.15	.09
576	Phil Roof	.30	.15	.09
577	John Morris	.30	.15	.09

		NR MT	EX	VG
578	Dave Tomlin	.30	.15	.09
579	Skip Pitlock	.30	.15	.09
580	Frank Robinson	4.00	2.00	1.25
581	Darrel Chaney	.30	.15	.09
582	Eduardo Rodriguez	.30	.15	.09
583	Andy Etchebarren	.30	.15	.09
584	Mike Garman	.30	.15	.09
585	Chris Chambliss	.40	.20	.12
586	Tim McCarver	.60	.30	.20
587	Chris Ward	.30	.15	.09
588	Rick Auerbach	.30	.15	.09
589	Braves Team (Clyde King)	.80	.40	.25
590	Cesar Cedeno	.40	.20	.12
591	Glenn Abbott	.30	.15	.09
592	Balor Moore	.30	.15	.09
593	Gene Lamont	.30	.15	.09
594	Jim Fuller	.30	.15	.09
595	Joe Niekro	.40	.20	.12
596	Ollie Brown	.30	.15	.09
597	Winston Llenas	.30	.15	.09
598	Bruce Kison	.30	.15	.09
599	Nate Colbert	.30	.15	.09
600	Rod Carew	12.00	6.00	3.50
601	Juan Beniquez	.35	.20	.11
602	John Vukovich	.30	.15	.09
603	Lew Krausse	.30	.15	.09
604	Oscar Zamora	.30	.15	.09
605	John Ellis	.30	.15	.09
606	Bruce Miller	.30	.15	.09
607	Jim Holt	.30	.15	.09
608	Gene Michael	.35	.20	.11
609	Ellie Hendricks	.30	.15	.09
610	Ron Hunt	.30	.15	.09
611	Yankees Team (Bill Virdon)	1.25	.60	.40
612	Terry Hughes	.30	.15	.09
613	Bill Parsons	.30	.15	.09
614	Rookie Pitchers (Jack Kucek, Dyar Miller, Vern Ruhle, Paul Siebert)	.30	.15	.09
615	Rookie Pitchers (Pat Darcy, *Dennis Leonard, Tom Underwood*, Hank Webb)	.60	.30	.20
616	Rookie Outfielders (Dave Augustine, Pepe Mangual, *Jim Rice*, John Scott)	25.00	12.50	7.50
617	Rookie Infielders (Mike Cubbage, *Doug DeCinces*, Reggie Sanders, Manny Trillo)	1.25	.60	.40
618	Rookie Pitchers (*Jamie Easterly*, Tom Johnson, *Scott McGregor, Rick Rhoden*)	2.25	1.25	.70
619	Rookie Outfielders (Benny Ayala, Nyls Nyman, Tommy Smith, Jerry Turner)	.30	.15	.09
620	Rookie Catchers-Outfielders (*Gary Carter*, Marc Hill, Danny Meyer, Leon Roberts)	50.00	25.00	15.00
621	Rookie Pitchers (*John Denny, Rawly Eastwick, Jim Kern*, Juan Veintidos)	.60	.30	.20
622	Rookie Outfielders (Ed Armbrister, *Fred Lynn*, Tom Poquette, Terry Whitfield)	10.00	5.00	3.00
623	Rookie Infielders (*Phil Garner, Keith Hernandez*, Bob Sheldon, Tom Veryzer)	20.00	10.00	6.00
624	Rookie Pitchers (Doug Konieczny, *Gary Lavelle*, Jim Otten, Eddie Solomon)	.35	.20	.11
625	Boog Powell	.70	.35	.20
626	Larry Haney	.30	.15	.09
627	Tom Walker	.30	.15	.09
628	*Ron LeFlore*	.80	.40	.25
629	Joe Hoerner	.30	.15	.09
630	Greg Luzinski	.70	.35	.20
631	Lee Lacy	.30	.15	.09
632	Morris Nettles	.30	.15	.09
633	Paul Casanova	.30	.15	.09
634	Cy Acosta	.30	.15	.09
635	Chuck Dobson	.30	.15	.09
636	Charlie Moore	.30	.15	.09
637	Ted Martinez	.30	.15	.09
638	Cubs Team (Jim Marshall)	.80	.40	.25
639	Steve Kline	.30	.15	.09
640	Harmon Killebrew	5.00	2.50	1.50
641	Jim Northrup	.30	.15	.09
642	Mike Phillips	.30	.15	.09
643	Brent Strom	.30	.15	.09
644	Bill Fahey	.30	.15	.09
645	Danny Cater	.30	.15	.09
646	Checklist 529-660	1.50	.70	.45
647	*Claudell Washington*	2.50	1.25	.70
648	Dave Pagan	.30	.15	.09
649	Jack Heidemann	.30	.15	.09
650	Dave May	.30	.15	.09
651	John Morlan	.30	.15	.09

		NR MT	EX	VG
652	Lindy McDaniel	.30	.15	.09
653	Lee Richards	.30	.15	.09
654	Jerry Terrell	.30	.15	.09
655	Rico Carty	.40	.20	.12
656	Bill Plummer	.30	.15	.09
657	Bob Oliver	.30	.15	.09
658	Vic Harris	.30	.15	.09
659	Bob Apodaca	.30	.15	.09
660	Hank Aaron	25.00	12.50	7.50

1976 Topps

These 2-1/2" by 3-1/2" cards begin a design trend for Topps. The focus was more on the photo quality than in past years with a corresponding trend toward simplicity in the borders. The front of the cards has the player's name and team in two strips while his position is in the lower left corner under a drawing of a player representing that position. The backs have a bat and ball with the card number on the left; statistics and personal information and career highlights on the right. The 660-card set features a number of specialty sets including record-setting performances, statistical leaders, playoff and World Series highlights, the Sporting News All-Time All-Stars and father and son combinations.

		NR MT	EX	VG
Complete Set:		450.00	225.00	135.00
Commmon Player:		.25	.13	.08
1	'75 Record Breaker (Hank Aaron)	15.00	7.50	4.50
2	'75 Record Breaker (Bobby Bonds)	.40	.20	.12
3	'75 Record Breaker (Mickey Lolich)	.35	.20	.11
4	'75 Record Breaker (Dave Lopes)	.35	.20	.11
5	'75 Record Breaker (Tom Seaver)	3.00	1.50	.90
6	'75 Record Breaker (Rennie Stennett)	.30	.15	.09
7	Jim Umbarger	.25	.13	.08
8	Tito Fuentes	.25	.13	.08
9	Paul Lindblad	.25	.13	.08
10	Lou Brock	4.00	2.00	1.25
11	Jim Hughes	.25	.13	.08
12	Richie Zisk	.25	.13	.08
13	Johnny Wockenfuss	.25	.13	.08
14	Gene Garber	.25	.13	.08
15	George Scott	.25	.13	.08
16	Bob Apodaca	.25	.13	.08
17	Yankees Team (Billy Martin)	1.25	.60	.40
18	Dale Murray	.25	.13	.08
19	George Brett	60.00	30.00	18.00
20	Bob Watson	.25	.13	.08
21	Dave LaRoche	.25	.13	.08
22	Bill Russell	.25	.13	.08
23	Brian Downing	.25	.13	.08
24	Cesar Geronimo	.25	.13	.08
25	Mike Torrez	.25	.13	.08
26	Andy Thornton	.25	.13	.08
27	Ed Figueroa	.25	.13	.08
28	Dusty Baker	.25	.13	.08
29	Rick Burleson	.30	.15	.09
30	*John Montefusco*	.35	.20	.11
31	Len Randle	.25	.13	.08
32	Danny Frisella	.25	.13	.08
33	Bill North	.25	.13	.08

		NR MT	EX	VG
34	Mike Garman	.25	.13	.08
35	Tony Oliva	.60	.30	.20
36	Frank Taveras	.25	.13	.08
37	John Hiller	.25	.13	.08
38	Garry Maddox	.25	.13	.08
39	Pete Broberg	.25	.13	.08
40	Dave Kingman	.80	.40	.25
41	*Tippy Martinez*	.40	.20	.12
42	Barry Foote	.25	.13	.08
43	Paul Splittorff	.25	.13	.08
44	Doug Rader	.25	.13	.08
45	Boog Powell	.60	.30	.20
46	Dodgers Team (Walter Alston)	1.00	.50	.30
47	Jesse Jefferson	.25	.13	.08
48	Dave Concepcion	.40	.20	.12
49	Dave Duncan	.25	.13	.08
50	Fred Lynn	2.00	1.00	.60
51	Ray Burris	.25	.13	.08
52	Dave Chalk	.25	.13	.08
53	Mike Beard	.25	.13	.08
54	Dave Rader	.25	.13	.08
55	Gaylord Perry	3.00	1.50	.90
56	Bob Tolan	.25	.13	.08
57	Phil Garner	.30	.15	.09
58	Ron Reed	.25	.13	.08
59	Larry Hisle	.25	.13	.08
60	Jerry Reuss	.30	.15	.09
61	Ron LeFlore	.30	.15	.09
62	Johnny Oates	.25	.13	.08
63	Bobby Darwin	.25	.13	.08
64	Jerry Koosman	.30	.15	.09
65	Chris Chambliss	.30	.15	.09
66	Father & Son (Buddy Bell, Gus Bell)	.50	.25	.15
67	Father & Son (Bob Boone, Ray Boone)	.40	.20	.12
68	Father & Son (Joe Coleman, Joe Coleman, Jr.)	.25	.13	.08
69	Father & Son (Jim Hegan, Mike Hegan)	.25	.13	.08
70	Father & Son (Roy Smalley, Roy Smalley, Jr.)	.25	.13	.08
71	Steve Rogers	.25	.13	.08
72	Hal McRae	.25	.13	.08
73	Orioles Team (Earl Weaver)	.80	.40	.25
74	Oscar Gamble	.25	.13	.08
75	Larry Dierker	.25	.13	.08
76	Willie Crawford	.25	.13	.08
77	Pedro Borbon	.25	.13	.08
78	Cecil Cooper	1.00	.50	.30
79	Jerry Morales	.25	.13	.08
80	Jim Kaat	.90	.45	.25
81	Darrell Evans	.50	.25	.15
82	Von Joshua	.25	.13	.08
83	Jim Spencer	.25	.13	.08
84	Brent Strom	.25	.13	.08
85	Mickey Rivers	.25	.13	.08
86	Mike Tyson	.25	.13	.08
87	Tom Burgmeier	.25	.13	.08
88	Duffy Dyer	.25	.13	.08
89	Vern Ruhle	.25	.13	.08
90	Sal Bando	.30	.15	.09
91	Tom Hutton	.25	.13	.08
92	Eduardo Rodriguez	.25	.13	.08
93	Mike Phillips	.25	.13	.08
94	Jim Dwyer	.30	.15	.09
95	Brooks Robinson	5.00	2.50	1.50
96	Doug Bird	.25	.13	.08
97	Wilbur Howard	.25	.13	.08
98	*Dennis Eckersley*	65.00	33.00	19.00
99	Lee Lacy	.25	.13	.08
100	Jim Hunter	3.00	1.50	.90
101	Pete LaCock	.25	.13	.08
102	Jim Willoughby	.25	.13	.08
103	Biff Pocoroba	.25	.13	.08
104	Reds Team (Sparky Anderson)	.90	.45	.25
105	Gary Lavelle	.25	.13	.08
106	Tom Grieve	.25	.13	.08
107	Dave Roberts	.25	.13	.08
108	Don Kirkwood	.25	.13	.08
109	Larry Lintz	.25	.13	.08
110	Carlos May	.25	.13	.08
111	Danny Thompson	.25	.13	.08
112	*Kent Tekulve*	.80	.40	.25
113	Gary Sutherland	.25	.13	.08
114	Jay Johnstone	.25	.13	.08
115	Ken Holtzman	.25	.13	.08
116	Charlie Moore	.25	.13	.08
117	Mike Jorgensen	.25	.13	.08
118	Red Sox Team (Darrell Johnson)	.90	.45	.25
119	Checklist 1-132	1.25	.60	.40
120	Rusty Staub	.35	.20	.11
121	Tony Solaita	.25	.13	.08
122	Mike Cosgrove	.25	.13	.08
123	Walt Williams	.25	.13	.08
124	Doug Rau	.25	.13	.08
125	Don Baylor	.50	.25	.15
126	Tom Dettore	.25	.13	.08
127	Larvell Blanks	.25	.13	.08
128	Ken Griffey	.35	.20	.11
129	Andy Etchebarren	.25	.13	.08
130	Luis Tiant	.40	.20	.12
131	Bill Stein	.25	.13	.08
132	Don Hood	.25	.13	.08
133	Gary Matthews	.25	.13	.08
134	Mike Ivie	.25	.13	.08
135	Bake McBride	.25	.13	.08
136	Dave Goltz	.25	.13	.08
137	Bill Robinson	.25	.13	.08
138	Lerrin LaGrow	.25	.13	.08
139	Gorman Thomas	.35	.20	.11
140	Vida Blue	.40	.20	.12
141	*Larry Parrish*	.80	.40	.25
142	Dick Drago	.25	.13	.08
143	Jerry Grote	.25	.13	.08
144	Al Fitzmorris	.25	.13	.08
145	Larry Bowa	.35	.20	.11
146	George Medich	.25	.13	.08
147	Astros Team (Bill Virdon)	.80	.40	.25
148	Stan Thomas	.25	.13	.08
149	Tommy Davis	.30	.15	.09
150	Steve Garvey	5.00	2.50	1.50
151	Bill Bonham	.25	.13	.08
152	Leroy Stanton	.25	.13	.08
153	Buzz Capra	.25	.13	.08
154	Bucky Dent	.30	.15	.09
155	Jack Billingham	.25	.13	.08
156	Rico Carty	.25	.13	.08
157	Mike Caldwell	.25	.13	.08
158	Ken Reitz	.25	.13	.08
159	Jerry Terrell	.25	.13	.08
160	Dave Winfield	25.00	12.50	7.50
161	Bruce Kison	.25	.13	.08
162	Jack Pierce	.25	.13	.08
163	Jim Slaton	.25	.13	.08
164	Pepe Mangual	.25	.13	.08
165	Gene Tenace	.25	.13	.08
166	Skip Lockwood	.25	.13	.08
167	Freddie Patek	.25	.13	.08
168	Tom Hilgendorf	.25	.13	.08
169	Graig Nettles	1.00	.50	.30
170	Rick Wise	.25	.13	.08
171	Greg Gross	.25	.13	.08
172	Rangers Team (Frank Lucchesi)	.80	.40	.25
173	Steve Swisher	.25	.13	.08
174	Charlie Hough	.25	.13	.08
175	Ken Singleton	.30	.15	.09
176	Dick Lange	.25	.13	.08
177	Marty Perez	.25	.13	.08
178	Tom Buskey	.25	.13	.08
179	George Foster	1.00	.50	.30
180	Rich Gossage	1.50	.70	.45
181	Willie Montanez	.25	.13	.08
182	Harry Rasmussen	.25	.13	.08
183	Steve Braun	.25	.13	.08
184	Bill Greif	.25	.13	.08
185	Dave Parker	7.00	3.50	2.00
186	Tom Walker	.25	.13	.08
187	Pedro Garcia	.25	.13	.08
188	Fred Scherman	.25	.13	.08
189	Claudell Washington	.40	.20	.12
190	Jon Matlack	.25	.13	.08
191	N.L. Batting Leaders (Bill Madlock, Manny Sanguillen, Ted Simmons)	.60	.30	.20
192	A.L. Batting Leaders (Rod Carew, Fred Lynn, Thurman Munson)	2.00	1.00	.60
193	N.L. Home Run Leaders (Dave Kingman, Greg Luzinski, Mike Schmidt)	1.25	.60	.40
194	A.L. Home Run Leaders (Reggie Jackson, John Mayberry, George Scott)	1.25	.60	.40
195	N.L. Runs Batted In Ldrs. (Johnny Bench, Greg Luzinski, Tony Perez)	1.25	.60	.40
196	A.L. Runs Batted In Ldrs. (Fred Lynn, John Mayberry, George Scott)	.60	.30	.20
197	N.L. Stolen Base Leaders (Lou Brock, Dave Lopes, Joe Morgan)	.90	.45	.25
198	A.L. Stolen Base Leaders (Amos Otis, Mickey Rivers, Claudell Washington)	.50	.25	.15
199	N.L. Victory Leaders (Randy Jones, Andy Messersmith, Tom Seaver)	.80	.40	.25
200	A.L. Victory Leaders (Vida Blue, Jim Hunter, Jim Palmer)	.90	.45	.25

	NR MT	EX	VG
201 N.L. Earned Run Avg. Ldrs. (Randy Jones, Andy Messersmith, Tom Seaver)	.80	.40	.25
202 A.L. Earned Run Avg. Ldrs. (Dennis Eckersley, Jim Hunter, Jim Palmer)	.90	.45	.25
203 N.L. Strikeout Leaders (Andy Messersmith, John Montefusco, Tom Seaver)	.80	.40	.25
204 A.L. Strikeout Leaders (Bert Blyleven, Gaylord Perry, Frank Tanana)	.70	.35	.20
205 Major League Leading Firemen (Rich Gossage, Al Hrabosky)	.50	.25	.15
206 Manny Trillo	.25	.13	.08
207 Andy Hassler	.25	.13	.08
208 Mike Lum	.25	.13	.08
209 Alan Ashby	.35	.20	.11
210 Lee May	.25	.13	.08
211 Clay Carroll	.25	.13	.08
212 Pat Kelly	.25	.13	.08
213 Dave Heaverlo	.25	.13	.08
214 Eric Soderholm	.25	.13	.08
215 Reggie Smith	.25	.13	.08
216 Expos Team (Karl Kuehl)	.80	.40	.25
217 Dave Freisleben	.25	.13	.08
218 John Knox	.25	.13	.08
219 Tom Murphy	.25	.13	.08
220 Manny Sanguillen	.25	.13	.08
221 Jim Todd	.25	.13	.08
222 Wayne Garrett	.25	.13	.08
223 Ollie Brown	.25	.13	.08
224 Jim York	.25	.13	.08
225 Roy White	.25	.13	.08
226 Jim Sundberg	.25	.13	.08
227 Oscar Zamora	.25	.13	.08
228 John Hale	.25	.13	.08
229 *Jerry Remy*	.30	.15	.09
230 Carl Yastrzemski	8.00	4.00	2.50
231 Tom House	.25	.13	.08
232 Frank Duffy	.25	.13	.08
233 Grant Jackson	.25	.13	.08
234 Mike Sadek	.25	.13	.08
235 Bert Blyleven	1.00	.50	.30
236 Royals Team (Whitey Herzog)	.80	.40	.25
237 Dave Hamilton	.25	.13	.08
238 Larry Biittner	.25	.13	.08
239 John Curtis	.25	.13	.08
240 Pete Rose	12.00	6.00	3.50
241 Hector Torres	.25	.13	.08
242 Dan Meyer	.25	.13	.08
243 Jim Rooker	.25	.13	.08
244 Bill Sharp	.25	.13	.08
245 Felix Millan	.25	.13	.08
246 Cesar Tovar	.25	.13	.08
247 Terry Harmon	.25	.13	.08
248 Dick Tidrow	.25	.13	.08
249 Cliff Johnson	.25	.13	.08
250 Fergie Jenkins	2.00	1.00	.60
251 Rick Monday	.30	.15	.09
252 Tim Nordbrook	.25	.13	.08
253 Bill Buckner	.50	.25	.15
254 Rudy Meoli	.25	.13	.08
255 Fritz Peterson	.25	.13	.08
256 Rowland Office	.25	.13	.08
257 Ross Grimsley	.25	.13	.08
258 Nyls Nyman	.25	.13	.08
259 Darrel Chaney	.25	.13	.08
260 Steve Busby	.25	.13	.08
261 Gary Thomasson	.25	.13	.08
262 Checklist 133-264	1.50	.70	.45
263 *Lyman Bostock*	.80	.40	.25
264 Steve Renko	.25	.13	.08
265 Willie Davis	.30	.15	.09
266 Alan Foster	.25	.13	.08
267 Aurelio Rodriguez	.25	.13	.08
268 Del Unser	.25	.13	.08
269 Rick Austin	.25	.13	.08
270 Willie Stargell	3.00	1.50	.90
271 Jim Lonborg	.25	.13	.08
272 Rick Dempsey	.25	.13	.08
273 Joe Niekro	.30	.15	.09
274 Tommy Harper	.25	.13	.08
275 *Rick Manning*	.40	.20	.12
276 Mickey Scott	.25	.13	.08
277 Cubs Team (Jim Marshall)	.80	.40	.25
278 Bernie Carbo	.25	.13	.08
279 Roy Howell	.25	.13	.08
280 Burt Hooton	.25	.13	.08
281 Dave May	.25	.13	.08
282 Dan Osborn	.25	.13	.08
283 Merv Rettenmund	.25	.13	.08
284 Steve Ontiveros	.25	.13	.08
285 Mike Cuellar	.25	.13	.08
286 Jim Wohlford	.25	.13	.08
287 Pete Mackanin	.25	.13	.08
288 Bill Campbell	.25	.13	.08
289 Enzo Hernandez	.25	.13	.08
290 Ted Simmons	.60	.30	.20
291 Ken Sanders	.25	.13	.08
292 Leon Roberts	.25	.13	.08
293 Bill Castro	.25	.13	.08
294 Ed Kirkpatrick	.25	.13	.08
295 Dave Cash	.25	.13	.08
296 Pat Dobson	.25	.13	.08
297 Roger Metzger	.25	.13	.08
298 Dick Bosman	.25	.13	.08
299 Champ Summers	.25	.13	.08
300 Johnny Bench	10.00	5.00	3.00
301 Jackie Brown	.25	.13	.08
302 Rick Miller	.25	.13	.08
303 Steve Foucault	.25	.13	.08
304 Angels Team (Dick Williams)	.80	.40	.25
305 Andy Messersmith	.25	.13	.08
306 Rod Gilbreath	.25	.13	.08
307 Al Bumbry	.25	.13	.08
308 Jim Barr	.25	.13	.08
309 Bill Melton	.25	.13	.08
310 Randy Jones	.30	.15	.09
311 Cookie Rojas	.25	.13	.08
312 Don Carrithers	.25	.13	.08
313 *Dan Ford*	.25	.13	.08
314 Ed Kranepool	.25	.13	.08
315 Al Hrabosky	.25	.13	.08
316 Robin Yount	60.00	30.00	18.00
317 *John Candelaria*	2.00	1.00	.60
318 Bob Boone	.30	.15	.09
319 Larry Gura	.25	.13	.08
320 Willie Horton	.25	.13	.08
321 Jose Cruz	.35	.20	.11
322 Glenn Abbott	.25	.13	.08
323 Rob Sperring	.25	.13	.08
324 Jim Bibby	.25	.13	.08
325 Tony Perez	2.00	1.00	.60
326 Dick Pole	.25	.13	.08
327 Dave Moates	.25	.13	.08
328 Carl Morton	.25	.13	.08
329 Joe Ferguson	.25	.13	.08
330 Nolan Ryan	50.00	25.00	15.00
331 Padres Team (John McNamara)	.80	.40	.25
332 Charlie Williams	.25	.13	.08
333 Bob Coluccio	.25	.13	.08
334 Dennis Leonard	.25	.13	.08
335 Bob Grich	.25	.13	.08
336 Vic Albury	.25	.13	.08
337 Bud Harrelson	.25	.13	.08
338 Bob Bailey	.25	.13	.08
339 John Denny	.25	.13	.08
340 Jim Rice	8.00	4.00	2.50
341 All Time All-Stars (Lou Gehrig)	5.00	2.50	1.50
342 All Time All-Stars (Rogers Hornsby)	1.25	.60	.40
343 All Time All-Stars (Pie Traynor)	.80	.40	.25
344 All Time All-Stars (Honus Wagner)	1.25	.60	.40
345 All Time All-Stars (Babe Ruth)	8.00	4.00	2.50
346 All Time All-Stars (Ty Cobb)	6.00	3.00	1.75
347 All Time All-Stars (Ted Williams)	6.00	3.00	1.75
348 All Time All-Stars (Mickey Cochrane)	.80	.40	.25
349 All Time All-Stars (Walter Johnson)	1.25	.60	.40
350 All Time All-Stars (Lefty Grove)	1.00	.50	.30
351 Randy Hundley	.25	.13	.08
352 Dave Giusti	.25	.13	.08
353 *Sixto Lezcano*	.30	.15	.09
354 Ron Blomberg	.25	.13	.08
355 Steve Carlton	7.00	3.50	2.00
356 Ted Martinez	.25	.13	.08
357 Ken Forsch	.25	.13	.08
358 Buddy Bell	.50	.25	.15
359 Rick Reuschel	.30	.15	.09
360 Jeff Burroughs	.25	.13	.08
361 Tigers Team (Ralph Houk)	1.00	.50	.30
362 Will McEnaney	.25	.13	.08
363 *Dave Collins*	.40	.20	.12
364 Elias Sosa	.25	.13	.08
365 Carlton Fisk	12.00	6.00	3.50
366 Bobby Valentine	.30	.15	.09
367 Bruce Miller	.25	.13	.08
368 Wilbur Wood	.25	.13	.08
369 Frank White	.30	.15	.09
370 Ron Cey	.40	.20	.12
371 Ellie Hendricks	.25	.13	.08
372 Rick Baldwin	.25	.13	.08
373 Johnny Briggs	.25	.13	.08

#	Player	NR MT	EX	VG
374	Dan Warthen	.25	.13	.08
375	Ron Fairly	.25	.13	.08
376	Rich Hebner	.25	.13	.08
377	Mike Hegan	.25	.13	.08
378	Steve Stone	.25	.13	.08
379	Ken Boswell	.25	.13	.08
380	Bobby Bonds	.35	.20	.11
381	Denny Doyle	.25	.13	.08
382	Matt Alexander	.25	.13	.08
383	John Ellis	.25	.13	.08
384	Phillies Team (Danny Ozark)	.80	.40	.25
385	Mickey Lolich	.40	.20	.12
386	Ed Goodson	.25	.13	.08
387	Mike Miley	.25	.13	.08
388	Stan Perzanowski	.25	.13	.08
389	Glenn Adams	.25	.13	.08
390	Don Gullett	.25	.13	.08
391	Jerry Hairston	.25	.13	.08
392	Checklist 265-396	1.50	.70	.45
393	Paul Mitchell	.25	.13	.08
394	Fran Healy	.25	.13	.08
395	Jim Wynn	.30	.15	.09
396	Bill Lee	.25	.13	.08
397	Tim Foli	.25	.13	.08
398	Dave Tomlin	.25	.13	.08
399	Luis Melendez	.25	.13	.08
400	Rod Carew	8.00	4.00	2.50
401	Ken Brett	.25	.13	.08
402	Don Money	.25	.13	.08
403	Geoff Zahn	.25	.13	.08
404	Enos Cabell	.25	.13	.08
405	Rollie Fingers	5.00	2.50	1.50
406	Ed Herrmann	.25	.13	.08
407	Tom Underwood	.25	.13	.08
408	Charlie Spikes	.25	.13	.08
409	Dave Lemanczyk	.25	.13	.08
410	Ralph Garr	.25	.13	.08
411	Bill Singer	.25	.13	.08
412	Toby Harrah	.25	.13	.08
413	Pete Varney	.25	.13	.08
414	Wayne Garland	.25	.13	.08
415	Vada Pinson	.50	.25	.15
416	Tommy John	1.25	.60	.40
417	Gene Clines	.25	.13	.08
418	Jose Morales	.25	.13	.08
419	Reggie Cleveland	.25	.13	.08
420	Joe Morgan	5.00	2.50	1.50
421	A's Team	.80	.40	.25
422	Johnny Grubb	.25	.13	.08
423	Ed Halicki	.25	.13	.08
424	Phil Roof	.25	.13	.08
425	Rennie Stennett	.25	.13	.08
426	Bob Forsch	.25	.13	.08
427	Kurt Bevacqua	.25	.13	.08
428	Jim Crawford	.25	.13	.08
429	Fred Stanley	.25	.13	.08
430	Jose Cardenal	.25	.13	.08
431	Dick Ruthven	.25	.13	.08
432	Tom Veryzer	.25	.13	.08
433	Rick Waits	.25	.13	.08
434	Morris Nettles	.25	.13	.08
435	Phil Niekro	2.00	1.00	.60
436	Bill Fahey	.25	.13	.08
437	Terry Forster	.25	.13	.08
438	Doug DeCinces	.50	.25	.15
439	Rick Rhoden	.60	.30	.20
440	John Mayberry	.25	.13	.08
441	Gary Carter	10.00	5.00	3.00
442	Hank Webb	.25	.13	.08
443	Giants Team	.80	.40	.25
444	Gary Nolan	.25	.13	.08
445	Rico Petrocelli	.25	.13	.08
446	Larry Haney	.25	.13	.08
447	Gene Locklear	.25	.13	.08
448	Tom Johnson	.25	.13	.08
449	Bob Robertson	.25	.13	.08
450	Jim Palmer	6.00	3.00	1.75
451	Buddy Bradford	.25	.13	.08
452	Tom Hausman	.25	.13	.08
453	Lou Piniella	.60	.30	.20
454	Tom Griffin	.25	.13	.08
455	Dick Allen	.50	.25	.15
456	Joe Coleman	.25	.13	.08
457	Ed Crosby	.25	.13	.08
458	Earl Williams	.25	.13	.08
459	Jim Brewer	.25	.13	.08
460	Cesar Cedeno	.30	.15	.09
461	NL & AL Championships	.80	.40	.25
462	1975 World Series	.80	.40	.25
463	Steve Hargan	.25	.13	.08
464	Ken Henderson	.25	.13	.08
465	Mike Marshall	.30	.15	.09
466	Bob Stinson	.25	.13	.08
467	Woodie Fryman	.25	.13	.08
468	Jesus Alou	.25	.13	.08
469	Rawly Eastwick	.25	.13	.08
470	Bobby Murcer	.35	.20	.11
471	Jim Burton	.25	.13	.08
472	Bob Davis	.25	.13	.08
473	Paul Blair	.25	.13	.08
474	Ray Corbin	.25	.13	.08
475	Joe Rudi	.30	.15	.09
476	Bob Moose	.25	.13	.08
477	Indians Team (Frank Robinson)	.80	.40	.25
478	Lynn McGlothen	.25	.13	.08
479	Bobby Mitchell	.25	.13	.08
480	Mike Schmidt	30.00	15.00	9.00
481	Rudy May	.25	.13	.08
482	Tim Hosley	.25	.13	.08
483	Mickey Stanley	.25	.13	.08
484	Eric Raich	.25	.13	.08
485	Mike Hargrove	.25	.13	.08
486	Bruce Dal Canton	.25	.13	.08
487	Leron Lee	.25	.13	.08
488	Claude Osteen	.25	.13	.08
489	Skip Jutze	.25	.13	.08
490	Frank Tanana	.30	.15	.09
491	Terry Crowley	.25	.13	.08
492	Marty Pattin	.25	.13	.08
493	Derrel Thomas	.25	.13	.08
494	Craig Swan	.25	.13	.08
495	Nate Colbert	.25	.13	.08
496	Juan Beniquez	.25	.13	.08
497	Joe McIntosh	.25	.13	.08
498	Glenn Borgmann	.25	.13	.08
499	Mario Guerrero	.25	.13	.08
500	Reggie Jackson	18.00	9.00	5.50
501	Billy Champion	.25	.13	.08
502	Tim McCarver	.50	.25	.15
503	Elliott Maddox	.25	.13	.08
504	Pirates Team (Danny Murtaugh)	.80	.40	.25
505	Mark Belanger	.25	.13	.08
506	George Mitterwald	.25	.13	.08
507	Ray Bare	.25	.13	.08
508	*Duane Kuiper*	.25	.13	.08
509	Bill Hands	.25	.13	.08
510	Amos Otis	.25	.13	.08
511	Jamie Easterly	.25	.13	.08
512	Ellie Rodriguez	.25	.13	.08
513	Bart Johnson	.25	.13	.08
514	Dan Driessen	.30	.15	.09
515	Steve Yeager	.25	.13	.08
516	Wayne Granger	.25	.13	.08
517	John Milner	.25	.13	.08
518	*Doug Flynn*	.25	.13	.08
519	Steve Brye	.25	.13	.08
520	Willie McCovey	2.50	1.25	.70
521	Jim Colborn	.25	.13	.08
522	Ted Sizemore	.25	.13	.08
523	Bob Montgomery	.25	.13	.08
524	Pete Falcone	.25	.13	.08
525	Billy Williams	2.25	1.25	.70
526	Checklist 397-528	1.50	.70	.45
527	Mike Anderson	.25	.13	.08
528	Dock Ellis	.25	.13	.08
529	Deron Johnson	.25	.13	.08
530	Don Sutton	1.50	.70	.45
531	Mets Team (Joe Frazier)	.90	.45	.25
532	Milt May	.25	.13	.08
533	Lee Richard	.25	.13	.08
534	Stan Bahnsen	.25	.13	.08
535	Dave Nelson	.25	.13	.08
536	Mike Thompson	.25	.13	.08
537	Tony Muser	.25	.13	.08
538	Pat Darcy	.25	.13	.08
539	John Balaz	.25	.13	.08
540	Bill Freehan	.25	.13	.08
541	Steve Mingori	.25	.13	.08
542	Keith Hernandez	6.00	3.00	1.75
543	Wayne Twitchell	.25	.13	.08
544	Pepe Frias	.25	.13	.08
545	Sparky Lyle	.35	.20	.11
546	Dave Rosello	.25	.13	.08
547	Roric Harrison	.25	.13	.08
548	Manny Mota	.25	.13	.08
549	Randy Tate	.25	.13	.08
550	Hank Aaron	20.00	10.00	6.00
551	Jerry DaVanon	.25	.13	.08
552	Terry Humphrey	.25	.13	.08
553	Randy Moffitt	.25	.13	.08
554	Ray Fosse	.25	.13	.08
555	Dyar Miller	.25	.13	.08

		NR MT	EX	VG
556	Twins Team (Gene Mauch)	.80	.40	.25
557	Dan Spillner	.25	.13	.08
558	Clarence Gaston	.25	.13	.08
559	Clyde Wright	.25	.13	.08
560	Jorge Orta	.25	.13	.08
561	Tom Carroll	.25	.13	.08
562	Adrian Garrett	.25	.13	.08
563	Larry Demery	.25	.13	.08
564	Bubble Gum Blowing Champ (Kurt Bevacqua)	.30	.15	.09
565	Tug McGraw	.35	.20	.11
566	Ken McMullen	.25	.13	.08
567	George Stone	.25	.13	.08
568	Rob Andrews	.25	.13	.08
569	Nelson Briles	.25	.13	.08
570	George Hendrick	.25	.13	.08
571	Don DeMola	.25	.13	.08
572	Rich Coggins	.25	.13	.08
573	Bill Travers	.25	.13	.08
574	Don Kessinger	.25	.13	.08
575	Dwight Evans	4.00	2.00	1.25
576	Maximino Leon	.25	.13	.08
577	Marc Hill	.25	.13	.08
578	Ted Kubiak	.25	.13	.08
579	Clay Kirby	.25	.13	.08
580	Bert Campaneris	.30	.15	.09
581	Cardinals Team (Red Schoendienst)	.80	.40	.25
582	Mike Kekich	.25	.13	.08
583	Tommy Helms	.25	.13	.08
584	Stan Wall	.25	.13	.08
585	Joe Torre	.50	.25	.15
586	Ron Schueler	.25	.13	.08
587	Leo Cardenas	.25	.13	.08
588	Kevin Kobel	.25	.13	.08
589	Rookie Pitchers (Santo Alcala, *Mike Flanagan*, Joe Pactwa, Pablo Torrealba)	2.00	1.00	.60
590	Rookie Outfielders (Henry Cruz, *Chet Lemon, Ellis Valentine*, Terry Whitfield)	1.00	.50	.30
591	Rookie Pitchers (Steve Grilli, Craig Mitchell, Jose Sosa, George Throop)	.25	.13	.08
592	Rookie Infielders (Dave McKay, *Willie Randolph, Jerry Royster*, Roy Staiger)	8.00	4.00	2.50
593	Rookie Pitchers (Larry Anderson, Ken Crosby, Mark Littell, *Butch Metzger*)	.25	.13	.08
594	Rookie Catchers & Outfielders (Andy Merchant, Ed Ott, Royle Stillman, Jerry White)	.25	.13	.08
595	Rookie Pitchers (Steve Barr, Art DeFilippis, Randy Lerch, Sid Monge)	.25	.13	.08
596	Rookie Infielders (Lamar Johnson, *Johnny LeMaster*, Jerry Manuel, *Craig Reynolds*)	.35	.20	.11
597	Rookie Pitchers (*Don Aase*, Jack Kucek, Frank LaCorte, Mike Pazik)	.50	.25	.15
598	Rookie Outfielders (Hector Cruz, *Jamie Quirk*, Jerry Turner, Joe Wallis)	.25	.13	.08
599	Rookie Pitchers (Rob Dressler, *Ron Guidry*, Bob McClure, Pat Zachry)	8.00	4.00	2.50
600	Tom Seaver	12.00	6.00	3.50
601	Ken Rudolph	.25	.13	.08
602	Doug Konieczny	.25	.13	.08
603	Jim Holt	.25	.13	.08
604	Joe Lovitto	.25	.13	.08
605	Al Downing	.25	.13	.08
606	Brewers Team (Alex Grammas)	.80	.40	.25
607	Rich Hinton	.25	.13	.08
608	Vic Correll	.25	.13	.08
609	Fred Norman	.25	.13	.08
610	Greg Luzinski	.40	.20	.12
611	Rich Folkers	.25	.13	.08
612	Joe Lahoud	.25	.13	.08
613	Tim Johnson	.25	.13	.08
614	Fernando Arroyo	.25	.13	.08
615	Mike Cubbage	.25	.13	.08
616	Buck Martinez	.25	.13	.08
617	Darold Knowles	.25	.13	.08
618	Jack Brohamer	.25	.13	.08
619	Bill Butler	.25	.13	.08
620	Al Oliver	.70	.35	.20
621	Tom Hall	.25	.13	.08
622	Rick Auerbach	.25	.13	.08
623	Bob Allietta	.25	.13	.08
624	Tony Taylor	.25	.13	.08
625	J.R. Richard	.25	.13	.08
626	Bob Sheldon	.25	.13	.08
627	Bill Plummer	.25	.13	.08
628	John D'Acquisto	.25	.13	.08
629	Sandy Alomar	.25	.13	.08
630	Chris Speier	.25	.13	.08
631	Braves Team (Dave Bristol)	.80	.40	.25
632	Rogelio Moret	.25	.13	.08
633	*John Stearns*	.30	.15	.09
634	Larry Christenson	.25	.13	.08
635	Jim Fregosi	.25	.13	.08
636	Joe Decker	.25	.13	.08
637	Bruce Bochte	.25	.13	.08
638	Doyle Alexander	.30	.15	.09
639	Fred Kendall	.25	.13	.08
640	Bill Madlock	1.00	.50	.30
641	Tom Paciorek	.25	.13	.08
642	Dennis Blair	.25	.13	.08
643	Checklist 529-660	1.50	.70	.45
644	Tom Bradley	.25	.13	.08
645	Darrell Porter	.25	.13	.08
646	John Lowenstein	.25	.13	.08
648	Al Cowens	.25	.13	.08
649	Dave Roberts	.25	.13	.08
650	Thurman Munson	7.00	3.50	2.00
651	John Odom	.25	.13	.08
652	Ed Armbrister	.25	.13	.08
653	*Mike Norris*	.30	.15	.09
654	Doug Griffin	.25	.13	.08
655	Mike Vail	.25	.13	.08
656	White Sox Team (Chuck Tanner)	.80	.40	.25
657	*Roy Smalley*	.40	.20	.12
658	Jerry Johnson	.25	.13	.08
659	Ben Oglivie	.25	.13	.08
660	Dave Lopes	.60	.13	.08

1976 Topps Traded

Similar to the Topps Traded set of 1974, the 2-1/2" by 3-1/2" cards feature photos of players traded after the printing deadline. The style of the cards is essentially the same as the regular issue but with a large "Sports Extra" headline announcing the trade and its date. The backs continue in newspaper style to detail the specifics of the trade. There are 43 player cards and one checklist in the set. Numbers remain the same as the player's regular card, with the addition of a "T" suffix.

		NR MT	EX	VG
Complete Set:		10.00	5.00	3.00
Common Player:		.15	.08	.05
27T	Ed Figueroa	.20	.10	.06
28T	Dusty Baker	.35	.20	.11
44T	Doug Rader	.15	.08	.05
58T	Ron Reed	.20	.10	.06
74T	Oscar Gamble	.25	.13	.08
80T	Jim Kaat	.60	.30	.20
83T	Jim Spencer	.15	.08	.05
85T	Mickey Rivers	.30	.15	.09
99T	Lee Lacy	.20	.10	.06
120T	Rusty Staub	.50	.25	.15
127T	Larvell Blanks	.15	.08	.05
146T	George Medich	.15	.08	.05
158T	Ken Reitz	.15	.08	.05
208T	Mike Lum	.15	.08	.05
211T	Clay Carroll	.20	.10	.06
231T	Tom House	.15	.08	.05
250T	Fergie Jenkins	1.00	.50	.30
259T	Darrel Chaney	.15	.08	.05

		NR MT	EX	VG
292T	Leon Roberts	.15	.08	.05
296T	Pat Dobson	.20	.10	.06
309T	Bill Melton	.20	.10	.06
338T	Bob Bailey	.15	.08	.05
380T	Bobby Bonds	.35	.20	.11
383T	John Ellis	.15	.08	.05
385T	Mickey Lolich	.50	.25	.15
401T	Ken Brett	.20	.10	.06
410T	Ralph Garr	.20	.10	.06
411T	Bill Singer	.20	.10	.06
428T	Jim Crawford	.15	.08	.05
434T	Morris Nettles	.15	.08	.05
464T	Ken Henderson	.15	.08	.05
497T	Joe McIntosh	.15	.08	.05
524T	Pete Falcone	.15	.08	.05
527T	Mike Anderson	.15	.08	.05
528T	Dock Ellis	.20	.10	.06
532T	Milt May	.15	.08	.05
554T	Ray Fosse	.15	.08	.05
579T	Clay Kirby	.15	.08	.05
583T	Tommy Helms	.15	.08	.05
592T	Willie Randolph	1.00	.50	.30
618T	Jack Brohamer	.15	.08	.05
632T	Rogelio Moret	.15	.08	.05
649T	Dave Roberts	.15	.08	.05
----	Traded Checklist	.80	.40	.25

1977 Topps

The 1977 Topps Set is a 660-card effort featuring front designs dominated by a color photograph on which there is a facsimile autograph. Above the picture are the player's name, team and position. The backs of the 2-1/2" by 3-1/2" cards include personal and career statistics along with newspaper-style highlights and a cartoon. Specialty cards include statistical leaders, record performances, a new "Turn Back The Clock" feature which highlighted great past moments and a "Big League Brothers" feature.

		NR MT	EX	VG
Complete Set:		400.00	200.00	125.00
Common Player:		.20	.10	.06
1	Batting Leaders (George Brett, Bill Madlock)	4.00	2.00	1.25
2	Home Run Leaders (Graig Nettles, Mike Schmidt)	1.25	.60	.40
3	Runs Batted In Leaders (George Foster, Lee May)	.50	.25	.15
4	Stolen Base Leaders (Dave Lopes, Bill North)	.30	.15	.09
5	Victory Leaders (Randy Jones, Jim Palmer)	.80	.40	.25
6	Strikeout Leaders (Nolan Ryan, Tom Seaver)	6.00	3.00	1.75
7	Earned Run Avg. Ldrs. (John Denny, Mark Fidrych)	.30	.15	.09
8	Leading Firemen (Bill Campbell, Rawly Eastwick)	.30	.15	.09
9	Doug Rader	.20	.10	.06
10	Reggie Jackson	15.00	7.50	4.50
11	Rob Dressler	.20	.10	.06
12	Larry Haney	.20	.10	.06
13	Luis Gomez	.20	.10	.06
14	Tommy Smith	.20	.10	.06
15	Don Gullett	.20	.10	.06

		NR MT	EX	VG
16	Bob Jones	.20	.10	.06
17	Steve Stone	.25	.13	.08
18	Indians Team (Frank Robinson)	.80	.40	.25
19	John D'Acquisto	.20	.10	.06
20	Graig Nettles	.90	.45	.25
21	Ken Forsch	.20	.10	.06
22	Bill Freehan	.25	.13	.08
23	Dan Driessen	.25	.13	.08
24	Carl Morton	.20	.10	.06
25	Dwight Evans	3.00	1.50	.90
26	Ray Sadecki	.20	.10	.06
27	Bill Buckner	.35	.20	.11
28	Woodie Fryman	.20	.10	.06
29	Bucky Dent	.25	.13	.08
30	Greg Luzinski	.40	.20	.12
31	Jim Todd	.20	.10	.06
32	Checklist 1-132	1.25	.60	.40
33	Wayne Garland	.20	.10	.06
34	Angels Team (Norm Sherry)	.70	.35	.20
35	Rennie Stennett	.20	.10	.06
36	John Ellis	.20	.10	.06
37	Steve Hargan	.20	.10	.06
38	Craig Kusick	.20	.10	.06
39	Tom Griffin	.20	.10	.06
40	Bobby Murcer	.30	.15	.09
41	Jim Kern	.20	.10	.06
42	Jose Cruz	.30	.15	.09
43	Ray Bare	.20	.10	.06
44	Bud Harrelson	.20	.10	.06
45	Rawly Eastwick	.20	.10	.06
46	Buck Martinez	.20	.10	.06
47	Lynn McGlothen	.20	.10	.06
48	Tom Paciorek	.20	.10	.06
49	Grant Jackson	.20	.10	.06
50	Ron Cey	.35	.20	.11
51	Brewers Team (Alex Grammas)	.70	.35	.20
52	Ellis Valentine	.20	.10	.06
53	Paul Mitchell	.20	.10	.06
54	Sandy Alomar	.20	.10	.06
55	Jeff Burroughs	.25	.13	.08
56	Rudy May	.20	.10	.06
57	Marc Hill	.20	.10	.06
58	Chet Lemon	.30	.15	.09
59	Larry Christenson	.20	.10	.06
60	Jim Rice	4.50	2.25	1.25
61	Manny Sanguillen	.20	.10	.06
62	Eric Raich	.20	.10	.06
63	Tito Fuentes	.20	.10	.06
64	Larry Biittner	.20	.10	.06
65	Skip Lockwood	.20	.10	.06
66	Roy Smalley	.20	.10	.06
67	*Joaquin Andujar*	.60	.30	.20
68	Bruce Bochte	.20	.10	.06
69	Jim Crawford	.20	.10	.06
70	Johnny Bench	10.00	5.00	3.00
71	Dock Ellis	.20	.10	.06
72	Mike Anderson	.20	.10	.06
73	Charlie Williams	.20	.10	.06
74	A's Team (Jack McKeon)	.70	.35	.20
75	Dennis Leonard	.20	.10	.06
76	Tim Foli	.20	.10	.06
77	Dyar Miller	.20	.10	.06
78	Bob Davis	.20	.10	.06
79	Don Money	.20	.10	.06
80	Andy Messersmith	.25	.13	.08
81	Juan Beniquez	.20	.10	.06
82	Jim Rooker	.20	.10	.06
83	Kevin Bell	.20	.10	.06
84	Ollie Brown	.20	.10	.06
85	Duane Kuiper	.20	.10	.06
86	Pat Zachry	.20	.10	.06
87	Glenn Borgmann	.20	.10	.06
88	Stan Wall	.20	.10	.06
89	*Butch Hobson*	.20	.10	.06
90	Cesar Cedeno	.30	.15	.09
91	John Verhoeven	.20	.10	.06
92	Dave Rosello	.20	.10	.06
93	Tom Poquette	.20	.10	.06
94	Craig Swan	.20	.10	.06
95	Keith Hernandez	3.00	1.50	.90
96	Lou Piniella	.40	.20	.12
97	Dave Heaverlo	.20	.10	.06
98	Milt May	.20	.10	.06
99	Tom Hausman	.20	.10	.06
100	Joe Morgan	4.00	2.00	1.25
101	Dick Bosman	.20	.10	.06
102	Jose Morales	.20	.10	.06
103	Mike Bacsik	.20	.10	.06
104	*Omar Moreno*	.25	.13	.08
105	Steve Yeager	.20	.10	.06
106	Mike Flanagan	.35	.20	.11

	NR MT	EX	VG			NR MT	EX	VG
107 Bill Melton	.20	.10	.06	196 Len Randle	.20	.10	.06
108 Alan Foster	.20	.10	.06	197 Ed Ott	.20	.10	.06
109 Jorge Orta	.20	.10	.06	198 Wilbur Wood	.20	.10	.06
110 Steve Carlton	8.00	4.00	2.40	199 Pepe Frias	.20	.10	.06
111 Rico Petrocelli	.25	.13	.08	200 Frank Tanana	.30	.15	.09
112 Bill Greif	.20	.10	.06	201 Ed Kranepool	.25	.13	.08
113 Blue Jays Mgr./Coaches (Roy Hartsfield,				202 Tom Johnson	.20	.10	.06
Don Leppert, Bob Miller, Jackie Moore, Harry				203 Ed Armbrister	.20	.10	.06
Warner)	.25	.13	.08	204 Jeff Newman	.20	.10	.06
114 Bruce Dal Canton	.20	.10	.06	205 Pete Falcone	.20	.10	.06
115 Rick Manning	.20	.10	.06	206 Boog Powell	.50	.25	.15
116 Joe Niekro	.30	.15	.09	207 Glenn Abbott	.20	.10	.06
117 Frank White	.25	.13	.08	208 Checklist 133-264	1.25	.60	.40
118 Rick Jones	.20	.10	.06	209 Rob Andrews	.20	.10	.06
119 John Stearns	.20	.10	.06	210 Fred Lynn	1.50	.70	.45
120 Rod Carew	8.00	4.00	2.50	211 Giants Team (Joe Altobelli)	.70	.35	.20
121 Gary Nolan	.20	.10	.06	212 Jim Mason	.20	.10	.06
122 Ben Oglivie	.20	.10	.06	213 Maximino Leon	.20	.10	.06
123 Fred Stanley	.20	.10	.06	214 Darrell Porter	.20	.10	.06
124 George Mitterwald	.20	.10	.06	215 Butch Metzger	.20	.10	.06
125 Bill Travers	.20	.10	.06	216 Doug DeCinces	.25	.13	.08
126 Rod Gilbreath	.20	.10	.06	217 Tom Underwood	.20	.10	.06
127 Ron Fairly	.25	.13	.08	218 *John Wathan*	.60	.30	.20
128 Tommy John	1.25	.60	.40	219 Joe Coleman	.20	.10	.06
129 Mike Sadek	.20	.10	.06	220 Chris Chambliss	.30	.15	.09
130 Al Oliver	.60	.30	.20	221 Bob Bailey	.20	.10	.06
131 Orlando Ramirez	.20	.10	.06	222 Francisco Barrios	.20	.10	.06
132 Chip Lang	.20	.10	.06	223 Earl Williams	.20	.10	.06
133 Ralph Garr	.20	.10	.06	224 Rusty Torres	.20	.10	.06
134 Padres Team (John McNamara)	.70	.35	.20	225 Bob Apodaca	.20	.10	.06
135 Mark Belanger	.20	.10	.06	226 Leroy Stanton	.20	.10	.06
136 *Jerry Mumphrey*	.20	.10	.06	227 *Joe Sambito*	.25	.13	.08
137 Jeff Terpko	.20	.10	.06	228 Twins Team (Gene Mauch)	.80	.40	.25
138 Bob Stinson	.20	.10	.06	229 Don Kessinger	.20	.10	.06
139 Fred Norman	.20	.10	.06	230 Vida Blue	.40	.20	.12
140 Mike Schmidt	25.00	12.50	7.50	231 Record Breaker (George Brett)	6.00	3.00	1.75
141 Mark Littell	.20	.10	.06	232 Record Breaker (Minnie Minoso)	.35	.20	.11
142 Steve Dillard	.20	.10	.06	233 Record Breaker (Jose Morales)	.20	.10	.06
143 Ed Herrmann	.20	.10	.06	234 Record Breaker (Nolan Ryan)	10.00	5.00	3.00
144 *Bruce Sutter*	3.00	1.50	.90	235 Cecil Cooper	.60	.30	.20
145 Tom Veryzer	.20	.10	.06	236 Tom Buskey	.20	.10	.06
146 Dusty Baker	.25	.13	.08	237 Gene Clines	.20	.10	.06
147 Jackie Brown	.20	.10	.06	238 Tippy Martinez	.20	.10	.06
148 Fran Healy	.20	.10	.06	239 Bill Plummer	.20	.10	.06
149 Mike Cubbage	.20	.10	.06	240 Ron LeFlore	.25	.13	.08
150 Tom Seaver	10.00	5.00	3.00	241 Dave Tomlin	.20	.10	.06
151 Johnnie LeMaster	.20	.10	.06	242 Ken Henderson	.20	.10	.06
152 Gaylord Perry	2.50	1.25	.70	243 Ron Reed	.20	.10	.06
153 Ron Jackson	.20	.10	.06	244 John Mayberry	.20	.10	.06
154 Dave Giusti	.20	.10	.06	245 Rick Rhoden	.30	.15	.09
155 Joe Rudi	.25	.13	.08	246 Mike Vail	.20	.10	.06
156 Pete Mackanin	.20	.10	.06	247 Chris Knapp	.20	.10	.06
157 Ken Brett	.20	.10	.06	248 Wilbur Howard	.20	.10	.06
158 Ted Kubiak	.20	.10	.06	249 Pete Redfern	.20	.10	.06
159 Bernie Carbo	.20	.10	.06	250 Bill Madlock	.40	.20	.12
160 Will McEnaney	.20	.10	.06	251 Tony Muser	.20	.10	.06
161 *Garry Templeton*	1.50	.70	.45	252 Dale Murray	.20	.10	.06
162 Mike Cuellar	.25	.13	.08	253 John Hale	.20	.10	.06
163 Dave Hilton	.20	.10	.06	254 Doyle Alexander	.30	.15	.09
164 Tug McGraw	.35	.20	.11	255 George Scott	.20	.10	.06
165 Jim Wynn	.25	.13	.08	256 Joe Hoerner	.20	.10	.06
166 Bill Campbell	.20	.10	.06	257 Mike Miley	.20	.10	.06
167 Rich Hebner	.20	.10	.06	258 Luis Tiant	.35	.20	.11
168 Charlie Spikes	.20	.10	.06	259 Mets Team (Joe Frazier)	.80	.40	.25
169 Darold Knowles	.20	.10	.06	260 J.R. Richard	.25	.13	.08
170 Thurman Munson	5.00	2.50	1.50	261 Phil Garner	.20	.10	.06
171 Ken Sanders	.20	.10	.06	262 Al Cowens	.20	.10	.06
172 John Milner	.20	.10	.06	263 Mike Marshall	.25	.13	.08
173 Chuck Scrivener	.20	.10	.06	264 Tom Hutton	.20	.10	.06
174 Nelson Briles	.20	.10	.06	265 *Mark Fidrych*	.70	.35	.20
175 *Butch Wynegar*	.40	.20	.12	266 Derrel Thomas	.20	.10	.06
176 Bob Robertson	.20	.10	.06	267 Ray Fosse	.20	.10	.06
177 Bart Johnson	.20	.10	.06	268 Rick Sawyer	.20	.10	.06
178 Bombo Rivera	.20	.10	.06	269 Joe Lis	.20	.10	.06
179 Paul Hartzell	.20	.10	.06	270 Dave Parker	4.00	2.00	1.25
180 Dave Lopes	.25	.13	.08	271 Terry Forster	.20	.10	.06
181 Ken McMullen	.20	.10	.06	272 Lee Lacy	.20	.10	.06
182 Dan Spillner	.20	.10	.06	273 Eric Soderholm	.20	.10	.06
183 Cardinals Team (Vern Rapp)	.70	.35	.20	274 Don Stanhouse	.20	.10	.06
184 Bo McLaughlin	.20	.10	.06	275 Mike Hargrove	.20	.10	.06
185 Sixto Lezcano	.20	.10	.06	276 A.L. Championship (Chambliss' Dramatic			
186 Doug Flynn	.20	.10	.06	Homer Decides It)	.70	.35	.20
187 Dick Pole	.20	.10	.06	277 N.L. Championship (Reds Sweep Phillies 3			
188 Bob Tolan	.20	.10	.06	In Row)	.70	.35	.20
189 Rick Dempsey	.20	.10	.06	278 Danny Frisella	.20	.10	.06
190 Ray Burris	.20	.10	.06	279 Joe Wallis	.20	.10	.06
191 Doug Griffin	.20	.10	.06	280 Jim Hunter	2.00	1.00	.60
192 Clarence Gaston	.20	.10	.06	281 Roy Staiger	.20	.10	.06
193 Larry Gura	.20	.10	.06	282 Sid Monge	.20	.10	.06
194 Gary Matthews	.25	.13	.08	283 Jerry DaVanon	.20	.10	.06
195 Ed Figueroa	.20	.10	.06	284 Mike Norris	.20	.10	.06

#	Player	NR MT	EX	VG
285	Brooks Robinson	2.50	1.25	.70
286	Johnny Grubb	.20	.10	.06
287	Reds Team (Sparky Anderson)	.80	.40	.25
288	Bob Montgomery	.20	.10	.06
289	Gene Garber	.20	.10	.06
290	Amos Otis	.20	.10	.06
291	*Jason Thompson*	.35	.20	.11
292	Rogelio Moret	.20	.10	.06
293	Jack Brohamer	.20	.10	.06
294	George Medich	.20	.10	.06
295	Gary Carter	6.00	3.00	1.75
296	Don Hood	.20	.10	.06
297	Ken Reitz	.20	.10	.06
298	Charlie Hough	.25	.13	.08
299	Otto Velez	.20	.10	.06
300	Jerry Koosman	.30	.15	.09
301	Toby Harrah	.20	.10	.06
302	Mike Garman	.20	.10	.06
303	Gene Tenace	.20	.10	.06
304	Jim Hughes	.20	.10	.06
305	Mickey Rivers	.25	.13	.08
306	Rick Waits	.20	.10	.06
307	Gary Sutherland	.20	.10	.06
308	Gene Pentz	.20	.10	.06
309	Red Sox Team (Don Zimmer)	.80	.40	.25
310	Larry Bowa	.30	.15	.09
311	Vern Ruhle	.20	.10	.06
312	Rob Belloir	.20	.10	.06
313	Paul Blair	.20	.10	.06
314	Steve Mingori	.20	.10	.06
315	Dave Chalk	.20	.10	.06
316	Steve Rogers	.20	.10	.06
317	Kurt Bevacqua	.20	.10	.06
318	Duffy Dyer	.20	.10	.06
319	Rich Gossage	1.00	.50	.30
320	Ken Griffey	.30	.15	.09
321	Dave Goltz	.20	.10	.06
322	Bill Russell	.20	.10	.06
323	Larry Lintz	.20	.10	.06
324	John Curtis	.20	.10	.06
325	Mike Ivie	.20	.10	.06
326	Jesse Jefferson	.20	.10	.06
327	Astros Team (Bill Virdon)	.70	.35	.20
328	Tommy Boggs	.20	.10	.06
329	Ron Hodges	.20	.10	.06
330	George Hendrick	.20	.10	.06
331	Jim Colborn	.20	.10	.06
332	Elliott Maddox	.20	.10	.06
333	Paul Reuschel	.20	.10	.06
334	Bill Stein	.20	.10	.06
335	Bill Robinson	.20	.10	.06
336	Denny Doyle	.20	.10	.06
337	Ron Schueler	.20	.10	.06
338	Dave Duncan	.20	.10	.06
339	Adrian Devine	.20	.10	.06
340	Hal McRae	.30	.15	.09
341	Joe Kerrigan	.20	.10	.06
342	Jerry Remy	.20	.10	.06
343	Ed Halicki	.20	.10	.06
344	Brian Downing	.25	.13	.08
345	Reggie Smith	.25	.13	.08
346	Bill Singer	.20	.10	.06
347	George Foster	1.25	.60	.40
348	Brent Strom	.20	.10	.06
349	Jim Holt	.20	.10	.06
350	Larry Dierker	.20	.10	.06
351	Jim Sundberg	.20	.10	.06
352	Mike Phillips	.20	.10	.06
353	Stan Thomas	.20	.10	.06
354	Pirates Team (Chuck Tanner)	.80	.40	.25
355	Lou Brock	3.00	1.50	.90
356	Checklist 265-396	1.25	.60	.40
357	Tim McCarver	.40	.20	.12
358	Tom House	.20	.10	.06
359	Willie Randolph	1.00	.50	.30
360	Rick Monday	.25	.13	.08
361	Eduardo Rodriguez	.20	.10	.06
362	Tommy Davis	.30	.15	.09
363	Dave Roberts	.20	.10	.06
364	Vic Correll	.20	.10	.06
365	Mike Torrez	.20	.10	.06
366	Ted Sizemore	.20	.10	.06
367	Dave Hamilton	.20	.10	.06
368	Mike Jorgensen	.20	.10	.06
369	Terry Humphrey	.20	.10	.06
370	John Montefusco	.20	.10	.06
371	Royals Team (Whitey Herzog)	.80	.40	.25
372	Rich Folkers	.20	.10	.06
373	Bert Campaneris	.30	.15	.09
374	Kent Tekulve	.30	.15	.09
375	Larry Hisle	.20	.10	.06

#	Player	NR MT	EX	VG
376	Nino Espinosa	.20	.10	.06
377	Dave McKay	.20	.10	.06
378	Jim Umbarger	.20	.10	.06
379	Larry Cox	.20	.10	.06
380	Lee May	.25	.13	.08
381	Bob Forsch	.20	.10	.06
382	Charlie Moore	.20	.10	.06
383	Stan Bahnsen	.20	.10	.06
384	Darrel Chaney	.20	.10	.06
385	Dave LaRoche	.20	.10	.06
386	Manny Mota	.25	.13	.08
387	Yankees Team (Billy Martin)	1.25	.60	.40
388	Terry Harmon	.20	.10	.06
389	Ken Kravec	.20	.10	.06
390	Dave Winfield	15.00	7.50	4.50
391	Dan Warthen	.20	.10	.06
392	Phil Roof	.20	.10	.06
393	John Lowenstein	.20	.10	.06
394	Bill Laxton	.20	.10	.06
395	Manny Trillo	.20	.10	.06
396	Tom Murphy	.20	.10	.06
397	*Larry Herndon*	.40	.20	.12
398	Tom Burgmeier	.20	.10	.06
399	Bruce Boisclair	.20	.10	.06
400	Steve Garvey	5.00	2.50	1.50
401	Mickey Scott	.20	.10	.06
402	Tommy Helms	.20	.10	.06
403	Tom Grieve	.20	.10	.06
404	Eric Rasmussen	.20	.10	.06
405	Claudell Washington	.25	.13	.08
406	Tim Johnson	.20	.10	.06
407	Dave Freisleben	.20	.10	.06
408	Cesar Tovar	.20	.10	.06
409	Pete Broberg	.20	.10	.06
410	Willie Montanez	.20	.10	.06
411	World Series Games 1 & 2	.70	.35	.20
412	World Series Games 3 & 4	.70	.35	.20
413	World Series Summary	.70	.35	.20
414	Tommy Harper	.20	.10	.06
415	Jay Johnstone	.20	.10	.06
416	Chuck Hartenstein	.20	.10	.06
417	Wayne Garrett	.20	.10	.06
418	White Sox Team (Bob Lemon)	.80	.40	.25
419	Steve Swisher	.20	.10	.06
420	Rusty Staub	.35	.20	.11
421	Doug Rau	.20	.10	.06
422	Freddie Patek	.20	.10	.06
423	Gary Lavelle	.20	.10	.06
424	Steve Brye	.20	.10	.06
425	Joe Torre	.40	.20	.12
426	Dick Drago	.20	.10	.06
427	Dave Rader	.20	.10	.06
428	Rangers Team (Frank Lucchesi)	.70	.35	.20
429	Ken Boswell	.20	.10	.06
430	Fergie Jenkins	1.75	.90	.50
431	Dave Collins	.25	.13	.08
432	Buzz Capra	.20	.10	.06
433	Turn Back The Clock (Nate Colbert)	.20	.10	.06
434	Turn Back The Clock (Carl Yastrzemski)	2.00	1.00	.60
435	Turn Back The Clock (Maury Wills)	.35	.20	.11
436	Turn Back The Clock (Bob Keegan)	.20	.10	.06
437	Turn Back The Clock (Ralph Kiner)	.50	.25	.15
438	Marty Perez	.20	.10	.06
439	Gorman Thomas	.30	.15	.09
440	Jon Matlack	.20	.10	.06
441	Larvell Blanks	.20	.10	.06
442	Braves Team (Dave Bristol)	.70	.35	.20
443	Lamar Johnson	.20	.10	.06
444	Wayne Twitchell	.20	.10	.06
445	Ken Singleton	.25	.13	.08
446	Bill Bonham	.20	.10	.06
447	Jerry Turner	.20	.10	.06
448	Ellie Rodriguez	.20	.10	.06
449	Al Fitzmorris	.20	.10	.06
450	Pete Rose	9.00	4.50	2.75
451	Checklist 397-528	1.25	.60	.40
452	Mike Caldwell	.20	.10	.06
453	Pedro Garcia	.20	.10	.06
454	Andy Etchebarren	.20	.10	.06
455	Rick Wise	.20	.10	.06
456	Leon Roberts	.20	.10	.06
457	Steve Luebber	.20	.10	.06
458	Leo Foster	.20	.10	.06
459	Steve Foucault	.20	.10	.06
460	Willie Stargell	3.00	1.50	.90
461	Dick Tidrow	.20	.10	.06
462	Don Baylor	.35	.20	.11
463	Jamie Quirk	.20	.10	.06
464	Randy Moffitt	.20	.10	.06

#	Player	NR MT	EX	VG
465	Rico Carty	.25	.13	.08
466	Fred Holdsworth	.20	.10	.06
467	Phillies Team (Danny Ozark)	.70	.35	.20
468	Ramon Hernandez	.20	.10	.06
469	Pat Kelly	.20	.10	.06
470	Ted Simmons	.60	.30	.20
471	Del Unser	.20	.10	.06
472	Rookie Pitchers (Don Aase, Bob McClure, Gil Patterson, Dave Wehrmeister)	.25	.13	.08
473	Rookie Outfielders (Andre Dawson, Gene Richards, John Scott, Denny Walling)	75.00	38.00	23.00
474	Rookie Shortstops (Bob Bailor, Kiko Garcia, Craig Reynolds, Alex Taveras)	.20	.10	.06
475	Rookie Pitchers (Chris Batton, Rick Camp, Scott McGregor, Manny Sarmiento)	.30	.15	.09
476	Rookie Catchers (Gary Alexander, Rick Cerone, Dale Murphy, Kevin Pasley)	40.00	20.00	12.00
477	Rookie Infielders (Doug Ault, Rich Dauer, Orlando Gonzalez, Phil Mankowski)	.25	.13	.08
478	Rookie Pitchers (Jim Gideon, Leon Hooten, Dave Johnson, Mark Lemongello)	.20	.10	.06
479	Rookie Outfielders (Brian Asselstine, Wayne Gross, Sam Mejias, Alvis Woods)	.25	.13	.08
480	Carl Yastrzemski	7.00	3.50	2.00
481	Roger Metzger	.20	.10	.06
482	Tony Solaita	.20	.10	.06
483	Richie Zisk	.20	.10	.06
484	Burt Hooton	.20	.10	.06
485	Roy White	.30	.15	.09
486	Ed Bane	.20	.10	.06
487	Rookie Pitchers (Larry Anderson, Ed Glynn, Joe Henderson, Greg Terlecky)	.20	.10	.06
488	Rookie Outfielders (Jack Clark, Ruppert Jones, Lee Mazzilli, Dan Thomas)	12.00	6.00	3.50
489	Rookie Pitchers (Len Barker, Randy Lerch, Greg Minton, Mike Overy)	.40	.20	.12
490	Rookie Shortstops (Billy Almon, Mickey Klutts, Tommy McMillan, Mark Wagner)	.25	.13	.08
491	Rookie Pitchers (Mike Dupree, Denny Martinez, Craig Mitchell, Bob Sykes)	5.00	2.50	1.50
492	Rookie Outfielders (Tony Armas, Steve Kemp, Carlos Lopez, Gary Woods)	1.00	.50	.30
493	Rookie Pitchers (Mike Krukow, Jim Otten, Gary Wheelock, Mike Willis)	.50	.25	.15
494	Rookie Infielders (Juan Bernhardt, Mike Champion, Jim Gantner, Bump Wills)	.50	.25	.15
495	Al Hrabosky	.20	.10	.06
496	Gary Thomasson	.20	.10	.06
497	Clay Carroll	.20	.10	.06
498	Sal Bando	.25	.13	.08
499	Pablo Torrealba	.20	.10	.06
500	Dave Kingman	.60	.30	.20
501	Jim Bibby	.20	.10	.06
502	Randy Hundley	.20	.10	.06
503	Bill Lee	.20	.10	.06
504	Dodgers Team (Tom Lasorda)	1.00	.50	.30
505	Oscar Gamble	.20	.10	.06
506	Steve Grilli	.20	.10	.06
507	Mike Hegan	.20	.10	.06
508	Dave Pagan	.20	.10	.06
509	Cookie Rojas	.20	.10	.06
510	John Candelaria	.80	.40	.25
511	Bill Fahey	.20	.10	.06
512	Jack Billingham	.20	.10	.06
513	Jerry Terrell	.20	.10	.06
514	Cliff Johnson	.20	.10	.06
515	Chris Speier	.20	.10	.06
516	Bake McBride	.20	.10	.06
517	Pete Vuckovich	.50	.25	.15
518	Cubs Team (Herman Franks)	.70	.35	.20
519	Don Kirkwood	.20	.10	.06
520	Garry Maddox	.20	.10	.06
521	Bob Grich	.25	.13	.08
522	Enzo Hernandez	.20	.10	.06
523	Rollie Fingers	2.50	1.25	.70
524	Rowland Office	.20	.10	.06
525	Dennis Eckersley	15.00	7.50	4.50
526	Larry Parrish	.35	.20	.11
527	Dan Meyer	.20	.10	.06
528	Bill Castro	.20	.10	.06
529	Jim Essian	.20	.10	.06
530	Rick Reuschel	.30	.15	.09
531	Lyman Bostock	.25	.13	.08
532	Jim Willoughby	.20	.10	.06
533	Mickey Stanley	.20	.10	.06
534	Paul Splittorff	.20	.10	.06
535	Cesar Geronimo	.20	.10	.06
536	Vic Albury	.20	.10	.06
537	Dave Roberts	.20	.10	.06
538	Frank Taveras	.20	.10	.06
539	Mike Wallace	.20	.10	.06
540	Bob Watson	.20	.10	.06
541	John Denny	.20	.10	.06
542	Frank Duffy	.20	.10	.06
543	Ron Blomberg	.20	.10	.06
544	Gary Ross	.20	.10	.06
545	Bob Boone	.25	.13	.08
546	Orioles Team (Earl Weaver)	.80	.40	.25
547	Willie McCovey	2.75	1.50	.80
548	Joel Youngblood	.30	.15	.09
549	Jerry Royster	.20	.10	.06
550	Randy Jones	.20	.10	.06
551	Bill North	.20	.10	.06
552	Pepe Mangual	.20	.10	.06
553	Jack Heidemann	.20	.10	.06
554	Bruce Kimm	.20	.10	.06
555	Dan Ford	.20	.10	.06
556	Doug Bird	.20	.10	.06
557	Jerry White	.20	.10	.06
558	Elias Sosa	.20	.10	.06
559	Alan Bannister	.20	.10	.06
560	Dave Concepcion	.35	.20	.11
561	Pete LaCock	.20	.10	.06
562	Checklist 529-660	1.25	.60	.40
563	Bruce Kison	.20	.10	.06
564	Alan Ashby	.20	.10	.06
565	Mickey Lolich	.50	.25	.15
566	Rick Miller	.20	.10	.06
567	Enos Cabell	.20	.10	.06
568	Carlos May	.20	.10	.06
569	Jim Lonborg	.20	.10	.06
570	Bobby Bonds	.35	.20	.11
571	Darrell Evans	.40	.20	.12
572	Ross Grimsley	.20	.10	.06
573	Joe Ferguson	.20	.10	.06
574	Aurelio Rodriguez	.20	.10	.06
575	Dick Ruthven	.20	.10	.06
576	Fred Kendall	.20	.10	.06
577	Jerry Augustine	.20	.10	.06
578	Bob Randall	.20	.10	.06
579	Don Carrithers	.20	.10	.06
580	George Brett	35.00	17.50	10.50
581	Pedro Borbon	.20	.10	.06
582	Ed Kirkpatrick	.20	.10	.06
583	Paul Lindblad	.20	.10	.06
584	Ed Goodson	.20	.10	.06
585	Rick Burleson	.20	.10	.06
586	Steve Renko	.20	.10	.06
587	Rick Baldwin	.20	.10	.06
588	Dave Moates	.20	.10	.06
589	Mike Cosgrove	.20	.10	.06
590	Buddy Bell	.30	.15	.09
591	Chris Arnold	.20	.10	.06
592	Dan Briggs	.20	.10	.06
593	Dennis Blair	.20	.10	.06
594	Biff Pocoroba	.20	.10	.06
595	John Hiller	.20	.10	.06
596	Jerry Martin	.25	.13	.08
597	Mariners Mgr./Coaches (Don Bryant, Jim Busby, Darrell Johnson, Vada Pinson, Wes Stock)	.25	.13	.08
598	Sparky Lyle	.35	.20	.11
599	Mike Tyson	.20	.10	.06
600	Jim Palmer	5.00	2.50	1.50
601	Mike Lum	.20	.10	.06
602	Andy Hassler	.20	.10	.06
603	Willie Davis	.25	.13	.08
604	Jim Slaton	.20	.10	.06
605	Felix Millan	.20	.10	.06
606	Steve Braun	.20	.10	.06
607	Larry Demery	.20	.10	.06
608	Roy Howell	.20	.10	.06
609	Jim Barr	.20	.10	.06
610	Jose Cardenal	.20	.10	.06
611	Dave Lemanczyk	.20	.10	.06
612	Barry Foote	.20	.10	.06
613	Reggie Cleveland	.20	.10	.06
614	Greg Gross	.20	.10	.06
615	Phil Niekro	1.50	.70	.45
616	Tommy Sandt	.20	.10	.06
617	Bobby Darwin	.20	.10	.06
618	Pat Dobson	.20	.10	.06
619	Johnny Oates	.20	.10	.06
620	Don Sutton	1.50	.70	.45
621	Tigers Team (Ralph Houk)	.80	.40	.25
622	Jim Wohlford	.20	.10	.06

		NR MT	EX	VG
623	Jack Kucek	.20	.10	.06
624	Hector Cruz	.20	.10	.06
625	Ken Holtzman	.25	.13	.08
626	Al Bumbry	.20	.10	.06
627	Bob Myrick	.20	.10	.06
628	Mario Guerrero	.20	.10	.06
629	Bobby Valentine	.25	.13	.08
630	Bert Blyleven	1.25	.60	.40
631	Big League Brothers (George Brett, Ken Brett)	3.00	1.50	.90
632	Big League Brothers (Bob Forsch, Ken Forsch)	.30	.15	.09
633	Big League Brothers (Carlos May, Lee May)	.30	.15	.09
634	Big League Brothers (Paul Reuschel, Rick Reuschel) (names switched)	.30	.15	.09
635	Robin Yount	35.00	17.50	10.50
636	Santo Alcala	.20	.10	.06
637	Alex Johnson	.20	.10	.06
638	Jim Kaat	.80	.40	.25
639	Jerry Morales	.20	.10	.06
640	Carlton Fisk	6.00	3.00	1.75
641	Dan Larson	.20	.10	.06
642	Willie Crawford	.20	.10	.06
643	Mike Pazik	.20	.10	.06
644	Matt Alexander	.20	.10	.06
645	Jerry Reuss	.25	.13	.08
646	Andres Mora	.20	.10	.06
647	Expos Team (Dick Williams)	.80	.40	.25
648	Jim Spencer	.20	.10	.06
649	Dave Cash	.20	.10	.06
650	Nolan Ryan	35.00	17.50	10.50
651	Von Joshua	.20	.10	.06
652	Tom Walker	.20	.10	.06
653	Diego Segui	.20	.10	.06
654	Ron Pruitt	.20	.10	.06
655	Tony Perez	2.00	1.00	.60
656	Ron Guidry	2.75	1.50	.80
657	Mick Kelleher	.20	.10	.06
658	Marty Pattin	.20	.10	.06
659	Merv Rettenmund	.20	.10	.06
660	Willie Horton	.40	.13	.08

		NR MT	EX	VG
10	Rod Carew	15.00	7.50	4.50
11	Steve Carlton	12.00	6.00	3.50
12	Dave Cash	.20	.10	.06
13	Cesar Cedeno	1.00	.50	.30
14	Ron Cey	.50	.25	.15
15	Mark Fidrych	.50	.25	.15
16	Dan Ford	.20	.10	.06
17	Wayne Garland	.20	.10	.06
18	Ralph Garr	.20	.10	.06
19	Steve Garvey	4.00	2.00	1.25
20	Mike Hargrove	.20	.10	.06
21	Jim Hunter	6.00	3.00	1.75
22	Reggie Jackson	12.00	6.00	3.50
23	Randy Jones	.20	.10	.06
24	Dave Kingman	1.00	.50	.30
25	Bill Madlock	.70	.35	.20
26	Lee May	.50	.25	.15
27	John Mayberry	.20	.10	.06
28	Andy Messersmith	.20	.10	.06
29	Willie Montanez	.20	.10	.06
30	John Montefusco	.50	.25	.15
31	Joe Morgan	6.00	3.00	1.75
32	Thurman Munson	6.00	3.00	1.75
33	Bobby Murcer	.50	.25	.15
34	Al Oliver	1.25	.60	.40
35	Dave Pagan	.20	.10	.06
36	Jim Palmer	15.00	7.50	4.50
37	Tony Perez	.70	.35	.20
38	Pete Rose	30.00	15.00	9.00
39	Joe Rudi	.50	.25	.15
40	Nolan Ryan	40.00	20.00	12.00
41	Mike Schmidt	30.00	15.00	9.00
42	Tom Seaver	25.00	12.50	7.50
43	Ted Simmons	.70	.35	.20
44	Bill Singer	.20	.10	.06
45	Willie Stargell	1.50	.70	.45
46	Rusty Staub	.50	.25	.15
47	Don Sutton	1.25	.60	.40
48	Luis Tiant	.70	.35	.20
49	Bill Travers	.20	.10	.06
50	Claudell Washington	.50	.25	.15
51	Bob Watson	.20	.10	.06
52	Dave Winfield	6.00	3.00	1.75
53	Carl Yastrzemski	4.50	2.25	1.25
54	Robin Yount	25.00	12.50	7.50
55	Richie Zisk	.20	.10	.06

1977 Topps Cloth Stickers

One of the few Topps specialty issues of the late 1970s, the 73-piece set of cloth stickers issued in 1977 includes 55 player stickers and 18 puzzle cards which could be joined to form a photo of the American League or National League All-Star teams. Issued as a separate issue, the 2-1/2" by 3-1/2" stickers have a paper backing which could be removed to allow the cloth to be adhered to a jacket, notebook, etc.

		NR MT	EX	VG
Complete Set:		300.00	150.00	90.00
Common Player:		.20	.10	.06
1	Alan Ashby	.20	.10	.06
2	Buddy Bell	1.00	.50	.30
3	Johnny Bench	5.00	2.50	1.50
4	Vida Blue	.50	.25	.15
5	Bert Blyleven	1.00	.50	.30
6	Steve Braun	.50	.25	.15
7	George Brett	15.00	7.50	4.50
8	Lou Brock	6.00	3.00	1.75
9	Jose Cardenal	.20	.10	.06

The values quoted are intended to reflect the market price.

1978 Topps

At 726 cards, this was the largest issue from Topps since 1972. In design, the color player photo is slightly larger than usual, with the player's name and team at the bottom. In the upper right-hand corner of the 2-1/2" by 3-1/2" cards there is a small white baseball with the player's position. Most of the starting All-Stars from the previous year had a red, white and blue shield instead of the baseball. Backs feature statistics and a baseball situation which made a card game of baseball possible. Specialty cards include baseball records, statistical leaders and the World Series and playoffs. As one row of cards per sheet had to be double-printed to accommodate the 726-card set size, some cards are more common, yet that seems to have no serious impact on their prices.

	NR MT	EX	VG
Complete Set:	350.00	175.00	105.00
Common Player:	.12	.06	.04

#	Player	NR MT	EX	VG
1	Record Breaker (Lou Brock)	3.00	1.50	.90
2	Record Breaker (Sparky Lyle)	.25	.13	.08
3	Record Breaker (Willie McCovey)	.70	.35	.20
4	Record Breaker (Brooks Robinson)	.90	.45	.25
5	Record Breaker (Pete Rose)	2.00	1.00	.60
6	Record Breaker (Nolan Ryan)	7.00	3.50	2.00
7	Record Breaker (Reggie Jackson)	3.00	1.50	.90
8	Mike Sadek	.12	.06	.04
9	Doug DeCinces	.25	.13	.08
10	Phil Niekro	1.25	.60	.40
11	Rick Manning	.12	.06	.04
12	Don Aase	.20	.10	.06
13	Art Howe	.12	.06	.04
14	Lerrin LaGrow	.12	.06	.04
15	Tony Perez	.25	.13	.08
16	Roy White	.25	.13	.08
17	Mike Krukow	.25	.13	.08
18	Bob Grich	.25	.13	.08
19	Darrell Porter	.20	.10	.06
20	Pete Rose	4.00	2.00	1.25
21	Steve Kemp	.25	.13	.08
22	Charlie Hough	.20	.10	.06
23	Bump Wills	.12	.06	.04
24	Don Money	.12	.06	.04
25	Jon Matlack	.20	.10	.06
26	Rich Hebner	.12	.06	.04
27	Geoff Zahn	.12	.06	.04
28	Ed Ott	.12	.06	.04
29	Bob Lacey	.12	.06	.04
30	George Hendrick	.20	.10	.06
31	Glenn Abbott	.12	.06	.04
32	Garry Templeton	.30	.15	.09
33	Dave Lemanczyk	.12	.06	.04
34	Willie McCovey	3.00	1.50	.90
35	Sparky Lyle	.30	.15	.09
36	*Eddie Murray*	75.00	38.00	23.00
37	Rick Waits	.12	.06	.04
38	Willie Montanez	.12	.06	.04
39	*Floyd Bannister*	.70	.35	.20
40	Carl Yastrzemski	5.00	2.50	1.50
41	Burt Hooton	.20	.10	.06
42	Jorge Orta	.12	.06	.04
43	Bill Atkinson	.12	.06	.04
44	Toby Harrah	.20	.10	.06
45	Mark Fidrych	.25	.13	.08
46	Al Cowens	.12	.06	.04
47	Jack Billingham	.12	.06	.04
48	Don Baylor	.35	.20	.11
49	Ed Kranepool	.20	.10	.06
50	Rick Reuschel	.40	.20	.12
51	Charlie Moore	.12	.06	.04
52	Jim Lonborg	.20	.10	.06
53	Phil Garner	.12	.06	.04
54	Tom Johnson	.12	.06	.04
55	Mitchell Page	.12	.06	.04
56	Randy Jones	.20	.10	.06
57	Dan Meyer	.12	.06	.04
58	Bob Forsch	.20	.10	.06
59	Otto Velez	.12	.06	.04
60	Thurman Munson	5.00	2.50	1.50
61	Larvell Blanks	.12	.06	.04
62	Jim Barr	.12	.06	.04
63	Don Zimmer	.20	.10	.06
64	Gene Pentz	.12	.06	.04
65	Ken Singleton	.25	.13	.08
66	White Sox Team	.50	.25	.15
67	Claudell Washington	.25	.13	.08
68	Steve Foucault	.12	.06	.04
69	Mike Vail	.12	.06	.04
70	Rich Gossage	1.00	.50	.30
71	Terry Humphrey	.12	.06	.04
72	Andre Dawson	20.00	10.00	6.00
73	Andy Hassler	.12	.06	.04
74	Checklist 1-121	.90	.45	.25
75	Dick Ruthven	.12	.06	.04
76	Steve Ontiveros	.12	.06	.04
77	Ed Kirkpatrick	.12	.06	.04
78	Pablo Torrealba	.12	.06	.04
79	Darrell Johnson	.12	.06	.04
80	Ken Griffey	.25	.13	.08
81	Pete Redfern	.12	.06	.04
82	Giants Team	.50	.25	.15
83	Bob Montgomery	.12	.06	.04
84	Kent Tekulve	.25	.13	.08
85	Ron Fairly	.20	.10	.06
86	Dave Tomlin	.12	.06	.04
87	John Lowenstein	.12	.06	.04
88	Mike Phillips	.12	.06	.04
89	Ken Clay	.20	.10	.06
90	Larry Bowa	.30	.15	.09
91	Oscar Zamora	.12	.06	.04
92	Adrian Devine	.12	.06	.04
93	Bobby Cox	.12	.06	.04
94	Chuck Scrivener	.12	.06	.04
95	Jamie Quirk	.12	.06	.04
96	Orioles Team	.50	.25	.15
97	Stan Bahnsen	.12	.06	.04
98	Jim Essian	.12	.06	.04
99	*Willie Hernandez*	.70	.35	.20
100	George Brett	20.00	10.00	6.00
101	Sid Monge	.12	.06	.04
102	Matt Alexander	.12	.06	.04
103	Tom Murphy	.12	.06	.04
104	Lee Lacy	.12	.06	.04
105	Reggie Cleveland	.12	.06	.04
106	Bill Plummer	.12	.06	.04
107	Ed Halicki	.12	.06	.04
108	Von Joshua	.12	.06	.04
109	Joe Torre	.30	.15	.09
110	Richie Zisk	.20	.10	.06
111	Mike Tyson	.12	.06	.04
112	Astros Team	.50	.25	.15
113	Don Carrithers	.12	.06	.04
114	Paul Blair	.20	.10	.06
115	Gary Nolan	.12	.06	.04
116	Tucker Ashford	.12	.06	.04
117	John Montague	.12	.06	.04
118	Terry Harmon	.12	.06	.04
119	Denny Martinez	.25	.13	.08
120	Gary Carter	4.00	2.00	1.25
121	Alvis Woods	.12	.06	.04
122	Dennis Eckersley	7.00	3.50	2.00
123	Manny Trillo	.20	.10	.06
124	*Dave Rozema*	.25	.13	.08
125	George Scott	.20	.10	.06
126	Paul Moskau	.12	.06	.04
127	Chet Lemon	.20	.10	.06
128	Bill Russell	.20	.10	.06
129	Jim Colborn	.12	.06	.04
130	Jeff Burroughs	.20	.10	.06
131	Bert Blyleven	.90	.45	.25
132	Enos Cabell	.20	.10	.06
133	Jerry Augustine	.12	.06	.04
134	*Steve Henderson*	.25	.13	.08
135	Ron Guidry	.70	.35	.20
136	Ted Sizemore	.12	.06	.04
137	Craig Kusick	.12	.06	.04
138	Larry Demery	.12	.06	.04
139	Wayne Gross	.12	.06	.04
140	Rollie Fingers	3.00	1.50	.90
141	Ruppert Jones	.20	.10	.06
142	John Montefusco	.20	.10	.06
143	Keith Hernandez	2.00	1.00	.60
144	Jesse Jefferson	.12	.06	.04
145	Rick Monday	.20	.10	.06
146	Doyle Alexander	.30	.15	.09
147	Lee Mazzilli	.25	.13	.08
148	Andre Thornton	.25	.13	.08
149	Dale Murray	.12	.06	.04
150	Bobby Bonds	.35	.20	.11
151	Milt Wilcox	.12	.06	.04
152	*Ivan DeJesus*	.20	.10	.06
153	Steve Stone	.25	.13	.08
154	Cecil Cooper	.20	.10	.06
155	Butch Hobson	.12	.06	.04
156	Andy Messersmith	.20	.10	.06
157	Pete LaCock	.12	.06	.04
158	Joaquin Andujar	.25	.13	.08
159	Lou Piniella	.35	.20	.11
160	Jim Palmer	4.00	2.00	1.25
161	Bob Boone	.25	.13	.08
162	Paul Thormodsgard	.12	.06	.04
163	Bill North	.12	.06	.04
164	Bob Owchinko	.12	.06	.04
165	Rennie Stennett	.12	.06	.04
166	Carlos Lopez	.12	.06	.04
167	Tim Foli	.12	.06	.04
168	Reggie Smith	.25	.13	.08
169	Jerry Johnson	.12	.06	.04
170	Lou Brock	3.00	1.50	.90
171	Pat Zachry	.12	.06	.04
172	Mike Hargrove	.20	.10	.06
173	Robin Yount	20.00	10.00	6.00
174	Wayne Garland	.12	.06	.04
175	Jerry Morales	.12	.06	.04
176	Milt May	.12	.06	.04
177	Gene Garber	.12	.06	.04
178	Dave Chalk	.12	.06	.04
179	Dick Tidrow	.20	.10	.06

#	Player	NR MT	EX	VG
180	Dave Concepcion	.35	.20	.11
181	Ken Forsch	.20	.10	.06
182	Jim Spencer	.12	.06	.04
183	Doug Bird	.12	.06	.04
184	Checklist 122-242	.90	.45	.25
185	Ellis Valentine	.20	.10	.06
186	*Bob Stanley*	.25	.13	.08
187	Jerry Royster	.12	.06	.04
188	Al Bumbry	.20	.10	.06
189	Tom Lasorda	.30	.15	.09
190	John Candelaria	.25	.13	.08
191	Rodney Scott	.12	.06	.04
192	Padres Team	.50	.25	.15
193	Rich Chiles	.12	.06	.04
194	Derrel Thomas	.12	.06	.04
195	Larry Dierker	.20	.10	.06
196	Bob Bailor	.12	.06	.04
197	Nino Espinosa	.12	.06	.04
198	Ron Pruitt	.12	.06	.04
199	Craig Reynolds	.12	.06	.04
200	Reggie Jackson	10.00	5.00	3.00
201	Batting Leaders (Rod Carew, Dave Parker)	1.00	.50	.30
202	Home Run Leaders (George Foster, Jim Rice)	.25	.13	.08
203	Runs Batted In Ldrs. (George Foster, Larry Hisle)	.25	.13	.08
204	Stolen Base Leaders (Freddie Patek, Frank Taveras)	.12	.06	.04
205	Victory Leaders (Steve Carlton, Dave Goltz, Dennis Leonard, Jim Palmer)	.60	.30	.20
206	Strikeout Leaders (Phil Niekro, Nolan Ryan)	.35	.20	.11
207	Earned Run Avg. Ldrs. (John Candelaria, Frank Tanana)	.12	.06	.04
208	Leading Firemen (Bill Campbell, Rollie Fingers)	.35	.20	.11
209	Dock Ellis	.12	.06	.04
210	Jose Cardenal	.12	.06	.04
211	Earl Weaver	.20	.10	.06
212	Mike Caldwell	.12	.06	.04
213	Alan Bannister	.12	.06	.04
214	Angels Team	.50	.25	.15
215	Darrell Evans	.35	.20	.11
216	Mike Paxton	.12	.06	.04
217	Rod Gilbreath	.12	.06	.04
218	Marty Pattin	.12	.06	.04
219	Mike Cubbage	.12	.06	.04
220	Pedro Borbon	.12	.06	.04
221	Chris Speier	.20	.10	.06
222	Jerry Martin	.12	.06	.04
223	Bruce Kison	.12	.06	.04
224	Jerry Tabb	.12	.06	.04
225	Don Gullett	.12	.06	.04
226	Joe Ferguson	.12	.06	.04
227	Al Fitzmorris	.12	.06	.04
228	Manny Mota	.12	.06	.04
229	Leo Foster	.12	.06	.04
230	Al Hrabosky	.20	.10	.06
231	Wayne Nordhagen	.12	.06	.04
232	Mickey Stanley	.20	.10	.06
233	Dick Pole	.12	.06	.04
234	Herman Franks	.12	.06	.04
235	Tim McCarver	.35	.20	.11
236	Terry Whitfield	.12	.06	.04
237	Rich Dauer	.12	.06	.04
238	Juan Beniquez	.20	.10	.06
239	Dyar Miller	.12	.06	.04
240	Gene Tenace	.20	.10	.06
241	Pete Vuckovich	.20	.10	.06
242	Barry Bonnell	.12	.06	.04
243	Bob McClure	.12	.06	.04
244	Expos Team	.20	.10	.06
245	Rick Burleson	.20	.10	.06
246	Dan Driessen	.20	.10	.06
247	Larry Christenson	.12	.06	.04
248	Frank White	.12	.06	.04
249	Dave Goltz	.12	.06	.04
250	Graig Nettles	.30	.15	.09
251	Don Kirkwood	.12	.06	.04
252	Steve Swisher	.12	.06	.04
253	Jim Kern	.12	.06	.04
254	Dave Collins	.20	.10	.06
255	Jerry Reuss	.20	.10	.06
256	Joe Altobelli	.12	.06	.04
257	Hector Cruz	.12	.06	.04
258	John Hiller	.20	.10	.06
259	Dodgers Team	.80	.40	.25
260	Bert Campaneris	.25	.13	.08
261	Tim Hosley	.12	.06	.04
262	Rudy May	.12	.06	.04
263	Danny Walton	.12	.06	.04
264	Jamie Easterly	.12	.06	.04
265	Sal Bando	.12	.06	.04
266	*Bob Shirley*	.20	.10	.06
267	Doug Ault	.12	.06	.04
268	Gil Flores	.12	.06	.04
269	Wayne Twitchell	.12	.06	.04
270	Carlton Fisk	5.00	2.50	1.50
271	Randy Lerch	.12	.06	.04
272	Royle Stillman	.12	.06	.04
273	Fred Norman	.12	.06	.04
274	Freddie Patek	.12	.06	.04
275	Dan Ford	.12	.06	.04
276	Bill Bonham	.12	.06	.04
277	Bruce Boisclair	.12	.06	.04
278	Enrique Romo	.12	.06	.04
279	Bill Virdon	.20	.10	.06
280	Buddy Bell	.30	.15	.09
281	Eric Rasmussen	.12	.06	.04
282	Yankees Team	1.00	.50	.30
283	Omar Moreno	.12	.06	.04
284	Randy Moffitt	.12	.06	.04
285	Steve Yeager	.12	.06	.04
286	Ben Oglivie	.20	.10	.06
287	Kiko Garcia	.12	.06	.04
288	Dave Hamilton	.12	.06	.04
289	Checklist 243-363	.90	.45	.25
290	Willie Horton	.20	.10	.06
291	Gary Ross	.12	.06	.04
292	Gene Richard	.12	.06	.04
293	Mike Willis	.12	.06	.04
294	Larry Parrish	.25	.13	.08
295	Bill Lee	.20	.10	.06
296	Biff Pocoroba	.12	.06	.04
297	Warren Brusstar	.12	.06	.04
298	Tony Armas	.25	.13	.08
299	Whitey Herzog	.30	.15	.09
300	Joe Morgan	3.00	1.50	.90
301	Buddy Schultz	.12	.06	.04
302	Cubs Team	.50	.25	.15
303	Sam Hinds	.12	.06	.04
304	John Milner	.12	.06	.04
305	Rico Carty	.20	.10	.06
306	Joe Niekro	.25	.13	.08
307	Glenn Borgmann	.12	.06	.04
308	Jim Rooker	.12	.06	.04
309	Cliff Johnson	.20	.10	.06
310	Don Sutton	2.00	1.00	.60
311	Jose Baez	.12	.06	.04
312	Greg Minton	.12	.06	.04
313	Andy Etchebarren	.12	.06	.04
314	Paul Lindblad	.12	.06	.04
315	Mark Belanger	.20	.10	.06
316	Henry Cruz	.12	.06	.04
317	Dave Johnson	.30	.15	.09
318	Tom Griffin	.12	.06	.04
319	Alan Ashby	.12	.06	.04
320	Fred Lynn	.90	.45	.25
321	Santo Alcala	.12	.06	.04
322	Tom Paciorek	.12	.06	.04
323	Jim Fregosi	.12	.06	.04
324	Vern Rapp	.12	.06	.04
325	Bruce Sutter	.50	.25	.15
326	Mike Lum	.12	.06	.04
327	Rick Langford	.12	.06	.04
328	Brewers Team	.50	.25	.15
329	John Verhoeven	.12	.06	.04
330	Bob Watson	.20	.10	.06
331	Mark Littell	.12	.06	.04
332	Duane Kuiper	.12	.06	.04
333	Jim Todd	.12	.06	.04
334	John Stearns	.12	.06	.04
335	Bucky Dent	.30	.15	.09
336	Steve Busby	.20	.10	.06
337	Tom Grieve	.12	.06	.04
338	Dave Heaverlo	.12	.06	.04
339	Mario Guerrero	.12	.06	.04
340	Bake McBride	.12	.06	.04
341	Mike Flanagan	.25	.13	.08
342	Aurelio Rodriguez	.20	.10	.06
343	John Wathan	.12	.06	.04
344	Sam Ewing	.12	.06	.04
345	Luis Tiant	.35	.20	.11
346	Larry Biittner	.12	.06	.04
347	Terry Forster	.20	.10	.06
348	Del Unser	.12	.06	.04
349	Rick Camp	.12	.06	.04
350	Steve Garvey	4.00	2.00	1.25
351	Jeff Torborg	.20	.10	.06
352	Tony Scott	.12	.06	.04
353	Doug Bair	.12	.06	.04

		NR MT	EX	VG			NR MT	EX	VG
354	Cesar Geronimo	.20	.10	.06	442	Elliott Maddox	.12	.06	.04
355	Bill Travers	.12	.06	.04	443	Darrel Chaney	.12	.06	.04
356	Mets Team	.70	.35	.20	444	Roy Hartsfield	.12	.06	.04
357	Tom Poquette	.12	.06	.04	445	Mike Ivie	.12	.06	.04
358	Mark Lemongello	.12	.06	.04	446	Tug McGraw	.35	.20	.11
359	Marc Hill	.12	.06	.04	447	Leroy Stanton	.12	.06	.04
360	Mike Schmidt	15.00	7.50	4.50	448	Bill Castro	.12	.06	.04
361	Chris Knapp	.12	.06	.04	449	Tim Blackwell	.12	.06	.04
362	Dave May	.12	.06	.04	450	Tom Seaver	7.00	3.50	2.00
363	Bob Randall	.12	.06	.04	451	Twins Team	.50	.25	.15
364	Jerry Turner	.12	.06	.04	452	Jerry Mumphrey	.20	.10	.06
365	Ed Figueroa	.20	.10	.06	453	Doug Flynn	.12	.06	.04
366	Larry Milbourne	.12	.06	.04	454	Dave LaRoche	.12	.06	.04
367	Rick Dempsey	.20	.10	.06	455	Bill Robinson	.12	.06	.04
368	Balor Moore	.12	.06	.04	456	Vern Ruhle	.12	.06	.04
369	Tim Nordbrook	.12	.06	.04	457	Bob Bailey	.12	.06	.04
370	Rusty Staub	.30	.15	.09	458	Jeff Newman	.12	.06	.04
371	Ray Burris	.12	.06	.04	459	Charlie Spikes	.12	.06	.04
372	Brian Asselstine	.12	.06	.04	460	Jim Hunter	2.00	1.00	.60
373	Jim Willoughby	.12	.06	.04	461	Rob Andrews	.12	.06	.04
374	Jose Morales	.12	.06	.04	462	Rogelio Moret	.12	.06	.04
375	Tommy John	.90	.45	.25	463	Kevin Bell	.12	.06	.04
376	Jim Wohlford	.12	.06	.04	464	Jerry Grote	.20	.10	.06
377	Manny Sarmiento	.12	.06	.04	465	Hal McRae	.30	.15	.09
378	Bobby Winkles	.12	.06	.04	466	Dennis Blair	.12	.06	.04
379	Skip Lockwood	.12	.06	.04	467	Alvin Dark	.20	.10	.06
380	Ted Simmons	.40	.20	.12	468	*Warren Cromartie*	.20	.10	.06
381	Phillies Team	.70	.35	.20	469	Rick Cerone	.20	.10	.06
382	Joe Lahoud	.12	.06	.04	470	J.R. Richard	.25	.13	.08
383	Mario Mendoza	.12	.06	.04	471	Roy Smalley	.20	.10	.06
384	Jack Clark	4.00	2.00	1.25	472	Ron Reed	.20	.10	.06
385	Tito Fuentes	.12	.06	.04	473	Bill Buckner	.30	.15	.09
386	Bob Gorinski	.12	.06	.04	474	Jim Slaton	.12	.06	.04
387	Ken Holtzman	.25	.13	.08	475	Gary Matthews	.20	.10	.06
388	Bill Fahey	.12	.06	.04	476	Bill Stein	.12	.06	.04
389	Julio Gonzalez	.12	.06	.04	477	Doug Capilla	.12	.06	.04
390	Oscar Gamble	.20	.10	.06	478	Jerry Remy	.12	.06	.04
391	Larry Haney	.12	.06	.04	479	Cardinals Team	.50	.25	.15
392	Billy Almon	.12	.06	.04	480	Ron LeFlore	.25	.13	.08
393	Tippy Martinez	.12	.06	.04	481	Jackson Todd	.12	.06	.04
394	Roy Howell	.12	.06	.04	482	Rick Miller	.12	.06	.04
395	Jim Hughes	.12	.06	.04	483	Ken Macha	.12	.06	.04
396	Bob Stinson	.12	.06	.04	484	Jim Norris	.12	.06	.04
397	Greg Gross	.12	.06	.04	485	Chris Chambliss	.30	.15	.09
398	Don Hood	.12	.06	.04	486	John Curtis	.12	.06	.04
399	Pete Mackanin	.12	.06	.04	487	Jim Tyrone	.12	.06	.04
400	Nolan Ryan	30.00	15.00	9.00	488	Dan Spillner	.12	.06	.04
401	Sparky Anderson	.30	.15	.09	489	Rudy Meoli	.12	.06	.04
402	Dave Campbell	.12	.06	.04	490	Amos Otis	.20	.10	.06
403	Bud Harrelson	.20	.10	.06	491	Scott McGregor	.20	.10	.06
404	Tigers Team	.60	.30	.20	492	Jim Sundberg	.20	.10	.06
405	Rawly Eastwick	.12	.06	.04	493	Steve Renko	.12	.06	.04
406	Mike Jorgensen	.12	.06	.04	494	Chuck Tanner	.20	.10	.06
407	Odell Jones	.12	.06	.04	495	Dave Cash	.12	.06	.04
408	Joe Zdeb	.12	.06	.04	496	*Jim Clancy*	.30	.15	.09
409	Ron Schueler	.12	.06	.04	497	Glenn Adams	.12	.06	.04
410	Bill Madlock	.50	.25	.15	498	Joe Sambito	.12	.06	.04
411	A.L. Championships (Yankees Rally To Defeat Royals)	.70	.35	.20	499	Mariners Team	.50	.25	.15
412	N.L. Championships (Dodgers Overpower Phillies In Four)	.50	.25	.15	500	George Foster	.70	.35	.20
					501	Dave Roberts	.12	.06	.04
413	World Series (Reggie & Yankees Reign Supreme)	3.00	1.50	.90	502	Pat Rockett	.12	.06	.04
					503	Ike Hampton	.12	.06	.04
414	Darold Knowles	.12	.06	.04	504	Roger Freed	.12	.06	.04
415	Ray Fosse	.12	.06	.04	505	Felix Millan	.12	.06	.04
416	Jack Brohamer	.12	.06	.04	506	Ron Blomberg	.12	.06	.04
417	Mike Garman	.12	.06	.04	507	Willie Crawford	.12	.06	.04
418	Tony Muser	.12	.06	.04	508	Johnny Oates	.12	.06	.04
419	Jerry Garvin	.12	.06	.04	509	Brent Strom	.12	.06	.04
420	Greg Luzinski	.35	.20	.11	510	Willie Stargell	3.00	1.50	.90
421	Junior Moore	.12	.06	.04	511	Frank Duffy	.12	.06	.04
422	Steve Braun	.12	.06	.04	512	Larry Herndon	.20	.10	.06
423	Dave Rosello	.12	.06	.04	513	Barry Foote	.12	.06	.04
424	Red Sox Team	.70	.35	.20	514	Rob Sperring	.12	.06	.04
425	Steve Rogers	.12	.06	.04	515	Tim Corcoran	.12	.06	.04
426	Fred Kendall	.12	.06	.04	516	Gary Beare	.12	.06	.04
427	*Mario Soto*	.40	.20	.12	517	Andres Mora	.12	.06	.04
428	Joel Youngblood	.20	.10	.06	518	Tommy Boggs	.12	.06	.04
429	Mike Barlow	.12	.06	.04	519	Brian Downing	.25	.13	.08
430	Al Oliver	.40	.20	.12	520	Larry Hisle	.20	.10	.06
431	Butch Metzger	.12	.06	.04	521	Steve Staggs	.12	.06	.04
432	Terry Bulling	.12	.06	.04	522	Dick Williams	.20	.10	.06
433	Fernando Gonzalez	.12	.06	.04	523	*Donnie Moore*	.25	.13	.08
434	Mike Norris	.12	.06	.04	524	Bernie Carbo	.12	.06	.04
435	Checklist 364-484	.90	.45	.25	525	Jerry Terrell	.12	.06	.04
436	Vic Harris	.12	.06	.04	526	Reds Team	.60	.30	.20
437	Bo McLaughlin	.12	.06	.04	527	Vic Correll	.12	.06	.04
438	John Ellis	.12	.06	.04	528	Rob Picciolo	.12	.06	.04
439	Ken Kravec	.12	.06	.04	529	Paul Hartzell	.12	.06	.04
440	Dave Lopes	.25	.13	.08	530	Dave Winfield	6.00	3.00	1.75
441	Larry Gura	.12	.06	.04	531	Tom Underwood	.12	.06	.04
					532	Skip Jutze	.12	.06	.04

		NR MT	EX	VG
533	Sandy Alomar	.12	.06	.04
534	Wilbur Howard	.12	.06	.04
535	Checklist 485-605	.90	.45	.25
536	Roric Harrison	.12	.06	.04
537	Bruce Bochte	.20	.10	.06
538	Johnnie LeMaster	.12	.06	.04
539	Vic Davalillo	.12	.06	.04
540	Steve Carlton	5.00	2.50	1.50
541	Larry Cox	.12	.06	.04
542	Tim Johnson	.12	.06	.04
543	Larry Harlow	.12	.06	.04
544	Len Randle	.12	.06	.04
545	Bill Campbell	.12	.06	.04
546	Ted Martinez	.12	.06	.04
547	John Scott	.12	.06	.04
548	Billy Hunter	.12	.06	.04
549	Joe Kerrigan	.12	.06	.04
550	John Mayberry	.20	.10	.06
551	Braves Team	.50	.25	.15
552	Francisco Barrios	.12	.06	.04
553	Terry Puhl	.35	.20	.11
554	Joe Coleman	.20	.10	.06
555	Butch Wynegar	.20	.10	.06
556	Ed Armbrister	.12	.06	.04
557	Tony Solaita	.12	.06	.04
558	Paul Mitchell	.12	.06	.04
559	Phil Mankowski	.12	.06	.04
560	Dave Parker	4.00	2.00	1.25
561	Charlie Williams	.12	.06	.04
562	Glenn Burke	.12	.06	.04
563	Dave Rader	.12	.06	.04
564	Mick Kelleher	.12	.06	.04
565	Jerry Koosman	.25	.13	.08
566	Merv Rettenmund	.12	.06	.04
567	Dick Drago	.12	.06	.04
568	Tom Hutton	.12	.06	.04
569	Lary Sorensen	.20	.10	.06
570	Dave Kingman	.60	.30	.20
571	Buck Martinez	.12	.06	.04
572	Rick Wise	.20	.10	.06
573	Luis Gomez	.12	.06	.04
574	Bob Lemon	.30	.15	.09
575	Pat Dobson	.20	.10	.06
576	Sam Mejias	.12	.06	.04
577	A's Team	.50	.25	.15
578	Buzz Capra	.12	.06	.04
579	Rance Mulliniks	.35	.20	.11
580	Rod Carew	6.00	3.00	1.75
581	Lynn McGlothen	.12	.06	.04
582	Fran Healy	.20	.10	.06
583	George Medich	.12	.06	.04
584	John Hale	.12	.06	.04
585	Woodie Fryman	.12	.06	.04
586	Ed Goodson	.12	.06	.04
587	John Urrea	.12	.06	.04
588	Jim Mason	.12	.06	.04
589	Bob Knepper	.70	.35	.20
590	Bobby Murcer	.30	.15	.09
591	George Zeber	.20	.10	.06
592	Bob Apodaca	.12	.06	.04
593	Dave Skaggs	.12	.06	.04
594	Dave Freisleben	.12	.06	.04
595	Sixto Lezcano	.12	.06	.04
596	Gary Wheelock	.12	.06	.04
597	Steve Dillard	.12	.06	.04
598	Eddie Solomon	.12	.06	.04
599	Gary Woods	.12	.06	.04
600	Frank Tanana	.25	.13	.08
601	Gene Mauch	.25	.13	.08
602	Eric Soderholm	.12	.06	.04
603	Will McEnaney	.12	.06	.04
604	Earl Williams	.12	.06	.04
605	Rick Rhoden	.25	.13	.08
606	Pirates Team	.50	.25	.15
607	Fernando Arroyo	.12	.06	.04
608	Johnny Grubb	.12	.06	.04
609	John Denny	.12	.06	.04
610	Garry Maddox	.20	.10	.06
611	Pat Scanlon	.12	.06	.04
612	Ken Henderson	.12	.06	.04
613	Marty Perez	.12	.06	.04
614	Joe Wallis	.12	.06	.04
615	Clay Carroll	.20	.10	.06
616	Pat Kelly	.12	.06	.04
617	Joe Nolan	.12	.06	.04
618	Tommy Helms	.12	.06	.04
619	Thad Bosley	.20	.10	.06
620	Willie Randolph	.30	.15	.09
621	Craig Swan	.12	.06	.04
622	Champ Summers	.12	.06	.04
623	Eduardo Rodriguez	.12	.06	.04
624	Gary Alexander	.12	.06	.04
625	Jose Cruz	.25	.13	.08
626	Blue Jays Team	.25	.13	.08
627	Dave Johnson	.12	.06	.04
628	Ralph Garr	.20	.10	.06
629	Don Stanhouse	.12	.06	.04
630	Ron Cey	.25	.13	.08
631	Danny Ozark	.20	.10	.06
632	Rowland Office	.12	.06	.04
633	Tom Veryzer	.12	.06	.04
634	Len Barker	.20	.10	.06
635	Joe Rudi	.25	.13	.08
636	Jim Bibby	.12	.06	.04
637	Duffy Dyer	.12	.06	.04
638	Paul Splittorff	.20	.10	.06
639	Gene Clines	.12	.06	.04
640	Lee May	.12	.06	.04
641	Doug Rau	.12	.06	.04
642	Denny Doyle	.12	.06	.04
643	Tom House	.12	.06	.04
644	Jim Dwyer	.12	.06	.04
645	Mike Torrez	.20	.10	.06
646	Rick Auerbach	.12	.06	.04
647	Steve Dunning	.12	.06	.04
648	Gary Thomasson	.12	.06	.04
649	Moose Haas	.25	.13	.08
650	Cesar Cedeno	.25	.13	.08
651	Doug Rader	.12	.06	.04
652	Checklist 606-726	.90	.45	.25
653	Ron Hodges	.12	.06	.04
654	Pepe Frias	.12	.06	.04
655	Lyman Bostock	.20	.10	.06
656	Dave Garcia	.12	.06	.04
657	Bombo Rivera	.12	.06	.04
658	Manny Sanguillen	.12	.06	.04
659	Rangers Team	.50	.25	.15
660	Jason Thompson	.20	.10	.06
661	Grant Jackson	.12	.06	.04
662	Paul Dade	.12	.06	.04
663	Paul Reuschel	.12	.06	.04
664	Fred Stanley	.20	.10	.06
665	Dennis Leonard	.20	.10	.06
666	Billy Smith	.12	.06	.04
667	Jeff Byrd	.12	.06	.04
668	Dusty Baker	.25	.13	.08
669	Pete Falcone	.12	.06	.04
670	Jim Rice	3.50	1.75	1.00
671	Gary Lavelle	.12	.06	.04
672	Don Kessinger	.20	.10	.06
673	Steve Brye	.12	.06	.04
674	Ray Knight	1.50	.70	.45
675	Jay Johnstone	.20	.10	.06
676	Bob Myrick	.12	.06	.04
677	Ed Herrmann	.12	.06	.04
678	Tom Burgmeier	.12	.06	.04
679	Wayne Garrett	.12	.06	.04
680	Vida Blue	.30	.15	.09
681	Rob Belloir	.12	.06	.04
682	Ken Brett	.20	.10	.06
683	Mike Champion	.12	.06	.04
684	Ralph Houk	.20	.10	.06
685	Frank Taveras	.12	.06	.04
686	Gaylord Perry	2.00	1.00	.60
687	Julio Cruz	.25	.13	.08
688	George Mitterwald	.12	.06	.04
689	Indians Team	.50	.25	.15
690	Mickey Rivers	.25	.13	.08
691	Ross Grimsley	.20	.10	.06
692	Ken Reitz	.12	.06	.04
693	Lamar Johnson	.12	.06	.04
694	Elias Sosa	.12	.06	.04
695	Dwight Evans	2.00	1.00	.60
696	Steve Mingori	.12	.06	.04
697	Roger Metzger	.12	.06	.04
698	Juan Bernhardt	.12	.06	.04
699	Jackie Brown	.12	.06	.04
700	Johnny Bench	5.00	2.50	1.50
701	Rookie Pitchers (Tom Hume, Larry Landreth, Steve McCatty, Bruce Taylor)	.25	.13	.08
702	Rookie Catchers (Bill Nahorodny, Kevin Pasley, Rick Sweet, Don Werner)	.12	.06	.04
703	Rookie Pitchers (Larry Andersen, Tim Jones, Mickey Mahler, Jack Morris)	18.00	9.00	5.50
704	Rookie 2nd Basemen (Garth Iorg, Dave Oliver, Sam Perlozzo, Lou Whitaker)	16.00	8.00	4.80
705	Rookie Outfielders (Dave Bergman, Miguel Dilone, Clint Hurdle, Willie Norwood)	.25	.13	.08
706	Rookie 1st Basemen (Wayne Cage, Ted Cox, Pat Putnam, Dave Revering)	.20	.10	.06

		NR MT	EX	VG
707	Rookie Shortstops (Mickey Klutts, *Paul Molitor*, Alan Trammell, *U.L. Washington*)	60.00	30.00	18.00
708	Rookie Catchers (*Bo Diaz*, Dale Murphy, *Lance Parrish*, Ernie Whitt)	15.00	7.50	4.50
709	Rookie Pitchers (Steve Burke, *Matt Keough*, Lance Rautzhan, *Dan Schatzeder*)	.20	.10	.06
710	Rookie Outfielders (Dell Alston, Rick Bosetti, *Mike Easler*, Keith Smith)	.50	.25	.15
711	Rookie Pitchers (Cardell Camper, Dennis Lamp, Craig Mitchell, Roy Thomas)	.12	.06	.04
712	Bobby Valentine	.25	.13	.08
713	Bob Davis	.12	.06	.04
714	Mike Anderson	.12	.06	.04
715	Jim Kaat	.60	.30	.20
716	Clarence Gaston	.12	.06	.04
717	Nelson Briles	.12	.06	.04
718	Ron Jackson	.12	.06	.04
719	Randy Elliott	.12	.06	.04
720	Fergie Jenkins	2.00	1.00	.60
721	Billy Martin	1.00	.50	.30
722	Pete Broberg	.12	.06	.04
723	Johnny Wockenfuss	.12	.06	.04
724	Royals Team	.70	.35	.20
725	Kurt Bevacqua	.12	.06	.04
726	Wilbur Wood	.40	.10	.06

1979 Topps

WILLIE McCOVEY 1B
GIANTS

The size of this issue remained the same as in 1978 with 726 cards making their appearance. Actually, the 2-1/2" by 3-1/2" cards have a relatively minor design change from the previous year. The large color photo still dominates the front, with the player's name, team and position below it. The baseball with the player's position was moved to the lower left and the position replaced by a Topps logo. On the back, the printing color was changed and the game situation was replaced by a quiz called "Baseball Dates". Specialty cards include statistical leaders, major league records set during the season and eight cards devoted to career records. For the first time, rookies were arranged by teams under the heading of "Prospects."

		NR MT	EX	VG
Complete Set:		250.00	125.00	75.00
Common Player:		.12	.06	.04
1	Batting Leaders (Rod Carew, Dave Parker)	3.00	1.50	.90
2	Home Run Leaders (George Foster, Jim Rice)	.50	.25	.15
3	Runs Batted In Leaders (George Foster, Jim Rice)	.50	.25	.15
4	Stolen Base Leaders (Ron LeFlore, Omar Moreno)	.25	.13	.08
5	Victory Leaders (Ron Guidry, Gaylord Perry)	.50	.25	.15
6	Strikeout Leaders (J.R. Richard, Nolan Ryan)	3.00	1.50	.90
7	Earned Run Avg. Leaders (Ron Guidry, Craig Swan)	.25	.13	.08
8	Leading Firemen (Rollie Fingers, Rich Gossage)	.40	.20	.12
9	Dave Campbell	.12	.06	.04
10	Lee May	.20	.10	.06

		NR MT	EX	VG
11	Marc Hill	.12	.06	.04
12	Dick Drago	.12	.06	.04
13	Paul Dade	.12	.06	.04
14	Rafael Landestoy	.12	.06	.04
15	Ross Grimsley	.20	.10	.06
16	Fred Stanley	.20	.10	.06
17	Donnie Moore	.20	.10	.06
18	Tony Solaita	.12	.06	.04
19	Larry Gura	.12	.06	.04
20	Joe Morgan	.40	.20	.12
21	Kevin Kobel	.12	.06	.04
22	Mike Jorgensen	.12	.06	.04
23	Terry Forster	.20	.10	.06
24	Paul Molitor	10.00	5.00	3.00
25	Steve Carlton	4.00	2.00	1.25
26	Jamie Quirk	.12	.06	.04
27	Dave Goltz	.20	.10	.06
28	Steve Brye	.12	.06	.04
29	Rick Langford	.12	.06	.04
30	Dave Winfield	9.00	4.50	2.75
31	Tom House	.12	.06	.04
32	Jerry Mumphrey	.12	.06	.04
33	Dave Rozema	.12	.06	.04
34	Rob Andrews	.12	.06	.04
35	Ed Figueroa	.20	.10	.06
36	Alan Ashby	.12	.06	.04
37	Joe Kerrigan	.12	.06	.04
38	Bernie Carbo	.12	.06	.04
39	Dale Murphy	6.00	3.00	1.75
40	Dennis Eckersley	6.00	3.00	1.75
41	Twins Team (Gene Mauch)	.50	.25	.15
42	Ron Blomberg	.12	.06	.04
43	Wayne Twitchell	.12	.06	.04
44	Kurt Bevacqua	.12	.06	.04
45	Al Hrabosky	.20	.10	.06
46	Ron Hodges	.12	.06	.04
47	Fred Norman	.12	.06	.04
48	Merv Rettenmund	.12	.06	.04
49	Vern Ruhle	.12	.06	.04
50	Steve Garvey	1.25	.60	.40
51	Ray Fosse	.12	.06	.04
52	Randy Lerch	.12	.06	.04
53	Mick Kelleher	.12	.06	.04
54	Dell Alston	.12	.06	.04
55	Willie Stargell	2.00	1.00	.60
56	John Hale	.12	.06	.04
57	Eric Rasmussen	.12	.06	.04
58	Bob Randall	.12	.06	.04
59	John Denny	.12	.06	.04
60	Mickey Rivers	.20	.10	.06
61	Bo Diaz	.20	.10	.06
62	Randy Moffitt	.12	.06	.04
63	Jack Brohamer	.12	.06	.04
64	Tom Underwood	.12	.06	.04
65	Mark Belanger	.20	.10	.06
66	Tigers Team (Les Moss)	.60	.30	.20
67	Jim Mason	.12	.06	.04
68	Joe Niekro	.12	.06	.04
69	Elliott Maddox	.12	.06	.04
70	John Candelaria	.25	.13	.08
71	Brian Downing	.20	.10	.06
72	Steve Mingori	.12	.06	.04
73	Ken Henderson	.12	.06	.04
74	*Shane Rawley*	.30	.15	.09
75	Steve Yeager	.12	.06	.04
76	Warren Cromartie	.12	.06	.04
77	Dan Briggs	.12	.06	.04
78	Elias Sosa	.12	.06	.04
79	Ted Cox	.12	.06	.04
80	Jason Thompson	.20	.10	.06
81	Roger Erickson	.12	.06	.04
82	Mets Team (Joe Torre)	.60	.30	.20
83	Fred Kendall	.12	.06	.04
84	Greg Minton	.12	.06	.04
85	Gary Matthews	.20	.10	.06
86	Rodney Scott	.12	.06	.04
87	Pete Falcone	.12	.06	.04
88	Bob Molinaro	.12	.06	.04
89	Dick Tidrow	.20	.10	.06
90	Bob Boone	.25	.13	.08
91	Terry Crowley	.12	.06	.04
92	Jim Bibby	.12	.06	.04
93	Phil Mankowski	.12	.06	.04
94	Len Barker	.12	.06	.04
95	Robin Yount	12.00	6.00	3.50
96	Indians Team (Jeff Torborg)	.50	.25	.15
97	Sam Mejias	.12	.06	.04
98	Ray Burris	.12	.06	.04
99	John Wathan	.20	.10	.06
100	Tom Seaver	4.00	2.00	1.25
101	Roy Howell	.12	.06	.04
102	Mike Anderson	.12	.06	.04

	NR MT	EX	VG			NR MT	EX	VG
103 Jim Todd	.12	.06	.04	194 Randy Jones		.20	.10	.06
104 Johnny Oates	.12	.06	.04	195 Bill Madlock		.40	.20	.12
105 Rick Camp	.12	.06	.04	196 Steve Kemp		.12	.06	.04
106 Frank Duffy	.12	.06	.04	197 Bob Apodaca		.12	.06	.04
107 Jesus Alou	.20	.10	.06	198 Johnny Grubb		.12	.06	.04
108 Eduardo Rodriguez	.12	.06	.04	199 Larry Milbourne		.12	.06	.04
109 Joel Youngblood	.12	.06	.04	200 Johnny Bench		2.00	1.00	.60
110 Vida Blue	.30	.15	.09	201 Record Breaker (Mike Edwards)		.12	.06	.04
111 Roger Freed	.12	.06	.04	202 Record Breaker (Ron Guidry)		.35	.20	.11
112 Phillies Team (Danny Ozark)	.50	.25	.15	203 Record Breaker (J.R. Richard)		.20	.10	.06
113 Pete Redfern	.12	.06	.04	204 Record Breaker (Pete Rose)		1.50	.70	.45
114 Cliff Johnson	.20	.10	.06	205 Record Breaker (John Stearns)		.12	.06	.04
115 Nolan Ryan	20.00	10.00	6.00	206 Record Breaker (Sammy Stewart)		.12	.06	.04
116 Ozzie Smith	70.00	35.00	21.00	207 Dave Lemanczyk		.12	.06	.04
117 Grant Jackson	.12	.06	.04	208 Clarence Gaston		.12	.06	.04
118 Bud Harrelson	.20	.10	.06	209 Reggie Cleveland		.12	.06	.04
119 Don Stanhouse	.12	.06	.04	210 Larry Bowa		.30	.15	.09
120 Jim Sundberg	.20	.10	.06	211 Denny Martinez		.20	.10	.06
121 Checklist 1-121	.25	.13	.08	212 Carney Lansford		5.00	2.50	1.50
122 Mike Paxton	.12	.06	.04	213 Bill Travers		.12	.06	.04
123 Lou Whitaker	3.00	1.50	.90	214 Red Sox Team (Don Zimmer)		.60	.30	.20
124 Dan Schatzeder	.12	.06	.04	215 Willie McCovey		2.00	1.00	.60
125 Rick Burleson	.20	.10	.06	216 Wilbur Wood		.20	.10	.06
126 Doug Bair	.12	.06	.04	217 Steve Dillard		.12	.06	.04
127 Thad Bosley	.12	.06	.04	218 Dennis Leonard		.20	.10	.06
128 Ted Martinez	.12	.06	.04	219 Roy Smalley		.20	.10	.06
129 Marty Pattin	.12	.06	.04	220 Cesar Geronimo		.20	.10	.06
130 Bob Watson	.12	.06	.04	221 Jesse Jefferson		.12	.06	.04
131 Jim Clancy	.25	.13	.08	222 Bob Beall		.12	.06	.04
132 Rowland Office	.12	.06	.04	223 Kent Tekulve		.25	.13	.08
133 Bill Castro	.12	.06	.04	224 Dave Revering		.12	.06	.04
134 Alan Bannister	.12	.06	.04	225 Rich Gossage		.70	.35	.20
135 Bobby Murcer	.25	.13	.08	226 Ron Pruitt		.12	.06	.04
136 Jim Kaat	.60	.30	.20	227 Steve Stone		.20	.10	.06
137 Larry Wolfe	.12	.06	.04	228 Vic Davalillo		.12	.06	.04
138 Mark Lee	.12	.06	.04	229 Doug Flynn		.12	.06	.04
139 Luis Pujols	.12	.06	.04	230 Bob Forsch		.20	.10	.06
140 Don Gullett	.20	.10	.06	231 Johnny Wockenfuss		.12	.06	.04
141 Tom Paciorek	.12	.06	.04	232 Jimmy Sexton		.12	.06	.04
142 Charlie Williams	.12	.06	.04	233 Paul Mitchell		.12	.06	.04
143 Tony Scott	.12	.06	.04	234 Toby Harrah		.20	.10	.06
144 Sandy Alomar	.12	.06	.04	235 Steve Rogers		.20	.10	.06
145 Rick Rhoden	.25	.13	.08	236 Jim Dwyer		.12	.06	.04
146 Duane Kuiper	.12	.06	.04	237 Billy Smith		.12	.06	.04
147 Dave Hamilton	.12	.06	.04	238 Balor Moore		.12	.06	.04
148 Bruce Boisclair	.12	.06	.04	239 Willie Horton		.20	.10	.06
149 Manny Sarmiento	.12	.06	.04	240 Rick Reuschel		.25	.13	.08
150 Wayne Cage	.12	.06	.04	241 Checklist 122-242		.25	.13	.08
151 John Hiller	.20	.10	.06	242 Pablo Torrealba		.12	.06	.04
152 Rick Cerone	.20	.10	.06	243 Buck Martinez		.12	.06	.04
153 Dennis Lamp	.12	.06	.04	244 Pirates Team (Chuck Tanner)		.80	.40	.25
154 Jim Gantner	.12	.06	.04	245 Jeff Burroughs		.20	.10	.06
155 Dwight Evans	1.25	.60	.40	246 Darrell Jackson		.12	.06	.04
156 Buddy Solomon	.12	.06	.04	247 Tucker Ashford		.12	.06	.04
157 U.L. Washington	.12	.06	.04	248 Pete LaCock		.12	.06	.04
158 Joe Sambito	.12	.06	.04	249 Paul Thormodsgard		.12	.06	.04
159 Roy White	.25	.13	.08	250 Willie Randolph		.30	.15	.09
160 Mike Flanagan	.30	.15	.09	251 Jack Morris		6.00	3.00	1.75
161 Barry Foote	.12	.06	.04	252 Bob Stinson		.12	.06	.04
162 Tom Johnson	.12	.06	.04	253 Rick Wise		.20	.10	.06
163 Glenn Burke	.12	.06	.04	254 Luis Gomez		.12	.06	.04
164 Mickey Lolich	.40	.20	.12	255 Tommy John		.80	.40	.25
165 Frank Taveras	.12	.06	.04	256 Mike Sadek		.12	.06	.04
166 Leon Roberts	.12	.06	.04	257 Adrian Devine		.12	.06	.04
167 Roger Metzger	.12	.06	.04	258 Mike Phillips		.12	.06	.04
168 Dave Freisleben	.12	.06	.04	259 Reds Team (Sparky Anderson)		.60	.30	.20
169 Bill Nahorodny	.12	.06	.04	260 Richie Zisk		.20	.10	.06
170 Don Sutton	1.25	.60	.40	261 Mario Guerrero		.12	.06	.04
171 Gene Clines	.12	.06	.04	262 Nelson Briles		.12	.06	.04
172 Mike Bruhert	.12	.06	.04	263 Oscar Gamble		.20	.10	.06
173 John Lowenstein	.12	.06	.04	264 Don Robinson		.50	.25	.15
174 Rick Auerbach	.12	.06	.04	265 Don Money		.12	.06	.04
175 George Hendrick	.20	.10	.06	266 Jim Willoughby		.12	.06	.04
176 Aurelio Rodriguez	.20	.10	.06	267 Joe Rudi		.20	.10	.06
177 Ron Reed	.20	.10	.06	268 Julio Gonzalez		.12	.06	.04
178 Alvis Woods	.12	.06	.04	269 Woodie Fryman		.20	.10	.06
179 Jim Beattie	.12	.06	.04	270 Butch Hobson		.12	.06	.04
180 Larry Hisle	.20	.10	.06	271 Rawly Eastwick		.12	.06	.04
181 Mike Garman	.12	.06	.04	272 Tim Corcoran		.12	.06	.04
182 Tim Johnson	.12	.06	.04	273 Jerry Terrell		.12	.06	.04
183 Paul Splittorff	.20	.10	.06	274 Willie Norwood		.12	.06	.04
184 Darrel Chaney	.12	.06	.04	275 Junior Moore		.12	.06	.04
185 Mike Torrez	.20	.10	.06	276 Jim Colborn		.12	.06	.04
186 Eric Soderholm	.12	.06	.04	277 Tom Grieve		.12	.06	.04
187 Mark Lemongello	.12	.06	.04	278 Andy Messersmith		.25	.13	.08
188 Pat Kelly	.12	.06	.04	279 Jerry Grote		.12	.06	.04
189 Eddie Whitson	.50	.25	.15	280 Andre Thornton		.25	.13	.08
190 Ron Cey	.25	.13	.08	281 Vic Correll		.12	.06	.04
191 Mike Norris	.12	.06	.04	282 Blue Jays Team (Roy Hartsfield)		.50	.25	.15
192 Cardinals Team (Ken Boyer)	.50	.25	.15	283 Ken Kravec		.12	.06	.04
193 Glenn Adams	.12	.06	.04	284 Johnnie LeMaster		.12	.06	.04

	NR MT	EX	VG			NR MT	EX	VG
285	Bobby Bonds	.30	.15	.09	375	Bill Campbell	.12	.06	.04
286	Duffy Dyer	.12	.06	.04	376	Gorman Thomas	.25	.13	.08
287	Andres Mora	.12	.06	.04	377	Paul Moskau	.12	.06	.04
288	Milt Wilcox	.20	.10	.06	378	Rob Picciolo	.12	.06	.04
289	Jose Cruz	.25	.13	.08	379	Dale Murray	.12	.06	.04
290	Dave Lopes	.25	.13	.08	380	John Mayberry	.20	.10	.06
291	Tom Griffin	.12	.06	.04	381	Astros Team (Bill Virdon)	.50	.25	.15
292	Don Reynolds	.12	.06	.04	382	Jerry Martin	.12	.06	.04
293	Jerry Garvin	.12	.06	.04	383	Phil Garner	.20	.10	.06
294	Pepe Frias	.12	.06	.04	384	Tommy Boggs	.12	.06	.04
295	Mitchell Page	.12	.06	.04	385	Dan Ford	.12	.06	.04
296	Preston Hanna	.12	.06	.04	386	Francisco Barrios	.12	.06	.04
297	Ted Sizemore	.12	.06	.04	387	Gary Thomasson	.12	.06	.04
298	Rich Gale	.12	.06	.04	388	Jack Billingham	.12	.06	.04
299	Steve Ontiveros	.12	.06	.04	389	Joe Zdeb	.12	.06	.04
300	Rod Carew	4.00	2.00	1.25	390	Rollie Fingers	2.50	1.25	.70
301	Tom Hume	.12	.06	.04	391	Al Oliver	.40	.20	.12
302	Braves Team (Bobby Cox)	.50	.25	.15	392	Doug Ault	.12	.06	.04
303	Lary Sorensen	.12	.06	.04	393	Scott McGregor	.20	.10	.06
304	Steve Swisher	.12	.06	.04	394	Randy Stein	.12	.06	.04
305	Willie Montanez	.12	.06	.04	395	Dave Cash	.12	.06	.04
306	Floyd Bannister	.30	.15	.09	396	Bill Plummer	.12	.06	.04
307	Larvell Blanks	.12	.06	.04	397	Sergio Ferrer	.12	.06	.04
308	Bert Blyleven	.60	.30	.20	398	Ivan DeJesus	.12	.06	.04
309	Ralph Garr	.20	.10	.06	399	David Clyde	.12	.06	.04
310	Thurman Munson	5.00	2.50	1.50	400	Jim Rice	2.00	1.00	.60
311	Gary Lavelle	.12	.06	.04	401	Ray Knight	.25	.13	.08
312	Bob Robertson	.12	.06	.04	402	Paul Hartzell	.12	.06	.04
313	Dyar Miller	.12	.06	.04	403	Tim Foli	.12	.06	.04
314	Larry Harlow	.12	.06	.04	404	White Sox Team (Don Kessinger)	.50	.25	.15
315	Jon Matlack	.20	.10	.06	405	Butch Wynegar	.20	.10	.06
316	Milt May	.12	.06	.04	406	Joe Wallis	.12	.06	.04
317	Jose Cardenal	.12	.06	.04	407	Pete Vuckovich	.20	.10	.06
318	*Bob Welch*	5.00	2.50	1.50	408	Charlie Moore	.12	.06	.04
319	Wayne Garrett	.12	.06	.04	409	*Willie Wilson*	2.00	1.00	.60
320	Carl Yastrzemski	4.00	2.00	1.25	410	Darrell Evans	.30	.15	.09
321	Gaylord Perry	2.00	1.00	.60	411	Hits Record Holders (Ty Cobb, George Sisler)	.70	.35	.20
322	Danny Goodwin	.12	.06	.04	412	Runs Batted In Record Holders (Hank Aaron, Hack Wilson)	.70	.35	.20
323	Lynn McGlothen	.12	.06	.04	413	Home Run Record Holders (Hank Aaron, Roger Maris)	1.00	.50	.30
324	Mike Tyson	.12	.06	.04	414	Batting Avg. Record Holders (Ty Cobb, Roger Hornsby)	.70	.35	.20
325	Cecil Cooper	.40	.20	.12	415	Stolen Bases Record Holders (Lou Brock)	.70	.35	.20
326	Pedro Borbon	.12	.06	.04	416	Wins Record Holders (Jack Chesbro, Cy Young)	.40	.20	.12
327	Art Howe	.12	.06	.04	417	Strikeouts Record Holders (Walter Johnson, Nolan Ryan)	.40	.20	.12
328	A's Team (Jack McKeon)	.50	.25	.15	418	Earned Run Avg. Record Holders (Walter Johnson, Dutch Leonard)	.20	.10	.06
329	Joe Coleman	.20	.10	.06	419	Dick Ruthven	.12	.06	.04
330	George Brett	12.00	6.00	3.50	420	Ken Griffey	.25	.13	.08
331	Mickey Mahler	.12	.06	.04	421	Doug DeCinces	.25	.13	.08
332	Gary Alexander	.12	.06	.04	422	Ruppert Jones	.12	.06	.04
333	Chet Lemon	.20	.10	.06	423	Bob Montgomery	.12	.06	.04
334	Craig Swan	.12	.06	.04	424	Angels Team (Jim Fregosi)	.60	.30	.20
335	Chris Chambliss	.25	.13	.08	425	Rick Manning	.12	.06	.04
336	Bobby Thompson	.12	.06	.04	426	Chris Speier	.20	.10	.06
337	John Montague	.12	.06	.04	427	Andy Replogle	.12	.06	.04
338	Vic Harris	.12	.06	.04	428	Bobby Valentine	.25	.13	.08
339	Ron Jackson	.12	.06	.04	429	John Urrea	.12	.06	.04
340	Jim Palmer	4.00	2.00	1.25	430	Dave Parker	2.00	1.00	.60
341	*Willie Upshaw*	.40	.20	.12	431	Glenn Borgmann	.12	.06	.04
342	Dave Roberts	.12	.06	.04	432	Dave Heaverlo	.12	.06	.04
343	Ed Glynn	.12	.06	.04	433	Larry Biittner	.12	.06	.04
344	Jerry Royster	.12	.06	.04	434	Ken Clay	.20	.10	.06
345	Tug McGraw	.30	.15	.09	435	Gene Tenace	.20	.10	.06
346	Bill Buckner	.30	.15	.09	436	Hector Cruz	.12	.06	.04
347	Doug Rau	.12	.06	.04	437	Rick Williams	.12	.06	.04
348	Andre Dawson	12.00	6.00	3.50	438	Horace Speed	.12	.06	.04
349	Jim Wright	.12	.06	.04	439	Frank White	.25	.13	.08
350	Garry Templeton	.20	.10	.06	440	Rusty Staub	.30	.15	.09
351	Wayne Nordhagen	.12	.06	.04	441	Lee Lacy	.12	.06	.04
352	Steve Renko	.12	.06	.04	442	Doyle Alexander	.25	.13	.08
353	Checklist 243-363	.60	.30	.20	443	Bruce Bochte	.12	.06	.04
354	Bill Bonham	.12	.06	.04	444	*Aurelio Lopez*	.20	.10	.06
355	Lee Mazzilli	.20	.10	.06	445	Steve Henderson	.12	.06	.04
356	Giants Team (Joe Altobelli)	.50	.25	.15	446	Jim Lonborg	.20	.10	.06
357	Jerry Augustine	.12	.06	.04	447	Manny Sanguillen	.12	.06	.04
358	Alan Trammell	8.00	4.00	2.50	448	Moose Haas	.12	.06	.04
359	Dan Spillner	.12	.06	.04	449	Bombo Rivera	.12	.06	.04
360	Amos Otis	.20	.10	.06	450	Dave Concepcion	.30	.15	.09
361	Tom Dixon	.12	.06	.04	451	Royals Team (Whitey Herzog)	.50	.25	.15
362	Mike Cubbage	.12	.06	.04	452	Jerry Morales	.12	.06	.04
363	Craig Skok	.12	.06	.04	453	Chris Knapp	.12	.06	.04
364	Gene Richards	.12	.06	.04	454	Len Randle	.12	.06	.04
365	Sparky Lyle	.30	.15	.09	455	Bill Lee	.12	.06	.04
366	Juan Bernhardt	.12	.06	.04	456	Chuck Baker	.12	.06	.04
367	Dave Skaggs	.12	.06	.04	457	Bruce Sutter	.60	.30	.20
368	Don Aase	.20	.10	.06					
369a	Bump Wills (Blue Jays)	2.00	1.00	.60					
369b	Bump Wills (Rangers)	2.50	1.25	.70					
370	Dave Kingman	.35	.20	.11					
371	Jeff Holly	.12	.06	.04					
372	Lamar Johnson	.12	.06	.04					
373	Lance Rautzhan	.12	.06	.04					
374	Ed Herrmann	.12	.06	.04					

		NR MT	EX	VG
458	Jim Essian	.12	.06	.04
459	Sid Monge	.12	.06	.04
460	Graig Nettles	.50	.25	.15
461	Jim Barr	.12	.06	.04
462	Otto Velez	.12	.06	.04
463	Steve Comer	.12	.06	.04
464	Joe Nolan	.12	.06	.04
465	Reggie Smith	.25	.13	.08
466	Mark Littell	.12	.06	.04
467	Don Kessinger	.12	.06	.04
468	Stan Bahnsen	.12	.06	.04
469	Lance Parrish	3.00	1.50	.90
470	Garry Maddox	.12	.06	.04
471	Joaquin Andujar	.20	.10	.06
472	Craig Kusick	.12	.06	.04
473	Dave Roberts	.12	.06	.04
474	Dick Davis	.12	.06	.04
475	Dan Driessen	.20	.10	.06
476	Tom Poquette	.12	.06	.04
477	Bob Grich	.25	.13	.08
478	Juan Beniquez	.12	.06	.04
479	Padres Team (Roger Craig)	.50	.25	.15
480	Fred Lynn	.70	.35	.20
481	Skip Lockwood	.12	.06	.04
482	Craig Reynolds	.12	.06	.04
483	Checklist 364-484	.25	.13	.08
484	Rick Waits	.12	.06	.04
485	Bucky Dent	.25	.13	.08
486	Bob Knepper	.25	.13	.08
487	Miguel Dilone	.12	.06	.04
488	Bob Owchinko	.12	.06	.04
489	Larry Cox (photo actually Dave Rader)	.12	.06	.04
490	Al Cowens	.12	.06	.04
491	Tippy Martinez	.12	.06	.04
492	Bob Bailor	.12	.06	.04
493	Larry Christenson	.12	.06	.04
494	Jerry White	.12	.06	.04
495	Tony Perez	.60	.30	.20
496	Barry Bonnell	.12	.06	.04
497	Glenn Abbott	.12	.06	.04
498	Rich Chiles	.12	.06	.04
499	Rangers Team (Pat Corrales)	.50	.25	.15
500	Ron Guidry	.90	.45	.25
501	Junior Kennedy	.12	.06	.04
502	Steve Braun	.12	.06	.04
503	Terry Humphrey	.12	.06	.04
504	*Larry McWilliams*	.20	.10	.06
505	Ed Kranepool	.20	.10	.06
506	John D'Acquisto	.12	.06	.04
507	Tony Armas	.20	.10	.06
508	Charlie Hough	.20	.10	.06
509	Mario Mendoza	.12	.06	.04
510	Ted Simmons	.40	.20	.12
511	Paul Reuschel	.12	.06	.04
512	Jack Clark	1.50	.70	.45
513	Dave Johnson	.30	.15	.09
514	Mike Proly	.12	.06	.04
515	Enos Cabell	.12	.06	.04
516	Champ Summers	.12	.06	.04
517	Al Bumbry	.20	.10	.06
518	Jim Umbarger	.12	.06	.04
519	Ben Oglivie	.20	.10	.06
520	Gary Carter	3.00	1.50	.90
521	Sam Ewing	.12	.06	.04
522	Ken Holtzman	.20	.10	.06
523	John Milner	.12	.06	.04
524	Tom Burgmeier	.12	.06	.04
525	Freddie Patek	.12	.06	.04
526	Dodgers Team (Tom Lasorda)	.60	.30	.20
527	Lerrin LaGrow	.12	.06	.04
528	Wayne Gross	.12	.06	.04
529	Brian Asselstine	.12	.06	.04
530	Frank Tanana	.25	.13	.08
531	Fernando Gonzalez	.12	.06	.04
532	Buddy Schultz	.12	.06	.04
533	Leroy Stanton	.12	.06	.04
534	Ken Forsch	.12	.06	.04
535	Ellis Valentine	.12	.06	.04
536	Jerry Reuss	.20	.10	.06
537	Tom Veryzer	.12	.06	.04
538	Mike Ivie	.12	.06	.04
539	John Ellis	.12	.06	.04
540	Greg Luzinski	.30	.15	.09
541	Jim Slaton	.12	.06	.04
542	Rick Bosetti	.12	.06	.04
543	Kiko Garcia	.12	.06	.04
544	Fergie Jenkins	1.50	.70	.45
545	John Stearns	.12	.06	.04
546	Bill Russell	.20	.10	.06
547	Clint Hurdle	.12	.06	.04
548	Enrique Romo	.12	.06	.04
549	Bob Bailey	.12	.06	.04
550	Sal Bando	.20	.10	.06
551	Cubs Team (Herman Franks)	.50	.25	.15
552	Jose Morales	.12	.06	.04
553	Denny Walling	.12	.06	.04
554	Matt Keough	.12	.06	.04
555	Biff Pocoroba	.12	.06	.04
556	Mike Lum	.12	.06	.04
557	Ken Brett	.20	.10	.06
558	Jay Johnstone	.20	.10	.06
559	Greg Pryor	.12	.06	.04
560	John Montefusco	.12	.06	.04
561	Ed Ott	.12	.06	.04
562	Dusty Baker	.25	.13	.08
563	Roy Thomas	.12	.06	.04
564	Jerry Turner	.12	.06	.04
565	Rico Carty	.25	.13	.08
566	Nino Espinosa	.12	.06	.04
567	Rich Hebner	.12	.06	.04
568	Carlos Lopez	.12	.06	.04
569	Bob Sykes	.12	.06	.04
570	Cesar Cedeno	.25	.13	.08
571	Darrell Porter	.20	.10	.06
572	Rod Gilbreath	.12	.06	.04
573	Jim Kern	.12	.06	.04
574	Claudell Washington	.20	.10	.06
575	Luis Tiant	.30	.15	.09
576	Mike Parrott	.12	.06	.04
577	Brewers Team (George Bamberger)	.50	.25	.15
578	Pete Broberg	.12	.06	.04
579	Greg Gross	.12	.06	.04
580	Ron Fairly	.20	.10	.06
581	Darold Knowles	.12	.06	.04
582	Paul Blair	.20	.10	.06
583	Julio Cruz	.12	.06	.04
584	Jim Rooker	.12	.06	.04
585	Hal McRae	.25	.13	.08
586	*Bob Horner*	.90	.45	.25
587	Ken Reitz	.12	.06	.04
588	Tom Murphy	.12	.06	.04
589	Terry Whitfield	.12	.06	.04
590	J.R. Richard	.20	.10	.06
591	Mike Hargrove	.20	.10	.06
592	Mike Krukow	.20	.10	.06
593	Rick Dempsey	.20	.10	.06
594	Bob Shirley	.12	.06	.04
595	Phil Niekro	1.25	.60	.40
596	Jim Wohlford	.12	.06	.04
597	Bob Stanley	.20	.10	.06
598	Mark Wagner	.12	.06	.04
599	Jim Spencer	.20	.10	.06
600	George Foster	.60	.30	.20
601	Dave LaRoche	.12	.06	.04
602	Checklist 485-605	.60	.30	.20
603	Rudy May	.12	.06	.04
604	Jeff Newman	.12	.06	.04
605	Rick Monday	.12	.06	.04
606	Expos Team (Dick Williams)	.50	.25	.15
607	Omar Moreno	.12	.06	.04
608	Dave McKay	.12	.06	.04
609	Silvio Martinez	.12	.06	.04
610	Mike Schmidt	12.00	6.00	3.50
611	Jim Norris	.12	.06	.04
612	*Rick Honeycutt*	.30	.15	.09
613	Mike Edwards	.12	.06	.04
614	Willie Hernandez	.20	.10	.06
615	Ken Singleton	.20	.10	.06
616	Billy Almon	.12	.06	.04
617	Terry Puhl	.12	.06	.04
618	Jerry Remy	.12	.06	.04
619	*Ken Landreaux*	.25	.13	.08
620	Bert Campaneris	.25	.13	.08
621	Pat Zachry	.12	.06	.04
622	Dave Collins	.20	.10	.06
623	Bob McClure	.12	.06	.04
624	Larry Herndon	.20	.10	.06
625	Mark Fidrych	.25	.13	.08
626	Yankees Team (Bob Lemon)	.80	.40	.25
627	Gary Serum	.12	.06	.04
628	Del Unser	.12	.06	.04
629	Gene Garber	.12	.06	.04
630	Bake McBride	.12	.06	.04
631	Jorge Orta	.12	.06	.04
632	Don Kirkwood	.12	.06	.04
633	Rob Wilfong	.12	.06	.04
634	Paul Lindblad	.20	.10	.06
635	Don Baylor	.80	.40	.25
636	Wayne Garland	.12	.06	.04
637	Bill Robinson	.12	.06	.04

		NR MT	EX	VG
638	Al Fitzmorris	.12	.06	.04
639	Manny Trillo	.20	.10	.06
640	Eddie Murray	21.00	10.50	6.30
641	*Bobby Castillo*	.12	.06	.04
642	Wilbur Howard	.12	.06	.04
643	Tom Hausman	.12	.06	.04
644	Manny Mota	.20	.10	.06
645	George Scott	.12	.06	.04
646	Rick Sweet	.12	.06	.04
647	Bob Lacey	.12	.06	.04
648	Lou Piniella	.35	.20	.11
649	John Curtis	.12	.06	.04
650	Pete Rose	4.50	2.25	1.25
651	Mike Caldwell	.12	.06	.04
652	Stan Papi	.12	.06	.04
653	Warren Brusstar	.12	.06	.04
654	Rick Miller	.12	.06	.04
655	Jerry Koosman	.30	.15	.09
656	Hosken Powell	.12	.06	.04
657	George Medich	.12	.06	.04
658	Taylor Duncan	.12	.06	.04
659	Mariners Team (Darrell Johnson)	.50	.25	.15
660	Ron LeFlore	.12	.06	.04
661	Bruce Kison	.12	.06	.04
662	Kevin Bell	.12	.06	.04
663	Mike Vail	.12	.06	.04
664	Doug Bird	.12	.06	.04
665	Lou Brock	3.00	1.50	.90
666	Rich Dauer	.12	.06	.04
667	Don Hood	.12	.06	.04
668	Bill North	.12	.06	.04
669	Checklist 606-726	.60	.30	.20
670	Jim Hunter	1.25	.60	.40
671	Joe Ferguson	.12	.06	.04
672	Ed Halicki	.12	.06	.04
673	Tom Hutton	.12	.06	.04
674	Dave Tomlin	.12	.06	.04
675	Tim McCarver	.30	.15	.09
676	Johnny Sutton	.12	.06	.04
677	Larry Parrish	.25	.13	.08
678	Geoff Zahn	.12	.06	.04
679	Derrel Thomas	.12	.06	.04
680	Carlton Fisk	5.00	2.50	1.50
681	*John Henry Johnson*	.12	.06	.04
682	Dave Chalk	.12	.06	.04
683	Dan Meyer	.12	.06	.04
684	Jamie Easterly	.12	.06	.04
685	Sixto Lezcano	.12	.06	.04
686	Ron Schueler	.12	.06	.04
687	Rennie Stennett	.12	.06	.04
688	Mike Willis	.12	.06	.04
689	Orioles Team (Earl Weaver)	.70	.35	.20
690	Buddy Bell	.12	.06	.04
691	Dock Ellis	.12	.06	.04
692	Mickey Stanley	.20	.10	.06
693	Dave Rader	.12	.06	.04
694	Burt Hooton	.20	.10	.06
695	Keith Hernandez	2.00	1.00	.60
696	Andy Hassler	.12	.06	.04
697	Dave Bergman	.12	.06	.04
698	Bill Stein	.12	.06	.04
699	Hal Dues	.12	.06	.04
700	Reggie Jackson	4.00	2.00	1.25
701	Orioles Prospects (Mark Corey, John Flinn, *Sammy Stewart*)	.20	.10	.06
702	Red Sox Prospects (Joel Finch, Garry Hancock, Allen Ripley)	.12	.06	.04
703	Angels Prospects (Jim Anderson, Dave Frost, Bob Slater)	.12	.06	.04
704	White Sox Prospects (Ross Baumgarten, Mike Colbern, *Mike Squires*)	.20	.10	.06
705	Indians Prospects (*Alfredo Griffin*, Tim Norrid, Dave Oliver)	.70	.35	.20
706	Tigers Prospects (Dave Stegman, Dave Tobik, Kip Young)	.12	.06	.04
707	Royals Prospects (Randy Bass, Jim Gaudet, Randy McGilberry)	.12	.06	.04
708	Brewers Prospects (*Kevin Bass, Eddie Romero*, Ned Yost)	1.00	.50	.30
709	Twins Prospects (Sam Perlozzo, Rick Sofield, Kevin Stanfield)	.12	.06	.04
710	Yankees Prospects (Brian Doyle, *Mike Heath*, Dave Rajsich)	.30	.15	.09
711	A's Prospects (*Dwayne Murphy*, Bruce Robinson, Alan Wirth)	.50	.25	.15
712	Mariners Prospects (Bud Anderson, Greg Biercevicz, Byron McLaughlin)	.12	.06	.04
713	Rangers Prospects (*Danny Darwin*, Pat Putnam, *Billy Sample*)	.70	.35	.20
714	Blue Jays Prospects (Victor Cruz, Pat Kelly, Ernie Whitt)	.20	.10	.06
715	Braves Prospects (*Bruce Benedict, Glenn Hubbard*, Larry Whisenton)	.40	.20	.12
716	Cubs Prospects (Dave Geisel, Karl Pagel, *Scot Thompson*)	.12	.06	.04
717	Reds Prospects (*Mike LaCoss, Ron Oester, Harry Spilman*)	.40	.20	.12
718	Astros Prospects (Bruce Bochy, Mike Fischlin, Don Pisker)	.12	.06	.04
719	Dodgers Prospects (*Pedro Guerrero, Rudy Law, Joe Simpson*)	7.00	3.50	2.00
720	Expos Prospects (Jerry Fry, Jerry Pirtle, *Scott Sanderson*)	.90	.45	.25
721	Mets Prospects (*Juan Berenguer*, Dwight Bernard, Dan Norman)	.30	.15	.09
722	Phillies Prospects (*Jim Morrison, Lonnie Smith*, Jim Wright)	2.00	1.00	.60
723	Pirates Prospects (*Dale Berra*, Eugenio Cotes, Ben Wiltbank)	.20	.10	.06
724	Cardinals Prospects (Tom Bruno, *George Frazier, Terry Kennedy*)	.50	.25	.15
725	Padres Prospects (Jim Beswick, Steve Mura, Broderick Perkins)	.12	.06	.04
726	Giants Prospects (Greg Johnston, Joe Strain, John Tamargo)	.25	.06	.04

1979 Topps Comics

Issued as the 3" by 3-3/4" wax wrapper for a piece of bubblegum, this "test" issue was bought up in great quantities by speculators and remains rather common. It is also inexpensive, because the comic-style player representations were not popular with collectors. The set is complete at 33 pieces.

		NR MT	EX	VG
	Complete Set:	8.00	4.00	2.50
	Common Player:	.10	.05	.03
1	Eddie Murray	.40	.20	.12
2	Jim Rice	.30	.15	.09
3	Carl Yastrzemski	.60	.30	.20
4	Nolan Ryan	.30	.15	.09
5	Chet Lemon	.10	.05	.03
6	Andre Thornton	.10	.05	.03
7	Rusty Staub	.15	.08	.05
8	Ron LeFlore	.10	.05	.03
9	George Brett	.50	.25	.15
10	Larry Hisle	.10	.05	.03
11	Rod Carew	.35	.20	.11
12	Reggie Jackson	.40	.20	.12
13	Ron Guidry	.20	.10	.06
14	Mitchell Page	.10	.05	.03
15	Leon Roberts	.10	.05	.03
16	Al Oliver	.15	.08	.05
17	John Mayberry	.10	.05	.03
18	Bob Horner	.20	.10	.06
19	Phil Niekro	.25	.13	.08
20	Dave Kingman	.15	.08	.05
21	John Bench	.40	.20	.12
22	Tom Seaver	.40	.20	.12
23	J.R. Richard	.10	.05	.03
24	Steve Garvey	.35	.20	.11
25	Reggie Smith	.15	.08	.05
26	Ross Grimsley	.10	.05	.03
27	Craig Swan	.10	.05	.03
28	Pete Rose	.90	.45	.25
29	Dave Parker	.20	.10	.06
30	Ted Simmons	.15	.08	.05

		NR MT	EX	VG
31	Dave Winfield	.30	.15	.09
32	Jack Clark	.20	.10	.06
33	Vida Blue	.15	.08	.05

1980 Topps

Again numbering 726 cards measuring 2-1/2" by 3-1/2", Topps did make some design changes in 1980. Fronts have the usual color picture with a facsimile autograph. The player's name appears above the picture, while his position is on a pennant at the upper left and his team on another pennant in the lower right. Backs no longer feature games, returning instead to statistics, personal information, a few headlines and a cartoon about the player. Specialty cards include statistical leaders, and previous season highlights. Many rookies again appear in team threesomes.

		NR MT	EX	VG
	Complete Set:	300.00	150.00	90.00
	Common Player:	.12	.06	.04
1	1979 Highlights (Lou Brock, Carl Yastrzemski)	2.00	1.00	.60
2	1979 Highlights (Willie McCovey)	.80	.40	.25
3	1979 Highlights (Manny Mota)	.20	.10	.06
4	1979 Highlights (Pete Rose)	2.00	1.00	.60
5	1979 Highlights (Garry Templeton)	.20	.10	.06
6	1979 Highlights (Del Unser)	.12	.06	.04
7	Mike Lum	.12	.06	.04
8	Craig Swan	.12	.06	.04
9	Steve Braun	.12	.06	.04
10	Denny Martinez	.20	.10	.06
11	Jimmy Sexton	.12	.06	.04
12	John Curtis	.12	.06	.04
13	Ron Pruitt	.12	.06	.04
14	Dave Cash	.12	.06	.04
15	Bill Campbell	.12	.06	.04
16	Jerry Narron	.20	.10	.06
17	Bruce Sutter	.35	.25	.14
18	Ron Jackson	.12	.06	.04
19	Balor Moore	.12	.06	.04
20	Dan Ford	.12	.06	.04
21	Manny Sarmiento	.12	.06	.04
22	Pat Putnam	.12	.06	.04
23	Derrel Thomas	.12	.06	.04
24	Jim Slaton	.12	.06	.04
25	Lee Mazzilli	.20	.10	.06
26	Marty Pattin	.12	.06	.04
27	Del Unser	.12	.06	.04
28	Bruce Kison	.12	.06	.04
29	Mark Wagner	.12	.06	.04
30	Vida Blue	.30	.15	.09
31	Jay Johnstone	.20	.10	.06
32	Julio Cruz	.12	.06	.04
33	Tony Scott	.12	.06	.04
34	Jeff Newman	.12	.06	.04
35	Luis Tiant	.30	.15	.09
36	Rusty Torres	.12	.06	.04
37	Kiko Garcia	.12	.06	.04
38	Dan Spillner	.12	.06	.04
39	Rowland Office	.12	.06	.04
40	Carlton Fisk	5.00	2.50	1.50
41	Rangers Team (Pat Corrales)	.50	.25	.15
42	*Dave Palmer*	.20	.10	.06
43	Bombo Rivera	.12	.06	.04

		NR MT	EX	VG
44	Bill Fahey	.12	.06	.04
45	Frank White	.25	.13	.08
46	Rico Carty	.20	.10	.06
47	Bill Bonham	.12	.06	.04
48	Rick Miller	.12	.06	.04
49	Mario Guerrero	.12	.06	.04
50	J.R. Richard	.20	.10	.06
51	Joe Ferguson	.12	.06	.04
52	Warren Brusstar	.12	.06	.04
53	Ben Oglivie	.20	.10	.06
54	Dennis Lamp	.12	.06	.04
55	Bill Madlock	.40	.20	.12
56	Bobby Valentine	.20	.10	.06
57	Pete Vuckovich	.20	.10	.06
58	Doug Flynn	.12	.06	.04
59	Eddy Putman	.12	.06	.04
60	Bucky Dent	.25	.13	.08
61	Gary Serum	.12	.06	.04
62	Mike Ivie	.12	.06	.04
63	Bob Stanley	.20	.10	.06
64	Joe Nolan	.12	.06	.04
65	Al Bumbry	.20	.10	.06
66	Royals Team (Jim Frey)	.60	.30	.20
67	Doyle Alexander	.25	.13	.08
68	Larry Harlow	.12	.06	.04
69	Rick Williams	.12	.06	.04
70	Gary Carter	2.25	1.25	.70
71	John Milner	.12	.06	.04
72	Fred Howard	.12	.06	.04
73	Dave Collins	.20	.10	.06
74	Sid Monge	.12	.06	.04
75	Bill Russell	.20	.10	.06
76	John Stearns	.12	.06	.04
77	*Dave Stieb*	3.00	1.50	.90
78	Ruppert Jones	.12	.06	.04
79	Bob Owchinko	.12	.06	.04
80	Ron LeFlore	.20	.10	.06
81	Ted Sizemore	.12	.06	.04
82	Astros Team (Bill Virdon)	.50	.25	.15
83	*Steve Trout*	.30	.15	.09
84	Gary Lavelle	.12	.06	.04
85	Ted Simmons	.40	.20	.12
86	Dave Hamilton	.12	.06	.04
87	Pepe Frias	.12	.06	.04
88	Ken Landreaux	.20	.10	.06
89	Don Hood	.20	.10	.06
90	Manny Trillo	.20	.10	.06
91	Rick Dempsey	.20	.10	.06
92	Rick Rhoden	.25	.13	.08
93	Dave Roberts	.12	.06	.04
94	*Neil Allen*	.30	.15	.09
95	Cecil Cooper	.35	.20	.11
96	A's Team (Jim Marshall)	.50	.25	.15
97	Bill Lee	.20	.10	.06
98	Jerry Terrell	.12	.06	.04
99	Victor Cruz	.12	.06	.04
100	Johnny Bench	4.00	2.00	1.25
101	Aurelio Lopez	.12	.06	.04
102	Rich Dauer	.12	.06	.04
103	*Bill Caudill*	.20	.10	.06
104	Manny Mota	.20	.10	.06
105	Frank Tanana	.20	.10	.06
106	*Jeff Leonard*	.80	.40	.25
107	Francisco Barrios	.12	.06	.04
108	Bob Horner	.40	.30	.15
109	Bill Travers	.12	.06	.04
110	Fred Lynn	.35	.20	.11
111	Bob Knepper	.20	.10	.06
112	White Sox Team (Tony LaRussa)	.50	.25	.15
113	Geoff Zahn	.12	.06	.04
114	Juan Beniquez	.12	.06	.04
115	Sparky Lyle	.25	.13	.08
116	Larry Cox	.12	.06	.04
117	Dock Ellis	.12	.06	.04
118	Phil Garner	.20	.10	.06
119	Sammy Stewart	.12	.06	.04
120	Greg Luzinski	.30	.15	.09
121	Checklist 1-121	.50	.25	.15
122	Dave Rosello	.12	.06	.04
123	Lynn Jones	.12	.06	.04
124	Dave Lemanczyk	.12	.06	.04
125	Tony Perez	.60	.30	.20
126	Dave Tomlin	.12	.06	.04
127	Gary Thomasson	.12	.06	.04
128	Tom Burgmeier	.12	.06	.04
129	Craig Reynolds	.12	.06	.04
130	Amos Otis	.20	.10	.06
131	Paul Mitchell	.12	.06	.04
132	Biff Pocoroba	.12	.06	.04
133	Jerry Turner	.12	.06	.04
134	Matt Keough	.12	.06	.04

#	Player	NR MT	EX	VG
135	Bill Buckner	.30	.15	.09
136	Dick Ruthven	.12	.06	.04
137	*John Castino*	.20	.10	.06
138	Ross Baumgarten	.12	.06	.04
139	*Dane Iorg*	.20	.10	.06
140	Rich Gossage	.60	.30	.20
141	Gary Alexander	.12	.06	.04
142	Phil Huffman	.12	.06	.04
143	Bruce Bochte	.12	.06	.04
144	Steve Comer	.12	.06	.04
145	Darrell Evans	.30	.15	.09
146	Bob Welch	2.00	1.00	.60
147	Terry Puhl	.12	.06	.04
148	Manny Sanguillen	.12	.06	.04
149	Tom Hume	.12	.06	.04
150	Jason Thompson	.20	.10	.06
151	Tom Hausman	.12	.06	.04
152	John Fulgham	.12	.06	.04
153	Tim Blackwell	.12	.06	.04
154	Lary Sorensen	.12	.06	.04
155	Jerry Remy	.12	.06	.04
156	Tony Brizzolara	.12	.06	.04
157	Willie Wilson	.20	.10	.06
158	Rob Picciolo	.12	.06	.04
159	Ken Clay	.20	.10	.06
160	Eddie Murray	11.00	5.50	3.30
161	Larry Christenson	.12	.06	.04
162	Bob Randall	.12	.06	.04
163	Steve Swisher	.12	.06	.04
164	Greg Pryor	.12	.06	.04
165	Omar Moreno	.12	.06	.04
166	Glenn Abbott	.12	.06	.04
167	Jack Clark	1.00	.50	.30
168	Rick Waits	.12	.06	.04
169	Luis Gomez	.12	.06	.04
170	Burt Hooton	.20	.10	.06
171	Fernando Gonzalez	.12	.06	.04
172	Ron Hodges	.12	.06	.04
173	John Henry Johnson	.12	.06	.04
174	Ray Knight	.20	.10	.06
175	Rick Reuschel	.25	.13	.08
176	Champ Summers	.12	.06	.04
177	Dave Heaverlo	.12	.06	.04
178	Tim McCarver	.30	.15	.09
179	*Ron Davis*	.20	.10	.06
180	Warren Cromartie	.12	.06	.04
181	Moose Haas	.12	.06	.04
182	Ken Reitz	.12	.06	.04
183	Jim Anderson	.12	.06	.04
184	Steve Renko	.12	.06	.04
185	Hal McRae	.25	.13	.08
186	Junior Moore	.12	.06	.04
187	Alan Ashby	.12	.06	.04
188	Terry Crowley	.12	.06	.04
189	Kevin Kobel	.12	.06	.04
190	Buddy Bell	.25	.13	.08
191	Ted Martinez	.12	.06	.04
192	Braves Team (Bobby Cox)	.50	.25	.15
193	Dave Goltz	.20	.10	.06
194	Mike Easler	.20	.10	.06
195	John Montefusco	.20	.10	.06
196	Lance Parrish	1.50	.70	.45
197	Byron McLaughlin	.12	.06	.04
198	Dell Alston	.12	.06	.04
199	Mike LaCoss	.20	.10	.06
200	Jim Rice	2.00	1.00	.60
201	Batting Leaders (Keith Hernandez, Fred Lynn)	.50	.25	.15
202	Home Run Leaders (Dave Kingman, Gorman Thomas)	.25	.13	.08
203	Runs Batted In Leaders (Don Baylor, Dave Winfield)	.50	.25	.15
204	Stolen Base Leaders (Omar Moreno, Willie Wilson)	.20	.10	.06
205	Victory Leaders (Mike Flanagan, Joe Niekro, Phil Niekro)	.40	.20	.12
206	Strikeout Leaders (J.R. Richard, Nolan Ryan)	2.00	1.00	.60
207	Earned Run Avg. Leaders (Ron Guidry, J.R. Richard)	.25	.13	.08
208	Wayne Cage	.12	.06	.04
209	Von Joshua	.12	.06	.04
210	Steve Carlton	4.00	2.00	1.25
211	Dave Skaggs	.12	.06	.04
212	Dave Roberts	.12	.06	.04
213	Mike Jorgensen	.12	.06	.04
214	Angels Team (Jim Fregosi)	.50	.25	.15
215	Sixto Lezcano	.12	.06	.04
216	Phil Mankowski	.12	.06	.04
217	Ed Halicki	.12	.06	.04
218	Jose Morales	.12	.06	.04
219	Steve Mingori	.12	.06	.04
220	Dave Concepcion	.30	.15	.09
221	Joe Cannon	.12	.06	.04
222	*Ron Hassey*	.50	.25	.15
223	Bob Sykes	.12	.06	.04
224	Willie Montanez	.12	.06	.04
225	Lou Piniella	.30	.15	.09
226	Bill Stein	.12	.06	.04
227	Len Barker	.12	.06	.04
228	Johnny Oates	.12	.06	.04
229	Jim Bibby	.12	.06	.04
230	Dave Winfield	6.00	3.00	1.75
231	Steve McCatty	.12	.06	.04
232	Alan Trammell	4.00	2.00	1.25
233	LaRue Washington	.12	.06	.04
234	Vern Ruhle	.12	.06	.04
235	Andre Dawson	7.50	3.75	2.25
236	Marc Hill	.12	.06	.04
237	Scott McGregor	.20	.10	.06
238	Rob Wilfong	.12	.06	.04
239	Don Aase	.12	.06	.04
240	Dave Kingman	.40	.20	.12
241	Checklist 122-242	.50	.25	.15
242	Lamar Johnson	.12	.06	.04
243	Jerry Augustine	.12	.06	.04
244	Cardinals Team (Ken Boyer)	.50	.25	.15
245	Phil Niekro	1.00	.50	.30
246	Tim Foli	.12	.06	.04
247	Frank Riccelli	.12	.06	.04
248	Jamie Quirk	.12	.06	.04
249	Jim Clancy	.20	.10	.06
250	Jim Kaat	.50	.25	.15
251	Kip Young	.12	.06	.04
252	Ted Cox	.12	.0€	.04
253	John Montague	.12	.06	.04
254	Paul Dade	.12	.06	.04
255	Dusty Baker	.12	.06	.04
256	Roger Erickson	.12	.06	.04
257	Larry Herndon	.20	.10	.06
258	Paul Moskau	.12	.06	.04
259	Mets Team (Joe Torre)	.60	.30	.20
260	Al Oliver	.35	.20	.11
261	Dave Chalk	.12	.06	.04
262	Benny Ayala	.12	.06	.04
263	Dave LaRoche	.12	.06	.04
264	Bill Robinson	.12	.06	.04
265	Robin Yount	12.00	6.00	3.50
266	Bernie Carbo	.12	.06	.04
267	Dan Schatzeder	.12	.06	.04
268	Rafael Landestoy	.12	.06	.04
269	Dave Tobik	.12	.06	.04
270	Mike Schmidt	6.00	3.00	1.75
271	Dick Drago	.12	.06	.04
272	Ralph Garr	.20	.10	.06
273	Eduardo Rodriguez	.12	.06	.04
274	Dale Murphy	4.00	2.00	1.25
275	Jerry Koosman	.25	.13	.08
276	Tom Veryzer	.12	.06	.04
277	Rick Bosetti	.12	.06	.04
278	Jim Spencer	.20	.10	.06
279	Rob Andrews	.12	.06	.04
280	Gaylord Perry	1.50	.70	.45
281	Paul Blair	.20	.10	.06
282	Mariners Team (Darrell Johnson)	.50	.25	.15
283	John Ellis	.12	.06	.04
284	Larry Murray	.12	.06	.04
285	Don Baylor	.35	.20	.11
286	Darold Knowles	.12	.06	.04
287	John Lowenstein	.12	.06	.04
288	Dave Rozema	.12	.06	.04
289	Bruce Bochy	.12	.06	.04
290	Steve Garvey	2.00	1.00	.60
291	Randy Scarbery	.12	.06	.04
292	Dale Berra	.12	.06	.04
293	Elias Sosa	.12	.06	.04
294	Charlie Spikes	.12	.06	.04
295	Larry Gura	.12	.06	.04
296	Dave Rader	.12	.06	.04
297	Tim Johnson	.12	.06	.04
298	Ken Holtzman	.20	.10	.06
299	Steve Henderson	.12	.06	.04
300	Ron Guidry	.70	.35	.20
301	Mike Edwards	.12	.06	.04
302	Dodgers Team (Tom Lasorda)	.60	.30	.20
303	Bill Castro	.12	.06	.04
304	Butch Wynegar	.20	.10	.06
305	Randy Jones	.20	.10	.06
306	Denny Walling	.12	.06	.04
307	Rick Honeycutt	.20	.10	.06
308	Mike Hargrove	.20	.10	.06
309	Larry McWilliams	.12	.06	.04

		NR MT	EX	VG			NR MT	EX	VG
310	Dave Parker	2.00	1.00	.60	400	George Foster	.50	.25	.15
311	Roger Metzger	.12	.06	.04	401	Pete Falcone	.12	.06	.04
312	Mike Barlow	.12	.06	.04	402	Merv Rettenmund	.12	.06	.04
313	Johnny Grubb	.12	.06	.04	403	Pete Redfern	.12	.06	.04
314	Tim Stoddard	.20	.10	.06	404	Orioles Team (Earl Weaver)	.60	.30	.20
315	Steve Kemp	.25	.13	.08	405	Dwight Evans	1.00	.50	.30
316	Bob Lacey	.12	.06	.04	406	Paul Molitor	5.00	2.50	1.50
317	Mike Anderson	.12	.06	.04	407	Tony Solaita	.12	.06	.04
318	Jerry Reuss	.20	.10	.06	408	Bill North	.12	.06	.04
319	Chris Speier	.12	.06	.04	409	Paul Splittorff	.20	.10	.06
320	Dennis Eckersley	3.00	1.50	.90	410	Bobby Bonds	.25	.13	.08
321	Keith Hernandez	1.50	.70	.45	411	Frank LaCorte	.12	.06	.04
322	Claudell Washington	.20	.10	.06	412	Thad Bosley	.12	.06	.04
323	Mick Kelleher	.12	.06	.04	413	Allen Ripley	.12	.06	.04
324	Tom Underwood	.12	.06	.04	414	George Scott	.20	.10	.06
325	Dan Driessen	.20	.10	.06	415	Bill Atkinson	.12	.06	.04
326	Bo McLaughlin	.12	.06	.04	416	Tom Brookens	.35	.20	.11
327	Ray Fosse	.12	.06	.04	417	Craig Chamberlain	.12	.06	.04
328	Twins Team (Gene Mauch)	.50	.25	.15	418	Roger Freed	.12	.06	.04
329	Bert Roberge	.12	.06	.04	419	Vic Correll	.12	.06	.04
330	Al Cowens	.12	.06	.04	420	Butch Hobson	.12	.06	.04
331	Rich Hebner	.12	.06	.04	421	Doug Bird	.12	.06	.04
332	Enrique Romo	.12	.06	.04	422	Larry Milbourne	.12	.06	.04
333	Jim Norris	.12	.06	.04	423	Dave Frost	.12	.06	.04
334	Jim Beattie	.20	.10	.06	424	Yankees Team (Dick Howser)	.70	.35	.20
335	Willie McCovey	1.50	.70	.45	425	Mark Belanger	.20	.10	.06
336	George Medich	.12	.06	.04	426	Grant Jackson	.12	.06	.04
337	Carney Lansford	.30	.15	.09	427	Tom Hutton	.12	.06	.04
338	Johnny Wockenfuss	.12	.06	.04	428	Pat Zachry	.12	.06	.04
339	John D'Acquisto	.12	.06	.04	429	Duane Kuiper	.12	.06	.04
340	Ken Singleton	.20	.10	.06	430	Larry Hisle	.12	.06	.04
341	Jim Essian	.12	.06	.04	431	Mike Krukow	.20	.10	.06
342	Odell Jones	.12	.06	.04	432	Willie Norwood	.12	.06	.04
343	Mike Vail	.12	.06	.04	433	Rich Gale	.12	.06	.04
344	Randy Lerch	.12	.06	.04	434	Johnnie LeMaster	.12	.06	.04
345	Larry Parrish	.20	.10	.06	435	Don Gullett	.20	.10	.06
346	Buddy Solomon	.12	.06	.04	436	Billy Almon	.12	.06	.04
347	Harry Chappas	.20	.10	.06	437	Joe Niekro	.20	.10	.06
348	Checklist 243-363	.50	.25	.15	438	Dave Revering	.12	.06	.04
349	Jack Brohamer	.12	.06	.04	439	Mike Phillips	.12	.06	.04
350	George Hendrick	.20	.10	.06	440	Don Sutton	1.00	.50	.30
351	Bob Davis	.12	.06	.04	441	Eric Soderholm	.12	.06	.04
352	Dan Briggs	.12	.06	.04	442	Jorge Orta	.12	.06	.04
353	Andy Hassler	.12	.06	.04	443	Mike Parrott	.12	.06	.04
354	Rick Auerbach	.12	.06	.04	444	Alvis Woods	.12	.06	.04
355	Gary Matthews	.20	.10	.06	445	Mark Fidrych	.20	.10	.06
356	Padres Team (Jerry Coleman)	.50	.25	.15	446	Duffy Dyer	.12	.06	.04
357	Bob McClure	.12	.06	.04	447	Nino Espinosa	.12	.06	.04
358	Lou Whitaker	1.25	.60	.40	448	Jim Wohlford	.12	.06	.04
359	Randy Moffitt	.12	.06	.04	449	Doug Bair	.12	.06	.04
360	Darrell Porter	.12	.06	.04	450	George Brett	11.00	5.50	3.30
361	Wayne Garland	.12	.06	.04	451	Indians Team (Dave Garcia)	.50	.25	.15
362	Danny Goodwin	.12	.06	.04	452	Steve Dillard	.12	.06	.04
363	Wayne Gross	.12	.06	.04	453	Mike Bacsik	.12	.06	.04
364	Ray Burris	.12	.06	.04	454	Tom Donohue	.12	.06	.04
365	Bobby Murcer	.25	.13	.08	455	Mike Torrez	.20	.10	.06
366	Rob Dressler	.12	.06	.04	456	Frank Taveras	.12	.06	.04
367	Billy Smith	.12	.06	.04	457	Bert Blyleven	.50	.25	.15
368	Willie Aikens	.20	.10	.06	458	Billy Sample	.12	.06	.04
369	Jim Kern	.12	.06	.04	459	Mickey Lolich	.12	.06	.04
370	Cesar Cedeno	.25	.13	.08	460	Willie Randolph	.25	.13	.08
371	Jack Morris	3.00	1.50	.90	461	Dwayne Murphy	.20	.10	.06
372	Joel Youngblood	.12	.06	.04	462	Mike Sadek	.12	.06	.04
373	Dan Petry	.30	.15	.09	463	Jerry Royster	.12	.06	.04
374	Jim Gantner	.20	.10	.06	464	John Denny	.12	.06	.04
375	Ross Grimsley	.12	.06	.04	465	Rick Monday	.20	.10	.06
376	Gary Allenson	.12	.06	.04	466	Mike Squires	.12	.06	.04
377	Junior Kennedy	.12	.06	.04	467	Jesse Jefferson	.12	.06	.04
378	Jerry Mumphrey	.12	.06	.04	468	Aurelio Rodriguez	.20	.10	.06
379	Kevin Bell	.12	.06	.04	469	Randy Niemann	.12	.06	.04
380	Garry Maddox	.20	.10	.06	470	Bob Boone	.20	.10	.06
381	Cubs Team (Preston Gomez)	.50	.25	.15	471	Hosken Powell	.12	.06	.04
382	Dave Freisleben	.12	.06	.04	472	Willie Hernandez	.20	.10	.06
383	Ed Ott	.12	.06	.04	473	Bump Wills	.12	.06	.04
384	Joey McLaughlin	.12	.06	.04	474	Steve Busby	.12	.06	.04
385	Enos Cabell	.12	.06	.04	475	Cesar Geronimo	.12	.06	.04
386	Darrell Jackson	.12	.06	.04	476	Bob Shirley	.12	.06	.04
387a	Fred Stanley (name in red)	.20	.10	.06	477	Buck Martinez	.12	.06	.04
387b	Fred Stanley (name in yellow)	3.00	1.50	.90	478	Gil Flores	.12	.06	.04
388	Mike Paxton	.12	.06	.04	479	Expos Team (Dick Williams)	.50	.25	.15
389	Pete LaCock	.12	.06	.04	480	Bob Watson	.20	.10	.06
390	Fergie Jenkins	.40	.20	.12	481	Tom Paciorek	.12	.06	.04
391	Tony Armas	.12	.06	.04	482	Rickey Henderson	100.00	50.00	30.00
392	Milt Wilcox	.12	.06	.04	483	Bo Diaz	.20	.10	.06
393	Ozzie Smith	15.00	7.50	4.50	484	Checklist 364-484	.50	.25	.15
394	Reggie Cleveland	.12	.06	.04	485	Mickey Rivers	.20	.10	.06
395	Ellis Valentine	.12	.06	.04	486	Mike Tyson	.12	.06	.04
396	Dan Meyer	.12	.06	.04	487	Wayne Nordhagen	.12	.06	.04
397	Roy Thomas	.12	.06	.04	488	Roy Howell	.12	.06	.04
398	Barry Foote	.12	.06	.04	489	Preston Hanna	.12	.06	.04
399	Mike Proly	.12	.06	.04	490	Lee May	.20	.10	.06

	NR MT	EX	VG
491 Steve Mura	.12	.06	.04
492 Todd Cruz	.12	.06	.04
493 Jerry Martin	.12	.06	.04
494 Craig Minetto	.12	.06	.04
495 Bake McBride	.12	.06	.04
496 Silvio Martinez	.12	.06	.04
497 Jim Mason	.12	.06	.04
498 Danny Darwin	.20	.10	.06
499 Giants Team (Dave Bristol)	.50	.25	.15
500 Tom Seaver	3.00	1.50	.90
501 Rennie Stennett	.12	.06	.04
502 Rich Wortham	.12	.06	.04
503 Mike Cubbage	.12	.06	.04
504 Gene Garber	.12	.06	.04
505 Bert Campaneris	.20	.10	.06
506 Tom Buskey	.12	.06	.04
507 Leon Roberts	.12	.06	.04
508 U.L. Washington	.12	.06	.04
509 Ed Glynn	.12	.06	.04
510 Ron Cey	.25	.13	.08
511 Eric Wilkins	.12	.06	.04
512 Jose Cardenal	.12	.06	.04
513 Tom Dixon	.12	.06	.04
514 Steve Ontiveros	.12	.06	.04
515 Mike Caldwell	.12	.06	.04
516 Hector Cruz	.12	.06	.04
517 Don Stanhouse	.12	.06	.04
518 Nelson Norman	.12	.06	.04
519 Steve Nicosia	.12	.06	.04
520 Steve Rogers	.20	.10	.06
521 Ken Brett	.12	.06	.04
522 Jim Morrison	.12	.06	.04
523 Ken Henderson	.12	.06	.04
524 Jim Wright	.12	.06	.04
525 Clint Hurdle	.12	.06	.04
526 Phillies Team (Dallas Green)	.70	.35	.20
527 Doug Rau	.12	.06	.04
528 Adrian Devine	.12	.06	.04
529 Jim Barr	.12	.06	.04
530 Jim Sundberg	.12	.06	.04
531 Eric Rasmussen	.12	.06	.04
532 Willie Horton	.20	.10	.06
533 Checklist 485-605	.50	.25	.15
534 Andre Thornton	.25	.13	.08
535 Bob Forsch	.20	.10	.06
536 Lee Lacy	.12	.06	.04
537 *Alex Trevino*	.20	.10	.06
538 Joe Strain	.12	.06	.04
539 Rudy May	.12	.06	.04
540 Pete Rose	4.00	2.00	1.25
541 Miguel Dilone	.12	.06	.04
542 Joe Coleman	.12	.06	.04
543 Pat Kelly	.12	.06	.04
544 *Rick Sutcliffe*	3.00	1.50	.90
545 Jeff Burroughs	.20	.10	.06
546 Rick Langford	.12	.06	.04
547 John Wathan	.20	.10	.06
548 Dave Rajsich	.12	.06	.04
549 Larry Wolfe	.12	.06	.04
550 Ken Griffey	.25	.13	.08
551 Pirates Team (Chuck Tanner)	.50	.25	.15
552 Bill Nahorodny	.12	.06	.04
553 Dick Davis	.12	.06	.04
554 Art Howe	.12	.06	.04
555 Ed Figueroa	.20	.10	.06
556 Joe Rudi	.20	.10	.06
557 Mark Lee	.12	.06	.04
558 Alfredo Griffin	.25	.13	.08
559 Dale Murray	.12	.06	.04
560 Dave Lopes	.25	.13	.08
561 Eddie Whitson	.20	.10	.06
562 Joe Wallis	.12	.06	.04
563 Will McEnaney	.12	.06	.04
564 Rick Manning	.12	.06	.04
565 Dennis Leonard	.20	.10	.06
566 Bud Harrelson	.20	.10	.06
567 Skip Lockwood	.12	.06	.04
568 *Gary Roenicke*	.25	.13	.08
569 Terry Kennedy	.25	.13	.08
570 Roy Smalley	.20	.10	.06
571 Joe Sambito	.12	.06	.04
572 Jerry Morales	.12	.06	.04
573 Kent Tekulve	.20	.10	.06
574 Scot Thompson	.12	.06	.04
575 Ken Kravec	.12	.06	.04
576 Jim Dwyer	.12	.06	.04
577 Blue Jays Team (Bobby Mattick)	.50	.25	.15
578 Scott Sanderson	.20	.10	.06
579 Charlie Moore	.12	.06	.04
580 Nolan Ryan	20.00	10.00	6.00
581 Bob Bailor	.12	.06	.04

	NR MT	EX	VG
582 Brian Doyle	.20	.10	.06
583 Bob Stinson	.12	.06	.04
584 Kurt Bevacqua	.12	.06	.04
585 Al Hrabosky	.20	.10	.06
586 Mitchell Page	.12	.06	.04
587 Garry Templeton	.20	.10	.06
588 Greg Minton	.12	.06	.04
589 Chet Lemon	.20	.10	.06
590 Jim Palmer	3.00	1.50	.90
591 Rick Cerone	.12	.06	.04
592 Jon Matlack	.20	.10	.06
593 Jesus Alou	.12	.06	.04
594 Dick Tidrow	.12	.06	.04
595 Don Money	.12	.06	.04
596 Rick Matula	.12	.06	.04
597 Tom Poquette	.12	.06	.04
598 Fred Kendall	.12	.06	.04
599 Mike Norris	.12	.06	.04
600 Reggie Jackson	7.00	3.50	2.00
601 Buddy Schultz	.12	.06	.04
602 Brian Downing	.20	.10	.06
603 Jack Billingham	.12	.06	.04
604 Glenn Adams	.12	.06	.04
605 Terry Forster	.20	.10	.06
606 Reds Team (John McNamara)	.50	.25	.15
607 Woodie Fryman	.20	.10	.06
608 Alan Bannister	.12	.06	.04
609 Ron Reed	.20	.10	.06
610 Willie Stargell	1.50	.70	.45
611 Jerry Garvin	.12	.06	.04
612 Cliff Johnson	.12	.06	.04
613 Randy Stein	.12	.06	.04
614 John Hiller	.20	.10	.06
615 Doug DeCinces	.20	.10	.06
616 Gene Richards	.12	.06	.04
617 Joaquin Andujar	.20	.10	.06
618 Bob Montgomery	.12	.06	.04
619 Sergio Ferrer	.12	.06	.04
620 Richie Zisk	.20	.10	.06
621 Bob Grich	.20	.10	.06
622 Mario Soto	.20	.10	.06
623 Gorman Thomas	.20	.10	.06
624 Lerrin LaGrow	.12	.06	.04
625 Chris Chambliss	.25	.13	.08
626 Tigers Team (Sparky Anderson)	.60	.30	.20
627 Pedro Borbon	.12	.06	.04
628 Doug Capilla	.12	.06	.04
629 Jim Todd	.12	.06	.04
630 Larry Bowa	.25	.13	.08
631 Mark Littell	.12	.06	.04
632 Barry Bonnell	.12	.06	.04
633 Bob Apodaca	.12	.06	.04
634 Glenn Borgmann	.12	.06	.04
635 John Candelaria	.20	.10	.06
636 Toby Harrah	.20	.10	.06
637 Joe Simpson	.12	.06	.04
638 *Mark Clear*	.20	.10	.06
639 Larry Biittner	.12	.06	.04
640 Mike Flanagan	.25	.13	.08
641 Ed Kranepool	.20	.10	.06
642 Ken Forsch	.12	.06	.04
643 John Mayberry	.20	.10	.06
644 Charlie Hough	.20	.10	.06
645 Rick Burleson	.20	.10	.06
646 Checklist 606-726	.50	.25	.15
647 Milt May	.12	.06	.04
648 Roy White	.20	.10	.06
649 Tom Griffin	.12	.06	.04
650 Joe Morgan	3.00	1.50	.90
651 Rollie Fingers	1.00	.50	.30
652 Mario Mendoza	.12	.06	.04
653 Stan Bahnsen	.12	.06	.04
654 Bruce Boisclair	.12	.06	.04
655 Tug McGraw	.25	.13	.08
656 Larvell Blanks	.12	.06	.04
657 Dave Edwards	.12	.06	.04
658 Chris Knapp	.12	.06	.04
659 Brewers Team (George Bamberger)	.50	.25	.15
660 Rusty Staub	.30	.15	.09
661 Orioles Future Stars (Mark Corey, Dave Ford, Wayne Krenchicki)	.12	.06	.04
662 Red Sox Future Stars (Joel Finch, Mike O'Berry, Chuck Rainey)	.12	.06	.04
663 Angels Future Stars (Ralph Botting, Bob Clark, *Dickie Thon*)	.30	.15	.09
664 White Sox Future Stars (Mike Colbern, *Guy Hoffman*, Dewey Robinson)	.20	.10	.06
665 Indians Future Stars (Larry Andersen, Bobby Cuellar, Sandy Wihtol)	.12	.06	.04
666 Tigers Future Stars (Mike Chris, Al Greene, Bruce Robbins)	.12	.06	.04

		NR MT	EX	VG
667	Royals Future Stars (Renie Martin, Bill Paschall, *Dan Quisenberry*)	1.00	.50	.30
668	Brewers Future Stars (Danny Boitano, Willie Mueller, Lenn Sakata)	.12	.06	.04
669	Twins Future Stars (Dan Graham, Rick Sofield, *Gary Ward*)	.35	.20	.11
670	Yankees Future Stars (Bobby Brown, Brad Gulden, Darryl Jones)	.20	.10	.06
671	A's Future Stars (Derek Bryant, Brian Kingman, *Mike Morgan*)	2.00	1.00	.60
672	Mariners Future Stars (Charlie Beamon, Rodney Craig, Rafael Vasquez)	.12	.06	.04
673	Rangers Future Stars (Brian Allard, Jerry Don Gleaton, Greg Mahlberg)	.12	.06	.04
674	Blue Jays Future Stars (Butch Edge, Pat Kelly, Ted Wilborn)	.12	.06	.04
675	Braves Future Stars (Bruce Benedict, Larry Bradford, Eddie Miller)	.12	.06	.04
676	Cubs Future Stars (Dave Geisel, Steve Macko, Karl Pagel)	.12	.06	.04
677	Reds Future Stars (Art DeFreites, *Frank Pastore*, Harry Spilman)	.12	.06	.04
678	Astros Future Stars (Reggie Baldwin, Alan Knicely, *Pete Ladd*)	.12	.06	.04
679	Dodgers Future Stars (Joe Beckwith, *Mickey Hatcher*, Dave Patterson)	.50	.25	.15
680	Expos Future Stars (*Tony Bernazard*, Randy Miller, John Tamargo)	.20	.10	.06
681	Mets Future Stars (Dan Norman, *Jesse Orosco, Mike Scott*)	3.00	1.50	.90
682	Phillies Future Stars (Ramon Aviles, *Dickie Noles*, Kevin Saucier)	.20	.10	.06
683	Pirates Future Stars (Dorian Boyland, Alberto Lois, Harry Saferight)	.12	.06	.04
684	Cardinals Future Stars (George Frazier, *Tom Herr*, Dan O'Brien)	1.50	.70	.45
685	Padres Future Stars (Tim Flannery, Brian Greer, Jim Wilhelm)	.12	.06	.04
686	Giants Future Stars (Greg Johnston, Dennis Littlejohn, Phil Nastu)	.12	.06	.04
687	Mike Heath	.12	.06	.04
688	Steve Stone	.20	.10	.06
689	Red Sox Team (Don Zimmer)	.60	.30	.20
690	Tommy John	.60	.30	.20
691	Ivan DeJesus	.12	.06	.04
692	Rawly Eastwick	.12	.06	.04
693	Craig Kusick	.12	.06	.04
694	Jim Rooker	.12	.06	.04
695	Reggie Smith	.20	.10	.06
696	Julio Gonzalez	.12	.06	.04
697	David Clyde	.12	.06	.04
698	Oscar Gamble	.20	.10	.06
699	Floyd Bannister	.20	.10	.06
700	Rod Carew	2.00	1.00	.60
701	*Ken Oberkfell*	.30	.15	.09
702	Ed Farmer	.12	.06	.04
703	Otto Velez	.12	.06	.04
704	Gene Tenace	.20	.10	.06
705	Freddie Patek	.12	.06	.04
706	Tippy Martinez	.12	.06	.04
707	Elliott Maddox	.12	.06	.04
708	Bob Tolan	.12	.06	.04
709	Pat Underwood	.12	.06	.04
710	Graig Nettles	.35	.20	.11
711	Bob Galasso	.12	.06	.04
712	Rodney Scott	.12	.06	.04
713	Terry Whitfield	.12	.06	.04
714	Fred Norman	.12	.06	.04
715	Sal Bando	.20	.10	.06
716	Lynn McGlothen	.12	.06	.04
717	Mickey Klutts	.12	.06	.04
718	Greg Gross	.12	.06	.04
719	Don Robinson	.20	.10	.06
720	Carl Yastrzemski	1.50	.70	.45
721	Paul Hartzell	.12	.06	.04
722	Jose Cruz	.20	.10	.06
723	Shane Rawley	.20	.10	.06
724	Jerry White	.12	.06	.04
725	Rick Wise	.20	.10	.06
726	Steve Yeager	.20	.06	.04

A player's name in italic indicates a rookie card. An (FC) indicates a player's first card for that particular card company.

1980 Topps
Superstar 5 X 7 Photos

In actuality, these cards measure 4-7/8" by 6-7/8". These were another Topps "test" issue that was bought out almost entirely by investors. The 60 cards have a color photo on the front and a blue ink facsimile autograph. Backs have the player's name, team position and card number. The issue was printed on different cardboard stocks, with the first on thick cardboard with a white back and the second on thinner cardboard with a gray back. Prices below are for the more common gray backs; white backs are valued about three times the figures shown. The issue was distributed in selected geographical areas, but they were hoarded quickly. Those who hoarded them still probably have much of their supply as the set has never taken off, despite the presence of many big-name stars.

		NR MT	EX	VG
	Complete Set:	9.00	4.50	2.75
	Common Player:	.10	.05	.03
1	Willie Stargell	.30	.15	.09
2	Mike Schmidt	.30	.15	.09
3	Johnny Bench	.50	.25	.15
4	Jim Palmer	.35	.20	.11
5	Jim Rice	.40	.20	.12
6	Reggie Jackson	.25	.13	.08
7	Ron Guidry	.20	.10	.06
8	Lee Mazzilli	.10	.05	.03
9	Don Baylor	.15	.08	.05
10	Fred Lynn	.20	.10	.06
11	Ken Singleton	.10	.05	.03
12	Rod Carew	.25	.13	.08
13	Steve Garvey	.25	.13	.08
14	George Brett	.30	.15	.09
15	Tom Seaver	.40	.20	.12
16	Dave Kingman	.15	.08	.05
17	Dave Parker	.10	.05	.03
18	Dave Winfield	.40	.20	.12
19	Pete Rose	1.00	.50	.30
20	Nolan Ryan	1.00	.50	.30
21	Graig Nettles	.15	.08	.05
22	Carl Yastrzemski	.60	.30	.20
23	Tommy John	.25	.13	.08
24	George Foster	.15	.08	.05
25	James Rodney Richard	.10	.05	.03
26	Keith Hernandez	.30	.15	.09
27	Bob Horner	.15	.08	.05
28	Eddie Murray	.40	.20	.12
29	Steve Kemp	.10	.05	.03
30	Gorman Thomas	.10	.05	.03
31	Sixto Lezcano	.10	.05	.03
32	Bruce Sutter	.15	.08	.05
33	Cecil Cooper	.15	.08	.05
34	Larry Bowa	.10	.05	.03
35	Al Oliver	.15	.08	.05
36	Ted Simmons	.15	.08	.05
37	Garry Templeton	.10	.05	.03
38	Jerry Koosman	.10	.05	.03
39	Darrell Porter	.10	.05	.03
40	Roy Smalley	.10	.05	.03
41	Craig Swan	.10	.05	.03
42	Jason Thompson	.10	.05	.03
43	Andre Thornton	.10	.05	.03

		NR MT	EX	VG
44	Rick Manning	.10	.05	.03
45	Kent Tekulve	.10	.05	.03
46	Phil Niekro	.30	.15	.09
47	Buddy Bell	.15	.08	.05
48	Randy Jones	.10	.05	.03
49	Brian Downing	.10	.05	.03
50	Amos Otis	.10	.05	.03
51	Rick Bosetti	.10	.05	.03
52	Gary Carter	.40	.20	.12
53	Larry Parrish	.15	.08	.05
54	Jack Clark	.20	.10	.06
55	Bruce Bochte	.10	.05	.03
56	Cesar Cedeno	.15	.08	.05
57	Chet Lemon	.10	.05	.03
58	Dave Revering	.10	.05	.03
59	Vida Blue	.15	.08	.05
60	Davey Lopes	.15	.08	.05

1981 Topps

This is another 726-card set of 2-1/2" by 3-1/2" cards from Topps. The cards have the usual color photo with all cards from the same team sharing the same color borders. The player's name appears under the photo with his team and position appearing on a baseball cap at the lower left. The Topps logo returned in a small baseball in the lower right corner. Card backs include the usual stats along with a headline and a cartoon if there was room. Specialty cards include previous season record-breakers, highlights of the playoffs and World Series, along with the final appearance of team cards.

		MT	NR MT	EX
	Complete Set:	100.00	75.00	40.00
	Common Player:	.08	.06	.03
1	Batting Leaders (George Brett, Bill Buckner)	2.00	1.50	.80
2	Home Run Leaders (Reggie Jackson, Ben Oglivie, Mike Schmidt)	.40	.30	.15
3	Runs Batted In Leaders (Cecil Cooper, Mike Schmidt)	.30	.25	.12
4	Stolen Base Leaders (Rickey Henderson, Ron LeFlore)	1.50	1.25	.60
5	Victory Leaders (Steve Carlton, Steve Stone)	.20	.15	.08
6	Strikeout Leaders (Len Barker, Steve Carlton)	.20	.15	.08
7	Earned Run Avg. Leaders (Rudy May, Don Sutton)	.15	.11	.06
8	Leading Firemen (Rollie Fingers, Tom Hume, Dan Quisenberry)	.10	.08	.04
9	Pete LaCock	.08	.06	.03
10	Mike Flanagan	.12	.09	.05
11	Jim Wohlford	.08	.06	.03
12	Mark Clear	.08	.06	.03
13	*Joe Charboneau*	.15	.11	.06
14	*John Tudor*	.40	.30	.15
15	Larry Parrish	.15	.11	.06
16	Ron Davis	.10	.08	.04
17	Cliff Johnson	.08	.06	.03
18	Glenn Adams	.08	.06	.03
19	Jim Clancy	.12	.09	.05
20	Jeff Burroughs	.10	.08	.04
21	Ron Oester	.08	.06	.03
22	Danny Darwin	.08	.06	.03

		MT	NR MT	EX
23	Alex Trevino	.08	.06	.03
24	Don Stanhouse	.08	.06	.03
25	Sixto Lezcano	.08	.06	.03
26	U.L. Washington	.08	.06	.03
27	Champ Summers	.08	.06	.03
28	Enrique Romo	.08	.06	.03
29	Gene Tenace	.10	.08	.04
30	Jack Clark	.50	.40	.20
31	Checklist 1-121	.08	.06	.03
32	Ken Oberkfell	.08	.06	.03
33	Rick Honeycutt	.08	.06	.03
34	Aurelio Rodriguez	.10	.08	.04
35	Mitchell Page	.08	.06	.03
36	Ed Farmer	.08	.06	.03
37	Gary Roenicke	.08	.06	.03
38	Win Remmerswaal	.08	.06	.03
39	Tom Veryzer	.08	.06	.03
40	Tug McGraw	.20	.15	.08
41	Rangers Future Stars (Bob Babcock, John Butcher, Jerry Don Gleaton)	.10	.08	.04
42	Jerry White	.08	.06	.03
43	Jose Morales	.08	.06	.03
44	Larry McWilliams	.08	.06	.03
45	Enos Cabell	.08	.06	.03
46	Rick Bosetti	.08	.06	.03
47	Ken Brett	.10	.08	.04
48	Dave Skaggs	.08	.06	.03
49	Bob Shirley	.08	.06	.03
50	Dave Lopes	.12	.09	.05
51	Bill Robinson	.08	.06	.03
52	Hector Cruz	.08	.06	.03
53	Kevin Saucier	.08	.06	.03
54	Ivan DeJesus	.08	.06	.03
55	Mike Norris	.08	.06	.03
56	Buck Martinez	.08	.06	.03
57	Dave Roberts	.08	.06	.03
58	Joel Youngblood	.08	.06	.03
59	Dan Petry	.12	.09	.05
60	Willie Randolph	.15	.11	.06
61	Butch Wynegar	.08	.06	.03
62	Joe Pettini	.08	.06	.03
63	Steve Renko	.08	.06	.03
64	Brian Asselstine	.08	.06	.03
65	Scott McGregor	.10	.08	.04
66	Royals Future Stars (Manny Castillo, Tim Ireland, Mike Jones)	.08	.06	.03
67	Ken Kravec	.08	.06	.03
68	Matt Alexander	.08	.06	.03
69	Ed Halicki	.08	.06	.03
70	Al Oliver	.15	.11	.06
71	Hal Dues	.08	.06	.03
72	Barry Evans	.08	.06	.03
73	Doug Bair	.08	.06	.03
74	Mike Hargrove	.08	.06	.03
75	Reggie Smith	.15	.11	.06
76	Mario Mendoza	.08	.06	.03
77	Mike Barlow	.08	.06	.03
78	Steve Dillard	.08	.06	.03
79	Bruce Robbins	.08	.06	.03
80	Rusty Staub	.15	.11	.06
81	Dave Stapleton	.08	.06	.03
82	Astros Future Stars (Danny Heep, Alan Knicely, Bobby Sprowl)	.08	.06	.03
83	Mike Proly	.08	.06	.03
84	Johnnie LeMaster	.08	.06	.03
85	Mike Caldwell	.08	.06	.03
86	Wayne Gross	.08	.06	.03
87	Rick Camp	.08	.06	.03
88	Joe Lefebvre	.08	.06	.03
89	Darrell Jackson	.08	.06	.03
90	Bake McBride	.08	.06	.03
91	Tim Stoddard	.08	.06	.03
92	Mike Easler	.10	.08	.04
93	Ed Glynn	.08	.06	.03
94	Harry Spilman	.08	.06	.03
95	Jim Sundberg	.10	.08	.04
96	A's Future Stars (Dave Beard, *Ernie Camacho*, Pat Dempsey)	.12	.09	.05
97	Chris Speier	.08	.06	.03
98	Clint Hurdle	.08	.06	.03
99	Eric Wilkins	.08	.06	.03
100	Rod Carew	3.00	2.25	1.25
101	Benny Ayala	.08	.06	.03
102	Dave Tobik	.08	.06	.03
103	Jerry Martin	.08	.06	.03
104	Terry Forster	.10	.08	.04
105	Jose Cruz	.15	.11	.06
106	Don Money	.08	.06	.03
107	Rich Wortham	.08	.06	.03
108	Bruce Benedict	.08	.06	.03
109	Mike Scott	.80	.60	.30

#	Player	MT	NR MT	EX
110	Carl Yastrzemski	2.00	1.50	.80
111	Greg Minton	.08	.06	.03
112	White Sox Future Stars (Rusty Kuntz, Fran Mullins, Leo Sutherland)	.08	.06	.03
113	Mike Phillips	.08	.06	.03
114	Tom Underwood	.08	.06	.03
115	Roy Smalley	.08	.06	.03
116	Joe Simpson	.08	.06	.03
117	Pete Falcone	.08	.06	.03
118	Kurt Bevacqua	.08	.06	.03
119	Tippy Martinez	.08	.06	.03
120	Larry Bowa	.20	.15	.08
121	Larry Harlow	.08	.06	.03
122	John Denny	.08	.06	.03
123	Al Cowens	.08	.06	.03
124	Jerry Garvin	.08	.06	.03
125	Andre Dawson	3.00	2.25	1.25
126	*Charlie Leibrandt*	.50	.40	.20
127	Rudy Law	.08	.06	.03
128	Gary Allenson	.08	.06	.03
129	Art Howe	.08	.06	.03
130	Larry Gura	.08	.06	.03
131	*Keith Moreland*	.35	.25	.14
132	Tommy Boggs	.08	.06	.03
133	Jeff Cox	.08	.06	.03
134	Steve Mura	.08	.06	.03
135	Gorman Thomas	.12	.09	.05
136	Doug Capilla	.08	.06	.03
137	Hosken Powell	.08	.06	.03
138	*Rich Dotson*	.20	.15	.08
139	Oscar Gamble	.10	.08	.04
140	Bob Forsch	.10	.08	.04
141	Miguel Dilone	.08	.06	.03
142	Jackson Todd	.08	.06	.03
143	Dan Meyer	.08	.06	.03
144	Allen Ripley	.08	.06	.03
145	Mickey Rivers	.10	.08	.04
146	Bobby Castillo	.08	.06	.03
147	Dale Berra	.08	.06	.03
148	Randy Niemann	.08	.06	.03
149	Joe Nolan	.08	.06	.03
150	Mark Fidrych	.12	.09	.05
151	Claudell Washington	.12	.09	.05
152	John Urrea	.08	.06	.03
153	Tom Poquette	.08	.06	.03
154	Rick Langford	.08	.06	.03
155	Chris Chambliss	.12	.09	.05
156	Bob McClure	.08	.06	.03
157	John Wathan	.12	.09	.05
158	Fergie Jenkins	1.00	.70	.40
159	Brian Doyle	.08	.06	.03
160	Garry Maddox	.12	.09	.05
161	Dan Graham	.08	.06	.03
162	Doug Corbett	.08	.06	.03
163	Billy Almon	.08	.06	.03
164	*Lamarr Hoyt (LaMarr)*	.20	.15	.08
165	Tony Scott	.08	.06	.03
166	Floyd Bannister	.12	.09	.05
167	Terry Whitfield	.08	.06	.03
168	Don Robinson	.08	.06	.03
169	John Mayberry	.10	.08	.04
170	Ross Grimsley	.08	.06	.03
171	Gene Richards	.08	.06	.03
172	Gary Woods	.08	.06	.03
173	Bump Wills	.08	.06	.03
174	Doug Rau	.08	.06	.03
175	Dave Collins	.10	.08	.04
176	Mike Krukow	.10	.08	.04
177	Rick Peters	.08	.06	.03
178	Jim Essian	.08	.06	.03
179	Rudy May	.08	.06	.03
180	Pete Rose	3.00	2.25	1.25
181	Elias Sosa	.08	.06	.03
182	Bob Grich	.15	.11	.06
183	Dick Davis	.08	.06	.03
184	Jim Dwyer	.08	.06	.03
185	Dennis Leonard	.10	.08	.04
186	Wayne Nordhagen	.08	.06	.03
187	Mike Parrott	.08	.06	.03
188	Doug DeCinces	.15	.11	.06
189	Craig Swan	.08	.06	.03
190	Cesar Cedeno	.15	.11	.06
191	Rick Sutcliffe	.40	.30	.15
192	Braves Future Stars (*Terry Harper*, Ed Miller, *Rafael Ramirez*)	.25	.20	.10
193	Pete Vuckovich	.10	.08	.04
194	*Rod Scurry*	.10	.08	.04
195	Rich Murray	.08	.06	.03
196	Duffy Dyer	.08	.06	.03
197	Jim Kern	.08	.06	.03
198	Jerry Dybzinski	.08	.06	.03
199	Chuck Rainey	.08	.06	.03
200	George Foster	.25	.20	.10
201	Record Breaker (Johnny Bench)	.40	.30	.15
202	Record Breaker (Steve Carlton)	.40	.30	.15
203	Record Breaker (Bill Gullickson)	.08	.06	.03
204	Record Breaker (Ron LeFlore, Rodney Scott)	.10	.08	.04
205	Record Breaker (Pete Rose)	.80	.60	.30
206	Record Breaker (Mike Schmidt)	.80	.60	.30
207	Record Breaker (Ozzie Smith)	.20	.15	.08
208	Record Breaker (Willie Wilson)	.20	.15	.08
209	Dickie Thon	.10	.08	.04
210	Jim Palmer	2.00	1.50	.80
211	Derrel Thomas	.08	.06	.03
212	Steve Nicosia	.08	.06	.03
213	*Al Holland*	.10	.08	.04
214	Angels Future Stars (Ralph Botting, Jim Dorsey, John Harris)	.08	.06	.03
215	Larry Hisle	.10	.08	.04
216	John Henry Johnson	.08	.06	.03
217	Rich Hebner	.08	.06	.03
218	Paul Splittorff	.08	.06	.03
219	Ken Landreaux	.08	.06	.03
220	Tom Seaver	3.00	2.25	1.25
221	Bob Davis	.08	.06	.03
222	Jorge Orta	.08	.06	.03
223	Roy Lee Jackson	.08	.06	.03
224	Pat Zachry	.08	.06	.03
225	Ruppert Jones	.08	.06	.03
226	Manny Sanguillen	.08	.06	.03
227	Fred Martinez	.08	.06	.03
228	Tom Paciorek	.08	.06	.03
229	Rollie Fingers	1.00	.70	.40
230	George Hendrick	.10	.08	.04
231	Joe Beckwith	.08	.06	.03
232	Mickey Klutts	.08	.06	.03
233	Skip Lockwood	.08	.06	.03
234	Lou Whitaker	.60	.45	.25
235	Scott Sanderson	.08	.06	.03
236	Mike Ivie	.08	.06	.03
237	Charlie Moore	.08	.06	.03
238	Willie Hernandez	.12	.09	.05
239	Rick Miller	.08	.06	.03
240	Nolan Ryan	10.00	7.50	4.00
241	Checklist 122-242	.08	.06	.03
242	Chet Lemon	.10	.08	.04
243	Sal Butera	.08	.06	.03
244	Cardinals Future Stars (*Tito Landrum*, Al Olmsted, Andy Rincon)	.15	.11	.06
245	Ed Figueroa	.08	.06	.03
246	Ed Ott	.08	.06	.03
247	Glenn Hubbard	.10	.08	.04
248	Joey McLaughlin	.08	.06	.03
249	Larry Cox	.08	.06	.03
250	Ron Guidry	.50	.40	.20
251	Tom Brookens	.10	.08	.04
252	Victor Cruz	.08	.06	.03
253	Dave Bergman	.08	.06	.03
254	Ozzie Smith	4.00	3.00	1.50
255	Mark Littell	.08	.06	.03
256	Bombo Rivera	.08	.06	.03
257	Rennie Stennett	.08	.06	.03
258	*Joe Price*	.12	.09	.05
259	Mets Future Stars (Juan Berenguer, *Hubie Brooks*, Mookie Wilson)	2.50	2.00	1.00
260	Ron Cey	.15	.11	.06
261	Rickey Henderson	20.00	15.00	8.00
262	Sammy Stewart	.08	.06	.03
263	Brian Downing	.12	.09	.05
264	Jim Norris	.08	.06	.03
265	John Candelaria	.12	.09	.05
266	Tom Herr	.15	.11	.06
267	Stan Bahnsen	.08	.06	.03
268	Jerry Royster	.08	.06	.03
269	Ken Forsch	.08	.06	.03
270	Greg Luzinski	.20	.15	.08
271	Bill Castro	.08	.06	.03
272	Bruce Kimm	.08	.06	.03
273	Stan Papi	.08	.06	.03
274	Craig Chamberlain	.08	.06	.03
275	Dwight Evans	.25	.20	.10
276	Dan Spillner	.08	.06	.03
277	Alfredo Griffin	.12	.09	.05
278	Rick Sofield	.08	.06	.03
279	Bob Knepper	.12	.09	.05
280	Ken Griffey	.15	.11	.06
281	Fred Stanley	.08	.06	.03
282	Mariners Future Stars (Rick Anderson, Greg Biercevicz, Rodney Craig)	.08	.06	.03
283	Billy Sample	.08	.06	.03
284	Brian Kingman	.08	.06	.03

#	Player	MT	NR MT	EX
285	Jerry Turner	.08	.06	.03
286	Dave Frost	.08	.06	.03
287	Lenn Sakata	.08	.06	.03
288	Bob Clark	.08	.06	.03
289	Mickey Hatcher	.10	.08	.04
290	Bob Boone	.08	.06	.03
291	Aurelio Lopez	.08	.06	.03
292	Mike Squires	.08	.06	.03
293	*Charlie Lea*	.15	.11	.06
294	Mike Tyson	.08	.06	.03
295	Hal McRae	.15	.11	.06
296	Bill Nahorodny	.08	.06	.03
297	Bob Bailor	.08	.06	.03
298	Buddy Solomon	.08	.06	.03
299	Elliott Maddox	.08	.06	.03
300	Paul Molitor	.40	.30	.15
301	Matt Keough	.08	.06	.03
302	Dodgers Future Stars (Jack Perconte, *Mike Scioscia, Fernando Valenzuela*)	6.00	4.50	2.50
303	Johnny Oates	.08	.06	.03
304	John Castino	.08	.06	.03
305	Ken Clay	.08	.06	.03
306	Juan Beniquez	.08	.06	.03
307	Gene Garber	.08	.06	.03
308	Rick Manning	.08	.06	.03
309	*Luis Salazar*	.20	.15	.08
310	Vida Blue	.08	.06	.03
311	Freddie Patek	.08	.06	.03
312	Rick Rhoden	.12	.09	.05
313	Luis Pujols	.08	.06	.03
314	Rich Dauer	.08	.06	.03
315	*Kirk Gibson*	3.50	2.75	1.50
316	Craig Minetto	.08	.06	.03
317	Lonnie Smith	.10	.08	.04
318	Steve Yeager	.08	.06	.03
319	Rowland Office	.08	.06	.03
320	Tom Burgmeier	.08	.06	.03
321	*Leon Durham*	.25	.20	.10
322	Neil Allen	.10	.08	.04
323	Jim Morrison	.08	.06	.03
324	Mike Willis	.08	.06	.03
325	Ray Knight	.12	.09	.05
326	Biff Pocoroba	.08	.06	.03
327	Moose Haas	.08	.06	.03
328	Twins Future Stars (*Dave Engle*, Greg Johnston, Gary Ward)	.12	.09	.05
329	Joaquin Andujar	.12	.09	.05
330	Frank White	.12	.09	.05
331	Dennis Lamp	.08	.06	.03
332	Lee Lacy	.08	.06	.03
333	Sid Monge	.08	.06	.03
334	Dane Iorg	.08	.06	.03
335	Rick Cerone	.08	.06	.03
336	Eddie Whitson	.08	.06	.03
337	Lynn Jones	.08	.06	.03
338	Checklist 243-363	.25	.20	.10
339	John Ellis	.08	.06	.03
340	Bruce Kison	.08	.06	.03
341	Dwayne Murphy	.10	.08	.04
342	Eric Rasmussen	.08	.06	.03
343	Frank Taveras	.08	.06	.03
344	Byron McLaughlin	.08	.06	.03
345	Warren Cromartie	.08	.06	.03
346	Larry Christenson	.08	.06	.03
347	*Harold Baines*	5.00	3.75	2.00
348	Bob Sykes	.08	.06	.03
349	Glenn Hoffman	.08	.06	.03
350	J.R. Richard	.12	.09	.05
351	Otto Velez	.08	.06	.03
352	Dick Tidrow	.08	.06	.03
353	Terry Kennedy	.12	.09	.05
354	Mario Soto	.10	.08	.04
355	Bob Horner	.25	.20	.10
356	Padres Future Stars (George Stablein, Craig Stimac, Tom Tellmann)	.08	.06	.03
357	Jim Slaton	.08	.06	.03
358	Mark Wagner	.08	.06	.03
359	Tom Hausman	.08	.06	.03
360	Willie Wilson	.30	.25	.12
361	Joe Strain	.08	.06	.03
362	Bo Diaz	.10	.08	.04
363	Geoff Zahn	.08	.06	.03
364	*Mike Davis*	.25	.20	.10
365	Graig Nettles	.12	.09	.05
366	Mike Ramsey	.08	.06	.03
367	Denny Martinez	.10	.08	.04
368	Leon Roberts	.08	.06	.03
369	Frank Tanana	.12	.09	.05
370	Dave Winfield	4.00	3.00	1.50
371	Charlie Hough	.15	.11	.06
372	Jay Johnstone	.10	.08	.04
373	Pat Underwood	.08	.06	.03
374	Tom Hutton	.08	.06	.03
375	Dave Concepcion	.20	.15	.08
376	Ron Reed	.08	.06	.03
377	Jerry Morales	.08	.06	.03
378	Dave Rader	.08	.06	.03
379	Lary Sorensen	.08	.06	.03
380	Willie Stargell	1.00	.70	.40
381	Cubs Future Stars (Carlos Lezcano, Steve Macko, Randy Martz)	.08	.06	.03
382	*Paul Mirabella* (FC)	.12	.09	.05
383	Eric Soderholm	.08	.06	.03
384	Mike Sadek	.08	.06	.03
385	Joe Sambito	.08	.06	.03
386	Dave Edwards	.08	.06	.03
387	Phil Niekro	.80	.60	.30
388	Andre Thornton	.12	.09	.05
389	Marty Pattin	.08	.06	.03
390	Cesar Geronimo	.08	.06	.03
391	Dave Lemanczyk	.08	.06	.03
392	Lance Parrish	.70	.50	.30
393	Broderick Perkins	.08	.06	.03
394	Woodie Fryman	.10	.08	.04
395	Scot Thompson	.08	.06	.03
396	Bill Campbell	.08	.06	.03
397	Julio Cruz	.08	.06	.03
398	Ross Baumgarten	.08	.06	.03
399	Orioles Future Stars (*Mike Boddicker*, Mark Corey, *Floyd Rayford*)	1.00	.70	.40
400	Reggie Jackson	3.25	2.40	1.30
401	A.L. Championships (Royals Sweep Yankees)	.50	.40	.20
402	N.L. Championships (Phillies Squeak Past Astros)	.40	.30	.15
403	World Series (Phillies Beat Royals In 6)	.25	.20	.10
404	World Series Summary (Phillies Win First World Series)	.25	.20	.10
405	Nino Espinosa	.08	.06	.03
406	Dickie Noles	.08	.06	.03
407	Ernie Whitt	.10	.08	.04
408	Fernando Arroyo	.08	.06	.03
409	Larry Herndon	.10	.08	.04
410	Bert Campaneris	.12	.09	.05
411	Terry Puhl	.08	.06	.03
412	*Britt Burns*	.12	.09	.05
413	Tony Bernazard	.08	.06	.03
414	John Pacella	.08	.06	.03
415	Ben Oglivie	.10	.08	.04
416	Gary Alexander	.08	.06	.03
417	Dan Schatzeder	.08	.06	.03
418	Bobby Brown	.08	.06	.03
419	Tom Hume	.08	.06	.03
420	Keith Hernandez	.50	.40	.20
421	Bob Stanley	.08	.06	.03
422	Dan Ford	.08	.06	.03
423	Shane Rawley	.15	.11	.06
424	Yankees Future Stars (Tim Lollar, Bruce Robinson, Dennis Werth)	.08	.06	.03
425	Al Bumbry	.10	.08	.04
426	Warren Brusstar	.08	.06	.03
427	John D'Acquisto	.08	.06	.03
428	John Stearns	.08	.06	.03
429	Mick Kelleher	.08	.06	.03
430	Jim Bibby	.08	.06	.03
431	Dave Roberts	.08	.06	.03
432	Len Barker	.10	.08	.04
433	Rance Mulliniks	.08	.06	.03
434	Roger Erickson	.08	.06	.03
435	Jim Spencer	.08	.06	.03
436	Gary Lucas	.08	.06	.03
437	Mike Heath	.08	.06	.03
438	John Montefusco	.10	.08	.04
439	Denny Walling	.08	.06	.03
440	Jerry Reuss	.12	.09	.05
441	Ken Reitz	.08	.06	.03
442	Ron Pruitt	.08	.06	.03
443	Jim Beattie	.08	.06	.03
444	Garth Iorg	.08	.06	.03
445	Ellis Valentine	.08	.06	.03
446	Checklist 364-484	.25	.20	.10
447	Junior Kennedy	.08	.06	.03
448	Tim Corcoran	.08	.06	.03
449	Paul Mitchell	.08	.06	.03
450	Dave Kingman	.10	.08	.04
451	Indians Future Stars (Chris Bando, Tom Brennan, Sandy Wihtol)	.12	.09	.05
452	Renie Martin	.08	.06	.03
453	Rob Wilfong	.08	.06	.03
454	Andy Hassler	.08	.06	.03

#	Player	MT	NR MT	EX
455	Rick Burleson	.10	.08	.04
456	*Jeff Reardon*	10.00	7.50	4.00
457	Mike Lum	.08	.06	.03
458	Randy Jones	.10	.08	.04
459	Greg Gross	.08	.06	.03
460	Rich Gossage	.40	.30	.15
461	Dave McKay	.08	.06	.03
462	Jack Brohamer	.08	.06	.03
463	Milt May	.08	.06	.03
464	Adrian Devine	.08	.06	.03
465	Bill Russell	.12	.09	.05
466	Bob Molinaro	.08	.06	.03
467	Dave Stieb	.80	.60	.30
468	Johnny Wockenfuss	.08	.06	.03
469	Jeff Leonard	.20	.15	.08
470	Manny Trillo	.10	.08	.04
471	Mike Vail	.08	.06	.03
472	Dyar Miller	.08	.06	.03
473	Jose Cardenal	.08	.06	.03
474	Mike LaCoss	.08	.06	.03
475	Buddy Bell	.15	.11	.06
476	Jerry Koosman	.15	.11	.06
477	Luis Gomez	.08	.06	.03
478	Juan Eichelberger	.08	.06	.03
479	Expos Future Stars (Bobby Pate, *Tim Raines*, Roberto Ramos)	7.00	5.25	2.75
480	Carlton Fisk	3.00	2.25	1.25
481	Bob Lacey	.08	.06	.03
482	Jim Gantner	.10	.08	.04
483	Mike Griffin	.08	.06	.03
484	Max Venable	.08	.06	.03
485	Garry Templeton	.12	.09	.05
486	Marc Hill	.08	.06	.03
487	Dewey Robinson	.08	.06	.03
488	*Damaso Garcia*	.12	.09	.05
489	John Littlefield (photo actually Mark Riggins)	.08	.06	.03
490	Eddie Murray	4.00	3.00	1.50
491	Gordy Pladson	.08	.06	.03
492	Barry Foote	.08	.06	.03
493	Dan Quisenberry	.20	.15	.08
494	*Bob Walk*	.50	.40	.20
495	Dusty Baker	.12	.09	.05
496	Paul Dade	.08	.06	.03
497	Fred Norman	.08	.06	.03
498	Pat Putnam	.08	.06	.03
499	Frank Pastore	.08	.06	.03
500	Jim Rice	1.00	.70	.40
501	Tim Foli	.08	.06	.03
502	Giants Future Stars (Chris Bourjos, Al Hargesheimer, Mike Rowland)	.08	.06	.03
503	Steve McCatty	.08	.06	.03
504	Dale Murphy	2.50	2.00	1.00
505	Jason Thompson	.08	.06	.03
506	Phil Huffman	.08	.06	.03
507	Jamie Quirk	.08	.06	.03
508	Rob Dressler	.08	.06	.03
509	Pete Mackanin	.08	.06	.03
510	Lee Mazzilli	.10	.08	.04
511	Wayne Garland	.08	.06	.03
512	Gary Thomasson	.08	.06	.03
513	Frank LaCorte	.08	.06	.03
514	George Riley	.08	.06	.03
515	Robin Yount	5.00	3.75	2.00
516	Doug Bird	.08	.06	.03
517	Richie Zisk	.10	.08	.04
518	Grant Jackson	.08	.06	.03
519	John Tamargo	.08	.06	.03
520	Steve Stone	.12	.09	.05
521	Sam Mejias	.08	.06	.03
522	Mike Colbern	.08	.06	.03
523	John Fulgham	.08	.06	.03
524	Willie Aikens	.08	.06	.03
525	Mike Torrez	.10	.08	.04
526	Phillies Future Stars (Marty Bystrom, Jay Loviglio, Jim Wright)	.08	.06	.03
527	Danny Goodwin	.08	.06	.03
528	Gary Matthews	.12	.09	.05
529	Dave LaRoche	.08	.06	.03
530	Steve Garvey	1.25	.90	.50
531	John Curtis	.08	.06	.03
532	Bill Stein	.08	.06	.03
533	Jesus Figueroa	.08	.06	.03
534	*Dave Smith*	.60	.45	.25
535	Omar Moreno	.08	.06	.03
536	Bob Owchinko	.08	.06	.03
537	Ron Hodges	.08	.06	.03
538	Tom Griffin	.08	.06	.03
539	Rodney Scott	.08	.06	.03
540	Mike Schmidt	4.00	3.00	1.50
541	Steve Swisher	.08	.06	.03
542	Larry Bradford	.08	.06	.03
543	Terry Crowley	.08	.06	.03
544	Rich Gale	.08	.06	.03
545	Johnny Grubb	.08	.06	.03
546	Paul Moskau	.08	.06	.03
547	Mario Guerrero	.08	.06	.03
548	Dave Goltz	.10	.08	.04
549	Jerry Remy	.08	.06	.03
550	Tommy John	.50	.40	.20
551	Pirates Future Stars (Vance Law, Tony Pena, Pascual Perez)	1.00	.70	.40
552	Steve Trout	.08	.06	.03
553	Tim Blackwell	.08	.06	.03
554	Bert Blyleven	.25	.20	.10
555	Cecil Cooper	.20	.15	.08
556	Jerry Mumphrey	.08	.06	.03
557	Chris Knapp	.08	.06	.03
558	Barry Bonnell	.08	.06	.03
559	Willie Montanez	.08	.06	.03
560	Joe Morgan	.70	.50	.30
561	Dennis Littlejohn	.08	.06	.03
562	Checklist 485-605	.25	.20	.10
563	Jim Kaat	.30	.25	.12
564	Ron Hassey	.08	.06	.03
565	Burt Hooton	.10	.08	.04
566	Del Unser	.08	.06	.03
567	Mark Bomback	.08	.06	.03
568	Dave Revering	.08	.06	.03
569	Al Williams	.08	.06	.03
570	Ken Singleton	.12	.09	.05
571	Todd Cruz	.08	.06	.03
572	Jack Morris	.60	.45	.25
573	Phil Garner	.10	.08	.04
574	Bill Caudill	.08	.06	.03
575	Tony Perez	.50	.40	.20
576	Reggie Cleveland	.08	.06	.03
577	Blue Jays Future Stars (Luis Leal, Brian Milner, *Ken Schrom*)	.20	.15	.08
578	*Bill Gullickson*	.20	.15	.08
579	Tim Flannery	.08	.06	.03
580	Don Baylor	.15	.11	.06
581	Roy Howell	.08	.06	.03
582	Gaylord Perry	.70	.50	.30
583	Larry Milbourne	.08	.06	.03
584	Randy Lerch	.08	.06	.03
585	Amos Otis	.10	.08	.04
586	Silvio Martinez	.08	.06	.03
587	Jeff Newman	.08	.06	.03
588	Gary Lavelle	.08	.06	.03
589	Lamar Johnson	.08	.06	.03
590	Bruce Sutter	.25	.20	.10
591	John Lowenstein	.08	.06	.03
592	Steve Comer	.08	.06	.03
593	Steve Kemp	.12	.09	.05
594	Preston Hanna	.08	.06	.03
595	Butch Hobson	.08	.06	.03
596	Jerry Augustine	.08	.06	.03
597	Rafael Landestoy	.08	.06	.03
598	George Vukovich	.08	.06	.03
599	Dennis Kinney	.08	.06	.03
600	Johnny Bench	2.00	1.50	.80
601	Don Aase	.08	.06	.03
602	Bobby Murcer	.15	.11	.06
603	John Verhoeven	.08	.06	.03
604	Rob Picciolo	.08	.06	.03
605	Don Sutton	.70	.50	.30
606	Reds Future Stars (Bruce Berenyi, Geoff Combe, Paul Householder)	.08	.06	.03
607	Dave Palmer	.08	.06	.03
608	Greg Pryor	.08	.06	.03
609	Lynn McGlothen	.08	.06	.03
610	Darrell Porter	.10	.08	.04
611	Rick Matula	.08	.06	.03
612	Duane Kuiper	.08	.06	.03
613	Jim Anderson	.08	.06	.03
614	Dave Rozema	.08	.06	.03
615	Rick Dempsey	.12	.09	.05
616	Rick Wise	.10	.08	.04
617	Craig Reynolds	.08	.06	.03
618	John Milner	.08	.06	.03
619	Steve Henderson	.08	.06	.03
620	Dennis Eckersley	2.00	1.50	.80
621	Tom Donohue	.08	.06	.03
622	Randy Moffitt	.08	.06	.03
623	Sal Bando	.12	.09	.05
624	Bob Welch	.70	.50	.30
625	Bill Buckner	.15	.11	.06
626	Tigers Future Stars (Dave Steffen, Jerry Ujdur, Roger Weaver)	.08	.06	.03
627	Luis Tiant	.20	.15	.08
628	Vic Correll	.08	.06	.03

		MT	NR MT	EX
629	Tony Armas	.12	.09	.05
630	Steve Carlton	2.00	1.50	.80
631	Ron Jackson	.08	.06	.03
632	Alan Bannister	.08	.06	.03
633	Bill Lee	.10	.08	.04
634	Doug Flynn	.08	.06	.03
635	Bobby Bonds	.15	.11	.06
636	Al Hrabosky	.10	.08	.04
637	Jerry Narron	.08	.06	.03
638	Checklist 606	.25	.20	.10
639	Carney Lansford	.15	.11	.06
640	Dave Parker	.60	.45	.25
641	Mark Belanger	.10	.08	.04
642	Vern Ruhle	.08	.06	.03
643	*Lloyd Moseby*	.40	.30	.15
644	Ramon Aviles	.08	.06	.03
645	Rick Reuschel	.15	.11	.06
646	Marvis Foley	.08	.06	.03
647	Dick Drago	.08	.06	.03
648	Darrell Evans	.25	.20	.10
649	Manny Sarmiento	.08	.06	.03
650	Bucky Dent	.12	.09	.05
651	Pedro Guerrero	1.25	.90	.50
652	John Montague	.08	.06	.03
653	Bill Fahey	.08	.06	.03
654	Ray Burris	.08	.06	.03
655	Dan Driessen	.12	.09	.05
656	Jon Matlack	.10	.08	.04
657	Mike Cubbage	.08	.06	.03
658	Milt Wilcox	.08	.06	.03
659	Brewers Future Stars (John Flinn, Ed Romero, Ned Yost)	.08	.06	.03
660	Gary Carter	1.00	.70	.40
661	Orioles Team (Earl Weaver)	.30	.25	.12
662	Red Sox Team (Ralph Houk)	.30	.25	.12
663	Angels Team (Jim Fregosi)	.25	.20	.10
664	White Sox Team (Tony LaRussa)	.25	.20	.10
665	Indians Team (Dave Garcia)	.25	.20	.10
666	Tigers Team (Sparky Anderson)	.30	.25	.12
667	Royals Team (Jim Frey)	.25	.20	.10
668	Brewers Team (Bob Rodgers)	.25	.20	.10
669	Twins Team (John Goryl)	.25	.20	.10
670	Yankees Team (Gene Michael)	.35	.25	.14
671	A's Team (Billy Martin)	.30	.25	.12
672	Mariners Team (Maury Wills)	.25	.20	.10
673	Rangers Team (Don Zimmer)	.25	.20	.10
674	Blue Jays Team (Bobby Mattick)	.25	.20	.10
675	Braves Team (Bobby Cox)	.25	.20	.10
676	Cubs Team (Joe Amalfitano)	.25	.20	.10
677	Reds Team (John McNamara)	.25	.20	.10
678	Astros Team (Bill Virdon)	.25	.20	.10
679	Dodgers Team (Tom Lasorda)	.35	.25	.14
680	Expos Team (Dick Williams)	.25	.20	.10
681	Mets Team (Joe Torre)	.30	.25	.12
682	Phillies Team (Dallas Green)	.25	.20	.10
683	Pirates Team (Chuck Tanner)	.25	.20	.10
684	Cardinals Team (Whitey Herzog)	.30	.25	.12
685	Padres Team (Frank Howard)	.25	.20	.10
686	Giants Team (Dave Bristol)	.25	.20	.10
687	Jeff Jones	.08	.06	.03
688	Kiko Garcia	.08	.06	.03
689	Red Sox Future Stars (*Bruce Hurst*, Keith MacWhorter, *Reid Nichols*)	2.00	1.50	.80
690	Bob Watson	.10	.08	.04
691	Dick Ruthven	.08	.06	.03
692	Lenny Randle	.08	.06	.03
693	*Steve Howe*	.20	.15	.08
694	Bud Harrelson	.08	.06	.03
695	Kent Tekulve	.10	.08	.04
696	Alan Ashby	.08	.06	.03
697	Rick Waits	.08	.06	.03
698	Mike Jorgensen	.08	.06	.03
699	Glenn Abbott	.08	.06	.03
700	George Brett	5.00	3.75	2.00
701	Joe Rudi	.12	.09	.05
702	George Medich	.08	.06	.03
703	Alvis Woods	.08	.06	.03
704	Bill Travers	.08	.06	.03
705	Ted Simmons	.25	.20	.10
706	Dave Ford	.08	.06	.03
707	Dave Cash	.08	.06	.03
708	Doyle Alexander	.12	.09	.05
709	Alan Trammell	.30	.25	.12
710	Ron LeFlore	.08	.06	.03
711	Joe Ferguson	.08	.06	.03
712	Bill Bonham	.08	.06	.03
713	Bill North	.08	.06	.03
714	Pete Redfern	.08	.06	.03
715	Bill Madlock	.25	.20	.10
716	Glenn Borgmann	.08	.06	.03
717	Jim Barr	.08	.06	.03

		MT	NR MT	EX
718	Larry Biittner	.08	.06	.03
719	Sparky Lyle	.12	.09	.05
720	Fred Lynn	.35	.25	.14
721	Toby Harrah	.10	.08	.04
722	Joe Niekro	.20	.15	.08
723	Bruce Bochte	.08	.06	.03
724	Lou Piniella	.20	.15	.08
725	Steve Rogers	.10	.08	.04
726	Rick Monday	.15	.11	.06

1981 Topps
Home Team 5 X 7 Photos

Once again testing the popularity of large cards, Topps issued 4-7/8" by 6-7/8" cards in two different sets. The Home Team cards feature a large color photo, facsimile autograph and white border on the front. Backs have the player's name, team, position and a checklist at the bottom. The 102 cards were sold in limited areas corresponding to the teams' geographic home. It was also possible to order the whole set by mail. Eleven teams are involved in the issue, with the number of players from each team ranging from 6 to 12. Although it is an attractive set featuring many stars, ready availability and many collectors' aversion to large cards keep prices relatively low today.

		MT	NR MT	EX
Complete Set:		40.00	30.00	16.00
Common Player:		.20	.15	.08
(1)	Dusty Baker	.25	.20	.10
(2)	Don Baylor	.40	.30	.15
(3)	Rick Burleson	.20	.15	.08
(4)	Rod Carew	.90	.70	.35
(5)	Ron Cey	.30	.25	.12
(6)	Steve Garvey	.90	.70	.35
(7)	Bobby Grich	.30	.25	.12
(8)	Butch Hobson	.20	.15	.08
(9)	Burt Hooton	.20	.15	.08
(10)	Steve Howe	.20	.15	.08
(11)	Dave Lopes	.25	.20	.10
(12)	Fred Lynn	.50	.40	.20
(13)	Rick Monday	.25	.20	.10
(14)	Jerry Reuss	.25	.20	.10
(15)	Bill Russell	.25	.20	.10
(16)	Reggie Smith	.30	.25	.12
(17)	Bob Welch	.40	.30	.15
(18)	Steve Yeager	.20	.15	.08
(19)	Buddy Bell	.30	.25	.12
(20)	Cesar Cedeno	.30	.25	.12
(21)	Jose Cruz	.30	.25	.12
(22)	Art Howe	.20	.15	.08
(23)	Jon Matlack	.20	.15	.08
(24)	Al Oliver	.40	.30	.15
(25)	Terry Puhl	.20	.15	.08
(26)	Mickey Rivers	.25	.20	.10
(27)	Nolan Ryan	.70	.50	.30
(28)	Jim Sundberg	.25	.20	.10
(29)	Don Sutton	.60	.45	.25
(30)	Bump Wills	.20	.15	.08
(31)	Tim Blackwell	.20	.15	.08
(32)	Bill Buckner	.40	.30	.15
(33)	Britt Burns	.20	.15	.08
(34)	Ivan DeJesus	.20	.15	.08

		MT	NR MT	EX
(35)	Rich Dotson	.25	.20	.10
(36)	Leon Durham	.25	.20	.10
(37)	Ed Farmer	.20	.15	.08
(38)	Lamar Johnson	.20	.15	.08
(39)	Dave Kingman	.40	.30	.15
(40)	Mike Krukow	.25	.20	.10
(41)	Ron LeFlore	.25	.20	.10
(42)	Chet Lemon	.25	.20	.10
(43)	Bob Molinaro	.20	.15	.08
(44)	Jim Morrison	.20	.15	.08
(45)	Wayne Nordhagen	.20	.15	.08
(46)	Ken Reitz	.20	.15	.08
(47)	Rick Reuschel	.30	.25	.12
(48)	Mike Tyson	.20	.15	.08
(49)	Neil Allen	.20	.15	.08
(50)	Rick Cerone	.20	.15	.08
(51)	Bucky Dent	.25	.20	.10
(52)	Doug Flynn	.20	.15	.08
(53)	Rich Gossage	.60	.45	.25
(54)	Ron Guidry	.60	.45	.25
(55)	Reggie Jackson	.90	.70	.35
(56)	Tommy John	.50	.40	.20
(57)	Ruppert Jones	.20	.15	.08
(58)	Rudy May	.20	.15	.08
(59)	Lee Mazzilli	.25	.20	.10
(60)	Graig Nettles	.40	.30	.15
(61)	Willie Randolph	.30	.25	.12
(62)	Rusty Staub	.40	.30	.15
(63)	Frank Taveras	.20	.15	.08
(64)	Alex Trevino	.20	.15	.08
(65)	Bob Watson	.25	.20	.10
(66)	Dave Winfield	.90	.70	.35
(67)	Bob Boone	.25	.20	.10
(68)	Larry Bowa	.40	.30	.15
(69)	Steve Carlton	.70	.50	.30
(70)	Greg Luzinski	.40	.30	.15
(71)	Garry Maddox	.25	.20	.10
(72)	Bake McBride	.20	.15	.08
(73)	Tug McGraw	.40	.30	.15
(74)	Pete Rose	1.75	1.25	.70
(75)	Dick Ruthven	.20	.15	.08
(76)	Mike Schmidt	.90	.70	.35
(77)	Manny Trillo	.25	.20	.10
(78)	Del Unser	.20	.15	.08
(79)	Tom Burgmeier	.20	.15	.08
(80)	Dennis Eckersley	.40	.30	.15
(81)	Dwight Evans	.50	.40	.20
(82)	Carlton Fisk	.60	.45	.25
(83)	Glenn Hoffman	.20	.15	.08
(84)	Carney Lansford	.30	.25	.12
(85)	Tony Perez	.50	.40	.20
(86)	Jim Rice	.70	.50	.30
(87)	Bob Stanley	.20	.15	.08
(88)	Dave Stapleton	.20	.15	.08
(89)	Frank Tanana	.25	.20	.10
(90)	Carl Yastrzemski	1.25	.90	.50
(91)	Johnny Bench	.90	.70	.35
(92)	Dave Collins	.25	.20	.10
(93)	Dave Concepcion	.40	.30	.15
(94)	Dan Driessen	.25	.20	.10
(95)	George Foster	.50	.40	.20
(96)	Ken Griffey	.30	.25	.12
(97)	Tom Hume	.20	.15	.08
(98)	Ray Knight	.25	.20	.10
(99)	Joe Nolan	.20	.15	.08
(100)	Ron Oester	.20	.15	.08
(101)	Tom Seaver	.70	.50	.30
(102)	Mario Soto	.25	.20	.10

1981 Topps National 5 X 7 Photos

This set is the other half of Topps' efforts with large

cards in 1981. Measuring 4-7/8" by 6-7/8", the National photo issue was limited to 15 cards. They were sold in areas not covered by the Home Team sets and feature ten cards which carry the same photos as found in the Home Team set, but with no checklist on the backs. Five cards are unique to the National set: George Brett, Cecil Cooper, Jim Palmer, Dave Parker and Ted Simmons. With their wide distribution and a limited demand, there are currently plenty of these cards to meet the demand, thus keeping prices fairly low.

		MT	NR MT	EX
Complete Set:		8.00	6.00	3.25
Common Player:		.30	.25	.12
(1)	Buddy Bell	.30	.25	.12
(2)	Johnny Bench	.60	.45	.25
(3)	George Brett	.90	.70	.35
(4)	Rod Carew	.60	.45	.25
(5)	Cecil Cooper	.40	.30	.15
(6)	Steve Garvey	.70	.50	.30
(7)	Rich Gossage	.40	.30	.15
(8)	Reggie Jackson	.70	.50	.30
(9)	Jim Palmer	.70	.50	.30
(10)	Dave Parker	.60	.45	.25
(11)	Jim Rice	.50	.40	.20
(12)	Pete Rose	1.25	.90	.50
(13)	Mike Schmidt	.70	.50	.30
(14)	Tom Seaver	.60	.45	.25
(15)	Ted Simmons	.50	.40	.20

1981 Topps Scratchoffs

Sold as a separate issue with bubble gum, this 108-card set was issued in three-card panels that measure 3-1/4" by 5-1/4". Each individual card measures 1-13/16" by 3-1/4" and contains a small player photo alongside a series of black dots designed to be scratched off as part of a baseball game. Cards of National League players have a green backgrounds, while American League players have a red background. While there are 108 different players in the set, there are 144 possible panel combinations. An intact panel of three cards is valued approximately 20-25 percent more the sum of the individual cards.

		MT	NR MT	EX
Complete Set:		4.00	3.00	1.50
Common Player:		.02	.02	.01
1	George Brett	.12	.09	.05
2	Cecil Cooper	.04	.03	.02
3	Reggie Jackson	.12	.09	.05
4	Al Oliver	.04	.03	.02
5	Fred Lynn	.06	.05	.02
6	Tony Armas	.02	.02	.01
7	Ben Oglivie	.02	.02	.01
8	Tony Perez	.06	.05	.02
9	Eddie Murray	.10	.08	.04
10	Robin Yount	.08	.06	.03
11	Steve Kemp	.04	.03	.02
12	Joe Charboneau	.04	.03	.02
13	Jim Rice	.10	.08	.04
14	Lance Parrish	.08	.06	.03
15	John Mayberry	.02	.02	.01

		MT	NR MT	EX
16	Richie Zisk	.02	.02	.01
17	Ken Singleton	.04	.03	.02
18	Rod Carew	.10	.08	.04
19	Rick Manning	.02	.02	.01
20	Willie Wilson	.04	.03	.02
21	Buddy Bell	.04	.03	.02
22	Dave Revering	.02	.02	.01
23	Tom Paciorek	.02	.02	.01
24	Champ Summers	.02	.02	.01
25	Carney Lansford	.04	.03	.02
26	Lamar Johnson	.02	.02	.01
27	Willie Aikens	.02	.02	.01
28	Rick Cerone	.02	.02	.01
29	Al Bumbry	.02	.02	.01
30	Bruce Bochte	.02	.02	.01
31	Mickey Rivers	.02	.02	.01
32	Mike Hargrove	.02	.02	.01
33	John Castino	.02	.02	.01
34	Chet Lemon	.04	.03	.02
35	Paul Molitor	.06	.05	.02
36	Willie Randolph	.04	.03	.02
37	Rick Burleson	.02	.02	.01
38	Alan Trammell	.08	.06	.03
39	Rickey Henderson	.10	.08	.04
40	Dan Meyer	.02	.02	.01
41	Ken Landreaux	.02	.02	.01
42	Damaso Garcia	.02	.02	.01
43	Roy Smalley	.02	.02	.01
44	Otto Velez	.02	.02	.01
45	Sixto Lezcano	.02	.02	.01
46	Toby Harrah	.02	.02	.01
47	Frank White	.04	.03	.02
48	Dave Stapleton	.02	.02	.01
49	Steve Stone	.04	.03	.02
50	Jim Palmer	.08	.06	.03
51	Larry Gura	.02	.02	.01
52	Tommy John	.06	.05	.02
53	Mike Norris	.02	.02	.01
54	Ed Farmer	.02	.02	.01
55	Bill Buckner	.04	.03	.02
56	Steve Garvey	.10	.08	.04
57	Reggie Smith	.04	.03	.02
58	Bake McBride	.02	.02	.01
59	Dave Parker	.06	.05	.02
60	Mike Schmidt	.12	.09	.05
61	Bob Horner	.04	.03	.02
62	Pete Rose	.20	.15	.08
63	Ted Simmons	.06	.05	.02
64	Johnny Bench	.12	.09	.05
65	George Foster	.06	.05	.02
66	Gary Carter	.10	.08	.04
67	Keith Hernandez	.08	.06	.03
68	Ozzie Smith	.06	.05	.02
69	Dave Kingman	.06	.05	.02
70	Jack Clark	.06	.05	.02
71	Dusty Baker	.04	.03	.02
72	Dale Murphy	.12	.09	.05
73	Ron Cey	.04	.03	.02
74	Greg Luzinski	.04	.03	.02
75	Lee Mazzilli	.02	.02	.01
76	Gary Matthews	.04	.03	.02
77	Cesar Cedeno	.04	.03	.02
78	Warren Cromartie	.02	.02	.01
79	Steve Henderson	.02	.02	.01
80	Ellis Valentine	.02	.02	.01
81	Mike Easler	.02	.02	.01
82	Garry Templeton	.04	.03	.02
83	Jose Cruz	.04	.03	.02
84	Dave Collins	.02	.02	.01
85	George Hendrick	.02	.02	.01
86	Gene Richards	.02	.02	.01
87	Terry Whitfield	.02	.02	.01
88	Terry Puhl	.02	.02	.01
89	Larry Parrish	.04	.03	.02
90	Andre Dawson	.08	.06	.03
91	Ken Griffey	.04	.03	.02
92	Dave Lopes	.02	.02	.01
93	Doug Flynn	.02	.02	.01
94	Ivan DeJesus	.02	.02	.01
95	Dave Concepcion	.04	.03	.02
96	John Stearns	.02	.02	.01
97	Jerry Mumphrey	.02	.02	.01
98	Jerry Martin	.02	.02	.01
99	Art Howe	.02	.02	.01
100	Omar Moreno	.02	.02	.01
101	Ken Reitz	.02	.02	.01
102	Phil Garner	.02	.02	.01
103	Jerry Reuss	.04	.03	.02
104	Steve Carlton	.10	.08	.04
105	Jim Bibby	.02	.02	.01
106	Steve Rogers	.02	.02	.01
107	Tom Seaver	.10	.08	.04

		MT	NR MT	EX
108	Vida Blue	.04	.03	.02

1981 Topps Stickers

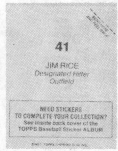

The 262 stickers in this full-color set measure 1-15/16" by 2-9/16" and are numbered on both the front and back. They were produced for Topps by the Panini Company of Italy. The set includes a series of "All-Star" stickers printed on silver or gold "foil". An album to house the stickers was also available.

		MT	NR MT	EX
Complete Set:		17.00	12.50	6.75
Common Player:		.03	.02	.01
Sticker Album:		.80	.60	.30
1	Steve Stone	.06	.05	.02
2	Tommy John, Mike Norris	.06	.05	.02
3	Rudy May	.03	.02	.01
4	Mike Norris	.03	.02	.01
5	Len Barker	.03	.02	.01
6	Mike Norris	.03	.02	.01
7	Dan Quisenberry	.06	.05	.02
8	Rich Gossage	.10	.08	.04
9	George Brett	.25	.20	.10
10	Cecil Cooper	.08	.06	.03
11	Reggie Jackson, Ben Oglivie	.06	.05	.02
12	Gorman Thomas	.06	.05	.02
13	Cecil Cooper	.08	.06	.03
14	George Brett, Ben Oglivie	.20	.15	.08
15	Rickey Henderson	.25	.20	.10
16	Willie Wilson	.08	.06	.03
17	Bill Buckner	.06	.05	.02
18	Keith Hernandez	.12	.09	.05
19	Mike Schmidt	.25	.20	.10
20	Bob Horner	.10	.08	.04
21	Mike Schmidt	.25	.20	.10
22	George Hendrick	.06	.05	.02
23	Ron LeFlore	.04	.03	.02
24	Omar Moreno	.03	.02	.01
25	Steve Carlton	.20	.15	.08
26	Joe Niekro	.06	.05	.02
27	Don Sutton	.10	.08	.04
28	Steve Carlton	.20	.15	.08
29	Steve Carlton	.20	.15	.08
30	Nolan Ryan	.20	.15	.08
31	Rollie Fingers, Tom Hume	.08	.06	.03
32	Bruce Sutter	.08	.06	.03
33	Ken Singleton	.06	.05	.02
34	Eddie Murray	.20	.15	.08
35	Al Bumbry	.03	.02	.01
36	Rich Dauer	.03	.02	.01
37	Scott McGregor	.04	.03	.02
38	Rick Dempsey	.04	.03	.02
39	Jim Palmer	.15	.11	.06
40	Steve Stone	.06	.05	.02
41	Jim Rice	.20	.15	.08
42	Fred Lynn	.10	.08	.04
43	Carney Lansford	.06	.05	.02
44	Tony Perez	.10	.08	.04
45	Carl Yastrzemski	.30	.25	.12
46	Carlton Fisk	.12	.09	.05
47	Dave Stapleton	.03	.02	.01
48	Dennis Eckersley	.06	.05	.02
49	Rod Carew	.20	.15	.08
50	Brian Downing	.04	.03	.02
51	Don Baylor	.08	.06	.03
52	Rick Burleson	.04	.03	.02

		MT	NR MT	EX
53	Bobby Grich	.06	.05	.02
54	Butch Hobson	.03	.02	.01
55	Andy Hassler	.03	.02	.01
56	Frank Tanana	.04	.03	.02
57	Chet Lemon	.04	.03	.02
58	Lamar Johnson	.03	.02	.01
59	Wayne Nordhagen	.03	.02	.01
60	Jim Morrison	.03	.02	.01
61	Bob Molinaro	.03	.02	.01
62	Rich Dotson	.04	.03	.02
63	Britt Burns	.03	.02	.01
64	Ed Farmer	.03	.02	.01
65	Toby Harrah	.04	.03	.02
66	Joe Charboneau	.04	.03	.02
67	Miguel Dilone	.03	.02	.01
68	Mike Hargrove	.04	.03	.02
69	Rick Manning	.03	.02	.01
70	Andre Thornton	.06	.05	.02
71	Ron Hassey	.03	.02	.01
72	Len Barker	.03	.02	.01
73	Lance Parrish	.12	.09	.05
74	Steve Kemp	.04	.03	.02
75	Alan Trammell	.15	.11	.06
76	Champ Summers	.03	.02	.01
77	Rick Peters	.03	.02	.01
78	Kirk Gibson	.15	.11	.06
79	Johnny Wockenfuss	.03	.02	.01
80	Jack Morris	.12	.09	.05
81	Willie Wilson	.08	.06	.03
82	George Brett	.25	.20	.10
83	Frank White	.06	.05	.02
84	Willie Aikens	.03	.02	.01
85	Clint Hurdle	.03	.02	.01
86	Hal McRae	.06	.05	.02
87	Dennis Leonard	.04	.03	.02
88	Larry Gura	.03	.02	.01
89	American League Pennant Winner (Kansas City Royals Team)	.04	.03	.02
90	American League Pennant Winner (Kansas City Royals Team)	.04	.03	.02
91	Paul Molitor	.10	.08	.04
92	Ben Oglivie	.04	.03	.02
93	Cecil Cooper	.08	.06	.03
94	Ted Simmons	.08	.06	.03
95	Robin Yount	.15	.11	.06
96	Gorman Thomas	.06	.05	.02
97	Mike Caldwell	.03	.02	.01
98	Moose Haas	.03	.02	.01
99	John Castino	.03	.02	.01
100	Roy Smalley	.03	.02	.01
101	Ken Landreaux	.03	.02	.01
102	Butch Wynegar	.04	.03	.02
103	Ron Jackson	.03	.02	.01
104	Jerry Koosman	.04	.03	.02
105	Roger Erickson	.03	.02	.01
106	Doug Corbett	.03	.02	.01
107	Reggie Jackson	.25	.20	.10
108	Willie Randolph	.04	.03	.02
109	Rick Cerone	.03	.02	.01
110	Bucky Dent	.04	.03	.02
111	Dave Winfield	.20	.15	.08
112	Ron Guidry	.12	.09	.05
113	Rich Gossage	.10	.08	.04
114	Tommy John	.10	.08	.04
115	Rickey Henderson	.25	.20	.10
116	Tony Armas	.04	.03	.02
117	Dave Revering	.03	.02	.01
118	Wayne Gross	.03	.02	.01
119	Dwayne Murphy	.04	.03	.02
120	Jeff Newman	.03	.02	.01
121	Rick Langford	.03	.02	.01
122	Mike Norris	.03	.02	.01
123	Bruce Bochte	.03	.02	.01
124	Tom Paciorek	.03	.02	.01
125	Dan Meyer	.03	.02	.01
126	Julio Cruz	.03	.02	.01
127	Richie Zisk	.04	.03	.02
128	Floyd Bannister	.04	.03	.02
129	Shane Rawley	.04	.03	.02
130	Buddy Bell	.06	.05	.02
131	Al Oliver	.06	.05	.02
132	Mickey Rivers	.04	.03	.02
133	Jim Sundberg	.03	.02	.01
134	Bump Wills	.03	.02	.01
135	Jon Matlack	.04	.03	.02
136	Danny Darwin	.03	.02	.01
137	Damaso Garcia	.04	.03	.02
138	Otto Velez	.03	.02	.01
139	John Mayberry	.04	.03	.02
140	Alfredo Griffin	.04	.03	.02
141	Alvis Woods	.03	.02	.01

		MT	NR MT	EX
142	Dave Stieb	.06	.05	.02
143	Jim Clancy	.04	.03	.02
144	Gary Matthews	.06	.05	.02
145	Bob Horner	.08	.06	.03
146	Dale Murphy	.25	.20	.10
147	Chris Chambliss	.04	.03	.02
148	Phil Niekro	.12	.09	.05
149	Glenn Hubbard	.03	.02	.01
150	Rick Camp	.03	.02	.01
151	Dave Kingman	.08	.06	.03
152	Bill Caudill	.03	.02	.01
153	Bill Buckner	.06	.05	.02
154	Barry Foote	.03	.02	.01
155	Mike Tyson	.03	.02	.01
156	Ivan DeJesus	.03	.02	.01
157	Rick Reuschel	.06	.05	.02
158	Ken Reitz	.03	.02	.01
159	George Foster	.08	.06	.03
160	Johnny Bench	.25	.20	.10
161	Dave Concepcion	.06	.05	.02
162	Dave Collins	.04	.03	.02
163	Ken Griffey	.06	.05	.02
164	Dan Driessen	.04	.03	.02
165	Tom Seaver	.20	.15	.08
166	Tom Hume	.03	.02	.01
167	Cesar Cedeno	.06	.05	.02
168	Rafael Landestoy	.03	.02	.01
169	Jose Cruz	.06	.05	.02
170	Art Howe	.03	.02	.01
171	Terry Puhl	.03	.02	.01
172	Joe Sambito	.03	.02	.01
173	Nolan Ryan	.20	.15	.08
174	Joe Niekro	.06	.05	.02
175	Dave Lopes	.04	.03	.02
176	Steve Garvey	.20	.15	.08
177	Ron Cey	.06	.05	.02
178	Reggie Smith	.06	.05	.02
179	Bill Russell	.04	.03	.02
180	Burt Hooton	.03	.02	.01
181	Jerry Reuss	.06	.05	.02
182	Dusty Baker	.04	.03	.02
183	Larry Parrish	.04	.03	.02
184	Gary Carter	.20	.15	.08
185	Rodney Scott	.03	.02	.01
186	Ellis Valentine	.03	.02	.01
187	Andre Dawson	.12	.09	.05
188	Warren Cromartie	.03	.02	.01
189	Chris Speier	.03	.02	.01
190	Steve Rogers	.03	.02	.01
191	Lee Mazzilli	.04	.03	.02
192	Doug Flynn	.03	.02	.01
193	Steve Henderson	.03	.02	.01
194	John Stearns	.03	.02	.01
195	Joel Youngblood	.03	.02	.01
196	Frank Taveras	.03	.02	.01
197	Pat Zachry	.03	.02	.01
198	Neil Allen	.03	.02	.01
199	Mike Schmidt	.25	.20	.10
200	Pete Rose	.40	.30	.15
201	Larry Bowa	.06	.05	.02
202	Bake McBride	.03	.02	.01
203	Bob Boone	.04	.03	.02
204	Garry Maddox	.04	.03	.02
205	Tug McGraw	.06	.05	.02
206	Steve Carlton	.20	.15	.08
207	National League Pennant Winner (Philadelphia Phillies Team)	.04	.03	.02
208	National League Pennant Winner (Philadelphia Phillies Team)	.04	.03	.02
209	Phil Garner	.04	.03	.02
210	Dave Parker	.12	.09	.05
211	Omar Moreno	.03	.02	.01
212	Mike Easler	.04	.03	.02
213	Bill Madlock	.06	.05	.02
214	Ed Ott	.03	.02	.01
215	Willie Stargell	.20	.15	.08
216	Jim Bibby	.03	.02	.01
217	Garry Templeton	.06	.05	.02
218	Sixto Lezcano	.03	.02	.01
219	Keith Hernandez	.12	.09	.05
220	George Hendrick	.04	.03	.02
221	Bruce Sutter	.08	.06	.03
222	Ken Oberkfell	.03	.02	.01
223	Tony Scott	.03	.02	.01
224	Darrell Porter	.04	.03	.02
225	Gene Richards	.03	.02	.01
226	Broderick Perkins	.03	.02	.01
227	Jerry Mumphrey	.03	.02	.01
228	Luis Salazar	.03	.02	.01
229	Jerry Turner	.03	.02	.01
230	Ozzie Smith	.10	.08	.04

#	Player	MT	NR MT	EX
231	John Curtis	.03	.02	.01
232	Rick Wise	.03	.02	.01
233	Terry Whitfield	.03	.02	.01
234	Jack Clark	.10	.08	.04
235	Darrell Evans	.08	.06	.03
236	Larry Herndon	.03	.02	.01
237	Milt May	.03	.02	.01
238	Greg Minton	.03	.02	.01
239	Vida Blue	.06	.05	.02
240	Eddie Whitson	.03	.02	.01
241	Cecil Cooper	.20	.15	.08
242	Willie Randolph	.20	.15	.08
243	George Brett	.40	.30	.15
244	Robin Yount	.30	.25	.12
245	Reggie Jackson	.40	.30	.15
246	Al Oliver	.20	.15	.08
247	Willie Wilson	.20	.15	.08
248	Rick Cerone	.15	.11	.06
249	Steve Stone	.15	.11	.06
250	Tommy John	.25	.20	.10
251	Rich Gossage	.25	.20	.10
252	Steve Garvey	.30	.25	.12
253	Phil Garner	.15	.11	.06
254	Mike Schmidt	.40	.30	.15
255	Garry Templeton	.20	.15	.08
256	George Hendrick	.15	.11	.06
257	Dave Parker	.25	.20	.10
258	Cesar Cedeno	.20	.15	.08
259	Gary Carter	.30	.25	.12
260	Jim Bibby	.15	.11	.06
261	Steve Carlton	.30	.25	.12
262	Tug McGraw	.20	.15	.08

1981 Topps Traded

The 132 cards in this extension set are numbered from 727 to 858, technically making them a high-numbered series of the regular Topps set. The set was not packaged in gum packs, but rather placed in a specially designed red box and sold through baseball card dealers only. While many complained about the method, the fact remains, even at higher prices, the set has done well for its owners as it features not only mid-season trades, but also single-player rookie cards of some of the hottest prospects. The cards measure 2-1/2" by 3-1/2".

	MT	NR MT	EX
Complete Set:	40.00	30.00	15.00
Common Player:	.10	.08	.04

#	Player	MT	NR MT	EX
727	Danny Ainge(FC)	3.00	2.25	1.25
728	Doyle Alexander	.20	.15	.08
729	Gary Alexander	.10	.08	.04
730	Billy Almon	.10	.08	.04
731	Joaquin Andujar	.15	.11	.06
732	Bob Bailor	.10	.08	.04
733	Juan Beniquez	.10	.08	.04
734	Dave Bergman	.10	.08	.04
735	Tony Bernazard	.10	.08	.04
736	Larry Biittner	.10	.08	.04
737	Doug Bird	.10	.08	.04
738	Bert Blyleven	1.00	.70	.40
739	Mark Bomback	.10	.08	.04
740	Bobby Bonds	.20	.15	.08
741	Rick Bosetti	.10	.08	.04
742	Hubie Brooks	1.75	1.25	.70

#	Player	MT	NR MT	EX
743	Rick Burleson	.15	.11	.06
744	Ray Burris	.10	.08	.04
745	Jeff Burroughs	.15	.11	.06
746	Enos Cabell	.10	.08	.04
747	Ken Clay	.10	.08	.04
748	Mark Clear	.10	.08	.04
749	Larry Cox	.10	.08	.04
750	Hector Cruz	.10	.08	.04
751	Victor Cruz	.10	.08	.04
752	Mike Cubbage	.10	.08	.04
753	Dick Davis	.10	.08	.04
754	Brian Doyle	.10	.08	.04
755	Dick Drago	.10	.08	.04
756	Leon Durham	.25	.20	.10
757	Jim Dwyer	.10	.08	.04
758	Dave Edwards	.10	.08	.04
759	Jim Essian	.10	.08	.04
760	Bill Fahey	.10	.08	.04
761	Rollie Fingers	5.00	3.75	2.00
762	Carlton Fisk	7.00	5.25	2.75
763	Barry Foote	.10	.08	.04
764	Ken Forsch	.10	.08	.04
765	Kiko Garcia	.10	.08	.04
766	Cesar Geronimo	.10	.08	.04
767	Gary Gray	.10	.08	.04
768	Mickey Hatcher	.15	.11	.06
769	Steve Henderson	.10	.08	.04
770	Marc Hill	.10	.08	.04
771	Butch Hobson	.10	.08	.04
772	Rick Honeycutt	.10	.08	.04
773	Roy Howell	.10	.08	.04
774	Mike Ivie	.10	.08	.04
775	Roy Lee Jackson	.10	.08	.04
776	Cliff Johnson	.10	.08	.04
777	Randy Jones	.15	.11	.06
778	Ruppert Jones	.10	.08	.04
779	Mick Kelleher	.10	.08	.04
780	Terry Kennedy	.20	.15	.08
781	Dave Kingman	.40	.30	.15
782	Bob Knepper	.15	.11	.06
783	Ken Kravec	.10	.08	.04
784	Bob Lacey	.10	.08	.04
785	Dennis Lamp	.10	.08	.04
786	Rafael Landestoy	.10	.08	.04
787	Ken Landreaux	.10	.08	.04
788	Carney Lansford	.80	.60	.30
789	Dave LaRoche	.10	.08	.04
790	Joe Lefebvre	.10	.08	.04
791	Ron LeFlore	.15	.11	.06
792	Randy Lerch	.10	.08	.04
793	Sixto Lezcano	.10	.08	.04
794	John Littlefield	.10	.08	.04
795	Mike Lum	.10	.08	.04
796	Greg Luzinski	.25	.20	.10
797	Fred Lynn	.50	.40	.20
798	Jerry Martin	.10	.08	.04
799	Buck Martinez	.10	.08	.04
800	Gary Matthews	.20	.15	.08
801	Mario Mendoza	.10	.08	.04
802	Larry Milbourne	.10	.08	.04
803	Rick Miller	.10	.08	.04
804	John Montefusco	.10	.08	.04
805	Jerry Morales	.10	.08	.04
806	Jose Morales	.10	.08	.04
807	Joe Morgan	2.00	1.50	.80
808	Jerry Mumphrey	.10	.08	.04
809	Gene Nelson(FC)	.30	.25	.12
810	Ed Ott	.10	.08	.04
811	Bob Owchinko	.10	.08	.04
812	Gaylord Perry	1.75	1.25	.60
813	Mike Phillips	.10	.08	.04
814	Darrell Porter	.15	.11	.06
815	Mike Proly	.10	.08	.04
816	Tim Raines	12.00	9.00	4.75
817	Lenny Randle	.10	.08	.04
818	Doug Rau	.10	.08	.04
819	Jeff Reardon	15.00	11.00	6.00
820	Ken Reitz	.10	.08	.04
821	Steve Renko	.10	.08	.04
822	Rick Reuschel	.25	.20	.10
823	Dave Revering	.10	.08	.04
824	Dave Roberts	.10	.08	.04
825	Leon Roberts	.10	.08	.04
826	Joe Rudi	.20	.15	.08
827	Kevin Saucier	.10	.08	.04
828	Tony Scott	.10	.08	.04
829	Bob Shirley	.10	.08	.04
830	Ted Simmons	.40	.30	.15
831	Lary Sorensen	.10	.08	.04
832	Jim Spencer	.10	.08	.04
833	Harry Spilman	.10	.08	.04

		MT	NR MT	EX
834	Fred Stanley	.10	.08	.04
835	Rusty Staub	.30	.25	.12
836	Bill Stein	.10	.08	.04
837	Joe Strain	.10	.08	.04
838	Bruce Sutter	.50	.40	.20
839	Don Sutton	1.50	1.25	.60
840	Steve Swisher	.10	.08	.04
841	Frank Tanana	.20	.15	.08
842	Gene Tenace	.15	.11	.06
843	Jason Thompson	.10	.08	.04
844	Dickie Thon	.15	.11	.06
845	Bill Travers	.10	.08	.04
846	Tom Underwood	.10	.08	.04
847	John Urrea	.10	.08	.04
848	Mike Vail	.10	.08	.04
849	Ellis Valentine	.10	.08	.04
850	Fernando Valenzuela	3.50	2.75	1.50
851	Pete Vuckovich	.15	.11	.06
852	Mark Wagner	.10	.08	.04
853	Bob Walk	.50	.40	.20
854	Claudell Washington	.15	.11	.06
855	Dave Winfield	10.00	7.50	4.00
856	Geoff Zahn	.10	.08	.04
857	Richie Zisk	.15	.11	.06
858	Checklist 727-858	.10	.08	.04

1982 Topps

At 792 cards, this was the largest issue produced up to that time, eliminating the need for double-printed cards. The 2-1/2" by 3-1/2" cards feature a front color photo with a pair of stripes down the left side. Under the player's photo are found his name, team and position. A facsimile autograph runs across the front of the picture. Specialty cards include great performances of the previous season, All-Stars, statistical leaders and "In Action" cards (indicated by "IA" in listings below). Managers and hitting/pitching leaders have cards, while rookies are shown as "Future Stars" on group cards.

		MT	NR MT	EX
	Complete Set:	150.00	110.00	60.00
	Common Player:	.08	.06	.03
1	1981 Highlight (Steve Carlton)	.50	.40	.20
2	1981 Highlight (Ron Davis)	.08	.06	.03
3	1981 Highlight (Tim Raines)	.30	.25	.12
4	1981 Highlight (Pete Rose)	.70	.50	.30
5	1981 Highlight (Nolan Ryan)	2.00	1.50	.80
6	1981 Highlight (Fernando Valenzuela)	.30	.25	.12
7	Scott Sanderson	.08	.06	.03
8	Rich Dauer	.08	.06	.03
9	Ron Guidry	.35	.25	.14
10	Ron Guidry IA	.15	.11	.06
11	Gary Alexander	.08	.06	.03
12	Moose Haas	.08	.06	.03
13	Lamar Johnson	.08	.06	.03
14	Steve Howe	.10	.08	.04
15	Ellis Valentine	.08	.06	.03
16	Steve Comer	.08	.06	.03
17	Darrell Evans	.25	.20	.10
18	Fernando Arroyo	.08	.06	.03
19	Ernie Whitt	.10	.08	.04
20	Garry Maddox	.12	.09	.05
21	Orioles Future Stars (Bob Bonner, *Cal Ripken*, Jeff Schneider)	70.00	52.00	27.00

		MT	NR MT	EX
22	Jim Beattie	.08	.06	.03
23	Willie Hernandez	.10	.08	.04
24	Dave Frost	.08	.06	.03
25	Jerry Remy	.08	.06	.03
26	Jorge Orta	.08	.06	.03
27	Tom Herr	.12	.09	.05
28	John Urrea	.08	.06	.03
29	Dwayne Murphy	.10	.08	.04
30	Tom Seaver	2.00	1.50	.80
31	Tom Seaver IA	1.00	.70	.40
32	Gene Garber	.08	.06	.03
33	Jerry Morales	.08	.06	.03
34	Joe Sambito	.08	.06	.03
35	Willie Aikens	.08	.06	.03
36	Rangers Batting & Pitching Ldrs. (George Medich, Al Oliver)	.12	.09	.05
37	Dan Graham	.08	.06	.03
38	Charlie Lea	.08	.06	.03
39	Lou Whitaker	.40	.30	.15
40	Dave Parker	.35	.25	.14
41	Dave Parker IA	.15	.11	.06
42	Rick Sofield	.08	.06	.03
43	Mike Cubbage	.08	.06	.03
44	Britt Burns	.08	.06	.03
45	Rick Cerone	.08	.06	.03
46	Jerry Augustine	.08	.06	.03
47	Jeff Leonard	.15	.11	.06
48	Bobby Castillo	.08	.06	.03
49	Alvis Woods	.08	.06	.03
50	Buddy Bell	.15	.11	.06
51	Cubs Future Stars (*Jay Howell*, Carlos Lezcano, Ty Waller)	.40	.30	.15
52	Larry Andersen	.08	.06	.03
53	Greg Gross	.08	.06	.03
54	Ron Hassey	.08	.06	.03
55	Rick Burleson	.10	.08	.04
56	Mark Littell	.08	.06	.03
57	Craig Reynolds	.08	.06	.03
58	John D'Acquisto	.08	.06	.03
59	*Rich Gedman*(FC)	.50	.40	.20
60	Tony Armas	.12	.09	.05
61	Tommy Boggs	.08	.06	.03
62	Mike Tyson	.08	.06	.03
63	Mario Soto	.10	.08	.04
64	Lynn Jones	.08	.06	.03
65	Terry Kennedy	.12	.09	.05
66	Astros Batting & Pitching Ldrs. (Art Howe, Nolan Ryan)	.25	.20	.10
67	Rich Gale	.08	.06	.03
68	Roy Howell	.08	.06	.03
69	Al Williams	.08	.06	.03
70	Tim Raines	3.00	2.25	1.25
71	Roy Lee Jackson	.08	.06	.03
72	Rick Auerbach	.08	.06	.03
73	Buddy Solomon	.08	.06	.03
74	Bob Clark	.08	.06	.03
75	Tommy John	.30	.25	.12
76	Greg Pryor	.08	.06	.03
77	Miguel Dilone	.08	.06	.03
78	George Medich	.08	.06	.03
79	Bob Bailor	.08	.06	.03
80	Jim Palmer	1.00	.70	.40
81	Jim Palmer IA	.30	.25	.12
82	Bob Welch	.60	.45	.25
83	Yankees Future Stars (*Steve Balboni, Andy McGaffigan, Andre Robertson*)(FC)	.25	.20	.10
84	Rennie Stennett	.08	.06	.03
85	Lynn McGlothen	.08	.06	.03
86	Dane Iorg	.08	.06	.03
87	Matt Keough	.08	.06	.03
88	Biff Pocoroba	.08	.06	.03
89	Steve Henderson	.08	.06	.03
90	Nolan Ryan	10.00	7.50	4.00
91	Carney Lansford	.12	.09	.05
92	Brad Havens	.08	.06	.03
93	Larry Hisle	.10	.08	.04
94	Andy Hassler	.08	.06	.03
95	Ozzie Smith	2.50	2.00	1.00
96	Royals Batting & Pitching Ldrs. (George Brett, Larry Gura)	.35	.25	.14
97	Paul Moskau	.08	.06	.03
98	Terry Bulling	.08	.06	.03
99	Barry Bonnell	.08	.06	.03
100	Mike Schmidt	3.00	2.25	1.25
101	Mike Schmidt IA	1.25	.90	.50
102	Dan Briggs	.08	.06	.03
103	Bob Lacey	.08	.06	.03
104	Rance Mulliniks	.08	.06	.03
105	Kirk Gibson	1.00	.70	.40
106	Enrique Romo	.08	.06	.03
107	Wayne Krenchicki	.08	.06	.03

#	Player	MT	NR MT	EX
108	Bob Sykes	.08	.06	.03
109	Dave Revering	.08	.06	.03
110	Carlton Fisk	2.00	1.50	.80
111	Carlton Fisk IA	1.25	.90	.50
112	Billy Sample	.08	.06	.03
113	Steve McCatty	.08	.06	.03
114	Ken Landreaux	.08	.06	.03
115	Gaylord Perry	.50	.40	.20
116	Jim Wohlford	.08	.06	.03
117	Rawly Eastwick	.08	.06	.03
118	Expos Future Stars (Terry Francona, Brad Mills, Bryn Smith)(FC)	.40	.30	.15
119	Joe Pittman	.08	.06	.03
120	Gary Lucas	.08	.06	.03
121	Ed Lynch	.08	.06	.03
122	Jamie Easterly	.08	.06	.03
123	Danny Goodwin	.08	.06	.03
124	Reid Nichols	.08	.06	.03
125	Danny Ainge	1.00	.70	.40
126	Braves Batting & Pitching Ldrs. (Rick Mahler, Claudell Washington)	.10	.08	.04
127	Lonnie Smith	.10	.08	.04
128	Frank Pastore	.08	.06	.03
129	Checklist 1-132	.12	.09	.05
130	Julio Cruz	.08	.06	.03
131	Stan Bahnsen	.08	.06	.03
132	Lee May	.10	.08	.04
133	Pat Underwood	.08	.06	.03
134	Dan Ford	.08	.06	.03
135	Andy Rincon	.08	.06	.03
136	Lenn Sakata	.08	.06	.03
137	George Cappuzzello	.08	.06	.03
138	Tony Pena	.20	.15	.08
139	Jeff Jones	.08	.06	.03
140	Ron LeFlore	.10	.08	.04
141	Indians Future Stars (Chris Bando, Tom Brennan, Von Hayes)(FC)	1.00	.70	.40
142	Dave LaRoche	.08	.06	.03
143	Mookie Wilson	.12	.09	.05
144	Fred Breining	.08	.06	.03
145	Bob Horner	.20	.15	.08
146	Mike Griffin	.08	.06	.03
147	Denny Walling	.08	.06	.03
148	Mickey Klutts	.08	.06	.03
149	Pat Putnam	.08	.06	.03
150	Ted Simmons	.20	.15	.08
151	Dave Edwards	.08	.06	.03
152	Ramon Aviles	.08	.06	.03
153	Roger Erickson	.08	.06	.03
154	Dennis Werth	.08	.06	.03
155	Otto Velez	.08	.06	.03
156	A's Batting & Pitching Ldrs. (Rickey Henderson, Steve McCatty)	.25	.20	.10
157	Steve Crawford	.08	.06	.03
158	Brian Downing	.12	.09	.05
159	Larry Biittner	.08	.06	.03
160	Luis Tiant	.15	.11	.06
161	Batting Leaders (Carney Lansford, Bill Madlock)	.20	.15	.08
162	Home Run Leaders (Tony Armas, Dwight Evans, Bobby Grich, Eddie Murray, Mike Schmidt)	.35	.25	.14
163	Runs Batted In Leaders (Eddie Murray, Mike Schmidt)	.40	.30	.15
164	Stolen Base Leaders (Rickey Henderson, Tim Raines)	.35	.25	.14
165	Victory Leaders (Denny Martinez, Steve McCatty, Jack Morris, Tom Seaver, Pete Vuckovich)	.20	.15	.08
166	Strikeout Leaders (Len Barker, Fernando Valenzuela)	.20	.15	.08
167	Earned Run Avg. Leaders (Steve McCatty, Nolan Ryan)	.20	.15	.08
168	Leading Relievers (Rollie Fingers, Bruce Sutter)	.20	.15	.08
169	Charlie Leibrandt	.12	.09	.05
170	Jim Bibby	.08	.06	.03
171	Giants Future Stars (Bob Brenly, Chili Davis, Bob Tufts)	2.50	2.00	1.00
172	Bill Gullickson	.10	.08	.04
173	Jamie Quirk	.08	.06	.03
174	Dave Ford	.08	.06	.03
175	Jerry Mumphrey	.08	.06	.03
176	Dewey Robinson	.08	.06	.03
177	John Ellis	.08	.06	.03
178	Dyar Miller	.08	.06	.03
179	Steve Garvey	.80	.60	.30
180	Steve Garvey IA	.40	.30	.15
181	Silvio Martinez	.08	.06	.03
182	Larry Herndon	.10	.08	.04
183	Mike Proly	.08	.06	.03
184	Mick Kelleher	.08	.06	.03
185	Phil Niekro	.50	.40	.20
186	Cardinals Batting & Pitching Ldrs. (Bob Forsch, Keith Hernandez)	.25	.20	.10
187	Jeff Newman	.08	.06	.03
188	Randy Martz	.08	.06	.03
189	Glenn Hoffman	.08	.06	.03
190	J.R. Richard	.12	.09	.05
191	Tim Wallach(FC)	2.00	1.50	.80
192	Broderick Perkins	.08	.06	.03
193	Darrell Jackson	.08	.06	.03
194	Mike Vail	.08	.06	.03
195	Paul Molitor	.35	.25	.14
196	Willie Upshaw	.12	.09	.05
197	Shane Rawley	.15	.11	.06
198	Chris Speier	.08	.06	.03
199	Don Aase	.08	.06	.03
200	George Brett	4.00	3.00	1.50
201	George Brett IA	1.50	1.25	.60
202	Rick Manning	.08	.06	.03
203	Blue Jays Future Stars (Jesse Barfield, Brian Milner, Boomer Wells)	1.00	.70	.40
204	Gary Roenicke	.08	.06	.03
205	Neil Allen	.08	.06	.03
206	Tony Bernazard	.08	.06	.03
207	Rod Scurry	.08	.06	.03
208	Bobby Murcer	.15	.11	.06
209	Gary Lavelle	.08	.06	.03
210	Keith Hernandez	.60	.45	.25
211	Dan Petry	.10	.08	.04
212	Mario Mendoza	.08	.06	.03
213	Dave Stewart(FC)	4.00	3.00	1.50
214	Brian Asselstine	.08	.06	.03
215	Mike Krukow	.10	.08	.04
216	White Sox Batting & Pitching Ldrs. (Dennis Lamp, Chet Lemon)	.10	.08	.04
217	Bo McLaughlin	.08	.06	.03
218	Dave Roberts	.08	.06	.03
219	John Curtis	.08	.06	.03
220	Manny Trillo	.10	.08	.04
221	Jim Slaton	.08	.06	.03
222	Butch Wynegar	.08	.06	.03
223	Lloyd Moseby	.20	.15	.08
224	Bruce Bochte	.08	.06	.03
225	Mike Torrez	.10	.08	.04
226	Checklist 133-264	.12	.09	.05
227	Ray Burris	.08	.06	.03
228	Sam Mejias	.08	.06	.03
229	Geoff Zahn	.08	.06	.03
230	Willie Wilson	.20	.15	.08
231	Phillies Future Stars (Mark Davis, Bob Dernier, Ozzie Virgil)(FC)	.60	.45	.25
232	Terry Crowley	.08	.06	.03
233	Duane Kuiper	.08	.06	.03
234	Ron Hodges	.08	.06	.03
235	Mike Easler	.10	.08	.04
236	John Martin	.08	.06	.03
237	Rusty Kuntz	.08	.06	.03
238	Kevin Saucier	.08	.06	.03
239	Jon Matlack	.10	.08	.04
240	Bucky Dent	.12	.09	.05
241	Bucky Dent IA	.10	.08	.04
242	Milt May	.08	.06	.03
243	Bob Owchinko	.08	.06	.03
244	Rufino Linares	.08	.06	.03
245	Ken Reitz	.08	.06	.03
246	Mets Batting & Pitching Ldrs. (Hubie Brooks, Mike Scott)	.20	.15	.08
247	Pedro Guerrero	.90	.70	.35
248	Frank LaCorte	.08	.06	.03
249	Tim Flannery	.08	.06	.03
250	Tug McGraw	.15	.11	.06
251	Fred Lynn	.30	.25	.12
252	Fred Lynn IA	.15	.11	.06
253	Chuck Baker	.08	.06	.03
254	Jorge Bell(FC)	10.00	7.50	4.00
255	Tony Perez	.30	.25	.12
256	Tony Perez IA	.15	.11	.06
257	Larry Harlow	.08	.06	.03
258	Bo Diaz	.10	.08	.04
259	Rodney Scott	.08	.06	.03
260	Bruce Sutter	.20	.15	.08
261	Tigers Future Stars (Howard Bailey, Marty Castillo, Dave Rucker)	.08	.06	.03
262	Doug Bair	.08	.06	.03
263	Victor Cruz	.08	.06	.03
264	Dan Quisenberry	.20	.15	.08
265	Al Bumbry	.10	.08	.04
266	Rick Leach	.15	.11	.06
267	Kurt Bevacqua	.08	.06	.03
268	Rickey Keeton	.08	.06	.03

#	Player	MT	NR MT	EX
269	Jim Essian	.08	.06	.03
270	Rusty Staub	.15	.11	.06
271	Larry Bradford	.08	.06	.03
272	Bump Wills	.08	.06	.03
273	Doug Bird	.08	.06	.03
274	Bob Ojeda(FC)	.70	.50	.30
275	Bob Watson	.10	.08	.04
276	Angels Batting & Pitching Ldrs. (Rod Carew, Ken Forsch)	.25	.20	.10
277	Terry Puhl	.08	.06	.03
278	John Littlefield	.08	.06	.03
279	Bill Russell	.10	.08	.04
280	Ben Oglivie	.10	.08	.04
281	John Verhoeven	.08	.06	.03
282	Ken Macha	.08	.06	.03
283	Brian Allard	.08	.06	.03
284	Bob Grich	.15	.11	.06
285	Sparky Lyle	.12	.09	.05
286	Bill Fahey	.08	.06	.03
287	Alan Bannister	.08	.06	.03
288	Garry Templeton	.12	.09	.05
289	Bob Stanley	.08	.06	.03
290	Ken Singleton	.12	.09	.05
291	Pirates Future Stars (Vance Law, Bob Long, *Johnny Ray*)(FC)	.60	.45	.25
292	Dave Palmer	.08	.06	.03
293	Rob Picciolo	.08	.06	.03
294	Mike LaCoss	.08	.06	.03
295	Jason Thompson	.08	.06	.03
296	Bob Walk	.12	.09	.05
297	Clint Hurdle	.08	.06	.03
298	Danny Darwin	.08	.06	.03
299	Steve Trout	.08	.06	.03
300	Reggie Jackson	2.00	1.50	.80
301	Reggie Jackson IA	1.25	.90	.50
302	Doug Flynn	.08	.06	.03
303	Bill Caudill	.08	.06	.03
304	Johnnie LeMaster	.08	.06	.03
305	Don Sutton	.50	.40	.20
306	Don Sutton IA	.25	.20	.10
307	Randy Bass	.08	.06	.03
308	Charlie Moore	.08	.06	.03
309	Pete Redfern	.08	.06	.03
310	Mike Hargrove	.08	.06	.03
311	Dodgers Batting & Pitching Leaders (Dusty Baker, Burt Hooton)	.12	.09	.05
312	Lenny Randle	.08	.06	.03
313	John Harris	.08	.06	.03
314	Buck Martinez	.08	.06	.03
315	Burt Hooton	.10	.08	.04
316	Steve Braun	.08	.06	.03
317	Dick Ruthven	.08	.06	.03
318	Mike Heath	.08	.06	.03
319	Dave Rozema	.08	.06	.03
320	Chris Chambliss	.10	.08	.04
321	Chris Chambliss IA	.10	.08	.04
322	Garry Hancock	.08	.06	.03
323	Bill Lee	.10	.08	.04
324	Steve Dillard	.08	.06	.03
325	Jose Cruz	.15	.11	.06
326	Pete Falcone	.08	.06	.03
327	Joe Nolan	.08	.06	.03
328	Ed Farmer	.08	.06	.03
329	U.L. Washington	.08	.06	.03
330	Rick Wise	.10	.08	.04
331	Benny Ayala	.08	.06	.03
332	Don Robinson	.10	.08	.04
333	Brewers Future Stars (*Frank DiPino*, Marshall Edwards, Chuck Porter)	.12	.09	.05
334	Aurelio Rodriguez	.10	.08	.04
335	Jim Sundberg	.10	.08	.04
336	Mariners Batting & Pitching Ldrs. (Glenn Abbott, Tom Paciorek)	.10	.08	.04
337	Pete Rose AS	.80	.60	.30
338	Dave Lopes AS	.12	.09	.05
339	Mike Schmidt AS	.80	.60	.30
340	Dave Concepcion AS	.12	.09	.05
341	Andre Dawson AS	.25	.20	.10
342a	George Foster AS (no autograph)	2.25	1.75	.90
342b	George Foster AS (autograph on front)	.40	.30	.15
343	Dave Parker AS	.20	.15	.08
344	Gary Carter AS	.35	.25	.14
345	Fernando Valenzuela AS	.35	.25	.14
346	Tom Seaver AS	.35	.25	.14
347	Bruce Sutter AS	.12	.09	.05
348	Derrel Thomas	.08	.06	.03
349	George Frazier	.08	.06	.03
350	Thad Bosley	.08	.06	.03
351	Reds Future Stars (Scott Brown, Geoff Combe, Paul Householder)	.08	.06	.03
352	Dick Davis	.08	.06	.03
353	Jack O'Connor	.08	.06	.03
354	Roberto Ramos	.08	.06	.03
355	Dwight Evans	.25	.20	.10
356	Denny Lewallyn	.08	.06	.03
357	Butch Hobson	.08	.06	.03
358	Mike Parrott	.08	.06	.03
359	Jim Dwyer	.08	.06	.03
360	Len Barker	.10	.08	.04
361	Rafael Landestoy	.08	.06	.03
362	Jim Wright	.08	.06	.03
363	Bob Molinaro	.08	.06	.03
364	Doyle Alexander	.12	.09	.05
365	Bill Madlock	.20	.15	.08
366	Padres Batting & Pitching Ldrs. (Juan Eichelberger, Luis Salazar)	.10	.08	.04
367	Jim Kaat	.25	.20	.10
368	Alex Trevino	.08	.06	.03
369	Champ Summers	.08	.06	.03
370	Mike Norris	.08	.06	.03
371	Jerry Don Gleaton	.08	.06	.03
372	Luis Gomez	.08	.06	.03
373	*Gene Nelson*	.15	.11	.06
374	Tim Blackwell	.08	.06	.03
375	Dusty Baker	.12	.09	.05
376	Chris Welsh	.08	.06	.03
377	Kiko Garcia	.08	.06	.03
378	Mike Caldwell	.08	.06	.03
379	Rob Wilfong	.08	.06	.03
380	Dave Stieb	.25	.20	.10
381	Red Sox Future Stars (Bruce Hurst, Dave Schmidt, Julio Valdez)	.25	.20	.10
382	Joe Simpson	.08	.06	.03
383a	Pascual Perez (no position on front)	18.00	13.50	7.25
383b	Pascual Perez (position on front)	.12	.09	.05
384	Keith Moreland	.12	.09	.05
385	Ken Forsch	.08	.06	.03
386	Jerry White	.08	.06	.03
387	Tom Veryzer	.08	.06	.03
388	Joe Rudi	.12	.09	.05
389	George Vukovich	.08	.06	.03
390	Eddie Murray	1.25	.90	.50
391	Dave Tobik	.08	.06	.03
392	Rick Bosetti	.08	.06	.03
393	Al Hrabosky	.10	.08	.04
394	Checklist 265-396	.12	.09	.05
395	Omar Moreno	.08	.06	.03
396	Twins Batting & Pitching Ldrs. (Fernando Arroyo, John Castino)	.10	.08	.04
397	Ken Brett	.10	.08	.04
398	Mike Squires	.08	.06	.03
399	Pat Zachry	.08	.06	.03
400	Johnny Bench	1.50	1.25	.60
401	Johnny Bench IA	.40	.30	.15
402	Bill Stein	.08	.06	.03
403	Jim Tracy	.08	.06	.03
404	Dickie Thon	.10	.08	.04
405	Rick Reuschel	.15	.11	.06
406	Al Holland	.08	.06	.03
407	Danny Boone	.08	.06	.03
408	Ed Romero	.08	.06	.03
409	Don Cooper	.08	.06	.03
410	Ron Cey	.15	.11	.06
411	Ron Cey IA	.10	.08	.04
412	Luis Leal	.08	.06	.03
413	Dan Meyer	.08	.06	.03
414	Elias Sosa	.08	.06	.03
415	Don Baylor	.15	.11	.06
416	Marty Bystrom	.08	.06	.03
417	Pat Kelly	.08	.06	.03
418	Rangers Future Stars (John Butcher, Bobby Johnson, *Dave Schmidt*)(FC)	.20	.15	.08
419	Steve Stone	.12	.09	.05
420	George Hendrick	.10	.08	.04
421	Mark Clear	.08	.06	.03
422	Cliff Johnson	.08	.06	.03
423	Stan Papi	.08	.06	.03
424	Bruce Benedict	.08	.06	.03
425	John Candelaria	.12	.09	.05
426	Orioles Batting & Pitching Ldrs. (Eddie Murray, Sammy Stewart)	.35	.25	.14
427	Ron Oester	.08	.06	.03
428	Lamarr Hoyt (LaMarr)	.08	.06	.03
429	John Wathan	.10	.08	.04
430	Vida Blue	.15	.11	.06
431	Vida Blue IA	.10	.08	.04
432	Mike Scott	.25	.20	.10
433	Alan Ashby	.08	.06	.03
434	Joe Lefebvre	.08	.06	.03
435	Robin Yount	4.00	3.00	1.50

		MT	NR MT	EX
436	Joe Strain	.08	.06	.03
437	Juan Berenguer	.08	.06	.03
438	Pete Mackanin	.08	.06	.03
439	*Dave Righetti*(FC)	2.50	2.00	1.00
440	Jeff Burroughs	.10	.08	.04
441	Astros Future Stars (Danny Heep, Billy Smith, Bobby Sprowl)	.08	.06	.03
442	Bruce Kison	.08	.06	.03
443	Mark Wagner	.08	.06	.03
444	Terry Forster	.10	.08	.04
445	Larry Parrish	.12	.09	.05
446	Wayne Garland	.08	.06	.03
447	Darrell Porter	.10	.08	.04
448	Darrell Porter IA	.10	.08	.04
449	*Luis Aguayo*(FC)	.12	.09	.05
450	Jack Morris	.50	.40	.20
451	Ed Miller	.08	.06	.03
452	*Lee Smith*(FC)	12.00	9.00	4.75
453	Art Howe	.08	.06	.03
454	Rick Langford	.08	.06	.03
455	Tom Burgmeier	.08	.06	.03
456	Cubs Batting & Pitching Ldrs. (Bill Buckner, Randy Martz)	.15	.11	.06
457	Tim Stoddard	.08	.06	.03
458	Willie Montanez	.08	.06	.03
459	Bruce Berenyi	.08	.06	.03
460	Jack Clark	.30	.25	.12
461	Rich Dotson	.12	.09	.05
462	Dave Chalk	.08	.06	.03
463	Jim Kern	.08	.06	.03
464	Juan Bonilla	.08	.06	.03
465	Lee Mazzilli	.10	.08	.04
466	Randy Lerch	.08	.06	.03
467	Mickey Hatcher	.10	.08	.04
468	Floyd Bannister	.12	.09	.05
469	Ed Ott	.08	.06	.03
470	John Mayberry	.10	.08	.04
471	Royals Future Stars (*Atlee Hammaker*, Mike Jones, Darryl Motley)	.25	.20	.10
472	Oscar Gamble	.10	.08	.04
473	Mike Stanton	.08	.06	.03
474	Ken Oberkfell	.08	.06	.03
475	Alan Trammell	.50	.40	.20
476	Brian Kingman	.08	.06	.03
477	Steve Yeager	.08	.06	.03
478	Ray Searage	.08	.06	.03
479	Rowland Office	.08	.06	.03
480	Steve Carlton	1.00	.70	.40
481	Steve Carlton IA	.40	.30	.15
482	Glenn Hubbard	.10	.08	.04
483	Gary Woods	.08	.06	.03
484	Ivan DeJesus	.08	.06	.03
485	Kent Tekulve	.10	.08	.04
486	Yankees Batting & Pitching Ldrs. (Tommy John, Jerry Mumphrey)	.20	.15	.08
487	Bob McClure	.08	.06	.03
488	Ron Jackson	.08	.06	.03
489	Rick Dempsey	.10	.08	.04
490	Dennis Eckersley	.20	.15	.08
491	Checklist 397-528	.12	.09	.05
492	Joe Price	.08	.06	.03
493	Chet Lemon	.10	.08	.04
494	Hubie Brooks	.20	.15	.08
495	Dennis Leonard	.10	.08	.04
496	Johnny Grubb	.08	.06	.03
497	Jim Anderson	.08	.06	.03
498	Dave Bergman	.08	.06	.03
499	Paul Mirabella	.08	.06	.03
500	Rod Carew	1.00	.70	.40
501	Rod Carew IA	.40	.30	.15
502	Braves Future Stars (*Steve Bedrosian, Brett Butler, Larry Owen*)	3.00	2.25	1.25
503	Julio Gonzalez	.08	.06	.03
504	Rick Peters	.08	.06	.03
505	Graig Nettles	.25	.20	.10
506	Graig Nettles IA	.12	.09	.05
507	Terry Harper	.08	.06	.03
508	*Jody Davis*(FC)	.25	.20	.10
509	Harry Spilman	.08	.06	.03
510	Fernando Valenzuela	1.50	1.25	.60
511	Ruppert Jones	.08	.06	.03
512	Jerry Dybzinski	.08	.06	.03
513	Rick Rhoden	.12	.09	.05
514	Joe Ferguson	.08	.06	.03
515	Larry Bowa	.20	.15	.08
516	Larry Bowa IA	.12	.09	.05
517	Mark Brouhard	.08	.06	.03
518	Garth Iorg	.08	.06	.03
519	Glenn Adams	.08	.06	.03
520	Mike Flanagan	.12	.09	.05
521	Billy Almon	.08	.06	.03

		MT	NR MT	EX
522	Chuck Rainey	.08	.06	.03
523	Gary Gray	.08	.06	.03
524	Tom Hausman	.08	.06	.03
525	Ray Knight	.12	.09	.05
526	Expos Batting & Pitching Ldrs. (Warren Cromartie, Bill Gullickson)	.10	.08	.04
527	John Henry Johnson	.08	.06	.03
528	Matt Alexander	.08	.06	.03
529	Allen Ripley	.08	.06	.03
530	Dickie Noles	.08	.06	.03
531	A's Future Stars (Rich Bordi, Mark Budaska, Kelvin Moore)	.08	.06	.03
532	Toby Harrah	.10	.08	.04
533	Joaquin Andujar	.10	.08	.04
534	Dave McKay	.08	.06	.03
535	Lance Parrish	.50	.40	.20
536	Rafael Ramirez	.10	.08	.04
537	Doug Capilla	.08	.06	.03
538	Lou Piniella	.15	.11	.06
539	Vern Ruhle	.08	.06	.03
540	Andre Dawson	2.00	1.50	.80
541	Barry Evans	.08	.06	.03
542	Ned Yost	.08	.06	.03
543	Bill Robinson	.08	.06	.03
544	Larry Christenson	.08	.06	.03
545	Reggie Smith	.15	.11	.06
546	Reggie Smith IA	.10	.08	.04
547	Rod Carew AS	.35	.25	.14
548	Willie Randolph AS	.12	.09	.05
549	George Brett AS	.60	.45	.25
550	Bucky Dent AS	.12	.09	.05
551	Reggie Jackson AS	.50	.40	.20
552	Ken Singleton AS	.12	.09	.05
553	Dave Winfield AS	.40	.30	.15
554	Carlton Fisk AS	.20	.15	.08
555	Scott McGregor AS	.12	.09	.05
556	Jack Morris AS	.20	.15	.08
557	Rich Gossage AS	.20	.15	.08
558	John Tudor	.30	.25	.12
559	Indians Batting & Pitching Ldrs. (Bert Blyleven, Mike Hargrove)	.15	.11	.06
560	Doug Corbett	.08	.06	.03
561	Cardinals Future Stars (Glenn Brummer, Luis DeLeon, Gene Roof)	.08	.06	.03
562	Mike O'Berry	.08	.06	.03
563	Ross Baumgarten	.08	.06	.03
564	Doug DeCinces	.15	.11	.06
565	Jackson Todd	.08	.06	.03
566	Mike Jorgensen	.08	.06	.03
567	Bob Babcock	.08	.06	.03
568	Joe Pettini	.08	.06	.03
569	Willie Randolph	.15	.11	.06
570	Willie Randolph IA	.10	.08	.04
571	Glenn Abbott	.08	.06	.03
572	Juan Beniquez	.08	.06	.03
573	Rick Waits	.08	.06	.03
574	Mike Ramsey	.08	.06	.03
575	Al Cowens	.08	.06	.03
576	Giants Batting & Pitching Ldrs. (Vida Blue, Milt May)	.15	.11	.06
577	Rick Monday	.12	.09	.05
578	Shooty Babitt	.08	.06	.03
579	*Rick Mahler*(FC)	.30	.25	.12
580	Bobby Bonds	.15	.11	.06
581	Ron Reed	.08	.06	.03
582	Luis Pujols	.08	.06	.03
583	Tippy Martinez	.08	.06	.03
584	Hosken Powell	.08	.06	.03
585	Rollie Fingers	.30	.25	.12
586	Rollie Fingers IA	.15	.11	.06
587	Tim Lollar	.08	.06	.03
588	Dale Berra	.08	.06	.03
589	Dave Stapleton	.08	.06	.03
590	Al Oliver	.20	.15	.08
591	Al Oliver IA	.10	.08	.04
592	Craig Swan	.08	.06	.03
593	Billy Smith	.08	.06	.03
594	Renie Martin	.08	.06	.03
595	Dave Collins	.10	.08	.04
596	Damaso Garcia	.08	.06	.03
597	Wayne Nordhagen	.08	.06	.03
598	Bob Galasso	.08	.06	.03
599	White Sox Future Stars (Jay Loviglio, Reggie Patterson, Leo Sutherland)	.08	.06	.03
600	Dave Winfield	3.00	2.25	1.25
601	Sid Monge	.08	.06	.03
602	Freddie Patek	.08	.06	.03
603	Rich Hebner	.08	.06	.03
604	Orlando Sanchez	.08	.06	.03
605	Steve Rogers	.10	.08	.04
606	Blue Jays Batting & Pitching Ldrs. (John Mayberry, Dave Stieb)	.15	.11	.06

#	Player	MT	NR MT	EX
607	Leon Durham	.10	.08	.04
608	Jerry Royster	.08	.06	.03
609	Rick Sutcliffe	.25	.20	.10
610	Rickey Henderson	8.00	6.00	3.25
611	Joe Niekro	.20	.15	.08
612	Gary Ward	.10	.08	.04
613	Jim Gantner	.10	.08	.04
614	Juan Eichelberger	.08	.06	.03
615	Bob Boone	.12	.09	.05
616	Bob Boone IA	.10	.08	.04
617	Scott McGregor	.10	.08	.04
618	Tim Foli	.08	.06	.03
619	Bill Campbell	.08	.06	.03
620	Ken Griffey	.15	.11	.06
621	Ken Griffey IA	.10	.08	.04
622	Dennis Lamp	.08	.06	.03
623	Mets Future Stars (Ron Gardenhire, *Terry Leach, Tim Leary*)(FC)	.50	.40	.20
624	Fergie Jenkins	.60	.45	.25
625	Hal McRae	.15	.11	.06
626	Randy Jones	.10	.08	.04
627	Enos Cabell	.08	.06	.03
628	Bill Travers	.08	.06	.03
629	Johnny Wockenfuss	.08	.06	.03
630	Joe Charboneau	.10	.08	.04
631	Gene Tenace	.10	.08	.04
632	Bryan Clark	.08	.06	.03
633	Mitchell Page	.08	.06	.03
634	Checklist 529-660	.12	.09	.05
635	Ron Davis	.10	.08	.04
636	Phillies Batting & Pitching Ldrs. (Steve Carlton, Pete Rose)	.50	.40	.20
637	Rick Camp	.08	.06	.03
638	John Milner	.08	.06	.03
639	Ken Kravec	.08	.06	.03
640	Cesar Cedeno	.15	.11	.06
641	Steve Mura	.08	.06	.03
642	Mike Scioscia	.10	.08	.04
643	Pete Vuckovich	.10	.08	.04
644	John Castino	.08	.06	.03
645	Frank White	.12	.09	.05
646	Frank White IA	.10	.08	.04
647	Warren Brusstar	.08	.06	.03
648	Jose Morales	.08	.06	.03
649	Ken Clay	.08	.06	.03
650	Carl Yastrzemski	1.50	1.25	.60
651	Carl Yastrzemski IA	.60	.45	.25
652	Steve Nicosia	.08	.06	.03
653	Angels Future Stars (*Tom Brunansky*, Luis Sanchez, Daryl Sconiers)	1.25	.90	.50
654	Jim Morrison	.08	.06	.03
655	Joel Youngblood	.08	.06	.03
656	Eddie Whitson	.08	.06	.03
657	Tom Poquette	.08	.06	.03
658	Tito Landrum	.08	.06	.03
659	Fred Martinez	.08	.06	.03
660	Dave Concepcion	.15	.11	.06
661	Dave Concepcion IA	.10	.08	.04
662	Luis Salazar	.08	.06	.03
663	Hector Cruz	.08	.06	.03
664	Dan Spillner	.08	.06	.03
665	Jim Clancy	.12	.09	.05
666	Tigers Batting & Pitching Ldrs. (Steve Kemp, Dan Petry)	.15	.11	.06
667	Jeff Reardon	2.00	1.50	.80
668	Dale Murphy	1.50	1.25	.60
669	Larry Milbourne	.08	.06	.03
670	Steve Kemp	.12	.09	.05
671	Mike Davis	.10	.08	.04
672	Bob Knepper	.12	.09	.05
673	Keith Drumright	.08	.06	.03
674	Dave Goltz	.10	.08	.04
675	Cecil Cooper	.20	.15	.08
676	Sal Butera	.08	.06	.03
677	Alfredo Griffin	.12	.09	.05
678	Tom Paciorek	.08	.06	.03
679	Sammy Stewart	.08	.06	.03
680	Gary Matthews	.12	.09	.05
681	Dodgers Future Stars (*Mike Marshall*, Ron Roenicke, *Steve Sax*)(FC)	5.00	3.75	2.00
682	Jesse Jefferson	.08	.06	.03
683	Phil Garner	.10	.08	.04
684	Harold Baines	.70	.50	.30
685	Bert Blyleven	.20	.15	.08
686	Gary Allenson	.08	.06	.03
687	Greg Minton	.08	.06	.03
688	Leon Roberts	.08	.06	.03
689	Lary Sorensen	.08	.06	.03
690	Dave Kingman	.20	.15	.08
691	Dan Schatzeder	.08	.06	.03
692	Wayne Gross	.08	.06	.03
693	Cesar Geronimo	.08	.06	.03
694	Dave Wehrmeister	.08	.06	.03
695	Warren Cromartie	.08	.06	.03
696	Pirates Batting & Pitching Ldrs. (Bill Madlock, Buddy Solomon)	.15	.11	.06
697	John Montefusco	.08	.06	.03
698	Tony Scott	.08	.06	.03
699	Dick Tidrow	.08	.06	.03
700	George Foster	.25	.20	.10
701	George Foster IA	.12	.09	.05
702	Steve Renko	.08	.06	.03
703	Brewers Batting & Pitching Ldrs. (Cecil Cooper, Pete Vuckovich)	.15	.11	.06
704	Mickey Rivers	.10	.08	.04
705	Mickey Rivers IA	.10	.08	.04
706	Barry Foote	.08	.06	.03
707	Mark Bomback	.08	.06	.03
708	Gene Richards	.08	.06	.03
709	Don Money	.08	.06	.03
710	Jerry Reuss	.12	.09	.05
711	Mariners Future Stars (Dave Edler, *Dave Henderson*, Reggie Walton)	1.25	.90	.50
712	Denny Martinez	.10	.08	.04
713	Del Unser	.08	.06	.03
714	Jerry Koosman	.12	.09	.05
715	Willie Stargell	.80	.60	.30
716	Willie Stargell IA	.30	.25	.12
717	Rick Miller	.08	.06	.03
718	Charlie Hough	.12	.09	.05
719	Jerry Narron	.08	.06	.03
720	Greg Luzinski	.20	.15	.08
721	Greg Luzinski IA	.12	.09	.05
722	Jerry Martin	.08	.06	.03
723	Junior Kennedy	.08	.06	.03
724	Dave Rosello	.08	.06	.03
725	Amos Otis	.10	.08	.04
726	Amos Otis IA	.10	.08	.04
727	Sixto Lezcano	.08	.06	.03
728	Aurelio Lopez	.08	.06	.03
729	Jim Spencer	.08	.06	.03
730	Gary Carter	.80	.60	.30
731	Padres Future Stars (Mike Armstrong, Doug Gwosdz, Fred Kuhaulua)	.08	.06	.03
732	Mike Lum	.08	.06	.03
733	Larry McWilliams	.08	.06	.03
734	Mike Ivie	.08	.06	.03
735	Rudy May	.08	.06	.03
736	Jerry Turner	.08	.06	.03
737	Reggie Cleveland	.08	.06	.03
738	Dave Engle	.08	.06	.03
739	Joey McLaughlin	.08	.06	.03
740	Dave Lopes	.12	.09	.05
741	Dave Lopes IA	.10	.08	.04
742	Dick Drago	.08	.06	.03
743	John Stearns	.08	.06	.03
744	*Mike Witt*(FC)	.80	.60	.30
745	Bake McBride	.08	.06	.03
746	Andre Thornton	.12	.09	.05
747	John Lowenstein	.08	.06	.03
748	Marc Hill	.08	.06	.03
749	Bob Shirley	.08	.06	.03
750	Jim Rice	.70	.50	.30
751	Rick Honeycutt	.08	.06	.03
752	Lee Lacy	.08	.06	.03
753	Tom Brookens	.08	.06	.03
754	Joe Morgan	.70	.50	.30
755	Joe Morgan IA	.20	.15	.08
756	Reds Batting & Pitching Ldrs. (Ken Griffey, Tom Seaver)	.30	.25	.12
757	Tom Underwood	.08	.06	.03
758	Claudell Washington	.12	.09	.05
759	Paul Splittorff	.08	.06	.03
760	Bill Buckner	.15	.11	.06
761	Dave Smith	.12	.09	.05
762	Mike Phillips	.08	.06	.03
763	Tom Hume	.08	.06	.03
764	Steve Swisher	.08	.06	.03
765	Gorman Thomas	.12	.09	.05
766	Twins Future Stars (Lenny Faedo, *Kent Hrbek, Tim Laudner*)(FC)	3.00	2.25	1.25
767	Roy Smalley	.08	.06	.03
768	Jerry Garvin	.08	.06	.03
769	Richie Zisk	.10	.08	.04
770	Rich Gossage	.35	.25	.14
771	Rich Gossage IA	.15	.11	.06
772	Bert Campaneris	.12	.09	.05
773	John Denny	.08	.06	.03
774	Jay Johnstone	.10	.08	.04
775	Bob Forsch	.10	.08	.04
776	Mark Belanger	.10	.08	.04
777	Tom Griffin	.08	.06	.03

		MT	NR MT	EX
778	Kevin Hickey	.08	.06	.03
779	Grant Jackson	.08	.06	.03
780	Pete Rose	2.25	1.75	.90
781	Pete Rose IA	1.00	.70	.40
782	Frank Taveras	.08	.06	.03
783	*Greg Harris*(FC)	.15	.11	.06
784	Milt Wilcox	.08	.06	.03
785	Dan Driessen	.10	.08	.04
786	Red Sox Batting & Pitching Ldrs. (Carney Lansford, Mike Torrez)	.12	.09	.05
787	Fred Stanley	.08	.06	.03
788	Woodie Fryman	.10	.08	.04
789	Checklist 661-792	.12	.09	.05
790	Larry Gura	.08	.06	.03
791	Bobby Brown	.08	.06	.03
792	Frank Tanana	.12	.09	.05

		MT	NR MT	EX
186	Milt Wilcox	.03	.02	.01
191	Dennis Leonard	.04	.03	.02
196	Willie Aikens	.03	.02	.01
201	Ted Simmons	.08	.06	.03
206	Hosken Powell	.03	.02	.01
211	Roger Erickson	.03	.02	.01
215	Graig Nettles	.06	.05	.02
216	Reggie Jackson	.25	.20	.10
221	Rickey Henderson	.25	.20	.10
226	Cliff Johnson	.03	.02	.01
231	Jeff Burroughs	.04	.03	.02
236	Tom Paciorek	.03	.02	.01
241	Pat Putnam	.03	.02	.01
246	Lloyd Moseby	.06	.05	.02
251	Barry Bonnell	.03	.02	.01

1982 Topps Insert Stickers

This 48-player set is actually an abbreviated version of the regular 1982 Topps sticker set with different backs. Used to promote the 1982 sticker set, Topps inserted these stickers in its baseball card wax packs. They are identical to the regular 1982 stickers, except for the backs, which advertise that the Topps sticker album will be "Coming Soon." The 48 stickers retain the same numbers used in the regular sticker set, resulting in the smaller set being skip-numbered.

		MT	NR MT	EX
	Complete Set:	2.00	1.50	.80
	Common Player:	.03	.02	.01
17	Chris Chambliss	.04	.03	.02
21	Bruce Benedict	.03	.02	.01
25	Leon Durham	.06	.05	.02
29	Bill Buckner	.06	.05	.02
33	Dave Collins	.04	.03	.02
37	Dave Concepcion	.06	.05	.02
41	Nolan Ryan	.15	.11	.06
45	Bob Knepper	.04	.03	.02
49	Ken Landreaux	.03	.02	.01
53	Burt Hooton	.03	.02	.01
57	Andre Dawson	.12	.09	.05
61	Gary Carter	.20	.15	.08
65	Joel Youngblood	.03	.02	.01
69	Ellis Valentine	.03	.02	.01
73	Garry Maddox	.04	.03	.02
77	Bob Boone	.04	.03	.02
81	Omar Moreno	.03	.02	.01
85	Willie Stargell	.20	.15	.08
89	Ken Oberkfell	.03	.02	.01
93	Darrell Porter	.04	.03	.02
97	Juan Eichelberger	.03	.02	.01
101	Luis Salazar	.03	.02	.01
105	Enos Cabell	.03	.02	.01
109	Larry Herndon	.03	.02	.01
143	Scott McGregor	.04	.03	.02
148	Mike Flanagan	.06	.05	.02
151	Mike Torrez	.04	.03	.02
156	Carney Lansford	.06	.05	.02
161	Fred Lynn	.10	.08	.04
166	Rich Dotson	.04	.03	.02
171	Tony Bernazard	.03	.02	.01
176	Bo Diaz	.04	.03	.02
181	Alan Trammell	.15	.11	.06

1982 Topps Stickers

The 1982 Topps sticker set is complete at 260 stickers and includes another series of "foil" All-Stars. The stickers measure 1-15/16" by 2-9/16" and feature full-color photos surrounded by a red border for American League players or a blue border for National League players. They are numbered on both the front and back and were designed to be mounted in a special album.

		MT	NR MT	EX
	Complete Set:	15.00	11.00	6.00
	Common Player:	.03	.02	.01
	Sticker Album:	.80	.60	.30
1	Bill Madlock	.06	.05	.02
2	Carney Lansford	.06	.05	.02
3	Mike Schmidt	.25	.20	.10
4	Tony Armas, Dwight Evans, Bobby Grich, Eddie Murray	.12	.09	.05
5	Mike Schmidt	.25	.20	.10
6	Eddie Murray	.20	.15	.08
7	Tim Raines	.03	.02	.01
8	Rickey Henderson	.25	.20	.10
9	Tom Seaver	.20	.15	.08
10	Denny Martinez, Steve McCatty, Jack Morris, Pete Vuckovich	.06	.05	.02
11	Fernando Valenzuela	.15	.11	.06
12	Len Barker	.03	.02	.01
13	Nolan Ryan	.20	.15	.08
14	Steve McCatty	.03	.02	.01
15	Bruce Sutter	.08	.06	.03
16	Rollie Fingers	.10	.08	.04
17	Chris Chambliss	.04	.03	.02
18	Bob Horner	.08	.06	.03
19	Dale Murphy	.25	.20	.10
20	Phil Niekro	.12	.09	.05
21	Bruce Benedict	.03	.02	.01
22	Claudell Washington	.04	.03	.02
23	Glenn Hubbard	.03	.02	.01
24	Rick Camp	.03	.02	.01
25	Leon Durham	.06	.05	.02
26	Ken Reitz	.03	.02	.01
27	Dick Tidrow	.03	.02	.01
28	Tim Blackwell	.03	.02	.01
29	Bill Buckner	.06	.05	.02
30	Steve Henderson	.03	.02	.01
31	Mike Krukow	.04	.03	.02
32	Ivan DeJesus	.03	.02	.01
33	Dave Collins	.04	.03	.02
34	Ron Oester	.03	.02	.01

#	Player	MT	NR MT	EX
35	Johnny Bench	.25	.20	.10
36	Tom Seaver	.20	.15	.08
37	Dave Concepcion	.06	.05	.02
38	Ken Griffey	.06	.05	.02
39	Ray Knight	.06	.05	.02
40	George Foster	.08	.06	.03
41	Nolan Ryan	.20	.15	.08
42	Terry Puhl	.03	.02	.01
43	Art Howe	.03	.02	.01
44	Jose Cruz	.06	.05	.02
45	Bob Knepper	.06	.05	.02
46	Craig Reynolds	.03	.02	.01
47	Cesar Cedeno	.06	.05	.02
48	Alan Ashby	.03	.02	.01
49	Ken Landreaux	.03	.02	.01
50	Fernando Valenzuela	.15	.11	.06
51	Ron Cey	.06	.05	.02
52	Dusty Baker	.04	.03	.02
53	Burt Hooton	.04	.03	.02
54	Steve Garvey	.20	.15	.08
55	Pedro Guerrero	.12	.09	.05
56	Jerry Reuss	.06	.05	.02
57	Andre Dawson	.12	.09	.05
58	Chris Speier	.03	.02	.01
59	Steve Rogers	.03	.02	.01
60	Warren Cromartie	.03	.02	.01
61	Gary Carter	.20	.15	.08
62	Tim Raines	.20	.15	.08
63	Scott Sanderson	.03	.02	.01
64	Larry Parrish	.06	.05	.02
65	Joel Youngblood	.03	.02	.01
66	Neil Allen	.03	.02	.01
67	Lee Mazzilli	.04	.03	.02
68	Hubie Brooks	.06	.05	.02
69	Ellis Valentine	.03	.02	.01
70	Doug Flynn	.03	.02	.01
71	Pat Zachry	.03	.02	.01
72	Dave Kingman	.08	.06	.03
73	Garry Maddox	.04	.03	.02
74	Mike Schmidt	.25	.20	.10
75	Steve Carlton	.20	.15	.08
76	Manny Trillo	.04	.03	.02
77	Bob Boone	.04	.03	.02
78	Pete Rose	.40	.30	.15
79	Gary Matthews	.04	.03	.02
80	Larry Bowa	.06	.05	.02
81	Omar Moreno	.03	.02	.01
82	Rick Rhoden	.04	.03	.02
83	Bill Madlock	.06	.05	.02
84	Mike Easler	.04	.03	.02
85	Willie Stargell	.20	.15	.08
86	Jim Bibby	.03	.02	.01
87	Dave Parker	.12	.09	.05
88	Tim Foli	.03	.02	.01
89	Ken Oberkfell	.03	.02	.01
90	Bob Forsch	.04	.03	.02
91	George Hendrick	.04	.03	.02
92	Keith Hernandez	.12	.09	.05
93	Darrell Porter	.04	.03	.02
94	Bruce Sutter	.08	.06	.03
95	Sixto Lezcano	.03	.02	.01
96	Garry Templeton	.04	.03	.02
97	Juan Eichelberger	.03	.02	.01
98	Broderick Perkins	.03	.02	.01
99	Ruppert Jones	.03	.02	.01
100	Terry Kennedy	.04	.03	.02
101	Luis Salazar	.03	.02	.01
102	Gary Lucas	.03	.02	.01
103	Gene Richards	.03	.02	.01
104	Ozzie Smith	.10	.08	.04
105	Enos Cabell	.03	.02	.01
106	Jack Clark	.10	.08	.04
107	Greg Minton	.03	.02	.01
108	Johnnie LeMaster	.03	.02	.01
109	Larry Herndon	.03	.02	.01
110	Milt May	.03	.02	.01
111	Vida Blue	.06	.05	.02
112	Darrell Evans	.08	.06	.03
113	Len Barker	.03	.02	.01
114	Julio Cruz	.03	.02	.01
115	Billy Martin	.08	.06	.03
116	Tim Raines	.20	.15	.08
117	Pete Rose	.40	.30	.15
118	Bill Stein	.03	.02	.01
119	Fernando Valenzuela	.15	.11	.06
120	Carl Yastrzemski	.25	.20	.10
121	Pete Rose	.50	.40	.20
122	Manny Trillo	.15	.11	.06
123	Mike Schmidt	.40	.30	.15
124	Dave Concepcion	.20	.15	.08
125	Andre Dawson	.25	.20	.10
126	George Foster	.20	.15	.08
127	Dave Parker	.25	.20	.10
128	Gary Carter	.30	.25	.12
129	Steve Carlton	.30	.25	.12
130	Bruce Sutter	.25	.20	.10
131	Rod Carew	.40	.30	.15
132	Jerry Remy	.15	.11	.06
133	George Brett	.40	.30	.15
134	Rick Burleson	.15	.11	.06
135	Dwight Evans	.25	.20	.10
136	Ken Singleton	.20	.15	.08
137	Dave Winfield	.30	.25	.12
138	Carlton Fisk	.25	.20	.10
139	Jack Morris	.25	.20	.10
140	Rich Gossage	.25	.20	.10
141	Al Bumbry	.04	.03	.02
142	Doug DeCinces	.06	.05	.02
143	Scott McGregor	.04	.03	.02
144	Ken Singleton	.06	.05	.02
145	Eddie Murray	.20	.15	.08
146	Jim Palmer	.15	.11	.06
147	Rich Dauer	.03	.02	.01
148	Mike Flanagan	.04	.03	.02
149	Jerry Remy	.03	.02	.01
150	Jim Rice	.20	.15	.08
151	Mike Torrez	.04	.03	.02
152	Tony Perez	.10	.08	.04
153	Dwight Evans	.10	.08	.04
154	Mark Clear	.03	.02	.01
155	Carl Yastrzemski	.25	.20	.10
156	Carney Lansford	.06	.05	.02
157	Rick Burleson	.04	.03	.02
158	Don Baylor	.08	.06	.03
159	Ken Forsch	.03	.02	.01
160	Rod Carew	.20	.15	.08
161	Fred Lynn	.10	.08	.04
162	Bob Grich	.06	.05	.02
163	Dan Ford	.03	.02	.01
164	Butch Hobson	.03	.02	.01
165	Greg Luzinski	.08	.06	.03
166	Rich Dotson	.04	.03	.02
167	Billy Almon	.03	.02	.01
168	Chet Lemon	.04	.03	.02
169	Steve Trout	.03	.02	.01
170	Carlton Fisk	.12	.09	.05
171	Tony Bernazard	.03	.02	.01
172	Ron LeFlore	.04	.03	.02
173	Bert Blyleven	.08	.06	.03
174	Andre Thornton	.06	.05	.02
175	Jorge Orta	.03	.02	.01
176	Bo Diaz	.04	.03	.02
177	Toby Harrah	.04	.03	.02
178	Len Barker	.03	.02	.01
179	Rick Manning	.03	.02	.01
180	Mike Hargrove	.04	.03	.02
181	Alan Trammell	.15	.11	.06
182	Al Cowens	.03	.02	.01
183	Jack Morris	.12	.09	.05
184	Kirk Gibson	.15	.11	.06
185	Steve Kemp	.04	.03	.02
186	Milt Wilcox	.03	.02	.01
187	Lou Whitaker	.12	.09	.05
188	Lance Parrish	.12	.09	.05
189	Willie Wilson	.08	.06	.03
190	George Brett	.25	.20	.10
191	Dennis Leonard	.04	.03	.02
192	John Wathan	.04	.03	.02
193	Frank White	.06	.05	.02
194	Amos Otis	.04	.03	.02
195	Larry Gura	.03	.02	.01
196	Willie Aikens	.03	.02	.01
197	Ben Oglivie	.06	.05	.02
198	Rollie Fingers	.10	.08	.04
199	Cecil Cooper	.08	.06	.03
200	Paul Molitor	.10	.08	.04
201	Ted Simmons	.08	.06	.03
202	Pete Vuckovich	.04	.03	.02
203	Robin Yount	.15	.11	.06
204	Gorman Thomas	.04	.03	.02
205	Rob Wilfong	.03	.02	.01
206	Hosken Powell	.03	.02	.01
207	Roy Smalley	.03	.02	.01
208	Butch Wynegar	.04	.03	.02
209	John Castino	.03	.02	.01
210	Doug Corbett	.03	.02	.01
211	Roger Erickson	.03	.02	.01
212	Mickey Hatcher	.03	.02	.01
213	Dave Winfield	.20	.15	.08
214	Tommy John	.10	.08	.04
215	Graig Nettles	.06	.05	.02
216	Reggie Jackson	.25	.20	.10

		MT	NR MT	EX
217	Rich Gossage	.10	.08	.04
218	Rick Cerone	.03	.02	.01
219	Willie Randolph	.06	.05	.02
220	Jerry Mumphrey	.03	.02	.01
221	Rickey Henderson	.20	.15	.08
222	Mike Norris	.03	.02	.01
223	Jim Spencer	.03	.02	.01
224	Tony Armas	.04	.03	.02
225	Matt Keough	.03	.02	.01
226	Cliff Johnson	.03	.02	.01
227	Dwayne Murphy	.04	.03	.02
228	Steve McCatty	.03	.02	.01
229	Richie Zisk	.04	.03	.02
230	Lenny Randle	.03	.02	.01
231	Jeff Burroughs	.04	.03	.02
232	Bruce Bochte	.03	.02	.01
233	Gary Gray	.03	.02	.01
234	Floyd Bannister	.04	.03	.02
235	Julio Cruz	.03	.02	.01
236	Tom Paciorek	.03	.02	.01
237	Danny Darwin	.03	.02	.01
238	Buddy Bell	.06	.05	.02
239	Al Oliver	.06	.05	.02
240	Jim Sundberg	.04	.03	.02
241	Pat Putnam	.03	.02	.01
242	Steve Comer	.03	.02	.01
243	Mickey Rivers	.04	.03	.02
244	Bump Wills	.03	.02	.01
245	Damaso Garcia	.04	.03	.02
246	Lloyd Moseby	.06	.05	.02
247	Ernie Whitt	.03	.02	.01
248	John Mayberry	.03	.02	.01
249	Otto Velez	.03	.02	.01
250	Dave Stieb	.06	.05	.02
251	Barry Bonnell	.03	.02	.01
252	Alfredo Griffin	.04	.03	.02
253	1981 N.L. Championship (Gary Carter)	.10	.08	.04
254	1981 A.L. Championship (Mike Heath, Larry Milbourne)	.03	.02	.01
255	1981 World Champions (Los Angeles Dodgers Team)	.04	.03	.02
256	1981 World Champions (Los Angeles Dodgers Team)	.04	.03	.02
257	1981 World Series - Game 3 (Fernando Valenzuela)	.10	.08	.04
258	1981 World Series - Game 4 (Steve Garvey)	.10	.08	.04
259	1981 World Series - Game 5 (Jerry Reuss, Steve Yeager)	.03	.02	.01
260	1981 World Series - Game 6 (Pedro Guerrero)	.08	.06	.03

1982 Topps Traded

Topps released its second straight 132-card Traded set in September of 1982. Again, the 2-1/2" by 3-1/2" cards feature not only players who had been traded during the season, but also promising rookies who were given their first individual cards. The cards follow the basic design of the regular issues, but have their backs printed in red rather than the regular-issue green. As in 1981, the cards were not available in normal retail outlets and could only be purchased through regular baseball card dealers. Unlike the previous year, the cards are numbered 1-132 with the letter "T" following the number.

		MT	NR MT	EX
Complete Set:		300.00	225.00	125.00
Common Player:		.10	.08	.04
1T	Doyle Alexander	.20	.15	.08
2T	Jesse Barfield	1.00	.70	.40
3T	Ross Baumgarten	.10	.08	.04
4T	Steve Bedrosian	.80	.60	.30
5T	Mark Belanger	.15	.11	.06
6T	Kurt Bevacqua	.10	.08	.04
7T	Tim Blackwell	.10	.08	.04
8T	Vida Blue	.25	.20	.10
9T	Bob Boone	.20	.15	.08
10T	Larry Bowa	.25	.20	.10
11T	Dan Briggs	.10	.08	.04
12T	Bobby Brown	.10	.08	.04
13T	Tom Brunansky	2.00	1.50	.80
14T	Jeff Burroughs	.15	.11	.06
15T	Enos Cabell	.10	.08	.04
16T	Bill Campbell	.10	.08	.04
17T	Bobby Castillo	.10	.08	.04
18T	Bill Caudill	.10	.08	.04
19T	Cesar Cedeno	.20	.15	.08
20T	Dave Collins	.15	.11	.06
21T	Doug Corbett	.10	.08	.04
22T	Al Cowens	.10	.08	.04
23T	Chili Davis	3.00	2.25	1.25
24T	Dick Davis	.10	.08	.04
25T	Ron Davis	.10	.08	.04
26T	Doug DeCinces	.20	.15	.08
27T	Ivan DeJesus	.10	.08	.04
28T	Bob Dernier	.20	.15	.08
29T	Bo Diaz	.15	.11	.06
30T	Roger Erickson	.10	.08	.04
31T	Jim Essian	.10	.08	.04
32T	Ed Farmer	.10	.08	.04
33T	Doug Flynn	.10	.08	.04
34T	Tim Foli	.10	.08	.04
35T	Dan Ford	.10	.08	.04
36T	George Foster	.40	.30	.15
37T	Dave Frost	.10	.08	.04
38T	Rich Gale	.10	.08	.04
39T	Ron Gardenhire	.10	.08	.04
40T	Ken Griffey	.25	.20	.10
41T	Greg Harris	.15	.11	.06
42T	Von Hayes	.80	.60	.30
43T	Larry Herndon	.15	.11	.06
44T	Kent Hrbek	5.00	3.75	2.00
45T	Mike Ivie	.10	.08	.04
46T	Grant Jackson	.10	.08	.04
47T	Reggie Jackson	9.00	6.75	3.50
48T	Ron Jackson	.10	.08	.04
49T	Fergie Jenkins	2.00	1.50	.80
50T	Lamar Johnson	.10	.08	.04
51T	Randy Johnson	.10	.08	.04
52T	Jay Johnstone	.15	.11	.06
53T	Mick Kelleher	.10	.08	.04
54T	Steve Kemp	.15	.11	.06
55T	Junior Kennedy	.10	.08	.04
56T	Jim Kern	.10	.08	.04
57T	Ray Knight	.20	.15	.08
58T	Wayne Krenchicki	.10	.08	.04
59T	Mike Krukow	.15	.11	.06
60T	Duane Kuiper	.10	.08	.04
61T	Mike LaCoss	.10	.08	.04
62T	Chet Lemon	.15	.11	.06
63T	Sixto Lezcano	.10	.08	.04
64T	Dave Lopes	.15	.11	.06
65T	Jerry Martin	.10	.08	.04
66T	Renie Martin	.10	.08	.04
67T	John Mayberry	.15	.11	.06
68T	Lee Mazzilli	.15	.11	.06
69T	Bake McBride	.10	.08	.04
70T	Dan Meyer	.10	.08	.04
71T	Larry Milbourne	.10	.08	.04
72T	Eddie Milner(FC)	.20	.15	.08
73T	Sid Monge	.10	.08	.04
74T	Jose Morales	.10	.08	.04
75T	Keith Moreland	.20	.15	.08
76T	John Montefusco	.10	.08	.04
77T	Jim Morrison	.10	.08	.04
78T	Rance Mulliniks	.10	.08	.04
79T	Steve Mura	.10	.08	.04
80T	Gene Nelson	.10	.08	.04
81T	Joe Nolan	.10	.08	.04
82T	Dickie Noles	.10	.08	.04
83T	Al Oliver	.30	.25	.12
84T	Jorge Orta	.10	.08	.04
85T	Tom Paciorek	.10	.08	.04
86T	Larry Parrish	.20	.15	.08
87T	Jack Perconte	.10	.08	.04
88T	Gaylord Perry	2.00	1.50	.80
89T	Rob Picciolo	.10	.08	.04

		MT	NR MT	EX
90T	Joe Pittman	.10	.08	.04
91T	Hosken Powell	.10	.08	.04
92T	Mike Proly	.10	.08	.04
93T	Greg Pryor	.10	.08	.04
94T	Charlie Puleo(FC)	.15	.11	.06
95T	Shane Rawley	.20	.15	.08
96T	Johnny Ray	.80	.60	.30
97T	Dave Revering	.10	.08	.04
98T	Cal Ripken	260.00	187.50	104.00
99T	Allen Ripley	.10	.08	.04
100T	Bill Robinson	.10	.08	.04
101T	Aurelio Rodriguez	.15	.11	.06
102T	Joe Rudi	.20	.15	.08
103T	Steve Sax	8.00	6.00	3.00
104T	Dan Schatzeder	.10	.08	.04
105T	Bob Shirley	.10	.08	.04
106T	Eric Show(FC)	.50	.40	.20
107T	Roy Smalley	.15	.11	.06
108T	Lonnie Smith	.15	.11	.06
109T	Ozzie Smith	15.00	11.00	6.00
110T	Reggie Smith	.20	.15	.08
111T	Lary Sorensen	.10	.08	.04
112T	Elias Sosa	.10	.08	.04
113T	Mike Stanton	.10	.08	.04
114T	Steve Stroughter	.10	.08	.04
115T	Champ Summers	.10	.08	.04
116T	Rick Sutcliffe	.80	.60	.30
117T	Frank Tanana	.20	.15	.08
118T	Frank Taveras	.10	.08	.04
119T	Garry Templeton	.20	.15	.08
120T	Alex Trevino	.10	.08	.04
121T	Jerry Turner	.10	.08	.04
122T	Ed Vande Berg(FC)	.15	.11	.06
123T	Tom Veryzer	.10	.08	.04
124T	Ron Washington	.10	.08	.04
125T	Bob Watson	.15	.11	.06
126T	Dennis Werth	.10	.08	.04
127T	Eddie Whitson	.15	.11	.06
128T	Rob Wilfong	.10	.08	.04
129T	Bump Wills	.10	.08	.04
130T	Gary Woods	.10	.08	.04
131T	Butch Wynegar	.15	.11	.06
132T	Checklist 1-132	.10	.08	.04

1983 Topps

The 1983 Topps set totals 792 cards. Missing among the regular 2-1/2" by 3-1/2" cards are some form of future stars cards, as Topps was saving them for the now-established late season "Traded" set. The 1983 cards carry a large color photo as well as a smaller color photo on the front, quite similar in design to the 1963 set. Team colors frame the card, which, at the bottom, have the player's name, position and team. At the upper right-hand corner is a Topps Logo. The backs are horizontal and include statistics, personal information and 1982 highlights. Specialty cards include record-breaking performances, league leaders, All-Stars, numbered checklists "Team Leaders" and "Super Veteran" cards which are horizontal with a current and first-season picture of the honyne player.

	MT	NR MT	EX
Complete Set:	175.00	125.00	75.00
Common Player:	.08	.06	.03

		MT	NR MT	EX
1	Record Breaker (Tony Armas)	.12	.09	.05
2	Record Breaker (Rickey Henderson)	1.50	1.25	.60
3	Record Breaker (Greg Minton)	.08	.06	.03
4	Record Breaker (Lance Parrish)	.20	.15	.08
5	Record Breaker (Manny Trillo)	.08	.06	.03
6	Record Breaker (John Wathan)	.08	.06	.03
7	Gene Richards	.08	.06	.03
8	Steve Balboni	.10	.08	.04
9	Joey McLaughlin	.08	.06	.03
10	Gorman Thomas	.12	.09	.05
11	Billy Gardner	.08	.06	.03
12	Paul Mirabella	.08	.06	.03
13	Larry Herndon	.10	.08	.04
14	Frank LaCorte	.08	.06	.03
15	Ron Cey	.15	.11	.06
16	George Vukovich	.08	.06	.03
17	Kent Tekulve	.10	.08	.04
18	Super Veteran (Kent Tekulve)	.10	.08	.04
19	Oscar Gamble	.10	.08	.04
20	Carlton Fisk	2.00	1.50	.80
21	Orioles Batting & Pitching Ldrs. (Eddie Murray, Jim Palmer)	.35	.25	.14
22	Randy Martz	.08	.06	.03
23	Mike Heath	.08	.06	.03
24	Steve Mura	.08	.06	.03
25	Hal McRae	.15	.11	.06
26	Jerry Royster	.08	.06	.03
27	Doug Corbett	.08	.06	.03
28	Bruce Bochte	.08	.06	.03
29	Randy Jones	.10	.08	.04
30	Jim Rice	.70	.50	.30
31	Bill Gullickson	.08	.06	.03
32	Dave Bergman	.08	.06	.03
33	Jack O'Connor	.08	.06	.03
34	Paul Householder	.08	.06	.03
35	Rollie Fingers	.60	.45	.25
36	Super Veteran (Rollie Fingers)	.15	.11	.06
37	Darrell Johnson	.08	.06	.03
38	Tim Flannery	.08	.06	.03
39	Terry Puhl	.08	.06	.03
40	Fernando Valenzuela	.50	.40	.20
41	Jerry Turner	.08	.06	.03
42	Dale Murray	.08	.06	.03
43	Bob Dernier	.08	.06	.03
44	Don Robinson	.10	.08	.04
45	John Mayberry	.10	.08	.04
46	Richard Dotson	.12	.09	.05
47	Dave McKay	.08	.06	.03
48	Lary Sorensen	.08	.06	.03
49	*Willie McGee*(FC)	5.00	3.75	2.00
50	Bob Horner	.20	.15	.08
51	Cubs Batting & Pitching Ldrs. (Leon Durham, Fergie Jenkins)	.15	.11	.06
52	*Onix Concepcion*(FC)	.08	.06	.03
53	Mike Witt	.30	.25	.12
54	Jim Maler	.08	.06	.03
55	Mookie Wilson	.12	.09	.05
56	Chuck Rainey	.08	.06	.03
57	Tim Blackwell	.08	.06	.03
58	Al Holland	.08	.06	.03
59	Benny Ayala	.08	.06	.03
60	Johnny Bench	1.50	1.25	.60
61	Super Veteran (Johnny Bench)	.30	.25	.12
62	Bob McClure	.08	.06	.03
63	Rick Monday	.12	.09	.05
64	Bill Stein	.08	.06	.03
65	Jack Morris	1.00	.70	.40
66	Bob Lillis	.08	.06	.03
67	Sal Butera	.08	.06	.03
68	*Eric Show*	.30	.25	.12
69	Lee Lacy	.08	.06	.03
70	Steve Carlton	1.25	.90	.50
71	Super Veteran (Steve Carlton)	.30	.25	.12
72	Tom Paciorek	.08	.06	.03
73	Allen Ripley	.08	.06	.03
74	Julio Gonzalez	.08	.06	.03
75	Amos Otis	.10	.08	.04
76	Rick Mahler	.12	.09	.05
77	Hosken Powell	.08	.06	.03
78	Bill Caudill	.08	.06	.03
79	Mick Kelleher	.08	.06	.03
80	George Foster	.20	.15	.08
81	Yankees Batting & Pitching Ldrs. (Jerry Mumphrey, Dave Righetti)	.15	.11	.06
82	Bruce Hurst	.15	.11	.06
83	*Ryne Sandberg*(FC)	60.00	45.00	25.00
84	Milt May	.08	.06	.03
85	Ken Singleton	.12	.09	.05
86	Tom Hume	.08	.06	.03
87	Joe Rudi	.12	.09	.05
88	Jim Gantner	.10	.08	.04

#	Player	MT	NR MT	EX
89	Leon Roberts	.08	.06	.03
90	Jerry Reuss	.12	.09	.05
91	Larry Milbourne	.08	.06	.03
92	Mike LaCoss	.08	.06	.03
93	John Castino	.08	.06	.03
94	Dave Edwards	.08	.06	.03
95	Alan Trammell	.50	.40	.20
96	Dick Howser	.08	.06	.03
97	Ross Baumgarten	.08	.06	.03
98	Vance Law	.10	.08	.04
99	Dickie Noles	.08	.06	.03
100	Pete Rose	1.75	1.25	.70
101	Super Veteran (Pete Rose)	.80	.60	.30
102	Dave Beard	.08	.06	.03
103	Darrell Porter	.10	.08	.04
104	Bob Walk	.08	.06	.03
105	Don Baylor	.15	.11	.06
106	Gene Nelson	.08	.06	.03
107	Mike Jorgensen	.08	.06	.03
108	Glenn Hoffman	.08	.06	.03
109	Luis Leal	.08	.06	.03
110	Ken Griffey	.15	.11	.06
111	Expos Batting & Pitching Ldrs. (Al Oliver, Steve Rogers)	.15	.11	.06
112	Bob Shirley	.08	.06	.03
113	Ron Roenicke	.08	.06	.03
114	Jim Slaton	.08	.06	.03
115	Chili Davis	.20	.15	.08
116	Dave Schmidt	.10	.08	.04
117	Alan Knicely	.08	.06	.03
118	Chris Welsh	.08	.06	.03
119	Tom Brookens	.08	.06	.03
120	Len Barker	.10	.08	.04
121	Mickey Hatcher	.10	.08	.04
122	Jimmy Smith	.08	.06	.03
123	George Frazier	.08	.06	.03
124	Marc Hill	.08	.06	.03
125	Leon Durham	.10	.08	.04
126	Joe Torre	.10	.08	.04
127	Preston Hanna	.08	.06	.03
128	Mike Ramsey	.08	.06	.03
129	Checklist 1-132	.12	.09	.05
130	Dave Stieb	.20	.15	.08
131	Ed Ott	.08	.06	.03
132	Todd Cruz	.08	.06	.03
133	Jim Barr	.08	.06	.03
134	Hubie Brooks	.15	.11	.06
135	Dwight Evans	.25	.20	.10
136	Willie Aikens	.08	.06	.03
137	Woodie Fryman	.10	.08	.04
138	Rick Dempsey	.10	.08	.04
139	Bruce Berenyi	.08	.06	.03
140	Willie Randolph	.12	.09	.05
141	Indians Batting & Pitching Ldrs. (Toby Harrah, Rick Sutcliffe)	.12	.09	.05
142	Mike Caldwell	.08	.06	.03
143	Joe Pettini	.08	.06	.03
144	Mark Wagner	.08	.06	.03
145	Don Sutton	.40	.30	.15
146	Super Veteran (Don Sutton)	.20	.15	.08
147	Rick Leach	.08	.06	.03
148	Dave Roberts	.08	.06	.03
149	Johnny Ray	.15	.11	.06
150	Bruce Sutter	.20	.15	.08
151	Super Veteran (Bruce Sutter)	.12	.09	.05
152	Jay Johnstone	.10	.08	.04
153	Jerry Koosman	.12	.09	.05
154	Johnnie LeMaster	.08	.06	.03
155	Dan Quisenberry	.20	.15	.08
156	Billy Martin	.12	.09	.05
157	Steve Bedrosian	.25	.20	.10
158	Rob Wilfong	.08	.06	.03
159	Mike Stanton	.08	.06	.03
160	Dave Kingman	.20	.15	.08
161	Super Veteran (Dave Kingman)	.10	.08	.04
162	Mark Clear	.08	.06	.03
163	Cal Ripken	25.00	18.00	10.00
164	Dave Palmer	.08	.06	.03
165	Dan Driessen	.10	.08	.04
166	John Pacella	.08	.06	.03
167	Mark Brouhard	.08	.06	.03
168	Juan Eichelberger	.08	.06	.03
169	Doug Flynn	.08	.06	.03
170	Steve Howe	.10	.08	.04
171	Giants Batting & Pitching Ldrs. (Bill Laskey, Joe Morgan)	.15	.11	.06
172	Vern Ruhle	.08	.06	.03
173	Jim Morrison	.08	.06	.03
174	Jerry Ujdur	.08	.06	.03
175	Bo Diaz	.10	.08	.04
176	Dave Righetti	.35	.25	.14
177	Harold Baines	.25	.20	.10
178	Luis Tiant	.15	.11	.06
179	Super Veteran (Luis Tiant)	.10	.08	.04
180	Rickey Henderson	7.00	5.25	2.75
181	Terry Felton	.08	.06	.03
182	Mike Fischlin	.08	.06	.03
183	Ed Vande Berg	.12	.09	.05
184	Bob Clark	.08	.06	.03
185	Tim Lollar	.08	.06	.03
186	Whitey Herzog	.10	.08	.04
187	Terry Leach	.12	.09	.05
188	Rick Miller	.08	.06	.03
189	Dan Schatzeder	.08	.06	.03
190	Cecil Cooper	.20	.15	.08
191	Joe Price	.08	.06	.03
192	Floyd Rayford	.08	.06	.03
193	Harry Spilman	.08	.06	.03
194	Cesar Geronimo	.08	.06	.03
195	Bob Stoddard	.08	.06	.03
196	Bill Fahey	.08	.06	.03
197	Jim Eisenreich(FC)	.15	.11	.06
198	Kiko Garcia	.08	.06	.03
199	Marty Bystrom	.08	.06	.03
200	Rod Carew	.70	.50	.30
201	Super Veteran (Rod Carew)	.35	.25	.14
202	Blue Jays Batting & Pitching Ldrs. (Damaso Garcia, Dave Stieb)	.12	.09	.05
203	Mike Morgan	.15	.11	.06
204	Junior Kennedy	.08	.06	.03
205	Dave Parker	.40	.30	.15
206	Ken Oberkfell	.08	.06	.03
207	Rick Camp	.08	.06	.03
208	Dan Meyer	.08	.06	.03
209	Mike Moore(FC)	1.00	.70	.40
210	Jack Clark	.30	.25	.12
211	John Denny	.08	.06	.03
212	John Stearns	.08	.06	.03
213	Tom Burgmeier	.08	.06	.03
214	Jerry White	.08	.06	.03
215	Mario Soto	.10	.08	.04
216	Tony LaRussa	.10	.08	.04
217	Tim Stoddard	.08	.06	.03
218	Roy Howell	.08	.06	.03
219	Mike Armstrong	.08	.06	.03
220	Dusty Baker	.12	.09	.05
221	Joe Niekro	.15	.11	.06
222	Damaso Garcia	.08	.06	.03
223	John Montefusco	.08	.06	.03
224	Mickey Rivers	.10	.08	.04
225	Enos Cabell	.08	.06	.03
226	Enrique Romo	.08	.06	.03
227	Chris Bando	.08	.06	.03
228	Joaquin Andujar	.10	.08	.04
229	Phillies Batting & Pitching Ldrs. (Steve Carlton, Bo Diaz)	.20	.15	.08
230	Fergie Jenkins	.60	.45	.25
231	Super Veteran (Fergie Jenkins)	.12	.09	.05
232	Tom Brunansky	.30	.25	.12
233	Wayne Gross	.08	.06	.03
234	Larry Andersen	.08	.06	.03
235	Claudell Washington	.10	.08	.04
236	Steve Renko	.08	.06	.03
237	Dan Norman	.08	.06	.03
238	Bud Black(FC)	.70	.50	.30
239	Dave Stapleton	.08	.06	.03
240	Rich Gossage	.30	.25	.12
241	Super Veteran (Rich Gossage)	.15	.11	.06
242	Joe Nolan	.08	.06	.03
243	Duane Walker	.08	.06	.03
244	Dwight Bernard	.08	.06	.03
245	Steve Sax	.35	.25	.14
246	George Bamberger	.08	.06	.03
247	Dave Smith	.12	.09	.05
248	Bake McBride	.08	.06	.03
249	Checklist 133-264	.12	.09	.05
250	Bill Buckner	.15	.11	.06
251	Alan Wiggins(FC)	.08	.06	.03
252	Luis Aguayo	.08	.06	.03
253	Larry McWilliams	.08	.06	.03
254	Rick Cerone	.08	.06	.03
255	Gene Garber	.08	.06	.03
256	Super Veteran (Gene Garber)	.08	.06	.03
257	Jesse Barfield	.50	.40	.20
258	Manny Castillo	.08	.06	.03
259	Jeff Jones	.08	.06	.03
260	Steve Kemp	.12	.09	.05
261	Tigers Batting & Pitching Ldrs. (Larry Herndon, Dan Petry)	.10	.08	.04
262	Ron Jackson	.08	.06	.03
263	Renie Martin	.08	.06	.03
264	Jamie Quirk	.08	.06	.03

#	Name	MT	NR MT	EX
265	Joel Youngblood	.08	.06	.03
266	Paul Boris	.08	.06	.03
267	Terry Francona	.08	.06	.03
268	Storm Davis (FC)	.30	.25	.12
269	Ron Oester	.08	.06	.03
270	Dennis Eckersley	2.00	1.50	.80
271	Ed Romero	.08	.06	.03
272	Frank Tanana	.12	.09	.05
273	Mark Belanger	.10	.08	.04
274	Terry Kennedy	.12	.09	.05
275	Ray Knight	.12	.09	.05
276	Gene Mauch	.10	.08	.04
277	Rance Mulliniks	.08	.06	.03
278	Kevin Hickey	.08	.06	.03
279	Greg Gross	.08	.06	.03
280	Bert Blyleven	.20	.15	.08
281	Andre Robertson	.08	.06	.03
282	Reggie Smith	.12	.09	.05
283	Super Veteran (Reggie Smith)	.10	.08	.04
284	Jeff Lahti	.08	.06	.03
285	Lance Parrish	.40	.30	.15
286	Rick Langford	.08	.06	.03
287	Bobby Brown	.08	.06	.03
288	Joe Cowley (FC)	.12	.09	.05
289	Jerry Dybzinski	.08	.06	.03
290	Jeff Reardon	2.00	1.50	.80
291	Pirates Batting & Pitching Ldrs. (John Candelaria, Bill Madlock)	.15	.11	.06
292	Craig Swan	.08	.06	.03
293	Glenn Gulliver	.08	.06	.03
294	Dave Engle	.08	.06	.03
295	Jerry Remy	.08	.06	.03
296	Greg Harris	.08	.06	.03
297	Ned Yost	.08	.06	.03
298	Floyd Chiffer	.08	.06	.03
299	George Wright	.08	.06	.03
300	Mike Schmidt	3.00	2.25	1.25
301	Super Veteran (Mike Schmidt)	1.00	.70	.40
302	Ernie Whitt	.10	.08	.04
303	Miguel Dilone	.08	.06	.03
304	Dave Rucker	.08	.06	.03
305	Larry Bowa	.15	.11	.06
306	Tom Lasorda	.12	.09	.05
307	Lou Piniella	.15	.11	.06
308	Jesus Vega	.08	.06	.03
309	Jeff Leonard	.12	.09	.05
310	Greg Luzinski	.15	.11	.06
311	Glenn Brummer	.08	.06	.03
312	Brian Kingman	.08	.06	.03
313	Gary Gray	.08	.06	.03
314	Ken Dayley (FC)	.15	.11	.06
315	Rick Burleson	.10	.08	.04
316	Paul Splittorff	.08	.06	.03
317	Gary Rajsich	.08	.06	.03
318	John Tudor	.15	.11	.06
319	Lenn Sakata	.08	.06	.03
320	Steve Rogers	.10	.08	.04
321	Brewers Batting & Pitching Ldrs. (Pete Vuckovich, Robin Yount)	.20	.15	.08
322	Dave Van Gorder	.08	.06	.03
323	Luis DeLeon	.08	.06	.03
324	Mike Marshall	.12	.09	.05
325	Von Hayes	.20	.15	.08
326	Garth Iorg	.08	.06	.03
327	Bobby Castillo	.08	.06	.03
328	Craig Reynolds	.08	.06	.03
329	Randy Niemann	.08	.06	.03
330	Buddy Bell	.15	.11	.06
331	Mike Krukow	.10	.08	.04
332	Glenn Wilson (FC)	.12	.09	.05
333	Dave LaRoche	.08	.06	.03
334	Super Veteran (Dave LaRoche)	.08	.06	.03
335	Steve Henderson	.08	.06	.03
336	Rene Lachemann	.08	.06	.03
337	Tito Landrum	.08	.06	.03
338	Bob Owchinko	.08	.06	.03
339	Terry Harper	.08	.06	.03
340	Larry Gura	.08	.06	.03
341	Doug DeCinces	.15	.11	.06
342	Atlee Hammaker	.10	.08	.04
343	Bob Bailor	.08	.06	.03
344	Roger LaFrancois	.08	.06	.03
345	Jim Clancy	.10	.08	.04
346	Joe Pittman	.08	.06	.03
347	Sammy Stewart	.08	.06	.03
348	Alan Bannister	.08	.06	.03
349	Checklist 265-396	.12	.09	.05
350	Robin Yount	4.00	3.00	1.50
351	Reds Batting & Pitching Ldrs. (Cesar Cedeno, Mario Soto)	.12	.09	.05
352	Mike Scioscia	.10	.08	.04
353	Steve Comer	.08	.06	.03
354	Randy Johnson	.08	.06	.03
355	Jim Bibby	.08	.06	.03
356	Gary Woods	.08	.06	.03
357	Len Matuszek (FC)	.08	.06	.03
358	Jerry Garvin	.08	.06	.03
359	Dave Collins	.10	.08	.04
360	Nolan Ryan	8.00	6.00	3.25
361	Super Veteran (Nolan Ryan)	.30	.25	.12
362	Bill Almon	.08	.06	.03
363	John Stuper (FC)	.08	.06	.03
364	Brett Butler	.20	.15	.08
365	Dave Lopes	.12	.09	.05
366	Dick Williams	.08	.06	.03
367	Bud Anderson	.08	.06	.03
368	Richie Zisk	.10	.08	.04
369	Jesse Orosco	.15	.11	.06
370	Gary Carter	.50	.40	.20
371	Mike Richardt	.08	.06	.03
372	Terry Crowley	.08	.06	.03
373	Kevin Saucier	.08	.06	.03
374	Wayne Krenchicki	.08	.06	.03
375	Pete Vuckovich	.10	.08	.04
376	Ken Landreaux	.08	.06	.03
377	Lee May	.10	.08	.04
378	Super Veteran (Lee May)	.10	.08	.04
379	Guy Sularz	.08	.06	.03
380	Ron Davis	.08	.06	.03
381	Red Sox Batting & Pitching Ldrs. (Jim Rice, Bob Stanley)	.25	.20	.10
382	Bob Knepper	.12	.09	.05
383	Ozzie Virgil	.10	.08	.04
384	Dave Dravecky (FC)	1.00	.70	.40
385	Mike Easler	.10	.08	.04
386	Rod Carew AS	.50	.40	.20
387	Bob Grich AS	.10	.08	.04
388	George Brett AS	.65	.50	.30
389	Robin Yount AS	.65	.50	.30
390	Reggie Jackson AS	.50	.40	.20
391	Rickey Henderson AS	1.75	1.25	.70
392	Fred Lynn AS	.15	.11	.06
393	Carlton Fisk AS	.15	.11	.06
394	Pete Vuckovich AS	.10	.08	.04
395	Larry Gura AS	.08	.06	.03
396	Dan Quisenberry AS	.12	.09	.05
397	Pete Rose AS	.70	.50	.30
398	Manny Trillo AS	.10	.08	.04
399	Mike Schmidt AS	.60	.45	.25
400	Dave Concepcion AS	.12	.09	.05
401	Dale Murphy AS	.70	.50	.30
402	Andre Dawson AS	.40	.30	.15
403	Tim Raines AS	.35	.25	.14
404	Gary Carter AS	.35	.25	.14
405	Steve Rogers AS	.10	.08	.04
406	Steve Carlton AS	.35	.25	.14
407	Bruce Sutter AS	.12	.09	.05
408	Rudy May	.08	.06	.03
409	Marvis Foley	.08	.06	.03
410	Phil Niekro	.40	.30	.15
411	Super Veteran (Phil Niekro)	.20	.15	.08
412	Rangers Batting & Pitching Ldrs. (Buddy Bell, Charlie Hough)	.15	.11	.06
413	Matt Keough	.08	.06	.03
414	Julio Cruz	.08	.06	.03
415	Bob Forsch	.10	.08	.04
416	Joe Ferguson	.08	.06	.03
417	Tom Hausman	.08	.06	.03
418	Greg Pryor	.08	.06	.03
419	Steve Crawford	.08	.06	.03
420	Al Oliver	.20	.15	.08
421	Super Veteran (Al Oliver)	.12	.09	.05
422	George Cappuzzello	.08	.06	.03
423	Tom Lawless (FC)	.10	.08	.04
424	Jerry Augustine	.08	.06	.03
425	Pedro Guerrero	.35	.25	.14
426	Earl Weaver	.10	.08	.04
427	Roy Lee Jackson	.08	.06	.03
428	Champ Summers	.08	.06	.03
429	Eddie Whitson	.08	.06	.03
430	Kirk Gibson	.50	.40	.20
431	Gary Gaetti (FC)	.70	.50	.30
432	Porfirio Altamirano	.08	.06	.03
433	Dale Berra	.08	.06	.03
434	Dennis Lamp	.08	.06	.03
435	Tony Armas	.12	.09	.05
436	Bill Campbell	.08	.06	.03
437	Rick Sweet	.08	.06	.03
438	Dave LaPoint (FC)	.40	.30	.15
439	Rafael Ramirez	.08	.06	.03
440	Ron Guidry	.30	.25	.12
441	Astros Batting & Pitching Ldrs. (Ray Knight, Joe Niekro)	.12	.09	.05

#	Player	MT	NR MT	EX
442	Brian Downing	.12	.09	.05
443	Don Hood	.08	.06	.03
444	Wally Backman(FC)	.25	.20	.10
445	Mike Flanagan	.12	.09	.05
446	Reid Nichols	.08	.06	.03
447	Bryn Smith	.10	.08	.04
448	Darrell Evans	.20	.15	.08
449	*Eddie Milner*	.12	.09	.05
450	Ted Simmons	.20	.15	.08
451	Super Veteran (Ted Simmons)	.12	.09	.05
452	Lloyd Moseby	.15	.11	.06
453	Lamar Johnson	.08	.06	.03
454	Bob Welch	.15	.11	.06
455	Sixto Lezcano	.08	.06	.03
456	Lee Elia	.08	.06	.03
457	Milt Wilcox	.08	.06	.03
458	Ron Washington	.08	.06	.03
459	Ed Farmer	.08	.06	.03
460	Roy Smalley	.08	.06	.03
461	Steve Trout	.08	.06	.03
462	Steve Nicosia	.08	.06	.03
463	Gaylord Perry	.40	.30	.15
464	Super Veteran (Gaylord Perry)	.20	.15	.08
465	Lonnie Smith	.10	.08	.04
466	Tom Underwood	.08	.06	.03
467	Rufino Linares	.08	.06	.03
468	Dave Goltz	.10	.08	.04
469	Ron Gardenhire	.08	.06	.03
470	Greg Minton	.08	.06	.03
471	Royals Batting & Pitching Ldrs. (Vida Blue, Willie Wilson)	.15	.11	.06
472	Gary Allenson	.08	.06	.03
473	John Lowenstein	.08	.06	.03
474	Ray Burris	.08	.06	.03
475	Cesar Cedeno	.12	.09	.05
476	Rob Picciolo	.08	.06	.03
477	Tom Niedenfuer(FC)	.15	.11	.06
478	Phil Garner	.10	.08	.04
479	Charlie Hough	.12	.09	.05
480	Toby Harrah	.10	.08	.04
481	Scot Thompson	.08	.06	.03
482	*Tony Gwynn*(FC)	40.00	30.00	15.00
483	Lynn Jones	.08	.06	.03
484	Dick Ruthven	.08	.06	.03
485	Omar Moreno	.08	.06	.03
486	Clyde King	.08	.06	.03
487	Jerry Hairston	.08	.06	.03
488	Alfredo Griffin	.10	.08	.04
489	Tom Herr	.12	.09	.05
490	Jim Palmer	1.00	.70	.40
491	Super Veteran (Jim Palmer)	.20	.15	.08
492	Paul Serna	.08	.06	.03
493	Steve McCatty	.08	.06	.03
494	Bob Brenly	.10	.08	.04
495	Warren Cromartie	.08	.06	.03
496	Tom Veryzer	.08	.06	.03
497	Rick Sutcliffe	.20	.15	.08
498	*Wade Boggs*(FC)	40.00	30.00	15.00
499	Jeff Little	.10	.08	.04
500	Reggie Jackson	1.50	1.25	.60
501	Super Veteran (Reggie Jackson)	.35	.25	.14
502	Braves Batting & Pitching Ldrs. (Dale Murphy, Phil Niekro)	.50	.40	.20
503	Moose Haas	.08	.06	.03
504	Don Werner	.08	.06	.03
505	Garry Templeton	.12	.09	.05
506	*Jim Gott*(FC)	.25	.20	.10
507	Tony Scott	.08	.06	.03
508	Tom Filer	.15	.11	.06
509	Lou Whitaker	.40	.30	.20
510	Tug McGraw	.15	.11	.06
511	Super Veteran (Tug McGraw)	.10	.08	.04
512	Doyle Alexander	.12	.09	.05
513	Fred Stanley	.08	.06	.03
514	Rudy Law	.08	.06	.03
515	Gene Tenace	.10	.08	.04
516	Bill Virdon	.08	.06	.03
517	Gary Ward	.10	.08	.04
518	Bill Laskey	.08	.06	.03
519	Terry Bulling	.08	.06	.03
520	Fred Lynn	.25	.20	.10
521	Bruce Benedict	.08	.06	.03
522	Pat Zachry	.08	.06	.03
523	Carney Lansford	.12	.09	.05
524	Tom Brennan	.08	.06	.03
525	Frank White	.12	.09	.05
526	Checklist 397-528	.12	.09	.05
527	Larry Biittner	.08	.06	.03
528	Jamie Easterly	.08	.06	.03
529	Tim Laudner	.10	.08	.04
530	Eddie Murray	.80	.60	.30

#	Player	MT	NR MT	EX
531	Athletics Batting & Pitching Ldrs. (Rickey Henderson, Rick Langford)	.30	.25	.12
532	Dave Stewart	1.25	.90	.50
533	Luis Salazar	.08	.06	.03
534	John Butcher	.08	.06	.03
535	Manny Trillo	.10	.08	.04
536	Johnny Wockenfuss	.08	.06	.03
537	Rod Scurry	.08	.06	.03
538	Danny Heep	.08	.06	.03
539	Roger Erickson	.08	.06	.03
540	Ozzie Smith	2.00	1.50	.80
541	Britt Burns	.08	.06	.03
542	Jody Davis	.12	.09	.05
543	Alan Fowlkes	.08	.06	.03
544	Larry Whisenton	.08	.06	.03
545	Floyd Bannister	.12	.09	.05
546	Dave Garcia	.08	.06	.03
547	Geoff Zahn	.08	.06	.03
548	Brian Giles	.08	.06	.03
549	*Charlie Puleo*	.15	.11	.06
550	Carl Yastrzemski	1.00	.70	.40
551	Super Veteran (Carl Yastrzemski)	.40	.30	.15
552	Tim Wallach	.30	.25	.12
553	Denny Martinez	.10	.08	.04
554	Mike Vail	.08	.06	.03
555	Steve Yeager	.08	.06	.03
556	Willie Upshaw	.10	.08	.04
557	Rick Honeycutt	.08	.06	.03
558	Dickie Thon	.10	.08	.04
559	Pete Redfern	.08	.06	.03
560	Ron LeFlore	.10	.08	.04
561	Cardinals Batting & Pitching Ldrs. (Joaquin Andujar, Lonnie Smith)	.12	.09	.05
562	Dave Rozema	.08	.06	.03
563	Juan Bonilla	.08	.06	.03
564	Sid Monge	.08	.06	.03
565	Bucky Dent	.12	.09	.05
566	Manny Sarmiento	.08	.06	.03
567	Joe Simpson	.08	.06	.03
568	Willie Hernandez	.12	.09	.05
569	Jack Perconte	.08	.06	.03
570	Vida Blue	.15	.11	.06
571	Mickey Klutts	.08	.06	.03
572	Bob Watson	.10	.08	.04
573	Andy Hassler	.08	.06	.03
574	Glenn Adams	.08	.06	.03
575	Neil Allen	.08	.06	.03
576	Frank Robinson	.12	.09	.05
577	Luis Aponte	.08	.06	.03
578	David Green	.08	.06	.03
579	Rich Dauer	.08	.06	.03
580	Tom Seaver	2.00	1.50	.80
581	Super Veteran (Tom Seaver)	.30	.25	.12
582	Marshall Edwards	.08	.06	.03
583	Terry Forster	.10	.08	.04
584	Dave Hostetler	.08	.06	.03
585	Jose Cruz	.15	.11	.06
586	*Frank Viola*(FC)	7.00	5.25	2.75
587	Ivan DeJesus	.08	.06	.03
588	Pat Underwood	.08	.06	.03
589	Alvis Woods	.08	.06	.03
590	Tony Pena	.12	.09	.05
591	White Sox Batting & Pitching Ldrs. (LaMarr Hoyt, Greg Luzinski)	.15	.11	.06
592	Shane Rawley	.12	.09	.05
593	Broderick Perkins	.08	.06	.03
594	Eric Rasmussen	.08	.06	.03
595	Tim Raines	1.00	.70	.40
596	Randy Johnson	.08	.06	.03
597	Mike Proly	.08	.06	.03
598	Dwayne Murphy	.10	.08	.04
599	Don Aase	.08	.06	.03
600	George Brett	4.00	3.00	1.50
601	Ed Lynch	.08	.06	.03
602	Rich Gedman	.12	.09	.05
603	Joe Morgan	.60	.45	.25
604	Super Veteran (Joe Morgan)	.15	.11	.06
605	Gary Roenicke	.08	.06	.03
606	Bobby Cox	.08	.06	.03
607	Charlie Leibrandt	.10	.08	.04
608	Don Money	.08	.06	.03
609	Danny Darwin	.08	.06	.03
610	Steve Garvey	.70	.50	.30
611	Bert Roberge	.08	.06	.03
612	Steve Swisher	.08	.06	.03
613	Mike Ivie	.08	.06	.03
614	Ed Glynn	.08	.06	.03
615	Garry Maddox	.12	.09	.05
616	Bill Nahorodny	.08	.06	.03
617	Butch Wynegar	.08	.06	.03
618	LaMarr Hoyt	.08	.06	.03

#	Name	MT	NR MT	EX
619	Keith Moreland	.10	.08	.04
620	Mike Norris	.08	.06	.03
621	Mets Batting & Pitching Ldrs. (Craig Swan, Mookie Wilson)	.12	.09	.05
622	Dave Edler	.08	.06	.03
623	Luis Sanchez	.08	.06	.03
624	Glenn Hubbard	.10	.08	.04
625	Ken Forsch	.08	.06	.03
626	Jerry Martin	.08	.06	.03
627	Doug Bair	.08	.06	.03
628	Julio Valdez	.08	.06	.03
629	Charlie Lea	.08	.06	.03
630	Paul Molitor	.30	.25	.12
631	Tippy Martinez	.08	.06	.03
632	Alex Trevino	.08	.06	.03
633	Vicente Romo	.08	.06	.03
634	Max Venable	.08	.06	.03
635	Graig Nettles	.20	.15	.08
636	Super Veteran (Graig Nettles)	.12	.09	.05
637	Pat Corrales	.08	.06	.03
638	Dan Petry	.10	.08	.04
639	Art Howe	.08	.06	.03
640	Andre Thornton	.12	.09	.05
641	Billy Sample	.08	.06	.03
642	Checklist 529-660	.12	.09	.05
643	Bump Wills	.08	.06	.03
644	Joe Lefebvre	.08	.06	.03
645	Bill Madlock	.15	.11	.06
646	Jim Essian	.08	.06	.03
647	Bobby Mitchell	.08	.06	.03
648	Jeff Burroughs	.10	.08	.04
649	Tommy Boggs	.08	.06	.03
650	George Hendrick	.10	.08	.04
651	Angels Batting & Pitching Ldrs. (Rod Carew, Mike Witt)	.30	.25	.12
652	Butch Hobson	.08	.06	.03
653	Ellis Valentine	.08	.06	.03
654	Bob Ojeda	.15	.11	.06
655	Al Bumbry	.10	.08	.04
656	Dave Frost	.08	.06	.03
657	Mike Gates	.08	.06	.03
658	Frank Pastore	.08	.06	.03
659	Charlie Moore	.08	.06	.03
660	Mike Hargrove	.08	.06	.03
661	Bill Russell	.10	.08	.04
662	Joe Sambito	.08	.06	.03
663	Tom O'Malley	.08	.06	.03
664	Bob Molinaro	.08	.06	.03
665	Jim Sundberg	.10	.08	.04
666	Sparky Anderson	.12	.09	.05
667	Dick Davis	.08	.06	.03
668	Larry Christenson	.08	.06	.03
669	Mike Squires	.08	.06	.03
670	Jerry Mumphrey	.08	.06	.03
671	Lenny Faedo	.08	.06	.03
672	Jim Kaat	.20	.15	.08
673	Super Veteran (Jim Kaat)	.12	.09	.05
674	Kurt Bevacqua	.08	.06	.03
675	Jim Beattie	.08	.06	.03
676	Biff Pocoroba	.08	.06	.03
677	Dave Revering	.08	.06	.03
678	Juan Beniquez	.08	.06	.03
679	Mike Scott	.20	.15	.08
680	Andre Dawson	2.00	1.50	.80
681	Dodgers Batting & Pitching Ldrs. (Pedro Guerrero, Fernando Valenzuela)	.25	.20	.10
682	Bob Stanley	.08	.06	.03
683	Dan Ford	.08	.06	.03
684	Rafael Landestoy	.08	.06	.03
685	Lee Mazzilli	.10	.08	.04
686	Randy Lerch	.08	.06	.03
687	U.L. Washington	.08	.06	.03
688	Jim Wohlford	.08	.06	.03
689	Ron Hassey	.08	.06	.03
690	Kent Hrbek	.70	.50	.30
691	Dave Tobik	.08	.06	.03
692	Denny Walling	.08	.06	.03
693	Sparky Lyle	.12	.09	.05
694	Super Veteran (Sparky Lyle)	.10	.08	.04
695	Ruppert Jones	.08	.06	.03
696	Chuck Tanner	.08	.06	.03
697	Barry Foote	.08	.06	.03
698	Tony Bernazard	.08	.06	.03
699	Lee Smith	2.50	2.00	1.00
700	Keith Hernandez	.50	.40	.20
701	Batting Leaders (Al Oliver, Willie Wilson)	.15	.11	.06
702	Home Run Leaders (Reggie Jackson, Dave Kingman, Gorman Thomas)	.25	.20	.10
703	Runs Batted In Leaders (Hal McRae, Dale Murphy, Al Oliver)	.35	.25	.14
704	Stolen Base Leaders (Rickey Henderson, Tim Raines)	.35	.25	.14
705	Victory Leaders (Steve Carlton, LaMarr Hoyt)	.20	.15	.08
706	Strikeout Leaders (Floyd Bannister, Steve Carlton)	.20	.15	.08
707	Earned Run Average Leaders (Steve Rogers, Rick Sutcliffe)	.12	.09	.05
708	Leading Firemen (Dan Quisenberry, Bruce Sutter)	.15	.11	.06
709	Jimmy Sexton	.08	.06	.03
710	Willie Wilson	.20	.15	.08
711	Mariners Batting & Pitching Ldrs. (Jim Beattie, Bruce Bochte)	.12	.09	.05
712	Bruce Kison	.08	.06	.03
713	Ron Hodges	.08	.06	.03
714	Wayne Nordhagen	.08	.06	.03
715	Tony Perez	.25	.20	.10
716	Super Veteran (Tony Perez)	.12	.09	.05
717	Scott Sanderson	.08	.06	.03
718	Jim Dwyer	.08	.06	.03
719	Rich Gale	.08	.06	.03
720	Dave Concepcion	.15	.11	.06
721	John Martin	.08	.06	.03
722	Jorge Orta	.08	.06	.03
723	Randy Moffitt	.08	.06	.03
724	Johnny Grubb	.08	.06	.03
725	Dan Spillner	.08	.06	.03
726	Harvey Kuenn	.10	.08	.04
727	Chet Lemon	.10	.08	.04
728	Ron Reed	.08	.06	.03
729	Jerry Morales	.08	.06	.03
730	Jason Thompson	.08	.06	.03
731	Al Williams	.08	.06	.03
732	Dave Henderson	.15	.11	.06
733	Buck Martinez	.08	.06	.03
734	Steve Braun	.08	.06	.03
735	Tommy John	.25	.20	.10
736	Super Veteran (Tommy John)	.12	.09	.05
737	Mitchell Page	.08	.06	.03
738	Tim Foli	.08	.06	.03
739	Rick Ownbey	.08	.06	.03
740	Rusty Staub	.15	.11	.06
741	Super Veteran (Rusty Staub)	.10	.08	.04
742	Padres Batting & Pitching Ldrs. (Terry Kennedy, Tim Lollar)	.12	.09	.05
743	Mike Torrez	.10	.08	.04
744	Brad Mills	.08	.06	.03
745	Scott McGregor	.10	.08	.04
746	John Wathan	.10	.08	.04
747	Fred Breining	.08	.06	.03
748	Derrel Thomas	.08	.06	.03
749	Jon Matlack	.10	.08	.04
750	Ben Oglivie	.10	.08	.04
751	Brad Havens	.08	.06	.03
752	Luis Pujols	.08	.06	.03
753	Elias Sosa	.08	.06	.03
754	Bill Robinson	.08	.06	.03
755	John Candelaria	.12	.09	.05
756	Russ Nixon	.08	.06	.03
757	Rick Manning	.08	.06	.03
758	Aurelio Rodriguez	.10	.08	.04
759	Doug Bird	.08	.06	.03
760	Dale Murphy	1.25	.90	.50
761	Gary Lucas	.08	.06	.03
762	Cliff Johnson	.08	.06	.03
763	Al Cowens	.08	.06	.03
764	Pete Falcone	.08	.06	.03
765	Bob Boone	.12	.09	.05
766	Barry Bonnell	.08	.06	.03
767	Duane Kuiper	.08	.06	.03
768	Chris Speier	.08	.06	.03
769	Checklist 661-792	.12	.09	.05
770	Dave Winfield	3.00	2.25	1.25
771	Twins Batting & Pitching Ldrs. (Bobby Castillo, Kent Hrbek)	.20	.15	.08
772	Jim Kern	.08	.06	.03
773	Larry Hisle	.10	.08	.04
774	Alan Ashby	.08	.06	.03
775	Burt Hooton	.10	.08	.04
776	Larry Parrish	.12	.09	.05
777	John Curtis	.08	.06	.03
778	Rich Hebner	.08	.06	.03
779	Rick Waits	.08	.06	.03
780	Gary Matthews	.12	.09	.05
781	Rick Rhoden	.12	.09	.05
782	Bobby Murcer	.12	.09	.05
783	Super Veteran (Bobby Murcer)	.10	.08	.04
784	Jeff Newman	.08	.06	.03
785	Dennis Leonard	.10	.08	.04
786	Ralph Houk	.10	.08	.04

		MT	NR MT	EX
787	Dick Tidrow	.08	.06	.03
788	Dane Iorg	.08	.06	.03
789	Bryan Clark	.08	.06	.03
790	Bob Grich	.12	.09	.05
791	Gary Lavelle	.08	.06	.03
792	Chris Chambliss	.10	.08	.04

1983 Topps All-Star Glossy Set Of 40

This set was a "consolation prize" in a scratch-off contest in regular packs of 1983 cards. The 2-1/2" by 3-1/2" cards have a large color photo surrounded by a yellow frame on the front. In very small type on a white border is printed the player's name. Backs carry the player's name, team, position and the card number along with a Topps identification. A major feature is that the surface of the front is glossy, which most collectors find very attractive. With many top stars, the set is a popular one, but the price has not moved too far above the issue price.

		MT	NR MT	EX
Complete Set:		13.00	9.75	5.25
Common Player:		.15	.11	.06
1	Carl Yastrzemski	1.00	.70	.40
2	Mookie Wilson	.15	.11	.06
3	Andre Thornton	.15	.11	.06
4	Keith Hernandez	.40	.30	.15
5	Robin Yount	.40	.30	.15
6	Terry Kennedy	.15	.11	.06
7	Dave Winfield	.60	.45	.25
8	Mike Schmidt	1.00	.70	.40
9	Buddy Bell	.20	.15	.08
10	Fernando Valenzuela	.50	.40	.20
11	Rich Gossage	.25	.20	.10
12	Bob Horner	.20	.15	.08
13	Toby Harrah	.15	.11	.06
14	Pete Rose	1.25	.90	.50
15	Cecil Cooper	.20	.15	.08
16	Dale Murphy	1.00	.70	.40
17	Carlton Fisk	.30	.25	.12
18	Ray Knight	.15	.11	.06
19	Jim Palmer	.40	.30	.15
20	Gary Carter	.50	.40	.20
21	Richard Zisk	.15	.11	.06
22	Dusty Baker	.15	.11	.06
23	Willie Wilson	.20	.15	.08
24	Bill Buckner	.15	.11	.06
25	Dave Stieb	.20	.15	.08
26	Bill Madlock	.20	.15	.08
27	Lance Parrish	.30	.25	.12
28	Nolan Ryan	1.00	.70	.40
29	Rod Carew	.60	.45	.25
30	Al Oliver	.20	.15	.08
31	George Brett	1.00	.70	.40
32	Jack Clark	.25	.20	.10
33	Rickey Henderson	.70	.50	.30
34	Dave Concepcion	.20	.15	.08
35	Kent Hrbek	.30	.25	.12
36	Steve Carlton	.50	.40	.20
37	Eddie Murray	.60	.45	.25
38	Ruppert Jones	.15	.11	.06
39	Reggie Jackson	.70	.50	.30
40	Bruce Sutter	.20	.15	.08

1983 Topps Foldouts

Another Topps test issue, these 3-1/2" by 5-5/16" cards were printed in booklets like souvenir postcards. Each of the booklets have a theme of currently playing statistical leaders in a specific category such as home runs. The cards feature a color player photo on each side. A black strip at the bottom gives the player's name, position and team along with statistics in the particular category. A facsimile autograph crosses the photograph. Booklets carry nine cards, with eight having players on both sides and one doubling as the back cover, for a total of 17 cards per booklet. There are 85 cards in the set, although some players appear in more than one category. Naturally, most of the players pictured are stars. Even so, the set is a problem as it seems to be most valuable when complete and unseparated, so the cards are difficult to display.

		MT	NR MT	EX
Complete Set:		10.00	7.50	4.00
Common Folder:		1.25	.90	.50
1	Pitching Leaders (Vida Blue, Bert Blyleven, Steve Carlton, Fergie Jenkins, Tommy John, Jim Kaat, Jerry Koosman, Joe Niekro, Phil Niekro, Jim Palmer, Gaylord Perry, Jerry Reuss, Nolan Ryan, Tom Seaver, Paul Splittorff, Don Sutton, Mike Torrez)			
		1.75	1.25	.70
2	Home Run Leaders (Johnny Bench, Ron Cey, Darrell Evans, George Foster, Reggie Jackson, Dave Kingman, Greg Luzinski, John Mayberry, Rick Monday, Joe Morgan, Bobby Murcer, Graig Nettles, Tony Perez, Jim Rice, Mike Schmidt, Rusty Staub, Carl Yastrzemski)			
		2.50	2.00	1.00
3	Batting Leaders (George Brett, Rod Carew, Cecil Cooper, Steve Garvey, Ken Griffey, Pedro Guerrero, Keith Hernandez, Dane Iorg, Fred Lynn, Bill Madlock, Bake McBride, Al Oliver, Dave Parker, Jim Rice, Pete Rose, Lonnie Smith, Willie Wilson)			
		2.50	2.00	1.00
4	Relief Aces (Tom Burgmeier, Bill Campbell, Ed Farmer, Rollie Fingers, Terry Forster, Gene Garber, Rich Gossage, Jim Kern, Gary Lavelle, Tug McGraw, Greg Minton, Randy Moffitt, Dan Quisenberry, Ron Reed, Elias Sosa, Bruce Sutter, Kent Tekulve)			
		1.25	.90	.50
5	Stolen Base Leaders (Don Baylor, Larry Bowa, Al Bumbry, Rod Carew, Cesar Cedeno, Dave Concepcion, Jose Cruz, Julio Cruz, Rickey Henderson, Ron LeFlore, Davey Lopes, Garry Maddox, Omar Moreno, Joe Morgan, Amos Otis, Mickey Rivers, Willie Wilson)			
		1.25	.90	.50

Regional interest may affect the value of a card.

1983 Topps Stickers

Topps increased the number of stickers in its set to 220 in 1983, but retained the same 1-15/16" by 2-9/16" size. The stickers are again numbered on both the front and back. Similar in style to previous sticker issues, the set includes 28 "foil" stickers, and various special stickers highlighting the 1982 season, playoffs and World Series. An album was also available.

		MT	NR MT	EX
Complete Set:		15.00	11.00	6.00
Common Player:		.03	.02	.01
Sticker Album:		.80	.60	.30
1	Hank Aaron	.40	.30	.15
2	Babe Ruth	.60	.45	.25
3	Willie Mays	.40	.30	.15
4	Frank Robinson	.30	.25	.12
5	Reggie Jackson	.20	.15	.08
6	Carl Yastrzemski	.25	.20	.10
7	Johnny Bench	.20	.15	.08
8	Tony Perez	.10	.08	.04
9	Lee May	.06	.05	.02
10	Mike Schmidt	.25	.20	.10
11	Dave Kingman	.08	.06	.03
12	Reggie Smith	.06	.05	.02
13	Graig Nettles	.06	.05	.02
14	Rusty Staub	.06	.05	.02
15	Willie Wilson	.06	.05	.02
16	LaMarr Hoyt	.03	.02	.01
17	Reggie Jackson, Gorman Thomas	.15	.11	.06
18	Floyd Bannister	.04	.03	.02
19	Hal McRae	.06	.05	.02
20	Rick Sutcliffe	.08	.06	.03
21	Rickey Henderson	.25	.20	.10
22	Dan Quisenberry	.06	.05	.02
23	Jim Palmer	.30	.25	.12
24	John Lowenstein	.03	.02	.01
25	Mike Flanagan	.04	.03	.02
26	Cal Ripken	.20	.15	.08
27	Rich Dauer	.03	.02	.01
28	Ken Singleton	.06	.05	.02
29	Eddie Murray	.20	.15	.08
30	Rick Dempsey	.04	.03	.02
31	Carl Yastrzemski	.40	.30	.15
32	Carney Lansford	.06	.05	.02
33	Jerry Remy	.03	.02	.01
34	Dennis Eckersley	.06	.05	.02
35	Dave Stapleton	.03	.02	.01
36	Mark Clear	.03	.02	.01
37	Jim Rice	.20	.15	.08
38	Dwight Evans	.08	.06	.03
39	Rod Carew	.20	.15	.08
40	Don Baylor	.08	.06	.03
41	Reggie Jackson	.40	.30	.15
42	Geoff Zahn	.03	.02	.01
43	Bobby Grich	.06	.05	.02
44	Fred Lynn	.10	.08	.04
45	Bob Boone	.04	.03	.02
46	Doug DeCinces	.06	.05	.02
47	Tom Paciorek	.03	.02	.01
48	Britt Burns	.03	.02	.01
49	Tony Bernazard	.03	.02	.01
50	Steve Kemp	.04	.03	.02
51	Greg Luzinski	.20	.15	.08
52	Harold Baines	.10	.08	.04
53	LaMarr Hoyt	.03	.02	.01
54	Carlton Fisk	.12	.09	.05
55	Andre Thornton	.15	.11	.06

		MT	NR MT	EX
56	Mike Hargrove	.04	.03	.02
57	Len Barker	.03	.02	.01
58	Toby Harrah	.04	.03	.02
59	Dan Spillner	.03	.02	.01
60	Rick Manning	.03	.02	.01
61	Rick Sutcliffe	.08	.06	.03
62	Ron Hassey	.03	.02	.01
63	Lance Parrish	.30	.25	.12
64	John Wockenfuss	.03	.02	.01
65	Lou Whitaker	.12	.09	.05
66	Alan Trammell	.15	.11	.06
67	Kirk Gibson	.15	.11	.06
68	Larry Herndon	.03	.02	.01
69	Jack Morris	.12	.09	.05
70	Dan Petry	.04	.03	.02
71	Frank White	.06	.05	.02
72	Amos Otis	.04	.03	.02
73	Willie Wilson	.25	.20	.10
74	Dan Quisenberry	.06	.05	.02
75	Hal McRae	.06	.05	.02
76	George Brett	.25	.20	.10
77	Larry Gura	.03	.02	.01
78	John Wathan	.04	.03	.02
79	Rollie Fingers	.10	.08	.04
80	Cecil Cooper	.08	.06	.03
81	Robin Yount	.30	.25	.12
82	Ben Oglivie	.06	.05	.02
83	Paul Molitor	.10	.08	.04
84	Gorman Thomas	.06	.05	.02
85	Ted Simmons	.06	.05	.02
86	Pete Vuckovich	.04	.03	.02
87	Gary Gaetti	.08	.06	.03
88	Kent Hrbek	.30	.25	.12
89	John Castino	.03	.02	.01
90	Tom Brunansky	.06	.05	.02
91	Bobby Mitchell	.03	.02	.01
92	Gary Ward	.04	.03	.02
93	Tim Laudner	.03	.02	.01
94	Ron Davis	.03	.02	.01
95	Willie Randolph	.06	.05	.02
96	Roy Smalley	.03	.02	.01
97	Jerry Mumphrey	.03	.02	.01
98	Ken Griffey	.06	.05	.02
99	Dave Winfield	.30	.25	.12
100	Rich Gossage	.10	.08	.04
101	Butch Wynegar	.04	.03	.02
102	Ron Guidry	.12	.09	.05
103	Rickey Henderson	.40	.30	.15
104	Mike Heath	.03	.02	.01
105	Dave Lopes	.06	.05	.02
106	Rick Langford	.03	.02	.01
107	Dwayne Murphy	.04	.03	.02
108	Tony Armas	.06	.05	.02
109	Matt Keough	.03	.02	.01
110	Dan Meyer	.03	.02	.01
111	Bruce Bochte	.03	.02	.01
112	Julio Cruz	.03	.02	.01
113	Floyd Bannister	.04	.03	.02
114	Gaylord Perry	.30	.25	.12
115	Al Cowens	.03	.02	.01
116	Richie Zisk	.04	.03	.02
117	Jim Essian	.03	.02	.01
118	Bill Caudill	.03	.02	.01
119	Buddy Bell	.20	.15	.08
120	Larry Parrish	.06	.05	.02
121	Danny Darwin	.03	.02	.01
122	Bucky Dent	.04	.03	.02
123	Johnny Grubb	.03	.02	.01
124	George Wright	.03	.02	.01
125	Charlie Hough	.06	.05	.02
126	Jim Sundberg	.04	.03	.02
127	Dave Stieb	.20	.15	.08
128	Willie Upshaw	.06	.05	.02
129	Alfredo Griffin	.04	.03	.02
130	Lloyd Moseby	.06	.05	.02
131	Ernie Whitt	.03	.02	.01
132	Jim Clancy	.04	.03	.02
133	Barry Bonnell	.03	.02	.01
134	Damaso Garcia	.04	.03	.02
135	Jim Kaat	.08	.06	.03
136	Jim Kaat	.06	.05	.02
137	Greg Minton	.03	.02	.01
138	Greg Minton	.03	.02	.01
139	Paul Molitor	.10	.08	.04
140	Paul Molitor	.08	.06	.03
141	Manny Trillo	.04	.03	.02
142	Manny Trillo	.04	.03	.02
143	Joel Youngblood	.03	.02	.01
144	Joel Youngblood	.03	.02	.01
145	Robin Yount	.15	.11	.06
146	Robin Yount	.12	.09	.05

#	Name	MT	NR MT	EX
147	Willie McGee	.08	.06	.03
148	Darrell Porter	.04	.03	.02
149	Darrell Porter	.04	.03	.02
150	Robin Yount	.15	.11	.06
151	Bruce Benedict	.03	.02	.01
152	Bruce Benedict	.03	.02	.01
153	George Hendrick	.04	.03	.02
154	Bruce Benedict	.03	.02	.01
155	Doug DeCinces	.06	.05	.02
156	Paul Molitor	.10	.08	.04
157	Charlie Moore	.03	.02	.01
158	Fred Lynn	.10	.08	.04
159	Rickey Henderson	.20	.15	.08
160	Dale Murphy	.25	.20	.10
161	Willie Wilson	.08	.06	.03
162	Jack Clark	.10	.08	.04
163	Reggie Jackson	.20	.15	.08
164	Andre Dawson	.15	.11	.06
165	Dan Quisenberry	.06	.05	.02
166	Bruce Sutter	.08	.06	.03
167	Robin Yount	.15	.11	.06
168	Ozzie Smith	.10	.08	.04
169	Frank White	.06	.05	.02
170	Phil Garner	.04	.03	.02
171	Doug DeCinces	.06	.05	.02
172	Mike Schmidt	.25	.20	.10
173	Cecil Cooper	.06	.05	.02
174	Al Oliver	.06	.05	.02
175	Jim Palmer	.15	.11	.06
176	Steve Carlton	.15	.11	.06
177	Carlton Fisk	.12	.09	.05
178	Gary Carter	.20	.15	.08
179	Joaquin Andujar	.04	.03	.02
180	Ozzie Smith	.10	.08	.04
181	Cecil Cooper	.06	.05	.02
182	Darrell Porter	.04	.03	.02
183	Darrell Porter	.04	.03	.02
184	Mike Caldwell	.03	.02	.01
185	Mike Caldwell	.03	.02	.01
186	Ozzie Smith	.10	.08	.04
187	Bruce Sutter	.08	.06	.03
188	Keith Hernandez	.12	.09	.05
189	Dane Iorg	.03	.02	.01
190	Dane Iorg	.03	.02	.01
191	Tony Armas	.04	.03	.02
192	Tony Armas	.04	.03	.02
193	Lance Parrish	.12	.09	.05
194	Lance Parrish	.12	.09	.05
195	John Wathan	.04	.03	.02
196	John Wathan	.04	.03	.02
197	Rickey Henderson	.12	.09	.05
198	Rickey Henderson	.12	.09	.05
199	Rickey Henderson	.12	.09	.05
200	Rickey Henderson	.12	.09	.05
201	Rickey Henderson	.12	.09	.05
202	Rickey Henderson	.12	.09	.05
203	Steve Carlton	.15	.11	.06
204	Steve Carlton	.12	.09	.05
205	Al Oliver	.06	.05	.02
206	Dale Murphy, Al Oliver	.20	.15	.08
207	Dave Kingman	.08	.06	.03
208	Steve Rogers	.04	.03	.02
209	Bruce Sutter	.08	.06	.03
210	Tim Raines	.20	.15	.08
211	Dale Murphy	.40	.30	.15
212	Chris Chambliss	.04	.03	.02
213	Gene Garber	.03	.02	.01
214	Bob Horner	.08	.06	.03
215	Glenn Hubbard	.03	.02	.01
216	Claudell Washington	.04	.03	.02
217	Bruce Benedict	.03	.02	.01
218	Phil Niekro	.12	.09	.05
219	Leon Durham	.20	.15	.08
220	Jay Johnstone	.04	.03	.02
221	Larry Bowa	.06	.05	.02
222	Keith Moreland	.06	.05	.02
223	Bill Buckner	.06	.05	.02
224	Fergie Jenkins	.08	.06	.03
225	Dick Tidrow	.03	.02	.01
226	Jody Davis	.06	.05	.02
227	Dave Concepcion	.06	.05	.02
228	Dan Driessen	.04	.03	.02
229	Johnny Bench	.20	.15	.08
230	Ron Oester	.03	.02	.01
231	Cesar Cedeno	.06	.05	.02
232	Alex Trevino	.03	.02	.01
233	Tom Seaver	.20	.15	.08
234	Mario Soto	.20	.15	.08
235	Nolan Ryan	.30	.25	.12
236	Art Howe	.03	.02	.01
237	Phil Garner	.04	.03	.02
238	Ray Knight	.06	.05	.02
239	Terry Puhl	.03	.02	.01
240	Joe Niekro	.06	.05	.02
241	Alan Ashby	.03	.02	.01
242	Jose Cruz	.06	.05	.02
243	Steve Garvey	.20	.15	.08
244	Ron Cey	.06	.05	.02
245	Dusty Baker	.04	.03	.02
246	Ken Landreaux	.03	.02	.01
247	Jerry Reuss	.06	.05	.02
248	Pedro Guerrero	.12	.09	.05
249	Bill Russell	.04	.03	.02
250	Fernando Valenzuela	.30	.25	.12
251	Al Oliver	.25	.20	.10
252	Andre Dawson	.15	.11	.06
253	Tim Raines	.20	.15	.08
254	Jeff Reardon	.08	.06	.03
255	Gary Carter	.20	.15	.08
256	Steve Rogers	.03	.02	.01
257	Tim Wallach	.08	.06	.03
258	Chris Speier	.03	.02	.01
259	Dave Kingman	.08	.06	.03
260	Bob Bailor	.03	.02	.01
261	Hubie Brooks	.06	.05	.02
262	Craig Swan	.03	.02	.01
263	George Foster	.08	.06	.03
264	John Stearns	.03	.02	.01
265	Neil Allen	.03	.02	.01
266	Mookie Wilson	.20	.15	.08
267	Steve Carlton	.30	.25	.12
268	Manny Trillo	.04	.03	.02
269	Gary Matthews	.06	.05	.02
270	Mike Schmidt	.25	.20	.10
271	Ivan DeJesus	.03	.02	.01
272	Pete Rose	.40	.30	.15
273	Bo Diaz	.04	.03	.02
274	Sid Monge	.03	.02	.01
275	Bill Madlock	.25	.20	.10
276	Jason Thompson	.03	.02	.01
277	Don Robinson	.03	.02	.01
278	Omar Moreno	.03	.02	.01
279	Dale Berra	.03	.02	.01
280	Dave Parker	.10	.08	.04
281	Tony Pena	.06	.05	.02
282	John Candelaria	.06	.05	.02
283	Lonnie Smith	.04	.03	.02
284	Bruce Sutter	.25	.20	.10
285	George Hendrick	.04	.03	.02
286	Tom Herr	.06	.05	.02
287	Ken Oberkfell	.03	.02	.01
288	Ozzie Smith	.10	.08	.04
289	Bob Forsch	.04	.03	.02
290	Keith Hernandez	.15	.11	.06
291	Garry Templeton	.06	.05	.02
292	Broderick Perkins	.03	.02	.01
293	Terry Kennedy	.20	.15	.08
294	Gene Richards	.03	.02	.01
295	Ruppert Jones	.03	.02	.01
296	Tim Lollar	.03	.02	.01
297	John Montefusco	.03	.02	.01
298	Sixto Lezcano	.03	.02	.01
299	Greg Minton	.03	.02	.01
300	Jack Clark	.25	.20	.10
301	Milt May	.03	.02	.01
302	Reggie Smith	.06	.05	.02
303	Joe Morgan	.10	.08	.04
304	John LeMaster	.03	.02	.01
305	Darrell Evans	.08	.06	.03
306	Al Holland	.03	.02	.01
307	Jesse Barfield	.08	.06	.03
308	Wade Boggs	.60	.45	.25
309	Tom Brunansky	.06	.05	.02
310	Storm Davis	.04	.03	.02
311	Von Hayes	.06	.05	.02
312	Dave Hostetler	.03	.02	.01
313	Kent Hrbek	.12	.09	.05
314	Tim Laudner	.03	.02	.01
315	Cal Ripken	.20	.15	.08
316	Andre Robertson	.03	.02	.01
317	Ed Vande Berg	.03	.02	.01
318	Glenn Wilson	.04	.03	.02
319	Chili Davis	.06	.05	.02
320	Bob Dernier	.03	.02	.01
321	Terry Francona	.03	.02	.01
322	Brian Giles	.03	.02	.01
323	David Green	.03	.02	.01
324	Atlee Hammaker	.03	.02	.01
325	Bill Laskey	.03	.02	.01
326	Willie McGee	.12	.09	.05
327	Johnny Ray	.06	.05	.02
328	Ryne Sandberg	.25	.20	.10

		MT	NR MT	EX
329	Steve Sax	.10	.08	.04
330	Eric Show	.04	.03	.02

1983 Topps Stickers Boxes

These eight cards were printed on the back panels of 1983 Topps sticker boxes, on card per box. The blank-backed cards measure the standard 2-1/2" by 3-1/2" and feature a full-color photo with the player's name at the top. The rest of the back panel advertises the sticker album, while the front of the box has an action photo of Reggie Jackson. The boxes are numbered on the front. Prices in the checklist that follows are for complete boxes.

		MT	NR MT	EX
Complete Set:		6.50	5.00	2.50
Common Player:		.75	.60	.30
1	Fernando Valenzuela	1.00	.70	.40
2	Gary Carter	1.25	.90	.50
3	Mike Schmidt	1.25	.90	.50
4	Reggie Jackson	1.25	.90	.50
5	Jim Palmer	1.00	.70	.40
6	Rollie Fingers	.75	.60	.30
7	Pete Rose	1.50	1.25	.60
8	Rickey Henderson	1.25	.90	.50

1983 Topps Traded

These 2-1/2" by 3-1/2" cards mark a continuation of the traded set introduced in 1981. The 132 cards retain the basic design of the year's regular issue, with their numbering being 1-132 with the "T" suffix. Cards in the set include traded players, new managers and promising rookies. Sold only through dealers, the set was in heavy demand as it contained the first cards of Darryl Strawberry, Ron Kittle, Julio Franco and Mel Hall. While some of those cards were very hot in 1983, it seems likely that some of the rookies may not live up to their initial promise.

	MT	NR MT	EX
Complete Set:	110.00	82.00	45.00

		MT	NR MT	EX
Common Player:		.10	.08	.04
1T	Neil Allen	.10	.08	.04
2T	Bill Almon	.10	.08	.04
3T	Joe Altobelli	.10	.08	.04
4T	Tony Armas	.20	.15	.08
5T	Doug Bair	.10	.08	.04
6T	Steve Baker	.10	.08	.04
7T	Floyd Bannister	.20	.15	.08
8T	Don Baylor	.30	.25	.12
9T	Tony Bernazard	.10	.08	.04
10T	Larry Biittner	.10	.08	.04
11T	Dann Bilardello	.10	.08	.04
12T	Doug Bird	.10	.08	.04
13T	Steve Boros	.10	.08	.04
14T	Greg Brock(FC)	.30	.25	.12
15T	Mike Brown	.10	.08	.04
16T	Tom Burgmeier	.10	.08	.04
17T	Randy Bush(FC)	.20	.15	.08
18T	Bert Campaneris	.20	.15	.08
19T	Ron Cey	.25	.20	.10
20T	Chris Codiroli(FC)	.15	.11	.06
21T	Dave Collins	.15	.11	.06
22T	Terry Crowley	.10	.08	.04
23T	Julio Cruz	.10	.08	.04
24T	Mike Davis	.15	.11	.06
25T	Frank DiPino	.10	.08	.04
26T	Bill Doran(FC)	2.00	1.50	.80
27T	Jerry Dybzinski	.10	.08	.04
28T	Jamie Easterly	.10	.08	.04
29T	Juan Eichelberger	.10	.08	.04
30T	Jim Essian	.10	.08	.04
31T	Pete Falcone	.10	.08	.04
32T	Mike Ferraro	.10	.08	.04
33T	Terry Forster	.15	.11	.06
34T	Julio Franco(FC)	10.00	7.50	4.00
35T	Rich Gale	.10	.08	.04
36T	Kiko Garcia	.10	.08	.04
37T	Steve Garvey	1.50	1.25	.60
38T	Johnny Grubb	.10	.08	.04
39T	Mel Hall(FC)	2.50	2.00	1.00
40T	Von Hayes	1.00	.70	.40
41T	Danny Heep	.10	.08	.04
42T	Steve Henderson	.10	.08	.04
43T	Keith Hernandez	1.00	.70	.40
44T	Leo Hernandez	.10	.08	.04
45T	Willie Hernandez	.25	.20	.10
46T	Al Holland	.10	.08	.04
47T	Frank Howard	.15	.11	.06
48T	Bobby Johnson	.10	.08	.04
49T	Cliff Johnson	.10	.08	.04
50T	Odell Jones	.10	.08	.04
51T	Mike Jorgensen	.10	.08	.04
52T	Bob Kearney	.10	.08	.04
53T	Steve Kemp	.15	.11	.06
54T	Matt Keough	.10	.08	.04
55T	Ron Kittle(FC)	.30	.25	.12
56T	Mickey Klutts	.10	.08	.04
57T	Alan Knicely	.10	.08	.04
58T	Mike Krukow	.15	.11	.06
59T	Rafael Landestoy	.10	.08	.04
60T	Carney Lansford	.30	.25	.12
61T	Joe Lefebvre	.10	.08	.04
62T	Bryan Little	.10	.08	.04
63T	Aurelio Lopez	.10	.08	.04
64T	Mike Madden	.10	.08	.04
65T	Rick Manning	.10	.08	.04
66T	Billy Martin	.20	.15	.08
67T	Lee Mazzilli	.15	.11	.06
68T	Andy McGaffigan	.10	.08	.04
69T	Craig McMurtry(FC)	.20	.15	.08
70T	John McNamara	.10	.08	.04
71T	Orlando Mercado	.10	.08	.04
72T	Larry Milbourne	.10	.08	.04
73T	Randy Moffitt	.10	.08	.04
74T	Sid Monge	.10	.08	.04
75T	Jose Morales	.10	.08	.04
76T	Omar Moreno	.10	.08	.04
77T	Joe Morgan	3.00	2.25	1.25
78T	Mike Morgan	.10	.08	.04
79T	Dale Murray	.10	.08	.04
80T	Jeff Newman	.10	.08	.04
81T	Pete O'Brien(FC)	1.00	.70	.40
82T	Jorge Orta	.10	.08	.04
83T	Alejandro Pena(FC)	1.00	.70	.40
84T	Pascual Perez	.20	.15	.08
85T	Tony Perez	1.00	.70	.40
86T	Broderick Perkins	.10	.08	.04
87T	Tony Phillips(FC)	2.50	2.00	1.00
88T	Charlie Puleo	.10	.08	.04
89T	Pat Putnam	.10	.08	.04
90T	Jamie Quirk	.10	.08	.04
91T	Doug Rader	.10	.08	.04

		MT	NR MT	EX
92T	Chuck Rainey	.10	.08	.04
93T	Bobby Ramos	.10	.08	.04
94T	Gary Redus(FC)	.30	.25	.12
95T	Steve Renko	.10	.08	.04
96T	Leon Roberts	.10	.08	.04
97T	Aurelio Rodriguez	.15	.11	.06
98T	Dick Ruthven	.10	.08	.04
99T	Daryl Sconiers	.10	.08	.04
100T	Mike Scott	.70	.50	.30
101T	Tom Seaver	8.50	6.40	3.20
102T	John Shelby(FC)	.25	.20	.10
103T	Bob Shirley	.10	.08	.04
104T	Joe Simpson	.10	.08	.04
105T	Doug Sisk(FC)	.15	.11	.06
106T	Mike Smithson(FC)	.20	.15	.08
107T	Elias Sosa	.10	.08	.04
108T	Darryl Strawberry(FC)	70.00	50.00	30.00
109T	Tom Tellmann	.10	.08	.04
110T	Gene Tenace	.15	.11	.06
111T	Gorman Thomas	.25	.20	.10
112T	Dick Tidrow	.10	.08	.04
113T	Dave Tobik	.10	.08	.04
114T	Wayne Tolleson(FC)	.20	.15	.08
115T	Mike Torrez	.15	.11	.06
116T	Manny Trillo	.15	.11	.06
117T	Steve Trout	.10	.08	.04
118T	Lee Tunnell(FC)	.15	.11	.06
119T	Mike Vail	.10	.08	.04
120T	Ellis Valentine	.10	.08	.04
121T	Tom Veryzer	.10	.08	.04
122T	George Vukovich	.10	.08	.04
123T	Rick Waits	.10	.08	.04
124T	Greg Walker(FC)	.20	.15	.08
125T	Chris Welsh	.10	.08	.04
126T	Len Whitehouse	.10	.08	.04
127T	Eddie Whitson	.15	.11	.06
128T	Jim Wohlford	.10	.08	.04
129T	Matt Young(FC)	.20	.15	.08
130T	Joel Youngblood	.10	.08	.04
131T	Pat Zachry	.10	.08	.04
132T	Checklist 1-132	.10	.08	.04

1984 Topps

Another 792-card regular set from Topps. For the second straight year, the 2-1/2" by 3-1/2" cards featured a color action photo on the front along with a small portrait photo in the lower left. The team name runs in big letters down the left side, while the player's name and position runs under the large action photo. In the upper right-hand corner is the Topps logo. Backs have a team logo in the upper right corner, along with statistics, personal information and a few highlights. The backs have an unusual and hard-to-read red and purple coloring. Specialty cards include past season highlights, team leaders, major league statistical leaders, All-Stars, active career leaders and numbered checklists. Again, promising rookies were saved for the traded set. Late in 1984, Topps introduced a specially boxed "Tiffany" edition of the 1984 set, with the cards printed on white cardboard with a glossy finish. A total of 10,000 sets were produced. Prices for Tiffany edition super- stars can run from six to eight times the value of the "regular" edition, while common cards sell in the 40¢ range.

		MT	NR MT	EX
Complete Set:		90.00	67.00	35.00
Common Player:		.08	.06	.03
1	1983 Highlight (Steve Carlton)	.30	.25	.12
2	1983 Highlight (Rickey Henderson)	1.00	.70	.40
3	1983 Highlight (Dan Quisenberry)	.10	.08	.04
4	1983 Highlight (Steve Carlton, Gaylord Perry, Nolan Ryan)	.30	.25	.12
5	1983 Highlight (Bob Forsch, Dave Righetti, Mike Warren)	.15	.11	.06
6	1983 Highlight (Johnny Bench, Gaylord Perry, Carl Yastrzemski)	.40	.30	.15
7	Gary Lucas	.08	.06	.03
8	*Don Mattingly*(FC)	12.00	9.00	4.75
9	Jim Gott	.10	.08	.04
10	Robin Yount	2.00	1.50	.80
11	Twins Batting & Pitching Leaders (Kent Hrbek, Ken Schrom)	.20	.15	.08
12	Billy Sample	.08	.06	.03
13	Scott Holman	.08	.06	.03
14	Tom Brookens	.08	.06	.03
15	Burt Hooton	.10	.08	.04
16	Omar Moreno	.08	.06	.03
17	John Denny	.08	.06	.03
18	Dale Berra	.08	.06	.03
19	*Ray Fontenot*(FC)	.10	.08	.04
20	Greg Luzinski	.12	.09	.05
21	Joe Altobelli	.08	.06	.03
22	Bryan Clark	.08	.06	.03
23	Keith Moreland	.10	.08	.04
24	John Martin	.08	.06	.03
25	Glenn Hubbard	.10	.08	.04
26	Bud Black	.10	.08	.04
27	Daryl Sconiers	.08	.06	.03
28	Frank Viola	.80	.60	.30
29	Danny Heep	.08	.06	.03
30	Wade Boggs	5.00	3.75	2.00
31	Andy McGaffigan	.08	.06	.03
32	Bobby Ramos	.08	.06	.03
33	Tom Burgmeier	.08	.06	.03
34	Eddie Milner	.08	.06	.03
35	Don Sutton	.30	.25	.12
36	Denny Walling	.08	.06	.03
37	Rangers Batting & Pitching Leaders (Buddy Bell, Rick Honeycutt)	.12	.09	.05
38	Luis DeLeon	.08	.06	.03
39	Garth Iorg	.08	.06	.03
40	Dusty Baker	.12	.09	.05
41	Tony Bernazard	.08	.06	.03
42	Johnny Grubb	.08	.06	.03
43	Ron Reed	.10	.08	.04
44	Jim Morrison	.08	.06	.03
45	Jerry Mumphrey	.08	.06	.03
46	Ray Smith	.08	.06	.03
47	Rudy Law	.08	.06	.03
48	Julio Franco(FC)	2.75	2.10	1.15
49	John Stuper	.08	.06	.03
50	Chris Chambliss	.10	.08	.04
51	Jim Frey	.08	.06	.03
52	Paul Splittorff	.08	.06	.03
53	Juan Beniquez	.08	.06	.03
54	Jesse Orosco	.10	.08	.04
55	Dave Concepcion	.15	.11	.06
56	Gary Allenson	.08	.06	.03
57	Dan Schatzeder	.08	.06	.03
58	Max Venable	.08	.06	.03
59	Sammy Stewart	.08	.06	.03
60	Paul Molitor	.20	.15	.08
61	*Chris Codiroli*	.10	.08	.04
62	Dave Hostetler	.08	.06	.03
63	Ed Vande Berg	.08	.06	.03
64	Mike Scioscia	.08	.06	.03
65	Kirk Gibson	.40	.30	.15
66	Astros Batting & Pitching Leaders (Jose Cruz, Nolan Ryan)	.25	.20	.10
67	Gary Ward	.10	.08	.04
68	Luis Salazar	.08	.06	.03
69	Rod Scurry	.08	.06	.03
70	Gary Matthews	.12	.09	.05
71	Leo Hernandez	.08	.06	.03
72	Mike Squires	.08	.06	.03
73	Jody Davis	.10	.08	.04
74	Jerry Martin	.08	.06	.03
75	Bob Forsch	.10	.08	.04
76	Alfredo Griffin	.10	.08	.04
77	Brett Butler	.10	.08	.04
78	Mike Torrez	.10	.08	.04
79	Rob Wilfong	.08	.06	.03

#	Player	MT	NR MT	EX
80	Steve Rogers	.10	.08	.04
81	Billy Martin	.12	.09	.05
82	Doug Bird	.08	.06	.03
83	Richie Zisk	.10	.08	.04
84	Lenny Faedo	.08	.06	.03
85	Atlee Hammaker	.08	.06	.03
86	*John Shelby*(FC)	.25	.20	.10
87	Frank Pastore	.08	.06	.03
88	Rob Picciolo	.08	.06	.03
89	*Mike Smithson*(FC)	.15	.11	.06
90	Pedro Guerrero	.35	.25	.14
91	Dan Spillner	.08	.06	.03
92	Lloyd Moseby	.12	.09	.05
93	Bob Knepper	.10	.08	.04
94	Mario Ramirez	.08	.06	.03
95	Aurelio Lopez	.08	.06	.03
96	Royals Batting & Pitching Leaders (Larry Gura, Hal McRae)	.10	.08	.04
97	LaMarr Hoyt	.08	.06	.03
98	Steve Nicosia	.08	.06	.03
99	*Craig Lefferts*(FC)	.30	.25	.12
100	Reggie Jackson	1.00	.70	.40
101	Porfirio Altamirano	.08	.06	.03
102	Ken Oberkfell	.08	.06	.03
103	Dwayne Murphy	.10	.08	.04
104	Ken Dayley	.08	.06	.03
105	Tony Armas	.12	.09	.05
106	Tim Stoddard	.08	.06	.03
107	Ned Yost	.08	.06	.03
108	Randy Moffitt	.08	.06	.03
109	Brad Wellman	.08	.06	.03
110	Ron Guidry	.30	.25	.12
111	Bill Virdon	.08	.06	.03
112	Tom Niedenfuer	.10	.08	.04
113	Kelly Paris	.08	.06	.03
114	Checklist 1-132	.08	.06	.03
115	Andre Thornton	.12	.09	.05
116	George Bjorkman	.08	.06	.03
117	Tom Veryzer	.08	.06	.03
118	Charlie Hough	.12	.09	.05
119	Johnny Wockenfuss	.08	.06	.03
120	Keith Hernandez	.40	.30	.15
121	*Pat Sheridan*(FC)	.15	.11	.06
122	Cecilio Guante(FC)	.10	.08	.04
123	Butch Wynegar	.08	.06	.03
124	Damaso Garcia	.08	.06	.03
125	Britt Burns	.08	.06	.03
126	Braves Batting & Pitching Leaders (Craig McMurtry, Dale Murphy)	.25	.20	.10
127	Mike Madden	.08	.06	.03
128	Rick Manning	.08	.06	.03
129	Bill Laskey	.08	.06	.03
130	Ozzie Smith	.70	.50	.30
131	Batting Leaders (Wade Boggs, Bill Madlock)	.50	.40	.20
132	Home Run Leaders (Jim Rice, Mike Schmidt)	.50	.40	.20
133	Runs Batted In Leaders (Cecil Cooper, Dale Murphy, Jim Rice)	.40	.30	.15
134	Stolen Base Leaders (Rickey Henderson, Tim Raines)	.30	.25	.12
135	Victory Leaders (John Denny, LaMarr Hoyt)	.10	.08	.04
136	Strikeout Leaders (Steve Carlton, Jack Morris)	.25	.20	.10
137	Earned Run Average Leaders (Atlee Hammaker, Rick Honeycutt)	.10	.08	.04
138	Leading Firemen (Al Holland, Dan Quisenberry)	.12	.09	.05
139	Bert Campaneris	.12	.09	.05
140	Storm Davis	.12	.09	.05
141	Pat Corrales	.08	.06	.03
142	Rich Gale	.08	.06	.03
143	Jose Morales	.08	.06	.03
144	Brian Harper	.08	.06	.03
145	Gary Lavelle	.08	.06	.03
146	Ed Romero	.08	.06	.03
147	Dan Petry	.10	.08	.04
148	Joe Lefebvre	.08	.06	.03
149	Jon Matlack	.10	.08	.04
150	Dale Murphy	.70	.50	.30
151	Steve Trout	.08	.06	.03
152	Glenn Brummer	.08	.06	.03
153	Dick Tidrow	.08	.06	.03
154	Dave Henderson	.12	.09	.05
155	Frank White	.12	.09	.05
156	Athletics Batting & Pitching Leaders (Tim Conroy, Rickey Henderson)	.25	.20	.10
157	Gary Gaetti	.70	.50	.30
158	John Curtis	.08	.06	.03
159	Darryl Cias	.08	.06	.03
160	Mario Soto	.10	.08	.04
161	*Junior Ortiz*(FC)	.10	.08	.04
162	Bob Ojeda	.12	.09	.05
163	Lorenzo Gray	.08	.06	.03
164	Scott Sanderson	.08	.06	.03
165	Ken Singleton	.12	.09	.05
166	Jamie Nelson	.08	.06	.03
167	Marshall Edwards	.08	.06	.03
168	Juan Bonilla	.08	.06	.03
169	Larry Parrish	.12	.09	.05
170	Jerry Reuss	.12	.09	.05
171	Frank Robinson	.12	.09	.05
172	Frank DiPino	.08	.06	.03
173	*Marvell Wynne*(FC)	.20	.15	.08
174	Juan Berenguer	.08	.06	.03
175	Graig Nettles	.20	.15	.08
176	Lee Smith	.15	.11	.06
177	Jerry Hairston	.08	.06	.03
178	Bill Krueger	.08	.06	.03
179	Buck Martinez	.08	.06	.03
180	Manny Trillo	.10	.08	.04
181	Roy Thomas	.08	.06	.03
182	*Darryl Strawberry*	15.00	11.00	6.00
183	Al Williams	.08	.06	.03
184	Mike O'Berry	.08	.06	.03
185	Sixto Lezcano	.08	.06	.03
186	Cardinals Batting & Pitching Leaders (Lonnie Smith, John Stuper)	.10	.08	.04
187	Luis Aponte	.08	.06	.03
188	Bryan Little	.08	.06	.03
189	*Tim Conroy*(FC)	.12	.09	.05
190	Ben Oglivie	.10	.08	.04
191	Mike Boddicker	.12	.09	.05
192	*Nick Esasky*(FC)	.40	.30	.15
193	Darrell Brown	.08	.06	.03
194	Domingo Ramos	.08	.06	.03
195	Jack Morris	.70	.50	.30
196	Don Slaught(FC)	.12	.09	.05
197	Garry Hancock	.08	.06	.03
198	*Bill Doran*	.80	.60	.30
199	Willie Hernandez	.12	.09	.05
200	Andre Dawson	1.00	.70	.40
201	Bruce Kison	.08	.06	.03
202	Bobby Cox	.08	.06	.03
203	Matt Keough	.08	.06	.03
204	Bobby Meacham(FC)	.15	.11	.06
205	Greg Minton	.08	.06	.03
206	*Andy Van Slyke*(FC)	3.25	2.45	1.35
207	Donnie Moore	.08	.06	.03
208	*Jose Oquendo*(FC)	.15	.11	.06
209	Manny Sarmiento	.08	.06	.03
210	Joe Morgan	.30	.25	.12
211	Rick Sweet	.08	.06	.03
212	Broderick Perkins	.08	.06	.03
213	Bruce Hurst	.15	.11	.06
214	Paul Householder	.08	.06	.03
215	Tippy Martinez	.08	.06	.03
216	White Sox Batting & Pitching Leaders (Richard Dotson, Carlton Fisk)	.15	.11	.06
217	Alan Ashby	.08	.06	.03
218	Rick Waits	.08	.06	.03
219	Joe Simpson	.08	.06	.03
220	Fernando Valenzuela	.40	.30	.15
221	Cliff Johnson	.08	.06	.03
222	Rick Honeycutt	.08	.06	.03
223	Wayne Krenchicki	.08	.06	.03
224	Sid Monge	.08	.06	.03
225	Lee Mazzilli	.10	.08	.04
226	Juan Eichelberger	.08	.06	.03
227	Steve Braun	.08	.06	.03
228	John Rabb	.08	.06	.03
229	Paul Owens	.08	.06	.03
230	Rickey Henderson	5.00	3.75	2.00
231	Gary Woods	.08	.06	.03
232	Tim Wallach	.15	.11	.06
233	Checklist 133-264	.08	.06	.03
234	Rafael Ramirez	.08	.06	.03
235	*Matt Young*	.15	.11	.06
236	Ellis Valentine	.08	.06	.03
237	John Castino	.08	.06	.03
238	Reid Nichols	.08	.06	.03
239	Jay Howell	.10	.08	.04
240	Eddie Murray	1.00	.70	.40
241	Billy Almon	.08	.06	.03
242	Alex Trevino	.08	.06	.03
243	Pete Ladd	.08	.06	.03
244	Candy Maldonado(FC)	.50	.40	.20
245	Rick Sutcliffe	.15	.11	.06
246	Mets Batting & Pitching Leaders (Tom Seaver, Mookie Wilson)	.25	.20	.10
247	Onix Concepcion	.08	.06	.03

#	Player	MT	NR MT	EX
248	*Bill Dawley*(FC)	.10	.08	.04
249	Jay Johnstone	.10	.08	.04
250	Bill Madlock	.12	.09	.05
251	Tony Gwynn	5.00	3.75	2.00
252	Larry Christenson	.08	.06	.03
253	Jim Wohlford	.08	.06	.03
254	Shane Rawley	.12	.09	.05
255	Bruce Benedict	.08	.06	.03
256	Dave Geisel	.08	.06	.03
257	Julio Cruz	.08	.06	.03
258	Luis Sanchez	.08	.06	.03
259	Sparky Anderson	.12	.09	.05
260	Scott McGregor	.10	.08	.04
261	Bobby Brown	.08	.06	.03
262	*Tom Candiotti*(FC)	.25	.20	.10
263	Jack Fimple	.08	.06	.03
264	Doug Frobel	.08	.06	.03
265	*Donnie Hill*(FC)	.15	.11	.06
266	Steve Lubratich	.08	.06	.03
267	*Carmelo Martinez*(FC)	.25	.20	.10
268	Jack O'Connor	.08	.06	.03
269	Aurelio Rodriguez	.10	.08	.04
270	*Jeff Russell*(FC)	.20	.15	.08
271	Moose Haas	.08	.06	.03
272	Rick Dempsey	.10	.08	.04
273	Charlie Puleo	.08	.06	.03
274	Rick Monday	.10	.08	.04
275	Len Matuszek	.08	.06	.03
276	Angels Batting & Pitching Leaders (Rod Carew, Geoff Zahn)	.20	.15	.08
277	Eddie Whitson	.08	.06	.03
278	Jorge Bell	1.00	.70	.40
279	Ivan DeJesus	.08	.06	.03
280	Floyd Bannister	.12	.09	.05
281	Larry Milbourne	.08	.06	.03
282	Jim Barr	.08	.06	.03
283	Larry Biittner	.08	.06	.03
284	Howard Bailey	.08	.06	.03
285	Darrell Porter	.10	.08	.04
286	Lary Sorensen	.08	.06	.03
287	Warren Cromartie	.08	.06	.03
288	Jim Beattie	.08	.06	.03
289	Randy Johnson	.08	.06	.03
290	Dave Dravecky	.10	.08	.04
291	Chuck Tanner	.08	.06	.03
292	Tony Scott	.08	.06	.03
293	Ed Lynch	.08	.06	.03
294	U.L. Washington	.08	.06	.03
295	Mike Flanagan	.12	.09	.05
296	Jeff Newman	.08	.06	.03
297	Bruce Berenyi	.08	.06	.03
298	Jim Gantner	.10	.08	.04
299	John Butcher	.08	.06	.03
300	Pete Rose	1.00	.70	.40
301	Frank LaCorte	.08	.06	.03
302	Barry Bonnell	.08	.06	.03
303	Marty Castillo	.08	.06	.03
304	Warren Brusstar	.08	.06	.03
305	Roy Smalley	.08	.06	.03
306	Dodgers Batting & Pitching Leaders (Pedro Guerrero, Bob Welch)	.15	.11	.06
307	Bobby Mitchell	.08	.06	.03
308	Ron Hassey	.08	.06	.03
309	*Tony Phillips*	.15	.11	.06
310	Willie McGee	.35	.25	.14
311	Jerry Koosman	.12	.09	.05
312	Jorge Orta	.08	.06	.03
313	Mike Jorgensen	.08	.06	.03
314	Orlando Mercado	.08	.06	.03
315	Bob Grich	.12	.09	.05
316	Mark Bradley	.08	.06	.03
317	Greg Pryor	.08	.06	.03
318	Bill Gullickson	.08	.06	.03
319	Al Bumbry	.10	.08	.04
320	Bob Stanley	.08	.06	.03
321	Harvey Kuenn	.10	.08	.04
322	Ken Schrom	.08	.06	.03
323	Alan Knicely	.08	.06	.03
324	*Alejandro Pena*	.30	.25	.12
325	Darrell Evans	.15	.11	.06
326	Bob Kearney	.08	.06	.03
327	Ruppert Jones	.08	.06	.03
328	Vern Ruhle	.08	.06	.03
329	Pat Tabler(FC)	.20	.15	.08
330	John Candelaria	.12	.09	.05
331	Bucky Dent	.12	.09	.05
332	*Kevin Gross*(FC)	.40	.30	.15
333	Larry Herndon	.10	.08	.04
334	Chuck Rainey	.08	.06	.03
335	Don Baylor	.15	.11	.06
336	Mariners Batting & Pitching Leaders (Pat Putnam, Matt Young)	.10	.08	.04
337	Kevin Hagen	.08	.06	.03
338	Mike Warren	.08	.06	.03
339	Roy Lee Jackson	.08	.06	.03
340	Hal McRae	.12	.09	.05
341	Dave Tobik	.08	.06	.03
342	Tim Foli	.08	.06	.03
343	Mark Davis	.08	.06	.03
344	Rick Miller	.08	.06	.03
345	Kent Hrbek	.40	.30	.15
346	Kurt Bevacqua	.08	.06	.03
347	Allan Ramirez	.08	.06	.03
348	Toby Harrah	.10	.08	.04
349	Bob Gibson	.08	.06	.03
350	George Foster	.20	.15	.08
351	Russ Nixon	.08	.06	.03
352	Dave Stewart	.70	.50	.30
353	Jim Anderson	.08	.06	.03
354	Jeff Burroughs	.10	.08	.04
355	Jason Thompson	.08	.06	.03
356	Glenn Abbott	.08	.06	.03
357	Ron Cey	.12	.09	.05
358	Bob Dernier	.08	.06	.03
359	*Jim Acker*(FC)	.12	.09	.05
360	Willie Randolph	.12	.09	.05
361	Dave Smith	.10	.08	.04
362	David Green	.08	.06	.03
363	Tim Laudner	.08	.06	.03
364	Scott Fletcher(FC)	.15	.11	.06
365	Steve Bedrosian	.12	.09	.05
366	Padres Batting & Pitching Leaders (Dave Dravecky, Terry Kennedy)	.12	.09	.05
367	Jamie Easterly	.08	.06	.03
368	Hubie Brooks	.15	.11	.06
369	Steve McCatty	.08	.06	.03
370	Tim Raines	.50	.40	.20
371	Dave Gumpert	.08	.06	.03
372	Gary Roenicke	.08	.06	.03
373	Bill Scherrer	.08	.06	.03
374	Don Money	.08	.06	.03
375	Dennis Leonard	.10	.08	.04
376	*Dave Anderson*(FC)	.15	.11	.06
377	Danny Darwin	.08	.06	.03
378	Bob Brenly	.08	.06	.03
379	Checklist 265-396	.08	.06	.03
380	Steve Garvey	.50	.40	.20
381	Ralph Houk	.10	.08	.04
382	Chris Nyman	.08	.06	.03
383	Terry Puhl	.08	.06	.03
384	*Lee Tunnell*	.10	.08	.04
385	Tony Perez	.20	.15	.08
386	George Hendrick AS	.10	.08	.04
387	Johnny Ray AS	.12	.09	.05
388	Mike Schmidt AS	.50	.40	.20
389	Ozzie Smith AS	.15	.11	.06
390	Tim Raines AS	.25	.20	.10
391	Dale Murphy AS	.40	.30	.15
392	Andre Dawson AS	.20	.15	.08
393	Gary Carter AS	.30	.25	.12
394	Steve Rogers AS	.10	.08	.04
395	Steve Carlton AS	.25	.20	.10
396	Jesse Orosco AS	.10	.08	.04
397	Eddie Murray AS	.35	.25	.14
398	Lou Whitaker AS	.20	.15	.08
399	George Brett AS	.50	.40	.20
400	Cal Ripken AS	1.25	.90	.50
401	Jim Rice AS	.30	.25	.12
402	Dave Winfield AS	.30	.25	.12
403	Lloyd Moseby AS	.12	.09	.05
404	Ted Simmons AS	.15	.11	.06
405	LaMarr Hoyt AS	.10	.08	.04
406	Ron Guidry AS	.20	.15	.08
407	Dan Quisenberry AS	.12	.09	.05
408	Lou Piniella	.15	.11	.06
409	*Juan Agosto*(FC)	.15	.11	.06
410	Claudell Washington	.10	.08	.04
411	Houston Jimenez	.08	.06	.03
412	Doug Rader	.08	.06	.03
413	*Spike Owen*(FC)	.20	.15	.08
414	Mitchell Page	.08	.06	.03
415	Tommy John	.25	.20	.10
416	Dane Iorg	.08	.06	.03
417	Mike Armstrong	.08	.06	.03
418	Ron Hodges	.08	.06	.03
419	John Henry Johnson	.08	.06	.03
420	Cecil Cooper	.15	.11	.06
421	Charlie Lea	.08	.06	.03
422	Jose Cruz	.12	.09	.05
423	Mike Morgan	.08	.06	.03
424	Dann Bilardello	.08	.06	.03
425	Steve Howe	.10	.08	.04
426	Orioles Batting & Pitching Leaders (Mike Boddicker, Cal Ripken)	.25	.20	.10

		MT	NR MT	EX
427	Rick Leach	.08	.06	.03
428	Fred Breining	.08	.06	.03
429	*Randy Bush*	.15	.11	.06
430	Rusty Staub	.12	.09	.05
431	Chris Bando	.08	.06	.03
432	*Charlie Hudson*(FC)	.20	.15	.08
433	Rich Hebner	.08	.06	.03
434	Harold Baines	.25	.20	.10
435	Neil Allen	.08	.06	.03
436	Rick Peters	.08	.06	.03
437	Mike Proly	.08	.06	.03
438	Biff Pocoroba	.08	.06	.03
439	Bob Stoddard	.08	.06	.03
440	Steve Kemp	.10	.08	.04
441	Bob Lillis	.08	.06	.03
442	Byron McLaughlin	.08	.06	.03
443	Benny Ayala	.08	.06	.03
444	Steve Renko	.08	.06	.03
445	Jerry Remy	.08	.06	.03
446	Luis Pujols	.08	.06	.03
447	Tom Brunansky	.20	.15	.08
448	Ben Hayes	.08	.06	.03
449	Joe Pettini	.08	.06	.03
450	Gary Carter	.40	.30	.15
451	Bob Jones	.08	.06	.03
452	Chuck Porter	.08	.06	.03
453	Willie Upshaw	.10	.08	.04
454	Joe Beckwith	.08	.06	.03
455	Terry Kennedy	.10	.08	.04
456	Cubs Batting & Pitching Leaders (Fergie Jenkins, Keith Moreland)	.15	.11	.06
457	Dave Rozema	.08	.06	.03
458	Kiko Garcia	.08	.06	.03
459	Kevin Hickey	.08	.06	.03
460	Dave Winfield	1.50	1.25	.60
461	Jim Maler	.08	.06	.03
462	Lee Lacy	.08	.06	.03
463	Dave Engle	.08	.06	.03
464	Jeff Jones	.08	.06	.03
465	Mookie Wilson	.12	.09	.05
466	Gene Garber	.08	.06	.03
467	Mike Ramsey	.08	.06	.03
468	Geoff Zahn	.08	.06	.03
469	Tom O'Malley	.08	.06	.03
470	Nolan Ryan	6.00	4.50	2.50
471	Dick Howser	.08	.06	.03
472	Mike Brown	.08	.06	.03
473	Jim Dwyer	.08	.06	.03
474	Greg Bargar	.08	.06	.03
475	*Gary Redus*	.25	.20	.10
476	Tom Tellmann	.08	.06	.03
477	Rafael Landestoy	.08	.06	.03
478	Alan Bannister	.08	.06	.03
479	Frank Tanana	.12	.09	.05
480	Ron Kittle(FC)	.20	.15	.08
481	*Mark Thurmond*(FC)	.10	.08	.04
482	Enos Cabell	.08	.06	.03
483	Fergie Jenkins	.20	.15	.08
484	Ozzie Virgil	.08	.06	.03
485	Rick Rhoden	.12	.09	.05
486	Yankees Batting & Pitching Leaders (Don Baylor, Ron Guidry)	.15	.11	.06
487	Ricky Adams	.08	.06	.03
488	Jesse Barfield	.25	.20	.10
489	Dave Von Ohlen	.08	.06	.03
490	Cal Ripken	9.00	6.75	3.50
491	Bobby Castillo	.08	.06	.03
492	Tucker Ashford	.08	.06	.03
493	Mike Norris	.08	.06	.03
494	Chili Davis	.12	.09	.05
495	Rollie Fingers	.25	.20	.10
496	Terry Francona	.08	.06	.03
497	Bud Anderson	.08	.06	.03
498	Rich Gedman	.10	.08	.04
499	Mike Witt	.15	.11	.06
500	George Brett	2.00	1.50	.80
501	Steve Henderson	.08	.06	.03
502	Joe Torre	.08	.06	.03
503	Elias Sosa	.08	.06	.03
504	Mickey Rivers	.10	.08	.04
505	Pete Vuckovich	.10	.08	.04
506	Ernie Whitt	.10	.08	.04
507	Mike LaCoss	.08	.06	.03
508	Mel Hall	.20	.15	.08
509	Brad Havens	.08	.06	.03
510	Alan Trammell	.40	.30	.15
511	Marty Bystrom	.08	.06	.03
512	Oscar Gamble	.10	.08	.04
513	Dave Beard	.08	.06	.03
514	Floyd Rayford	.08	.06	.03
515	Gorman Thomas	.10	.08	.04
516	Expos Batting & Pitching Leaders (Charlie Lea, Al Oliver)	.12	.09	.05
517	John Moses	.12	.09	.05
518	*Greg Walker*	.25	.20	.10
519	Ron Davis	.08	.06	.03
520	Bob Boone	.10	.08	.04
521	Pete Falcone	.08	.06	.03
522	Dave Bergman	.08	.06	.03
523	Glenn Hoffman	.08	.06	.03
524	Carlos Diaz	.08	.06	.03
525	Willie Wilson	.15	.11	.06
526	Ron Oester	.08	.06	.03
527	Checklist 397-528	.08	.06	.03
528	Mark Brouhard	.08	.06	.03
529	*Keith Atherton*(FC)	.20	.15	.08
530	Dan Ford	.08	.06	.03
531	Steve Boros	.08	.06	.03
532	Eric Show	.12	.09	.05
533	Ken Landreaux	.08	.06	.03
534	*Pete O'Brien*	.70	.50	.30
535	Bo Diaz	.10	.08	.04
536	Doug Bair	.08	.06	.03
537	Johnny Ray	.12	.09	.05
538	Kevin Bass	.15	.11	.06
539	George Frazier	.08	.06	.03
540	George Hendrick	.10	.08	.04
541	Dennis Lamp	.08	.06	.03
542	Duane Kuiper	.08	.06	.03
543	*Craig McMurtry*	.12	.09	.05
544	Cesar Geronimo	.08	.06	.03
545	Bill Buckner	.15	.11	.06
546	Indians Batting & Pitching Leaders (Mike Hargrove, Lary Sorensen)	.10	.08	.04
547	Mike Moore	.10	.08	.04
548	Ron Jackson	.08	.06	.03
549	*Walt Terrell*	.50	.40	.20
550	Jim Rice	.40	.30	.15
551	Scott Ullger	.08	.06	.03
552	Ray Burris	.08	.06	.03
553	Joe Nolan	.08	.06	.03
554	Ted Power(FC)	.12	.09	.05
555	Greg Brock	.15	.11	.06
556	Joey McLaughlin	.08	.06	.03
557	Wayne Tolleson	.10	.08	.04
558	Mike Davis	.10	.08	.04
559	Mike Scott	.20	.15	.08
560	Carlton Fisk	1.00	.70	.40
561	Whitey Herzog	.10	.08	.04
562	Manny Castillo	.08	.06	.03
563	Glenn Wilson	.10	.08	.04
564	Al Holland	.08	.06	.03
565	Leon Durham	.10	.08	.04
566	Jim Bibby	.08	.06	.03
567	Mike Heath	.08	.06	.03
568	Pete Filson	.08	.06	.03
569	Bake McBride	.08	.06	.03
570	Dan Quisenberry	.12	.09	.05
571	Bruce Bochy	.08	.06	.03
572	Jerry Royster	.08	.06	.03
573	Dave Kingman	.15	.11	.06
574	Brian Downing	.12	.09	.05
575	Jim Clancy	.10	.08	.04
576	Giants Batting & Pitching Leaders (Atlee Hammaker, Jeff Leonard)	.10	.08	.04
577	Mark Clear	.08	.06	.03
578	Lenn Sakata	.08	.06	.03
579	Bob James	.08	.06	.03
580	Lonnie Smith	.10	.08	.04
581	*Jose DeLeon*(FC)	.30	.25	.12
582	Bob McClure	.08	.06	.03
583	Derrel Thomas	.08	.06	.03
584	Dave Schmidt	.08	.06	.03
585	Dan Driessen	.10	.08	.04
586	Joe Niekro	.15	.11	.06
587	Von Hayes	.15	.11	.06
588	Milt Wilcox	.08	.06	.03
589	Mike Easler	.10	.08	.04
590	Dave Stieb	.15	.11	.06
591	Tony LaRussa	.10	.08	.04
592	Andre Robertson	.08	.06	.03
593	Jeff Lahti	.08	.06	.03
594	Gene Richards	.08	.06	.03
595	Jeff Reardon	.60	.45	.25
596	Ryne Sandberg	10.00	7.50	4.00
597	Rick Camp	.08	.06	.03
598	Rusty Kuntz	.08	.06	.03
599	*Doug Sisk*	.10	.08	.04
600	Rod Carew	.50	.40	.20
601	John Tudor	.12	.09	.05
602	John Wathan	.10	.08	.04
603	Renie Martin	.08	.06	.03

#	Player	MT	NR MT	EX
604	John Lowenstein	.08	.06	.03
605	Mike Caldwell	.08	.06	.03
606	Blue Jays Batting & Pitching Leaders (Lloyd Moseby, Dave Stieb)	.15	.11	.06
607	Tom Hume	.08	.06	.03
608	Bobby Johnson	.08	.06	.03
609	Dan Meyer	.08	.06	.03
610	Steve Sax	.30	.25	.12
611	Chet Lemon	.10	.08	.04
612	Harry Spilman	.08	.06	.03
613	Greg Gross	.08	.06	.03
614	Len Barker	.10	.08	.04
615	Garry Templeton	.12	.09	.05
616	Don Robinson	.10	.08	.04
617	Rick Cerone	.08	.06	.03
618	Dickie Noles	.08	.06	.03
619	Jerry Dybzinski	.08	.06	.03
620	Al Oliver	.20	.15	.08
621	Frank Howard	.10	.08	.04
622	Al Cowens	.08	.06	.03
623	Ron Washington	.08	.06	.03
624	Terry Harper	.08	.06	.03
625	Larry Gura	.10	.08	.04
626	Bob Clark	.08	.06	.03
627	Dave LaPoint	.10	.08	.04
628	Ed Jurak	.08	.06	.03
629	Rick Langford	.08	.06	.03
630	Ted Simmons	.15	.11	.06
631	Denny Martinez	.10	.08	.04
632	Tom Foley	.08	.06	.03
633	Mike Krukow	.10	.08	.04
634	Mike Marshall	.15	.11	.06
635	Dave Righetti	.25	.20	.10
636	Pat Putnam	.08	.06	.03
637	Phillies Batting & Pitching Leaders (John Denny, Gary Matthews)	.10	.08	.04
638	George Vukovich	.08	.06	.03
639	Rick Lysander	.08	.06	.03
640	Lance Parrish	.35	.25	.14
641	Mike Richardt	.08	.06	.03
642	Tom Underwood	.08	.06	.03
643	Mike Brown	.08	.06	.03
644	Tim Lollar	.08	.06	.03
645	Tony Pena	.12	.09	.05
646	Checklist 529-660	.08	.06	.03
647	Ron Roenicke	.08	.06	.03
648	Len Whitehouse	.08	.06	.03
649	Tom Herr	.12	.09	.05
650	Phil Niekro	.30	.25	.12
651	John McNamara	.08	.06	.03
652	Rudy May	.08	.06	.03
653	Dave Stapleton	.08	.06	.03
654	Bob Bailor	.08	.06	.03
655	Amos Otis	.10	.08	.04
656	Bryn Smith	.08	.06	.03
657	Thad Bosley	.08	.06	.03
658	Jerry Augustine	.08	.06	.03
659	Duane Walker	.08	.06	.03
660	Ray Knight	.12	.09	.05
661	Steve Yeager	.08	.06	.03
662	Tom Brennan	.08	.06	.03
663	Johnnie LeMaster	.08	.06	.03
664	Dave Stegman	.08	.06	.03
665	Buddy Bell	.15	.11	.06
666	Tigers Batting & Pitching Leaders (Jack Morris, Lou Whitaker)	.15	.11	.06
667	Vance Law	.10	.08	.04
668	Larry McWilliams	.08	.06	.03
669	Dave Lopes	.10	.08	.04
670	Rich Gossage	.25	.20	.10
671	Jamie Quirk	.08	.06	.03
672	Ricky Nelson	.08	.06	.03
673	Mike Walters	.08	.06	.03
674	Tim Flannery	.08	.06	.03
675	Pascual Perez	.10	.08	.04
676	Brian Giles	.08	.06	.03
677	Doyle Alexander	.12	.09	.05
678	Chris Speier	.08	.06	.03
679	Art Howe	.08	.06	.03
680	Fred Lynn	.25	.20	.10
681	Tom Lasorda	.12	.09	.05
682	Dan Morogiello	.08	.06	.03
683	Marty Barrett (FC)	.35	.25	.14
684	Bob Shirley	.08	.06	.03
685	Willie Aikens	.08	.06	.03
686	Joe Price	.08	.06	.03
687	Roy Howell	.08	.06	.03
688	George Wright	.08	.06	.03
689	Mike Fischlin	.08	.06	.03
690	Jack Clark	.25	.20	.10
691	Steve Lake (FC)	.10	.08	.04
692	Dickie Thon	.10	.08	.04
693	Alan Wiggins	.08	.06	.03
694	Mike Stanton	.08	.06	.03
695	Lou Whitaker	.40	.30	.15
696	Pirates Batting & Pitching Leaders (Bill Madlock, Rick Rhoden)	.15	.11	.06
697	Dale Murray	.08	.06	.03
698	Marc Hill	.08	.06	.03
699	Dave Rucker	.08	.06	.03
700	Mike Schmidt	2.00	1.50	.80
701	NL Active Career Batting Leaders (Bill Madlock, Dave Parker, Pete Rose)	.35	.25	.14
702	NL Active Career Hit Leaders (Tony Perez, Pete Rose, Rusty Staub)	.35	.25	.14
703	NL Active Career Home Run Leaders (Dave Kingman, Tony Perez, Mike Schmidt)	.30	.25	.12
704	NL Active Career RBI Leaders (Al Oliver, Tony Perez, Rusty Staub)	.15	.11	.06
705	NL Active Career Stolen Bases Leaders (Larry Bowa, Cesar Cedeno, Joe Morgan)	.12	.09	.05
706	NL Active Career Victory Leaders (Steve Carlton, Fergie Jenkins, Tom Seaver)	.30	.25	.12
707	NL Active Career Strikeout Leaders (Steve Carlton, Nolan Ryan, Tom Seaver)	.35	.25	.14
708	NL Active Career ERA Leaders (Steve Carlton, Steve Rogers, Tom Seaver)	.25	.20	.10
709	NL Active Career Save Leaders (Gene Garber, Tug McGraw, Bruce Sutter)	.12	.09	.05
710	AL Active Career Batting Leaders (George Brett, Rod Carew, Cecil Cooper)	.30	.25	.12
711	AL Active Career Hit Leaders (Bert Campaneris, Rod Carew, Reggie Jackson)	.30	.25	.12
712	AL Active Career Home Run Leaders (Reggie Jackson, Greg Luzinski, Graig Nettles)	.20	.15	.08
713	AL Active Career RBI Leaders (Reggie Jackson, Graig Nettles, Ted Simmons)	.20	.15	.08
714	AL Active Career Stolen Bases Leaders (Bert Campaneris, Dave Lopes, Omar Moreno)	.10	.08	.04
715	AL Active Career Victory Leaders (Tommy John, Jim Palmer, Don Sutton)	.25	.20	.10
716	AL Active Strikeout Leaders (Bert Blyleven, Jerry Koosman, Don Sutton)	.15	.11	.06
717	AL Active Career ERA Leaders (Rollie Fingers, Ron Guidry, Jim Palmer)	.15	.11	.06
718	AL Active Career Save Leaders (Rollie Fingers, Rich Gossage, Dan Quisenberry)	.15	.11	.06
719	Andy Hassler	.08	.06	.03
720	Dwight Evans	.20	.15	.08
721	Del Crandall	.08	.06	.03
722	Bob Welch	.15	.11	.06
723	Rich Dauer	.08	.06	.03
724	Eric Rasmussen	.08	.06	.03
725	Cesar Cedeno	.12	.09	.05
726	Brewers Batting & Pitching Leaders (Moose Haas, Ted Simmons)	.12	.09	.05
727	Joel Youngblood	.08	.06	.03
728	Tug McGraw	.12	.09	.05
729	Gene Tenace	.10	.08	.04
730	Bruce Sutter	.20	.15	.08
731	Lynn Jones	.08	.06	.03
732	Terry Crowley	.08	.06	.03
733	Dave Collins	.10	.08	.04
734	Odell Jones	.08	.06	.03
735	Rick Burleson	.10	.08	.04
736	Dick Ruthven	.08	.06	.03
737	Jim Essian	.08	.06	.03
738	Bill Schroeder (FC)	.20	.15	.08
739	Bob Watson	.10	.08	.04
740	Tom Seaver	1.75	1.25	.70
741	Wayne Gross	.08	.06	.03
742	Dick Williams	.08	.06	.03
743	Don Hood	.08	.06	.03
744	Jamie Allen	.08	.06	.03
745	Dennis Eckersley	.15	.11	.06
746	Mickey Hatcher	.10	.08	.04
747	Pat Zachry	.08	.06	.03
748	Jeff Leonard	.12	.09	.05
749	Doug Flynn	.08	.06	.03
750	Jim Palmer	1.00	.70	.40
751	Charlie Moore	.08	.06	.03
752	Phil Garner	.10	.08	.04
753	Doug Gwosdz	.08	.06	.03
754	Kent Tekulve	.10	.08	.04
755	Garry Maddox	.10	.08	.04

		MT	NR MT	EX
756	Reds Batting & Pitching Leaders (Ron Oester, Mario Soto)	.10	.08	.04
757	Larry Bowa	.15	.11	.06
758	Bill Stein	.08	.06	.03
759	Richard Dotson	.12	.09	.05
760	Bob Horner	.15	.11	.06
761	John Montefusco	.08	.06	.03
762	Rance Mulliniks	.08	.06	.03
763	Craig Swan	.08	.06	.03
764	Mike Hargrove	.08	.06	.03
765	Ken Forsch	.08	.06	.03
766	Mike Vail	.08	.06	.03
767	Carney Lansford	.12	.09	.05
768	Champ Summers	.08	.06	.03
769	Bill Caudill	.08	.06	.03
770	Ken Griffey	.12	.09	.05
771	Billy Gardner	.08	.06	.03
772	Jim Slaton	.08	.06	.03
773	Todd Cruz	.08	.06	.03
774	Tom Gorman	.08	.06	.03
775	Dave Parker	.30	.25	.12
776	Craig Reynolds	.08	.06	.03
777	Tom Paciorek	.08	.06	.03
778	*Andy Hawkins*(FC)	.25	.20	.10
779	Jim Sundberg	.10	.08	.04
780	Steve Carlton	.80	.60	.30
781	Checklist 661-792	.08	.06	.03
782	Steve Balboni	.10	.08	.04
783	Luis Leal	.08	.06	.03
784	Leon Roberts	.08	.06	.03
785	Joaquin Andujar	.10	.08	.04
786	Red Sox Batting & Pitching Leaders (Wade Boggs, Bob Ojeda)	.40	.30	.15
787	Bill Campbell	.08	.06	.03
788	Milt May	.08	.06	.03
789	Bert Blyleven	.20	.15	.08
790	Doug DeCinces	.12	.09	.05
791	Terry Forster	.10	.08	.04
792	Bill Russell	.10	.08	.04

		MT	NR MT	EX
3	Manny Trillo	.20	.15	.08
4	George Brett	.80	.60	.30
5	Robin Yount	.40	.30	.15
6	Jim Rice	.50	.40	.20
7	Fred Lynn	.25	.20	.10
8	Dave Winfield	.50	.40	.20
9	Ted Simmons	.25	.20	.10
10	Dave Stieb	.25	.20	.10
11	Carl Yastrzemski	.80	.60	.30
12	Whitey Herzog	.20	.15	.08
13	Al Oliver	.25	.20	.10
14	Steve Sax	.30	.25	.12
15	Mike Schmidt	.80	.60	.30
16	Ozzie Smith	.30	.25	.12
17	Tim Raines	.50	.40	.20
18	Andre Dawson	.35	.25	.14
19	Dale Murphy	.80	.60	.30
20	Gary Carter	.50	.40	.20
21	Mario Soto	.20	.15	.08
22	Johnny Bench	.60	.45	.25

1984 Topps All-Star Glossy Set Of 40

For the second straight year in 1984, Topps produced a 40-card All-Star "Collector's Edition" set as a "consolation prize" for its sweepstakes game. By collecting game cards and sending them in with a bit of cash, the collector could receive one of eight different five-card series. As the previous year, the 2-1/2" by 3-1/2" cards feature a nearly full-frame color photo on its glossy finish front. Backs are printed in red and blue.

		MT	NR MT	EX
Complete Set:		16.00	12.00	6.50
Common Player:		.15	.11	.06
1	Pete Rose	1.25	.90	.50
2	Lance Parrish	.30	.25	.12
3	Steve Rogers	.15	.11	.06
4	Eddie Murray	.60	.45	.25
5	Johnny Ray	.20	.15	.08
6	Rickey Henderson	.70	.50	.30
7	Atlee Hammaker	.15	.11	.06
8	Wade Boggs	3.00	2.25	1.25
9	Gary Carter	.50	.40	.20
10	Jack Morris	.30	.25	.12
11	Darrell Evans	.20	.15	.08
12	George Brett	1.00	.70	.40
13	Bob Horner	.20	.15	.08
14	Ron Guidry	.30	.25	.12
15	Nolan Ryan	.50	.40	.20
16	Dave Winfield	.60	.45	.25
17	Ozzie Smith	.25	.20	.10
18	Ted Simmons	.20	.15	.08
19	Bill Madlock	.20	.15	.08
20	Tony Armas	.15	.11	.06
21	Al Oliver	.20	.15	.08
22	Jim Rice	.50	.40	.20
23	George Hendrick	.15	.11	.06
24	Dave Stieb	.20	.15	.08
25	Pedro Guerrero	.25	.20	.10
26	Rod Carew	.60	.45	.25
27	Steve Carlton	.50	.40	.20
28	Dave Righetti	.30	.25	.12

1984 Topps All-Star Glossy Set Of 22

These 2-1/2" by 3-1/2" cards were a result of the success of Topps' efforts the previous year with glossy cards on a mail-in basis. A 22-card set, the cards are divided evenly between the two leagues. Each All-Star Game starter for both leagues, the managers and the honorary team captains have an All-Star Glossy card. The cards feature a large color photo on the front with an All-Star banner across the top and the league emblem in the lower left. The player's name and position appear below the photo. Backs have a name, team, position and card number along with the phrase "1983 All-Star Game Commemorative Set". The '84 Glossy All-Stars were distributed one card per pack in Topps rack packs that year.

		MT	NR MT	EX
Complete Set:		6.00	4.50	2.50
Common Player:		.20	.15	.08
1	Harvey Kuenn	.20	.15	.08
2	Rod Carew	.50	.40	.20

		MT	NR MT	EX
29	Darryl Strawberry	3.00	2.25	1.25
30	Lou Whitaker	.30	.25	.12
31	Dale Murphy	1.00	.70	.40
32	LaMarr Hoyt	.15	.11	.06
33	Jesse Orosco	.15	.11	.06
34	Cecil Cooper	.20	.15	.08
35	Andre Dawson	.35	.25	.14
36	Robin Yount	.40	.30	.15
37	Tim Raines	.50	.40	.20
38	Dan Quisenberry	.15	.11	.06
39	Mike Schmidt	1.00	.70	.40
40	Carlton Fisk	.30	.25	.12

		MT	NR MT	EX
(9a)	Pete Rose (aluminum)	2.50	2.00	1.00
(9b)	Pete Rose (bronze)	25.00	18.50	10.00
(9c)	Pete Rose (silver)	110.00	82.00	44.00
(10a)	Nolan Ryan (aluminum)	1.50	1.25	.60
(10b)	Nolan Ryan (bronze)	12.50	9.50	5.00
(10c)	Nolan Ryan (silver)	80.00	60.00	33.00
(11a)	Mike Schmidt (aluminum)	1.50	1.25	.60
(11b)	Mike Schmidt (bronze)	15.00	11.00	6.00
(11c)	Mike Schmidt (silver)	80.00	60.00	32.00
(12a)	Tom Seaver (aluminum)	1.50	1.25	.60
(12b)	Tom Seaver (bronze)	12.50	9.50	5.00
(12c)	Tom Seaver (silver)	50.00	37.00	20.00

1984 Topps Gallery of Immortals

The Gallery of Immortals set of aluminum, bronze and silver replicas was the first miniature set of 12 from Topps and the start of an annual tradition in 1985, the name was changed to Gallery of Champions) .Each mini is an exact replica (one-quarter scale) of the featured player's official Topps baseball card card, both front and back, in minute detail. The bronze and silver sets include a dozen three-dimensional raised metal cards packaged in a velvet-lined case that bears the title of the set in gold-embossed letters. A certificate of authenticity is included with each set. A Tom Seaver pewter metal mini-card was given as a premium to dealers who purchased bronze and silver sets (value $75). A Darryl Strawberry bronze was given as a premium to dealers who purchased cases of the 1984 Topps Traded sets (value $12). Additionally, a Steve Carlton bronze was issued as a premium in 1983 to dealers who purchased 1983 Topps Traded sets (value $50).

		MT	NR MT	EX
Complete Aluminum Set:		30.00	22.00	12.00
Complete Bronze Set:		175.00	131.00	70.00
Complete Silver Set:		600.00	450.00	240.00
(1a)	George Brett (aluminum)	1.50	1.25	.60
(1b)	George Brett (bronze)	15.00	11.00	6.00
(1c)	George Brett (silver)	80.00	60.00	32.00
(2a)	Rod Carew (aluminum)	1.50	1.25	.60
(2b)	Rod Carew (bronze)	12.50	9.50	5.00
(2c)	Rod Carew (silver)	50.00	37.00	20.00
(3a)	Steve Carlton (aluminum)	1.50	1.25	.60
(3b)	Steve Carlton (bronze)	12.50	9.50	5.00
(3c)	Steve Carlton (silver)	50.00	37.00	20.00
(4a)	Rollie Fingers (aluminum)	1.25	.90	.50
(4b)	Rollie Fingers (bronze)	10.00	7.50	4.00
(4c)	Rollie Fingers (silver)	20.00	15.00	8.00
(5a)	Steve Garvey (aluminum)	1.50	1.25	.60
(5b)	Steve Garvey (bronze)	12.50	9.50	5.00
(5c)	Steve Garvey (silver)	50.00	37.00	20.00
(6a)	Reggie Jackson (aluminum)	1.50	1.25	.60
(6b)	Reggie Jackson (bronze)	15.00	11.00	6.00
(6c)	Reggie Jackson (silver)	80.00	60.00	32.00
(7a)	Joe Morgan (aluminum)	1.25	.90	.50
(7b)	Joe Morgan (bronze)	10.00	7.50	4.00
(7c)	Joe Morgan (silver)	20.00	15.00	8.00
(8a)	Jim Palmer (aluminum)	1.25	.90	.50
(8b)	Jim Palmer (bronze)	10.00	7.50	4.00
(8c)	Jim Palmer (silver)	20.00	15.00	8.00

1984 Topps Rub Downs

This set, produced by Topps in 1984, consists of 32 "Rub Down" sheets featuring 112 different players. Each sheet measures 2-3/8" by 3-15/16" and includes small, color baseball player figures along with bats, balls and gloves. The pictures can be transferred to another surface by rubbing the paper backing. The sheets, which were sold as a separate issue, are somewhat reminiscent of earlier tattoo sets issued by Topps. The sheets are not numbered.

		MT	NR MT	EX
Complete Set:		9.00	6.75	3.50
Common Player:		.10	.08	.04
(1)	Tony Armas, Harold Baines, Lonnie Smith	.10	.08	.04
(2)	Don Baylor, George Hendrick, Ron Kittle, Johnnie LeMaster	.10	.08	.04
(3)	Buddy Bell, Ray Knight, Lloyd Moseby	.10	.08	.04
(4)	Bruce Benedict, Atlee Hammaker, Frank White	.10	.08	.04
(5)	Wade Boggs, Rick Dempsey, Keith Hernandez	.60	.45	.25
(6)	George Brett, Andre Dawson, Paul Molitor, Alan Wiggins	.30	.25	.12
(7)	Tom Brunansky, Pedro Guerrero, Darryl Strawberry	.40	.30	.15
(8)	Bill Buckner, Rich Gossage, Dave Stieb, Rick Sutcliffe	.15	.11	.06
(9)	Rod Carew, Carlton Fisk, Johnny Ray, Matt Young	.25	.20	.10
(10)	Steve Carlton, Bob Horner, Dan Quisenberry	.25	.20	.10
(11)	Gary Carter, Phil Garner, Ron Guidry	.25	.20	.10
(12)	Ron Cey, Steve Kemp, Greg Luzinski, Kent Tekulve	.10	.08	.04
(13)	Chris Chambliss, Dwight Evans, Julio Franco	.15	.11	.06
(14)	Jack Clark, Damaso Garcia, Hal McRae, Lance Parrish	.20	.15	.08
(15)	Dave Concepcion, Cecil Cooper, Fred Lynn, Jesse Orosco	.15	.11	.06
(16)	Jose Cruz, Gary Matthews, Jack Morris, Jim Rice	.20	.15	.08
(17)	Ron Davis, Kent Hrbek, Tom Seaver	.25	.20	.10
(18)	John Denny, Carney Lansford, Mario Soto, Lou Whitaker	.10	.08	.04
(19)	Leon Durham, Dave Lopes, Steve Sax	.15	.11	.06
(20)	George Foster, Gary Gaetti, Bobby Grich, Gary Redus	.15	.11	.06

		MT	NR MT	EX
(21)	Steve Garvey, Bill Russell, Jerry REmy, George Wright .20		.15	.08
(22)	Moose Haas, Bruce Sutter, Dickie Thon, Andre Thornton .10		.08	.04
(23)	Toby Harrah, Pat Putnam, Tim Raines, Mike Schmidt .30		.25	.12
(24)	Rickey Henderson, Dave Righetti, Pete Rose .70		.50	.30
(25)	Steve Henderson, Bill Madlock, Alan Trammell .20		.15	.08
(26)	LaMarr Hoyt, Larry Parrish, Nolan Ryan .25		.20	.10
(27)	Reggie Jackson, Eric Show, Jason Thompson .30		.25	.12
(28)	Tommy John, Terry Kennedy, Eddie Murray, Ozzie Smith .25		.20	.10
(29)	Jeff Leonard, Dale Murphy, Ken Singleton, Dave Winfield .30		.25	.12
(30)	Craig McMurtry, Cal Ripken, Steve Rogers, Willie Upshaw .25		.20	.10
(31)	Ben Oglivie, Jim Palmer, Darrell Porter .20		.15	.08
(32)	Tony Pena, Fernando Valenzuela, Robin Yount .20		.15	.08

1984 Topps Stickers

The largest sticker set issued by Topps, the 1984 set consists of 386 stickers, each measuring 1-15/16" by 2-9/16". The full color photos have stars in each of the corners and are numbered on both the front and the back. The back includes information about the sticker album and a promotion to order stickers through the mail:

		MT	NR MT	EX
Complete Set:		15.00	11.00	6.00
Common Player:		.03	.02	.01
Sticker Album:		.80	.60	.30
1	Steve Carlton	.15	.11	.06
2	Steve Carlton	.12	.09	.05
3	Rickey Henderson	.20	.15	.08
4	Rickey Henderson	.15	.11	.06
5	Fred Lynn	.12	.09	.05
6	Fred Lynn	.10	.08	.04
7	Greg Luzinski	.08	.06	.03
8	Greg Luzinski	.06	.05	.02
9	Dan Quisenberry	.08	.06	.03
10	Dan Quisenberry	.06	.05	.02
11	1983 Championship (LaMarr Hoyt)	.03	.02	.01
12	1983 Championship (Mike Flanagan) .04		.03	.02
13	1983 Championship (Mike Boddicker) .04		.03	.02
14	1983 Championship (Tito Landrum) .03		.02	.01
15	1983 Championship (Steve Carlton) .12		.09	.05
16	1983 Championship (Fernando Valenzuela) .12		.09	.05
17	1983 Championship (Charlie Hudson) .03		.02	.01
18	1983 Championship (Gary Matthews) .04		.03	.02
19	1983 World Series (John Denny)	.03	.02	.01
20	1983 World Series (John Lowenstein) .03		.02	.01

		MT	NR MT	EX
21	1983 World Series (Jim Palmer)	.10	.08	.04
22	1983 World Series (Benny Ayala)	.03	.02	.01
23	1983 World Series (Rick Dempsey)	.03	.02	.01
24	1983 World Series (Cal Ripken)	.15	.11	.06
25	1983 World Series (Sammy Stewart) .03		.02	.01
26	1983 World Series (Eddie Murray)	.15	.11	.06
27	Dale Murphy	.25	.20	.10
28	Chris Chambliss	.04	.03	.02
29	Glenn Hubbard	.04	.03	.02
30	Bob Horner	.08	.06	.03
31	Phil Niekro	.12	.09	.05
32	Claudell Washington	.04	.03	.02
33	Rafael Ramirez	.03	.02	.01
34	Bruce Benedict	.04	.03	.02
35	Gene Garber	.03	.02	.01
36	Pascual Perez	.04	.03	.02
37	Jerry Royster	.03	.02	.01
38	Steve Bedrosian	.06	.05	.02
39	Keith Moreland	.06	.05	.02
40	Leon Durham	.06	.05	.02
41	Ron Cey	.06	.05	.02
42	Bill Buckner	.06	.05	.02
43	Jody Davis	.06	.05	.02
44	Lee Smith	.06	.05	.02
45	Ryne Sandberg	.10	.08	.04
46	Larry Bowa	.04	.03	.02
47	Chuck Rainey	.04	.03	.02
48	Fergie Jenkins	.06	.05	.02
49	Dick Ruthven	.03	.02	.01
50	Jay Johnstone	.04	.03	.02
51	Mario Soto	.06	.05	.02
52	Gary Redus	.04	.03	.02
53	Ron Oester	.04	.03	.02
54	Cesar Cedeno	.06	.05	.02
55	Dan Driessen	.04	.03	.02
56	Dave Concepcion	.06	.05	.02
57	Dann Bilardello	.03	.02	.01
58	Joe Price	.03	.02	.01
59	Tom Hume	.03	.02	.01
60	Eddie Milner	.03	.02	.01
61	Paul Householder	.04	.03	.02
62	Bill Scherrer	.04	.03	.02
63	Phil Garner	.04	.03	.02
64	Dickie Thon	.04	.03	.02
65	Jose Cruz	.06	.05	.02
66	Nolan Ryan	.15	.11	.06
67	Terry Puhl	.03	.02	.01
68	Ray Knight	.06	.05	.02
69	Joe Niekro	.06	.05	.02
70	Jerry Mumphrey	.10	.08	.04
71	Bill Dawley	.03	.02	.01
72	Alan Ashby	.04	.03	.02
73	Denny Walling	.04	.03	.02
74	Frank DiPino	.04	.03	.02
75	Pedro Guerrero	.12	.09	.05
76	Ken Landreaux	.03	.02	.01
77	Bill Russell	.04	.03	.02
78	Steve Sax	.10	.08	.04
79	Fernando Valenzuela	.15	.11	.06
80	Dusty Baker	.04	.03	.02
81	Jerry Reuss	.04	.03	.02
82	Alejandro Pena	.04	.03	.02
83	Rick Monday	.06	.05	.02
84	Rick Honeycutt	.03	.02	.01
85	Mike Marshall	.06	.05	.02
86	Steve Yeager	.04	.03	.02
87	Al Oliver	.06	.05	.02
88	Steve Rogers	.03	.02	.01
89	Jeff Reardon	.08	.06	.03
90	Gary Carter	.20	.15	.08
91	Tim Raines	.15	.11	.06
92	Andre Dawson	.12	.09	.05
93	Manny Trillo	.04	.03	.02
94	Tim Wallach	.06	.05	.02
95	Chris Speier	.03	.02	.01
96	Bill Gullickson	.04	.03	.02
97	Doug Flynn	.04	.03	.02
98	Charlie Lea	.03	.02	.01
99	Bill Madlock	.06	.05	.02
100	Wade Boggs	.25	.20	.10
101	Mike Schmidt	.15	.11	.06
102a	Jim Rice	.06	.05	.02
102b	Reggie Jackson	.06	.05	.02
103	Hubie Brooks	.06	.05	.02
104	Jesse Orosco	.04	.03	.02
105	George Foster	.08	.06	.03
106	Tom Seaver	.20	.15	.08
107	Keith Hernandez	.15	.11	.06
108	Mookie Wilson	.06	.05	.02
109	Bob Bailor	.03	.02	.01

#	Player	MT	NR MT	EX	#	Player	MT	NR MT	EX
110	Walt Terrell	.04	.03	.02	200b	Jim Rice	.25	.20	.10
111	Brian Giles	.06	.05	.02	201	Tim Raines	.10	.08	.04
112	Jose Oquendo	.06	.05	.02	202	Rickey Henderson	.15	.11	.06
113	Mike Torrez	.03	.02	.01	203	Eddie Murray	.20	.15	.08
114	Junior Ortiz	.03	.02	.01	204	Cal Ripken	.20	.15	.08
115	Pete Rose	.40	.30	.15	205	Gary Roenicke	.03	.02	.01
116	Joe Morgan	.12	.09	.05	206	Ken Singleton	.06	.05	.02
117	Mike Schmidt	.25	.20	.10	207	Scott McGregor	.04	.03	.02
118	Gary Matthews	.06	.05	.02	208	Tippy Martinez	.03	.02	.01
119	Steve Carlton	.15	.11	.06	209	John Lowenstein	.04	.03	.02
120	Bo Diaz	.04	.03	.02	210	Mike Flanagan	.04	.03	.02
121	Ivan DeJesus	.04	.03	.02	211	Jim Palmer	.10	.08	.04
122	John Denny	.03	.02	.01	212	Dan Ford	.12	.09	.05
123	Garry Maddox	.03	.02	.01	213	Rick Dempsey	.04	.03	.02
124	Von Hayes	.08	.06	.03	214	Rich Dauer	.03	.02	.01
125	Al Holland	.03	.02	.01	215	Jerry Remy	.03	.02	.01
126	Tony Perez	.06	.05	.02	216	Wade Boggs	.50	.40	.20
127	John Candelaria	.06	.05	.02	217	Jim Rice	.20	.15	.08
128	Jason Thompson	.03	.02	.01	218	Tony Armas	.06	.05	.02
129	Tony Pena	.06	.05	.02	219	Dwight Evans	.08	.06	.03
130	Dave Parker	.12	.09	.05	220	Bob Stanley	.04	.03	.02
131	Bill Madlock	.08	.06	.03	221	Dave Stapleton	.06	.05	.02
132	Kent Tekulve	.04	.03	.02	222	Rich Gedman	.04	.03	.02
133	larry McWilliams	.03	.02	.01	223	Glenn Hoffman	.06	.05	.02
134	Johnny Ray	.04	.03	.02	224	Dennis Eckersley	.08	.06	.03
135	Marvell Wynne	.03	.02	.01	225	John Tudor	.06	.05	.02
136	Dale Berra	.03	.02	.01	226	Bruce Hurst	.04	.03	.02
137	Mike Easler	.03	.02	.01	227	Rod Carew	.20	.15	.08
138	Lee Lacy	.03	.02	.01	228	Bobby Grich	.06	.05	.02
139	George Hendrick	.04	.03	.02	229	Doug DeCinces	.06	.05	.02
140	Lonnie Smith	.04	.03	.02	230	Fred Lynn	.10	.08	.04
141	Willie McGee	.08	.06	.03	231	Reggie Jackson	.20	.15	.08
142	Tom Herr	.06	.05	.02	232	Tommy John	.10	.08	.04
143	Darrell Porter	.04	.03	.02	233	Luis Sanchez	.03	.02	.01
144	Ozzie Smith	.10	.08	.04	234	Bob Boone	.04	.03	.02
145	Bruce Sutter	.06	.05	.02	235	Bruce Kison	.04	.03	.02
146	Dave LaPoint	.03	.02	.01	236	Brian Downing	.04	.03	.02
147	Neil Allen	.03	.02	.01	237	Ken Forsch	.03	.02	.01
148	Ken Oberkfell	.04	.03	.02	238	Rick Burleson	.04	.03	.02
149	David Green	.03	.02	.01	239	Dennis Lamp	.03	.02	.01
150	Andy Van Slyke	.04	.03	.02	240	LaMarr Hoyt	.03	.02	.01
151	Garry Templeton	.06	.05	.02	241	Richard Dotson	.04	.03	.02
152	Juan Bonilla	.03	.02	.01	242	Harold Baines	.10	.08	.04
153	Alan Wiggins	.03	.02	.01	243	Carlton Fisk	.12	.09	.05
154	Terry Kennedy	.04	.03	.02	244	Greg Luzinski	.08	.06	.03
155	Dave Dravecky	.04	.03	.02	245	Rudy Law	.06	.05	.02
156	Steve Garvey	.15	.11	.06	246	Tom Paciorek	.03	.02	.01
157	Bobby Brown	.04	.03	.02	247	Floyd Bannister	.04	.03	.02
158	Ruppert Jones	.03	.02	.01	248	Julio Cruz	.04	.03	.02
159	Luis Salazar	.03	.02	.01	249	Vance Law	.03	.02	.01
160	Tony Gwynn	.12	.09	.05	250	Scott Fletcher	.04	.03	.02
161	Gary Lucas	.10	.08	.04	251	Toby Harrah	.04	.03	.02
162	Eric Show	.04	.03	.02	252	Pat Tabler	.04	.03	.02
163	Darrell Evans	.08	.06	.03	253	Gorman Thomas	.06	.05	.02
164	Gary Lavelle	.03	.02	.01	254	Rick Sutcliffe	.08	.06	.03
165	Atlee Hammaker	.03	.02	.01	255	Andre Thornton	.06	.05	.02
166	Jeff Leonard	.06	.05	.02	256	Bake McBride	.03	.02	.01
167	Jack Clark	.10	.08	.04	257	Alan Bannister	.03	.02	.01
168	Johnny LeMaster	.03	.02	.01	258	Jamie Easterly	.03	.02	.01
169	Duane Kuiper	.03	.02	.01	259	Lary Sorenson	.03	.02	.01
170	Tom O'Malley	.06	.05	.02	260	Mike Hargrove	.03	.02	.01
171	Chili Davis	.06	.05	.02	261	Bert Blyleven	.06	.05	.02
172	Bill Laskey	.03	.02	.01	262	Ron Hassey	.04	.03	.02
173	Joel Youngblood	.06	.05	.02	263	Jack Morris	.12	.09	.05
174	Bob Brenly	.06	.05	.02	264	Larry Herndon	.03	.02	.01
175	Atlee Hammaker	.15	.11	.06	265	Lance Parrish	.12	.09	.05
176	Rick Honeycutt	.15	.11	.06	266	Alan Trammell	.15	.11	.06
177	John Denny	.06	.05	.02	267	Lou Whitaker	.12	.09	.05
178	LaMarr Hoyt	.03	.02	.01	268	Aurelio Lopez	.03	.02	.01
179	Tim Raines	.30	.25	.12	269	Dan Petry	.04	.03	.02
180	Dale Murphy	.40	.30	.15	270	Glenn Wilson	.04	.03	.02
181	Andre Dawson	.25	.20	.10	271	Chet Lemon	.04	.03	.02
182	Steve Rogers	.15	.11	.06	272	Kirk Gibson	.06	.05	.02
183	Gary Carter	.30	.25	.12	273	Enos Cabell	.04	.03	.02
184	Steve Carlton	.25	.20	.10	274	Johnny Wockenfuss	.03	.02	.01
185	George Hendrick	.15	.11	.06	275	George Brett	.25	.20	.10
186	Johnny Ray	.15	.11	.06	276	Willie Aikens	.03	.02	.01
187	Ozzie Smith	.20	.15	.08	277	Frank White	.04	.03	.02
188	Mike Schmidt	.40	.30	.15	278	Hal McRae	.06	.05	.02
189	Jim Rice	.30	.25	.12	279	Dan Quisenberry	.06	.05	.02
190	Dave Winfield	.30	.25	.12	280	Willie Wilson	.08	.06	.03
191	Lloyd Moseby	.15	.11	.06	281	Paul Splittorff	.03	.02	.01
192	LaMarr Hoyt	.15	.11	.06	282	U.L. Washington	.03	.02	.01
193	Ted Simmons	.15	.11	.06	283	Bud Black	.06	.05	.02
194	Ron Guidry	.20	.15	.08	284	John Wathan	.04	.03	.02
195	Eddie Murray	.40	.30	.15	285	Larry Gura	.03	.02	.01
196	Lou Whitaker	.25	.20	.10	286	Pat Sheridan	.03	.02	.01
197	Cal Ripken	.40	.30	.15	287a	Rusty Staub	.06	.05	.02
198	George Brett	.40	.30	.15	287b	Dave Righetti	.25	.20	.10
199	Dale Murphy	.15	.11	.06	288a	Bob Forsch	.03	.02	.01
200a	Cecil Cooper	.03	.02	.01	288b	Mike Warren	.06	.05	.02

		MT	NR MT	EX
289	Al Holland	.10	.08	.04
290	Dan Quisenberry	.15	.11	.06
291	Cecil Cooper	.06	.05	.02
292	Moose Haas	.03	.02	.01
293	Ted Simmons	.08	.06	.03
294	Paul Molitor	.10	.08	.04
295	Robin Yount	.15	.11	.06
296	Ben Oglivie	.04	.03	.02
297	Tom Tellmann	.50	.40	.20
298	Jim Gantner	.04	.03	.02
299	Rick Manning	.03	.02	.01
300	Don Sutton	.06	.05	.02
301	Charlie Moore	.04	.03	.02
302	Jim Slaton	.03	.02	.01
303	Gary Ward	.04	.03	.02
304	Tom Brunansky	.08	.06	.03
305	Kent Hrbek	.12	.09	.05
306	Gary Gaetti	.10	.08	.04
307	John Castino	.03	.02	.01
308	Ken Schrom	.03	.02	.01
309	Ron Davis	.03	.02	.01
310	Lenny Faedo	.03	.02	.01
311	Darrell Brown	.06	.05	.02
312	Frank Viola	.06	.05	.02
313	Dave Engle	.03	.02	.01
314	Randy Bush	.03	.02	.01
315	Dave Righetti	.12	.09	.05
316	Rich Gossage	.12	.09	.05
317	Ken Griffey	.06	.05	.02
318	Ron Guidry	.12	.09	.05
319	Dave Winfield	.15	.11	.06
320	Don Baylor	.08	.06	.03
321	Butch Wynegar	.03	.02	.01
322	Omar Moreno	.03	.02	.01
323	Andre Robertson	.03	.02	.01
324	Willie Randolph	.04	.03	.02
325	Don Mattingly	.50	.40	.20
326	Graig Nettles	.06	.05	.02
327	Rickey Henderson	.25	.20	.10
328	Carney Lansford	.08	.06	.03
329	Jeff Burroughs	.04	.03	.02
330	Chris Codiroli	.03	.02	.01
331	Dave Lopes	.06	.05	.02
332	Dwayne Murphy	.04	.03	.02
333	Wayne Gross	.03	.02	.01
334	Bill Almon	.03	.02	.01
335	Tom Underwood	.04	.03	.02
336	Dave Beard	.03	.02	.01
337	Mike Heath	.03	.02	.01
338	Mike Davis	.04	.03	.02
339	Pat Putnam	.03	.02	.01
340	Tony Bernazard	.03	.02	.01
341	Steve Henderson	.03	.02	.01
342	Richie Zisk	.04	.03	.02
343	Dave Henderson	.06	.05	.02
344	Al Cowens	.03	.02	.01
345	Bill Caudill	.03	.02	.01
346	Jim Beattie	.06	.05	.02
347	Ricky Nelson	.04	.03	.02
348	Roy Thomas	.06	.05	.02
349	Spike Owen	.04	.03	.02
350	Jamie Allen	.03	.02	.01
351	Buddy Bell	.06	.05	.02
352	Billy Sample	.03	.02	.01
353	George Wright	.03	.02	.01
354	Larry Parrish	.06	.05	.02
355	Jim Sundberg	.04	.03	.02
356	Charlie Hough	.06	.05	.02
357	Pete O'Brien	.06	.05	.02
358	Wayne Tolleson	.03	.02	.01
359	Danny Darwin	.03	.02	.01
360	Dave Stewart	.04	.03	.02
361	Mickey Rivers	.04	.03	.02
362	Bucky Dent	.04	.03	.02
363	Willie Upshaw	.06	.05	.02
364	Damaso Garcia	.04	.03	.02
365	Lloyd Moseby	.06	.05	.02
366	Cliff Johnson	.03	.02	.01
367	Jim Clancy	.04	.03	.02
368	Dave Stieb	.06	.05	.02
369	Alfredo Griffin	.04	.03	.02
370	Barry Bonnell	.04	.03	.02
371	Luis Leal	.03	.02	.01
372	Jesse Barfield	.06	.05	.02
373	Ernie Whitt	.03	.02	.01
374	Rance Mulliniks	.06	.05	.02
375	Mike Boddicker	.06	.05	.02
376	Greg Brock	.06	.05	.02
377	Bill Doran	.06	.05	.02
378	Nick Esasky	.06	.05	.02
379	Julio Franco	.08	.06	.03

		MT	NR MT	EX
380	Mel Hall	.06	.05	.02
381	Bob Kearney	.03	.02	.01
382	Ron Kittle	.06	.05	.02
383	Carmelo Martinez	.06	.05	.02
384	Craig McMurtry	.03	.02	.01
385	Darryl Strawberry	.30	.25	.12
386	Matt Young	.04	.03	.02

1984 Topps Stickers Boxes

For the second straight year, Topps printed baseball cards on the back of its sticker boxes. The 1984 set, titled "The Super Bats" features 24 hitting leaders. The cards are blank-backed and measure 2-1/2" by 3-1/2". Two cards were printed on each of 12 different boxes. The player's name appears inside a bat above his photo. Prices listed are for complete boxes.

		MT	NR MT	EX
Complete Set:		8.50	6.50	3.50
Common Player:		.75	.60	.30
1	Al Oliver, Lou Whitaker	1.00	.70	.40
2	Ken Oberkfell, Ted Simmons	.75	.60	.30
3	Hal McRae, Alan Wiggins	.75	.60	.30
4	Lloyd Moseby, Tim Raines	1.00	.70	.40
5	Lonnie Smith, Willie Wilson	.75	.60	.30
6	Keith Hernandez, Robin Yount	.75	.60	.30
7	Wade Boggs, Johnny Ray	1.50	1.25	.60
8	Willie McGee, Ken Singleton	.75	.60	.30
9	Ray Knight, Alan Trammell	1.00	.70	.40
11	Rod Carew, George Hendrick	1.25	.90	.50
12	Bill Madlock, Eddie Murray	1.25	.90	.50
13	Jose Cruz, Cal Ripken, Jr.	1.25	.90	.50

1984 Topps Super

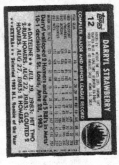

The next installment in Topps' continuing production of large-format cards, these 4-7/8" by 6-7/8" cards were sold in cellophane packs with a complete set being 30 cards. Other than their size and the change in card number on the back, there is nothing to distinguish the Supers from the regular 1984 Topps cards of the same players. One plus is that the players are all big name stars, and are likely to remain in demand.

		MT	NR MT	EX
Complete Set:		12.00	9.00	4.75
Common Player:		.20	.15	.08
1	Cal Ripken	.70	.50	.30
2	Dale Murphy	.90	.70	.35
3	LaMarr Hoyt	.20	.15	.08
4	John Denny	.20	.15	.08
5	Jim Rice	.50	.40	.20
6	Mike Schmidt	.90	.70	.35
7	Wade Boggs	1.25	.90	.50
8	Bill Madlock	.20	.15	.08
9	Dan Quisenberry	.20	.15	.08
10	Al Holland	.20	.15	.08
11	Ron Kittle	.20	.15	.08
12	Darryl Strawberry	1.25	.90	.50
13	George Brett	.90	.70	.35
14	Bill Buckner	.25	.20	.10
15	Carlton Fisk	.30	.25	.12
16	Steve Carlton	.50	.40	.20
17	Ron Guidry	.35	.25	.14
18	Gary Carter	.50	.40	.20
19	Rickey Henderson	1.00	.70	.40
20	Andre Dawson	.35	.25	.14
21	Reggie Jackson	.60	.45	.25
22	Steve Garvey	.50	.40	.20
23	Fred Lynn	.30	.25	.12
24	Pedro Guerrero	.25	.20	.10
25	Eddie Murray	.60	.45	.25
26	Keith Hernandez	.50	.40	.20
27	Dave Winfield	.50	.40	.20
28	Nolan Ryan	1.00	.70	.40
29	Robin Yount	.40	.30	.15
30	Fernando Valenzuela	.40	.30	.15

1984 Topps Traded

The popular Topps Traded set returned for its fourth year in 1984 with another 132-card set. The 2-1/2" by 3-1/2" cards have an identical design to the regular Topps cards except that the back cardboard is white and the card numbers carry a "T" suffix. As before, the set was sold only through hobby dealers. Also as before, players who changed teams, new managers and promising rookies are included in the set. The presence of several promising young rookies in especially high demand from investors and speculators had made this one of the most expensive Topps issues of recent years. A glossy-finish "Tiffany" version of the set was also issued, valued at four to five times the price of the normal Traded cards.

		MT	NR MT	EX
Complete Set:		80.00	60.00	32.00
Common Player:		.10	.08	.04
1T	Willie Aikens	.10	.08	.04
2T	Luis Aponte	.10	.08	.04
3T	Mike Armstrong	.10	.08	.04
4T	Bob Bailor	.10	.08	.04
5T	Dusty Baker	.20	.15	.08
6T	Steve Balboni	.20	.15	.08
7T	Alan Bannister	.10	.03	.04
8T	Dave Beard	.10	.08	.04
9T	Joe Beckwith	.10	.08	.04

		MT	NR MT	EX
10T	Bruce Berenyi	.10	.08	.04
11T	Dave Bergman	.10	.08	.04
12T	Tony Bernazard	.10	.08	.04
13T	Yogi Berra	.20	.15	.08
14T	Barry Bonnell	.10	.08	.04
15T	Phil Bradley(FC)	1.25	.90	.50
16T	Fred Breining	.10	.08	.04
17T	Bill Buckner	.25	.20	.10
18T	Ray Burris	.10	.08	.04
19T	John Butcher	.10	.08	.04
20T	Brett Butler	.20	.15	.08
21T	Enos Cabell	.10	.08	.04
22T	Bill Campbell	.10	.08	.04
23T	Bill Caudill	.10	.08	.04
24T	Bob Clark	.10	.08	.04
25T	Bryan Clark	.10	.08	.04
26T	Jaime Cocanower	.10	.08	.04
27T	Ron Darling(FC)	3.00	2.25	1.25
28T	Alvin Davis(FC)	3.00	2.25	1.25
29T	Ken Dayley	.10	.08	.04
30T	Jeff Dedmon(FC)	.15	.11	.06
31T	Bob Dernier	.10	.08	.04
32T	Carlos Diaz	.10	.08	.04
33T	Mike Easler	.15	.11	.06
34T	Dennis Eckersley	6.00	4.50	2.50
35T	Jim Essian	.10	.08	.04
36T	Darrell Evans	.25	.20	.10
37T	Mike Fitzgerald(FC)	.15	.11	.06
38T	Tim Foli	.10	.08	.04
39T	George Frazier	.10	.08	.04
40T	Rich Gale	.10	.08	.04
41T	Barbaro Garbey	.15	.11	.06
42T	Dwight Gooden(FC)	30.00	22.00	12.00
43T	Rich Gossage	.40	.30	.15
44T	Wayne Gross	.10	.08	.04
45T	Mark Gubicza(FC)	2.00	1.50	.80
46T	Jackie Gutierrez	.10	.08	.04
47T	Mel Hall	1.00	.70	.40
48T	Toby Harrah	.15	.11	.06
49T	Ron Hassey	.10	.08	.04
50T	Rich Hebner	.10	.08	.04
51T	Willie Hernandez	.30	.25	.12
52T	Ricky Horton(FC)	.40	.30	.15
53T	Art Howe	.10	.08	.04
54T	Dane Iorg	.10	.08	.04
55T	Brook Jacoby(FC)	1.50	1.25	.60
56T	Mike Jeffcoat(FC)	.15	.11	.06
57T	Dave Johnson	.15	.11	.06
58T	Lynn Jones	.10	.08	.04
59T	Ruppert Jones	.10	.08	.04
60T	Mike Jorgensen	.10	.08	.04
61T	Bob Kearney	.10	.08	.04
62T	Jimmy Key(FC)	5.00	3.75	2.00
63T	Dave Kingman	.40	.30	.15
64T	Jerry Koosman	.25	.20	.10
65T	Wayne Krenchicki	.10	.08	.04
66T	Rusty Kuntz	.10	.08	.04
67T	Rene Lachemann	.10	.08	.04
68T	Frank LaCorte	.10	.08	.04
69T	Dennis Lamp	.10	.08	.04
70T	Mark Langston(FC)	10.00	7.50	4.00
71T	Rick Leach	.10	.08	.04
72T	Craig Lefferts	.15	.11	.06
73T	Gary Lucas	.10	.08	.04
74T	Jerry Martin	.10	.08	.04
75T	Carmelo Martinez	.25	.20	.10
76T	Mike Mason(FC)	.15	.11	.06
77T	Gary Matthews	.25	.20	.10
78T	Andy McGaffigan	.10	.08	.04
79T	Larry Milbourne	.10	.08	.04
80T	Sid Monge	.10	.08	.04
81T	Jackie Moore	.10	.08	.04
82T	Joe Morgan	3.00	2.25	1.25
83T	Graig Nettles	.50	.40	.20
84T	Phil Niekro	2.00	1.50	.80
85T	Ken Oberkfell	.10	.08	.04
86T	Mike O'Berry	.10	.08	.04
87T	Al Oliver	.30	.25	.12
88T	Jorge Orta	.10	.08	.04
89T	Amos Otis	.15	.11	.06
90T	Dave Parker	2.00	1.50	.80
91T	Tony Perez	.70	.50	.30
92T	Gerald Perry(FC)	1.00	.70	.40
93T	Gary Pettis(FC)	.25	.20	.10
94T	Rob Picciolo	.10	.08	.04
95T	Vern Rapp	.10	.08	.04
96T	Floyd Rayford	.10	.08	.04
97T	Randy Ready(FC)	.25	.20	.10
98T	Ron Reed	.15	.11	.06
99T	Gene Richards	.10	.08	.04
100T	Jose Rijo(FC)	7.00	5.25	2.75
101T	Jeff Robinson(FC)	.25	.20	.10

		MT	NR MT	EX
102T	Ron Romanick(FC)	.20	.15	.08
103T	Pete Rose	8.00	6.00	3.25
104T	Bret Saberhagen(FC)	15.00	11.00	6.00
105T	Juan Samuel(FC)	2.00	1.50	.80
106T	Scott Sanderson	.10	.08	.04
107T	Dick Schofield(FC)	.35	.25	.14
108T	Tom Seaver	8.00	6.00	3.25
109T	Jim Slaton	.10	.08	.04
110T	Mike Smithson	.10	.08	.04
111T	Lary Sorensen	.10	.08	.04
112T	Tim Stoddard	.10	.08	.04
113T	Champ Summers	.10	.08	.04
114T	Jim Sundberg	.15	.11	.06
115T	Rick Sutcliffe	.40	.30	.15
116T	Craig Swan	.10	.08	.04
117T	Tim Teufel(FC)	.30	.25	.12
118T	Derrel Thomas	.10	.08	.04
119T	Gorman Thomas	.25	.20	.10
120T	Alex Trevino	.10	.08	.04
121T	Manny Trillo	.15	.11	.06
122T	John Tudor	.25	.20	.10
123T	Tom Underwood	.10	.08	.04
124T	Mike Vail	.10	.08	.04
125T	Tom Waddell	.10	.08	.04
126T	Gary Ward	.10	.08	.04
127T	Curt Wilkerson	.10	.08	.04
128T	Frank Williams(FC)	.25	.20	.10
129T	Glenn Wilson	.20	.15	.08
130T	Johnny Wockenfuss	.10	.08	.04
131T	Ned Yost	.10	.08	.04
132T	Checklist 1-132	.10	.08	.04

1985 Topps

Holding the line at 792 cards, Topps did initiate some major design changes in its 2-1/2" by 3-1/2" cards in 1985. The use of two photos on the front was discontinued in favor of one large color photo. The Topps logo appears in the upper left-hand corner. At the bottom runs a diagonal rectangular box with the team name. It joins a team logo, and below that point runs the player's position and name. The backs feature statistics, biographical information and a trivia question. Some interesting specialty sets were introduced in 1985, including the revival of the father/son theme from 1976, a subset of the 1984 U.S. Olympic Baseball Team members and a set featuring #1 draft choices since the inception of the baseball draft in 1965. Again in 1985, a glossy-finish "Tiffany" edition of the regular set was produced, though the number was cut back to 5,000 sets. Values range from four times regular value for common cards to five-six times for high-demand stars and rookie cards.

	MT	NR MT	EX
Complete Set:	85.00	65.00	33.00
Common Player:	.06	.05	.02

		MT	NR MT	EX
1	Record Breaker (Carlton Fisk)	.15	.11	.06
2	Record Breaker (Steve Garvey)	.20	.15	.08
3	Record Breaker (Dwight Gooden)	1.00	.70	.40
4	Record Breaker (Cliff Johnson)	.08	.06	.03
5	Record Breaker (Joe Morgan)	.15	.11	.06
6	Record Breaker (Pete Rose)	.60	.45	.25
7	Record Breaker (Nolan Ryan)	1.00	.70	.40

		MT	NR MT	EX
8	Record Breaker (Juan Samuel)(FC)	.20	.15	.08
9	Record Breaker (Bruce Sutter)	.12	.09	.05
10	Record Breaker (Don Sutton)	.20	.15	.08
11	Ralph Houk	.08	.06	.03
12	Dave Lopes	.08	.06	.03
13	Tim Lollar	.06	.05	.02
14	Chris Bando	.06	.05	.02
15	Jerry Koosman	.10	.08	.04
16	Bobby Meacham	.06	.05	.02
17	Mike Scott	.15	.11	.06
18	Mickey Hatcher	.06	.05	.02
19	George Frazier	.06	.05	.02
20	Chet Lemon	.08	.06	.03
21	Lee Tunnell	.06	.05	.02
22	Duane Kuiper	.06	.05	.02
23	*Bret Saberhagen*	4.00	3.00	1.50
24	Jesse Barfield	.25	.20	.10
25	Steve Bedrosian	.12	.09	.05
26	Roy Smalley	.06	.05	.02
27	Bruce Berenyi	.06	.05	.02
28	Dann Bilardello	.06	.05	.02
29	Odell Jones	.06	.05	.02
30	Cal Ripken	4.00	3.00	1.50
31	Terry Whitfield	.06	.05	.02
32	Chuck Porter	.06	.05	.02
33	Tito Landrum	.06	.05	.02
34	Ed Nunez(FC)	.08	.06	.03
35	Graig Nettles	.15	.11	.06
36	Fred Breining	.06	.05	.02
37	Reid Nichols	.06	.05	.02
38	Jackie Moore	.06	.05	.02
39	Johnny Wockenfuss	.06	.05	.02
40	Phil Niekro	.25	.20	.10
41	Mike Fischlin	.06	.05	.02
42	Luis Sanchez	.06	.05	.02
43	Andre David	.06	.05	.02
44	Dickie Thon	.08	.06	.03
45	Greg Minton	.06	.05	.02
46	Gary Woods	.06	.05	.02
47	Dave Rozema	.06	.05	.02
48	Tony Fernandez(FC)	.80	.60	.30
49	Butch Davis	.06	.05	.02
50	John Candelaria	.10	.08	.04
51	Bob Watson	.08	.06	.03
52	Jerry Dybzinski	.06	.05	.02
53	Tom Gorman	.06	.05	.02
54	Cesar Cedeno	.10	.08	.04
55	Frank Tanana	.10	.08	.04
56	Jim Dwyer	.06	.05	.02
57	Pat Zachry	.06	.05	.02
58	Orlando Mercado	.06	.05	.02
59	Rick Waits	.06	.05	.02
60	George Hendrick	.08	.06	.03
61	Curt Kaufman	.06	.05	.02
62	Mike Ramsey	.06	.05	.02
63	Steve McCatty	.06	.05	.02
64	*Mark Bailey*(FC)	.10	.08	.04
65	Bill Buckner	.12	.09	.05
66	Dick Williams	.06	.05	.02
67	*Rafael Santana*(FC)	.20	.15	.08
68	Von Hayes	.10	.08	.04
69	*Jim Winn*(FC)	.10	.08	.04
70	Don Baylor	.12	.09	.05
71	Tim Laudner	.06	.05	.02
72	Rick Sutcliffe	.12	.09	.05
73	Rusty Kuntz	.06	.05	.02
74	Mike Krukow	.08	.06	.03
75	Willie Upshaw	.08	.06	.03
76	Alan Bannister	.06	.05	.02
77	Joe Beckwith	.06	.05	.02
78	Scott Fletcher	.08	.06	.03
79	Rick Mahler	.06	.05	.02
80	Keith Hernandez	.30	.25	.12
81	Lenn Sakata	.06	.05	.02
82	Joe Price	.06	.05	.02
83	Charlie Moore	.06	.05	.02
84	Spike Owen	.08	.06	.03
85	Mike Marshall	.15	.11	.06
86	Don Aase	.06	.05	.02
87	David Green	.06	.05	.02
88	Bryn Smith	.06	.05	.02
89	Jackie Gutierrez	.06	.05	.02
90	Rich Gossage	.20	.15	.08
91	Jeff Burroughs	.08	.06	.03
92	Paul Owens	.06	.05	.02
93	*Don Schulze*(FC)	.10	.08	.04
94	Toby Harrah	.08	.06	.03
95	Jose Cruz	.10	.08	.04
96	Johnny Ray	.12	.09	.05
97	Pete Filson	.06	.05	.02
98	Steve Lake	.06	.05	.02

#	Player	MT	NR MT	EX
99	Milt Wilcox	.06	.05	.02
100	George Brett	1.00	.70	.40
101	Jim Acker	.06	.05	.02
102	Tommy Dunbar	.06	.05	.02
103	Randy Lerch	.06	.05	.02
104	Mike Fitzgerald	.08	.06	.03
105	Ron Kittle	.10	.08	.04
106	Pascual Perez	.08	.06	.03
107	Tom Foley	.06	.05	.02
108	Darnell Coles(FC)	.15	.11	.06
109	Gary Roenicke	.06	.05	.02
110	Alejandro Pena	.08	.06	.03
111	Doug DeCinces	.10	.08	.04
112	Tom Tellmann	.06	.05	.02
113	Tom Herr	.10	.08	.04
114	Bob James	.06	.05	.02
115	Rickey Henderson	2.00	1.50	.80
116	Dennis Boyd(FC)	.15	.11	.06
117	Greg Gross	.06	.05	.02
118	Eric Show	.08	.06	.03
119	Pat Corrales	.06	.05	.02
120	Steve Kemp	.08	.06	.03
121	Checklist 1-132	.06	.05	.02
122	Tom Brunansky	.12	.09	.05
123	Dave Smith	.08	.06	.03
124	Rich Hebner	.06	.05	.02
125	Kent Tekulve	.08	.06	.03
126	Ruppert Jones	.06	.05	.02
127	*Mark Gubicza*	.40	.30	.15
128	Ernie Whitt	.08	.06	.03
129	Gene Garber	.06	.05	.02
130	Al Oliver	.12	.09	.05
131	Father - Son (Buddy Bell, Gus Bell)	.12	.09	.05
132	Father - Son (Dale Berra, Yogi Berra)	.20	.15	.08
133	Father - Son (Bob Boone, Ray Boone)	.12	.09	.05
134	Father - Son (Terry Francona, Tito Francona)	.08	.06	.03
135	Father - Son (Bob Kennedy, Terry Kennedy)	.08	.06	.03
136	Father - Son (Bill Kunkel, Jeff Kunkel)(FC)	.08	.06	.03
137	Father - Son (Vance Law, Vern Law)	.10	.08	.04
138	Father - Son (Dick Schofield, Dick Schofield)	.08	.06	.03
139	Father - Son (Bob Skinner, Joel Skinner)	.08	.06	.03
140	Father - Son (Roy Smalley, Roy Smalley)	.08	.06	.03
141	Father - Son (Dave Stenhouse, Mike Stenhouse)	.08	.06	.03
142	Father - Son (Dizzy Trout, Steve Trout)	.08	.06	.03
143	Father - Son (Ossie Virgil, Ozzie Virgil)	.08	.06	.03
144	Ron Gardenhire	.06	.05	.02
145	*Alvin Davis*	.60	.45	.25
146	Gary Redus	.08	.06	.03
147	Bill Swaggerty	.06	.05	.02
148	Steve Yeager	.06	.05	.02
149	Dickie Noles	.06	.05	.02
150	Jim Rice	.35	.25	.14
151	Moose Haas	.06	.05	.02
152	Steve Braun	.06	.05	.02
153	Frank LaCorte	.06	.05	.02
154	Argenis Salazar(FC)	.06	.05	.02
155	Yogi Berra	.12	.09	.05
156	Craig Reynolds	.06	.05	.02
157	Tug McGraw	.10	.08	.04
158	Pat Tabler	.08	.06	.03
159	Carlos Diaz	.06	.05	.02
160	Lance Parrish	.25	.20	.10
161	Ken Schrom	.06	.05	.02
162	*Benny Distefano*(FC)	.10	.08	.04
163	Dennis Eckersley	.12	.09	.05
164	Jorge Orta	.06	.05	.02
165	Dusty Baker	.08	.06	.03
166	Keith Atherton	.06	.05	.02
167	Rufino Linares	.06	.05	.02
168	Garth Iorg	.06	.05	.02
169	Dan Spillner	.06	.05	.02
170	George Foster	.15	.11	.06
171	Bill Stein	.06	.05	.02
172	Jack Perconte	.06	.05	.02
173	Mike Young(FC)	.12	.09	.05
174	Rick Honeycutt	.06	.05	.02
175	Dave Parker	.25	.20	.10
176	Bill Schroeder	.06	.05	.02
177	Dave Von Ohlen	.06	.05	.02
178	Miguel Dilone	.06	.05	.02
179	Tommy John	.20	.15	.08
180	Dave Winfield	1.25	.90	.50
181	*Roger Clemens*(FC)	20.00	15.00	8.00
182	Tim Flannery	.06	.05	.02
183	Larry McWilliams	.06	.05	.02
184	Carmen Castillo(FC)	.10	.08	.04
185	Al Holland	.06	.05	.02
186	Bob Lillis	.06	.05	.02
187	Mike Walters	.06	.05	.02
188	Greg Pryor	.06	.05	.02
189	Warren Brusstar	.06	.05	.02
190	Rusty Staub	.12	.09	.05
191	Steve Nicosia	.08	.06	.03
192	Howard Johnson(FC)	4.00	3.00	1.50
193	*Jimmy Key*	1.00	.70	.40
194	Dave Stegman	.06	.05	.02
195	Glenn Hubbard	.06	.05	.02
196	Pete O'Brien	.12	.09	.05
197	Mike Warren	.06	.05	.02
198	Eddie Milner	.06	.05	.02
199	Denny Martinez	.08	.06	.03
200	Reggie Jackson	.60	.45	.25
201	Burt Hooton	.08	.06	.03
202	Gorman Thomas	.10	.08	.04
203	Bob McClure	.06	.05	.02
204	Art Howe	.06	.05	.02
205	Steve Rogers	.08	.06	.03
206	Phil Garner	.08	.06	.03
207	Mark Clear	.06	.05	.02
208	Champ Summers	.06	.05	.02
209	Bill Campbell	.06	.05	.02
210	Gary Matthews	.10	.08	.04
211	Clay Christiansen	.06	.05	.02
212	George Vukovich	.06	.05	.02
213	Billy Gardner	.06	.05	.02
214	John Tudor	.10	.08	.04
215	Bob Brenly	.06	.05	.02
216	Jerry Don Gleaton	.06	.05	.02
217	Leon Roberts	.06	.05	.02
218	Doyle Alexander	.10	.08	.04
219	Gerald Perry	.35	.25	.14
220	Fred Lynn	.20	.15	.08
221	Ron Reed	.06	.05	.02
222	Hubie Brooks	.10	.08	.04
223	Tom Hume	.06	.05	.02
224	Al Cowens	.06	.05	.02
225	Mike Boddicker	.10	.08	.04
226	Juan Beniquez	.06	.05	.02
227	Danny Darwin	.06	.05	.02
228	Dion James(FC)	.20	.15	.08
229	Dave LaPoint	.08	.06	.03
230	Gary Carter	.35	.25	.14
231	Dwayne Murphy	.08	.06	.03
232	Dave Beard	.06	.05	.02
233	Ed Jurak	.06	.05	.02
234	Jerry Narron	.06	.05	.02
235	Garry Maddox	.10	.08	.04
236	Mark Thurmond	.06	.05	.02
237	Julio Franco	.50	.40	.20
238	*Jose Rijo*	1.50	1.25	.60
239	Tim Teufel	.12	.09	.05
240	Dave Stieb	.12	.09	.05
241	Jim Frey	.06	.05	.02
242	Greg Harris	.06	.05	.02
243	Barbaro Garbey	.10	.08	.04
244	Mike Jones	.06	.05	.02
245	Chili Davis	.10	.08	.04
246	Mike Norris	.06	.05	.02
247	Wayne Tolleson	.06	.05	.02
248	Terry Forster	.08	.06	.03
249	Harold Baines	.15	.11	.06
250	Jesse Orosco	.08	.06	.03
251	Brad Gulden	.06	.05	.02
252	Dan Ford	.06	.05	.02
253	*Sid Bream*(FC)	.50	.40	.20
254	Pete Vuckovich	.08	.06	.03
255	Lonnie Smith	.08	.06	.03
256	Mike Stanton	.06	.05	.02
257	Brian Little (Bryan)	.06	.05	.02
258	Mike Brown	.06	.05	.02
259	Gary Allenson	.06	.05	.02
260	Dave Righetti	.20	.15	.08
261	Checklist 133-264	.06	.05	.02
262	*Greg Booker*(FC)	.12	.09	.05
263	Mel Hall	.08	.06	.03
264	Joe Sambito	.06	.05	.02
265	Juan Samuel(FC)	.50	.40	.20
266	Frank Viola	.20	.15	.08
267	*Henry Cotto*(FC)	.15	.11	.06
268	Chuck Tanner	.06	.05	.02

		MT	NR MT	EX
269	Doug Baker(FC)	.10	.08	.04
270	Dan Quisenberry	.10	.08	.04
271	1968 #1 Draft Pick (Tim Foli)	.08	.06	.03
272	1969 #1 Draft Pick (Jeff Burroughs)			
		.08	.06	.03
273	1974 #1 Draft Pick (Bill Almon)	.08	.06	.03
274	1976 #1 Draft Pick (Floyd Bannister)			
		.10	.08	.04
275	1977 #1 Draft Pick (Harold Baines)			
		.15	.11	.06
276	1978 #1 Draft Pick (Bob Horner)	.15	.11	.06
277	1979 #1 Draft Pick (Al Chambers)	.08	.06	.03
278	1980 #1 Draft Pick (Darryl Strawberry)			
		2.00	1.50	.80
279	1981 #1 Draft Pick (Mike Moore)(FC)			
		.20	.15	.08
280	1982 #1 Draft Pick (Shawon Dunston)(FC)	1.00	.70	.40
281	1983 #1 Draft Pick (Tim Belcher)(FC)			
		1.25	.90	.50
282	1984 #1 Draft Pick (Shawn Abner)(FC)			
		.20	.15	.08
283	Fran Mullins	.06	.05	.02
284	Marty Bystrom	.06	.05	.02
285	Dan Driessen	.08	.06	.03
286	Rudy Law	.06	.05	.02
287	Walt Terrell	.08	.06	.03
288	Jeff Kunkel(FC)	.10	.08	.04
289	Tom Underwood	.06	.05	.02
290	Cecil Cooper	.12	.09	.05
291	Bob Welch	.12	.09	.05
292	Brad Komminsk(FC)	.08	.06	.03
293	Curt Young(FC)	.35	.25	.14
294	Tom Nieto(FC)	.10	.08	.04
295	Joe Niekro	.10	.08	.04
296	Ricky Nelson	.06	.05	.02
297	Gary Lucas	.06	.05	.02
298	Marty Barrett	.15	.11	.06
299	Andy Hawkins	.08	.06	.03
300	Rod Carew	.50	.40	.20
301	John Montefusco	.06	.05	.02
302	Tim Corcoran	.06	.05	.02
303	Mike Jeffcoat	.08	.06	.03
304	Gary Gaetti	.25	.20	.10
305	Dale Berra	.06	.05	.02
306	Rick Reuschel	.10	.08	.04
307	Sparky Anderson	.08	.06	.03
308	John Wathan	.08	.06	.03
309	Mike Witt	.12	.09	.05
310	Manny Trillo	.08	.06	.03
311	Jim Gott	.06	.05	.02
312	Marc Hill	.06	.05	.02
313	Dave Schmidt	.06	.05	.02
314	Ron Oester	.06	.05	.02
315	Doug Sisk	.06	.05	.02
316	John Lowenstein	.06	.05	.02
317	Jack Lazorko(FC)	.10	.08	.04
318	Ted Simmons	.12	.09	.05
319	Jeff Jones	.06	.05	.02
320	Dale Murphy	.60	.45	.25
321	Ricky Horton	.30	.25	.12
322	Dave Stapleton	.06	.05	.02
323	Andy McGaffigan	.06	.05	.02
324	Bruce Bochy	.06	.05	.02
325	John Denny	.06	.05	.02
326	Kevin Bass	.10	.08	.04
327	Brook Jacoby	.30	.25	.12
328	Bob Shirley	.06	.05	.02
329	Ron Washington	.06	.05	.02
330	Leon Durham	.08	.06	.03
331	Bill Laskey	.06	.05	.02
332	Brian Harper	.06	.05	.02
333	Willie Hernandez	.08	.06	.03
334	Dick Howser	.06	.05	.02
335	Bruce Benedict	.06	.05	.02
336	Rance Mulliniks	.06	.05	.02
337	Billy Sample	.06	.05	.02
338	Britt Burns	.06	.05	.02
339	Danny Heep	.06	.05	.02
340	Robin Yount	1.00	.70	.40
341	Floyd Rayford	.06	.05	.02
342	Ted Power	.06	.05	.02
343	Bill Russell	.08	.06	.03
344	Dave Henderson	.10	.08	.04
345	Charlie Lea	.06	.05	.02
346	Terry Pendleton(FC)	4.00	3.00	1.50
347	Rick Langford	.06	.05	.02
348	Bob Boone	.08	.06	.03
349	Domingo Ramos	.06	.05	.02
350	Wade Boggs	2.00	1.50	.80
351	Juan Agosto	.06	.05	.02

		MT	NR MT	EX
352	Joe Morgan	.30	.25	.12
353	Julio Solano	.06	.05	.02
354	Andre Robertson	.06	.05	.02
355	Bert Blyleven	.12	.09	.05
356	Dave Meier	.06	.05	.02
357	Rich Bordi	.06	.05	.02
358	Tony Pena	.10	.08	.04
359	Pat Sheridan	.06	.05	.02
360	Steve Carlton	.60	.45	.25
361	Alfredo Griffin	.08	.06	.03
362	Craig McMurtry	.06	.05	.02
363	Ron Hodges	.06	.05	.02
364	Richard Dotson	.10	.08	.04
365	Danny Ozark	.06	.05	.02
366	Todd Cruz	.06	.05	.02
367	Keefe Cato	.06	.05	.02
368	Dave Bergman	.06	.05	.02
369	R.J. Reynolds(FC)	.25	.20	.10
370	Bruce Sutter	.12	.09	.05
371	Mickey Rivers	.08	.06	.03
372	Roy Howell	.06	.05	.02
373	Mike Moore	.06	.05	.02
374	Brian Downing	.10	.08	.04
375	Jeff Reardon	.12	.09	.05
376	Jeff Newman	.06	.05	.02
377	Checklist 265-396	.06	.05	.02
378	Alan Wiggins	.06	.05	.02
379	Charles Hudson	.08	.06	.03
380	Ken Griffey	.10	.08	.04
381	Roy Smith	.06	.05	.02
382	Denny Walling	.06	.05	.02
383	Rick Lysander	.06	.05	.02
384	Jody Davis	.10	.08	.04
385	Jose DeLeon	.08	.06	.03
386	Dan Gladden(FC)	.30	.25	.12
387	Buddy Biancalana(FC)	.12	.09	.05
388	Bert Roberge	.06	.05	.02
389	1984 United States Baseball Team (Rod Dedeaux)	.06	.05	.02
390	1984 United States Baseball Team (Sid Akins)(FC)	.10	.08	.04
391	1984 United States Baseball Team (Flavio Alfaro)	.06	.05	.02
392	1984 United States Baseball Team (Don August)(FC)	.20	.15	.08
393	1984 United States Baseball Team (Scott Bankhead)(FC)	.60	.45	.25
394	1984 United States Baseball Team (Bob Caffrey)(FC)	.08	.06	.03
395	1984 United States Baseball Team (Mike Dunne)(FC)	.20	.15	.08
396	1984 United States Baseball Team (Gary Green)(FC)	.08	.06	.03
397	1984 United States Baseball Team (John Hoover)(FC)	.06	.05	.02
398	1984 United States Baseball Team (Shane Mack)(FC)	4.00	3.00	1.50
399	1984 United States Baseball Team (John Marzano)(FC)	.25	.20	.10
400	1984 United States Baseball Team (Oddibe McDowell)(FC)	.20	.15	.08
401	1984 United States Baseball Team (Mark McGwire)(FC)	30.00	22.00	12.00
402	1984 United States Baseball Team (Pat Pacillo)(FC)	.20	.15	.08
403	1984 United States Baseball Team (Cory Snyder)(FC)	1.25	.90	.50
404	1984 United States Baseball Team (Billy Swift)(FC)	1.50	1.25	.60
405	Tom Veryzer	.06	.05	.02
406	Len Whitehouse	.06	.05	.02
407	Bobby Ramos	.06	.05	.02
408	Sid Monge	.06	.05	.02
409	Brad Wellman	.06	.05	.02
410	Bob Horner	.15	.11	.06
411	Bobby Cox	.06	.05	.02
412	Bud Black	.06	.05	.02
413	Vance Law	.08	.06	.03
414	Gary Ward	.08	.06	.03
415	Ron Darling	.60	.45	.25
416	Wayne Gross	.06	.05	.02
417	John Franco(FC)	1.50	1.25	.70
418	Ken Landreaux	.06	.05	.02
419	Mike Caldwell	.06	.05	.02
420	Andre Dawson	.50	.40	.20
421	Dave Rucker	.06	.05	.02
422	Carney Lansford	.10	.08	.04
423	Barry Bonnell	.06	.05	.02
424	Al Nipper(FC)	.15	.11	.06
425	Mike Hargrove	.06	.05	.02
426	Verne Ruhle	.06	.05	.02

	MT	NR MT	EX			MT	NR MT	EX
427 Mario Ramirez	.06	.05	.02	518 Chris Chambliss	.08	.06	.03
428 Larry Andersen	.06	.05	.02	519 Doug Rader	.06	.05	.02
429 Rick Cerone	.06	.05	.02	520 LaMarr Hoyt	.06	.05	.02
430 Ron Davis	.06	.05	.02	521 Rick Dempsey	.08	.06	.03
431 U.L. Washington	.06	.05	.02	522 Paul Molitor	.15	.11	.06
432 Thad Bosley	.06	.05	.02	523 Candy Maldonado	.10	.08	.04
433 Jim Morrison	.06	.05	.02	524 Rob Wilfong	.06	.05	.02
434 Gene Richards	.06	.05	.02	525 Darrell Porter	.08	.06	.03
435 Dan Petry	.08	.06	.03	526 Dave Palmer	.06	.05	.02
436 Willie Aikens	.06	.05	.02	527 Checklist 397-528	.06	.05	.02
437 Al Jones	.06	.05	.02	528 Bill Krueger	.06	.05	.02
438 Joe Torre	.08	.06	.03	529 Rich Gedman	.10	.08	.04
439 Junior Ortiz	.06	.05	.02	530 Dave Dravecky	.08	.06	.03
440 Fernando Valenzuela	.30	.25	.12	531 Joe Lefebvre	.06	.05	.02
441 Duane Walker	.06	.05	.02	532 Frank DiPino	.06	.05	.02
442 Ken Forsch	.06	.05	.02	533 Tony Bernazard	.06	.05	.02
443 George Wright	.06	.05	.02	534 Brian Dayett(FC)	.06	.05	.02
444 Tony Phillips	.06	.05	.02	535 Pat Putnam	.06	.05	.02
445 Tippy Martinez	.06	.05	.02	536 Kirby Puckett(FC)	21.00	15.70	8.40
446 Jim Sundberg	.08	.06	.03	537 Don Robinson	.08	.06	.03
447 Jeff Lahti	.06	.05	.02	538 Keith Moreland	.08	.06	.03
448 Derrel Thomas	.06	.05	.02	539 Aurelio Lopez	.06	.05	.02
449 *Phil Bradley*	.20	.15	.08	540 Claudell Washington	.08	.06	.03
450 Steve Garvey	.40	.30	.15	541 Mark Davis	.06	.05	.02
451 Bruce Hurst	.12	.09	.05	542 Don Slaught	.06	.05	.02
452 John Castino	.06	.05	.02	543 Mike Squires	.06	.05	.02
453 Tom Waddell	.06	.05	.02	544 Bruce Kison	.06	.05	.02
454 Glenn Wilson	.08	.06	.03	545 Lloyd Moseby	.10	.08	.04
455 Bob Knepper	.08	.06	.03	546 Brent Gaff	.06	.05	.02
456 Tim Foli	.06	.05	.02	547 Pete Rose	.60	.45	.25
457 Cecilio Guante	.06	.05	.02	548 Larry Parrish	.10	.08	.04
458 Randy Johnson	.06	.05	.02	549 Mike Scioscia	.08	.06	.03
459 Charlie Leibrandt	.08	.06	.03	550 Scott McGregor	.08	.06	.03
460 Ryne Sandberg	3.00	2.25	1.25	551 Andy Van Slyke	.35	.25	.14
461 Marty Castillo	.06	.05	.02	552 Chris Codiroli	.06	.05	.02
462 Gary Lavelle	.06	.05	.02	553 Bob Clark	.06	.05	.02
463 Dave Collins	.08	.06	.03	554 Doug Flynn	.06	.05	.02
464 *Mike Mason*(FC)	.10	.08	.04	555 Bob Stanley	.06	.05	.02
465 Bob Grich	.10	.08	.04	556 Sixto Lezcano	.06	.05	.02
466 Tony LaRussa	.08	.06	.03	557 Len Barker	.08	.06	.03
467 Ed Lynch	.06	.05	.02	558 Carmelo Martinez	.08	.06	.03
468 Wayne Krenchicki	.06	.05	.02	559 Jay Howell	.08	.06	.03
469 Sammy Stewart	.06	.05	.02	560 Bill Madlock	.12	.09	.05
470 Steve Sax	.20	.15	.08	561 Darryl Motley	.06	.05	.02
471 Pete Ladd	.06	.05	.02	562 Houston Jimenez	.06	.05	.02
472 Jim Essian	.06	.05	.02	563 Dick Ruthven	.06	.05	.02
473 Tim Wallach	.12	.09	.05	564 Alan Ashby	.06	.05	.02
474 Kurt Kepshire	.06	.05	.02	565 Kirk Gibson	.35	.25	.14
475 Andre Thornton	.10	.08	.04	566 Ed Vande Berg	.06	.05	.02
476 *Jeff Stone*(FC)	.12	.09	.05	567 Joel Youngblood	.06	.05	.02
477 Bob Ojeda	.10	.08	.04	568 Cliff Johnson	.06	.05	.02
478 Kurt Bevacqua	.06	.05	.02	569 Ken Oberkfell	.06	.05	.02
479 Mike Madden	.06	.05	.02	570 Darryl Strawberry	5.00	3.75	2.00
480 Lou Whitaker	.30	.25	.12	571 Charlie Hough	.08	.06	.03
481 Dale Murray	.06	.05	.02	572 Tom Paciorek	.06	.05	.02
482 Harry Spilman	.06	.05	.02	573 *Jay Tibbs*(FC)	.15	.11	.06
483 Mike Smithson	.06	.05	.02	574 Joe Altobelli	.06	.05	.02
484 Larry Bowa	.10	.08	.04	575 Pedro Guerrero	.25	.20	.10
485 Matt Young	.06	.05	.02	576 Jaime Cocanower	.06	.05	.02
486 Steve Balboni	.08	.06	.03	577 Chris Speier	.06	.05	.02
487 *Frank Williams*	.15	.11	.06	578 Terry Francona	.06	.05	.02
488 Joel Skinner(FC)	.08	.06	.03	579 *Ron Romanick*	.10	.08	.04
489 Bryan Clark	.06	.05	.02	580 Dwight Evans	.12	.09	.05
490 Jason Thompson	.06	.05	.02	581 Mark Wagner	.06	.05	.02
491 Rick Camp	.06	.05	.02	582 Ken Phelps(FC)	.20	.15	.08
492 Dave Johnson	.08	.06	.03	583 Bobby Brown	.06	.05	.02
493 *Orel Hershiser*(FC)	2.50	2.00	1.00	584 Kevin Gross	.10	.08	.04
494 Rich Dauer	.06	.05	.02	585 Butch Wynegar	.06	.05	.02
495 Mario Soto	.08	.06	.03	586 Bill Scherrer	.06	.05	.02
496 Donnie Scott	.06	.05	.02	587 Doug Frobel	.06	.05	.02
497 Gary Pettis	.15	.11	.06	588 Bobby Castillo	.06	.05	.02
498 Ed Romero	.06	.05	.02	589 Bob Dernier	.06	.05	.02
499 Danny Cox(FC)	.20	.20	.10	590 Ray Knight	.10	.08	.04
500 Mike Schmidt	1.00	.70	.40	591 Larry Herndon	.08	.06	.03
501 Dan Schatzeder	.06	.05	.02	592 *Jeff Robinson*	.30	.25	.12
502 Rick Miller	.06	.05	.02	593 Rick Leach	.06	.05	.02
503 Tim Conroy	.06	.05	.02	594 Curt Wilkerson(FC)	.08	.06	.03
504 Jerry Willard	.06	.05	.02	595 Larry Gura	.06	.05	.02
505 Jim Beattie	.06	.05	.02	596 Jerry Hairston	.06	.05	.02
506 *Franklin Stubbs*(FC)	.40	.30	.15	597 Brad Lesley	.06	.05	.02
507 Ray Fontenot	.06	.05	.02	598 Jose Oquendo	.06	.05	.02
508 John Shelby	.08	.06	.03	599 Storm Davis	.10	.08	.04
509 Milt May	.06	.05	.02	600 Pete Rose	1.00	.70	.40
510 Kent Hrbek	.25	.20	.10	601 Tom Lasorda	.10	.08	.04
511 Lee Smith	.10	.08	.04	602 *Jeff Dedmon*	.12	.09	.05
512 Tom Brookens	.06	.05	.02	603 Rick Manning	.06	.05	.02
513 Lynn Jones	.06	.05	.02	604 Daryl Sconiers	.06	.05	.02
514 Jeff Cornell	.06	.05	.02	605 Ozzie Smith	.15	.11	.06
515 Dave Concepcion	.12	.09	.05	606 Rich Gale	.06	.05	.02
516 Roy Lee Jackson	.06	.05	.02	607 Bill Almon	.06	.05	.02
517 Jerry Martin	.06	.05	.02	608 Craig Lefferts	.08	.06	.03

#	Name	MT	NR MT	EX
609	Broderick Perkins	.06	.05	.02
610	Jack Morris	.25	.20	.10
611	Ozzie Virgil	.06	.05	.02
612	Mike Armstrong	.06	.05	.02
613	Terry Puhl	.06	.05	.02
614	Al Williams	.06	.05	.02
615	Marvell Wynne	.06	.05	.02
616	Scott Sanderson	.06	.05	.02
617	Willie Wilson	.12	.09	.05
618	Pete Falcone	.06	.05	.02
619	Jeff Leonard	.10	.08	.04
620	*Dwight Gooden*	4.00	3.00	1.50
621	Marvis Foley	.06	.05	.02
622	Luis Leal	.06	.05	.02
623	Greg Walker	.12	.09	.05
624	Benny Ayala	.06	.05	.02
625	*Mark Langston*	2.25	1.75	.90
626	German Rivera	.06	.05	.02
627	*Eric Davis*(FC)	4.00	3.00	1.50
628	Rene Lachemann	.06	.05	.02
629	Dick Schofield	.12	.09	.05
630	Tim Raines	.35	.25	.14
631	Bob Forsch	.08	.06	.03
632	Bruce Bochte	.06	.05	.02
633	Glenn Hoffman	.06	.05	.02
634	Bill Dawley	.06	.05	.02
635	Terry Kennedy	.08	.06	.03
636	Shane Rawley	.10	.08	.04
637	Brett Butler	.08	.06	.03
638	*Mike Pagliarulo*(FC)	.80	.60	.30
639	Ed Hodge	.06	.05	.02
640	Steve Henderson	.06	.05	.02
641	Rod Scurry	.06	.05	.02
642	Dave Owen	.06	.05	.02
643	Johnny Grubb	.06	.05	.02
644	Mark Huismann(FC)	.06	.05	.02
645	Damaso Garcia	.06	.05	.02
646	Scot Thompson	.06	.05	.02
647	Rafael Ramirez	.06	.05	.02
648	Bob Jones	.06	.05	.02
649	Sid Fernandez(FC)	.90	.70	.35
650	Greg Luzinski	.10	.08	.04
651	Jeff Russell	.08	.06	.03
652	Joe Nolan	.06	.05	.02
653	Mark Brouhard	.06	.05	.02
654	Dave Anderson	.06	.05	.02
655	Joaquin Andujar	.08	.06	.03
656	Chuck Cottier	.06	.05	.02
657	Jim Slaton	.06	.05	.02
658	Mike Stenhouse	.06	.05	.02
659	Checklist 529-660	.06	.05	.02
660	Tony Gwynn	.80	.60	.30
661	Steve Crawford	.06	.05	.02
662	Mike Heath	.06	.05	.02
663	Luis Aguayo	.06	.05	.02
664	*Steve Farr*(FC)	.30	.25	.12
665	Don Mattingly	3.00	2.25	1.25
666	Mike LaCoss	.06	.05	.02
667	Dave Engle	.06	.05	.02
668	Steve Trout	.06	.05	.02
669	Lee Lacy	.06	.05	.02
670	Tom Seaver	.30	.25	.12
671	Dane Iorg	.06	.05	.02
672	Juan Berenguer	.06	.05	.02
673	Buck Martinez	.06	.05	.02
674	Atlee Hammaker	.06	.05	.02
675	Tony Perez	.15	.11	.06
676	*Albert Hall*(FC)	.15	.11	.06
677	Wally Backman	.08	.06	.03
678	Joey McLaughlin	.06	.05	.02
679	Bob Kearney	.06	.05	.02
680	Jerry Reuss	.08	.06	.03
681	Ben Oglivie	.08	.06	.03
682	Doug Corbett	.06	.05	.02
683	Whitey Herzog	.08	.06	.03
684	Bill Doran	.12	.09	.05
685	Bill Caudill	.06	.05	.02
686	Mike Easler	.08	.06	.03
687	Bill Gullickson	.06	.05	.02
688	Len Matuszek	.06	.05	.02
689	Luis DeLeon	.06	.05	.02
690	Alan Trammell	.35	.25	.14
691	Dennis Rasmussen(FC)	.30	.25	.12
692	Randy Bush	.06	.05	.02
693	Tim Stoddard	.06	.05	.02
694	Joe Carter(FC)	5.00	3.75	2.00
695	Rick Rhoden	.10	.08	.04
696	John Rabb	.06	.05	.02
697	Onix Concepcion	.06	.05	.02
698	Jorge Bell	.40	.30	.15
699	Donnie Moore	.06	.05	.02
700	Eddie Murray	.50	.40	.20
701	Eddie Murray AS	.30	.25	.12
702	Damaso Garcia AS	.08	.06	.03
703	George Brett AS	.35	.25	.14
704	Cal Ripken AS	.30	.25	.12
705	Dave Winfield AS	.20	.15	.08
706	Rickey Henderson AS	.30	.25	.12
707	Tony Armas AS	.08	.06	.03
708	Lance Parrish AS	.15	.11	.06
709	Mike Boddicker AS	.08	.06	.03
710	Frank Viola AS	.12	.09	.05
711	Dan Quisenberry AS	.10	.08	.04
712	Keith Hernandez AS	.20	.15	.08
713	Ryne Sandberg AS	.60	.45	.25
714	Mike Schmidt AS	.30	.25	.12
715	Ozzie Smith AS	.12	.09	.05
716	Dale Murphy AS	.35	.25	.14
717	Tony Gwynn AS	.35	.25	.14
718	Jeff Leonard AS	.10	.08	.04
719	Gary Carter AS	.20	.15	.08
720	Rick Sutcliffe AS	.12	.09	.05
721	Bob Knepper AS	.08	.06	.03
722	Bruce Sutter AS	.10	.08	.04
723	Dave Stewart	.12	.09	.05
724	Oscar Gamble	.08	.06	.03
725	Floyd Bannister	.10	.08	.04
726	Al Bumbry	.08	.06	.03
727	Frank Pastore	.06	.05	.02
728	Bob Bailor	.06	.05	.02
729	Don Sutton	.30	.25	.12
730	Dave Kingman	.15	.11	.06
731	Neil Allen	.06	.05	.02
732	John McNamara	.06	.05	.02
733	Tony Scott	.06	.05	.02
734	John Henry Johnson	.06	.05	.02
735	Garry Templeton	.08	.06	.03
736	Jerry Mumphrey	.06	.05	.02
737	Bo Diaz	.08	.06	.03
738	Omar Moreno	.06	.05	.02
739	Ernie Camacho	.06	.05	.02
740	Jack Clark	.20	.15	.08
741	John Butcher	.06	.05	.02
742	Ron Hassey	.06	.05	.02
743	Frank White	.10	.08	.04
744	Doug Bair	.06	.05	.02
745	Buddy Bell	.12	.09	.05
746	Jim Clancy	.08	.06	.03
747	Alex Trevino	.06	.05	.02
748	Lee Mazzilli	.08	.06	.03
749	Julio Cruz	.06	.05	.02
750	Rollie Fingers	.20	.15	.08
751	Kelvin Chapman	.06	.05	.02
752	Bob Owchinko	.06	.05	.02
753	Greg Brock	.08	.06	.03
754	Larry Milbourne	.06	.05	.02
755	Ken Singleton	.08	.06	.03
756	Rob Picciolo	.06	.05	.02
757	Willie McGee	.30	.25	.12
758	Ray Burris	.06	.05	.02
759	Jim Fanning	.06	.05	.02
760	Nolan Ryan	4.00	3.00	1.50
761	Jerry Remy	.06	.05	.02
762	Eddie Whitson	.06	.05	.02
763	Kiko Garcia	.06	.05	.02
764	Jamie Easterly	.06	.05	.02
765	Willie Randolph	.10	.08	.04
766	Paul Mirabella	.06	.05	.02
767	Darrell Brown	.06	.05	.02
768	Ron Cey	.10	.08	.04
769	Joe Cowley	.06	.05	.02
770	Carlton Fisk	.40	.30	.15
771	Geoff Zahn	.06	.05	.02
772	Johnnie LeMaster	.06	.05	.02
773	Hal McRae	.10	.08	.04
774	Dennis Lamp	.06	.05	.02
775	Mookie Wilson	.10	.08	.04
776	Jerry Royster	.06	.05	.02
777	Ned Yost	.06	.05	.02
778	Mike Davis	.08	.06	.03
779	Nick Esasky	.08	.06	.03
780	Mike Flanagan	.10	.08	.04
781	Jim Gantner	.08	.06	.03
782	Tom Niedenfuer	.08	.06	.03
783	Mike Jorgensen	.06	.05	.02
784	Checklist 661-792	.06	.05	.02
785	Tony Armas	.10	.08	.04
786	Enos Cabell	.06	.05	.02
787	Jim Wohlford	.06	.05	.02
788	Steve Comer	.06	.05	.02
789	Luis Salazar	.06	.05	.02
790	Ron Guidry	.25	.20	.10

		MT	NR MT	EX
791	Ivan DeJesus	.06	.05	.02
792	Darrell Evans	.12	.09	.05

1985 Topps All-Star Glossy Set Of 22

This was the second straight year for this set of 22 cards featuring the starting players, the honorary captains and the managers in the All-Star Game. The set is virtually identical to that of the previous year in design with a color photo, All-Star banner, league emblem, and player's name and position on the front. What makes the cards special is their high gloss finish. The cards were available as inserts in Topps rack packs. With their combination of attractive appearance and big-name stars, these 2-1/2" by 3-1/2" cards will probably continue to enjoy a great deal of popularity.

		MT	NR MT	EX
Complete Set:		7.00	5.25	2.75
Common Player:		.20	.15	.08
1	Paul Owens	.20	.15	.08
2	Steve Garvey	.50	.40	.20
3	Ryne Sandberg	.40	.30	.15
4	Mike Schmidt	.60	.45	.25
5	Ozzie Smith	.30	.25	.12
6	Tony Gwynn	.60	.45	.25
7	Dale Murphy	.80	.60	.30
8	Darryl Strawberry	1.00	.70	.40
9	Gary Carter	.50	.40	.20
10	Charlie Lea	.20	.15	.08
11	Willie McCovey	.40	.30	.15
12	Joe Altobelli	.20	.15	.08
13	Rod Carew	.50	.40	.20
14	Lou Whitaker	.30	.25	.12
15	George Brett	.80	.60	.30
16	Cal Ripken	.60	.45	.25
17	Dave Winfield	.50	.40	.20
18	Chet Lemon	.20	.15	.08
19	Reggie Jackson	.60	.45	.25
20	Lance Parrish	.30	.25	.12
21	Dave Stieb	.25	.20	.10
22	Hank Greenberg	.20	.15	.08

1985 Topps All-Star Glossy Set Of 40

Similar to previous years' glossy sets, the 1985 All-Star "Collector's Edition" glossy set of 40 could be obtained through the mail in eight five-card subsets. To obtain the 2-1/2" by 3-1/2" cards, collectors had to accumulate sweepstakes insert cards from Topps packs, and pay 75¢ postage and handling. Under the circumstances, the complete set of 40 cards was not inexpensive. They are however, rather attractive and popular cards, and the set size enabled Topps to include some players who didn't make their 22-card set.

		MT	NR MT	EX
Complete Set:		18.00	13.50	7.25
Common Player:		.15	.11	.06
1	Dale Murphy	1.00	.70	.40
2	Jesse Orosco	.15	.11	.06
3	Bob Brenly	.15	.11	.06
4	Mike Boddicker	.15	.11	.06
5	Dave Kingman	.25	.20	.10
6	Jim Rice	.50	.40	.20
7	Frank Viola	.30	.25	.12
8	Alvin Davis	.35	.25	.14
9	Rick Sutcliffe	.20	.15	.08
10	Pete Rose	1.25	.90	.50
11	Leon Durham	.15	.11	.06
12	Joaquin Andujar	.15	.11	.06
13	Keith Hernandez	.40	.30	.15
14	Dave Winfield	.60	.45	.25
15	Reggie Jackson	.70	.50	.30
16	Alan Trammell	.35	.25	.14
17	Bert Blyleven	.20	.15	.08
18	Tony Armas	.15	.11	.06
19	Rich Gossage	.25	.20	.10
20	Jose Cruz	.15	.11	.06
21	Ryne Sandberg	.40	.30	.15
22	Bruce Sutter	.20	.15	.08
23	Mike Schmidt	1.00	.70	.40
24	Cal Ripken	.70	.50	.30
25	Dan Petry	.15	.11	.06
26	Jack Morris	.30	.25	.12
27	Don Mattingly	3.50	2.75	1.50
28	Eddie Murray	.60	.45	.25
29	Tony Gwynn	.60	.45	.25
30	Charlie Lea	.15	.11	.06
31	Juan Samuel	.30	.25	.12
32	Phil Niekro	.35	.25	.14
33	Alejandro Pena	.15	.11	.06
34	Harold Baines	.25	.20	.10
35	Dan Quisenberry	.15	.11	.06
36	Gary Carter	.50	.40	.20
37	Mario Soto	.15	.11	.06
38	Dwight Gooden	2.50	2.00	1.00
39	Tom Brunansky	.20	.15	.08
40	Dave Stieb	.20	.15	.08

1985 Topps All-Time Record Holders

This 44-card boxed set was produced by Topps for

the Woolworth's chain stores. Many hobbyists refer to this as the "Woolworth's" set, but that name does not appear anywhere on the cards. Featuring a combination of black and white and color photos of baseball record holders from all eras, the set is in the standard 2-1/2" by 3-1/2" format. Backs, printed in blue and orange, give career details and personal data. Because it combined old-timers with current players, the set did not achieve a great deal of collector popularity.

		MT	NR MT	EX
	Complete Set:	5.00	3.75	2.00
	Common Player:	.05	.04	.02
1	Hank Aaron	.25	.20	.10
2	Grover Alexander	.10	.08	.04
3	Ernie Banks	.12	.09	.05
4	Yogi Berra	.15	.11	.06
5	Lou Brock	.12	.09	.05
6	Steve Carlton	.12	.09	.05
7	Jack Chesbro	.07	.05	.03
8	Ty Cobb	.30	.25	.12
9	Sam Crawford	.07	.05	.03
10	Rollie Fingers	.07	.05	.03
11	Whitey Ford	.12	.09	.05
12	Johnny Frederick	.05	.04	.02
13	Frankie Frisch	.07	.05	.03
14	Lou Gehrig	.30	.25	.12
15	Jim Gentile	.05	.04	.02
16	Dwight Gooden	.60	.45	.25
17	Rickey Henderson	.15	.11	.06
18	Rogers Hornsby	.12	.09	.05
19	Frank Howard	.07	.05	.03
20	Cliff Johnson	.05	.04	.02
21	Walter Johnson	.15	.11	.06
22	Hub Leonard	.05	.04	.02
23	Mickey Mantle	1.00	.70	.40
24	Roger Maris	.12	.09	.05
25	Christy Mathewson	.12	.09	.05
26	Willie Mays	.20	.15	.08
27	Stan Musial	.20	.15	.08
28	Dan Quisenberry	.05	.04	.02
29	Frank Robinson	.12	.09	.05
30	Pete Rose	.40	.30	.15
31	Babe Ruth	.60	.45	.25
32	Nolan Ryan	.12	.09	.05
33	George Sisler	.10	.08	.04
34	Tris Speaker	.10	.08	.04
35	Ed Walsh	.07	.05	.03
36	Lloyd Waner	.07	.05	.03
37	Earl Webb	.05	.04	.02
38	Ted Williams	.30	.25	.12
39	Maury Wills	.07	.05	.03
40	Hack Wilson	.07	.05	.03
41	Owen Wilson	.05	.04	.02
42	Willie Wilson	.07	.05	.03
43	Rudy York	.05	.04	.02
44	Cy Young	.12	.09	.05

1985 Topps Gallery of Champions

This second annual aluminum, bronze, and silver miniature issues honors 12 award winners from the previous season (MVP, Cy Young, Rookie of Year, Fireman, etc.). Each mini is an exact reproduction, at one-quarter scale of the player's official Topps baseball card, both front and back. The bronze and silver sets were issued in a specially-designed velvet-like case. Aluminum sets came cello-wrapped. A Dwight Gooden pewter replica was given as a premium to dealers who bought bronze and silver sets (value $75). A Pete Rose bronze was issued as a premium to dealers purchasing cases of 1985 Topps Traded sets (value $12).

		MT	NR MT	EX
	Complete Aluminum Set:	30.00	22.00	12.00
	Complete Bronze Set:	175.00	131.00	70.00
	Complete Silver Set:	600.00	450.00	240.00
(1a)	Tony Armas (aluminum)	.70	.50	.30
(1b)	Tony Armas (bronze)	7.50	5.75	3.00
(1c)	Tony Armas (silver)	20.00	15.00	8.00
(2a)	Alvin Davis (aluminum)	1.00	.70	.40
(2b)	Alvin Davis (bronze)	10.00	7.50	4.00
(2c)	Alvin Davis (silver)	30.00	22.00	12.00
(3a)	Dwight Gooden (aluminum)	3.00	2.25	1.25
(3b)	Dwight Gooden (bronze)	25.00	18.50	10.00
(3c)	Dwight Gooden (silver)	125.00	94.00	50.00
(4a)	Tony Gwynn (aluminum)	1.25	.90	.50
(4b)	Tony Gwynn (bronze)	12.00	9.00	4.75
(4c)	Tony Gwynn (silver)	50.00	37.00	20.00
(5a)	Willie Hernandez (aluminum)	.70	.50	.30
(5b)	Willie Hernandez (bronze)	7.50	5.75	3.00
(5c)	Willie Hernandez (silver)	20.00	15.00	8.00
(6a)	Don Mattingly (aluminum)	8.00	6.00	3.25
(6b)	Don Mattingly (bronze)	50.00	37.00	20.00
(6c)	Don Mattingly (silver)	200.00	150.00	80.00
(7a)	Dale Murphy (aluminum)	1.50	1.25	.60
(7b)	Dale Murphy (bronze)	15.00	11.00	6.00
(7c)	Dale Murphy (silver)	80.00	60.00	32.00
(8a)	Dan Quisenberry (aluminum)	.70	.50	.30
(8b)	Dan Quisenberry (bronze)	7.50	5.75	3.00
(8c)	Dan Quisenberry (silver)	20.00	15.00	8.00
(9a)	Ryne Sandberg (aluminum)	1.25	.90	.50
(9b)	Ryne Sandberg (bronze)	12.50	9.50	5.00
(9c)	Ryne Sandberg (silver)	70.00	52.00	27.00
(10a)	Mike Schmidt (aluminum)	1.50	1.25	.60
(10b)	Mike Schmidt (bronze)	15.00	11.00	6.00
(10c)	Mike Schmidt (silver)	80.00	60.00	32.00
(11a)	Rick Sutcliffe (aluminum)	.70	.50	.30
(11b)	Rick Sutcliffe (bronze)	7.50	5.75	3.00
(11c)	Rick Sutcliffe (silver)	20.00	15.00	8.00
(12a)	Bruce Sutter (aluminum)	.70	.50	.30
(12b)	Bruce Sutter (bronze)	7.50	5.75	3.00
(12c)	Bruce Sutter (silver)	20.00	15.00	8.00

1985 Topps Rub Downs

Similar in size and design to the Rub Downs of the previous year, the 1985 set again consisted of 32 unnumbered sheets featuring 112 different players. The set was sold by Topps as a separate issue.

		MT	NR MT	EX
	Complete Set:	6.00	4.50	2.50
	Common Player:	.10	.08	.04
(1)	Tony Armas, Harold Baines, Lonnie Smith	.10	.08	.04
(2)	Don Baylor, George Hendrick, Ron Kittle, Johnnie LeMaster	.10	.08	.04

		MT	NR MT	EX
(3)	Buddy Bell, Tony Gwynn, Lloyd Moseby			
		.25	.20	.10
(4)	Bruce Benedict, Atlee Hammaker, Frank White			
		.10	.08	.04
(5)	Mike Boddicker, Rod Carew, Carlton Fisk, Johnny Ray			
		.25	.20	.10
(6)	Wade Boggs, Rick Dempsey, Keith Hernandez			
		.60	.45	.25
(7)	George Brett, Andre Dawson, Paul Molitor, Alan Wiggins			
		.30	.25	.12
(8)	Tom Brunansky, Pedro Guerrero, Darryl Strawberry			
		.40	.30	.15
(9)	Bill Buckner, Tim Raines, Ryne Sandberg, Mike Schmidt			
		.30	.25	.12
(10)	Steve Carlton, Bob Horner, Dan Quisenberry			
		.25	.20	.10
(11)	Gary Carter, Phil Garner, Ron Guidry			
		.25	.20	.10
(12)	Jack Clark, Damaso Garcia, Hal McRae, Lance Parrish			
		.20	.15	.08
(13)	Dave Concepcion, Cecil Cooper, Fred Lynn, Jesse Orosco			
		.15	.11	.06
(14)	Jose Cruz, Jack Morris, Jim Rice, Rick Sutcliffe			
		.20	.15	.08
(15)	Alvin Davis, Steve Kemp, Greg Luzinski, Kent Tekulve			
		.20	.15	.08
(16)	Ron Davis, Kent Hrbek, Juan Samuel			
		.20	.15	.08
(17)	John Denny, Carney Lansford, Mario Soto, Lou Whitaker			
		.15	.11	.06
(18)	Leon Durham, Willie Hernandez, Steve Sax			
		.15	.11	.06
(19)	Dwight Evans, Julio Franco, Dwight Gooden			
		.40	.30	.15
(20)	George Foster, Gary Gaetti, Bobby Grich, Gary Redus			
		.15	.11	.06
(21)	Steve Garvey, Jerry Remy, Bill Russell, George Wright			
		.20	.15	.08
(22)	Kirk Gibson, Rich Gossage, Don Mattingly, Dave Stieb			
		.90	.70	.35
(23)	Moose Haas, Bruce Sutter, Dickie Thon, Andre Thornton			
		.10	.08	.04
(24)	Rickey Henderson, Dave Righetti, Pete Rose			
		.70	.50	.30
(25)	Steve Henderson, Bill Madlock, Alan Trammell			
		.15	.11	.06
(26)	LaMarr Hoyt, Larry Parrish, Nolan Ryan			
		.25	.20	.10
(27)	Reggie Jackson, Eric Show, Jason Thompson			
		.30	.25	.12
(28)	Terry Kennedy, Eddie Murray, Tom Seaver, Ozzie Smith			
		.25	.20	.10
(29)	Mark Langston, Ben Oglivie, Darrell Porter			
		.15	.11	.06
(30)	Jeff Leonard, Gary Matthews, Dale Murphy, Dave Winfield			
		.30	.25	.12
(31)	Craig McMurtry, Cal Ripken, Steve Rogers, Willie Upshaw			
		.25	.20	.10
(32)	Tony Pena, Fernando Valenzuela, Robin Yount			
		.20	.15	.08

1985 Topps Stickers

Topps went to a larger size for its stickers in 1985. Each of the 376 stickers measures 2-1/8" by 3" and is numbered on both the front and the back. The backs contain either an offer to obtain an autographed team ball or a poster. An album was also available.

		MT	NR MT	EX
	Complete Set:	16.00	12.00	6.50
	Common Player:	.03	.02	.01
	Sticker Album:	.80	.60	.30
1	Steve Garvey	.25	.20	.10
2	Steve Garvey	.25	.20	.10
3	Dwight Gooden	.25	.20	.10
4	Dwight Gooden	.25	.20	.10
5	Joe Morgan	.10	.08	.04
6	Joe Morgan	.10	.08	.04
7	Don Sutton	.10	.08	.04
8	Don Sutton	.10	.08	.04
9	1984 A.L. Championships (Jack Morris)	.06	.05	.02
10	1984 A.L. Championships (Milt Wilcox)	.03	.02	.01
11	1984 A.L. Championships (Kirk Gibson)	.08	.06	.03
12	1984 N.L. Championships (Gary Matthews)	.04	.03	.02
13	1984 N.L. Championships (Steve Garvey)	.10	.08	.04
14	1984 N.L. Championships (Steve Garvey)	.15	.11	.06
15	1984 World Series (Jack Morris)	.06	.05	.02
16	1984 World Series (Kurt Bevacqua)	.03	.02	.01
17	1984 World Series (Milt Wilcox)	.03	.02	.01
18	1984 World Series (Alan Trammell)	.08	.06	.03
19	1984 World Series (Kirk Gibson)	.08	.06	.03
20	1984 World Series (Alan Trammell)	.12	.09	.05
21	1984 World Series (Chet Lemon)	.03	.02	.01
22	Dale Murphy	.25	.20	.10
23	Steve Bedrosian	.10	.08	.04
24	Bob Horner	.10	.08	.04
25	Claudell Washington	.06	.05	.02
26	Rick Mahler	.06	.05	.02
27	Rafael Ramirez	.04	.03	.02
28	Craig McMurtry	.04	.03	.02
29	Chris Chambliss	.04	.03	.02
30	Alex Trevino	.03	.02	.01
31	Bruce Benedict	.04	.03	.02
32	Ken Oberkfell	.03	.02	.01
33	Glenn Hubbard	.04	.03	.02
34	Ryne Sandberg	.15	.11	.06
35	Rick Sutcliffe	.08	.06	.03
36	Leon Durham	.06	.05	.02
37	Jody Davis	.06	.05	.02
38	Bob Dernier	.04	.03	.02
39	Keith Moreland	.06	.05	.02
40	Scott Sanderson	.04	.03	.02
41	Lee Smith	.06	.05	.02
42	Ron Cey	.06	.05	.02
43	Steve Trout	.06	.05	.02
44	Gary Matthews	.06	.05	.02
45	Larry Bowa	.04	.03	.02
46	Mario Soto	.06	.05	.02
47	Dave Parker	.12	.09	.05
48	Dave Concepcion	.06	.05	.02
49	Gary Redus	.06	.05	.02
50	Ted Power	.06	.05	.02
51	Nick Esasky	.04	.03	.02
52	Duane Walker	.06	.05	.02
53	Eddie Milner	.03	.02	.01
54	Ron Oester	.03	.02	.01
55	Cesar Cedeno	.04	.03	.02
56	Joe Price	.03	.02	.01
57	Pete Rose	.20	.15	.08
58	Nolan Ryan	.15	.11	.06
59	Jose Cruz	.06	.05	.02
60	Jerry Mumphrey	.04	.03	.02
61	Enos Cabell	.03	.02	.01
62	Bob Knepper	.04	.03	.02
63	Dickie Thon	.04	.03	.02
64	Phil Garner	.04	.03	.02
65	Craig Reynolds	.06	.05	.02
66	Frank DiPino	.03	.02	.01
67	Terry Puhl	.03	.02	.01
68	Bill Doran	.06	.05	.02
69	Joe Niekro	.04	.03	.02
70	Pedro Guerrero	.12	.09	.05
71	Fernando Valenzuela	.15	.11	.06
72	Mike Marshall	.08	.06	.03
73	Alejandro Pena	.04	.03	.02
74	Orel Hershiser	.10	.08	.04
75	Ken Landreaux	.06	.05	.02
76	Bill Russell	.06	.05	.02
77	Steve Sax	.06	.05	.02
78	Rick Honeycutt	.03	.02	.01
79	Mike Scioscia	.03	.02	.01
80	Tom Niedenfuer	.06	.05	.02

#	Player	MT	NR MT	EX
81	Candy Maldonado	.03	.02	.01
82	Tim Raines	.15	.11	.06
83	Gary Carter	.20	.15	.08
84	Charlie Lea	.03	.02	.01
85	Jeff Reardon	.08	.06	.03
86	Andre Dawson	.06	.05	.02
87	Tim Wallach	.04	.03	.02
88	Terry Francona	.04	.03	.02
89	Steve Rogers	.03	.02	.01
90	Bryn Smith	.03	.02	.01
91	Bill Gullickson	.04	.03	.02
92	Dan Driessen	.03	.02	.01
93	Doug Flynn	.03	.02	.01
94	Mike Schmidt	.20	.15	.08
95	Tony Armas	.30	.25	.12
96	Dale Murphy	.15	.11	.06
97	Rick Sutcliffe	.10	.08	.04
98	Keith Hernandez	.12	.09	.05
99	George Foster	.08	.06	.03
100	Darryl Strawberry	.30	.25	.12
101	Jesse Orosco	.04	.03	.02
102	Mookie Wilson	.04	.03	.02
103	Doug Sisk	.03	.02	.01
104	Hubie Brooks	.06	.05	.02
105	Ron Darling	.04	.03	.02
106	Wally Backman	.04	.03	.02
107	Dwight Gooden	.15	.11	.06
108	Mike Fitzgerald	.04	.03	.02
109	Walt Terrell	.03	.02	.01
110	Ozzie Virgil	.04	.03	.02
111	Mike Schmidt	.25	.20	.10
112	Steve Carlton	.15	.11	.06
113	Al Holland	.03	.02	.01
114	Juan Samuel	.06	.05	.02
115	Von Hayes	.04	.03	.02
116	Jeff Stone	.06	.05	.02
117	Jerry Koosman	.04	.03	.02
118	Al Oliver	.04	.03	.02
119	John Denny	.03	.02	.01
120	Charles Hudson	.03	.02	.01
121	Garry Maddox	.06	.05	.02
122	Bill Madlock	.06	.05	.02
123	John Candelaria	.06	.05	.02
124	Tony Pena	.06	.05	.02
125	Jason Thompson	.03	.02	.01
126	Lee Lacy	.04	.03	.02
127	Rick Rhoden	.06	.05	.02
128	Doug Frobel	.06	.05	.02
129	Kent Tekulve	.04	.03	.02
130	Johnny Ray	.04	.03	.02
131	Marvell Wynne	.08	.06	.03
132	Larry McWilliams	.03	.02	.01
133	Dale Berra	.03	.02	.01
134	George Hendrick	.06	.05	.02
135	Bruce Sutter	.08	.06	.03
136	Joaquin Andujar	.04	.03	.02
137	Ozzie Smith	.10	.08	.04
138	Andy Van Slyke	.04	.03	.02
139	Lonnie Smith	.06	.05	.02
140	Darrell Porter	.03	.02	.01
141	Willie McGee	.06	.05	.02
142	Tom Herr	.04	.03	.02
143	Dave LaPoint	.03	.02	.01
144	Neil Allen	.04	.03	.02
145	David Green	.03	.02	.01
146	Tony Gwynn	.20	.15	.08
147	Rich Gossage	.12	.09	.05
148	Terry Kennedy	.04	.03	.02
149	Steve Garvey	.15	.11	.06
150	Alan Wiggins	.03	.02	.01
151	Garry Templeton	.08	.06	.03
152	Ed Whitson	.04	.03	.02
153	Tim Lollar	.03	.02	.01
154	Dave Dravecky	.04	.03	.02
155	Graig Nettles	.04	.03	.02
156	Eric Show	.03	.02	.01
157	Carmelo Martinez	.03	.02	.01
158	Bob Brenly	.03	.02	.01
159	Gary Lavelle	.03	.02	.01
160	Jack Clark	.10	.08	.04
161	Jeff Leonard	.04	.03	.02
162	Chili Davis	.06	.05	.02
163	Mike Krukow	.03	.02	.01
164	Johnnie LeMaster	.03	.02	.01
165	Atlee Hammaker	.03	.02	.01
166	Dan Gladden	.06	.05	.02
167	Greg Minton	.03	.02	.01
168	Joel Youngblood	.03	.02	.01
169	Frank Williams	.04	.03	.02
170	Tony Gwynn	.20	.15	.08
171	Don Mattingly	.30	.25	.12
172	Bruce Sutter	.15	.11	.06
173	Dan Quisenberry	.10	.08	.04
174	Tony Gwynn	.40	.30	.15
175	Ryne Sandberg	.35	.25	.14
176	Steve Garvey	.30	.25	.12
177	Dale Murphy	.40	.30	.15
178	Mike Schmidt	.40	.30	.15
179	Darryl Strawberry	.50	.40	.20
180	Gary Carter	.30	.25	.12
181	Ozzie Smith	.20	.15	.08
182	Charlie Lea	.15	.11	.06
183	Lou Whitaker	.25	.20	.10
184	Rod Carew	.30	.25	.12
185	Cal Ripken	.40	.30	.15
186	Dave Winfield	.30	.25	.12
187	Reggie Jackson	.40	.30	.15
188	George Brett	.40	.30	.15
189	Lance Parrish	.25	.20	.10
190	Chet Lemon	.15	.11	.06
191	Dave Stieb	.15	.11	.06
192	Gary Carter	.20	.15	.08
193	Mike Schmidt	.30	.25	.12
194	Tony Armas	.15	.11	.06
195	Mike Witt	.10	.08	.04
196	Eddie Murray	.20	.15	.08
197	Cal Ripken	.20	.15	.08
198	Scott McGregor	.04	.03	.02
199	Rick Dempsey	.04	.03	.02
200	Tippy Martinez	.08	.06	.03
201	Ken Singleton	.04	.03	.02
202	Mike Boddicker	.06	.05	.02
203	Rich Dauer	.03	.02	.01
204	John Shelby	.04	.03	.02
205	Al Bumbry	.04	.03	.02
206	John Lowenstein	.04	.03	.02
207	Mike Flanagan	.04	.03	.02
209	Tony Armas	.04	.03	.02
210	Wade Boggs	.60	.45	.25
211	Bruce Hurst	.06	.05	.02
212	Dwight Evans	.06	.05	.02
213	Mike Easler	.04	.03	.02
214	Bill Buckner	.04	.03	.02
215	Bob Stanley	.04	.03	.02
216	Jackie Gutierrez	.03	.02	.01
217	Rich Gedman	.04	.03	.02
218	Jerry Remy	.03	.02	.01
219	Marty Barrett	.04	.03	.02
220	Reggie Jackson	.20	.15	.08
221	Geoff Zahn	.03	.02	.01
222	Doug DeCinces	.06	.05	.02
223	Rod Carew	.20	.15	.08
224	Brian Downing	.04	.03	.02
225	Fred Lynn	.06	.05	.02
226	Gary Pettis	.04	.03	.02
227	Mike Witt	.06	.05	.02
228	Bob Boone	.06	.05	.02
229	Tommy John	.06	.05	.02
230	Bobby Grich	.06	.05	.02
231	Ron Romanick	.04	.03	.02
232	Ron Kittle	.06	.05	.02
233	Richard Dotson	.06	.05	.02
234	Harold Baines	.08	.06	.03
235	Tom Seaver	.15	.11	.06
236	Greg Walker	.06	.05	.02
237	Roy Smalley	.04	.03	.02
238	Greg Luzinski	.06	.05	.02
239	Julio Cruz	.03	.02	.01
240	Scott Fletcher	.03	.02	.01
241	Rudy Law	.04	.03	.02
242	Vance Law	.03	.02	.01
243	Carlton Fisk	.20	.15	.08
244	Andre Thornton	.06	.05	.02
245	Julio Franco	.08	.06	.03
246	Brett Butler	.06	.05	.02
247	Bert Blyleven	.08	.06	.03
248	Mike Hargrove	.04	.03	.02
249	George Vukovich	.04	.03	.02
250	Pat Tabler	.06	.05	.02
251	Brook Jacoby	.03	.02	.01
252	Tony Bernazard	.03	.02	.01
253	Ernie Camacho	.03	.02	.01
254	Mel Hall	.06	.05	.02
255	Carmen Castillo	.04	.03	.02
256	Jack Morris	.12	.09	.05
257	Willie Hernandez	.06	.05	.02
258	Alan Trammell	.15	.11	.06
259	Lance Parrish	.12	.09	.05
260	Chet Lemon	.10	.08	.04
261	Lou Whitaker	.06	.05	.02
262	Howard Johnson	.06	.05	.02
263	Barbaro Garbey	.06	.05	.02

		MT	NR MT	EX
264	Dan Petry	.03	.02	.01
265	Aurelio Lopez	.03	.02	.01
266	Larry Herndon	.03	.02	.01
267	Kirk Gibson	.06	.05	.02
268	George Brett	.25	.20	.10
269	Dan Quisenberry	.06	.05	.02
270	Hal McRae	.06	.05	.02
271	Steve Balboni	.06	.05	.02
272	Pat Sheridan	.06	.05	.02
273	Jorge Orta	.04	.03	.02
274	Frank White	.04	.03	.02
275	Bud Black	.03	.02	.01
276	Darryl Motley	.03	.02	.01
277	Willie Wilson	.04	.03	.02
278	Larry Gura	.03	.02	.01
279	Don Slaught	.03	.02	.01
280	Dwight Gooden	.20	.15	.08
281	Mark Langston	.30	.25	.12
282	Tim Raines	.15	.11	.06
283	Rickey Henderson	.10	.08	.04
284	Robin Yount	.15	.11	.06
285	Rollie Fingers	.10	.08	.04
286	Jim Sundberg	.03	.02	.01
287	Cecil Cooper	.06	.05	.02
288	Jaime Cocanower	.04	.03	.02
289	Mike Caldwell	.03	.02	.01
290	Don Sutton	.06	.05	.02
291	Rick Manning	.04	.03	.02
292	Ben Oglivie	.04	.03	.02
293	Moose Haas	.15	.11	.06
294	Ted Simmons	.04	.03	.02
295	Jim Gantner	.03	.02	.01
296	Kent Hrbek	.12	.09	.05
297	Ron Davis	.03	.02	.01
298	Dave Engle	.03	.02	.01
299	Tom Brunansky	.06	.05	.02
300	Frank Viola	.06	.05	.02
301	Mike Smithson	.04	.03	.02
302	Gary Gaetti	.06	.05	.02
303	Tim Teufel	.04	.03	.02
304	Mickey Hatcher	.04	.03	.02
305	John Butcher	.03	.02	.01
306	Darrell Brown	.03	.02	.01
307	Kirby Puckett	.06	.05	.02
308	Dave Winfield	.15	.11	.06
309	Phil Niekro	.12	.09	.05
310	Don Mattingly	.70	.50	.30
311	Don Baylor	.08	.06	.03
312	Willie Randolph	.04	.03	.02
313	Ron Guidry	.06	.05	.02
314	Dave Righetti	.06	.05	.02
315	Bobby Meacham	.04	.03	.02
316	Butch Wynegar	.04	.03	.02
317	Mike Pagliarulo	.08	.06	.03
318	Joe Cowley	.03	.02	.01
319	John Montefusco	.03	.02	.01
320	Dave Kingman	.08	.06	.03
321	Rickey Henderson	.20	.15	.08
322	Bill Caudill	.03	.02	.01
323	Dwayne Murphy	.04	.03	.02
324	Steve McCatty	.04	.03	.02
325	Joe Morgan	.06	.05	.02
326	Mike Heath	.03	.02	.01
327	Chris Codiroli	.06	.05	.02
328	Ray Burris	.04	.03	.02
329	Tony Phillips	.03	.02	.01
330	Carney Lansford	.04	.03	.02
331	Bruce Bochte	.03	.02	.01
332	Alvin Davis	.15	.11	.06
333	Al Cowens	.03	.02	.01
334	Jim Beattie	.03	.02	.01
335	Bob Kearney	.03	.02	.01
336	Ed Vande Berg	.03	.02	.01
337	Mark Langston	.08	.06	.03
338	Dave Henderson	.04	.03	.02
339	Spike Owen	.03	.02	.01
340	Matt Young	.04	.03	.02
341	Jack Perconte	.04	.03	.02
342	Barry Bonnell	.03	.02	.01
343	Mike Stanton	.03	.02	.01
344	Pete O'Brien	.08	.06	.03
345	Charlie Hough	.06	.05	.02
346	Larry Parrish	.06	.05	.02
347	Buddy Bell	.08	.06	.03
348	Frank Tanana	.06	.05	.02
349	Curt Wilkerson	.03	.02	.01
350	Jeff Kunkel	.03	.02	.01
351	Billy Sample	.03	.02	.01
352	Danny Darwin	.03	.02	.01
353	Gary Ward	.03	.02	.01
354	Mike Mason	.03	.02	.01

		MT	NR MT	EX
355	Mickey Rivers	.04	.03	.02
356	Dave Stieb	.08	.06	.03
357	Damaso Garcia	.04	.03	.02
358	Willie Upshaw	.06	.05	.02
359	Lloyd Moseby	.08	.06	.03
360	George Bell	.08	.06	.03
361	Luis Leal	.04	.03	.02
362	Jesse Barfield	.06	.05	.02
363	Dave Collins	.03	.02	.01
364	Roy Lee Jackson	.04	.03	.02
365	Doyle Alexander	.04	.03	.02
366	Alfredo Griffin	.04	.03	.02
367	Cliff Johnson	.04	.03	.02
368	Alvin Davis	.15	.11	.06
369	Juan Samuel	.10	.08	.04
370	Brook Jacoby	.08	.06	.03
371	Dwight Gooden, Mark Langston	.30	.25	.12
372	Mike Fitzgerald	.04	.03	.02
373	Jackie Gutierrez	.03	.02	.01
374	Dan Gladden	.08	.06	.03
375	Carmelo Martinez	.06	.05	.02
376	Kirby Puckett	.20	.15	.08

1985 Topps Super

Still trying to sell collectors on the idea of jumbo-sized cards, Topps returned for a second year with its 4-7/8" by 6-7/8" "Super" set. In fact, the set size was doubled from the previous year, to 60 cards. The Supers are identical to the regular-issue 1985 cards of the same players, only the card numbers on back were changed. The cards were again sold three per pack for 50¢.

		MT	NR MT	EX
Complete Set:		14.00	10.50	5.50
Common Player:		.20	.15	.08
1	Ryne Sandberg	.50	.40	.20
2	Willie Hernandez	.20	.15	.08
3	Rick Sutcliffe	.25	.20	.10
4	Don Mattingly	2.25	1.75	.90
5	Tony Gwynn	.70	.50	.30
6	Alvin Davis	.35	.25	.14
7	Dwight Gooden	2.00	1.50	.80
8	Dan Quisenberry	.20	.15	.08
9	Bruce Sutter	.25	.20	.10
10	Tony Armas	.20	.15	.08
11	Dale Murphy	.90	.70	.35
12	Mike Schmidt	.90	.70	.35
13	Gary Carter	.50	.40	.20
14	Rickey Henderson	.70	.50	.30
15	Tim Raines	.50	.40	.20
16	Mike Boddicker	.20	.15	.08
17	Alejandro Pena	.20	.15	.08
18	Eddie Murray	.60	.45	.25
19	Gary Matthews	.20	.15	.08
20	Mark Langston	.30	.25	.12
21	Mario Soto	.20	.15	.08
22	Dave Stieb	.20	.15	.08
23	Nolan Ryan	.50	.40	.20
24	Steve Carlton	.50	.40	.20
25	Alan Trammell	.40	.30	.15
26	Steve Garvey	.50	.40	.20
27	Kirk Gibson	.35	.25	.14
28	Juan Samuel	.35	.25	.14
29	Reggie Jackson	.60	.45	.25
30	Darryl Strawberry	.90	.70	.35

		MT	NR MT	EX
31	Tom Seaver	.50	.40	.20
32	Pete Rose	1.25	.90	.50
33	Dwight Evans	.30	.25	.12
34	Jose Cruz	.20	.15	.08
35	Bert Blyleven	.25	.20	.10
36	Keith Hernandez	.50	.40	.20
37	Robin Yount	.40	.30	.15
38	Joaquin Andujar	.20	.15	.08
39	Lloyd Moseby	.20	.15	.08
40	Chili Davis	.20	.15	.08
41	Kent Hrbek	.35	.25	.14
42	Dave Parker	.30	.25	.12
43	Jack Morris	.35	.25	.14
44	Pedro Guerrero	.30	.25	.12
45	Mike Witt	.20	.15	.08
46	George Brett	.90	.70	.35
47	Ozzie Smith	.30	.25	.12
48	Cal Ripken	.70	.50	.30
49	Rich Gossage	.25	.20	.10
50	Jim Rice	.50	.40	.20
51	Harold Baines	.25	.20	.10
52	Fernando Valenzuela	.40	.30	.15
53	Buddy Bell	.25	.20	.10
54	Jesse Orosco	.20	.15	.08
55	Lance Parrish	.35	.25	.14
56	Jason Thompson	.20	.15	.08
57	Tom Brunansky	.25	.20	.10
58	Dave Righetti	.30	.25	.12
59	Dave Kingman	.25	.20	.10
60	Dave Winfield	.50	.40	.20

1985 Topps 3-D

These 4-1/4" by 6" cards were something new. Printed on plastic, rather than paper, the player picture on the card is actually raised above the surface much like might be found on a relief map; a true 3-D baseball card. The plastic cards include the player's name, a Topps logo and card number across the top, and a team logo on the side. The backs are blank but have two peel-off adhesive strips so that the card may be attached to a flat surface. There are 30 cards in the set, the bulk of whom are stars.

		MT	NR MT	EX
Complete Set:		16.00	12.00	6.50
Common Player:		.20	.15	.08
1	Mike Schmidt	.90	.70	.35
2	Eddie Murray	.70	.50	.30
3	Dale Murphy	.90	.70	.35
4	George Brett	.90	.70	.35
5	Pete Rose	1.25	.90	.50
6	Jim Rice	.60	.45	.25
7	Ryne Sandberg	.50	.40	.20
8	Don Mattingly	2.50	2.00	1.00
9	Darryl Strawberry	.90	.70	.35
10	Rickey Henderson	.80	.60	.30
11	Keith Hernandez	.50	.40	.20
12	Dave Kingman	.20	.15	.08
13	Tony Gwynn	.80	.60	.30
14	Reggie Jackson	.70	.50	.30
15	Gary Carter	.60	.45	.25
16	Cal Ripken	.80	.60	.30
17	Tim Raines	.50	.40	.20
18	Dave Winfield	.60	.45	.25
19	Dwight Gooden	2.00	1.50	.80

		MT	NR MT	EX
20	Dave Stieb	.20	.15	.08
21	Fernando Valenzuela	.50	.40	.20
22	Mark Langston	.30	.25	.12
23	Bruce Sutter	.25	.20	.10
24	Dan Quisenberry	.20	.15	.08
25	Steve Carlton	.60	.45	.25
26	Mike Boddicker	.20	.15	.08
27	Goose Gossage	.30	.25	.12
28	Jack Morris	.40	.30	.15
29	Rick Sutcliffe	.25	.20	.10
30	Tom Seaver	.60	.45	.25

1985 Topps Traded

By 1985, the Topps Traded set had become a yearly feature, and Topps continued the tradition with another 132-card set. The 2-1/2" by 3-1/2" cards followed the pattern of being virtually identical in design to the regular cards issued by Topps. Sold only through established hobby dealers, the set features traded veterans and promising rookies. A glossy-finish "Tiffany" edition of the set is valued at four times normal Traded card value for commons, up to five or six times normal value for superstars and hot rookies.

		MT	NR MT	EX
Complete Set:		25.00	18.00	10.00
Common Player:		.10	.08	.04
1T	Don Aase	.10	.08	.04
2T	Bill Almon	.10	.08	.04
3T	Benny Ayala	.10	.08	.04
4T	Dusty Baker	.15	.11	.06
5T	George Bamberger	.10	.08	.04
6T	Dale Berra	.10	.08	.04
7T	Rich Bordi	.10	.08	.04
8T	Daryl Boston(FC)	.20	.15	.08
9T	Hubie Brooks	.25	.20	.10
10T	Chris Brown(FC)	.25	.20	.10
11T	Tom Browning(FC)	1.25	.90	.50
12T	Al Bumbry	.10	.08	.04
13T	Ray Burris	.10	.08	.04
14T	Jeff Burroughs	.15	.11	.06
15T	Bill Campbell	.10	.08	.04
16T	Don Carman(FC)	.15	.11	.06
17T	Gary Carter	1.00	.70	.40
18T	Bobby Castillo	.10	.08	.04
19T	Bill Caudill	.10	.08	.04
20T	Rick Cerone	.10	.08	.04
21T	Bryan Clark	.10	.08	.04
22T	Jack Clark	.35	.25	.14
23T	Pat Clements(FC)	.20	.15	.08
24T	Vince Coleman(FC)	5.00	3.75	2.00
25T	Dave Collins	.15	.11	.06
26T	Danny Darwin	.15	.11	.06
27T	Jim Davenport	.10	.08	.04
28T	Jerry Davis	.10	.08	.04
29T	Brian Dayett	.10	.08	.04
30T	Ivan DeJesus	.10	.08	.04
31T	Ken Dixon	.10	.08	.04
32T	Mariano Duncan(FC)	.20	.15	.08
33T	John Felske	.10	.08	.04
34T	Mike Fitzgerald	.10	.08	.04
35T	Ray Fontenot	.10	.08	.04
36T	Greg Gagne(FC)	.35	.25	.14
37T	Oscar Gamble	.15	.11	.06

		MT	NR MT	EX
38T	Scott Garrelts(FC)	.50	.40	.20
39T	Bob Gibson	.10	.08	.04
40T	Jim Gott	.10	.08	.04
41T	David Green	.10	.08	.04
42T	Alfredo Griffin	.15	.11	.06
43T	Ozzie Guillen(FC)	1.25	.90	.50
44T	Eddie Haas	.10	.08	.04
45T	Terry Harper	.10	.08	.04
46T	Toby Harrah	.15	.11	.06
47T	Greg Harris	.10	.08	.04
48T	Ron Hassey	.10	.08	.04
49T	Rickey Henderson	5.00	3.75	2.00
50T	Steve Henderson	.10	.08	.04
51T	George Hendrick	.15	.11	.06
52T	Joe Hesketh(FC)	.20	.15	.08
53T	Teddy Higuera(FC)	.70	.50	.30
54T	Donnie Hill	.10	.08	.04
55T	Al Holland	.10	.08	.04
56T	Burt Hooton	.15	.11	.06
57T	Jay Howell	.15	.11	.06
58T	Ken Howell(FC)	.15	.11	.06
59T	LaMarr Hoyt	.10	.08	.04
60T	Tim Hulett(FC)	.15	.11	.06
61T	Bob James	.10	.08	.04
62T	Steve Jeltz(FC)	.15	.11	.06
63T	Cliff Johnson	.10	.08	.04
64T	Howard Johnson	2.50	2.00	1.00
65T	Ruppert Jones	.10	.08	.04
66T	Steve Kemp	.15	.11	.06
67T	Bruce Kison	.10	.08	.04
68T	Alan Knicely	.10	.08	.04
69T	Mike LaCoss	.10	.08	.04
70T	Lee Lacy	.10	.08	.04
71T	Dave LaPoint	.20	.15	.08
72T	Gary Lavelle	.10	.08	.04
73T	Vance Law	.15	.11	.06
74T	Johnnie LeMaster	.10	.08	.04
75T	Sixto Lezcano	.10	.08	.04
76T	Tim Lollar	.10	.08	.04
77T	Fred Lynn	.30	.25	.12
78T	Billy Martin	.20	.15	.08
79T	Ron Mathis	.10	.08	.04
80T	Len Matuszek	.10	.08	.04
81T	Gene Mauch	.15	.11	.06
82T	Oddibe McDowell	.25	.20	.10
83T	Roger McDowell(FC)	.50	.40	.20
84T	John McNamara	.10	.08	.04
85T	Donnie Moore	.10	.08	.04
86T	Gene Nelson	.10	.08	.04
87T	Steve Nicosia	.10	.08	.04
88T	Al Oliver	.30	.25	.12
89T	Joe Orsulak(FC)	.20	.15	.08
90T	Rob Picciolo	.10	.08	.04
91T	Chris Pittaro	.10	.08	.04
92T	Jim Presley(FC)	.60	.45	.25
93T	Rick Reuschel	.25	.20	.10
94T	Bert Roberge	.10	.08	.04
95T	Bob Rodgers	.10	.08	.04
96T	Jerry Royster	.10	.08	.04
97T	Dave Rozema	.10	.08	.04
98T	Dave Rucker	.10	.08	.04
99T	Vern Ruhle	.10	.08	.04
100T	Paul Runge(FC)	.15	.11	.06
101T	Mark Salas(FC)	.15	.11	.06
102T	Luis Salazar	.10	.08	.04
103T	Joe Sambito	.10	.08	.04
104T	Rick Schu(FC)	.20	.15	.08
105T	Donnie Scott	.10	.08	.04
106T	Larry Sheets(FC)	.50	.40	.20
107T	Don Slaught	.10	.08	.04
108T	Roy Smalley	.15	.11	.06
109T	Lonnie Smith	.15	.11	.06
110T	Nate Snell	.10	.08	.04
111T	Chris Speier	.10	.08	.04
112T	Mike Stenhouse	.10	.08	.04
113T	Tim Stoddard	.10	.08	.04
114T	Jim Sundberg	.15	.11	.06
115T	Bruce Sutter	.25	.20	.10
116T	Don Sutton	.60	.45	.25
117T	Kent Tekulve	.15	.11	.06
118T	Tom Tellmann	.10	.08	.04
119T	Walt Terrell	.15	.11	.06
120T	Mickey Tettleton(FC)	5.00	3.75	2.00
121T	Derrel Thomas	.10	.08	.04
122T	Rich Thompson	.10	.08	.04
123T	Alex Trevino	.10	.08	.04
124T	John Tudor	.25	.20	.10
125T	Jose Uribe(FC)	.25	.20	.10
126T	Bobby Valentine	.10	.08	.04
127T	Dave Von Ohlen	.10	.08	.04
128T	U.L. Washington	.10	.08	.04

		MT	NR MT	EX
129T	Earl Weaver	.15	.11	.06
130T	Eddie Whitson	.10	.08	.04
131T	Herm Winningham(FC)	.20	.15	.08
132T	Checklist 1-132	.10	.08	.04

1986 Topps

DAVE HENDERSON

The 1986 Topps set consists of 792 cards. Fronts of the 2-1/2" by 3-1/2" cards feature color photos with the Topps logo in the upper right-hand corner while the player's position is in the lower left-hand corner. Above the picture is the team name, while below it is the player's name. The borders are a departure from previous practice, as the top 7/8" is black, while the remainder was white. There are no card numbers 51 and 171 in the set; the card that should have been #51, Bobby Wine, shares #57 with Bill Doran, while #171, Bob Rodgers, shares #141 with Chuck Cottier. Once again, a 5,000-set glossy-finish "Tiffany" edition was produced. Values are four to six times higher than the same card in the regular issue.

		MT	NR MT	EX
	Complete Set:	35.00	28.00	13.00
	Common Player:	.05	.04	.02
1	Pete Rose	.90	.70	.35
2	Rose Special 1963-66	.30	.25	.12
3	Rose Special 1967-70	.30	.25	.12
4	Rose Special 1971-74	.30	.25	.12
5	Rose Special 1975-78	.30	.25	.12
6	Rose Special 1979-82	.30	.25	.12
7	Rose Special 1983-85	.30	.25	.12
8	Dwayne Murphy	.07	.05	.03
9	Roy Smith	.05	.04	.02
10	Tony Gwynn	1.00	.70	.40
11	Bob Ojeda	.07	.05	.03
12	Jose Uribe(FC)	.20	.15	.08
13	Bob Kearney	.05	.04	.02
14	Julio Cruz	.05	.04	.02
15	Eddie Whitson	.05	.04	.02
16	Rick Schu(FC)	.07	.05	.03
17	Mike Stenhouse	.05	.04	.02
18	Brent Gaff	.05	.04	.02
19	Rich Hebner	.05	.04	.02
20	Lou Whitaker	.25	.20	.10
21	George Bamberger	.05	.04	.02
22	Duane Walker	.05	.04	.02
23	Manny Lee(FC)	.15	.11	.06
24	Len Barker	.07	.05	.03
25	Willie Wilson	.12	.09	.05
26	Frank DiPino	.05	.04	.02
27	Ray Knight	.07	.05	.03
28	Eric Davis	1.00	.70	.40
29	Tony Phillips	.05	.04	.02
30	Eddie Murray	.40	.30	.15
31	Jamie Easterly	.05	.04	.02
32	Steve Yeager	.05	.04	.02
33	Jeff Lahti	.05	.04	.02
34	Ken Phelps(FC)	.07	.05	.03
35	Jeff Reardon	.12	.09	.05
36	Tigers Leaders (Lance Parrish)	.12	.09	.05
37	Mark Thurmond	.05	.04	.02
38	Glenn Hoffman	.05	.04	.02
39	Dave Rucker	.05	.04	.02
40	Ken Griffey	.10	.08	.04

		MT	NR MT	EX
41	Brad Wellman	.05	.04	.02
42	Geoff Zahn	.05	.04	.02
43	Dave Engle	.05	.04	.02
44	*Lance McCullers*(FC)	.25	.20	.10
45	Damaso Garcia	.05	.04	.02
46	Billy Hatcher(FC)	.20	.15	.08
47	Juan Berenguer	.05	.04	.02
48	Bill Almon	.05	.04	.02
49	Rick Manning	.05	.04	.02
50	Dan Quisenberry	.07	.05	.03
51	Not Issued			
52	Chris Welsh	.05	.04	.02
53	*Len Dykstra*(FC)	1.25	.90	.50
54	John Franco	.12	.09	.05
55	Fred Lynn	.15	.11	.06
56	Tom Niedenfuer	.07	.05	.03
57a	Bobby Wine	.05	.04	.02
57b	Bill Doran	.10	.08	.04
58	Bill Krueger	.05	.04	.02
59	Andre Thornton	.07	.05	.03
60	Dwight Evans	.12	.09	.05
61	Karl Best	.05	.04	.02
62	Bob Boone	.07	.05	.03
63	Ron Roenicke	.05	.04	.02
64	Floyd Bannister	.10	.08	.04
65	Dan Driessen	.07	.05	.03
66	Cardinals Leaders (Bob Forsch)	.07	.05	.03
67	Carmelo Martinez	.07	.05	.03
68	Ed Lynch	.05	.04	.02
69	Luis Aguayo	.05	.04	.02
70	Dave Winfield	.60	.45	.25
71	Ken Schrom	.05	.04	.02
72	Shawon Dunston	.20	.15	.08
73	Randy O'Neal(FC)	.07	.05	.03
74	Rance Mulliniks	.05	.04	.02
75	Jose DeLeon	.07	.05	.03
76	Dion James	.07	.05	.03
77	Charlie Leibrandt	.07	.05	.03
78	Bruce Benedict	.05	.04	.02
79	Dave Schmidt	.07	.05	.03
80	Darryl Strawberry	1.50	1.25	.60
81	Gene Mauch	.07	.05	.03
82	Tippy Martinez	.05	.04	.02
83	Phil Garner	.07	.05	.03
84	Curt Young	.07	.05	.03
85	Tony Perez	.15	.11	.06
86	Tom Waddell	.05	.04	.02
87	Candy Maldonado	.10	.08	.04
88	Tom Nieto	.05	.04	.02
89	Randy St. Claire(FC)	.07	.05	.03
90	Garry Templeton	.07	.05	.03
91	Steve Crawford	.05	.04	.02
92	Al Cowens	.05	.04	.02
93	Scot Thompson	.05	.04	.02
94	Rick Bordi	.05	.04	.02
95	Ozzie Virgil	.05	.04	.02
96	Blue Jay Leaders (Jim Clancy)	.07	.05	.03
97	Gary Gaetti	.20	.15	.08
98	Dick Ruthven	.05	.04	.02
99	Buddy Biancalana	.05	.04	.02
100	Nolan Ryan	2.50	2.00	1.00
101	Dave Bergman	.05	.04	.02
102	*Joe Orsulak*	.15	.11	.06
103	Luis Salazar	.05	.04	.02
104	Sid Fernandez	.12	.09	.05
105	Gary Ward	.07	.05	.03
106	Ray Burris	.05	.04	.02
107	Rafael Ramirez	.05	.04	.02
108	Ted Power	.05	.04	.02
109	Len Matuszek	.05	.04	.02
110	Scott McGregor	.07	.05	.03
111	Roger Craig	.07	.05	.03
112	Bill Campbell	.05	.04	.02
113	U.L. Washington	.05	.04	.02
114	Mike Brown	.05	.04	.02
115	Jay Howell	.07	.05	.03
116	Brook Jacoby	.10	.08	.04
117	Bruce Kison	.05	.04	.02
118	Jerry Royster	.05	.04	.02
119	Barry Bonnell	.05	.04	.02
120	Steve Carlton	.40	.30	.15
121	Nelson Simmons	.05	.04	.02
122	Pete Filson	.05	.04	.02
123	Greg Walker	.10	.08	.04
124	Luis Sanchez	.05	.04	.02
125	Dave Lopes	.07	.05	.03
126	Mets Leaders (Mookie Wilson)	.07	.05	.03
127	*Jack Howell*(FC)	.20	.15	.08
128	John Wathan	.07	.05	.03
129	Jeff Dedmon(FC)	.05	.04	.02
130	Alan Trammell	.30	.25	.12
131	Checklist 1-132	.05	.04	.02

		MT	NR MT	EX
132	Razor Shines	.05	.04	.02
133	Andy McGaffigan	.05	.04	.02
134	Carney Lansford	.10	.08	.04
135	Joe Niekro	.10	.08	.04
136	Mike Hargrove	.05	.04	.02
137	Charlie Moore	.05	.04	.02
138	Mark Davis	.05	.04	.02
139	Daryl Boston	.10	.08	.04
140	John Candelaria	.10	.08	.04
141a	Bob Rodgers	.05	.04	.02
141b	Chuck Cottier	.05	.04	.02
142	Bob Jones	.05	.04	.02
143	Dave Van Gorder	.05	.04	.02
144	Doug Sisk	.05	.04	.02
145	Pedro Guerrero	.20	.15	.08
146	Jack Perconte	.05	.04	.02
147	Larry Sheets	.20	.15	.08
148	Mike Heath	.05	.04	.02
149	Brett Butler	.07	.05	.03
150	Joaquin Andujar	.07	.05	.03
151	Dave Stapleton	.05	.04	.02
152	Mike Morgan	.05	.04	.02
153	Ricky Adams	.05	.04	.02
154	Bert Roberge	.05	.04	.02
155	Bob Grich	.10	.08	.04
156	White Sox Leaders (Richard Dotson)	.07	.05	.03
157	Ron Hassey	.05	.04	.02
158	Derrel Thomas	.05	.04	.02
159	Orel Hershiser	.50	.40	.20
160	Chet Lemon	.07	.05	.03
161	Lee Tunnell	.05	.04	.02
162	Greg Gagne	.10	.08	.04
163	Pete Ladd	.05	.04	.02
164	Steve Balboni	.07	.05	.03
165	Mike Davis	.07	.05	.03
166	Dickie Thon	.07	.05	.03
167	Zane Smith(FC)	.15	.11	.06
168	Jeff Burroughs	.07	.05	.03
169	George Wright	.05	.04	.02
170	Gary Carter	.25	.20	.10
171	Not Issued			
172	Jerry Reed	.05	.04	.02
173	Wayne Gross	.05	.04	.02
174	Brian Snyder	.05	.04	.02
175	Steve Sax	.15	.11	.06
176	Jay Tibbs	.05	.04	.02
177	Joel Youngblood	.05	.04	.02
178	Ivan DeJesus	.05	.04	.02
179	*Stu Cliburn*(FC)	.10	.08	.04
180	Don Mattingly	1.00	.70	.40
181	Al Nipper	.05	.04	.02
182	Bobby Brown	.05	.04	.02
183	Larry Andersen	.05	.04	.02
184	Tim Laudner	.05	.04	.02
185	Rollie Fingers	.30	.25	.12
186	Astros Leaders (Jose Cruz)	.07	.05	.03
187	Scott Fletcher	.07	.05	.03
188	Bob Dernier	.05	.04	.02
189	Mike Mason	.05	.04	.02
190	George Hendrick	.07	.05	.03
191	Wally Backman	.07	.05	.03
192	Milt Wilcox	.05	.04	.02
193	Daryl Sconiers	.05	.04	.02
194	Craig McMurtry	.05	.04	.02
195	Dave Concepcion	.12	.09	.05
196	Doyle Alexander	.10	.08	.04
197	Enos Cabell	.05	.04	.02
198	Ken Dixon	.05	.04	.02
199	Dick Howser	.05	.04	.02
200	Mike Schmidt	1.00	.70	.40
201	Record Breaker (Vince Coleman)(FC)	.30	.25	.12
202	Record Breaker (Dwight Gooden)	.40	.30	.15
203	Record Breaker (Keith Hernandez)	.20	.15	.08
204	Record Breaker (Phil Niekro)	.15	.11	.06
205	Record Breaker (Tony Perez)	.10	.08	.04
206	Record Breaker (Pete Rose)	.50	.40	.20
207	Record Breaker (Fernando Valenzuela)	.20	.15	.08
208	Ramon Romero	.05	.04	.02
209	Randy Ready	.10	.08	.04
210	Calvin Schiraldi(FC)	.10	.08	.04
211	Ed Wojna	.05	.04	.02
212	Chris Speier	.05	.04	.02
213	Bob Shirley	.05	.04	.02
214	Randy Bush	.05	.04	.02
215	Frank White	.10	.08	.04
216	A's Leaders (Dwayne Murphy)	.07	.05	.03
217	Bill Scherrer	.05	.04	.02
218	Randy Hunt	.05	.04	.02

		MT	NR MT	EX			MT	NR MT	EX
219	Dennis Lamp	.05	.04	.02	310	Greg Minton	.05	.04	.02
220	Bob Horner	.10	.08	.04	311	Dick Schofield	.05	.04	.02
221	Dave Henderson	.10	.08	.04	312	Tom Filer	.05	.04	.02
222	Craig Gerber	.05	.04	.02	313	Joe DeSa	.05	.04	.02
223	Atlee Hammaker	.05	.04	.02	314	Frank Pastore	.05	.04	.02
224	Cesar Cedeno	.10	.08	.04	315	Mookie Wilson	.10	.08	.04
225	Ron Darling	.15	.11	.06	316	Sammy Khalifa	.05	.04	.02
226	Lee Lacy	.05	.04	.02	317	Ed Romero	.05	.04	.02
227	Al Jones	.05	.04	.02	318	Terry Whitfield	.05	.04	.02
228	Tom Lawless	.05	.04	.02	319	Rick Camp	.05	.04	.02
229	Bill Gullickson	.05	.04	.02	320	Jim Rice	.30	.25	.12
230	Terry Kennedy	.07	.05	.03	321	Earl Weaver	.07	.05	.03
231	Jim Frey	.05	.04	.02	322	Bob Forsch	.05	.04	.02
232	Rick Rhoden	.10	.08	.04	323	Jerry Davis	.05	.04	.02
233	Steve Lyons(FC)	.07	.05	.03	324	Dan Schatzeder	.05	.04	.02
234	Doug Corbett	.05	.04	.02	325	Juan Beniquez	.05	.04	.02
235	Butch Wynegar	.05	.04	.02	326	Kent Tekulve	.07	.05	.03
236	Frank Eufemia	.05	.04	.02	327	Mike Pagliarulo	.20	.15	.08
237	Ted Simmons	.12	.09	.05	328	Pete O'Brien	.10	.08	.04
238	Larry Parrish	.10	.08	.04	329	Kirby Puckett	4.00	3.00	1.50
239	Joel Skinner	.05	.04	.02	330	Rick Sutcliffe	.12	.09	.05
240	Tommy John	.20	.15	.08	331	Alan Ashby	.05	.04	.02
241	Tony Fernandez	.20	.15	.08	332	Darryl Motley	.05	.04	.02
242	Rich Thompson	.05	.04	.02	333	Tom Henke(FC)	.15	.11	.06
243	Johnny Grubb	.05	.04	.02	334	Ken Oberkfell	.05	.04	.02
244	Craig Lefferts	.05	.04	.02	335	Don Sutton	.25	.20	.10
245	Jim Sundberg	.07	.05	.03	336	Indians Leaders (Andre Thornton)	.07	.05	.03
246	Phillies Leaders (Steve Carlton)	.15	.11	.06	337	Darnell Coles	.07	.05	.03
247	Terry Harper	.05	.04	.02	338	Jorge Bell	.25	.20	.10
248	Spike Owen	.05	.04	.02	339	Bruce Berenyi	.05	.04	.02
249	Rob Deer(FC)	.40	.30	.15	340	Cal Ripken	3.00	2.25	1.25
250	Dwight Gooden	1.00	.70	.40	341	Frank Williams	.05	.04	.02
251	Rich Dauer	.05	.04	.02	342	Gary Redus	.05	.04	.02
252	Bobby Castillo	.05	.04	.02	343	Carlos Diaz	.05	.04	.02
253	Dann Bilardello	.05	.04	.02	344	Jim Wohlford	.05	.04	.02
254	Ozzie Guillen	.70	.50	.30	345	Donnie Moore	.05	.04	.02
255	Tony Armas	.07	.05	.03	346	Bryan Little	.05	.04	.02
256	Kurt Kepshire	.05	.04	.02	347	Teddy Higuera	.70	.50	.30
257	Doug DeCinces	.10	.08	.04	348	Cliff Johnson	.05	.04	.02
258	Tim Burke(FC)	.25	.20	.10	349	Mark Clear	.05	.04	.02
259	Dan Pasqua(FC)	.20	.15	.08	350	Jack Clark	.20	.15	.08
260	Tony Pena	.10	.08	.04	351	Chuck Tanner	.05	.04	.02
261	Bobby Valentine	.05	.04	.02	352	Harry Spilman	.05	.04	.02
262	Mario Ramirez	.05	.04	.02	353	Keith Atherton	.05	.04	.02
263	Checklist 133-264	.05	.04	.02	354	Tony Bernazard	.05	.04	.02
264	Darren Daulton(FC)	.12	.09	.05	355	Lee Smith	.10	.08	.04
265	Ron Davis	.05	.04	.02	356	Mickey Hatcher	.05	.04	.02
266	Keith Moreland	.07	.05	.03	357	Ed Vande Berg	.05	.04	.02
267	Paul Molitor	.15	.11	.06	358	Rick Dempsey	.07	.05	.03
268	Mike Scott	.15	.11	.06	359	Mike LaCoss	.05	.04	.02
269	Dane Iorg	.05	.04	.02	360	Lloyd Moseby	.10	.08	.04
270	Jack Morris	.20	.15	.08	361	Shane Rawley	.10	.08	.04
271	Dave Collins	.07	.05	.03	362	Tom Paciorek	.05	.04	.02
272	Tim Tolman	.05	.04	.02	363	Terry Forster	.07	.05	.03
273	Jerry Willard	.05	.04	.02	364	Reid Nichols	.05	.04	.02
274	Ron Gardenhire	.05	.04	.02	365	Mike Flanagan	.10	.08	.04
275	Charlie Hough	.08	.06	.03	366	Reds Leaders (Dave Concepcion)	.07	.05	.03
276	Yankees Leaders (Willie Randolph)	.07	.05	.03	367	Aurelio Lopez	.05	.04	.02
277	Jaime Cocanower	.05	.04	.02	368	Greg Brock	.07	.05	.03
278	Sixto Lezcano	.05	.04	.02	369	Al Holland	.05	.04	.02
279	Al Pardo	.05	.04	.02	370	Vince Coleman	1.50	1.25	.60
280	Tim Raines	.30	.25	.12	371	Bill Stein	.05	.04	.02
281	Steve Mura	.05	.04	.02	372	Ben Oglivie	.07	.05	.03
282	Jerry Mumphrey	.05	.04	.02	373	Urbano Lugo(FC)	.07	.05	.03
283	Mike Fischlin	.05	.04	.02	374	Terry Francona	.05	.04	.02
284	Brian Dayett	.05	.04	.02	375	Rich Gedman	.10	.08	.04
285	Buddy Bell	.10	.08	.04	376	Bill Dawley	.05	.04	.02
286	Luis DeLeon	.05	.04	.02	377	Joe Carter	.70	.50	.30
287	John Christensen(FC)	.10	.08	.04	378	Bruce Bochte	.05	.04	.02
288	Don Aase	.05	.04	.02	379	Bobby Meacham	.05	.04	.02
289	Johnnie LeMaster	.05	.04	.02	380	LaMarr Hoyt	.05	.04	.02
290	Carlton Fisk	.50	.40	.20	381	Ray Miller	.05	.04	.02
291	Tom Lasorda	.07	.05	.03	382	Ivan Calderon(FC)	1.25	.90	.50
292	Chuck Porter	.05	.04	.02	383	Chris Brown	.15	.11	.06
293	Chris Chambliss	.07	.05	.03	384	Steve Trout	.05	.04	.02
294	Danny Cox	.10	.08	.04	385	Cecil Cooper	.10	.08	.04
295	Kirk Gibson	.30	.25	.12	386	Cecil Fielder(FC)	8.00	6.00	3.25
296	Geno Petralli(FC)	.07	.05	.03	387	Steve Kemp	.07	.05	.03
297	Tim Lollar	.05	.04	.02	388	Dickie Noles	.05	.04	.02
298	Craig Reynolds	.05	.04	.02	389	Glenn Davis(FC)	.50	.40	.20
299	Bryn Smith	.05	.04	.02	390	Tom Seaver	.40	.30	.15
300	George Brett	.50	.40	.20	391	Julio Franco	.10	.08	.04
301	Dennis Rasmussen	.12	.09	.05	392	John Russell(FC)	.10	.08	.04
302	Greg Gross	.05	.04	.02	393	Chris Pittaro	.05	.04	.02
303	Curt Wardle	.05	.04	.02	394	Checklist 265-396	.05	.04	.02
304	Mike Gallego(FC)	.12	.09	.05	395	Scott Garrelts	.07	.05	.03
305	Phil Bradley	.15	.11	.06	396	Red Sox Leaders (Dwight Evans)	.07	.05	.03
306	Padres Leaders (Terry Kennedy)	.07	.05	.03	397	Steve Buechele(FC)	.20	.15	.08
307	Dave Sax	.05	.04	.02	398	Earnie Riles(FC)	.15	.11	.06
308	Ray Fontenot	.05	.04	.02	399	Bill Swift	.12	.09	.05
309	John Shelby	.05	.04	.02	400	Rod Carew	.30	.25	.12

#	Name	MT	NR MT	EX
401	Turn Back The Clock (Fernando Valenzuela)	.15	.11	.06
402	Turn Back The Clock (Tom Seaver)	.15	.11	.06
403	Turn Back The Clock (Willie Mays)	.20	.15	.08
404	Turn Back The Clock (Frank Robinson)	.15	.11	.06
405	Turn Back The Clock (Roger Maris)	.20	.15	.08
406	Scott Sanderson	.05	.04	.02
407	Sal Butera	.05	.04	.02
408	Dave Smith	.07	.05	.03
409	Paul Runge	.07	.05	.03
410	Dave Kingman	.15	.11	.06
411	Sparky Anderson	.07	.05	.03
412	Jim Clancy	.07	.05	.03
413	Tim Flannery	.05	.04	.02
414	Tom Gorman	.05	.04	.02
415	Hal McRae	.10	.08	.04
416	Denny Martinez	.07	.05	.03
417	R.J. Reynolds	.07	.05	.03
418	Alan Knicely	.05	.04	.02
419	Frank Wills	.05	.04	.02
420	Von Hayes	.10	.08	.04
421	Dave Palmer	.05	.04	.02
422	Mike Jorgensen	.05	.04	.02
423	Dan Spillner	.05	.04	.02
424	Rick Miller	.05	.04	.02
425	Larry McWilliams	.05	.04	.02
426	Brewers Leaders (Charlie Moore)	.07	.05	.03
427	Joe Cowley	.05	.04	.02
428	Max Venable	.05	.04	.02
429	Greg Booker	.05	.04	.02
430	Kent Hrbek	.20	.15	.08
431	George Frazier	.05	.04	.02
432	Mark Bailey	.05	.04	.02
433	Chris Codiroli	.05	.04	.02
434	Curt Wilkerson	.05	.04	.02
435	Bill Caudill	.05	.04	.02
436	Doug Flynn	.05	.04	.02
437	Rick Mahler	.05	.04	.02
438	Clint Hurdle	.05	.04	.02
439	Rick Honeycutt	.05	.04	.02
440	Alvin Davis	.30	.25	.12
441	Whitey Herzog	.07	.05	.03
442	Ron Robinson(FC)	.12	.09	.05
443	Bill Buckner	.10	.08	.04
444	Alex Trevino	.05	.04	.02
445	Bert Blyleven	.12	.09	.05
446	Lenn Sakata	.05	.04	.02
447	Jerry Don Gleaton	.05	.04	.02
448	Herm Winningham	.15	.11	.06
449	Rod Scurry	.05	.04	.02
450	Graig Nettles	.15	.11	.06
451	Mark Brown	.05	.04	.02
452	Bob Clark	.05	.04	.02
453	Steve Jeltz	.07	.05	.03
454	Burt Hooton	.07	.05	.03
455	Willie Randolph	.10	.08	.04
456	Braves Leaders (Dale Murphy)	.25	.20	.10
457	Mickey Tettleton	.90	.70	.35
458	Kevin Bass	.10	.08	.04
459	Luis Leal	.05	.04	.02
460	Leon Durham	.07	.05	.03
461	Walt Terrell	.07	.05	.03
462	Domingo Ramos	.05	.04	.02
463	Jim Gott	.05	.04	.02
464	Ruppert Jones	.05	.04	.02
465	Jesse Orosco	.07	.05	.03
466	Tom Foley	.05	.04	.02
467	Bob James	.05	.04	.02
468	Mike Scioscia	.07	.05	.03
469	Storm Davis	.10	.08	.04
470	Bill Madlock	.12	.09	.05
471	Bobby Cox	.05	.04	.02
472	Joe Hesketh	.07	.05	.03
473	Mark Brouhard	.05	.04	.02
474	John Tudor	.10	.08	.04
475	Juan Samuel	.12	.09	.05
476	Ron Mathis	.05	.04	.02
477	Mike Easler	.07	.05	.03
478	Andy Hawkins	.05	.04	.02
479	Bob Melvin(FC)	.12	.09	.05
480	Oddibe McDowell	.15	.11	.06
481	Scott Bradley(FC)	.10	.08	.04
482	Rick Lysander	.05	.04	.02
483	George Vukovich	.05	.04	.02
484	Donnie Hill	.05	.04	.02
485	Gary Matthews	.10	.08	.04
486	Angels Leaders (Bob Grich)	.07	.05	.03
487	Bret Saberhagen	.70	.50	.30
488	Lou Thornton	.05	.04	.02
489	Jim Winn	.05	.04	.02
490	Jeff Leonard	.07	.05	.03
491	Pascual Perez	.07	.05	.03
492	Kelvin Chapman	.05	.04	.02
493	Gene Nelson	.05	.04	.02
494	Gary Roenicke	.05	.04	.02
495	Mark Langston	.20	.15	.08
496	Jay Johnstone	.07	.05	.03
497	John Stuper	.05	.04	.02
498	Tito Landrum	.05	.04	.02
499	Bob Gibson	.05	.04	.02
500	Rickey Henderson	1.25	.90	.50
501	Dave Johnson	.07	.05	.03
502	Glen Cook	.05	.04	.02
503	Mike Fitzgerald	.05	.04	.02
504	Denny Walling	.05	.04	.02
505	Jerry Koosman	.10	.08	.04
506	Bill Russell	.07	.05	.03
507	Steve Ontiveros(FC)	.12	.09	.05
508	Alan Wiggins	.05	.04	.02
509	Ernie Camacho	.05	.04	.02
510	Wade Boggs	1.25	.90	.50
511	Ed Nunez	.05	.04	.02
512	Thad Bosley	.05	.04	.02
513	Ron Washington	.05	.04	.02
514	Mike Jones	.05	.04	.02
515	Darrell Evans	.12	.09	.05
516	Giants Leaders (Greg Minton)	.07	.05	.03
517	Milt Thompson(FC)	.25	.20	.10
518	Buck Martinez	.05	.04	.02
519	Danny Darwin	.05	.04	.02
520	Keith Hernandez	.30	.25	.12
521	Nate Snell	.05	.04	.02
522	Bob Bailor	.05	.04	.02
523	Joe Price	.05	.04	.02
524	Darrell Miller(FC)	.07	.05	.03
525	Marvell Wynne	.05	.04	.02
526	Charlie Lea	.05	.04	.02
527	Checklist 397-528	.05	.04	.02
528	Terry Pendleton	.15	.11	.06
529	Marc Sullivan	.05	.04	.02
530	Rich Gossage	.20	.15	.08
531	Tony LaRussa	.07	.05	.03
532	Don Carman	.25	.20	.10
533	Billy Sample	.05	.04	.02
534	Jeff Calhoun	.05	.04	.02
535	Toby Harrah	.07	.05	.03
536	Jose Rijo	.10	.08	.04
537	Mark Salas	.07	.05	.03
538	Dennis Eckersley	.40	.30	.15
539	Glenn Hubbard	.05	.04	.02
540	Dan Petry	.07	.05	.03
541	Jorge Orta	.05	.04	.02
542	Don Schulze	.05	.04	.02
543	Jerry Narron	.05	.04	.02
544	Eddie Milner	.05	.04	.02
545	Jimmy Key	.15	.11	.06
546	Mariners Leaders (Dave Henderson)	.07	.05	.03
547	Roger McDowell	.20	.15	.08
548	Mike Young	.05	.04	.02
549	Bob Welch	.12	.09	.05
550	Tom Herr	.10	.08	.04
551	Dave LaPoint	.07	.05	.03
552	Marc Hill	.05	.04	.02
553	Jim Morrison	.05	.04	.02
554	Paul Householder	.05	.04	.02
555	Hubie Brooks	.10	.08	.04
556	John Denny	.05	.04	.02
557	Gerald Perry	.12	.09	.05
558	Tim Stoddard	.05	.04	.02
559	Tommy Dunbar	.05	.04	.02
560	Dave Righetti	.20	.15	.08
561	Bob Lillis	.05	.04	.02
562	Joe Beckwith	.05	.04	.02
563	Alejandro Sanchez	.05	.04	.02
564	Warren Brusstar	.05	.04	.02
565	Tom Brunansky	.12	.09	.05
566	Alfredo Griffin	.07	.05	.03
567	Jeff Barkley	.05	.04	.02
568	Donnie Scott	.05	.04	.02
569	Jim Acker	.05	.04	.02
570	Rusty Staub	.10	.08	.04
571	Mike Jeffcoat	.05	.04	.02
572	Paul Zuvella	.05	.04	.02
573	Tom Hume	.05	.04	.02
574	Ron Kittle	.10	.08	.04
575	Mike Boddicker	.07	.05	.03
576	Expos Leaders (Andre Dawson)	.12	.09	.05
577	Jerry Reuss	.07	.05	.03
578	Lee Mazzilli	.07	.05	.03
579	Jim Slaton	.05	.04	.02

		MT	NR MT	EX			MT	NR MT	EX
580	Willie McGee	.15	.11	.06	671	Lynn Jones	.05	.04	.02
581	Bruce Hurst	.12	.09	.05	672	Rob Picciolo	.05	.04	.02
582	Jim Gantner	.07	.05	.03	673	Ernie Whitt	.07	.05	.03
583	Al Bumbry	.05	.04	.02	674	Pat Tabler	.07	.05	.03
584	Brian Fisher(FC)	.12	.09	.05	675	Claudell Washington	.07	.05	.03
585	Garry Maddox	.07	.05	.03	676	Matt Young	.05	.04	.02
586	Greg Harris	.05	.04	.02	677	Nick Esasky	.07	.05	.03
587	Rafael Santana	.05	.04	.02	678	Dan Gladden	.07	.05	.03
588	Steve Lake	.05	.04	.02	679	Britt Burns	.05	.04	.02
589	Sid Bream	.10	.08	.04	680	George Foster	.15	.11	.06
590	Bob Knepper	.07	.05	.03	681	Dick Williams	.05	.04	.02
591	Jackie Moore	.05	.04	.02	682	Junior Ortiz	.05	.04	.02
592	Frank Tanana	.10	.08	.04	683	Andy Van Slyke	.15	.11	.06
593	Jesse Barfield	.20	.15	.08	684	Bob McClure	.05	.04	.02
594	Chris Bando	.05	.04	.02	685	Tim Wallach	.12	.09	.05
595	Dave Parker	.20	.15	.08	686	Jeff Stone	.05	.04	.02
596	Onix Concepcion	.05	.04	.02	687	Mike Trujillo	.05	.04	.02
597	Sammy Stewart	.05	.04	.02	688	Larry Herndon	.07	.05	.03
598	Jim Presley	.25	.20	.10	689	Dave Stewart	.12	.09	.05
599	Rick Aguilera(FC)	.40	.30	.15	690	Ryne Sandberg	2.00	1.50	.80
600	Dale Murphy	.50	.40	.20	691	Mike Madden	.05	.04	.02
601	Gary Lucas	.05	.04	.02	692	Dale Berra	.05	.04	.02
602	Mariano Duncan	.15	.11	.06	693	Tom Tellmann	.05	.04	.02
603	Bill Laskey	.05	.04	.02	694	Garth Iorg	.05	.04	.02
604	Gary Pettis	.05	.04	.02	695	Mike Smithson	.05	.04	.02
605	Dennis Boyd	.07	.05	.03	696	Dodgers Leaders (Bill Russell)	.07	.05	.03
606	Royals Leaders (Hal McRae)	.07	.05	.03	697	Bud Black	.05	.04	.02
607	Ken Dayley	.05	.04	.02	698	Brad Komminsk	.05	.04	.02
608	Bruce Bochy	.05	.04	.02	699	Pat Corrales	.05	.04	.02
609	Barbaro Garbey	.05	.04	.02	700	Reggie Jackson	.35	.25	.14
610	Ron Guidry	.15	.11	.06	701	Keith Hernandez AS	.15	.11	.06
611	Gary Woods	.05	.04	.02	702	Tom Herr AS	.07	.05	.03
612	Richard Dotson	.10	.08	.04	703	Tim Wallach AS	.07	.05	.03
613	Roy Smalley	.05	.04	.02	704	Ozzie Smith AS	.10	.08	.04
614	Rick Waits	.05	.04	.02	705	Dale Murphy AS	.30	.25	.12
615	Johnny Ray	.10	.08	.04	706	Pedro Guerrero AS	.12	.09	.05
616	Glenn Brummer	.05	.04	.02	707	Willie McGee AS	.12	.09	.05
617	Lonnie Smith	.07	.05	.03	708	Gary Carter AS	.20	.15	.08
618	Jim Pankovits	.05	.04	.02	709	Dwight Gooden AS	.40	.30	.15
619	Danny Heep	.05	.04	.02	710	John Tudor AS	.07	.05	.03
620	Bruce Sutter	.12	.09	.05	711	Jeff Reardon AS	.07	.05	.03
621	John Felske	.05	.04	.02	712	Don Mattingly AS	.40	.30	.15
622	Gary Lavelle	.05	.04	.02	713	Damaso Garcia AS	.05	.04	.02
623	Floyd Rayford	.05	.04	.02	714	George Brett AS	.30	.25	.12
624	Steve McCatty	.05	.04	.02	715	Cal Ripken AS	.25	.20	.10
625	Bob Brenly	.05	.04	.02	716	Rickey Henderson AS	.25	.20	.10
626	Roy Thomas	.05	.04	.02	717	Dave Winfield AS	.20	.15	.08
627	Ron Oester	.05	.04	.02	718	Jorge Bell AS	.20	.15	.08
628	Kirk McCaskill(FC)	.35	.25	.14	719	Carlton Fisk AS	.12	.09	.05
629	Mitch Webster(FC)	.25	.20	.10	720	Bret Saberhagen AS	.15	.11	.06
630	Fernando Valenzuela	.30	.25	.12	721	Ron Guidry AS	.10	.08	.04
631	Steve Braun	.05	.04	.02	722	Dan Quisenberry AS	.07	.05	.03
632	Dave Von Ohlen	.05	.04	.02	723	Marty Bystrom	.05	.04	.02
633	Jackie Gutierrez	.05	.04	.02	724	Tim Hulett	.07	.05	.03
634	Roy Lee Jackson	.05	.04	.02	725	Mario Soto	.07	.05	.03
635	Jason Thompson	.05	.04	.02	726	Orioles Leaders (Rick Dempsey)	.07	.05	.03
636	Cubs Leaders (Lee Smith)	.07	.05	.03	727	David Green	.05	.04	.02
637	Rudy Law	.05	.04	.02	728	Mike Marshall	.12	.09	.05
638	John Butcher	.05	.04	.02	729	Jim Beattie	.05	.04	.02
639	Bo Diaz	.07	.05	.03	730	Ozzie Smith	.15	.11	.06
640	Jose Cruz	.10	.08	.04	731	Don Robinson	.07	.05	.03
641	Wayne Tolleson	.05	.04	.02	732	Floyd Youmans(FC)	.12	.09	.05
642	Ray Searage	.05	.04	.02	733	Ron Romanick	.05	.04	.02
643	Tom Brookens	.05	.04	.02	734	Marty Barrett	.10	.08	.04
644	Mark Gubicza	.12	.09	.05	735	Dave Dravecky	.07	.05	.03
645	Dusty Baker	.07	.05	.03	736	Glenn Wilson	.07	.05	.03
646	Mike Moore	.05	.04	.02	737	Pete Vuckovich	.07	.05	.03
647	Mel Hall	.07	.05	.03	738	Andre Robertson	.05	.04	.02
648	Steve Bedrosian	.10	.08	.04	739	Dave Rozema	.05	.04	.02
649	Ronn Reynolds	.05	.04	.02	740	Lance Parrish	.20	.15	.08
650	Dave Stieb	.12	.09	.05	741	Pete Rose	.40	.30	.15
651	Billy Martin	.12	.09	.05	742	Frank Viola	.15	.11	.06
652	Tom Browning	.25	.20	.10	743	Pat Sheridan	.05	.04	.02
653	Jim Dwyer	.05	.04	.02	744	Lary Sorensen	.05	.04	.02
654	Ken Howell	.07	.05	.03	745	Willie Upshaw	.07	.05	.03
655	Manny Trillo	.07	.05	.03	746	Denny Gonzalez	.05	.04	.02
656	Brian Harper	.05	.04	.02	747	Rick Cerone	.05	.04	.02
657	Juan Agosto	.05	.04	.02	748	Steve Henderson	.05	.04	.02
658	Rob Wilfong	.05	.04	.02	749	Ed Jurak	.05	.04	.02
659	Checklist 529-660	.05	.04	.02	750	Gorman Thomas	.10	.08	.04
660	Steve Garvey	.30	.25	.12	751	Howard Johnson	.40	.30	.15
661	Roger Clemens	5.00	3.75	2.00	752	Mike Krukow	.07	.05	.03
662	Bill Schroeder	.05	.04	.02	753	Dan Ford	.05	.04	.02
663	Neil Allen	.05	.04	.02	754	Pat Clements	.12	.09	.05
664	Tim Corcoran	.05	.04	.02	755	Harold Baines	.15	.11	.06
665	Alejandro Pena	.07	.05	.03	756	Pirates Leaders (Rick Rhoden)	.07	.05	.03
666	Rangers Leaders (Charlie Hough)	.07	.05	.03	757	Darrell Porter	.07	.05	.03
667	Tim Teufel	.05	.04	.02	758	Dave Anderson	.05	.04	.02
668	Cecilio Guante	.05	.04	.02	759	Moose Haas	.05	.04	.02
669	Ron Cey	.10	.08	.04	760	Andre Dawson	.20	.15	.08
670	Willie Hernandez	.07	.05	.03	761	Don Slaught	.05	.04	.02

		MT	NR MT	EX
762	Eric Show	.07	.05	.03
763	Terry Puhl	.05	.04	.02
764	Kevin Gross	.07	.05	.03
765	Don Baylor	.12	.09	.05
766	Rick Langford	.05	.04	.02
767	Jody Davis	.10	.08	.04
768	Vern Ruhle	.05	.04	.02
769	*Harold Reynolds*(FC)	.40	.30	.15
770	Vida Blue	.10	.08	.04
771	John McNamara	.05	.04	.02
772	Brian Downing	.07	.05	.03
773	Greg Pryor	.05	.04	.02
774	Terry Leach	.05	.04	.02
775	Al Oliver	.10	.08	.04
776	Gene Garber	.05	.04	.02
777	Wayne Krenchicki	.05	.04	.02
778	Jerry Hairston	.05	.04	.02
779	Rick Reuschel	.10	.08	.04
780	Robin Yount	.50	.40	.20
781	Joe Nolan	.05	.04	.02
782	Ken Landreaux	.05	.04	.02
783	Ricky Horton	.07	.05	.03
784	Alan Bannister	.05	.04	.02
785	Bob Stanley	.05	.04	.02
786	Twins Leaders (Mickey Hatcher)	.07	.05	.03
787	Vance Law	.07	.05	.03
788	Marty Castillo	.05	.04	.02
789	Kurt Bevacqua	.05	.04	.02
790	Phil Niekro	.25	.20	.10
791	Checklist 661-792	.05	.04	.02
792	Charles Hudson	.06	.05	.02

1986 Topps All-Star Glossy Set Of 22

As in previous years, Topps continued to make the popular glossy-surfaced cards as an insert in rack packs. The All-Star Glossy set of 22 2-1/2" by 3-1/2" cards shows little design change from previous years. Cards feature a front color photo and All-Star banner at the top. The bottom has the player's name and position. The set includes the All-Star starting teams as well as the managers and honorary captains.

		MT	NR MT	EX
Complete Set:		6.00	4.50	2.50
Common Player:		.20	.15	.08
1	Sparky Anderson	.20	.15	.08
2	Eddie Murray	.50	.40	.20
3	Lou Whitaker	.30	.25	.12
4	George Brett	.80	.60	.30
5	Cal Ripken	.60	.45	.25
6	Jim Rice	.50	.40	.20
7	Rickey Henderson	.60	.45	.25
8	Dave Winfield	.50	.40	.20
9	Carlton Fisk	.30	.25	.12
10	Jack Morris	.30	.25	.12
11	A.L. All-Star Team	.20	.15	.08
12	Dick Williams	.20	.15	.08
13	Steve Garvey	.50	.40	.20
14	Tom Herr	.20	.15	.08
15	Graig Nettles	.20	.15	.08
16	Ozzie Smith	.30	.25	.12
17	Tony Gwynn	.60	.45	.25
18	Dale Murphy	.80	.60	.30
19	Darryl Strawberry	.80	.60	.30
20	Terry Kennedy	.20	.15	.08
21	LaMarr Hoyt	.20	.15	.08
22	N.L. All-Star Team	.20	.15	.08

1986 Topps All-Star Glossy Set Of 60

The Topps All-Star & Hot Prospects Glossy Set of 60 cards represents an expansion of a good idea. The 2-1/2" by 3-1/2" cards had a good following when they were limited to stars, but Topps realized that the addition of top young players would spice up the set even further, so in 1986 it was expanded from 40 to 60 cards. The cards themselves are basically all color glossy pictures with the player's name in very small print in the lower left-hand corner. To obtain the set, it was necessary to send $1 plus six special offer cards from wax packs to Topps for each series. At 60 cards, that meant the process had to be repeated six times as there were 10 cards in each series, making the set quite expensive from the outset.

		MT	NR MT	EX
Complete Set:		15.00	11.00	6.00
Common Player:		.15	.11	.06
1	Oddibe McDowell	.25	.20	.10
2	Reggie Jackson	.70	.50	.30
3	Fernando Valenzuela	.35	.25	.14
4	Jack Clark	.25	.20	.10
5	Rickey Henderson	.70	.50	.30
6	Steve Balboni	.15	.11	.06
7	Keith Hernandez	.40	.30	.15
8	Lance Parrish	.30	.25	.12
9	Willie McGee	.25	.20	.10
10	Chris Brown	.40	.30	.15
11	Darryl Strawberry	.90	.70	.35
12	Ron Guidry	.30	.25	.12
13	Dave Parker	.25	.20	.10
14	Cal Ripken	.70	.50	.30
15	Tim Raines	.50	.40	.20
16	Rod Carew	.60	.45	.25
17	Mike Schmidt	.90	.70	.35
18	George Brett	.90	.70	.35
19	Joe Hesketh	.15	.11	.06
20	Dan Pasqua	.20	.15	.08
21	Vince Coleman	1.00	.70	.40
22	Tom Seaver	.50	.40	.20
23	Gary Carter	.50	.40	.20
24	Orel Hershiser	.40	.30	.15
25	Pedro Guerrero	.30	.25	.12
26	Wade Boggs	1.25	.90	.50
27	Bret Saberhagen	.30	.25	.12
28	Carlton Fisk	.25	.20	.10
29	Kirk Gibson	.35	.25	.14
30	Brian Fisher	.20	.15	.08
31	Don Mattingly	3.00	2.25	1.25
32	Tom Herr	.15	.11	.06
33	Eddie Murray	.60	.45	.25
34	Ryne Sandberg	.40	.30	.15
35	Dan Quisenberry	.15	.11	.06
36	Jim Rice	.50	.40	.20
37	Dale Murphy	.90	.70	.35
38	Steve Garvey	.50	.40	.20
39	Roger McDowell	.25	.20	.10

		MT	NR MT	EX
40	Earnie Riles	.15	.11	.06
41	Dwight Gooden	1.25	.90	.50
42	Dave Winfield	.50	.40	.20
43	Dave Stieb	.20	.15	.08
44	Bob Horner	.20	.15	.08
45	Nolan Ryan	.50	.40	.20
46	Ozzie Smith	.25	.20	.10
47	Jorge Bell	.50	.40	.20
48	Gorman Thomas	.15	.11	.06
49	Tom Browning	.25	.20	.10
50	Larry Sheets	.20	.15	.08
51	Pete Rose	1.25	.90	.50
52	Brett Butler	.15	.11	.06
53	John Tudor	.20	.15	.08
54	Phil Bradley	.20	.15	.08
55	Jeff Reardon	.20	.15	.08
56	Rich Gossage	.25	.20	.10
57	Tony Gwynn	.60	.45	.25
58	Ozzie Guillen	.25	.20	.10
59	Glenn Davis	.35	.25	.14
60	Darrell Evans	.15	.11	.06

A player's name in *italic* type indicates a rookie card. An (FC) indicates a player's first card for that particular card company.

1986 Topps Box Panels

DALE MURPHY

Following the lead of Donruss, which introduced the concept in 1985, Topps produced special cards on the bottom panels of wax boxes. Individual cards measure 2-1/2" by 3-1/2", the same as regular cards. Design of the cards is virtually identical with regular '86 Topps, though the top border is in red, rather than black. The cards are lettered "A" through "P", rather than numbered on the back.

		MT	NR MT	EX
Complete Panel Set:		10.00	7.50	4.00
Complete Singles Set:		5.00	3.75	2.00
Common Panel:		2.00	1.50	.80
Common Single Player:		.15	.11	.06
	Panel	3.50	2.75	1.50
A	Jorge Bell	.20	.15	.08
B	Wade Boggs	.60	.45	.25
C	George Brett	.35	.25	.14
D	Vince Coleman	.35	.25	.14
	Panel	2.00	1.50	.80
E	Carlton Fisk	.15	.11	.06
F	Dwight Gooden	.40	.30	.15
G	Pedro Guerrero	.15	.11	.06
H	Ron Guidry	.15	.11	.06
	Panel	3.50	2.75	1.50
I	Reggie Jackson	.30	.25	.12
J	Don Mattingly	.90	.70	.35
K	Oddibe McDowell	.15	.11	.06
L	Willie McGee	.15	.11	.06
	Panel	3.00	2.25	1.25
M	Dale Murphy	.35	.25	.14
N	Pete Rose	.50	.40	.20
O	Bret Saberhagen	.15	.11	.06
P	Fernando Valenzuela	.20	.15	.08

1986 Topps Gallery Of Champions

For the third consecutive year Topps issued 12 "metal mini-cards" as a dealer-ordering incentive. The metal replicas were minted 1/4-size (approximately 1-1/4" by 1-3/4") of the regular cards and come in silver, aluminum and bronze. The bronze and silver sets were issued in leather-like velvet-lined display cases. A bronze 1952 Topps Mickey Mantle was given as a premium for dealers purchasing 1986 Traded sets, while a pewter Don Mattingly was issued as a premium to those ordering the aluminum, bronze and silver sets. The Mantle bronze is valued at $12 and the Mattingly pewter at $100.

		MT	NR MT	EX
Complete Aluminum Set:		30.00	22.00	12.00
Complete Bronze Set:		175.00	131.00	70.00
Complete Silver Set:		650.00	487.00	260.00
(1a)	Wade Boggs (aluminum)	3.00	2.25	1.25
(1b)	Wade Boggs (bronze)	25.00	18.50	10.00
(1c)	Wade Boggs (silver)	125.00	94.00	50.00
(2a)	Vince Coleman (aluminum)	1.25	.90	.50
(2b)	Vince Coleman (bronze)	12.00	9.00	4.75
(2c)	Vince Coleman (silver)	50.00	37.00	20.00
(3a)	Darrell Evans (aluminum)	.70	.50	.30
(3b)	Darrell Evans (bronze)	7.50	5.75	3.00
(3c)	Darrell Evans (silver)	20.00	15.00	8.00
(4a)	Dwight Gooden (aluminum)	2.00	1.50	.80
(4b)	Dwight Gooden (bronze)	20.00	15.00	40.00
(4c)	Dwight Gooden (silver)	100.00	75.00	40.00
(5a)	Ozzie Guillen (aluminum)	.70	.50	.30
(5b)	Ozzie Guillen (bronze)	7.50	5.75	3.00
(5c)	Ozzie Guillen (silver)	20.00	15.00	8.00
(6a)	Don Mattingly (aluminum)	8.00	6.00	3.25
(6b)	Don Mattingly (bronze)	50.00	37.00	20.00
(6c)	Don Mattingly (silver)	200.00	150.00	80.00
(7a)	Willie McGee (aluminum)	1.00	.70	.40
(7b)	Willie McGee (bronze)	10.00	7.50	4.00
(7c)	Willie McGee (silver)	30.00	22.00	12.00
(8a)	Dale Murphy (aluminum)	1.50	1.25	.60
(8b)	Dale Murphy (bronze)	15.00	11.00	6.00
(8c)	Dale Murphy (silver)	80.00	60.00	32.00
(9a)	Dan Quisenberry (aluminum)	.70	.50	.30
(9b)	Dan Quisenberry (bronze)	7.50	5.75	3.00
(9c)	Dan Quisenberry (silver)	20.00	15.00	8.00
(10a)	Jeff Reardon (aluminum)	.70	.50	.30
(10b)	Jeff Reardon (bronze)	7.50	5.75	3.00
(10c)	Jeff Reardon (silver)	20.00	15.00	8.00
(11a)	Pete Rose (aluminum)	2.50	2.00	1.00
(11b)	Pete Rose (bronze)	25.00	18.50	10.00
(11c)	Pete Rose (silver)	110.00	82.00	44.00
(12a)	Bret Saberhagen (aluminum)	1.00	.70	.40
(12b)	Bret Saberhagen (bronze)	10.00	7.50	4.00
(12c)	Bret Saberhagen (silver)	30.00	22.00	12.00

Regional interest may affect the value of a card.

1986 Topps
Mini League Leaders

MIKE SCHMIDT

Topps had long experimented with bigger cards, but in 1986, they also decided to try smaller ones. These 2-1/8" by 2-15/16" cards feature top players in a number of categories. Sold in plastic packs as a regular Topps issue, the 66-card set is attractive as well as innovative. The cards feature color photos and a minimum of added information on the fronts where only the player's name and Topps logo appear. Backs limited information as well, but do feature whatever information was required to justify the player's inclusion in a set of league leaders.

		MT	NR MT	EX
	Complete Set:	8.00	6.00	3.25
	Common Player:	.09	.07	.04
1	Eddie Murray	.40	.30	.15
2	Cal Ripken	.40	.30	.15
3	Wade Boggs	.80	.60	.30
4	Dennis Boyd	.09	.07	.04
5	Dwight Evans	.15	.11	.06
6	Bruce Hurst	.15	.11	.06
7	Gary Pettis	.09	.07	.04
8	Harold Baines	.15	.11	.06
9	Floyd Bannister	.09	.07	.04
10	Britt Burns	.09	.07	.04
11	Carlton Fisk	.20	.15	.08
12	Brett Butler	.15	.11	.06
13	Darrell Evans	.15	.11	.06
14	Jack Morris	.25	.20	.10
15	Lance Parrish	.25	.20	.10
16	Walt Terrell	.09	.07	.04
17	Steve Balboni	.09	.07	.04
18	George Brett	.50	.40	.20
19	Charlie Leibrandt	.09	.07	.04
20	Bret Saberhagen	.20	.15	.08
21	Lonnie Smith	.09	.07	.04
22	Willie Wilson	.15	.11	.06
23	Bert Blyleven	.15	.11	.06
24	Mike Smithson	.09	.07	.04
25	Frank Viola	.20	.15	.08
26	Ron Guidry	.20	.15	.08
27	Rickey Henderson	.40	.30	.15
28	Don Mattingly	1.25	.90	.50
29	Dave Winfield	.30	.25	.12
30	Mike Moore	.09	.07	.04
31	Gorman Thomas	.09	.07	.04
32	Toby Harrah	.09	.07	.04
33	Charlie Hough	.09	.07	.04
34	Doyle Alexander	.09	.07	.04
35	Jimmy Key	.15	.11	.06
36	Dave Stieb	.15	.11	.06
37	Dale Murphy	.50	.40	.20
38	Keith Moreland	.09	.07	.04
39	Ryne Sandberg	.30	.25	.12
40	Tom Browning	.15	.11	.06
41	Dave Parker	.20	.15	.08
42	Mario Soto	.09	.07	.04
43	Nolan Ryan	.30	.25	.12
44	Pedro Guerrero	.20	.15	.08
45	Orel Hershiser	.30	.25	.12
46	Mike Scioscia	.09	.07	.04
47	Fernando Valenzuela	.25	.20	.10
48	Bob Welch	.15	.11	.06
49	Tim Raines	.30	.25	.12

		MT	NR MT	EX
50	Gary Carter	.30	.25	.12
51	Sid Fernandez	.15	.11	.06
52	Dwight Gooden	.70	.50	.30
53	Keith Hernandez	.25	.20	.10
54	Juan Samuel	.20	.15	.08
55	Mike Schmidt	.50	.40	.20
56	Glenn Wilson	.09	.07	.04
57	Rick Reuschel	.15	.11	.06
58	Joaquin Andujar	.09	.07	.04
59	Jack Clark	.20	.15	.08
60	Vince Coleman	.60	.45	.25
61	Danny Cox	.09	.07	.04
62	Tom Herr	.09	.07	.04
63	Willie McGee	.15	.11	.06
64	John Tudor	.15	.11	.06
65	Tony Gwynn	.40	.30	.15
66	Checklist	.09	.07	.04

1986 Topps Stickers

The 1986 Topps stickers are 2-1/8" by 3". The 200-piece set features 316 different subjects, with some stickers including two or three players. Numbers run only to 315, however. The set includes some specialty stickers such as League Championships and World Series themes. Stickers are numbered both front and back and included a chance to win a trip to spring training as well as an offer to buy a complete 1986 Topps regular set. An album for the stickers was available in stores.

		MT	NR MT	EX
	Complete Set:	15.00	11.00	6.00
	Common Player:	.03	.02	.01
	Sticker Album:	.70	.50	.30
1	Pete Rose	.25	.20	.10
2	Pete Rose	.25	.20	.10
3	George Brett	.12	.09	.05
4	Rod Carew	.10	.08	.04
5	Vince Coleman	.12	.09	.05
6	Dwight Gooden	.15	.11	.06
7	Phil Niekro	.08	.06	.03
8	Tony Perez	.06	.05	.02
9	Nolan Ryan	.10	.08	.04
10	Tom Seaver	.10	.08	.04
11	N.L. Championship Series (Ozzie Smith)			
		.06	.05	.02
12	N.L. Championship Series (Bill Madlock)			
		.04	.03	.02
13	N.L. Championship Series (Cardinals Celebrate)	.03	.02	.01
14	A.L. Championship Series (Al Oliver)			
		.04	.03	.02
15	A.L. Championship Series (Jim Sundberg)			
		.03	.02	.01
16	A.L. Championship Series (George Brett)			
		.10	.08	.04
17	World Series (Bret Saberhagen)	.06	.05	.02
18	World Series (Dane Iorg)	.03	.02	.01
19	World Series (Tito Landrum)	.03	.02	.01
20	World Series (John Tudor)	.04	.03	.02
21	World Series (Buddy Biancalana)	.03	.02	.01
22	World Series (Darryl Motley, Darrell Porter)	.03	.02	.01
23	World Series (George Brett, Frank White)			
		.10	.08	.04

#	Name	MT	NR MT	EX	#	Name	MT	NR MT	EX
24	Nolan Ryan	.15	.11	.06	115	Ozzie Virgil	.06	.05	.02
25	Bill Doran	.08	.06	.03	116	Steve Carlton	.10	.08	.04
26	Jose Cruz	.04	.03	.02	117	Garry Maddox	.03	.02	.01
27	Mike Scott	.08	.06	.03	118	Glenn Wilson	.06	.05	.02
28	Kevin Bass	.04	.03	.02	119	Kevin Gross	.03	.02	.01
29	Glenn Davis	.10	.08	.04	120	Von Hayes	.04	.03	.02
30	Mark Bailey	.06	.05	.02	121	Juan Samuel	.06	.05	.02
31	Dave Smith	.10	.08	.04	122	Rick Schu	.08	.06	.03
32	Phil Garner	.03	.02	.01	123	Shane Rawley	.06	.05	.02
33	Dickie Thon	.06	.05	.02	124	Johnny Ray	.06	.05	.02
34	Bob Horner	.12	.09	.05	125	Tony Pena	.06	.05	.02
35	Dale Murphy	.25	.20	.10	126	Rick Reuschel	.12	.09	.05
36	Glenn Hubbard	.04	.03	.02	127	Sammy Khalifa	.06	.05	.02
37	Bruce Sutter	.08	.06	.03	128	Marvell Wynne	.04	.03	.02
38	Ken Oberkfell	.04	.03	.02	129	Jason Thompson	.03	.02	.01
39	Claudell Washington	.04	.03	.02	130	Rick Rhoden	.04	.03	.02
40	Steve Bedrosian	.04	.03	.02	131	Bill Almon	.03	.02	.01
41	Terry Harper	.03	.02	.01	132	Joe Orsulak	.06	.05	.02
42	Rafael Ramirez	.06	.05	.02	133	Jim Morrison	.06	.05	.02
43	Rick Mahler	.03	.02	.01	134	Pete Rose	.40	.30	.15
44	Joaquin Andujar	.06	.05	.02	135	Dave Parker	.12	.09	.05
45	Willie McGee	.10	.08	.04	136	Mario Soto	.03	.02	.01
46	Ozzie Smith	.06	.05	.02	137	Dave Concepcion	.10	.08	.04
47	Vince Coleman	.12	.09	.05	138	Ron Oester	.03	.02	.01
48	Danny Cox	.04	.03	.02	139	Buddy Bell	.06	.05	.02
49	Tom Herr	.04	.03	.02	140	Ted Power	.03	.02	.01
50	Jack Clark	.08	.06	.03	141	Tom Browning	.06	.05	.02
51	Andy Van Slyke	.04	.03	.02	142	John Franco	.08	.06	.03
52	John Tudor	.08	.06	.03	143	Tony Perez	.06	.05	.02
53	Terry Pendleton	.03	.02	.01	144	Willie McGee	.08	.06	.03
54	Keith Moreland	.06	.05	.02	145	Dale Murphy	.15	.11	.06
55	Ryne Sandberg	.15	.11	.06	146	Tony Gwynn	.40	.30	.15
56	Lee Smith	.04	.03	.02	147	Tom Herr	.15	.11	.06
57	Steve Trout	.06	.05	.02	148	Steve Garvey	.30	.25	.12
58	Jody Davis	.08	.06	.03	149	Dale Murphy	.40	.30	.15
59	Gary Matthews	.04	.03	.02	150	Darryl Strawberry	.40	.30	.15
60	Leon Durham	.04	.03	.02	151	Graig Nettles	.15	.11	.06
61	Rick Sutcliffe	.06	.05	.02	152	Terry Kennedy	.15	.11	.06
62	Dennis Eckersley	.04	.03	.02	153	Ozzie Smith	.20	.15	.08
63	Bob Dernier	.03	.02	.01	154	LaMarr Hoyt	.15	.11	.06
64	Fernando Valenzuela	.15	.11	.06	155	Rickey Henderson	.40	.30	.15
65	Pedro Guerrero	.12	.09	.05	156	Lou Whitaker	.25	.20	.10
66	Jerry Reuss	.06	.05	.02	157	George Brett	.40	.30	.15
67	Greg Brock	.06	.05	.02	158	Eddie Murray	.40	.30	.15
68	Mike Scioscia	.03	.02	.01	159	Cal Ripken	.40	.30	.15
69	Ken Howell	.04	.03	.02	160	Dave Winfield	.30	.25	.12
70	Bill Madlock	.04	.03	.02	161	Jim Rice	.30	.25	.12
71	Mike Marshall	.06	.05	.02	162	Carlton Fisk	.25	.20	.10
72	Steve Sax	.06	.05	.02	163	Jack Morris	.25	.20	.10
73	Orel Hershiser	.06	.05	.02	164	Wade Boggs	.15	.11	.06
74	Andre Dawson	.12	.09	.05	165	Darrell Evans	.06	.05	.02
75	Tim Raines	.12	.09	.05	166	Mike Davis	.06	.05	.02
76	Jeff Reardon	.06	.05	.02	167	Dave Kingman	.08	.06	.03
77	Hubie Brooks	.04	.03	.02	168	Alfredo Griffin	.04	.03	.02
78	Bill Gullickson	.04	.03	.02	169	Carney Lansford	.04	.03	.02
79	Bryn Smith	.04	.03	.02	170	Bruce Bochte	.10	.08	.04
80	Terry Francona	.04	.03	.02	171	Dwayne Murphy	.08	.06	.03
81	Vance Law	.03	.02	.01	172	Dave Collins	.04	.03	.02
82	Tim Wallach	.04	.03	.02	173	Chris Codiroli	.10	.08	.04
83	Herm Winningham	.04	.03	.02	174	Mike Heath	.03	.02	.01
84	Jeff Leonard	.06	.05	.02	175	Jay Howell	.12	.09	.05
85	Chris Brown	.20	.15	.08	176	Rod Carew	.20	.15	.08
86	Scott Garrelts	.03	.02	.01	177	Reggie Jackson	.20	.15	.08
87	Jose Uribe	.04	.03	.02	178	Doug DeCinces	.10	.08	.04
88	Manny Trillo	.04	.03	.02	179	Bob Boone	.12	.09	.05
89	Dan Driessen	.04	.03	.02	180	Ron Romanick	.15	.11	.06
90	Dan Gladden	.06	.05	.02	181	Bob Grich	.08	.06	.03
91	Mark Davis	.04	.03	.02	182	Donnie Moore	.06	.05	.02
92	Bob Brenly	.03	.02	.01	183	Brian Downing	.10	.08	.04
93	Mike Krukow	.04	.03	.02	184	Ruppert Jones	.10	.08	.04
94	Dwight Gooden	.35	.25	.14	185	Juan Beniquez	.04	.03	.02
95	Darryl Strawberry	.25	.20	.10	186	Dave Stieb	.06	.05	.02
96	Gary Carter	.10	.08	.04	187	Jorge Bell	.20	.15	.08
97	Wally Backman	.06	.05	.02	188	Willie Upshaw	.08	.06	.03
98	Ron Darling	.06	.05	.02	189	Tom Henke	.04	.03	.02
99	Keith Hernandez	.12	.09	.05	190	Damaso Garcia	.10	.08	.04
100	George Foster	.06	.05	.02	191	Jimmy Key	.06	.05	.02
101	Howard Johnson	.06	.05	.02	192	Jesse Barfield	.10	.08	.04
102	Rafael Santana	.04	.03	.02	193	Dennis Lamp	.03	.02	.01
103	Roger McDowell	.06	.05	.02	194	Tony Fernandez	.06	.05	.02
104	Steve Garvey	.15	.11	.06	195	Lloyd Moseby	.04	.03	.02
105	Tony Gwynn	.20	.15	.08	196	Cecil Cooper	.08	.06	.03
106	Graig Nettles	.06	.05	.02	197	Robin Yount	.15	.11	.06
107	Rich Gossage	.10	.08	.04	198	Rollie Fingers	.08	.06	.03
108	Andy Hawkins	.04	.03	.02	199	Ted Simmons	.04	.03	.02
109	Carmelo Martinez	.04	.03	.02	200	Ben Oglivie	.04	.03	.02
110	Garry Templeton	.04	.03	.02	201	Moose Haas	.04	.03	.02
111	Terry Kennedy	.06	.05	.02	202	Jim Gantner	.03	.02	.01
112	Tim Flannery	.08	.06	.03	203	Paul Molitor	.06	.05	.02
113	LaMarr Hoyt	.03	.02	.01	204	Charlie Moore	.03	.02	.01
114	Mike Schmidt	.25	.20	.10	205	Danny Darwin	.06	.05	.02

		MT	NR MT	EX
206	Brett Butler	.06	.05	.02
207	Brook Jacoby	.08	.06	.03
208	Andre Thornton	.12	.09	.05
209	Tom Waddell	.04	.03	.02
210	Tony Bernazard	.04	.03	.02
211	Julio Franco	.08	.06	.03
212	Pat Tabler	.04	.03	.02
213	Joe Carter	.08	.06	.03
214	George Vukovich	.03	.02	.01
215	Rich Thompson	.04	.03	.02
216	Gorman Thomas	.06	.05	.02
217	Phil Bradley	.10	.08	.04
218	Alvin Davis	.06	.05	.02
219	Jim Presley	.08	.06	.03
220	Matt Young	.04	.03	.02
221	Mike Moore	.04	.03	.02
222	Dave Henderson	.06	.05	.02
223	Ed Nunez	.04	.03	.02
224	Spike Owen	.03	.02	.01
225	Mark Langston	.06	.05	.02
226	Cal Ripken	.20	.15	.08
227	Eddie Murray	.20	.15	.08
228	Fred Lynn	.06	.05	.02
229	Lee Lacy	.03	.02	.01
230	Scott McGregor	.04	.03	.02
231	Storm Davis	.04	.03	.02
232	Rick Dempsey	.06	.05	.02
233	Mike Boddicker	.06	.05	.02
234	Mike Young	.06	.05	.02
235	Sammy Stewart	.06	.05	.02
236	Pete O'Brien	.08	.06	.03
237	Oddibe McDowell	.15	.11	.06
238	Toby Harrah	.04	.03	.02
239	Gary Ward	.04	.03	.02
240	Larry Parrish	.04	.03	.02
241	Charlie Hough	.04	.03	.02
242	Burt Hooton	.03	.02	.01
243	Don Slaught	.04	.03	.02
244	Curt Wilkerson	.04	.03	.02
245	Greg Harris	.03	.02	.01
246	Jim Rice	.15	.11	.06
247	Wade Boggs	.60	.45	.25
248	Rich Gedman	.04	.03	.02
249	Dennis Boyd	.04	.03	.02
250	Marty Barrett	.04	.03	.02
251	Dwight Evans	.06	.05	.02
252	Bill Buckner	.04	.03	.02
253	Bob Stanley	.03	.02	.01
254	Tony Armas	.04	.03	.02
255	Mike Easler	.10	.08	.04
256	George Brett	.25	.20	.10
257	Dan Quisenberry	.06	.05	.02
258	Willie Wilson	.06	.05	.02
259	Jim Sundberg	.06	.05	.02
260	Bret Saberhagen	.12	.09	.05
261	Bud Black	.06	.05	.02
262	Charlie Leibrandt	.06	.05	.02
263	Frank White	.04	.03	.02
264	Lonnie Smith	.06	.05	.02
265	Steve Balboni	.06	.05	.02
266	Kirk Gibson	.15	.11	.06
267	Alan Trammell	.15	.11	.06
268	Jack Morris	.10	.08	.04
269	Darrell Evans	.04	.03	.02
270	Dan Petry	.04	.03	.02
271	Larry Herndon	.04	.03	.02
272	Lou Whitaker	.06	.05	.02
273	Lance Parrish	.08	.06	.03
274	Chet Lemon	.03	.02	.01
275	Willie Hernandez	.10	.08	.04
276	Tom Brunansky	.08	.06	.03
277	Kent Hrbek	.12	.09	.05
278	Mark Salas	.03	.02	.01
279	Bert Blyleven	.06	.05	.02
280	Tim Teufel	.03	.02	.01
281	Ron Davis	.04	.03	.02
282	Mike Smithson	.06	.05	.02
283	Gary Gaetti	.08	.06	.03
284	Frank Viola	.06	.05	.02
285	Kirby Puckett	.12	.09	.05
286	Carlton Fisk	.12	.09	.05
287	Tom Seaver	.15	.11	.06
288	Harold Baines	.06	.05	.02
289	Ron Kittle	.04	.03	.02
290	Bob James	.03	.02	.01
291	Rudy Law	.04	.03	.02
292	Britt Burns	.03	.02	.01
293	Greg Walker	.06	.05	.02
294	Ozzie Guillen	.06	.05	.02
295	Tim Hulett	.03	.02	.01
296	Don Mattingly	.70	.50	.30

		MT	NR MT	EX
297	Rickey Henderson	.20	.15	.08
298	Dave Winfield	.10	.08	.04
299	Butch Wynegar	.03	.02	.01
300	Don Baylor	.06	.05	.02
301	Eddie Whitson	.03	.02	.01
302	Ron Guidry	.06	.05	.02
303	Dave Righetti	.08	.06	.03
304	Bobby Meacham	.06	.05	.02
305	Willie Randolph	.08	.06	.03
306	Vince Coleman	.15	.11	.06
307	Oddibe McDowell	.15	.11	.06
308	Larry Sheets	.06	.05	.02
309	Ozzie Guillen	.06	.05	.02
310	Earnie Riles	.04	.03	.02
311	Chris Brown	.10	.08	.04
312	Brian Fisher, Roger McDowell	.08	.06	.03
313	Tom Browning	.04	.03	.02
314	Glenn Davis	.10	.08	.04
315	Mark Salas	.03	.02	.01

1986 Topps Super

A third year of oversize, 4-7/8" by 6-7/8", versions of Topps' regular issue cards saw the set once again hit the 60-card mark. Besides being four times the size of a normal card, the Supers differ only in the number on the back of the card.

		MT	NR MT	EX
Complete Set:		12.00	9.00	4.75
Common Player:		.20	.15	.08
1	Don Mattingly	2.25	1.75	.90
2	Willie McGee	.35	.25	.14
3	Bret Saberhagen	.35	.25	.14
4	Dwight Gooden	1.50	1.25	.60
5	Dan Quisenberry	.20	.15	.08
6	Jeff Reardon	.25	.20	.10
7	Ozzie Guillen	.25	.20	.10
8	Vince Coleman	.70	.50	.30
9	Harold Baines	.25	.20	.10
10	Jorge Bell	.50	.40	.20
11	Bert Blyleven	.25	.20	.10
12	Wade Boggs	1.25	.90	.50
13	Phil Bradley	.25	.20	.10
14	George Brett	.80	.60	.30
15	Hubie Brooks	.20	.15	.08
16	Tom Browning	.25	.20	.10
17	Bill Buckner	.20	.15	.08
18	Brett Butler	.20	.15	.08
19	Gary Carter	.50	.40	.20
20	Cecil Cooper	.25	.20	.10
21	Darrell Evans	.25	.20	.10
22	Dwight Evans	.20	.15	.08
23	Carlton Fisk	.30	.25	.12
24	Steve Garvey	.50	.40	.20
25	Kirk Gibson	.35	.25	.14
26	Rich Gossage	.25	.20	.10
27	Pedro Guerrero	.30	.25	.12
28	Ron Guidry	.30	.25	.12
29	Tony Gwynn	.70	.50	.30
30	Rickey Henderson	.70	.50	.30
31	Keith Hernandez	.50	.40	.20
32	Tom Herr	.20	.15	.08
33	Orel Hershiser	.50	.40	.20
34	Jay Howell	.20	.15	.08
35	Reggie Jackson	.60	.45	.25
36	Bob James	.20	.15	.08

		MT	NR MT	EX
37	Charlie Leibrandt	.20	.15	.08
38	Jack Morris	.35	.25	.14
39	Dale Murphy	.80	.60	.30
40	Eddie Murray	.60	.45	.25
41	Dave Parker	.35	.25	.14
42	Tim Raines	.50	.40	.20
43	Jim Rice	.50	.40	.20
44	Dave Righetti	.30	.25	.12
45	Cal Ripken	.70	.50	.30
46	Pete Rose	1.00	.70	.40
47	Nolan Ryan	.50	.40	.20
48	Ryne Sandberg	.50	.40	.20
49	Mike Schmidt	.80	.60	.30
50	Tom Seaver	.50	.40	.20
51	Bryn Smith	.20	.15	.08
52	Lee Smith	.20	.15	.08
53	Ozzie Smith	.30	.25	.12
54	Dave Stieb	.20	.15	.08
55	Darryl Strawberry	.80	.60	.30
56	Gorman Thomas	.20	.15	.08
57	John Tudor	.20	.15	.08
58	Fernando Valenzuela	.40	.30	.15
59	Willie Wilson	.25	.20	.10
60	Dave Winfield	.50	.40	.20

1986 Topps Super Star

Labeled "Topps' Collector Series" in a red band at the top of the front, this set marked the second year of Topps' production of a special boxed set for the Woolworth chain of stores, though Woolworth's name does not appear anywhere on the card. The cards, which measure 2-1/2" by 3-1/2", feature a color photo with its lower right corner rolled up to reveal the words "Super Star" on a bright yellow border. The player's name appears in the lower left corner. The 66-card set features stars and retains a certain measure of popularity on that basis.

		MT	NR MT	EX
	Complete Set:	5.00	3.75	2.00
	Common Player:	.09	.07	.04
1	Tony Armas	.09	.07	.04
2	Don Baylor	.12	.09	.05
3	Wade Boggs	.80	.60	.30
4	George Brett	.40	.30	.15
5	Bill Buckner	.09	.07	.04
6	Rod Carew	.30	.25	.12
7	Gary Carter	.30	.25	.12
8	Cecil Cooper	.12	.09	.05
9	Darrell Evans	.12	.09	.05
10	Dwight Evans	.15	.11	.06
11	George Foster	.12	.09	.05
12	Bobby Grich	.09	.07	.04
13	Tony Gwynn	.35	.25	.14
14	Keith Hernandez	.25	.20	.10
15	Reggie Jackson	.30	.25	.12
16	Dave Kingman	.12	.09	.05
17	Carney Lansford	.09	.07	.04
18	Fred Lynn	.12	.09	.05
19	Bill Madlock	.12	.09	.05
20	Don Mattingly	1.50	1.25	.60
21	Willie McGee	.20	.15	.08
22	Hal McRae	.09	.07	.04
23	Dale Murphy	.40	.30	.15
24	Eddie Murray	.35	.25	.14

		MT	NR MT	EX
25	Ben Oglivie	.09	.07	.04
26	Al Oliver	.12	.09	.05
27	Dave Parker	.20	.15	.08
28	Jim Rice	.30	.25	.12
29	Pete Rose	.90	.70	.35
30	Mike Schmidt	.40	.30	.15
31	Gorman Thomas	.09	.07	.04
32	Willie Wilson	.12	.09	.05
33	Dave Winfield	.30	.25	.12

NOTE: A card number in parentheses ( ) indicates the set is unnumbered.

1986 Topps Tattoos

Topps returned to tattoos in 1986, marketing a set of 24 different tattoo sheets. Each sheet of tattoos measures 3-7/16" by 14" and includes both player and smaller action tattoos. As the action tattoos were uniform and not of any particular player, they add little value 'to the sheet. The player tattoos measure 1-3/16" by 2-3/8". With 24 sheets, eight players per sheet, there are 192 players represented in the set. The sheets are numbered.

		MT	NR MT	EX
	Complete Set:	5.00	3.75	2.00
	Common Player:	.20	.15	.08
1	Julio Franco, Rich Gossage, Keith Hernandez, Charlie Leibrandt, Jack Perconte, Lee Smith, Dickie Thon, Dave Winfield	.25	.20	.10
2	Jesse Barfield, Shawon Dunston, Dennis Eckersley, Brian Fisher, Moose Haas, Mike Moore, Dale Murphy, Bret Saberhagen	.30	.25	.12
3	George Bell, Bob Brenly, Steve Carlton, Jose DeLeon, Bob Horner, Bob James, Dan Quisenberry, Andre Thornton	.25	.20	.10
4	Mike Davis, Leon Durham, Darrell Evans, Glenn Hubbard, Johnny Ray, Cal Ripken, Ted Simmons	.25	.20	.10
5	John Candelaria, Rick Dempsey, Steve Garvey, Ozzie Guillen, Gary Matthews, Jesse Orosco, Tony Pena	.25	.20	.10
6	Bruce Bochte, George Brett, Cecil Cooper, Sammy Khalifa, Ron Kittle, Scott McGregor, Pete Rose, Mookie Wilson	.45	.35	.20
7	John Franco, Carney Lansford, Don Mattingly, Graig Nettles, Rick Reuschel, Mike Schmidt, Larry Sheets, Don Sutton	.45	.35	.20
8	Cecilio Guante, Willie Hernandez, Mike Krukow, Fred Lynn, Phil Niekro, Ed Nunez, Ryne Sandberg, Pat Tabler	.25	.20	.10
9	Brett Butler, Chris Codiroli, Jim Gantner, Charlie Hough, Dave Parker, Rick Rhoden, Glenn Wilson, Robin Yount	.20	.15	.08
10	Tom Browning, Ron Darling, Von Hayes, Chet Lemon, Tom Seaver, Mike Smithson, Bruce Sutter, Alan Trammell	.25	.20	.10
11	Tony Armas, Jose Cruz, Jay Howell, Rick Mahler, Jack Morris, Rafael Ramirez, Dave Righetti, Mike Young	.20	.15	.08
12	Alvin Davis, Doug DeCinces, Andy Hawkins, Dennis Lamp, Keith Moreland, Jim Presley, Mario Soto, John Tudor	.20	.15	.08
13	Hubie Brooks, Jody Davis, Dwight Evans, Ron Hassey, Charles Hudson, Kirby Puckett, Jose Uribe	.20	.15	.08
14	Tony Bernazard, Phil Bradley, Bill Buckner, Brian Downing, Dan Driessen, Ron Guidry, LaMarr Hoyt, Garry Maddox	.20	.15	.08

		MT	NR MT	EX
15	Buddy Bell, Joe Carter, Tony Fernandez, Tito Landrum, Jeff Leonard, Hal McRae, Willie Randolph, Juan Samuel	.20	.15	.08
16	Dennis Boyd, Vince Coleman, Scott Garrelts, Alfredo Griffin, Donnie Moore, Tony Perez, Ozzie Smith, Frank White	.25	.20	.10
17	Rich Gedman, Kent Hrbek, Reggie Jackson, Mike Marshall, Terry Pendleton, Tim Raines, Mark Salas, Claudell Washington	.25	.20	.10
18	Chris Brown, Tom Brunansky, Glenn Davis, Ron Davis, Burt Hooton, Darryl Strawberry, Frank Viola, Tim Wallach	.30	.25	.12
19	Jack Clark, Bill Doran, Toby Harrah, Bill Madlock, Pete O'Brien, Larry Parrish, Mike Scioscia, Garry Templeton	.20	.15	.08
20	Gary Carter, Andre Dawson, Dwight Gooden, Orel Hershiser, Oddibe McDowell, Roger McDowell, Dwayne Murphy, Jim Rice	.40	.30	.15
21	Steve Balboni, Mike Easler, Charlie Lea, Lloyd Moseby, Steve Sax, Rick Sutcliffe, Gary Ward, Willie Wilson	.20	.15	.08
22	Wade Boggs, Dave Concepcion, Kirk Gibson, Tom Herr, Lance Parrish, Jeff Reardon, Bryn Smith, Gorman Thomas	.30	.25	.12
23	Carlton Fisk, Bob Grich, Pedro Guerrero, Willie McGee, Paul Molitor, Mike Scott, Dave Stieb, Lou Whitaker	.20	.15	.08
24	Bert Blyleven, Damaso Garcia, Phil Garner, Tony Gwynn, Rickey Henderson, Ben Oglivie, Nolan Ryan, Fernando Valenzuela	.30	.25	.12

1986 Topps Traded

PHIL NIEKRO

This 132-card set of 2-1/2" by 3-1/2" cards is one of the most popular sets of recent times. As always, the set features traded veterans, including such players as Phil Niekro and Tom Seaver. They are not, however, the reason for the excitement. The demand is there because of a better than usual crop of rookies who also appear in the sets. Among those are Jose Canseco, Wally Joyner, Pete Incaviglia, Todd Worrell and the first card of Bo Jackson. As in the previous two years, a glossy-finish "Tiffany" edition of 5,000 Traded sets was produced. The "Tiffany" cards are worth four to six times the value of the regular Traded cards.

		MT	NR MT	EX
Complete Set:		25.00	18.00	10.00
Common Player:		.08	.06	.03
1T	Andy Allanson(FC)	.20	.15	.08
2T	Neil Allen	.08	.06	.03
3T	Joaquin Andujar	.10	.08	.04
4T	Paul Assenmacher(FC)	.20	.15	.08
5T	Scott Bailes(FC)	.20	.15	.08
6T	Don Baylor	.15	.11	.06
7T	Steve Bedrosian	.15	.11	.06
8T	Juan Beniquez	.08	.06	.03
9T	Juan Berenguer	.08	.06	.03
10T	Mike Bielecki(FC)	.20	.15	.08
11T	Barry Bonds(FC)	5.00	3.75	2.25
12T	Bobby Bonilla(FC)	3.00	2.25	1.25

		MT	NR MT	EX
13T	Juan Bonilla	.08	.06	.03
14T	Rich Bordi	.08	.06	.03
15T	Steve Boros	.08	.06	.03
16T	Rick Burleson	.10	.08	.04
17T	Bill Campbell	.08	.06	.03
18T	Tom Candiotti	.08	.06	.03
19T	John Cangelosi(FC)	.20	.15	.08
20T	Jose Canseco(FC)	9.00	6.75	3.50
21T	Carmen Castillo	.08	.06	.03
22T	Rick Cerone	.08	.06	.03
23T	John Cerutti(FC)	.20	.15	.08
24T	Will Clark(FC)	9.00	6.75	3.50
25T	Mark Clear	.08	.06	.03
26T	Darnell Coles	.12	.09	.05
27T	Dave Collins	.10	.08	.04
28T	Tim Conroy	.08	.06	.03
29T	Joe Cowley	.08	.06	.03
30T	Joel Davis(FC)	.12	.09	.05
31T	Rob Deer	.15	.11	.06
32T	John Denny	.08	.06	.03
33T	Mike Easler	.10	.08	.04
34T	Mark Eichhorn(FC)	.20	.15	.08
35T	Steve Farr	.08	.06	.03
36T	Scott Fletcher	.15	.11	.06
37T	Terry Forster	.10	.08	.04
38T	Terry Francona	.08	.06	.03
39T	Jim Fregosi	.08	.06	.03
40T	Andres Galarraga(FC)	.25	.20	.10
41T	Ken Griffey	.12	.09	.05
42T	Bill Gullickson	.08	.06	.03
43T	Jose Guzman(FC)	.35	.25	.14
44T	Moose Haas	.08	.06	.03
45T	Billy Hatcher	.20	.15	.08
46T	Mike Heath	.08	.06	.03
47T	Tom Hume	.08	.06	.03
48T	Pete Incaviglia(FC)	.40	.30	.15
49T	Dane Iorg	.08	.06	.03
50T	Bo Jackson(FC)	5.00	3.75	2.00
51T	Wally Joyner(FC)	2.00	1.50	.80
52T	Charlie Kerfeld(FC)	.15	.11	.06
53T	Eric King(FC)	.20	.15	.08
54T	Bob Kipper(FC)	.12	.09	.05
55T	Wayne Krenchicki	.08	.06	.03
56T	John Kruk(FC)	.50	.40	.20
57T	Mike LaCoss	.08	.06	.03
58T	Pete Ladd	.08	.06	.03
59T	Mike Laga	.08	.06	.03
60T	Hal Lanier	.08	.06	.03
61T	Dave LaPoint	.12	.09	.05
62T	Rudy Law	.08	.06	.03
63T	Rick Leach	.08	.06	.03
64T	Tim Leary	.08	.06	.03
65T	Dennis Leonard	.10	.08	.04
66T	Jim Leyland	.08	.06	.03
67T	Steve Lyons	.12	.09	.05
68T	Mickey Mahler	.08	.06	.03
69T	Candy Maldonado	.15	.11	.06
70T	Roger Mason(FC)	.10	.08	.04
71T	Bob McClure	.08	.06	.03
72T	Andy McGaffigan	.08	.06	.03
73T	Gene Michael	.08	.06	.03
74T	Kevin Mitchell(FC)	3.00	2.25	1.25
75T	Omar Moreno	.08	.06	.03
76T	Jerry Mumphrey	.08	.06	.03
77T	Phil Niekro	.40	.30	.15
78T	Randy Niemann	.08	.06	.03
79T	Juan Nieves(FC)	.15	.11	.06
80T	Otis Nixon(FC)	.12	.09	.05
81T	Bob Ojeda	.12	.09	.05
82T	Jose Oquendo	.08	.06	.03
83T	Tom Paciorek	.08	.06	.03
84T	Dave Palmer	.08	.06	.03
85T	Frank Pastore	.08	.06	.03
86T	Lou Piniella	.12	.09	.05
87T	Dan Plesac(FC)	.20	.15	.08
88T	Darrell Porter	.10	.08	.04
89T	Rey Quinones(FC)	.20	.15	.08
90T	Gary Redus	.10	.08	.04
91T	Bip Roberts	.60	.45	.25
92T	Billy Jo Robidoux(FC)	.15	.11	.06
93T	Jeff Robinson	.12	.09	.05
94T	Gary Roenicke	.08	.06	.03
95T	Ed Romero	.08	.06	.03
96T	Argenis Salazar	.08	.06	.03
97T	Joe Sambito	.08	.06	.03
98T	Billy Sample	.08	.06	.03
99T	Dave Schmidt	.08	.06	.03
100T	Ken Schrom	.08	.06	.03
101T	Tom Seaver	.60	.45	.25
102T	Ted Simmons	.20	.15	.08
103T	Sammy Stewart	.08	.06	.03

		MT	NR MT	EX
104T	Kurt Stillwell(FC)	.20	.15	.08
105T	Franklin Stubbs	.12	.09	.05
106T	Dale Sveum(FC)	.20	.15	.08
107T	Chuck Tanner	.08	.06	.03
108T	Danny Tartabull(FC)	1.25	.90	.50
109T	Tim Teufel	.08	.06	.03
110T	Bob Tewksbury(FC)	.15	.11	.06
111T	Andres Thomas(FC)	.12	.09	.05
112T	Milt Thompson	.12	.09	.05
113T	Robby Thompson(FC)	.30	.25	.12
114T	Jay Tibbs	.08	.06	.03
115T	Wayne Tolleson	.08	.06	.03
116T	Alex Trevino	.08	.06	.03
117T	Manny Trillo	.10	.08	.04
118T	Ed Vande Berg	.08	.06	.03
119T	Ozzie Virgil	.08	.06	.03
120T	Bob Walk	.08	.06	.03
121T	Gene Walter(FC)	.12	.09	.05
122T	Claudell Washington	.12	.09	.05
123T	Bill Wegman(FC)	.20	.15	.08
124T	Dick Williams	.08	.06	.03
125T	Mitch Williams(FC)	.50	.40	.20
126T	Bobby Witt(FC)	.35	.25	.14
127T	Todd Worrell(FC)	.20	.15	.08
128T	George Wright	.08	.06	.03
129T	Ricky Wright	.08	.06	.03
130T	Steve Yeager	.08	.06	.03
131T	Paul Zuvella	.08	.06	.03
132T	Checklist	.08	.06	.03

1986 Topps 3-D

This set is a second effort in the production of over-size (4-1/2" by 6") plastic cards on which the player figure is embossed. Cards were sold one per pack for approximately 50¢. The 30 players in the set are among the game's top stars. The embossed color photo is bordered at bottom by a strip of contrasting color on which the player name appears. At the top, a row of white baseballs each contain a letter of the team nickname. Backs have no printing, and contain two self-adhesive strips with which the cards can be attached to a hard surface.

		MT	NR MT	EX
	Complete Set:	10.00	7.50	4.00
	Common Player:	.20	.15	.08
1	Bert Blyleven	.30	.25	.12
2	Gary Carter	.60	.45	.25
3	Wade Boggs	1.00	.70	.40
4	Dwight Gooden	1.00	.70	.40
5	George Brett	.80	.60	.30
6	Rich Gossage	.30	.25	.12
7	Darrell Evans	.20	.15	.08
8	Pedro Guerrero	.30	.25	.12
9	Ron Guidry	.30	.25	.12
10	Keith Hernandez	.50	.40	.20
11	Rickey Henderson	.70	.50	.30
12	Orel Hershiser	.50	.40	.20
13	Reggie Jackson	.60	.45	.25
14	Willie McGee	.30	.25	.12
15	Don Mattingly	1.75	1.25	.70
16	Dale Murphy	.40	.30	.15
17	Jack Morris	.30	.25	.12
18	Dave Parker	.30	.25	.12
19	Eddie Murray	.60	.45	.25

		MT	NR MT	EX
20	Jeff Reardon	.30	.25	.12
21	Dan Quisenberry	.20	.15	.08
22	Pete Rose	1.00	.70	.40
23	Jim Rice	.50	.40	.20
24	Mike Schmidt	.80	.60	.30
25	Bret Saberhagen	.30	.25	.12
26	Darryl Strawberry	.80	.60	.30
27	Dave Stieb	.20	.15	.08
28	John Tudor	.20	.15	.08
29	Dave Winfield	.50	.40	.20
30	Fernando Valenzuela	.40	.30	.15

1987 Topps

Many collectors feel that Topps' 1987 set of 792 card is a future classic. The 2-1/2" by 3-1/2" design is closely akin to the 1962 set in that the player photo is set against a woodgrain border. Instead of a rolling corner, as in 1962, the player photos in '87 feature a couple of clipped corners at top left and bottom right, where the team logo and player name appear. The player's position is not given on the front of the card. For the first time in several years, the trophy which designates members of Topps All-Star Rookie Team returned to the card design. As in the previous three years, Topps issued a glossy-finish "Tiffany" edition of their 792-card set. However, it was speculated that as many as 50,000 sets were produced as opposed to the 5,000 sets printed in 1985 and 1986. Because of the large print run, the values for the Tiffany cards are only 3-4 times higher than the same card in the regular issue.

		MT	NR MT	EX
	Complete Set:	25.00	18.00	10.00
	Common Player:	.05	.04	.02
1	Record Breaker (Roger Clemens)	.35	.25	.14
2	Record Breaker (Jim Deshaies)	.07	.05	.03
3	Record Breaker (Dwight Evans)	.07	.05	.03
4	Record Breaker (Dave Lopes)	.07	.05	.03
5	Record Breaker (Dave Righetti)	.07	.05	.03
6	Record Breaker (Ruben Sierra)	.25	.20	.10
7	Record Breaker (Todd Worrell)	.07	.05	.03
8	Terry Pendleton	.07	.05	.03
9	Jay Tibbs	.05	.04	.02
10	Cecil Cooper	.10	.08	.04
11	Indians Leaders (Jack Aker, Chris Bando, Phil Niekro)	.07	.05	.03
12	*Jeff Sellers*(FC)	.15	.11	.06
13	Nick Esasky	.07	.05	.03
14	Dave Stewart	.12	.09	.05
15	Claudell Washington	.07	.05	.03
16	Pat Clements	.05	.04	.02
17	Pete O'Brien	.10	.08	.04
18	Dick Howser	.05	.04	.02
19	Matt Young	.05	.04	.02
20	Gary Carter	.20	.15	.08
21	Mark Davis	.05	.04	.02
22	Doug DeCinces	.07	.05	.03
23	Lee Smith	.10	.08	.04
24	Tony Walker	.05	.04	.02
25	Bert Blyleven	.12	.09	.05
26	Greg Brock	.07	.05	.03
27	Joe Cowley	.05	.04	.02
28	Rick Dempsey	.07	.05	.03

#	Player	MT	NR MT	EX
29	Jimmy Key	.10	.08	.04
30	Tim Raines	.25	.20	.10
31	Braves Leaders (Glenn Hubbard, Rafael Ramirez)	.07	.05	.03
32	Tim Leary	.07	.05	.03
33	Andy Van Slyke	.12	.09	.05
34	Jose Rijo	.07	.05	.03
35	Sid Bream	.07	.05	.03
36	*Eric King*	.25	.20	.10
37	Marvell Wynne	.05	.04	.02
38	Dennis Leonard	.07	.05	.03
39	Marty Barrett	.07	.05	.03
40	Dave Righetti	.12	.09	.05
41	Bo Diaz	.07	.05	.03
42	Gary Redus	.05	.04	.02
43	Gene Michael	.05	.04	.02
44	Greg Harris	.05	.04	.02
45	Jim Presley	.10	.08	.04
46	Danny Gladden	.05	.04	.02
47	Dennis Powell	.07	.05	.03
48	Wally Backman	.07	.05	.03
49	Terry Harper	.05	.04	.02
50	Dave Smith	.07	.05	.03
51	Mel Hall	.07	.05	.03
52	Keith Atherton	.05	.04	.02
53	Ruppert Jones	.05	.04	.02
54	Bill Dawley	.05	.04	.02
55	Tim Wallach	.10	.08	.04
56	Brewers Leaders (Jamie Cocanower, Paul Molitor, Charlie Moore, Herm Starrette)	.07	.05	.03
57	*Scott Nielsen*(FC)	.10	.08	.04
58	Thad Bosley	.05	.04	.02
59	Ken Dayley	.05	.04	.02
60	Tony Pena	.07	.05	.03
61	*Bobby Thigpen*(FC)	.70	.50	.30
62	Bobby Meacham	.05	.04	.02
63	Fred Toliver(FC)	.07	.05	.03
64	Harry Spilman	.05	.04	.02
65	Tom Browning	.10	.08	.04
66	Marc Sullivan	.05	.04	.02
67	Bill Swift	.05	.04	.02
68	Tony LaRussa	.07	.05	.03
69	Lonnie Smith	.07	.05	.03
70	Charlie Hough	.07	.05	.03
71	*Mike Aldrete*(FC)	.15	.11	.06
72	Walt Terrell	.07	.05	.03
73	Dave Anderson	.05	.04	.02
74	Dan Pasqua	.10	.08	.04
75	Ron Darling	.12	.09	.05
76	Rafael Ramirez	.05	.04	.02
77	Bryan Oelkers	.05	.04	.02
78	Tom Foley	.05	.04	.02
79	Juan Nieves	.10	.08	.04
80	*Wally Joyner*	.80	.60	.30
81	Padres Leaders (Andy Hawkins, Terry Kennedy)	.07	.05	.03
82	*Rob Murphy*(FC)	.15	.11	.06
83	Mike Davis	.07	.05	.03
84	Steve Lake	.05	.04	.02
85	Kevin Bass	.07	.05	.03
86	Nate Snell	.05	.04	.02
87	Mark Salas	.05	.04	.02
88	Ed Wojna	.05	.04	.02
89	Ozzie Guillen	.25	.20	.10
90	Dave Stieb	.10	.08	.04
91	Harold Reynolds	.10	.08	.04
92a	Urbano Lugo (no trademark on front)	.30	.25	.12
92b	Urbano Lugo (trademark on front)	.07	.05	.03
93	Jim Leyland	.05	.04	.02
94	Calvin Schiraldi	.05	.04	.02
95	Oddibe McDowell	.07	.05	.03
96	Frank Williams	.05	.04	.02
97	Glenn Wilson	.07	.05	.03
98	Bill Scherrer	.05	.04	.02
99	Darryl Motley	.05	.04	.02
100	Steve Garvey	.20	.15	.08
101	*Carl Willis*(FC)	.10	.08	.04
102	Paul Zuvella	.05	.04	.02
103	Rick Aguilera	.06	.05	.02
104	Billy Sample	.05	.04	.02
105	Floyd Youmans	.07	.05	.03
106	Blue Jays Leaders (George Bell, Willie Upshaw)	.07	.05	.03
107	John Butcher	.05	.04	.02
108	Jim Gantner (photo reversed)	.07	.05	.03
109	R.J. Reynolds	.05	.04	.02
110	John Tudor	.10	.08	.04
111	Alfredo Griffin	.07	.05	.03
112	Alan Ashby	.05	.04	.02
113	Neil Allen	.05	.04	.02
114	Billy Beane	.05	.04	.02
115	Donnie Moore	.05	.04	.02
116	Bill Russell	.07	.05	.03
117	Jim Beattie	.05	.04	.02
118	Bobby Valentine	.05	.04	.02
119	Ron Robinson	.05	.04	.02
120	Eddie Murray	.30	.25	.12
121	*Kevin Romine*(FC)	.12	.09	.05
122	Jim Clancy	.07	.05	.03
123	*John Kruk*	.40	.30	.15
124	Ray Fontenot	.05	.04	.02
125	Bob Brenly	.05	.04	.02
126	*Mike Loynd*(FC)	.15	.11	.06
127	Vance Law	.07	.05	.03
128	Checklist 1-132	.05	.04	.02
129	Rick Cerone	.05	.04	.02
130	Dwight Gooden	.60	.45	.25
131	Pirates Leaders (Sid Bream, Tony Pena)	.07	.05	.03
132	*Paul Assenmacher*	.15	.11	.06
133	Jose Oquendo	.05	.04	.02
134	*Rich Yett*(FC)	.12	.09	.05
135	Mike Easler	.07	.05	.03
136	Ron Romanick	.05	.04	.02
137	Jerry Willard	.05	.04	.02
138	Roy Lee Jackson	.05	.04	.02
139	*Devon White*(FC)	.60	.45	.25
140	Bret Saberhagen	.15	.11	.06
141	Herm Winningham	.05	.04	.02
142	Rick Sutcliffe	.10	.08	.04
143	Steve Boros	.05	.04	.02
144	Mike Scioscia	.07	.05	.03
145	Charlie Kerfeld	.07	.05	.03
146	*Tracy Jones*(FC)	.25	.20	.10
147	Randy Niemann	.05	.04	.02
148	Dave Collins	.07	.05	.03
149	Ray Searage	.05	.04	.02
150	Wade Boggs	.70	.50	.30
151	Mike LaCoss	.05	.04	.02
152	Toby Harrah	.07	.05	.03
153	*Duane Ward*(FC)	.12	.09	.05
154	Tom O'Malley	.05	.04	.02
155	Eddie Whitson	.05	.04	.02
156	Mariners Leaders (Bob Kearney, Phil Regan, Matt Young)	.07	.05	.03
157	Danny Darwin	.05	.04	.02
158	Tim Teufel	.05	.04	.02
159	Ed Olwine	.05	.04	.02
160	Julio Franco	.10	.08	.04
161	Steve Ontiveros	.05	.04	.02
162	*Mike LaValliere*	.25	.20	.10
163	Kevin Gross	.07	.05	.03
164	Sammy Khalifa	.05	.04	.02
165	Jeff Reardon	.10	.08	.04
166	Bob Boone	.07	.05	.03
167	*Jim Deshaies*	.25	.20	.10
168	Lou Piniella	.07	.05	.03
169	Ron Washington	.05	.04	.02
170	Future Stars (Bo Jackson)	1.00	.70	.40
171	*Chuck Cary*(FC)	.10	.08	.04
172	Ron Oester	.05	.04	.02
173	Alex Trevino	.05	.04	.02
174	Henry Cotto	.05	.04	.02
175	Bob Stanley	.05	.04	.02
176	Steve Buechele	.07	.05	.03
177	Keith Moreland	.07	.05	.03
178	Cecil Fielder	1.75	1.25	.70
179	Bill Wegman	.10	.08	.04
180	Chris Brown	.07	.05	.03
181	Cardinals Leaders (Mike LaValliere, Ozzie Smith, Ray Soff)	.07	.05	.03
182	Lee Lacy	.05	.04	.02
183	Andy Hawkins	.05	.04	.02
184	*Bobby Bonilla*	2.00	1.50	.80
185	Roger McDowell	.10	.08	.04
186	Bruce Benedict	.05	.04	.02
187	Mark Huismann	.05	.04	.02
188	Tony Phillips	.05	.04	.02
189	Joe Hesketh	.05	.04	.02
190	Jim Sundberg	.07	.05	.03
191	Charles Hudson	.05	.04	.02
192	Cory Snyder(FC)	.40	.30	.15
193	Roger Craig	.07	.05	.03
194	Kirk McCaskill	.07	.05	.03
195	Mike Pagliarulo	.10	.08	.04
196	Randy O'Neal	.05	.04	.02
197	Mark Bailey	.05	.04	.02
198	Lee Mazzilli	.07	.05	.03
199	Mariano Duncan	.05	.04	.02
200	Pete Rose	.40	.30	.15

#	Player	MT	NR MT	EX
201	John Cangelosi	.12	.09	.05
202	Ricky Wright	.05	.04	.02
203	Mike Kingery(FC)	.15	.11	.06
204	Sammy Stewart	.05	.04	.02
205	Graig Nettles	.10	.08	.04
206	Twins Leaders (Tim Laudner, Frank Viola)	.07	.05	.03
207	George Frazier	.05	.04	.02
208	John Shelby	.05	.04	.02
209	Rick Schu	.05	.04	.02
210	Lloyd Moseby	.07	.05	.03
211	John Morris(FC)	.07	.05	.03
212	Mike Fitzgerald	.05	.04	.02
213	Randy Myers(FC)	.30	.25	.12
214	Omar Moreno	.05	.04	.02
215	Mark Langston	.12	.09	.05
216	Future Stars (B.J. Surhoff)(FC)	.30	.25	.12
217	Chris Codiroli	.05	.04	.02
218	Sparky Anderson	.07	.05	.03
219	Cecilio Guante	.05	.04	.02
220	Joe Carter	.12	.09	.05
221	Vern Ruhle	.05	.04	.02
222	Denny Walling	.05	.04	.02
223	Charlie Leibrandt	.07	.05	.03
224	Wayne Tolleson	.05	.04	.02
225	Mike Smithson	.05	.04	.02
226	Max Venable	.05	.04	.02
227	Jamie Moyer(FC)	.20	.15	.08
228	Curt Wilkerson	.05	.04	.02
229	Mike Birkbeck(FC)	.15	.11	.06
230	Don Baylor	.10	.08	.04
231	Giants Leaders (Bob Brenly, Mike Krukow)	.07	.05	.03
232	Reggie Williams	.10	.08	.04
233	Russ Morman(FC)	.10	.08	.04
234	Pat Sheridan	.05	.04	.02
235	Alvin Davis	.10	.08	.04
236	Tommy John	.15	.11	.06
237	Jim Morrison	.05	.04	.02
238	Bill Krueger	.05	.04	.02
239	Juan Espino	.05	.04	.02
240	Steve Balboni	.07	.05	.03
241	Danny Heep	.05	.04	.02
242	Rick Mahler	.05	.04	.02
243	Whitey Herzog	.07	.05	.03
244	Dickie Noles	.05	.04	.02
245	Willie Upshaw	.07	.05	.03
246	Jim Dwyer	.05	.04	.02
247	Jeff Reed(FC)	.07	.05	.03
248	Gene Walter	.07	.05	.03
249	Jim Pankovits	.05	.04	.02
250	Teddy Higuera	.15	.11	.06
251	Rob Wilfong	.05	.04	.02
252	Denny Martinez	.05	.04	.02
253	Eddie Milner	.05	.04	.02
254	Bob Tewksbury	.12	.09	.05
255	Juan Samuel	.10	.08	.04
256	Royals Leaders (George Brett, Frank White)	.10	.08	.04
257	Bob Forsch	.07	.05	.03
258	Steve Yeager	.05	.04	.02
259	Mike Greenwell(FC)	.40	.30	.15
260	Vida Blue	.07	.05	.03
261	Ruben Sierra(FC)	2.75	2.00	1.00
262	Jim Winn	.05	.04	.02
263	Stan Javier(FC)	.07	.05	.03
264	Checklist 133-264	.05	.04	.02
265	Darrell Evans	.10	.08	.04
266	Jeff Hamilton(FC)	.25	.20	.10
267	Howard Johnson	.10	.08	.04
268	Pat Corrales	.05	.04	.02
269	Cliff Speck	.05	.04	.02
270	Jody Davis	.07	.05	.03
271	Mike Brown	.05	.04	.02
272	Andres Galarraga	.35	.25	.14
273	Gene Nelson	.05	.04	.02
274	Jeff Hearron(FC)	.05	.04	.02
275	LaMarr Hoyt	.05	.04	.02
276	Jackie Gutierrez	.05	.04	.02
277	Juan Agosto	.05	.04	.02
278	Gary Pettis	.05	.04	.02
279	Dan Plesac	.30	.25	.12
280	Jeffrey Leonard	.07	.05	.03
281	Reds Leaders (Bo Diaz, Bill Gullickson, Pete Rose)	.10	.08	.04
282	Jeff Calhoun	.05	.04	.02
283	Doug Drabek(FC)	.80	.60	.30
284	John Moses	.05	.04	.02
285	Dennis Boyd	.07	.05	.03
286	Mike Woodard(FC)	.07	.05	.03
287	Dave Von Ohlen	.05	.04	.02
288	Tito Landrum	.05	.04	.02
289	Bob Kipper	.07	.05	.03
290	Leon Durham	.07	.05	.03
291	Mitch Williams(FC)	.40	.30	.15
292	Franklin Stubbs	.07	.05	.03
293	Bob Rodgers	.05	.04	.02
294	Steve Jeltz	.05	.04	.02
295	Len Dykstra	.12	.09	.05
296	Andres Thomas	.15	.11	.06
297	Don Schulze	.05	.04	.02
298	Larry Herndon	.05	.04	.02
299	Joel Davis	.07	.05	.03
300	Reggie Jackson	.30	.25	.12
301	Luis Aquino(FC)	.10	.08	.04
302	Bill Schroeder	.05	.04	.02
303	Juan Berenguer	.05	.04	.02
304	Phil Garner	.05	.04	.02
305	John Franco	.10	.08	.04
306	Red Sox Leaders (Rich Gedman, John McNamara, Tom Seaver)	.07	.05	.03
307	Lee Guetterman(FC)	.15	.11	.06
308	Don Slaught	.05	.04	.02
309	Mike Young	.05	.04	.02
310	Frank Viola	.15	.11	.06
311	Turn Back The Clock (Rickey Henderson)	.10	.08	.04
312	Turn Back The Clock (Reggie Jackson)	.10	.08	.04
313	Turn Back The Clock (Roberto Clemente)	.15	.11	.06
314	Turn Back The Clock (Carl Yastrzemski)	.10	.08	.04
315	Turn Back The Clock (Maury Wills)	.07	.05	.03
316	Brian Fisher	.07	.05	.03
317	Clint Hurdle	.05	.04	.02
318	Jim Fregosi	.05	.04	.02
319	Greg Swindell(FC)	.60	.45	.25
320	Barry Bonds	2.00	1.50	.80
321	Mike Laga	.05	.04	.02
322	Chris Bando	.05	.04	.02
323	Al Newman	.07	.05	.03
324	Dave Palmer	.05	.04	.02
325	Garry Templeton	.07	.05	.03
326	Mark Gubicza	.10	.08	.04
327	Dale Sveum	.20	.15	.08
328	Bob Welch	.10	.08	.04
329	Ron Roenicke	.05	.04	.02
330	Mike Scott	.12	.09	.05
331	Mets Leaders (Gary Carter, Keith Hernandez, Dave Johnson, Darryl Strawberry)	.10	.08	.04
332	Joe Price	.05	.04	.02
333	Ken Phelps	.07	.05	.03
334	Ed Correa	.15	.11	.06
335	Candy Maldonado	.07	.05	.03
336	Allan Anderson(FC)	.25	.20	.10
337	Darrell Miller	.05	.04	.02
338	Tim Conroy	.05	.04	.02
339	Donnie Hill	.05	.04	.02
340	Roger Clemens	1.00	.70	.40
341	Mike Brown	.05	.04	.02
342	Bob James	.05	.04	.02
343	Hal Lanier	.05	.04	.02
344a	Joe Niekro (copyright outside yellow on back)	.30	.25	.12
344b	Joe Niekro (copyright inside yellow on back)	.07	.05	.03
345	Andre Dawson	.20	.15	.08
346	Shawon Dunston	.07	.05	.03
347	Mickey Brantley(FC)	.07	.05	.03
348	Carmelo Martinez	.07	.05	.03
349	Storm Davis	.10	.08	.04
350	Keith Hernandez	.20	.15	.08
351	Gene Garber	.05	.04	.02
352	Mike Felder(FC)	.07	.05	.03
353	Ernie Camacho	.05	.04	.02
354	Jamie Quirk	.05	.04	.02
355	Don Carman	.07	.05	.03
356	White Sox Leaders (Ed Brinkman, Julio Cruz)	.07	.05	.03
357	Steve Fireovid(FC)	.07	.05	.03
358	Sal Butera	.05	.04	.02
359	Doug Corbett	.05	.04	.02
360	Pedro Guerrero	.15	.11	.06
361	Mark Thurmond	.05	.04	.02
362	Luis Quinones(FC)	.12	.09	.05
363	Jose Guzman	.12	.09	.05
364	Randy Bush	.05	.04	.02
365	Rick Rhoden	.07	.05	.03
366	Mark McGwire	1.50	1.25	.60
367	Jeff Lahti	.05	.04	.02

#	Player	MT	NR MT	EX
368	John McNamara	.05	.04	.02
369	Brian Dayett	.05	.04	.02
370	Fred Lynn	.15	.11	.06
371	*Mark Eichhorn*	.15	.11	.06
372	Jerry Mumphrey	.05	.04	.02
373	Jeff Dedmon	.05	.04	.02
374	Glenn Hoffman	.05	.04	.02
375	Ron Guidry	.12	.09	.04
376	Scott Bradley	.05	.04	.02
377	John Henry Johnson	.05	.04	.02
378	Rafael Santana	.05	.04	.02
379	John Russell	.05	.04	.02
380	Rich Gossage	.15	.11	.06
381	Expos Leaders (Mike Fitzgerald, Bob Rodgers)	.07	.05	.03
382	Rudy Law	.05	.04	.02
383	Ron Davis	.05	.04	.02
384	Johnny Grubb	.05	.04	.02
385	Orel Hershiser	.30	.25	.12
386	Dickie Thon	.07	.05	.03
387	*T.R. Bryden*(FC)	.10	.08	.04
388	Geno Petralli	.05	.04	.02
389	Jeff Robinson	.07	.05	.03
390	Gary Matthews	.07	.05	.03
391	Jay Howell	.07	.05	.03
392	Checklist 265-396	.05	.04	.02
393	Pete Rose	.40	.30	.15
394	Mike Bielecki	.07	.05	.03
395	Damaso Garcia	.05	.04	.02
396	Tim Lollar	.05	.04	.02
397	Greg Walker	.07	.05	.03
398	Brad Havens	.05	.04	.02
399	Curt Ford(FC)	.07	.05	.03
400	George Brett	.35	.25	.14
401	Billy Jo Robidoux	.07	.05	.03
402	Mike Trujillo	.05	.04	.02
403	Jerry Royster	.05	.04	.02
404	Doug Sisk	.05	.04	.02
405	Brook Jacoby	.10	.08	.04
406	Yankees Leaders (Rickey Henderson, Don Mattingly)	.25	.20	.10
407	Jim Acker	.05	.04	.02
408	John Mizerock	.05	.04	.02
409	Milt Thompson	.07	.05	.03
410	Fernando Valenzuela	.25	.20	.10
411	Darnell Coles	.07	.05	.03
412	Eric Davis	.90	.70	.35
413	Moose Haas	.05	.04	.02
414	Joe Orsulak	.05	.04	.02
415	*Bobby Witt*	.50	.40	.20
416	Tom Nieto	.05	.04	.02
417	Pat Perry(FC)	.07	.05	.03
418	Dick Williams	.05	.04	.02
419	*Mark Portugal*(FC)	.10	.08	.04
420	*Will Clark*	3.00	2.25	1.25
421	Jose DeLeon	.07	.05	.03
422	Jack Howell	.07	.05	.03
423	Jaime Cocanower	.05	.04	.02
424	Chris Speier	.05	.04	.02
425	Tom Seaver	.30	.25	.12
426	Floyd Rayford	.05	.04	.02
427	Ed Nunez	.05	.04	.02
428	Bruce Bochy	.05	.04	.02
429	Future Stars *(Tim Pyznarski)*(FC)	.10	.08	.04
430	Mike Schmidt	.40	.30	.15
431	Dodgers Leaders (Tom Niedenfuer, Ron Perranoski, Alex Trevino)	.07	.05	.03
432	Jim Slaton	.05	.04	.02
433	*Ed Hearn*(FC)	.10	.08	.04
434	Mike Fischlin	.05	.04	.02
435	Bruce Sutter	.12	.09	.05
436	*Andy Allanson*	.15	.11	.06
437	Ted Power	.05	.04	.02
438	*Kelly Downs*(FC)	.30	.25	.12
439	Karl Best	.05	.04	.02
440	Willie McGee	.10	.08	.04
441	*Dave Leiper*(FC)	.10	.08	.04
442	Mitch Webster	.07	.05	.03
443	John Felske	.05	.04	.02
444	Jeff Russell	.05	.04	.02
445	Dave Lopes	.07	.05	.03
446	*Chuck Finley*(FC)	1.00	.70	.40
447	Bill Almon	.05	.04	.02
448	*Chris Bosio*(FC)	.25	.20	.10
449	Future Stars *(Pat Dodson)*(FC)	.10	.08	.04
450	Kirby Puckett	1.00	.70	.40
451	Joe Sambito	.05	.04	.02
452	Dave Henderson	.10	.08	.04
453	*Scott Terry*(FC)	.12	.09	.05
454	Luis Salazar	.05	.04	.02
455	Mike Boddicker	.07	.05	.03
456	A's Leaders (Carney Lansford, Tony LaRussa, Mickey Tettleton, Dave Von Ohlen)	.07	.05	.03
457	Len Matuszek	.05	.04	.02
458	Kelly Gruber(FC)	1.00	.70	.40
459	Dennis Eckersley	.10	.08	.04
460	Darryl Strawberry	.35	.25	.14
461	Craig McMurtry	.05	.04	.02
462	Scott Fletcher	.07	.05	.03
463	Tom Candiotti	.05	.04	.02
464	Butch Wynegar	.05	.04	.02
465	Todd Worrell	.30	.25	.12
466	Kal Daniels(FC)	.30	.25	.12
467	Randy St. Claire	.05	.04	.02
468	George Bamberger	.05	.04	.02
469	*Mike Diaz*(FC)	.15	.11	.06
470	Dave Dravecky	.07	.05	.03
471	Ronn Reynolds	.05	.04	.02
472	Bill Doran	.07	.05	.03
473	Steve Farr	.05	.04	.02
474	Jerry Narron	.05	.04	.02
475	Scott Garrelts	.05	.04	.02
476	Danny Tartabull	.70	.50	.30
477	Ken Howell	.05	.04	.02
478	Tim Laudner	.05	.04	.02
479	*Bob Sebra*(FC)	.10	.08	.04
480	Jim Rice	.25	.20	.10
481	Phillies Leaders (Von Hayes, Juan Samuel, Glenn Wilson)	.07	.05	.03
482	Daryl Boston	.05	.04	.02
483	Dwight Lowry	.05	.04	.02
484	Jim Traber(FC)	.15	.11	.06
485	Tony Fernandez	.10	.08	.04
486	Otis Nixon	.05	.04	.02
487	Dave Gumpert	.05	.04	.02
488	Ray Knight	.07	.05	.03
489	Bill Gullickson	.05	.04	.02
490	Dale Murphy	.40	.30	.15
491	*Ron Karkovice*(FC)	.10	.08	.04
492	Mike Heath	.05	.04	.02
493	Tom Lasorda	.07	.05	.03
494	*Barry Jones*(FC)	.12	.09	.05
495	Gorman Thomas	.10	.08	.04
496	Bruce Bochte	.05	.04	.02
497	*Dale Mohorcic*(FC)	.15	.11	.06
498	Bob Kearney	.05	.04	.02
499	*Bruce Ruffin*(FC)	.20	.15	.08
500	Don Mattingly	.60	.45	.25
501	Craig Lefferts	.05	.04	.02
502	Dick Schofield	.05	.04	.02
503	Larry Andersen	.05	.04	.02
504	Mickey Hatcher	.05	.04	.02
505	Bryn Smith	.05	.04	.02
506	Orioles Leaders (Rich Bordi, Rick Dempsey, Earl Weaver)	.07	.05	.03
507	Dave Stapleton	.05	.04	.02
508	*Scott Bankhead*	.25	.20	.10
509	Enos Cabell	.05	.04	.02
510	Tom Henke	.07	.05	.03
511	Steve Lyons	.05	.04	.02
512	*Dave Magadan*(FC)	.30	.25	.12
513	Carmen Castillo	.05	.04	.02
514	Orlando Mercado	.05	.04	.02
515	Willie Hernandez	.07	.05	.03
516	Ted Simmons	.10	.08	.04
517	Mario Soto	.07	.05	.03
518	Gene Mauch	.07	.05	.03
519	Curt Young	.07	.05	.03
520	Jack Clark	.15	.11	.06
521	Rick Reuschel	.10	.08	.04
522	Checklist 397-528	.05	.04	.02
523	Earnie Riles	.05	.04	.02
524	Bob Shirley	.05	.04	.02
525	Phil Bradley	.10	.08	.04
526	Roger Mason	.05	.04	.02
527	Jim Wohlford	.05	.04	.02
528	Ken Dixon	.05	.04	.02
529	*Alvaro Espinoza*(FC)	.07	.05	.03
530	Tony Gwynn	.50	.40	.20
531	Astros Leaders (Yogi Berra, Hal Lanier, Denis Menke, Gene Tenace)	.07	.05	.03
532	Jeff Stone	.05	.04	.02
533	Argenis Salazar	.05	.04	.02
534	Scott Sanderson	.05	.04	.02
535	Tony Armas	.07	.05	.03
536	*Terry Mulholland*(FC)	.10	.08	.04
537	Rance Mulliniks	.05	.04	.02
538	Tom Niedenfuer	.07	.05	.03
539	Reid Nichols	.05	.04	.02
540	Terry Kennedy	.07	.05	.03
541	*Rafael Belliard*(FC)	.10	.08	.04

#	Player	MT	NR MT	EX
542	Ricky Horton	.07	.05	.03
543	Dave Johnson	.07	.05	.03
544	Zane Smith	.07	.05	.03
545	Buddy Bell	.07	.05	.03
546	Mike Morgan	.05	.04	.02
547	Rob Deer	.10	.08	.04
548	*Bill Mooneyham*(FC)	.10	.08	.04
549	Bob Melvin	.05	.04	.02
550	*Pete Incaviglia*	.20	.15	.08
551	Frank Wills	.05	.04	.02
552	Larry Sheets	.07	.05	.03
553	*Mike Maddux*(FC)	.15	.11	.06
554	Buddy Biancalana	.05	.04	.02
555	Dennis Rasmussen	.10	.08	.04
556	Angels Leaders (Bob Boone, Marcel Lachemann, Mike Witt)	.07	.05	.03
557	*John Cerutti*	.15	.11	.06
558	Greg Gagne	.05	.04	.02
559	Lance McCullers	.07	.05	.03
560	Glenn Davis	.25	.20	.10
561	*Rey Quinones*	.15	.11	.06
562	*Bryan Clutterbuck*(FC)	.10	.08	.04
563	John Stefero	.05	.04	.02
564	Larry McWilliams	.05	.04	.02
565	Dusty Baker	.07	.05	.03
566	Tim Hulett	.05	.04	.02
567	*Greg Mathews*(FC)	.20	.15	.08
568	Earl Weaver	.07	.05	.03
569	Wade Rowdon(FC)	.07	.05	.03
570	Sid Fernandez	.10	.08	.04
571	Ozzie Virgil	.05	.04	.02
572	Pete Ladd	.05	.04	.02
573	Hal McRae	.07	.05	.03
574	Manny Lee	.05	.04	.02
575	Pat Tabler	.07	.05	.03
576	Frank Pastore	.05	.04	.02
577	Dann Bilardello	.05	.04	.02
578	Billy Hatcher	.07	.05	.03
579	Rick Burleson	.07	.05	.03
580	Mike Krukow	.07	.05	.03
581	Cubs Leaders (Ron Cey, Steve Trout)	.07	.05	.03
582	Bruce Berenyi	.05	.04	.02
583	Junior Ortiz	.05	.04	.02
584	Ron Kittle	.07	.05	.03
585	*Scott Bailes*	.15	.11	.06
586	Ben Oglivie	.07	.05	.03
587	Eric Plunk(FC)	.10	.08	.04
588	Wallace Johnson	.05	.04	.02
589	Steve Crawford	.05	.04	.02
590	Vince Coleman	.30	.25	.12
591	Spike Owen	.05	.04	.02
592	Chris Welsh	.05	.04	.02
593	Chuck Tanner	.05	.04	.02
594	Rick Anderson	.05	.04	.02
595	Keith Hernandez AS	.12	.09	.05
596	Steve Sax AS	.07	.05	.03
597	Mike Schmidt AS	.20	.15	.08
598	Ozzie Smith AS	.07	.05	.03
599	Tony Gwynn AS	.20	.15	.08
600	Dave Parker AS	.10	.08	.04
601	Darryl Strawberry AS	.20	.15	.08
602	Gary Carter AS	.15	.11	.06
603a	Dwight Gooden AS (no trademark on front)	.80	.60	.30
603b	Dwight Gooden AS (trademark on front)	.30	.25	.12
604	Fernando Valenzuela AS	.12	.09	.05
605	Todd Worrell AS	.10	.08	.04
606a	Don Mattingly AS (no trademark on front)	1.25	.90	.50
606b	Don Mattingly AS (trademark on front)	.70	.50	.30
607	Tony Bernazard AS	.05	.04	.02
608	Wade Boggs AS	.40	.30	.15
609	Cal Ripken AS	.20	.15	.08
610	Jim Rice AS	.15	.11	.06
611	Kirby Puckett AS	.15	.11	.06
612	George Bell AS	.12	.09	.05
613	Lance Parrish AS	.10	.08	.04
614	Roger Clemens AS	.30	.25	.12
615	Teddy Higuera AS	.10	.08	.04
616	Dave Righetti AS	.10	.08	.04
617	Al Nipper	.05	.04	.02
618	Tom Kelly	.05	.04	.02
619	Jerry Reed	.05	.04	.02
620	Jose Canseco	3.00	2.25	1.25
621	Danny Cox	.07	.05	.03
622	*Glenn Braggs*(FC)	.30	.25	.12
623	*Kurt Stillwell*(FC)	.30	.25	.12
624	Tim Burke	.05	.04	.02
625	Mookie Wilson	.07	.05	.03
626	Joel Skinner	.05	.04	.02
627	Ken Oberkfell	.05	.04	.02
628	Bob Walk	.05	.04	.02
629	Larry Parrish	.07	.05	.03
630	John Candelaria	.07	.05	.03
631	Tigers Leaders (Sparky Anderson, Mike Heath, Willie Hernandez)	.07	.05	.03
632	Rob Woodward(FC)	.07	.05	.03
633	Jose Uribe	.07	.05	.03
634	Future Stars *(Rafael Palmeiro)*(FC)	1.75	1.25	.70
635	Ken Schrom	.05	.04	.02
636	Darren Daulton	.05	.04	.02
637	*Bip Roberts*	.40	.30	.15
638	Rich Bordi	.05	.04	.02
639	Gerald Perry	.10	.08	.04
640	Mark Clear	.05	.04	.02
641	Domingo Ramos	.05	.04	.02
642	Al Pulido	.05	.04	.02
643	Ron Shepherd	.05	.04	.02
644	John Denny	.05	.04	.02
645	Dwight Evans	.12	.09	.05
646	Mike Mason	.05	.04	.02
647	Tom Lawless	.05	.04	.02
648	*Barry Larkin*	1.75	1.25	.70
649	Mickey Tettleton	.05	.04	.02
650	Hubie Brooks	.07	.05	.03
651	Benny Distefano	.05	.04	.02
652	Terry Forster	.07	.05	.03
653	*Kevin Mitchell*	1.25	.90	.50
654	Checklist 529-660	.05	.04	.02
655	Jesse Barfield	.15	.11	.06
656	Rangers Leaders (Bobby Valentine, Rickey Wright)	.07	.05	.03
657	Tom Waddell	.05	.04	.02
658	*Robby Thompson*	.30	.25	.12
659	Aurelio Lopez	.05	.04	.02
660	Bob Horner	.10	.08	.04
661	Lou Whitaker	.15	.11	.06
662	Frank DiPino	.05	.04	.02
663	Cliff Johnson	.05	.04	.02
664	Mike Marshall	.10	.08	.04
665	Rod Scurry	.05	.04	.02
666	Von Hayes	.07	.05	.03
667	Ron Hassey	.05	.04	.02
668	Juan Bonilla	.05	.04	.02
669	Bud Black	.05	.04	.02
670	Jose Cruz	.07	.05	.03
671a	Ray Soff (no "D*" before copyright line)	.20	.15	.08
671b	Ray Soff ("D*" before copyright line)	.05	.04	.02
672	Chili Davis	.07	.05	.03
673	Don Sutton	.15	.11	.06
674	Bill Campbell	.05	.04	.02
675	Ed Romero	.05	.04	.02
676	Charlie Moore	.05	.04	.02
677	Bob Grich	.07	.05	.03
678	Carney Lansford	.07	.05	.03
679	Kent Hrbek	.15	.11	.06
680	Ryne Sandberg	1.00	.70	.40
681	George Bell	.25	.20	.10
682	Jerry Reuss	.07	.05	.03
683	Gary Roenicke	.05	.04	.02
684	Kent Tekulve	.07	.05	.03
685	Jerry Hairston	.05	.04	.02
686	Doyle Alexander	.07	.05	.03
687	Alan Trammell	.25	.20	.10
688	Juan Beniquez	.05	.04	.02
689	Darrell Porter	.07	.05	.03
690	Dane Iorg	.05	.04	.02
691	Dave Parker	.20	.15	.08
692	Frank White	.07	.05	.03
693	Terry Puhl	.05	.04	.02
694	Phil Niekro	.20	.15	.08
695	Chico Walker	.05	.04	.02
696	Gary Lucas	.05	.04	.02
697	Ed Lynch	.05	.04	.02
698	Ernie Whitt	.07	.05	.03
699	Ken Landreaux	.05	.04	.02
700	Dave Bergman	.05	.04	.02
701	Willie Randolph	.07	.05	.03
702	Greg Gross	.05	.04	.02
703	Dave Schmidt	.05	.04	.02
704	Jesse Orosco	.07	.05	.03
705	Bruce Hurst	.10	.08	.04
706	Rick Manning	.05	.04	.02
707	Bob McClure	.05	.04	.02
708	Scott McGregor	.07	.05	.03
709	Dave Kingman	.10	.08	.04

		MT	NR MT	EX
710	Gary Gaetti	.15	.11	.06
711	Ken Griffey	.07	.05	.03
712	Don Robinson	.07	.05	.03
713	Tom Brookens	.05	.04	.02
714	Dan Quisenberry	.07	.05	.03
715	Bob Dernier	.05	.04	.02
716	Rick Leach	.05	.04	.02
717	Ed Vande Berg	.05	.04	.02
718	Steve Carlton	.25	.20	.10
719	Tom Hume	.05	.04	.02
720	Richard Dotson	.07	.05	.03
721	Tom Herr	.07	.05	.03
722	Bob Knepper	.07	.05	.03
723	Brett Butler	.07	.05	.03
724	Greg Minton	.05	.04	.02
725	George Hendrick	.07	.05	.03
726	Frank Tanana	.07	.05	.03
727	Mike Moore	.05	.04	.02
728	Tippy Martinez	.05	.04	.02
729	Tom Paciorek	.05	.04	.02
730	Eric Show	.07	.05	.03
731	Dave Concepcion	.10	.08	.04
732	Manny Trillo	.07	.05	.03
733	Bill Caudill	.05	.04	.02
734	Bill Madlock	.10	.08	.04
735	Rickey Henderson	.70	.50	.30
736	Steve Bedrosian	.10	.08	.04
737	Floyd Bannister	.07	.05	.03
738	Jorge Orta	.05	.04	.02
739	Chet Lemon	.07	.05	.03
740	Rich Gedman	.07	.05	.03
741	Paul Molitor	.12	.09	.05
742	Andy McGaffigan	.05	.04	.02
743	Dwayne Murphy	.07	.05	.03
744	Roy Smalley	.05	.04	.02
745	Glenn Hubbard	.05	.04	.02
746	Bob Ojeda	.07	.05	.03
747	Johnny Ray	.07	.05	.03
748	Mike Flanagan	.07	.05	.03
749	Ozzie Smith	.35	.25	.14
750	Steve Trout	.07	.05	.03
751	Garth Iorg	.05	.04	.02
752	Dan Petry	.07	.05	.03
753	Rick Honeycutt	.05	.04	.02
754	Dave LaPoint	.07	.05	.03
755	Luis Aguayo	.05	.04	.02
756	Carlton Fisk	.25	.20	.10
757	Nolan Ryan	1.25	.90	.50
758	Tony Bernazard	.05	.04	.02
759	Joel Youngblood	.05	.04	.02
760	Mike Witt	.07	.05	.03
761	Greg Pryor	.05	.04	.02
762	Gary Ward	.07	.05	.03
763	Tim Flannery	.05	.04	.02
764	Bill Buckner	.07	.05	.03
765	Kirk Gibson	.20	.15	.08
766	Don Aase	.05	.04	.02
767	Ron Cey	.07	.05	.03
768	Dennis Lamp	.05	.04	.02
769	Steve Sax	.15	.11	.06
770	Dave Winfield	.25	.20	.10
771	Shane Rawley	.07	.05	.03
772	Harold Baines	.12	.09	.05
773	Robin Yount	.35	.25	.14
774	Wayne Krenchicki	.05	.04	.02
775	Joaquin Andujar	.07	.05	.03
776	Tom Brunansky	.10	.08	.04
777	Chris Chambliss	.07	.05	.03
778	Jack Morris	.20	.15	.08
779	Craig Reynolds	.05	.04	.02
780	Andre Thornton	.07	.05	.03
781	Atlee Hammaker	.05	.04	.02
782	Brian Downing	.07	.05	.03
783	Willie Wilson	.10	.08	.04
784	Cal Ripken	1.25	.90	.50
785	Terry Francona	.05	.04	.02
786	Jimy Williams	.05	.04	.02
787	Alejandro Pena	.07	.05	.03
788	Tim Stoddard	.05	.04	.02
789	Dan Schatzeder	.05	.04	.02
790	Julio Cruz	.05	.04	.02
791	Lance Parrish	.15	.11	.06
792	Checklist 661-792	.05	.04	.02

The values quoted are intended to reflect the market price.

1987 Topps All-Star Glossy Set Of 22

For the fourth consecutive year, Topps produced an All-Star Game commemorative set of 22 cards. The glossy cards, which measure 2-1/2" by 3-1/2", were included in rack packs. Using the same basic card design as in previous efforts with a few minor changes, the 1987 edition features American and National League logos on the card fronts. Card #'s 1-12 feature representatives from the American League, while #'s 13-22 are National Leaguers.

		MT	NR MT	EX
Complete Set:		5.00	3.75	2.00
Common Player:		.15	.11	.06
1	Whitey Herzog	.15	.11	.06
2	Keith Hernandez	.40	.30	.15
3	Ryne Sandberg	.40	.30	.15
4	Mike Schmidt	.70	.50	.30
5	Ozzie Smith	.30	.25	.12
6	Tony Gwynn	.50	.40	.20
7	Dale Murphy	.50	.40	.20
8	Darryl Strawberry	.80	.60	.30
9	Gary Carter	.40	.30	.15
10	Dwight Gooden	.60	.45	.25
11	Fernando Valenzuela	.30	.25	.12
12	Dick Howser	.15	.11	.06
13	Wally Joyner	.70	.50	.30
14	Lou Whitaker	.30	.25	.12
15	Wade Boggs	.70	.50	.30
16	Cal Ripken	.50	.40	.20
17	Dave Winfield	.40	.30	.15
18	Rickey Henderson	.80	.60	.30
19	Kirby Puckett	.40	.30	.15
20	Lance Parrish	.30	.25	.12
21	Roger Clemens	.60	.45	.25
22	Teddy Higuera	.30	.25	.12

1987 Topps All-Star Glossy Set Of 60

Using the same design as the previous year, the 1987 Topps All-Star Glossy set includes 48 All-Star performers plus 12 potential superstars branded as "Hot Prospects". The card fronts are uncluttered, save the player's name found in very small print at the bottom. The set was available via a mail-in offer. Six subsets make up the 60-card set, with each subset being available for $1.00 plus six special offer cards that were found in wax packs.

		MT	NR MT	EX
Complete Set:		12.00	9.00	4.75
Common Player:		.15	.11	.06
1	Don Mattingly	2.50	2.00	1.00
2	Tony Gwynn	.60	.45	.25
3	Gary Gaetti	.25	.20	.10
4	Glenn Davis	.30	.25	.12
5	Roger Clemens	.70	.50	.30
6	Dale Murphy	.90	.70	.35
7	Lou Whitaker	.30	.25	.12
8	Roger McDowell	.15	.11	.06
9	Cory Snyder	.50	.40	.20
10	Todd Worrell	.20	.15	.08
11	Gary Carter	.50	.40	.20
12	Eddie Murray	.60	.45	.25
13	Bob Knepper	.15	.11	.06
14	Harold Baines	.20	.15	.08
15	Jeff Reardon	.20	.15	.08
16	Joe Carter	.25	.20	.10
17	Dave Parker	.25	.20	.10
18	Wade Boggs	1.25	.90	.50
19	Danny Tartabull	.35	.25	.14
20	Jim Deshaies	.20	.15	.08
21	Rickey Henderson	.70	.50	.30
22	Rob Deer	.15	.11	.06
23	Ozzie Smith	.25	.20	.10
24	Dave Righetti	.25	.20	.10
25	Kent Hrbek	.30	.25	.12
26	Keith Hernandez	.40	.30	.15
27	Don Baylor	.15	.11	.06
28	Mike Schmidt	.90	.70	.35
29	Pete Incaviglia	.50	.40	.20
30	Barry Bonds	.50	.40	.20
31	George Brett	.90	.70	.35
32	Darryl Strawberry	.90	.70	.35
33	Mike Witt	.15	.11	.06
34	Kevin Bass	.15	.11	.06
35	Jesse Barfield	.20	.15	.08
36	Bob Ojeda	.15	.11	.06
37	Cal Ripken	.70	.50	.30
38	Vince Coleman	.25	.20	.10
39	Wally Joyner	1.75	1.25	.70
40	Robby Thompson	.20	.15	.08
41	Pete Rose	1.25	.90	.50
42	Jim Rice	.50	.40	.20
43	Tony Bernazard	.15	.11	.06
44	Eric Davis	1.00	.70	.40
45	George Bell	.50	.40	.20
46	Hubie Brooks	.15	.11	.06
47	Jack Morris	.30	.25	.12
48	Tim Raines	.50	.40	.20
49	Mark Eichhorn	.20	.15	.08
50	Kevin Mitchell	.25	.20	.10
51	Dwight Gooden	.80	.60	.30
52	Doug DeCinces	.15	.11	.06
53	Fernando Valenzuela	.35	.25	.14
54	Reggie Jackson	.70	.50	.30
55	Johnny Ray	.15	.11	.06
56	Mike Pagliarulo	.20	.15	.08
57	Kirby Puckett	.50	.40	.20
58	Lance Parrish	.30	.25	.12
59	Jose Canseco	2.50	2.00	1.00
60	Greg Mathews	.25	.20	.10

NOTE: A card number in parentheses ( ) indicates the set is unnumbered.

1987 Topps Baseball Highlights

The "Baseball Highlights" boxed set of 33 cards was prepared by Topps for distribution at stores in the Woolworth's chain. Each card measures 2-1/2" by 3-1/2" in size and features a memorable baseball event that occurred during the 1986 season. The glossy set sold for $1.99 in Woolworth's stores.

		MT	NR MT	EX
Complete Set:		5.00	3.75	2.00
Common Player:		.09	.07	.04
1	Steve Carlton	.30	.25	.12
2	Cecil Cooper	.12	.09	.05
3	Rickey Henderson	.50	.40	.20
4	Reggie Jackson	.30	.25	.12
5	Jim Rice	.25	.20	.10
6	Don Sutton	.20	.15	.08
7	Roger Clemens	.50	.40	.20
8	Mike Schmidt	.35	.25	.14
9	Jesse Barfield	.15	.11	.06
10	Wade Boggs	.70	.50	.30
11	Tim Raines	.30	.25	.12
12	Jose Canseco	1.00	.70	.40
13	Todd Worrell	.15	.11	.06
14	Dave Righetti	.15	.11	.06
15	Don Mattingly	1.25	.90	.50
16	Tony Gwynn	.35	.25	.14
17	Marty Barrett	.09	.07	.04
18	Mike Scott	.12	.09	.05
19	World Series Game #1 (Bruce Hurst)	.12	.09	.05
20	World Series Game #1 (Calvin Schiraldi)	.09	.07	.04
21	World Series Game #2 (Dwight Evans)	.12	.09	.05
22	World Series Game #2 (Dave Henderson)	.09	.07	.04
23	World Series Game #3 (Len Dykstra)	.12	.09	.05
24	World Series Game #3 (Bob Ojeda)	.09	.07	.04
25	World Series Game #4 (Gary Carter)	.30	.25	.12
26	World Series Game #4 (Ron Darling)	.15	.11	.06
27	Jim Rice	.30	.25	.12
28	Bruce Hurst	.09	.07	.04
29	World Series Game #6 (Darryl Strawberry)	.35	.25	.14
30	World Series Game #6 (Ray Knight)	.09	.07	.04
31	World Series Game #6 (Keith Hernandez)	.25	.20	.10
32	World Series Games #7 (Mets Celebrate)	.12	.09	.05
33	Ray Knight	.09	.07	.04

1987 Topps Box Panels

Offering baseball cards on retail boxes for a second straight year, Topps reduced the size of the cards to 2-1/8" by 3". Four different wax pack boxes were available, each featuring two cards that were placed on the sides of the boxes. The card fronts are identical in design to the regular issue cards. The backs are printed in blue and yellow and carry a commentary imitating a newspaper format. The cards are numbered A through H.

		MT	NR MT	EX
	Complete Panel Set:	5.00	3.75	2.00
	Complete Singles Set:	2.00	1.50	.80
	Common Panel:	.75	.60	.30
	Common Single Player:	.15	.11	.06
	Panel	1.25	.90	.50
A	Don Baylor	.15	.11	.06
B	Steve Carlton	.30	.25	.12
	Panel	.75	.60	.30
C	Ron Cey	.15	.11	.06
D	Cecil Cooper	.15	.11	.06
	Panel	1.75	1.25	.70
E	Rickey Henderson	.40	.30	.15
F	Jim Rice	.25	.20	.10
	Panel	1.25	.90	.50
G	Don Sutton	.20	.15	.08
H	Dave Winfield	.30	.25	.12

		MT	NR MT	EX
19	Eddie Murray	.25	.20	.10
20	Kirby Puckett	.30	.25	.12
21	Jim Rice	.25	.20	.10
22	Dave Righetti	.20	.15	.08
23	Cal Ripken	.25	.20	.10
24	Cory Snyder	.25	.20	.10
25	Danny Tartabull	.20	.15	.08
26	Dave Winfield	.25	.20	.10
27	Hubie Brooks	.15	.11	.06
28	Gary Carter	.25	.20	.10
29	Vince Coleman	.20	.15	.08
30	Eric Davis	.70	.50	.30
31	Glenn Davis	.15	.11	.06
32	Steve Garvey	.25	.20	.10
33	Dwight Gooden	.40	.30	.15
34	Tony Gwynn	.30	.25	.12
35	Von Hayes	.15	.11	.06
36	Keith Hernandez	.20	.15	.08
37	Dale Murphy	.30	.25	.12
38	Dave Parker	.20	.15	.08
39	Tony Pena	.15	.11	.06
40	Nolan Ryan	.25	.20	.10
41	Ryne Sandberg	.20	.15	.08
42	Steve Sax	.15	.11	.06
43	Mike Schmidt	.30	.25	.12
44	Mike Scott	.15	.11	.06
45	Ozzie Smith	.15	.11	.06
46	Darryl Strawberry	.40	.30	.15
47	Fernando Valenzuela	.20	.15	.08
48	Todd Worrell	.15	.11	.06

1987 Topps Coins

For the first time since 1971, Topps issued a set of baseball "coins". Similar in design to the 1964 edition of Topps coins, the metal discs measure 1-1/2" in diameter. The aluminum coins were sold on a limited basis in retail outlets. Three coins and three sticks of gum were found in a pack. The coin fronts feature a full-color photo along with the player's name, team ans position in a white band at the bottom of the coin. Gold-colored rims are found for American League players; National League players have silver-colored rims. Backs are silver in color and carry the coin number, player's name and personal and statistical information.

		MT	NR MT	EX
	Complete Set:	10.00	7.50	4.00
	Common Player:	.15	.11	.06
1	Harold Baines	.15	.11	.06
2	Jesse Barfield	.15	.11	.06
3	George Bell	.20	.15	.08
4	Wade Boggs	.70	.50	.30
5	George Brett	.30	.25	.12
6	Jose Canseco	1.00	.70	.40
7	Joe Carter	.15	.11	.06
8	Roger Clemens	.40	.30	.15
9	Alvin Davis	.15	.11	.06
10	Rob Deer	.15	.11	.06
11	Kirk Gibson	.20	.15	.08
12	Rickey Henderson	.25	.20	.10
13	Kent Hrbek	.20	.15	.08
14	Pete Incaviglia	.20	.15	.08
15	Reggie Jackson	.25	.20	.10
16	Wally Joyner	.60	.45	.25
17	Don Mattingly	1.25	.90	.50
18	Jack Morris	.20	.15	.08

1987 Topps Gallery Of Champions

Designed as a tribute to the 1986 season's winners of baseball's most prestigious awards, the Gallery of Champions are metal "cards" that are one-quarter size replicas of the regular issue Topps cards. The bronze and silver sets were issued in leather-like velvet-lined display cases; the aluminum sets came cello-wrapped. Hobby dealers who purchased one bronze set or a 16-set case of aluminum "cards" received one free Jose Canseco pewter metal mini-card (value $60). The purchase of a silver set included five Canseco pewters. A 1953 Willie Mays bronze was given to dealers who brought cases of 1987 Topps Traded sets (value $10).

		MT	NR MT	EX
	Complete Aluminum Set:	30.00	22.00	12.00
	Complete Bronze Set:	175.00	131.00	70.00
	Complete Silver Set:	700.00	525.00	280.00
(1a)	Jesse Barfield (aluminum)	.70	.50	.30
(1b)	Jesse Barfield (bronze)	7.50	5.75	3.00
(1c)	Jesse Barfield (silver)	20.00	15.00	8.00
(2a)	Wade Boggs (aluminum)	3.00	2.25	1.25
(2b)	Wade Boggs (bronze)	25.00	18.50	10.00
(2c)	Wade Boggs (silver)	125.00	94.00	50.00
(3a)	Jose Canseco (aluminum)	3.00	2.25	1.25
(3b)	Jose Canseco (bronze)	25.00	18.50	10.00
(3c)	Jose Canseco (silver)	125.00	94.00	50.00
(4a)	Joe Carter (aluminum)	.70	.50	.30
(4b)	Joe Carter (bronze)	7.50	5.75	3.00
(4c)	Joe Carter (silver)	20.00	15.00	8.00
(5a)	Roger Clemens (aluminum)	2.00	1.50	.80

		MT	NR MT	EX
(5b)	Roger Clemens (bronze)	20.00	15.00	8.00
(5c)	Roger Clemens (silver)	90.00	67.00	36.00
(6a)	Tony Gwynn (aluminum)	1.25	.90	.50
(6b)	Tony Gwynn (bronze)	12.00	9.00	4.75
(6c)	Tony Gwynn (silver)	50.00	37.00	20.00
(7a)	Don Mattingly (aluminum)	8.00	6.00	3.25
(7b)	Don Mattingly (bronze)	50.00	37.00	20.00
(7c)	Don Mattingly (silver)	200.00	150.00	80.00
(8a)	Tim Raines (aluminum)	1.00	.70	.40
(8b)	Tim Raines (bronze)	10.00	7.50	4.00
(8c)	Tim Raines (silver)	30.00	22.00	12.00
(9a)	Dave Righetti (aluminum)	1.00	.70	.40
(9b)	Dave Righetti (bronze)	10.00	7.50	4.00
(9c)	Dave Righetti (silver)	30.00	22.00	12.00
(10a)	Mike Schmidt (aluminum)	1.50	1.25	.60
(10b)	Mike Schmidt (bronze)	15.00	11.00	6.00
(10c)	Mike Schmidt (silver)	80.00	60.00	32.00
(11a)	Mike Scott (aluminum)	.70	.50	.30
(11b)	Mike Scott (bronze)	7.50	5.75	3.00
(11c)	Mike Scott (silver)	20.00	15.00	8.00
(12a)	Todd Worrell (aluminum)	.70	.50	.30
(12b)	Todd Worrell (bronze)	10.00	7.50	4.00
(12c)	Todd Worrell (silver)	20.00	15.00	8.00

1987 Topps Glossy Rookies

The 1987 Topps Glossy Rookies set of 22 cards was introduced with Topps' new 100-card "Jumbo Packs". Intended for sale in supermarkets, the jumbo packs contained one glossy card. Measuring the standard 2-1/2" by 3-1/2" size, the special insert cards feature the top rookies from the previous season.

		MT	NR MT	EX
	Complete Set:	12.00	9.00	4.75
	Common Player:	.20	.15	.08
1	Andy Allanson	.20	.15	.08
2	John Cangelosi	.20	.15	.08
3	Jose Canseco	3.00	2.25	1.25
4	Will Clark	3.00	1.50	.90
5	Mark Eichhorn	.40	.30	.15
6	Pete Incaviglia	.70	.50	.30
7	Wally Joyner	1.00	.70	.40
8	Eric King	.30	.25	.12
9	Dave Magadan	.60	.45	.25
10	John Morris	.20	.15	.08
11	Juan Nieves	.40	.30	.15
12	Rafael Palmeiro	1.00	.70	.40
13	Billy Jo Robidoux	.20	.15	.08
14	Bruce Ruffin	.40	.30	.15
15	Ruben Sierra	1.25	.90	.50
16	Cory Snyder	.80	.60	.30
17	Kurt Stillwell	.60	.45	.25
18	Dale Sveum	.40	.30	.15
19	Danny Tartabull	.80	.60	.30
20	Andres Thomas	.40	.30	.15
21	Robby Thompson	.40	.30	.15
22	Todd Worrell	.40	.30	.15

A player's name in italic type indicates a rookie card. An (FC) indicates a player's first card for that particular card company.

1987 Topps Mini League Leaders

Returning for 1987, the Topps "Major League Leaders" set was increased in size from 66 to 76 cards. The 2-1/8" by 3" cards feature wood grain borders that encompass a white-bordered full-color photo. The card backs are printed in yellow, orange and brown and list the player's official ranking based on his 1986 American or National League statistics. The players featured are those who finished the top five in their leagues' various batting and pitching statistics. The cards were sold in plastic-wrapped packs, seven cards plus a game card per pack.

		MT	NR MT	EX
	Complete Set:	8.00	6.00	3.25
	Common Player:	.09	.07	.04
1	Bob Horner	.20	.15	.08
2	Dale Murphy	.50	.40	.20
3	Lee Smith	.09	.07	.04
4	Eric Davis	.60	.45	.25
5	John Franco	.15	.11	.06
6	Dave Parker	.20	.15	.08
7	Kevin Bass	.09	.07	.04
8	Glenn Davis	.20	.15	.08
9	Bill Doran	.15	.11	.06
10	Bob Knepper	.09	.07	.04
11	Mike Scott	.20	.15	.08
12	Dave Smith	.09	.07	.04
13	Mariano Duncan	.09	.07	.04
14	Orel Hershiser	.30	.25	.12
15	Steve Sax	.20	.15	.08
16	Fernando Valenzuela	.25	.20	.10
17	Tim Raines	.30	.25	.12
18	Jeff Reardon	.15	.11	.06
19	Floyd Youmans	.09	.07	.04
20	Gary Carter	.30	.25	.12
21	Ron Darling	.20	.15	.08
22	Sid Fernandez	.15	.11	.06
23	Dwight Gooden	.60	.45	.25
24	Keith Hernandez	.25	.20	.10
25	Bob Ojeda	.09	.07	.04
26	Darryl Strawberry	.50	.40	.20
27	Steve Bedrosian	.15	.11	.06
28	Von Hayes	.15	.11	.06
29	Juan Samuel	.20	.15	.08
30	Mike Schmidt	.50	.40	.20
31	Rick Rhoden	.09	.07	.04
32	Vince Coleman	.20	.15	.08
33	Danny Cox	.09	.07	.04
34	Todd Worrell	.15	.11	.06
35	Tony Gwynn	.40	.30	.15
36	Mike Krukow	.09	.07	.04
37	Candy Maldonado	.09	.07	.04
38	Don Aase	.09	.07	.04
39	Eddie Murray	.40	.30	.15
40	Cal Ripken	.40	.30	.15
41	Wade Boggs	.80	.60	.30
42	Roger Clemens	.60	.45	.25
43	Bruce Hurst	.15	.11	.06
44	Jim Rice	.30	.25	.12
45	Wally Joyner	.80	.60	.30
46	Donnie Moore	.09	.07	.04
47	Gary Pettis	.09	.07	.04
48	Mike Witt	.09	.07	.04
49	John Cangelosi	.09	.07	.04

		MT	NR MT	EX
50	Tom Candiotti	.09	.07	.04
51	Joe Carter	.20	.15	.08
52	Pat Tabler	.09	.07	.04
53	Kirk Gibson	.25	.20	.10
54	Willie Hernandez	.09	.07	.04
55	Jack Morris	.25	.20	.10
56	Alan Trammell	.30	.25	.12
57	George Brett	.50	.40	.20
58	Willie Wilson	.15	.11	.06
59	Rob Deer	.09	.07	.04
60	Teddy Higuera	.15	.11	.06
61	Bert Blyleven	.15	.11	.06
62	Gary Gaetti	.20	.15	.08
63	Kirby Puckett	.35	.25	.14
64	Rickey Henderson	.40	.30	.15
65	Don Mattingly	1.25	.90	.50
66	Dennis Rasmussen	.15	.11	.06
67	Dave Righetti	.20	.15	.08
68	Jose Canseco	1.00	.70	.40
69	Dave Kingman	.15	.11	.06
70	Phil Bradley	.15	.11	.06
71	Mark Langston	.15	.11	.06
72	Pete O'Brien	.09	.07	.04
73	Jesse Barfield	.15	.11	.06
74	George Bell	.25	.20	.10
75	Tony Fernandez	.15	.11	.06
76	Tom Henke	.09	.07	.04
77	Checklist	.09	.07	.04

1987 Topps Stickers

For the seventh consecutive year, Topps issued stickers to be housed in a specially designed yearbook. The stickers, which measure 2-1/8" by 3", offer a full-color front with a peel-off back printed in blue ink on white stock. The sticker fronts feature either one full-size player picture or two half-size individual stickers. The sticker yearbook measures 9" by 10-3/4" and contains 36 glossy, magazine-style pages, all printed in full color. Mike Schmidt, 1986 National League MVP, is featured on the cover. The yearbook sold in retail outlets for 35¢, while stickers were sold five in a pack for 25¢. The number in parentheses in the following checklist is the sticker number the player shares the sticker with.

		MT	NR MT	EX
Complete Set:		18.00	13.50	7.25
Common Player:		.03	.02	.01
Sticker Album:		.70	.50	.30
1	1986 Highlights (Jim Deshaies) (172)	.04	.03	.02
2	1986 Highlights (Roger Clemens) (175)	.15	.11	.06
3	1986 Highlights (Roger Clemens) (176)	.15	.11	.06
4	1986 Highlights (Dwight Evans) (177)	.06	.05	.02
5	1986 Highlights (Dwight Gooden) (178)	.15	.11	.06
6	1986 Highlights (Dwight Gooden) (180)	.15	.11	.06
7	1986 Highlights (Dave Lopes) (181)	.03	.02	.01
8	1986 Highlights (Dave Righetti) (182)	.06	.05	.02

		MT	NR MT	EX
9	1986 Highlights (Dave Righetti) (183)	.10	.08	.04
10	1986 Highlights (Ruben Sierra) (185)	.15	.11	.06
11	1986 Highlights (Todd Worrell) (186)	.06	.05	.02
12	1986 Highlights (Todd Worrell) (187)	.06	.05	.02
13	N.L. Championship Series (Lenny Dykstra)	.06	.05	.02
14	N.L. Championship Series (Gary Carter)	.08	.06	.03
15	N.L. Championship Series (Mike Scott)	.06	.05	.02
16	A.L. Championship Series (Gary Pettis)	.03	.02	.01
17	A.L. Championship Series (Jim Rice)	.08	.06	.03
18	A.L. Championship Series (Bruce Hurst)	.04	.03	.02
19	1986 World Series (Bruce Hurst)	.04	.03	.02
20	1986 World Series (Wade Boggs)	.15	.11	.06
21	1986 World Series (Lenny Dykstra)	.06	.05	.02
22	1986 World Series (Gary Carter)	.08	.06	.03
23	1986 World Series (Dave Henderson)	.04	.03	.02
24	1986 World Series (Howard Johnson)	.04	.03	.02
25	1986 World Series (Mets Celebrate)	.08	.06	.03
26	Glenn Davis	.15	.11	.06
27	Nolan Ryan (188)	.10	.08	.04
28	Charlie Kerfeld (189)	.03	.02	.01
29	Jose Cruz (190)	.04	.03	.02
30	Phil Garner (191)	.06	.05	.02
31	Bill Doran (192)	.06	.05	.02
32	Bob Knepper (195)	.03	.02	.01
33	Denny Walling (196)	.10	.08	.04
34	Kevin Bass (197)	.04	.03	.02
35	Mike Scott	.10	.08	.04
36	Dale Murphy	.25	.20	.10
37	Paul Assenmacher (198)	.06	.05	.02
38	Ken Oberkfell (200)	.06	.05	.02
39	Andres Thomas (201)	.08	.06	.03
40	Gene Garber (202)	.03	.02	.01
41	Bob Horner	.08	.06	.03
42	Rafael Ramirez (203)	.03	.02	.01
43	Rick Mahler (204)	.03	.02	.01
44	Omar Moreno (205)	.03	.02	.01
45	Dave Palmer (206)	.03	.02	.01
46	Ozzie Smith	.12	.09	.05
47	Bob Forsch (207)	.03	.02	.01
48	Willie McGee (209)	.06	.05	.02
49	Tom Herr (210)	.06	.05	.02
50	Vince Coleman (211)	.08	.06	.03
51	Andy Van Slyke (212)	.06	.05	.02
52	Jack Clark (215)	.08	.06	.03
53	John Tudor (216)	.04	.03	.02
54	Terry Pendleton (217)	.03	.02	.01
55	Todd Worrell	.10	.08	.04
56	Lee Smith	.06	.05	.02
57	Leon Durham (218)	.03	.02	.01
58	Jerry Mumphrey (219)	.06	.05	.02
59	Shawon Dunston (220)	.06	.05	.02
60	Scott Sanderson (221)	.06	.05	.02
61	Ryne Sandberg (222)	.15	.11	.06
62	Gary Matthews (222)	.04	.03	.02
63	Dennis Eckersley (225)	.06	.05	.02
64	Jody Davis (226)	.06	.05	.02
65	Keith Moreland (227)	.04	.03	.02
66	Mike Marshall (228)	.06	.05	.02
67	Bill Madlock (229)	.06	.05	.02
68	Greg Brock (230)	.04	.03	.02
69	Pedro Guerrero (231)	.08	.06	.03
70	Steve Sax	.12	.09	.05
71	Rick Honeycutt (232)	.03	.02	.01
72	Franklin Stubbs (235)	.03	.02	.01
73	Mike Scioscia (236)	.10	.08	.04
74	Mariano Duncan (237)	.03	.02	.01
75	Fernando Valenzuela	.15	.11	.06
76	Hubie Brooks	.06	.05	.02
77	Andre Dawson (238)	.08	.06	.03
78	Tim Burke (240)	.04	.03	.02
79	Floyd Youmans (241)	.03	.02	.01
80	Tim Wallach (242)	.04	.03	.02
81	Jeff Reardon (243)	.06	.05	.02
82	Mitch Webster (244)	.15	.11	.06
83	Bryn Smith (245)	.03	.02	.01
84	Andres Galarraga (246)	.12	.09	.05
85	Tim Raines	.15	.11	.06
86	Chris Brown	.08	.06	.03

		MT	NR MT	EX			MT	NR MT	EX
87	Bob Brenly (247)	.03	.02	.01	178	Brian Downing (5)	.15	.11	.06
88	Will Clark (249)	.25	.20	.10	179	Mike Witt	.06	.05	.02
89	Scott Garrelts (250)	.04	.03	.02	180	Bob Boone (6)	.15	.11	.06
90	Jeffrey Leonard (251)	.06	.05	.02	181	Kirk McCaskill (7)	.03	.02	.01
91	Robby Thompson (252)	.06	.05	.02	182	Doug DeCinces (8)	.06	.05	.02
92	Mike Krukow (255)	.03	.02	.01	183	Don Sutton (9)	.10	.08	.04
93	Danny Gladden (256)	.03	.02	.01	184	Jessie Barfield	.10	.08	.04
94	Candy Maldonado (257)	.04	.03	.02	185	Tom Henke (10)	.15	.11	.06
95	Chili Davis	.04	.03	.02	186	Willie Upshaw (11)	.06	.05	.02
96	Dwight Gooden	.30	.25	.12	187	Mark Eichhorn (12)	.06	.05	.02
97	Sid Fernandez (258)	.04	.03	.02	188	Damaso Garcia (27)	.10	.08	.04
98	Len Dykstra (259)	.06	.05	.02	189	Jim Clancy (28)	.03	.02	.01
99	Bob Ojeda (260)	.04	.03	.02	190	Lloyd Moseby (29)	.04	.03	.02
100	Wally Backman (261)	.04	.03	.02	191	Tony Fernandez (30)	.06	.05	.02
101	Gary Carter	.15	.11	.06	192	Jimmy Key (31)	.06	.05	.02
102	Keith Hernandez (262)	.10	.08	.04	193	George Bell	.20	.15	.08
103	Darryl Strawberry (265)	.15	.11	.06	194	Rob Deer	.06	.05	.02
104	Roger McDowell (266)	.08	.06	.03	195	Mark Clear (32)	.03	.02	.01
105	Ron Darling (267)	.08	.06	.03	196	Robin Yount (33)	.10	.08	.04
106	Tony Gwynn	.20	.15	.08	197	Jim Gantner (34)	.04	.03	.02
107	Dave Dravecky (268)	.04	.03	.02	198	Cecil Cooper (37)	.06	.05	.02
108	Terry Kennedy (269)	.08	.06	.03	199	Teddy Higuera	.08	.06	.03
109	Rich Gossage (270)	.10	.08	.04	200	Paul Molitor (38)	.08	.06	.03
110	Garry Templeton (271)	.04	.03	.02	201	Dan Plesac (39)	.08	.06	.03
111	Lance McCullers (272)	.04	.03	.02	202	Billy Jo Robidoux (40)	.03	.02	.01
112	Eric Show (275)	.04	.03	.02	203	Earnie Riles (42)	.03	.02	.01
113	John Kruk (276)	.12	.09	.05	204	Ken Schrom (43)	.03	.02	.01
114	Tim Flannery (277)	.06	.05	.02	205	Pat Tabler (44)	.03	.02	.01
115	Steve Garvey	.15	.11	.06	206	Mel Hall (45)	.03	.02	.01
116	Mike Schmidt	.25	.20	.10	207	Tony Bernazard (47)	.03	.02	.01
117	Glenn Wilson (278)	.06	.05	.02	208	Joe Carter	.10	.08	.04
118	Kent Tekulve (280)	.06	.05	.02	209	Ernie Camacho (48)	.06	.05	.02
119	Gary Redus (281)	.08	.06	.03	210	Julio Franco (49)	.06	.05	.02
120	Shane Rawley (282)	.03	.02	.01	211	Tom Candiotti (50)	.08	.06	.03
121	Von Hayes	.06	.05	.02	212	Brook Jacoby (51)	.06	.05	.02
122	Don Carman (283)	.04	.03	.02	213	Cory Snyder	.30	.25	.12
123	Bruce Ruffin (285)	.04	.03	.02	214	Jim Presley	.08	.06	.03
124	Steve Bedrosian (286)	.06	.05	.02	215	Mike Moore (52)	.08	.06	.03
125	Juan Samuel (287)	.06	.05	.02	216	Harold Reynolds (53)	.04	.03	.02
126	Sid Bream (288)	.06	.05	.02	217	Scott Bradley (54)	.03	.02	.01
127	Cecilio Guante (289)	.03	.02	.01	218	Matt Young (57)	.03	.02	.01
128	Rick Reuschel (290)	.04	.03	.02	219	Mark Langston (58)	.06	.05	.02
129	Tony Pena (291)	.04	.03	.02	220	Alvin Davis (59)	.06	.05	.02
130	Rick Rhoden	.06	.05	.02	221	Phil Bradley (60)	.06	.05	.02
131	Barry Bonds (292)	.10	.08	.04	222	Ken Phelps (62)	.04	.03	.02
132	Joe Orsulak (295)	.03	.02	.01	223	Danny Tartabull	.20	.15	.08
133	Jim Morrison (296)	.12	.09	.05	224	Eddie Murray	.20	.15	.08
134	R.J. Reynolds (297)	.04	.03	.02	225	Rick Dempsey (63)	.06	.05	.02
135	Johnny Ray	.06	.05	.02	226	Fred Lynn (64)	.06	.05	.02
136	Eric Davis	.30	.25	.12	227	Mike Boddicker (65)	.04	.03	.02
137	Tom Browning (298)	.10	.08	.04	228	Don Aase (66)	.06	.05	.02
138	John Franco (300)	.06	.05	.02	229	Larry Sheets (67)	.06	.05	.02
139	Pete Rose (301)	.20	.15	.08	230	Storm Davis (68)	.04	.03	.02
140	Bill Gullickson (302)	.04	.03	.02	231	Lee Lacy (69)	.08	.06	.03
141	Ron Oester (303)	.04	.03	.02	232	Jim Traber (71)	.03	.02	.01
142	Bo Diaz (304)	.40	.30	.15	233	Cal Ripken	.20	.15	.08
143	Buddy Bell (305)	.04	.03	.02	234	Larry Parrish	.06	.05	.02
144	Eddie Milner (306)	.08	.06	.03	235	Gary Ward (72)	.03	.02	.01
145	Dave Parker	.10	.08	.04	236	Pete Incaviglia (73)	.10	.08	.04
146	Kirby Puckett	.35	.25	.14	237	Scott Fletcher (74)	.03	.02	.01
147	Rickey Henderson	.40	.30	.15	238	Greg Harris (77)	.08	.06	.03
148	Wade Boggs	.60	.45	.25	239	Pete O'Brien	.06	.05	.02
149	Lance Parrish	.25	.20	.10	240	Charlie Hough (78)	.04	.03	.02
150	Wally Joyner	.70	.50	.30	241	Don Slaught (79)	.03	.02	.01
151	Cal Ripken	.40	.30	.15	242	Steve Buechele (80)	.04	.03	.02
152	Dave Winfield	.30	.25	.12	243	Oddibe McDowell (81)	.06	.05	.02
153	Lou Whitaker	.25	.20	.10	244	Roger Clemens (82)	.15	.11	.06
154	Roger Clemens	.50	.40	.20	245	Bob Stanley (83)	.03	.02	.01
155	Tony Gwynn	.40	.30	.15	246	Tom Seaver (84)	.12	.09	.05
156	Ryne Sandberg	.25	.20	.10	247	Rich Gedman (87)	.03	.02	.01
157	Keith Hernandez	.25	.20	.10	248	Jim Rice	.15	.11	.06
158	Gary Carter	.30	.25	.12	249	Dennis Boyd (88)	.25	.20	.10
159	Darryl Strawberry	.50	.40	.20	250	Bill Buckner (89)	.04	.03	.02
160	Mike Schmidt	.40	.30	.15	251	Dwight Evans (90)	.06	.05	.02
161	Dale Murphy	.40	.30	.15	252	Don Baylor (91)	.06	.05	.02
162	Ozzie Smith	.20	.15	.08	253	Wade Boggs	.40	.30	.15
163	Dwight Gooden	.50	.40	.20	254	George Brett	.25	.20	.10
164	Jose Canseco	.80	.60	.30	255	Steve Farr (92)	.03	.02	.01
165	Curt Young (307)	.04	.03	.02	256	Jim Sundberg (93)	.03	.02	.01
166	Alfredo Griffin (308)	.12	.09	.05	257	Dan Quisenberry (94)	.04	.03	.02
167	Dave Stewart (309)	.06	.05	.02	258	Charlie Leibrandt (97)	.04	.03	.02
168	Mike Davis (310)	.06	.05	.02	259	Argenis Salazar (98)	.06	.05	.02
169	Bruce Bochte (311)	.03	.02	.01	260	Frank White (99)	.04	.03	.02
170	Dwayne Murphy (312)	.04	.03	.02	261	Willie Wilson (100)	.04	.03	.02
171	Carney Lansford (313)	.20	.15	.08	262	Lonnie Smith (102)	.10	.08	.04
172	Joaquin Andujar (1)	.04	.03	.02	263	Steve Balboni	.04	.03	.02
173	Dave Kingman	.08	.06	.03	264	Darrell Evans	.06	.05	.02
174	Wally Joyner	.40	.30	.15	265	Johnny Grubb (103)	.15	.11	.06
175	Gary Pettis (2)	.15	.11	.06	266	Jack Morris (104)	.08	.06	.03
176	Dick Schofield (3)	.15	.11	.06	267	Lou Whitaker (105)	.08	.06	.03
177	Donnie Moore (4)	.06	.05	.02	268	Chet Lemon (107)	.04	.03	.02

		MT	NR MT	EX
269	Lance Parrish (108)	.08	.06	.03
270	Alan Trammell (109)	.10	.08	.04
271	Darnell Coles (110)	.04	.03	.02
272	Willie Hernandez (111)	.04	.03	.02
273	Kirk Gibson	.15	.11	.06
274	Kirby Puckett	.20	.15	.08
275	Mike Smithson (112)	.04	.03	.02
276	Mickey Hatcher (113)	.12	.09	.05
277	Frank Viola (114)	.06	.05	.02
278	Bert Blyleven (117)	.06	.05	.02
279	Gary Gaetti	.10	.08	.04
280	Tom Brunansky (118)	.06	.05	.02
281	Kent Hrbek (119)	.08	.06	.03
282	Roy Smalley (120)	.03	.02	.01
283	Greg Gagne (122)	.04	.03	.02
284	Harold Baines	.10	.08	.04
285	Ron Hassey (123)	.04	.03	.02
286	Floyd Bannister (124)	.06	.05	.02
287	Ozzie Guillen (125)	.06	.05	.02
288	Carlton Fisk (126)	.06	.05	.02
289	Tim Hulett (127)	.03	.02	.01
290	Joe Cowley (128)	.04	.03	.02
291	Greg Walker (129)	.04	.03	.02
292	Neil Allen (131)	.10	.08	.04
293	John Cangelosi	.04	.03	.02
294	Don Mattingly	.90	.70	.35
295	Mike Easler (132)	.03	.02	.01
296	Rickey Henderson (133)	.12	.09	.05
297	Dan Pasqua (134)	.04	.03	.02
298	Dave Winfield (137)	.10	.08	.04
299	Dave Righetti	.12	.09	.05
300	Mike Pagliarulo (138)	.06	.05	.02
301	Ron Guidry (139)	.20	.15	.08
302	Willie Randolph (140)	.04	.03	.02
303	Dennis Rasmussen (141)	.04	.03	.02
304	Jose Canseco (142)	.40	.30	.15
305	Andres Thomas (143)	.04	.03	.02
306	Danny Tartabull (144)	.08	.06	.03
307	Robby Thompson (165)	.04	.03	.02
308	Pete Incaviglia, Cory Snyder (166)	.12	.09	.05
309	Dale Sveum (167)	.06	.05	.02
310	Todd Worrell (168)	.06	.05	.02
311	Andy Allanson (169)	.03	.02	.01
312	Bruce Ruffin (170)	.04	.03	.02
313	Wally Joyner (171)	.20	.15	.08

1987 Topps Traded

The Topps Traded set consists of 132 cards as have all Traded sets issued by Topps since 1981. The cards measure the standard 2 1/2" by 3 1/2" and are identical in design to the regular edition set. The purpose of the set is to update player trades and feature rookies not included in the regular issue. As they had done the previous three years, Topps produced a glossy-coated "Tiffany" edition of the Traded set. The Tiffany edition cards are valued at two to three times greater than the regular Traded cards.

		MT	NR MT	EX
Complete Set:		10.00	7.50	4.00
Common Player:		.06	.05	.02
1T	Bill Almon	.06	.05	.02
2T	Scott Bankhead	.08	.06	.03
3T	Eric Bell(FC)	.15	.11	.06

		MT	NR MT	EX
4T	Juan Beniquez	.06	.05	.02
5T	Juan Berenguer	.06	.05	.02
6T	Greg Booker	.06	.05	.02
7T	Thad Bosley	.06	.05	.02
8T	Larry Bowa	.10	.08	.04
9T	Greg Brock	.10	.08	.04
10T	Bob Brower(FC)	.15	.11	.06
11T	Jerry Browne(FC)	.30	.25	.12
12T	Ralph Bryant(FC)	.12	.09	.05
13T	DeWayne Buice(FC)	.15	.11	.06
14T	Ellis Burks(FC)	.60	.45	.25
15T	Ivan Calderon	.25	.20	.10
16T	Jeff Calhoun	.06	.05	.02
17T	Casey Candaele(FC)	.10	.08	.04
18T	John Cangelosi	.06	.05	.02
19T	Steve Carlton	.30	.25	.12
20T	Juan Castillo(FC)	.06	.05	.02
21T	Rick Cerone	.06	.05	.02
22T	Ron Cey	.10	.08	.04
23T	John Christensen	.06	.05	.02
24T	Dave Cone(FC)	2.00	1.50	.80
25T	Chuck Crim(FC)	.15	.11	.06
26T	Storm Davis	.06	.05	.02
27T	Andre Dawson	.40	.30	.15
28T	Rick Dempsey	.08	.06	.03
29T	Doug Drabek	.40	.30	.15
30T	Mike Dunne	.30	.25	.12
31T	Dennis Eckersley	.30	.25	.12
32T	Lee Elia	.06	.05	.02
33T	Brian Fisher	.10	.08	.04
34T	Terry Francona	.06	.05	.02
35T	Willie Fraser(FC)	.15	.11	.06
36T	Billy Gardner	.06	.05	.02
37T	Ken Gerhart(FC)	.15	.11	.06
38T	Danny Gladden	.06	.05	.02
39T	Jim Gott	.06	.05	.02
40T	Cecilio Guante	.06	.05	.02
41T	Albert Hall	.06	.05	.02
42T	Terry Harper	.06	.05	.02
43T	Mickey Hatcher	.06	.05	.02
44T	Brad Havens	.06	.05	.02
45T	Neal Heaton	.06	.05	.02
46T	Mike Henneman(FC)	.30	.25	.12
47T	Donnie Hill	.06	.05	.02
48T	Guy Hoffman	.06	.05	.02
49T	Brian Holton(FC)	.15	.11	.06
50T	Charles Hudson	.06	.05	.02
51T	Danny Jackson(FC)	.30	.25	.12
52T	Reggie Jackson	.50	.40	.20
53T	Chris James(FC)	.40	.30	.15
54T	Dion James	.10	.08	.04
55T	Stan Jefferson(FC)	.20	.15	.08
56T	Joe Johnson(FC)	.08	.06	.03
57T	Terry Kennedy	.08	.06	.03
58T	Mike Kingery	.08	.06	.03
59T	Ray Knight	.10	.08	.04
60T	Gene Larkin(FC)	.30	.25	.12
61T	Mike LaValliere	.10	.08	.04
62T	Jack Lazorko	.06	.05	.02
63T	Terry Leach	.06	.05	.02
64T	Tim Leary	.06	.05	.02
65T	Jim Lindeman(FC)	.15	.11	.06
66T	Steve Lombardozzi(FC)	.06	.05	.02
67T	Bill Long(FC)	.20	.15	.08
68T	Barry Lyons(FC)	.15	.11	.06
69T	Shane Mack	.40	.30	.15
70T	Greg Maddux(FC)	3.00	2.25	1.25
71T	Bill Madlock	.15	.11	.06
72T	Joe Magrane(FC)	.50	.40	.20
73T	Dave Martinez(FC)	.25	.20	.10
74T	Fred McGriff(FC)	3.00	2.25	1.25
75T	Mark McLemore(FC)	.10	.08	.04
76T	Kevin McReynolds(FC)	.40	.30	.15
77T	Dave Meads(FC)	.15	.11	.06
78T	Eddie Milner	.06	.05	.02
79T	Greg Minton	.06	.05	.02
80T	John Mitchell(FC)	.15	.11	.06
81T	Kevin Mitchell	.70	.50	.30
82T	Charlie Moore	.06	.05	.02
83T	Jeff Musselman(FC)	.12	.09	.05
84T	Gene Nelson	.06	.05	.02
85T	Graig Nettles	.12	.09	.05
86T	Al Newman	.06	.05	.02
87T	Reid Nichols	.06	.05	.02
88T	Tom Niedenfuer	.08	.06	.03
89T	Joe Niekro	.10	.08	.04
90T	Tom Nieto	.06	.05	.02
91T	Matt Nokes(FC)	.40	.30	.15
92T	Dickie Noles	.06	.05	.02
93T	Pat Pacillo	.15	.11	.06
94T	Lance Parrish	.20	.15	.08

		MT	NR MT	EX
95T	Tony Pena	.10	.08	.04
96T	Luis Polonia(FC)	.40	.30	.15
97T	Randy Ready	.06	.05	.02
98T	Jeff Reardon	.12	.09	.05
99T	Gary Redus	.08	.06	.03
100T	Jeff Reed	.06	.05	.02
101T	Rick Rhoden	.10	.08	.04
102T	Cal Ripken, Sr.	.06	.05	.02
103T	Wally Ritchie(FC)	.15	.11	.06
104T	Jeff Robinson(FC)	.40	.30	.15
105T	Gary Roenicke	.06	.05	.02
106T	Jerry Royster	.06	.05	.02
107T	Mark Salas	.06	.05	.02
108T	Luis Salazar	.06	.05	.02
109T	Benny Santiago(FC)	.50	.40	.20
110T	Dave Schmidt	.08	.06	.03
111T	Kevin Seitzer(FC)	.50	.40	.20
112T	John Shelby	.06	.05	.02
113T	Steve Shields(FC)	.08	.06	.03
114T	John Smiley(FC)	.60	.45	.25
115T	Chris Speier	.06	.05	.02
116T	Mike Stanley(FC)	.20	.15	.08
117T	Terry Steinbach(FC)	.40	.30	.15
118T	Les Straker(FC)	.20	.15	.08
119T	Jim Sundberg	.08	.06	.03
120T	Danny Tartabull	.35	.25	.14
121T	Tom Trebelhorn	.08	.06	.03
122T	Dave Valle(FC)	.12	.09	.05
123T	Ed Vande Berg	.06	.05	.02
124T	Andy Van Slyke	.20	.15	.08
125T	Gary Ward	.06	.05	.02
126T	Alan Wiggins	.06	.05	.02
127T	Bill Wilkinson(FC)	.15	.11	.06
128T	Frank Williams	.08	.06	.03
129T	Matt Williams(FC)	1.50	1.25	.60
130T	Jim Winn	.06	.05	.02
131T	Matt Young	.06	.05	.02
132T	Checklist 1T-132T	.06	.05	.02

1988 Topps

The 1988 Topps set features a clean, attractive design that should prove to be very popular with collectors for many years to come. The full-color player photo is surrounded by a thin yellow frame which is encompassed by a white border. The player's name appears in the lower right corner in a colored band which appears to wrap around the player photo. The player's team nickname is located in large letters at the top of the card. The Topps logo is placed in the lower left corner of the card. The card backs feature black print on orange and gray stock and includes the usual player personal and career statistics. Many of the cards contain a new feature entitled "This Way To The Clubhouse", which explains how the player joined his current team, be it by trade, free agency, etc. The 792-card set includes a number of special subsets including "Future Stars", "Turn Back The Clock", All-Star teams, All-Star rookie selections, and Record Breakers. All cards measure 2-1/2" by 3-1/2". For the fifth consecutive year, Topps issued a glossy "Tiffany" edition of its 792-card regular-issue set. The Tiffany cards have a value of 3-4 times greater than the same card in the regular issue. The Tiffany edition could be purchased by collectors directly from Topps for $99. The company

placed ads for the Tiffany set in publications such as USA Today and The Sporting News.

		MT	NR MT	EX
Complete Set:		18.00	13.50	7.25
Common Player:		.04	.03	.02
1	'87 Record Breakers (Vince Coleman)	.08	.06	.03
2	'87 Record Breakers (Don Mattingly)	.40	.30	.15
3a	'87 Record Breakers (Mark McGwire) (white triangle by left foot)	.40	.30	.15
3b	'87 Record Breakers (Mark McGwire) (no triangle by left foot)	.25	.20	.10
4a	'87 Record Breakers (Eddie Murray) (no mention of record on front)	.10	.08	.04
4b	'87 Record Breakers (Eddie Murray) (record stated on card front)	.60	.45	.25
5	'87 Record Breakers (Joe Niekro, Phil Niekro)	.10	.08	.04
6	'87 Record Breakers (Nolan Ryan)	.10	.08	.04
7	'87 Record Breakers (Benito Santiago)	.15	.11	.06
8	Kevin Elster(FC)	.25	.20	.10
9	Andy Hawkins	.04	.03	.02
10	Ryne Sandberg	.35	.25	.12
11	Mike Young	.04	.03	.02
12	Bill Schroeder	.04	.03	.02
13	Andres Thomas	.06	.05	.02
14	Sparky Anderson	.06	.05	.02
15	Chili Davis	.06	.05	.02
16	Kirk McCaskill	.06	.05	.02
17	Ron Oester	.04	.03	.02
18a	*Al Leiter* (no "NY" on shirt, photo actually Steve George)(FC)	.40	.30	.15
18b	*Al Leiter* ("NY" on shirt, correct photo)(FC)	.20	.15	.08
19	*Mark Davidson*(FC)	.12	.09	.05
20	Kevin Gross	.06	.05	.02
21	Red Sox Leaders (Wade Boggs, Spike Owen)	.15	.11	.06
22	Greg Swindell	.15	.11	.06
23	Ken Landreaux	.04	.03	.02
24	Jim Deshaies	.06	.05	.02
25	Andres Galarraga	.12	.09	.05
26	Mitch Williams	.06	.05	.02
27	R.J. Reynolds	.04	.03	.02
28	*Jose Nunez*(FC)	.10	.08	.04
29	Argenis Salazar	.04	.03	.02
30	Sid Fernandez	.08	.06	.03
31	Bruce Bochy	.04	.03	.02
32	Mike Morgan	.04	.03	.02
33	Rob Deer	.06	.05	.02
34	Ricky Horton	.06	.05	.02
35	Harold Baines	.10	.08	.04
36	Jamie Moyer	.06	.05	.02
37	Ed Romero	.04	.03	.02
38	Jeff Calhoun	.04	.03	.02
39	Gerald Perry	.08	.06	.03
40	Orel Hershiser	.20	.15	.08
41	Bob Melvin	.04	.03	.02
42	*Bill Landrum*(FC)	.10	.08	.04
43	Dick Schofield	.04	.03	.02
44	Lou Piniella	.06	.05	.02
45	Kent Hrbek	.12	.09	.05
46	Darnell Coles	.06	.05	.02
47	Joaquin Andujar	.06	.05	.02
48	Alan Ashby	.04	.03	.02
49	Dave Clark(FC)	.10	.08	.04
50	Hubie Brooks	.08	.06	.03
51	Orioles Leaders (Eddie Murray, Cal Ripken)	.12	.09	.05
52	Don Robinson	.06	.05	.02
53	Curt Wilkerson	.04	.03	.02
54	Jim Clancy	.06	.05	.02
55	Phil Bradley	.08	.06	.03
56	Ed Hearn	.04	.03	.02
57	*Tim Crews*(FC)	.15	.11	.06
58	Dave Magadan	.10	.08	.04
59	Danny Cox	.06	.05	.02
60	Rickey Henderson	.35	.25	.14
61	*Mark Knudson*(FC)	.10	.08	.04
62	Jeff Hamilton	.08	.06	.03
63	Jimmy Jones(FC)	.10	.08	.04
64	*Ken Caminiti*(FC)	.30	.25	.12
65	Leon Durham	.06	.05	.02
66	Shane Rawley	.06	.05	.02
67	Ken Oberkfell	.04	.03	.02
68	Dave Dravecky	.06	.05	.02
69	*Mike Hart*(FC)	.10	.08	.04

		MT	NR MT	EX
70	Roger Clemens	.50	.40	.20
71	Gary Pettis	.04	.03	.02
72	Dennis Eckersley	.10	.08	.04
73	Randy Bush	.04	.03	.02
74	Tom Lasorda	.06	.05	.02
75	Joe Carter	.10	.08	.04
76	Denny Martinez	.04	.03	.02
77	Tom O'Malley	.04	.03	.02
78	Dan Petry	.06	.05	.02
79	Ernie Whitt	.06	.05	.02
80	Mark Langston	.10	.08	.04
81	Reds Leaders (John Franco, Ron Robinson)	.06	.05	.02
82	*Darrel Akerfelds*(FC)	.12	.09	.05
83	Jose Oquendo	.04	.03	.02
84	Cecilio Guante	.04	.03	.02
85	Howard Johnson	.08	.06	.03
86	Ron Karkovice	.04	.03	.02
87	Mike Mason	.04	.03	.02
88	Earnie Riles	.04	.03	.02
89	*Gary Thurman*(FC)	.20	.15	.08
90	Dale Murphy	.30	.25	.12
91	*Joey Cora*(FC)	.12	.09	.05
92	Len Matuszek	.04	.03	.02
93	Bob Sebra	.04	.03	.02
94	*Chuck Jackson*(FC)	.15	.11	.06
95	Lance Parrish	.12	.09	.05
96	*Todd Benzinger*(FC)	.25	.20	.10
97	Scott Garrelts	.04	.03	.02
98	*Rene Gonzales*(FC)	.15	.11	.06
99	Chuck Finley	.06	.05	.02
100	Jack Clark	.12	.09	.05
101	Allan Anderson	.06	.05	.02
102	Barry Larkin	.35	.25	.14
103	Curt Young	.06	.05	.02
104	Dick Williams	.04	.03	.02
105	Jesse Orosco	.06	.05	.02
106	*Jim Walewander*(FC)	.12	.09	.05
107	Scott Bailes	.06	.05	.02
108	Steve Lyons	.04	.03	.02
109	Joel Skinner	.04	.03	.02
110	Teddy Higuera	.08	.06	.03
111	Expos Leaders (Hubie Brooks, Vance Law)	.06	.05	.02
112	*Les Lancaster*(FC)	.15	.11	.06
113	Kelly Gruber	.04	.03	.02
114	Jeff Russell	.04	.03	.02
115	Johnny Ray	.06	.05	.02
116	Jerry Don Gleaton	.04	.03	.02
117	*James Steels*(FC)	.10	.08	.04
118	Bob Welch	.08	.06	.03
119	*Robbie Wine*(FC)	.12	.09	.05
120	Kirby Puckett	.40	.30	.15
121	Checklist 1-132	.04	.03	.02
122	Tony Bernazard	.04	.03	.02
123	Tom Candiotti	.06	.05	.02
124	Ray Knight	.06	.05	.02
125	Bruce Hurst	.08	.06	.03
126	Steve Jeltz	.04	.03	.02
127	Jim Gott	.04	.03	.02
128	Johnny Grubb	.04	.03	.02
129	Greg Minton	.04	.03	.02
130	Buddy Bell	.08	.06	.03
131	Don Schulze	.04	.03	.02
132	Donnie Hill	.04	.03	.02
133	Greg Mathews	.06	.05	.02
134	Chuck Tanner	.04	.03	.02
135	Dennis Rasmussen	.08	.06	.03
136	Brian Dayett	.04	.03	.02
137	Chris Bosio	.06	.05	.02
138	Mitch Webster	.06	.05	.02
139	Jerry Browne	.06	.05	.02
140	Jesse Barfield	.10	.08	.04
141	Royals Leaders (George Brett, Bret Saberhagen)	.12	.09	.05
142	Andy Van Slyke	.10	.08	.04
143	Mickey Tettleton	.04	.03	.02
144	*Don Gordon*(FC)	.08	.06	.03
145	Bill Madlock	.08	.06	.03
146	*Donell Nixon*(FC)	.15	.11	.06
147	Bill Buckner	.08	.06	.03
148	Carmelo Martinez	.06	.05	.02
149	Ken Howell	.04	.03	.02
150	Eric Davis	.40	.30	.15
151	Bob Knepper	.06	.05	.02
152	*Jody Reed*(FC)	.35	.25	.14
153	John Habyan	.04	.03	.02
154	Jeff Stone	.04	.03	.02
155	Bruce Sutter	.10	.08	.04
156	Gary Matthews	.06	.05	.02
157	Atlee Hammaker	.04	.03	.02
158	Tim Hulett	.04	.03	.02
159	*Brad Arnsberg*(FC)	.12	.09	.05
160	Willie McGee	.10	.08	.04
161	Bryn Smith	.06	.05	.02
162	Mark McLemore	.06	.05	.02
163	Dale Mohorcic	.04	.03	.02
164	Dave Johnson	.06	.05	.02
165	Robin Yount	.20	.15	.08
166	*Rick Rodriguez*(FC)	.10	.08	.04
167	Rance Mulliniks	.04	.03	.02
168	Barry Jones	.04	.03	.02
169	*Ross Jones*(FC)	.12	.09	.05
170	Rich Gossage	.12	.09	.05
171	Cubs Leaders (Shawon Dunston, Manny Trillo)	.06	.05	.02
172	*Lloyd McClendon*(FC)	.10	.08	.04
173	Eric Plunk	.04	.03	.02
174	Phil Garner	.04	.03	.02
175	Kevin Bass	.06	.05	.02
176	Jeff Reed	.04	.03	.02
177	Frank Tanana	.06	.05	.02
178	Dwayne Henry(FC)	.06	.05	.02
179	Charlie Puleo	.04	.03	.02
180	Terry Kennedy	.06	.05	.02
181	Dave Cone	.50	.40	.20
182	Ken Phelps	.06	.05	.02
183	Tom Lawless	.04	.03	.02
184	Ivan Calderon	.08	.06	.03
185	Rick Rhoden	.06	.05	.02
186	Rafael Palmeiro	.35	.25	.14
187	Steve Kiefer(FC)	.06	.05	.02
188	John Russell	.04	.03	.02
189	*Wes Gardner*(FC)	.20	.15	.08
190	Candy Maldonado	.06	.05	.02
191	John Cerutti	.06	.05	.02
192	Devon White	.20	.15	.08
193	Brian Fisher	.06	.05	.02
194	Tom Kelly	.04	.03	.02
195	Dan Quisenberry	.06	.05	.02
196	Dave Engle	.04	.03	.02
197	Lance McCullers	.06	.05	.02
198	Franklin Stubbs	.06	.05	.02
199	*Dave Meads*	.12	.09	.05
200	Wade Boggs	.30	.25	.12
201	Rangers Leaders (Steve Buechele, Pete Incaviglia, Pete O'Brien, Bobby Valentine)	.06	.05	.02
202	Glenn Hoffman	.04	.03	.02
203	Fred Toliver	.04	.03	.02
204	Paul O'Neill(FC)	.12	.09	.05
205	*Nelson Liriano*(FC)	.12	.09	.05
206	Domingo Ramos	.04	.03	.02
207	*John Mitchell, John Mitchell*(FC)	.20	.15	.08
208	Steve Lake	.04	.03	.02
209	Richard Dotson	.06	.05	.02
210	Willie Randolph	.06	.05	.02
211	Frank DiPino	.04	.03	.02
212	Greg Brock	.06	.05	.02
213	Albert Hall	.04	.03	.02
214	Dave Schmidt	.04	.03	.02
215	Von Hayes	.06	.05	.02
216	Jerry Reuss	.06	.05	.02
217	Harry Spilman	.04	.03	.02
218	Dan Schatzeder	.04	.03	.02
219	Mike Stanley	.08	.06	.03
220	Tom Henke	.06	.05	.02
221	Rafael Belliard	.04	.03	.02
222	Steve Farr	.04	.03	.02
223	Stan Jefferson	.08	.06	.03
224	Tom Trebelhorn	.04	.03	.02
225	Mike Scioscia	.06	.05	.02
226	Dave Lopes	.06	.05	.02
227	Ed Correa	.04	.03	.02
228	Wallace Johnson	.04	.03	.02
229	Jeff Musselman	.08	.06	.03
230	Pat Tabler	.06	.05	.02
231	Pirates Leaders (Barry Bonds, Bobby Bonilla)	.10	.08	.04
232	Bob James	.04	.03	.02
233	Rafael Santana	.04	.03	.02
234	Ken Dayley	.04	.03	.02
235	Gary Ward	.06	.05	.02
236	Ted Power	.04	.03	.02
237	Mike Heath	.04	.03	.02
238	*Luis Polonia*	.30	.25	.12
239	Roy Smalley	.04	.03	.02
240	Lee Smith	.08	.06	.03
241	Damaso Garcia	.04	.03	.02
242	Tom Niedenfuer	.06	.05	.02
243	Mark Ryal(FC)	.04	.03	.02

#	Player	MT	NR MT	EX
244	Jeff Robinson	.04	.03	.02
245	Rich Gedman	.06	.05	.02
246	*Mike Campbell*(FC)	.10	.08	.04
247	Thad Bosley	.04	.03	.02
248	Storm Davis	.08	.06	.03
249	Mike Marshall	.10	.08	.04
250	Nolan Ryan	.60	.45	.25
251	Tom Foley	.04	.03	.02
252	Bob Brower	.06	.05	.02
253	Checklist 133-264	.04	.03	.02
254	Lee Elia	.04	.03	.02
255	Mookie Wilson	.06	.05	.02
256	Ken Schrom	.04	.03	.02
257	Jerry Royster	.04	.03	.02
258	Ed Nunez	.04	.03	.02
259	Ron Kittle	.06	.05	.02
260	Vince Coleman	.15	.11	.06
261	Giants Leaders (Will Clark, Candy Maldonado, Kevin Mitchell, Robby Thompson, Jose Uribe)	.10	.08	.04
262	Drew Hall(FC)	.12	.09	.05
263	Glenn Braggs	.08	.06	.03
264	*Les Straker*	.15	.11	.06
265	Bo Diaz	.06	.05	.02
266	Paul Assenmacher	.04	.03	.02
267	*Billy Bean*(FC)	.10	.08	.04
268	Bruce Ruffin	.06	.05	.02
269	*Ellis Burks*	.60	.45	.25
270	Mike Witt	.06	.05	.02
271	Ken Gerhart	.06	.05	.02
272	Steve Ontiveros	.04	.03	.02
273	Garth Iorg	.04	.03	.02
274	Junior Ortiz	.04	.03	.02
275	Kevin Seitzer	.15	.11	.06
276	Luis Salazar	.04	.03	.02
277	Alejandro Pena	.06	.05	.02
278	Jose Cruz	.06	.05	.02
279	Randy St. Claire	.04	.03	.02
280	Pete Incaviglia	.12	.09	.05
281	Jerry Hairston	.04	.03	.02
282	Pat Perry	.04	.03	.02
283	Phil Lombardi(FC)	.06	.05	.02
284	Larry Bowa	.06	.05	.02
285	Jim Presley	.08	.06	.03
286	*Chuck Crim*	.12	.09	.05
287	Manny Trillo	.06	.05	.02
288	*Pat Pacillo*	.15	.11	.06
289	Dave Bergman	.04	.03	.02
290	Tony Fernandez	.10	.08	.04
291	Astros Leaders (Kevin Bass, Billy Hatcher)	.06	.05	.02
292	Carney Lansford	.08	.06	.03
293	*Doug Jones*(FC)	.25	.20	.10
294	*Al Pedrique*(FC)	.12	.09	.05
295	Bert Blyleven	.10	.08	.04
296	Floyd Rayford	.04	.03	.02
297	Zane Smith	.06	.05	.02
298	Milt Thompson	.04	.03	.02
299	Steve Crawford	.04	.03	.02
300	Don Mattingly	.30	.25	.12
301	Bud Black	.04	.03	.02
302	Jose Uribe	.04	.03	.02
303	Eric Show	.06	.05	.02
304	George Hendrick	.06	.05	.02
305	Steve Sax	.12	.09	.05
306	Billy Hatcher	.06	.05	.02
307	Mike Trujillo	.04	.03	.02
308	Lee Mazzilli	.06	.05	.02
309	*Bill Long*	.15	.11	.06
310	Tom Herr	.06	.05	.02
311	Scott Sanderson	.04	.03	.02
312	Joey Meyer(FC)	.20	.15	.08
313	Bob McClure	.04	.03	.02
314	Jimy Williams	.04	.03	.02
315	Dave Parker	.12	.09	.05
316	Jose Rijo	.06	.05	.02
317	Tom Nieto	.04	.03	.02
318	Mel Hall	.06	.05	.02
319	Mike Loynd	.04	.03	.02
320	Alan Trammell	.15	.11	.06
321	White Sox Leaders (Harold Baines, Carlton Fisk)	.08	.06	.03
322	*Vicente Palacios*(FC)	.15	.11	.06
323	Rick Leach	.04	.03	.02
324	Danny Jackson	.20	.15	.08
325	Glenn Hubbard	.04	.03	.02
326	Al Nipper	.04	.03	.02
327	Larry Sheets	.06	.05	.02
328	*Greg Cadaret*(FC)	.15	.11	.06
329	Chris Speier	.04	.03	.02
330	Eddie Whitson	.04	.03	.02
331	Brian Downing	.06	.05	.02
332	Jerry Reed	.04	.03	.02
333	Wally Backman	.06	.05	.02
334	Dave LaPoint	.06	.05	.02
335	Claudell Washington	.06	.05	.02
336	Ed Lynch	.04	.03	.02
337	Jim Gantner	.04	.03	.02
338	Brian Holton	.08	.06	.03
339	Kurt Stillwell	.08	.06	.03
340	Jack Morris	.15	.11	.06
341	Carmen Castillo	.04	.03	.02
342	Larry Andersen	.04	.03	.02
343	Greg Gagne	.04	.03	.02
344	Tony LaRussa	.04	.03	.02
345	Scott Fletcher	.06	.05	.02
346	Vance Law	.06	.05	.02
347	Joe Johnson	.04	.03	.02
348	Jim Eisenreich	.04	.03	.02
349	Bob Walk	.04	.03	.02
350	Will Clark	.80	.60	.30
351	Cardinals Leaders (Tony Pena, Red Schoendienst)	.06	.05	.02
352	*Billy Ripken*(FC)	.20	.15	.08
353	Ed Olwine	.04	.03	.02
354	Marc Sullivan	.04	.03	.02
355	Roger McDowell	.08	.06	.03
356	Luis Aguayo	.04	.03	.02
357	Floyd Bannister	.06	.05	.02
358	Rey Quinones	.04	.03	.02
359	Tim Stoddard	.04	.03	.02
360	Tony Gwynn	.25	.20	.10
361	Greg Maddux	.35	.25	.14
362	Juan Castillo	.04	.03	.02
363	Willie Fraser	.06	.05	.02
364	Nick Esasky	.06	.05	.02
365	Floyd Youmans	.04	.03	.02
366	Chet Lemon	.06	.05	.02
367	Tim Leary	.06	.05	.02
368	*Gerald Young*(FC)	.15	.11	.06
369	Greg Harris	.04	.03	.02
370	Jose Canseco	.80	.60	.30
371	Joe Hesketh	.04	.03	.02
372	*Matt Williams*	1.50	1.25	.60
373	Checklist 265-396	.04	.03	.02
374	Doc Edwards	.04	.03	.02
375	Tom Brunansky	.08	.06	.03
376	*Bill Wilkinson*	.12	.09	.05
377	Sam Horn(FC)	.20	.15	.08
378	*Todd Frohwirth*(FC)	.15	.11	.06
379	Rafael Ramirez	.04	.03	.02
380	*Joe Magrane*	.30	.25	.12
381	Angels Leaders (Jack Howell, Wally Joyner)	.12	.09	.05
382	*Keith Miller*(FC)	.15	.11	.06
383	Eric Bell	.06	.05	.02
384	Neil Allen	.04	.03	.02
385	Carlton Fisk	.30	.25	.12
386	Don Mattingly AS	.40	.30	.15
387	Willie Randolph AS	.06	.05	.02
388	Wade Boggs AS	.35	.25	.14
389	Alan Trammell AS	.08	.06	.03
390	George Bell AS	.10	.08	.04
391	Kirby Puckett AS	.12	.09	.05
392	Dave Winfield AS	.12	.09	.05
393	Matt Nokes AS	.15	.11	.06
394	Roger Clemens AS	.15	.11	.06
395	Jimmy Key AS	.06	.05	.02
396	Tom Henke AS	.06	.05	.02
397	Jack Clark AS	.06	.05	.02
398	Juan Samuel AS	.06	.05	.02
399	Tim Wallach AS	.06	.05	.02
400	Ozzie Smith AS	.08	.06	.03
401	Andre Dawson AS	.10	.08	.04
402	Tony Gwynn AS	.15	.11	.05
403	Tim Raines AS	.12	.09	.05
404	Benny Santiago AS	.10	.08	.04
405	Dwight Gooden AS	.15	.11	.06
406	Shane Rawley AS	.06	.05	.02
407	Steve Bedrosian AS	.08	.06	.03
408	Dion James	.06	.05	.02
409	Joel McKeon(FC)	.04	.03	.02
410	Tony Pena	.06	.05	.02
411	Wayne Tolleson	.04	.03	.02
412	Randy Myers	.10	.08	.04
413	John Christensen	.04	.03	.02
414	John McNamara	.04	.03	.02
415	Don Carman	.06	.05	.02
416	Keith Moreland	.06	.05	.02
417	*Mark Ciardi*(FC)	.10	.08	.04
418	Joel Youngblood	.04	.03	.02
419	Scott McGregor	.06	.05	.02

	MT	NR MT	EX
420 Wally Joyner	.25	.20	.10
421 Ed Vande Berg	.04	.03	.02
422 Dave Concepcion	.06	.05	.02
423 *John Smiley*	.50	.40	.20
424 Dwayne Murphy	.06	.05	.02
425 Jeff Reardon	.08	.06	.03
426 Randy Ready	.04	.03	.02
427 *Paul Kilgus*(FC)	.20	.15	.08
428 John Shelby	.04	.03	.02
429 Tigers Leaders (Kirk Gibson, Alan Trammell)	.08	.06	.03
430 Glenn Davis	.12	.09	.05
431 Casey Candaele	.04	.03	.02
432 Mike Moore	.04	.03	.02
433 *Bill Pecota*(FC)	.15	.11	.06
434 Rick Aguilera	.04	.03	.02
435 Mike Pagliarulo	.08	.06	.03
436 Mike Bielecki	.04	.03	.02
437 *Fred Manrique*(FC)	.12	.09	.05
438 *Rob Ducey*(FC)	.12	.09	.05
439 Dave Martinez	.08	.06	.03
440 Steve Bedrosian	.10	.08	.04
441 Rick Manning	.04	.03	.02
442 *Tom Bolton*(FC)	.15	.11	.06
443 Ken Griffey	.06	.05	.02
444 Cal Ripken, Sr.	.04	.03	.02
445 Mike Krukow	.06	.05	.02
446 Doug DeCinces	.06	.05	.02
447 *Jeff Montgomery*(FC)	.30	.25	.12
448 Mike Davis	.06	.05	.02
449 *Jeff Robinson*	.15	.11	.06
450 Barry Bonds	.40	.30	.15
451 Keith Atherton	.04	.03	.02
452 Willie Wilson	.08	.06	.03
453 Dennis Powell	.04	.03	.02
454 Marvell Wynne	.04	.03	.02
455 *Shawn Hillegas*(FC)	.15	.11	.06
456 Dave Anderson	.04	.03	.02
457 Terry Leach	.04	.03	.02
458 Ron Hassey	.04	.03	.02
459 Yankees Leaders (Willie Randolph, Dave Winfield)	.08	.06	.03
460 Ozzie Smith	.12	.09	.05
461 Danny Darwin	.04	.03	.02
462 Don Slaught	.04	.03	.02
463 *Fred McGriff*	.80	.60	.30
464 Jay Tibbs	.04	.03	.02
465 Paul Molitor	.10	.08	.04
466 Jerry Mumphrey	.04	.03	.02
467 Don Aase	.04	.03	.02
468 Darren Daulton	.04	.03	.02
469 Jeff Dedmon	.04	.03	.02
470 Dwight Evans	.10	.08	.04
471 Donnie Moore	.04	.03	.02
472 Robby Thompson	.06	.05	.02
473 Joe Niekro	.06	.05	.02
474 Tom Brookens	.04	.03	.02
475 Pete Rose	.20	.15	.08
476 Dave Stewart	.08	.06	.03
477 Jamie Quirk	.04	.03	.02
478 Sid Bream	.06	.05	.02
479 Brett Butler	.06	.05	.02
480 Dwight Gooden	.40	.30	.15
481 Mariano Duncan	.04	.03	.02
482 Mark Davis	.04	.03	.02
483 *Rod Booker*(FC)	.12	.09	.05
484 Pat Clements	.04	.03	.02
485 Harold Reynolds	.06	.05	.02
486 *Pat Keedy*(FC)	.10	.08	.04
487 Jim Pankovits	.04	.03	.02
488 Andy McGaffigan	.04	.03	.02
489 Dodgers Leaders (Pedro Guerrero, Fernando Valenzuela)	.08	.06	.03
490 Larry Parrish	.06	.05	.02
491 B.J. Surhoff	.10	.08	.04
492 Doyle Alexander	.06	.05	.02
493 Mike Greenwell	.25	.20	.10
494 *Wally Ritchie*	.12	.09	.05
495 Eddie Murray	.25	.20	.10
496 Guy Hoffman	.04	.03	.02
497 Kevin Mitchell	.30	.25	.12
498 Bob Boone	.06	.05	.02
499 Eric King	.06	.05	.02
500 Andre Dawson	.15	.11	.06
501 Tim Birtsas(6)	.06	.05	.02
502 Danny Gladden	.04	.03	.02
503 *Junior Noboa*(FC)	.10	.08	.04
504 Bob Rodgers	.04	.03	.02
505 Willie Upshaw	.06	.05	.02
506 John Cangelosi	.04	.03	.02
507 Mark Gubicza	.10	.08	.04

	MT	NR MT	EX
508 Tim Teufel	.04	.03	.02
509 Bill Dawley	.04	.03	.02
510 Dave Winfield	.20	.15	.08
511 Joel Davis	.04	.03	.02
512 Alex Trevino	.04	.03	.02
513 Tim Flannery	.04	.03	.02
514 Pat Sheridan	.04	.03	.02
515 Juan Nieves	.06	.05	.02
516 Jim Sundberg	.06	.05	.02
517 Ron Robinson	.04	.03	.02
518 Greg Gross	.04	.03	.02
519 Mariners Leaders (Phil Bradley, Harold Reynolds)	.06	.05	.02
520 Dave Smith	.06	.05	.02
521 Jim Dwyer	.04	.03	.02
522 *Bob Patterson*(FC)	.12	.09	.05
523 Gary Roenicke	.04	.03	.02
524 Gary Lucas	.04	.03	.02
525 Marty Barrett	.06	.05	.02
526 Juan Berenguer	.04	.03	.02
527 Steve Henderson	.04	.03	.02
528a Checklist 397-528 (#455 is Steve Carlton)	.80	.60	.30
528b Checklist 397-528 (#455 is Shawn Hillegas)	.06	.05	.02
529 Tim Burke	.04	.03	.02
530 Gary Carter	.15	.11	.06
531 Rich Yett	.04	.03	.02
532 Mike Kingery	.04	.03	.02
533 *John Farrell*(FC)	.15	.11	.06
534 John Wathan	.06	.05	.02
535 Ron Guidry	.12	.09	.05
536 John Morris	.04	.03	.02
537 Steve Buechele	.04	.03	.02
538 Bill Wegman	.04	.03	.02
539 Mike LaValliere	.06	.05	.02
540 Bret Saberhagen	.25	.20	.10
541 Juan Beniquez	.04	.03	.02
542 *Paul Noce*(FC)	.10	.08	.04
543 Kent Tekulve	.06	.05	.02
544 Jim Traber	.06	.05	.02
545 Don Baylor	.08	.06	.03
546 John Candelaria	.06	.05	.02
547 *Felix Fermin*(FC)	.12	.09	.05
548 *Shane Mack*	.15	.11	.06
549 Braves Leaders (Ken Griffey, Dion James, Dale Murphy, Gerald Perry)	.08	.06	.03
550 Pedro Guerrero	.15	.11	.06
551 Terry Steinbach	.15	.11	.06
552 Mark Thurmond	.04	.03	.02
553 Tracy Jones	.10	.08	.04
554 Mike Smithson	.04	.03	.02
555 Brook Jacoby	.08	.06	.03
556 *Stan Clarke*(FC)	.12	.09	.05
557 Craig Reynolds	.04	.03	.02
558 Bob Ojeda	.06	.05	.02
559 *Ken Williams*(FC)	.20	.15	.08
560 Tim Wallach	.08	.06	.03
561 Rick Cerone	.04	.03	.02
562 Jim Lindeman	.10	.08	.04
563 Jose Guzman	.06	.05	.02
564 Frank Lucchesi	.04	.03	.02
565 Lloyd Moseby	.06	.05	.02
566 *Charlie O'Brien*(FC)	.12	.09	.05
567 Mike Diaz	.06	.05	.02
568 Chris Brown	.06	.05	.02
569 Charlie Leibrandt	.06	.05	.02
570 Jeffrey Leonard	.06	.05	.02
571 *Mark Williamson*(FC)	.12	.09	.05
572 Chris James	.15	.11	.06
573 Bob Stanley	.04	.03	.02
574 Graig Nettles	.08	.06	.03
575 Don Sutton	.12	.09	.05
576 *Tommy Hinzo*(FC)	.12	.09	.05
577 Tom Browning	.08	.06	.03
578 Gary Gaetti	.10	.08	.04
579 Mets Leaders (Gary Carter, Kevin McReynolds)	.08	.06	.03
580 Mark McGwire	.40	.30	.15
581 Tito Landrum	.04	.03	.02
582 *Mike Henneman*	.25	.20	.10
583 Dave Valle(FC)	.06	.05	.02
584 Steve Trout	.04	.03	.02
585 Ozzie Guillen	.06	.05	.02
586 Bob Forsch	.04	.03	.02
587 Terry Puhl	.04	.03	.02
588 *Jeff Parrett*(FC)	.20	.15	.08
589 Geno Petralli	.04	.03	.02
590 George Bell	.20	.15	.08
591 Doug Drabek	.06	.05	.02
592 Dale Sveum	.06	.05	.02

#	Name	MT	NR MT	EX
593	Bob Tewksbury	.04	.03	.02
594	Bobby Valentine	.04	.03	.02
595	Frank White	.06	.05	.02
596	John Kruk	.08	.06	.03
597	Gene Garber	.04	.03	.02
598	Lee Lacy	.04	.03	.02
599	Calvin Schiraldi	.04	.03	.02
600	Mike Schmidt	.40	.30	.15
601	Jack Lazorko	.04	.03	.02
602	Mike Aldrete	.06	.05	.02
603	Rob Murphy	.06	.05	.02
604	Chris Bando	.04	.03	.02
605	Kirk Gibson	.15	.11	.06
606	Moose Haas	.04	.03	.02
607	Mickey Hatcher	.04	.03	.02
608	Charlie Kerfeld	.04	.03	.02
609	Twins Leaders (Gary Gaetti, Kent Hrbek)	.08	.06	.03
610	Keith Hernandez	.15	.11	.06
611	Tommy John	.12	.09	.05
612	Curt Ford	.04	.03	.02
613	Bobby Thigpen	.08	.06	.03
614	Herm Winningham	.04	.03	.02
615	Jody Davis	.06	.05	.02
616	*Jay Aldrich*(FC)	.10	.08	.04
617	Oddibe McDowell	.06	.05	.02
618	Cecil Fielder	.60	.45	.25
619	*Mike Dunne*	.15	.11	.06
620	Cory Snyder	.15	.11	.06
621	Gene Nelson	.04	.03	.02
622	Kal Daniels	.15	.11	.06
623	Mike Flanagan	.06	.05	.02
624	Jim Leyland	.04	.03	.02
625	Frank Viola	.12	.09	.05
626	Glenn Wilson	.06	.05	.02
627	*Joe Boever*(FC)	.12	.09	.05
628	Dave Henderson	.08	.06	.03
629	Kelly Downs	.08	.06	.03
630	Darrell Evans	.08	.06	.03
631	Jack Howell	.06	.05	.02
632	*Steve Shields*	.12	.09	.05
633	*Barry Lyons*	.12	.09	.05
634	Jose DeLeon	.06	.05	.02
635	Terry Pendleton	.06	.05	.02
636	Charles Hudson	.04	.03	.02
637	*Jay Bell*(FC)	.35	.25	.14
638	Steve Balboni	.06	.05	.02
639	Brewers Leaders (Glenn Braggs, Tony Muser)	.06	.05	.02
640	Garry Templeton	.06	.05	.02
641	Rick Honeycutt	.04	.03	.02
642	Bob Dernier	.04	.03	.02
643	*Rocky Childress*(FC)	.12	.09	.05
644	Terry McGriff(FC)	.06	.05	.02
645	*Matt Nokes*	.30	.25	.12
646	Checklist 529-660	.04	.03	.02
647	Pascual Perez	.06	.05	.02
648	Al Newman	.04	.03	.02
649	*DeWayne Buice*	.15	.11	.06
650	Cal Ripken	.40	.30	.15
651	*Mike Jackson*(FC)	.15	.11	.06
652	Bruce Benedict	.04	.03	.02
653	Jeff Sellers	.06	.05	.02
654	Roger Craig	.06	.05	.02
655	Len Dykstra	.08	.06	.03
656	Lee Guetterman	.04	.03	.02
657	Gary Redus	.04	.03	.02
658	Tim Conroy	.04	.03	.02
659	Bobby Meacham	.04	.03	.02
660	Rick Reuschel	.08	.06	.03
661	Turn Back The Clock (Nolan Ryan)	.08	.06	.03
662	Turn Back The Clock (Jim Rice)	.08	.06	.03
663	Turn Back The Clock (Ron Blomberg)	.04	.03	.02
664	Turn Back The Clock (Bob Gibson)	.08	.06	.03
665	Turn Back The Clock (Stan Musial)	.12	.09	.05
666	Mario Soto	.06	.05	.02
667	Luis Quinones	.04	.03	.02
668	Walt Terrell	.06	.05	.02
669	Phillies Leaders (Lance Parrish, Mike Ryan)	.06	.05	.02
670	Dan Plesac	.08	.06	.03
671	Tim Laudner	.04	.03	.02
672	*John Davis*(FC)	.15	.11	.06
673	Tony Phillips	.04	.03	.02
674	Mike Fitzgerald	.04	.03	.02
675	Jim Rice	.20	.15	.08
676	Ken Dixon	.04	.03	.02
677	Eddie Milner	.04	.03	.02
678	Jim Acker	.04	.03	.02
679	Darrell Miller	.04	.03	.02
680	Charlie Hough	.06	.05	.02
681	Bobby Bonilla	.40	.30	.15
682	Jimmy Key	.08	.06	.03
683	Julio Franco	.08	.06	.03
684	Hal Lanier	.04	.03	.02
685	Ron Darling	.10	.08	.04
686	Terry Francona	.04	.03	.02
687	Mickey Brantley	.04	.03	.02
688	Jim Winn	.04	.03	.02
689	*Tom Pagnozzi*(FC)	.25	.20	.10
690	Jay Howell	.06	.05	.02
691	Dan Pasqua	.08	.06	.03
692	Mike Birkbeck	.06	.05	.02
693	Benny Santiago	.30	.25	.12
694	*Eric Nolte*(FC)	.12	.09	.05
695	Shawon Dunston	.08	.06	.03
696	Duane Ward	.04	.03	.02
697	Steve Lombardozzi	.08	.06	.03
698	Brad Havens	.04	.03	.02
699	Padres Leaders (Tony Gwynn, Benny Santiago)	.12	.09	.05
700	George Brett	.30	.25	.12
701	Sammy Stewart	.04	.03	.02
702	Mike Gallego	.04	.03	.02
703	Bob Brenly	.04	.03	.02
704	Dennis Boyd	.06	.05	.02
705	Juan Samuel	.10	.08	.04
706	Rick Mahler	.04	.03	.02
707	Fred Lynn	.10	.08	.04
708	Gus Polidor(FC)	.06	.05	.02
709	George Frazier	.04	.03	.02
710	Darryl Strawberry	.30	.25	.12
711	Bill Gullickson	.04	.03	.02
712	John Moses	.04	.03	.02
713	Willie Hernandez	.06	.05	.02
714	Jim Fregosi	.04	.03	.02
715	Todd Worrell	.08	.06	.03
716	Lenn Sakata	.04	.03	.02
717	Jay Baller(FC)	.06	.05	.02
718	Mike Felder	.04	.03	.02
719	Denny Walling	.04	.03	.02
720	Tim Raines	.20	.15	.08
721	Pete O'Brien	.06	.05	.02
722	Manny Lee	.04	.03	.02
723	Bob Kipper	.04	.03	.02
724	Danny Tartabull	.20	.15	.08
725	Mike Boddicker	.06	.05	.02
726	Alfredo Griffin	.06	.05	.02
727	Greg Booker	.04	.03	.02
728	Andy Allanson	.06	.05	.02
729	Blue Jays Leaders (George Bell, Fred McGriff)	.10	.08	.04
730	John Franco	.08	.06	.03
731	Rick Schu	.04	.03	.02
732	Dave Palmer	.04	.03	.02
733	Spike Owen	.04	.03	.02
734	Craig Lefferts	.04	.03	.02
735	Kevin McReynolds	.20	.15	.08
736	Matt Young	.04	.03	.02
737	Butch Wynegar	.04	.03	.02
738	Scott Bankhead	.04	.03	.02
739	Daryl Boston	.04	.03	.02
740	Rick Sutcliffe	.08	.06	.03
741	Mike Easler	.06	.05	.02
742	Mark Clear	.04	.03	.02
743	Larry Herndon	.04	.03	.02
744	Whitey Herzog	.06	.05	.02
745	Bill Doran	.06	.05	.02
746	*Gene Larkin*	.25	.20	.10
747	Bobby Witt	.08	.06	.03
748	Reid Nichols	.04	.03	.02
749	Mark Eichhorn	.06	.05	.02
750	Bo Jackson	.70	.50	.30
751	Jim Morrison	.04	.03	.02
752	Mark Grant	.04	.03	.02
753	Danny Heep	.04	.03	.02
754	Mike LaCoss	.04	.03	.02
755	Ozzie Virgil	.04	.03	.02
756	Mike Maddux	.06	.05	.02
757	*John Marzano*	.15	.11	.06
758	*Eddie Williams*(FC)	.08	.06	.03
759	A's Leaders (Jose Canseco, Mark McGwire)	.40	.30	.15
760	Mike Scott	.10	.08	.04
761	Tony Armas	.06	.05	.02
762	Scott Bradley	.04	.03	.02
763	Doug Sisk	.04	.03	.02
764	Greg Walker	.06	.05	.02
765	Neal Heaton	.06	.05	.02
766	Henry Cotto	.04	.03	.02
767	*Jose Lind*(FC)	.25	.20	.10

		MT	NR MT	EX
768	Dickie Noles	.04	.03	.02
769	Cecil Cooper	.08	.06	.03
770	Lou Whitaker	.20	.15	.08
771	Ruben Sierra	.50	.40	.20
772	Sal Butera	.04	.03	.02
773	Frank Williams	.04	.03	.02
774	Gene Mauch	.06	.05	.02
775	Dave Stieb	.08	.06	.03
776	Checklist 661-792	.04	.03	.02
777	Lonnie Smith	.06	.05	.02
778a	*Keith Comstock* (white team letters)(FC)			
		2.00	1.50	.80
778b	*Keith Comstock* (blue team letters)(FC)			
		.25	.20	.10
779	*Tom Glavine*(FC)	2.00	1.50	.80
780	Fernando Valenzuela	.15	.11	.06
781	*Keith Hughes*(FC)	.15	.11	.06
782	*Jeff Ballard*(FC)	.15	.11	.06
783	Ron Roenicke	.04	.03	.02
784	Joe Sambito	.04	.03	.02
785	Alvin Davis	.10	.08	.04
786	Joe Price	.04	.03	.02
787	Bill Almon	.04	.03	.02
788	Ray Searage	.04	.03	.02
789	Indians Leaders (Joe Carter, Cory			
	Snyder)	.08	.06	.03
790	Dave Righetti	.12	.09	.05
791	Ted Simmons	.08	.06	.03
792	John Tudor	.08	.06	.03

		MT	NR MT	EX
13	Jack Clark	.25	.20	.10
14	Ryne Sandberg	.40	.30	.15
15	Mike Schmidt	.60	.45	.25
16	Ozzie Smith	.25	.20	.10
17	Eric Davis	.60	.45	.25
18	Andre Dawson	.25	.20	.10
19	Darryl Strawberry	.60	.45	.25
20	Gary Carter	.40	.30	.15
21	Mike Scott	.15	.11	.06
22	Billy Williams	.25	.20	.10

1988 Topps All-Star
Glossy Set Of 60

This standard-size collectors set includes 60 full-color glossy cards featuring All-Stars and Prospects in six separate 10-card sets. In 1986, Topps issued a similar set that included only All-Stars. Card fronts have a white border and a thin red line framing the player photo, with the player's name in the lower left corner. Card backs, in red and blue, include very basic player information (name, team and position), along with the card set logo and card number. Topps glossy collector sets were marketed via a special offer printed on a card packaged in all Topps wax packs. For six special offer cards and $1.25, collectors received one of the six 10-card sets; 18 special offer cards and $7.50 earned the entire 60-card collection.

		MT	NR MT	EX
Complete Set:		14.00	10.50	5.50
Common Player:		.15	.11	.06
1	Andre Dawson	.30	.25	.12
2	Jesse Barfield	.20	.15	.08
3	Mike Schmidt	.70	.50	.30
4	Ruben Sierra	.40	.30	.15
5	Mike Scott	.20	.15	.08
6	Cal Ripken	.70	.50	.30
7	Gary Carter	.50	.40	.20
8	Kent Hrbek	.30	.25	.12
9	Kevin Seitzer	.70	.50	.30
10	Mike Henneman	.25	.20	.10
11	Don Mattingly	2.00	1.50	.80
12	Tim Raines	.40	.30	.15
13	Roger Clemens	.80	.60	.30
14	Ryne Sandberg	.40	.30	.15
15	Tony Fernandez	.20	.15	.08
16	Eric Davis	.80	.60	.30
17	Jack Morris	.30	.25	.12
18	Tim Wallach	.20	.15	.08
19	Mike Dunne	.25	.20	.10
20	Mike Greenwell	1.00	.70	.40
21	Dwight Evans	.20	.15	.08
22	Darryl Strawberry	.80	.60	.30
23	Cory Snyder	.30	.25	.12
24	Pedro Guerrero	.25	.20	.10
25	Rickey Henderson	.60	.45	.25
26	Dale Murphy	.70	.50	.30
27	Kirby Puckett	.50	.40	.20
28	Steve Bedrosian	.20	.15	.08
29	Devon White	.25	.20	.10
30	Benny Santiago	.25	.20	.10
31	George Bell	.40	.30	.15

1988 Topps All-Star
Glossy Set Of 22

The fifth edition of Topps' special All-Star inserts (22 cards) was included in the company's 1988 rack packs. The 1987 American and National League All-Star lineup, plus honorary captains Jim Hunter and Billy Williams, are featured on the standard-size All-Star inserts. The glossy full-color card fronts contain player photos centered between a red and yellow "1987 All-Star" logo printed across the card top and the player name (also red and yellow) which is printed across the bottom margin. A National or American League logo appears in the lower left corner. Card backs are printed in red and blue on a white background, with the title and All-Star logo emblem printed above the player name and card number.

		MT	NR MT	EX
Complete Set:		4.00	3.00	1.50
Common Player:		.15	.11	.06
1	John McNamara	.15	.11	.06
2	Don Mattingly	1.00	.70	.40
3	Willie Randolph	.15	.11	.06
4	Wade Boggs	.80	.60	.30
5	Cal Ripken	.50	.40	.20
6	George Bell	.30	.25	.12
7	Rickey Henderson	.50	.40	.20
8	Dave Winfield	.40	.30	.15
9	Terry Kennedy	.15	.11	.06
10	Bret Saberhagen	.25	.20	.10
11	Jim Hunter	.25	.20	.10
12	Davey Johnson	.15	.11	.06

		MT	NR MT	EX
32	Keith Hernandez	.40	.30	.15
33	Dave Stewart	.15	.11	.06
34	Dave Parker	.25	.20	.10
35	Tom Henke	.15	.11	.06
36	Willie McGee	.20	.15	.08
37	Alan Trammell	.30	.25	.12
38	Tony Gwynn	.60	.45	.25
39	Mark McGwire	.80	.60	.30
40	Joe Magrane	.25	.20	.10
41	Jack Clark	.25	.20	.10
42	Willie Randolph	.15	.11	.06
43	Juan Samuel	.25	.20	.10
44	Joe Carter	.25	.20	.10
45	Shane Rawley	.15	.11	.06
46	Dave Winfield	.50	.40	.20
47	Ozzie Smith	.25	.20	.10
48	Wally Joyner	.70	.50	.30
49	B.J. Surhoff	.20	.15	.08
50	Ellis Burks	.80	.60	.30
51	Wade Boggs	.80	.60	.30
52	Howard Johnson	.20	.15	.08
53	George Brett	.70	.50	.30
54	Dwight Gooden	.80	.60	.30
55	Jose Canseco	2.00	1.50	.80
56	Lee Smith	.15	.11	.06
57	Paul Molitor	.20	.15	.08
58	Andres Galarraga	.30	.25	.12
59	Matt Nokes	.40	.30	.15
60	Casey Candaele	.15	.11	.06

		MT	NR MT	EX
6	Bob Boone	.08	.06	.03
7	George Brett	.40	.30	.15
8	Hubie Brooks	.08	.06	.03
9	Ivan Calderon	.10	.08	.04
10	Jose Canseco	1.25	.90	.50
11	Gary Carter	.30	.25	.12
12	Joe Carter	.15	.11	.06
13	Jack Clark	.20	.15	.08
14	Will Clark	.50	.40	.20
15	Roger Clemens	.60	.45	.25
16	Vince Coleman	.20	.15	.08
17	Alvin Davis	.15	.11	.06
18	Eric Davis	.70	.50	.30
19	Glenn Davis	.20	.15	.08
20	Andre Dawson	.25	.20	.10
21	Mike Dunne	.15	.11	.06
22	Dwight Evans	.10	.08	.04
23	Tony Fernandez	.15	.11	.06
24	John Franco	.10	.08	.04
25	Gary Gaetti	.20	.15	.08
26	Kirk Gibson	.25	.20	.10
27	Dwight Gooden	.60	.45	.25
28	Pedro Guerrero	.20	.15	.08
29	Tony Gwynn	.35	.25	.14
30	Billy Hatcher	.08	.06	.03
31	Rickey Henderson	.35	.25	.14
32	Tom Henke	.08	.06	.03
33	Keith Hernandez	.25	.20	.10
34	Orel Hershiser	.30	.25	.12
35	Teddy Higuera	.10	.08	.04
36	Charlie Hough	.08	.06	.03
37	Kent Hrbek	.25	.20	.10
38	Brook Jacoby	.10	.08	.04
39	Dion James	.08	.06	.03
40	Wally Joyner	.50	.40	.20
41	John Kruk	.15	.11	.06
42	Mark Langston	.15	.11	.06
43	Jeffrey Leonard	.08	.06	.03
44	Candy Maldonaldo	.08	.06	.03
45	Don Mattingly	1.25	.90	.50
46	Willie McGee	.15	.11	.06
47	Mark McGwire	.80	.60	.30
48	Kevin Mitchell	.08	.06	.03
49	Paul Molitor	.15	.11	.06
50	Jack Morris	.15	.11	.06
51	Lloyd Moseby	.10	.08	.04
52	Dale Murphy	.40	.30	.15
53	Eddie Murray	.30	.25	.12
54	Matt Nokes	.40	.30	.15
55	Dave Parker	.20	.15	.08
56	Larry Parrish	.08	.06	.03
57	Kirby Puckett	.35	.25	.14
58	Tim Raines	.30	.25	.12
59	Willie Randolph	.08	.06	.03
60	Harold Reynolds	.08	.06	.03
61	Cal Ripken	.35	.25	.14
62	Nolan Ryan	.80	.60	.30
63	Bret Saberhagen	.20	.15	.08
64	Juan Samuel	.15	.11	.06
65	Ryne Sandberg	.25	.20	.10
66	Benny Santiago	.15	.11	.06
67	Mike Schmidt	.40	.30	.15
68	Mike Scott	.10	.08	.04
69	Kevin Seitzer	.40	.30	.15
70	Larry Sheets	.08	.06	.03
71	Ruben Sierra	.15	.11	.06
72	Ozzie Smith	.15	.11	.06
73	Zane Smith	.08	.06	.03
74	Cory Snyder	.15	.11	.06
75	Dave Stewart	.10	.08	.04
76	Darryl Strawberry	.50	.40	.20
77	Rick Sutcliffe	.15	.11	.06
78	Danny Tartabull	.20	.15	.08
79	Alan Trammell	.25	.20	.10
80	Fernando Valenzuela	.20	.15	.08
81	Andy Van Slyke	.15	.11	.06
82	Frank Viola	.15	.11	.06
83	Greg Walker	.10	.08	.04
84	Tim Wallach	.10	.08	.04
85	Dave Winfield	.30	.25	.12
86	Mike Witt	.08	.06	.03
87	Robin Yount	.25	.20	.10
88	Checklist	.08	.06	.03

1988 Topps American Baseball

DWIGHT EVANS OF/1B

This 88-card set, unlike Topps' United Kingdom football cards, was made available for distribution by U.S. hobby dealers. The cards were packaged in checklist-backed boxes with an American flag on the top flap. The 2-1/4" by 3" cards feature full-color player photos printed on white stock with a red line framing the photo. The team name, printed in individual team colors, intersects the red frame at the top of the card. A bright yellow name banner appears below the photo. Card backs have bright blue borders and cartoon-style horizontal layouts. The card number appears within a circle of red stars upper left, beside the player's name and team logo. A red banner containing the player career stats runs the length of the card back. The lower half of the flip side features a caricature of the player and a one-line caption. Below the cartoon, a short "Talkin' Baseball" paragraph provides elementary baseball information, obviously designed to acquaint soccer-playing European collectors with American baseball rules and terminology. A glossy edition of the set was issued and is valued at 2-3 times greater than the regular issue.

		MT	NR MT	EX
Complete Set:		10.00	7.50	4.00
Common Player:		.08	.06	.03
1	Harold Baines	.15	.11	.06
2	Steve Bedrosian	.10	.08	.04
3	George Bell	.25	.20	.10
4	Wade Boggs	.70	.50	.30
5	Barry Bonds	.20	.15	.08

Regional interest may affect the value of a card.

1988 Topps Big Baseball

1988 Topps Big Baseball cards (2-5/8" by 3-3/4") were issued in three series, 88 cards per series (a total set of 264 cards). Each series features current star players, sold in 7-card packages. The glossy cards are similar in format, both front and back, to the 1956 Topps 340-card set. Each card features a posed head shot and a close-up action photo on the front, framed by a wide white border and a dark blue inner border. A white outlines highlights the player closeup. The player's name appears below his head shot, in reversed type on a splash of color that fades from yellow to orange to red to pink. On the card back, the player's name is printed in large red letters across the top, followed by his team name and position in black. Personal info is printed in a red rectangle beside a Topps baseball logo bearing the card number. A triple cartoon strip, in full-color, illustrates career highlights, performance, personal background, etc. A red, white and blue statistics box (pitching, batting, fielding) is printed across the bottom.

		MT	NR MT	EX
	Complete Set:	20.00	15.00	8.00
	Common Player:	.05	.04	.02
1	Paul Molitor	.12	.09	.05
2	Milt Thompson	.05	.04	.02
3	Billy Hatcher	.05	.04	.02
4	Mike Witt	.05	.04	.02
5	Vince Coleman	.12	.09	.05
6	Dwight Evans	.10	.08	.04
7	Tim Wallach	.10	.08	.04
8	Alan Trammell	.15	.11	.06
9	Will Clark	.80	.60	.30
10	Jeff Reardon	.08	.06	.03
11	Dwight Gooden	.50	.40	.20
12	Benny Santiago	.12	.09	.05
13	Jose Canseco	1.25	.90	.50
14	Dale Murphy	.30	.25	.12
15	George Bell	.20	.15	.08
16	Ryne Sandberg	.20	.15	.08
17	Brook Jacoby	.08	.06	.03
18	Fernando Valenzuela	.15	.11	.06
19	Scott Fletcher	.05	.04	.02
20	Eric Davis	.60	.45	.25
21	Willie Wilson	.10	.08	.04
22	B.J. Surhoff	.10	.08	.04
23	Steve Bedrosian	.08	.06	.03
24	Dave Winfield	.25	.20	.10
25	Bobby Bonilla	.15	.11	.06
26	Larry Sheets	.08	.06	.03
27	Ozzie Guillen	.08	.06	.03
28	Checklist 1-88	.05	.04	.02
29	Nolan Ryan	.80	.60	.30
30	Bob Boone	.05	.04	.02
31	Tom Herr	.08	.06	.03
32	Wade Boggs	.90	.70	.35
33	Neal Heaton	.05	.04	.02
34	Doyle Alexander	.05	.04	.02
35	Candy Maldonado	.08	.06	.03
36	Kirby Puckett	.25	.20	.10
37	Gary Carter	.20	.15	.08
38	Lance McCullers	.08	.06	.03
39a	Terry Steinbach (black Topps logo on front)	.12	.09	.05
39b	Terry Steinbach (white Topps logo on front)	.12	.09	.05
40	Gerald Perry	.10	.08	.04
41	Tom Henke	.05	.04	.02
42	Leon Durham	.05	.04	.02
43	Cory Snyder	.12	.09	.05
44	Dale Sveum	.05	.04	.02
45	Lance Parrish	.12	.09	.05
46	Steve Sax	.12	.09	.05
47	Charlie Hough	.05	.04	.02
48	Kal Daniels	.15	.11	.06
49	Bo Jackson	1.00	.70	.40
50	Ron Guidry	.10	.08	.04
51	Bill Doran	.08	.06	.03
52	Wally Joyner	.40	.30	.15
53	Terry Pendleton	.08	.06	.03
54	Marty Barrett	.08	.06	.03
55	Andres Galarraga	.15	.11	.06
56	Larry Herndon	.05	.04	.02
57	Kevin Mitchell	.08	.06	.03
58	Greg Gagne	.05	.04	.02
59	Keith Hernandez	.15	.11	.06
60	John Kruk	.10	.08	.04
61	Mike LaValliere	.08	.06	.03
62	Cal Ripken	.30	.25	.12
63	Ivan Calderon	.08	.06	.03
64	Alvin Davis	.10	.08	.04
65	Luis Polonia	.08	.06	.03
66	Robin Yount	.20	.15	.08
67	Juan Samuel	.12	.09	.05
68	Andres Thomas	.05	.04	.02
69	Jeff Musselman	.05	.04	.02
70	Jerry Mumphrey	.05	.04	.02
71	Joe Carter	.12	.09	.05
72	Mike Scioscia	.05	.04	.02
73	Pete Incaviglia	.10	.08	.04
74	Barry Larkin	.15	.11	.06
75	Frank White	.08	.06	.03
76	Willie Randolph	.08	.06	.03
77	Kevin Bass	.05	.04	.02
78	Brian Downing	.08	.06	.03
79	Willie McGee	.10	.08	.04
80	Ellis Burks	.40	.30	.15
81	Hubie Brooks	.08	.06	.03
82	Darrell Evans	.08	.06	.03
83	Robby Thompson	.05	.04	.02
84	Kent Hrbek	.15	.11	.06
85	Ron Darling	.12	.09	.05
86	Stan Jefferson	.05	.04	.02
87	Teddy Higuera	.10	.08	.04
88	Mike Schmidt	.30	.25	.12
89	Barry Bonds	.15	.11	.06
90	Jim Presley	.08	.06	.03
91	Orel Hershiser	.25	.20	.10
92	Jesse Barfield	.10	.08	.04
93	Tom Candiotti	.05	.04	.02
94	Bret Saberhagen	.12	.09	.05
95	Jose Uribe	.05	.04	.02
96	Tom Browning	.10	.08	.04
97	Johnny Ray	.08	.06	.03
98	Mike Morgan	.05	.04	.02
100	Jim Sundberg	.05	.04	.02
101	Roger McDowell	.08	.06	.03
102	Randy Ready	.05	.04	.02
103	Mike Gallego	.05	.04	.02
104	Steve Buechele	.05	.04	.02
105	Greg Walker	.08	.06	.03
106	Jose Lind	.12	.09	.05
107	Steve Trout	.05	.04	.02
108	Rick Rhoden	.08	.06	.03
109	Jim Pankovits	.05	.04	.02
110	Ken Griffey	.08	.06	.03
111	Danny Cox	.08	.06	.03
112	Franklin Stubbs	.05	.04	.02
113	Lloyd Moseby	.08	.06	.03
114	Mel Hall	.08	.06	.03
115	Kevin Seitzer	.25	.20	.10
116	Tim Raines	.25	.20	.10
117	Juan Castillo	.05	.04	.02
118	Roger Clemens	.50	.40	.20
119	Mike Aldrete	.08	.06	.03
120	Mario Soto	.05	.04	.02
121	Jack Howell	.05	.04	.02
122	Rick Schu	.05	.04	.02
123	Jeff Robinson	.10	.08	.04
124	Doug Drabek	.08	.06	.03
125	Henry Cotto	.05	.04	.02
126	Checklist 89-176	.05	.04	.02

		MT	NR MT	EX
127	Gary Gaetti	.12	.09	.05
128	Rick Sutcliffe	.10	.08	.04
129	Howard Johnson	.08	.06	.03
130	Chris Brown	.08	.06	.03
131	Dave Henderson	.08	.06	.03
132	Curt Wilkerson	.05	.04	.02
133	Mike Marshall	.10	.08	.04
134	Kelly Gruber	.05	.04	.02
135	Julio Franco	.10	.08	.04
136	Kurt Stillwell	.12	.09	.05
137	Donnie Hill	.05	.04	.02
138	Mike Pagliarulo	.10	.08	.04
139	Von Hayes	.08	.06	.03
140	Mike Scott	.10	.08	.04
141	Bob Kipper	.05	.04	.02
142	Harold Reynolds	.08	.06	.03
143	Bob Brenly	.05	.04	.02
144	Dave Concepcion	.08	.06	.03
145	Devon White	.12	.09	.05
146	Jeff Stone	.05	.04	.02
147	Chet Lemon	.05	.04	.02
148	Ozzie Virgil	.05	.04	.02
149	Todd Worrell	.10	.08	.04
150	Mitch Webster	.05	.04	.02
151	Rob Deer	.08	.06	.03
152	Rich Gedman	.08	.06	.03
153	Andre Dawson	.15	.11	.06
154	Mike Davis	.05	.04	.02
155	Nelson Liriano	.08	.06	.03
156	Greg Swindell	.10	.08	.04
157	George Brett	.30	.25	.12
158	Kevin McReynolds	.15	.11	.06
159	Brian Fisher	.08	.06	.03
160	Mike Kingery	.05	.04	.02
161	Tony Gwynn	.25	.20	.10
162	Don Baylor	.10	.08	.04
163	Jerry Browne	.05	.04	.02
164	Dan Pasqua	.08	.06	.03
165	Rickey Henderson	.25	.20	.10
166	Brett Butler	.08	.06	.03
167	Nick Esasky	.05	.04	.02
168	Kirk McCaskill	.05	.04	.02
169	Fred Lynn	.10	.08	.04
170	Jack Morris	.12	.09	.05
171	Pedro Guerrero	.12	.09	.05
172	Dave Stieb	.10	.08	.04
173	Pat Tabler	.08	.06	.03
174	Floyd Bannister	.05	.04	.02
175	Rafael Belliard	.05	.04	.02
176	Mark Langston	.10	.08	.04
177	Greg Mathews	.08	.06	.03
178	Claudell Washington	.05	.04	.02
179	Mark McGwire	1.00	.70	.40
180	Bert Blyleven	.10	.08	.04
181	Jim Rice	.20	.15	.08
182	Mookie Wilson	.08	.06	.03
183	Willie Fraser	.05	.04	.02
184	Andy Van Slyke	.10	.08	.04
185	Matt Nokes	.10	.08	.04
186	Eddie Whitson	.05	.04	.02
187	Tony Fernandez	.10	.08	.04
188	Rick Reuschel	.08	.06	.03
189	Ken Phelps	.05	.04	.02
190	Juan Nieves	.08	.06	.03
191	Kirk Gibson	.20	.15	.08
192	Glenn Davis	.15	.11	.06
193	Zane Smith	.05	.04	.02
194	Jose DeLeon	.08	.06	.03
195	Gary Ward	.05	.04	.02
196	Pascual Perez	.05	.04	.02
197	Carlton Fisk	.12	.09	.05
198	Oddibe McDowell	.08	.06	.03
199	Mark Gubicza	.10	.08	.04
200	Glenn Hubbard	.05	.04	.02
201	Frank Viola	.15	.11	.06
202	Jody Reed	.12	.09	.05
203	Len Dykstra	.08	.06	.03
204	Dick Schofield	.05	.04	.02
205	Sid Bream	.05	.04	.02
206	Guillermo Hernandez	.05	.04	.02
207	Keith Moreland	.05	.04	.02
208	Mark Eichhorn	.05	.04	.02
209	Rene Gonzales	.08	.06	.03
210	Dave Valle	.05	.04	.02
211	Tom Brunansky	.10	.08	.04
212	Charles Hudson	.05	.04	.02
213	John Farrell	.10	.08	.04
214	Jeff Treadway	.12	.09	.05
215	Eddie Murray	.25	.20	.10
216	Checklist 177-264	.05	.04	.02
217	Greg Brock	.08	.06	.03

		MT	NR MT	EX
218	John Shelby	.05	.04	.02
219	Craig Reynolds	.05	.04	.02
220	Dion James	.05	.04	.02
221	Carney Lansford	.08	.06	.03
222	Juan Berenguer	.05	.04	.02
223	Luis Rivera	.08	.06	.03
224	Harold Baines	.12	.09	.05
225	Shawon Dunston	.08	.06	.03
226	Luis Aguayo	.05	.04	.02
227	Pete O'Brien	.08	.06	.03
228	Ozzie Smith	.12	.09	.05
229	Don Mattingly	1.50	1.25	.60
230	Danny Tartabull	.15	.11	.06
231	Andy Allanson	.05	.04	.02
232	John Franco	.08	.06	.03
233	Mike Greenwell	.80	.60	.30
234	Bob Ojeda	.08	.06	.03
235	Chili Davis	.08	.06	.03
236	Mike Dunne	.12	.09	.05
237	Jim Morrison	.05	.04	.02
238	Carmelo Martinez	.05	.04	.02
239	Ernie Whitt	.05	.04	.02
240	Scott Garrelts	.05	.04	.02
241	Mike Moore	.05	.04	.02
242	Dave Parker	.10	.08	.04
243	Tim Laudner	.05	.04	.02
244	Bill Wegman	.05	.04	.02
245	Bob Horner	.08	.06	.03
246	Rafael Santana	.05	.04	.02
247	Alfredo Griffin	.05	.04	.02
248	Mark Bailey	.05	.04	.02
249	Ron Gant	.12	.09	.05
250	Bryn Smith	.05	.04	.02
251	Lance Johnson	.10	.08	.04
252	Sam Horn	.10	.08	.04
253	Darryl Strawberry	.40	.30	.15
254	Chuck Finley	.05	.04	.02
255	Darnell Coles	.08	.06	.03
256	Mike Henneman	.10	.08	.04
257	Andy Hawkins	.08	.06	.03
258	Jim Clancy	.08	.06	.03
259	Atlee Hammaker	.05	.04	.02
260	Glenn Wilson	.05	.04	.02
261	Larry McWilliams	.05	.04	.02
262	Jack Clark	.12	.09	.05
263	Walt Weiss	.80	.60	.30
264	Gene Larkin	.08	.06	.03

1988 Topps Box Panels

After a one-year hiatus during which they appeared on the sides of Topps wax pack display boxes, Topps retail box cards returned to box bottoms in 1988. Topps first issued box-bottom cards in 1986, following the introduction of the concept by Donruss in 1985. Topps 1988 box-bottom series includes 16 standard-size baseball cards, four cards per each of four different display boxes. Card fronts follow the same design as the 1988 Topps basic issue; full-color player photos, framed in yellow, surrounded by a white border; diagonal player name lower right; team name in large letters at the top of the card front. Card backs are "numbered" A through P and are printed in black and orange.

	MT	NR MT	EX
Complete Panel Set:	7.00	5.25	2.75

		MT	NR MT	EX
	Complete Singles Set:	3.00	2.25	1.25
	Common Panel:	1.00	.70	.40
	Common Single Player:	.08	.06	.03
	Panel	1.00	.70	.40
A	Don Baylor	.12	.09	.05
B	Steve Bedrosian	.12	.09	.05
C	Juan Beniquez	.08	.06	.03
D	Bob Boone	.08	.06	.03
	Panel	1.75	1.25	.70
E	Darrell Evans	.12	.09	.05
F	Tony Gwynn	.30	.25	.12
G	John Kruk	.15	.11	.06
H	Marvell Wynne	.08	.06	.03
	Panel	2.75	2.00	1.00
I	Joe Carter	.15	.11	.06
J	Eric Davis	.50	.40	.20
K	Howard Johnson	.12	.09	.05
L	Darryl Strawberry	.35	.25	.14
	Panel	2.50	2.00	1.00
M	Rickey Henderson	.50	.40	.20
N	Nolan Ryan	.35	.25	.14
O	Mike Schmidt	.08	.06	.03
P	Kent Tekulve	.08	.06	.03

1988 Topps Coins

This edition of 60 lightweight metal coins is similar in design to Topps' 1964 set. The 1988 coins are 1-1/2" in diameter and feature full-color player closeups under crimped edges in silver, gold and pink. Curved under the photo is a red and white player name banner pinned by two gold stars. Coin backs list the coin number, player name, personal information and career summary in black letters on a silver background.

		MT	NR MT	EX
	Complete Set:	8.00	6.00	3.25
	Common Player:	.10	.08	.04
1	George Bell	.25	.20	.10
2	Roger Clemens	.40	.30	.15
3	Mark McGwire	.60	.45	.25
4	Wade Boggs	.70	.50	.30
5	Harold Baines	.15	.11	.06
6	Ivan Calderon	.10	.08	.04
7	Jose Canseco	.80	.60	.30
8	Joe Carter	.15	.11	.06
9	Jack Clark	.15	.11	.06
10	Alvin Davis	.15	.11	.06
11	Dwight Evans	.15	.11	.06
12	Tony Fernandez	.15	.11	.06
13	Gary Gaetti	.15	.11	.06
14	Mike Greenwell	.40	.30	.15
15	Charlie Hough	.10	.08	.04
16	Wally Joyner	.30	.25	.12
17	Jimmy Key	.10	.08	.04
18	Mark Langston	.15	.11	.06
19	Don Mattingly	1.00	.70	.40
20	Paul Molitor	.15	.11	.06
21	Jack Morris	.15	.11	.06
22	Eddie Murray	.20	.15	.08
23	Kirby Puckett	.25	.20	.10
24	Cal Ripken	.25	.20	.10
25	Bret Saberhagen	.15	.11	.06
26	Ruben Sierra	.15	.11	.06
27	Cory Snyder	.15	.11	.06
28	Terry Steinbach	.15	.11	.06
29	Danny Tartabull	.15	.11	.06
30	Alan Trammell	.15	.11	.06
31	Devon White	.15	.11	.06
32	Robin Yount	.15	.11	.06
33	Andre Dawson	.15	.11	.06
34	Steve Bedrosian	.15	.11	.06
35	Benny Santiago	.15	.11	.06
36	Tony Gwynn	.25	.20	.10
37	Bobby Bonilla	.15	.11	.06
38	Will Clark	.30	.25	.12
39	Eric Davis	.40	.30	.15
40	Mike Dunne	.15	.11	.06
41	John Franco	.10	.08	.04
42	Dwight Gooden	.40	.30	.15
43	Pedro Guerrero	.15	.11	.06
44	Dion James	.10	.08	.04
45	John Kruk	.15	.11	.06
46	Jeffrey Leonard	.10	.08	.04
47	Carmelo Martinez	.10	.08	.04
48	Dale Murphy	.30	.25	.12
49	Tim Raines	.20	.15	.08
50	Nolan Ryan	.20	.15	.08
51	Juan Samuel	.15	.11	.06
52	Ryne Sandberg	.20	.15	.08
53	Mike Schmidt	.30	.25	.12
54	Mike Scott	.15	.11	.06
55	Ozzie Smith	.15	.11	.06
56	Darryl Strawberry	.40	.30	.15
57	Rick Sutcliffe	.15	.11	.06
58	Fernando Valenzuela	.15	.11	.06
59	Tim Wallach	.15	.11	.06
60	Todd Worrell	.15	.11	.06

1988 Topps Gallery Of Champions

These bronze replicas are exact reproductions at one-quarter scale of Topps official 1988 cards, both front and back. The set includes 12 three-dimensional raised metal cards packaged in a velvet-lined case that bears the title of the set in gold embossed letters. A deluxe limited edition of the set (1,000) was produced in sterling silver and an economy version in aluminum. Topps first issued the metal mini-cards in 1984 (the initial set was called Gallery of Immortals). Since 1985, the metal cards have honored award-winning players from the previous season. A Mark McGwire pewter replica was given as a premium to dealers ordering the aluminum, bronze and silver sets ($50 value). The special pewter card is distinguished from the regular issue by a diagonal name banner in the lower right corner (regular) replicas have a rectangular name banner printer parallel to the lower edge of the card). A 1955 Topps Duke Snider bronze (value $10) was available to dealers purchasing cases of the 1988 Topps Traded sets.

		MT	NR MT	EX
	Complete Aluminum Set:	20.00	15.00	8.00
	Complete Bronze Set:	125.00	94.00	50.00
	Complete Silver Set:	500.00	375.00	200.00
(1a)	Steve Bedrosian (aluminum)	.70	.50	.30

		MT	NR MT	EX
(1b)	Steve Bedrosian (bronze)	7.50	5.75	3.00
(1c)	Steve Bedrosian (silver)	20.00	15.00	8.00
(2a)	George Bell (aluminum)	1.00	.70	.40
(2b)	George Bell (bronze)	10.00	7.50	4.00
(2c)	George Bell (silver)	20.00	15.00	8.00
(3a)	Wade Boggs (aluminum)	3.00	2.25	1.25
(3b)	Wade Boggs (bronze)	25.00	18.50	10.00
(3c)	Wade Boggs (silver)	125.00	94.00	50.00
(4a)	Jack Clark (aluminum)	1.00	.70	.40
(4b)	Jack Clark (bronze)	10.00	7.50	4.00
(4c)	Jack Clark (silver)	20.00	15.00	8.00
(5a)	Roger Clemens (aluminum)	2.00	1.50	.80
(5b)	Roger Clemens (bronze)	20.00	15.00	8.00
(5c)	Roger Clemens (silver)	90.00	67.00	36.00
(6a)	Andre Dawson (aluminum)	1.00	.70	.40
(6b)	Andre Dawson (bronze)	10.00	7.50	4.00
(6c)	Andre Dawson (silver)	20.00	15.00	8.00
(7a)	Tony Gwynn (aluminum)	1.25	.90	.50
(7b)	Tony Gwynn (bronze)	12.00	9.00	4.75
(7c)	Tony Gwynn (silver)	50.00	37.00	20.00
(8a)	Mark Langston (aluminum)	.70	.50	.30
(8b)	Mark Langston (bronze)	7.50	5.75	3.00
(8c)	Mark Langston (silver)	20.00	15.00	8.00
(9a)	Mark McGwire (aluminum)	3.00	2.25	1.25
(9b)	Mark McGwire (bronze)	25.00	18.50	10.00
(9c)	Mark McGwire (silver)	125.00	94.00	50.00
(10a)	Dave Righetti (aluminum)	1.00	.70	.40
(10b)	Dave Righetti (bronze)	10.00	7.50	4.00
(10c)	Dave Righetti (silver)	20.00	15.00	8.00
(11a)	Nolan Ryan (aluminum)	1.00	.70	.40
(11b)	Nolan Ryan (bronze)	10.00	7.50	4.00
(11c)	Nolan Ryan (silver)	20.00	15.00	8.00
(12a)	Benny Santiago (aluminum)	1.00	.70	.40
(12b)	Benny Santiago (bronze)	10.00	7.50	4.00
(12c)	Benny Santiago (silver)	20.00	15.00	8.00

1988 Topps
Glossy Rookies

The Topps 1988 Rookies special insert cards follow the same basic design as the All-Star inserts. The set consists of 22 standard-size cards. Large, glossy color player photos are printed on a white background below a red, yellow and blue "1987 Rookies" banner. A red and yellow player name appears beneath the photo. Red, white and blue card backs bear the title of the special insert set, the Rookies logo emblem, player name and card number.

		MT	NR MT	EX
	Complete Set:	10.00	7.50	4.00
	Common Player:	.20	.15	.08
1	Billy Ripken	.30	.25	.12
2	Ellis Burks	1.50	1.25	.60
3	Mike Greenwell	2.00	1.50	.80
4	DeWayne Buice	.20	.15	.08
5	Devon White	.40	.30	.15
6	Fred Manrique	.20	.15	.08
7	Mike Henneman	.40	.30	.15
8	Matt Nokes	.60	.45	.25
9	Kevin Seitzer	.80	.60	.30
10	B.J. Surhoff	.40	.30	.15
11	Casey Candaele	.20	.15	.08
12	Randy Myers	.60	.45	.25
13	Mark McGwire	1.50	1.25	.60
14	Luis Polonia	.25	.20	.10

		MT	NR MT	EX
15	Terry Steinbach	.40	.30	.15
16	Mike Dunne	.40	.30	.15
17	Al Pedrique	.20	.15	.08
18	Benny Santiago	.70	.50	.30
19	Kelly Downs	.40	.30	.15
20	Joe Magrane	.40	.30	.15
21	Jerry Browne	.20	.15	.08
22	Jeff Musselman	.25	.20	.10

1988 Topps
Mini League Leaders

The third consecutive issue of Topps mini-cards (2-1/8" by 3") includes 77 cards spotlighting the top five ranked pitchers and batters. This set is unique in that it was the first time Topps included full-color player photos on both the front and back. Glossy action shots on the card fronts fade into a white border with a Topps logo in an upper corner. The player's name is printed in bold black letters beneath the photo. Horizontal reverses feature circular player photos on a blue and white background with the card number, player name, personal information, 1987 ranking and lifetime/1987 stats printed in red, black and yellow lettering.

		MT	NR MT	EX
	Complete Set:	6.00	4.50	2.50
	Common Player:	.09	.07	.04
1	Wade Boggs	.80	.60	.30
2	Roger Clemens	.60	.45	.25
3	Dwight Evans	.15	.11	.06
4	DeWayne Buice	.09	.07	.04
5	Brian Downing	.09	.07	.04
6	Wally Joyner	.60	.45	.25
7	Ivan Calderon	.15	.11	.06
8	Carlton Fisk	.20	.15	.08
9	Gary Redus	.09	.07	.04
10	Darrell Evans	.15	.11	.06
11	Jack Morris	.25	.20	.10
12	Alan Trammell	.30	.25	.12
13	Lou Whitaker	.20	.15	.08
14	Bret Saberhagen	.20	.15	.08
15	Kevin Seitzer	.50	.40	.20
16	Danny Tartabull	.25	.20	.10
17	Willie Wilson	.15	.11	.06
18	Teddy Higuera	.15	.11	.06
19	Paul Molitor	.20	.15	.08
20	Dan Plesac	.15	.11	.06
21	Robin Yount	.25	.20	.10
22	Kent Hrbek	.25	.20	.10
23	Kirby Puckett	.35	.25	.14
24	Jeff Reardon	.15	.11	.06
25	Frank Viola	.20	.15	.08
26	Rickey Henderson	.60	.45	.25
27	Don Mattingly	1.25	.90	.50
28	Willie Randolph	.15	.11	.06
29	Dave Righetti	.20	.15	.08
30	Jose Canseco	1.00	.70	.40
31	Mark McGwire	.90	.70	.35
32	Dave Stewart	.09	.07	.04
33	Phil Bradley	.15	.11	.06
34	Mark Langston	.15	.11	.06
35	Harold Reynolds	.09	.07	.04
36	Charlie Hough	.09	.07	.04

		MT	NR MT	EX
37	George Bell	.25	.20	.10
38	Tom Henke	.09	.07	.04
39	Jimmy Key	.15	.11	.06
40	Dion James	.09	.07	.04
41	Dale Murphy	.50	.40	.20
42	Zane Smith	.09	.07	.04
43	Andre Dawson	.25	.20	.10
44	Lee Smith	.09	.07	.04
45	Rick Sutcliffe	.15	.11	.06
46	Eric Davis	.60	.45	.25
47	John Franco	.15	.11	.06
48	Dave Parker	.20	.15	.08
49	Billy Hatcher	.09	.07	.04
50	Nolan Ryan	.60	.45	.25
51	Mike Scott	.20	.15	.08
52	Pedro Guerrero	.20	.15	.08
53	Orel Hershiser	.30	.25	.12
54	Fernando Valenzuela	.25	.20	.10
55	Bob Welch	.15	.11	.06
56	Andres Galarraga	.25	.20	.10
57	Tim Raines	.30	.25	.12
58	Tim Wallach	.15	.11	.06
59	Len Dykstra	.15	.11	.06
60	Dwight Gooden	.60	.45	.25
61	Howard Johnson	.15	.11	.06
62	Roger McDowell	.15	.11	.06
63	Darryl Strawberry	.50	.40	.20
64	Steve Bedrosian	.15	.11	.06
65	Shane Rawley	.09	.07	.04
66	Juan Samuel	.20	.15	.08
67	Mike Schmidt	.50	.40	.20
68	Mike Dunne	.15	.11	.06
69	Jack Clark	.25	.20	.10
70	Vince Coleman	.20	.15	.08
71	Willie McGee	.15	.11	.06
72	Ozzie Smith	.20	.15	.08
73	Todd Worrell	.15	.11	.06
74	Tony Gwynn	.40	.30	.15
75	John Kruk	.20	.15	.08
76	Rick Rueschel	.15	.11	.06
77	Checklist	.09	.07	.04

1988 Topps Stickercards

Actually a part of the 1988 Topps Stickers issue, this set consists of 67 cards. The cards are the backs of the peel-off stickers and measure 2-1/8" by 3". To determine total value, combine the prices of the stickers (found in the 1988 Topps Stickers checklist) on the stickercard front with the value assigned to the stickercard in the following checklist.

		MT	NR MT	EX
Complete Set:		2.00	1.50	.80
Common Player:		.02	.02	.01
1	Jack Clark	.03	.02	.01
2	Andres Galarraga	.03	.02	.01
3	Keith Hernandez	.04	.03	.02
4	Tom Herr	.02	.02	.01
5	Juan Samuel	.03	.02	.01
6	Ryne Sandberg	.04	.03	.02
7	Terry Pendleton	.02	.02	.01
8	Mike Schmidt	.06	.05	.02
9	Tim Wallach	.02	.02	.01
10	Hubie Brooks	.02	.02	.01
11	Shawon Dunston	.02	.02	.01
12	Ozzie Smith	.03	.02	.01

		MT	NR MT	EX
13	Andre Dawson	.04	.03	.02
14	Eric Davis	.06	.05	.02
15	Pedro Guerrero	.03	.02	.01
16	Tony Gwynn	.05	.04	.02
17	Jeffrey Leonard	.02	.02	.01
18	Dale Murphy	.06	.05	.02
19	Dave Parker	.03	.02	.01
20	Tim Raines	.04	.03	.02
21	Darryl Strawberry	.06	.05	.02
22	Gary Carter	.04	.03	.02
23	Jody Davis	.02	.02	.01
24	Ozzie Virgil	.02	.02	.01
25	Dwight Gooden	.08	.06	.03
26	Mike Scott	.02	.02	.01
27	Rick Sutcliffe	.02	.02	.01
28	Sid Fernandez	.02	.02	.01
29	Neal Heaton	.02	.02	.01
30	Fernando Valenzuela	.03	.02	.01
31	Steve Bedrosian	.02	.02	.01
32	John Franco	.02	.02	.01
33	Lee Smith	.02	.02	.01
34	Wally Joyner	.06	.05	.02
35	Don Mattingly	.12	.09	.05
36	Mark McGwire	.08	.06	.03
37	Willie Randolph	.02	.02	.01
38	Lou Whitaker	.03	.02	.01
39	Frank White	.02	.02	.01
40	Wade Boggs	.10	.08	.04
41	George Brett	.06	.05	.02
42	Paul Molitor	.02	.02	.01
43	Tony Fernandez	.02	.02	.01
44	Cal Ripken	.06	.05	.02
45	Alan Trammell	.04	.03	.02
46	Jesse Barfield	.03	.02	.01
47	George Bell	.04	.03	.02
48	Jose Canseco	.10	.08	.04
49	Joe Carter	.03	.02	.01
50	Dwight Evans	.02	.02	.01
51	Rickey Henderson	.05	.04	.02
52	Kirby Puckett	.05	.04	.02
53	Cory Snyder	.03	.02	.01
54	Dave Winfield	.04	.03	.02
55	Terry Kennedy	.02	.02	.01
56	Matt Nokes	.03	.02	.01
57	B.J. Surhoff	.02	.02	.01
58	Roger Clemens	.08	.06	.03
59	Jack Morris	.03	.02	.01
60	Bret Saberhagen	.03	.02	.01
61	Ron Guidry	.03	.02	.01
62	Bruce Hurst	.02	.02	.01
63	Mark Langston	.02	.02	.01
64	Tom Henke	.02	.02	.01
65	Dan Plesac	.02	.02	.01
66	Dave Righetti	.03	.02	.01
67	Checklist	.02	.02	.01

1988 Topps Stickers

This set of 313 stickers (on 198 cards) offers a new addition for 1988 - 66 different players are pictured on the reverse of the sticker cards. The stickers come in two sizes (2-1/8" by 3" or 1-1/2" by 2-1/8"). Larger stickers fill an entire card, smaller ones are attached in pairs. A 36-page sticker yearbook produced by Topps has a designated space inside for each sticker, with one page per team and special pages of 1987 Highlights, World Series, All-Stars and Future Stars. No printing appears on the full-color action shot stickers except for a small black number in the lower left corner. Sticker card backs carry a Super Star header, player close-up and stats. Stickers were sold in packages of five (with gum) for 25 cents per pack. Unlike the 1987 Topps Stickers set, different pairings can be found, rather than the same two players/numbers always sharing the same sticker. To determine total value, combine the value of the stickercard (found in the 1988 Topps Stickercard checklist) with the values assigned the stickers in the following checklist.

		MT	NR MT	EX
Complete Set:		15.00	11.00	6.00
Common Player:		.02	.02	.01
Sticker Album:		.60	.45	.25
1	1987 Highlights (Mark McGwire)	.20	.15	.08
2	1987 Highlights (Benny Santiago)	.04	.03	.02
3	1987 Highlights (Don Mattingly)	.25	.20	.10
4	1987 Highlights (Vince Coleman)	.04	.03	.02
5	1987 Highlights (Bob Boone)	.02	.02	.01
6	1987 Highlights (Steve Bedrosian)	.02	.02	.01
7	1987 Highlights (Nolan Ryan)	.08	.06	.03
8	1987 Highlights (Darrell Evans)	.02	.02	.01
9	1987 Highlights (Mike Schmidt)	.10	.08	.04
10	1987 Highlights (Don Baylor)	.04	.03	.02
11	1987 Highlights (Eddie Murray)	.08	.06	.03
12	1987 Highlights (Juan Beniquez)	.02	.02	.01
13	1987 Championship Series (John Tudor)	.04	.03	.02
14	1987 Championship Series (Jeff Reardon)	.04	.03	.02
15	1987 Championship Series (Tom Brunansky)	.06	.05	.02
16	1987 Championship Series (Jeffrey Leonard)	.04	.03	.02
17	1987 Championship Series (Gary Gaetti)	.10	.08	.04
18	1987 Championship Series (Cardinals Celebrate)	.04	.03	.02
19	1987 World Series (Danny Gladden)	.04	.03	.02
20	1987 World Series (Bert Blyleven)	.08	.06	.03
21	1987 World Series (John Tudor)	.06	.05	.02
22	1987 World Series (Tom Lawless)	.04	.03	.02
23	1987 World Series (Curt Ford)	.04	.03	.02
24	1987 World Series (Kent Hrbek)	.12	.09	.05
25	1987 World Series (Frank Viola)	.10	.08	.04
26	Dave Smith	.02	.02	.01
27	Jim Deshaies	.02	.02	.01
28	Billy Hatcher	.02	.02	.01
29	Kevin Bass	.02	.02	.01
30	Mike Scott	.04	.03	.02
31	Danny Walling	.02	.02	.01
32	Alan Ashby	.02	.02	.01
33	Ken Caminiti	.02	.02	.01
34	Bill Doran	.02	.02	.01
35	Glenn Davis	.12	.09	.05
36	Ozzie Virgil	.02	.02	.01
37	Ken Oberkfell	.02	.02	.01
38	Ken Griffey	.02	.02	.01
39	Albert Hall	.02	.02	.01
40	Zane Smith	.02	.02	.01
41	Andres Thomas	.02	.02	.01
42	Dion James	.02	.02	.01
43	Jim Acker	.02	.02	.01
44	Tom Glavine	.04	.03	.02
45	Dale Murphy	.25	.20	.10
46	Jack Clark	.10	.08	.04
47	Vince Coleman	.04	.03	.02
48	Ricky Horton	.02	.02	.01
49	Terry Pendleton	.02	.02	.01
50	Tom Herr	.02	.02	.01
51	Joe Magrane	.04	.03	.02
52	Tony Pena	.02	.02	.01
53	Ozzie Smith	.04	.03	.02
54	Todd Worrell	.04	.03	.02
55	Willie McGee	.10	.08	.04
56	Andre Dawson	.15	.11	.06
57	Ryne Sandberg	.06	.05	.02
58	Keith Moreland	.02	.02	.01
59	Greg Maddux	.04	.03	.02
60	Jody Davis	.02	.02	.01
61	Rick Sutcliffe	.08	.06	.03
62	Jamie Moyer	.02	.02	.01
63	Leon Durham	.02	.02	.01
64	Lee Smith	.02	.02	.01
65	Shawon Dunston	.02	.02	.01
66	Franklin Stubbs	.02	.02	.01

		MT	NR MT	EX
67	Mike Scioscia	.02	.02	.01
68	Orel Hershiser	.06	.05	.02
69	Mike Marshall	.04	.03	.02
70	Fernando Valenzuela	.15	.11	.06
71	Mickey Hatcher	.02	.02	.01
72	Matt Young	.02	.02	.01
73	Bob Welch	.04	.03	.02
74	Steve Sax	.04	.03	.02
75	Pedro Guerrero	.12	.09	.05
76	Tim Raines	.15	.11	.06
77	Casey Candaele	.02	.02	.01
78	Mike Fitzgerald	.02	.02	.01
79	Andres Galarraga	.04	.03	.02
80	Neal Heaton	.02	.02	.01
81	Hubie Brooks	.02	.02	.01
82	Floyd Youmans	.02	.02	.01
83	Herm Winningham	.02	.02	.01
84	Denny Martinez	.02	.02	.01
85	Tim Wallach	.08	.06	.03
86	Jeffrey Leonard	.04	.03	.02
87	Will Clark	.10	.08	.04
88	Kevin Mitchell	.04	.03	.02
89	Mike Aldrete	.02	.02	.01
90	Scott Garrelts	.02	.02	.01
91	Jose Uribe	.02	.02	.01
92	Bob Brenly	.02	.02	.01
93	Robby Thompson	.02	.02	.01
94	Don Robinson	.02	.02	.01
95	Candy Maldonado	.04	.03	.02
96	Darryl Strawberry	.25	.20	.10
97	Keith Hernandez	.06	.05	.02
98	Ron Darling	.04	.03	.02
99	Howard Johnson	.04	.03	.02
100	Roger McDowell	.02	.02	.01
101	Dwight Gooden	.30	.25	.12
102	Kevin McReynolds	.04	.03	.02
103	Sid Fernandez	.02	.02	.01
104	Dave Magadan	.04	.03	.02
105	Gary Carter	.08	.06	.03
106	Carmelo Martinez	.02	.02	.01
107	Eddie Whitson	.02	.02	.01
108	Tim Flannery	.02	.02	.01
109	Stan Jefferson	.02	.02	.01
110	John Kruk	.10	.08	.04
111	Chris Brown	.04	.03	.02
112	Benny Santiago	.04	.03	.02
113	Garry Templeton	.02	.02	.01
114	Lance McCullers	.02	.02	.01
115	Tony Gwynn	.20	.15	.08
116	Steve Bedrosian	.06	.05	.02
117	Von Hayes	.02	.02	.01
118	Kevin Gross	.02	.02	.01
119	Bruce Ruffin	.02	.02	.01
120	Juan Samuel	.04	.03	.02
121	Shane Rawley	.02	.02	.01
122	Chris James	.04	.03	.02
123	Lance Parrish	.04	.03	.02
124	Glenn Wilson	.02	.02	.01
125	Mike Schmidt	.25	.20	.10
126	Andy Van Slyke	.08	.06	.03
127	Jose Lind	.04	.03	.02
128	Al Pedrique	.02	.02	.01
129	Bobby Bonilla	.04	.03	.02
130	Sed Bream	.02	.02	.01
131	Mike LaValliere	.02	.02	.01
132	Mike Dunne	.04	.03	.02
133	Jeff Robinson	.02	.02	.01
134	Doug Drabek	.02	.02	.01
135	Barry Bonds	.10	.08	.04
136	Dave Parker	.08	.06	.03
137	Nick Esasky	.02	.02	.01
138	Buddy Bell	.02	.02	.01
139	Kal Daniels	.04	.03	.02
140	Barry Larkin	.04	.03	.02
141	Eric Davis	.25	.20	.10
142	John Franco	.02	.02	.01
143	Bo Diaz	.02	.02	.01
144	Ron Oester	.02	.02	.01
145	Dennis Rasmussen	.02	.02	.01
146	Eric Davis	.40	.30	.15
147	Ryne Sandberg	.30	.25	.12
148	Andre Dawson	.20	.15	.08
149	Mike Schmidt	.40	.30	.15
150	Jack Clark	.20	.15	.08
151	Darryl Strawberry	.40	.30	.15
152	Gary Carter	.30	.25	.12
153	Ozzie Smith	.20	.15	.08
154	Mike Scott	.20	.15	.08
155	Rickey Henderson	.40	.30	.15
156	Don Mattingly	.90	.70	.35
157	Wade Boggs	.60	.45	.25

#	Player	MT	NR MT	EX
158	George Bell	.30	.25	.12
159	Dave Winfield	.30	.25	.12
160	Cal Ripken	.40	.30	.15
161	Terry Kennedy	.15	.11	.06
162	Willie Randolph	.15	.11	.06
163	Bret Saberhagen	.25	.20	.10
164	Mark McGwire	.35	.25	.14
165	Tony Phillips	.02	.02	.01
166	Jay Howell	.02	.02	.01
167	Carney Lansford	.02	.02	.01
168	Dave Stewart	.02	.02	.01
169	Alfredo Griffin	.02	.02	.01
170	Dennis Eckersley	.04	.03	.02
171	Mike Davis	.02	.02	.01
172	Luis Polonia	.02	.02	.01
173	Jose Canseco	.60	.45	.25
174	Mike Witt	.06	.05	.02
175	Jack Howell	.02	.02	.01
176	Greg Minton	.02	.02	.01
177	Dick Schofield	.02	.02	.01
178	Gary Pettis	.02	.02	.01
179	Wally Joyner	.25	.20	.10
180	DeWayne Buice	.02	.02	.01
181	Brian Downing	.02	.02	.01
182	Bob Boone	.02	.02	.01
183	Devon White	.04	.03	.02
184	Jim Clancy	.02	.02	.01
185	Willie Upshaw	.02	.02	.01
186	Tom Henke	.02	.02	.01
187	Ernie Whitt	.02	.02	.01
188	George Bell	.20	.15	.08
189	Lloyd Moseby	.02	.02	.01
190	Jimmy Key	.02	.02	.01
191	Dave Stieb	.02	.02	.01
192	Jesse Barfield	.04	.03	.02
193	Tony Fernandez	.10	.08	.04
194	Paul Molitor	.06	.05	.02
195	Jim Gantner	.02	.02	.01
196	Teddy Higuera	.04	.03	.02
197	Glenn Braggs	.02	.02	.01
198	Rob Deer	.02	.02	.01
199	Dale Sveum	.02	.02	.01
200	Bill Wegman	.02	.02	.01
201	Robin Yount	.06	.05	.02
202	B.J. Surhoff	.04	.03	.02
203	Dan Plesac	.06	.05	.02
204	Pat Tabler	.04	.03	.02
205	Mel Hall	.02	.02	.01
206	Scott Bailes	.02	.02	.01
207	Julio Franco	.04	.03	.02
208	Cory Snyder	.06	.05	.02
209	Chris Bando	.02	.02	.01
210	Greg Swindell	.04	.03	.02
211	Brook Jacoby	.02	.02	.01
212	Brett Butler	.02	.02	.01
213	Joe Carter	.10	.08	.04
214	Mark Langston	.08	.06	.03
215	Rey Quinones	.02	.02	.01
216	Ed Nunez	.02	.02	.01
217	Jim Presley	.02	.02	.01
218	Phil Bradley	.04	.03	.02
219	Alvin Davis	.10	.08	.04
220	Dave Valle	.02	.02	.01
221	Harold Reynolds	.02	.02	.01
222	Scott Bradley	.02	.02	.01
223	Gary Matthews	.02	.02	.01
224	Eric Bell	.02	.02	.01
225	Terry Kennedy	.02	.02	.01
226	Dave Schmidt	.02	.02	.01
227	Billy Ripken	.04	.03	.02
228	Cal Ripken	.20	.15	.08
229	Ray Knight	.02	.02	.01
230	Larry Sheets	.02	.02	.01
231	Mike Boddicker	.02	.02	.01
232	Tom Niedenfuer	.02	.02	.01
233	Eddie Murray	.20	.15	.08
234	Ruben Sierra	.12	.09	.05
235	Steve Buechele	.02	.02	.01
236	Charlie Hough	.02	.02	.01
237	Oddibe McDowell	.02	.02	.01
238	Mike Stanley	.02	.02	.01
239	Pete Incaviglia	.04	.03	.02
240	Pete O'Brien	.02	.02	.01
241	Scott Fletcher	.02	.02	.01
242	Dale Mohorcic	.02	.02	.01
243	Larry Parrish	.04	.03	.02
244	Wade Boggs	.35	.25	.14
245	Dwight Evans	.04	.03	.02
246	Sam Horn	.04	.03	.02
247	Jim Rice	.06	.05	.02
248	Marty Barrett	.02	.02	.01
249	Mike Greenwell	.15	.11	.06
250	Ellis Burks	.10	.08	.04
251	Roger Clemens	.12	.09	.05
252	Rich Gedman	.02	.02	.01
253	Bruce Hurst	.06	.05	.02
254	Bret Saberhagen	.15	.11	.06
255	Frank White	.02	.02	.01
256	Dan Quisenberry	.02	.02	.01
257	Danny Tartabull	.06	.05	.02
258	Bo Jackson	.08	.06	.03
259	George Brett	.25	.20	.10
260	Charlie Leibrandt	.02	.02	.01
261	Kevin Seitzer	.10	.08	.04
262	Mark Gubicza	.04	.03	.02
263	Willie Wilson	.04	.03	.02
264	Frank Tanana	.02	.02	.01
265	Darrell Evans	.02	.02	.01
266	Bill Madlock	.04	.03	.02
267	Kirk Gibson	.06	.05	.02
268	Jack Morris	.12	.09	.05
269	Matt Nokes	.06	.05	.02
270	Lou Whitaker	.04	.03	.02
271	Eric King	.02	.02	.01
272	Jim Morrison	.02	.02	.01
273	Alan Trammell	.20	.15	.08
274	Kent Hrbek	.12	.09	.05
275	Tom Brunansky	.04	.03	.02
276	Bert Blyleven	.04	.03	.02
277	Gary Gaetti	.04	.03	.02
278	Tim Laudner	.04	.03	.02
279	Gene Larkin	.02	.02	.01
280	Jeff Reardon	.02	.02	.01
281	Danny Gladden	.02	.02	.01
282	Frank Viola	.04	.03	.02
283	Kirby Puckett	.20	.15	.08
284	Ozzie Guillen	.06	.05	.02
285	Ivan Calderon	.02	.02	.01
286	Donnie Hill	.02	.02	.01
287	Ken Williams	.04	.03	.02
288	Jim Winn	.02	.02	.01
289	Bob James	.02	.02	.01
290	Carlton Fisk	.04	.03	.02
291	Richard Dotson	.02	.02	.01
292	Greg Walker	.02	.02	.01
293	Harold Baines	.10	.08	.04
294	Willie Randolph	.06	.05	.02
295	Mike Pagliarulo	.04	.03	.02
296	Ron Guidry	.04	.03	.02
297	Rickey Henderson	.10	.08	.04
298	Rick Rhoden	.02	.02	.01
299	Don Mattingly	.70	.50	.30
300	Dave Righetti	.04	.03	.02
301	Claudell Washington	.02	.02	.01
302	Dave Winfield	.08	.06	.03
303	Gary Ward	.02	.02	.01
304	Al Pedrique	.02	.02	.01
305	Casey Candaele	.02	.02	.01
306	Kevin Seitzer	.10	.08	.04
307	Mike Dunne	.04	.03	.02
308	Jeff Musselman	.02	.02	.01
309	Mark McGwire	.20	.15	.08
310	Ellis Burks	.10	.08	.04
311	Matt Nokes	.06	.05	.02
312	Mike Greenwell	.15	.11	.06
313	Devon White	.04	.03	.02

1988 Topps Traded

In addition to new players and traded veterans, 21 members of the U.S.A. Olympic Baseball team are showcased in this 132-card set, numbered 1T-132T. The standard-size (2-1/2" by 3-1/2") set follows the same design as the basic Topps issue - white borders, large full-color photos, team name (or U.S.A.) in large bold letters at the top of the card face, player name on a diagonal stripe across the lower right corner. Topps has issued its traded series each year since 1981 in boxed complete sets available through hobby dealers.

		MT	NR MT	EX
Complete Set:		40.00	30.00	15.00
Common Player:		.06	.05	.02
1T	Jim Abbott (U.S.A.)(FC)	7.00	5.25	2.75
2T	Juan Agosto	.06	.05	.02
3T	Luis Alicea(FC)	.15	.11	.06
4T	Roberto Alomar(FC)	10.00	7.50	4.00
5T	Brady Anderson(FC)	1.50	1.25	.60
6T	Jack Armstrong(FC)	.25	.20	.10
7T	Don August	.15	.11	.06
8T	Floyd Bannister	.08	.06	.03
9T	Bret Barberie (U.S.A.)(FC)	.60	.45	.25
10T	Jose Bautista(FC)	.15	.11	.06
11T	Don Baylor	.10	.08	.04
12T	Tim Belcher	.20	.15	.08
13T	Buddy Bell	.10	.08	.04
14T	Andy Benes (U.S.A.)(FC)	3.00	2.25	1.25
15T	Damon Berryhill(FC)	.25	.20	.10
16T	Bud Black	.06	.05	.02
17T	Pat Borders(FC)	.30	.25	.12
18T	Phil Bradley	.10	.08	.04
19T	Jeff Branson (U.S.A.)(FC)	.20	.15	.08
20T	Tom Brunansky	.12	.09	.05
21T	Jay Buhner(FC)	.40	.30	.15
22T	Brett Butler	.08	.06	.03
23T	Jim Campanis (U.S.A.)(FC)	.20	.15	.08
24T	Sil Campusano(FC)	.20	.15	.08
25T	John Candelaria	.08	.06	.03
26T	Jose Cecena(FC)	.15	.11	.06
27T	Rick Cerone	.06	.05	.02
28T	Jack Clark	.15	.11	.06
29T	Kevin Coffman(FC)	.10	.08	.04
30T	Pat Combs (U.S.A.)(FC)	.30	.25	.12
31T	Henry Cotto	.06	.05	.02
32T	Chili Davis	.08	.06	.03
33T	Mike Davis	.08	.06	.03
34T	Jose DeLeon	.08	.06	.03
35T	Richard Dotson	.10	.08	.04
36T	Cecil Espy(FC)	.08	.06	.03
37T	Tom Filer	.06	.05	.02
38T	Mike Fiore (U.S.A.)(FC)	.20	.15	.08
39T	Ron Gant(FC)	5.00	3.75	2.00
40T	Kirk Gibson	.20	.15	.08
41T	Rich Gossage	.15	.11	.06
42T	Mark Grace(FC)	2.00	1.50	.80
43T	Alfredo Griffin	.08	.06	.03
44T	Ty Griffin (U.S.A.)(FC)	.15	.11	.06
45T	Bryan Harvey(FC)	.40	.30	.15
46T	Ron Hassey	.06	.05	.02
47T	Ray Hayward(FC)	.08	.06	.03
48T	Dave Henderson	.20	.15	.08
49T	Tom Herr	.10	.08	.04
50T	Bob Horner	.10	.08	.04
51T	Ricky Horton	.08	.06	.03
52T	Jay Howell	.08	.06	.03
53T	Glenn Hubbard	.06	.05	.02
54T	Jeff Innis(FC)	.15	.11	.06
55T	Danny Jackson	.15	.11	.06
56T	Darrin Jackson(FC)	.10	.08	.04
57T	Roberto Kelly(FC)	1.00	.70	.40
58T	Ron Kittle	.10	.08	.04
59T	Ray Knight	.08	.06	.03
60T	Vance Law	.08	.06	.03
61T	Jeffrey Leonard	.08	.06	.03
62T	Mike Macfarlane(FC)	.25	.20	.10
63T	Scotti Madison(FC)	.15	.11	.06
64T	Kirt Manwaring(FC)	.20	.15	.08
65T	Mark Marquess (U.S.A.)	.06	.05	.02
66T	Tino Martinez (U.S.A.)(FC)	3.00	2.25	1.25
67T	Billy Masse (U.S.A.)(FC)	.30	.25	.12
68T	Jack McDowell(FC)	3.50	2.75	1.50
69T	Jack McKeon	.06	.05	.02
70T	Larry McWilliams	.06	.05	.02
71T	Mickey Morandini (U.S.A.)(FC)	.50	.40	.20
72T	Keith Moreland	.08	.06	.03
73T	Mike Morgan	.06	.05	.02
74T	Charles Nagy (U.S.A.)(FC)	2.00	1.50	.80
75T	Al Nipper	.06	.05	.02
76T	Russ Nixon	.06	.05	.02
77T	Jesse Orosco	.08	.06	.03
78T	Joe Orsulak	.06	.05	.02
79T	Dave Palmer	.06	.05	.02
80T	Mark Parent(FC)	.20	.15	.08
81T	Dave Parker	.12	.09	.05
82T	Dan Pasqua	.10	.08	.04
83T	Melido Perez(FC)	.40	.30	.15
84T	Steve Peters(FC)	.15	.11	.06
85T	Dan Petry	.08	.06	.03
86T	Gary Pettis	.08	.06	.03
87T	Jeff Pico(FC)	.20	.15	.08
88T	Jim Poole (U.S.A.)(FC)	.20	.15	.08
89T	Ted Power	.06	.05	.02
90T	Rafael Ramirez	.06	.05	.02
91T	Dennis Rasmussen	.10	.08	.04
92T	Jose Rijo	.08	.06	.03
93T	Earnie Riles	.06	.05	.02
94T	Luis Rivera(FC)	.08	.06	.03
95T	Doug Robbins (U.S.A.)(FC)	.20	.15	.08
96T	Frank Robinson	.10	.08	.04
97T	Cookie Rojas	.06	.05	.02
98T	Chris Sabo(FC)	1.00	.70	.40
99T	Mark Salas	.06	.05	.02
100T	Luis Salazar	.06	.05	.02
101T	Rafael Santana	.06	.05	.02
102T	Nelson Santovenia(FC)	.20	.15	.08
103T	Mackey Sasser(FC)	.25	.20	.10
104T	Calvin Schiraldi	.06	.05	.02
105T	Mike Schooler(FC)	.30	.25	.12
106T	Scott Servais (U.S.A.)(FC)	.30	.25	.12
107T	Dave Silvestri (U.S.A.)(FC)	.20	.15	.08
108T	Don Slaught	.06	.05	.02
109T	Joe Slusarski (U.S.A.)(FC)	.35	.25	.14
110T	Lee Smith	.10	.08	.04
111T	Pete Smith(FC)	.10	.08	.04
112T	Jim Snyder	.06	.05	.02
113T	Ed Sprague (U.S.A.)(FC)	.60	.45	.25
114T	Pete Stanicek(FC)	.15	.11	.06
115T	Kurt Stillwell	.10	.08	.04
116T	Todd Stottlemyre(FC)	.90	.70	.35
117T	Bill Swift	.06	.05	.02
118T	Pat Tabler	.08	.06	.03
119T	Scott Terry(FC)	.10	.08	.04
120T	Mickey Tettleton	.06	.05	.02
121T	Dickie Thon	.08	.06	.03
122T	Jeff Treadway(FC)	.20	.15	.08
123T	Willie Upshaw	.08	.06	.03
124T	Robin Ventura(FC)	12.00	9.00	4.75
125T	Ron Washington	.06	.05	.02
126T	Walt Weiss(FC)	.30	.25	.12
127T	Bob Welch	.10	.08	.04
128T	David Wells(FC)	.15	.11	.06
129T	Glenn Wilson	.08	.06	.03
130T	Ted Wood (U.S.A.)(FC)	.30	.25	.12
131T	Don Zimmer	.06	.05	.02
132T	Checklist 1T-132T	.06	.05	.02

1989 Topps

Ten top young players who led the June 1988 draft picks are featured on "#1 Draft Pick" cards in this full-color basic set of 792 standard-size baseball cards. An additional five cards salute 1989 Future Stars, 22 cards highlight All-Stars, seven contain Record Breakers, five are designated Turn Back The Clock, and six contain checklists. This set features the familiar white borders, but two inner photo corners (upper left and lower right) have been rounded off and the rectangular player name was replaced by a curved name banner in bright red or blue that leads to the team name in large script in the lower right corner. The card backs are printed in black on a red background and include personal information and complete minor and major league stats. Another new addition in this set is the special Monthly Scoreboard chart that lists monthly stats (April through September) in two of several categories (hits, run, home runs, stolen bases, RBIs, wins, strikeouts, games or saves).

		MT	NR MT	EX
	Complete Set:	20.00	15.00	8.00
	Common Player:	.03	.02	.01
1	Record Breaker (George Bell)	.08	.06	.03
2	Record Breaker (Wade Boggs)	.20	.15	.08
3	Record Breaker (Gary Carter)	.10	.08	.04
4	Record Breaker (Andre Dawson)	.08	.06	.03
5	Record Breaker (Orel Hershiser)	.10	.08	.04
6	Record Breaker (Doug Jones)	.06	.05	.02
7	Record Breaker (Kevin McReynolds)	.08	.06	.03
8	*Dave Eiland*(FC)	.20	.15	.08
9	Tim Teufel	.03	.02	.01
10	Andre Dawson	.15	.11	.06
11	Bruce Sutter	.08	.06	.03
12	Dale Sveum	.06	.05	.02
13	Doug Sisk	.03	.02	.01
14	Tom Kelly	.03	.02	.01
15	Robby Thompson	.06	.05	.02
16	Ron Robinson	.03	.02	.01
17	Brian Downing	.06	.05	.02
18	Rick Rhoden	.06	.05	.02
19	Greg Gagne	.03	.02	.01
20	Steve Bedrosian	.08	.06	.03
21	White Sox Leaders (Greg Walker)	.06	.05	.02
22	Tim Crews	.06	.05	.02
23	Mike Fitzgerald	.03	.02	.01
24	Larry Andersen	.03	.02	.01
25	Frank White	.06	.05	.02
26	Dale Mohorcic	.03	.02	.01
27	*Orestes Destrade*(FC)	.12	.09	.05
28	Mike Moore	.03	.02	.01
29	Kelly Gruber	.03	.02	.01
30	Doc Gooden	.20	.15	.08
31	Terry Francona	.03	.02	.01
32	Dennis Rasmussen	.08	.06	.03
33	B.J. Surhoff	.08	.06	.03
34	Ken Williams	.06	.05	.02
35	John Tudor	.08	.06	.03
36	Mitch Webster	.06	.05	.02
37	Bob Stanley	.03	.02	.01
38	Paul Runge	.03	.02	.01
39	Mike Maddux	.03	.02	.01
40	Steve Sax	.12	.09	.05
41	Terry Mulholland	.03	.02	.01
42	Jim Eppard(FC)	.08	.06	.03
43	Guillermo Hernandez	.06	.05	.02
44	Jim Snyder	.03	.02	.01
45	Kal Daniels	.12	.09	.05
46	Mark Portugal	.03	.02	.01
47	Carney Lansford	.06	.05	.02
48	Tim Burke	.03	.02	.01
49	*Craig Biggio*(FC)	.35	.25	.12
50	George Bell	.20	.15	.08
51	Angels Leaders (Mark McLemore)	.06	.05	.02
52	Bob Brenly	.03	.02	.01
53	Ruben Sierra	.30	.25	.12
54	Steve Trout	.03	.02	.01
55	Julio Franco	.08	.06	.03
56	Pat Tabler	.06	.05	.02
57	Alejandro Pena	.06	.05	.02
58	Lee Mazzilli	.06	.05	.02
59	Mark Davis	.03	.02	.01
60	Tom Brunansky	.10	.08	.04
61	Neil Allen	.03	.02	.01
62	Alfredo Griffin	.06	.05	.02
63	Mark Clear	.03	.02	.01
64	Alex Trevino	.03	.02	.01
65	Rick Reuschel	.08	.06	.03
66	Manny Trillo	.03	.02	.01
67	Dave Palmer	.03	.02	.01
68	Darrell Miller	.03	.02	.01
69	Jeff Ballard	.06	.05	.02
70	Mark McGwire	.25	.20	.10
71	Mike Boddicker	.06	.05	.02
72	John Moses	.03	.02	.01
73	Pascual Perez	.06	.05	.02

		MT	NR MT	EX
74	Nick Leyva	.03	.02	.01
75	Tom Henke	.06	.05	.02
76	*Terry Blocker*(FC)	.12	.09	.05
77	Doyle Alexander	.06	.05	.02
78	Jim Sundberg	.06	.05	.02
79	Scott Bankhead	.03	.02	.01
80	Cory Snyder	.15	.11	.06
81	Expos Leaders (Tim Raines)	.08	.06	.03
82	Dave Leiper	.03	.02	.01
83	Jeff Blauser(FC)	.15	.11	.06
84	#1 Draft Pick *(Bill Bene)*(FC)	.15	.11	.06
85	Kevin McReynolds	.12	.09	.05
86	Al Nipper	.03	.02	.01
87	Larry Owen	.03	.02	.01
88	*Darryl Hamilton*(FC)	.35	.25	.14
89	Dave LaPoint	.06	.05	.02
90	Vince Coleman	.12	.09	.05
91	Floyd Youmans	.03	.02	.01
92	Jeff Kunkel	.03	.02	.01
93	Ken Howell	.03	.02	.01
94	Chris Speier	.03	.02	.01
95	Gerald Young	.10	.08	.04
96	Rick Cerone	.03	.02	.01
97	Greg Mathews	.06	.05	.02
98	Larry Sheets	.06	.05	.02
99	*Sherman Corbett*(FC)	.12	.09	.05
100	Mike Schmidt	.35	.25	.14
101	Les Straker	.06	.05	.02
102	Mike Gallego	.03	.02	.01
103	Tim Birtsas	.03	.02	.01
104	Dallas Green	.03	.02	.01
105	Ron Darling	.10	.08	.04
106	Willie Upshaw	.06	.05	.02
107	Jose DeLeon	.06	.05	.02
108	Fred Manrique	.06	.05	.02
109	*Hipolito Pena*(FC)	.12	.09	.05
110	Paul Molitor	.12	.09	.05
111	Reds Leaders (Eric Davis)	.10	.08	.04
112	Jim Presley	.06	.05	.02
113	Lloyd Moseby	.06	.05	.02
114	Bob Kipper	.03	.02	.01
115	Jody Davis	.06	.05	.02
116	Jeff Montgomery	.06	.05	.02
117	Dave Anderson	.03	.02	.01
118	Checklist 1-132	.03	.02	.01
119	Terry Puhl	.03	.02	.01
120	Frank Viola	.12	.09	.05
121	Garry Templeton	.06	.05	.02
122	Lance Johnson(FC)	.10	.08	.04
123	Spike Owen	.03	.02	.01
124	Jim Traber	.06	.05	.02
125	Mike Krukow	.06	.05	.02
126	Sid Bream	.06	.05	.02
127	Walt Terrell	.06	.05	.02
128	Milt Thompson	.03	.02	.01
129	*Terry Clark*(FC)	.12	.09	.05
130	Gerald Perry	.08	.06	.03
131	Dave Otto(FC)	.08	.06	.03
132	Curt Ford	.03	.02	.01
133	Bill Long	.06	.05	.02
134	Don Zimmer	.03	.02	.01
135	Jose Rijo	.06	.05	.02
136	Joey Meyer	.08	.06	.03
137	Geno Petralli	.03	.02	.01
138	Wallace Johnson	.03	.02	.01
139	Mike Flanagan	.06	.05	.02
140	Shawon Dunston	.08	.06	.03
141	Indians Leaders (Brook Jacoby)	.06	.05	.02
142	Mike Diaz	.06	.05	.02
143	Mike Campbell	.08	.06	.03
144	Jay Bell	.06	.05	.02
145	Dave Stewart	.08	.06	.03
146	Gary Pettis	.03	.02	.01
147	DeWayne Buice	.03	.02	.01
148	Bill Pecota	.06	.05	.02
149	*Doug Dascenzo*(FC)	.20	.15	.08
150	Fernando Valenzuela	.15	.11	.06
151	Terry McGriff	.03	.02	.01
152	Mark Thurmond	.03	.02	.01
153	Jim Pankovits	.03	.02	.01
154	Don Carman	.06	.05	.02
155	Marty Barrett	.06	.05	.02
156	*Dave Gallagher*(FC)	.15	.11	.06
157	Tom Glavine	.08	.06	.03
158	Mike Aldrete	.06	.05	.02
159	Pat Clements	.03	.02	.01
160	Jeffrey Leonard	.06	.05	.02
161	#1 Draft Pick *(Gregg Olson)*(FC)	.40	.30	.15
162	John Davis	.03	.02	.01
163	Bob Forsch	.06	.05	.02
164	Hal Lanier	.03	.02	.01

#	Player	MT	NR MT	EX
165	Mike Dunne	.08	.06	.03
166	*Doug Jennings*(FC)	.12	.09	.05
167	Future Star *(Steve Searcy)*(FC)	.25	.20	.10
168	Willie Wilson	.08	.06	.03
169	Mike Jackson	.06	.05	.02
170	Tony Fernandez	.10	.08	.04
171	Braves Leaders (Andres Thomas)	.06	.05	.02
172	Frank Williams	.03	.02	.01
173	Mel Hall	.06	.05	.02
174	*Todd Burns*(FC)	.12	.09	.05
175	John Shelby	.03	.02	.01
176	Jeff Parrett	.08	.06	.03
177	#1 Draft Pick *(Monty Fariss)*(FC)	.25	.20	.10
178	Mark Grant	.03	.02	.01
179	Ozzie Virgil	.03	.02	.01
180	Mike Scott	.10	.08	.04
181	*Craig Worthington*(FC)	.12	.09	.05
182	Bob McClure	.03	.02	.01
183	Oddibe McDowell	.06	.05	.02
184	*John Costello*	.20	.15	.08
185	Claudell Washington	.06	.05	.02
186	Pat Perry	.03	.02	.01
187	Darren Daulton	.03	.02	.01
188	Dennis Lamp	.03	.02	.01
189	Kevin Mitchell	.20	.15	.08
190	Mike Witt	.06	.05	.02
191	*Sil Campusano*	.20	.15	.08
192	Paul Mirabella	.03	.02	.01
193	Sparky Anderson	.06	.05	.02
194	*Greg Harris*(FC)	.25	.20	.10
195	Ozzie Guillen	.06	.05	.02
196	Denny Walling	.03	.02	.01
197	Neal Heaton	.03	.02	.01
198	Danny Heep	.03	.02	.01
199	*Mike Schooler*	.30	.25	.12
200	George Brett	.30	.25	.12
201	Blue Jays Leaders (Kelly Gruber)	.06	.05	.02
202	*Brad Moore*(FC)	.12	.09	.05
203	Rob Ducey	.03	.02	.01
204	Brad Havens	.03	.02	.01
205	Dwight Evans	.10	.08	.04
206	Roberto Alomar	.50	.40	.20
207	Terry Leach	.03	.02	.01
208	Tom Pagnozzi	.06	.05	.02
209	*Jeff Bittiger*(FC)	.12	.09	.05
210	Dale Murphy	.30	.25	.12
211	Mike Pagliarulo	.08	.06	.03
212	Scott Sanderson	.03	.02	.01
213	Rene Gonzales	.06	.05	.02
214	Charlie O'Brien	.03	.02	.01
215	Kevin Gross	.06	.05	.02
216	Jack Howell	.06	.05	.02
217	Joe Price	.03	.02	.01
218	Mike LaValliere	.06	.05	.02
219	Jim Clancy	.06	.05	.02
220	Gary Gaetti	.12	.09	.05
221	Cecil Espy	.08	.06	.03
222	#1 Draft Pick *(Mark Lewis)*(FC)	.70	.50	.30
223	Jay Buhner	.10	.08	.04
224	Tony LaRussa	.06	.05	.02
225	*Ramon Martinez*(FC)	.80	.60	.30
226	Bill Doran	.06	.05	.02
227	John Farrell	.08	.06	.03
228	*Nelson Santovenia*	.15	.11	.06
229	Jimmy Key	.08	.06	.03
230	Ozzie Smith	.12	.09	.05
231	Padres Leaders (Roberto Alomar)	.10	.08	.04
232	Ricky Horton	.06	.05	.02
233	Future Star (Gregg Jefferies)(FC)	.30	.25	.12
234	Tom Browning	.08	.06	.03
235	John Kruk	.06	.05	.02
236	Charles Hudson	.03	.02	.01
237	Glenn Hubbard	.03	.02	.01
238	Eric King	.03	.02	.01
239	Tim Laudner	.03	.02	.01
240	Greg Maddux	.10	.08	.04
241	Brett Butler	.06	.05	.02
242	Ed Vande Berg	.03	.02	.01
243	Bob Boone	.06	.05	.02
244	Jim Acker	.03	.02	.01
245	Jim Rice	.20	.15	.08
246	Rey Quinones	.03	.02	.01
247	Shawn Hillegas	.06	.05	.02
248	Tony Phillips	.03	.02	.01
249	Tim Leary	.06	.05	.02
250	Cal Ripken	.40	.30	.15
251	*John Dopson*(FC)	.20	.15	.08
252	Billy Hatcher	.06	.05	.02
253	*Jose Alvarez*(FC)	.12	.09	.05
254	Tom LaSorda	.06	.05	.02
255	Ron Guidry	.12	.09	.05
256	Benny Santiago	.12	.09	.05
257	Rick Aguilera	.03	.02	.01
258	Checklist 133-264	.03	.02	.01
259	Larry McWilliams	.03	.02	.01
260	Dave Winfield	.25	.20	.10
261	Cardinals Leaders (Tom Brunansky)	.06	.05	.02
262	*Jeff Pico*	.15	.11	.06
263	Mike Felder	.03	.02	.01
264	*Rob Dibble*(FC)	.40	.30	.15
265	Kent Hrbek	.15	.11	.06
266	Luis Aquino	.03	.02	.01
267	Jeff Robinson	.06	.05	.02
268	Keith Miller	.06	.05	.02
269	Tom Bolton	.06	.05	.02
270	Wally Joyner	.20	.15	.08
271	Jay Tibbs	.03	.02	.01
272	Ron Hassey	.03	.02	.01
273	Jose Lind	.08	.06	.03
274	Mark Eichhorn	.06	.05	.02
275	Danny Tartabull	.15	.11	.06
276	Paul Kilgus	.08	.06	.03
277	Mike Davis	.06	.05	.02
278	Andy McGaffigan	.03	.02	.01
279	Scott Bradley	.03	.02	.01
280	Bob Knepper	.06	.05	.02
281	Gary Redus	.03	.02	.01
282	*Cris Carpenter*(FC)	.15	.11	.06
283	Andy Allanson	.03	.02	.01
284	Jim Leyland	.03	.02	.01
285	John Candelaria	.06	.05	.02
286	Darrin Jackson	.08	.06	.03
287	Juan Nieves	.06	.05	.02
288	Pat Sheridan	.03	.02	.01
289	Ernie Whitt	.06	.05	.02
290	John Franco	.08	.06	.03
291	Mets Leaders (Darryl Strawberry)	.12	.09	.05
292	*Jim Corsi*(FC)	.15	.11	.06
293	Glenn Wilson	.06	.05	.02
294	Juan Berenguer	.03	.02	.01
295	Scott Fletcher	.06	.05	.02
296	Ron Gant	.40	.30	.15
297	*Oswald Peraza*(FC)	.15	.11	.06
298	Chris James	.08	.06	.03
299	*Steve Ellsworth*(FC)	.12	.09	.05
300	Darryl Strawberry	.35	.25	.14
301	Charlie Leibrandt	.06	.05	.02
302	Gary Ward	.06	.05	.02
303	Felix Fermin	.06	.05	.02
304	Joel Youngblood	.03	.02	.01
305	Dave Smith	.06	.05	.02
306	Tracy Woodson(FC)	.10	.08	.04
307	Lance McCullers	.06	.05	.02
308	Ron Karkovice	.03	.02	.01
309	Mario Diaz(FC)	.10	.08	.04
310	Rafael Palmeiro	.20	.15	.08
311	Chris Bosio	.03	.02	.01
312	Tom Lawless	.03	.02	.01
313	Denny Martinez	.06	.05	.02
314	Bobby Valentine	.03	.02	.01
315	Greg Swindell	.10	.08	.04
316	Walt Weiss	.20	.15	.08
317	*Jack Armstrong*	.35	.25	.14
318	Gene Larkin	.08	.06	.03
319	Greg Booker	.03	.02	.01
320	Lou Whitaker	.15	.11	.06
321	Red Sox Leaders (Jody Reed)	.06	.05	.02
322	John Smiley	.10	.08	.04
323	Gary Thurman	.10	.08	.04
324	*Bob Milacki*(FC)	.25	.20	.10
325	Jesse Barfield	.08	.06	.03
326	Dennis Boyd	.06	.05	.02
327	*Mark Lemke*(FC)	.20	.15	.08
328	Rick Honeycutt	.03	.02	.01
329	Bob Melvin	.03	.02	.01
330	Eric Davis	.35	.25	.14
331	Curt Wilkerson	.03	.02	.01
332	Tony Armas	.06	.05	.02
333	Bob Ojeda	.06	.05	.02
334	Steve Lyons	.03	.02	.01
335	Dave Righetti	.10	.08	.04
336	Steve Balboni	.06	.05	.02
337	Calvin Schiraldi	.03	.02	.01
338	Jim Adduci(FC)	.06	.05	.02
339	Scott Bailes	.03	.02	.01
340	Kirk Gibson	.15	.11	.06
341	Jim Deshaies	.03	.02	.01
342	Tom Brookens	.03	.02	.01
343	Future Star *(Gary Sheffield)*(FC)	1.25	.90	.50
344	Tom Trebelhorn	.03	.02	.01
345	Charlie Hough	.06	.05	.02

#	Player	MT	NR MT	EX
346	Rex Hudler(FC)	.06	.05	.02
347	John Cerutti	.06	.05	.02
348	Ed Hearn	.03	.02	.01
349	Ron Jones(FC)	.15	.11	.06
350	Andy Van Slyke	.12	.09	.05
351	Giants Leaders (Bob Melvin)	.06	.05	.02
352	Rick Schu	.03	.02	.01
353	Marvell Wynne	.03	.02	.01
354	Larry Parrish	.06	.05	.02
355	Mark Langston	.08	.06	.03
356	Kevin Elster	.08	.06	.03
357	Jerry Reuss	.06	.05	.02
358	Ricky Jordan(FC)	.40	.30	.15
359	Tommy John	.10	.08	.04
360	Ryne Sandberg	.30	.25	.12
361	Kelly Downs	.08	.06	.03
362	Jack Lazorko	.03	.02	.01
363	Rich Yett	.03	.02	.01
364	Rob Deer	.06	.05	.02
365	Mike Henneman	.08	.06	.03
366	Herm Winningham	.03	.02	.01
367	Johnny Paredes(FC)	.15	.11	.06
368	Brian Holton	.06	.05	.02
369	Ken Caminiti	.06	.05	.02
370	Dennis Eckersley	.10	.08	.04
371	Manny Lee	.03	.02	.01
372	Craig Lefferts	.03	.02	.01
373	Tracy Jones	.08	.06	.03
374	John Wathan	.06	.05	.02
375	Terry Pendleton	.08	.06	.03
376	Steve Lombardozzi	.03	.02	.01
377	Mike Smithson	.03	.02	.01
378	Checklist 265-396	.03	.02	.01
379	Tim Flannery	.03	.02	.01
380	Rickey Henderson	.30	.25	.12
381	Orioles Leaders (Larry Sheets)	.06	.05	.02
382	John Smoltz(FC)	.70	.50	.30
383	Howard Johnson	.08	.06	.03
384	Mark Salas	.03	.02	.01
385	Von Hayes	.08	.06	.03
386	Andres Galarraga AS	.08	.06	.03
387	Ryne Sandberg AS	.10	.08	.04
388	Bobby Bonilla AS	.08	.06	.03
389	Ozzie Smith AS	.08	.06	.03
390	Darryl Strawberry AS	.15	.11	.06
391	Andre Dawson AS	.10	.08	.04
392	Andy Van Slyke AS	.08	.06	.03
393	Gary Carter AS	.10	.08	.04
394	Orel Hershiser AS	.12	.09	.05
395	Danny Jackson AS	.08	.06	.03
396	Kirk Gibson AS	.08	.06	.03
397	Don Mattingly AS	.30	.25	.12
398	Julio Franco AS	.06	.05	.02
399	Wade Boggs AS	.20	.15	.08
400	Alan Trammell AS	.08	.06	.03
401	Jose Canseco AS	.30	.25	.12
402	Mike Greenwell AS	.15	.11	.06
403	Kirby Puckett AS	.12	.09	.05
404	Bob Boone AS	.06	.05	.02
405	Roger Clemens AS	.15	.11	.06
406	Frank Viola AS	.08	.06	.03
407	Dave Winfield AS	.12	.09	.05
408	Greg Walker	.06	.05	.02
409	Ken Dayley	.03	.02	.01
410	Jack Clark	.12	.09	.05
411	Mitch Williams	.06	.05	.02
412	Barry Lyons	.03	.02	.01
413	Mike Kingery	.03	.02	.01
414	Jim Fregosi	.03	.02	.01
415	Rich Gossage	.10	.08	.04
416	Fred Lynn	.10	.08	.04
417	Mike LaCoss	.03	.02	.01
418	Bob Dernier	.03	.02	.01
419	Tom Filer	.03	.02	.01
420	Joe Carter	.10	.08	.04
421	Kirk McCaskill	.06	.05	.02
422	Bo Diaz	.06	.05	.02
423	Brian Fisher	.06	.05	.02
424	Luis Polonia	.06	.05	.02
425	Jay Howell	.06	.05	.02
426	Danny Gladden	.03	.02	.01
427	Eric Show	.06	.05	.02
428	Craig Reynolds	.03	.02	.01
429	Twins Leaders (Greg Gagne)	.06	.05	.02
430	Mark Gubicza	.08	.06	.03
431	Luis Rivera	.06	.05	.02
432	Chad Kreuter(FC)	.15	.11	.06
433	Albert Hall	.03	.02	.01
434	Ken Patterson(FC)	.15	.11	.06
435	Len Dykstra	.08	.06	.03
436	Bobby Meacham	.03	.02	.01
437	#1 Draft Pick (Andy Benes)	.70	.50	.30
438	Greg Gross	.03	.02	.01
439	Frank DiPino	.03	.02	.01
440	Bobby Bonilla	.25	.20	.10
441	Jerry Reed	.03	.02	.01
442	Jose Oquendo	.03	.02	.01
443	Rod Nichols(FC)	.15	.11	.06
444	Moose Stubing	.03	.02	.01
445	Matt Nokes	.15	.11	.06
446	Rob Murphy	.03	.02	.01
447	Donell Nixon	.03	.02	.01
448	Eric Plunk	.03	.02	.01
449	Carmelo Martinez	.03	.02	.01
450	Roger Clemens	.40	.30	.15
451	Mark Davidson	.06	.05	.02
452	Israel Sanchez	.12	.09	.05
453	Tom Prince(FC)	.08	.06	.03
454	Paul Assenmacher	.03	.02	.01
455	Johnny Ray	.06	.05	.02
456	Tim Belcher	.08	.06	.03
457	Mackey Sasser	.06	.05	.02
458	Donn Pall(FC)	.12	.09	.05
459	Mariners Leaders (Dave Valle)	.06	.05	.02
460	Dave Stieb	.08	.06	.03
461	Buddy Bell	.06	.05	.02
462	Jose Guzman	.08	.06	.03
463	Steve Lake	.03	.02	.01
464	Bryn Smith	.03	.02	.01
465	Mark Grace	.70	.50	.30
466	Chuck Crim	.03	.02	.01
467	Jim Walewander	.03	.02	.01
468	Henry Cotto	.03	.02	.01
469	Jose Bautista	.20	.15	.08
470	Lance Parrish	.12	.09	.05
471	Steve Curry(FC)	.15	.11	.06
472	Brian Harper	.03	.02	.01
473	Don Robinson	.03	.02	.01
474	Bob Rodgers	.03	.02	.01
475	Dave Parker	.10	.08	.04
476	Jon Perlman(FC)	.06	.05	.02
477	Dick Schofield	.03	.02	.01
478	Doug Drabek	.06	.05	.02
479	Mike Macfarlane	.25	.20	.10
480	Keith Hernandez	.15	.11	.06
481	Chris Brown	.06	.05	.02
482	Steve Peters	.12	.09	.05
483	Mickey Hatcher	.03	.02	.01
484	Steve Shields	.03	.02	.01
485	Hubie Brooks	.08	.06	.03
486	Jack McDowell	.20	.15	.08
487	Scott Lusader(FC)	.08	.06	.03
488	Kevin Coffman	.06	.05	.02
489	Phillies Leaders (Mike Schmidt)	.12	.09	.05
490	Chris Sabo	.40	.30	.15
491	Mike Birkbeck	.03	.02	.01
492	Alan Ashby	.03	.02	.01
493	Todd Benzinger	.10	.08	.04
494	Shane Rawley	.06	.05	.02
495	Candy Maldonado	.06	.05	.02
496	Dwayne Henry	.03	.02	.01
497	Pete Stanicek	.12	.09	.05
498	Dave Valle	.03	.02	.01
499	Don Heinkel(FC)	.15	.11	.06
500	Jose Canseco	.40	.30	.15
501	Vance Law	.06	.05	.02
502	Duane Ward	.03	.02	.01
503	Al Newman	.03	.02	.01
504	Bob Walk	.03	.02	.01
505	Pete Rose	.20	.15	.08
506	Kirt Manwaring	.10	.08	.04
507	Steve Farr	.03	.02	.01
508	Wally Backman	.06	.05	.02
509	Bud Black	.03	.02	.01
510	Bob Horner	.08	.06	.03
511	Richard Dotson	.06	.05	.02
512	Donnie Hill	.03	.02	.01
513	Jesse Orosco	.06	.05	.02
514	Chet Lemon	.06	.05	.02
515	Barry Larkin	.20	.15	.08
516	Eddie Whitson	.03	.02	.01
517	Greg Brock	.06	.05	.02
518	Bruce Ruffin	.03	.02	.01
519	Yankees Leaders (Willie Randolph)	.03	.02	.01
520	Rick Sutcliffe	.08	.06	.03
521	Mickey Tettleton	.03	.02	.01
522	Randy Kramer(FC)	.12	.09	.05
523	Andres Thomas	.06	.05	.02
524	Checklist 397-528	.03	.02	.01
525	Chili Davis	.06	.05	.02
526	Wes Gardner	.06	.05	.02
527	Dave Henderson	.08	.06	.03

		MT	NR MT	EX
528	Luis Medina(FC)	.15	.11	.06
529	Tom Foley	.03	.02	.01
530	Nolan Ryan	.50	.40	.20
531	Dave Hengel(FC)	.08	.06	.03
532	Jerry Browne	.03	.02	.01
533	Andy Hawkins	.03	.02	.01
534	Doc Edwards	.03	.02	.01
535	Todd Worrell	.08	.06	.03
536	Joel Skinner	.03	.02	.01
537	Pete Smith	.08	.06	.03
538	Juan Castillo	.03	.02	.01
539	Barry Jones	.03	.02	.01
540	Bo Jackson	.30	.25	.12
541	Cecil Fielder	.30	.25	.12
542	Todd Frohwirth	.06	.05	.02
543	Damon Berryhill	.15	.11	.06
544	Jeff Sellers	.03	.02	.01
545	Mookie Wilson	.06	.05	.02
546	Mark Williamson	.06	.05	.02
547	Mark McLemore	.03	.02	.01
548	Bobby Witt	.08	.06	.03
549	Cubs Leaders (Jamie Moyer)	.03	.02	.01
550	Orel Hershiser	.20	.15	.08
551	Randy Ready	.03	.02	.01
552	Greg Cadaret	.06	.05	.02
553	Luis Salazar	.03	.02	.01
554	Nick Esasky	.06	.05	.02
555	Bert Blyleven	.10	.08	.04
556	Bruce Fields(FC)	.06	.05	.02
557	Keith Miller(FC)	.15	.11	.06
558	Dan Pasqua	.08	.06	.03
559	Juan Agosto	.03	.02	.01
560	Rock Raines	.15	.11	.06
561	Luis Aguayo	.03	.02	.01
562	Danny Cox	.06	.05	.02
563	Bill Schroeder	.03	.02	.01
564	Russ Nixon	.03	.02	.01
565	Jeff Russell	.03	.02	.01
566	Al Pedrique	.03	.02	.01
567	David Wells	.08	.06	.03
568	Mickey Brantley	.03	.02	.01
569	German Jimenez(FC)	.08	.06	.03
570	Tony Gwynn	.30	.25	.12
571	Billy Ripken	.06	.05	.02
572	Atlee Hammaker	.03	.02	.01
573	#1 Draft Pick (Jim Abbott)	1.25	.90	.50
574	Dave Clark	.06	.05	.02
575	Juan Samuel	.10	.08	.04
576	Greg Minton	.03	.02	.01
577	Randy Bush	.03	.02	.01
578	John Morris	.03	.02	.01
579	Astros Leaders (Glenn Davis)	.08	.06	.03
580	Harold Reynolds	.06	.05	.02
581	Gene Nelson	.03	.02	.01
582	Mike Marshall	.10	.08	.04
583	Paul Gibson(FC)	.15	.11	.06
584	Randy Velarde(FC)	.10	.08	.04
585	Harold Baines	.10	.08	.04
586	Joe Boever	.03	.02	.01
587	Mike Stanley	.03	.02	.01
588	Luis Alicea	.15	.11	.06
589	Dave Meads	.03	.02	.01
590	Andres Galarraga	.12	.09	.05
591	Jeff Musselman	.06	.05	.02
592	John Cangelosi	.03	.02	.01
593	Drew Hall	.10	.08	.04
594	Jimy Williams	.03	.02	.01
595	Teddy Higuera	.08	.06	.03
596	Kurt Stillwell	.06	.05	.02
597	Terry Taylor(FC)	.12	.09	.05
598	Ken Gerhart	.06	.05	.02
599	Tom Candiotti	.03	.02	.01
600	Wade Boggs	.40	.30	.15
601	Dave Dravecky	.06	.05	.02
602	Devon White	.10	.08	.04
603	Frank Tanana	.06	.05	.02
604	Paul O'Neill	.03	.02	.01
605a	Bob Welch (missing Complete Major League Pitching Record line)	3.00	2.25	1.25
605b	Bob Welch (contains Complete Major League Pitching Record line)	.08	.06	.03
606	Rick Dempsey	.06	.05	.02
607	#1 Draft Pick (Willie Ansley)(FC)	.15	.11	.06
608	Phil Bradley	.08	.06	.03
609	Tigers Leaders (Frank Tanana)	.06	.05	.02
610	Randy Myers	.08	.06	.03
611	Don Slaught	.03	.02	.01
612	Dan Quisenberry	.06	.05	.02
613	Gary Varsho(FC)	.15	.11	.06
614	Joe Hesketh	.03	.02	.01
615	Robin Yount	.25	.20	.10
616	Steve Rosenberg(FC)	.15	.11	.06
617	Mark Parent	.15	.11	.06
618	Rance Mulliniks	.03	.02	.01
619	Checklist 529-660	.03	.02	.01
620	Barry Bonds	.20	.15	.08
621	Rick Mahler	.03	.02	.01
622	Stan Javier	.03	.02	.01
623	Fred Toliver	.03	.02	.01
624	Jack McKeon	.03	.02	.01
625	Eddie Murray	.25	.20	.10
626	Jeff Reed	.03	.02	.01
627	Greg Harris	.03	.02	.01
628	Matt Williams	.10	.08	.04
629	Pete O'Brien	.06	.05	.02
630	Mike Greenwell	.30	.25	.12
631	Dave Bergman	.03	.02	.01
632	Bryan Harvey	.25	.20	.10
633	Daryl Boston	.03	.02	.01
634	Marvin Freeman(FC)	.08	.06	.03
635	Willie Randolph	.06	.05	.02
636	Bill Wilkinson	.06	.05	.02
637	Carmen Castillo	.03	.02	.01
638	Floyd Bannister	.06	.05	.02
639	Athletics Leaders (Walt Weiss)	.15	.11	.06
640	Willie McGee	.10	.08	.04
641	Curt Young	.06	.05	.02
642	Argenis Salazar	.03	.02	.01
643	Louie Meadows(FC)	.12	.09	.05
644	Lloyd McClendon	.03	.02	.01
645	Jack Morris	.12	.09	.05
646	Kevin Bass	.06	.05	.02
647	Randy Johnson(FC)	.30	.25	.12
648	Future Star (Sandy Alomar)(FC)	.40	.30	.15
649	Stewart Cliburn	.03	.02	.01
650	Kirby Puckett	.25	.20	.10
651	Tom Niedenfuer	.06	.05	.02
652	Rich Gedman	.06	.05	.02
653	Tommy Barrett(FC)	.12	.09	.05
654	Whitey Herzog	.06	.05	.02
655	Dave Magadan	.08	.06	.03
656	Ivan Calderon	.06	.05	.02
657	Joe Magrane	.08	.06	.03
658	R.J. Reynolds	.03	.02	.01
659	Al Leiter	.15	.11	.06
660	Will Clark	.50	.40	.20
661	Turn Back The Clock (Dwight Gooden)	.10	.08	.04
662	Turn Back The Clock (Lou Brock)	.08	.06	.03
663	Turn Back The Clock (Hank Aaron)	.15	.11	.06
664	Turn Back The Clock (Gil Hodges)	.06	.05	.02
665	Turn Back The Clock (Tony Oliva)	.06	.05	.02
666	Randy St. Claire	.03	.02	.01
667	Dwayne Murphy	.06	.05	.02
668	Mike Bielecki	.03	.02	.01
669	Dodgers Leaders (Orel Hershiser)	.12	.09	.05
670	Kevin Seitzer	.12	.09	.05
671	Jim Gantner	.03	.02	.01
672	Allan Anderson	.06	.05	.02
673	Don Baylor	.08	.06	.03
674	Otis Nixon	.03	.02	.01
675	Bruce Hurst	.08	.06	.03
676	Ernie Riles	.03	.02	.01
677	Dave Schmidt	.03	.02	.01
678	Dion James	.03	.02	.01
679	Willie Fraser	.03	.02	.01
680	Gary Carter	.15	.11	.06
681	Jeff Robinson	.10	.08	.04
682	Rick Leach	.03	.02	.01
683	Jose Cecena	.15	.11	.06
684	Dave Johnson	.06	.05	.02
685	Jeff Treadway	.10	.08	.04
686	Scott Terry	.08	.06	.03
687	Alvin Davis	.10	.08	.04
688	Zane Smith	.06	.05	.02
689	Stan Jefferson	.03	.02	.01
690	Doug Jones	.10	.08	.04
691	Roberto Kelly	.25	.20	.10
692	Steve Ontiveros	.03	.02	.01
693	Pat Borders	.30	.25	.12
694	Les Lancaster	.06	.05	.02
695	Carlton Fisk	.20	.15	.08
696	Don August	.08	.06	.03
697	Franklin Stubbs	.03	.02	.01
698	Keith Atherton	.03	.02	.01
699	Pirates Leaders (Al Pedrique)	.06	.05	.02
700	Don Mattingly	.60	.45	.25
701	Storm Davis	.08	.06	.03
702	Jamie Quirk	.03	.02	.01
703	Scott Garrelts	.03	.02	.01
704	Carlos Quintana(FC)	.20	.15	.08
705	Terry Kennedy	.06	.05	.02

		MT	NR MT	EX
706	Pete Incaviglia	.08	.06	.03
707	Steve Jeltz	.03	.02	.01
708	Chuck Finley	.03	.02	.01
709	Tom Herr	.06	.05	.02
710	Dave Cone	.20	.15	.08
711	Candy Sierra(FC)	.12	.09	.05
712	Bill Swift	.03	.02	.01
713	#1 Draft Pick (Ty Griffin)	.10	.08	.04
714	Joe Morgan	.03	.02	.01
715	Tony Pena	.06	.05	.02
716	Wayne Tolleson	.03	.02	.01
717	Jamie Moyer	.03	.02	.01
718	Glenn Braggs	.06	.05	.02
719	Danny Darwin	.03	.02	.01
720	Tim Wallach	.08	.06	.03
721	Ron Tingley(FC)	.12	.09	.05
722	Todd Stottlemyre	.15	.11	.06
723	Rafael Belliard	.03	.02	.01
724	Jerry Don Gleaton	.03	.02	.01
725	Terry Steinbach	.08	.06	.03
726	Dickie Thon	.03	.02	.01
727	Joe Orsulak	.03	.02	.01
728	Charlie Puleo	.03	.02	.01
729	Rangers Leaders (Steve Buechele)	.06	.05	.02
730	Danny Jackson	.12	.09	.05
731	Mike Young	.03	.02	.01
732	Steve Buechele	.03	.02	.01
733	Randy Bockus(FC)	.06	.05	.02
734	Jody Reed	.10	.08	.04
735	Roger McDowell	.08	.06	.03
736	Jeff Hamilton	.06	.05	.02
737	Norm Charlton(FC)	.30	.25	.12
738	Darnell Coles	.06	.05	.02
739	Brook Jacoby	.08	.06	.03
740	Dan Plesac	.08	.06	.03
741	Ken Phelps	.06	.05	.02
742	Future Star (Mike Harkey)(FC)	.30	.25	.12
743	Mike Heath	.03	.02	.01
744	Roger Craig	.06	.05	.02
745	Fred McGriff	.30	.25	.12
746	German Gonzalez(FC)	.15	.11	.06
747	Wil Tejada(FC)	.06	.05	.02
748	Jimmy Jones	.03	.02	.01
749	Rafael Ramirez	.03	.02	.01
750	Bret Saberhagen	.12	.09	.05
751	Ken Oberkfell	.03	.02	.01
752	Jim Gott	.03	.02	.01
753	Jose Uribe	.03	.02	.01
754	Bob Brower	.03	.02	.01
755	Mike Scioscia	.06	.05	.02
756	Scott Medvin(FC)	.12	.09	.05
757	Brady Anderson	.50	.40	.20
758	Gene Walter	.03	.02	.01
759	Brewers Leaders (Rob Deer)	.06	.05	.02
760	Lee Smith	.08	.06	.03
761	Dante Bichette(FC)	.25	.20	.10
762	Bobby Thigpen	.08	.06	.03
763	Dave Martinez	.06	.05	.02
764	#1 Draft Pick (Robin Ventura)	2.50	2.00	1.00
765	Glenn Davis	.15	.11	.06
766	Cecilio Guante	.03	.02	.01
767	Mike Capel(FC)	.15	.11	.06
768	Bill Wegman	.03	.02	.01
769	Junior Ortiz	.03	.02	.01
770	Alan Trammell	.15	.11	.06
771	Ron Kittle	.06	.05	.02
772	Ron Oester	.03	.02	.01
773	Keith Moreland	.06	.05	.02
774	Frank Robinson	.08	.06	.03
775	Jeff Reardon	.08	.06	.03
776	Nelson Liriano	.06	.05	.02
777	Ted Power	.03	.02	.01
778	Bruce Benedict	.03	.02	.01
779	Craig McMurtry	.03	.02	.01
780	Pedro Guerrero	.12	.09	.05
781	Greg Briley(FC)	.30	.25	.12
782	Checklist 661-792	.03	.02	.01
783	Trevor Wilson(FC)	.20	.15	.08
784	#1 Draft Pick (Steve Avery)(FC)	1.50	1.25	.60
785	Ellis Burks	.40	.30	.15
786	Melido Perez	.08	.06	.03
787	Dave West(FC)	.20	.15	.08
788	Mike Morgan	.03	.02	.01
789	Royals Leaders (Bo Jackson)	.15	.11	.06
790	Sid Fernandez	.08	.06	.03
791	Jim Lindeman	.03	.02	.01
792	Rafael Santana	.03	.02	.01

Definitions for grading conditions are located in the Introduction of this price guide.

1989 Topps All-Star Glossy Set Of 22

Bearing the same design and style of the past two years, Topps featured the top first-year players from the 1988 season in this glossy set. The full-color player photos appears beneath the "1988 Rookies" banner. The player's name is displayed beneath the photo. The flip side features the "1988 Rookies Commemorative Set" logo followed by the player's name, position, team, and card number. The glossy All-Stars are included in the Topps 1989 Jumbo Paks.

		MT	NR MT	EX
Complete Set:		3.50	2.75	1.50
Common Player:		.15	.11	.06
1	Roberto Alomar	.25	.20	.10
2	Brady Anderson	.20	.15	.08
3	Tim Belcher	.20	.15	.08
4	Damon Berryhill	.15	.11	.06
5	Jay Buhner	.20	.15	.11
6	Kevin Elster	.15	.11	.06
7	Cecil Espy	.15	.11	.06
8	Dave Gallagher	.15	.11	.06
9	Ron Gant	.15	.11	.06
10	Paul Gibson	.15	.11	.06
11	Mark Grace	.60	.45	.25
12	Darrin Jackson	.15	.11	.06
13	Gregg Jefferies	.70	.50	.30
14	Ricky Jordan	.50	.40	.20
15	Al Leiter	.15	.11	.06
16	Melido Perez	.15	.11	.06
17	Chris Sabo	.35	.25	.14
18	Nelson Santovenia	.20	.15	.08
19	Mackey Sasser	.15	.11	.06
20	Gary Sheffield	.50	.40	.20
21	Walt Weiss	.15	.11	.06
22	David Wells	.15	.11	.06

1989 Topps All-Star Glossy Set Of 60

For the seventh straight year Topps issued this "send-away" glossy set. Divided into six 10-card sets, it was available only by sending in special offer cards from the 1989 Topps wax packs. The 2-1/2" by 3-1/2" cards feature full-color photos bordered in white with a thin yellow frame. The player's name appears in small print in the lower right corner. Red-and-blue-printed flip sides provide basic information including player's name, team, and position. Any of the six 10-card sets were available for $1.25 and six special offer cards. The set was also made available in its complete 60-card set form for $7.50 and 18 special offer cards.

		MT	NR MT	EX
	Complete Set:	10.00	7.50	4.00
	Common Player:	.15	.11	.06
1	Kirby Puckett	.50	.40	.20
2	Eric Davis	.70	.50	.30
3	Joe Carter	.20	.15	.08
4	Andy Van Slyke	.20	.15	.08
5	Wade Boggs	.70	.50	.30
6	Dave Cone	.25	.20	.10
7	Kent Hrbek	.15	.11	.06
8	Darryl Strawberry	.70	.50	.30
9	Jay Buhner	.15	.11	.06
10	Ron Gant	.30	.25	.12
11	Will Clark	1.00	.70	.40
12	Jose Canseco	1.25	.90	.50
13	Juan Samuel	.15	.11	.06
14	George Brett	.25	.20	.10
15	Benny Santiago	.20	.15	.08
16	Dennis Eckersley	.15	.11	.06
17	Gary Carter	.15	.11	.06
18	Frank Viola	.20	.15	.08
19	Roberto Alomar	.30	.25	.12
20	Paul Gibson	.15	.11	.06
21	Dave Winfield	.20	.15	.08
22	Howard Johnson	.35	.25	.14
23	Roger Clemens	.40	.30	.15
24	Bobby Bonilla	.25	.20	.10
25	Alan Trammell	.20	.15	.08
26	Kevin McReynolds	.20	.15	.08
27	George Bell	.20	.15	.08
28	Bruce Hurst	.15	.11	.06
29	Mark Grace	.70	.50	.30
30	Tim Belcher	.20	.15	.08
31	Mike Greenwell	.70	.50	.30
32	Glenn Davis	.15	.11	.06
33	Gary Gaetti	.15	.11	.06
34	Ryne Sandberg	.70	.50	.30
35	Rickey Henderson	.70	.50	.30
36	Dwight Evans	.15	.11	.06
37	Doc Gooden	.50	.40	.20
38	Robin Yount	.25	.20	.10
39	Damon Berryhill	.15	.11	.06
40	Chris Sabo	.20	.15	.11
41	Mark McGwire	.70	.50	.30
42	Ozzie Smith	.25	.20	.10
43	Paul Molitor	.20	.15	.08
44	Andres Galarraga	.30	.25	.12
45	Dave Stewart	.15	.11	.06
46	Tom Browning	.15	.11	.06
47	Cal Ripken	.50	.40	.20
48	Orel Hershiser	.40	.30	.15
49	Dave Gallagher	.15	.11	.06
50	Walt Weiss	.20	.15	.08
51	Don Mattingly	1.50	1.25	.60
52	Tony Fernandez	.20	.15	.08
53	Rock Raines	.20	.15	.08
54	Jeff Reardon	.15	.11	.06
55	Kirk Gibson	.20	.15	.08
56	Jack Clark	.20	.15	.08
57	Danny Jackson	.15	.11	.06
58	Tony Gwynn	.60	.45	.25
59	Cecil Espy	.15	.11	.06
60	Jody Reed	.15	.11	.06

1989 Topps Batting Leaders

The active career batting leaders are showcased in this 22-card set. The standard-size cards are printed on super glossy stock with full-color photos. A unique left-handed or right-handed batter creates one of the vertical borders. The Topps logo appears in the upper left portion of the photo, while a "Top Active Career Batting Leaders" cup is displayed in the lower left. The player's name appears above the photo. This set is specially numbered in accordance to career batting

average. Wade Boggs is featured on card number one as the top active career batting leader. The flip sides present batting statistics. One batting leader card was included in each K-mart blister pack, which also includes 100 cards from the 1989 regular Topps set.

		MT	NR MT	EX
	Complete Set:	25.00	18.00	9.00
	Common Player:	.40	.30	.15
1	Wade Boggs	2.00	1.50	.80
2	Tony Gwynn	2.00	1.50	.80
3	Don Mattingly	2.00	1.50	.80
4	Kirby Puckett	2.50	2.00	1.00
5	George Brett	2.00	1.50	.80
6	Pedro Guerrero	.40	.30	.15
7	Rock Raines	.50	.40	.20
8	Keith Hernandez	.40	.30	.15
9	Jim Rice	.50	.40	.20
10	Paul Molitor	1.50	1.25	.60
11	Eddie Murray	1.00	.70	.40
12	Willie McGee	.40	.30	.15
13	Dave Parker	.40	.30	.15
14	Julio Franco	.40	.30	.15
15	Rickey Henderson	1.50	1.25	.60
16	Kent Hrbek	.40	.30	.15
17	Willie Wilson	.40	.30	.15
18	Johnny Ray	.40	.30	.15
19	Pat Tabler	.40	.30	.15
20	Carney Lansford	.40	.30	.15
21	Robin Yount	2.50	2.00	1.00
22	Alan Trammell	1.00	.70	.40

1989 Topps Big Baseball

Known by collectors as Topps "Big Baseball," the cards in this 330-card set measure 2-5/8" by 3-3/4" and are patterned after the 1956 Topps cards. The glossy card fronts are horizontally-designed and include two photos of each player, a posed head shot alongside an action photo. The backs include 1988 and career stats, but are dominated by a color cartoon featuring the player. The set was issued in three series of 110 cards each.

		MT	NR MT	EX
	Complete Set:	20.00	15.00	8.00
	Common Player:	.05	.04	.02
1	Orel Hershiser	.15	.11	.06
2	Harold Reynolds	.08	.06	.03
3	Jody Davis	.05	.04	.02
4	Greg Walker	.05	.04	.02
5	Barry Bonds	.08	.06	.03
6	Bret Saberhagen	.12	.09	.05
7	Johnny Ray	.05	.04	.02
8	Mike Fiore	.20	.15	.08
9	Juan Castillo	.05	.04	.02
10	Todd Burns	.05	.04	.02
11	Carmelo Martinez	.05	.04	.02
12	Geno Petralli	.05	.04	.02
13	Mel Hall	.05	.04	.02
14	Tom Browning	.08	.06	.03
15	Fred McGriff	.15	.11	.06
16	Kevin Elster	.05	.04	.02
17	Tim Leary	.05	.04	.02
18	Jim Rice	.05	.04	.02
19	Bret Barberie	.15	.11	.06
20	Jay Buhner	.05	.04	.02
21	Atlee Hammaker	.05	.04	.02
22	Lou Whitaker	.05	.04	.02
23	Paul Runge	.05	.04	.02
24	Carlton Fisk	.08	.06	.03
25	Jose Lind	.05	.04	.02
26	Mark Gubicza	.08	.06	.03
27	Billy Ripken	.05	.04	.02
28	Mike Pagliarulo	.05	.04	.02
29	Jim Deshaies	.05	.04	.02
30	Mark McLemore	.05	.04	.02
31	Scott Terry	.05	.04	.02
32	Franklin Stubbs	.05	.04	.02
33	Don August	.05	.04	.02
34	Mark McGwire	1.00	.70	.40
35	Eric Show	.05	.04	.02
36	Cecil Espy	.05	.04	.02
37	Ron Tingley	.05	.04	.02
38	Mickey Brantley	.05	.04	.02
39	Paul O'Neill	.05	.04	.02
40	Ed Sprague	.35	.25	.14
41	Len Dykstra	.05	.04	.02
42	Roger Clemens	.25	.20	.10
43	Ron Gant	.05	.04	.02
44	Dan Pasqua	.05	.04	.02
45	Jeff Robinson	.05	.04	.02
46	George Brett	.15	.11	.06
47	Bryn Smith	.05	.04	.02
48	Mike Marshall	.05	.04	.02
49	Doug Robbins	.15	.11	.06
50	Don Mattingly	1.50	1.25	.60
51	Mike Scott	.08	.06	.03
52	Steve Jeltz	.05	.04	.02
53	Dick Schofield	.05	.04	.02
54	Tom Brunansky	.08	.06	.03
55	Gary Sheffield	1.00	.70	.40
56	Dave Valle	.05	.04	.02
57	Carney Lansford	.08	.06	.03
58	Tony Gwynn	.15	.11	.06
59	Checklist	.05	.04	.02
60	Damon Berryhill	.05	.04	.02
61	Jack Morris	.05	.04	.02
62	Brett Butler	.05	.04	.02
63	Mickey Hatcher	.05	.04	.02
64	Bruce Sutter	.05	.04	.02
65	Robin Ventura	.80	.60	.30
66	Junior Ortiz	.05	.04	.02
67	Pat Tabler	.05	.04	.02
68	Greg Swindell	.08	.06	.03
69	Jeff Branson	.20	.15	.08
70	Manny Lee	.05	.04	.02
71	Dave Magadan	.05	.04	.02
72	Rich Gedman	.05	.04	.02
73	Rock Raines	.08	.06	.03
74	Mike Maddux	.05	.04	.02
75	Jim Presley	.05	.04	.02
76	Chuck Finley	.05	.04	.02
77	Jose Oquendo	.05	.04	.02
78	Rob Deer	.05	.04	.02
79	Jay Howell	.05	.04	.02
80	Terry Steinbach	.08	.06	.03
81	Eddie Whitson	.05	.04	.02
82	Ruben Sierra	.20	.15	.08
83	Bruce Benedict	.05	.04	.02
84	Fred Manrique	.05	.04	.02
85	John Smiley	.05	.04	.02
86	Mike Macfarlane	.05	.04	.02
87	Rene Gonzales	.05	.04	.02
88	Charles Hudson	.05	.04	.02
90	Les Straker	.05	.04	.02
91	Carmen Castillo	.05	.04	.02
92	Tracy Woodson	.05	.04	.02
93	Tino Martinez	.70	.50	.30
94	Herm Winningham	.05	.04	.02
95	Kelly Gruber	.05	.04	.02
96	Terry Leach	.05	.04	.02
97	Jody Reed	.05	.04	.02
98	Nelson Santovenia	.05	.04	.02
99	Tony Armas	.05	.04	.02
100	Greg Brock	.05	.04	.02
101	Dave Stewart	.05	.04	.02
102	Roberto Alomar	.08	.06	.03
103	Jim Sundberg	.05	.04	.02
104	Albert Hall	.05	.04	.02
105	Steve Lyons	.05	.04	.02
106	Sid Bream	.05	.04	.02
107	Danny Tartabull	.08	.06	.03
108	Rick Dempsey	.05	.04	.02
109	Rich Renteria	.05	.04	.02
110	Ozzie Smith	.08	.06	.03
111	Steve Sax	.08	.06	.03
112	Kelly Downs	.05	.04	.02
113	Larry Sheets	.05	.04	.02
114	Andy Benes	.50	.40	.20
115	Pete O'Brien	.05	.04	.02
116	Kevin McReynolds	.08	.06	.03
117	Juan Berenguer	.05	.04	.02
118	Billy Hatcher	.05	.04	.02
119	Rick Cerone	.05	.04	.02
120	Andre Dawson	.08	.06	.03
121	Storm Davis	.05	.04	.02
122	Devon White	.05	.04	.02
123	Alan Trammell	.08	.06	.03
124	Vince Coleman	.08	.06	.03
125	Al Leiter	.05	.04	.02
126	Dale Sveum	.05	.04	.02
127	Pete Incaviglia	.05	.04	.02
128	Dave Stieb	.08	.06	.03
129	Kevin Mitchell	.30	.25	.12
130	Dave Schmidt	.05	.04	.02
131	Gary Redus	.05	.04	.02
132	Ron Robinson	.05	.04	.02
133	Darnell Coles	.05	.04	.02
134	Benny Santiago	.08	.06	.03
135	John Farrell	.05	.04	.02
136	Willie Wilson	.05	.04	.02
137	Steve Bedrosian	.05	.04	.02
138	Don Slaught	.05	.04	.02
139	Darryl Strawberry	.25	.20	.10
140	Frank Viola	.10	.08	.04
141	Dave Silvestri	.20	.15	.08
142	Carlos Quintana	.05	.04	.02
143	Vance Law	.05	.04	.02
144	Dave Parker	.05	.04	.02
145	Tim Belcher	.05	.04	.02
146	Will Clark	.90	.70	.35
147	Mark Williamson	.05	.04	.02
148	Ozzie Guillen	.05	.04	.02
149	Kirk McCaskill	.05	.04	.02
150	Pat Sheridan	.05	.04	.02
151	Terry Pendleton	.05	.04	.02
152	Roberto Kelly	.05	.04	.02
153	Joey Meyer	.05	.04	.02
154	Mark Grant	.05	.04	.02
155	Joe Carter	.08	.06	.03
156	Steve Buechele	.05	.04	.02
157	Tony Fernandez	.08	.06	.03
158	Jeff Reed	.05	.04	.02
159	Bobby Bonilla	.08	.06	.03
160	Henry Cotto	.05	.04	.02
161	Kurt Stillwell	.05	.04	.02
162	Mickey Morandini	.25	.20	.10
163	Robby Thompson	.05	.04	.02
164	Rick Schu	.05	.04	.02
165	Stan Jefferson	.05	.04	.02
166	Ron Darling	.05	.04	.02
167	Kirby Puckett	.25	.20	.10
168	Bill Doran	.05	.04	.02
169	Dennis Lamp	.05	.04	.02
170	Ty Griffin	.60	.45	.25
171	Ron Hassey	.05	.04	.02
172	Dale Murphy	.08	.06	.03
173	Andres Galarraga	.08	.06	.03
174	Tim Flannery	.05	.04	.02
175	Cory Snyder	.05	.04	.02
176	Checklist	.05	.04	.02
177	Tommy Barrett	.05	.04	.02
178	Dan Petry	.05	.04	.02
179	Billy Masse	.20	.15	.08
180	Terry Kennedy	.05	.04	.02
181	Joe Orsulak	.05	.04	.02

		MT	NR MT	EX
182	Doyle Alexander	.05	.04	.02
183	Willie McGee	.05	.04	.02
184	Jim Gantner	.05	.04	.02
185	Keith Hernandez	.05	.04	.02
186	Greg Gagne	.05	.04	.02
187	Kevin Bass	.05	.04	.02
188	Mark Eichhorn	.05	.04	.02
189	Mark Grace	.25	.20	.10
190	Jose Canseco	1.00	.70	.40
191	Bobby Witt	.05	.04	.02
192	Rafael Santana	.05	.04	.02
193	Dwight Evans	.05	.04	.02
194	Greg Booker	.05	.04	.02
195	Brook Jacoby	.05	.04	.02
196	Rafael Belliard	.05	.04	.02
197	Candy Maldonado	.05	.04	.02
198	Mickey Tettleton	.08	.06	.03
199	Barry Larkin	.08	.06	.03
200	Frank White	.05	.04	.02
201	Wally Joyner	.15	.11	.06
202	Chet Lemon	.05	.04	.02
203	Joe Magrane	.05	.04	.02
204	Glenn Braggs	.05	.04	.02
205	Scott Fletcher	.05	.04	.02
206	Gary Ward	.05	.04	.02
207	Nelson Liriano	.05	.04	.02
208	Howard Johnson	.15	.11	.06
209	Kent Hrbek	.08	.06	.03
210	Ken Caminiti	.05	.04	.02
211	Mike Greenwell	.50	.40	.20
212	Ryne Sandberg	.25	.20	.10
213	Joe Slusarski	.25	.20	.10
214	Donnell Nixon	.05	.04	.02
215	Tim Wallach	.05	.04	.02
216	John Kruk	.05	.04	.02
217	Charles Nagy	.25	.20	.10
218	Alvin Davis	.08	.06	.03
219	Oswald Peraza	.05	.04	.02
220	Mike Schmidt	.30	.25	.12
221	Spike Owen	.05	.04	.02
222	Mike Smithson	.05	.04	.02
223	Dion James	.05	.04	.02
224	Ernie Whitt	.05	.04	.02
225	Mike Davis	.05	.04	.02
226	Gene Larkin	.05	.04	.02
227	Pat Combs	.50	.40	.20
228	Jack Howell	.05	.04	.02
229	Ron Oester	.05	.04	.02
230	Paul Gibson	.05	.04	.02
231	Mookie Wilson	.05	.04	.02
232	Glenn Hubbard	.05	.04	.02
233	Shawon Dunston	.05	.04	.02
234	Otis Nixon	.05	.04	.02
235	Melido Perez	.05	.04	.02
236	Jerry Browne	.05	.04	.02
237	Rick Rhoden	.05	.04	.02
238	Bo Jackson	.50	.40	.20
239	Randy Velarde	.05	.04	.02
240	Jack Clark	.05	.04	.02
241	Wade Boggs	.80	.60	.30
242	Lonnie Smith	.05	.04	.02
243	Mike Flanagan	.05	.04	.02
244	Willie Randolph	.05	.04	.02
245	Oddibe McDowell	.05	.04	.02
246	Ricky Jordan	.35	.25	.14
247	Greg Briley	.20	.15	.08
248	Rex Hudler	.05	.04	.02
249	Robin Yount	.20	.15	.08
250	Lance Parrish	.05	.04	.02
251	Chris Sabo	.20	.15	.08
252	Mike Henneman	.05	.04	.02
253	Gregg Jefferies	1.00	.70	.40
254	Curt Young	.05	.04	.02
255	Andy Van Slyke	.08	.06	.03
256	Rod Booker	.05	.04	.02
257	Rafael Palmeiro	.05	.04	.02
258	Jose Uribe	.05	.04	.02
259	Ellis Burks	.20	.15	.08
260	John Smoltz	.10	.08	.04
261	Tom Foley	.05	.04	.02
262	Lloyd Moseby	.05	.04	.02
263	Jim Poole	.15	.11	.06
264	Gary Gaetti	.08	.06	.03
265	Bob Dernier	.05	.04	.02
266	Harold Baines	.08	.06	.03
267	Tom Candiotti	.05	.04	.02
268	Rafael Ramirez	.05	.04	.02
269	Bob Boone	.05	.04	.02
270	Buddy Bell	.05	.04	.02
271	Rickey Henderson	.15	.11	.06
272	Willie Fraser	.05	.04	.02

		MT	NR MT	EX
273	Eric Davis	.25	.20	.10
274	Jeff Robinson	.05	.04	.02
275	Damaso Garcia	.05	.04	.02
276	Sid Fernandez	.05	.04	.02
277	Stan Javier	.05	.04	.02
278	Marty Barrett	.05	.04	.02
279	Gerald Perry	.05	.04	.02
280	Rob Ducey	.05	.04	.02
281	Mike Scioscia	.05	.04	.02
282	Randy Bush	.05	.04	.02
283	Tom Herr	.05	.04	.02
284	Glenn Wilson	.05	.04	.02
285	Pedro Guerrero	.10	.08	.04
286	Cal Ripken	.10	.08	.04
287	Randy Johnson	.15	.11	.06
288	Julio Franco	.08	.06	.03
289	Ivan Calderon	.05	.04	.02
290	Rich Yett	.05	.04	.02
291	Scott Servais	.20	.15	.08
292	Bill Pecota	.05	.04	.02
293	Ken Phelps	.05	.04	.02
294	Chili Davis	.05	.04	.02
295	Manny Trillo	.05	.04	.02
296	Mike Boddicker	.05	.04	.02
297	Geronimo Berroa	.05	.04	.02
298	Todd Stottlemyre	.05	.04	.02
299	Kirk Gibson	.05	.04	.02
300	Wally Backman	.05	.04	.02
301	Hubie Brooks	.05	.04	.02
302	Von Hayes	.05	.04	.02
303	Matt Nokes	.05	.04	.02
304	Doc Gooden	.20	.15	.08
305	Walt Weiss	.10	.08	.04
306	Mike LaValliere	.05	.04	.02
307	Cris Carpenter	.10	.08	.04
308	Ted Wood	.20	.15	.08
309	Jeff Russell	.05	.04	.02
310	Dave Gallagher	.05	.04	.02
311	Andy Allanson	.05	.04	.02
312	Craig Reynolds	.05	.04	.02
313	Kevin Seitzer	.08	.06	.03
314	Dave Winfield	.10	.08	.04
315	Andy McGaffigan	.05	.04	.02
316	Nick Esasky	.05	.04	.02
317	Jeff Blauser	.05	.04	.02
318	George Bell	.10	.08	.04
319	Eddie Murray	.10	.08	.04
320	Mark Davidson	.05	.04	.02
321	Juan Samuel	.05	.04	.02
322	Jim Abbott	.50	.40	.20
323	Kal Daniels	.05	.04	.02
324	Mike Brumley	.05	.04	.02
325	Gary Carter	.05	.04	.02
326	Dave Henderson	.05	.04	.02
327	Checklist	.05	.04	.02
328	Garry Templeton	.05	.04	.02
329	Pat Perry	.05	.04	.02
330	Paul Molitor	.08	.06	.03

1989 Topps Box Panels

Continuing its practice of printing baseball cards on the bottom panels of its wax pack boxes, Topps in 1989 issued a special 16-card set, printing four cards on each of four different box-bottom panels. The cards are identical in design to the regular 1989 Topps cards. They are designated by letter (from A through P) rather than by number.

		MT	NR MT	EX
Complete Panel Set:		5.00	3.75	2.00
Complete Singles Set:		2.00	1.50	.80
Common Panel:		.50	.40	.20
Common Single Player:		.08	.06	.03
	Panel	.50	.40	.20
A	George Brett	.25	.20	.10
B	Bill Buckner	.08	.06	.03
C	Darrell Evans	.08	.06	.03
D	Rich Gossage	.08	.06	.03
	Panel	1.00	.70	.40
E	Greg Gross	.08	.06	.03
F	Rickey Henderson	.30	.25	.12
G	Keith Hernandez	.15	.11	.06
H	Tom Lasorda	.08	.06	.03
	Panel	2.50	2.00	1.00
I	Jim Rice	.15	.11	.06
J	Cal Ripken	.35	.25	.14
K	Nolan Ryan	.50	.40	.20
L	Mike Schmidt	.25	.20	.10
	Panel	1.00	.70	.40
M	Bruce Sutter	.15	.11	.06
N	Don Sutton	.10	.08	.04
O	Kent Tekulve	.08	.06	.03
P	Dave Winfield	.25	.20	.10

1989 Topps Major League Debut

This 150-card set highlights the debut date of 1989 Major League rookies. Two checklist cards are also included in this boxed set. The checklist cards list the players in order of debut date, but the cards are numbered alphabetically. The card fronts resemble the 1990 Topps cards in style. A debut banner appears in an upper corner of the card. The flip sides are horizontal and are printed in black on yellow stock. An overview of the player's first game is provided on the card back. The set is packaged in an attractive red, blue, green and yellow collectors box. The set was available through select hobby dealers.

		MT	NR MT	EX
Complete Set:		18.00	13.50	7.25
Common Player:		.08	.06	.03
1	Jim Abbott	.30	.25	.12
2	Beau Allred	.15	.11	.06
3	Wilson Alvarez	.25	.20	.10
4	Kent Anderson	.08	.06	.03
5	Eric Anthony	.40	.30	.15
6	Kevin Appier	.25	.20	.10
7	Larry Arndt	.08	.06	.03
8	John Barfield	.08	.06	.03
9	Billy Bates	.08	.06	.03
10	Kevin Batiste	.10	.08	.04
11	Blaine Beatty	.20	.15	.08
12	Stan Belinda	.15	.11	.06
13	Juan Bell	.15	.11	.06
14	Joey Belle	.20	.15	.08
15	Andy Benes	.30	.25	.12
16	Mike Benjamin	.20	.15	.08
17	Geronimo Berroa	.08	.06	.03
18	Mike Blowers	.10	.08	.04

		MT	NR MT	EX
19	Brian Brady	.08	.06	.03
20	Francisco Cabrera	.25	.20	.10
21	George Canale	.08	.06	.03
22	Jose Cano	.08	.06	.03
23	Steve Carter	.10	.08	.04
24	Pat Combs	.30	.25	.12
25	Scott Coolbaugh	.15	.11	.06
26	Steve Cummings	.10	.08	.04
27	Pete Dalena	.08	.06	.03
28	Jeff Datz	.08	.06	.03
29	Bobby Davidson	.08	.06	.03
30	Drew Denson	.08	.06	.03
31	Gary DiSarcina	.20	.15	.08
32	Brian DuBois	.15	.11	.06
33	Mike Dyer	.10	.08	.04
34	Wayne Edwards	.10	.08	.04
35	Junior Felix	.30	.25	.12
36	Mike Fetters	.15	.11	.06
37	Steve Finley	.15	.11	.06
38	Darren Fletcher	.15	.11	.06
39	LaVel Freeman	.08	.06	.03
40	Steve Frey	.10	.08	.04
41	Mark Gardner	.20	.15	.08
42	Joe Girardi	.25	.20	.08
43	Juan Gonzalez	2.00	1.50	.80
44	Goose Gozzo	.15	.11	.06
45	Tommy Greene	.15	.11	.06
46	Ken Griffey, Jr.	3.50	2.75	1.50
47	Jason Grimsley	.20	.15	.08
48	Marquis Grissom	.40	.30	.15
49	Mark Guthrie	.10	.08	.04
50	Chip Hale	.08	.06	.03
51	John Hardy	.08	.06	.03
52	Gene Harris	.10	.08	.04
53	Mike Hartley	.10	.08	.04
54	Scott Hemond	.10	.08	.04
55	Xavier Hernandez	.10	.08	.04
56	Eric Hetzel	.15	.11	.06
57	Greg Hibbard	.25	.20	.10
58	Mark Higgins	.08	.06	.03
59	Glenallen Hill	.20	.15	.08
60	Chris Hoiles	.30	.25	.12
61	Shawn Holman	.10	.08	.04
62	Dann Howitt	.10	.08	.04
63	Mike Huff	.10	.08	.04
64	Terry Jorgenson	.10	.08	.04
65	Dave Justice	2.00	1.50	.80
66	Jeff King	.20	.15	.08
67	Matt Kinzer	.08	.06	.03
68	Joe Kraemer	.08	.06	.03
69	Marcus Lawton	.08	.06	.03
70	Derek Lilliquist	.15	.11	.06
71	Scott Little	.08	.06	.03
72	Greg Litton	.15	.11	.06
73	Rick Lueken	.10	.08	.04
74	Julio Machado	.15	.11	.06
75	Tom Magrann	.08	.06	.03
76	Kelly Mann	.20	.15	.08
77	Randy McCament	.08	.06	.03
78	Ben McDonald	.50	.40	.20
79	Chuck McElroy	.20	.15	.08
80	Jeff McKnight	.10	.08	.04
81	Kent Mercker	.25	.20	.10
82	Matt Merullo	.08	.06	.03
83	Hensley Meulens	.15	.11	.06
84	Kevin Mmahat	.08	.06	.03
85	Mike Munoz	.08	.06	.03
86	Dan Murphy	.08	.06	.03
87	Jaime Navarro	.20	.15	.08
88	Randy Nosek	.10	.08	.04
89	John Olerud	.50	.40	.20
90	Steve Olin	.10	.08	.04
91	Joe Oliver	.20	.15	.08
92	Francisco Oliveras	.10	.08	.04
93	Greg Olson	.15	.11	.06
94	John Orton	.10	.08	.04
95	Dean Palmer	.20	.15	.08
96	Ramon Pena	.08	.06	.03
97	Jeff Peterek	.08	.06	.03
98	Marty Pevey	.08	.06	.03
99	Rusty Richards	.08	.06	.03
100	Jeff Richardson	.08	.06	.03
101	Rob Richie	.08	.06	.03
102	Kevin Ritz	.10	.08	.04
103	Rosario Rodriguez	.25	.20	.10
104	Mike Roesler	.10	.08	.04
105	Kenny Rogers	.15	.11	.06
106	Bobby Rose	.20	.15	.08
107	Alex Sanchez	.15	.11	.06
108	Deion Sanders	.25	.20	.10
109	Jeff Schaefer	.08	.06	.03

		MT	NR MT	EX
110	Jeff Schulz	.10	.08	.04
111	Mike Schwabe	.10	.08	.04
112	Dick Scott	.08	.06	.03
113	Scott Scudder	.25	.20	.10
114	Rudy Seanez	.15	.11	.06
115	Joe Skalski	.08	.06	.03
116	Dwight Smith	.20	.15	.08
117	Greg Smith	.15	.11	.06
118	Mike Smith	.10	.08	.04
119	Paul Sorrento	.15	.11	.06
120	Sammy Sosa	.50	.40	.20
121	Billy Spiers	.15	.11	.06
122	Mike Stanton	.20	.15	.08
123	Phil Stephenson	.08	.06	.03
124	Doug Strange	.08	.06	.03
125	Russ Swan	.10	.08	.04
126	Kevin Tapani	.35	.25	.14
127	Stu Tate	.08	.06	.03
128	Greg Vaughn	.40	.30	.15
129	Robin Ventura	.25	.20	.10
130	Randy Veres	.08	.06	.03
131	Jose Vizcaino	.15	.11	.06
132	Omar Vizquel	.10	.08	.04
133	Larry Walker	.40	.30	.15
134	Jerome Walton	.50	.40	.20
135	Gary Wayne	.10	.08	.04
136	Lenny Webster	.10	.08	.04
137	Mickey Weston	.10	.08	.04
138	Jeff Wetherby	.08	.06	.03
139	John Wetteland	.25	.20	.10
140	Ed Whited	.08	.06	.03
141	Wally Whitehurst	.10	.08	.04
142	Kevin Wickander	.15	.11	.06
143	Dean Wilkins	.10	.08	.04
144	Dana Williams	.10	.08	.04
145	Paul Wilmet	.08	.06	.03
146	Craig Wilson	.15	.11	.06
147	Matt Winters	.08	.06	.03
148	Eric Yelding	.25	.20	.10
149	Clint Zavaras	.15	.11	.06
150	Todd Zeile	.50	.40	.20
-----	Checklist (1 of 2)	.08	.06	.03
-----	Checklist (2 of 2)	.08	.06	.03

1989 Topps Mini League Leaders

This 77-card set from Topps features baseball's statistical leaders from the 1988 season, and is referred to as a "mini" set because of the cards' small (2-1/8" by 3") size. The glossy cards feature action photos that have a soft focus on all edges. The player's team and name appear along the bottom of the card. The back features a head-shot of the player along with his 1988 season ranking and stats.

		MT	NR MT	EX
Complete Set:		6.00	4.50	2.50
Common Player:		.09	.07	.04
1	Dale Murphy	.35	.25	.14
2	Gerald Perry	.09	.07	.04
3	Andre Dawson	.20	.15	.08
4	Greg Maddux	.20	.15	.08
5	Rafael Palmeiro	.15	.11	.06

		MT	NR MT	EX
6	Tom Browning	.12	.09	.05
7	Kal Daniels	.15	.11	.06
8	Eric Davis	.60	.45	.25
9	John Franco	.09	.07	.04
10	Danny Jackson	.09	.07	.04
11	Barry Larkin	.15	.11	.06
12	Jose Rijo	.12	.09	.05
13	Chris Sabo	.20	.15	.08
14	Mike Scott	.09	.07	.04
15	Nolan Ryan	.50	.40	.20
16	Gerald Young	.09	.07	.04
17	Kirk Gibson	.12	.09	.05
18	Orel Hershiser	.25	.20	.10
19	Steve Sax	.12	.09	.05
20	John Tudor	.09	.07	.04
21	Hubie Brooks	.09	.07	.04
22	Andres Galarraga	.15	.11	.06
23	Otis Nixon	.09	.07	.04
24	Dave Cone	.15	.11	.06
25	Sid Fernandez	.12	.09	.05
26	Doc Gooden	.30	.25	.12
27	Kevin McReynolds	.20	.15	.08
28	Darryl Strawberry	.35	.25	.14
29	Juan Samuel	.09	.07	.04
30	Bobby Bonilla	.12	.09	.05
31	Sid Bream	.09	.07	.04
32	Andy Van Slyke	.12	.09	.05
33	Vince Coleman	.12	.09	.05
34	Jose DeLeon	.09	.07	.04
35	Joe Magrane	.12	.09	.05
36	Ozzie Smith	.12	.09	.05
37	Todd Worrell	.09	.07	.04
38	Tony Gwynn	.30	.25	.12
39	Brett Butler	.12	.09	.05
40	Will Clark	.80	.60	.30
41	Jim Gott	.09	.07	.04
42	Rick Reuschel	.12	.09	.05
43	Checklist	.09	.07	.04
44	Eddie Murray	.20	.15	.08
45	Wade Boggs	.80	.60	.30
46	Roger Clemens	.30	.25	.12
47	Dwight Evans	.12	.09	.05
48	Mike Greenwell	.70	.50	.30
49	Bruce Hurst	.12	.09	.05
50	Johnny Ray	.09	.07	.04
51	Doug Jones	.09	.07	.04
52	Greg Swindell	.15	.11	.06
53	Gary Pettis	.09	.07	.04
54	George Brett	.15	.11	.06
55	Mark Gubicza	.15	.11	.06
56	Willie Wilson	.09	.07	.04
57	Teddy Higuera	.12	.09	.05
58	Paul Molitor	.15	.11	.06
59	Robin Yount	.25	.20	.10
60	Allan Anderson	.09	.07	.04
61	Gary Gaetti	.12	.09	.04
62	Kirby Puckett	.40	.30	.15
63	Jeff Reardon	.09	.07	.04
64	Frank Viola	.12	.09	.05
65	Jack Clark	.12	.09	.05
66	Rickey Henderson	.25	.20	.10
67	Dave Winfield	.15	.11	.06
68	Jose Canseco	.80	.60	.30
69	Dennis Eckersley	.12	.09	.05
70	Mark McGwire	.80	.60	.30
71	Dave Stewart	.12	.09	.05
72	Alvin Davis	.12	.09	.05
73	Mark Langston	.12	.09	.05
74	Harold Reynolds	.12	.09	.05
75	George Bell	.15	.11	.06
76	Tony Fernandez	.15	.11	.06
77	Fred McGriff	.25	.20	.10

1989 Topps American Baseball

For the second consecutive year Topps released an 88-card set of baseball cards available in both the United States and the United Kingdom. The mini-sized cards (2-1/4" by 3") feature full-color photos on the card fronts. The cards are printed on white stock with a low gloss finish. The player action photo is outlined in red, white, and blue and framed in white. The card backs are printed horizontally and include a characterization cartoon along with biographical information and statistics. The cards are sold in packs of five cards with a stick of bubble gum.

		MT	NR MT	EX
	Complete Set:	8.00	6.00	3.25
	Common Player:	.08	.06	.03
1	Brady Anderson	.08	.06	.03
2	Harold Baines	.15	.11	.06
3	George Bell	.15	.11	.06
4	Wade Boggs	1.00	.70	.40
5	Barry Bonds	.20	.15	.08
6	Bobby Bonilla	.20	.15	.08
7	George Brett	.15	.11	.06
8	Hubie Brooks	.08	.06	.03
9	Tom Brunansky	.08	.06	.03
10	Jay Buhner	.08	.06	.03
11	Brett Butler	.08	.06	.03
12	Jose Canseco	1.25	.90	.50
13	Joe Carter	.15	.11	.06
14	Jack Clark	.08	.06	.03
15	Will Clark	.80	.60	.30
16	Roger Clemens	.30	.25	.12
17	Dave Cone	.08	.06	.03
18	Alvin Davis	.08	.06	.03
19	Eric Davis	.30	.25	.12
20	Glenn Davis	.08	.06	.03
21	Andre Dawson	.12	.09	.05
22	Bill Doran	.08	.06	.03
23	Dennis Eckersley	.08	.06	.03
24	Dwight Evans	.08	.06	.03
25	Tony Fernandez	.08	.06	.03
26	Carlton Fisk	.08	.06	.03
27	John Franco	.08	.06	.03
28	Andres Galarraga	.15	.11	.06
29	Ron Gant	.08	.06	.03
30	Kirk Gibson	.08	.06	.03
31	Doc Gooden	.25	.20	.10
32	Mike Greenwell	.50	.40	.20
33	Mark Gubicza	.08	.06	.03
34	Pedro Gurrero	.12	.09	.05
35	Ozzie Guillen	.08	.06	.03
36	Tony Gwynn	.15	.11	.06
37	Rickey Henderson	.15	.11	.06
38	Orel Hershiser	.15	.11	.06
39	Teddy Higuera	.08	.06	.03
40	Charlie Hough	.08	.06	.03
41	Kent Hrbek	.12	.09	.05
42	Bruce Hurst	.08	.06	.03
43	Bo Jackson	.50	.40	.20
44	Gregg Jefferies	.60	.45	.25
45	Ricky Jordan	.25	.20	.10
46	Wally Joyner	.15	.11	.06
47	Mark Langston	.12	.09	.05
48	Mike Marshall	.08	.06	.03
49	Don Mattingly	2.00	1.50	.80
50	Fred McGriff	.35	.25	.14
51	Mark McGwire	1.00	.70	.40
52	Kevin McReynolds	.15	.11	.06
53	Paul Molitor	.08	.06	.03
54	Jack Morris	.08	.06	.03
55	Dale Murphy	.15	.11	.06
56	Eddie Murray	.10	.08	.04
57	Pete O'Brien	.08	.06	.03
58	Rafael Palmeiro	.08	.06	.03
59	Gerald Perry	.08	.06	.03
60	Kirby Puckett	.30	.25	.12
61	Rock Raines	.15	.11	.06
62	Johnny Ray	.08	.06	.03
63	Rick Reuschel	.08	.06	.03
64	Cal Ripken	.15	.11	.06
65	Chris Sabo	.15	.11	.06
66	Juan Samuel	.08	.06	.03
67	Ryane Sandberg	.15	.11	.06
68	Benny Santiago	.15	.11	.06
69	Steve Sax	.08	.06	.03
70	Mike Schmidt	.20	.15	.11
71	Ruben Sierra	.20	.15	.11

		MT	NR MT	EX
72	Ozzie Smith	.15	.11	.06
73	Cory Snyder	.08	.06	.03
74	Dave Stewart	.08	.06	.03
75	Darryl Strawberry	.25	.20	.10
76	Greg Swindell	.15	.11	.06
77	Alan Trammell	.15	.11	.06
78	Fernando Valenzuela	.08	.06	.03
79	Andy Van Slyke	.20	.15	.08
80	Frank Viola	.20	.15	.08
81	Claudell Washington	.08	.06	.03
82	Walt Weiss	.08	.06	.03
83	Lou Whitaker	.08	.06	.03
84	Dave Winfield	.20	.15	.08
85	Mike Witt	.08	.06	.03
86	Gerald Young	.08	.06	.03
87	Robin Yount	.20	.15	.08
88	Checklist	.08	.06	.03

1990 Topps

The 1990 Topps set again included 792 cards, and sported a newly-designed front that featured six different color schemes. The set led off with a special four-card salute to Nolan Ryan, and featured various other specials, including All-Stars, Number 1 Draft Picks, Record Breakers, manager cards, rookies, and "Turn Back the Clock" cards. The set also includes a special card commemorating A. Bartlett Giamatti, the late Baseball Commissioner. The backs are printed in black on a chartreuse background with the card number in the upper left corner. The set features 725 different individual player cards, the most ever, including 138 players making their first appearance in a regular Topps set.

		MT	NR MT	EX
	Complete Set:	20.00	15.00	8.00
	Common Player:	.03	.02	.01
1	Nolan Ryan	.35	.25	.14
2	Nolan Ryan (The Mets Years)	.20	.15	.08
3	Nolan Ryan (The Angels Years)	.20	.15	.08
4	Nolan Ryan (The Astros Years)	.20	.15	.08
5	Nolan Ryan (The Rangers)	.20	.15	.08
6	1989 Record Breaker (Vince Coleman)	.10	.08	.04
7	1989 Record Breaker (Rickey Henderson)	.20	.15	.08
8	1989 Record Breaker (Cal Ripken)	.15	.11	.06
9	Eric Plunk	.03	.02	.01
10	Barry Larkin	.15	.11	.06
11	Paul Gibson	.04	.03	.02
12	Joe Girardi(FC)	.15	.11	.06
13	Mark Williamson	.03	.02	.01
14	Mike Fetters(FC)	.20	.15	.08
15	Teddy Higuera	.06	.05	.02
16	Kent Anderson	.10	.08	.04
17	Kelly Downs	.05	.04	.02
18	Carlos Quintana	.09	.07	.04
19	Al Newman	.03	.02	.01
20	Mark Gubicza	.12	.09	.05
21	Jeff Torborg	.03	.02	.01
22	Bruce Ruffin	.03	.02	.01
23	Randy Velarde	.07	.05	.03
24	Joe Hesketh	.03	.02	.01
25	Willie Randolph	.08	.06	.03
26	Don Slaught	.03	.02	.01
27	Rick Leach	.03	.02	.01
28	Duane Ward	.04	.03	.02

#	Name	MT	NR MT	EX
29	John Cangelosi	.03	.02	.01
30	David Cone	.10	.08	.04
31	Henry Cotto	.03	.02	.01
32	John Farrell	.05	.04	.02
33	Greg Walker	.05	.04	.02
34	Tony Fossas(FC)	.07	.05	.03
35	Benito Santiago	.12	.09	.05
36	John Costello	.04	.03	.02
37	Domingo Ramos	.03	.02	.01
38	Wes Gardner	.04	.03	.02
39	Curt Ford	.04	.03	.02
40	Jay Howell	.06	.05	.02
41	Matt Williams	.15	.11	.06
42	Jeff Robinson	.05	.04	.02
43	Dante Bichette	.07	.05	.03
44	#1 Draft Pick (Roger Salkeld)(FC)	.50	.40	.20
45	Dave Parker	.09	.07	.04
46	Rob Dibble	.07	.05	.03
47	Brian Harper	.04	.03	.02
48	Zane Smith	.03	.02	.01
49	Tom Lawless	.03	.02	.01
50	Glenn Davis	.08	.06	.03
51	Doug Rader	.03	.02	.01
52	Jack Daugherty(FC)	.20	.15	.08
53	Mike LaCoss	.04	.03	.02
54	Joel Skinner	.04	.03	.02
55	Darrell Evans	.05	.04	.02
56	Franklin Stubbs	.04	.03	.02
57	Greg Vaughn(FC)	.60	.45	.25
58	Keith Miller	.10	.08	.04
59	Ted Power	.03	.02	.01
60	George Brett	.15	.11	.06
61	Deion Sanders	.30	.25	.12
62	Ramon Martinez	.30	.25	.12
63	Mike Pagliarulo	.04	.03	.02
64	Danny Darwin	.03	.02	.01
65	Devon White	.07	.05	.03
66	Greg Litton(FC)	.15	.11	.06
67	Scott Sanderson	.04	.03	.02
68	Dave Henderson	.06	.05	.02
69	Todd Frohwirth	.03	.02	.01
70	Mike Greenwell	.30	.25	.12
71	Allan Anderson	.05	.04	.02
72	Jeff Huson(FC)	.25	.20	.10
73	Bob Milacki	.05	.04	.02
74	#1 Draft Pick (Jeff Jackson)(FC)	.20	.15	.08
75	Doug Jones	.05	.04	.02
76	Dave Valle	.03	.02	.01
77	Dave Bergman	.03	.02	.01
78	Mike Flanagan	.04	.03	.02
79	Ron Kittle	.05	.04	.02
80	Jeff Russell	.05	.04	.02
81	Bob Rodgers	.03	.02	.01
82	Scott Terry	.04	.03	.02
83	Hensley Meulens	.30	.25	.12
84	Ray Searage	.03	.02	.01
85	Juan Samuel	.05	.04	.02
86	Paul Kilgus	.03	.02	.01
87	Rick Luecken(FC)	.15	.11	.06
88	Glenn Braggs	.05	.04	.02
89	Clint Zavaras(FC)	.15	.11	.06
90	Jack Clark	.06	.05	.02
91	Steve Frey(FC)	.20	.15	.08
92	Mike Stanley	.03	.02	.01
93	Shawn Hillegas	.03	.02	.01
94	Herm Winningham	.03	.02	.01
95	Todd Worrell	.05	.04	.02
96	Jody Reed	.04	.03	.02
97	Curt Schilling(FC)	.10	.08	.04
98	Jose Gonzalez(FC)	.10	.08	.04
99	Rich Monteleone(FC)	.15	.11	.06
100	Will Clark	.50	.40	.20
101	Shane Rawley	.04	.03	.02
102	Stan Javier	.04	.03	.02
103	Marvin Freeman	.09	.07	.04
104	Bob Knepper	.03	.02	.01
105	Randy Myers	.05	.04	.02
106	Charlie O'Brien	.03	.02	.01
107	Fred Lynn	.05	.04	.02
108	Rod Nichols	.04	.03	.02
109	Roberto Kelly	.08	.06	.03
110	Tommy Helms	.03	.02	.01
111	Ed Whited	.20	.15	.08
112	Glenn Wilson	.03	.02	.01
113	Manny Lee	.03	.02	.01
114	Mike Bielecki	.05	.04	.02
115	Tony Pena	.06	.05	.02
116	Floyd Bannister	.04	.03	.02
117	Mike Sharperson(FC)	.09	.07	.04
118	Erik Hanson	.10	.08	.04
119	Billy Hatcher	.04	.03	.02
120	John Franco	.05	.04	.02
121	Robin Ventura	.60	.45	.25
122	Shawn Abner	.03	.02	.01
123	Rich Gedman	.04	.03	.02
124	Dave Dravecky	.04	.03	.02
125	Kent Hrbek	.07	.05	.03
126	Randy Kramer	.03	.02	.01
127	Mike Devereaux	.06	.05	.02
128	Checklist 1-132	.03	.02	.01
129	Ron Jones	.10	.08	.04
130	Bert Blyleven	.05	.04	.02
131	Matt Nokes	.06	.05	.02
132	Lance Blankenship(FC)	.10	.08	.04
133	Ricky Horton	.03	.02	.01
134	#1 Draft Pick (Earl Cunningham)(FC)	.15	.11	.06
135	Dave Magadan	.05	.04	.02
136	Kevin Brown	.06	.05	.02
137	Marty Pevey(FC)	.15	.11	.06
138	Al Leiter	.04	.03	.02
139	Greg Brock	.04	.03	.02
140	Andre Dawson	.12	.09	.05
141	John Hart	.05	.04	.02
142	Jeff Wetherby(FC)	.15	.11	.06
143	Rafael Belliard	.03	.02	.01
144	Bud Black	.03	.02	.01
145	Terry Steinbach	.07	.05	.03
146	Rob Richie(FC)	.15	.11	.06
147	Chuck Finley	.04	.03	.02
148	Edgar Martinez(FC)	.09	.07	.04
149	Steve Farr	.04	.03	.02
150	Kirk Gibson	.09	.07	.04
151	Rick Mahler	.03	.02	.01
152	Lonnie Smith	.05	.04	.02
153	Randy Milligan	.05	.04	.02
154	Mike Maddux	.05	.04	.02
155	Ellis Burks	.25	.20	.10
156	Ken Patterson	.04	.03	.02
157	Craig Biggio	.15	.11	.06
158	Craig Lefferts	.04	.03	.02
159	Mike Felder	.03	.02	.01
160	Dave Righetti	.06	.05	.02
161	Harold Reynolds	.06	.05	.02
162	Todd Zeile(FC)	.60	.45	.25
163	Phil Bradley	.05	.04	.02
164	#1 Draft Pick (Jeff Juden)(FC)	.30	.25	.12
165	Walt Weiss	.08	.06	.03
166	Bobby Witt	.04	.03	.02
167	Kevin Appier(FC)	.35	.25	.14
168	Jose Lind	.04	.03	.02
169	Richard Dotson	.03	.02	.01
170	George Bell	.12	.09	.05
171	Russ Nixon	.03	.02	.01
172	Tom Lampkin(FC)	.10	.08	.04
173	Tim Belcher	.12	.09	.05
174	Jeff Kunkel	.03	.02	.01
175	Mike Moore	.07	.05	.02
176	Luis Quinones	.03	.02	.01
177	Mike Henneman	.05	.04	.02
178	Chris James	.06	.05	.02
179	Brian Holton	.04	.03	.02
180	Rock Raines	.10	.08	.04
181	Juan Agosto	.03	.02	.01
182	Mookie Wilson	.05	.04	.02
183	Steve Lake	.03	.02	.01
184	Danny Cox	.04	.03	.02
185	Ruben Sierra	.20	.15	.08
186	Dave LaPoint	.03	.02	.01
187	Rick Wrona(FC)	.12	.09	.05
188	Mike Smithson	.03	.02	.01
189	Dick Schofield	.04	.03	.02
190	Rick Reuschel	.06	.05	.02
191	Pat Borders	.08	.06	.03
192	Don August	.04	.03	.02
193	Andy Benes	.25	.20	.10
194	Glenallen Hill(FC)	.25	.20	.10
195	Tim Burke	.05	.04	.02
196	Gerald Young	.04	.03	.02
197	Doug Drabek	.07	.05	.03
198	Mike Marshall	.06	.05	.02
199	Sergio Valdez(FC)	.20	.15	.08
200	Don Mattingly	.40	.30	.15
201	Cito Gaston	.03	.02	.01
202	Mike Macfarlane	.03	.02	.01
203	Mike Roesler(FC)	.15	.11	.06
204	Bob Dernier	.03	.02	.01
205	Mark Davis	.09	.07	.04
206	Nick Esasky	.07	.05	.02
207	Bob Ojeda	.04	.03	.02
208	Brook Jacoby	.04	.03	.02
209	Greg Mathews	.04	.03	.02

#	Player	MT	NR MT	EX
210	Ryne Sandberg	.30	.25	.12
211	John Cerutti	.04	.03	.02
212	Joe Orsulak	.03	.02	.01
213	Scott Bankhead	.05	.04	.02
214	Terry Francona	.03	.02	.01
215	Kirk McCaskill	.04	.03	.02
216	Ricky Jordan	.20	.15	.08
217	Don Robinson	.04	.03	.02
218	Wally Backman	.04	.03	.02
219	Donn Pall	.03	.02	.01
220	Barry Bonds	.10	.08	.04
221	*Gary Mielke*(FC)	.15	.11	.06
222	Kurt Stillwell	.05	.04	.02
223	Tommy Gregg	.06	.05	.02
224	*Delino DeShields*(FC)	.60	.45	.25
225	Jim Deshaies	.05	.04	.02
226	Mickey Hatcher	.03	.02	.01
227	*Kevin Tapani*(FC)	.30	.25	.12
228	Dave Martinez	.03	.02	.01
229	David Wells	.03	.02	.01
230	Keith Hernandez	.07	.05	.03
231	Jack McKeon	.03	.02	.01
232	Darnell Coles	.04	.03	.02
233	Ken Hill	.10	.08	.06
234	Mariano Duncan	.05	.04	.02
235	Jeff Reardon	.04	.03	.02
236	Hal Morris(FC)	.50	.40	.20
237	*Kevin Ritz*(FC)	.15	.11	.06
238	Felix Jose(FC)	.10	.08	.04
239	Eric Show	.04	.03	.02
240	Mark Grace	.40	.30	.15
241	Mike Krukow	.04	.03	.02
242	Fred Manrique	.03	.02	.01
243	Barry Jones	.03	.02	.01
244	Bill Schroeder	.03	.02	.01
245	Roger Clemens	.25	.20	.10
246	Jim Eisenreich	.03	.02	.01
247	Jerry Reed	.03	.02	.01
248	Dave Anderson	.03	.02	.01
249	*Mike Smith*(FC)	.12	.09	.05
250	Jose Canseco	.70	.50	.30
251	Jeff Blauser	.05	.04	.02
252	Otis Nixon	.03	.02	.01
253	Mark Portugal	.03	.02	.01
254	Francisco Cabrera	.25	.20	.10
255	Bobby Thigpen	.07	.05	.03
256	Marvell Wynne	.03	.02	.01
257	Jose DeLeon	.07	.05	.03
258	Barry Lyons	.03	.02	.01
259	Lance McCullers	.05	.04	.02
260	Eric Davis	.30	.25	.12
261	Whitey Herzog	.03	.02	.01
262	Checklist 133-264	.03	.02	.01
263	*Mel Stottlemyre, Jr.*(FC)	.12	.09	.05
264	Bryan Clutterbuck	.03	.02	.01
265	Pete O'Brien	.06	.05	.02
266	German Gonzalez	.04	.03	.02
267	Mark Davidson	.03	.02	.01
268	Rob Murphy	.03	.02	.01
269	Dickie Thon	.03	.02	.01
270	Dave Stewart	.08	.06	.03
271	Chet Lemon	.05	.04	.02
272	Bryan Harvey	.04	.03	.02
273	Bobby Bonilla	.15	.11	.06
274	*Goose Gozzo*(FC)	.15	.11	.06
275	Mickey Tettleton	.07	.05	.03
276	Gary Thurman	.03	.02	.01
277	Lenny Harris(FC)	.12	.09	.05
278	Pascual Perez	.04	.03	.02
279	Steve Buechele	.04	.03	.02
280	Lou Whitaker	.07	.05	.03
281	Kevin Bass	.05	.04	.02
282	Derek Lilliquist	.10	.08	.04
283	*Joey Belle*(FC)	.70	.50	.30
284	*Mark Gardner*(FC)	.30	.25	.12
285	Willie McGee	.06	.05	.02
286	Lee Guetterman	.03	.02	.01
287	Vance Law	.03	.02	.01
288	Greg Briley	.15	.11	.06
289	Norm Charlton	.10	.08	.04
290	Robin Yount	.20	.15	.08
291	Dave Johnson	.03	.02	.01
292	Jim Gott	.04	.03	.02
293	Mike Gallego	.04	.03	.02
294	Craig McMurtry	.03	.02	.01
295	Fred McGriff	.25	.20	.10
296	Jeff Ballard	.07	.05	.03
297	Tom Herr	.06	.05	.02
298	Danny Gladden	.05	.04	.02
299	Adam Peterson(FC)	.09	.07	.04
300	Bo Jackson	.60	.45	.25
301	Don Aase	.03	.02	.01
302	*Marcus Lawton*(FC)	.08	.06	.03
303	Rick Cerone	.03	.02	.01
304	Marty Clary(FC)	.08	.06	.03
305	Eddie Murray	.15	.11	.06
306	Tom Niedenfuer	.03	.02	.01
307	Bip Roberts	.08	.06	.03
308	Jose Guzman	.05	.04	.02
309	*Eric Yelding*(FC)	.20	.15	.08
310	Steve Bedrosian	.05	.04	.02
311	Dwight Smith	.25	.20	.10
312	Dan Quisenberry	.05	.04	.02
313	Gus Polidor	.03	.02	.01
314	#1 Draft Pick *(Donald Harris)*(FC)	.20	.15	.08
315	Bruce Hurst	.06	.05	.02
316	Carney Lansford	.06	.05	.02
317	*Mark Guthrie*(FC)	.20	.15	.08
318	Wallace Johnson	.03	.02	.01
319	Dion James	.04	.03	.02
320	Dave Steib	.07	.05	.03
321	Joe Morgan	.03	.02	.01
322	Junior Ortiz	.03	.02	.01
323	Willie Wilson	.04	.03	.02
324	Pete Harnisch(FC)	.10	.08	.04
325	Robby Thompson	.06	.05	.02
326	*Tom McCarthy*	.10	.08	.04
327	Ken Williams	.03	.02	.01
328	Curt Young	.03	.02	.01
329	Oddibe McDowell	.06	.05	.02
330	Ron Darling	.09	.07	.04
331	*Juan Gonzalez*(FC)	1.50	1.25	.60
332	Paul O'Neill	.07	.05	.03
333	Bill Wegman	.03	.02	.01
334	Johnny Ray	.05	.04	.02
335	Andy Hawkins	.05	.04	.02
336	Ken Griffey, Jr.	1.00	.70	.40
337	Lloyd McClendon	.06	.05	.02
338	Dennis Lamp	.03	.02	.01
339	Dave Clark	.04	.03	.02
340	Fernando Valenzuela	.06	.05	.02
341	Tom Foley	.03	.02	.01
342	Alex Trevino	.03	.02	.01
343	Frank Tanana	.04	.03	.02
344	*George Canale*(FC)	.15	.11	.06
345	Harold Baines	.09	.07	.04
346	Jim Presley	.04	.03	.02
347	*Junior Felix*	.20	.15	.08
348	*Gary Wayne*(FC)	.12	.09	.05
349	*Steve Finley*(FC)	.30	.25	.12
350	Bret Saberhagen	.10	.08	.04
351	Roger Craig	.03	.02	.01
352	Bryn Smith	.05	.04	.02
353	Sandy Alomar	.25	.20	.10
354	*Stan Belinda*(FC)	.20	.15	.08
355	Marty Barrett	.05	.04	.02
356	Randy Ready	.03	.02	.01
357	Dave West	.20	.15	.08
358	Andres Thomas	.04	.03	.02
359	Jimmy Jones	.03	.02	.01
360	Paul Molitor	.09	.07	.04
361	*Randy McCament*(FC)	.15	.11	.06
362	Damon Berryhill	.06	.05	.02
363	Dan Petry	.03	.02	.01
364	Rolando Roomes(FC)	.15	.11	.06
365	Ozzie Guillen	.05	.04	.02
366	Mike Heath	.03	.02	.01
367	Mike Morgan	.03	.02	.01
368	Bill Doran	.06	.05	.02
369	Todd Burns	.04	.03	.02
370	Tim Wallach	.07	.05	.03
371	Jimmy Key	.03	.02	.01
372	Terry Kennedy	.03	.02	.01
373	Alvin Davis	.08	.06	.03
374	*Steve Cummings*(FC)	.15	.11	.06
375	Dwight Evans	.08	.06	.03
376	Checklist 265-396	.03	.02	.01
377	*Mickey Weston*(FC)	.15	.11	.06
378	Luis Salazar	.03	.02	.01
379	Steve Rosenberg	.03	.02	.01
380	Dave Winfield	.15	.11	.06
381	Frank Robinson	.03	.02	.01
382	Jeff Musselman	.03	.02	.01
383	John Morris	.04	.03	.02
384	Pat Combs	.20	.15	.08
385	Fred McGriff AS	.20	.15	.08
386	Julio Franco AS	.10	.08	.04
387	Wade Boggs AS	.20	.15	.08
388	Cal Ripken AS	.15	.11	.06
389	Robin Yount AS	.20	.15	.08
390	Ruben Sierra AS	.20	.15	.08
391	Kirby Puckett AS	.20	.15	.08

		MT	NR MT	EX
392	Carlton Fisk AS	.08	.06	.03
393	Bret Saberhagen AS	.10	.08	.04
394	Jeff Ballard AS	.08	.06	.03
395	Jeff Russell AS	.08	.06	.03
396	A. Bartlett Giamatti	.30	.25	.12
397	Will Clark AS	.25	.20	.10
398	Ryne Sandberg AS	.15	.11	.06
399	Howard Johnson AS	.15	.11	.06
400	Ozzie Smith AS	.10	.08	.04
401	Kevin Mitchell AS	.20	.15	.08
402	Eric Davis AS	.20	.15	.08
403	Tony Gwynn AS	.15	.11	.06
404	Craig Biggio AS	.15	.11	.06
405	Mike Scott AS	.08	.06	.03
406	Joe Magrane AS	.08	.06	.03
407	Mark Davis AS	.08	.06	.03
408	Trevor Wilson	.06	.05	.02
409	Tom Brunansky	.09	.07	.04
410	Joe Boever	.06	.05	.02
411	Ken Phelps	.03	.02	.01
412	Jamie Moyer	.04	.03	.02
413	Brian DuBois(FC)	.15	.11	.06
414	#1 Draft Pick (Frank Thomas)(FC)			
		4.00	3.00	1.50
415	Shawon Dunston	.06	.05	.02
416	Dave Johnson(FC)	.12	.09	.05
417	Jim Gantner	.06	.05	.02
418	Tom Browning	.08	.06	.03
419	Beau Allred(FC)	.20	.15	.08
420	Carlton Fisk	.08	.06	.03
421	Greg Minton	.03	.02	.01
422	Pat Sheridan	.03	.02	.01
423	Fred Toliver	.03	.02	.01
424	Jerry Reuss	.05	.04	.02
425	Bill Landrum	.05	.04	.02
426	Jeff Hamilton	.05	.04	.02
427	Carmem Castillo	.03	.02	.01
428	Steve Davis(FC)	.12	.09	.05
429	Tom Kelly	.03	.02	.01
430	Pete Incaviglia	.06	.05	.02
431	Randy Johnson	.10	.08	.04
432	Damaso Garcia	.03	.02	.01
433	Steve Olin(FC)	.12	.08	.04
434	Mark Carreon(FC)	.09	.07	.04
435	Kevin Seitzer	.09	.07	.04
436	Mel Hall	.05	.04	.02
437	Les Lancaster	.05	.04	.02
438	Greg Myers(FC)	.10	.08	.04
439	Jeff Parrett	.06	.05	.02
440	Alan Trammell	.09	.07	.04
441	Bob Kipper	.03	.02	.01
442	Jerry Browne	.07	.05	.02
443	Cris Carpenter	.09	.07	.04
444	Kyle Abbott (Number 1 Daft Pick)(FC)			
		.30	.25	.12
445	Danny Jackson	.05	.04	.02
446	Dan Pasqua	.05	.04	.02
447	Atlee Hammaker	.03	.02	.01
448	Greg Gagne	.04	.03	.02
449	Dennis Rasmussen	.04	.03	.02
450	Rickey Henderson	.25	.20	.10
451	Mark Lemke(FC)	.10	.08	.04
452	Luis de los Santos(FC)	.10	.08	.04
453	Jody Davis	.03	.02	.01
454	Jeff King(FC)	.15	.11	.06
455	Jeffrey Leonard	.06	.05	.02
456	Chris Gwynn(FC)	.09	.07	.03
457	Gregg Jefferies	.30	.25	.12
458	Bob McClure	.03	.02	.01
459	Jim Lefebvre	.03	.02	.01
460	Mike Scott	.09	.07	.03
461	Carlos Martinez(FC)	.15	.11	.06
462	Denny Walling	.03	.02	.01
463	Drew Hall	.03	.02	.01
464	Jerome Walton	.25	.20	.10
465	Kevin Gross	.06	.05	.02
466	Rance Mulliniks	.03	.02	.01
467	Juan Nieves	.04	.03	.02
468	Billy Ripken	.04	.03	.02
469	John Kruk	.07	.05	.02
470	Frank Viola	.09	.07	.04
471	Mike Brumley	.03	.02	.01
472	Jose Uribe	.04	.03	.02
473	Joe Price	.03	.02	.01
474	Rich Thompson	.04	.03	.02
475	Bob Welch	.06	.05	.02
476	Brad Komminsk	.03	.02	.02
477	Willie Fraser	.03	.02	.01
478	Mike LaValliere	.04	.03	.02
479	Frank White	.06	.05	.02
480	Sid Fernandez	.09	.07	.04

		MT	NR MT	EX
481	Garry Templeton	.05	.04	.02
482	Steve Carter(FC)	.15	.11	.06
483	Alejandro Pena	.04	.03	.02
484	Mike Fitzgerald	.03	.02	.01
485	John Candelaria	.05	.04	.02
486	Jeff Treadway	.05	.04	.02
487	Steve Searcy	.05	.04	.02
488	Ken Oberkfell	.03	.02	.01
489	Nick Leyva	.03	.02	.01
490	Dan Plesac	.07	.05	.03
491	Dave Cochrane(FC)	.15	.11	.06
492	Ron Oester	.04	.03	.02
493	Jason Grimsley(FC)	.25	.20	.10
494	Terry Puhl	.03	.02	.01
495	Lee Smith	.06	.05	.02
496	Cecil Espy	.06	.05	.02
497	Dave Schmidt	.03	.02	.01
498	Rick Schu	.03	.02	.01
499	Bill Long	.04	.03	.02
500	Kevin Mitchell	.35	.25	.14
501	Matt Young	.03	.02	.01
502	Mitch Webster	.04	.03	.02
503	Randy St. Claire	.03	.02	.01
504	Tom O'Malley	.03	.02	.01
505	Kelly Gruber	.08	.06	.03
506	Tom Glavine	.20	.15	.08
507	Gary Redus	.04	.03	.02
508	Terry Leach	.03	.02	.01
509	Tom Pagnozzi	.03	.02	.01
510	Doc Gooden	.25	.20	.10
511	Clay Parker	.07	.05	.03
512	Gary Pettis	.03	.02	.01
513	Mark Eichhorn	.03	.02	.01
514	Andy Allanson	.03	.02	.01
515	Len Dykstra	.06	.05	.02
516	Tim Leary	.05	.04	.02
517	Roberto Alomar	.15	.11	.06
518	Bill Krueger	.03	.02	.01
519	Bucky Dent	.03	.02	.01
520	Mitch Williams	.09	.07	.03
521	Craig Worthington	.15	.11	.06
522	Mike Dunne	.04	.03	.02
523	Jay Bell	.03	.02	.01
524	Daryl Boston	.03	.02	.01
525	Wally Joyner	.20	.15	.08
526	Checklist 397-528	.03	.02	.01
527	Ron Hassey	.03	.02	.01
528	Kevin Wickander(FC)	.20	.15	.08
529	Greg Harris	.03	.02	.01
530	Mark Langston	.10	.08	.04
531	Ken Caminiti	.06	.05	.02
532	Cecilio Guante	.03	.02	.01
533	Tim Jones(FC)	.07	.05	.03
534	Louie Meadows	.07	.05	.03
535	John Smoltz	.15	.11	.06
536	Bob Geren	.15	.11	.06
537	Mark Grant	.03	.02	.01
538	Billy Spiers	.20	.15	.08
539	Neal Heaton	.03	.02	.01
540	Danny Tartabull	.09	.07	.03
541	Pat Perry	.03	.02	.01
542	Darren Daulton	.03	.02	.01
543	Nelson Liriano	.03	.02	.01
544	Dennis Boyd	.05	.04	.02
545	Kevin McReynolds	.09	.07	.04
546	Kevin Hickey	.05	.04	.02
547	Jack Howell	.05	.04	.02
548	Pat Clements	.03	.02	.01
549	Don Zimmer	.03	.02	.01
550	Julio Franco	.09	.07	.04
551	Tim Crews	.03	.02	.01
552	Mike Smith(FC)	.12	.09	.05
553	Scott Scudder(FC)	.20	.15	.11
554	Jay Buhner	.08	.06	.03
555	Jack Morris	.07	.05	.03
556	Gene Larkin	.03	.02	.01
557	Jeff Innis	.15	.11	.06
558	Rafael Ramirez	.04	.03	.02
559	Andy McGaffigan	.04	.03	.02
560	Steve Sax	.08	.06	.03
561	Ken Dayley	.03	.02	.01
562	Chad Kreuter	.10	.08	.04
563	Alex Sanchez	.10	.08	.04
564	#1 Draft Pick (Tyler Houston)(FC)	.20	.15	.08
565	Scott Fletcher	.05	.04	.02
566	Mark Knudson	.06	.05	.02
567	Ron Gant	.10	.08	.04
568	John Smiley	.07	.05	.03
569	Ivan Calderon	.05	.04	.02
570	Cal Ripken	.35	.25	.14
571	Brett Butler	.06	.05	.02

#	Player	MT	NR MT	EX
572	Greg Harris	.09	.07	.04
573	Danny Heep	.03	.02	.01
574	Bill Swift	.04	.03	.02
575	Lance Parrish	.07	.05	.03
576	*Mike Dyer*(FC)	.20	.15	.08
577	Charlie Hayes(FC)	.10	.08	.04
578	Joe Magrane	.09	.07	.04
579	Art Howe	.03	.02	.01
580	Joe Carter	.15	.11	.06
581	Ken Griffey	.05	.04	.02
582	Rick Honeycutt	.03	.02	.01
583	Bruce Benedict	.03	.02	.01
584	*Phil Stephenson*(FC)	.09	.07	.04
585	Kal Daniels	.10	.08	.04
586	Ed Nunez	.03	.02	.01
587	Lance Johnson	.08	.06	.03
588	Rick Rhoden	.03	.02	.01
589	Mike Aldrete	.03	.02	.01
590	Ozzie Smith	.10	.08	.04
591	Todd Stottlemyre	.08	.06	.03
592	R.J. Reynolds	.03	.02	.01
593	Scott Bradley	.03	.02	.01
594	*Luis Sojo*(FC)	.20	.15	.08
595	Greg Swindell	.10	.08	.04
596	Jose DeJesus(FC)	.10	.08	.04
597	Chris Bosio	.07	.05	.03
598	Brady Anderson	.05	.04	.02
599	Frank Williams	.03	.02	.01
600	Darryl Strawberry	.30	.15	.08
601	Luis Rivera	.04	.03	.02
602	Scott Garrelts	.07	.05	.03
603	Tony Armas	.03	.02	.01
604	Ron Robinson	.03	.02	.01
605	Mike Scioscia	.07	.05	.03
606	Storm Davis	.07	.05	.03
607	Steve Jeltz	.03	.02	.01
608	*Eric Anthony*(FC)	.20	.15	.08
609	Sparky Anderson	.03	.02	.01
610	Pedro Guerrero	.12	.09	.05
611	Walt Terrell	.05	.04	.02
612	Dave Gallagher	.07	.05	.02
613	Jeff Pico	.04	.03	.02
614	Nelson Santovenia	.09	.07	.04
615	Rob Deer	.07	.05	.03
616	Brian Holman	.10	.08	.04
617	Geronimo Berroa	.08	.06	.03
618	Eddie Whitson	.05	.04	.02
619	Rob Ducey	.08	.06	.03
620	*Tony Castillo*(FC)	.20	.15	.08
621	Melido Perez	.07	.05	.03
622	Sid Bream	.05	.04	.02
623	Jim Corsi	.05	.04	.02
624	Darrin Jackson	.04	.03	.02
625	Roger McDowell	.07	.05	.03
626	Bob Melvin	.03	.02	.01
627	Jose Rijo	.07	.05	.03
628	Candy Maldonado	.04	.03	.02
629	Eric Hetzel(FC)	.10	.08	.04
630	Gary Gaetti	.10	.08	.04
631	*John Wetteland*(FC)	.25	.20	.10
632	Scott Lusader	.06	.05	.02
633	Dennis Cook(FC)	.25	.20	.10
634	Luis Polonia	.06	.05	.02
635	Brian Downing	.06	.05	.02
636	Jesse Orosco	.03	.02	.01
637	Craig Reynolds	.03	.02	.01
638	Jeff Montgomery	.07	.05	.03
639	Tony LaRussa	.03	.02	.01
640	Rick Sutcliffe	.06	.05	.02
641	*Doug Strange*(FC)	.15	.11	.06
642	Jack Armstrong	.04	.03	.02
643	Alfredo Griffin	.04	.03	.02
644	Paul Assenmacher	.04	.03	.02
645	Jose Oquendo	.06	.05	.02
646	Checklist 529-660	.03	.02	.01
647	Rex Hudler	.03	.02	.01
648	Jim Clancy	.03	.02	.01
649	*Dan Murphy*(FC)	.15	.11	.06
650	Mike Witt	.06	.05	.02
651	Rafael Santana	.06	.05	.02
652	Mike Boddicker	.06	.05	.02
653	John Moses	.03	.02	.01
654	#1 Draft Pick *(Paul Coleman)*(FC)	.20	.15	.08
655	Gregg Olson	.30	.25	.12
656	Mackey Sasser	.05	.04	.02
657	Terry Mulholland	.06	.05	.02
658	Donell Nixon	.03	.02	.01
659	Greg Cadaret	.03	.02	.01
660	Vince Coleman	.10	.08	.04
661	Turn Back The Clock - 1985 (Dick Howser)	.07	.05	.03
662	Turn Back The Clock - 1980 (Mike Schmidt)	.07	.05	.03
663	Turn Back The Clock - 1975 (Fred Lynn)	.07	.05	.03
664	Turn Back The Clock - 1970 (Johnny Bench)	.07	.05	.03
665	Turn Back The Clock - 1965 (Sandy Koufax)	.07	.05	.03
666	Brian Fisher	.05	.04	.02
667	Curt Wilkerson	.03	.02	.01
668	*Joe Oliver*(FC)	.30	.25	.12
669	Tom Lasorda	.03	.02	.01
670	Dennis Eckersley	.09	.07	.04
671	Bob Boone	.09	.07	.04
672	Roy Smith	.03	.02	.01
673	Joey Meyer	.03	.02	.01
674	Spike Owen	.05	.04	.02
675	Jim Abbott	.35	.25	.12
676	Randy Kutcher(FC)	.07	.05	.03
677	Jay Tibbs	.03	.02	.01
678	Kirt Manwaring	.10	.08	.04
679	Gary Ward	.04	.03	.02
680	Howard Johnson	.15	.11	.06
681	Mike Schooler	.07	.05	.03
682	Dann Bilardello	.03	.02	.01
683	*Kenny Rogers*	.10	.08	.04
684	*Julio Machado*(FC)	.20	.15	.08
685	Tony Fernandez	.09	.07	.04
686	Carmelo Martinez	.06	.05	.02
687	Tim Birtsas	.03	.02	.01
688	Milt Thompson	.06	.05	.02
689	Rich Yett	.03	.02	.01
690	Mark McGwire	.30	.25	.12
691	Chuck Cary	.03	.02	.01
692	Sammy Sosa	.35	.25	.14
693	Calvin Schiraldi	.03	.02	.01
694	*Mike Stanton*(FC)	.15	.11	.06
695	Tom Henke	.06	.05	.02
696	B.J. Surhoff	.07	.05	.03
697	Mike Davis	.03	.02	.01
698	*Omar Vizquel*	.10	.08	.04
699	Jim Leyland	.03	.02	.01
700	Kirby Puckett	.25	.20	.10
701	*Bernie Williams*(FC)	.30	.25	.12
702	Tony Phillips	.04	.03	.02
703	*Jeff Brantley*	.12	.09	.05
704	*Chip Hale*(FC)	.15	.11	.06
705	Claudell Washington	.07	.05	.03
706	Geno Petralli	.03	.02	.01
707	Luis Aquino	.03	.02	.01
708	Larry Sheets	.03	.02	.01
709	Juan Berneguer	.03	.02	.01
710	Von Hayes	.05	.04	.02
711	Rick Aguilera	.09	.07	.04
712	Todd Benzinger	.09	.07	.04
713	*Tim Drummond*(FC)	.15	.11	.06
714	*Marquis Grissom*(FC)	.50	.40	.20
715	Greg Maddux	.15	.11	.06
716	Steve Balboni	.03	.02	.01
717	Ron Kakovice	.03	.02	.01
718	Gary Sheffield	.30	.25	.12
719	*Wally Whitehurst*(FC)	.15	.11	.06
720	Andres Galarraga	.15	.11	.06
721	Lee Mazzilli	.03	.02	.01
722	Felix Fermin	.03	.02	.01
723	Jeff Robinson	.05	.04	.02
724	Juan Bell(FC)	.10	.08	.04
725	Terry Pendleton	.07	.05	.03
726	Gene Nelson	.03	.02	.01
727	Pat Tabler	.05	.04	.02
728	Jim Acker	.03	.02	.01
729	Bobby Valentine	.03	.02	.01
730	Tony Gwynn	.20	.15	.08
731	Don Carman	.05	.04	.02
732	Ernie Riles	.03	.02	.01
733	John Dopson	.09	.07	.04
734	Kevin Elster	.06	.05	.02
735	Charlie Hough	.15	.11	.06
736	Rick Dempsey	.03	.02	.01
737	Chris Sabo	.15	.11	.06
738	*Gene Harris*	.10	.08	.04
739	Dale Sveum	.04	.03	.02
740	Jesse Barfield	.08	.06	.03
741	Steve Wilson	.10	.08	.04
742	Ernie Whitt	.05	.04	.02
743	Tom Candiotti	.05	.04	.02
744	*Kelly Mann*(FC)	.20	.15	.08
745	Hubie Brooks	.06	.05	.02
746	Dave Smith	.06	.05	.02
747	Randy Bush	.03	.02	.01
748	Doyle Alexander	.06	.05	.02

		MT	NR MT	EX
749	Mark Parent	.04	.03	.02
750	Dale Murphy	.10	.08	.04
751	Steve Lyons	.04	.03	.02
752	Tom Gordon	.25	.20	.10
753	Chris Speier	.03	.02	.01
754	Bob Walk	.05	.04	.02
755	Rafael Palmeiro	.08	.06	.03
756	Ken Howell	.03	.02	.01
757	*Larry Walker*(FC)	.40	.30	.15
758	Mark Thurmond	.03	.02	.01
759	Tom Trebelhorn	.03	.02	.01
760	Wade Boggs	.25	.20	.10
761	Mike Jackson	.05	.04	.02
762	Doug Dascenzo	.07	.05	.03
763	Denny Martinez	.07	.05	.03
764	Tim Teufel	.05	.04	.02
765	Chili Davis	.07	.05	.03
766	Brian Meyer(FC)	.10	.08	.04
767	Tracy Jones	.06	.05	.02
768	Chuck Crim	.04	.03	.02
769	*Greg Hibbard*(FC)	.30	.25	.12
770	Cory Snyder	.09	.07	.04
771	Pete Smith	.06	.05	.02
772	Jeff Reed	.03	.02	.01
773	Dave Leiper	.03	.02	.01
774	*Ben McDonald*(FC)	.60	.45	.25
775	Andy Van Slyke	.09	.07	.04
776	Charlie Leibrandt	.04	.03	.02
777	Tim Laudner	.03	.02	.01
778	Mike Jeffcoat	.03	.02	.01
779	Lloyd Moseby	.06	.05	.02
780	Orel Hershiser	.15	.11	.06
781	Mario Diaz	.03	.02	.01
782	Jose Alvarez	.03	.02	.01
783	Checklist 661-792	.03	.02	.01
784	Scott Bailes	.03	.02	.01
785	Jim Rice	.07	.05	.03
786	Eric King	.04	.03	.02
787	Rene Gonzales	.03	.02	.01
788	Frank DiPino	.03	.02	.01
789	John Wathan	.03	.02	.01
790	Gary Carter	.07	.05	.03
791	Alvaro Espinoza	.15	.11	.06
792	Gerald Perry	.06	.05	.02

1990 Topps All-Star
Glossy Set of 22

One glossy All-Star card was included in each 1990 Topps rack pack. The cards measure 2-1/2" by 3-1/2" and feature a similar style to past glossy All-Star cards. Special cards of All-Star team captains Carl Yastrzemski and Don Drysdale are included in the set.

		MT	NR MT	EX
Complete Set:		3.50	2.75	1.50
Common Player:		.12	.09	.05
1	Tom Lasorda	.12	.09	.05
2	Will Clark	.35	.25	.14
3	Ryne Sandberg	.30	.25	.12
4	Howard Johnson	.15	.11	.06
5	Ozzie Smith	.15	.11	.06
6	Kevin Mitchell	.25	.20	.10
7	Eric Davis	.25	.20	.10
8	Tony Gwynn	.20	.15	.08
9	Benny Santiago	.15	.11	.06
10	Rick Rueschel	.12	.09	.05

		MT	NR MT	EX
11	Don Drysdale	.12	.09	.05
12	Tony LaRussa	.12	.09	.05
13	Mark McGwire	.30	.25	.12
14	Julio Franco	.15	.11	.06
15	Wade Boggs	.25	.20	.10
16	Cal Ripken	.20	.15	.08
17	Bo Jackson	.60	.45	.25
18	Kirby Puckett	.25	.20	.10
19	Ruben Sierra	.25	.20	.10
20	Terry Steinbach	.12	.09	.05
21	Dave Stewart	.15	.11	.06
22	Carl Yastrzemski	.15	.11	.06

1990 Topps All Star
Glossy Set of 60

Sharp color photographs and a clutter-free design are features of the cards in this 60-card send away set. Topps initiated the redemption series in 1983 and increased the size of the set to 60 in 1986. Six special offer cards, which were included in Topps baseball wax packs, are necessary to obtain each of the six 10-card sets in the series.

		MT	NR MT	EX
Complete Set:		9.00	6.75	3.50
Common Player:		.10	.08	.04
1	Ryne Sandberg	.70	.50	.30
2	Nolan Ryan	.70	.50	.30
3	Glenn Davis	.15	.11	.06
4	Dave Stewart	.15	.11	.06
5	Barry Larkin	.15	.11	.06
6	Carney Lansford	.15	.11	.06
7	Darryl Strawberry	.60	.45	.25
8	Steve Sax	.15	.11	.06
9	Carlos Martinez	.10	.08	.04
10	Gary Sheffield	.40	.30	.15
11	Don Mattingly	.80	.60	.30
12	Mark Grace	.40	.30	.15
13	Bret Saberhagen	.20	.15	.08
14	Mike Scott	.10	.08	.04
15	Robin Yount	.20	.15	.08
16	Ozzie Smith	.15	.11	.06
17	Jeff Ballard	.10	.08	.04
18	Rick Reuschel	.10	.08	.04
19	Greg Briley	.10	.08	.04
20	Ken Griffey,Jr.	1.75	1.25	.70
21	Kevin Mitchell	.30	.25	.12
22	Wade Boggs	.60	.45	.25
23	Doc Gooden	.50	.40	.20
24	George Bell	.15	.11	.06
25	Eric Davis	.40	.30	.15
26	Ruben Sierra	.25	.20	.10
27	Roberto Alomar	.20	.15	.08
28	Gary Gaetti	.15	.11	.06
29	Gregg Olson	.20	.15	.08
30	Tom Gordon	.20	.15	.08
31	Jose Canseco	.80	.60	.30
32	Pedro Guerrero	.15	.11	.06
33	Joe Carter	.15	.11	.06
34	Mike Scioscia	.10	.08	.04
35	Julio Franco	.15	.11	.06
36	Joe Magrane	.10	.08	.04
37	Rickey Henderson	.40	.30	.15
38	Rock Raines	.15	.11	.06
39	Jerome Walton	.35	.25	.14
40	Bob Geren	.10	.08	.04
41	Andre Dawson	.20	.15	.08

		MT	NR MT	EX
42	Mark McGwire	.60	.45	.25
43	Howard Johnson	.20	.15	.08
44	Bo Jackson	.80	.60	.30
45	Shawon Dunston	.20	.15	.08
46	Carlton Fisk	.20	.15	.08
47	Mitch Williams	.15	.11	.06
48	Kirby Puckett	.35	.25	.14
49	Craig Worthington	.10	.08	.04
50	Jim Abbott	.20	.15	.08
51	Cal Ripken	.25	.20	.10
52	Will Clark	.70	.50	.30
53	Dennis Eckersley	.20	.15	.08
54	Craig Biggio	.15	.11	.06
55	Fred McGriff	.20	.15	.08
56	Tony Gwynn	.20	.15	.08
57	Mickey Tettleton	.10	.08	.04
58	Mark Davis	.10	.08	.04
59	Omar Vizquel	.10	.08	.04
60	Gregg Jefferies	.30	.25	.12

1990 Topps Big Baseball

For the third consecutive year, Topps issued a 330-card set of the oversized cards (2-5/8" by 3-3/4"). The cards were issued in three 110-card series. The cards are reminiscent of Topps cards from the mid-1950s in that they feature players in portrait and action shots. The 1990 set has action photos in freeze frames. As in previous years, the cards are printed on white card stock with a glossy finish on the front. The card backs include 1989 and career hitting, fielding and pitching stats and a player cartoon.

		MT	NR MT	EX
Complete Set:		18.00	13.50	7.25
Common Player:		.05	.04	.02
1	Dwight Evans	.08	.06	.03
2	Kirby Puckett	.25	.20	.10
3	Kevin Gross	.06	.05	.02
4	Ron Hassey	.05	.04	.02
5	Lloyd McClendon	.05	.04	.02
6	Bo Jackson	1.00	.70	.40
7	Lonnie Smith	.06	.05	.02
8	Alvaro Espinoza	.06	.05	.02
9	Roberto Alomar	.15	.11	.06
10	Glenn Braggs	.06	.05	.02
11	David Cone	.10	.08	.04
12	Clauudell Washington	.05	.04	.02
13	Pedro Guerrero	.10	.08	.04
14	Todd Benzinger	.06	.05	.02
15	Jeff Russell	.06	.05	.02
16	Terry Kennedy	.05	.04	.02
17	Kelly Gruber	.15	.11	.06
18	Alfredo Griffin	.05	.04	.02
19	Mark Grace	.20	.15	.08
20	Dave Winfield	.12	.09	.05
21	Bret Saberhagen	.15	.11	.06
22	Roger Clemens	.30	.25	.12
23	Bob Walk	.05	.04	.02
24	Dave Magadan	.15	.11	.06
25	Spike Owen	.06	.05	.02
26	Jody Davis	.05	.04	.02
27	Kent Hrbek	.12	.09	.05
28	Mark McGwire	.50	.40	.20
29	Eddie Murray	.15	.11	.06
30	Paul O'Neill	.06	.05	.02

		MT	NR MT	EX
31	Jose DeLeon	.06	.05	.02
32	Steve Lyons	.05	.04	.02
33	Dan Plesac	.06	.05	.02
34	Jack Howell	.05	.04	.02
35	Greg Briley	.06	.05	.02
36	Andy Hawkins	.06	.05	.02
37	Cecil Espy	.05	.04	.02
38	Rick Sutcliffe	.08	.06	.03
39	Jack Clark	.12	.09	.05
40	Dale Murphy	.12	.09	.05
41	Mike Henneman	.06	.05	.02
42	Rick Honeycutt	.05	.04	.02
43	Willie Randolph	.06	.05	.02
44	Marty Barrett	.06	.05	.02
45	Willie Wilson	.06	.05	.02
46	Wallace Johnson	.05	.04	.02
47	Greg Brock	.06	.05	.02
48	Tom Browning	.06	.05	.02
49	Gerald Young	.05	.04	.02
50	Dennis Eckersley	.15	.11	.06
51	Scott Garrelts	.06	.05	.02
52	Gary Redus	.05	.04	.02
53	Al Newman	.05	.04	.02
54	Darryl Boston	.05	.04	.02
55	Ron Oester	.05	.04	.02
56	Danny Tartabull	.08	.06	.03
57	Gregg Jefferies	.30	.25	.12
58	Tom Foley	.05	.04	.02
59	Robin Yount	.20	.15	.08
60	Pat Borders	.06	.05	.02
61	Mike Greenwell	.30	.25	.12
62	Shawon Dunston	.10	.08	.04
63	Steve Buechele	.05	.04	.02
64	Dave Stewart	.12	.09	.05
65	Jose Oquendo	.05	.04	.02
66	Ron Gant	.20	.15	.08
67	Mike Scioscia	.06	.05	.02
68	Randy Velarde	.05	.04	.02
69	Charlie Hayes	.06	.05	.02
70	Tim Wallach	.08	.06	.03
71	Eric Show	.06	.05	.02
72	Eric Davis	.25	.20	.10
73	Mike Gallego	.05	.04	.02
74	Rob Deer	.06	.05	.02
75	Ryne Sandberg	.40	.30	.15
76	Kevin Seitzer	.08	.06	.03
77	Wade Boggs	.50	.40	.20
78	Greg Gagne	.06	.05	.02
79	John Smiley	.06	.05	.02
80	Ivan Calderon	.08	.06	.03
81	Pete Incaviglia	.06	.05	.02
82	Orel Hershiser	.12	.09	.05
83	Carney Lansford	.08	.06	.03
84	Mike Fitzgerald	.05	.04	.02
85	Don Mattingly	.60	.45	.25
86	Chet Lemon	.06	.05	.02
87	Rolando Roomes	.05	.04	.02
88	Bill Spiers	.06	.05	.02
89	Pat Tabler	.06	.05	.02
90	Danny Heep	.05	.04	.02
91	Andre Dawson	.15	.11	.06
92	Randy Bush	.05	.04	.02
93	Tony Gwynn	.15	.11	.06
94	Tom Brunansky	.08	.06	.03
95	Johnny Ray	.06	.05	.02
96	Matt Williams	.15	.11	.06
97	Barry Lyons	.05	.04	.02
98	Jeff Hamilton	.05	.04	.02
99	Tom Glavine	.06	.05	.02
100	Ken Griffey, Sr.	.06	.05	.02
101	Tom Henke	.06	.05	.02
102	Dave Righetti	.08	.06	.03
103	Paul Molitor	.12	.09	.05
104	Mike LaValliere	.06	.05	.02
105	Frank White	.06	.05	.02
106	Bob Welch	.08	.06	.03
107	Ellis Burks	.25	.20	.10
108	Andres Galarraga	.08	.06	.03
109	Mitch Williams	.08	.06	.03
110	Checklist	.05	.04	.02
111	Craig Biggio	.08	.06	.03
112	Dave Steib	.08	.06	.03
113	Ron Darling	.06	.05	.02
114	Bert Blyleven	.10	.08	.04
115	Dickie Thon	.05	.04	.02
116	Carlos Martinez	.06	.05	.02
117	Jeff King	.06	.05	.02
118	Terry Steinbach	.06	.05	.02
119	Frank Tanana	.06	.05	.02
120	Mark Lemke	.10	.08	.04
121	Chris Sabo			

#	Name	MT	NR MT	EX
122	Glenn Davis	.15	.11	.06
123	Mel Hall	.06	.05	.02
124	Jim Gantner	.06	.05	.02
125	Benito Santiago	.10	.08	.04
126	Milt Thompson	.06	.05	.02
127	Rafael Palmeiro	.12	.09	.05
128	Barry Bonds	.20	.15	.08
129	Mike Bielecki	.06	.05	.02
130	Lou Whitaker	.10	.08	.04
131	Bob Ojeda	.05	.04	.02
132	Dion James	.05	.04	.02
133	Denny Martinez	.06	.05	.02
134	Fred McGriff	.20	.15	.08
135	Terry Pendleton	.06	.05	.02
136	Pat Combs	.10	.08	.04
137	Kevin Mitchell	.30	.25	.12
138	Marquis Grissom	.50	.40	.20
139	Chris Bosio	.06	.05	.02
140	Omar Vizquel	.05	.04	.02
141	Steve Sax	.10	.08	.04
142	Nelson Liriano	.05	.04	.02
143	Kevin Elster	.06	.05	.02
144	Dan Pasqua	.06	.05	.02
145	Dave Smith	.06	.05	.02
146	Craig Worthington	.06	.05	.02
147	Dan Gladden	.06	.05	.02
148	Oddibe McDowell	.05	.04	.02
149	Bip Roberts	.06	.05	.02
150	Randy Ready	.05	.04	.02
151	Dwight Smith	.10	.08	.04
152	Ed Whitson	.06	.05	.02
153	George Bell	.12	.09	.05
154	Tim Raines	.15	.11	.06
155	Sid Fernandez	.08	.06	.03
156	Henry Cotto	.05	.04	.02
157	Harold Baines	.12	.09	.05
158	Willie McGee	.10	.08	.04
159	Bill Doran	.06	.05	.02
160	Steve Balboni	.05	.04	.02
161	Pete Smith	.06	.05	.02
162	Frank Viola	.12	.09	.05
163	Gary Sheffield	.25	.20	.10
164	Bill Landrum	.06	.05	.02
165	Tony Fernandez	.08	.06	.03
166	Mike Heath	.05	.04	.02
167	Jody Reed	.08	.06	.03
168	Wally Joyner	.08	.06	.03
169	Robby Thompson	.06	.05	.02
170	Ken Caminiti	.06	.05	.02
171	Nolan Ryan	.40	.30	.15
172	Ricky Jordan	.08	.06	.03
173	Lance Blankenship	.05	.04	.02
174	Dwight Gooden	.30	.25	.12
175	Ruben Sierra	.20	.15	.08
176	Carlton Fisk	.15	.11	.06
177	Garry Templeton	.06	.05	.02
178	Mike Devereaux	.06	.05	.02
179	Mookie Wilson	.06	.05	.02
180	Jeff Blauser	.06	.05	.02
181	Scott Bradley	.05	.04	.02
182	Luis Salazar	.05	.04	.02
183	Rafael Ramirez	.06	.05	.02
184	Vince Coleman	.08	.06	.03
185	Doug Drabek	.10	.08	.04
186	Darryl Strawberry	.30	.25	.12
187	Tim Burke	.06	.05	.02
188	Jesse Barfield	.08	.06	.03
189	Barry Larkin	.15	.11	.06
190	Alan Trammell	.10	.08	.04
191	Steve Lake	.05	.04	.02
192	Derek Lilliquist	.06	.05	.02
193	Don Robinson	.06	.05	.02
194	Kevin McReynolds	.08	.06	.03
195	Melido Perez	.06	.05	.02
196	Jose Lind	.06	.05	.02
197	Eric Anthony	.50	.40	.20
198	B.J. Surhoff	.06	.05	.02
199	John Olerud	1.00	.70	.40
200	Mike Moore	.06	.05	.02
201	Mark Gubicza	.08	.06	.03
202	Phil Bradley	.06	.05	.02
203	Ozzie Smith	.12	.09	.05
204	Greg Maddux	.08	.06	.03
205	Julio Franco	.12	.09	.05
206	Tom Herr	.06	.05	.02
207	Scott Fletcher	.05	.04	.02
208	Bobby Bonilla	.15	.11	.06
209	Bob Geren	.06	.05	.02
210	Junior Felix	.20	.15	.08
211	Dick Schofield	.05	.04	.02
212	Jim Deshaies	.06	.05	.02
213	Jose Uribe	.06	.05	.02
214	John Kruk	.06	.05	.02
215	Ozzie Guillen	.08	.06	.03
216	Howard Johnson	.10	.08	.04
217	Andy Van Slyke	.08	.06	.03
218	Tim Laudner	.05	.04	.02
219	Manny Lee	.06	.05	.02
220	Checklist	.05	.04	.02
221	Cory Snyder	.08	.06	.03
222	Billy Hatcher	.06	.05	.02
223	Bud Black	.05	.04	.02
224	Will Clark	.40	.30	.15
225	Kevin Tapani	.20	.15	.08
226	Mike Pagliarulo	.06	.05	.02
227	Dave Parker	.12	.09	.05
228	Ben McDonald	1.00	.70	.40
229	Carlos Baerga	.50	.40	.20
230	Roger McDowell	.06	.05	.02
231	Delino DeShields	.50	.40	.20
232	Mark Langston	.10	.08	.04
233	Wally Backman	.06	.05	.02
234	Jim Eisenreich	.06	.05	.02
235	Mike Schooler	.06	.05	.02
236	Kevin Bass	.06	.05	.02
237	John Farrell	.05	.04	.02
238	Kal Daniels	.10	.08	.04
239	Tony Phillips	.06	.05	.02
240	Todd Stottlemyre	.06	.05	.02
241	Greg Olson	.15	.11	.06
242	Charlie Hough	.06	.05	.02
243	Mariano Duncan	.06	.05	.02
244	Billy Ripken	.05	.04	.02
245	Joe Carter	.12	.09	.05
246	Tim Belcher	.08	.06	.03
247	Roberto Kelly	.08	.06	.03
248	Candy Maldonado	.08	.06	.03
249	Mike Scott	.08	.06	.03
250	Ken Griffey,Jr.	1.25	.90	.50
251	Nick Esasky	.06	.05	.02
252	Tom Gordon	.15	.11	.06
253	John Tudor	.06	.05	.02
254	Gary Gaetti	.10	.08	.04
255	Neal Heaton	.06	.05	.02
256	Jerry Browne	.06	.05	.02
257	Joe Rijo	.06	.05	.02
258	Mike Boddicker	.06	.05	.02
259	Brett Butler	.06	.05	.02
260	Andy Benes	.10	.08	.04
261	Kevin Brown	.08	.06	.03
262	Hubie Brooks	.08	.06	.03
263	Randy Milligan	.06	.05	.02
264	John Franco	.10	.08	.04
265	Sandy Alomar	.30	.25	.12
266	Dave Valle	.06	.05	.02
267	Jerome Walton	.25	.20	.10
268	Bob Boone	.08	.06	.03
269	Ken Howell	.06	.05	.02
270	Jose Canseco	1.00	.70	.40
271	Joe Magrane	.08	.06	.03
272	Brian DuBois	.08	.06	.03
273	Carlos Quintana	.08	.06	.03
274	Lance Johnson	.06	.05	.02
275	Steve Bedrosian	.06	.05	.02
276	Brook Jacoby	.08	.06	.03
277	Fred Lynn	.06	.05	.02
278	Jeff Ballard	.06	.05	.02
279	Otis Nixon	.05	.04	.02
280	Chili Davis	.06	.05	.02
281	Joe Oliver	.12	.09	.05
282	Brian Holman	.08	.06	.03
283	Juan Samuel	.08	.06	.03
284	Rick Aguilera	.06	.05	.02
285	Jeff Reardon	.08	.06	.03
286	Sammy Sosa	.30	.25	.12
287	Carmelo Martinez	.06	.05	.02
288	Greg Swindell	.08	.06	.03
289	Erik Hanson	.15	.11	.06
290	Tony Pena	.08	.06	.03
291	Pascual Perez	.06	.05	.02
292	Rickey Henderson	.35	.25	.14
293	Kurt Stillwell	.06	.05	.02
294	Todd Zeile	.50	.40	.20
295	Bobby Thigpen	.10	.08	.04
296	Larry Walker	.30	.25	.12
297	Rob Murphy	.05	.04	.02
298	Mitch Webster	.05	.04	.02
299	Devon White	.06	.05	.02
300	Len Dykstra	.10	.08	.04
301	Keith Hernandez	.06	.05	.02
302	Gene Larkin	.06	.05	.02
303	Jeffrey Leonard	.06	.05	.02

		MT	NR MT	EX
304	Jim Presley	.06	.05	.02
305	Lloyd Moseby	.08	.06	.03
306	John Smoltz	.08	.06	.03
307	Sam Horn	.06	.05	.02
308	Greg Litton	.06	.05	.02
309	Dave Henderson	.08	.06	.03
310	Mark McLemore	.05	.04	.02
311	Gary Pettis	.06	.05	.02
312	Mark Davis	.05	.04	.02
313	Cecil Fielder	.50	.40	.20
314	Jack Armstrong	.08	.06	.03
315	Alvin Davis	.08	.06	.03
316	Doug Jones	.08	.06	.03
317	Eric Yelding	.08	.06	.03
318	Joe Orsulak	.06	.05	.02
319	Chuck Finley	.08	.06	.03
320	Glenn Wilson	.06	.05	.02
321	Harold Reynolds	.08	.06	.03
322	Teddy Higuera	.08	.06	.03
323	Lance Parrish	.08	.06	.03
324	Bruce Hurst	.06	.05	.02
325	Dave West	.06	.05	.02
326	Kirk Gibson	.10	.08	.04
327	Cal Ripken	.15	.11	.06
328	Rick Reuschel	.06	.05	.02
329	Jim Abbott	.15	.11	.06
330	Checklist	.05	.04	.02

1990 Topps Box Panels

This special 16-card set features four cards on four different box-bottom panels. The cards are identical in design to the regular 1990 Topps cards. The cards are designated by letter.

		MT	NR MT	EX
	Complete Panel Set:	3.00	2.25	1.25
	Complete Singles Set:	1.50	1.25	.60
	Common Panel:	.40	.30	.15
	Common Single Player:	.06	.05	.02
	Panel	.60	.45	.25
A	Wade Boggs	.25	.20	.10
B	George Brett	.20	.15	.08
C	Andre Dawson	.15	.11	.06
D	Darrell Evans	.06	.05	.02
	Panel	.60	.45	.25
E	Doc Gooden	.25	.20	.10
F	Rickey Henderson	.25	.20	.10
G	Tom Lasorda	.06	.05	.02
H	Fred Lynn	.06	.05	.02
	Panel	.40	.30	.15
I	Mark McGwire	.25	.20	.10
J	Dave Parker	.10	.08	.04
K	Jeff Reardon	.06	.05	.02
L	Rick Reuschel	.06	.05	.02
	Panel	.60	.45	.25
M	Jim Rice	.06	.05	.02
N	Cal Ripken	.10	.08	.04
O	Nolan Ryan	.25	.20	.10
P	Ryne Sandberg	.25	.20	.10

A player's name in italic type indicates a rookie card. An (FC) indicates a player's first card for that particular card company.

1990 Topps Traded

For the first time, Topps "Traded" series cards were made available nationwide in retail wax packs. The 132-card set was also sold in complete boxed form as it has been in recent years. The wax pack traded cards feature gray backs, while the boxed set cards feature white backs. The cards are numbered 1T-132T and showcase rookies, players who changed teams and new managers.

		MT	NR MT	EX
	Complete Set:	8.00	6.00	3.25
	Common Player:	.05	.04	.02
1T	Darrel Akerfelds	.05	.04	.02
2T	Sandy Alomar,Jr.	.20	.15	.08
3T	Brad Arnsberg	.05	.04	.02
4T	Steve Avery	.80	.60	.30
5T	Wally Backman	.05	.04	.02
6T	Carlos Baerga(FC)	1.00	.70	.40
7T	Kevin Bass	.06	.05	.02
8T	Willie Blair(FC)	.10	.08	.04
9T	Mike Blowers(FC)	.20	.15	.08
10T	Shawn Boskie(FC)	.20	.15	.08
11T	Daryl Boston	.05	.04	.02
12T	Dennis Boyd	.06	.05	.02
13T	Glenn Braggs	.06	.05	.02
14T	Hubie Brooks	.08	.06	.03
15T	Tom Brunansky	.08	.06	.03
16T	John Burkett(FC)	.25	.20	.10
17T	Casey Candaele	.05	.04	.02
18T	John Candelaria	.06	.05	.02
19T	Gary Carter	.10	.08	.04
20T	Joe Carter	.10	.08	.04
21T	Rick Cerone	.05	.04	.02
22T	Scott Coolbaugh(FC)	.15	.11	.06
23T	Bobby Cox	.05	.04	.02
24T	Mark Davis	.06	.05	.02
25T	Storm Davis	.06	.05	.02
26T	Edgar Diaz(FC)	.10	.08	.04
27T	Wayne Edwards(FC)	.20	.15	.08
28T	Mark Eichhorn	.05	.04	.02
29T	Scott Erickson(FC)	.70	.50	.30
30T	Nick Esasky	.06	.05	.02
31T	Cecil Fielder	.50	.40	.20
32T	John Franco	.08	.06	.03
33T	Travis Fryman(FC)	1.25	.90	.50
34T	Bill Gullickson	.05	.04	.02
35T	Darryl Hamilton	.15	.11	.06
36T	Mike Harkey	.20	.15	.08
37T	Bud Harrelson	.05	.04	.02
38T	Billy Hatcher	.06	.05	.02
39T	Keith Hernandez	.08	.06	.03
40T	Joe Hesketh	.05	.04	.02
41T	Dave Hollins(FC)	.25	.20	.10
42T	Sam Horn	.08	.06	.03
43T	Steve Howard(FC)	.20	.15	.08
44T	Todd Hundley(FC)	.25	.20	.10
45T	Jeff Huson	.10	.08	.04
46T	Chris James	.05	.04	.02
47T	Stan Javier	.05	.04	.02
48T	Dave Justice(FC)	1.50	1.25	.60
49T	Jeff Kaiser(FC)	.12	.09	.05
50T	Dana Kiecker(FC)	.20	.15	.08
51T	Joe Klink(FC)	.10	.08	.04
52T	Brent Knackert(FC)	.12	.09	.05
53T	Brad Komminsk	.05	.04	.02
54T	Mark Langston	.10	.08	.04
55T	Tim Layana(FC)	.25	.20	.10

56T	Rick Leach	.05	.04	.02
57T	Terry Leach	.05	.04	.02
58T	Tim Leary	.05	.04	.02
59T	Craig Lefferts	.05	.04	.02
60T	Charlie Leibrandt	.05	.04	.02
61T	Jim Leyritz(FC)	.20	.15	.08
62T	Fred Lynn	.06	.05	.02
63T	Kevin Maas(FC)	2.00	1.50	.80
64T	Shane Mack	.08	.06	.03
65T	Candy Maldonado	.06	.05	.02
66T	Fred Manrique	.05	.04	.02
67T	Mike Marshall	.05	.04	.02
68T	Carmelo Martinez	.05	.04	.02
69T	John Marzano	.06	.05	.02
70T	Ben McDonald	1.00	.70	.40
71T	Jack McDowell	.08	.06	.03
72T	John McNamara	.05	.04	.02
73T	Orlando Mercado	.05	.04	.02
74T	Stump Merrill	.05	.04	.02
75T	Alan Mills(FC)	.20	.15	.08
76T	Hal Morris	.40	.30	.15
77T	Lloyd Moseby	.06	.05	.02
78T	Randy Myers	.08	.06	.03
79T	Tim Naehring(FC)	.35	.25	.14
80T	Junior Noboa	.06	.05	.02
81T	Matt Nokes	.06	.05	.02
82T	Pete O'Brien	.05	.04	.02
83T	John Olerud(FC)	1.25	.90	.50
84T	Greg Olson(FC)	.15	.11	.06
85T	Junior Ortiz	.05	.04	.02
86T	Dave Parker	.15	.11	.06
87T	Rick Parker(FC)	.15	.11	.06
88T	Bob Patterson	.05	.04	.02
89T	Alejandro Pena	.05	.04	.02
90T	Tony Pena	.08	.06	.03
91T	Pascual Perez	.05	.04	.02
92T	Gerald Perry	.05	.04	.02
93T	Dan Petry	.05	.04	.02
94T	Gary Pettis	.06	.05	.02
95T	Tony Phillips	.05	.04	.02
96T	Lou Pinella	.05	.04	.02
97T	Luis Polonia	.05	.04	.02
98T	Jim Presley	.06	.05	.02
99T	Scott Radinsky(FC)	.25	.20	.10
100T	Willie Randolph	.08	.06	.03
101T	Jeff Reardon	.08	.06	.03
102T	Greg Riddoch	.05	.04	.02
103T	Jeff Robinson	.05	.04	.02
104T	Ron Robinson	.05	.04	.02
105T	Kevin Romine	.05	.04	.02
106T	Scott Ruskin(FC)	.20	.15	.08
107T	John Russell	.05	.04	.02
108T	Bill Sampen(FC)	.20	.15	.08
109T	Juan Samuel	.08	.06	.03
110T	Scott Sanderson	.06	.05	.02
111T	Jack Savage(FC)	.10	.08	.04
112T	Dave Schmidt	.05	.04	.02
113T	Red Schoendienst	.05	.04	.02
114T	Terry Shumpert(FC)	.20	.15	.08
115T	Matt Sinatro	.05	.04	.02
116T	Don Slaught	.05	.04	.02
117T	Bryn Smith	.05	.04	.02
118T	Lee Smith	.08	.06	.03
119T	Paul Sorrento(FC)	.20	.15	.08
120T	Franklin Stubbs	.05	.04	.02
121T	Russ Swan(FC)	.20	.15	.08
122T	Bob Tewksbury	.05	.04	.02
123T	Wayne Tolleson	.05	.04	.02
124T	John Tudor	.06	.05	.02
125T	Randy Veres(FC)	.10	.08	.04
126T	Hector Villanueva(FC)	.20	.15	.08
127T	Mitch Webster	.05	.04	.02
128T	Ernie Whitt	.06	.05	.02
129T	Frank Wills	.06	.05	.02
130T	Dave Winfield	.15	.11	.06
131T	Matt Young	.05	.04	.02
132T	Checklist	.05	.04	.02

1991 Topps

Topps celebrated its 40th anniversary in 1991 with the biggest promotional campaign in baseball card history. More than 300,000 vintage Topps cards (or certificates which can be redeemed for valuable older cards) produced from 1952 to present were randomly inserted in packs. Also a grand prize winner will receive one complete set from each year, and

others will receive a single set from 1952-present. The 1991 Topps card fronts feature the "Topps 40 Years of Baseball" logo in the upper left corner. Card borders frame the player photos. All players of the same team have cards with the same frame/border colors. Both action and posed shots appear in full-color on the card fronts. The flip sides are printed horizontally and feature complete statistics. Record Breakers and other special cards were once again included in the set. The cards measure 2-1/2" by 3-1/2". Several cards feature horizontal fronts. 6,313 forms of this set were released with gold "Operation Desert Shield" stamps on the fronts of the cards. The cards were released to U.S. troops serving in the Persian Gulf. Due to scarcity, these cards are quite valuable. Complete "Desert Shield" sets list for $4,000.

		MT	NR MT	EX
Complete Set:		18.00	13.50	7.25
Common Player:		.03	.02	.01
1	Nolan Ryan	.30	.25	.12
2	Record Breaker (George Brett)	.08	.06	.03
3	Record Breaker (Carlton Fisk)	.08	.06	.03
4	Record Breaker (Kevin Maas)	.10	.08	.04
5	Record Breaker (Cal Ripken)	.08	.04	.02
6	Record Breaker (Nolan Ryan)	.20	.15	.08
7	Record Breaker (Ryne Sandberg)	.10	.08	.04
8	Record Breaker (Bobby Thigpen)	.08	.06	.03
9	Darrin Fletcher(FC)	.10	.08	.04
10	Gregg Olson	.08	.06	.03
11	Roberto Kelly	.08	.06	.03
12	Paul Assenmacher	.04	.03	.02
13	Mariano Duncan	.06	.05	.02
14	Dennis Lamp	.03	.02	.01
15	Von Hayes	.08	.06	.03
16	Mike Heath	.04	.03	.02
17	Jeff Brantley	.06	.05	.02
18	Nelson Liriano	.03	.02	.01
19	Jeff Robinson	.04	.03	.02
20	Pedro Guerrero	.08	.06	.03
21	Joe Morgan	.03	.02	.01
22	Storm Davis	.06	.05	.02
23	Jim Gantner	.04	.03	.02
24	Dave Martinez	.05	.04	.02
25	Tim Belcher	.08	.06	.03
26	Luis Sojo	.06	.05	.02
27	Bobby Witt	.08	.06	.03
28	Alvaro Espinoza	.05	.04	.02
29	Bob Walk	.03	.02	.01
30	Gregg Jefferies	.15	.11	.06
31	*Colby Ward*(FC)	.15	.11	.06
32	*Mike Simms*(FC)	.20	.15	.08
33	Barry Jones	.05	.04	.02
34	Atlee Hammaker	.03	.02	.01
35	Greg Maddux	.08	.06	.03
36	Donnie Hill	.03	.02	.01
37	Tom Bolton	.05	.04	.02

A player's name in italic indicates a rookie card. An (FC) indicates a player's first card for that particular card company.

Values for recent cards and sets are listed in Mint (MT), Near Mint (NM) and Excellent (EX), reflecting the fact that many cards from recent years have been preserved in top condition. Recent cards and sets in less than Excellent condition have little collector interest.

		MT	NR MT	EX
38	Scott Bradley	.03	.02	.01
39	*Jim Neidlinger*(FC)	.15	.11	.06
40	Kevin Mitchell	.20	.15	.08
41	Ken Dayley	.04	.03	.02
42	*Chris Hoiles*(FC)	.20	.15	.08
43	Roger McDowell	.06	.05	.02
44	Mike Felder	.04	.03	.02
45	Chris Sabo	.10	.08	.04
46	Tim Drummond	.06	.05	.02
47	Brook Jacoby	.06	.05	.02
48	Dennis Boyd	.05	.04	.02
49a	Pat Borders (40 stolen bases in 1986)	.20	.15	.06
49b	Pat Borders (0 stolen bases in 1986)	.15	.11	.06
50	Bob Welch	.08	.06	.03
51	Art Howe	.03	.02	.01
52	*Francisco Oliveras*(FC)	.10	.08	.04
53	Mike Sahrperson	.06	.05	.02
54	Gary Mielke	.05	.04	.02
55	Jeffrey Leonard	.05	.04	.02
56	Jeff Parrett	.04	.03	.02
57	Jack Howell	.04	.03	.02
58	Mel Stottlemyre	.08	.06	.03
59	Eric Yelding	.06	.05	.02
60	Frank Viola	.12	.09	.05
61	Stan Javier	.04	.03	.02
62	Lee Guetterman	.03	.02	.01
63	Milt Thompson	.04	.03	.02
64	Tom Herr	.05	.04	.02
65	Bruce Hurst	.06	.05	.02
66	Terry Kennedy	.03	.02	.01
67	Rick Honeycutt	.03	.02	.01
68	Gary Sheffield	.15	.11	.06
69	Steve Wilson	.06	.05	.02
70	Ellis Burks	.15	.11	.06
71	Jim Acker	.03	.02	.01
72	Junior Ortiz	.03	.02	.01
73	Craig Worthington	.06	.05	.02
74	#1 Draft Pick (*Shane Andrews*)(FC)	.20	.15	.08
75	Jack Morris	.08	.06	.03
76	Jerry Browne	.05	.04	.02
77	Drew Hall	.03	.02	.01
78	Geno Petralli	.03	.02	.01
79	Frank Thomas	1.00	.70	.40
80a	Fernando Valenzuela (italics error)	.25	.20	.10
80b	Fernando Valenzuela (correct italics)	.15	.11	.06
81	Cito Gaston	.03	.02	.01
82	Tom Glavine	.05	.04	.02
83	Daryl Boston	.03	.02	.01
84	Bob McClure	.03	.02	.01
85	Jesse Barfield	.08	.06	.03
86	Les Lancaster	.04	.03	.02
87	Tracy Jones	.03	.02	.01
88	Bob Tewksbury	.04	.03	.02
89	Darren Daulton	.06	.05	.02
90	Danny Tartabull	.08	.06	.03
91	*Greg Colbrunn*(FC)	.15	.11	.06
92	Danny Jackson	.06	.05	.02
93	Ivan Calderon	.08	.06	.03
94	John Dopson	.05	.04	.02
95	Paul Molitor	.10	.08	.04
96	Trevor Wilson	.04	.03	.02
97	Brady Anderson	.04	.03	.02
98	Sergio Valdez	.05	.04	.02
99	Chris Gwynn	.05	.04	.02
100a	Don Mattingly (10 hits in 1990)	.60	.45	.25
100b	Don Mattingly (101 hits in 1990)	.40	.30	.15

		MT	NR MT	EX
101	Rob Ducey	.04	.03	.02
102	Gene Larkin	.06	.05	.02
103	#1 Draft Pick (*Tim Costo*)(FC)	.35	.25	.14
104	Don Robinson	.04	.03	.02
105	Kevin McReynolds	.05	.04	.02
106	Ed Nunez	.03	.02	.01
107	Luis Polonia	.04	.03	.02
108	Matt Young	.04	.03	.02
109	Greg Riddoch	.03	.02	.01
110	Tom Henke	.06	.05	.02
111	Andres Thomas	.03	.02	.01
112	Frank DiPino	.03	.02	.01
113	#1 Draft Pick (*Carl Everett*)(FC)	.35	.25	.14
114	*Lance Dickson*(FC)	.40	.30	.15
115	Hubie Brooks	.08	.06	.03
116	Mark Davis	.05	.04	.02
117	Dion James	.03	.02	.01
118	*Tom Edens*(FC)	.10	.08	.04
119	Carl Nichols(FC)	.05	.04	.02
120	Joe Carter	.08	.06	.03
121	Eric King	.05	.04	.02
122	Paul O'Neill	.06	.05	.02
123	Greg Harris	.05	.04	.02
124	Randy Bush	.04	.03	.02
125	Steve Bedrosian	.06	.05	.02
126	*Bernard Gilkey*(FC)	.20	.15	.08
127	Joe Price	.03	.02	.01
128	*Travis Fryman*	.60	.45	.25
129	Mark Eichhorn	.03	.02	.01
130	Ozzie Smith	.08	.06	.03
131	Checklist 1	.03	.02	.01
132	Jamie Quirk	.03	.02	.01
133	Greg Briley	.08	.06	.03
134	Kevin Elster	.04	.03	.02
135	Jerome Walton	.08	.06	.03
136	Dave Schmidt	.03	.02	.01
137	Randy Ready	.03	.02	.01
138	Jamie Moyer	.04	.03	.02
139	Jeff Treadway	.05	.04	.02
140	Fred McGriff	.10	.08	.04
141	Nick Leyva	.03	.02	.01
142	Curtis Wilkerson	.04	.03	.02
143	John Smiley	.04	.03	.02
144	Dave Henderson	.06	.05	.02
145	Lou Whitaker	.08	.06	.03
146	Dan Plesac	.06	.05	.02
147	*Carlos Baerga*	.20	.15	.08
148	Rey Palacios	.04	.03	.02
149	*Al Osuna*(FC)	.15	.11	.06
150	Cal Ripken	.12	.09	.05
151	Tom Browning	.06	.05	.02
152	Mickey Hatcher	.04	.03	.02
153	Bryan Harvey	.06	.05	.02
154	Jay Buhner	.06	.05	.02
155	Dwight Evans	.08	.06	.03
156	Carlos Martinez	.06	.05	.02
157	John Smoltz	.08	.06	.03
158	Jose Uribe	.04	.03	.02
159	Joe Boever	.03	.02	.01
160	Vince Coleman	.08	.06	.03
161	Tim Leary	.04	.03	.02
162	*Ozzie Canseco*(FC)	.15	.11	.06
163	Dave Johnson	.04	.03	.02
164	Edgar Diaz	.05	.04	.02
165	Sandy Alomar	.15	.11	.06
166	Harold Baines	.08	.06	.03
167	*Randy Tomlin*(FC)	.25	.20	.10
168	John Olerud	.30	.25	.12
169	Luis Aquino	.04	.03	.02
170	Carlton Fisk	.10	.08	.04
171	Tony LaRussa	.04	.03	.02
172	Pete Incaviglia	.06	.05	.02
173	Jason Grimsley	.06	.05	.02
174	Ken Caminiti	.05	.04	.02
175	Jack Armstrong	.08	.06	.03
176	John Orton(FC)	.06	.05	.02
177	*Reggie Harris*(FC)	.15	.11	.06
178	Dave Valle	.04	.03	.02
179	Pete Harnisch	.06	.05	.02
180	Tony Gwynn	.12	.09	.05
181	Duane Ward	.04	.03	.02
182	Junior Noboa	.04	.03	.02
183	Clay Parker	.04	.03	.02
184	Gary Green	.10	.08	.04
185	Joe Magrane	.06	.05	.02
186	Rod Booker	.03	.02	.01
187	Greg Cadaret	.03	.02	.01
188	Damon Berryhill	.06	.05	.02
189	*Daryl Irvine*(FC)	.15	.11	.06
190	Matt Williams	.15	.11	.06
191	*Willie Blair*	.10	.08	.04

#	Player	MT	NR MT	EX
192	Rob Deer	.06	.05	.02
193	Felix Fermin	.03	.02	.01
194	Xavier Hernandez(FC)	.08	.06	.02
195	Wally Joyner	.10	.08	.04
196	*Jim Vatcher*(FC)	.12	.09	.05
197	*Chris Nabholz*(FC)	.20	.15	.08
198	R.J. Reynolds	.04	.03	.02
199	Mike Hartley(FC)	.15	.11	.06
200	Darryl Strawberry	.20	.15	.08
201	Tom Kelly	.03	.02	.01
202	*Jim Leyritz*	.12	.09	.05
203	Gene Harris	.05	.04	.02
204	Herm Winningham	.04	.03	.02
205	*Mike Perez*(FC)	.15	.11	.06
206	Carlos Quintana	.08	.06	.03
207	Gary Wayne	.05	.04	.02
208	Willie Wilson	.06	.05	.02
209	Ken Howell	.05	.04	.02
210	Lance Parrish	.08	.06	.03
211	*Brian Barnes*(FC)	.20	.15	.08
212	Steve Finley	.06	.05	.02
213	Frank Wills	.06	.05	.02
214	Joe Girardi	.06	.05	.02
215	Dave Smith	.06	.05	.02
216	Greg Gagne	.04	.03	.02
217	Chris Bosio	.05	.04	.02
218	*Rick Parker*	.03	.02	.01
219	Jack McDowell	.06	.05	.02
220	Tim Wallach	.08	.06	.03
221	Don Slaught	.04	.03	.02
222	*Brian McRae*(FC)	.40	.30	.15
223	Allan Anderson	.04	.03	.02
224	Juan Gonzalez	.35	.25	.14
225	Randy Johnson	.06	.05	.02
226	Alfredo Griffin	.04	.03	.02
227	Steve Avery	.15	.11	.06
228	Rex Hudler	.04	.03	.02
229	Rance Mulliniks	.03	.02	.01
230	Sid Fernandez	.08	.06	.03
231	Doug Rader	.03	.02	.01
232	Jose DeJesus	.08	.06	.03
233	Al Leiter	.03	.02	.01
234	*Scott Erickson*	.80	.60	.30
235	Dave Parker	.10	.08	.04
236	Frank Tanana	.06	.05	.02
237	Rick Cerone	.03	.02	.01
238	Mike Dunne	.03	.02	.01
239	*Darren Lewis*(FC)	.30	.25	.12
240	Mike Scott	.08	.06	.03
241	Dave Clark	.04	.03	.02
242	Mike LaCoss	.03	.02	.01
243	Lance Johnson	.06	.05	.02
244	Mike Jeffcoat	.03	.02	.01
245	Kal Daniels	.08	.06	.03
246	Kevin Wickander	.05	.04	.02
247	Jody Reed	.08	.06	.03
248	Tom Gordon	.08	.06	.03
249	Bob Melvin	.03	.02	.01
250	Dennis Eckersley	.10	.08	.04
251	Mark Lemke	.05	.04	.02
252	*Mel Rojas*(FC)	.15	.11	.06
253	Garry Templeton	.04	.03	.02
254	*Shawn Boskie*	.15	.11	.06
255	Brian Downing	.05	.04	.02
256	Greg Hibbard	.08	.06	.03
257	Tom O'Malley	.03	.02	.01
258	Chris Hammond(FC)	.15	.11	.06
259	Hensley Meulens	.08	.06	.03
260	Harold Reynolds	.06	.05	.02
261	Bud Harrelson	.03	.02	.01
262	Tim Jones	.04	.03	.02
263	Checklist 2	.03	.02	.01
264	*Dave Hollins*	.25	.20	.10
265	Mark Gubicza	.06	.05	.02
266	Carmen Castillo	.03	.02	.01
267	Mark Knudson	.03	.02	.01
268	Tom Brookens	.04	.03	.02
269	Joe Hesketh	.03	.02	.01
270	Mark McGwire	.25	.20	.10
271	*Omar Olivares*(FC)	.15	.11	.06
272	Jeff King	.06	.05	.02
273	Johnny Ray	.05	.04	.02
274	Ken Williams	.03	.02	.01
275	Alan Trammell	.10	.08	.04
276	Bill Swift	.05	.04	.02
277	Scott Coolbaugh	.06	.05	.02
278	*Alex Fernandez*(FC)	.60	.45	.25
279a	Jose Gonzalez (photo of Billy Bean)	.20	.15	.08
279b	Jose Gonzalez (correct photo)	.12	.09	.05
280	Bret Saberhagen	.08	.06	.03
281	Larry Sheets	.04	.03	.02
282	Don Carman	.04	.03	.02
283	Marquis Grissom	.10	.08	.04
284	Bill Spiers	.06	.05	.02
285	Jim Abbott	.10	.08	.04
286	Ken Oberkfell	.04	.03	.02
287	Mark Grant	.03	.02	.01
288	Derrick May(FC)	.40	.30	.15
289	Tim Birtsas	.03	.02	.01
290	Steve Sax	.08	.06	.03
291	John Wathan	.03	.02	.01
292	Bud Black	.04	.03	.02
293	Jay Bell	.06	.05	.02
294	Mike Moore	.06	.05	.02
295	Rafael Palmeiro	.08	.06	.03
296	Mark Williamson	.04	.03	.02
297	Manny Lee	.04	.03	.02
298	Omar Vizquel	.04	.03	.02
299	*Scott Radinsky*	.15	.11	.06
300	Kirby Puckett	.15	.11	.06
301	Steve Farr	.04	.03	.02
302	Tim Teufel	.03	.02	.01
303	Mike Boddicker	.06	.05	.02
304	Kevin Reimer(FC)	.10	.08	.04
305	Mike Scioscia	.06	.05	.02
306	Lonnie Smith	.06	.05	.02
307	Andy Benes	.08	.06	.03
308	Tom Pagnozzi	.04	.03	.02
309	Norm Charlton	.08	.06	.03
310	Gary Carter	.08	.06	.03
311	Jeff Pico	.03	.02	.01
312	Charlie Hayes	.06	.05	.02
313	Ron Robinson	.06	.05	.02
314	Gary Pettis	.04	.03	.02
315	Roberto Alomar	.10	.08	.04
316	Gene Nelson	.03	.02	.01
317	Mike Fitzgerald	.03	.02	.01
318	Rick Aguilera	.06	.05	.02
319	Jeff McKnight(FC)	.06	.05	.02
320	Tony Fernandez	.08	.06	.03
321	Bob Rodgers	.03	.02	.01
322	*Terry Shumpert*	.15	.11	.06
323	Cory Snyder	.08	.06	.03
324	Ron Kittle	.08	.06	.03
325	Brett Butler	.06	.05	.02
326	Ken Patterson	.04	.03	.02
327	Ron Hassey	.03	.02	.01
328	Walt Terrell	.04	.03	.02
329	Dave Justice	.50	.40	.20
330	Doc Gooden	.20	.15	.08
331	Eric Anthony	.10	.08	.04
332	Kenny Rogers	.06	.05	.02
333	#1 Draft Pick *(Chipper Jones)*(FC)	.50	.40	.20
334	Todd Benzinger	.05	.04	.02
335	Mitch Williams	.08	.06	.03
336	Matt Nokes	.06	.05	.02
337	Keith Comstock	.03	.02	.01
338	Luis Rivera	.04	.03	.02
339	Larry Walker	.08	.06	.03
340	Ramon Martinez	.15	.11	.06
341	John Moses	.03	.02	.01
342	*Mickey Morandini*	.15	.11	.06
343	Jose Oquendo	.04	.03	.02
344	Jeff Russell	.06	.05	.02
345	Jose DeJesus	.06	.05	.02
346	Jesse Orosco	.04	.03	.02
347	Greg Vaughn	.10	.08	.04
348	Todd Stottlemyre	.06	.05	.02
349	Dave Gallagher	.04	.03	.02
350	Glenn Davis	.12	.09	.05
351	Joe Torre	.03	.02	.01
352	Frank White	.06	.05	.02
353	Tony Castillo	.05	.04	.02
354	Sid Bream	.05	.04	.02
355	Chili Davis	.06	.05	.02
356	Mike Marshall	.06	.05	.02
357	Jack Savage	.10	.08	.04
358	Mark Parent	.03	.02	.01
359	Chuck Cary	.04	.03	.02
360	Rock Raines	.15	.11	.06
361	Scott Garrelts	.05	.04	.02
362	*Hector Villanueva*	.15	.11	.06
363	Rick Mahler	.04	.03	.02
364	Dan Pasqua	.06	.05	.02
365	Mike Schooler	.06	.05	.02
366	Checklist 3	.03	.02	.01
367	*Dave Walsh*(FC)	.15	.11	.06
368	Felix Jose	.06	.05	.02
369	Steve Searcy	.06	.05	.02
370	Kelly Gruber	.12	.09	.05
371	Jeff Montgomery	.06	.05	.02

#	Name	MT	NR MT	EX
372	Spike Owen	.05	.04	.02
373	Darrin Jackson	.04	.03	.02
374	Larry Casian(FC)	.15	.11	.06
375	Tony Pena	.06	.05	.02
376	Mike Harkey	.08	.06	.03
377	Rene Gonzales	.03	.02	.01
378	Wilson Alvarez(FC)	.40	.30	.15
379	Randy Velarde	.04	.03	.02
380	Willie McGee	.08	.06	.03
381	Jose Lind	.05	.04	.02
382	Mackey Sasser	.05	.04	.02
383	Pete Smith	.06	.05	.02
384	Gerald Perry	.05	.04	.02
385	Mickey Tettleton	.05	.04	.02
386	Cecil Fielder (AS)	.10	.08	.04
387	Julio Franco (AS)	.08	.06	.03
388	Kelly Gruber (AS)	.08	.06	.03
389	Alan Trammell (AS)	.06	.05	.02
390	Jose Canseco (AS)	.10	.08	.04
391	Rickey Henderson (AS)	.10	.08	.04
392	Ken Griffey,Jr. (AS)	.30	.25	.12
393	Carlton Fisk (AS)	.08	.06	.03
394	Bob Welch (AS)	.06	.05	.02
395	Chuck Finley (AS)	.06	.05	.02
396	Bobby Thigpen (AS)	.08	.06	.03
397	Eddie Murray (AS)	.08	.06	.03
398	Ryne Sandberg (AS)	.10	.08	.04
399	Matt Williams (AS)	.08	.06	.03
400	Barry Larkin (AS)	.08	.06	.03
401	Barry Bonds (AS)	.10	.08	.04
402	Darryl Strawberry (AS)	.10	.08	.04
403	Bobby Bonilla (AS)	.10	.08	.04
404	Mike Scoscia (AS)	.06	.05	.02
405	Doug Drabek (AS)	.08	.06	.03
406	Frank Viola (AS)	.08	.06	.03
407	John Franco (AS)	.06	.05	.02
408	Ernie Riles	.04	.03	.02
409	Mike Stanley	.03	.02	.01
410	Dave Righetti	.08	.06	.03
411	Lance Blankenship	.04	.03	.02
412	Dave Bergman	.03	.02	.01
413	Terry Mulholland	.06	.05	.02
414	Sammy Sosa	.15	.11	.06
415	Rick Sutcliffe	.08	.06	.03
416	Randy Milligan	.06	.05	.02
417	Bill Krueger	.03	.02	.01
418	Nick Esasky	.06	.05	.02
419	Jeff Reed	.03	.02	.01
420	Bobby Thigpen	.08	.06	.03
421	Alex Cole(FC)	.20	.15	.08
422	Rick Rueschel	.06	.05	.02
423	Rafael Ramirez	.04	.03	.02
424	Calvin Schiraldi	.03	.02	.01
425	Andy Van Slyke	.08	.06	.03
426	Joe Grahe(FC)	.15	.11	.06
427	Rick Dempsey	.03	.02	.01
428	John Barfield(FC)	.10	.08	.04
429	Stump Merrill	.03	.02	.01
430	Gary Gaetti	.08	.06	.03
431	Paul Gibson	.03	.02	.01
432	Delino DeShields	.20	.15	.08
433	Pat Tabler	.04	.03	.02
434	Julio Machado(FC)	.10	.08	.04
435	Kevin Maas	.25	.20	.10
436	Scott Bankhead	.05	.04	.02
437	Doug Dascenzo	.04	.03	.02
438	Vicente Palacios	.05	.04	.02
439	Dickie Thon	.03	.02	.01
440	George Bell	.08	.06	.03
441	Zane Smith	.04	.03	.02
442	Charlie O'Brien	.04	.03	.02
443	Jeff Innis	.05	.04	.02
444	Glenn Braggs	.05	.04	.02
445	Greg Swindell	.06	.05	.02
446	Craig Grebeck(FC)	.15	.11	.06
447	John Burkett	.12	.09	.05
448	Craig Lefferts	.05	.04	.02
449	Juan Berenguer	.03	.02	.01
450	Wade Boggs	.15	.11	.06
451	Neal Heaton	.05	.04	.02
452	Bill Schroeder	.03	.02	.01
453	Lenny Harris	.05	.04	.02
454	Kevin Appier	.08	.06	.03
455	Walt Weiss	.06	.05	.02
456	Charlie Leibrandt	.05	.04	.02
457	Todd Hundley	.20	.15	.08
458	Brian Holman	.06	.05	.02
459	Tom Trebelhorn	.03	.02	.01
460	Dave Steib	.08	.06	.03
461	Robin Ventura	.08	.06	.03
462	Steve Frey	.06	.05	.02
463	Dwight Smith	.06	.05	.02
464	Steve Buechele	.04	.03	.02
465	Ken Griffey	.05	.04	.02
466	Charles Nagy(FC)	.10	.08	.04
467	Dennis Cook	.06	.05	.02
468	Tim Hulett	.04	.03	.02
469	Chet Lemon	.05	.04	.02
470	Howard Johnson	.10	.08	.04
471	#1 Draft Pick (Mike Lieberthal)(FC)	.30	.25	.12
472	Kirt Manwaring	.05	.04	.02
473	Curt Young	.04	.03	.02
474	Phil Plantier(FC)	.40	.30	.15
475	Teddy Higuera	.08	.06	.03
476	Glenn Wilson	.05	.04	.02
477	Mike Fetters	.06	.05	.02
478	Kurt Stillwell	.05	.04	.02
479	Bob Patterson	.03	.02	.01
480	Dave Magadan	.10	.08	.04
481	Eddie Whitson	.05	.04	.02
482	Tino Martinez	.40	.30	.15
483	Mike Aldrete	.04	.03	.02
484	Dave LaPoint	.03	.02	.02
485	Terry Pendleton	.06	.05	.02
486	Tommy Greene(FC)	.10	.08	.04
487	Rafael Belliard	.03	.02	.01
488	Jeff Manto(FC)	.15	.11	.06
489	Bobby Valentine	.03	.02	.01
490	Kirk Gibson	.08	.06	.03
491	#1 Draft Pick (Kurt Miller)(FC)	.30	.25	.12
492	Ernie Whitt	.05	.04	.02
493	Jose Rijo	.08	.06	.03
494	Chris James	.06	.05	.02
495	Charlie Hough	.04	.03	.02
496	Marty Barrett	.05	.04	.02
497	Ben McDonald	.30	.25	.12
498	Mark Salas	.03	.02	.01
499	Melido Perez	.06	.05	.02
500	Will Clark	.30	.25	.12
501	Mike Bielecki	.05	.04	.02
502	Carney Lansford	.06	.05	.02
503	Roy Smith	.04	.03	.02
504	Julio Valera(FC)	.15	.11	.06
505	Chuck Finley	.08	.06	.03
506	Darnell Coles	.04	.03	.02
507	Steve Jeltz	.03	.02	.01
508	Mike York(FC)	.15	.11	.06
509	Glenallen Hill	.06	.05	.02
510	John Franco	.08	.06	.03
511	Steve Balboni	.03	.02	.01
512	Jose Mesa(FC)	.05	.04	.02
513	Jerald Clark	.05	.04	.02
514	Mike Stanton	.08	.06	.03
515	Alvin Davis	.08	.06	.03
516	Karl Rhodes(FC)	.20	.15	.08
517	Joe Oliver	.06	.05	.02
518	Cris Carpenter	.05	.04	.02
519	Sparky Anderson	.04	.03	.02
520	Mark Grace	.15	.11	.06
521	Joe Orsulak	.05	.04	.02
522	Stan Belinda	.06	.05	.02
523	Rodney McCray(FC)	.15	.11	.06
524	Darrel Akerfelds	.04	.03	.02
525	Willie Randolph	.06	.05	.02
526	Moises Alou(FC)	.15	.11	.06
527	Checklist 4	.03	.02	.01
528	Denny Martinez	.06	.05	.02
529	#1 Draft Pick (Mark Newfield)(FC)	.60	.45	.25
530	Roger Clemens	.20	.15	.08
531	Dave Rhode(FC)	.15	.11	.06
532	Kirk McCaskill	.06	.05	.02
533	Oddibe McDowell	.05	.04	.02
534	Mike Jackson	.04	.03	.02
535	Ruben Sierra	.15	.11	.06
536	Mike Witt	.04	.03	.02
537	Mike LaValliere	.05	.04	.02
538	Bip Roberts	.05	.04	.02
539	Scott Terry	.03	.02	.01
540	George Brett	.12	.09	.05
541	Domingo Ramos	.03	.02	.01
542	Rob Murphy	.03	.02	.01
543	Junior Felix	.08	.06	.03
544	Alejandro Pena	.03	.02	.01
545	Dale Murphy	.10	.08	.04
546	Jeff Ballard	.05	.04	.02
547	Mike Pagliarulo	.04	.03	.02
548	Jaime Navarro	.10	.08	.04
549	John McNamara	.03	.02	.01
550	Eric Davis	.15	.11	.06
551	Bob Kipper	.03	.02	.01
552	Jeff Hamilton	.04	.03	.02

		MT	NR MT	EX			MT	NR MT	EX
553	Joe Klink	.10	.08	.04	641	Mike Henneman	.06	.05	.02
554	Brian Harper	.06	.05	.02	642	Hal Morris	.15	.11	.06
555	Turner Ward(FC)	.20	.15	.08	643	Jim Presley	.06	.05	.02
556	Gary Ward	.04	.03	.02	644	Chuck Crim	.04	.03	.02
557	Wally Whitehurst	.06	.05	.02	645	Juan Samuel	.06	.05	.02
558	Otis Nixon	.03	.02	.01	646	Andujar Cedeno(FC)	.30	.25	.12
559	Adam Peterson	.06	.05	.02	647	Mark Portugal	.04	.03	.02
560	Greg Smith(FC)	.15	.11	.06	648	Lee Stevens(FC)	.15	.11	.06
561	Tim McIntosh(FC)	.15	.11	.06	649	Bill Sampen	.15	.11	.06
562	Jeff Kunkel	.03	.02	.01	650	Jack Clark	.08	.06	.03
563	Brent Knackert	.10	.08	.04	651	Alan Mills	.12	.09	.05
564	Dante Bichette	.08	.06	.03	652	Kevin Romine	.03	.02	.01
565	Craig Biggio	.08	.06	.03	653	Anthony Telford(FC)	.20	.15	.08
566	Craig Wilson(FC)	.15	.11	.06	654	Paul Sorrento(FC)	.15	.11	.06
567	Dwayne Henry	.03	.02	.01	655	Erik Hanson	.08	.06	.03
568	Ron Karkovice	.04	.03	.02	656	Checklist 5	.03	.02	.01
569	Curt Schilling	.05	.04	.02	657	Mike Kingery	.03	.02	.01
570	Barry Bonds	.15	.11	.06	658	Scott Aldred(FC)	.15	.11	.06
571	Pat Combs	.08	.06	.03	659	Oscar Azocar(FC)	.15	.11	.06
572	Dave Anderson	.03	.02	.01	660	Lee Smith	.06	.05	.02
573	Rich Rodriguez(FC)	.15	.11	.06	661	Steve Lake	.03	.02	.01
574	John Marzano	.04	.03	.02	662	Rob Dibble	.08	.06	.03
575	Robin Yount	.15	.11	.06	663	Greg Brock	.05	.04	.02
576	Jeff Kaiser(FC)	.10	.08	.04	664	John Farrell	.04	.03	.02
577	Bill Doran	.06	.05	.02	665	Jim Leyland	.03	.02	.01
578	Dave West	.06	.05	.02	666	Danny Darwin	.06	.05	.02
579	Roger Craig	.03	.02	.01	667	Kent Anderson	.04	.03	.02
580	Dave Stewart	.12	.09	.05	668	Bill Long	.04	.03	.02
581	Luis Quinones	.03	.02	.01	669	Lou Pinella	.04	.03	.02
582	Marty Clary	.03	.02	.01	670	Rickey Henderson	.35	.25	.14
583	Tony Phillips	.04	.03	.02	671	Andy McGaffigan	.03	.02	.01
584	Kevin Brown	.06	.05	.02	672	Shane Mack	.06	.05	.02
585	Pete O'Brien	.04	.03	.02	673	Greg Olson	.20	.15	.08
586	Fred Lynn	.05	.04	.02	674	Kevin Gross	.06	.05	.02
587	Jose Offerman(FC)	.25	.20	.10	675	Tom Brunansky	.08	.06	.03
588	Mark Whiten(FC)	.35	.25	.14	676	Scott Chiamparino(FC)	.20	.15	.08
589	Scott Ruskin	.10	.08	.04	677	Billy Ripken	.04	.03	.02
590	Eddie Murray	.12	.09	.05	678	Mark Davidson	.03	.02	.01
591	Ken Hill	.05	.04	.02	679	Bill Bathe(FC)	.04	.03	.02
592	B.J. Surhoff	.06	.05	.02	680	David Cone	.06	.05	.02
593	Mike Walker(FC)	.15	.11	.06	681	Jeff Schaefer(FC)	.10	.08	.04
594	Rich Garces(FC)	.15	.11	.06	682	Ray Lankford(FC)	.70	.50	.30
595	Bill Landrum	.05	.04	.02	683	Derek Lilliquist	.05	.04	.02
596	#1 Draft Pick (Ronnie Walden)(FC)	.30	.25	.12	684	Milt Cuyler(FC)	.25	.20	.10
597	Jerry Don Gleaton	.03	.02	.01	685	Doug Drabek	.08	.06	.03
598	Sam Horn	.05	.04	.02	686	Mike Gallego	.03	.02	.01
599	Greg Myers	.04	.03	.02	687	John Cerutti	.03	.02	.01
600	Bo Jackson	.40	.30	.15	688	Rosario Rodriguez(FC)	.15	.11	.06
601	Bob Ojeda	.04	.03	.02	689	John Kruk	.06	.05	.02
602	Casey Candaele	.04	.03	.02	690	Orel Hershiser	.10	.08	.04
603a	Wes Chamberlain (photo of Louie Meadows)(FC)	1.25	.90	.50	691	Mike Blowers	.10	.08	.04
603b	Wes Chamberlain (correct photo)(FC)	.40	.30	.15	692	Efrain Valdez(FC)	.15	.11	.06
					693	Francisco Cabrera	.08	.06	.03
604	Billy Hatcher	.05	.04	.02	694	Randy Veres	.03	.02	.01
605	Jeff Reardon	.08	.06	.03	695	Kevin Seitzer	.08	.06	.03
606	Jim Gott	.04	.03	.02	696	Steve Olin	.05	.04	.02
607	Edgar Martinez	.06	.05	.02	697	Shawn Abner	.04	.03	.02
608	Todd Burns	.03	.02	.01	698	Mark Guthrie	.05	.04	.02
609	Jeff Torborg	.03	.02	.01	699	Jim Lefebvre	.03	.02	.01
610	Andres Galarraga	.08	.06	.03	700	Jose Canseco	.40	.30	.15
611	Dave Eiland	.04	.03	.02	701	Pascual Perez	.05	.04	.02
612	Steve Lyons	.04	.03	.02	702	Tim Naehring	.20	.15	.08
613	Eric Show	.04	.03	.02	703	Juan Agosto	.03	.02	.01
614	Luis Salazar	.04	.03	.02	704	Devon White	.06	.05	.02
615	Bert Blyleven	.08	.06	.03	705	Robby Thompson	.05	.04	.02
616	Todd Zeile	.15	.11	.06	706	Brad Arnsberg	.04	.03	.02
617	Bill Wegman	.04	.03	.02	707	Jim Eisenreich	.04	.03	.02
618	Sil Campusano	.04	.03	.02	708	John Mitchell(FC)	.12	.09	.05
619	David Wells	.04	.03	.02	709	Matt Sinatro	.03	.02	.01
620	Ozzie Guillen	.08	.06	.03	710	Kent Hrbek	.08	.06	.03
621	Ted Power	.03	.02	.01	711	Gary Redus, Jose DeLeon	.05	.04	.02
622	Jack Daugherty	.05	.04	.02	712	Ricky Jordan	.06	.05	.02
623	Jeff Blauser	.04	.03	.02	713	Scott Scudder	.08	.06	.03
624	Tom Candiotti	.04	.03	.02	714	Marvell Wynne	.04	.03	.02
625	Terry Steinbach	.06	.05	.02	715	Tim Burke	.06	.05	.02
626	Gerald Young	.03	.02	.01	716	Bob Geren	.06	.05	.02
627	Tim Layana	.15	.11	.06	717	Phil Bradley	.06	.05	.02
628	Greg Litton	.05	.04	.02	718	Steve Crawford	.03	.02	.01
629	Wes Gardner	.04	.03	.02	719	Keith Miller	.06	.05	.02
630	Dave Winfield	.10	.08	.04	720	Cecil Fielder	.20	.15	.08
631	Mike Morgan	.04	.03	.02	721	Mark Lee(FC)	.15	.11	.06
632	Lloyd Moseby	.06	.05	.02	722	Wally Backman	.04	.03	.02
633	Kevin Tapani	.10	.08	.04	723	Candy Maldonado	.08	.06	.03
634	Henry Cotto	.03	.02	.01	724	David Segui(FC)	.25	.20	.10
635	Andy Hawkins	.04	.03	.02	725	Ron Gant	.15	.11	.06
636	Geronimo Pena(FC)	.20	.15	.08	726	Phil Stephenson	.04	.03	.02
637	Bruce Ruffin	.04	.03	.02	727	Mookie Wilson	.06	.05	.02
638	Mike Macfarlane	.04	.03	.02	728	Scott Sanderson	.04	.03	.02
639	Frank Robinson	.05	.04	.02	729	Don Zimmer	.04	.03	.02
640	Andre Dawson	.10	.08	.04	730	Barry Larkin	.12	.09	.06
					731	Jeff Gray(FC)	.15	.11	.06

		MT	NR MT	EX
732	Franklin Stubbs	.05	.04	.02
733	Kelly Downs	.04	.03	.02
734	John Russell	.03	.02	.01
735	Ron Darling	.06	.05	.02
736	Dick Schofield	.04	.03	.02
737	Tim Crews	.03	.02	.01
738	Mel Hall	.04	.03	.02
739	*Russ Swan*	.10	.08	.04
740	Ryne Sandberg	.20	.15	.08
741	Jimmy Key	.06	.05	.02
742	Tommy Gregg	.04	.03	.02
743	Bryn Smith	.04	.03	.02
744	Nelson Santovenia	.05	.04	.02
745	Doug Jones	.08	.06	.03
746	John Shelby	.03	.02	.01
747	Tony Fossas	.03	.02	.01
748	Al Newman	.03	.02	.01
749	Greg Harris	.04	.03	.02
750	Bobby Bonilla	.12	.09	.05
751	*Wayne Edwards*	.10	.08	.04
752	Kevin Bass	.05	.04	.02
753	*Paul Marak*(FC)	.15	.11	.06
754	Bill Pecota	.04	.03	.02
755	Mark Langston	.10	.08	.04
756	Jeff Huson	.05	.04	.02
757	Mark Gardner	.06	.05	.02
758	Mike Devereaux	.06	.05	.02
759	Bobby Cox	.03	.02	.01
760	Benny Santiago	.08	.06	.03
761	Larry Andersen	.04	.03	.02
762	Mitch Webster	.04	.03	.02
763	*Dana Kiecker*	.10	.08	.04
764	Mark Carreon	.05	.04	.02
765	Shawon Dunston	.08	.06	.03
766	Jeff Robinson	.05	.04	.02
767	#1 Draft Pick *(Dan Wilson)*(FC)	.30	.25	.12
768	Donn Pall	.04	.03	.02
769	*Tim Sherrill*(FC)	.15	.11	.06
770	Jay Howell	.06	.05	.02
772	Kent Mercker(FC)	.10	.08	.04
773	Tom Foley	.03	.02	.01
774	Dennis Rasmussen	.04	.03	.02
775	Julio Franco	.08	.06	.03
776	Brent Mayne(FC)	.15	.11	.06
777	John Candelaria	.05	.04	.02
778	Dan Gladden	.05	.04	.02
779	Carmelo Martinez	.04	.03	.02
780	Randy Myers	.08	.06	.03
781	Darryl Hamilton	.05	.04	.02
782	Jim Deshaies	.05	.04	.02
783	Joel Skinner	.03	.02	.01
784	Willie Fraser	.04	.03	.02
785	Scott Fletcher	.04	.03	.02
786	Eric Plunk	.03	.02	.01
787	Checklist 6	.03	.02	.01
788	Bob Milacki	.06	.05	.02
789	Tom Lasorda	.04	.03	.02
790	Ken Griffey,Jr.	1.00	.70	.40
791	Mike Benjamin(FC)	.15	.11	.06
792	Mike Greenwell	.15	.11	.06

GRADING GUIDE

Mint (MT): A perfect card. Well-centered with all corners sharp and square. No creases, stains, edge nicks, surface marks, yellowing or fading.

Near Mint (NM): A nearly perfect card. At first glance, a NM card appears to be perfect. May be slightly off-center. No surface marks, creases or loss of gloss.

Excellent (EX): Corners are still fairly sharp with only moderate wear. Borders may be off-center. No creases or stains on fronts or backs, but may show slight loss of surface luster.

Very Good (VG): Shows obvious handling. May have rounded corners, minor creases, major gum or wax stains. No major creases, tape marks, writing, etc.

Good (G): A well-worn card, but exhibits no intentional damage. May have major or multiple creases. Corners may be rounded well beyond card border.

Card Company Addresses

AW Sports, 17842 Mitchell North, Suite 200, Irvine, CA 92714.

Action Packed, 851 N. Villa, Suite 101, Villa Park, Il 60181.

Bowman — See Topps.

Classic Games Inc., 8055 Troon Circle, Suite C, Austell, GA 30001.

Collector's Edge, P.O. Box 9010, Denver, CO 80209.

Courtside, 1247 Broadway Ave., Burlingame, CA 94010

Fleer Corporation, 1120 Rte. 73, Mt. Laurel, NJ 08054.

Front Row, 201 W. Main St., Dalton, PA 18414.

Kayo, One Meadowlands Plaza, Suite 1020, East Rutherford, NJ 07073.

Leaf/Donruss, 2355 Waukegan Road, Bannockburn, Il 60015.

Megacards, Inc., 5650 Wattsburg Rd., Erie, PA 16509

NBA Hoops, P.O. Box 14930, Research Triangle Park, NC 27709-4930.

O-Pee-Chee, P.O. Box 6306, London, Ontario, Canada, N5W 5S1.

Pacific Trading Cards, 18424 Hwy. 99, Lynwood, WA 98039.

Pro Line Portraits, P.O. Box 14930, Research Triangle Park, NC 27709-4930.

Pro Set, 17250 Dallas Parkway, Dallas, TX 75248.

Score, 25 Ford Road, Westport, CT 06880.

SilverStar Holograms, P.O. Box 8195, Van Nuys, CA 91406.

SkyBox Int'l., P.O. Box 14930, Research Triangle Park, NC 27709-4930.

Topps, 254 36th St., Brooklyn, NY 11232.

Upper Deck, 5909 Sea Otter Place, Carlsbad, CA 92008.

Wild Card, 2715 Dixie Highway, Hamilton, OH 45015.

1991 Topps Box Panels

Styled like the standard 1991 Topps cards, this 16-card set honors milestones of the featured players. The cards were found on the bottom of wax pack boxes. The cards are designated in alphabetical order by (A-P) and are not numbered.

		MT	NR MT	EX
Complete Set:		2.50	2.00	1.00
Common Player:		.08	.06	.03
(1)	Bert Blyleven	.08	.06	.03
(2)	George Brett	.20	.15	.08
(3)	Brett Butler	.10	.08	.04
(4)	Andre Dawson	.15	.11	.06
(5)	Dwight Evans	.10	.08	.04
(6)	Carlton Fisk	.20	.15	.08
(7)	Alfredo Griffin	.08	.06	.03
(8)	Rickey Henderson	.30	.25	.12
(9)	Willie McGee	.15	.11	.06
(10)	Dale Murphy	.20	.15	.08
(11)	Eddie Murray	.20	.15	.08
(12)	Dave Parker	.15	.11	.06
(13)	Jeff Reardon	.15	.11	.06
(14)	Nolan Ryan	.40	.30	.15
(15)	Juan Samuel	.08	.06	.03
(16)	Robin Yount	.20	.15	.08

The values quoted are intended to reflect the market price.

A player's name in *italic* indicates a rookie card. An (FC) indicates a player's first card for that particular card company.

1991 Topps Babe Ruth

This 11-card set by Topps was released in honor of the NBC movie about Babe Ruth. The cards were released on a limited basis. The card fronts feature full-color photos from the movie, while the flip sides are printed horizontally and describe the front photo. The cards are numbered on the back.

		MT	NR MT	EX
Complete Set:		30.00	22.00	12.00
Common Player:		2.00	1.50	.80
1	Sunday October 6th NBC	2.00	1.50	.80
2	Stephen Lang as Babe Ruth	2.00	1.50	.80
3	Bruce Weitz as Miller Huggins	2.00	1.50	.80
4	Lisa Zane as Claire Ruth	2.00	1.50	.80
5	Donald Moffat as Jacob Ruppert . cards are numbered on the back.	2.00	1.50	.80
6	Neil McDonough as Lou Gehrig	2.00	1.50	.80
7	Pete Rose as Ty Cobb	10.00	7.50	4.00
8	Rod Carew Baseball Consultant	6.00	4.50	2.50
9	Ruth and Manager Huggins	2.00	1.50	.80
10	Ruth In Action	2.00	1.50	.80
11	Babe Calls His Shot	2.00	1.50	.80

1991 Topps Major League Debut

This 194-card set highlights the debut date of 1991 Major League rookies. Two checklist cards are also included in this boxed set. The card fronts resemble the 1992 Topps cards. A debut banner appears in the lower right hand corner of the card front. The set is packaged in an attractive collector box and the cards are numbered alphabetically. This set was available through select hobby dealers.

		MT	NR MT	EX
Complete Set:		15.00	11.00	6.00
Common Player:		.08	.06	.03
1	Kyle Abbott	.20	.15	.08
2	Dana Allison	.15	.11	.06
3	Rich Amaral	.08	.06	.03
4	Ruben Amaro	.10	.08	.04
5	Andy Ashby	.15	.11	.06
6	Jim Austin	.08	.06	.03
7	Jeff Bagwell	1.50	1.25	.60
8	Jeff Banister	.10	.08	.04
9	Willie Banks	.25	.20	.10
10	Bret Barberie	.20	.15	.08
11	Kim Batiste	.10	.08	.04
12	Chris Beasley	.10	.08	.04
13	Rodd Beck	.08	.06	.03
14	Derek Bell	.50	.40	.20
15	Esteban Beltre	.08	.06	.03
16	Freddie Benavides	.10	.08	.04
17	Rickey Bones	.10	.08	.04
18	Denis Boucher	.15	.11	.06
19	Ryan Bowen	.20	.15	.08
20	Cliff Brantley	.10	.08	.04
21	John Briscoe	.10	.08	.04
22	Scott Brosius	.10	.08	.04
23	Terry Bross	.08	.06	.03
24	Jarvis Brown	.10	.08	.04
25	Scott Bullett	.10	.08	.04
26	Kevin Campbell	.08	.06	.03
27	Amalio Carreno	.08	.06	.03
28	Matias Carrillo	.10	.08	.04
29	Jeff Carter	.08	.06	.03
30	Vinny Castilla	.10	.08	.04
31	Braulio Castillo	.10	.08	.04
32	Frank Castillo	.25	.20	.10
33	Darrin Chapin	.10	.08	.04
34	Mike Christopher	.08	.06	.03
35	Mark Clark	.15	.11	.06
36	Royce Clayton	.25	.20	.10
37	Stu Cole	.10	.08	.04
38	Gary Cooper	.08	.06	.03
39	Archie Corbin	.10	.08	.04
40	Rheal Cormier	.20	.15	.08
41	Chris Cron	.08	.06	.03
42	Mike Dalton	.08	.06	.03
43	Mark Davis	.08	.06	.03
44	Francisco de la Rosa	.08	.06	.03
45	Chris Donnels	.35	.25	.14

		MT	NR MT	EX
46	Brian Drahman	.25	.20	.10
47	Tom Drees	.15	.11	.06
48	Kirk Dressendorfer	.40	.30	.15
49	Bruce Egloff	.30	.25	.12
50	Cal Eldred	.30	.25	.12
51	Jose Escobar	.30	.25	.12
52	Tony Eusebio	.08	.06	.03
53	Hector Fajardo	.10	.08	.04
54	Monty Farriss	.10	.08	.04
55	Jeff Fassero	.15	.11	.06
56	Dave Fleming	.10	.08	.04
57	Kevin Flora	.10	.08	.04
58	Steve Foster	.10	.08	.04
59	Dan Gakeler	.08	.06	.03
60	Ramon Garcia	.15	.11	.06
61	Chris Gardner	.10	.08	.04
62	Jeff Gardner	.15	.11	.06
63	Chris George	.15	.11	.06
64	Ray Giannelli	.08	.06	.03
65	Tom Goodwin	.20	.15	.08
66	Mark Grater	.08	.06	.03
67	Johnny Guzman	.15	.11	.06
68	Juan Guzman	.60	.45	.25
69	Dave Haas	.08	.06	.03
70	Chris Haney	.25	.20	.10
71	Shawn Hare	.08	.06	.03
72	Donald Harris	.20	.15	.08
73	Doug Henry	.20	.15	.08
74	Pat Hentgen	.10	.08	.04
75	Gil Heredia	.20	.15	.08
76	Jeremy Hernandez	.20	.15	.08
77	Jose Hernandez	.08	.06	.03
78	Roberto Hernandez	.10	.08	.04
79	Bryan Hickerson	.15	.11	.06
80	Milt Hill	.08	.06	.03
81	Vince Horsman	.08	.06	.03
82	Wayne Housie	.08	.06	.03
83	Chris Howard	.15	.11	.06
84	David Howard	.20	.15	.08
85	Mike Humphreys	.15	.11	.06
86	Brian Hunter	.70	.50	.30
87	Jim Hunter	.08	.06	.03
88	Mike Ignasiak	.08	.06	.03
89	Reggie Jefferson	.35	.25	.14
90	Jeff Johnson	.20	.15	.08
91	Joel Johnson	.10	.08	.04
92	Calvin Jones	.15	.11	.06
93	Chris Jones	.25	.20	.10
94	Stacy Jones	.08	.06	.03
95	Jeff Juden	.25	.20	.10
96	Scott Kamieniecki	.20	.15	.08
97	Eric Karros	.60	.45	.25
98	Pat Kelly	.50	.40	.20
99	John Kiely	.08	.06	.03
100	Darryl Kile	.20	.15	.08
101	Wayne Kirby	.08	.06	.03
102	Garland Kiser	.10	.08	.04
103	Chuck Knoblauch	.60	.45	.25
104	Randy Knorr	.08	.06	.03
105	Tom Kramer	.08	.06	.03
106	Ced Landrum	.20	.15	.08
107	Patrick Lennon	.20	.15	.08
108	Jim Lewis	.08	.06	.03
109	Mark Lewis	.35	.25	.14
110	Doug Lindsey	.08	.06	.03
111	Scott Livingstone	.30	.25	.12
112	Kenny Lofton	.40	.30	.15
113	Ever Magallanes	.10	.08	.04
114	Mike Magnante	.10	.08	.04
115	Barry Manuel	.10	.08	.04
116	Josias Manzanillo	.10	.08	.04
117	Chito Martinez	.60	.45	.25
118	Terry Mathews	.08	.06	.03
119	Rob Mauer	.10	.08	.04
120	Tim Mauser	.08	.06	.03
121	Terry McDaniel	.20	.15	.08
122	Rusty Meacham	.15	.11	.06
123	Luis Mercedes	.25	.20	.10
124	Paul Miller	.15	.11	.06
125	Keith Mitchell	.25	.20	.10
126	Bobby Moore	.08	.06	.03
127	Kevin Morton	.30	.25	.12
128	Andy Mota	.25	.20	.10
129	Jose Mota	.15	.11	.06
130	Mike Mussina	.25	.20	.10
131	Jeff Mutis	.08	.06	.03
132	Denny Neagle	.40	.30	.15
133	Warren Newson	.15	.11	.06
134	Jim Olander	.08	.06	.03
135	Erik Pappas	.15	.11	.06
136	Jorge Pedre	.10	.08	.04

		MT	NR MT	EX
137	Yorkis Perez	.15	.11	.06
138	Mark Petkovsek	.15	.11	.06
139	Doug Piatt	.15	.11	.06
140	Jeff Plympton	.15	.11	.06
141	Harvey Pulliam	.15	.11	.06
142	John Ramos	.15	.11	.06
143	Mike Remlinger	.10	.08	.04
144	Laddie Renfroe	.10	.08	.04
145	Armando Reynoso	.10	.08	.04
146	Arthur Rhodes	.20	.15	.08
147	Pat Rice	.15	.11	.06
148	Nikco Riesgo	.10	.08	.04
149	Carlos Rodriguez	.10	.08	.04
150	Ivan Rodriguez	1.50	1.25	.60
151	Wayne Rosenthal	.10	.08	.04
152	Rico Rossy	.08	.06	.03
153	Stan Royer	.15	.11	.06
154	Rey Sanchez	.08	.06	.03
155	Reggie Sanders	.40	.30	.15
156	Mo Sanford	.35	.25	.14
157	Bob Scanlan	.15	.11	.06
158	Pete Schourek	.15	.11	.06
159	Gary Scott	.25	.20	.10
160	Tim Scott	.08	.06	.03
161	Tony Scruggs	.10	.08	.04
162	Scott Servais	.10	.08	.04
163	Doug Simons	.15	.11	.06
164	Heathcliff Slocumb	.10	.08	.04
165	Joe Slusarski	.10	.08	.04
166	Tim Spehr	.15	.11	.06
167	Ed Sprague	.10	.08	.04
168	Jeff Tackett	.08	.06	.03
169	Eddie Taubensee	.15	.11	.06
170	Wade Taylor	.15	.11	.06
171	Jim Thome	.60	.45	.25
172	Mike Timlin	.25	.20	.10
173	Jose Tolentino	.10	.08	.04
174	John Vander Wal	.08	.06	.03
175	Todd Van Poppel	.80	.60	.30
176	Mo Vaughn	.50	.40	.20
177	Dave Wainhouse	.15	.11	.06
178	Don Wakamatsu	.10	.08	.04
179	Bruce Walton	.08	.06	.03
180	Kevin Ward	.08	.06	.03
181	Dave Weathers	.08	.06	.03
182	Eric Wedge	.08	.06	.03
183	John Wehner	.25	.20	.10
184	Rick Wilkins	.30	.25	.12
185	Bernie Williams	.35	.25	.14
186	Brian Williams	.15	.11	.06
187	Ron Witmeyer	.08	.06	.03
188	Mark Wohlers	.25	.20	.10
189	Ted Wood	.20	.15	.08
190	Anthony Young	.50	.40	.20
191	Eddie Zosky	.20	.15	.08
192	Bob Zupcic	.15	.11	.06
193	Checklist	.08	.06	.03
194	Checklist	.08	.06	.03

1991 Topps Stadium Club

One of the most popular sets of 1991, this 600-card issue was released in two 300-card series. The cards were available in foil packs only. No factory sets were available. The cards feature orderless high gloss photos on the front and a player evaluation and card photo on the back. Stadium Club cards were considered scarce in many areas, thus driving up the price per pack. A special Stadium Club membership package was made available for $29.95 with 10 proof of purchase seals from wrappers.

		MT	NR MT	EX
	Complete Set:	300.00	225.00	125.00
	Common Player:	.20	.15	.08
1	Dave Stewart	1.00	.70	.40
2	Wally Joyner	.30	.25	.12
3	Shawon Dunston	.25	.20	.10
4	Darren Daulton	.20	.15	.08
5	Will Clark	4.00	3.00	1.50
6	Sammy Sosa	.25	.20	.10
7	Dan Plesac	.20	.15	.08
8	Marquis Grissom	.80	.60	.30
9	Erik Hanson	.30	.25	.12
10	Geno Petralli	.20	.15	.08
11	Jose Rijo	.25	.20	.10
12	Carlos Quintana	.20	.15	.08
13	Junior Ortiz	.20	.15	.08
14	Bob Walk	.20	.15	.08
15	Mike Macfarlane	.20	.15	.08
16	Eric Yelding	.20	.15	.08
17	Bryn Smith	.20	.15	.08
18	Bip Roberts	.20	.15	.08
19	Mike Scioscia	.20	.15	.08
20	Mark Williamson	.20	.15	.08
21	Don Mattingly	1.50	1.25	.60
22	John Franco	.20	.15	.08
23	Chet Lemon	.20	.15	.08
24	Tom Henke	.20	.15	.08
25	Jerry Browne	.20	.15	.08
26	Dave Justice	10.00	7.50	4.00
27	Mark Langston	.30	.25	.12
28	Damon Berryhill	.20	.15	.08
29	Kevin Bass	.20	.15	.08
30	Scott Fletcher	.20	.15	.08
31	Moises Alou	.25	.20	.10
32	Dave Valle	.20	.15	.08
33	Jody Reed	.20	.15	.08
34	Dave West	.20	.15	.08
35	Kevin McReynolds	.25	.20	.10
36	Pat Combs	.20	.15	.08
37	Eric Davis	.50	.40	.20
38	Bret Saberhagen	.30	.25	.12
39	Stan Javier	.20	.15	.08
40	Chuck Cary	.20	.15	.08
41	Tony Phillips	.20	.15	.08
42	Lee Smith	.25	.20	.10
43	Tim Teufel	.20	.15	.08
44	Lance Dickson	.80	.60	.30
45	Greg Litton	.20	.15	.08
46	Teddy Higuera	.25	.20	.10
47	Edgar Martinez	.30	.25	.12
48	Steve Avery	9.00	6.75	3.50
49	Walt Weiss	.20	.15	.08
50	David Segui	.30	.25	.12
51	Andy Benes	.30	.25	.12
52	Karl Rhodes	.30	.25	.12
53	Neal Heaton	.20	.15	.08
54	Danny Gladden	.20	.15	.08
55	Luis Rivera	.20	.15	.08
56	Kevin Brown	.20	.15	.08
57	Frank Thomas	30.00	22.00	12.00
58	Terry Mulholland	.25	.20	.10
59	Dick Schofield	.20	.15	.08
60	Ron Darling	.20	.15	.08
61	Sandy Alomar, Jr.	.35	.25	.14
62	Dave Stieb	.20	.15	.08
63	Alan Trammell	.40	.30	.15
64	Matt Nokes	.20	.15	.08
65	Lenny Harris	.20	.15	.08
66	Milt Thompson	.20	.15	.08
67	Storm Davis	.20	.15	.08
68	Joe Oliver	.20	.15	.08
69	Andres Galarraga	.20	.15	.08
70	Ozzie Guillen	.25	.20	.10
71	Ken Howell	.20	.15	.08
72	Garry Templeton	.20	.15	.08
73	Derrick May	.35	.25	.14
74	Xavier Hernandez	.20	.15	.08
75	Dave Parker	.25	.20	.10
76	Rick Aguilera	.20	.15	.08
77	Robby Thompson	.20	.15	.08
78	Pete Incaviglia	.20	.15	.08
79	Bob Welch	.25	.20	.10
80	Randy Milligan	.25	.20	.10
81	Chuck Finley	.35	.25	.14
82	Alvin Davis	.20	.15	.08
83	Tim Naehring	.35	.25	.14
84	Jay Bell	.25	.20	.10
85	Joe Magrane	.25	.20	.10
86	Howard Johnson	.40	.30	.15
87	Jack McDowell	.40	.30	.15
88	Kevin Seitzer	.20	.15	.08
89	Bruce Ruffin	.20	.15	.08
90	Fernando Valenzuela	.30	.25	.12
91	Terry Kennedy	.20	.15	.08
92	Barry Larkin	.80	.60	.30
93	Larry Walker	.30	.25	.12
94	Luis Salazar	.20	.15	.08
95	Gary Sheffield	4.00	3.00	1.50
96	Bobby Witt	.20	.15	.08
97	Lonnie Smith	.20	.15	.08
98	Bryan Harvey	.25	.20	.10
99	Mookie Wilson	.25	.20	.10
100	Doc Gooden	.70	.50	.30
101	Lou Whitaker	.25	.20	.10
102	Ron Karkovice	.20	.15	.08
103	Jesse Barfield	.25	.20	.10
104	Jose DeJesus	.25	.20	.10
105	Benito Santiago	.25	.20	.10
106	Brian Holman	.20	.15	.08
107	Rafael Ramirez	.20	.15	.08
108	Ellis Burks	.50	.40	.20
109	Mike Bielecki	.20	.15	.08
110	Kirby Puckett	3.00	2.25	1.25
111	Terry Shumpert	.25	.20	.10
112	Chuck Crim	.20	.15	.08
113	Todd Benzinger	.20	.15	.08
114	Brian Barnes	.40	.30	.15
115	Carlos Baerga	.80	.60	.30
116	Kal Daniels	.25	.20	.10
117	Dave Johnson	.20	.15	.08
118	Andy Van Slyke	.35	.25	.14
119	John Burkett	.20	.15	.08
120	Rickey Henderson	2.50	2.00	1.00
121	Tim Jones	.20	.15	.08
122	Daryl Irvine	.30	.20	.10
123	Ruben Sierra	1.50	1.25	.60
124	Jim Abbott	.80	.60	.30
125	Daryl Boston	.20	.15	.08
126	Greg Maddux	.25	.20	.10
127	Von Hayes	.20	.15	.08
128	Mike Fitzgerald	.20	.15	.08
129	Wayne Edwards	.20	.15	.08
130	Greg Briley	.20	.15	.08
131	Rob Dibble	.30	.25	.12
132	Gene Larkin	.20	.15	.08
133	David Wells	.20	.15	.08
134	Steve Balboni	.20	.15	.08
135	Greg Vaughn	1.25	.90	.50
136	Mark Davis	.20	.15	.08
137	Dave Rohde	.20	.15	.08
138	Eric Show	.20	.15	.08
139	Bobby Bonilla	1.00	.70	.40
140	Dana Kiecker	.25	.20	.10
141	Gary Pettis	.20	.15	.08
142	Dennis Boyd	.20	.15	.08
143	Mike Benjamin	.20	.15	.08
144	Luis Polonia	.20	.15	.08
145	Doug Jones	.20	.15	.08
146	Al Newman	.20	.15	.08
147	Alex Fernandez	.80	.60	.30
148	Bill Doran	.20	.15	.08
149	Kevin Elster	.20	.15	.08
150	Len Dykstra	.30	.25	.12
151	Mike Gallego	.20	.15	.08
152	Tim Belcher	.20	.15	.08
153	Jay Buhner	.20	.15	.08
154	Ozzie Smith	.70	.50	.30
155	Jose Canseco	4.00	3.00	1.50
156	Gregg Olson	.30	.25	.12
157	Charlie O'Brien	.20	.15	.08
158	Frank Tanana	.20	.15	.08
159	George Brett	.80	.60	.30
160	Jeff Huson	.20	.15	.08
161	Kevin Tapani	.35	.25	.14
162	Jerome Walton	.25	.20	.10
163	Charlie Hayes	.20	.15	.08
164	Chris Bosio	.20	.15	.08
165	Chris Sabo	.40	.30	.15
166	Lance Parrish	.20	.15	.08
167	Don Robinson	.20	.15	.08
168	Manuel Lee	.20	.15	.08
169	Dennis Rasmussen	.20	.15	.08
170	Wade Boggs	1.50	1.25	.60
171	Bob Geren	.20	.15	.08
172	Mackey Sasser	.20	.15	.08
173	Julio Franco	.50	.40	.20
174	Otis Nixon	.20	.15	.08
175	Bert Blyleven	.20	.15	.08
176	Craig Biggio	.40	.30	.15
177	Eddie Murray	.60	.45	.25

#	Player	MT	NR MT	EX
178	Randy Tomlin	.80	.60	.30
179	Tino Martinez	.80	.60	.30
180	Carlton Fisk	.80	.60	.30
181	Dwight Smith	.20	.15	.08
182	Scott Garrelts	.20	.15	.08
183	Jim Gantner	.20	.15	.08
184	Dickie Thon	.20	.15	.08
185	John Farrell	.20	.15	.08
186	Cecil Fielder	3.00	2.25	1.25
187	Glenn Braggs	.20	.15	.08
188	Allan Anderson	.20	.15	.08
189	Kurt Stillwell	.20	.15	.08
190	Jose Oquendo	.20	.15	.08
191	Joe Orsulak	.20	.15	.08
192	Ricky Jordan	.20	.15	.08
193	Kelly Downs	.20	.15	.08
194	Delino DeShields	.60	.45	.25
195	Omar Vizquel	.20	.15	.08
196	Mark Carreon	.20	.15	.08
197	Mike Harkey	.20	.15	.08
198	Jack Howell	.20	.15	.08
199	Lance Johnson	.20	.15	.08
200	Nolan Ryan	15.00	11.00	6.00
201	John Marzano	.20	.15	.08
202	Doug Drabek	.30	.25	.12
203	Mark Lemke	.30	.25	.12
204	Steve Sax	.30	.25	.12
205	Greg Harris	.20	.15	.08
206	B.J. Surhoff	.20	.15	.08
207	Todd Burns	.20	.15	.08
208	Jose Gonzalez	.20	.15	.08
209	Mike Scott	.20	.15	.08
210	Dave Magadan	.30	.25	.12
211	Dante Bichette	.20	.15	.08
212	Trevor Wilson	.20	.15	.08
213	Hector Villanueva	.20	.15	.08
214	Dan Pasqua	.20	.15	.08
215	Greg Colbrunn	.30	.25	.12
216	Mike Jeffcoat	.20	.15	.08
217	Harold Reynolds	.25	.20	.10
218	Paul O'Neill	.25	.20	.10
219	Mark Guthrie	.25	.20	.10
220	Barry Bonds	1.00	.70	.40
221	Jimmy Key	.25	.20	.10
222	Billy Ripken	.20	.15	.08
223	Tom Pagnozzi	.20	.15	.08
224	Bo Jackson	4.00	3.00	1.50
225	Sid Fernandez	.20	.15	.08
226	Mike Marshall	.20	.15	.08
227	John Kruk	.25	.20	.10
228	Mike Fetters	.20	.15	.08
229	Eric Anthony	.20	.15	.08
230	Ryne Sandberg	3.00	2.25	1.25
231	Carney Lansford	.20	.15	.08
232	Melido Perez	.20	.15	.08
233	Jose Lind	.20	.15	.08
234	Darryl Hamilton	.20	.15	.08
235	Tom Browning	.20	.15	.08
236	Spike Owen	.20	.15	.08
237	Juan Gonzalez	15.00	11.00	6.00
238	Felix Fermin	.20	.15	.08
239	Keith Miller	.20	.15	.08
240	Mark Gubicza	.20	.15	.08
241	Kent Anderson	.20	.15	.08
242	Alvaro Espinoza	.20	.15	.08
243	Dale Murphy	.50	.40	.20
244	Orel Hershiser	.30	.25	.12
245	Paul Molitor	.30	.25	.12
246	Eddie Whitson	.20	.15	.08
247	Joe Girardi	.20	.15	.08
248	Kent Hrbek	.25	.20	.10
249	Bill Sampen	.20	.15	.08
250	Kevin Mitchell	.50	.40	.20
251	Mariano Duncan	.20	.15	.08
252	Scott Bradley	.20	.15	.08
253	Mike Greenwell	.50	.40	.20
254	Tom Gordon	.25	.20	.10
255	Todd Zeile	.80	.60	.30
256	Bobby Thigpen	.25	.20	.10
257	Gregg Jefferies	.40	.30	.15
258	Kenny Rogers	.20	.15	.08
259	Shane Mack	.30	.25	.12
260	Zane Smith	.20	.15	.08
261	Mitch Williams	.25	.20	.10
262	Jim DeShaies	.20	.15	.08
263	Dave Winfield	.50	.40	.20
264	Ben McDonald	1.00	.70	.40
265	Randy Ready	.20	.15	.08
266	Pat Borders	.20	.15	.08
267	Jose Uribe	.20	.15	.08
268	Derek Lilliquist	.20	.15	.08
269	Greg Brock	.20	.15	.08
270	Ken Griffey, Jr.	18.00	13.50	7.25
271	Jeff Gray	.25	.20	.10
272	Danny Tartabull	.40	.30	.15
273	Dennis Martinez	.20	.15	.08
274	Robin Ventura	5.00	3.75	2.00
275	Randy Myers	.20	.15	.08
276	Jack Daugherty	.20	.15	.08
277	Greg Gagne	.20	.15	.08
278	Jay Howell	.20	.15	.08
279	Mike LaValliere	.20	.15	.08
280	Rex Hudler	.20	.15	.08
281	Mike Simms	.50	.40	.20
282	Kevin Maas	1.00	.70	.40
283	Jeff Ballard	.20	.15	.08
284	Dave Henderson	.30	.25	.14
285	Pete O'Brien	.20	.15	.08
286	Brook Jacoby	.20	.15	.08
287	Mike Henneman	.20	.15	.08
288	Greg Olson	.20	.15	.08
289	Greg Myers	.20	.15	.08
290	Mark Grace	.50	.40	.20
291	Shawn Abner	.20	.15	.08
292	Frank Viola	.30	.25	.12
293	Lee Stevens	.30	.25	.12
294	Jason Grimsley	.20	.15	.08
295	Matt Williams	.70	.50	.30
296	Ron Robinson	.20	.15	.08
297	Tom Brunansky	.20	.15	.08
298	Checklist	.20	.15	.08
299	Checklist	.20	.15	.08
300	Checklist	.20	.15	.08
301	Darryl Strawberry	2.00	1.50	.80
302	Bud Black	.20	.15	.08
303	Harold Baines	.30	.25	.12
304	Roberto Alomar	4.00	3.00	1.50
305	Norm Charlton	.20	.15	.08
306	Gary Thurman	.20	.15	.08
307	Mike Felder	.20	.15	.08
308	Tony Gwynn	2.00	1.50	.80
309	Roger Clemens	2.00	1.50	.80
310	Andre Dawson	.50	.40	.20
311	Scott Radinsky	.20	.15	.08
312	Bob Melvin	.20	.15	.08
313	Kirk McCaskill	.20	.15	.08
314	Pedro Guerrero	.35	.25	.14
315	Walt Terrell	.20	.15	.08
316	Sam Horn	.20	.15	.08
317	Wes Chamberlain	3.00	2.25	1.25
318	Pedro Munoz	3.00	2.25	1.25
319	Roberto Kelly	.35	.25	.14
320	Mark Portugal	.20	.15	.08
321	Tim McIntosh	.20	.15	.08
322	Jesse Orosco	.20	.15	.08
323	Gary Green	.20	.15	.08
324	Greg Harris	.20	.15	.08
325	Hubie Brooks	.20	.15	.08
326	Chris Nabholz	.20	.15	.08
327	Terry Pendleton	.35	.25	.14
328	Eric King	.20	.15	.08
329	Chili Davis	.20	.15	.08
330	Anthony Telford	.20	.15	.08
331	Kelly Gruber	.35	.25	.14
332	Dennis Eckersley	.35	.25	.14
333	Mel Hall	.20	.15	.08
334	Bob Kipper	.20	.15	.08
335	Willie McGee	.30	.25	.12
336	Steve Olin	.20	.15	.08
337	Steve Buechele	.20	.15	.08
338	Scott Leius	.35	.25	.14
339	Hal Morris	1.00	.70	.40
340	Jose Offerman	.40	.30	.15
341	Kent Mercker	.30	.25	.14
342	Ken Griffey	.20	.15	.08
343	Pete Harnisch	.20	.15	.08
344	Kirk Gibson	.30	.25	.12
345	Dave Smith	.20	.15	.08
346	Dave Martinez	.20	.15	.08
347	Atlee Hammaker	.20	.15	.08
348	Brian Downing	.20	.15	.08
349	Todd Hundley	.35	.25	.14
350	Candy Maldonado	.20	.15	.08
351	Dwight Evans	.30	.25	.12
352	Steve Searcy	.20	.15	.08
353	Gary Gaetti	.25	.20	.10
354	Jeff Reardon	.25	.20	.10
355	Travis Fryman	8.00	6.00	3.25
356	Dave Righetti	.20	.15	.08
357	Fred McGriff	.50	.40	.20
358	Don Slaught	.20	.15	.08
359	Gene Nelson	.20	.15	.08

		MT	NR MT	EX			MT	NR MT	EX
360	Billy Spiers	.20	.15	.08	451	Luis Aquino	.20	.15	.08
361	Lee Guetterman	.20	.15	.08	452	Mark Whiten	.60	.45	.25
362	Darren Lewis	1.00	.70	.40	453	Stan Belinda	.20	.15	.08
363	Duane Ward	.20	.15	.08	454	Ron Gant	1.00	.70	.40
364	Lloyd Moseby	.20	.15	.08	455	Jose DeLeon	.20	.15	.08
365	John Smoltz	.50	.40	.20	456	Mark Salas	.20	.15	.08
366	Felix Jose	.80	.60	.30	457	Junior Felix	.20	.15	.08
367	David Cone	.30	.25	.12	458	Wally Whitehurst	.20	.15	.08
368	Wally Backman	.20	.15	.08	459	Phil Plantier	8.00	6.00	3.25
369	Jeff Montgomery	.20	.15	.08	460	Juan Berenguer	.20	.15	.08
370	Rich Garces	.35	.25	.14	461	Franklin Stubbs	.20	.15	.08
371	Billy Hatcher	.20	.15	.08	462	Joe Boever	.20	.15	.08
372	Bill Swift	.20	.15	.08	463	Tim Wallach	.30	.25	.12
373	Jim Eisenreich	.20	.15	.08	464	Mike Moore	.20	.15	.08
374	Rob Ducey	.20	.15	.08	465	Albert Belle	2.00	1.50	.80
375	Tim Crews	.20	.15	.08	466	Mike Witt	.20	.15	.08
376	Steve Finley	.20	.15	.08	467	Craig Worthington	.20	.15	.08
377	Jeff Blauser	.20	.15	.08	468	Jerald Clark	.20	.15	.08
378	Willie Wilson	.20	.15	.08	469	Scott Terry	.20	.15	.08
379	Gerald Perry	.20	.15	.08	470	Milt Cuyler	.60	.45	.25
380	Jose Mesa	.20	.15	.08	471	John Smiley	.25	.20	.10
381	Pat Kelly	2.00	1.50	.80	472	Charles Nagy	.25	.20	.10
382	Matt Merullo	.20	.15	.08	473	Alan Mills	.20	.15	.08
383	Ivan Calderon	.30	.25	.12	474	John Russell	.20	.15	.08
384	Scott Chiamparino	.20	.15	.08	475	Bruce Hurst	.20	.15	.08
385	Lloyd McClendon	.20	.15	.08	476	Andujar Cedeno	3.00	2.25	1.25
386	Dave Bergman	.20	.15	.08	477	Dave Eiland	.20	.15	.08
387	Ed Sprague	.40	.30	.15	478	Brian McRae	3.00	2.25	1.25
388	Jeff Bagwell	14.00	10.30	5.70	479	Mike LaCoss	.20	.15	.08
389	Brett Butler	.25	.20	.10	480	Chris Gwynn	.20	.15	.08
390	Larry Andersen	.20	.15	.08	481	Jamie Moyer	.20	.15	.08
391	Glenn Davis	.30	.25	.12	482	John Olerud	.80	.60	.30
392	Alex Cole (photo of Otis Nixon)	.30	.25	.12	483	Efrain Valdez	.20	.15	.08
393	Mike Heath	.20	.15	.08	484	Sil Campusano	.20	.15	.08
394	Danny Darwin	.20	.15	.08	485	Pascual Perez	.20	.15	.08
395	Steve Lake	.20	.15	.08	486	Gary Redus	.20	.15	.08
396	Tim Layana	.20	.15	.08	487	Andy Hawkins	.20	.15	.08
397	Terry Leach	.20	.15	.08	488	Cory Snyder	.20	.15	.08
398	Bill Wegman	.20	.15	.08	489	Chris Hoiles	.25	.20	.10
399	Mark McGwire	.50	.40	.20	490	Ron Hassey	.20	.15	.08
400	Mike Boddicker	.20	.15	.08	491	Gary Wayne	.20	.15	.08
401	Steve Howe	.20	.15	.08	492	Mark Lewis	.80	.60	.30
402	Bernard Gilkey	.40	.30	.15	493	Scott Coolbaugh	.20	.15	.08
403	Thomas Howard	.20	.15	.08	494	Gerald Young	.20	.15	.08
404	Rafael Belliard	.20	.15	.08	495	Juan Samuel	.20	.15	.08
405	Tom Candiotti	.20	.15	.08	496	Willie Fraser	.20	.15	.08
406	Rene Gonzalez	.25	.20	.10	497	Jeff Treadway	.20	.15	.08
407	Chuck McElroy	.25	.20	.10	498	Vince Coleman	.30	.25	.12
408	Paul Sorrento	.25	.20	.10	499	Cris Carpenter	.20	.15	.08
409	Randy Johnson	.25	.20	.10	500	Jack Clark	.30	.25	.12
410	Brady Anderson	.20	.15	.08	501	Kevin Appier	.25	.20	.10
411	Dennis Cook	.20	.15	.08	502	Rafael Palmeiro	.60	.45	.25
412	Mickey Tettleton	.25	.20	.10	503	Hensley Meulens	.30	.25	.12
413	Mike Stanton	.20	.15	.08	504	George Bell	.30	.25	.12
414	Ken Oberkfell	.20	.15	.08	505	Tony Pena	.30	.25	.12
415	Rick Honeycutt	.20	.15	.08	506	Roger McDowell	.20	.15	.08
416	Nelson Santovenia	.20	.15	.08	507	Luis Sojo	.20	.15	.08
417	Bob Tewksbury	.20	.15	.08	508	Mike Schooler	.20	.15	.08
418	Brent Mayne	.20	.15	.08	509	Robin Yount	1.00	.70	.40
419	Steve Farr	.20	.15	.08	510	Jack Armstrong	.20	.15	.08
420	Phil Stephenson	.20	.15	.08	511	Rick Cerone	.20	.15	.08
421	Jeff Russell	.20	.15	.08	512	Curt Wilkerson	.20	.15	.08
422	Chris James	.20	.15	.08	513	Joe Carter	.60	.45	.25
423	Tim Leary	.20	.15	.08	514	Tim Burke	.20	.15	.08
424	Gary Carter	.30	.25	.12	515	Tony Fernandez	.25	.20	.10
425	Glenallen Hill	.30	.25	.12	516	Ramon Martinez	2.00	1.50	.80
426	Matt Young	.20	.15	.08	517	Tim Hulett	.20	.15	.08
427	Sid Bream	.20	.15	.08	518	Terry Steinbach	.20	.15	.08
428	Greg Swindell	.30	.25	.12	519	Pete Smith	.20	.15	.08
429	Scott Aldred	.30	.25	.12	520	Ken Caminiti	.20	.15	.08
430	Cal Ripken	2.50	2.00	1.00	521	Shawn Boskie	.20	.15	.08
431	Bill Landrum	.20	.15	.08	522	Mike Pagliarulo	.20	.15	.08
432	Ernie Riles	.20	.15	.08	523	Tim Raines	.35	.25	.14
433	Danny Jackson	.20	.15	.08	524	Alfredo Griffin	.20	.15	.08
434	Casey Candaele	.20	.15	.08	525	Henry Cotto	.20	.15	.08
435	Ken Hill	.20	.15	.08	526	Mike Stanley	.20	.15	.08
436	Jaime Navarro	.20	.15	.08	527	Charlie Leibrandt	.20	.15	.08
437	Lance Blankenship	.20	.15	.08	528	Jeff King	.20	.15	.08
438	Randy Velarde	.20	.15	.08	529	Eric Plunk	.20	.15	.08
439	Frank DiPino	.20	.15	.08	530	Tom Lampkin	.20	.15	.08
440	Carl Nichols	.20	.15	.08	531	Steve Bedrosian	.20	.15	.08
441	Jeff Robinson	.20	.15	.08	532	Tom Herr	.20	.15	.08
442	Deion Sanders	.35	.25	.14	533	Craig Lefferts	.20	.15	.08
443	Vincente Palacios	.20	.15	.08	534	Jeff Reed	.20	.15	.08
444	Devon White	.30	.25	.12	535	Mickey Morandini	.35	.25	.14
445	John Cerutti	.20	.15	.08	536	Greg Cadaret	.20	.15	.08
446	Tracy Jones	.20	.15	.08	537	Ray Lankford	2.00	1.50	.80
447	Jack Morris	.30	.25	.12	538	John Candelaria	.20	.15	.08
448	Mitch Webster	.20	.15	.08	539	Rob Deer	.20	.15	.08
449	Bob Ojeda	.20	.15	.08	540	Brad Arnsberg	.20	.15	.08
450	Oscar Azocar	.20	.15	.08	541	Mike Sharperson-	.20	.15	.08

		MT	NR MT	EX
542	Jeff Robinson	.20	.15	.08
543	Mo Vaughn	3.00	2.25	1.25
544	Jeff Parrett	.20	.15	.08
545	Willie Randolph	.20	.15	.08
546	Herm Winningham	.20	.15	.08
547	Jeff Innis	.20	.15	.08
548	Chuck Knoblauch	5.00	3.75	2.00
549	Tommy Greene	.25	.20	.10
550	Jeff Hamilton	.20	.15	.08
551	Barry Jones	.20	.15	.08
552	Ken Dayley	.20	.15	.08
553	Rick Dempsey	.20	.15	.08
554	Greg Smith	.20	.15	.08
555	Mike Devereaux	.20	.15	.08
556	Keith Comstock	.20	.15	.08
557	Paul Faries	.20	.15	.08
558	Tom Glavine	1.50	1.25	.60
559	Craig Grebeck	.20	.15	.08
560	Scott Erickson	4.00	3.00	1.50
561	Joel Skinner	.20	.15	.08
562	Mike Morgan	.20	.15	.08
563	Dave Gallagher	.20	.15	.08
564	Todd Stottlemyre	.25	.20	.10
565	Rich Rodriguez	.25	.20	.10
566	Craig Wilson	.25	.20	.10
567	Jeff Brantley	.25	.20	.10
568	Scott Kamieniecki	.30	.25	.12
569	Steve Decker	.80	.60	.30
570	Juan Agosto	.20	.15	.08
571	Tommy Gregg	.20	.15	.08
572	Kevin Wickander	.20	.15	.08
573	Jamie Quirk	.20	.15	.08
574	Jerry Don Gleaton	.20	.15	.08
575	Chris Hammond	.20	.15	.08
576	Luis Gonzalez	2.00	1.50	.80
577	Russ Swan	.20	.15	.08
578	Jeff Conine	.40	.30	.15
579	Charlie Hough	.20	.15	.08
580	Jeff Kunkel	.20	.15	.08
581	Darrel Akerfelds	.20	.15	.08
582	Jeff Manto	.25	.20	.10
583	Alejandro Pena	.20	.15	.08
584	Mark Davidson	.20	.15	.08
585	Bob MacDonald	.25	.20	.10
586	Paul Assenmacher	.20	.15	.08
587	Dan Wilson	.60	.45	.25
588	Tom Bolton	.20	.15	.08
589	Brian Harper	.20	.15	.08
590	John Habyan	.20	.15	.08
591	John Orton	.20	.15	.08
592	Mark Gardner	.20	.15	.08
593	Turner Ward	.40	.30	.15
594	Bob Patterson	.20	.15	.08
595	Edwin Nunez	.20	.15	.08
596	Gary Scott	.40	.30	.15
597	Scott Bankhead	.20	.15	.08
598	Checklist	.20	.15	.08
599	Checklist	.20	.15	.08
600	Checklist	.20	.15	.08

1991 Topps Traded

"Team USA" is featured in the 1991 Topps Traded set. The cards feature the same style as the regular 1991 issue, including the 40th anniversary logo. The set includes 132 cards and showcases rookies and traded players along with "Team USA." The cards are numbered with a "T" designation in alphabetical order.

		MT	NR MT	EX
	Complete Set:	10.00	7.50	4.00
	Common Player:	.05	.04	.02
1	Juan Agosto	.05	.04	.02
2	Roberto Alomar	.25	.20	.10
3	Wally Backman	.05	.04	.02
4	Jeff Bagwell(FC)	2.00	1.50	.80
5	Skeeter Barnes(FC)	.15	.11	.06
6	Steve Bedrosian	.06	.05	.02
7	Derek Bell(FC)	.35	.25	.14
8	George Bell	.10	.08	.04
9	Rafael Belliard	.05	.04	.02
10	Dante Bichette	.06	.05	.02
11	Bud Black	.05	.04	.02
12	Mike Boddicker	.06	.05	.02
13	Sid Bream	.06	.05	.02
14	Hubie Brooks	.06	.05	.02
15	Brett Butler	.08	.06	.03
16	Ivan Calderon	.08	.06	.03
17	John Candelaria	.05	.04	.02
18	Tom Candiotti	.06	.05	.02
19	Gary Carter	.08	.06	.03
20	Joe Carter	.12	.09	.05
21	Rick Cerone	.05	.04	.02
22	Jack Clark	.08	.06	.03
23	Vince Coleman	.15	.11	.06
24	Scott Coolbaugh	.10	.08	.04
25	Danny Cox	.05	.04	.02
26	Danny Darwin	.05	.04	.02
27	Chili Davis	.08	.06	.03
28	Glenn Davis	.08	.06	.03
29	Steve Decker(FC)	.25	.20	.10
30	Rob Deer	.06	.05	.02
31	Rich DeLucia(FC)	.15	.11	.06
32	John Dettmer (U.S.A.)(FC)	.20	.15	.08
33	Brian Downing	.05	.04	.02
34	Darren Dreifort (U.S.A.)(FC)	.20	.15	.08
35	Kirk Dressendorfer(FC)	.40	.30	.15
36	Jim Essian	.05	.04	.02
37	Dwight Evans	.08	.06	.03
38	Steve Farr	.06	.05	.02
39	Jeff Fassero(FC)	.20	.15	.08
40	Junior Felix	.08	.06	.03
41	Tony Fernandez	.08	.06	.03
42	Steve Finley	.08	.06	.03
43	Jim Fregosi	.05	.04	.02
44	Gary Gaetti	.06	.05	.02
45	Jason Giambi (U.S.A.)(FC)	.30	.25	.12
46	Kirk Gibson	.08	.06	.03
47	Leo Gomez(FC)	.30	.25	.12
48	Luis Gonzalez(FC)	.30	.25	.12
49	Jeff Granger (U.S.A.)(FC)	.20	.15	.08
50	Todd Greene (U.S.A.)(FC)	.20	.15	.08
51	Jeffrey Hammonds (U.S.A.)(FC)	1.00	.70	.40
52	Mike Hargrove	.05	.04	.02
53	Pete Harnisch	.08	.06	.03
54	Rick Helling (U.S.A.)(FC)	.20	.15	.08
55	Glenallen Hill	.08	.06	.03
56	Charlie Hough	.06	.05	.02
57	Pete Incaviglia	.08	.06	.03
58	Bo Jackson	.50	.40	.20
59	Danny Jackson	.06	.05	.02
60	Reggie Jefferson(FC)	.30	.25	.12
61	Charles Johnson (U.S.A.)(FC)	1.25	.90	.50
62	Jeff Johnson(FC)	.20	.15	.08
63	Todd Johnson (U.S.A.)(FC)	.20	.15	.08
64	Barry Jones	.05	.04	.02
65	Chris Jones(FC)	.20	.15	.08
66	Scott Kamieniecki(FC)	.20	.15	.08
67	Pat Kelly(FC)	.50	.40	.20
68	Darryl Kile(FC)	.20	.15	.08
69	Chuck Knoblauch(FC)	.40	.30	.15
70	Bill Krueger	.05	.04	.02
71	Scott Leius(FC)	.15	.11	.06
72	Donnie Leshnock (U.S.A.)(FC)	.20	.15	.08
73	Mark Lewis	.30	.25	.12
74	Candy Maldonado	.06	.05	.02
75	Jason McDonald (U.S.A.)(FC)	.25	.20	.10
76	Willie McGee	.08	.06	.03
77	Fred McGriff	.10	.08	.04
78	Billy McMillon (U.S.A.)(FC)	.20	.15	.08
79	Hal McRae	.06	.05	.02
80	Dan Melendez (U.S.A.)(FC)	.30	.25	.12
81	Orlando Merced(FC)	.40	.30	.15
82	Jack Morris	.08	.06	.03
83	Phil Nevin (U.S.A.)(FC)	1.50	1.25	.60
84	Otis Nixon	.06	.05	.02
85	Johnny Oates	.05	.04	.02
86	Bob Ojeda	.05	.04	.02
87	Mike Pagliarulo	.05	.04	.02
88	Dean Palmer(FC)	.35	.25	.14

		MT	NR MT	EX
89	Dave Parker	.08	.06	.03
90	Terry Pendleton	.08	.06	.03
91	Tony Phillips (U.S.A.)(FC)	.20	.15	.08
92	Doug Piatt(FC)	.20	.15	.08
93	Ron Polk (U.S.A.)	.06	.05	.02
94	Rock Raines	.12	.09	.05
95	Willie Randolph	.06	.05	.02
96	Dave Righetti	.06	.05	.02
97	Ernie Riles	.05	.04	.02
98	Chris Roberts (U.S.A.)(FC)	.30	.25	.12
99	Jeff Robinson (Angels)	.05	.04	.02
100	Jeff Robinson (Orioles)	.05	.04	.02
101	Ivan Rodriguez(FC)	2.00	1.50	.80
102	Steve Rodriguez (U.S.A.)(FC)	.20	.15	.08
103	Tom Runnells	.05	.04	.02
104	Scott Sanderson	.06	.05	.02
105	Bob Scanlan(FC)	.15	.11	.06
106	Pete Schourek(FC)	.15	.11	.06
107	Gary Scott(FC)	.35	.25	.14
108	Paul Shuey (U.S.A.)(FC)	.40	.30	.15
109	Doug Simons(FC)	.20	.15	.08
110	Dave Smith	.06	.05	.02
111	Cory Snyder	.05	.04	.02
112	Luis Sojo	.06	.05	.02
113	Kennie Steenstra (U.S.A.)(FC)	.20	.15	.08
114	Darryl Strawberry	.30	.25	.12
115	Franklin Stubbs	.05	.04	.02
116	Todd Taylor (U.S.A.)(FC)	.20	.15	.08
117	Wade Taylor(FC)	.20	.15	.08
118	Garry Templeton	.06	.05	.02
119	Mickey Tettleton	.06	.05	.02
120	Tim Teufel	.05	.04	.02
121	Mike Timlin(FC)	.20	.15	.08
122	David Tuttle (U.S.A.)(FC)	.20	.15	.08
123	Mo Vaughn(FC)	.50	.40	.20
124	Jeff Ware (U.S.A.)(FC)	.20	.15	.08
125	Devon White	.08	.06	.03
126	Mark Whiten	.20	.15	.08
127	Mitch Williams	.08	.06	.03
128	Craig Wilson (U.S.A.)(FC)	.20	.15	.08
129	Willie Wilson	.06	.05	.02
130	Chris Wimmer (U.S.A.)(FC)	.30	.25	.12
131	Ivan Zweig (U.S.A.)(FC)	.20	.15	.08
132	Checklist	.05	.04	.02

1992 Topps

This 792-card set features white stock much like the 1991 issue. The card fronts feature full-color action and posed photos with a gray inner frame and the player name and position on the bottom. The backs feature biographical information, statistics and stadium photos on player cards where space is available. All-Star cards and #1 Draft Pick cards are once again included. Topps brought back four-player rookie cards in 1992. Nine Top Prospect cards of this nature can be found within the set. Several cards can once again be found with horizontal fronts. "Match the Stats" game cards were inserted into packs of 1992 Topps cards. Special bonus cards were given away to winners of this insert game. Record Breaker cards are also featured in this set.

		MT	NR MT	EX
	Complete Set:	20.00	15.00	8.00
	Common Player:	.03	.02	.01
1	Nolan Ryan	.30	.25	.12
2	Record Breaker (Rickey Henderson)	.10	.08	.04
3	Record Breaker (Jeff Reardon)	.05	.04	.02
4	Record Breaker (Nolan Ryan)	.10	.08	.04
5	Record Breaker (Dave Winfield)	.06	.05	.02
6	#1 Draft Pick (Brien Taylor)(FC)	2.75	2.00	1.00
7	Jim Olander(FC)	.10	.08	.04
8	Bryan Hickerson(FC)	.10	.08	.04
9	John Farrell	.03	.02	.01
10	Wade Boggs	.15	.11	.06
11	Jack McDowell	.08	.06	.03
12	Luis Gonzalez	.15	.11	.06
13	Mike Scioscia	.04	.03	.02
14	Wes Chamberlain	.20	.15	.08
15	Denny Martinez	.04	.03	.02
16	Jeff Montgomery	.04	.03	.02
17	Randy Milligan	.06	.05	.02
18	Greg Cadaret	.03	.02	.01
19	Jamie Quirk	.03	.02	.01
20	Bip Roberts	.05	.04	.02
21	Buck Rogers	.03	.02	.01
22	Bill Wegman	.04	.03	.02
23	Chuck Knoblauch	.20	.15	.08
24	Randy Myers	.05	.04	.02
25	Ron Gant	.15	.11	.06
26	Mike Bielecki	.03	.02	.01
27	Juan Gonzalez	.20	.15	.08
28	Mike Schooler	.04	.03	.02
29	Mickey Tettleton	.05	.04	.02
30	John Kruk	.06	.05	.02
31	Bryn Smith	.03	.02	.01
32	Chris Nabholz	.06	.05	.02
33	Carlos Baerga	.08	.06	.03
34	Jeff Juden	.15	.11	.06
35	Dave Righetti	.06	.05	.02
36	#1 Draft Pick (Scott Ruffcorn)(FC)	.25	.20	.10
37	Luis Polonia	.04	.03	.02
38	Tom Candiotti	.04	.03	.02
39	Greg Olson	.04	.03	.02
40	Cal Ripken	.20	.15	.08
41	Craig Lefferts	.04	.03	.02
42	Mike Macfarlane	.04	.03	.02
43	Jose Lind	.04	.03	.02
44	Rick Aguilera	.05	.04	.02
45	Gary Carter	.08	.06	.03
46	Steve Farr	.04	.03	.02
47	Rex Hudler	.04	.03	.02
48	Scott Scudder	.05	.04	.02
49	Damon Berryhill	.04	.03	.02
50	Ken Griffey, Jr.	.50	.40	.20
51	Tom Runnells	.03	.02	.01
52	Juan Bell	.05	.04	.02
53	Tommy Gregg	.03	.02	.01
54	David Wells	.04	.03	.02
55	Rafael Palmeiro	.10	.08	.04
56	Charlie O'Brien	.03	.02	.01
57	Donn Pall	.03	.02	.01
58	Top Prospects-Catchers (Brad Ausmus, Jim Campanis, Dave Nilsson, Doug Robbins)(FC)	.50	.40	.20
59	Mo Vaughn	.25	.20	.10
60	Tony Fernandez	.05	.04	.02
61	Paul O'Neill	.06	.05	.02
62	Gene Nelson	.03	.02	.01
63	Randy Ready	.03	.02	.01
64	Bob Kipper	.03	.02	.01
65	Willie McGee	.08	.06	.03
66	#1 Draft Pick (Scott Stahoviak)(FC)	.30	.25	.12
67	Luis Salazar	.03	.02	.01
68	Marvin Freeman	.03	.02	.01
69	Kenny Lofton(FC)	.40	.30	.15
70	Gary Gaetti	.06	.05	.02
71	Erik Hanson	.08	.06	.03
72	Eddie Zosky(FC)	.10	.08	.04
73	Brian Barnes	.10	.08	.04
74	Scott Leius	.10	.08	.04
75	Bret Saberhagen	.08	.06	.03
76	Mike Gallego	.03	.02	.01
77	Jack Armstrong	.05	.04	.02
78	Ivan Rodriguez	.60	.45	.25
79	Jesse Orosco	.03	.02	.01
80	David Justice	.20	.15	.08
81	Ced Landrum(FC)	.15	.11	.06
82	Doug Simons	.10	.08	.04
83	Tommy Greene	.06	.05	.02
84	Leo Gomez	.15	.11	.06
85	Jose DeLeon	.04	.03	.02
86	Steve Finley	.06	.05	.02
87	Bob MacDonald(FC)	.15	.11	.06
88	Darrin Jackson	.04	.03	.02
89	Neal Heaton	.03	.02	.01
90	Robin Yount	.12	.09	.05
91	Jeff Reed	.03	.02	.01

#	Name	MT	NR MT	EX
92	Lenny Harris	.04	.03	.02
93	Reggie Jefferson	.15	.11	.06
94	Sammy Sosa	.08	.06	.03
95	Scott Bailes	.03	.02	.01
96	#1 Draft Pick (Tom McKinnon)(FC)	.15	.11	.06
97	Luis Rivera	.03	.02	.01
98	Mike Harkey	.06	.05	.02
99	Jeff Treadway	.04	.03	.02
100	Jose Canseco	.20	.15	.08
101	Omar Vizquel	.03	.02	.01
102	Scott Kamieniecki	.12	.09	.05
103	Ricky Jordan	.06	.05	.02
104	Jeff Ballard	.04	.03	.02
105	Felix Jose	.10	.08	.04
106	Mike Boddicker	.05	.04	.02
107	Dan Pasqua	.04	.03	.02
108	Mike Timlin	.12	.09	.05
109	Roger Craig	.04	.03	.02
110	Ryne Sandberg	.20	.15	.08
111	Mark Carreon	.03	.02	.01
112	Oscar Azocar	.04	.03	.02
113	Mike Greenwell	.10	.08	.04
114	Mark Portugal	.03	.02	.01
115	Terry Pendleton	.08	.06	.03
116	Willie Randolph	.05	.04	.02
117	Scott Terry	.03	.02	.01
118	Chili Davis	.08	.06	.03
119	Mark Gardner	.05	.04	.02
120	Alan Trammell	.10	.08	.04
121	Derek Bell	.25	.20	.10
122	Gary Varsho	.03	.02	.01
123	Bob Ojeda	.04	.03	.02
124	#1 Draft Pick (Shawn Livsey)(FC)	.15	.11	.06
125	Chris Hoiles	.08	.06	.03
126	Top Prospects-1st Baseman (Rico Brogna, John Jaha, Ryan Klesko, Dave Staton)(FC)	1.00	.70	.40
127	Carlos Quintana	.06	.05	.02
128	Kurt Stillwell	.04	.03	.02
129	Melido Perez	.04	.03	.02
130	Alvin Davis	.06	.05	.02
131	Checklist 1	.03	.02	.01
132	Eric Show	.03	.02	.01
133	Rance Mulliniks	.03	.02	.01
134	Darryl Kile	.08	.06	.03
135	Von Hayes	.05	.04	.02
136	Bill Doran	.05	.04	.02
137	Jeff Robinson	.03	.02	.01
138	Monty Fariss	.08	.06	.03
139	Jeff Innis	.05	.04	.03
140	Mark Grace	.12	.09	.05
141	Jim Leyland	.03	.02	.01
142	Todd Van Poppel(FC)	.50	.40	.20
143	Paul Gibson	.03	.02	.01
144	Bill Swift	.04	.03	.02
145	Danny Tartabull	.08	.06	.03
146	Al Newman	.03	.02	.01
147	Cris Carpenter	.04	.03	.02
148	Anthony Young(FC)	.25	.20	.10
149	Brian Bohanon(FC)	.15	.11	.06
150	Roger Clemens	.15	.11	.06
151	Jeff Hamilton	.03	.02	.01
152	Charlie Leibrandt	.04	.03	.02
153	Ron Karkovice	.04	.03	.02
154	Hensley Meulens	.08	.06	.03
155	Scott Bankhead	.04	.03	.02
156	#1 Draft Pick (Manny Ramirez)(FC)	.70	.50	.30
157	Keith Miller	.03	.02	.01
158	Todd Frohwirth	.03	.02	.01
159	Darrin Fletcher	.05	.04	.02
160	Bobby Bonilla	.12	.09	.05
161	Casey Candaele	.03	.02	.01
162	Paul Faries(FC)	.10	.08	.04
163	Dana Kiecker	.03	.02	.01
164	Shane Mack	.08	.06	.03
165	Mark Langston	.10	.08	.04
166	Geronimo Pena	.06	.05	.02
167	Andy Allanson	.03	.02	.01
168	Dwight Smith	.04	.03	.02
169	Chuck Crim	.03	.02	.01
170	Alex Cole	.05	.04	.02
171	Bill Plummer	.03	.02	.01
172	Juan Berenguer	.03	.02	.01
173	Brian Downing	.04	.03	.02
174	Steve Frey	.03	.02	.01
175	Orel Hershiser	.08	.06	.03
176	Ramon Garcia(FC)	.15	.11	.06
177	Danny Gladden	.04	.03	.02
178	Jim Acker	.03	.02	.01
179	Top Prospects-2nd Baseman (Cesar Bernhardt, Bobby DeJardin, Armando Moreno, Andy Stankiewicz)(FC)	.25	.20	.10
180	Kevin Mitchell	.10	.08	.04
181	Hector Villanueva	.06	.05	.02
182	Jeff Reardon	.06	.05	.02
183	Brent Mayne	.06	.05	.02
184	Jimmy Jones	.03	.02	.01
185	Benny Santiago	.08	.06	.03
186	#1 Draft Pick (Cliff Floyd)(FC)	.60	.45	.25
187	Ernie Riles	.03	.02	.01
188	Jose Guzman	.05	.04	.02
189	Junior Felix	.06	.05	.02
190	Glenn Davis	.08	.06	.03
191	Charlie Hough	.04	.03	.02
192	Dave Fleming(FC)	.40	.30	.15
193	Omar Oliveras(FC)	.08	.06	.03
194	Eric Karros(FC)	.30	.25	.12
195	David Cone	.08	.06	.03
196	Frank Castillo(FC)	.12	.09	.05
197	Glenn Braggs	.04	.03	.02
198	Scott Aldred	.06	.05	.02
199	Jeff Blauser	.04	.03	.02
200	Len Dykstra	.08	.06	.03
201	Buck Showalter	.03	.02	.01
202	Rick Honeycutt	.03	.02	.01
203	Greg Myers	.03	.02	.01
204	Trevor Wilson	.05	.04	.02
205	Jay Howell	.04	.03	.02
206	Luis Sojo	.05	.04	.02
207	Jack Clark	.08	.06	.03
208	Julio Machado	.03	.02	.01
209	Lloyd McClendon	.03	.02	.01
210	Ozzie Guillen	.06	.05	.02
211	Jeremy Hernandez(FC)	.15	.11	.06
212	Randy Velarde	.03	.02	.01
213	Les Lancaster	.03	.02	.01
214	Andy Mota(FC)	.15	.11	.06
215	Rich Gossage	.05	.04	.02
216	#1 Draft Pick (Brent Gates)(FC)	.25	.20	.10
217	Brian Harper	.05	.04	.02
218	Mike Flanagan	.03	.02	.01
219	Jerry Browne	.04	.03	.02
220	Jose Rijo	.08	.06	.03
221	Skeeter Barnes	.04	.03	.02
222	Jaime Navarro	.04	.03	.02
223	Mel Hall	.04	.03	.02
224	Brett Barberie	.20	.15	.08
225	Roberto Alomar	.10	.08	.04
226	Pete Smith	.03	.02	.01
227	Daryl Boston	.03	.02	.01
228	Eddie Whitson	.04	.03	.02
229	Shawn Boskie	.04	.03	.02
230	Dick Schofield	.03	.02	.01
231	Brian Drahman(FC)	.10	.08	.04
232	John Smiley	.05	.04	.02
233	Mitch Webster	.04	.03	.02
234	Terry Steinbach	.05	.04	.02
235	Jack Morris	.08	.06	.03
236	Bill Pecota	.04	.03	.02
237	Jose Hernandez(FC)	.10	.08	.04
238	Greg Litton	.03	.02	.01
239	Brian Holman	.05	.04	.02
240	Andres Galarraga	.06	.05	.02
241	Gerald Young	.03	.02	.01
242	Mike Mussina(FC)	.50	.40	.20
243	Alvaro Espinoza	.03	.02	.01
244	Darren Daulton	.04	.03	.02
245	John Smoltz	.08	.06	.03
246	#1 Draft Pick (Jason Pruitt)(FC)	.15	.11	.06
247	Chuck Finley	.08	.06	.03
248	Jim Gantner	.04	.03	.02
249	Tony Fossas	.03	.02	.01
250	Ken Griffey	.05	.04	.02
251	Kevin Elster	.04	.03	.02
252	Dennis Rasmussen	.03	.02	.01
253	Terry Kennedy	.03	.02	.01
254	Ryan Bowen(FC)	.15	.11	.06
255	Robin Ventura	.15	.11	.06
256	Mike Aldrete	.03	.02	.01
257	Jeff Russell	.04	.03	.02
258	Jim Lindeman	.03	.02	.01
259	Ron Darling	.05	.04	.02
260	Devon White	.06	.05	.02
261	Tom Lasorda	.04	.03	.02
262	Terry Lee(FC)	.10	.08	.04
263	Bob Patterson	.03	.02	.01
264	Checklist 2	.03	.02	.01
265	Teddy Higuera	.05	.04	.02
266	Roberto Kelly	.08	.06	.03
267	Steve Bedrosian	.04	.03	.02
268	Brady Anderson	.03	.02	.01
269	Ruben Amaro(FC)	.15	.11	.06
270	Tony Gwynn	.12	.09	.05

#	Player	MT	NR MT	EX
271	Tracy Jones	.03	.02	.01
272	Jerry Don Gleaton	.03	.02	.01
273	Craig Grebeck	.04	.03	.02
274	*Bob Scanlan*	.10	.08	.04
275	Todd Zeile	.10	.08	.04
276	#1 Draft Pick *(Shawn Green)*(FC)	.25	.20	.10
277	Scott Chiamparino	.04	.03	.02
278	Darryl Hamilton	.04	.03	.02
279	Jim Clancy	.03	.02	.01
280	Carlos Martinez	.04	.03	.02
281	Kevin Appier	.05	.04	.02
282	*John Wehner*(FC)	.15	.11	.06
283	Reggie Sanders(FC)	.30	.25	.12
284	Gene Larkin	.04	.03	.02
285	Bob Welch	.06	.05	.02
286	Gilberto Reyes(FC)	.05	.04	.02
287	*Pete Schourek*	.15	.11	.06
288	Andujar Cedeno	.15	.11	.06
289	Mike Morgan	.04	.03	.02
290	Bo Jackson	.20	.15	.08
291	Phil Garner	.03	.02	.01
292	Ray Lankford	.15	.11	.06
293	Mike Henneman	.05	.04	.02
294	Dave Valle	.03	.02	.01
295	Alonzo Powell(FC)	.08	.06	.03
296	Tom Brunansky	.05	.04	.02
297	Kevin Brown	.05	.04	.02
298	Kelly Gruber	.08	.06	.03
299	Charles Nagy	.06	.05	.02
300	Don Mattingly	.15	.11	.06
301	Kirk McCaskill	.04	.03	.02
302	Joey Cora	.04	.03	.02
303	Dan Plesac	.04	.03	.02
304	Joe Oliver	.04	.03	.02
305	Tom Glavine	.08	.06	.03
306	#1 Draft Pick *(Al Shirley)*(FC)	.25	.20	.10
307	Bruce Ruffin	.03	.02	.01
308	*Craig Shipley*(FC)	.08	.06	.03
309	Dave Martinez	.04	.03	.02
310	Jose Mesa	.03	.02	.01
311	Henry Cotto	.03	.02	.01
312	Mike LaValliere	.04	.03	.02
313	Kevin Tapani	.08	.06	.03
314	Jeff Huson	.04	.03	.02
315	Juan Samuel	.06	.05	.02
316	Curt Schilling	.06	.05	.02
317	Mike Bordick(FC)	.06	.05	.02
318	Steve Howe	.04	.03	.02
319	Tony Phillips	.04	.03	.02
320	George Bell	.10	.08	.04
321	Lou Pinella	.03	.02	.01
322	Tim Burke	.04	.03	.02
323	Milt Thompson	.04	.03	.02
324	Danny Darwin	.04	.03	.02
325	Joe Orsulak	.03	.02	.01
326	Eric King	.04	.03	.02
327	Jay Buhner	.05	.04	.02
328	*Joel Johnson*(FC)	.15	.11	.06
329	Franklin Stubbs	.03	.02	.01
330	Will Clark	.20	.15	.08
331	Steve Lake	.03	.02	.01
332	*Chris Jones*	.10	.08	.04
333	Pat Tabler	.03	.02	.01
334	Kevin Gross	.03	.02	.01
335	Dave Henderson	.08	.06	.03
336	#1 Draft Pick *(Greg Anthony)*(FC)	.15	.11	.06
337	Alejandro Pena	.04	.03	.02
338	Shawn Abner	.03	.02	.01
339	Tom Browning	.06	.05	.02
340	Otis Nixon	.04	.03	.02
341	Bob Geren	.03	.02	.01
342	*Tim Spehr*(FC)	.10	.08	.04
343	*Jon Vander Wal*(FC)	.20	.15	.08
344	Jack Daugherty	.03	.02	.01
345	Zane Smith	.04	.03	.02
346	*Rheal Cormier*(FC)	.15	.11	.06
347	Kent Hrbek	.06	.05	.02
348	*Rick Wilkins*(FC)	.15	.11	.06
349	Steve Lyons	.03	.02	.01
350	Gregg Olson	.08	.06	.03
351	Greg Riddoch	.03	.02	.01
352	Ed Nunez	.03	.02	.01
353	*Braulio Castillo*(FC)	.08	.06	.03
354	Dave Bergman	.03	.02	.01
355	*Warren Newson*(FC)	.15	.11	.06
356	Luis Quinones	.03	.02	.01
357	Mike Witt	.04	.03	.02
358	*Ted Wood*	.15	.11	.06
359	Mike Moore	.04	.03	.02
360	Lance Parrish	.06	.05	.02
361	Barry Jones	.03	.02	.01
362	*Javier Ortiz*(FC)	.10	.08	.04
363	John Candelaria	.04	.03	.02
364	Glenallen Hill	.06	.05	.02
365	Duane Ward	.04	.03	.02
366	Checklist 3	.03	.02	.01
367	Rafael Belliard	.03	.02	.01
368	Bill Krueger	.03	.02	.01
369	#1 Draft Pick *(Steve Whitaker)*(FC)	.20	.15	.08
370	Shawon Dunston	.06	.05	.02
371	Dante Bichette	.04	.03	.02
372	*Kip Gross*(FC)	.10	.08	.04
373	Don Robinson	.03	.02	.01
374	Bernie Williams	.03	.02	.01
375	Bert Blyleven	.05	.04	.02
376	*Chris Donnels*(FC)	.15	.11	.06
377	*Bob Zupcic*(FC)	.30	.25	.12
378	Joel Skinner	.03	.02	.01
379	Steve Chitren	.06	.05	.02
380	Barry Bonds	.15	.11	.06
381	Sparky Anderson	.03	.02	.01
382	Sid Fernandez	.05	.04	.02
383	Dave Hollins	.06	.05	.02
384	Mark Lee	.03	.02	.01
385	Tim Wallach	.05	.04	.02
386	Will Clark (AS)	.10	.08	.04
387	Ryne Sandberg (AS)	.10	.08	.04
388	Howard Johnson (AS)	.05	.04	.02
389	Barry Larkin (AS)	.05	.04	.02
390	Barry Bonds (AS)	.10	.08	.04
391	Ron Gant (AS)	.08	.06	.03
392	Bobby Bonilla (AS)	.08	.06	.03
393	Craig Biggio (AS)	.05	.04	.02
394	Denny Martinez (AS)	.04	.03	.02
395	Tom Glavine (AS)	.05	.04	.02
396	Ozzie Smith (AS)	.08	.06	.03
397	Cecil Fielder (AS)	.10	.08	.04
398	Julio Franco (AS)	.08	.06	.03
399	Wade Boggs (AS)	.10	.08	.04
400	Cal Ripken (AS)	.15	.11	.06
401	Jose Canseco (AS)	.15	.11	.06
402	Joe Carter (AS)	.08	.06	.03
403	Ruben Sierra (AS)	.10	.08	.04
404	Matt Nokes (AS)	.04	.03	.02
405	Roger Clemens (AS)	.12	.09	.05
406	Jim Abbott (AS)	.08	.06	.03
407	Bryan Harvey (AS)	.05	.04	.02
408	Bob Milacki	.03	.02	.01
409	Geno Petralli	.03	.02	.01
410	Dave Stewart	.08	.06	.03
411	Mike Jackson	.03	.02	.01
412	Luis Aquino	.03	.02	.01
413	Tim Teufel	.03	.02	.01
414	#1 Draft Pick *(Jeff Ware)*(FC)	.15	.11	.06
415	Jim Deshaies	.04	.03	.02
416	Ellis Burks	.10	.08	.04
417	Allan Anderson	.03	.02	.01
418	Alfredo Griffin	.03	.02	.01
419	Wally Whitehurst	.05	.04	.02
420	Sandy Alomar	.08	.06	.03
421	Juan Agosto	.03	.02	.01
422	Sam Horn	.03	.02	.01
423	*Jeff Fassero*	.10	.08	.04
424	Paul McClellan(FC)	.10	.08	.04
425	Cecil Fielder	.15	.11	.06
426	Rock Raines	.10	.08	.04
427	*Eddie Taubensee*(FC)	.20	.15	.08
428	Dennis Boyd	.05	.04	.02
429	Tony LaRussa	.03	.02	.01
430	Steve Sax	.06	.05	.02
431	Tom Gordon	.08	.06	.03
432	Billy Hatcher	.04	.03	.02
433	Cal Eldred(FC)	.25	.20	.10
434	Wally Backman	.03	.02	.01
435	Mark Eichhorn	.03	.02	.01
436	Mookie Wilson	.03	.02	.01
437	*Scott Servais*	.10	.08	.04
438	Mike Maddux	.03	.02	.01
439	*Chico Walker*(FC)	.10	.08	.04
440	Doug Drabek	.08	.06	.03
441	Rob Deer	.04	.03	.02
442	Dave West	.04	.03	.02
443	Spike Owen	.03	.02	.01
444	#1 Draft Pick *(Tyrone Hill)*(FC)	.25	.20	.10
445	Matt Williams	.12	.09	.05
446	Mark Lewis	.12	.09	.05
447	David Segui	.08	.06	.03
448	Tom Pagnozzi	.04	.03	.02
449	*Jeff Johnson*	.12	.09	.05
450	Mark McGwire	.12	.09	.05
451	Tom Henke	.05	.04	.02
452	Wilson Alvarez	.08	.06	.03

No.	Player	MT	NR MT	EX
453	Gary Redus	.03	.02	.01
454	Darren Holmes	.03	.02	.01
455	Pete O'Brien	.03	.02	.01
456	Pat Combs	.04	.03	.02
457	Hubie Brooks	.04	.03	.02
458	Frank Tanana	.03	.02	.01
459	Tom Kelly	.03	.02	.01
460	Andre Dawson	.12	.09	.05
461	Doug Jones	.04	.03	.02
462	Rich Rodriguez	.04	.03	.02
463	*Mike Simms*	.10	.08	.04
464	Mike Jeffcoat	.03	.02	.01
465	Barry Larkin	.12	.09	.05
466	Stan Belinda	.04	.03	.02
467	Lonnie Smith	.04	.03	.02
468	Greg Harris	.03	.02	.01
469	Jim Eisenreich	.03	.02	.01
470	Pedro Guerrero	.08	.06	.03
471	Jose DeJesus	.04	.03	.02
472	*Rich Rowland*(FC)	.15	.11	.06
473	Top Prospects-3rd Baseman *(Frank Bolick, Craig Paquette, Tom Redington, Paul Russo)*(FC)	.35	.25	.14
474	#1 Draft Pick *(Mike Rossiter)*(FC)	.25	.20	.10
475	Robby Thompson	.04	.03	.02
476	Randy Bush	.03	.02	.01
477	Greg Hibbard	.04	.03	.02
478	Dale Sveum	.03	.02	.01
479	*Chito Martinez*(FC)	.15	.11	.06
480	Scott Sanderson	.04	.03	.02
481	Tino Martinez	.10	.08	.04
482	Jimmy Key	.05	.04	.02
483	Terry Shumpert	.03	.02	.01
484	Mike Hartley	.03	.02	.01
485	Chris Sabo	.08	.06	.03
486	Bob Walk	.03	.02	.01
487	John Cerutti	.03	.02	.01
488	Scott Cooper(FC)	.10	.08	.04
489	Bobby Cox	.03	.02	.01
490	Julio Franco	.10	.08	.04
491	Jeff Brantley	.04	.03	.02
492	Mike Devereaux	.04	.03	.02
493	Jose Offerman	.10	.08	.04
494	Gary Thurman	.03	.02	.01
495	Carney Lansford	.06	.05	.02
496	Joe Grahe	.04	.03	.02
497	*Andy Ashby*(FC)	.15	.11	.06
498	Gerald Perry	.03	.02	.01
499	Dave Otto	.03	.02	.01
500	Vince Coleman	.08	.06	.03
501	*Rob Mallicoat*(FC)	.15	.11	.06
502	Greg Briley	.03	.02	.01
503	Pascual Perez	.03	.02	.01
504	#1 Draft Pick *(Aaron Sele)*(FC)	.30	.25	.12
505	Bobby Thigpen	.08	.06	.03
506	Todd Benzinger	.04	.03	.02
507	Candy Maldonado	.04	.03	.02
508	Bill Gullickson	.05	.04	.02
509	Doug Dascenzo	.03	.02	.01
510	Frank Viola	.08	.06	.03
511	Kenny Rogers	.04	.03	.02
512	Mike Heath	.03	.02	.01
513	Kevin Bass	.04	.03	.02
514	*Kim Batiste*(FC)	.15	.11	.06
515	Delino DeShields	.08	.06	.03
516	*Ed Sprague*	.10	.08	.04
517	Jim Gott	.03	.02	.01
518	*Jose Melendez*(FC)	.10	.08	.04
519	Hal McRae	.03	.02	.01
520	*Jeff Bagwell*	.50	.40	.20
521	Joe Hesketh	.03	.02	.01
522	Milt Cuyler	.12	.09	.05
523	Shawn Hillegas	.03	.02	.01
524	Don Slaught	.03	.02	.01
525	Randy Johnson	.06	.05	.02
526	*Doug Piatt*	.10	.08	.04
527	Checklist 4	.03	.02	.01
528	*Steve Foster*(FC)	.15	.11	.06
529	Joe Girardi	.04	.03	.02
530	Jim Abbott	.10	.08	.04
531	Larry Walker	.08	.06	.03
532	Mike Huff	.04	.03	.02
533	Mackey Sasser	.03	.02	.01
534	#1 Draft Pick *(Benji Gil)*(FC)	.20	.15	.08
535	Dave Stieb	.06	.05	.02
536	Willie Wilson	.04	.03	.02
537	*Mark Leiter*(FC)	.10	.08	.04
538	Jose Uribe	.03	.02	.01
539	Thomas Howard	.03	.02	.01
540	Ben McDonald	.12	.09	.05
541	*Jose Tolentino*(FC)	.15	.11	.06
542	*Keith Mitchell*(FC)	.20	.15	.08
543	Jerome Walton	.08	.06	.03
544	*Cliff Brantley*(FC)	.15	.11	.06
545	Andy Van Slyke	.08	.06	.03
546	Paul Sorrento	.04	.03	.02
547	Herm Winningham	.03	.02	.01
548	Mark Guthrie	.04	.03	.02
549	Joe Torre	.03	.02	.01
550	Darryl Strawberry	.12	.09	.05
551	Top Prospects-Shortstops *(Manny Alexander, Alex Arias, Wil Cordero, Chipper Jones)*	.50	.40	.20
552	Dave Gallagher	.04	.03	.02
553	Edgar Martinez	.06	.05	.02
554	Donald Harris	.15	.11	.06
555	Frank Thomas	.60	.45	.25
556	Storm Davis	.04	.03	.02
557	Dickie Thon	.03	.02	.01
558	Scott Garrelts	.03	.02	.01
559	Steve Olin	.03	.02	.01
560	Rickey Henderson	.15	.11	.06
561	Jose Vizcaino	.04	.03	.02
562	*Wade Taylor*	.10	.08	.04
563	Pat Borders	.04	.03	.02
564	#1 Draft Pick *(Jimmy Gonzalez)*(FC)	.20	.15	.08
565	Lee Smith	.05	.04	.02
566	Bill Sampen	.05	.04	.02
567	Dean Palmer	.12	.09	.05
568	Bryan Harvey	.05	.04	.02
569	Tony Pena	.05	.04	.02
570	Lou Whitaker	.06	.05	.02
571	Randy Tomlin	.06	.05	.02
572	Greg Vaughn	.12	.09	.05
573	Kelly Downs	.03	.02	.01
574	Steve Avery	.20	.15	.08
575	Kirby Puckett	.15	.11	.06
576	*Heathcliff Slocumb*(FC)	.10	.08	.04
577	Kevin Seitzer	.04	.03	.02
578	Lee Guetterman	.03	.02	.01
579	Johnny Oates	.03	.02	.01
580	Greg Maddux	.05	.04	.02
581	Stan Javier	.03	.02	.01
582	Vicente Palacios	.03	.02	.01
583	Mel Rojas	.03	.02	.01
584	*Wayne Rosenthal*(FC)	.10	.08	.04
585	*Lenny Webster*(FC)	.10	.08	.04
586	Rod Nichols	.03	.02	.01
587	Mickey Morandini	.08	.06	.03
588	Russ Swan	.03	.02	.01
589	Mariano Duncan	.04	.03	.02
590	Howard Johnson	.10	.08	.04
591	Top Prospects-Outfielders *(Jacob Brumfield, Jeromy Burnitz, Alan Cockrell, D.J. Dozier)*(FC)	.60	.45	.25
592	*Denny Neagle*(FC)	.15	.11	.06
593	Steve Decker	.10	.08	.04
594	#1 Draft Pick *(Brian Barber)*(FC)	.15	.11	.06
595	Bruce Hurst	.04	.03	.02
596	Kent Mercker	.04	.03	.02
597	*Mike Magnante*(FC)	.10	.08	.04
598	Jody Reed	.04	.03	.02
599	Steve Searcy	.03	.02	.01
600	Paul Molitor	.10	.08	.04
601	Dave Smith	.05	.04	.02
602	Mike Fetters	.04	.03	.02
603	*Luis Mercedes*(FC)	.25	.20	.10
604	Chris Gwynn	.03	.02	.01
605	Scott Erickson	.20	.15	.08
606	Brook Jacoby	.04	.03	.02
607	Todd Stottlemyre	.05	.04	.02
608	Scott Bradley	.03	.02	.01
609	Mike Hargrove	.03	.02	.01
610	Eric Davis	.12	.09	.05
611	*Brian Hunter*(FC)	.25	.20	.10
612	Pat Kelly	.10	.08	.04
613	Pedro Munoz(FC)	.15	.11	.06
614	Al Osuna	.04	.03	.02
615	Matt Merullo	.03	.02	.01
616	Larry Andersen	.03	.02	.01
617	Junior Ortiz	.03	.02	.01
618	Top Prospects-Outfielders *(Cesar Hernandez, Steve Hosey, Dan Peltier, Jeff McNeely)*(FC)	.60	.45	.25
619	Danny Jackson	.04	.03	.02
620	George Brett	.12	.09	.05
621	*Dan Gakeler*(FC)	.10	.08	.04
622	Steve Buechele	.04	.03	.02
623	Bob Tewksbury	.03	.02	.01
624	#1 Draft Pick *(Shawn Estes)*(FC)	.15	.11	.06
625	Kevin McReynolds	.08	.06	.03

		MT	NR MT	EX
626	*Chris Haney*(FC)	.15	.11	.06
627	Mike Sharperson	.03	.02	.01
628	Mark Williamson	.03	.02	.01
629	Wally Joyner	.10	.08	.04
630	Carlton Fisk	.12	.09	.05
631	*Armando Reynoso*(FC)	.10	.08	.04
632	Felix Fermin	.03	.02	.01
633	Mitch Williams	.05	.04	.02
634	Manuel Lee	.04	.03	.02
635	Harold Baines	.08	.06	.03
636	Greg Harris	.05	.04	.02
637	Orlando Merced	.12	.09	.05
638	Chris Bosio	.04	.03	.02
639	*Wayne Housie*(FC)	.10	.08	.04
640	Xavier Hernandez	.04	.03	.02
641	*David Howard*(FC)	.10	.08	.04
642	Tim Crews	.03	.02	.01
643	Rick Cerone	.03	.02	.01
644	Terry Leach	.03	.02	.01
645	Deion Sanders	.12	.09	.05
646	Craig Wilson	.04	.03	.02
647	Marquis Grissom	.12	.09	.05
648	Scott Fletcher	.03	.02	.01
649	Norm Charlton	.04	.03	.02
650	Jesse Barfield	.06	.05	.02
651	*Joe Slusarski*	.10	.08	.04
652	Bobby Rose	.04	.03	.02
653	Dennis Lamp	.03	.02	.01
654	#1 Draft Pick *(Allen Watson)*(FC)	.15	.11	.06
655	Brett Butler	.06	.05	.02
656	Top Prospects-Outfielders *(Rudy Pemberton, Henry Rodriguez, Lee Tinsley, Gerald Williams)*(FC)	.50	.40	.20
657	Dave Johnson	.03	.02	.01
658	Checklist 5	.03	.02	.01
659	Brian McRae	.12	.09	.05
660	Fred McGriff	.10	.08	.04
661	Bill Landrum	.03	.02	.01
662	*Juan Guzman*(FC)	.50	.40	.20
663	Greg Gagne	.03	.02	.01
664	Ken Hill	.04	.03	.02
665	*Dave Haas*(FC)	.15	.11	.06
666	Tom Foley	.03	.02	.01
667	*Roberto Hernandez*(FC)	.10	.08	.04
668	Dwayne Henry	.03	.02	.01
669	Jim Fregosi	.03	.02	.01
670	Harold Reynolds	.05	.04	.02
671	Mark Whiten	.10	.08	.04
672	Eric Plunk	.03	.02	.01
673	Todd Hundley	.10	.08	.04
674	*Mo Sanford*(FC)	.25	.20	.10
675	Bobby Witt	.04	.03	.02
676	Top Prospects-Pitchers *(Pat Mahomes, Sam Militello, Roger Salkeld, Turk Wendell)*(FC)	.70	.50	.30
677	John Marzano	.03	.02	.01
678	Joe Klink	.03	.02	.01
679	Pete Incaviglia	.04	.03	.02
680	Dale Murphy	.08	.06	.03
681	Rene Gonzales	.03	.02	.01
682	Andy Benes	.08	.06	.03
683	Jim Poole(FC)	.08	.06	.03
684	#1 Draft Pick *(Trever Miller)*(FC)	.15	.11	.06
685	*Scott Livingstone*(FC)	.12	.09	.05
686	Rich DeLucia	.04	.03	.02
687	*Harvey Pulliam*(FC)	.15	.11	.06
688	Tim Belcher	.04	.03	.02
689	Mark Lemke	.05	.04	.02
690	John Franco	.06	.05	.02
691	Walt Weiss	.06	.05	.02
692	Scott Ruskin	.04	.03	.02
693	Jeff King	.04	.03	.02
694	Mike Gardiner(FC)	.06	.05	.02
695	Gary Sheffield	.12	.09	.05
696	Joe Boever	.03	.02	.01
697	Mike Felder	.03	.02	.01
698	John Habyan	.03	.02	.01
699	Cito Gaston	.03	.02	.01
700	Ruben Sierra	.15	.11	.06
701	Scott Radinsky	.03	.02	.01
702	Lee Stevens	.06	.05	.02
703	*Mark Wohlers*(FC)	.15	.11	.06
704	Curt Young	.03	.02	.01
705	Dwight Evans	.06	.05	.02
706	Rob Murphy	.03	.02	.01
707	Gregg Jefferies	.12	.09	.05
708	Tom Bolton	.03	.02	.01
709	Chris James	.03	.02	.01
710	Kevin Maas	.12	.09	.05
711	*Ricky Bones*(FC)	.10	.08	.04
712	Curt Wilkerson	.03	.02	.01

		MT	NR MT	EX
713	Roger McDowell	.04	.03	.02
714	#1 Draft Pick *(Calvin Reese)*(FC)	.50	.40	.20
715	Craig Biggio	.08	.06	.03
716	*Kirk Dressendorfer*	.15	.11	.06
717	Ken Dayley	.03	.02	.01
718	B.J. Surhoff	.05	.04	.02
719	Terry Mulholland	.05	.04	.02
720	Kirk Gibson	.06	.05	.02
721	Mike Pagliarulo	.04	.03	.02
722	Walt Terrell	.03	.02	.01
723	Jose Oquendo	.03	.02	.01
724	Kevin Morton(FC)	.08	.06	.03
725	Doc Gooden	.12	.09	.05
726	Kirt Manwaring	.04	.03	.02
727	Chuck McElroy	.03	.02	.01
728	Dave Burba(FC)	.06	.05	.02
729	Art Howe	.03	.02	.01
730	Ramon Martinez	.15	.11	.06
731	Donnie Hill	.03	.02	.01
732	Nelson Santovenia	.03	.02	.01
733	Bob Melvin	.03	.02	.01
734	#1 Draft Pick *(Scott Hatteberg)*(FC)	.15	.11	.06
735	Greg Swindell	.05	.04	.02
736	Lance Johnson	.03	.02	.01
737	Kevin Reimer	.05	.04	.02
738	Dennis Eckersley	.08	.06	.03
739	Rob Ducey	.03	.02	.01
740	Ken Caminiti	.04	.03	.02
741	Mark Gubicza	.04	.03	.02
742	Billy Spiers	.04	.03	.02
743	Darren Lewis	.15	.11	.06
744	Chris Hammond	.05	.04	.02
745	Dave Magadan	.05	.04	.02
746	Bernard Gilkey	.10	.08	.04
747	Willie Banks(FC)	.15	.11	.06
748	Matt Nokes	.04	.03	.02
749	Jerald Clark	.04	.03	.02
750	Travis Fryman	.15	.11	.06
751	Steve Wilson	.03	.02	.01
752	Billy Ripken	.03	.02	.01
753	Paul Assenmacher	.03	.02	.01
754	Charlie Hayes	.04	.03	.02
755	Alex Fernandez	.15	.11	.06
756	Gary Pettis	.03	.02	.01
757	Rob Dibble	.08	.06	.03
758	Tim Naehring	.08	.06	.03
759	Jeff Torborg	.03	.02	.01
760	Ozzie Smith	.10	.08	.04
761	Mike Fitzgerald	.03	.02	.01
762	John Burkett	.04	.03	.02
763	Kyle Abbott	.06	.05	.02
764	#1 Draft Pick *(Tyler Green)*(FC)	.50	.40	.20
765	Pete Harnisch	.06	.05	.02
766	Mark Davis	.03	.02	.01
767	Kal Daniels	.06	.05	.02
768	*Jim Thome*(FC)	.35	.25	.14
769	Jack Howell	.03	.02	.01
770	Sid Bream	.05	.04	.02
771	*Arthur Rhodes*(FC)	.20	.15	.08
772	Garry Templeton	.04	.03	.02
773	Hal Morris	.12	.09	.05
774	Bud Black	.04	.03	.02
775	Ivan Calderon	.06	.05	.02
776	*Doug Henry*(FC)	.15	.11	.06
777	John Olerud	.12	.09	.05
778	Tim Leary	.04	.03	.02
779	Jay Bell	.05	.04	.02
780	Eddie Murray	.10	.08	.04
781	Paul Abbott(FC)	.08	.06	.03
782	Phil Plantier	.20	.15	.08
783	Joe Magrane	.05	.04	.02
784	Ken Patterson	.03	.02	.01
785	Albert Belle	.15	.11	.06
786	Royce Clayton(FC)	.25	.20	.10
787	Checklist 6	.03	.02	.01
788	Mike Stanton	.04	.03	.02
789	Bobby Valentine	.03	.02	.01
790	Joe Carter	.10	.08	.04
791	Danny Cox	.03	.02	.01
792	Dave Winfield	.12	.09	.05

A player's name in italic indicates a rookie card. An (FC) indicates a player's first card for that particular card company.

1992 Topps Stadium Club Dome

This 200-card special Stadium Club set from Topps was uniquely packaged in a plastic replica of the Toronto SkyDome, the home of the 1991 All-Star Game. Featured in the set are members of Team USA, All-Stars, draft picks, top prospects and highlight cards from the World Series between the Twins and Braves. The cards are styled much like the regular Stadium Club cards.

		MT	NR MT	EX
Complete Set:		45.00	33.00	18.00
Common Player:		.20	.15	.08
1	Terry Adams	.30	.25	.12
2	Tommy Adams	.40	.30	.15
3	Rick Aguilera	.20	.15	.08
4	Ron Allen	.25	.20	.10
5	Roberto Alomar (AS)	.60	.45	.25
6	Sandy Alomar	.25	.20	.10
7	Greg Anthony	.40	.30	.15
8	James Austin	.25	.20	.10
9	Steve Avery	.80	.60	.30
10	Harold Baines	.20	.15	.08
11	Brian Barber	.80	.60	.30
12	Jon Barnes	.25	.20	.10
13	George Bell	.20	.15	.08
14	Doug Bennett	.25	.20	.10
15	Sean Bergman	.25	.20	.10
16	Bill Bliss	.25	.20	.10
17	Craig Biggio	.20	.15	.08
18	Wade Boggs (AS)	.30	.25	.12
19	Bobby Bonilla (AS)	.35	.25	.14
20	Russell Brock	.30	.25	.12
21	Tarrik Brock	.50	.40	.20
22	Tom Browning	.20	.15	.08
23	Brett Butler	.20	.15	.08
24	Ivan Calderon	.20	.15	.08
25	Joe Carter	.20	.15	.08
26	Joe Caruso	.25	.20	.10
27	Dan Cholowsky	.40	.30	.15
28	Will Clark (AS)	.80	.60	.30
29	Roger Clemens (AS)	.80	.60	.30
30	Shawn Curran	.25	.20	.10
31	Chris Curtis	.30	.25	.12
32	Chili Davis	.20	.15	.08
33	Andre Dawson	.20	.15	.08
34	Joe DeBerry	.40	.30	.15
35	John Dettmer	.40	.30	.15
36	Rob Dibble	.20	.15	.08
37	John Donati	.30	.25	.12
38	Dave Doorneweerd	.50	.40	.20
39	Darren Dreifort	.70	.50	.30
40	Mike Durant	.30	.25	.12
41	Chris Durkin	.30	.25	.12
42	Dennis Eckersley	.30	.25	.12
43	Brian Edmondson	.30	.25	.12
44	Vaughn Eshelman	.40	.30	.15
45	Shawn Estes	1.00	.70	.40
46	Jorge Fabregas	.40	.30	.15
47	Jon Farrell	.60	.45	.25
48	Cecil Fielder (AS)	.80	.60	.30
49	Carlton Fisk	.20	.15	.08
50	Tim Flannelly	.25	.20	.10
51	Cliff Floyd	2.00	1.50	.80
52	Julio Franco	.20	.15	.08

		MT	NR MT	EX
53	Greg Gagne	.20	.15	.08
54	Chris Gambs	.30	.25	.12
55	Ron Gant (NLCS)	.35	.25	.14
56	Brent Gates	.50	.40	.20
57	Dwayne Gerald	.30	.25	.12
58	Jason Giambi	.70	.50	.30
59	Benji Gil	1.00	.70	.40
60	Mark Gipner	.30	.25	.12
61	Danny Gladden	.20	.15	.08
62	Tom Glavine	.25	.20	.10
63	Jimmy Gonzalez	.50	.40	.20
64	Jeff Granger	.80	.60	.30
65	Dan Grapenthien	.25	.20	.10
66	Dennis Gray	.25	.20	.10
67	Shawn Green	1.25	.90	.50
68	Tyler Green	3.00	2.25	1.25
69	Todd Greene	.50	.40	.20
70	Ken Griffey, Jr. (AS)	4.00	3.00	1.50
71	Kelly Gruber	.20	.15	.08
72	Ozzie Guillen	.20	.15	.08
73	Tony Gwynn (AS)	.30	.25	.12
74	Shane Halter	.25	.20	.10
75	Jeffrey Hammonds	5.00	3.75	2.00
76	Larry Hanlon	.25	.20	.10
77	Pete Harnisch	.20	.15	.08
78	Mike Harrison	.25	.20	.10
79	Bryan Harvey	.20	.15	.08
80	Scott Hatteberg	.60	.45	.25
81	Rick Helling	.30	.25	.12
82	Dave Henderson	.20	.15	.08
83	Rickey Henderson (AS)	.50	.40	.20
84	Tyrone Hill	1.00	.70	.40
85	Todd Hollandsworth	.35	.25	.14
86	Brian Holliday	.25	.20	.10
87	Terry Horn	.40	.30	.15
88	Jeff Hostetler	.40	.30	.15
89	Kent Hrbek	.20	.15	.08
90	Mark Hubbard	.25	.20	.10
91	Charles Johnson	4.00	3.00	1.50
92	Howard Johnson	.20	.15	.08
93	Todd Johnson	.40	.30	.15
94	Bobby Jones	.80	.60	.30
95	Dan Jones	.25	.20	.10
96	Felix Jose	.20	.15	.08
97	Dave Justice (WS)	1.50	1.25	.60
98	Jimmy Key	.20	.15	.08
99	Marc Kroom	.25	.20	.10
100	John Kruk	.20	.15	.08
101	Mark Langston	.20	.15	.08
102	Barry Larkin	.20	.15	.08
103	Mike LaValliere	.20	.15	.08
104	Scott Leius	.20	.15	.08
105	Mark Lemke	.20	.15	.08
106	Donnie Leshnock	.40	.30	.15
107	Jimmy Lewis	.25	.20	.10
108	Shawn Livesy	.40	.30	.15
109	Ryan Long	.40	.30	.15
110	Trevor Mallory	.25	.20	.10
111	Denny Martinez	.20	.15	.08
112	Justin Mashore	.25	.20	.10
113	Jason McDonald	.25	.20	.10
114	Jack McDowell	.25	.20	.10
115	Tom McKinnon	.35	.25	.14
116	Billy McKinnon	.25	.20	.10
117	Buck McNabb	.25	.20	.10
118	Jim Mecir	.25	.20	.10
119	Dan Melendez	1.00	.70	.40
120	Shawn Miller	.25	.20	.10
121	Trever Miller	.40	.30	.15
122	Paul Molitor	.25	.20	.10
123	Vincent Moore	.25	.20	.10
124	Mike Morgan	.20	.15	.08
125	Jack Morris	.20	.15	.08
126	Jack Morris	.20	.15	.08
127	Sean Mulligan	.25	.20	.10
128	Eddie Murray	.25	.20	.10
129	Mike Neill	.60	.45	.25
130	Phil Nevin	6.00	4.50	2.50
131	Mark O'Brien	.25	.20	.10
132	Alex Ochoa	.25	.20	.10
133	Chad Ogea	.25	.20	.10
134	Greg Olson	.20	.15	.08
135	Paul O'Neill	.20	.15	.08
136	Jared Osentowski	.30	.25	.12
137	Mike Pagliarulo	.20	.15	.08
138	Rafael Palmeiro	.20	.15	.08
139	Rodney Pedraza	.25	.20	.10
140	Tony Phillips	.25	.20	.10
141	Scott Pisciotta	.30	.25	.12
142	Chris Pritchett	.30	.25	.12

		MT	NR MT	EX
143	Jason Pruitt	.50	.40	.20
144	Kirby Puckett (WS)	.80	.60	.30
145	Kirby Puckett (AS)	.80	.60	.30
146	Manny Ramirez	4.00	3.00	1.50
147	Eddie Ramos	.30	.25	.12
148	Mark Ratekin	.30	.25	.12
149	Jeff Reardon	.20	.15	.08
150	Sean Rees	.25	.20	.10
151	Calvin Reese	.80	.60	.30
152	Desmond Relaford	.25	.20	.10
153	Eric Richardson	.25	.20	.10
154	Cal Ripken (AS)	3.00	2.25	1.25
155	Chris Roberts	1.25	.90	.50
156	Mike Robertson	.35	.25	.14
157	Steve Rodriguez	.35	.25	.14
158	Mike Rossiter	.30	.25	.12
159	Scott Ruffcorn	.50	.40	.20
160	Chris Sabo	.20	.15	.08
161	Juan Samuel	.20	.15	.08
162	Ryne Sandberg (AS)	1.00	.70	.40
163	Scott Sanderson	.20	.15	.08
164	Benito Santiago	.20	.15	.08
165	Gene Schall	.30	.25	.12
166	Chad Schoenvogel	.30	.25	.12
167	Chris Seelbach	.30	.25	.12
168	Aaron Sele	.70	.50	.30
169	Basil Shabazz	.50	.40	.20
170	Al Shirley	1.00	.70	.40
171	Paul Shuey	.60	.45	.25
172	Ruben Sierra	.50	.40	.20
173	John Smiley	.30	.25	.12
174	Lee Smith	.30	.25	.12
175	Ozzie Smith	.30	.25	.12
176	Tim Smith	.25	.20	.10
177	Zane Smith	.20	.15	.08
178	John Smoltz	.20	.15	.08
179	Scott Stahoviak	1.00	.70	.40
180	Kennie Steenstra	.60	.45	.25
181	Kevin Stocker	.20	.15	.08
182	Chris Stynes	.20	.15	.08
183	Danny Tartabull	.20	.15	.08
184	Brien Taylor	12.00	9.00	4.75
185	Todd Taylor	.30	.25	.12
186	Larry Thomas	.30	.25	.12
187	Ozzie Timmons	.30	.25	.12
188	David Tuttle	.30	.25	.12
189	Andy Van Slyke	.20	.15	.08
190	Frank Viola	.20	.15	.08
191	Michael Walkden	.30	.25	.12
192	Jeff Ware	.60	.45	.25
193	Allen Watson	.50	.40	.20
194	Steve Whitaker	.40	.30	.15
195	Jerry Willard	.20	.15	.08
196	Craig Wilson	.50	.40	.20
197	Chris Wimmer	.50	.40	.20
198	Steve Wojciechowski	.30	.25	.12
199	Joel Wolfe	.40	.30	.15
200	Ivan Zweig	.50	.40	.20

1992 Topps Stadium Club

This 900-card set was released in three 300-card series. Like the 1991 issue, the cards feature borderless high gloss photos on the front. The flip sides feature the player's first Topps card and a player evaluation. Topps released updated cards in the third series for traded players and free agents. Several players appear on two cards. Special Members Choice cards are included in the set. Series III featured special inserts of the last three number one picks overall, Phil Nevin, Brien Taylor and Chipper Jones.

		MT	NR MT	EX
Complete Set:		110.00	82.00	44.00
Common Player:		.12	.09	.05
1	Cal Ripken	4.00	3.00	1.50
2	Eric Yelding	.12	.09	.05
3	Geno Petralli	.12	.09	.05
4	Wally Backman	.12	.09	.05
5	Milt Cuyler	.12	.09	.05
6	Kevin Bass	.12	.09	.05
7	Dante Bichette	.12	.09	.05
8	Ray Lankford	.80	.60	.30
9	Mel Hall	.15	.11	.06
10	Joe Carter	.30	.25	.12
11	Juan Samuel	.12	.09	.05
12	Jeff Motngomery	.15	.11	.06
13	Glenn Braggs	.15	.11	.06
14	Henry Cotto	.12	.09	.05
15	Deion Sanders	.30	.25	.12
16	Dick Schofield	.12	.09	.05
17	David Cone	.20	.15	.08
18	Chili Davis	.20	.15	.08
19	Tom Foley	.12	.09	.05
20	Ozzie Guillen	.15	.11	.06
21	Luis Salazar	.12	.09	.05
22	Terry Steinbach	.15	.11	.06
23	Chris James	.12	.09	.05
24	Jeff King	.12	.09	.05
25	Carlos Quintana	.12	.09	.05
26	Mike Maddux	.12	.09	.05
27	Tommy Greene	.15	.11	.06
28	Jeff Russell	.15	.11	.06
29	Steve Finley	.20	.10	.08
30	Mike Flanagan	.12	.09	.05
31	Darren Lewis	.12	.09	.05
32	Kevin Maas, Mark Lee	.12	.09	.05
33	Willie Fraser	.12	.09	.05
34	Mike Henneman	.15	.11	.06
35	Kevin Maas	.15	.11	.06
36	Dave Hansen, Dave Hansen	.12	.09	.05
37	Erik Hanson	.12	.09	.05
38	Bill Doran	.12	.09	.05
39	Mike Boddicker	.12	.09	.05
40	Vince Coleman	.15	.11	.06
41	Devon White	.15	.11	.06
42	Mark Gardner	.12	.09	.05
43	Scott Lewis	.25	.20	.10
44	Juan Berenguer	.12	.09	.05
45	Carney Lansford	.12	.09	.05
46	Curt Wilkerson	.12	.09	.05
47	Shane Mack	.15	.11	.06
48	Bip Roberts	.15	.11	.06
49	Greg Harris	.12	.09	.05
50	Ryne Sandberg	2.00	1.50	.80
51	Mark Whiten	.30	.25	.12
52	Jack McDowell	.20	.15	.08
53	Jimmy Jones	.12	.09	.05
54	Steve Lake	.12	.09	.05
55	Bud Black	.12	.09	.05
56	Dave Valle	.12	.09	.05
57	Kevin Reimer	.12	.09	.05
58	Rich Gedman	.12	.09	.05
59	Travis Fryman	1.25	.90	.50
60	Steve Avery	2.00	1.50	.80
61	Francisco DeLaRosa	.25	.20	.10
62	Scott Hemond	.12	.09	.05
63	Hal Morris	.30	.25	.12
64	Hensley Meulens	.12	.09	.05
65	Frank Castillo	.25	.20	.10
66	Gene Larkin	.12	.09	.05
67	Jose DeLeon	.12	.09	.05
68	Al Osuna	.12	.09	.05
69	Dave Cochrane	.12	.09	.05
70	Robin Ventura	2.00	1.50	.80
71	John Cerutti	.12	.09	.05
72	Kevin Gross	.12	.09	.05
73	Ivan Calderon	.15	.11	.06
74	Mike Macfarlane	.12	.09	.05
75	Stan Belinda	.12	.09	.05
76	Shawn Hillegas	.12	.09	.05
77	Pat Borders	.12	.09	.05
78	Jim Vatcher	.12	.09	.05
79	Bobby Rose	.12	.09	.05
80	Roger Clemens	1.50	1.25	.60
81	Craig Worthington	.12	.09	.05
82	Jeff Treadway	.12	.09	.05
83	Jamie Quirk	.12	.09	.05
84	Randy Bush	.12	.09	.05
85	Anthony Young	.50	.40	.20
86	Trevor Wilson	.12	.09	.05
87	Jaime Navarro	.15	.11	.06
88	Les Lancaster	.12	.09	.05

		MT	NR MT	EX			MT	NR MT	EX
89	Pat Kelly	.30	.25	.12	179	Candy Maldonado	.12	.09	.05
90	Alvin Davis	.12	.09	.05	180	Lee Smith	.15	.11	.06
91	Larry Andersen	.12	.09	.05	181	Harold Reynolds	.12	.09	.05
92	Rob Deer	.12	.09	.05	182	Dave Justice	2.00	1.50	.80
93	Mike Sharperson	.12	.09	.05	183	Lenny Webster	.12	.09	.05
94	Lance Parrish	.12	.09	.05	184	Donn Pall	.12	.09	.05
95	Cecil Espy	.12	.09	.05	185	Gerald Alexander	.12	.09	.05
96	Tim Spehr	.15	.11	.06	186	Jack Clark	.12	.09	.05
97	Dave Stieb	.15	.11	.06	187	Stan Javier	.12	.09	.05
98	Terry Mulholland	.15	.11	.06	188	Ricky Jordan	.15	.11	.06
99	Dennis Boyd	.12	.09	.05	189	Franklin Stubbs	.12	.09	.05
100	Barry Larkin	.30	.25	.12	190	Dennis Eckersley	.25	.20	.10
101	Ryan Bowen	.40	.30	.15	191	Danny Tartabull	.20	.15	.08
102	Felix Fermin	.12	.09	.05	192	Pete O'Brien	.12	.09	.05
103	Luis Alicea	.12	.09	.05	193	Mark Lewis	.30	.25	.12
104	Tim Huulett	.12	.09	.05	194	Mike Felder	.12	.09	.05
105	Rafael Belliard	.12	.09	.05	195	Mickey Tettleton	.15	.11	.06
106	Mike Gallego	.12	.09	.05	196	Dwight Smith	.12	.09	.05
107	Dave Righetti	.12	.09	.05	197	Shawn Abner	.12	.09	.05
108	Jeff Schaefer	.12	.09	.05	198	Jim Leyritz	.12	.09	.05
109	Ricky Bones	.40	.30	.15	199	Mike Devereaux	.20	.15	.08
110	Scott Erickson	.60	.45	.25	200	Craig Biggio	.15	.11	.06
111	Matt Nokes	.12	.09	.05	201	Kevin Elster	.12	.09	.05
112	Bob Scanlan	.12	.09	.05	202	Rance Mulliniks	.12	.09	.05
113	Tom Candiotti	.15	.11	.06	203	Tony Fernandez	.15	.11	.06
114	Sean Berry	.15	.11	.06	204	Allan Anderson	.12	.09	.05
115	Kevin Morton	.30	.25	.12	205	Herm Winningham	.12	.09	.05
116	Scott Fletcher	.12	.09	.05	206	Tim Jones	.12	.09	.05
117	B.J. Surhoff	.12	.09	.05	207	Ramon Martinez	.30	.25	.12
118	Dave Magadan	.12	.09	.05	208	Teddy Higuera	.12	.09	.05
119	Bill Gullickson	.12	.09	.05	209	John Kruk	.15	.11	.06
120	Marquis Grissom	.25	.20	.10	210	Jim Abbott	.30	.25	.12
121	Lenny Harris	.12	.09	.05	211	Dean Palmer, Dean Palmer	.20	.15	.08
122	Wally Joyner	.20	.15	.08	212	Mark Davis	.12	.09	.05
123	Kevin Brown	.15	.11	.06	213	Jay Buhner	.12	.09	.05
124	Braulio Castillo	.60	.45	.25	214	Jesse Barfield	.12	.09	.05
125	Eric King	.12	.09	.05	215	Kevin Mitchell, Kevin Mitchell	.15	.11	.06
126	Mark Portugal	.12	.09	.05	216	Mike LaValliere	.15	.11	.06
127	Calvin Jones	.30	.25	.12	217	Mark Wohlers, Mark Wohlers	.15	.11	.06
128	Mike Heath	.12	.09	.05	218	Dave Henderson	.15	.11	.06
129	Todd Van Poppel	1.00	.70	.40	219	Dave Smith	.12	.09	.05
130	Benny Santiago	.15	.11	.06	220	Albert Belle	.60	.45	.25
131	Gary Thurman	.12	.09	.05	221	Spike Owen	.12	.09	.05
132	Joe Girardi	.12	.09	.05	222	Jeff Gray	.12	.09	.05
133	Dave Eiland	.12	.09	.05	223	Paul Gibson	.12	.09	.05
134	Orlando Merced	1.00	.70	.40	224	Bobby Thigpen	.15	.11	.06
135	Joe Orsulak	.12	.09	.05	225	Mike Mussina	4.00	3.00	1.50
136	John Burkett	.12	.09	.05	226	Darrin Jackson	.12	.09	.05
137	Ken Dayley	.12	.09	.05	227	Luis Gonzalez	.70	.50	.30
138	Ken Hill	.15	.11	.06	228	Greg Briley	.12	.09	.05
139	Walt Terrell	.12	.09	.05	229	Brent Mayne	.12	.09	.05
140	Mike Scioscia	.12	.09	.05	230	Paul Molitor	.20	.15	.08
141	Junior Felix	.12	.09	.05	231	Al Leiter	.12	.09	.05
142	Ken Caminiti	.12	.09	.05	232	Andy Van Slyke	.15	.11	.06
143	Carlos Baerga	.35	.25	.14	233	Ron Tingley	.12	.09	.05
144	Tony Fossas	.12	.09	.05	234	Bernard Gilkey	.15	.11	.06
145	Craig Grebeck	.12	.09	.05	235	Kent Hrbek	.15	.11	.06
146	Scott Bradley	.12	.09	.05	236	Eric Karros	3.00	2.25	1.25
147	Kent Mercker	.12	.09	.05	237	Randy Velarde	.12	.09	.05
148	Derrick May	.20	.15	.08	238	Andy Allanson	.12	.09	.05
149	Jerald Clark	.15	.11	.06	239	Willie McGee	.15	.11	.06
150	George Brett	.40	.30	.15	240	Juan Gonzalez	2.50	2.00	1.00
151	Luis Quinones	.15	.11	.06	241	Karl Rhodes	.12	.09	.05
152	Mike Pagliarulo	.15	.11	.06	242	Luis Mercedes	.50	.40	.20
153	Jose Guzman	.15	.11	.06	243	Billy Swift	.15	.11	.06
154	Charlie O'Brien	.15	.11	.06	244	Tommy Gregg	.12	.09	.05
155	Darren Holmes	.15	.11	.06	245	David Howard	.12	.09	.05
156	Joe Boever	.15	.11	.06	246	Dave Hollins	.20	.15	.08
157	Rich Monteleone	.15	.11	.06	247	Kip Gross	.30	.25	.12
158	Reggie Harris	.15	.11	.06	248	Walt Weiss	.12	.09	.05
159	Roberto Alomar	1.00	.70	.40	249	Mackey Sasser	.12	.09	.05
160	Robby Thompson	.15	.11	.06	250	Cecil Fielder	1.00	.70	.40
161	Chris Hoiles	.25	.20	.10	251	Jerry Browne	.12	.09	.05
162	Tom Pagnozzi	.12	.09	.05	252	Doug Dascenzo	.12	.09	.05
163	Omar Vizquel	.12	.09	.05	253	Darryl Hamilton	.12	.09	.05
164	John Candelaria	.12	.09	.05	254	Dann Bilardello	.12	.09	.05
165	Terry Shumpert	.12	.09	.05	255	Luis Rivera	.12	.09	.05
166	Andy Mota	.25	.20	.10	256	Larry Walker	.20	.15	.08
167	Scott Bailes	.12	.09	.05	257	Ron Karkovice	.12	.09	.05
168	Jeff Blauser	.12	.09	.05	258	Bob Tewksbury	.15	.11	.06
169	Steve Olin	.12	.09	.05	259	Jimmy Key	.15	.11	.06
170	Doug Drabek	.20	.15	.08	260	Bernie Williams	.60	.45	.25
171	Dave Bergman	.12	.09	.05	261	Gary Wayne	.12	.09	.05
172	Eddie Whitson	.12	.09	.05	262	Mike Simms	.12	.09	.05
173	Gilberto Reyes	.12	.09	.05	263	John Orton	.12	.09	.05
174	Mark Grace	.25	.20	.10	264	Marvin Freeman	.12	.09	.05
175	Paul O'Neill	.15	.11	.06	265	Mike Jeffcoat	.12	.09	.05
176	Greg Cadaret	.12	.09	.05	266	Roger Mason	.12	.09	.05
177	Mark Williamson	.12	.09	.05	267	Edgar Martinez	.20	.15	.08
178	Casey Candaele	.12	.09	.05	268	Henry Rodriguez	.35	.25	.14

		MT	NR MT	EX
269	Sam Horn	.12	.09	.05
270	Brian McRae	.60	.45	.25
271	Kirt Manwaring	.12	.09	.05
272	Mike Bordick	.15	.11	.06
273	Chris Sabo	.15	.11	.06
274	Jim Olander	.12	.09	.05
275	Greg Harris	.12	.09	.05
276	Dan Gakeler	.12	.09	.05
277	Bill Sampen	.12	.09	.05
278	Joel Skinner	.12	.09	.05
279	Curt Schilling	.12	.09	.05
280	Dale Murphy	.25	.20	.10
281	Lee Stevens	.12	.09	.05
282	Lonnie Smith	.12	.09	.05
283	Manuel Lee	.12	.09	.05
284	Shawn Boskie	.12	.09	.05
285	Kevin Seitzer	.12	.09	.05
286	Stan Royer	.15	.11	.06
287	John Dopson	.12	.09	.05
288	Scott Bullett	.35	.25	.12
289	Ken Patterson	.12	.09	.05
290	Todd Hundley	.15	.11	.06
291	Tim Leary	.12	.09	.05
292	Brett Butler	.12	.09	.05
293	Gregg Olson	.15	.11	.06
294	Jeff Brantley	.12	.09	.05
295	Brian Holman	.12	.09	.05
296	Brian Harper	.15	.11	.06
297	Brian Bohanon	.15	.11	.06
298	Checklist 1-100	.15	.11	.06
299	Checklist 101-200	.15	.11	.06
300	Checklist 201-300	.15	.11	.06
301	Frank Thomas	6.00	4.50	2.50
302	Lloyd McClendon	.15	.11	.06
303	Brady Anderson	.30	.25	.12
304	Julio Valera	.15	.11	.06
305	Mike Aldrete	.15	.11	.06
306	Joe Oliver	.15	.11	.06
307	Todd Stottlemyre	.15	.11	.06
308	Rey Sanchez	.15	.11	.06
309	Gary Sheffield	1.00	.70	.40
310	Andujar Cedeno	.30	.25	.12
311	Kenny Rogers	.12	.09	.05
312	Bruce Hurst	.15	.11	.06
313	Mike Schooler	.12	.09	.05
314	Mike Benjamin	.12	.09	.05
315	Chuck Finley	.15	.11	.06
316	Mark Lemke	.12	.09	.05
317	Scott Livingstone	.15	.11	.06
318	Chris Nabholz	.12	.09	.05
319	Mike Humphreys	.15	.11	.06
320	Pedro Guerrero	.15	.11	.06
321	Willie Banks	.15	.11	.06
322	Tom Goodwin	.15	.11	.06
323	Hector Wagner	.25	.20	.10
324	Wally Ritchie	.12	.09	.05
325	Mo Vaughn	.25	.20	.10
326	Joe Klink	.12	.09	.05
327	Cal Eldred	2.00	1.50	.80
328	Daryl Boston	.12	.09	.05
329	Mike Huff	.12	.09	.05
330	Jeff Bagwell	2.50	2.00	1.00
331	Bob Milacki	.12	.09	.05
332	Tom Prince	.12	.09	.05
333	Pat Tabler	.12	.09	.05
334	Ced Landrum	.12	.09	.05
335	Reggie Jefferson	.30	.25	.12
336	Mo Sanford	.35	.25	.14
337	Kevin Ritz	.12	.09	.05
338	Gerald Perry	.12	.09	.05
339	Jeff Hamilton	.12	.09	.05
340	Tim Wallach	.15	.11	.06
341	Jeff Huson	.15	.11	.06
342	Jose Melendez	.15	.11	.06
343	Willie Wilson	.15	.11	.06
344	Mike Stanton	.12	.09	.05
345	Joel Johnston	.15	.11	.06
346	Lee Guetterman	.12	.09	.05
347	Francisco Olivares	.12	.09	.05
348	Dave Burba	.12	.09	.05
349	Tim Crews	.12	.09	.05
350	Scott Leius	.15	.11	.06
351	Danny Cox	.12	.09	.05
352	Wayne Housie	.35	.25	.14
353	Chris Donnels	.20	.15	.08
354	Chris George	.20	.15	.08
355	Gerald Young	.12	.09	.05
356	Roberto Hernandez	.15	.11	.06
357	Neal Heaton	.12	.09	.05
358	Todd Frohwirth	.12	.09	.05
359	Jose Vizcaino	.12	.09	.05
360	Jim Thome	1.00	.70	.40
361	Craig Wilson	.12	.09	.05
362	Dave Haas	.20	.15	.08
363	Billy Hatcher	.12	.09	.05
364	John Barfield	.12	.09	.05
365	Luis Aquino	.12	.09	.05
366	Charlie Leibrandt	.12	.09	.05
367	Howard Farmer	.12	.09	.05
368	Bryn Smith	.12	.09	.05
369	Mickey Morandini	.15	.11	.06
370	Jose Canseco	2.00	1.50	.80
370b	Jose Canseco (Members Choice - should be numbered 597)	3.00	2.25	1.25
371	Jose Uribe	.12	.09	.05
372	Bob MacDonald	.12	.09	.05
373	Luis Sojo	.12	.09	.05
374	Craig Shipley	.12	.09	.05
375	Scott Bankhead	.12	.09	.05
376	Greg Gagne	.12	.09	.05
377	Scott Cooper	.12	.09	.05
378	Jose Offerman	.12	.09	.05
379	Billy Spiers	.12	.09	.05
380	John Smiley	.15	.11	.06
381	Jeff Carter	.12	.09	.05
382	Heathcliff Slocumb	.12	.09	.05
383	Jeff Tackett	.20	.15	.08
384	John Kiely	.25	.20	.10
385	John Vander Wal	.50	.40	.20
386	Omar Olivares	.12	.09	.05
387	Ruben Sierra	.80	.60	.30
388	Tom Gordon	.12	.09	.05
389	Charles Nagy	.35	.25	.14
390	Dave Stewart	.15	.11	.06
391	Pete Harnisch	.15	.11	.06
392	Tim Burke	.12	.09	.05
393	Roberto Kelly	.25	.20	.10
394	Freddie Benavides	.12	.09	.05
395	Tom Glavine	.50	.40	.20
396	Wes Chamberlain	.40	.30	.15
397	Eric Gunderson	.12	.09	.05
398	Dave West	.12	.09	.05
399	Ellis Burks	.20	.15	.08
400	Ken Griffey, Jr.	4.00	3.00	1.50
401	Thomas Howard	.12	.09	.05
402	Juan Guzman	4.00	3.00	1.50
403	Mitch Webster	.12	.09	.05
404	Matt Merullo	.12	.09	.05
405	Steve Buechele	.12	.09	.05
406	Danny Jackson	.12	.09	.05
407	Felix Jose	.30	.25	.12
408	Doug Piatt	.20	.15	.08
409	Jim Eisenreich	.12	.09	.05
410	Bryan Harvey	.15	.11	.06
411	Jim Austin	.15	.11	.06
412	Jim Poole	.12	.09	.05
413	Glenallen Hill	.15	.11	.06
414	Gene Nelson	.12	.09	.05
415	Ivan Rodriguez	2.50	2.00	1.00
416	Frank Tanana	.12	.09	.05
417	Steve Decker	.12	.09	.05
418	Jason Grimsley	.12	.09	.05
419	Tim Layana	.12	.09	.05
420	Don Mattingly	.60	.45	.25
421	Jerome Walton	.12	.09	.05
422	Rob Ducey	.12	.09	.05
423	Andy Benes	.60	.45	.25
424	John Marzano	.12	.09	.05
425	Gene Harris	.12	.09	.05
426	Rock Raines	.20	.15	.08
427	Bret Barberie	.30	.25	.12
428	Harvey Pulliam	.30	.25	.12
429	Cris Carpenter	.12	.09	.05
430	Howard Johnson	.30	.25	.12
431	Orel Hershiser	.25	.20	.10
432	Brian Hunter	.40	.30	.15
433	Kevin Tapani	.15	.11	.06
434	Rick Reed	.15	.11	.06
435	Ron Witmeyer	.30	.25	.12
436	Gary Gaetti	.15	.11	.06
437	Alex Cole	.15	.11	.06
438	Chito Martinez	.25	.20	.10
439	Greg Litton	.15	.11	.06
440	Julio Franco	.20	.15	.08
441	Mike Munoz	.15	.11	.06
442	Erik Pappas	.15	.11	.06
443	Pat Combs	.15	.11	.06
444	Lance Johnson	.15	.11	.06
445	Ed Sprague	.15	.11	.06
446	Mike Greenwell	.25	.20	.10

		MT	NR MT	EX
447	Milt Thompson	.15	.11	.06
448	Mike Magnante	.25	.20	.10
449	Chris Haney	.20	.15	.08
450	Robin Yount	.50	.40	.20
451	Rafael Ramirez	.15	.11	.06
452	Gino Minutelli	.15	.11	.06
453	Tom Lampkin	.15	.11	.06
454	Tony Perezchica	.15	.11	.06
455	Doc Gooden	.40	.30	.15
456	Mark Guthrie	.15	.11	.06
457	Jay Howell	.15	.11	.06
458	Gary DiSarcina	.15	.11	.06
459	John Smoltz	.25	.20	.10
460	Will Clark	1.50	1.25	.60
461	Dave Otto	.15	.11	.06
462	Rob Maurer	.80	.60	.30
463	Dwight Evans	.15	.11	.06
464	Tom Brunansky	.12	.09	.05
465	Shawn Hare	.50	.40	.20
466	Geronimo Pena	.20	.15	.08
467	Alex Fernandez	.20	.15	.08
468	Greg Myers	.12	.09	.05
469	Jeff Fassero	.12	.09	.05
470	Len Dykstra	.20	.15	.08
471	Jeff Johnson	.15	.11	.06
472	Russ Swan	.12	.09	.05
473	Archie Corbin	.30	.25	.12
474	Chuck McElroy	.12	.09	.05
475	Mark McGwire	1.00	.70	.40
476	Wally Whitehurst	.12	.09	.05
477	Tim McIntosh	.12	.09	.05
478	Sid Bream	.12	.09	.05
479	Jeff Juden	.50	.40	.20
480	Carlton Fisk	.50	.40	.20
481	Jeff Plympton	.30	.25	.12
482	Carlos Martinez	.12	.09	.05
483	Jim Gott	.12	.09	.05
484	Bob McClure	.12	.09	.05
485	Tim Teufel	.12	.09	.05
486	Vicente Palacios	.12	.09	.05
487	Jeff Reed	.12	.09	.05
488	Tony Phillips	.15	.11	.06
489	Mel Rojas	.12	.09	.05
490	Ben McDonald	.50	.40	.20
491	Andres Santana	.15	.11	.06
492	Chris Beasley	.20	.15	.08
493	Mike Timlin	.15	.11	.06
494	Brian Downing	.12	.09	.05
495	Kirk Gibson	.12	.09	.05
496	Scott Sanderson	.12	.09	.05
497	Nick Esasky	.12	.09	.05
498	Johnny Guzman	.30	.25	.12
499	Mitch Williams	.15	.11	.06
500	Kirby Puckett	1.25	.90	.50
501	Mike Harkey	.12	.09	.05
502	Jim Gantner	.12	.09	.05
503	Bruce Egloff	.20	.15	.08
504	Josias Manzanillo	.20	.15	.08
505	Delino DeShields	.20	.15	.08
506	Rheal Cormier	.30	.25	.12
507	Jay Bell	.15	.11	.06
508	Rich Rowland	.25	.20	.10
509	Scott Servais	.15	.11	.06
510	Terry Pendleton	.20	.15	.08
511	Rich DeLucia	.12	.09	.05
512	Warren Newson	.12	.09	.05
513	Paul Faries	.12	.09	.05
514	Kal Daniels	.12	.09	.05
515	Jarvis Brown	.20	.15	.08
516	Rafael Palmeiro	.30	.25	.12
517	Kelly Downs	.12	.09	.05
518	Steve Chitren	.12	.09	.05
519	Moises Alou	.20	.15	.08
520	Wade Boggs	.80	.60	.30
521	Pete Schourek	.12	.09	.05
522	Scott Terry	.12	.09	.05
523	Kevin Appier	.20	.15	.08
524	Gary Redus	.12	.09	.05
525	George Bell	.20	.15	.08
526	Jeff Kaiser	.20	.15	.08
527	Alvaro Espinoza	.12	.09	.05
528	Luis Polonia	.12	.09	.05
529	Darren Daulton	.25	.20	.10
530	Norm Charlton	.20	.15	.08
531	John Olerud	.20	.15	.08
532	Dan Plesac	.12	.09	.05
533	Billy Ripken	.12	.09	.05
534	Rod Nichols	.12	.09	.05
535	Joey Cora	.12	.09	.05
536	Harold Baines	.20	.15	.08
537	Bob Ojeda	.12	.09	.05
538	Mark Leonard	.12	.09	.05
539	Danny Darwin	.12	.09	.05
540	Shawon Dunston	.15	.11	.06
541	Pedro Munoz	.60	.45	.25
542	Mark Gubicza	.15	.11	.06
543	Kevin Baez	.20	.15	.08
544	Todd Zeile	.20	.15	.08
545	Don Slaught	.12	.09	.05
546	Tony Eusebio	.20	.15	.08
547	Alonzo Powell	.12	.09	.05
548	Gary Pettis	.12	.09	.05
549	Brian Barnes	.15	.11	.06
550	Lou Whitaker	.15	.11	.06
551	Keith Mitchell	.40	.30	.15
552	Oscar Azocar	.12	.09	.05
553	Stu Cole	.15	.11	.06
554	Steve Wapnick	.20	.15	.08
555	Derek Bell	.50	.40	.20
556	Luis Lopez	.20	.15	.08
557	Anthony Telford	.15	.11	.06
558	Tim Mauser	.20	.15	.08
559	Glenn Sutko	.20	.15	.08
560	Darryl Strawberry	.80	.60	.30
561	Tom Bolton	.12	.09	.05
562	Cliff Young	.20	.15	.08
563	Bruce Walton	.12	.09	.05
564	Chico Walker	.12	.09	.05
565	John Franco	.15	.11	.06
566	Paul McClellan	.15	.11	.06
567	Paul Abbott	.15	.11	.06
568	Gary Varsho	.12	.09	.05
569	Carlos Maldonado	.20	.15	.08
570	Kelly Gruber	.20	.15	.08
571	Jose Oquendo	.12	.09	.05
572	Steve Frey	.12	.09	.05
573	Tino Martinez	.20	.15	.08
574	Bill Haselman	.12	.09	.05
575	Eric Anthony	.15	.11	.06
576	John Habyan	.12	.09	.05
577	Jeffrey McNeely	.80	.60	.30
578	Chris Bosio	.15	.11	.06
579	Joe Grahe	.15	.11	.06
580	Fred McGriff	.35	.25	.14
581	Rick Honeycutt	.12	.09	.05
582	Matt Williams	.25	.20	.10
583	Cliff Brantley	.20	.15	.08
584	Rob Dibble	.20	.15	.08
585	Skeeter Barnes	.12	.09	.05
586	Greg Hibbard	.12	.09	.05
587	Randy Milligan	.12	.09	.05
588	Checklist 301-400	.12	.09	.05
589	Checklist 401-500	.12	.09	.05
590	Checklist 501-600	.12	.09	.05
591	Frank Thomas (Members Choice)	5.00	3.75	2.00
592	David Justice (Members Choice)	1.00	.70	.40
593	Roger Clemens (Members Choice)	.80	.60	.30
594	Steve Avery (Members Choice)	1.00	.70	.40
595	Cal Ripken (Members Choice)	1.50	1.25	.60
596	Barry Larkin (Members Choice)	.40	.30	.15
598	Will Clark (Members Choice)	1.00	.70	.40
599	Cecil Fielder (Members Choice)	.60	.45	.25
600	Ryne Sandberg (Members Choice)	1.00	.70	.40
601	Chuck Knoblauch (Members Choice)	1.00	.70	.40
602	Dwight Gooden (Members Choice)	.50	.40	.20
603	Ken Griffey, Jr. (Members Choice)	3.00	2.25	1.25
604	Barry Bonds (Members Choice)	1.00	.70	.40
605	Nolan Ryan (Members Choice)	3.00	2.25	1.25
606	Jeff Bagwell (Members Choice)	1.25	.90	.50
607	Robin Yount (Members Choice)	.60	.45	.25
608	Bobby Bonilla (Members Choice)	.30	.25	.12
609	George Brett (Members Choice)	.60	.45	.25
610	Howard Johnson	.25	.20	.10
611	Esteban Beltre	.12	.09	.05
612	Mike Christopher	.20	.15	.08
613	Troy Afenir	.12	.09	.05
614	Mariano Duncan	.12	.09	.05
615	Doug Henry	.15	.11	.06
616	Doug Jones	.15	.11	.06
617	Alvin Davis	.12	.09	.05
618	Craig Lefferts	.12	.09	.05
619	Kevin McReynolds	.20	.15	.08
620	Barry Bonds	.80	.60	.30
621	Turner Ward	.20	.15	.08
622	Joe Magrane	.15	.11	.06
623	Mark Parent	.12	.09	.05
624	Tom Browning	.15	.11	.06
625	John Smiley	.15	.11	.06
626	Steve Wilson	.12	.09	.05

		MT	NR MT	EX
627	Mike Gallego	.12	.09	.05
628	Sammy Sosa	.15	.11	.06
629	Rico Rossy	.15	.11	.06
630	Royce Clayton	.60	.45	.25
631	Clay Parker	.12	.09	.05
632	Pete Smith	.12	.09	.05
633	Jeff McKnight	.12	.09	.05
634	Jack Daugherty	.12	.09	.05
635	Steve Sax	.20	.15	.08
636	Joe Hesketh	.12	.09	.05
637	Vince Horsman	.20	.15	.08
638	Joe Boever	.12	.09	.05
640	Jack Morris	.30	.25	.12
641	Arthur Rhodes	.50	.40	.20
642	Bob Melvin	.12	.09	.05
643	Rick Wilkins	.20	.15	.08
644	Scott Scudder	.12	.09	.05
645	Bip Roberts	.20	.15	.08
646	Julio Valera	.20	.15	.08
647	Kevin Campbell	.20	.15	.08
648	Steve Searcy	.12	.09	.05
649	Scott Kamieniecki	.12	.09	.05
650	Kurt Stillwell	.12	.09	.05
651	Bob Welch	.15	.11	.06
652	Andres Galarraga	.15	.11	.06
653	Mike Jackson	.12	.09	.05
654	Bo Jackson	.60	.45	.25
655	Sid Fernandez	.15	.11	.06
656	Mike Bielecki	.12	.09	.05
657	Jeff Reardon	.15	.11	.06
658	Wayne Rosenthal	.12	.09	.05
659	Eric Bullock	.12	.09	.05
660	Eric Davis	.25	.20	.10
661	Randy Tomlin	.20	.15	.08
662	Tom Edens	.12	.09	.05
663	Rob Murphy	.12	.09	.05
664	Leo Gomez	.30	.25	.12
665	Greg Maddux	.25	.20	.10
666	Greg Vaughn	.15	.11	.06
667	Wade Taylor	.12	.09	.05
668	Brad Arnsberg	.12	.09	.05
669	Mike Moore	.15	.11	.06
670	Mark Langston	.15	.11	.06
671	Barry Jones	.12	.09	.05
672	Bill Landrum	.12	.09	.05
673	Greg Swindell	.20	.15	.08
674	Wayne Edwards	.12	.09	.05
675	Greg Olson	.12	.09	.05
676	Bill Pulsipher	.20	.15	.08
677	Bobby Witt	.15	.11	.06
678	Mark Carreon	.12	.09	.05
679	Patrick Lennon	.30	.25	.12
680	Ozzie Smith	.40	.30	.15
681	John Briscoe	.20	.15	.08
682	Matt Young	.12	.09	.05
683	Jeff Conine	.20	.15	.08
684	Phil Stephenson	.12	.09	.05
685	Ron Darling	.15	.11	.06
686	Bryan Hickerson	.15	.11	.06
687	Dale Sveum	.12	.09	.05
688	Kirk McCaskill	.12	.09	.05
689	Rich Amaral	.15	.11	.06
690	Danny Tartabull	.40	.30	.15
691	Donald Harris	.15	.11	.06
692	Doug Davis	.20	.15	.08
693	John Farrell	.12	.09	.05
694	Paul Gibson	.12	.09	.05
695	Kenny Lofton	2.50	2.00	1.00
696	Mike Fetters	.12	.09	.05
697	Rosario Rodriguez	.12	.09	.05
698	Chris Jones	.15	.11	.06
699	Jeff Manto	.12	.09	.05
700	Rick Sutcliffe	.15	.11	.06
701	Scott Bankhead	.12	.09	.05
702	Donnie Hill	.12	.09	.05
703	Todd Worrell	.15	.11	.06
704	Rene Gonzales	.12	.09	.05
705	Rick Cerone	.12	.09	.05
706	Tony Pena	.12	.09	.05
707	Paul Sorrento	.12	.09	.05
708	Gary Scott	.15	.11	.06
709	Junior Noboa	.12	.09	.05
710	Wally Joyner	.20	.15	.08
711	Charlie Hayes	.15	.11	.06
712	Rich Rodriguez	.12	.09	.05
713	Rudy Seanez	.12	.09	.05
714	Jim Bullinger	.40	.30	.15
715	Jeff Robinson	.12	.09	.05
716	Jeff Branson	.25	.20	.10
717	Andy Ashby	.12	.09	.05
718	Dave Burba	.12	.09	.05

		MT	NR MT	EX
719	Rich Gossage	.20	.15	.08
720	Randy Johnson	.20	.15	.08
721	David Wells	.12	.09	.05
722	Paul Kilgus	.12	.09	.05
723	Dave Martinez	.12	.09	.05
724	Denny Neagle	.15	.11	.06
725	Andy Stankiewicz	.40	.30	.15
726	Rick Aguilera	.15	.11	.06
727	Junior Noboa	.12	.09	.05
728	Storm Davis	.12	.09	.05
729	Don Robinson	.12	.09	.05
730	Ron Gant	.40	.30	.15
731	Paul Assenmacher	.12	.09	.05
732	Mark Gardiner	.12	.09	.05
733	Milt Hill	.12	.09	.05
734	Jeremy Hernandez	.15	.11	.06
735	Ken Hill	.20	.15	.08
736	Xavier Hernandez	.12	.09	.05
737	Gregg Jefferies	.25	.20	.10
738	Dick Schofield	.12	.09	.05
739	Ron Robinson	.12	.09	.05
740	Sandy Alomar	.20	.15	.08
741	Mike Stanley	.12	.09	.05
742	Butch Henry	.30	.25	.12
743	Floyd Bannister	.12	.09	.05
744	Brian Drahman	.15	.11	.06
745	Dave Winfield	.50	.40	.20
746	Bob Walk	.12	.09	.05
747	Chris James	.12	.09	.05
748	Don Prybylinski	.20	.15	.08
749	Dennis Rasmussen	.12	.09	.05
750	Rickey Henderson	.80	.60	.30
751	Chris Hammond	.15	.11	.06
752	Bob Kipper	.12	.09	.05
753	Dave Rohde	.12	.09	.05
754	Hubie Brooks	.12	.09	.05
755	Bret Saberhagen	.20	.15	.08
756	Jeff Robinson	.12	.09	.05
757	Pat Listach	4.00	3.00	1.50
758	Bill Wegman	.15	.11	.06
759	John Wetteland	.15	.11	.06
760	Phil Plantier	.80	.60	.30
761	Wilson Alvarez	.12	.09	.05
762	Scott Aldred	.12	.09	.05
763	Armando Reynoso	.30	.25	.12
764	Todd Benzinger	.12	.09	.05
765	Kevin Mitchell	.20	.15	.08
766	Gary Sheffield	1.25	.90	.50
767	Allan Anderson	.12	.09	.05
768	Rusty Meacham	.15	.11	.06
769	Rick Parker	.12	.09	.05
770	Nolan Ryan	2.50	2.00	1.00
771	Jeff Ballard	.12	.09	.05
772	Cory Snyder	.12	.09	.05
773	Denis Boucher	.15	.11	.06
774	Jose Gonzales	.12	.09	.05
775	Juan Guerrero	.40	.30	.15
776	Ed Nunez	.12	.09	.05
777	Scott Ruskin	.12	.09	.05
778	Terry Leach	.12	.09	.05
779	Carl Willis	.12	.09	.05
780	Bobby Bonilla	.20	.15	.08
781	Duane Ward	.15	.11	.06
782	Joe Slusarski	.15	.11	.06
783	David Segui	.15	.11	.06
784	Kirk Gibson	.12	.09	.05
785	Frank Viola	.20	.15	.08
786	Keith Miller	.12	.09	.05
787	Mike Morgan	.12	.09	.05
788	Kim Batiste	.15	.11	.06
789	Sergio Valdez	.15	.11	.06
790	Eddie Taubensee	.30	.25	.12
791	Jack Armstrong	.12	.09	.05
792	Scott Fletcher	.12	.09	.05
793	Steve Farr	.12	.09	.05
794	Dan Pasqua	.12	.09	.05
795	Eddie Murray	.20	.15	.08
796	John Morris	.12	.09	.05
797	Francisco Cabrera	.12	.09	.05
798	Mike Perez	.20	.15	.08
799	Ted Wood	.20	.15	.08
800	Jose Rijo	.20	.15	.08
801	Danny Gladden	.12	.09	.05
802	Arci Cianfrocco	.50	.40	.20
803	Monty Fariss	.15	.11	.06
804	Roger McDowell	.12	.09	.05
805	Randy Myers	.15	.11	.06
806	Kirk Dressendorfer	.15	.11	.06
807	Zane Smith	.12	.09	.05
808	Glenn Davis	.15	.11	.06
809	Tory Lovullo	.12	.09	.05

		MT	NR MT	EX
810	Andre Dawson	.40	.30	.15
811	Bill Pecota	.12	.09	.05
812	Ted Power	.12	.09	.05
813	Willie Blair	.12	.09	.05
814	Dave Fleming	2.00	1.50	.80
815	Chris Gwynn	.12	.09	.05
816	Jody Reed	.12	.09	.05
817	Mark Dewey	.12	.09	.05
818	Kyle Abbott	.12	.09	.05
819	Tom Henke	.12	.09	.05
820	Kevin Seitzer	.12	.09	.05
821	Al Newman	.12	.09	.05
822	Tim Sherrill	.20	.15	.08
823	Chuck Crim	.12	.09	.05
824	Darren Reed	.15	.11	.06
825	Tony Gwynn	.80	.60	.30
826	Steve Foster	.20	.15	.08
827	Steve Howe	.12	.09	.05
828	Brook Jacoby	.12	.09	.05
829	Rodney McCray	.12	.09	.05
830	Chuck Knoblauch	1.00	.70	.40
831	John Wehner	.15	.11	.06
832	Scott Garrelts	.12	.09	.05
833	Alejandro Pena	.12	.09	.05
834	Jeff Parrett	.12	.09	.05
835	Juan Bell	.12	.09	.05
836	Lance Dickson	.12	.09	.05
837	Darryl Kile	.15	.11	.06
838	Efrain Valdez	.15	.11	.06
839	Bob Zupcic	.60	.45	.25
840	George Bell	.15	.11	.06
841	Dave Gallagher	.12	.09	.05
842	Tim Belcher	.15	.11	.06
843	Jeff Shaw	.12	.09	.05
844	Mike Fitgerald	.12	.09	.05
845	Gary Carter	.20	.15	.08
846	John Russell	.12	.09	.05
847	Eric Hillman	.30	.25	.12
848	Mike Witt	.12	.09	.05
849	Curt Wilkerson	.12	.09	.05
850	Alan Trammell	.15	.11	.06
851	Rex Hudler	.12	.09	.05
852	Michael Walkden	.30	.25	.12
853	Kevin Ward	.30	.25	.12
854	Tim Naehring	.15	.11	.06
855	Bill Swift	.15	.11	.06
856	Damon Berryhill	.12	.09	.05
857	Mark Eichhorn	.12	.09	.05
858	Hector Villanueva	.12	.09	.05
859	Jose Lind	.12	.09	.05
860	Denny Martinez	.15	.11	.06
861	Bill Krueger	.12	.09	.05
862	Mike Kingery	.12	.09	.05
863	Jeff Innis	.12	.09	.05
864	Derek Lilliquist	.12	.09	.05
865	Reggie Sanders	1.75	1.25	.70
866	Ramon Garcia	.20	.15	.08
867	Bruce Ruffin	.12	.09	.05
868	Dickie Thon	.12	.09	.05
869	Melido Perez	.15	.11	.06
870	Ruben Amaro	.15	.11	.06
871	Alan Mills	.12	.09	.05
872	Matt Sinatro	.12	.09	.05
873	Eddie Zosky	.20	.15	.08
874	Pete Incaviglia	.12	.09	.05
875	Tom Candiotti	.12	.09	.05
876	Bob Patterson	.12	.09	.05
877	Neal Heaton	.12	.09	.05
878	Terrel Hansen	.35	.25	.14
879	Dave Eiland	.12	.09	.05
880	Von Hayes	.12	.09	.05
881	Tim Scott	.20	.15	.08
882	Otis Nixon	.15	.11	.06
883	Herm Winningham	.12	.09	.05
884	Dion James	.12	.09	.05
885	Dave Wainhouse	.15	.11	.06
886	Frank DiPino	.12	.09	.05
887	Dennis Cook	.12	.09	.05
888	Jose Mesa	.12	.09	.05
889	Mark Leiter	.12	.09	.05
890	Willie Randolph	.15	.11	.06
891	Craig Colbert	.15	.11	.06
892	Dwayne Henry	.12	.09	.05
893	Jim Lindeman	.12	.09	.05
894	Charlie Hough	.12	.09	.05
895	Gil Heredia	.12	.09	.05
896	Scott Chiamparino	.12	.09	.05
897	Lance Blankenship	.12	.09	.05
898	Checklist 601-700	.12	.00	.05
899	Checklist 701-800	.12	.09	.05
900	Checklist 801-900	.12	.09	.05

		MT	NR MT	EX
----	Chipper Jones (#1 Draft Pick)	8.00	6.00	3.25
----	Brien Taylor (#1 Draft Pick)	15.00	11.00	6.00
----	Phil Nevin (#1 Draft Pick)	10.00	7.50	4.00

Values for recent cards and sets are listed in Mint (MT), Near Mint (NM) and Excellent (EX), reflecting the fact that many cards from recent years have been preserved in top condition. Recent cards and sets in less than Excellent condition have little collector interest.

1992 Topps Traded

Members of the United States baseball team are featured in this 132-card boxed set released by Topps. The cards are styled after the regular 1992 Topps cards and are numbered alphabetically. Several United States baseball players featured in this set were also featuured in the 1991 Topps Traded set.

		MT	NR MT	EX
Complete Set:		10.00	7.50	4.00
Common Player:		.05	.04	.02
1	Willie Adams (U.S.A.)(FC)	.20	.15	.08
2	Jeff Alkire (U.S.A.)(FC)	.20	.15	.08
3	Felipe Alou	.05	.04	.02
4	Moises Alou	.20	.15	.08
5	Ruben Amaro(FC)	.10	.08	.04
6	Jack Armstrong	.05	.04	.02
7	Scott Bankhead	.05	.04	.02
8	Tim Belcher	.08	.06	.03
9	George Bell	.08	.06	.03
10	Freddie Benavides(FC)	.12	.09	.05
11	Todd Benzinger	.05	.04	.02
12	Joe Boever	.05	.04	.02
13	Ricky Bones	.10	.08	.04
15	Hubie Brooks	.05	.04	.02
16	Jerry Browne	.05	.04	.02
17	Jim Bullinger(FC)	.10	.08	.04
18	Dave Burba	.05	.04	.02
19	Kevin Campbell(FC)	.12	.09	.05
20	Tom Candiotti	.05	.04	.02
21	Mark Carreon	.05	.04	.02
23	Archi Cianfrocco(FC)	.30	.25	.12
24	Phil Clark(FC)	.10	.08	.04
25	Chad Curtis(FC)	.15	.11	.06
26	Eric Davis	.08	.06	.03
27	Tim Davis (U.S.A.)(FC)	.20	.15	.08
28	Gary DiSarcina	.05	.04	.02
29	Darren Dreifort (U.S.A.)	.12	.09	.05
30	Mariano Duncan	.05	.04	.02
31	Mike Fitzgerald	.05	.04	.02
32	John Flaherty(FC)	.12	.09	.05
33	Darrin Fletcher	.05	.04	.02
34	Scott Fletcher	.05	.04	.02
35	Ron Fraser (U.S.A.)	.08	.06	.03
36	Andres Galarraga	.06	.05	.02
37	Dave Gallagher	.05	.04	.02
38	Mike Gallego	.05	.04	.02
39	Nomar Garciaparra (U.S.A.)(FC)	.20	.15	.08
40	Jason Giambi (U.S.A.)	.12	.09	.05
41	Danny Gladden	.05	.04	.02
42	Rene Gonzales	.05	.04	.02
43	Jeff Granger (U.S.A.)	.12	.09	.05
44	Rick Greene (U.S.A.)	.20	.15	.08
45	Jeffrey Hammonds (U.S.A.)	.20	.15	.08
46	Charlie Hayes	.05	.04	.02
47	Von Hayes	.05	.04	.02
48	Rick Helling (U.S.A.)	.15	.11	.06
49	Butch Henry(FC)	.12	.09	.05
50	Carlos Hernandez(FC)	.12	.09	.05
51	Ken Hill	.08	.06	.03
52	Butch Hobson	.05	.04	.02

		MT	NR MT	EX
53	Vince Horsman(FC)	.10	.08	.04
54	Pete Incaviglia	.06	.05	.02
55	Gregg Jefferies	.08	.06	.03
56	Charles Johnson (U.S.A.)	.25	.20	.10
57	Doug Jones	.05	.04	.02
58	Brian Jordan(FC)	.30	.25	.12
59	Wally Joyner	.08	.06	.03
60	Daron Kirkreit (U.S.A.)(FC)	.20	.15	.08
61	Bill Krueger	.06	.05	.02
62	Gene Lamont	.06	.05	.02
63	Jim Lefebvre	.06	.05	.02
64	Danny Leon(FC)	.20	.15	.08
65	Pat Listach(FC)	1.00	.70	.40
66	Kenny Lofton	.25	.20	.10
67	Dave Martinez	.05	.04	.02
68	Derrick May	.10	.08	.04
69	Kirk McCaskill	.06	.05	.02
70	Chad McConnell (U.S.A.)(FC)	.20	.15	.08
71	Kevin McReynolds	.06	.05	.02
72	Rusty Meacham(FC)	.10	.08	.04
73	Keith Miller	.06	.05	.02
74	Kevin Mitchell	.08	.06	.03
75	Jason Moler (U.S.A.)(FC)	.20	.15	.08
76	Mike Morgan	.06	.05	.02
77	Jack Morris	.08	.06	.03
78	Calvin Murray (U.S.A.)(FC)	.25	.20	.10
79	Eddie Murray	.08	.06	.03
80	Randy Myers	.06	.05	.02
81	Denny Neagle(FC)	.10	.08	.04
82	Phil Nevin (U.S.A.)	.20	.15	.08
83	Dave Nilsson	.20	.15	.08
84	Junior Ortiz	.05	.04	.02
85	Donovan Osborne(FC)	.20	.15	.08
86	Bill Pecota	.05	.04	.02
87	Melido Perez	.05	.04	.02
88	Mike Perez(FC)	.10	.08	.04
89	Hipolito Pena(FC)	.10	.08	.04
90	Willie Randolph	.06	.05	.02
91	Darren Reed(FC)	.12	.09	.05
92	Bip Roberts	.08	.06	.03
93	Chris Roberts (U.S.A.)	.12	.09	.05
94	Steve Rodriguez (U.S.A.)	.12	.09	.05
95	Bruce Ruffin	.05	.04	.02
96	Scott Ruskin	.05	.04	.02
97	Bret Saberhagen	.08	.06	.03
98	Rey Sanchez(FC)	.12	.09	.05
99	Steve Sax	.08	.06	.03
100	Curt Schilling	.06	.05	.02
101	Dick Schofield	.05	.04	.02
102	Gary Scott	.10	.08	.04
103	Kevin Seitzer	.06	.05	.02
104	Frank Seminara(FC)	.12	.09	.05
105	Gary Sheffield	.10	.08	.04
106	John Smiley	.06	.05	.02
107	Cory Snyder	.06	.05	.02
108	Paul Sorrento	.06	.05	.02
109	Sammy Sosa	.06	.05	.02
110	Matt Stairs(FC)	.12	.09	.05
111	Andy Stankiewicz	.20	.15	.08
112	Kurt Stillwell	.06	.05	.02
113	Rick Sutcliffe	.06	.05	.02
114	Bill Swift	.06	.05	.02
115	Jeff Tackett(FC)	.12	.09	.05
116	Danny Tartabull	.08	.06	.03
117	Eddie Taubensee(FC)	.12	.09	.05
118	Dickie Thon	.05	.04	.02
119	Michael Tucker (U.S.A.)(FC)	.20	.15	.08
120	Scooter Tucker(FC)	.12	.09	.05
121	Marc Valdes (U.S.A.)(FC)	.20	.15	.08
122	Julio Valera(FC)	.10	.08	.04
123	Jason Vilaitek (U.S.A.)(FC)	.20	.15	.08
124	Ron Villone (U.S.A.)(FC)	.20	.15	.08
125	Frank Viola	.08	.06	.03
126	B.J. Wallace (U.S.A.)(FC)	.25	.20	.10
127	Dan Walters(FC)	.12	.09	.05
128	Craig Wilson (U.S.A.)	.12	.09	.05
129	Chris Wimmer (U.S.A.)	.12	.09	.05
130	Dave Winfield	.08	.06	.03
131	Herm Winningham	.05	.04	.02
132	Checklist	.05	.04	.02

A player's name in italic indicates a rookie card. An (FC) indicates a player's first card for that particular card company.

1993 Topps Series I

Topps used a two series format in 1993. Series I featured cards 1-396. The card fronts feature full-color photos enclosed by a white border. The player's name and team appear at the bottom. The backs feature an additional player photo and biographical information at the top. The bottom box includes statistics and player information. Like in recent years, several cards are printed horizontally. The cards are numbered in red on the back. The number appears in a yellow flag in the upper left corner of the card.

		MT	NR MT	EX
Complete Set:		15.00	11.00	8.00
Common Player:		.03	.02	.01
1	Robin Yount	.10	.08	.04
2	Barry Bonds	.15	.11	.06
3	Ryne Sandberg	.15	.11	.06
4	Roger Clemens	.15	.11	.06
5	Tony Gwynn	.12	.09	.05
6	*Jeff Tackett*	.12	.09	.05
7	Pete Incaviglia	.05	.04	.02
8	Mark Wohlers	.05	.04	.02
9	Kent Hrbek	.06	.05	.02
10	Will Clark	.15	.11	.06
11	Eric Karros	.15	.11	.06
12	Lee Smith	.06	.05	.02
13	Esteban Beltre	.05	.04	.02
14	Greg Briley	.03	.02	.01
15	Marquis Grissom	.08	.06	.03
16	Dan Plesac	.04	.03	.02
17	Dave Hollins	.08	.06	.03
18	Terry Steinbach	.06	.05	.02
19	Ed Nunez	.03	.02	.01
20	*Tim Salmon*	.15	.11	.06
21	Luis Salazar	.04	.03	.02
22	Jim Eisenreich	.03	.02	.01
23	Todd Stottlemyre	.05	.04	.02
24	Tim Naehring	.05	.04	.02
25	John Franco	.06	.05	.02
26	Skeeter Barnes	.06	.05	.02
27	*Carlos Garcia*	.15	.11	.06
28	Joe Orsulak	.04	.03	.02
29	Dwayne Henry	.03	.02	.01
30	Fred McGriff	.10	.08	.04
31	Derek Lilliquist	.03	.02	.01
32	Don Mattingly	.12	.09	.05
33	B.J. Wallace	.12	.09	.05
34	Juan Gonzalez	.15	.11	.06
35	John Smoltz	.08	.06	.03
36	Scott Servais	.08	.06	.03
37	Lenny Webster	.08	.06	.03
38	Chris James	.04	.03	.02
39	Roger McDowell	.04	.03	.02
40	Ozzie Smith	.10	.08	.04
41	Alex Fernandez	.08	.06	.03
42	Spike Owen	.03	.02	.01
43	Ruben Amaro	.05	.04	.02
44	Kevin Seitzer	.05	.04	.02
45	Dave Fleming	.10	.08	.04
46	*Eric Fox*	.12	.09	.05
47	Bob Scanlan	.03	.02	.01
48	Bert Blyleven	.06	.05	.02
49	Brian McRae	.06	.05	.02
50	Roberto Alomar	.12	.09	.05
51	Mo Vaughn	.05	.04	.02
52	Bobby Bonilla	.10	.08	.04

		MT	NR MT	EX
53	Frank Tanana	.04	.03	.02
54	Mike LaValliere	.04	.03	.02
55	Mark McLemore	.03	.02	.01
56	*Chad Mottola* (FC)	.15	.11	.06
57	Norm Charlton	.06	.05	.02
58	Jose Melendez	.08	.06	.03
59	Carlos Martinez	.03	.02	.01
60	Roberto Kelly	.08	.06	.03
61	Gene Larkin	.03	.02	.01
62	Rafael Belliard	.03	.02	.01
63	Al Osuna	.03	.02	.01
64	Scott Chiamparino	.03	.02	.01
65	Brett Butler	.06	.05	.02
66	John Burkett	.04	.03	.02
67	Felix Jose	.08	.06	.03
68	Omar Vizquel	.03	.02	.01
69	*John Vander Wal*	.12	.09	.05
70	Roberto Hernandez	.08	.06	.03
71	Ricky Bones	.05	.04	.02
72	*Jeff Grotewold*	.12	.09	.05
73	Mike Moore	.05	.04	.02
74	Steve Buechele	.05	.04	.02
75	Juan Guzman	.10	.08	.04
76	Kevin Appier	.08	.06	.03
77	Junior Felix	.05	.04	.02
78	Greg Harris	.04	.03	.02
79	Dick Schofield	.04	.03	.02
80	Cecil Fielder	.10	.08	.04
81	Lloyd McClendon	.04	.03	.02
82	David Segui	.05	.04	.02
83	Reggie Sanders	.15	.11	.06
84	Kurt Stillwell	.04	.03	.02
85	Sandy Alomar	.08	.06	.03
86	John Habyan	.03	.02	.01
87	Kevin Reimer	.05	.04	.02
88	Mike Stanton	.05	.04	.02
89	Eric Anthony	.06	.05	.02
90	Scott Erickson	.08	.06	.03
91	Craig Colbert	.06	.05	.02
92	Tom Pagnozzi	.06	.05	.02
93	*Pedro Astacio* (FC)	.15	.11	.06
94	Lance Johnson	.04	.03	.02
95	Larry Walker	.10	.08	.04
96	Russ Swan	.03	.02	.01
97	Scott Fletcher	.03	.02	.01
98	*Derek Jeter* (FC)	.15	.11	.06
99	*Mike Williams* (FC)	.15	.11	.06
100	Mark McGwire	.15	.11	.06
101	*Jim Bullinger*	.12	.09	.05
102	Brian Hunter	.08	.06	.03
103	Jody Reed	.04	.03	.02
104	*Mike Butcher* (FC)	.15	.11	.06
105	Gregg Jefferies	.08	.06	.03
106	Howard Johnson	.08	.06	.03
107	*John Kiely*	.12	.09	.05
108	Jose Lind	.04	.03	.02
109	Sam Horn	.03	.02	.01
110	Barry Larkin	.08	.06	.03
111	Bruce Hurst	.05	.04	.02
112	Brian Barnes	.04	.03	.02
113	Thomas Howard	.04	.03	.02
114	Mel Hall	.06	.05	.02
115	Robby Thompson	.04	.03	.02
116	Mark Lemke	.04	.03	.02
117	Eddie Taubensee	.08	.06	.03
118	David Justice	.10	.08	.04
119	Pedro Munoz	.10	.08	.04
120	Ramon Martinez	.08	.06	.03
121	Todd Worrell	.05	.04	.02
122	Joey Cora	.03	.02	.01
123	Moises Alou	.08	.06	.03
124	Franklin Stubbs	.03	.02	.01
125	Pete O'Brien	.03	.02	.01
126	*Bob Aryault* (FC)	.12	.09	.05
127	Carney Lansford	.05	.04	.02
128	Kal Daniels	.05	.04	.02
129	Joe Grahe	.05	.04	.02
130	Jeff Montgomery	.05	.04	.02
131	Dave Winfield	.10	.08	.04
132	*Preston Wilson* (FC)	.15	.11	.06
133	Steve Wilson	.04	.03	.02
134	Lee Guetterman	.03	.02	.01
135	Mickey Tettleton	.08	.06	.03
136	Jeff King	.04	.03	.02
137	Alan Mills	.03	.02	.01
138	Joe Oliver	.04	.03	.02
139	Gary Gaetti	.04	.03	.02
140	Gary Sheffield	.10	.08	.04
141	Dennis Cook	.03	.02	.01
142	Charlie Hayes	.04	.03	.02
143	Jeff Huson	.04	.03	.02

		MT	NR MT	EX
144	Kent Mercker	.04	.03	.02
145	*Eric Young* (FC)	.15	.11	.06
146	Scott Leius	.04	.03	.02
147	Bryan Hickerson	.04	.03	.02
148	Steve Finley	.06	.05	.02
149	Rheal Cormier	.08	.06	.03
150	Frank Thomas	.30	.25	.12
151	*Archi Cianfrocco*	.15	.11	.06
152	Rich DeLucia	.04	.03	.02
153	Greg Vaughn	.06	.05	.02
154	Wes Chamberlain	.05	.04	.02
155	Dennis Eckersley	.08	.06	.03
156	Sammy Sosa	.04	.03	.02
157	Gary DiSarcina	.06	.05	.02
158	*Kevin Koslofski* (FC)	.12	.09	.05
159	*Doug Linton* (FC)	.12	.09	.05
160	Lou Whitaker	.06	.05	.02
161	Chad McDonnell	.12	.09	.05
162	Joe Hesketh	.03	.02	.01
163	*Tim Wakefield*	.15	.11	.06
164	Leo Gomez	.05	.04	.02
165	Jose Rijo	.06	.05	.02
166	*Tim Scott* (FC)	.12	.09	.05
167	Steve Olin	.05	.04	.02
168	Kevin Maas	.05	.04	.02
169	Kenny Rogers	.04	.03	.02
170	David Justice	.10	.08	.04
171	Doug Jones	.04	.03	.02
172	*Jeff Reboulet* (FC)	.12	.09	.05
173	Andres Galarraga	.05	.04	.02
174	Randy Velarde	.03	.02	.01
175	Kirk McCaskill	.04	.03	.02
176	Darren Lewis	.04	.03	.02
177	Lenny Harris	.04	.03	.02
178	Jeff Fassero	.04	.03	.02
179	Ken Griffey, Jr.	.30	.25	.12
180	Darren Daulton	.08	.06	.03
181	John Jaha	.12	.09	.05
182	Ron Darling	.05	.04	.02
183	Greg Maddux	.08	.06	.03
184	*Damion Easley* (FC)	.15	.11	.06
185	Jack Morris	.08	.06	.03
186	Mike Magnante	.05	.04	.02
187	John Dopson	.05	.04	.02
188	Sid Fernandez	.08	.06	.03
189	Tony Phillips	.08	.06	.03
190	Doug Drabek	.08	.06	.03
191	Sean Lowe	.15	.11	.06
192	Bob Milacki	.03	.02	.01
193	*Steve Foster* (FC)	.15	.11	.06
194	Jerald Clark	.05	.04	.02
195	Pete Harnisch	.06	.05	.02
196	Pat Kelly	.06	.05	.02
197	*Jeff Frye* (FC)	.12	.09	.05
198	Alejandro Pena	.04	.03	.02
199	Junior Ortiz	.03	.02	.01
200	Kirby Puckett	.15	.11	.06
201	Jose Uribe	.03	.02	.01
202	Mike Scioscia	.04	.03	.02
203	Bernard Gilkey	.06	.05	.02
204	Dan Pasqua	.04	.03	.02
205	Gary Carter	.08	.06	.03
206	Henry Cotto	.03	.02	.01
207	Paul Molitor	.08	.06	.03
208	Mike Hartley	.04	.03	.02
209	Jeff Parrett	.03	.02	.01
210	Mark Langston	.08	.06	.03
211	Doug Dascenzo	.03	.02	.01
212	Rick Reed	.03	.02	.01
213	Candy Maldonado	.05	.04	.02
214	Danny Darwin	.03	.02	.01
215	*Pat Howell* (FC)	.12	.09	.05
216	Mark Leiter	.03	.02	.01
217	Kevin Mitchell	.08	.06	.03
218	Ben McDonald	.08	.06	.03
219	Bip Roberts	.08	.06	.03
220	Benny Santiago	.08	.06	.03
221	Carlos Baerga	.10	.08	.04
222	Bernie Williams	.10	.08	.04
223	*Roger Pavlik* (FC)	.12	.09	.05
224	Sid Bream	.04	.03	.02
225	Matt Williams	.08	.06	.03
226	Willie Banks	.08	.06	.03
227	Jeff Bagwell	.12	.09	.05
228	Tom Goodwin	.08	.06	.03
229	Mike Perez	.08	.06	.03
230	Carlton Fisk	.08	.06	.03
231	John Wetteland	.08	.06	.03
232	Tino Martinez	.08	.06	.03
233	*Rick Greene* (FC)	.12	.09	.05
234	Tim McIntosh	.04	.03	.02

		MT	NR MT	EX
235	Mitch Williams	.06	.05	.02
236	*Kevin Campbell*	.10	.08	.04
237	Jose Vizcaino	.03	.02	.01
238	Chris Donnels	.05	.04	.02
239	Mike Boddicker	.04	.03	.02
240	John Olerud	.12	.09	.05
241	Mike Gardiner	.04	.03	.02
242	Charlie O'Brien	.03	.02	.01
243	Rob Deer	.04	.03	.02
244	Denny Neagle	.08	.06	.03
245	Chris Sabo	.08	.06	.03
246	Gregg Olson	.08	.06	.03
247	Frank Seminara	.08	.06	.03
248	Scott Scudder	.03	.02	.01
249	Tim Burke	.03	.02	.01
250	Chuck Knoblauch	.10	.08	.04
251	Mike Bielecki	.04	.03	.02
252	Xavier Hernandez	.03	.02	.01
253	Jose Guzman	.04	.03	.02
254	Cory Snyder	.04	.03	.02
255	Orel Hershiser	.08	.06	.03
256	Wil Cordero	.12	.09	.05
257	Luis Alicea	.04	.03	.02
258	Mike Schooler	.04	.03	.02
259	Craig Grebeck	.03	.02	.01
260	Duane Ward	.04	.03	.02
261	Bill Wegman	.04	.03	.02
262	Mickey Morandini	.08	.06	.03
263	*Vince Horsman*	.12	.09	.05
264	Paul Sorrento	.06	.05	.02
265	Andre Dawson	.10	.08	.04
266	Rene Gonzales	.03	.02	.01
267	Keith Miller	.04	.03	.02
268	Derek Bell	.10	.08	.04
269	*Todd Steverson*(FC)	.20	.15	.08
270	Frank Viola	.08	.06	.03
271	Wally Whitehurst	.04	.03	.02
272	*Kurt Knudsen*	.12	.09	.05
273	*Dan Walters*	.12	.09	.05
274	Rick Sutcliffe	.06	.05	.02
275	Andy Van Slyke	.08	.06	.03
276	Paul O'Neill	.06	.05	.02
277	Mark Whiten	.10	.08	.04
278	Chris Nabholz	.06	.05	.02
279	Todd Burns	.03	.02	.01
280	Tom Glavine	.10	.08	.04
281	*Butch Henry*(FC)	.12	.09	.05
282	Shane Mack	.08	.06	.03
283	Mike Jackson	.03	.02	.01
284	Henry Rodriguez	.06	.05	.02
285	Bob Tewksbury	.06	.05	.02
286	Ron Karkovice	.04	.03	.02
287	Mike Gallego	.04	.03	.02
288	Dave Cochrane	.03	.02	.01
289	Jesse Orosco	.03	.02	.01
290	Dave Stewart	.08	.06	.03
291	Tommy Greene	.08	.06	.03
292	Rey Sanchez	.08	.06	.03
293	Rob Ducey	.03	.02	.01
294	Brent Mayne	.04	.03	.02
295	Dave Stieb	.05	.04	.02
296	Luis Rivera	.03	.02	.01
297	Jeff Innis	.04	.03	.02
298	Scott Livingstone	.08	.06	.03
299	Bob Patterson	.03	.02	.01
300	Cal Ripken	.20	.15	.08
301	Cesar Hernandez	.10	.08	.04
302	Randy Myers	.06	.05	.02
303	Brook Jacoby	.04	.03	.02
304	Melido Perez	.04	.03	.02
305	Rafael Palmeiro	.08	.06	.03
306	Damon Berryhill	.03	.02	.01
307	*Dan Serafini*(FC)	.20	.15	.08
308	Darryl Kile	.06	.05	.02
309	*J.T. Bruett*	.15	.11	.06
310	Dave Righetti	.05	.04	.02
311	Jay Howell	.05	.04	.02
312	Geronimo Pena	.05	.04	.02
313	Greg Hibbard	.05	.04	.02
314	Mark Gardner	.05	.04	.02
315	Edgar Martinez	.08	.06	.03
316	Dave Nilsson	.10	.08	.04
317	Kyle Abbott	.08	.06	.03
318	Willie Wilson	.06	.05	.02
319	Paul Assenmacher	.04	.03	.02
320	*Tim Fortugno*	.12	.09	.05
321	Rusty Meacham	.08	.06	.03
322	Pat Borders	.05	.04	.02
323	Mike Greenwell	.06	.05	.02
324	Willie Randolph	.06	.05	.02
325	Bill Gullickson	.05	.04	.02

		MT	NR MT	EX
326	Gary Varsho	.03	.02	.01
327	Tim Hulett	.03	.02	.01
328	Scott Ruskin	.03	.02	.01
329	Mike Maddux	.03	.02	.01
330	Danny Tartabull	.08	.06	.03
331	Kenny Lofton	.15	.11	.06
332	Geno Petralli	.03	.02	.01
333	Otis Nixon	.05	.04	.02
334	*Jason Kendall*(FC)	.20	.15	.08
335	Mark Portugal	.03	.02	.01
336	Mike Pagliarulo	.04	.03	.02
337	Kirt Manwaring	.04	.03	.02
338	Bob Ojeda	.04	.03	.02
339	*Mark Clark*(FC)	.12	.09	.05
340	John Kruk	.08	.06	.03
341	Mel Rojas	.04	.03	.02
342	Erik Hanson	.06	.05	.02
343	Doug Henry	.06	.05	.02
344	Jack McDowell	.08	.06	.03
345	Harold Baines	.08	.06	.03
346	Chuck McElroy	.03	.02	.01
347	Luis Sojo	.03	.02	.01
348	Andy Stankiewicz	.10	.08	.04
349	*Hipolito Pichardo*	.10	.08	.04
350	Joe Carter	.08	.06	.03
351	Ellis Burks	.06	.05	.02
352	Pete Schourek	.06	.05	.02
353	Buddy Groom	.20	.15	.08
354	Jay Bell	.06	.05	.02
355	Brady Anderson	.08	.06	.03
356	Freddie Benavides	.06	.05	.02
357	Phil Stepheson	.03	.02	.01
358	Kevin Wickander	.03	.02	.01
359	Mike Stanley	.03	.02	.01
360	Ivan Rodriguez	.12	.09	.05
361	Scott Bankhead	.04	.03	.02
362	Luis Gonzalez	.08	.06	.03
363	John Smiley	.06	.05	.02
364	Trevor Wilson	.04	.03	.02
365	Tom Candiotti	.04	.03	.02
366	Craig Wilson	.04	.03	.02
367	Steve Sax	.06	.05	.02
368	Delino Deshields	.06	.05	.02
369	Jaime Navarro	.06	.05	.02
370	Dave Valle	.03	.02	.01
371	Mariano Duncan	.04	.03	.02
372	Rod Nichols	.03	.02	.01
373	Mike Morgan	.05	.04	.02
374	Julio Valera	.08	.06	.03
375	Wally Joyner	.08	.06	.03
376	Tom Henke	.08	.06	.03
377	Herm Winningham	.03	.02	.01
378	Orlando Merced	.06	.05	.02
379	Mike Munoz	.08	.06	.03
380	Todd Hundley	.08	.06	.03
381	Mike Flanagan	.03	.02	.01
382	Tim Belcher	.06	.05	.02
383	Jerry Browne	.03	.02	.01
384	Mike Benjamin	.03	.02	.01
385	Jim Leyritz	.03	.02	.01
386	Ray Lankford	.12	.09	.05
387	Devon White	.06	.05	.02
388	Jeremy Hernandez	.08	.06	.03
389	Brian Harper	.06	.05	.02
390	Wade Boggs	.12	.09	.05
391	Derrick May	.10	.08	.04
392	Travis Fryman	.15	.11	.06
393	Ron Gant	.10	.08	.04
394	Checklist 1-132	.03	.02	.01
395	Checklist 133-264	.03	.02	.01
396	Checklist 265-396	.03	.02	.01

Values quoted in this guide reflect the retail price of a card — the price a collector can expect to pay when buying a card from a dealer. The wholesale price — that which a collector can expect to receive from a dealer when selling cards — will be significantly lower, depending on desirability and condition.

1993 Topps Baseball Series II

The checklist for 1993 Topps Baseball Series II arrived in time to be included in this catalog, but because the cards were not available in the hobby market no prices were available at press time.

397. George Brett
398. Bobby Witt
399. Daryl Boston
400. Bo Jackson
401. F. McGriff/F. Thomas
402. R. Sandberg/C. Baerga
403. G. Sheffield/E. Martinez
404. B. Larkin/T. Fryman
405. A. Van Slyke/K. Griffey Jr.
406. L. Walker/K. Puckett
407. B. Bonds/J. Carter
408. D. Daulton/B. Harper
409. g. Maddux/R. Clemens
410. T. Glavine/D. Fleming
411. L. Smith/D. Eckersley
412. Jamie McAndrew
413. Pete Smith
414. Juan Guerrero
415. Todd Frohwirth
416. Randy Tomlin
417. B.J. Surhoff
418. Jim Gott
419. Mark Thompson
420. Kevin Tapani
421. Curt Schilling
422. J.T. Snow
423. 1993 Prospects
424. John Valentin
425. Joe Girardi
426. Nigel Wilson
427. Bob MacDonald
428. Todd Zeile
429. Milt Cuyler
430. Eddie Murray
431. Rich Amaral
432. Pete Young
433. R. Bailey/T. Schmidt
434. Jack Armstrong
435. Willie McGee
436. Greg Harris
437. Chris Hammond
438. Ritchie Moody
439. Bryan Harvey
440. Ruben Sierra
441. D. Lemon/T. Pridy
442. Kevin McReynolds
443. Terry Leach
444. David Nied
445. Dale Murphy
446. Luis Mercedes
447. Keith Shepherd
448. Ken Caminiti
449. James Austin
450. Darryl Strawberry
451. Victor Cole
452. Bob Wickman
453. Victor Cole
454. John Johnstone
455. Chili Davis
456. Scott Taylor
457. Tracy Woodson
458. David Wells
459. Derek Wallace
460. Randy Johnson
461. Steve Reed
462. Felix Fermin
463. Scott Aldred
464. Greg Colbrunn
465. Tony Fernandez

466. Mike Felder
467. Lee Stevens
468. Matt Whiteside
469. Dave Hansen
470. Rob Dibble
471. Dave Gallagher
472. Chris Gwynn
473. Dave Henderson
474. Ozzie Guillen
475. Jeff Reardon
476. M. Voisard/W. Scalzitti
477. Jimmy Jones
478. Greg Cadaret
479. Todd Pratt
480. Patt Listach
481. Ryan Luzinski
482. Darren Reed
483. Brian Griffiths
484. John Wehner
485. Glenn Davis
486. Eric Wedge
487. Jesse Hollins
488. Manuel Lee
489. Scott Fredrickson
490. Omar Olivares
491. Shawn Hare
492. Tom Lampkin
493. Jeff Nelson
494. 1993 Prospects
495. Ken Hill
496. Reggie Jefferson
497. M. petersen/W. Brown
498. Bud Black
499. Chuck Crim
500. Jose Canseco
501. Johnny Oates
502. Butch Hobson
503. Buck Rodgers
504. Gene Lamont
505. Mike Hargrove
506. Sparky Anderson
507. Hal McRae
508. Phil Garner
509. Tom Kelly'
510. Buck Showalter
511. Tony LaRussa
512. Lou Piniella
513. Toby Harrah
514. Cito Gason
515. Greg Swindell
516. Alex Arias
517. Bill Pecota
518. Benji Grigsby
519. David Howard
520. Charlie Hough
521. Kevin Flora
522. Shane Reynolds
523. Doug Bochtler
524. Chris Hoiles
525. Scott Sanderson
526. Mike Sharperson
527. Mike Fetters
528. Paul Quantrill
529. 1993 Prospects
530. Sterling Hitchcock
531. Joe Millette
532. Tom Brunansky
533. Frank Castillo
534. Randy Knorr

535. Jose Oquendo
536. Dave Haas
537. J. Hutchins/R. Turner
538. Jimmy Baron
539. Kerry Woodson
540. Ivan Calderon
541. Denis Boucher
542. Royce Clayton
543. Reggie Williams
544. Steve Deckers
545. Dean Palmer
546. Hal Morris
547. Ryan Thompson
548. Lance Blankenship
549. Hensley Meulens
550. Scott Radinksy
551. Eric Young
552. Jeff Blauser
553. Andujar Cedeno
554. Arthur Rhodes
555. Terry Mulholland
556. Darryl Hamilton
557. Pedro Martinez
558. R. Whitman/M. Skeels
559. Jamie Arnold
560. Zane Smith
561. Matt Nokes
562. Bob Zupcic
563. Shawn Boskie
564. Mike Timlin
565. Jerald Clark
566. Rod Brewer
567. Mark Carreon
568. Andy Benes
569. Shawn Barton
570. Tim Wallach
571. Dave Mlicki
572. Trevor Hoffman
573. John Patterson
574. De Shawn Warren
575. Monty Fariss
576. 1993 Prospects
577. Tim Costo
578. Dave Magadan
579. N. Garret/J. Bates
580. Walt Weiss
581. Chris Haney
582. Shawn Abner
583. Marvin Freeman
584. Casey Candaele
585. Ricky Jordan
586. Jeff Tabaka
587. Manny Alexander
588. Mike Trombley
589. Carlos Hernandez
590. Cal Eldred
591. Alex Cole
592. Phil Plantier
593. Brett Merriman
594. Jerry Nielsen
595. Shawn Dunston
596. Jimmy Key
597. Gerald Perry
598. Rico Brogna
599. C. Nunez/D. Robinson
600. Breg Saberhagen
601. Craig Shipley
602. Henry Mercedes
603. Jim Thome

604. Rod Beck
605. Chuck Finley
606. J. Owens
607. Dan Smith
608. Bill Doran
609. Lance Parrish
610. Denny Martinez
611. tom Gordon
612. Byron Mathews
613. Joel Adamson
614. Brian Williams
615. Steve Avery
616. 1993 Prospects
617. Craig Lefferts
618. Tony Pena
619. Billy Spiers
620. Todd Benzinger
621. M. Kotarski/G. Boyd
622. Ben Rivera
623. Al Martin
624. Sam Militello
625. Rick Aguilera
626. Danny Gladden
627. Andres Berumen
628. Kelly Gruber
629. Cris Carpenter
630. Mark Grace
631. Jeff Brantley
632. Chris Widger
633. Three Russians
634. Mo Sanford
635. Albert Belle
636. Tim Teufel
637. Greg Myers
638. Brian Bohanon
639. Mike Bordick
640. Doc Gooden
641. P. leahy/G. Baugh
642. Milt Hill
643. Luis Aquino
644. Dante Bichette
645. Bobby Thigpen
646. Rich Scheid
647. Brian Sackinsky
648. Ryan Hawblitzel
649. Tom Marsh
650. Terry Pendleton
651. Rafael Bournigal
652. Dave West
653. Steve Hosey
654. Gerald Williams
655. Scott Cooper
656. Gary Scott
657. Mike Harkey
658. 1993 Prospects
659. Ed Sprague
660. Alan Trammel
661. G. Alston/M. Case
662. Donovan Osborne
663. Jeff Gardner
664. Calvin Jones
665. Darrin Fletcher
666. Glenallen Hill
667. Jim Rosenbohm
668. Scott Lewis
669. Kip Vaughn
670. Julio Franco
671. Dave Martinez
672. Kevin Bass
673. Todd Van Poppel
674. Mark Gubicza
675. Tim Raines
676. Rudy Seanez
677. Charlie Leibrandt

678. Randy Milligan
679. Kim Batiste
680. Craig Biggio
681. Darren Holmes
682. John Candelaria
683. J. Stafford/E. Christian
684. Pat Mahomes
685. Bob Walk
686. Russ Springer
687. Tony Sheffield
688. Dwight Smith
689. Eddie Zosky
690. Bien Figueroa
691. Jim Tatum
692. Chad Kreuter
693. Rich Rodriguez
694. Shane Turner
695. Kent Bottenfield
696. Jose Mesa
697. Darrell Whitmore
698. Ted Wood
699. Chad Curtis
700. Nolan Ryan
701. 1993 Prospects
702. Tim Pugh
703. Jeff Kent
704. J. goodrich/D. Figueroa
705. Bob Welch
706. Sherard Clinkscales
707. Donn Pall
708. Greg Olson
709. Jeff Juden
710. Mike Mussina
711. Scott Chiamparino
712. Stan Javier
713. John Doherty
714. Kevin Gross
715. Greg Gagne
716. Steve Cooke
717. Steve Farr
718. Jay Buhner
719. Butch Henry
720. David Cone
721. Rick Wilkins
722. Chuck Carr
723. Kenny Felder
724. Guillermo Velasquez
725. Billy Hatcher
726. M. Veneziale/K. Kendrena
727. Jonathan Hurst
728. Steve Frey
729. Mark Leonard
730. Charles Nagy
731. Donald Harris
732. Travis Buckley
733. Tom Browning
734. Anthony Young
735. Steve Shifflett
736. Jeff Russell
737. Wilson Alvarez
738. Lance Painter
739. Dave Weathers
740. Len Dykstra
741. Mike Devereaux
742. 1993 Prospects
743. Dave Landaker
744. Chris George
745. Eric Davis
746. Strittmatter/L. Rogers
747. Carl Willis
748. Stan Belinda
749. Scott Kamieniecki
750. Rickey Henderson
751. Eric Hillman

752. Pat Hentgen
753. Jim Corsi
754. Brian Jordan
755. Bill Swift
756. Mike Henneman
757. Harold Reynolds
758. Sean Berry
759. Charlie Hayes
760. Luis Polonia
761. Darrin Jackson
762. Mark Lewis
763. Rob Maurer
764. Willie Greene
765. Vince Coleman
766. Todd Revenig
767. Rich Ireland
768. Mike MacFarlane
769. Francisco Cabrera
770. Robin Ventura
771. Kevin Ritz
772. Chito Martinez
773. Cliff Brantley
774. Curtis Leskanic
775. Chris Bosio
776. Jose Offerman
777. Mark Guthrie
778. Don Slaught
779. Rich Monteleone
780. Jim Abbott
781. Jack Clark
782. R. Mendoza/D. Roman
783. Heathcliff Slocumb
784. Jeff Branson
785. Kevin Brown
786. 1993 Prospects
787. Mike Matthews
788. Mackey Sasser
789. Jeff Conine
790. George Bell
791. Pat Rapp
792. Joe boever
793. Jim Poole
794. Andy Ashby
795. Deion Sanders
796. Scott Brosius
797. Brad Pennington
798. Greg Blosser
799. Jim Edmonds
800. Shawn Jeter
801. Jesse Levis
802. Phil Clark
803. Ed Pierce
804. Jose Valentin
805. Terry Jorgensen
806. Mark Hutton
807. Troy Neel
808. Bret Boone
809. Cris Conlon
810. Domingo Martinez
811. Davy Lopez
812. Matt Walbeck
813. Dan Wilson
814. Scooter Tucker
815. Billy Ashley
816. Tim Laker
817. Bobby Jones
818. Brad Brink
819. William Pennyfeather
820. Stan Royer
821. Doug Brocail
822. Kevin Rogers
823. Checklist 4 of 6
824. Checklist 5 of 6
825. Checklist 6 of 6

1987 Toys "R" Us

Marked as a collectors' edition set and titled "Baseball Rookies," the 1987 Toys "R" Us issue was produced by Topps for the toy store chain. The set is comprised of 33 glossy-coated cards, each measuring 2-1/2" by 3-1/2". The card fronts are very colorful, employing nine different colors including deep black borders. The backs, printed in blue and orange, contain career highlights and composite minor and major league statistics. The set was distributed in a specially designed box and sold for $1.99 in retail outlets.

		MT	NR MT	EX
Complete Set:		6.00	4.50	2.50
Common Player:		.09	.07	.04
1	Andy Allanson	.09	.07	.04
2	Paul Assenmacher	.09	.07	.04
3	Scott Bailes	.09	.07	.04
4	Barry Bonds	.40	.30	.15
5	Jose Canseco	1.50	1.25	.60
6	John Cerutti	.09	.07	.04
7	Will Clark	.90	.70	.35
8	Kal Daniels	.25	.20	.10
9	Jim Deshaies	.09	.07	.04
10	Mark Eichhorn	.09	.07	.04
11	Ed Hearn	.09	.07	.04
12	Pete Incaviglia	.12	.09	.05
13	Bo Jackson	.60	.45	.25
14	Wally Joyner	.60	.45	.25
15	Charlie Kerfeld	.09	.07	.04
16	Eric King	.12	.09	.05
17	John Kruk	.40	.30	.15
18	Barry Larkin	.50	.40	.20
19	Mike LaValliere	.15	.11	.06
20	Greg Mathews	.09	.07	.04
21	Kevin Mitchell	.20	.15	.08
22	Dan Plesac	.20	.15	.08
23	Bruce Ruffin	.15	.11	.06
24	Ruben Sierra	.50	.40	.20
25	Cory Snyder	.10	.08	.04
26	Kurt Stillwell	.20	.15	.08
27	Dale Sveum	.12	.09	.05
28	Danny Tartabull	.30	.25	.12
29	Andres Thomas	.09	.07	.04
30	Robby Thompson	.15	.11	.06
31	Jim Traber	.09	.07	.04
32	Mitch Williams	.15	.11	.06
33	Todd Worrell	.15	.11	.06

1988 Toys "R" Us Rookies

This 33-card boxed edition was produced by Topps for exclusive distribution at Toys "R" Us stores. The glossy standard-size cards spotlight rookies in both closeups and action photos on a bright blue background inlaid with yellow. The Toys "R" Us logo frames the top left corner, above a curving white banner that reads "Topps 1988 Collectors' Edition Rookies". A black Topps logo hugs the upper right-hand edge of the photo. The player name,

red-lettered on a tube of yellow, frames the bottom. Card backs are horizontal, blue and pink on a bright pink background and include the player name, personal information and career highlights and stats.

		MT	NR MT	EX
Complete Set:		5.00	3.75	2.00
Common Player:		.09	.07	.04
1	Todd Benzinger	.20	.15	.08
2	Bob Brower	.09	.07	.04
3	Jerry Browne	.09	.07	.04
4	DeWayne Buice	.09	.07	.04
5	Ellis Burks	.70	.50	.30
6	Ken Caminiti	.12	.09	.05
7	Casey Candaele	.09	.07	.04
8	Dave Cone	.50	.40	.20
9	Kelly Downs	.20	.15	.08
10	Mike Dunne	.15	.11	.06
11	Ken Gerhart	.12	.09	.05
12	Mike Greenwell	.40	.30	.15
13	Mike Henneman	.12	.09	.05
14	Sam Horn	.20	.15	.08
15	Joe Magrane	.20	.15	.08
16	Fred Manrique	.12	.09	.05
17	John Marzano	.12	.09	.05
18	Fred McGriff	.15	.11	.06
19	Mark McGwire	.50	.40	.20
20	Jeff Musselman	.12	.09	.05
21	Randy Myers	.20	.15	.08
22	Matt Nokes	.40	.30	.15
23	Al Pedrique	.12	.09	.05
24	Luis Polonia	.15	.11	.06
25	Billy Ripken	.25	.20	.10
26	Benny Santiago	.25	.20	.10
27	Kevin Seitzer	.10	.08	.04
28	John Smiley	.20	.15	.08
29	Mike Stanley	.09	.07	.04
30	Terry Steinbach	.20	.15	.08
31	B.J. Surhoff	.25	.20	.10
32	Bobby Thigpen	.25	.20	.10
33	Devon White	.25	.20	.10

1989 Toys "R" Us Rookies

This glossy set of 33 top rookies was produced by Topps for the Toys 'R' Us chain and was sold in a special box. Each player's name and position appear below the full-color photo, while the Toys 'R' Us logo and "Topps 1989 Collector's Edition" appear along the top. Major and minor league stats are on the back. The set is numbered alphabetically.

		MT	NR MT	EX
Complete Set:		4.00	3.00	1.50
Common Player:		.09	.07	.04
1	Roberto Alomar	.50	.40	.20
2	Brady Anderson	.09	.07	.04
3	Tim Belcher	.20	.15	.08
4	Damon Berryhill	.12	.09	.05
5	Jay Buhner	.12	.09	.05
6	Sherman Corbett	.09	.07	.04
7	Kevin Elster	.12	.09	.05
8	Cecil Espy	.12	.09	.05
9	Dave Gallagher	.12	.09	.05
10	Ron Gant	.12	.09	.05
11	Paul Gibson	.09	.07	.04
12	Mark Grace	.90	.70	.35
13	Bryan Harvey	.12	.09	.05
14	Darrin Jackson	.09	.07	.04
15	Gregg Jefferies	.70	.50	.30
16	Ron Jones	.15	.11	.06
17	Ricky Jordan	.35	.25	.14
18	Roberto Kelly	.25	.20	.10
19	Al Leiter	.09	.07	.04
20	Jack McDowell	.09	.07	.04
21	Melido Perez	.12	.09	.05
22	Jeff Pico	.09	.07	.04
23	Jody Reed	.12	.09	.05
24	Chris Sabo	.25	.20	.10
25	Nelson Santovenia	.15	.11	.06
26	Mackey Sasser	.09	.07	.04
27	Mike Schooler	.12	.09	.05
28	Gary Sheffield	.60	.45	.25
29	Pete Smith	.12	.09	.05
30	Pete Stanicek	.09	.07	.04
31	Jeff Treadway	.09	.07	.04
32	Walt Weiss	.25	.20	.10
33	Dave West	.10	.08	.04

10	Mark Gardner	.15	.11	.06
11	Bob Geren	.08	.06	.03
12	Tom Gordon	.20	.15	.08
13	Ken Griffey,Jr.	2.00	1.50	.80
14	Pete Harnisch	.10	.08	.04
15	Ken Hill	.08	.06	.03
16	Gregg Jefferies	.30	.25	.12
17	Derek Lilliquist	.08	.06	.03
18	Carlos Martinez	.10	.08	.04
19	Ramon Martinez	.60	.45	.25
20	Bob Milacki	.08	.06	.03
21	Gregg Olson	.15	.11	.06
22	Kenny Rogers	.10	.08	.04
23	Alex Sanchez	.10	.08	.04
24	Gary Sheffield	.30	.25	.12
25	Dwight Smith	.10	.08	.04
26	Billy Spiers	.08	.06	.03
27	Greg Vaughn	.40	.30	.15
28	Robin Ventura	.25	.20	.10
29	Jerome Walton	.40	.30	.15
30	Dave West	.08	.06	.03
31	John Wetteland	.15	.11	.06
32	Craig Worthington	.10	.08	.04
33	Todd Zeile	.40	.30	.15

1991 Toys "R" Us Rookies

Produced by Topps, this 33-card set features baseball's top young players. The cards are styled much like past Toys "R" Us issues featuring glossy photos. The backs are printed horizontally and include player information and statistics. This set is the fifth of its kind produced by Topps for Toys "R" Us.

		MT	NR MT	EX
Complete Set:		5.00	3.75	2.00
Common Player:		.08	.06	.03
1	Sandy Alomar, Jr.	.15	.11	.06
2	Kevin Appier	.15	.11	.06
3	Steve Avery	.40	.30	.15
4	Carlos Baerga	.30	.25	.12
5	Alex Cole	.08	.06	.03
6	Pat Combs	.08	.06	.03
7	Delino DeShields	.30	.25	.12
8	Travis Fryman	.40	.30	.15
9	Marquis Grissom	.30	.25	.12
10	Mike Harkey	.10	.08	.04
11	Glenallen Hill	.08	.06	.03
12	Jeff Huson	.08	.06	.03
13	Felix Jose	.40	.30	.15
14	Dave Justice	.50	.40	.20
15	Dana Kiecker	.08	.06	.03
16	Kevin Maas	.25	.20	.10
17	Ben McDonald	.30	.25	.12
18	Brian McRae	.30	.25	.12
19	Kent Mercker	.10	.08	.04
20	Hal Morris	.20	.15	.08
21	Chris Nabholz	.10	.08	.04
22	Tim Naehring	.10	.08	.04
23	Jose Offerman	.15	.11	.06
24	John Olerud	.25	.20	.10
25	Scott Radinsky	.08	.06	.03
26	Bill Sampen	.08	.06	.03
27	Frank Thomas	.80	.60	.30
28	Randy Tomlin	.15	.11	.06
29	Greg Vaughn	.20	.15	.08
30	Robin Ventura	.40	.30	.15

1990 Toys "R" Us Rookies

This 33-card set marks the fourth straigh year that Topps has produced a set to be sold exclusively at Toys "R" Us stores. The card fronts contain full- color photos of 1989 rookies. The flip sides are horizontal and provide both minor and major league totals. The complete set is packaged in a special box which features a checklist uon the back.

		MT	NR MT	EX
Complete Set:		5.00	3.75	2.00
Common Player:		.08	.06	.03
1	Jim Abbott	.15	.11	.06
2	Eric Anthony	.40	.30	.15
3	Joey Belle	.15	.11	.06
4	Andy Benes	.20	.15	.08
5	Greg Briley	.08	.06	.03
6	Kevin Brown	.10	.08	.04
7	Mark Carreon	.08	.06	.03
8	Mike Devereaux	.08	.06	.03
9	Junior Felix	.25	.20	.10

		MT	NR MT	EX
31	Larry Walker	.30	.25	.12
32	Wally Whitehurst	.08	.06	.03
33	Todd Zeile	.20	.15	.08

1969 Transogram

Produced by the Transogram toy company, the 2-1/2" by 3-1/2" cards were printed on the bottom of toy baseball player statue boxes. The cards feature a color photo of the player surrounded by a rounded white border. Below the photo is the player's name in red and his team and other personal details all printed in black. The overall background is yellow. The cards were designed to be cut off the box, but collectors prefer to find the box intact and better still, with the statue inside. Although the 60-card set features a lot of stars, and is fairly scarce, it does not not have a lot of popularity today.

		NR MT	EX	VG
Complete Set:		650.00	325.00	195.00
Common Player:		.80	.40	.25
(1)	Hank Aaron	30.00	15.00	9.00
(2)	Richie Allen	4.00	2.00	1.25
(3)	Felipe Alou	3.00	1.50	.90
(4)	Matty Alou	3.00	1.50	.90
(5)	Luis Aparicio	20.00	10.00	6.00
(6)	Joe Azcue	2.00	1.00	.60
(7)	Ernie Banks	20.00	10.00	6.00
(8)	Lou Brock	20.00	10.00	6.00
(9)	John Callison	3.00	1.50	.90
(10)	Jose Cardenal	2.00	1.00	.60
(11)	Danny Cater	2.00	1.00	.60
(12)	Roberto Clemente	30.00	15.00	9.00
(13)	Willie Davis	1.00	.50	.30
(14)	Mike Epstein	2.00	1.00	.60
(15)	Jim Fregosi	1.00	.50	.30
(16)	Bob Gibson	8.00	4.00	2.50
(17)	Tom Haller	2.00	1.00	.60
(18)	Ken Harrelson	3.00	1.50	.90
(19)	Willie Horton	3.00	1.50	.90
(20)	Frank Howard	1.50	.70	.45
(21)	Tommy John	8.00	4.00	2.50
(22)	Al Kaline	20.00	10.00	6.00
(23)	Harmon Killebrew	20.00	10.00	6.00
(24)	Bobby Knoop	2.00	1.00	.60
(25)	Jerry Koosman	.80	.40	.25
(26)	Jim Lefebvre	2.00	1.00	.60
(27)	Mickey Mantle	125.00	62.00	37.00
(28)	Juan Marichal	8.00	4.00	2.50
(29)	Lee May	3.00	1.50	.90
(30)	Willie Mays	30.00	15.00	9.00
(31)	Bill Mazeroski	4.00	2.00	1.25
(32)	Tim McCarver	4.00	2.00	1.25
(33)	Willie McCovey	20.00	10.00	6.00
(34)	Denny McLain	1.50	.70	.45
(35)	Dave McNally	3.00	1.50	.90
(36)	Rick Monday	3.00	1.50	.90
(37)	Blue Moon Odom	.80	.40	.25
(38)	Tony Oliva	1.50	.70	.45
(39)	Camilo Pascual	3.00	1.50	.90
(40)	Tony Perez	7.00	3.50	2.00
(41)	Rico Petrocelli	1.00	.50	.30
(42)	Rick Reichardt	.80	.40	.25
(43)	Brooks Robinson	30.00	15.00	9.00
(44)	Frank Robinson	8.00	4.00	2.50

		NR MT	EX	VG
(45)	Cookie Rojas	2.00	1.00	.60
(46)	Pete Rose	30.00	15.00	9.00
(47)	Ron Santo	1.50	.70	.45
(48)	Tom Seaver	20.00	10.00	6.00
(49)	Rusty Staub	4.00	2.00	1.25
(50)	Mel Stottlemyre	1.00	.50	.30
(51)	Ron Swoboda	.80	.40	.25
(52)	Luis Tiant	3.00	1.50	.90
(53)	Joe Torre	4.00	2.00	1.25
(54)	Cesar Tovar	2.00	1.00	.60
(55)	Pete Ward	2.00	1.00	.60
(56)	Roy White	3.00	1.50	.90
(57)	Billy Williams	20.00	10.00	6.00
(58)	Don Wilson	2.00	1.00	.60
(59)	Jim Wynn	.80	.40	.25
(60)	Carl Yastrzemski	30.00	15.00	9.00

1970 Transogram

Like the 1969 cards, the 1970 Transogram cards were available on boxes of Transogram baseball statues. The cards are slightly larger at 2-9/16" by 3- 1/2". The 30-card set has the same pictures as the 1969 set except for Joe Torre. All players in the '70 set were included in the '69 Transogram issue except for Reggie Jackson, Sam McDowell and Boog Powell. Three cards and three statues were part of each Transogram box in 1970. When available, most collectors prefer to find the cards as uncut panels of three, better yet, as complete boxes.

		NR MT	EX	VG
Complete Set:		325.00	162.00	97.00
Common Player:		.80	.40	.25
(1)	Hank Aaron	30.00	15.00	9.00
(2)	Ernie Banks	8.00	4.00	2.50
(3)	Roberto Clemente	30.00	15.00	9.00
(4)	Willie Davis	1.00	.50	.30
(5)	Jim Fregosi	1.00	.50	.30
(6)	Bob Gibson	8.00	4.00	2.50
(7)	Frank Howard	1.50	.70	.45
(8)	Reggie Jackson	40.00	20.00	12.00
(9)	Cleon Jones	.80	.40	.25
(10)	Al Kaline	18.00	9.00	5.50
(11)	Harmon Killebrew	18.00	9.00	5.50
(12)	Jerry Koosman	.80	.40	.25
(13)	Willie McCovey	18.00	9.00	5.50
(14)	Sam McDowell	3.00	1.50	.90
(15)	Denny McLain	1.50	.70	.45
(16)	Juan Marichal	8.00	4.00	2.50
(17)	Willie Mays	30.00	15.00	9.00
(18)	Blue Moon Odom	.80	.40	.25
(19)	Tony Oliva	1.50	.70	.45
(20)	Rico Petrocelli	1.00	.50	.30
(21)	Boog Powell	4.00	2.00	1.25
(22)	Rick Reichardt	.80	.40	.25
(23)	Frank Robinson	18.00	9.00	5.50
(24)	Pete Rose	30.00	15.00	9.00
(25)	Ron Santo	1.50	.70	.45
(26)	Tom Seaver	18.00	9.00	5.50
(27)	Mel Stottlemyre	1.00	.50	.30
(28)	Joe Torre	4.00	2.00	1.25
(29)	Jim Wynn	.80	.40	.25
(30)	Carl Yastrzemski	30.00	15.00	9.00

1970 Transogram Mets

The Transogram Mets set is a second set that the company produced in 1970. The cards are 2-9/16" by 3-1/2" and feature members of the World Champions Mets team. There are 15 cards in the set which retains the basic color picture with player's names in red and team, position and biographical details in ablack format. As with the other Transogram sets, the cards are most valuable when they are still part of their original box with the statues. Values decrease for them if the cards are removed from the box. While the Mets set does not have the attraction of many Hall of Famers as was the case with the regular set, it does make a very nice item for the Mets team collector.

		NR MT	EX	VG
Complete Set:		200.00	100.00	60.00
Common Player:		.80	.40	.25
(1)	Tommie Agee	3.00	1.50	.90
(2)	Ken Boswell	2.00	1.00	.60
(3)	Donn Clendenon	3.00	1.50	.90
(4)	Gary Gentry	2.00	1.00	.60
(5)	Jerry Grote	3.00	1.50	.90
(6)	Bud Harrelson	3.00	1.50	.90
(7)	Cleon Jones	.80	.40	.25
(8)	Jerry Koosman	.80	.40	.25
(9)	Ed Kranepool	3.00	1.50	.90
(10)	Tug McGraw	7.00	3.50	2.00
(11)	Nolan Ryan	125.00	62.00	37.00
(12)	Art Shamsky	2.00	1.00	.60
(13)	Tom Seaver	40.00	20.00	12.00
(14)	Ron Swoboda	.80	.40	.25
(15)	Al Weis	2.00	1.00	.60

1983 True Value White Sox

Issued by the Chicago White Sox and True Value hardware stores, these 2-5/8" by 4-1/8" cards are a rather expensive and scarce regional set. The 23-card set was originally scheduled as part of a promotion in which cards were given out at special Tuesday night games. The idea was sound, but rainouts forced the cancellation of some games so those scheduled cards were never given out. They were, however, smuggled out to hobby channels making it possible, although not easy, to assemble complete sets. The cards feature a large color photo with a wide white border. A red and blue White Sox logo is in the lower left corner, while the player's name, position and team number are in the lower right. Backs feature a True Value ad along with statistics. The three cards which were never given out through the normal channels are considered more scarce than the others. They are Marc Hill, Harold Baines and Salome Barojas.

		MT	NR MT	EX
Complete Set:		30.00	22.00	12.00
Common Player:		.40	.30	.15
1	Scott Fletcher	.60	.45	.25
2	Harold Baines	7.00	5.25	2.75
5	Vance Law	.50	.40	.20
7	Marc Hill	3.25	2.50	1.25
10	Tony LaRussa	.50	.40	.20
11	Rudy Law	.40	.30	.15
14	Tony Bernazard	.40	.30	.15
17	Jerry Hairston	.40	.30	.15
19	Greg Luzinski	1.00	.70	.40
24	Floyd Bannister	.60	.45	.25
25	Mike Squires	.40	.30	.15
30	Salome Barojas	3.25	2.50	1.25
31	LaMarr Hoyt	.50	.40	.20
34	Richard Dotson	.70	.50	.30
36	Jerry Koosman	.70	.50	.30
40	Britt Burns	.50	.40	.20
41	Dick Tidrow	.40	.30	.15
42	Ron Kittle	1.75	1.25	.70
44	Tom Paciorek	.40	.30	.15
45	Kevin Hickey	.40	.30	.15
53	Dennis Lamp	.40	.30	.15
67	Jim Kern	.40	.30	.15
72	Carlton Fisk	3.00	2.25	1.25

1984 True Value White Sox

True Value hardware stores and the Chicago White Sox gave their Tuesday night baseball card promotion at Comiskey Park another try in 1984. The cards measure 2-5/8" by 4-1/8" with 30 cards comprising the set. In addition to the players, there are cards for manager Tony LaRussa, the coaching staff, and former Sox greats Luis Aparicio and Minnie Minoso. Cards designs are very similar to the 1983 cards. As the cards were given out two at a time, it was very difficult to acquire a complete set. Additionally, as numbers available vary because of attendance, some cards are scarcer than others.

		MT	NR MT	EX
Complete Set:		25.00	18.50	10.00
Common Player:		.40	.30	.15
1	Scott Fletcher	.60	.45	.25
3	Harold Baines	2.25	1.75	.90
5	Vance Law	.50	.40	.20
7	Marc Hill	.40	.30	.15
8	Dave Stegman	.40	.30	.15
10	Tony LaRussa	.50	.40	.20
11	Rudy Law	.40	.30	.15

		MT	NR MT	EX
16	Julio Cruz	.40	.30	.15
17	Jerry Hairston	.40	.30	.15
19	Greg Luzinski	.90	.70	.35
20	Jerry Dybzinski	.40	.30	.15
24	Floyd Bannister	.60	.45	.25
25	Mike Squires	.40	.30	.15
27	Ron Reed	.40	.30	.15
29	Greg Walker	.50	.40	.20
30	Salome Barojas	.40	.30	.15
31	LaMarr Hoyt	.50	.40	.20
32	Tim Hulett	1.00	.70	.40
34	Richard Dotson	.70	.50	.30
40	Britt Burns	.40	.30	.15
41	Tom Seaver	4.00	3.00	1.50
42	Ron Kittle	1.00	.70	.40
44	Tom Paciorek	.40	.30	.15
50	Juan Agosto	.40	.30	.15
59	Tom Brennan	1.00	.70	.40
72	Carlton Fisk	2.00	1.50	.80
----	Minnie Minoso	2.00	1.50	.80
----	Luis Aparicio	2.00	1.50	.80
----	Nancy Faust (organist)	1.00	.70	.40
----	The Coaching Staff (Ed Brinkman, Dave Duncan, Art Kusnyer, Tony LaRussa, Jim Leyland, Dave Nelson, Joe Nossek)	.40	.30	.15

		MT	NR MT	EX
15	Bruce Sutter	.05	.04	.02
	Panel	1.00	.70	.40
16	Gary Carter	.15	.11	.06
17	George Brett	.20	.15	.08
18	Rick Sutcliffe	.05	.04	.02
	Panel	.40	.30	.15
19	Dave Stieb	.05	.04	.02
20	Buddy Bell	.05	.04	.02
21	Alvin Davis	.08	.06	.03
	Panel	.60	.45	.25
22	Cal Ripken, Jr.	.20	.15	.08
23	Bill Madlock	.05	.04	.02
24	Kent Hrbek	.10	.08	.04
	Panel	1.50	1.25	.60
25	Lou Whitaker	.08	.06	.03
26	Nolan Ryan	.40	.30	.15
27	Dwayne Murphy	.05	.04	.02
	Panel	2.00	1.50	.80
28	Mike Schmidt	.20	.15	.08
29	Andre Dawson	.10	.08	.04
30	Wade Boggs	.50	.40	.20

1986 True Value

A 30-card set of 2-1/2" by 3-1/2" cards was available in three-card packets at True Value hardware stores with a purchase of $5 or more. Cards feature a photo enclosed by stars and a ball and bat at the bottom. The player's name and team are in the lower left while his position and a Major League Baseball logo are in the lower right. The True Value logo is in the upper left. Above the picture runs the phrase "Collector Series." Backs feature some personal information and brief 1985 statistics. Along with the player cards, the folders contained a sweepstakes card offering trips to post-season games and other prizes.

		MT	NR MT	EX
Complete Panel Set:		12.00	9.00	4.75
Complete Singles Set:		6.00	4.50	2.50
Common Panel:		.40	.30	.15
Common Single Player:		.05	.04	.02
	Panel	1.00	.70	.40
1	Pedro Guerrero	.08	.06	.03
2	Steve Garvey	.15	.11	.06
3	Eddie Murray	.20	.15	.08
	Panel	3.25	2.50	1.25
4	Pete Rose	.30	.25	.12
5	Don Mattingly	.80	.60	.30
6	Fernando Valenzuela	.10	.08	.04
	Panel	.60	.45	.25
7	Jim Rice	.15	.11	.06
8	Kirk Gibson	.10	.08	.04
9	Ozzie Smith	.15	.11	.06
	Panel	1.00	.70	.40
10	Dale Murphy	.20	.15	.08
11	Robin Yount	.15	.11	.06
12	Tom Seaver	.15	.11	.06
	Panel	.80	.60	.30
13	Reggie Jackson	.15	.11	.06
14	Ryne Sandberg	.15	.11	.06

1989 Upper Deck

Matt Williams

This premiere "Collector's Choice" issue from Upper Deck contains 700 cards (2-1/2" by 3-1/2") with full-color photos on both sides. The first 26 cards feature Star Rookies. The set also includes 26 special portrait cards with team checklist backs and seven numberical checklist cards (one for each 100 numbers). Team Checklist cards feature individual player portraits by artist Vernon Wells. Major 1988 award winners (Cy Young, Rookie of Year, MVP) are honored on 10 cards in the set, in addition to their individual player cards. There are also special cards for the Most Valuable Players in both League Championship series and the World Series. The card fronts feature head-and-shoulder poses framed by a white border. A vertical brown and green artist's rendition of the runner's lane that leads from home plate to first base is found along the right margin. The backs carry full-color action poses that fill the card back, except for a compact (yet complete) stats chart. A high-number series, cards 701-800, featuring rookies and traded players, was released in mid-season in foil packs mixed within the complete set, in boxed complete sets and in high number set boxes.

		MT	NR MT	EX
Complete Set: 1-700		125.00	90.00	50.00
Common Player: 1-700		.08	.06	.03
Complete Set: 1-800		150.00	125.00	60.00
Common Player: 701-800		.10	.08	.04
1	Star Rookie (Ken Griffey, Jr.)	60.00	45.00	25.00
2	Star Rookie (Luis Medina)	.30	.25	.12
3	Star Rookie (Tony Chance)	.15	.11	.06

#	Player	MT	NR MT	EX
4	Star Rookie (Dave Otto)	.08	.06	.03
5	Star Rookie (Sandy Alomar, Jr.)	1.00	.70	.40
6	Star Rookie (Rolando Roomes)	.20	.15	.08
7	Star Rookie (David West)	.25	.20	.10
8	Star Rookie (Cris Carpenter)	.30	.25	.12
9	Star Rookie (Gregg Jefferies)	1.00	.70	.40
10	Star Rookie (Doug Dascenzo)	.25	.20	.10
11	Star Rookie (Ron Jones)	.20	.15	.08
12	Star Rookie (Luis de los Santos)	.25	.20	.10
13a	Star Rookie (Gary Sheffield) (SS position on front is upside down)	8.00	6.00	3.25
13b	Star Rookie (Gary Sheffield) (SS position on front is correct)	12.00	9.00	4.75
14	Star Rookie (Mike Harkey)	.30	.25	.12
15	Star Rookie (Lance Blankenship)	.25	.20	.10
16	Star Rookie (William Brennan)	.15	.11	.06
17	Star Rookie (John Smoltz)	4.00	3.00	1.50
18	Star Rookie (Ramon Martinez)	2.00	1.50	.80
19	Star Rookie (Mark Lemke)	.50	.40	.20
20	Star Rookie (Juan Bell)	.25	.20	.10
21	Star Rookie (Rey Palacios)	.15	.11	.06
22	Star Rookie (Felix Jose)	3.00	2.25	1.25
23	Star Rookie (Van Snider)	.25	.20	.10
24	Star Rookie (Dante Bichette)	.40	.30	.15
25	Star Rookie (Randy Johnson)	.70	.50	.30
26	Star Rookie (Carlos Quintana)	.40	.30	.15
27	Star Rookie Checklist 1-26	.08	.06	.03
28	*Mike Schooler*	.40	.30	.15
29	Randy St. Claire	.08	.06	.03
30	*Jerald Clark*	.35	.25	.14
31	Kevin Gross	.08	.06	.03
32	*Dan Firova*	.20	.15	.08
33	Jeff Calhoun	.08	.06	.03
34	Tommy Hinzo	.08	.06	.03
35	*Ricky Jordan*	.60	.45	.25
36	Larry Parrish	.08	.06	.03
37	Bret Saberhagen	.15	.11	.06
38	Mike Smithson	.08	.06	.03
39	Dave Dravecky	.08	.06	.03
40	Ed Romero	.08	.06	.03
41	Jeff Musselman	.08	.06	.03
42	Ed Hearn	.08	.06	.03
43	Rance Mulliniks	.08	.06	.03
44	Jim Eisenreich	.08	.06	.03
45	*Sil Campusano*	.20	.15	.08
46	Mike Krukow	.08	.06	.03
47	*Paul Gibson*	.20	.15	.08
48	Mike LaCoss	.08	.06	.03
49	Larry Herndon	.08	.06	.03
50	Scott Garrelts	.08	.06	.03
51	Dwayne Henry	.08	.06	.03
52	Jim Acker	.08	.06	.03
53	Steve Sax	.15	.11	.06
54	Pete O'Brien	.08	.06	.03
55	Paul Runge	.08	.06	.03
56	Rick Rhoden	.08	.06	.03
57	*John Dopson*	.25	.20	.10
58	Casey Candaele	.08	.06	.03
59	Dave Righetti	.12	.09	.05
60	Joe Hesketh	.08	.06	.03
61	Frank DiPino	.08	.06	.03
62	Tim Laudner	.08	.06	.03
63	Jamie Moyer	.08	.06	.03
64	Fred Toliver	.08	.06	.03
65	Mitch Webster	.08	.06	.03
66	John Tudor	.10	.08	.04
67	John Cangelosi	.08	.06	.03
68	Mike Devereaux	.15	.11	.06
69	Brian Fisher	.08	.06	.03
70	Mike Marshall	.12	.09	.05
71	Zane Smith	.08	.06	.03
72a	Brian Holton (ball not visible on card front, photo actually Shawn Hillegas)	1.50	1.25	.60
72b	Brian Holton (ball visible, correct photo)	.15	.11	.06
73	Jose Guzman	.10	.08	.04
74	Rick Mahler	.08	.06	.03
75	John Shelby	.08	.06	.03
76	Jim Deshaies	.08	.06	.03
77	Bobby Meacham	.08	.06	.03
78	Bryn Smith	.08	.06	.03
79	Joaquin Andujar	.08	.06	.03
80	Richard Dotson	.08	.06	.03
81	Charlie Lea	.08	.06	.03
82	Calvin Schiraldi	.08	.06	.03
83	Les Straker	.08	.06	.03
84	Les Lancaster	.08	.06	.03
85	Allan Anderson	.08	.06	.03
86	Junior Ortiz	.08	.06	.03
87	Jesse Orosco	.08	.06	.03
88	Felix Fermin	.08	.06	.03
89	Dave Anderson	.08	.06	.03
90	Rafael Belliard	.08	.06	.03
91	Franklin Stubbs	.08	.06	.03
92	Cecil Espy	.08	.06	.03
93	Albert Hall	.08	.06	.03
94	Tim Leary	.08	.06	.03
95	Mitch Williams	.08	.06	.03
96	Tracy Jones	.10	.08	.04
97	Danny Darwin	.08	.06	.03
98	Gary Ward	.08	.06	.03
99	Neal Heaton	.08	.06	.03
100	Jim Pankovits	.08	.06	.03
101	Bill Doran	.08	.06	.03
102	Tim Wallach	.10	.08	.04
103	Joe Magrane	.10	.08	.04
104	Ozzie Virgil	.08	.06	.03
105	Alvin Davis	.12	.09	.05
106	Tom Brookens	.08	.06	.03
107	Shawon Dunston	.10	.08	.04
108	Tracy Woodson	.10	.08	.04
109	Nelson Liriano	.08	.06	.03
110	Devon White	.12	.09	.05
111	Steve Balboni	.08	.06	.03
112	Buddy Bell	.08	.06	.03
113	*German Jimenez*	.08	.06	.03
114	Ken Dayley	.08	.06	.03
115	Andres Galarraga	.15	.11	.06
116	Mike Scioscia	.08	.06	.03
117	Gary Pettis	.08	.06	.03
118	Ernie Whitt	.08	.06	.03
119	Bob Boone	.08	.06	.03
120	Ryne Sandberg	.80	.60	.30
121	Bruce Benedict	.08	.06	.03
122	Hubie Brooks	.10	.08	.04
123	Mike Moore	.08	.06	.03
124	Wallace Johnson	.08	.06	.03
125	Bob Horner	.10	.08	.04
126	Chili Davis	.08	.06	.03
127	Manny Trillo	.08	.06	.03
128	Chet Lemon	.08	.06	.03
129	John Cerutti	.08	.06	.03
130	Orel Hershiser	.25	.20	.10
131	Terry Pendleton	.10	.08	.04
132	Jeff Blauser	.10	.08	.04
133	Mike Fitzgerald	.08	.06	.03
134	Henry Cotto	.08	.06	.03
135	Gerald Young	.12	.09	.05
136	Luis Salazar	.08	.06	.03
137	Alejandro Pena	.08	.06	.03
138	Jack Howell	.08	.06	.03
139	Tony Fernandez	.12	.09	.05
140	Mark Grace	1.25	.90	.50
141	Ken Caminiti	.08	.06	.03
142	Mike Jackson	.08	.06	.03
143	Larry McWilliams	.08	.06	.03
144	Andres Thomas	.08	.06	.03
145	Nolan Ryan	4.00	3.00	1.50
146	Mike Davis	.08	.06	.03
147	DeWayne Buice	.08	.06	.03
148	Jody Davis	.08	.06	.03
149	Jesse Barfield	.10	.08	.04
150	Matt Nokes	.15	.11	.06
151	Jerry Reuss	.08	.06	.03
152	Rick Cerone	.08	.06	.03
153	Storm Davis	.10	.08	.04
154	Marvell Wynne	.08	.06	.03
155	Will Clark	2.00	1.50	.80
156	Luis Aguayo	.08	.06	.03
157	Willie Upshaw	.08	.06	.03
158	Randy Bush	.08	.06	.03
159	Ron Darling	.12	.09	.05
160	Kal Daniels	.15	.11	.06
161	Spike Owen	.08	.06	.03
162	Luis Polonia	.08	.06	.03
163	Kevin Mitchell	.50	.40	.20
164	*Dave Gallagher*	.25	.20	.10
165	Benito Santiago	.15	.11	.06
166	Greg Gagne	.08	.06	.03
167	Ken Phelps	.08	.06	.03
168	Sid Fernandez	.10	.08	.04
169	Bo Diaz	.08	.06	.03
170	Cory Snyder	.15	.11	.06
171	Eric Show	.08	.06	.03
172	Rob Thompson	.08	.06	.03
173	Marty Barrett	.08	.06	.03
174	Dave Henderson	.10	.08	.04
175	Ozzie Guillen	.08	.06	.03
176	Barry Lyons	.08	.06	.03
177	*Kelvin Torve* (FC)	.20	.15	.08
178	Don Slaught	.08	.06	.03
179	Steve Lombardozzi	.08	.06	.03
180	*Chris Sabo*	1.00	.70	.40

		MT	NR MT	EX
181	Jose Uribe	.08	.06	.03
182	Shane Mack	.08	.06	.03
183	Ron Karkovice	.08	.06	.03
184	Todd Benzinger	.12	.09	.05
185	Dave Stewart	.10	.08	.04
186	Julio Franco	.10	.08	.04
187	Ron Robinson	.08	.06	.03
188	Wally Backman	.08	.06	.03
189	Randy Velarde	.08	.06	.03
190	Joe Carter	.12	.09	.05
191	Bob Welch	.10	.08	.04
192	Kelly Paris	.08	.06	.03
193	Chris Brown	.08	.06	.03
194	Rick Reuschel	.10	.08	.04
195	Roger Clemens	.50	.40	.20
196	Dave Concepcion	.10	.08	.04
197	Al Newman	.08	.06	.03
198	Brook Jacoby	.10	.08	.04
199	Mookie Wilson	.08	.06	.03
200	Don Mattingly	1.00	.70	.40
201	Dick Schofield	.08	.06	.03
202	Mark Gubicza	.10	.08	.04
203	Gary Gaetti	.15	.11	.06
204	Dan Pasqua	.10	.08	.04
205	Andre Dawson	.20	.15	.08
206	Chris Speier	.08	.06	.03
207	Kent Tekulve	.08	.06	.03
208	Rod Scurry	.08	.06	.03
209	Scott Bailes	.08	.06	.03
210	Rickey Henderson	1.50	1.25	.60
211	Harold Baines	.12	.09	.05
212	Tony Armas	.08	.06	.03
213	Kent Hrbek	.20	.15	.08
214	Darrin Jackson	.08	.06	.03
215	George Brett	.35	.25	.14
216	Rafael Santana	.08	.06	.03
217	Andy Allanson	.08	.06	.03
218	Brett Butler	.08	.06	.03
219	Steve Jeltz	.08	.06	.03
220	Jay Buhner	.10	.08	.04
221	Bo Jackson	1.00	.70	.40
222	Angel Salazar	.08	.06	.03
223	Kirk McCaskill	.08	.06	.03
224	Steve Lyons	.08	.06	.03
225	Bert Blyleven	.10	.08	.04
226	Scott Bradley	.08	.06	.03
227	Bob Melvin	.08	.06	.03
228	Ron Kittle	.08	.06	.03
229	Phil Bradley	.10	.08	.04
230	Tommy John	.12	.09	.05
231	Greg Walker	.08	.06	.03
232	Juan Berenguer	.08	.06	.03
233	Pat Tabler	.08	.06	.03
234	Terry Clark	.20	.15	.08
235	Rafael Palmeiro	.25	.20	.10
236	Paul Zuvella	.08	.06	.03
237	Willie Randolph	.08	.06	.03
238	Bruce Fields	.08	.06	.03
239	Mike Aldrete	.08	.06	.03
240	Lance Parrish	.15	.11	.06
241	Greg Maddux	.12	.09	.05
242	John Moses	.08	.06	.03
243	Melido Perez	.10	.08	.04
244	Willie Wilson	.10	.08	.04
245	Mark McLemore	.08	.06	.03
246	Von Hayes	.10	.08	.04
247	Matt Williams	.12	.09	.05
248	John Candelaria	.08	.06	.03
249	Harold Reynolds	.08	.06	.03
250	Greg Swindell	.12	.09	.05
251	Juan Agosto	.08	.06	.03
252	Mike Felder	.08	.06	.03
253	Vince Coleman	.15	.11	.06
254	Larry Sheets	.08	.06	.03
255	George Bell	.25	.20	.10
256	Terry Steinbach	.10	.08	.04
257	Jack Armstrong	.20	.15	.08
258	Dickie Thon	.08	.06	.03
259	Ray Knight	.08	.06	.03
260	Darryl Strawberry	.40	.30	.15
261	Doug Sisk	.08	.06	.03
262	Alex Trevino	.08	.06	.03
263	Jeff Leonard	.08	.06	.03
264	Tom Henke	.08	.06	.03
265	Ozzie Smith	.15	.11	.06
266	Dave Bergman	.08	.06	.03
267	Tony Phillips	.08	.06	.03
268	Mark Davis	.08	.06	.03
269	Kevin Elster	.10	.08	.04
270	Barry Larkin	.20	.15	.08
271	Manny Lee	.08	.06	.03
272	Tom Brunansky	.12	.09	.05
273	Craig Biggio	1.50	1.25	.60
274	Jim Gantner	.08	.06	.03
275	Eddie Murray	.25	.20	.10
276	Jeff Reed	.08	.06	.03
277	Tim Teufel	.08	.06	.03
278	Rick Honeycutt	.08	.06	.03
279	Guillermo Hernandez	.08	.06	.03
280	John Kruk	.10	.08	.04
281	Luis Alicea	.20	.15	.08
282	Jim Clancy	.08	.06	.03
283	Billy Ripken	.08	.06	.03
284	Craig Reynolds	.08	.06	.03
285	Robin Yount	.35	.25	.14
286	Jimmy Jones	.08	.06	.03
287	Ron Oester	.08	.06	.03
288	Terry Leach	.08	.06	.03
289	Dennis Eckersley	.12	.09	.05
290	Alan Trammell	.20	.15	.08
291	Jimmy Key	.10	.08	.04
292	Chris Bosio	.08	.06	.03
293	Jose DeLeon	.08	.06	.03
294	Jim Traber	.08	.06	.03
295	Mike Scott	.12	.09	.05
296	Roger McDowell	.10	.08	.04
297	Garry Templeton	.08	.06	.03
298	Doyle Alexander	.08	.06	.03
299	Nick Esasky	.08	.06	.03
300	Mark McGwire	.70	.50	.30
301	Darryl Hamilton	.40	.30	.15
302	Dave Smith	.08	.06	.03
303	Rick Sutcliffe	.10	.08	.04
304	Dave Stapleton	.08	.06	.03
305	Alan Ashby	.08	.06	.03
306	Pedro Guerrero	.15	.11	.06
307	Ron Guidry	.12	.09	.05
308	Steve Farr	.08	.06	.03
309	Curt Ford	.08	.06	.03
310	Claudell Washington	.08	.06	.03
311	Tom Prince	.08	.06	.03
312	Chad Kreuter	.15	.11	.06
313	Ken Oberkfell	.08	.06	.03
314	Jerry Browne	.08	.06	.03
315	R.J. Reynolds	.08	.06	.03
316	Scott Bankhead	.08	.06	.03
317	Milt Thompson	.08	.06	.03
318	Mario Diaz	.10	.08	.04
319	Bruce Ruffin	.08	.06	.03
320	Dave Valle	.08	.06	.03
321a	Gary Varsho (batting righty on card back, photo actually Mike Bielecki)	2.00	1.50	.80
321b	Gary Varsho (batting lefty on card back, correct photo)	.30	.25	.12
322	Paul Mirabella	.08	.06	.03
323	Chuck Jackson	.08	.06	.03
324	Drew Hall	.10	.08	.04
325	Don August	.10	.08	.04
326	Israel Sanchez	.15	.11	.06
327	Denny Walling	.08	.06	.03
328	Joel Skinner	.08	.06	.03
329	Danny Tartabull	.15	.11	.06
330	Tony Pena	.08	.06	.03
331	Jim Sundberg	.08	.06	.03
332	Jeff Robinson	.12	.09	.05
333	Odibbe McDowell	.08	.06	.03
334	Jose Lind	.10	.08	.04
335	Paul Kilgus	.10	.08	.04
336	Juan Samuel	.12	.09	.05
337	Mike Campbell	.10	.08	.04
338	Mike Maddux	.08	.06	.03
339	Darnell Coles	.08	.06	.03
340	Bob Dernier	.08	.06	.03
341	Rafael Ramirez	.08	.06	.03
342	Scott Sanderson	.08	.06	.03
343	B.J. Surhoff	.10	.08	.04
344	Billy Hatcher	.08	.06	.03
345	Pat Perry	.08	.06	.03
346	Jack Clark	.15	.11	.06
347	Gary Thurman	.12	.09	.05
348	Timmy Jones	.20	.15	.08
349	Dave Winfield	.30	.25	.12
350	Frank White	.08	.06	.03
351	Dave Collins	.08	.06	.03
352	Jack Morris	.15	.11	.06
353	Eric Plunk	.08	.06	.03
354	Leon Durham	.08	.06	.03
355	Ivan DeJesus	.08	.06	.03
356	Brian Holman	.40	.30	.15
357a	Dale Murphy (photo on card front reversed)	60.00	45.00	25.00
357b	Dale Murphy (correct photo)	.35	.25	.14

#	Player	MT	NR MT	EX
358	Mark Portugal	.08	.06	.03
359	Andy McGaffigan	.08	.06	.03
360	Tom Glavine	2.50	2.00	1.00
361	Keith Moreland	.08	.06	.03
362	Todd Stottlemyre	.15	.11	.06
363	Dave Leiper	.08	.06	.03
364	Cecil Fielder	.80	.60	.30
365	Carmelo Martinez	.08	.06	.03
366	Dwight Evans	.10	.08	.04
367	Kevin McReynolds	.15	.11	.06
368	Rich Gedman	.08	.06	.03
369	Len Dykstra	.10	.08	.04
370	Jody Reed	.12	.09	.05
371	Jose Canseco	2.00	1.50	.80
372	Rob Murphy	.08	.06	.03
373	Mike Henneman	.10	.08	.04
374	Walt Weiss	.40	.30	.15
375	*Rob Dibble*	1.00	.70	.40
376	Kirby Puckett	.30	.25	.12
377	Denny Martinez	.08	.06	.03
378	Ron Gant	2.00	1.50	.80
379	Brian Harper	.08	.06	.03
380	*Nelson Santovenia*	.20	.15	.08
381	Lloyd Moseby	.08	.06	.03
382	Lance McCullers	.08	.06	.03
383	Dave Stieb	.10	.08	.04
384	Tony Gwynn	.30	.25	.12
385	Mike Flanagan	.08	.06	.03
386	Bob Ojeda	.08	.06	.03
387	Bruce Hurst	.10	.08	.04
388	Dave Magadan	.10	.08	.04
389	Wade Boggs	.60	.45	.25
390	Gary Carter	.25	.20	.10
391	Frank Tanana	.08	.06	.03
392	Curt Young	.08	.06	.03
393	Jeff Treadway	.10	.08	.04
394	Darrell Evans	.10	.08	.04
395	Glenn Hubbard	.08	.06	.03
396	Chuck Cary	.08	.06	.03
397	Frank Viola	.15	.11	.06
398	Jeff Parrett	.10	.08	.04
399	*Terry Blocker*	.15	.11	.06
400	Dan Gladden	.08	.06	.03
401	*Louie Meadows*	.15	.11	.06
402	Tim Raines	.25	.20	.10
403	Joey Meyer	.10	.08	.04
404	Larry Andersen	.08	.06	.03
405	Rex Hudler	.08	.06	.03
406	Mike Schmidt	2.00	1.50	.80
407	John Franco	.10	.08	.04
408	*Brady Anderson*	1.25	.90	.50
409	Don Carman	.08	.06	.03
410	Eric Davis	.40	.30	.15
411	Bob Stanley	.08	.06	.03
412	Pete Smith	.10	.08	.04
413	Jim Rice	.25	.20	.10
414	Bruce Sutter	.10	.08	.04
415	Oil Can Boyd	.08	.06	.03
416	Ruben Sierra	.50	.40	.20
417	Mike LaValliere	.08	.06	.03
418	Steve Buechele	.08	.06	.03
419	Gary Redus	.08	.06	.03
420	Scott Fletcher	.08	.06	.03
421	Dale Sveum	.08	.06	.03
422	Bob Knepper	.08	.06	.03
423	Luis Rivera	.08	.06	.03
424	Ted Higuera	.10	.08	.04
425	Kevin Bass	.08	.06	.03
426	Ken Gerhart	.08	.06	.03
427	Shane Rawley	.08	.06	.03
428	Paul O'Neill	.08	.06	.03
429	Joe Orsulak	.08	.06	.03
430	Jackie Gutierrez	.08	.06	.03
431	Gerald Perry	.10	.08	.04
432	Mike Greenwell	.60	.45	.25
433	Jerry Royster	.08	.06	.03
434	Ellis Burks	.60	.45	.25
435	Ed Olwine	.08	.06	.03
436	Dave Rucker	.08	.06	.03
437	Charlie Hough	.08	.06	.03
438	Bob Walk	.08	.06	.03
439	Bob Brower	.08	.06	.03
440	Barry Bonds	1.50	1.25	.60
441	Tom Foley	.08	.06	.03
442	Rob Deer	.08	.06	.03
443	Glenn Davis	.15	.11	.06
444	Dave Martinez	.08	.06	.03
445	Bill Wegman	.08	.06	.03
446	Lloyd McClendon	.08	.06	.03
447	Dave Schmidt	.08	.06	.03
448	Darren Daulton	.08	.06	.03
449	Frank Williams	.08	.06	.03
450	Don Aase	.08	.06	.03
451	Lou Whitaker	.15	.11	.06
452	Goose Gossage	.12	.09	.05
453	Ed Whitson	.08	.06	.03
454	Jim Walewander	.08	.06	.03
455	Damon Berryhill	.12	.09	.05
456	Tim Burke	.08	.06	.03
457	Barry Jones	.08	.06	.03
458	Joel Youngblood	.08	.06	.03
459	Floyd Youmans	.08	.06	.03
460	Mark Salas	.08	.06	.03
461	Jeff Russell	.08	.06	.03
462	Darrell Miller	.08	.06	.03
463	Jeff Kunkel	.08	.06	.03
464	*Sherman Corbett*	.20	.15	.08
465	Curtis Wilkerson	.08	.06	.03
466	Bud Black	.08	.06	.03
467	Cal Ripken, Jr.	3.00	2.25	1.25
468	John Farrell	.10	.08	.04
469	Terry Kennedy	.08	.06	.03
470	Tom Candiotti	.08	.06	.03
471	Roberto Alomar	5.00	3.75	2.00
472	Jeff Robinson	.12	.09	.05
473	Vance Law	.08	.06	.03
474	Randy Ready	.08	.06	.03
475	Walt Terrell	.08	.06	.03
476	Kelly Downs	.10	.08	.04
477	*Johnny Paredes*	.15	.11	.06
478	Shawn Hillegas	.08	.06	.03
479	Bob Brenly	.08	.06	.03
480	Otis Nixon	.08	.06	.03
481	Johnny Ray	.08	.06	.03
482	Geno Petralli	.08	.06	.03
483	Stu Cliburn	.08	.06	.03
484	Pete Incaviglia	.10	.08	.04
485	Brian Downing	.08	.06	.03
486	Jeff Stone	.08	.06	.03
487	Carmen Castillo	.08	.06	.03
488	Tom Niedenfuer	.08	.06	.03
489	Jay Bell	.08	.06	.03
490	Rick Schu	.08	.06	.03
491	*Jeff Pico*	.15	.11	.06
492	*Mark Parent*	.20	.15	.08
493	Eric King	.08	.06	.03
494	Al Nipper	.08	.06	.03
495	Andy Hawkins	.08	.06	.03
496	Daryl Boston	.08	.06	.03
497	Ernie Riles	.08	.06	.03
498	Pascual Perez	.08	.06	.03
499	Bill Long	.08	.06	.03
500	Kirt Manwaring	.10	.08	.04
501	Chuck Crim	.08	.06	.03
502	Candy Maldonado	.08	.06	.03
503	Dennis Lamp	.08	.06	.03
504	Glenn Braggs	.08	.06	.03
505	Joe Price	.08	.06	.03
506	Ken Williams	.08	.06	.03
507	Bill Pecota	.08	.06	.03
508	Rey Quinones	.08	.06	.03
509	*Jeff Bittiger*	.15	.11	.06
510	Kevin Seitzer	.30	.25	.12
511	Steve Bedrosian	.10	.08	.04
512	Todd Worrell	.10	.08	.04
513	Chris James	.10	.08	.04
514	Jose Oquendo	.08	.06	.03
515	David Palmer	.08	.06	.03
516	John Smiley	.12	.09	.05
517	Dave Clark	.08	.06	.03
518	Mike Dunne	.10	.08	.04
519	Ron Washington	.08	.06	.03
520	Bob Kipper	.08	.06	.03
521	Lee Smith	.10	.08	.04
522	Juan Castillo	.08	.06	.03
523	Don Robinson	.08	.06	.03
524	Kevin Romine	.08	.06	.03
525	Paul Molitor	.15	.11	.06
526	Mark Langston	.10	.08	.04
527	Donnie Hill	.08	.06	.03
528	Larry Owen	.08	.06	.03
529	Jerry Reed	.08	.06	.03
530	Jack McDowell	.10	.08	.04
531	Greg Mathews	.08	.06	.03
532	John Russell	.08	.06	.03
533	Don Quisenberry	.08	.06	.03
534	Greg Gross	.08	.06	.03
535	Danny Cox	.08	.06	.03
536	Terry Francona	.08	.06	.03
537	Andy Van Slyke	.15	.11	.06
538	Mel Hall	.08	.06	.03
539	Jim Gott	.08	.06	.03

#	Player	MT	NR MT	EX
540	Doug Jones	.10	.08	.04
541	Criag Lefferts	.08	.06	.03
542	Mike Boddicker	.08	.06	.03
543	Greg Brock	.08	.06	.03
544	Atlee Hammaker	.08	.06	.03
545	Tom Bolton	.08	.06	.03
546	*Mike Macfarlane*	.20	.15	.08
547	*Rich Renteria*	.15	.11	.06
548	John Davis	.08	.06	.03
549	Floyd Bannister	.08	.06	.03
550	Mickey Brantley	.08	.06	.03
551	Duane Ward	.08	.06	.03
552	Dan Petry	.08	.06	.03
553	Mickey Tettleton	.08	.06	.03
554	Rick Leach	.08	.06	.03
555	Mike Witt	.08	.06	.03
556	Sid Bream	.08	.06	.03
557	Bobby Witt	.10	.08	.04
558	Tommy Herr	.08	.06	.03
559	Randy Milligan	.08	.06	.03
560	*Jose Cecena*	.20	.15	.08
561	Mackey Sasser	.08	.06	.03
562	Carney Lansford	.08	.06	.03
563	Rick Aguilera	.08	.06	.03
564	Ron Hassey	.08	.06	.03
565	Dwight Gooden	.50	.40	.20
566	Paul Assenmacher	.08	.06	.03
567	Neil Allen	.08	.06	.03
568	Jim Morrison	.08	.06	.03
569	Mike Pagliarulo	.10	.08	.04
570	Ted Simmons	.10	.08	.04
571	Mark Thurmond	.08	.06	.03
572	Fred McGriff	.40	.30	.15
573	Wally Joyner	.25	.20	.10
574	*Jose Bautista*	.20	.15	.08
575	Kelly Gruber	.08	.06	.03
576	Cecilio Guante	.08	.06	.03
577	Mark Davidson	.08	.06	.03
578	Bobby Bonilla	.12	.09	.05
579	Mike Stanley	.08	.06	.03
580	Gene Larkin	.10	.08	.04
581	Stan Javier	.08	.06	.03
582	Howard Johnson	.10	.08	.04
583a	Mike Gallego (photo on card back reversed)	1.00	.70	.40
583b	Mike Gallego (correct photo)	.15	.11	.06
584	David Cone	.35	.25	.14
585	*Doug Jennings*	.20	.15	.08
586	Charlie Hudson	.08	.06	.03
587	Dion James	.08	.06	.03
588	Al Leiter	.15	.11	.06
589	Charlie Puleo	.08	.06	.03
590	Roberto Kelly	.25	.20	.10
591	Thad Bosley	.08	.06	.03
592	Pete Stanicek	.10	.08	.04
593	*Pat Borders*	.60	.45	.25
594	*Bryan Harvey*	.60	.45	.25
595	Jeff Ballard	.10	.08	.04
596	Jeff Reardon	.10	.08	.04
597	Doug Drabek	.08	.06	.03
598	Edwin Correa	.08	.06	.03
599	Keith Atherton	.08	.06	.03
600	Dave LaPoint	.08	.06	.03
601	Don Baylor	.10	.08	.04
602	Tom Pagnozzi	.08	.06	.03
603	Tim Flannery	.08	.06	.03
604	Gene Walter	.08	.06	.03
605	Dave Parker	.12	.09	.05
606	Mike Diaz	.08	.06	.03
607	Chris Gwynn	.10	.08	.04
608	Odell Jones	.08	.06	.03
609	Carlton Fisk	.60	.45	.25
610	Jay Howell	.08	.06	.03
611	Tim Crews	.08	.06	.03
612	Keith Hernandez	.20	.15	.08
613	Willie Fraser	.08	.06	.03
614	Jim Eppard	.08	.06	.03
615	Jeff Hamilton	.08	.06	.03
616	Kurt Stillwell	.08	.06	.03
617	Tom Browning	.10	.08	.04
618	Jeff Montgomery	.08	.06	.03
619	Jose Rijo	.08	.06	.03
620	Jamie Quirk	.08	.06	.03
621	Willie McGee	.12	.09	.05
622	Mark Grant	.08	.06	.03
623	Bill Swift	.08	.06	.03
624	Orlando Mercado	.08	.06	.03
625	*John Costello*	.15	.11	.06
626	Jose Gonzalez	.08	.06	.03
627a	Bill Schroeder (putting on shin guards on card back, photo actually Ronn Reynolds)	1.25	.90	.50
627b	Bill Schroeder (arms crossed on card back, correct photo)	.15	.11	.06
628a	Fred Manrique (throwing on card back, photo actually Ozzie Guillen)	1.25	.90	.50
628b	Fred Manrique (batting on card back, correct photo)	.15	.11	.06
629	Ricky Horton	.08	.06	.03
630	Dan Plesac	.10	.08	.04
631	Alfredo Griffin	.08	.06	.03
632	Chuck Finley	.08	.06	.03
633	Kirk Gibson	.20	.15	.08
634	Randy Myers	.10	.08	.04
635	Greg Minton	.08	.06	.03
636	Herm Winningham	.08	.06	.03
637	Charlie Leibrandt	.08	.06	.03
638	Tim Birtsas	.08	.06	.03
639	Bill Buckner	.10	.08	.04
640	Danny Jackson	.15	.11	.06
641	Greg Booker	.08	.06	.03
642	Jim Presley	.08	.06	.03
643	Gene Nelson	.08	.06	.03
644	Rod Booker	.08	.06	.03
645	Dennis Rasmussen	.10	.08	.04
646	Juan Nieves	.08	.06	.03
647	Bobby Thigpen	.10	.08	.04
648	Tim Belcher	.10	.08	.04
649	Mike Young	.08	.06	.03
650	Ivan Calderon	.08	.06	.03
651	*Oswaldo Peraza*	.20	.15	.08
652a	Pat Sheridan (no position on front)	30.00	22.00	12.00
652b	Pat Sheridan (position on front)	.08	.06	.03
653	Mike Morgan	.08	.06	.03
654	Mike Heath	.08	.06	.03
655	Jay Tibbs	.08	.06	.03
656	Fernando Valenzuela	.20	.15	.08
657	Lee Mazzilli	.08	.06	.03
658	Frank Viola	.08	.06	.03
659	Jose Canseco	.08	.06	.03
660	Walt Weiss	.08	.06	.03
661	Orel Hershiser	.08	.06	.03
662	Kirk Gibson	.08	.06	.03
663	Chris Sabo	.08	.06	.03
664	Dennis Eckersley	.08	.06	.03
665	Orel Hershiser	.08	.06	.03
666	Kirk Gibson	.08	.06	.03
667	Orel Hershiser	.08	.06	.03
668	Angels Checklist (Wally Joyner)	.08	.06	.03
669	Astros Checklist (Nolan Ryan)	.60	.45	.25
670	Athletics Checklist (Jose Canseco)	.08	.06	.03
671	Blue Jays Checklist (Fred McGriff)	.08	.06	.03
672	Braves Checklist (Dale Murphy)	.08	.06	.03
673	Brewers Checklist (Paul Molitor)	.08	.06	.03
674	Cardinals Checklist (Ozzie Smith)	.08	.06	.03
675	Cubs Checklist (Ryne Sandberg)	.08	.06	.03
676	Dodgers Checklist (Kirk Gibson)	.08	.06	.03
677	Expos Checklist (Andres Galarraga)	.08	.06	.03
678	Giants Checklist (Will Clark)	.08	.06	.03
679	Indians Checklist (Cory Snyder)	.08	.06	.03
680	Mariners Checklist (Alvin Davis)	.08	.06	.03
681	Mets Checklist (Darryl Strawberry)	.08	.06	.03
682	Orioles Checklist (Cal Ripken, Jr.)	.08	.06	.03
683	Padres Checklist (Tony Gwynn)	.08	.06	.03
684	Phillies Checklist (Mike Schmidt)	.08	.06	.03
685	Pirates Checklist (Andy Van Slyke)	.08	.06	.03
686	Rangers Checklist (Ruben Sierra)	.08	.06	.03
687	Red Sox Checklist (Wade Boggs)	.08	.06	.03
688	Reds Checklist (Eric Davis)	.08	.06	.03
689	Royals Checklist (George Brett)	.08	.06	.03
690	Tigers Checklist (Alan Trammell)	.08	.06	.03
691	Twins Checklist (Frank Viola)	.08	.06	.03
692	White Sox Checklist (Harold Baines)	.08	.06	.03
693	Yankees Checklist (Don Mattingly)	.08	.06	.03
694	Checklist 1-100	.08	.06	.03
695	Checklist 101-200	.08	.06	.03
696	Checklist 201-300	.08	.06	.03
697	Checklist 301-400	.08	.06	.03
698	Checklist 401-500	.08	.06	.03
699	Checklist 501-600	.08	.06	.03
700	Checklist 601-700	.08	.06	.03
701	Checklist 701-800	.20	.15	.08
702	Jessie Barfield	.10	.08	.04
703	Walt Terrell	.10	.08	.04
704	Dickie Thon	.10	.08	.04
705	Al Leiter	.10	.08	.04
706	Dave LaPoint	.10	.08	.04
707	Charlie Hayes(FC)	.20	.15	.08
708	Andy Hawkins	.10	.08	.04
709	Mickey Hatcher	.10	.08	.04

		MT	NR MT	EX
710	Lance McCullers	.10	.08	.04
711	Ron Kittle	.10	.08	.04
712	Bert Blyleven	.10	.08	.04
713	Rick Dempsey	.10	.08	.04
714	Ken Williams	.10	.08	.04
715	Steve Rosenberg(FC)	.15	.11	.06
716	Joe Skalski(FC)	.20	.15	.08
717	Spike Owen	.10	.08	.04
718	Todd Burns	.10	.08	.04
719	Kevin Gross	.10	.08	.04
720	Tommy Herr	.10	.08	.04
721	Rob Ducey	.10	.08	.04
722	Gary Green(FC)	.15	.11	.06
723	Gregg Olson(FC)	2.00	1.50	.80
724	Greg Harris(FC)	.15	.11	.06
725	Craig Worthington(FC)	.50	.40	.20
726	Tom Howard(FC)	.25	.20	.10
727	Dale Mohorcic	.10	.08	.04
728	Rich Yett	.10	.08	.04
729	Mel Hall	.10	.08	.04
730	Floyd Youmans	.10	.08	.04
731	Lonnie Smith	.15	.11	.06
732	Wally Backman	.10	.08	.04
733	Trevor Wilson	.10	.08	.04
734	Jose Alvarez	.10	.08	.04
735	Bob Milacki(FC)	.15	.11	.06
736	Tom Gordon(FC)	.80	.60	.30
737	Wally Whitehurst(FC)	.25	.20	.10
738	Mike Aldrete	.10	.08	.04
739	Keith Miller	.10	.08	.04
740	Randy Milligan	.10	.08	.04
741	Jeff Parrett	.10	.08	.04
742	Steve Finley(FC)	.60	.45	.25
743	Junior Felix(FC)	.80	.60	.30
744	Pete Harnisch(FC)	.50	.40	.20
745	Bill Spiers(FC)	.40	.30	.15
746	Hensley Meulens(FC)	.50	.40	.20
747	Juan Bell	.20	.15	.08
748	Steve Sax	.15	.11	.06
749	Phil Bradley	.10	.08	.04
750	Rey Quinones	.10	.08	.04
751	Tommy Gregg(FC)	.15	.11	.06
752	Kevin Brown(FC)	.10	.08	.04
753	Derek Lilliquist(FC)	.15	.11	.06
754	Todd Zeile(FC)	3.00	2.25	1.25
755	Jim Abbott(FC)	4.00	3.00	1.50
756	Ozzie Canseco(FC)	.30	.25	.12
757	Nick Esasky	.10	.08	.04
758	Mike Moore	.15	.11	.06
759	Rob Murphy	.10	.08	.04
760	Rick Mahler	.10	.08	.04
761	Fred Lynn	.10	.08	.04
762	Kevin Blankenship(FC)	.10	.08	.04
763	Eddie Murray	.15	.11	.06
764	Steve Searcy(FC)	.10	.08	.04
765	Jerome Walton(FC)	.50	.40	.20
766	Erik Hanson(FC)	.60	.45	.25
767	Bob Boone	.15	.11	.06
768	Edgar Martinez(FC)	2.00	1.50	.80
769	Jose DeJesus(FC)	.10	.08	.04
770	Greg Briley(FC)	.30	.25	.12
771	Steve Peters(FC)	.10	.08	.04
772	Rafael Palmeiro	.60	.45	.25
773	Jack Clark	.15	.11	.06
774	Nolan Ryan	4.00	3.00	1.50
775	Lance Parrish	.10	.08	.04
776	Joe Girardi(FC)	.25	.20	.10
777	Willie Randolph	.10	.08	.04
778	Mitch Williams	.30	.25	.12
779	Dennis Cook(FC)	.40	.30	.15
780	Dwight Smith(FC)	.25	.20	.10
781	Lenny Harris(FC)	.40	.30	.15
782	Torey Lovullo(FC)	.15	.11	.06
783	Norm Charlton(FC)	.10	.08	.04
784	Chris Brown	.10	.08	.04
785	Todd Benzinger	.10	.08	.04
786	Shane Rawley	.10	.08	.04
787	Omar Vizquel(FC)	.25	.20	.10
788	LaVel Freeman(FC)	.25	.20	.10
789	Jeffrey Leonard	.10	.08	.04
790	Eddie Williams(FC)	.10	.08	.04
791	Jamie Moyer	.10	.08	.04
792	Bruce Hurst	.10	.08	.04
793	Julio Franco	.30	.25	.12
794	Claudell Washington	.10	.08	.04
795	Jody Davis	.10	.08	.04
796	Odibbe McDowell	.10	.08	.04
797	Paul Kilgus	.10	.08	.04
798	Tracy Jones	.10	.08	.04
799	Steve Wilson(FC)	.20	.15	.08
800	Pete O'Brien,	.10	.08	.04

1989 Upper Deck Promos

DeWAYNE BUICE

In 1988 Upper Deck produced a two card test set to be distributed as samples for the 1989 set. 18,000 of each card was produced. The cards were distributed to dealers at the 1988 National Sports Collectors Convention. Two other variations of the promo cards exist. Both variations involve differences in how the hologram was produced. 2,000-5,000 of one of the hologram variations exist, while less than 1,000 of the third variation exist. These sets are valued at $300 and $500 respectively. Joyner and Buice were selected for the promo cards because of a reported investment interest in Upper Deck. Joyner and Buice were not allowed to invest in the company due to their player status.

		MT	NR MT	EX
Complete Set:		150.00	110.00	60.00
Common Player:		50.00	37.00	20.00
1	DeWayne Buice	50.00	37.00	20.00
700	Wally Joyner	75.00	55.00	30.00

Regional interest may affect the value of a card.

1990 Upper Deck

Tom Candiotti

Following the success of its first issue, Upper Deck released another 800-card set in 1990. The cards contain full-color photos on both sides and are 2-1/2" by 3-1/2" in size. The artwork of Vernon Wells is featured on the front of all team checklist cards. The 1990 set also introduces two new Wells illustrations - a tribute to Mike Schmidt upon his retirement and one commemorating Nolan Ryan's 5,000 career strikeouts. The cards are similar in design to the 1989 issue. The Wade Boggs card depicts the Red Sox star in four stages of his batting swing via a quad-action photograph, much like the Jim Abbott card of 1989. The high-number series (701-800) was released as a boxed set, in factory sets and in wax packs at mid-season.

		MT	NR MT	EX
	Complete Set: 1-700	40.00	30.00	15.00
	Common Player: 1-700	.06	.05	.02
	Complete Set: 1-800	50.00	37.00	20.00
	Common Player: 701-800	.10	.08	.04
1	Star Rookie Checklist	.06	.05	.02
2	Randy Nosek(FC)	.15	.11	.06
3	Tom Dress(FC)	.15	.11	.06
4	Curt Young	.06	.05	.02
5	Angels Checklist	.06	.05	.02
6	Luis Salazar	.06	.05	.02
7	Phillies Checklist	.06	.05	.02
8	Jose Bautista	.08	.06	.03
9	Marquis Grissom(FC)	2.00	1.50	.80
10	Dodgers Checklist	.06	.05	.02
11	Rick Aguilera	.08	.06	.03
12	Padres Checklist	.06	.05	.02
13	Deion Sanders(FC)	2.00	1.50	.80
14	Marvell Wynne	.06	.05	.02
15	David West	.15	.11	.06
16	Pirates Checklist	.06	.05	.02
17	Sammy Sosa(FC)	.70	.50	.30
18	Yankees Checklist	.06	.05	.02
19	Jack Howell	.06	.05	.02
20	Mike Schmidt (Special Card)	1.00	.70	.40
21	Robin Ventura(FC)	3.00	2.25	1.25
22	Brian Meyer(FC)	.20	.15	.08
23	Blaine Beatty(FC)	.20	.15	.08
24	Mariners Checklist	.06	.05	.02
25	Greg Vaughn(FC)	1.00	.70	.40
26	Xavier Hernandez(FC)	.15	.11	.06
27	Jason Grimsley(FC)	.25	.20	.10
28	Eric Anthony(FC)	.50	.40	.20
29	Expos Checklist	.06	.05	.02
30	David Wells	.06	.05	.02
31	Hal Morris(FC)	1.25	.90	.50
32	Royals Checklist	.25	.20	.10
33	Kelly Mann(FC)	.15	.11	.06
34	Nolan Ryan (Special Card)	1.25	.90	.50
35	Scott Service(FC)	.20	.15	.08
36	Athletics Checklist	.06	.05	.02
37	Tino Martinez(FC)	1.00	.70	.40
38	Chili Davis	.09	.07	.04
39	Scott Sanderson	.06	.05	.02
40	Giants Checklist	.06	.05	.02
41	Tigers Checklist	.06	.05	.02
42	Scott Coolbaugh(FC)	.20	.15	.08
43	Jose Cano(FC)	.15	.11	.06
44	Jose Vizcaino(FC)	.30	.25	.12
45	Bob Hamelin(FC)	.20	.15	.08
46	Jose Offerman(FC)	.50	.40	.20
47	Kevin Blankenship	.10	.08	.04
48	Twins Checklist	.06	.05	.02
49	Tommy Greene(FC)	.50	.40	.20
50	Will Clark (Special Card)	.40	.30	.15
51	Rob Nelson(FC)	.09	.07	.04
52	Chris Hammond(FC)	.30	.25	.12
53	Indians Checklist	.06	.05	.02
54a	Ben McDonald (Orioles Logo)(FC)	15.00	11.00	6.00
54b	Ben McDonald (Rookies Logo)(FC)	2.00	1.50	.80
55	Andy Benes(FC)	1.00	.70	.40
56	John Olerud(FC)	1.50	1.25	.60
57	Red Sox Checklist	.06	.05	.02
58	Tony Armas	.06	.05	.02
59	George Canale(FC)	.20	.15	.08
60a	Orioles Checklist (Jamie Weston)	4.00	3.00	1.50
60b	Orioles Checklist (Mickey Weston)	.08	.06	.03
61	Mike Stanton(FC)	.15	.11	.06
62	Mets Checklist	.06	.05	.02
63	Kent Mercker(FC)	.50	.40	.20
64	Francisco Cabrera(FC)	.30	.25	.20
65	Steve Avery(FC)	3.00	2.25	1.25
66	Jose Canseco	.90	.70	.50
67	Matt Merullo(FC)	.15	.11	.06
68	Cardinals Checklist	.06	.05	.02
69	Ron Karkovice	.06	.05	.02
70	Kevin Maas(FC)	.80	.60	.30
71	Dennis Cook	.10	.08	.04
72	Juan Gonzalez(FC)	9.00	6.75	3.50

		MT	NR MT	EX
73	Cubs Checklist	.06	.05	.02
74	Dean Palmer(FC)	3.00	2.25	1.25
75	Bo Jackson (Special Card)	.60	.45	.25
76	Rob Richie(FC)	.20	.15	.08
77	Bobby Rose(FC)	.20	.15	.08
78	Brian DuBois(FC)	.15	.11	.06
79	White Sox Checklist	.06	.05	.02
80	Gene Nelson	.06	.05	.02
81	Bob McClure	.06	.05	.02
82	Rangers Checklist	.06	.05	.02
83	Greg Minton	.06	.05	.02
84	Braves Checklist	.06	.05	.02
85	Willie Fraser	.06	.05	.02
86	Neal Heaton	.06	.05	.02
87	Kevin Tapani(FC)	.60	.45	.25
88	Astros Checklist	.06	.05	.02
89a	Jim Gott (Incorrect Photo)	5.00	3.75	2.00
89b	Jim Gott (Photo of Gott)	.10	.08	.04
90	Lance Johnson(FC)	.09	.07	.04
91	Brewers Checklist	.06	.05	.02
92	Jeff Parrett	.08	.06	.03
93	Julio Machado(FC)	.25	.20	.10
94	Ron Jones	.10	.08	.04
95	Blue Jays Checklist	.06	.05	.02
96	Jerry Reuss	.06	.05	.02
97	Brian Fisher	.06	.05	.02
98	Kevin Ritz(FC)	.25	.20	.10
99	Reds Checklist	.06	.05	.02
100	Checklist 1-100	.06	.05	.02
101	Gerald Perry	.06	.05	.02
102	Kevin Appier(FC)	.40	.30	.15
103	Julio Franco	.10	.08	.04
104	Craig Biggio	.20	.15	.08
105	Bo Jackson	1.00	.70	.40
106	Junior Felix	.30	.25	.12
107	Mike Harkey(FC)	.30	.25	.12
108	Fred McGriff	.25	.20	.10
109	Rick Sutcliffe	.08	.06	.03
110	Pete O'Brien	.08	.06	.03
111	Kelly Gruber	.10	.08	.04
112	Pat Borders	.10	.08	.04
113	Dwight Evans	.10	.08	.04
114	Dwight Gooden	.20	.15	.08
115	Kevin Batiste(FC)	.15	.11	.06
116	Eric Davis	.25	.20	.10
117	Kevin Mitchell	.40	.30	.15
118	Ron Oester	.06	.05	.02
119	Brett Butler	.09	.07	.04
120	Danny Jackson	.06	.05	.02
121	Tommy Gregg	.06	.05	.02
122	Ken Caminiti	.08	.06	.03
123	Kevin Brown	.10	.08	.04
124	George Brett	.15	.11	.06
125	Mike Scott	.10	.08	.04
126	Cory Snyder	.10	.08	.04
127	George Bell	.15	.11	.06
128	Mark Grace	.50	.40	.20
129	Devon White	.10	.08	.04
130	Tony Fernandez	.15	.11	.06
131	Dan Aase	.06	.05	.02
132	Rance Mulliniks	.06	.05	.02
133	Marty Barrett	.08	.06	.03
134	Nelson Liriano	.07	.05	.03
135	Mark Carreon(FC)	.15	.11	.06
136	Candy Maldonado	.06	.05	.02
137	Tim Birtsas	.06	.05	.02
138	Tom Brookens	.06	.05	.02
139	John Franco	.08	.06	.03
140	Mike LaCoss	.06	.05	.02
141	Jeff Treadway	.07	.05	.03
142	Pat Tabler	.07	.05	.03
143	Darrell Evans	.06	.05	.02
144	Rafael Ramirez	.06	.05	.02
145	Oddibe McDowell	.07	.05	.04
146	Brian Downing	.09	.07	.04
147	Curtis Wilkerson	.06	.05	.02
148	Ernie Whitt	.07	.05	.02
149	Bill Schroeder	.06	.05	.02
150	Domingo Ramos	.06	.05	.02
151	Rick Honeycutt	.06	.05	.02
152	Don Slaught	.06	.05	.02
153	Mitch Webster	.06	.05	.02
154	Tony Phillips	.07	.05	.02
155	Paul Kilgus	.06	.05	.02
156	Ken Griffey, Jr.	4.00	3.00	1.50
157	Gary Sheffield	.80	.60	.30
158	Wally Backman	.06	.05	.02
159	B.J. Surhoff	.08	.06	.03
160	Louie Meadows	.08	.06	.03
161	Paul O'Neill	.09	.07	.04
162	Jeff McKnight(FC)	.15	.11	.06

		MT	NR MT	EX
163	Alvaro Espinoza(FC)	.15	.11	.06
164	*Scott Scudder*(FC)	.20	.15	.08
165	Jeff Reed	.06	.05	.02
166	Gregg Jefferies	.30	.25	.12
167	Barry Larkin	.15	.11	.06
168	Gary Carter	.10	.08	.04
169	Robby Thompson	.09	.07	.04
170	Rolando Roomes	.15	.11	.06
171	Mark McGwire	.50	.40	.20
172	Steve Sax	.10	.08	.04
173	Mark Williamson	.06	.05	.02
174	Mitch Williams	.15	.11	.06
175	Brian Holton	.06	.05	.02
176	Rob Deer	.08	.06	.03
177	Tim Raines	.12	.09	.05
178	Mike Felder	.06	.05	.02
179	Harold Reynolds	.10	.08	.04
180	Terry Francona	.06	.05	.02
181	Chris Sabo	.15	.11	.06
182	Darryl Strawberry	.30	.25	.14
183	Willie Randolph	.10	.08	.04
184	Billy Ripken	.06	.05	.02
185	Mackey Sasser	.08	.06	.03
186	Todd Benzinger	.08	.06	.03
187	Kevin Elster	.07	.05	.03
188	Jose Uribe	.06	.05	.02
189	Tom Browning	.10	.08	.04
190	Keith Miller	.09	.07	.04
191	Don Mattingly	.60	.45	.25
192	Dave Parker	.12	.09	.05
193	Roberto Kelly	.12	.09	.05
194	Phil Bradley	.09	.07	.04
195	Ron Hassey	.07	.05	.03
196	Gerald Young	.06	.05	.02
197	Hubie Brooks	.08	.06	.03
198	Bill Doran	.09	.07	.04
199	Al Newman	.06	.05	.02
200	Checklist 101-200	.06	.05	.02
201	Terry Puhl	.06	.05	.02
202	Frank DiPino	.06	.05	.02
203	Jim Clancy	.06	.05	.02
204	Bob Ojeda	.07	.05	.03
205	Alex Trevino	.06	.05	.02
206	Dave Henderson	.10	.08	.04
207	Henry Cotto	.06	.05	.02
208	Rafael Belliard	.06	.05	.02
209	Stan Javier	.07	.05	.03
210	Jerry Reed	.06	.05	.02
211	Doug Dascenzo	.08	.06	.03
212	Andres Thomas	.07	.05	.03
213	Greg Maddux	.20	.15	.08
214	Mike Schooler	.09	.07	.04
215	Lonnie Smith	.09	.07	.04
216	Jose Rijo	.10	.08	.04
217	Greg Gagne	.08	.06	.03
218	Jim Gantner	.08	.06	.03
219	Allan Anderson	.09	.07	.04
220	Rick Mahler	.06	.05	.02
221	Jim Deshaies	.09	.07	.04
222	Keith Hernandez	.10	.08	.04
223	Vince Coleman	.12	.09	.05
224	David Cone	.20	.15	.08
225	Ozzie Smith	.20	.15	.08
226	Matt Nokes	.10	.08	.04
227	Barry Bonds	.10	.08	.04
228	Felix Jose	.10	.08	.04
229	Dennis Powell	.06	.05	.02
230	Mike Gallego	.06	.05	.02
231	Shawon Dunston	.09	.07	.04
232	Ron Gant	.10	.08	.04
233	*Omar Vizquel*	.10	.08	.04
234	Derek Lilliquist	.10	.08	.04
235	Erik Hanson	.10	.08	.04
236	Kirby Puckett	.35	.25	.14
237	*Bill Spiers*	.25	.20	.10
238	Dan Gladden	.07	.05	.03
239	Bryan Clutterbuck(FC)	.07	.05	.03
240	John Moses	.06	.05	.02
241	Ron Darling	.12	.09	.05
242	Joe Magrane	.12	.09	.05
243	Dave Magadan	.09	.07	.03
244	Pedro Guererro	.15	.11	.06
245	Glenn Davis	.10	.08	.04
246	Terry Steinbach	.12	.09	.05
247	Fred Lynn	.09	.07	.04
248	Gary Redus	.06	.05	.02
249	Kenny Williams	.06	.05	.02
250	Sid Bream	.06	.05	.02
251	Bob Welch	.08	.06	.03
252	Bill Buckner	.07	.05	.03
253	Carney Lansford	.09	.07	.04

		MT	NR MT	EX
254	Paul Molitor	.12	.09	.05
255	Jose DeJesus	.15	.11	.06
256	Orel Hershiser	.25	.20	.10
257	Tom Brunansky	.10	.08	.04
258	Mike Davis	.06	.05	.02
259	Jeff Ballard	.12	.09	.05
260	Scott Terry	.09	.07	.04
261	Sid Fernandez	.10	.08	.04
262	Mike Marshall	.08	.06	.03
263	Howard Johnson	.20	.15	.08
264	Kirk Gibson	.09	.07	.04
265	Kevin McReynolds	.15	.11	.06
266	Cal Ripken, Jr.	.30	.25	.12
267	Ozzie Guillen	.07	.05	.03
268	Jim Traber	.06	.05	.02
269	Bobby Thigpen	.09	.07	.04
270	Joe Orsulak	.06	.05	.02
271	Bob Boone	.09	.07	.04
272	Dave Stewart	.09	.07	.04
273	Tim Wallach	.09	.07	.04
274	Luis Aquino	.06	.05	.02
275	Mike Moore	.10	.08	.04
276	Tony Pena	.08	.06	.03
277	Eddie Murray	.15	.11	.06
278	Milt Thompson	.07	.05	.03
279	Alejandro Pena	.06	.05	.02
280	Ken Dayley	.06	.05	.02
281	Carmen Castillo	.06	.05	.02
282	Tom Henke	.08	.06	.03
283	Mickey Hatcher	.06	.05	.02
284	Roy Smith(FC)	.06	.05	.02
285	Manny Lee	.06	.05	.02
286	Dan Pasqua	.07	.05	.02
287	Larry Sheets	.06	.05	.02
288	Garry Templeton	.07	.05	.03
289	Eddie Williams	.07	.05	.03
290	Brady Anderson	.07	.05	.03
291	Spike Owen	.07	.05	.03
292	Storm Davis	.09	.07	.04
293	Chris Bosio	.09	.07	.04
294	Jim Eisenreich	.07	.05	.03
295	Don August	.07	.05	.03
296	Jeff Hamilton	.07	.05	.03
297	Mickey Tettleton	.10	.08	.04
298	Mike Scioscia	.09	.07	.04
299	Kevin Hickey(FC)	.06	.05	.02
300	Checklist 201-300	.06	.05	.02
301	Shawn Abner	.06	.05	.02
302	Kevin Bass	.08	.06	.03
303	Bip Roberts(FC)	.08	.06	.03
304	Joe Girardi	.10	.08	.04
305	Danny Darwin	.06	.05	.02
306	Mike Heath	.06	.05	.02
307	Mike Macfarlane	.06	.05	.02
308	Ed Whitson	.08	.06	.03
309	Tracy Jones	.07	.05	.02
310	Scott Fletcher	.07	.05	.02
311	Darnell Coles	.07	.05	.02
312	Mike Brumley	.06	.05	.02
313	Bill Swift	.06	.05	.02
314	Charlie Hough	.07	.05	.03
315	Jim Presley	.08	.06	.03
316	Luis Polonia	.07	.05	.03
317	Mike Morgan	.06	.05	.02
318	Lee Guetterman	.06	.05	.02
319	Jose Oquendo	.08	.06	.03
320	Wayne Tollenson	.06	.05	.02
321	Jody Reed	.07	.05	.03
322	Damon Berryhill	.09	.07	.04
323	Roger Clemens	.40	.30	.15
324	Ryne Sandberg	.30	.25	.12
325	Benito Santiago	.10	.08	.04
326	Bret Saberhagen	.15	.11	.06
327	Lou Whitaker	.10	.08	.04
328	Dave Gallagher	.10	.08	.04
329	Mike Pagliarulo	.07	.05	.03
330	Doyle Alexander	.07	.05	.03
331	Jeffrey Leonard	.09	.07	.04
332	Torey Lovullo	.20	.15	.08
333	Pete Incaviglia	.09	.07	.04
334	Rickey Henderson	.30	.25	.12
335	Rafael Palmeiro	.10	.08	.04
336	Ken Hill	.10	.08	.04
337	Dave Winfield	.12	.09	.05
338	Alfredo Griffin	.07	.05	.03
339	Andy Hawkins	.07	.05	.03
340	Ted Power	.06	.05	.02
341	Steve Wilson	.10	.08	.04
342	Jack Clark	.10	.08	.04
343	Ellis Burks	.25	.20	.10
344	Tony Gwynn	.20	.15	.08

#	Name	MT	NR MT	EX
345	*Jerome Walton*	.25	.20	.10
346	Roberto Alomar	.10	.08	.04
347	Carlos Martinez(FC)	.15	.11	.06
348	Chet Lemon	.07	.05	.03
349	Willie Wilson	.07	.05	.03
350	Greg Walker	.07	.05	.03
351	Tom Bolton	.06	.05	.02
352	German Gonzalez(FC)	.08	.06	.03
353	Harold Baines	.10	.08	.04
354	Mike Greenwell	.30	.25	.12
355	Ruben Sierra	.20	.15	.08
356	Anres Galarraga	.12	.09	.05
357	Andre Dawson	.15	.11	.06
358	*Jeff Brantley*(FC)	.10	.08	.04
359	Mike Bielecki	.08	.06	.03
360	Ken Oberkfell	.06	.05	.02
361	Kurt Stillwell	.07	.05	.03
362	Brian Holman	.09	.07	.04
363	Kevin Seitzer	.12	.09	.05
364	Alvin Davis	.15	.11	.06
365	Tom Gordon	.35	.25	.14
366	Bobby Bonilla	.10	.08	.04
367	Carlton Fisk	.10	.08	.04
368	*Steve Carter*(FC)	.15	.11	.06
369	Joel Skinner	.06	.05	.02
370	John Cangelosi	.06	.05	.02
371	Cecil Espy	.08	.06	.03
372	*Gary Wayne*(FC)	.15	.11	.06
373	Jim Rice	.08	.06	.03
374	*Mike Dyer*(FC)	.15	.11	.06
375	Joe Carter	.12	.09	.05
376	Dwight Smith	.20	.15	.08
377	*John Wetteland*(FC)	.35	.25	.14
378	Ernie Riles	.06	.05	.02
379	Otis Nixon	.06	.05	.02
380	Vance Law	.06	.05	.02
381	Dave Bergman	.06	.05	.02
382	Frank White	.07	.05	.03
383	Scott Bradley	.06	.05	.02
384	Israel Sanchez	.06	.05	.02
385	Gary Pettis	.06	.05	.02
386	Donn Pall(FC)	.06	.05	.02
387	John Smiley	.10	.08	.04
388	Tom Candiotti	.07	.05	.03
389	Junior Ortiz	.06	.05	.02
390	Steve Lyons	.06	.05	.02
391	Brian Harper	.06	.05	.02
392	Fred Manrique	.06	.05	.02
393	Lee Smith	.08	.06	.03
394	Jeff Kunkel	.06	.05	.02
395	Claudell Washington	.08	.06	.03
396	John Tudor	.07	.05	.03
397	Terry Kennedy	.07	.05	.03
398	Lloyd McClendon	.09	.07	.04
399	Craig Lefferts	.06	.05	.02
400	Checklist 301-400	.06	.05	.02
401	Keith Moreland	.06	.05	.02
402	Rich Gedman	.07	.05	.03
403	Jeff Robinson	.07	.05	.03
404	Randy Ready	.06	.05	.02
405	Rick Cerone	.06	.05	.02
406	Jeff Blauser	.07	.05	.03
407	Larry Andersen	.06	.05	.02
408	Joe Boever	.08	.06	.03
409	Felix Fermin	.06	.05	.02
410	Glenn Wilson	.06	.05	.02
411	Rex Hudler	.06	.05	.02
412	Mark Grant	.06	.05	.02
413	Dennis Martinez	.08	.06	.03
414	Darrin Jackson	.06	.05	.02
415	Mike Aldrete	.06	.05	.02
416	Roger McDowell	.09	.07	.04
417	Jeff Reardon	.10	.08	.04
418	Darren Daulton	.06	.05	.02
419	Tim Laudner	.08	.06	.03
420	Don Carman	.07	.05	.03
421	Lloyd Moseby	.09	.07	.04
422	Doug Drabek	.10	.08	.04
423	Lenny Harris	.09	.07	.04
424	Jose Lind	.07	.05	.03
425	*Dave Johnson*(FC)	.20	.15	.08
426	Jerry Browne	.09	.07	.04
427	*Eric Yelding*(FC)	.12	.09	.05
428	Brad Komminsk(FC)	.06	.05	.02
429	Jody Davis	.06	.05	.02
430	Mariano Duncan(FC)	.09	.07	.04
431	Mark Davis	.12	.09	.05
432	Nelson Santovenia	.10	.08	.04
433	Bruce Hurst	.10	.08	.04
434	*Jeff Huson*(FC)	.25	.20	.10
435	Chris James	.09	.07	.04

#	Name	MT	NR MT	EX
436	*Mark Guthrie*(FC)	.15	.11	.06
437	Charlie Hayes(FC)	.10	.08	.04
438	Shane Rawley	.08	.06	.03
439	Dickie Thon	.06	.05	.02
440	Juan Berenguer	.06	.05	.02
441	Kevin Romine	.06	.05	.02
442	Bill Landrum	.09	.07	.04
443	Todd Frohwirth	.07	.05	.03
444	Craig Worthington	.10	.08	.04
445	Fernando Valenzuela	.09	.07	.04
446	Joey Belle(FC)	2.00	1.50	.80
447	Ed Whited(FC)	.15	.11	.06
448	Dave Smith	.09	.07	.04
449	Dave Clark	.07	.05	.03
450	Juan Agosto	.06	.05	.02
451	Dave Valle	.06	.05	.02
452	Kent Hrbek	.15	.11	.06
453	Von Hayes	.10	.08	.04
454	Gary Gaetti	.15	.11	.06
455	Greg Briley	.20	.15	.08
456	Glenn Braggs	.08	.06	.03
457	Kirt Manwaring	.10	.08	.04
458	Mel Hall	.07	.05	.03
459	Brook Jacoby	.08	.06	.03
460	Pat Sheridan	.06	.05	.02
461	Rob Murphy	.06	.05	.02
462	Jimmy Key	.10	.08	.04
463	Nick Esasky	.10	.08	.04
464	Rob Ducey	.09	.07	.04
465	Carlos Quintana	.09	.07	.04
466	*Larry Walker*(FC)	2.00	1.50	.80
467	Todd Worrell	.10	.08	.04
468	Kevin Gross	.09	.07	.04
469	Terry Pendleton	.09	.07	.04
470	Dave Martinez	.07	.05	.02
471	Gene Larkin	.06	.05	.02
472	Len Dykstra	.09	.07	.04
473	Barry Lyons	.06	.05	.02
474	Terry Mulholland(FC)	.10	.08	.04
475	*Chip Hale*(FC)	.15	.11	.06
476	Jesse Barfield	.08	.06	.03
477	Dan Plesac	.09	.07	.04
478a	Scott Garrelts (Photo actually Bill Bathe)	3.00	2.25	1.25
478b	Scott Garrelts (Correct photo)	.10	.08	.04
479	Dave Righetti	.10	.08	.04
480	Gus Polidor(FC)	.06	.05	.02
481	Mookie Wilson	.09	.07	.04
482	Luis Rivera	.06	.05	.02
483	Mike Flanagan	.07	.05	.03
484	Dennis "Oil Can" Boyd	.07	.05	.03
485	John Cerutti	.07	.05	.03
486	John Costello	.07	.05	.03
487	Pascual Perez	.07	.05	.03
488	Tommy Herr	.09	.07	.04
489	Tom Foley	.06	.05	.02
490	Curt Ford	.06	.05	.02
491	Steve Lake	.06	.05	.02
492	Tim Teufel	.06	.05	.02
493	Randy Bush	.06	.05	.02
494	Mike Jackson	.06	.05	.02
495	Steve Jeltz	.06	.05	.02
496	Paul Gibson	.08	.06	.03
497	Steve Balboni	.06	.05	.02
498	Bud Black	.06	.05	.02
499	Dale Sveum	.06	.05	.02
500	Checklist 401-500	.06	.05	.02
501	Timmy Jones	.06	.05	.02
502	Mark Portugal	.06	.05	.02
503	Ivan Calderon	.07	.05	.03
504	Rick Rhoden	.06	.05	.02
505	Willie McGee	.09	.07	.04
506	Kirk McCaskill	.08	.06	.03
507	Dave LaPoint	.07	.05	.03
508	Jay Howell	.10	.08	.04
509	Johnny Ray	.08	.06	.03
510	Dave Anderson	.06	.05	.02
511	Chuck Crim	.06	.05	.02
512	Joe Hesketh	.06	.05	.02
513	Dennis Eckersley	.10	.08	.04
514	Greg Brock	.08	.06	.03
515	Tim Burke	.08	.06	.03
516	Frank Tanana	.07	.05	.03
517	Jay Bell	.07	.05	.03
518	Guillermo Hernandez	.07	.05	.03
519	Randy Kramer(FC)	.08	.06	.03
520	Charles Hudson	.06	.05	.02
521	Jim Corsi(FC)	.08	.06	.03
522	Steve Rosenberg	.08	.06	.03
523	Cris Carpenter	.10	.08	.04
524	*Matt Winters*(FC)	.12	.09	.05

		MT	NR MT	EX
525	Melido Perez	.08	.06	.03
526	Chris Gwynn	.08	.06	.03
527	Bert Blyleven	.09	.07	.04
528	Chuck Cary	.07	.05	.03
529	Daryl Boston	.06	.05	.02
530	Dale Mohorcic	.06	.05	.02
531	Geronimo Berroa(FC)	.09	.07	.04
532	Edgar Martinez	.09	.07	.04
533	Dale Murphy	.15	.11	.06
534	Jay Buhner	.09	.07	.04
535	John Smoltz	.15	.11	.06
536	Andy Van Slyke	.15	.11	.06
537	Mike Henneman	.09	.07	.04
538	Miguel Garcia(FC)	.07	.05	.03
539	Frank Williams	.06	.05	.02
540	R.J. Reynolds	.06	.05	.02
541	Shawn Hillegas	.06	.05	.02
542	Walt Weiss	.10	.08	.04
543	Greg Hibbard(FC)	.15	.11	.06
544	Nolan Ryan	1.00	.70	.40
545	Todd Zeile	.80	.60	.30
546	Hensley Meulens	.20	.15	.08
547	Tim Belcher	.10	.08	.04
548	Mike Witt	.08	.06	.03
549	Greg Cadaret	.06	.05	.02
550	Franklin Stubbs	.06	.05	.02
551	Tony Castillo(FC)	.12	.09	.05
552	Jeff Robinson	.08	.06	.03
553	Steve Olin(FC)	.12	.09	.05
554	Alan Trammell	.10	.08	.04
555	Wade Boggs	.50	.40	.20
556	Will Clark	.60	.45	.25
557	Jeff King(FC)	.10	.08	.04
558	Mike Fitzgerald	.06	.05	.02
559	Ken Howell	.06	.05	.02
560	Bob Kipper	.06	.05	.02
561	Scott Bankhead	.09	.07	.04
562a	Jeff Innis (Photo actually David West)(FC)	3.00	2.25	1.25
562b	Jeff Innis (Corrected)(FC)	.20	.15	.08
563	Randy Johnson	.10	.08	.04
564	Wally Whithurst	.10	.08	.04
565	Gene Harris(FC)	.10	.08	.04
566	Norm Charlton	.09	.07	.04
567	Robin Yount	.40	.30	.15
568	Joe Oliver(FC)	.35	.25	.14
569	Mark Parent	.07	.05	.03
570	John Farrell	.07	.05	.03
571	Tom Glavine	.10	.08	.04
572	Rod Nichols(FC)	.06	.05	.02
573	Jack Morris	.09	.07	.04
574	Greg Swindell	.12	.09	.05
575	Steve Searcy(FC)	.09	.07	.04
576	Ricky Jordan	.20	.15	.08
577	Matt Williams	.35	.25	.14
578	Mike LaValliere	.07	.05	.03
579	Bryn Smith	.08	.06	.03
580	Bruce Ruffin	.06	.05	.02
581	Randy Myers	.08	.06	.03
582	Rick Wrona(FC)	.15	.11	.06
583	Juan Samuel	.09	.07	.04
584	Les Lancaster	.07	.05	.03
585	Jeff Musselman	.07	.05	.03
586	Rob Dibble	.09	.07	.04
587	Eric Show	.07	.05	.03
588	Jesse Orosco	.06	.05	.02
589	Herm Winningham	.06	.05	.02
590	Andy Allanson	.06	.05	.02
591	Dion James	.08	.06	.03
592	Carmelo Martinez	.08	.06	.03
593	Luis Quinones(FC)	.08	.06	.03
594	Dennis Rasmussen	.06	.05	.02
595	Rich Yett	.08	.06	.03
596	Bob Walk	.07	.05	.03
597	Andy McGaffigan	.07	.05	.03
598	Billy Hatcher	.06	.05	.02
599	Bob Knepper	.06	.05	.02
600	Checklist 501-600	.10	.08	.04
601	Joey Cora	.20	.15	.08
602	Steve Finley	.10	.08	.04
603	Kal Daniels	.30	.25	.12
604	Gregg Olson	.09	.07	.04
605	Dave Steib	.15	.11	.06
606	Kenny Rogers(FC)	.06	.05	.02
607	Zane Smith	.15	.11	.06
608	Bob Geren(FC)	.10	.08	.04
609	Chad Kreuter	.06	.05	.02
610	Mike Smithson	.15	.11	.06
611	Jeff Wetherby(FC)	.15	.11	.06
612	Gary Mielke(FC)	.08	.06	.03
613	Pete Smith			

		MT	NR MT	EX
614	Jack Daugherty(FC)	.15	.11	.06
615	Lance McCullers	.08	.06	.03
616	Don Robinson	.06	.05	.02
617	Jose Guzman	.06	.05	.02
618	Steve Bedrosian	.08	.06	.03
619	Jamie Moyer	.06	.05	.02
620	Atlee Hammaker	.06	.05	.02
621	Rick Luecken(FC)	.15	.11	.06
622	Greg W. Harris	.09	.07	.04
623	Pete Harnisch	.10	.08	.04
624	Jerald Clark	.10	.08	.04
625	Jack McDowell	.07	.05	.03
626	Frank Viola	.12	.09	.05
627	Ted Higuera	.09	.07	.04
628	Marty Pevey(FC)	.15	.11	.06
629	Bill Wegman	.06	.05	.02
630	Eric Plunk	.06	.05	.02
631	Drew Hall	.06	.05	.02
632	Doug Jones	.08	.06	.03
633	Geno Petralli	.06	.05	.02
634	Jose Alvarez	.06	.05	.02
635	Bob Milacki(FC)	.10	.08	.04
636	Bobby Witt	.07	.05	.03
637	Trevor Wilson	.08	.06	.03
638	Jeff Russell	.08	.06	.03
639	Mike Krukow	.07	.05	.03
640	Rick Leach	.06	.05	.02
641	Dave Schmidt	.06	.05	.02
642	Terry Leach	.06	.05	.02
643	Calvin Schiraldi	.06	.05	.02
644	Bob Melvin	.06	.05	.02
645	Jim Abbott	.40	.30	.15
646	Jaime Navarro(FC)	.30	.25	.12
647	Mark Langston	.10	.08	.04
648	Juan Nieves	.08	.06	.03
649	Damaso Garcia	.06	.05	.02
650	Charlie O'Brien	.06	.05	.02
651	Eric King	.06	.05	.02
652	Mike Boddicker	.08	.06	.03
653	Duan Ward	.07	.05	.03
654	Bob Stanley	.06	.05	.02
655	Sandy Alomar, Jr.	.30	.25	.12
656	Danny Tartabull	.10	.08	.04
657	Randy McCament	.15	.11	.06
658	Charlie Leibrandt	.07	.05	.03
659	Dan Quisenberry	.07	.05	.03
660	Paul Assenmacher	.06	.05	.02
661	Walt Terrell	.07	.05	.03
662	Tim Leary	.07	.05	.03
663	Randy Milligan	.08	.06	.03
664	Bo Diaz	.06	.05	.02
665	Mark Lemke	.07	.05	.03
666	Jose Gonzalez	.08	.06	.03
667	Chuck Finley	.07	.05	.03
668	John Kruk	.08	.06	.03
669	Dick Schofield	.07	.05	.03
670	Tim Crews	.06	.05	.02
671	John Dopson	.09	.07	.04
672	John Orton(FC)	.15	.11	.06
673	Eric Hetzel(FC)	.10	.08	.04
674	Lance Parrish	.08	.06	.03
675	Ramon Martinez	.50	.40	.20
676	Mark Gubicza	.10	.08	.04
677	Greg Litton	.20	.15	.08
678	Greg Mathews	.07	.05	.03
679	Dave Dravecky	.07	.05	.03
680	Steve Farr	.07	.05	.03
681	Mike Devereaux	.09	.07	.04
682	Ken Griffey, Sr.	.08	.06	.03
683a	Mickey Weston (Jamie)(FC)	4.00	3.00	1.50
683b	Mickey Weston (corrected)(FC)	.30	.25	.12
684	Jack Armstrong	.07	.05	.03
685	Steve Buechele	.07	.05	.03
686	Bryan Harvey	.07	.05	.03
687	Lance Blankenship	.09	.07	.04
688	Dante Bichette	.09	.07	.04
689	Todd Burns	.09	.07	.04
690	Dan Petry	.06	.05	.02
691	Kent Anderson(FC)	.15	.11	.06
692	Todd Stottlemyre	.08	.06	.03
693	Wally Joyner	.15	.11	.06
694	Mike Rochford(FC)	.10	.08	.04
695	Floyd Bannister	.07	.05	.03
696	Rick Reuschel	.09	.07	.04
697	Jose DeLeon	.09	.07	.04
698	Jeff Montgomery	.08	.06	.03
699	Jeff Montgomery	.08	.06	.03
700a	Checklist 601-700 (Jamie Weston)	4.00	3.00	1.50
700b	Checklist 601-700 (Mickey Weston)	.10	.08	.04

		MT	NR MT	EX
701	Jim Gott	.10	.08	.04
702	"Rookie Threats" (Delino DeShields, Larry			
	Walker, Marquis Grissom)	.60	.45	.25
703	Alejandro Pena	.10	.08	.04
704	Willie Randolph	.12	.09	.05
705	Tim Leary	.10	.08	.04
706	Chuck McElroy(FC)	.20	.15	.08
707	Gerald Perry	.10	.08	.04
708	Tom Brunansky	.12	.09	.05
709	John Franco	.15	.11	.06
710	Mark Davis	.10	.08	.04
711	Dave Justice(FC)	6.00	4.50	2.50
712	Storm Davis	.10	.08	.04
713	Scott Ruskin(FC)	.20	.15	.08
714	Glenn Braggs	.10	.08	.04
715	Kevin Bearse(FC)	.20	.15	.08
716	Jose Nunez(FC)	.15	.11	.06
717	Tim Layana(FC)	.20	.15	.08
718	Greg Myers(FC)	.12	.09	.05
719	Pete O'Brien	.10	.08	.04
720	John Candelaria	.10	.08	.04
721	Craig Grebeck(FC)	.25	.20	.10
722	Shawn Boskie(FC)	.30	.25	.12
723	Jim Leyritz(FC)	.20	.15	.08
724	Bill Sampen(FC)	.30	.25	.12
725	Scott Radinsky(FC)	.35	.25	.14
726	Todd Hundley(FC)	.30	.25	.12
727	Scott Hemond(FC)	.20	.15	.08
728	Lenny Webster(FC)	.25	.20	.10
729	Jeff Reardon	.12	.09	.05
730	Mitch Webster	.10	.08	.04
731	Brian Bohanon(FC)	.25	.20	.10
732	Rick Parker(FC)	.20	.15	.08
733	Terry Shumpert(FC)	.25	.20	.10
734a	6th No-Hitter (Nolan Ryan) (with 300 win			
	stripe)	2.00	1.50	.80
734b	6th No-Hitter (Nolan Ryan) (without			
	stripe)	8.00	6.00	3.25
735	John Burkett(FC)	.40	.30	.15
736	Derrick May(FC)	.80	.60	.30
737	Carlos Baerga(FC)	3.00	2.25	1.25
738	Greg Smith(FC)	.15	.11	.06
739	Joe Kraemer(FC)	.15	.11	.06
740	Scott Sanderson	.10	.08	.04
741	Hector Villanueva(FC)	.30	.25	.12
742	Mike Fetters(FC)	.25	.20	.10
743	Mark Gardner(FC)	.30	.25	.12
744	Matt Nokes	.10	.08	.04
745	Dave Winfield	.20	.15	.08
746	Delino DeShields(FC)	1.00	.70	.40
747	Dann Howitt(FC)	.20	.15	.08
748	Tony Pena	.12	.09	.05
749	Oil Can Boyd	.12	.09	.05
750	Mike Benjamin(FC)	.25	.20	.10
751	Alex Cole(FC)	.80	.60	.30
752	Eric Gunderson(FC)	.20	.15	.08
753	Howard Farmer(FC)	.25	.20	.10
754	Joe Carter	.15	.11	.06
755	Ray Lankford(FC)	2.50	2.00	1.00
756	Sandy Alomar,Jr.	.40	.30	.15
757	Alex Sanchez(FC)	.15	.11	.06
758	Nick Esasky	.10	.08	.04
759	Stan Belinda(FC)	.20	.15	.08
760	Jim Presley	.10	.08	.04
761	Gary DiSarcina(FC)	.20	.15	.08
762	Wayne Edwards(FC)	.20	.15	.08
763	Pat Combs(FC)	.20	.15	.08
764	Mickey Pina(FC)	.20	.15	.08
765	Wilson Alvarez(FC)	.50	.40	.20
766	Dave Parker	.15	.11	.06
767	Mike Blowers(FC)	.20	.15	.08
768	Tony Phillips	.10	.08	.04
769	Pascual Perez	.10	.08	.04
770	Gary Pettis	.10	.08	.04
771	Fred Lynn	.10	.08	.04
772	Mel Rojas(FC)	.20	.15	.08
773	David Segui(FC)	.30	.25	.12
774	Gary Carter	.15	.11	.06
775	Rafael Valdez(FC)	.15	.11	.06
776	Glenallen Hill(FC)	.15	.11	.06
777	Keith Hernandez	.12	.09	.05
778	Billy Hatcher	.12	.09	.05
779	Marty Clary(FC)	.10	.08	.04
780	Candy Maldonado	.12	.09	.05
781	Mike Marshall	.10	.08	.04
782	Billy Jo Robidoux(FC)	.10	.08	.04
783	Mark Langston	.12	.09	.05
784	Paul Sorrento(FC)	.25	.20	.10
785	Dave Hollins(FC)	1.50	1.25	.60
786	Cecil Fielder	.50	.40	.20
787	Matt Young	.10	.08	.04

		MT	NR MT	EX
788	Jeff Huson	.15	.11	.06
789	Lloyd Moseby	.12	.09	.05
790	Ron Kittle	.12	.09	.05
791	Hubie Brooks	.12	.09	.05
792	Craig Lefferts	.10	.08	.04
793	Kevin Bass	.10	.08	.04
794	Bryn Smith	.10	.08	.04
795	Juan Samuel	.12	.09	.05
796	Sam Horn(FC)	.15	.11	.06
797	Randy Myers	.12	.09	.05
798	Chris James	.10	.08	.04
799	Bill Gullickson	.10	.08	.04
800	Checklist 701-800	.10	.08	.04

1991 Upper Deck

115 rookies are included among the first 700 cards in the 1991 Upper Deck set. A 100-card high # series was once again planned for release in July or August. The 1991 Upper Deck cards feature high quality white stock and color photos on both the front and backs of the cards. A nine-card "Baseball Heroes" bonus set honoring Nolan Ryan, is among the many insert specials in the 1991 Upper Deck set. Others include a card of Chicago Bulls superstar Michael Jordan. Along with the Ryan bonus cards, 2,500 limited-edition cards personally autographed and numbered by Ryan will be randomly inserted. Upper Deck cards are packaged in tamper-proof foil packs. Each pack contains 15 cards and a 3-D team logo hologram sticker. The 1991 hologram stickers are full size.

		MT	NR MT	EX
Complete Set: 1-700		15.00	11.00	6.00
Common Player: 1-700		.05	.04	.02
Complete Set: 1-800		40.00	30.00	15.00
Common Player: 701-800		.10	.08	.04
1	Star Rookie Checklist	.05	.04	.02
2	Star Rookie (Phil Plantier)(FC)	1.00	.70	.40
3	Star Rookie (D.J. Dozier)(FC)	.40	.30	.15
4	Star Rookie (Dave Hansen)(FC)	.25	.20	.10
5	Star Rookie (Maurice Vaughn)(FC)	.70	.50	.30
6	Star Rookie (Leo Gomez)(FC)	.60	.45	.25
7	Star Rookie (Scott Aldred)(FC)	.25	.20	.10
8	Star Rookie (Scott Chiamparino)(FC)			
		.30	.25	.12
9	Star Rookie (Lance Dickson)(FC)	.30	.25	.12
10	Star Rookie (Sean Berry)(FC)	.20	.15	.08
11	Star Rookie (Bernie Williams)(FC)	.70	.50	.30
12	Star Rookie (Brian Barnes)(FC)	.30	.25	.12
13	Star Rookie (Narciso Elvira)(FC)	.20	.15	.08
14	Star Rookie (Mike Gardiner)(FC)	.30	.25	.12
15	Star Rookie (Greg Colbrunn)(FC)	.20	.15	.08
16	Star Rookie (Bernard Gilkey)(FC)	.50	.40	.20
17	Star Rookie (Mark Lewis)(FC)	.70	.50	.30
18	Star Rookie (Mickey Morandini)(FC)			
		.15	.11	.06
19	Star Rookie (Charles Nagy)(FC)	.60	.45	.25
20	Star Rookie (Geronimo Pena)(FC)	.25	.20	.10
21	Star Rookie (Henry Rodriguez)(FC)	.50	.40	.20
22	Star Rookie (Scott Cooper)(FC)	.20	.15	.08
23	Star Rookie (Andujar Cedeno)(FC)	.60	.45	.25
24	Star Rookie (Eric Karros)(FC)	2.50	2.00	1.00
25	Star Rookie (Steve Decker)(FC)	.25	.20	.10
26	Star Rookie (Kevin Belcher)(FC)	.20	.15	.08
27	Star Rookie (Jeff Conine)(FC)	.20	.15	.08

#	Player	MT	NR MT	EX
28	Oakland Athletics Checklist	.10	.08	.04
29	Chicago White Sox Checklist	.08	.06	.03
30	Texas Rangers Checklist	.08	.06	.03
31	California Angels Checklist	.08	.06	.03
32	Seattle Mariners Checklist	.10	.08	.04
33	Kansas City Royals Checklist	.10	.08	.04
34	Minnesota Twins Checklist	.08	.06	.03
35	Scott Leius(FC)	.10	.08	.04
36	Neal Heaton	.06	.05	.02
37	*Terry Lee*(FC)	.20	.15	.08
38	Gary Redus	.05	.04	.02
39	Barry Jones	.06	.05	.02
40	Chuck Knoblauch(FC)	1.75	1.25	.70
41	Larry Andersen	.05	.04	.02
43	Darryl Hamilton	.06	.05	.02
44	Toronto Blue Jays Checklist	.08	.06	.03
45	Detroit Tigers Checklist	.10	.08	.04
46	Cleveland Indians Checklist	.08	.06	.03
47	Baltimore Orioles Checklist	.08	.06	.03
48	Milwaukee Brewers Checklist	.08	.06	.03
49	New York Yankees Checklist	.08	.06	.03
50	Top Prospect Checklist	.05	.04	.02
51	Top Prospect (Kyle Abbott)(FC)	.25	.20	.10
52	Top Prospect (Jeff Juden)(FC)	.25	.20	.10
53	Top Prospect *(Todd Van Poppel)*(FC)	1.00	.70	.40
54	Top Prospect (Steve Karsay)(FC)	.40	.30	.15
55	Top Prospect *(Chipper Jones)*(FC)	1.25	.90	.50
56	Top Prospect (Chris Johnson)(FC)	.25	.20	.10
57	Top Prospect *(John Ericks)*(FC)	.25	.20	.10
58	Top Prospect *(Gary Scott)*(FC)	.50	.40	.20
59	Top Prospect (Kiki Jones)(FC)	.50	.40	.20
60	Top Prospect *(Wilfredo Cordero)*(FC)	.80	.60	.30
61	Top Prospect (Royce Clayton)(FC)	.80	.60	.30
62	Top Prospect *(Tim Costo)*(FC)	.30	.25	.12
63	Top Prospect (Roger Salkeld)(FC)	.40	.30	.15
64	Top Prospect *(Brook Fordyce)*(FC)	.25	.20	.10
65	Top Prospect *(Mike Mussina)*(FC)	2.50	2.00	1.00
66	Top Prospect *(Dave Staton)*(FC)	.40	.30	.15
67	Top Prospect *(Mike Lieberthal)*(FC)	.30	.25	.12
68	Top Prospect *(Kurt Miller)*(FC)	.30	.25	.12
69	Top Prospect *(Dan Peltier)*(FC)	.25	.20	.10
70	Top Prospect (Greg Blosser)(FC)	.40	.30	.15
71	Top Prospect *(Reggie Sanders)*(FC)	2.50	2.00	1.00
72	Top Prospect (Brent Mayne)(FC)	.15	.11	.06
73	Top Prospect *(Rico Brogna)*(FC)	.35	.25	.14
74	Top Prospect *(Willie Banks)*(FC)	.40	.30	.15
75	Top Prospect (Len Brutcher)(FC)	.25	.20	.10
76	Top Prospect (Pat Kelly)(FC)	.30	.25	.12
77	Cincinnati Reds Checklist	.08	.06	.03
78	Los Angeles Dodgers Checklist	.08	.06	.03
79	San Francisco Giants Checklist	.08	.06	.03
80	San Diego Padres Checklist	.08	.06	.03
81	Houston Astros Checklist	.08	.06	.03
82	Atlanta Braves Checklist	.10	.08	.04
83	"Fielder's Feat"	.20	.15	.08
84	*Orlando Merced*(FC)	.60	.45	.25
85	Domingo Ramos	.05	.04	.02
86	Tom Bolton	.05	.04	.02
87	*Andres Santana*(FC)	.20	.15	.08
88	John Dopson	.05	.04	.02
89	Kenny Williams	.05	.04	.02
90	Marty Barrett	.06	.05	.02
91	Tom Pagnozzi	.06	.05	.02
92	Carmelo Martinez	.06	.05	.02
93	"Save Master"	.10	.08	.04
94	Pittsburgh Pirates Checklist	.10	.08	.04
95	New York Mets Checklist	.10	.08	.04
96	Montreal Expos Checklist	.08	.06	.03
97	Philadelphia Phillies Checklist	.08	.06	.03
98	St. Louis Cardinals Checklist	.08	.06	.03
99	Chicago Cubs Checklist	.10	.08	.04
100	Checklist 1-100	.05	.04	.02
101	Kevin Elster	.06	.05	.02
102	Tom Brookens	.05	.04	.02
103	Mackey Sasser	.08	.06	.03
104	Felix Fermin	.05	.04	.02
105	Kevin McReynolds	.12	.09	.05
106	Dave Steib	.12	.09	.05
107	Jeffrey Leonard	.06	.05	.02
108	Dave Henderson	.08	.06	.03
109	Sid Bream	.06	.05	.02
110	Henry Cotto	.05	.04	.02
111	Shawon Dunston	.12	.09	.05
112	Mariano Duncan	.08	.06	.03
113	Joe Girardi	.08	.06	.03
114	Billy Hatcher	.08	.06	.03
115	Greg Maddux	.12	.09	.05
116	Jerry Browne	.08	.06	.03
117	Juan Samuel	.08	.06	.03
118	Steve Olin	.06	.05	.02
119	Alfredo Griffin	.06	.05	.02
120	Mitch Webster	.06	.05	.02
121	Joel Skinner	.05	.04	.02
122	Frank Viola	.15	.11	.06
123	Cory Snyder	.10	.08	.04
124	Howard Johnson	.12	.09	.05
125	*Carlos Baerga*	.60	.45	.25
126	Tony Fernandez	.12	.09	.05
127	Dave Stewart	.15	.11	.06
128	Jay Buhner	.08	.06	.03
129	Mike LaValliere	.06	.05	.02
130	Scott Bradley	.05	.04	.02
131	Tony Phillips	.06	.05	.02
132	Ryne Sandberg	.20	.15	.08
133	Paul O'Neill	.08	.06	.03
134	Mark Grace	.15	.11	.06
135	Chris Sabo	.12	.09	.05
136	Ramon Martinez	.20	.15	.08
137	Brook Jacoby	.08	.06	.03
138	Candy Maldonado	.08	.06	.03
139	Mike Scioscia	.08	.06	.03
140	Chris James	.08	.06	.03
141	Craig Worthington	.08	.06	.03
142	Manny Lee	.06	.05	.02
143	Tim Raines	.15	.11	.06
144	Sandy Alomar, Jr.	.15	.11	.06
145	John Olerud	.40	.30	.15
146	*Ozzie Canseco*	.15	.11	.06
147	Pat Borders	.06	.05	.02
148	Harold Reynolds	.10	.08	.04
149	Tom Henke	.08	.06	.03
150	R.J. Reynolds	.05	.04	.02
151	Mike Gallego	.05	.04	.02
152	Bobby Bonilla	.20	.15	.08
153	Terry Steinbach	.06	.05	.02
154	Barry Bonds	.20	.15	.08
155	Jose Canseco	.50	.40	.20
156	Gregg Jefferies	.15	.11	.06
157	Matt Williams	.20	.15	.08
158	Craig Biggio	.08	.06	.03
159	Daryl Boston	.05	.04	.02
160	Ricky Jordan	.08	.06	.03
161	Stan Belinda	.20	.15	.08
162	Ozzie Smith	.10	.08	.04
163	Tom Brunansky	.08	.06	.03
164	Todd Zeile	.30	.25	.12
165	Mike Greenwell	.15	.11	.06
166	Kal Daniels	.10	.08	.04
167	Kent Hrbek	.12	.09	.05
168	Franklin Stubbs	.06	.05	.02
169	Dick Schofield	.05	.04	.02
170	Junior Ortiz	.05	.04	.02
171	*Hector Villanueva*	.20	.15	.08
172	Dennis Eckersley	.15	.11	.06
173	Mitch Williams	.08	.06	.03
174	Mark McGwire	.35	.25	.14
175	Fernando Valenzuela	.10	.08	.04
176	Gary Carter	.10	.08	.04
177	Dave Magadan	.08	.06	.03
178	Robby Thompson	.05	.04	.02
179	Bob Ojeda	.05	.04	.02
180	Ken Caminiti	.06	.05	.02
181	Don Slaught	.05	.04	.02
182	Luis Rivera	.05	.04	.02
183	Jay Bell	.06	.05	.02
184	Jody Reed	.08	.06	.03
185	Wally Backman	.06	.05	.02
186	Dave Martinez	.06	.05	.02
187	Luis Polonia	.06	.05	.02
188	Shane Mack	.06	.05	.02
189	Spike Owen	.05	.04	.02
190	Scott Bailes	.05	.04	.02
191	John Russell	.08	.06	.03
192	Walt Weiss	.06	.05	.02
193	Jose Oquendo	.08	.06	.03
194	Carney Lansford	.08	.06	.03
195	Jeff Huson	.06	.05	.02
196	Keith Miller	.10	.08	.04
197	Eric Yelding	.06	.05	.02
198	Ron Darling	.06	.05	.02
199	John Kruk	.05	.04	.02
200	Checklist 101-200	.05	.04	.02
201	John Shelby	.06	.05	.02
202	Bob Geren	.05	.04	.02
203	Lance McCullers	.06	.05	.02
204	Alvaro Espinoza	.06	.05	.02
205	Mark Salas	.05	.04	.02
206	Mike Pagliarulo	.06	.05	.02

#	Player	MT	NR MT	EX
207	Jose Uribe	.06	.05	.02
208	Jim Deshaies	.06	.05	.02
209	Ron Karkovice	.05	.04	.02
210	Rafael Ramirez	.06	.05	.02
211	Donnie Hill	.05	.04	.02
212	Brian Harper	.08	.06	.03
213	Jack Howell	.05	.04	.02
214	Wes Gardner	.05	.04	.02
215	Tim Burke	.08	.06	.03
216	Doug Jones	.08	.06	.03
217	Hubie Brooks	.10	.08	.04
218	Tom Candiotti	.06	.05	.02
219	Gerald Perry	.06	.05	.02
220	Jose DeLeon	.06	.05	.02
221	Wally Whitehurst	.08	.06	.03
222	*Alan Mills*(FC)	.15	.11	.06
223	Alan Trammell	.12	.09	.05
224	Dwight Gooden	.25	.20	.10
225	*Travis Fryman*(FC)	1.50	1.25	.60
226	Joe Carter	.10	.08	.04
227	Julio Franco	.10	.08	.04
228	Craig Lefferts	.06	.05	.02
229	Gary Pettis	.06	.05	.02
230	Dennis Rasmussen	.06	.05	.02
231	Brian Downing	.06	.05	.02
232	Carlos Quintana	.10	.08	.04
233	Gary Gaetti	.12	.09	.05
234	Mark Langston	.15	.11	.06
235	Tim Wallach	.10	.08	.04
236	Greg Swindell	.10	.08	.04
237	Eddie Murray	.15	.11	.06
238	Jeff Manto(FC)	.20	.15	.08
239	Lenny Harris	.08	.06	.03
240	Jesse Orosco	.05	.04	.02
241	Scott Lusader	.05	.04	.02
242	Sid Fernandez	.08	.06	.03
243	*Jim Leyritz*	.25	.20	.10
244	Cecil Fielder	.20	.15	.08
245	Darryl Strawberry	.25	.20	.10
246	Frank Thomas(FC)	4.00	3.00	1.50
247	Kevin Mitchell	.20	.15	.08
248	Lance Johnson	.06	.05	.02
249	Rick Rueschel	.08	.06	.03
250	Mark Portugal	.05	.04	.02
251	Derek Lilliquist	.06	.05	.02
252	Brian Holman	.08	.06	.03
253	Rafael Valdez	.08	.06	.03
254	B.J. Surhoff	.06	.05	.02
255	Tony Gwynn	.15	.11	.06
256	Andy Van Slyke	.12	.09	.05
257	Todd Stottlemyre	.08	.06	.03
258	Jose Lind	.06	.05	.02
259	Greg Myers	.06	.05	.02
260	Jeff Ballard	.06	.05	.02
261	Bobby Thigpen	.10	.08	.04
262	*Jimmy Kremers*(FC)	.15	.11	.06
263	Robin Ventura	.30	.25	.12
264	John Smoltz	.10	.08	.04
265	Sammy Sosa	.20	.15	.08
266	Gary Sheffield	.15	.11	.06
267	Lenny Dykstra	.10	.08	.04
268	Bill Spiers	.06	.05	.02
269	Charlie Hayes	.08	.06	.03
270	Brett Butler	.08	.06	.03
271	Bip Roberts	.08	.06	.03
272	Rob Deer	.06	.05	.02
273	Fred Lynn	.08	.06	.03
274	Dave Parker	.15	.11	.06
275	Andy Benes	.10	.08	.04
276	Glenallen Hill	.08	.06	.03
277	*Steve Howard*(FC)	.12	.09	.05
278	Doug Drabek	.10	.08	.04
279	Joe Oliver	.08	.06	.03
280	Todd Benzinger	.06	.05	.02
281	Eric King	.06	.05	.02
282	Jim Presley	.06	.05	.02
283	Ken Patterson(FC)	.06	.05	.02
284	Jack Daugherty	.08	.06	.03
285	Ivan Calderon	.10	.08	.04
286	*Edgar Diaz*(FC)	.10	.08	.04
287	Kevin Bass	.08	.06	.03
288	Don Carman	.06	.05	.02
289	Greg Brock	.06	.05	.02
290	John Franco	.10	.08	.04
291	Joey Cora	.06	.05	.02
292	Bill Wegman	.06	.05	.02
293	Eric Show	.06	.05	.02
294	Scott Bankhead	.08	.06	.03
295	Garry Templeton	.06	.05	.02
296	Mickey Tettleton	.06	.05	.02
297	Luis Sojo(FC)	.15	.11	.06
298	Jose Rijo	.08	.06	.03
299	Dave Johnson	.06	.05	.02
300	Checklist 201-300	.05	.04	.02
301	Mark Grant	.05	.04	.02
302	Pete Harnisch	.08	.06	.03
303	Greg Olson(FC)	.10	.08	.04
304	*Anthony Telford*(FC)	.15	.11	.06
305	Lonnie Smith	.06	.05	.02
306	*Chris Hoiles*(FC)	.50	.40	.20
307	Bryn Smith	.06	.05	.02
308	Mike Devereaux	.06	.05	.02
309	Milt Thompson	.06	.05	.02
310	Bob Melvin	.05	.04	.02
311	Luis Salazar	.05	.04	.02
312	Ed Whitson	.06	.05	.02
313	Charlie Hough	.06	.05	.02
314	Dave Clark	.05	.04	.02
315	*Eric Gunderson*	.15	.11	.06
316	Dan Petry	.05	.04	.02
317	Dante Bichette	.08	.06	.03
318	Mike Heath	.05	.04	.02
319	Damon Berryhill	.06	.05	.02
320	Walt Terrell	.05	.04	.02
321	Scott Fletcher	.05	.04	.02
322	Dan Plesac	.08	.06	.03
323	Jack McDowell	.08	.06	.03
324	Paul Molitor	.12	.09	.05
325	Ozzie Guillen	.10	.08	.04
326	Gregg Olson	.10	.08	.04
327	Pedro Guerrero	.10	.08	.04
328	Bob Milacki	.06	.05	.02
329	John Tudor	.06	.05	.02
330	Steve Finley	.08	.06	.03
331	Jack Clark	.10	.08	.04
332	Jerome Walton	.15	.11	.06
333	Andy Hawkins	.06	.05	.02
334	Derrick May	.20	.15	.08
335	Roberto Alomar	.10	.08	.04
336	Jack Morris	.08	.06	.03
337	Dave Winfield	.15	.11	.06
338	Steve Searcy	.08	.06	.03
339	Chili Davis	.08	.06	.03
340	Larry Sheets	.06	.05	.02
341	Ted Higuera	.08	.06	.03
342	*David Segui*	.30	.25	.12
343	Greg Cadaret	.05	.04	.02
344	Robin Yount	.15	.11	.06
345	Nolan Ryan	.30	.25	.12
346	*Ray Lankford*	.80	.60	.30
347	Cal Ripken, Jr.	.15	.11	.06
348	Lee Smith	.08	.06	.03
349	Brady Anderson	.05	.04	.02
350	Frank DiPino	.05	.04	.02
351	Hal Morris	.30	.25	.12
352	Deion Sanders	.10	.08	.04
353	Barry Larkin	.10	.08	.04
354	Don Mattingly	.35	.25	.14
355	Eric Davis	.20	.15	.08
356	Jose Offerman	.30	.25	.12
357	*Mel Rojas*	.12	.09	.05
358	Rudy Seanez(FC)	.10	.08	.04
359	Oil Can Boyd	.06	.05	.02
360	Nelson Liriano	.05	.04	.02
361	Ron Gant	.15	.11	.06
362	*Howard Farmer*	.15	.11	.06
363	David Justice	1.00	.70	.40
364	Delino DeShields	.30	.25	.12
365	Steve Avery	.25	.20	.10
366	David Cone	.12	.09	.05
367	lou Whitaker	.10	.08	.04
368	Von Hayes	.10	.08	.04
369	Frank Tanana	.06	.05	.02
370	Tim Teufel	.05	.04	.02
371	Randy Myers	.10	.08	.04
372	Roberto Kelly	.10	.08	.04
373	Jack Armstrong	.08	.06	.03
374	Kelly Gruber	.10	.08	.04
375	Kevin Maas	.50	.40	.20
376	Randy Johnson	.10	.08	.04
377	David West	.06	.05	.02
378	*Brent Knackert*(FC)	.12	.09	.05
379	Rick Honeycutt	.05	.04	.02
380	Kevin Gross	.08	.06	.03
381	Tom Foley	.05	.04	.02
382	Jeff Blauser	.06	.05	.02
383	*Scott Ruskin*	.15	.11	.06
384	Andres Thomas	.05	.04	.02
385	Dennis Martinez	.08	.06	.03
386	Mike Henneman	.08	.06	.03
387	Felix Jose	.15	.11	.06
388	Alejandro Pena	.05	.04	.02

		MT	NR MT	EX				MT	NR MT	EX
389	Chet Lemon	.06	.05	.02		480	Tom Glavine	.08	.06	.03
390	Craig Wilson(FC)	.20	.15	.08		481	Lee Guetterman	.05	.04	.02
391	Chuck Crim	.05	.04	.02		482	Rex Hudler	.06	.05	.02
392	Mel Hall	.06	.05	.02		483	Dave LaPoint	.06	.05	.02
393	Mark Knudson	.05	.04	.02		484	Terry Pendleton	.08	.06	.03
394	Norm Charlton	.08	.06	.03		485	Jesse Barfield	.08	.06	.03
395	Mike Felder	.05	.04	.02		486	Jose DeJesus	.08	.06	.03
396	Tim Layana	.15	.11	.06		487	Paul Abbott(FC)	.15	.11	.06
397	Steve Frey(FC)	.06	.05	.02		488	Ken Howell	.06	.05	.02
398	Bill Doran	.08	.06	.03		489	Greg W. Harris	.06	.05	.02
399	Dion James	.05	.04	.02		490	Roy Smith	.05	.04	.02
400	Checklist 301-400	.05	.04	.02		491	Paul Assenmacher	.05	.04	.02
401	Ron Hassey	.05	.04	.02		492	Geno Petralli	.05	.04	.02
402	Don Robinson	.06	.05	.02		493	Steve Wilson	.08	.06	.03
403	Gene Nelson	.05	.04	.02		494	Kevin Reimer(FC)	.08	.06	.03
404	Terry Kennedy	.05	.04	.02		495	Bill Long	.05	.04	.02
405	Todd Burns	.05	.04	.02		496	Mike Jackson	.06	.05	.02
406	Roger McDowell	.08	.06	.03		497	Oddibe McDowell	.06	.05	.02
407	Bob Kipper	.05	.04	.02		498	Bill Swift	.06	.05	.02
408	Darren Daulton	.08	.06	.03		499	Jeff Treadway	.06	.05	.02
409	Chuck Cary	.06	.05	.02		500	Checklist 401-500	.05	.04	.02
410	Bruce Ruffin	.06	.05	.02		501	Gene Larkin	.06	.05	.02
411	Juan Berenguer	.05	.04	.02		502	Bob Boone	.08	.06	.03
412	Gary Ward	.05	.04	.02		503	Allan Anderson	.06	.05	.02
413	Al Newman	.05	.04	.02		504	Luis Aquino	.06	.05	.02
414	Danny Jackson	.08	.06	.02		505	Mark Guthrie	.06	.05	.02
415	Greg Gagne	.06	.05	.02		506	Joe Orsulak	.06	.05	.02
416	Tom Herr	.06	.05	.02		507	Dana Kiecker(FC)	.15	.11	.06
417	Jeff Parrett	.06	.05	.02		508	Dave Gallagher	.05	.04	.02
418	Jeff Reardon	.08	.06	.03		509	Greg W. Harris	.06	.05	.02
419	Mark Lemke	.06	.05	.02		510	Mark Williamson	.05	.04	.02
420	Charlie O'Brien	.05	.04	.02		511	Casey Candaele	.05	.04	.02
421	Willie Randolph	.08	.06	.03		512	Mookie Wilson	.06	.05	.02
422	Steve Bedrosian	.08	.06	.03		513	Dave Smith	.08	.06	.03
423	Mike Moore	.08	.06	.03		514	Chuck Carr(FC)	.15	.11	.06
424	Jeff Brantley	.08	.06	.03		515	Glenn Wilson	.06	.05	.02
425	Bob Welch	.10	.08	.04		516	Mike Fitzgerald	.05	.04	.02
426	Terry Mulholland	.08	.06	.03		517	Devon White	.08	.06	.03
427	Willie Blair(FC)	.15	.11	.06		518	Dave Hollins	.25	.20	.10
428	Darrin Fletcher(FC)	.10	.08	.04		519	Mark Eichhorn	.05	.04	.02
429	Mike Witt	.06	.05	.02		520	Otis Nixon	.05	.04	.02
430	Joe Boever	.05	.04	.02		521	Terry Shumpert	.20	.15	.08
431	Tom Gordon	.12	.09	.05		522	Scott Erickson(FC)	.50	.40	.20
432	Pedro Munoz(FC)	1.00	.70	.40		523	Danny Tartabull	.10	.08	.04
433	Kevin Seitzer	.10	.08	.04		524	Orel Hershiser	.15	.11	.06
434	Kevin Tapani	.15	.11	.06		525	George Brett	.15	.11	.06
435	Bret Saberhagen	.12	.09	.05		526	Greg Vaughn	.20	.15	.08
436	Ellis Burks	.20	.15	.08		527	Tim Naehring(FC)	.40	.30	.15
437	Chuck Finley	.10	.08	.04		528	Curt Schilling(FC)	.06	.05	.02
438	Mike Boddicker	.08	.06	.03		529	Chris Bosio	.06	.05	.02
439	Francisco Cabrera	.08	.06	.03		530	Sam Horn	.08	.06	.03
440	Todd Hundley	.25	.20	.10		531	Mike Scott	.10	.08	.04
441	Kelly Downs	.06	.05	.02		532	George Bell	.15	.11	.06
442	Dann Howitt(FC)	.15	.11	.06		533	Eric Anthony	.20	.15	.08
443	Scott Garrelts	.08	.06	.03		534	Julio Valera(FC)	.15	.11	.06
444	Rickey Henderson	.40	.30	.15		535	Glenn Davis	.15	.11	.06
445	Will Clark	.40	.30	.15		536	Larry Walker	.15	.11	.06
446	Ben McDonald	.50	.40	.20		537	Pat Combs	.15	.11	.06
447	Dale Murphy	.12	.09	.05		538	Chris Nabholz(FC)	.20	.15	.08
448	Dave Righetti	.10	.08	.04		539	Kirk McCaskill	.08	.06	.03
449	Dickie Thon	.05	.04	.02		540	Randy Ready	.05	.04	.02
450	Ted Power	.05	.04	.02		541	Mark Gubicza	.10	.08	.04
451	Scott Coolbaugh	.08	.06	.03		542	Rick Aguilera	.08	.06	.03
452	Dwight Smith	.08	.06	.03		543	Brian McRae(FC)	.60	.45	.25
453	Pete Incaviglia	.08	.06	.03		544	Kirby Puckett	.20	.15	.08
454	Andre Dawson	.15	.11	.06		545	Bo Jackson	.50	.40	.20
455	Ruben Sierra	.20	.15	.08		546	Wade Boggs	.25	.20	.10
456	Andres Galarraga	.10	.08	.04		547	Tim McIntosh(FC)	.20	.15	.08
457	Alvin Davis	.10	.08	.04		548	Randy Milligan	.08	.06	.03
458	Tony Castillo	.06	.05	.02		549	Dwight Evans	.08	.06	.03
459	Pete O'Brien	.06	.05	.02		550	Billy Ripken	.05	.04	.02
460	Charlie Leibrandt	.06	.05	.02		551	Erik Hanson	.15	.11	.06
461	Vince Coleman	.10	.08	.04		552	Lance Parrish	.10	.08	.04
462	Steve Sax	.10	.08	.04		553	Tino Martinez	.20	.15	.08
463	Omar Oliveras(FC)	.15	.11	.06		554	Jim Abbott	.15	.11	.06
464	Oscar Azocar(FC)	.20	.15	.08		555	Ken Griffey,Jr.	1.50	1.25	.60
465	Joe Magrane	.08	.06	.03		556	Milt Cuyler(FC)	.30	.25	.12
466	Karl Rhodes(FC)	.30	.25	.12		557	Mark Leonard(FC)	.25	.20	.10
467	Benito Santiago	.10	.08	.04		558	Jay Howell	.08	.06	.03
468	Joe Klink(FC)	.10	.08	.04		559	Lloyd Moseby	.08	.06	.03
469	Sil Campusano	.05	.04	.02		560	Chris Gwynn	.06	.05	.02
470	Mark Parent	.05	.04	.02		561	Mark Whiten(FC)	.70	.50	.30
471	Shawn Boskie	.20	.15	.08		562	Harold Baines	.10	.08	.04
472	Kevin Brown	.10	.08	.04		563	Junior Felix	.15	.11	.06
473	Rick Sutcliffe	.08	.06	.03		564	Darren Lewis(FC)	.50	.40	.20
474	Rafael Palmeiro	.12	.09	.05		565	Fred McGriff	.15	.11	.06
475	Mike Harkey	.10	.08	.04		566	Kevin Appier	.15	.11	.06
476	Jaime Navarro	.15	.11	.06		567	Luis Gonzalez(FC)	.40	.30	.15
477	Marquis Grissom	.20	.15	.08		568	Frank White	.08	.06	.03
478	Marty Clary	.05	.04	.02		569	Juan Agosto	.05	.04	.02
479	Greg Briley	.10	.08	.04		570	Mike Macfarlane	.06	.05	.02

#	Player	MT	NR MT	EX
571	Bert Blyleven	.10	.08	.04
572	Ken Griffey,Sr.	.10	.08	.04
573	Lee Stevens(FC)	.20	.15	.08
574	Edgar Martinez	.08	.06	.03
575	Wally Joyner	.10	.08	.04
576	Tim Belcher	.08	.06	.03
577	John Burkett	.10	.08	.04
578	Mike Morgan	.06	.05	.02
579	Paul Gibson	.05	.04	.02
580	Jose Vizcaino	.10	.08	.04
581	Duane Ward	.06	.05	.02
582	Scott Sanderson	.06	.05	.02
583	David Wells	.06	.05	.02
584	Willie McGee	.10	.08	.04
585	John Cerutti	.05	.04	.02
586	Danny Darwin	.08	.06	.03
587	Kurt Stillwell	.08	.06	.03
588	Rich Gedman	.05	.04	.02
589	Mark Davis	.08	.06	.03
590	Bill Gullickson	.06	.05	.02
591	Matt Young	.06	.05	.02
592	Bryan Harvey	.08	.06	.03
593	Omar Vizquel	.06	.05	.02
594	Scott Lewis(FC)	.20	.15	.08
595	Dave Valle	.06	.05	.02
596	Tim Crews	.05	.04	.02
597	Mike Bielecki	.06	.05	.02
598	Mike Sharperson	.06	.05	.02
599	Dave Bergman	.05	.04	.02
600	Checklist 501-600	.05	.04	.02
601	Steve Lyons	.06	.05	.02
602	Bruce Hurst	.08	.06	.03
603	Donn Pall	.05	.04	.02
604	Jim Vatcher(FC)	.15	.11	.06
605	Dan Pasqua	.06	.05	.02
606	Kenny Rogers	.08	.06	.03
607	Jeff Schulz(FC)	.15	.11	.06
608	Brad Arnsberg(FC)	.10	.08	.04
609	Willie Wilson	.08	.06	.03
610	Jamie Moyer	.06	.05	.02
611	Ron Oester	.05	.04	.02
612	Dennis Cook	.08	.06	.03
613	Rick Mahler	.05	.04	.02
614	Bill Landrum	.06	.05	.02
615	Scott Scudder	.15	.11	.06
616	Tom Edens(FC)	.08	.06	.03
617	"1917 Revisited"	.25	.20	.10
618	Jim Gantner	.06	.05	.02
619	Darrel Akerfelds(FC)	.06	.05	.02
620	Ron Robinson	.06	.05	.02
621	Scott Radinsky	.20	.15	.08
622	Pete Smith	.06	.05	.02
623	Melido Perez	.08	.06	.03
624	Jerald Clark	.06	.05	.02
625	Carlos Martinez	.08	.06	.03
626	Wes Chamberlain(FC)	1.00	.70	.40
627	Bobby Witt	.08	.06	.03
628	Ken Dayley	.06	.05	.02
629	John Barfield(FC)	.10	.08	.04
630	Bob Tewksbury	.06	.05	.02
631	Glenn Braggs	.06	.05	.02
632	Jim Neidlinger(FC)	.20	.15	.08
633	Tom Browning	.08	.06	.03
634	Kirk Gibson	.12	.09	.05
635	Rob Dibble	.12	.09	.05
636	"Stolen Base Leaders"	.30	.25	.12
637	Jeff Montgomery	.08	.06	.03
638	Mike Schooler	.08	.06	.03
639	Storm Davis	.06	.05	.02
640	Rich Rodriguez(FC)	.15	.11	.06
641	Phil Bradley	.08	.06	.03
642	Kent Mercker	.15	.11	.06
643	Carlton Fisk	.12	.09	.05
644	Mike Bell(FC)	.15	.11	.06
645	Alex Fernandez(FC)	.40	.30	.15
646	Juan Gonzalez	.50	.40	.20
647	Ken Hill	.06	.05	.02
648	Jeff Russell	.08	.06	.03
649	Chuck Malone(FC)	.15	.11	.06
650	Steve Buechele	.06	.05	.02
651	Mike Benjamin	.15	.11	.06
652	Tony Pena	.08	.06	.03
653	Trevor Wilson	.08	.06	.03
654	Alex Cole	.30	.25	.12
655	Roger Clemens	.25	.20	.10
656	"The Bashing Years"	.25	.20	.10
657	Joe Grahe(FC)	.20	.15	.08
658	Jim Eisenreich	.06	.05	.02
659	Dan Gladden	.06	.05	.02
660	Steve Farr	.06	.05	.02
661	Bill Sampen	.20	.15	.08
662	Dave Rohde(FC)	.15	.11	.06
663	Mark Gardner	.20	.15	.08
664	Mike Simms(FC)	.25	.20	.10
665	Moises Alou(FC)	.15	.11	.06
666	Mickey Hatcher	.06	.05	.02
667	Jimmy Key	.08	.06	.03
668	John Wetteland	.10	.08	.04
669	John Smiley	.06	.05	.02
670	Jim Acker	.05	.04	.02
671	Pascual Perez	.06	.05	.02
672	Reggie Harris(FC)	.30	.25	.12
673	Matt Nokes	.08	.06	.03
674	Rafael Novoa(FC)	.15	.11	.06
675	Hensley Meulens	.10	.08	.04
676	Jeff M. Robinson	.06	.05	.02
677	"Ground Breaking"	.25	.20	.10
678	Johnny Ray	.06	.05	.02
679	Greg Hibbard	.10	.08	.04
680	Paul Sorrento	.20	.15	.08
681	Mike Marshall	.06	.05	.02
682	Jim Clancy	.05	.04	.02
683	Rob Murphy	.05	.04	.02
684	Dave Schmidt	.05	.04	.02
685	Jeff Gray(FC)	.15	.11	.06
686	Mike Hartley(FC)	.20	.15	.08
687	Jeff King	.08	.06	.03
688	Stan Javier	.06	.05	.02
689	Bob Walk	.06	.05	.02
690	Jim Gott	.06	.05	.02
691	Mike LaCoss	.05	.04	.02
692	John Farrell	.06	.05	.02
693	Tim Leary	.06	.05	.02
694	Mike Walker(FC)	.20	.15	.08
695	Eric Plunk	.05	.04	.02
696	Mike Fetters(FC)	.15	.11	.06
697	Wayne Edwards	.10	.08	.04
698	Tim Drummond(FC)	.15	.11	.06
699	Willie Fraser	.05	.04	.02
700	Checklist 601-700	.05	.04	.02
701	Mike Heath	.10	.08	.04
702	"Rookie Threats"	.60	.45	.25
703	Jose Mesa	.10	.08	.04
704	Dave Smith	.10	.08	.04
705	Danny Darwin	.10	.08	.04
706	Rafael Belliard	.10	.08	.04
707	Rob Murphy	.10	.08	.04
708	Terry Pendleton	.15	.11	.06
709	Mike Pagliarulo	.10	.08	.04
710	Sid Bream	.12	.09	.05
711	Junior Felix	.12	.09	.05
712	Dante Bichette	.10	.08	.04
713	Kevin Gross	.10	.08	.04
714	Luis Sojo	.12	.09	.05
715	Bob Ojeda	.10	.08	.04
716	Julio Machado	.12	.09	.05
717	Steve Farr	.10	.08	.04
718	Franklin Stubbs	.10	.08	.04
719	Mike Boddicker	.12	.09	.05
720	Willie Randolph	.12	.09	.05
721	Willie McGee	.15	.11	.06
722	Chili Davis	.15	.11	.06
723	Danny Jackson	.12	.09	.05
724	Cory Snyder	.10	.08	.04
725	"MVP Lineup"	.25	.20	.10
726	Rob Deer	.10	.08	.04
727	Rich DeLucia(FC)	.15	.11	.06
728	Mike Perez(FC)	.15	.11	.06
729	Mickey Tettleton	.12	.09	.05
730	Mike Blowers	.10	.08	.04
731	Gary Gaetti	.12	.09	.05
732	Brett Butler	.12	.09	.05
733	Dave Parker	.15	.11	.06
734	Eddie Zosky(FC)	.20	.15	.08
735	Jack Clark	.12	.09	.05
736	Jack Morris	.12	.09	.05
737	Kirk Gibson	.12	.09	.05
738	Steve Bedrosian	.10	.08	.04
739	Candy Maldonado	.10	.08	.04
740	Matt Young	.10	.08	.04
741	Rich Garces(FC)	.20	.15	.08
742	George Bell	.15	.11	.06
743	Deion Sanders	.15	.11	.06
744	Bo Jackson	1.00	.70	.40
745	Luis Mercedes(FC)	.40	.30	.15
746	Reggie Jefferson(FC)	.80	.60	.30
747	Pete Incaviglia	.10	.08	.04
748	Chris Hammond(FC)	.20	.15	.08
749	Mike Stanton	.12	.09	.05
750	Scott Sanderson	.10	.08	.04
751	Paul Faries(FC)	.20	.15	.08
752	Al Osuna(FC)	.15	.11	.06

		MT	NR MT	EX
753	Steve Chitren(FC)	.15	.11	.06
754	Tony Fernandez	.15	.11	.06
755	Jeff Bagwell(FC)	3.00	2.25	1.25
756	Kirk Dressendorfer(FC)	.50	.40	.20
757	Glenn Davis	.15	.11	.06
758	Gary Carter	.12	.09	.05
759	Zane Smith	.10	.08	.04
760	Vance Law	.10	.08	.04
761	Denis Boucher(FC)	.20	.15	.08
762	Turner Ward(FC)	.20	.15	.08
763	Roberto Alomar	.15	.11	.06
764	Albert Belle	.25	.20	.10
765	Joe Carter	.15	.11	.06
766	Pete Schourek(FC)	.15	.11	.06
767	Heathcliff Slocumb(FC)	.15	.11	.06
768	Vince Coleman	.15	.11	.06
769	Mitch Williams	.12	.09	.05
770	Brian Downing	.10	.08	.04
771	Dana Allison(FC)	.15	.11	.06
772	Pete Harnisch	.12	.09	.05
773	Tim Raines	.15	.11	.06
774	Darryl Kile(FC)	.25	.20	.10
775	Fred McGriff	.15	.11	.06
776	Dwight Evans	.12	.09	.05
777	Joe Slusarski(FC)	.20	.15	.08
778	Dave Righetti	.12	.09	.05
779	Jeff Hamilton	.10	.08	.04
780	Ernest Riles	.10	.08	.04
781	Ken Dayley	.10	.08	.04
782	Eric King	.10	.08	.04
783	Devon White	.12	.09	.05
784	Beau Allred	.10	.08	.04
785	Mike Timlin(FC)	.25	.20	.10
786	Ivan Calderon	.15	.11	.06
787	Hubie Brooks	.12	.09	.05
788	Juan Agosto	.10	.08	.04
789	Barry Jones	.10	.08	.04
790	Wally Backman	.10	.08	.04
791	Jim Presley	.10	.08	.04
792	Charlie Hough	.10	.08	.04
793	Larry Andersen	.10	.08	.04
794	Steve Finley	.12	.09	.05
795	Shawn Abner	.10	.08	.04
796	Jeff M. Robinson	.10	.08	.04
797	Joe Bitker(FC)	.10	.08	.04
798	Eric Show	.10	.08	.04
799	Bud Black	.10	.08	.04
800	Checklist 701-800	.10	.08	.04
-----	Michael Jordan (Special Insert)	8.00	6.00	3.25

1991 Upper Deck
Final Edition

Upper Deck surprised the hobby with the release of this 100-card boxed set. The cards are numbered with an "F" designation. A special diamond skills subset features several top prospects. An all-star subset is also included in this set. The cards are styled like the regular 1991 Upper Deck issue. Special team hologram cards are also included with the set.

		MT	NR MT	EX
	Complete Set:	20.00	15.00	8.00
	Common Player:	.20	.15	.08
1	Diamond Skills Checklist (Klesko Sanders)	.80	.60	.30
2	Pedro Martinez(FC)	2.00	1.50	.80
3	Lance Dickson	.30	.25	.12

		MT	NR MT	EX
4	Royce Clayton	.80	.60	.30
5	Scott Bryant(FC)	.35	.25	.14
6	Dan Wilson(FC)	.40	.30	.15
7	Dmitri Young(FC)	1.25	.90	.50
8	Ryan Klesko(FC)	1.50	1.25	.60
9	Tom Goodwin(FC)	.35	.25	.14
10	Rondell White(FC)	1.00	.70	.40
11	Reggie Sanders	1.00	.70	.40
12	Todd Van Poppel	1.00	.70	.40
13	Arthur Rhodes(FC)	.50	.40	.20
14	Eddie Zosky	.20	.15	.08
15	Gerald Williams(FC)	.80	.60	.30
16	Robert Eenhoorn(FC)	.30	.25	.12
17	Jim Thome(FC)	.60	.45	.25
18	Marc Newfield(FC)	1.00	.70	.40
19	Kerwin Moore(FC)	.50	.40	.20
20	Jeff McNeely(FC)	.60	.45	.25
21	Frankie Rodriguez(FC)	2.00	1.50	.80
22	Andy Mota(FC)	.30	.25	.12
23	Chris Haney(FC)	.30	.25	.12
24	Kenny Lofton(FC)	1.50	1.25	.60
25	Dave Nilsson(FC)	.80	.60	.30
26	Derek Bell(FC)	.70	.50	.30
27	Frank Castillo(FC)	.50	.40	.20
28	Candy Maldonado	.20	.15	.08
29	Chuck McElroy	.20	.15	.08
30	Chito Martinez(FC)	.70	.50	.30
31	Steve Howe	.20	.15	.08
32	Freddie Benavides(FC)	.30	.25	.12
33	Scott Kamieniecki(FC)	.35	.25	.14
34	Denny Neagle(FC)	.70	.50	.30
35	Mike Humphreys(FC)	.35	.25	.14
36	Mike Remlinger(FC)	.25	.20	.10
37	Scott Coolbaugh	.20	.15	.08
38	Darren Lewis	.35	.25	.14
39	Thomas Howard(FC)	.20	.15	.08
40	John Candelaria	.20	.15	.08
41	Todd Benzinger	.20	.15	.08
42	Wilson Alvarez	.30	.25	.12
43	Patrick Lennon(FC)	.50	.40	.20
44	Rusty Meacham(FC)	.35	.25	.14
45	Ryan Bowen(FC)	.40	.30	.15
46	Rick Wilkins(FC)	.50	.40	.20
47	Ed Sprague(FC)	.30	.25	.14
48	Bob Scanlan(FC)	.20	.15	.08
49	Tom Candiotti	.20	.15	.08
50	Dennis Martinez (Perfecto)	.20	.15	.08
51	Oil Can Boyd	.20	.15	.08
52	Glenallen Hill	.30	.25	.12
53	Scott Livingstone(FC)	.50	.40	.20
54	Brian Hunter(FC)	.40	.30	.15
55	Ivan Rodriguez(FC)	2.00	1.50	.80
56	Keith Mitchell(FC)	.80	.60	.30
57	Roger McDowell	.20	.15	.08
58	Otis Nixon	.20	.15	.08
59	Juan Bell	.20	.15	.08
60	Bill Krueger	.20	.15	.08
61	Chris Donnels(FC)	.50	.40	.20
62	Tommy Greene	.25	.20	.10
63	Doug Simons(FC)	.25	.20	.10
64	Andy Ashby(FC)	.25	.20	.10
65	Anthony Young(FC)	.60	.45	.25
66	Kevin Morton(FC)	.40	.30	.15
67	Bret Barberie(FC)	.50	.40	.20
68	Scott Servais(FC)	.25	.20	.10
69	Ron Darling	.20	.15	.08
70	Vicente Palacios	.20	.15	.08
71	Tim Burke	.20	.15	.08
72	Gerald Alexander(FC)	.20	.15	.08
73	Reggie Jefferson	.50	.40	.20
74	Dean Palmer	.60	.45	.25
75	Mark Whiten	.30	.25	.12
76	Randy Tomlin(FC)	.50	.40	.20
77	Mark Wohlers(FC)	.50	.40	.20
78	Brook Jacoby	.20	.15	.08
79	All-Star Checklist (Griffey/Sandberg)(FC)	1.00	.70	.40
80	Jack Morris (AS)	.30	.25	.12
81	Sandy Alomar, Jr. (AS)	.25	.20	.10
82	Cecil Fielder (AS)	.30	.25	.12
83	Roberto Alomar (AS)	.30	.25	.12
84	Wade Boggs (AS)	.30	.25	.12
85	Cal Ripken, Jr. (AS)	.50	.40	.20
86	Rickey Henderson (AS)	.40	.30	.15
87	Ken Griffey, Jr. (AS)	.60	.45	.25
88	Dave Henderson (AS)	.25	.20	.10
89	Danny Tartabull (AS)	.25	.20	.10
90	Tom Glavine (AS)	.30	.25	.12
91	Benito Santiago (AS)	.25	.20	.10
92	Will Clark (AS)	.50	.40	.20
93	Ryne Sandberg (AS)	.50	.40	.20

		MT	NR MT	EX
94	Chris Sabo (AS)	.25	.20	.10
95	Ozzie Smith (AS)	.30	.25	.14
96	Ivan Calderon (AS)	.25	.20	.10
97	Tony Gwynn (AS)	.30	.25	.12
98	Andre Dawson (AS)	.30	.25	.12
99	Bobby Bonilla (AS)	.30	.25	.12
100	Checklist	.20	.15	.08

1991 Upper Deck Silver Sluggers

Each year the "Silver Slugger" award is presented to the top slugger at each position in the American and National Leagues. Upper Deck produced special cards in honor of the players who received this award for the 1990 season. The cards were randomly inserted in jumbo packs of Upper Deck cards. The cards feature a "SS" designation along with the card number. The cards are designed like the regular issue Upper Deck cards from 1991, but feature a Silver Slugger bat along the left border of the card.

		MT	NR MT	EX
	Complete Set:	40.00	30.00	15.00
	Common Player:	1.00	.70	.40
1	Julio Franco	1.50	1.25	.60
2	Alan Trammell	1.50	1.25	.60
3	Rickey Henderson	4.00	3.00	1.50
4	Jose Canseco	8.00	6.00	3.25
5	Barry Bonds	4.00	3.00	1.50
6	Eddie Murray	1.50	1.25	.60
7	Kelly Gruber	1.25	.90	.50
8	Ryne Sandberg	6.00	4.50	2.50
9	Darryl Strawberry	4.00	3.00	1.50
10	Ellis Burks	1.25	.90	.50
11	Lance Parrish	1.25	.90	.50
12	Cecil Fielder	4.00	3.00	1.50
13	Matt Williams	1.50	1.25	.60
14	Dave Parker	1.25	.90	.50
15	Bobby Bonilla	2.50	2.00	1.00
16	Don Robinson	1.00	.70	.40
17	Benito Santiago	1.25	.90	.50
18	Barry Larkin	2.00	1.50	.80

1992 Upper Deck

Upper Deck introduced a new look in 1992. The baseline style was no longer used. The 1992 cards feature full-color action photos on white stock, with the player's name and the Upper Deck logo along the top border. The team name is inserted in the bottom right corner of the photo.. Once again a 100-card high number series was set for release in July or August. 2,500 Ted Williams autographed Baseball Heroes cards were randomly inserted into Upper Deck packs. Several subsets are also featured in the 1992 issue including Star Rookies and Top Prospects. At press time, Upper Deck was considering changes in its 1992 card set. This explains any discrepancies in the price list from what was actually released from Upper Deck.

		MT	NR MT	EX
	Complete Set:	40.00	30.00	15.00
	Common Player:	.05	.04	.02
1	Star Rookie Checklist	.06	.05	.02
2	Star Rookie (Royce Clayton)	.20	.15	.08
3	Star Rookie (Brian Jordan)(FC)	.60	.45	.25
4	Star Rookie (Dave Fleming)(FC)	.60	.45	.25
5	Star Rookie (Jim Thome)	.25	.20	.10
6	Star Rookie (Jeff Juden)	.20	.15	.08
7	Star Rookie (Roberto Hernandez)(FC)	.20	.15	.08
8	Star Rookie (Kyle Abbott)(FC)	.10	.08	.04
9	Star Rookie (Chris George)(FC)	.20	.15	.08
10	Star Rookie (Rob Maurer)(FC)	.30	.25	.12
11	Star Rookie (Donald Harris)(FC)	.20	.15	.08
12	Star Rookie (Ted Wood)(FC)	.25	.20	.10
13	Star Rookie (Patrick Lennon)	.20	.15	.08
14	Star Rookie (Willie Banks)	.15	.11	.06
15	Star Rookie (Roger Salkeld)	.25	.20	.10
16	Star Rookie (Wilfredo Cordero)	.20	.15	.08
17	Star Rookie (Arthur Rhodes)	.40	.30	.15
18	Star Rookie (Pedro Martinez)	.80	.60	.30
19	Star Rookie (Andy Ashby)	.10	.08	.04
20	Star Rookie (Tom Goodwin)	.15	.11	.06
21	Star Rookie (Braulio Castillo)(FC)	.20	.15	.08
22	Star Rookie (Todd Van Poppel)	.35	.25	.14
23	Star Rookie (Brian Williams)(FC)	.30	.25	.12
24	Star Rookie (Ryan Klesko)	.70	.50	.30
25	Star Rookie (Kenny Lofton)	.70	.50	.30
26	Star Rookie (Derek Bell)	.35	.25	.14
27	Star Rookie (Reggie Sanders)	.40	.30	.15
28	"Winfield's 400th"	.10	.08	.04
29	Atlanta Checklist	.05	.04	.02
30	Cincinnati Checklist	.05	.04	.02
31	Houston Checklist	.05	.04	.02
32	Los Angeles Checklist	.05	.04	.02
33	San Diego Checklist	.05	.04	.02
34	San Francisco Checklist	.05	.04	.02
35	Chicago Checklist	.05	.04	.02
36	Montreal Checklist	.05	.04	.02
37	New York Checklist	.05	.04	.02
38	Philadelphia Checklist	.05	.04	.02
39	Pittsburgh Checklist	.05	.04	.02
40	St. Louis Checklist	.05	.04	.02
41	"Playoff Perfection"	.10	.08	.04
42	Jeremy Hernandez(FC)	.20	.15	.08
43	Doug Henry(FC)	.20	.15	.08
44	Chris Donnels	.25	.20	.10
45	Mo Sanford(FC)	.20	.15	.08
46	Scott Kamieniecki	.15	.11	.06
47	Mark Lemke	.06	.05	.02
48	Steve Farr	.05	.04	.02
49	Francisco Oliveras	.05	.04	.02
50	Ced Landrum(FC)	.10	.08	.04
51	Top Prospect Checklist	.06	.05	.02
52	Top Prospect (Eduardo Perez)(FC)	.50	.40	.20
53	Top Prospect (Tom Nevers)(FC)	.20	.15	.08
54	Top Prospect (David Zancanaro)(FC)	.20	.15	.08
55	Top Prospect (Shawn Green)(FC)	.20	.15	.08
56	Top Prospect (Mark Wohlers)	.20	.15	.08
57	Top Prospect (Dave Nilsson)	.50	.40	.20
58	Top Prospect (Dmitri Young)	.50	.40	.20
59	Top Prospect (Ryan Hawblitzel)(FC)	.30	.25	.12
60	Top Prospect (Raul Mondesi)(FC)	.30	.25	.12
61	Top Prospect (Rondell White)(FC)	.35	.25	.14
62	Top Prospect (Steve Hosey)(FC)	.20	.15	.08
63	Top Prospect (Manny Ramirez)(FC)	1.25	.90	.50
64	Top Prospect (Marc Newfield)	.50	.40	.20
65	Top Prospect (Jeromy Burnitz)(FC)	.80	.60	.30
66	Top Prospect (Mark Smith)	.30	.25	.12

#	Player	MT	NR MT	EX
67	Top Prospect (*Joey Hamilton*)(FC)	.40	.30	.15
68	Top Prospect (*Tyler Green*)(FC)	.80	.60	.30
69	Top Prospect (*John Farrell*)(FC)	.30	.25	.12
70	Top Prospect (*Kurt Miller*)(FC)	.20	.15	.08
71	Top Prospect (*Jeff Plympton*)(FC)	.30	.25	.12
72	Top Prospect (*Dan Wilson*)(FC)	.35	.25	.14
73	Top Prospect (*Joe Vitiello*)(FC)	.40	.30	.15
74	Top Prospect (*Rico Brogna*)(FC)	.10	.08	.04
75	Top Prospect (*David McCarty*)(FC)	1.50	1.25	.60
76	Top Prospect (*Bob Wickman*)(FC)	.60	.45	.25
77	Top Prospect (*Carlos Rodriguez*)(FC)	.30	.25	.12
78	"Stay In School"	.10	.08	.04
79	Bloodlines (Ramon & Pedro Martinez)	.40	.30	.15
80	Bloodlines (Kevin & Keith Mitchell)	.10	.08	.04
81	Bloodlines (Sandy Jr. & Roberto Alomar)	.10	.08	.04
82	Bloodlines (Cal Jr. & Billy Ripken)	.15	.11	.06
83	Bloodlines (Tony & Chris Gwynn)	.10	.08	.04
84	Bloodlines (Dwight Gooden & Gary Sheffield)	.10	.08	.04
85	Bloodlines (Ken Sr., Ken Jr. & Craig Griffey)	.80	.60	.30
86	California Checklist	.05	.04	.02
87	Chicago Checklist	.05	.04	.02
88	Kansas City Checklist	.05	.04	.02
89	Minnesota Checklist	.05	.04	.02
90	Oakland Checklist	.05	.04	.02
91	Seattle Checklist	.05	.04	.02
92	Texas Checklist	.05	.04	.02
93	Baltimore Checklist	.05	.04	.02
94	Boston Checklist	.05	.04	.02
95	Cleveland Checklist	.05	.04	.02
96	Detroit Checklist	.05	.04	.02
97	Milwaukee Checklist	.05	.04	.02
98	New York Checklist	.05	.04	.02
99	Toronto Checklist	.05	.04	.02
100	Checklist 1-100	.05	.04	.02
101	Joe Oliver	.06	.05	.02
102	Hector Villanueva	.05	.04	.02
103	Ed Whitson	.05	.04	.02
104	Danny Jackson	.05	.04	.02
105	Chris Hammond	.06	.05	.02
106	Ricky Jordan	.06	.05	.02
107	Kevin Bass	.05	.04	.02
108	Darrin Fletcher	.05	.04	.02
109	Junior Ortiz	.05	.04	.02
110	Tom Bolton	.05	.04	.02
111	Jeff King	.06	.05	.02
112	Dave Magadan	.08	.06	.03
113	Mike LaValliere	.06	.05	.02
114	Hubie Brooks	.06	.05	.02
115	Jay Bell	.06	.05	.02
116	David Wells	.05	.04	.02
117	Jim Leyritz	.05	.04	.02
118	Manuel Lee	.05	.04	.02
119	Alvaro Espinoza	.05	.04	.02
120	B.J. Surhoff	.06	.05	.02
121	Hal Morris	.20	.15	.08
122	Shawon Dunston	.08	.06	.03
123	Chris Sabo	.10	.08	.04
124	Andre Dawson	.15	.11	.06
125	Eric Davis	.15	.11	.06
126	Chili Davis	.08	.06	.03
127	Dale Murphy	.10	.08	.04
128	Kirk McCaskill	.06	.05	.02
129	Terry Mulholland	.06	.05	.02
130	Rick Aguilera	.08	.06	.03
131	Vince Coleman	.10	.08	.04
132	Andy Van Slyke	.12	.09	.05
133	Gregg Jefferies	.15	.11	.06
134	Barry Bonds	.20	.15	.08
135	Dwight Gooden	.15	.11	.06
136	Dave Stieb	.08	.06	.03
137	Albert Belle	.25	.20	.10
138	Teddy Higuera	.08	.06	.03
139	Jesse Barfield	.08	.06	.03
140	Pat Borders	.06	.05	.02
141	Bip Roberts	.06	.05	.02
142	Rob Dibble	.10	.08	.04
143	Mark Grace	.15	.11	.06
144	Barry Larkin	.15	.11	.06
145	Ryne Sandberg	.25	.20	.10
146	Scott Erickson	.25	.20	.10
147	Luis Polonia	.06	.05	.02
148	John Burkett	.06	.05	.02
149	Luis Sojo	.06	.05	.02
150	Dickie Thon	.05	.04	.02
151	Walt Weiss	.06	.05	.02
152	Mike Scioscia	.06	.05	.02
153	Mark McGwire	.15	.11	.06
154	Matt Williams	.15	.11	.06
155	Rickey Henderson	.25	.20	.10
156	Sandy Alomar, Jr.	.10	.08	.04
157	Brian McRae	.25	.20	.10
158	Harold Baines	.08	.06	.03
159	Kevin Appier	.06	.05	.02
160	Felix Fermin	.05	.04	.02
161	Leo Gomez	.15	.11	.06
162	Craig Biggio	.10	.08	.04
163	Ben McDonald	.20	.15	.08
164	Randy Johnson	.08	.06	.03
165	Cal Ripken, Jr.	.30	.25	.12
166	Frank Thomas	1.00	.70	.40
167	Delino DeShields	.08	.06	.03
168	Greg Gagne	.05	.04	.02
169	Ron Karkovice	.05	.04	.02
170	Charlie Leibrandt	.05	.04	.02
171	Dave Righetti	.08	.06	.03
172	Dave Henderson	.10	.08	.04
173	Steve Decker	.15	.11	.06
174	Darryl Strawberry	.15	.11	.06
175	Will Clark	.25	.20	.10
176	Ruben Sierra	.15	.11	.06
177	Ozzie Smith	.15	.11	.06
178	Charles Nagy	.08	.06	.03
179	Gary Pettis	.05	.04	.02
180	Kirk Gibson	.08	.06	.03
181	Randy Milligan	.06	.05	.02
182	Dave Valle	.05	.04	.02
183	Chris Hoiles	.10	.08	.04
184	Tony Phillips	.05	.04	.02
185	Brady Anderson	.05	.04	.02
186	Scott Fletcher	.05	.04	.02
187	Gene Larkin	.05	.04	.02
188	Lance Johnson	.05	.04	.02
189	Greg Olson	.05	.04	.02
190	Melido Perez	.05	.04	.02
191	Lenny Harris	.05	.04	.02
192	Terry Kennedy	.05	.04	.02
193	Mike Gallego	.05	.04	.02
194	Willie McGee	.08	.06	.03
195	Juan Samuel	.06	.05	.02
196	Jeff Huson	.05	.04	.02
197	Alex Cole	.05	.04	.02
198	Ron Robinson	.06	.05	.02
199	Joel Skinner	.06	.05	.02
200	Checklist 101-200	.06	.05	.02
201	Kevin Reimer	.06	.05	.02
202	Stan Belinda	.05	.04	.02
203	Pat Tabler	.05	.04	.02
204	Jose Guzman	.05	.04	.02
205	Jose Lind	.05	.04	.02
206	Spike Owen	.05	.04	.02
207	Joe Orsulak	.05	.04	.02
208	Charlie Hayes	.05	.04	.02
209	Mike Devereaux	.06	.05	.02
210	Mike Fitzgerald	.05	.04	.02
211	Willie Randolph	.05	.04	.02
212	Rod Nichols	.05	.04	.02
213	Mike Boddicker	.05	.04	.02
214	Bill Spiers	.05	.04	.02
215	Steve Olin	.05	.04	.02
216	*David Howard*(FC)	.15	.11	.06
217	Gary Varsho	.05	.04	.02
218	Mike Harkey	.06	.05	.02
219	Luis Aquino	.05	.04	.02
220	Chuck McElroy	.05	.04	.02
221	Doug Drabek	.08	.06	.03
222	Dave Winfield	.15	.11	.06
223	Rafael Palmeiro	.12	.09	.05
224	Joe Carter	.12	.09	.05
225	Bobby Bonilla	.12	.09	.05
226	Ivan Calderon	.10	.08	.04
227	Gregg Olson	.10	.08	.04
228	Tim Wallach	.08	.06	.03
229	Terry Pendleton	.10	.08	.04
230	Gilberto Reyes(FC)	.08	.06	.03
231	Carlos Baerga	.10	.08	.04
232	Greg Vaughn	.10	.08	.04
233	Bret Saberhagen	.10	.08	.04
234	Gary Sheffield	.10	.08	.04
235	Mark Lewis	.15	.11	.06
236	George Bell	.10	.08	.04
237	Danny Tartabull	.10	.08	.04
238	Willie Wilson	.06	.05	.02
239	Doug Dascenzo	.05	.04	.02
240	Bill Pecota	.05	.04	.02
241	Julio Franco	.12	.09	.05
242	Ed Sprague	.10	.08	.04

		MT	NR MT	EX			MT	NR MT	EX
243	Juan Gonzalez	.35	.25	.14	334	Kent Hrbek	.06	.05	.02
244	Chuck Finley	.10	.08	.04	335	Ken Griffey, Sr.	.06	.05	.02
245	*Ivan Rodriguez*	.80	.60	.30	336	Greg Swindell	.08	.06	.03
246	Lenny Dykstra	.10	.08	.04	337	Trevor Wilson	.06	.05	.02
247	Deion Sanders	.15	.11	.06	338	Sam Horn	.05	.04	.02
248	Dwight Evans	.08	.06	.03	339	Mike Henneman	.06	.05	.02
249	Larry Walker	.10	.08	.04	340	Jerry Browne	.05	.04	.02
250	Billy Ripken	.05	.04	.02	341	Glenn Braggs	.05	.04	.02
251	Mickey Tettleton	.06	.05	.02	342	Tom Glavine	.10	.08	.04
252	Tony Pena	.06	.05	.02	343	Wally Joyner	.10	.08	.04
253	Benito Santiago	.08	.06	.03	344	Fred McGriff	.10	.08	.04
254	Kirby Puckett	.20	.15	.08	345	Ron Gant	.15	.11	.06
255	Cecil Fielder	.20	.15	.08	346	Ramon Martinez	.15	.11	.06
256	Howard Johnson	.12	.09	.05	347	Wes Chamberlain	.20	.15	.08
257	Andujar Cedeno	.20	.15	.08	348	Terry Shumpert	.05	.04	.02
258	Jose Rijo	.08	.06	.03	349	Tim Teufel	.05	.04	.02
259	Al Osuna	.05	.04	.02	350	Wally Backman	.05	.04	.02
260	Todd Hundley	.15	.11	.06	351	Joe Girardi	.05	.04	.02
261	Orel Hershiser	.08	.06	.03	352	Devon White	.08	.06	.03
262	Ray Lankford	.15	.11	.06	353	Greg Maddux	.08	.06	.03
263	Robin Ventura	.15	.11	.06	354	*Ryan Bowen*	.15	.11	.06
264	Felix Jose	.10	.08	.04	355	Roberto Alomar	.10	.08	.04
265	Eddie Murray	.15	.11	.06	356	Don Mattingly	.25	.20	.10
266	Kevin Mitchell	.15	.11	.06	357	Pedro Guerrero	.10	.08	.04
267	Gary Carter	.10	.08	.04	358	Steve Sax	.10	.08	.04
268	Mike Benjamin	.05	.04	.02	359	Joey Cora	.05	.04	.02
269	Dick Schofield	.05	.04	.02	360	Jim Gantner	.10	.08	.04
270	Jose Uribe	.05	.04	.02	361	Brian Barnes	.10	.08	.04
271	Pete Incaviglia	.06	.05	.02	362	Kevin McReynolds	.10	.08	.04
272	Tony Fernandez	.08	.06	.03	363	*Bret Barberie*(FC)	.15	.11	.06
273	Alan Trammell	.10	.08	.04	364	David Cone	.08	.06	.03
274	Tony Gwynn	.15	.11	.06	365	Dennis Martinez	.08	.06	.03
275	Mike Greenwell	.10	.08	.04	366	*Brian Hunter*	.25	.20	.10
276	*Jeff Bagwell*	.70	.50	.30	367	Edgar Martinez	.08	.06	.03
277	Frank Viola	.10	.08	.04	368	Steve Finley	.08	.06	.03
278	Randy Myers	.06	.05	.02	369	Greg Briley	.05	.04	.02
279	Ken Caminiti	.06	.05	.02	370	Jeff Blauser	.05	.04	.02
280	Bill Doran	.06	.05	.02	371	Todd Stottlemyre	.06	.05	.02
281	Dan Pasqua	.05	.04	.02	372	Luis Gonzalez	.20	.15	.08
282	Alfredo Griffin	.05	.04	.02	373	*Rick Wilkins*	.20	.15	.08
283	Jose Oquendo	.05	.04	.02	374	*Darryl Kile*	.15	.11	.06
284	Kal Daniels	.08	.06	.03	375	John Olerud	.15	.11	.06
285	Bobby Thigpen	.08	.06	.03	376	Lee Smith	.08	.06	.03
286	Robby Thompson	.05	.04	.02	377	Kevin Maas	.20	.15	.08
287	Mark Eichhorn	.05	.04	.02	378	Dante Bichette	.06	.05	.02
288	Mike Felder	.05	.04	.02	379	Tom Pagnozzi	.06	.05	.02
289	Dave Gallagher	.05	.04	.02	380	Mike Flanagan	.05	.04	.02
290	Dave Anderson	.05	.04	.02	381	Charlie O'Brien	.05	.04	.02
291	Mel Hall	.06	.05	.02	382	Dave Martinez	.05	.04	.02
292	Jerald Clark	.06	.05	.02	383	Keith Miller	.05	.04	.02
293	Al Newman	.05	.04	.02	384	Scott Ruskin	.05	.04	.02
294	Rob Deer	.05	.04	.02	385	Kevin Elster	.05	.04	.02
295	Matt Nokes	.06	.05	.02	386	Alvin Davis	.08	.06	.03
296	Jack Armstrong	.06	.05	.02	387	Casey Candaele	.05	.04	.02
297	Jim Deshaies	.05	.04	.02	388	Pete O'Brien	.05	.04	.02
298	Jeff Innis	.05	.04	.02	389	Jeff Treadway	.05	.04	.02
299	Jeff Reed	.05	.04	.02	390	Scott Bradley	.05	.04	.02
300	Checklist 201-300	.05	.04	.02	391	Mookie Wilson	.05	.04	.02
301	Lonnie Smith	.05	.04	.02	392	Jimmy Jones	.05	.04	.02
302	Jimmy Key	.06	.05	.02	393	Candy Maldonado	.05	.04	.02
303	Junior Felix	.08	.06	.03	394	Eric Yelding	.05	.04	.02
304	Mike Heath	.05	.04	.02	395	Tom Henke	.06	.05	.02
305	Mark Langston	.10	.08	.04	396	Franklin Stubbs	.05	.04	.02
306	Greg W. Harris	.06	.05	.02	397	Milt Thompson	.05	.04	.02
307	Brett Butler	.08	.06	.03	398	Mark Carreon	.05	.04	.02
308	Luis Rivera	.05	.04	.02	399	Randy Velarde	.05	.04	.02
309	Bruce Ruffin	.05	.04	.02	400	Checklist 301-400	.05	.04	.02
310	Paul Faries	.08	.06	.03	401	Omar Vizquel	.05	.04	.02
311	Terry Leach	.05	.04	.02	402	Joe Boever	.05	.04	.02
312	*Scott Brosius*(FC)	.15	.11	.06	403	Bill Krueger	.05	.04	.02
313	Scott Leius	.15	.11	.06	404	Jody Reed	.06	.05	.02
314	Harold Reynolds	.08	.06	.03	405	Mike Schooler	.06	.05	.02
315	Jack Morris	.10	.08	.04	406	Jason Grimsley	.06	.05	.02
316	David Segui	.10	.08	.04	407	Greg Myers	.05	.04	.02
317	Bill Gullickson	.06	.05	.02	408	Randy Ready	.05	.04	.02
318	Todd Frohwirth	.05	.04	.02	409	*Mike Timlin*	.15	.11	.06
319	*Mark Leiter*(FC)	.10	.08	.04	410	Mitch Williams	.08	.06	.03
320	Jeff M. Robinson	.05	.04	.02	411	Garry Templeton	.06	.05	.02
321	Gary Gaetti	.08	.06	.03	412	Greg Cadaret	.05	.04	.02
322	John Smoltz	.10	.08	.04	413	Donnie Hill	.05	.04	.02
323	Andy Benes	.10	.08	.04	414	Wally Whitehurst	.05	.04	.02
324	Kelly Gruber	.08	.06	.03	415	Scott Sanderson	.06	.05	.02
325	Jim Abbott	.10	.08	.04	416	Thomas Howard	.06	.05	.02
326	John Kruk	.06	.05	.02	417	Neal Heaton	.05	.04	.02
327	Kevin Seitzer	.06	.05	.02	418	Charlie Hough	.06	.05	.02
328	Darrin Jackson	.05	.04	.02	419	Jack Howell	.05	.04	.02
329	Kurt Stillwell	.05	.04	.02	420	Greg Hibbard	.06	.05	.02
330	Mike Maddux	.05	.04	.02	421	Carlos Quintana	.06	.05	.02
331	Dennis Eckersley	.10	.08	.04	422	*Kim Batiste*(FC)	.10	.08	.04
332	Dan Gladden	.05	.04	.02	423	Paul Molitor	.10	.08	.04
333	Jose Canseco	.25	.20	.10	424	Ken Griffey, Jr.	.80	.60	.30

		MT	NR MT	EX			MT	NR MT	EX
425	Phil Plantier	.60	.45	.25	516	Lou Whitaker	.08	.06	.03
426	Denny Neagle(FC)	.20	.15	.08	517	Orlando Merced	.20	.15	.08
427	Von Hayes	.06	.05	.02	518	Todd Benzinger	.05	.04	.02
428	Shane Mack	.08	.06	.03	519	Gary Redus	.05	.04	.02
429	Darren Daulton	.06	.05	.02	520	Walt Terrell	.05	.04	.02
430	Dwayne Henry	.05	.04	.02	521	Jack Clark	.08	.06	.03
431	Lance Parrish	.06	.05	.02	522	Dave Parker	.10	.08	.04
432	Mike Humphreys(FC)	.10	.08	.04	523	Tim Naehring	.15	.11	.06
433	Tim Burke	.05	.04	.02	524	Mark Whiten	.15	.11	.06
434	Bryan Harvey	.06	.05	.02	525	Ellis Burks	.10	.08	.04
435	Pat Kelly	.15	.11	.06	526	Frank Castillo	.20	.15	.08
436	Ozzie Guillen	.08	.06	.03	527	Brian Harper	.06	.05	.02
437	Bruce Hurst	.06	.03	.02	528	Brook Jacoby	.06	.05	.02
438	Sammy Sosa	.08	.06	.03	529	Rick Sutcliffe	.06	.05	.02
439	Dennis Rasmussen	.05	.04	.02	530	Joe Klink	.05	.04	.02
440	Ken Patterson	.05	.04	.02	531	Terry Bross	.05	.04	.02
441	Jay Buhner	.08	.06	.03	532	Jose Offerman	.15	.11	.06
442	Pat Combs	.06	.05	.02	533	Todd Zeile	.15	.11	.06
443	Wade Boggs	.15	.11	.06	534	Eric Karros	.30	.25	.12
444	George Brett	.15	.11	.06	535	Anthony Young	.25	.20	.10
445	Mo Vaughn	.35	.25	.12	536	Milt Cuyler	.10	.08	.04
446	Chuck Knoblauch	.35	.25	.14	537	Randy Tomlin	.08	.06	.03
447	Tom Candiotti	.06	.05	.02	538	Scott Livingstone	.20	.15	.08
448	Mark Portugal	.05	.04	.02	539	Jim Eisenreich	.05	.04	.02
449	Mickey Morandini	.10	.08	.04	540	Don Slaught	.05	.04	.02
450	Duane Ward	.05	.04	.02	541	Scott Cooper(FC)	.20	.15	.08
451	Otis Nixon	.05	.04	.02	542	Joe Grahe	.06	.05	.02
452	Bob Welch	.08	.06	.03	543	Tom Brunansky	.06	.05	.02
453	Rusty Meacham(FC)	.10	.08	.04	544	Eddie Zosky	.10	.08	.04
454	Keith Mitchell	.20	.15	.08	545	Roger Clemens	.20	.15	.08
455	Marquis Grissom	.10	.08	.04	546	David Justice	.30	.25	.12
456	Robin Yount	.20	.15	.08	547	Dave Stewart	.10	.08	.04
457	Harvey Pulliam(FC)	.20	.15	.08	548	David West	.05	.04	.02
458	Jose DeLeon	.05	.04	.02	549	Dave Smith	.06	.05	.02
459	Mark Gubicza	.06	.05	.02	550	Dan Plesac	.06	.05	.02
460	Darryl Hamilton	.06	.05	.02	551	Alex Fernandez	.20	.15	.08
461	Tom Browning	.08	.06	.03	552	Bernard Gilkey	.10	.08	.04
462	Monty Fariss	.10	.08	.04	553	Jack McDowell	.10	.08	.04
463	Jerome Walton	.10	.08	.04	554	Tino Martinez	.30	.25	.12
464	Paul O'Neill	.08	.06	.03	555	Bo Jackson	.25	.20	.10
465	Dean Palmer	.20	.15	.08	556	Bernie Williams	.15	.11	.06
466	Travis Fryman	.20	.15	.08	557	Mark Gardner	.06	.05	.02
467	John Smiley	.06	.05	.02	558	Glenallen Hill	.08	.06	.03
468	Lloyd Moseby	.05	.04	.02	559	Oil Can Boyd	.05	.04	.02
469	John Wehner(FC)	.15	.11	.06	560	Chris James	.05	.04	.02
470	Skeeter Barnes(FC)	.06	.05	.02	561	Scott Servais	.15	.11	.06
471	Steve Chitren	.06	.05	.02	562	Rey Sanchez(FC)	.20	.15	.08
472	Kent Mercker	.06	.05	.02	563	Paul McClellan(FC)	.15	.11	.06
473	Terry Steinbach	.08	.06	.03	564	Andy Mota	.15	.11	.06
474	Andres Galarraga	.20	.15	.08	565	Darren Lewis	.15	.11	.06
475	Steve Avery	.10	.08	.04	566	Jose Melendez(FC)	.15	.11	.06
476	Tom Gordon	.50	.40	.20	567	Tommy Greene	.08	.06	.03
477	Cal Eldred(FC)	.08	.06	.03	568	Rich Rodriguez	.06	.05	.02
478	Omar Olivares(FC)	.05	.04	.02	569	Heathcliff Slocumb	.10	.08	.04
479	Julio Machado	.05	.04	.02	570	Joe Hesketh	.05	.04	.02
480	Bob Milacki	.05	.04	.02	571	Carlton Fisk	.15	.11	.06
481	Les Lancaster	.05	.04	.02	572	Erik Hanson	.10	.08	.04
482	John Candelaria	.05	.04	.02	573	Wilson Alvarez	.10	.08	.04
483	Brian Downing	.05	.04	.02	574	Rheal Cormier(FC)	.20	.15	.08
484	Roger McDowell	.05	.04	.02	575	Tim Raines	.10	.08	.04
485	Scott Scudder	.05	.04	.02	576	Bobby Witt	.06	.05	.02
486	Zane Smith	.06	.05	.02	577	Roberto Kelly	.10	.08	.04
487	John Cerutti	.05	.04	.02	578	Kevin Brown	.06	.05	.02
488	Steve Buechele	.06	.05	.02	579	Chris Nabholz	.06	.05	.02
489	Paul Gibson	.05	.04	.02	580	Jesse Orosco	.05	.04	.02
490	Curtis Wilkerson	.05	.04	.02	581	Jeff Brantley	.06	.05	.02
491	Marvin Freeman	.05	.04	.02	582	Rafael Ramirez	.05	.04	.02
492	Tom Foley	.05	.04	.02	583	Kelly Downs	.05	.04	.02
493	Juan Berenguer	.05	.04	.02	584	Mike Simms	.10	.08	.04
494	Ernest Riles	.05	.04	.02	585	Mike Remlinger	.10	.08	.04
495	Sid Bream	.06	.05	.02	586	Dave Hollins	.08	.06	.03
496	Chuck Crim	.05	.04	.02	587	Larry Andersen	.05	.04	.02
497	Mike Macfarlane	.05	.04	.02	588	Mike Gardiner	.08	.06	.03
498	Dale Sveum	.05	.04	.02	589	Craig Lefferts	.05	.04	.02
499	Storm Davis	.05	.04	.02	590	Paul Assenmacher	.05	.04	.02
500	Checklist 401-500	.05	.04	.02	591	Bryn Smith	.05	.04	.02
501	Jeff Reardon	.08	.06	.03	592	Donn Pall	.05	.04	.02
502	Shawn Abner	.05	.04	.02	593	Mike Jackson	.05	.04	.02
503	Tony Fossas	.05	.04	.02	594	Scott Radinsky	.05	.04	.02
504	Cory Snyder	.05	.04	.02	595	Brian Holman	.06	.05	.02
505	Matt Young	.05	.04	.02	596	Geronimo Pena	.08	.06	.03
506	Allan Anderson	.05	.04	.02	597	Mike Jeffcoat	.05	.04	.02
507	Mark Lee	.05	.04	.02	598	Carlos Martinez	.05	.04	.02
508	Gene Nelson	.05	.04	.02	599	Geno Petralli	.05	.04	.02
509	Mike Pagliarulo	.05	.04	.02	600	Checklist 501-600	.05	.04	.02
510	Rafael Belliard	.05	.04	.02	601	Jerry Don Gleaton	.05	.04	.02
511	Jay Howell	.06	.05	.02	602	Adam Peterson	.05	.04	.02
512	Bob Tewksbury	.05	.04	.02	603	Craig Grebeck	.05	.04	.02
513	Mike Morgan	.05	.04	.02	604	Mark Guthrie	.05	.04	.02
514	John Franco	.06	.05	.02	605	Frank Tanana	.05	.04	.02
515	Kevin Gross	.05	.04	.02	606	Hensley Meulens	.08	.06	.03

#	Name	MT	NR MT	EX
607	Mark Davis	.05	.04	.02
608	Eric Plunk	.05	.04	.02
609	Mark Williamson	.05	.04	.02
610	Lee Guetterman	.05	.04	.02
611	Bobby Rose	.05	.04	.02
612	Bill Wegman	.06	.05	.02
613	Mike Hartley	.05	.04	.02
614	Chris Beasley(FC)	.10	.08	.04
615	Chris Bosio	.05	.04	.02
616	Henry Cotto	.05	.04	.02
617	Chico Walker(FC)	.10	.08	.04
618	Russ Swan	.05	.04	.02
619	Bob Walk	.05	.04	.02
620	Billy Swift	.05	.04	.02
621	Warren Newson	.15	.11	.06
622	Steve Bedrosian	.05	.04	.02
623	Ricky Bones(FC)	.15	.11	.06
624	Kevin Tapani	.10	.08	.04
625	Juan Guzman(FC)	1.25	.90	.50
626	Jeff Johnson(FC)	.15	.11	.06
627	Jeff Montgomery	.06	.05	.02
628	Ken Hill	.06	.05	.02
629	Gary Thurman	.05	.04	.02
630	Steve Howe	.06	.05	.02
631	Jose DeJesus	.06	.05	.02
632	Bert Blyleven	.06	.05	.02
633	Jaime Navarro	.06	.05	.02
634	Lee Stevens	.08	.06	.03
635	Pete Harnisch	.08	.06	.03
636	Bill Landrum	.05	.04	.02
637	Rich DeLucia	.06	.05	.02
638	Luis Salazar	.05	.04	.02
639	Rob Murphy	.05	.04	.02
640	Diamond Skills Checklist	.05	.04	.02
641	Roger Clemens (DS)	.25	.20	.10
642	Jim Abbott (DS)	.15	.11	.06
643	Travis Fryman (DS)	.25	.20	.10
644	Jesse Barfield (DS)	.10	.08	.04
645	Cal Ripken, Jr. (DS)	.25	.20	.10
646	Wade Boggs (DS)	.20	.15	.08
647	Cecil Fielder (DS)	.20	.15	.08
648	Rickey Henderson (DS)	.25	.20	.10
649	Jose Canseco (DS)	.25	.20	.10
650	Ken Griffey, Jr. (DS)	.50	.40	.20
651	Kenny Rogers	.05	.04	.02
652	Luis Mercedes(FC)	.20	.15	.08
653	Mike Stanton	.06	.05	.02
654	Glenn Davis	.10	.08	.04
655	Nolan Ryan	.40	.30	.15
656	Reggie Jefferson	.20	.15	.08
657	Javier Ortiz(FC)	.15	.11	.06
658	Greg A. Harris	.05	.04	.02
659	Mariano Duncan	.06	.05	.02
660	Jeff Shaw	.05	.04	.02
661	Mike Moore	.06	.05	.02
662	Chris Haney	.20	.15	.08
663	Joe Slusarski	.20	.15	.08
664	Wayne Housie(FC)	.20	.15	.08
665	Carlos Garcia(FC)	.08	.06	.03
666	Bob Ojeda	.05	.04	.02
667	Bryan Hickerson(FC)	.20	.15	.08
668	Tim Belcher	.06	.05	.02
669	Ron Darling	.06	.05	.02
670	Rex Hudler	.05	.04	.02
671	Sid Fernandez	.08	.06	.03
672	Chito Martinez	.20	.15	.08
673	Pete Schourek	.15	.11	.06
674	Armando Renoso(FC)	.15	.11	.06
675	Mike Mussina	.50	.40	.20
676	Kevin Morton(FC)	.15	.11	.06
677	Norm Charlton	.06	.05	.02
678	Danny Darwin	.05	.04	.02
679	Eric King	.05	.04	.02
680	Ted Power	.05	.04	.02
681	Barry Jones	.05	.04	.02
682	Carney Lansford	.08	.06	.03
683	Mel Rojas	.06	.05	.02
684	Rick Honeycutt	.05	.04	.02
685	Jeff Fassero(FC)	.15	.11	.06
686	Cris Carpenter	.06	.05	.02
687	Tim Crews	.05	.04	.02
688	Scott Terry	.05	.04	.02
689	Chris Gwynn	.05	.04	.02
690	Gerald Perry	.05	.04	.02
691	John Barfield	.05	.04	.02
692	Bob Melvin	.05	.04	.02
693	Juan Agosto	.05	.04	.02
694	Alejandro Pena	.06	.05	.02
695	Jeff Russell	.06	.05	.02
696	Carmelo Martinez	.05	.04	.02
697	Bud Black	.05	.04	.02
698	Dave Otto	.05	.04	.02
699	Billy Hatcher	.05	.04	.02
700	Checklist 601-700	.05	.04	.02
701	Clemente Nunez(FC)	.40	.30	.15
702	"Rookie Threats"	.25	.20	.10
703	Mike Morgan	.06	.05	.02
704	Keith Miller	.06	.05	.02
705	Kurt Stillwell	.06	.05	.02
706	Damon Berryhill	.06	.05	.02
707	Von Hayes	.06	.05	.02
708	Rick Sutcliffe	.10	.08	.04
709	Hubie Brooks	.06	.05	.02
710	Ryan Turner(FC)	.50	.40	.20
711	Diamond Skills Checklist	.06	.05	.02
712	Jose Rijo (DS)	.06	.05	.02
713	Tom Glavine (DS)	.10	.08	.04
714	Shawon Dunston (DS)	.08	.06	.03
715	Andy Van Slyke (DS)	.08	.06	.03
716	Ozzie Smith (DS)	.15	.11	.06
717	Tony Gwynn (DS)	.20	.15	.08
718	Will Clark (DS)	.20	.15	.08
719	Marquis Grissom (DS)	.08	.06	.03
720	Howard Johnson (DS)	.08	.06	.03
721	Barry Bonds (DS)	.20	.15	.08
722	Kirk McCaskill	.06	.05	.02
723	Sammy Sosa	.06	.05	.02
724	George Bell	.08	.06	.03
725	Gregg Jefferies	.12	.09	.05
726	Gary DiSarcina	.06	.05	.02
727	Mike Bordick	.12	.09	.05
728	"400 Homerun Club"	.12	.09	.05
729	Rene Gonzales	.06	.05	.02
730	Mike Bielecki	.06	.05	.02
731	Calvin Jones(FC)	.12	.09	.05
732	Jack Morris	.12	.09	.05
733	Frank Viola	.12	.09	.05
734	Dave Winfield	.15	.11	.06
735	Kevin Mitchell	.12	.09	.05
736	Billy Swift	.08	.06	.03
737	Dan Gladden	.06	.05	.02
738	Mike Jackson	.06	.05	.02
739	Mark Carreon	.06	.05	.02
740	Kirt Manwaring	.06	.05	.02
741	Randy Myers	.06	.05	.02
742	Kevin McReynolds	.08	.06	.03
743	Steve Sax	.08	.06	.03
744	Wally Joyner	.12	.09	.05
745	Gary Sheffield	.30	.25	.12
746	Danny Tartabull	.15	.11	.06
747	Julio Valera	.10	.08	.04
748	Denny Neagle	.10	.08	.04
749	Lance Blankenship	.06	.05	.02
750	Mike Gallego	.06	.05	.02
751	Bret Saberhagen	.12	.09	.05
752	Ruben Amaro(FC)	.15	.11	.06
753	Eddie Murray	.15	.11	.06
754	Kyle Abbott	.15	.11	.06
755	Bobby Bonilla	.15	.11	.06
756	Eric Davis	.15	.11	.06
757	Eddie Taubensee(FC)	.20	.15	.08
758	Andres Galarraga	.08	.06	.03
759	Pete Incaviglia	.08	.06	.03
760	Tom Candiotti	.08	.06	.03
761	Tim Belcher	.08	.06	.03
762	Ricky Bones	.15	.11	.06
763	Bip Roberts	.08	.06	.03
764	Pedro Munoz	.20	.15	.08
765	Greg Swindell	.08	.06	.03
766	Kenny Lofton	.25	.20	.10
767	Gary Carter	.08	.06	.03
768	Charlie Hayes	.06	.05	.02
769	Dickie Thon	.06	.05	.02
770	Diamond Debut Checklist	.06	.05	.02
771	Bret Boone (DD)(FC)	.60	.45	.25
772	Arol Cianfroco (DD)(FC)	.25	.20	.10
773	Mark Clark (DD)(FC)	.25	.20	.10
774	Chad Curtis (DD)(FC)	.25	.20	.10
775	Pat Listach (DD)(FC)	2.00	1.50	.80
776	Pat Mahomes (DD)(FC)	.50	.40	.20
777	Donovan Osborne (DD)(FC)	.40	.30	.15
778	John Patterson (DD)(FC)	.15	.11	.06
779	Andy Stankiewicz (DD)(FC)	.25	.20	.10
780	Turk Wendell (DD)(FC)	.25	.20	.10
781	Bill Krueger	.06	.05	.02
782	"Grand Theft"	.15	.11	.06
783	Kevin Seitzer	.06	.05	.02
784	Dave Martinez	.06	.05	.02
785	John Smiley	.08	.06	.03
786	Matt Stairs(FC)	.08	.06	.03
787	Scott Scudder	.06	.05	.02
788	John Wetteland	.10	.08	.04

		MT	NR MT	EX
789	Jack Armstrong	.06	.05	.02
790	Ken Hill	.08	.06	.03
791	Dick Schofield	.06	.05	.02
792	Mariano Duncan	.06	.05	.02
793	Bill Pecota	.06	.05	.02
794	Mike Kelly(FC)	1.25	.90	.50
795	Willie Randolph	.06	.05	.02
796	Butch Henry(FC)	.20	.15	.08
797	Carlos Hernandez(FC)	.10	.08	.04
798	Doug Jones	.06	.05	.02
799	Melido Perez	.06	.05	.02
800	Checklist	.06	.05	.02

		MT	NR MT	EX
42	Ozzie Smith	.30	.25	.12
43	Darryl Strawberry	.25	.20	.10
44	Robin Yount	.30	.25	.12
45	Rollie Fingers	.30	.25	.12
46	Reggie Jackson	.60	.45	.25
47	Billy Williams	.10	.08	.04
48	Lou Brock	.30	.25	.12
49	Gaylord Perry	.25	.20	.10
50	Ted Williams	.70	.50	.30
51	Brooks Robinson	.50	.40	.20
52	Bob Gibson	.25	.20	.10
53	Bobby Bonds	.10	.08	.04
54	Robin Roberts	.10	.08	.04

1992 Upper Deck FanFest

This 54-card boxed set was made available through special offers at the 1992 National Sports Collectors Convention and at the 1992 All-Star FanFest. The card fronts feature a glossy finish and the All-Star FanFest logo is displayed. The card backs include a player profile. Both "Future Heroes" and past and present "All-Star Heroes" are featured. The complete set was packaged in an attractive blue box with white pinstripes.

		MT	NR MT	EX
Complete Set:		16.00	12.00	6.50
Common Player:		.10	.08	.04
1	Steve Avery	.30	.25	.12
2	Ivan Rodriguez	.60	.45	.25
3	Jeff Bagwell	.30	.25	.12
4	Delino DeShields	.15	.11	.06
5	Royce Clayton	.25	.20	.10
6	Robin Ventura	.30	.25	.12
7	Phil Plantier	.25	.20	.10
8	Ray Lankford	.20	.15	.08
9	Juan Gonzalez	.60	.45	.25
10	Frank Thomas	1.25	.90	.50
11	Roberto Alomar	.80	.60	.30
12	Sandy Alomar, Jr.	.10	.08	.04
13	Wade Boggs	.30	.25	.12
14	Barry Bonds	.25	.20	.10
15	Bobby Bonilla	.25	.20	.10
16	George Brett	.30	.25	.12
17	Jose Canseco	.60	.45	.25
18	Will Clark	.60	.45	.25
19	Roger Clemens	.30	.25	.12
20	Eric Davis	.10	.08	.04
21	Rob Dibble	.10	.08	.04
22	Cecil Fielder	.25	.20	.10
23	Dwight Gooden	.20	.15	.08
24	Ken Griffey, Jr.	1.00	.70	.40
25	Tony Gwynn	.60	.45	.25
26	Bryan Harvey	.10	.08	.04
27	Rickey Henderson	.30	.25	.12
28	Howard Johnson	.10	.08	.04
29	Wally Joyner	.10	.08	.04
30	Barry Larkin	.20	.15	.08
31	Don Mattingly	.25	.20	.10
32	Mark McGwire	.35	.25	.14
33	Dale Murphy	.10	.08	.04
34	Rafael Palmeiro	.10	.08	.04
35	Kirby Puckett	.50	.40	.20
36	Cal Ripken, Jr.	1.00	.70	.40
37	Nolan Ryan	.80	.60	.30
38	Chris Sabo	.10	.08	.04
39	Ryne Sandberg	.60	.45	.25
40	Benito Santiago	.10	.08	.04
41	Ruben Sierra	.25	.20	.10

1992 Upper Deck Ted Williams' Best

Twenty of the best hitters in baseball according to legend Ted Williams are featured in this special insert set from Upper Deck. The cards are styled much like the 1992 FanFest cards and showcase each chosen player. Each card is numbered with a "T" designation.

		MT	NR MT	EX
Complete Set:		60.00	45.00	25.00
Common Player:		1.50	1.25	.60
1	Wade Boggs	2.50	2.00	1.00
2	Barry Bonds	3.00	2.25	1.25
3	Jose Canseco	3.00	2.25	1.25
4	Will Clark	3.00	2.25	1.25
5	Cecil Fielder	3.00	2.25	1.25
6	Tony Gwynn	2.50	2.00	1.00
7	Rickey Henderson	3.00	2.25	1.25
8	Fred McGriff	2.50	2.00	1.00
9	Kirby Puckett	3.00	2.25	1.25
10	Ruben Sierra	3.00	2.25	1.25
11	Roberto Alomar	4.00	3.00	1.50
12	Jeff Bagwell	3.00	2.25	1.25
13	Albert Belle	2.50	2.00	1.00
14	Juan Gonzalez	5.00	3.75	2.00
15	Ken Griffey, Jr.	6.00	4.50	2.50
16	Chris Hoiles	1.50	1.25	.60
17	David Justice	3.00	2.25	1.25
18	Phil Plantier	1.50	1.25	.60
19	Frank Thomas	10.00	7.50	4.00
20	Robin Ventura	3.00	2.25	1.25

Values for recent cards and sets are listed in Mint (MT), Near Mint (NM) and Excellent (EX), reflecting the fact that many cards from recent years have been preserved in top condition. Recent cards and sets in less than Excellent condition have little collector interest.

1993 Upper Deck

Upper Deck introduced its 1993 set in a two series format to adjust to expansion. Cards 1-420 make up the first series. Special subsets in series one include rookies, teammates and community heroes. The card fronts feature full-color player photos surrounded by a white border. "Upper Deck" appears at the top of the photo and the player's name, team and position appear at the bottom. The backs feature vertical photos which is a change from the past and more ccmplete statistics than what Upper Deck has had in the past. The hologram appears in the lower left corner on the card back.

		MT	NR MT	EX
Complete Set:		18.00	13.50	7.25
Common Player:		.05	.04	.02
1	Star Rookie Checklist	.05	.04	.02
2	Mike Piazza(FC)	.30	.25	.12
3	Rene Arocha(FC)	.15	.11	.06
4	Willie Greene(FC)	.15	.11	.06
5	Manny Alexander(FC)	.25	.20	.10
6	Dan Wilson	.12	.09	.05
7	Dan Smith(FC)	.20	.15	.08
8	Kevin Rogers(FC)	.20	.15	.08
9	Nigel Wilson(FC)	.35	.25	.14
10	Joe Vitko(FC)	.15	.11	.06
11	Tim Costo	.15	.11	.06
12	Alan Embree(FC)	.15	.11	.06
13	Jim Tatum(FC)	.25	.20	.10
14	Cris Colon(FC)	.15	.11	.06
15	Steve Hosey(FC)	.12	.09	.05
16	Sterling Hitchcock(FC)	.20	.15	.08
17	Dave Mlicki(FC)	.15	.11	.06
18	Jessie Hollins(FC)	.15	.11	.06
19	Bobby Jones(FC)	.15	.11	.06
20	Kurt Miller(FC)	.15	.11	.06
21	Melvin Nieves(FC)	.20	.15	.08
22	Billy Ashley(FC)	.20	.15	.08
23	J.T. Snow(FC)	.25	.20	.10
24	Chipper Jones	.20	.15	.08
25	Tim Simon(FC)	.15	.11	.06
26	Tim Pugh(FC)	.15	.11	.06
27	Dave Nied(FC)	.30	.25	.12
28	Mike Trombley(FC)	.20	.15	.08
29	Javy Lopez(FC)	.30	.25	.12
30	Community Heroes Checklist	.05	.04	.02
31	Jim Abbott	.10	.08	.04
32	Dale Murphy	.10	.08	.04
33	Tony Pena	.10	.08	.04
34	Kirby Puckett	.20	.15	.08
35	Harold Reynolds	.10	.08	.04
36	Cal Ripken Jr	.20	.15	.08
37	Nolan Ryan	.20	.15	.08
38	Ryne Sandberg	.20	.15	.08
39	Dave Stewart	.10	.08	.04
40	Dave Winfield	.15	.11	.06
41	Teammates Checklist	.05	.04	.02
42	Blockbuster Trade	.12	.09	.05
43	Brew Crew	.12	.09	.05
44	Iron and Steal	.12	.09	.05
45	Youthful Tribe	.12	.09	.05
46	Motown Mashers	.12	.09	.05
47	Yankee Pride	.12	.09	.05
48	Boston Cy Sox	.12	.09	.05
49	Bash Brothers	.12	.09	.05
50	Twin Titles	.12	.09	.05
51	Southside Sluggers	.20	.15	.08

		MT	NR MT	EX
52	Latin Stars	.15	.11	.06
53	Lethal Lefties	.12	.09	.05
54	Royal Family	.12	.09	.05
55	Pacific Sox Exchange	.12	.09	.05
56	George Brett	.15	.11	.06
57	Scott Cooper	.08	.06	.03
58	Mike Maddux	.05	.04	.02
59	Rusty Meacham(FC)	.12	.09	.05
60	Wilfredo Cordero	.15	.11	.06
61	Tim Teufel	.05	.04	.02
62	Jeff Montgomery	.06	.05	.02
63	Scott Livingstone	.08	.06	.03
64	Doug Dascenzo	.05	.04	.02
65	Bret Boone	.20	.15	.08
66	Tim Wakefield(FC)	.20	.15	.08
67	Curt Schilling	.08	.06	.03
68	Frank Tanana	.05	.04	.02
69	Lenny Dykstra	.08	.06	.03
70	Derek Lilliquist	.05	.04	.02
71	Anthony Young	.08	.06	.03
72	Hipolito Pichardo(FC)	.12	.09	.05
73	Rob Beck	.06	.05	.02
74	Kent Hrbek	.08	.06	.03
75	Tom Glavine	.12	.09	.05
76	Kevin Brown	.08	.06	.03
77	Chuck Finley	.08	.06	.03
78	Bob Walk	.05	.04	.02
79	Rheal Cormier	.10	.08	.04
80	Rick Sutcliffe	.08	.06	.03
81	Harold Baines	.08	.06	.03
82	Lee Smith	.08	.06	.03
83	Geno Petralli	.05	.04	.02
84	Jose Oquendo	.05	.04	.02
85	Mark Gubicza	.06	.05	.02
86	Mickey Tettleton	.08	.06	.03
87	Bobby Witt	.06	.05	.02
88	Mark Lewis	.06	.05	.02
89	Kevin Appier	.08	.06	.03
90	Mike Stanton	.05	.04	.02
91	Rafael Belliard	.05	.04	.02
92	Kenny Rogers	.05	.04	.02
93	Randy Velarde	.05	.04	.02
94	Luis Sojo	.05	.04	.02
95	Mark Leiter	.05	.04	.02
96	Jody Reed	.06	.05	.02
97	Pete Harnisch	.06	.05	.02
98	Tom Candiotti	.06	.05	.02
99	Mark Portugal	.05	.04	.02
100	Dave Valle	.05	.04	.02
101	Shawon Dunston	.08	.06	.03
102	B.J. Surhoff	.08	.06	.03
103	Jay Bell	.08	.06	.03
104	Sid Bream	.05	.04	.02
105	Checklist 1-105	.05	.04	.02
106	Mike Morgan	.05	.04	.02
107	Bill Doran	.05	.04	.02
108	Lance Blankenship	.05	.04	.02
109	Mark Lemke	.05	.04	.02
110	Brian Harper	.06	.05	.02
111	Brady Anderson	.08	.06	.03
112	Bip Roberts	.08	.06	.03
113	Mitch Williams	.08	.06	.03
114	Craig Biggio	.08	.06	.03
115	Eddie Murray	.08	.06	.03
116	Matt Nokes	.06	.05	.02
117	Lance Parrish	.06	.05	.02
118	Bill Swift	.06	.05	.02
119	Jeff Innis	.05	.04	.02
120	Mike LaValliere	.05	.04	.02
121	Hal Morris	.08	.06	.03
122	Walt Weiss	.06	.05	.02
123	Ivan Rodriguez	.15	.11	.06
124	Andy Van Slyke	.08	.06	.03
125	Roberto Alomar	.15	.11	.06
126	Robby Thompson	.06	.05	.02
127	Sammy Sosa	.06	.05	.02
128	Mark Langston	.06	.05	.02
129	Jerry Browne	.05	.04	.02
130	Chuck McElroy	.05	.04	.02
131	Frank Viola	.08	.06	.03
132	Leo Gomez	.08	.06	.03
133	Ramon Martinez	.10	.08	.04
134	Don Mattingly	.12	.09	.05
135	Roger Clemens	.15	.11	.06
136	Rickey Henderson	.15	.11	.06
137	Darren Daulton	.12	.09	.05
138	Ken Hill	.08	.06	.03
139	Ozzie Guillen	.08	.06	.03
140	Jerald Clark	.08	.06	.03
141	Dave Fleming	.15	.11	.06
142	Delino DeShields	.12	.09	.05

#	Player	MT	NR MT	EX
143	Matt Williams	.08	.06	.03
144	Larry Walker	.08	.06	.03
145	Ruben Sierra	.12	.09	.05
146	Ozzie Smith	.12	.09	.05
147	Chris Sabo	.08	.06	.03
148	Carlos Hernandez(FC)	.12	.09	.05
149	Pat Borders	.08	.06	.03
150	Orlando Merced	.08	.06	.03
151	Royce Clayton	.08	.06	.03
152	Kurt Stillwell	.06	.05	.02
153	Dave Hollins	.10	.08	.04
154	Mike Greenwell	.08	.06	.03
155	Nolan Ryan	.20	.15	.08
156	Felix Jose	.08	.06	.03
157	Junior Felix	.06	.05	.03
158	Derek Bell	.10	.08	.04
159	Steve Buechele	.06	.05	.02
160	John Burkett	.06	.05	.02
161	Pat Howell(FC)	.15	.11	.06
162	Milt Cuyler	.06	.05	.02
163	Terry Pendleton	.10	.08	.04
164	Jack Morris	.10	.08	.04
165	Tony Gwynn	.15	.11	.06
166	Deion Sanders	.15	.11	.06
167	Mike Devereaux	.08	.06	.03
168	Ron Darling	.08	.06	.03
169	Orel Hershiser	.08	.06	.03
170	Mike Jackson	.05	.04	.02
171	Doug Jones	.06	.05	.02
172	Dan Walters(FC)	.12	.09	.05
173	Darren Lewis	.08	.06	.03
174	Carlos Baerga	.12	.09	.05
175	Ryne Sandberg	.15	.11	.06
176	Gregg Jefferies	.12	.09	.05
177	John Jaha(FC)	.20	.15	.08
178	Luis Polonia	.05	.04	.02
179	Kirt Manwaring	.05	.04	.02
180	Mike Magnante	.08	.06	.03
181	Billy Ripken	.05	.04	.02
182	Mike Moore	.06	.05	.02
183	Eric Anthony	.06	.05	.02
184	Lenny Harris	.05	.04	.02
185	Tony Pena	.06	.05	.02
186	Mike Felder	.05	.04	.02
187	Greg Olson	.05	.04	.02
188	Rene Gonzales	.05	.04	.02
189	Mike Bordick	.08	.06	.03
190	Mel Rojas	.05	.04	.02
191	Todd Frohwirth	.05	.04	.02
192	Darryl Hamilton	.08	.06	.03
193	Mike Fetters	.05	.04	.02
194	Omar Olivares	.05	.04	.02
195	Tony Phillips	.08	.06	.03
196	Paul Sorrento	.08	.06	.03
197	Trevor Wilson	.06	.05	.02
198	Kevin Gross	.05	.04	.02
199	Ron Karkovice	.05	.04	.02
200	Brook Jacoby	.05	.04	.02
201	Mariano Duncan	.05	.04	.02
202	Dennis Cook	.05	.04	.02
203	Daryl Boston	.05	.04	.02
204	Mike Perez	.08	.06	.03
205	Manuel Lee	.05	.04	.02
206	Steve Olin	.05	.04	.02
207	Charlie Hough	.05	.04	.02
208	Scott Scudder	.05	.04	.02
209	Charlie O'Brien	.05	.04	.02
210	Checklist 106-210	.05	.04	.02
211	Jose Vizcaino	.05	.04	.02
212	Scott Leius	.05	.04	.02
213	Kevin Mitchell	.08	.06	.03
214	Brian Barnes	.08	.06	.03
215	Pat Kelly	.08	.06	.03
216	Chris Hammond	.08	.06	.03
217	Rob Deer	.06	.05	.02
218	Cory Snyder	.06	.05	.02
219	Gary Carter	.10	.08	.04
220	Danny Darwin	.05	.04	.02
221	Tom Gordon	.05	.04	.02
222	Gary Sheffield	.10	.08	.04
223	Joe Carter	.10	.08	.04
224	Jay Buhner	.06	.05	.02
225	Jose Offerman	.06	.05	.02
226	Jose Rijo	.06	.05	.02
227	Mark Whiten	.08	.06	.03
228	Randy Milligan	.05	.04	.02
229	Bud Black	.05	.04	.02
230	Gary DiSarcina	.05	.04	.02
231	Steve Finley	.08	.06	.03
232	Dennis Martinez	.08	.06	.03
233	Mike Mussina	.20	.15	.08
234	Joe Oliver	.06	.05	.02
235	Chad Curtis	.15	.11	.06
236	Shane Mack	.08	.06	.03
237	Jaime Navarro	.08	.06	.03
238	Brian McRae	.08	.06	.03
239	Chili Davis	.06	.05	.02
240	Jeff King	.06	.05	.02
241	Dean Palmer	.06	.05	.02
242	Danny Tartabull	.10	.08	.04
243	Charles Nagy	.10	.08	.04
244	Ray Lankford	.15	.11	.06
245	Barry Larkin	.15	.11	.06
246	Steve Avery	.15	.11	.06
247	John Kruk	.08	.06	.03
248	Derrick May	.08	.06	.03
249	Stan Javier	.05	.04	.02
250	Roger McDowell	.05	.04	.02
251	Dan Gladden	.05	.04	.02
252	Wally Joyner	.08	.06	.03
253	Pat Listach	.25	.20	.10
254	Chuck Knoblauch	.10	.08	.04
255	Sandy Alomar Jr.	.10	.08	.04
256	Jeff Bagwell	.15	.11	.06
257	Andy Stankiewicz	.15	.11	.06
258	Darrin Jackson	.06	.05	.02
259	Brett Butler	.08	.06	.03
260	Joe Orsulak	.06	.05	.02
261	Andy Benes	.10	.08	.04
262	Kenny Lofton	.20	.15	.08
263	Robin Ventura	.15	.11	.06
264	Ron Gant	.15	.11	.06
265	Ellis Burks	.08	.06	.03
266	Juan Guzman	.15	.11	.06
267	Wes Chamberlain	.08	.06	.03
268	John Smiley	.06	.05	.02
269	Franklin Stubs	.05	.04	.02
270	Tom Browning	.06	.05	.02
271	Dennis Eckersley	.12	.09	.05
272	Carlton Fisk	.12	.09	.05
273	Lou Whitaker	.08	.06	.03
274	Phil Plantier	.15	.11	.06
275	Bobby Bonilla	.10	.08	.04
276	Ben McDonald	.10	.08	.04
277	Bob Zupcic	.10	.08	.04
278	Terry Steinbach	.06	.05	.02
279	Terry Mulholland	.06	.05	.02
280	Lance Johnson	.06	.05	.02
281	Willie McGee	.06	.05	.02
282	Bret Saberhagen	.08	.06	.03
283	Randy Myers	.08	.06	.03
284	Randy Tomlin	.08	.06	.03
285	Mickey Morandini	.08	.06	.03
286	Brian Williams	.08	.06	.03
287	Tino Martinez	.08	.06	.03
288	Jose Melendez	.08	.06	.03
289	Jeff Huson	.05	.04	.02
290	Joe Grahe	.05	.04	.02
291	Mel Hall	.06	.05	.02
292	Otis Nixon	.06	.05	.02
293	Todd Hundley	.08	.06	.03
294	Casey Candaele	.05	.04	.02
295	Kevin Seitzer	.06	.05	.02
296	Eddie Taubensee	.10	.08	.04
297	Moises Alou	.10	.08	.04
298	Scott Radinsky	.05	.04	.02
299	Thomas Howard	.05	.04	.02
300	Kyle Abbott	.08	.06	.03
301	Omar Vizquel	.05	.04	.02
302	Keith Miller	.05	.04	.02
303	Rick Aguilera	.08	.06	.03
304	Bruce Hurst	.08	.06	.03
305	Ken Caminiti	.06	.05	.02
306	Mike Pagliarulo	.05	.04	.02
307	Frank Seminara(FC)	.12	.09	.05
308	Andre Dawson	.15	.11	.06
309	Jose Lind	.06	.05	.02
310	Joe Boever	.05	.04	.02
311	Jeff Parrett	.05	.04	.02
312	Alan Mills	.05	.04	.02
313	Kevin Tapani	.08	.06	.03
314	Daryl Kile	.08	.06	.03
315	Checklist 211-315	.05	.04	.02
316	Mike Sharperson	.05	.04	.02
317	John Orton	.05	.04	.02
318	Bob Tewksbury	.08	.06	.03
319	Xavier Hernandez	.05	.04	.02
320	Paul Assenmacher	.05	.04	.02
321	John Franco	.08	.06	.03
322	Mike Timlin	.06	.05	.02
323	Jose Guzman	.06	.05	.02
324	Pedro Martinez	.15	.11	.06

		MT	NR MT	EX				MT	NR MT	EX
325	Bill Spiers	.06	.05	.02		373	Ryan Thompson(FC)	.20	.15	.08
326	Melido Perez	.06	.05	.02		374	David Hulse	.15	.11	.06
327	Mike Macfarlane	.06	.05	.02		375	Cal Eldred	.20	.15	.08
328	Ricky Bones	.06	.05	.02		376	Ryan Klesko	.20	.15	.08
329	Scott Bankhead	.06	.05	.02		377	Damion Easley(FC)	.20	.15	.08
330	Rich Rodriguez	.05	.04	.02		378	John Kiely(FC)	.20	.15	.08
331	Geronimo Pena	.06	.05	.02		379	Jim Bullinger(FC)	.12	.09	.05
332	Bernie Williams	.10	.08	.04		380	Brian Bohanon	.08	.06	.03
333	Paul Molitor	.10	.08	.04		381	Rod Brewer	.08	.06	.03
334	Roger Mason	.05	.04	.02		382	Fernando Ramsey(FC)	.15	.11	.06
335	David Cone	.10	.08	.04		383	Sam Militello	.15	.11	.06
336	Randy Johnson	.06	.05	.02		384	Arthur Rhodes	.15	.11	.06
337	Pat Mahomes	.15	.11	.06		385	Eric Karros	.25	.20	.10
338	Erik Hanson	.08	.06	.03		386	Rico Brogna	.12	.09	.05
339	Duane Ward	.06	.05	.02		387	John Valentin(FC)	.12	.09	.05
340	Al Martin(FC)	.15	.11	.06		388	Kerry Woodson(FC)	.12	.09	.05
341	Pedro Munoz	.10	.08	.04		389	Ben Rivera(FC)	.12	.09	.05
342	Greg Colbrunn	.06	.05	.02		390	Matt Whiteside(FC)	.15	.11	.06
343	Julio Valera	.06	.05	.02		391	Henry Rodriguez	.08	.06	.03
344	John Olerud	.10	.08	.04		392	John Wetteland	.08	.06	.03
345	George Bell	.10	.08	.04		393	Kent Mercker	.06	.05	.02
346	Devon White	.08	.06	.03		394	Bernard Gilkey	.08	.06	.03
347	Donovan Osborne	.15	.11	.06		395	Doug Henry	.08	.06	.03
348	Mark Gardner	.06	.05	.02		396	Mo Vaughn	.08	.06	.03
349	Zane Smith	.06	.05	.02		397	Scott Erickson	.08	.06	.03
350	Wilson Alvarez	.06	.05	.02		398	Bill Gullickson	.08	.06	.03
351	Kevin Koslofski(FC)	.15	.11	.06		399	Mark Guthrie	.05	.04	.02
352	Roberto Hernandez	.10	.08	.04		400	Dave Martinez	.05	.04	.02
353	Glenn Davis	.08	.06	.03		401	Jeff Kent	.15	.11	.06
354	Reggie Sanders	.15	.11	.06		402	Chris Hoiles	.15	.11	.06
355	Ken Griffey Jr.	.40	.30	.15		403	Mike Henneman	.08	.06	.03
356	Marquis Grissom	.12	.09	.05		404	Chris Nabholz	.08	.06	.03
357	Jack McDowell	.12	.09	.05		405	Tom Pagnozzi	.08	.06	.03
358	Jimmy Key	.06	.05	.02		406	Kelly Gruber	.08	.06	.03
359	Stan Belinda	.05	.04	.02		407	Bob Welch	.08	.06	.03
360	Gerald Williams	.10	.08	.04		408	Frank Castillo	.08	.06	.03
361	Sid Fernandez	.08	.06	.03		409	John Dopson	.05	.04	.02
362	Alex Fernandez	.08	.06	.03		410	Steve Farr	.06	.05	.02
363	John Smoltz	.10	.08	.04		411	Henry Cotto	.05	.04	.02
364	Travis Fryman	.15	.11	.06		412	Bob Patterson	.05	.04	.02
365	Jose Canseco	.25	.20	.10		413	Todd Stottlemyre	.06	.05	.02
366	David Justice	.15	.11	.06		414	Greg A. Harris	.05	.04	.02
367	Pedro Astacio(FC)	.25	.20	.10		415	Denny Neagle	.08	.06	.03
368	Tim Belcher	.08	.06	.03		416	Bill Wegman	.06	.05	.02
369	Steve Sax	.08	.06	.03		417	Willie Wilson	.06	.05	.02
370	Gary Gaetti	.06	.05	.02		418	Terry Leach	.05	.04	.02
371	Jeff Frye(FC)	.12	.09	.05		419	Willie Randolph	.06	.05	.02
372	Bob Wickman	.20	.15	.08		420	Checklist 316-420	.05	.04	.02

1993 Upper Deck Series II Checklist Was Unavailable at Press Time

V

1989 Very Fine Pirates

This 30-card set Pittsburgh Pirates team set was sponsored by Veryfine fruit juices, and was issued in the form of two uncut, perforated panels, each containing 15 standard-size cards. A third panel featured color action photographs. The panels were distributed in a stadium promotion to fans attending the April 23 Pirates game at Three Rivers Stadium. The cards display the Pirates traditional black and gold   color scheme, and include the player's names and uniform number along the bottom. The "Veryfine" logo appears in the lower right corner. The backs include player data and complete stats.

		MT	NR MT	EX
Complete 3-Panel Set:		20.00	15.00	8.00
Complete Singles Card Set:		12.00	9.00	4.75
Common Player:		.20	.15	.08
0	Junior Ortiz	.20	.15	.08
2	Gary Redus	.30	.25	.12
3	Jay Bell	.30	.25	.12
5	Sid Bream	.30	.25	.12
6	Rafael Belliard	.25	.20	.10
10	Jim Leyland	.30	.25	.12
11	Glenn Wilson	.30	.25	.12
12	Mike La Valliere	.30	.25	.12
13	Jose Lind	.40	.30	.15
14	Ken Oberkfell	.25	.20	.10
15	Doug Drabek	.70	.50	.30
16	Bob Kipper	.20	.15	.08
17	Bob Walk	.25	.20	.10
18	Andy Van Slyke	1.00	.70	.40
23	R.J. Reynolds	.30	.25	.12
24	Barry Bonds	1.50	1.25	.60
25	Bobby Bonilla	1.50	1.25	.60
26	Neal Heaton	.30	.25	.12
30	Benny Distefano	.30	.25	.12
35	Jim Gott	.35	.25	.14
41	Mike Dunne	.30	.25	.12
43	Bill Landrum	.40	.30	.15
44	John Cangelosi	.25	.20	.10
49	Jeff Robinson	.35	.25	.12
52	Dorn Taylor	.30	.25	.12
54	Brian Fisher	.25	.20	.10
57	John Smiley	.50	.40	.20
----	Ray Miller, Tommy Sandt (31-37)	.20	.15	.08
----	Bruce Kimm (32-36)	.20	.15	.08
----	Gene Lamont (32-36)	.20	.15	.08
----	Milt May (39-45)	.20	.15	.08
----	Rich Donnelly (39-45)	.20	.15	.08

W

1950 W576
Callahan Hall Of Fame

These cards, which feature drawings of Hall of Famers, were produced from 1950 through 1956 and sold by the Baseball Hall of Fame in Cooperstown. The cards measure 1-3/4" by 2-1/2" and include a detailed player biography on the back. When introduced in 1950 the set included all members of the Hall of Fame up to that time, and then new cards were added each year as more players were elected. Therefore, cards of players appearing in all previous editions are lesser in value than those players who appeared in just one or two years. When the set was discontinued in 1956 it consisted of 82 cards, which is now considered a complete set. The cards are not numbered and are listed here alphabetically.

		NR MT	EX	VG
Complete Set:		600.00	300.00	180.00
Common Player:		3.00	1.50	.90
(1)	Grover Alexander	6.00	3.00	1.75
(2)	"Cap" Anson	6.00	3.00	1.75
(3)	J. Franklin "Home Run" Baker	7.00	3.50	2.00
(4)	Edward G. Barrow	7.00	3.50	2.00
(5a)	Charles "Chief" Bender (different biography)	7.00	3.50	2.00
(5b)	Charles "Chief" Bender (different biography)	7.00	3.50	2.00
(6)	Roger Bresnahan	3.00	1.50	.90
(7)	Dan Brouthers	3.00	1.50	.90
(8)	Mordecai Brown	3.00	1.50	.90
(9)	Morgan G. Bulkeley	3.00	1.50	.90
(10)	Jesse Burkett	3.00	1.50	.90
(11)	Alexander Cartwright	3.00	1.50	.90
(12)	Henry Chadwick	3.00	1.50	.90
(13)	Frank Chance	3.00	1.50	.90
(14)	Albert B. Chandler	30.00	15.00	9.00
(15)	Jack Chesbro	3.00	1.50	.90
(16)	Fred Clarke	3.00	1.50	.90
(17)	Ty Cobb	50.00	25.00	15.00
(18a)	Mickey Cochran (name incorrect)	50.00	25.00	15.00
(18b)	Mickey Cochrane (name correct)	6.00	3.00	1.75
(19a)	Eddie Collins (different biography)	6.00	3.00	1.75
(19b)	Eddie Collins (different biography)	6.00	3.00	1.75
(20)	Jimmie Collins	3.00	1.50	.90
(21)	Charles A. Comiskey	3.00	1.50	.90
(22)	Tom Connolly	7.00	3.50	2.00
(23)	"Candy" Cummings	3.00	1.50	.90
(24)	Dizzy Dean	30.00	15.00	9.00
(25)	Ed Delahanty	3.00	1.50	.90
(26a)	Bill Dickey (different biography)	30.00	15.00	9.00
(26b)	Bill Dickey (different biography)	30.00	15.00	9.00
(27)	Joe DiMaggio	100.00	50.00	30.00
(28)	Hugh Duffy	3.00	1.50	.90
(29)	Johnny Evers	3.00	1.50	.90
(30)	Buck Ewing	3.00	1.50	.90
(31)	Jimmie Foxx	7.00	3.50	2.00
(32)	Frank Frisch	3.00	1.50	.90
(33)	Lou Gehrig	50.00	25.00	15.00
(34)	Charles Gehringer	3.00	1.50	.90
(35)	Clark Griffith	3.00	1.50	.90
(36)	Lefty Grove	6.00	3.00	1.75
(37)	Leo "Gabby" Hartnett	7.00	3.50	2.00
(38)	Harry Heilmann	3.00	1.50	.90

		NR MT	EX	VG
(39)	Rogers Hornsby	7.00	3.50	2.00
(40)	Carl Hubbell	6.00	3.00	1.75
(41)	Hughey Jennings	3.00	1.50	.90
(42)	Ban Johnson	3.00	1.50	.90
(43)	Walter Johnson	7.00	3.50	2.00
(44)	Willie Keeler	3.00	1.50	.90
(45)	Mike Kelly	3.00	1.50	.90
(46)	Bill Klem	7.00	3.50	2.00
(47)	Napoleon Lajoie	3.00	1.50	.90
(48)	Kenesaw M. Landis	3.00	1.50	.90
(49)	Ted Lyons	7.00	3.50	2.00
(50)	Connie Mack	7.00	3.50	2.00
(51)	Walter Maranville	7.00	3.50	2.00
(52)	Christy Mathewson	7.00	3.50	2.00
(53)	Tommy McCarthy	3.00	1.50	.90
(54)	Joe McGinnity	3.00	1.50	.90
(55)	John McGraw	6.00	3.00	1.75
(56)	Charles Nichols	3.00	1.50	.90
(57)	Jim O'Rourke	3.00	1.50	.90
(58)	Mel Ott	6.00	3.00	1.75
(59)	Herb Pennock	3.00	1.50	.90
(60)	Eddie Plank	3.00	1.50	.90
(61)	Charles Radbourne	3.00	1.50	.90
(62)	Wilbert Robinson	3.00	1.50	.90
(63)	Babe Ruth	100.00	50.00	30.00
(64)	Ray "Cracker" Schalk	7.00	3.50	2.00
(65)	Al Simmons	7.00	3.50	2.00
(66a)	George Sisler (different biography)	3.00	1.50	.90
(66b)	George Sisler (different biography)	3.00	1.50	.90
(67)	A. G. Spalding	3.00	1.50	.90
(68)	Tris Speaker	3.00	1.50	.90
(69)	Bill Terry	7.00	3.50	2.00
(70)	Joe Tinker	3.00	1.50	.90
(71)	"Pie" Traynor	3.00	1.50	.90
(72)	Clarence A. "Dizzy" Vance	7.00	3.50	2.00
(73)	Rube Waddell	3.00	1.50	.90
(74)	Hans Wagner	30.00	15.00	9.00
(75)	Bobby Wallace	7.00	3.50	2.00
(76)	Ed Walsh	3.00	1.50	.90
(77)	Paul Waner	6.00	3.00	1.75
(78)	George Wright	3.00	1.50	.90
(79)	Harry Wright	7.00	3.50	2.00
(80)	Cy Young	7.00	3.50	2.00
---a)	Museum Exterior View (different biography)	7.00	3.50	2.00
---b)	Museum Exterior View (different biography)	7.00	3.50	2.00
---a)	Museum Interior View (different biography)	7.00	3.50	2.00
---b)	Museum Interior View (different biography)	7.00	3.50	2.00

1985 Wendy's Tigers

This 22-card set of cards measuring 2-1/2" by 3-1/2", which carry both Wendy's Hamburgers and Coca-Cola logos was produced by Topps. The cards feature a color photo with the player's team, name and position underneath the picture and the Wendy's logo in the lower left and Coke logo in the upper right. Backs are identical to 1985 Topps cards except they have different card numbers and are done in a red and black color scheme. Cards were distributed three to a pack along with a "Header" checklist in a cellophane package at selected Wendy's outlets in Michigan only.

		MT	NR MT	EX
	Complete Set:	8.00	6.00	3.25
	Common Player:	.15	.11	.06
1	Sparky Anderson	.30	.25	.12
2	Doug Bair	.15	.11	.06
3	Juan Berenguer	.15	.11	.06
4	Dave Bergman	.15	.11	.06
5	Tom Brookens	.15	.11	.06
6	Marty Castillo	.15	.11	.06
7	Darrell Evans	.40	.30	.15
8	Barbaro Garbey	.15	.11	.06
9	Kirk Gibson	.60	.45	.25
10	Johnny Grubb	.15	.11	.06
11	Willie Hernandez	.25	.20	.10
12	Larry Herndon	.15	.11	.06
13	Rusty Kuntz	.15	.11	.06
14	Chet Lemon	.25	.20	.10
15	Aurelio Lopez	.15	.11	.06
16	Jack Morris	1.00	.70	.40
17	Lance Parrish	.80	.60	.30
18	Dan Petry	.25	.20	.10
19	Bill Scherrer	.15	.11	.06
20	Alan Trammell	1.00	.70	.40
21	Lou Whitaker	.80	.60	.30
22	Milt Wilcox	.15	.11	.06

1951 Wheaties

Printed as the backs of single-serving size boxes of Wheaties, the six-card 1951 set includes three baseball players and one football player, basketball player and golfer. Well-trimmed cards measure 2-1/2" by 3-1/4". The cards feature blue line drawings of the athletes with a facsimile autograph and descriptive title below. There is a wide white border.

		NR MT	EX	VG
	Complete Set:	600.00	300.00	180.00
	Common Player:	50.00	25.00	15.00
(1)	Bob Feller (baseball)	125.00	62.00	37.00
(2)	John Lujack (football)	75.00	38.00	23.00
(3)	George K. Mikan (basketball)	125.00	62.00	37.00
(4)	Stan Musial (baseball)	175.00	87.00	52.00
(5)	Sam Snead (golfer)	50.00	25.00	15.00
(6)	Ted Williams (baseball)	200.00	100.00	60.00

1952 Wheaties

These 2" by 2-3/4" cards appeared on the back of the popular cereal boxes. Actually, sports figures had been appearing on the backs of the boxes for many years, but in 1952, of the 30 athletes depicted, 10 were baseball players. That means there are 20 baseball cards, as each player appears in both a portrait and an action drawing. The cards have a blue line drawing on an orange background with a white border. The player's name, team, and position appear at the bottom. The cards have rounded corners and are not widely collected because they have an outdated look, are mixed with other athletes and are often poorly cut from the boxes.

		NR MT	EX	VG
Complete Set:		800.00	400.00	240.00
Common Player:		15.00	7.50	4.50
(1)	Larry "Yogi" Berra (portrait)	50.00	25.00	15.00
(2)	Larry "Yogi" Berra (action pose)	50.00	25.00	15.00
(3)	Roy Campanella (portrait)	50.00	25.00	15.00
(4)	Roy Campanella (action pose)	50.00	25.00	15.00
(5)	Bob Feller (portrait)	40.00	20.00	12.00
(6)	Bob Feller (action pose)	40.00	20.00	12.00
(7)	George Kell (portrait)	18.00	9.00	5.50
(8)	George Kell (action pose)	18.00	9.00	5.50
(9)	Ralph Kiner (portrait)	25.00	12.50	7.50
(10)	Ralph Kiner (action pose)	25.00	12.50	7.50
(11)	Bob Lemon (portrait)	25.00	12.50	7.50
(12)	Bob Lemon (action pose)	25.00	12.50	7.50
(13)	Stan Musial (portrait)	75.00	37.00	22.00
(14)	Stan Musial (action pose)	75.00	37.00	22.00
(15)	Phil Rizzuto (portrait)	30.00	15.00	9.00
(16)	Phil Rizzuto (action pose)	30.00	15.00	9.00
(17)	Elwin "Preacher" Roe (portrait)	15.00	7.50	4.50
(18)	Elwin "Preacher" Roe (action pose)			
		15.00	7.50	4.50
(19)	Ted Williams (portrait)	100.00	50.00	30.00
(20)	Ted Williams (action pose)	100.00	50.00	30.00

1982 Wheaties Indians

TOBY HARRAH
Infield

GET THE

EATIES FOR WHEATIES

—that undeniable, irresistible urge for the crispy, crunchy whole wheat taste of

WHEATIES

The Breakfast of Champions.

These 2-13/16" by 4-1/8" cards were given out ten at a time during three special promotional games; later the complete set was placed on sale at the Indians' gift shop. The 30-card set represented the first time in 30 years that Wheaties had been associated with a baseball card set. The cards feature color photos surrounded by a wide white border with the player's name and position below the picture. The Indians logo is in the lower left corner while the Wheaties logo is in the lower right. Card backs have a Wheaties ad.

		MT	NR MT	EX
Complete Set:		10.00	7.50	4.00
Common Player:		.25	.20	.10
(1)	Chris Bando	.25	.20	.10
(2)	Alan Bannister	.25	.20	.10
(3)	Len Barker	.40	.30	.15
(4)	Bert Blyleven	.90	.70	.35
(5)	Tom Brennan	.25	.20	.10
(6)	Joe Charboneau	.40	.30	.15
(7)	Rodney Craig	.25	.20	.10
(8)	John Denny	.40	.30	.15

		MT	NR MT	EX
(9)	Miguel Dilone	.25	.20	.10
(10)	Jerry Dybzinski	.25	.20	.10
(11)	Mike Fischlin	.25	.20	.10
(12)	Dave Garcia	.25	.20	.10
(13)	Johnny Goryl	.25	.20	.10
(14)	Mike Hargrove	.40	.30	.15
(15)	Toby Harrah	.40	.30	.15
(16)	Ron Hassey	.25	.20	.10
(17)	Von Hayes	.70	.50	.30
(18)	Dennis Lewallyn	.25	.20	.10
(19)	Rick Manning	.25	.20	.10
(20)	Bake McBride	.25	.20	.10
(21)	Tommy McCraw	.25	.20	.10
(22)	Jack Perconte	.25	.20	.10
(23)	Mel Queen	.25	.20	.10
(24)	Dennis Sommers	.25	.20	.10
(25)	Lary Sorensen	.25	.20	.10
(26)	Dan Spillner	.25	.20	.10
(27)	Rick Sutcliffe	.90	.70	.35
(28)	Andre Thornton	.50	.40	.20
(29)	Rick Waits	.25	.20	.10
(30)	Eddie Whitson	.50	.40	.20

1983 Wheaties Indians

JULIO FRANCO
Infield   WHEATIES

A 32-card set marked the second year of Wheaties involvement with the Indians. Distribution of the 2-13/16" by 4-1/8" cards changed slightly in that the entire set was given away on the day of the special promotional game. As happened in 1982, the set was then placed on sale at the team's gift shop. The set includes 27 players, four coaches and the manager. The format of the cards remained basically the same on the front although the backs of player cards were changed to include complete major and minor league statistics.

		MT	NR MT	EX
Complete Set:		8.00	6.00	3.25
Common Player:		.15	.11	.06
(1)	Bud Anderson	.15	.11	.06
(2)	Jay Baller	.20	.15	.08
(3)	Chris Bando	.15	.11	.06
(4)	Alan Bannister	.15	.11	.06
(5)	Len Barker	.25	.20	.10
(6)	Bert Blyleven	.60	.45	.25
(7)	Wil Culmer	.15	.11	.06
(8)	Miguel Dilone	.15	.11	.06
(9)	Juan Eichelberger	.15	.11	.06
(10)	Jim Essian	.15	.11	.06
(11)	Mike Ferraro	.15	.11	.06
(12)	Mike Fischlin	.15	.11	.06
(13)	Julio Franco	1.75	1.25	.70
(14)	Ed Glynn	.15	.11	.06
(15)	Johnny Goryl	.15	.11	.06
(16)	Mike Hargrove	.25	.20	.10
(17)	Toby Harrah	.25	.20	.10
(18)	Ron Hassey	.15	.11	.06
(19)	Neal Heaton	.35	.25	.14
(20)	Rick Manning	.15	.11	.06
(21)	Bake McBride	.15	.11	.06
(22)	Don McMahon	.15	.11	.06
(23)	Ed Napoleon	.15	.11	.06
(24)	Broderick Perkins	.15	.11	.06
(25)	Dennis Sommers	.15	.11	.06

		MT	NR MT	EX
(26)	Lary Sorensen	.15	.11	.06
(27)	Dan Spillner	.15	.11	.06
(28)	Rick Sutcliffe	.60	.45	.25
(29)	Andre Thornton	.50	.40	.20
(30)	Manny Trillo	.25	.20	.10
(31)	George Vukovich	.15	.11	.06
(32)	Rick Waits	.15	.11	.06

1984 Wheaties Indians

BRETT BUTLER
Outfield

The 2-13/16" by 4-1/8" cards again were given out at Municipal Stadium as part of a promotion involving Wheaties and the Indians on July 22. The set was down from 32 cards in 1983 to 29. There are 26 players as well as cards for the manager, coaches and team mascot, Tom-E-Hawk. Designs of the cards are identical to prior years. The 1984 set is numbered by uniform number. A total of 15,000 sets were printed and any left over from the promotion were placed on sale in the team's gift shop.

		MT	NR MT	EX
Complete Set		10.00	7.50	4.00
Common Player		.15	.11	.06
2	Brett Butler	.40	.30	.15
4	Tony Bernazard	.20	.15	.08
8	Carmelo Castillo	.15	.11	.06
10	Pat Tabler	.50	.40	.20
13	Ernie Camacho	.15	.11	.06
14	Julio Franco	1.50	1.25	.60
15	Broderick Perkins	.15	.11	.06
16	Jerry Willard	.15	.11	.06
18	Pat Corrales	.15	.11	.06
21	Mike Hargrove	.25	.20	.10
22	Mike Fischlin	.15	.11	.06
23	Chris Bando	.15	.11	.06
24	George Vukovich	.15	.11	.06
26	Brook Jacoby	.80	.60	.30
27	Steve Farr	.25	.20	.10
28	Bert Blyleven	.60	.45	.25
29	Andre Thornton	.50	.40	.20
30	Joe Carter	2.00	1.50	.80
31	Steve Comer	.15	.11	.06
33	Roy Smith	.15	.11	.06
34	Mel Hall	.40	.30	.15
36	Jamie Easterly	.15	.11	.06
37	Don Schulze	.20	.15	.08
38	Luis Aponte	.15	.11	.06
44	Neal Heaton	.25	.20	.10
46	Mike Jeffcoat	.15	.11	.06
54	Tom Waddell	.20	.15	.08
-----	Coaching Staff (Bobby Bonds, John Goryl, Don McMahon, Ed Napoleon, Dennis Sommers)	.15	.11	.06
-----	Tom-E-Hawk (mascot)	.15	.11	.06

1954 Wilson Franks

The 2-5/8" by 3-3/4" cards are among the most popular and difficult to find baseball card sets issued

with hot dogs during the 1950s. The cards feature color-added photos on the front where the player's name, team and position appear at the top. The front also has a facsimile autograph and a color picture of a package of Wilson's frankfurters. The card backs feature personal information, a short career summary and 1953 and career statistics. The 20-card set includes players from a number of teams and was distributed nationally in the frankfurter packages. The problem with such distribution is that the cards are very tough to find without grease stains from the hot dogs.

		NR MT	EX	VG
Complete Set:		6500.00	3250.00	1950.
Common Player:		175.00	87.00	52.00
(1)	Roy Campanella	750.00	375.00	225.00
(2)	Del Ennis	175.00	87.00	52.00
(3)	Carl Erskine	300.00	150.00	90.00
(4)	Ferris Fain	175.00	87.00	52.00
(5)	Bob Feller	600.00	300.00	180.00
(6)	Nelson Fox	300.00	150.00	90.00
(7)	Johnny Groth	175.00	87.00	52.00
(8)	Stan Hack	175.00	87.00	52.00
(9)	Gil Hodges	500.00	250.00	150.00
(10)	Ray Jablonski	175.00	87.00	52.00
(11)	Harvey Kuenn	300.00	150.00	90.00
(12)	Roy McMillan	175.00	87.00	52.00
(13)	Andy Pafko	175.00	87.00	52.00
(14)	Paul Richards	175.00	87.00	52.00
(15)	Hank Sauer	175.00	87.00	52.00
(16)	Red Schoendienst	300.00	150.00	90.00
(17)	Enos Slaughter	450.00	225.00	135.00
(18)	Vern Stephens	175.00	87.00	52.00
(19)	Sammy White	175.00	87.00	52.00
(20)	Ted Williams	3000.00	1500.00	900.00

1988 Woolworth

This 33-card boxed set was produced by Topps for exclusive distribution at Woolworth stores. The set includes 18 individual player cards and 15 World Series game action photo cards. World Series cards include two for each game of the Series, plus a card of 1987 Series MVP Frank Viola. Card front carry a

Woolworth's Baseball Highlights heading on a red and yellow banner above the blue-bordered super glossy player photo. A white-lettered caption beneath the photo consists of either the player's name or a World Series game notation. Card backs are red, white and blue and contain the Topps logo, card number and "Collector's Series" label above a "1987 Baseball Highlights" logo and a brief description of the photo on the front.

		MT	NR MT	EX
	Complete Set:	4.00	3.00	1.50
	Common Player:	.09	.07	.04
1	Don Baylor	.12	.09	.05
2	Vince Coleman	.15	.11	.06
3	Darrell Evans	.12	.09	.05
4	Don Mattingly	.90	.70	.35
5	Eddie Murray	.30	.25	.12
6	Nolan Ryan	.30	.25	.12
7	Mike Schmidt	.35	.25	.14
8	Andre Dawson	.20	.15	.08
9	George Bell	.25	.20	.10
10	Steve Bedrosian	.12	.09	.05
11	Roger Clemens	.50	.40	.20
12	Tony Gwynn	.35	.25	.14
13	Wade Boggs	.40	.30	.15
14	Benny Santiago	.35	.25	.14
15	Mark McGwire	.40	.30	.15
16	Dave Righetti	.15	.11	.06
17	Jeffrey Leonard	.09	.07	.04
18	Gary Gaetti	.12	.09	.05
19	World Series Game #1 (Frank Viola)	.12	.09	.05
20	World Series Game #1 (Dan Gladden)	.09	.07	.04
21	World Series Game #2 (Bert Blyleven)	.12	.09	.05
22	World Series Game #2 (Gary Gaetti)	.12	.09	.05
23	World Series Game #3 (John Tudor)	.12	.09	.05
24	World Series Game #3 (Todd Worrell)	.12	.09	.05
25	World Series Game #4 (Tom Lawless)	.09	.07	.04
26	World Series Game #4 (Willie McGee)	.12	.09	.05
27	World Series Game #5 (Danny Cox)	.09	.07	.04
28	World Series Game #5 (Curt Ford)	.09	.07	.04
29	World Series Game #6 (Don Baylor)	.12	.09	.05
30	World Series Game #6 (Kent Hrbek)	.15	.11	.06
31	World Series Game #7 (Kirby Puckett)	.25	.20	.10
32	World Series Game #7 (Greg Gagne)	.09	.07	.04
33	World Series MVP (Frank Viola)	.12	.09	.05

1989 Woolworth

This 33-card set was produced by Topps for the Woolworth store chain and was sold in a special box with a checklist on the back. The glossy-coated cards commemorate the most memorable moments in baseball from the the 1988 season, and include the

logo "Woolworth's Baseball Highlights" along the top. The player photos are framed in red, yellow and white and feature the player's name beneath the photo. The backs include a description of the various highlights. Orel Hershiser is pictured on four of the cards, and Jose Canseco appears on two.

		MT	NR MT	EX
	Complete Set:	5.00	3.75	2.00
	Common Player:	.09	.07	.04
1	Jose Canseco	.70	.50	.30
2	Kirk Gibson	.15	.11	.06
3	Frank Viola	.15	.11	.06
4	Orel Hershiser	.15	.11	.06
5	Walt Weiss	.20	.15	.11
6	Chris Sabo	.20	.15	.11
7	George Bell	.15	.11	.06
8	Wade Boggs	.50	.40	.20
9	Tom Browning	.12	.09	.05
10	Gary Carter	.12	.09	.05
11	Andre Dawson	.15	.11	.06
12	John Franco	.09	.07	.04
13	Randy Johnson	.15	.11	.06
14	Doug Jones	.09	.07	.04
15	Kevin McReynolds	.20	.15	.11
16	Gene Nelson	.09	.07	.04
17	Jeff Reardon	.09	.07	.04
18	Pat Tabler	.09	.07	.04
19	Tim Belcher	.25	.20	.10
20	Dennis Eckersley	.15	.11	.06
21	Orel Hershiser	.20	.15	.08
22	Gregg Jefferies	.50	.40	.20
23	Jose Canseco	.70	.50	.30
24	Kirk Gibson	.20	.15	.08
25	Orel Hershiser	.20	.15	.08
26	Mike Marshall	.09	.07	.04
27	Mark McGwire	.50	.40	.20
28	Rick Honeycutt	.09	.07	.04
29	Tim Belcher	.20	.15	.08
30	Jay Howell	.12	.09	.05
31	Mickey Hatcher	.09	.07	.04
32	Mike Davis	.09	.07	.04
33	Orel Hershiser	.15	.11	.06

1990 Woolworth

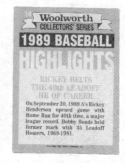

This 33-card set highlights the great baseball moments of 1989. The cards are styled like past Woolworth sets. The set features award winners and regular and post-season highlights.

		MT	NR MT	EX
	Complete Set:	3.00	2.25	1.25
	Common Player:	.06	.05	.02
1	Robin Yount	.20	.15	.08
2	Kevin Mitchell	.15	.11	.06
3	Bret Saberhagen	.10	.08	.04
4	Mark Davis	.06	.05	.02
5	Gregg Olson	.10	.08	.04
6	Jerome Walton	.10	.08	.04
7	Bert Blyleven	.06	.05	.02
8	Wade Boggs	.25	.20	.10
9	George Brett	.20	.15	.08
10	Vince Coleman	.10	.08	.04
11	Andre Dawson	.20	.15	.08
12	Dwight Evans	.10	.08	.04

		MT	NR MT	EX
13	Carlton Fisk	.20	.15	.08
14	Rickey Henderson	.40	.30	.15
15	Dale Murphy	.20	.15	.08
16	Eddie Murray	.20	.15	.08
17	Jeff Reardon	.08	.06	.03
18	Rick Reuschel	.06	.05	.02
19	Cal Ripken, Jr.	.25	.20	.10
20	Nolan Ryan	.40	.30	.15
21	Ryne Sandberg	.25	.20	.10
22	Robin Yount	.20	.15	.08
23	Rickey Henderson	.40	.30	.15
24	Will Clark	.40	.30	.15
25	Dave Stewart	.10	.08	.04
26	Walt Weiss	.08	.06	.03
27	Mike Moore	.06	.05	.02
28	Terry Steinbach	.08	.06	.03
29	Dave Henderson	.08	.06	.03
30	Matt Williams	.20	.15	.08
31	Rickey Henderson	.40	.30	.15
32	Kevin Mitchell	.15	.11	.06
33	Dave Stewart	.10	.08	.04

1991 Woolworth

This 33-card boxed set was produced by Topps for distribution at Woolworth stores. Yellow borders are featured on the fronts of the glossy cards. The back feature baseball highlights from the previous season. Award winners, regular season and World Series highlights are showcased. The cards are numbered on back.

		MT	NR MT	EX
Complete Set:		4.00	3.00	1.50
Common Player:		.08	.06	.03
1	Barry Bonds	.25	.20	.10
2	Rickey Henderson	.25	.20	.10
3	Doug Drabek	.10	.08	.04
4	Bob Welch	.10	.08	.04
5	Dave Justice	.40	.30	.15
6	Sandy Alomar, Jr.	.20	.15	.08
7	Bert Blyleven	.10	.08	.04
8	George Brett	.25	.20	.10
9	Andre Dawson	.25	.20	.10
10	Dwight Evans	.10	.08	.04
11	Alex Fernandez	.20	.15	.08
12	Carlton Fisk	.20	.15	.08
13	Kevin Maas	.20	.15	.08
14	Dale Murphy	.20	.15	.08
15	Eddie Murray	.20	.15	.08
16	Dave Parker	.15	.11	.06
17	Jeff Reardon	.15	.11	.06
18	Cal Ripken	.60	.45	.25
19	Nolan Ryan	.60	.45	.25
20	Ryne Sandberg	.60	.45	.25
21	Bobby Thigpen	.10	.08	.04
22	Robin Yount	.20	.15	.08
23	Nasty Boys	.10	.08	.04
24	Dave Stewart	.10	.08	.04
25	Eric Davis	.15	.11	.06
26	Rickey Henderson	.25	.20	.10
27	Billy Hatcher	.08	.06	.03
28	Joe Oliver	.08	.06	.03
29	Chris Sabo	.15	.11	.06
30	Barry Larkin	.15	.11	.06
31	Jose Rijo	.10	.08	.04
32	Reds Celebrate	.10	.08	.04
33	Jose Rijo	.10	.08	.04

1982 Zellers Expos

Produced and distributed by the Zellers department stores in Canada, this 60-card set was produced in the form of 20 three-card panels. The

Tim Raines
Sliding
Glissade

cards feature a photo of the player surrounded by rings and a yellow background. A red "Zellers" is above the photo and on either side of it are the words "Baseball Pro Tips" in English on the left and in French on the right. The player's name and the title of the playing tip are under the photo. Backs have the playing tip in both languages. Single cards measure 2-1/2" by 3-1/2" while the whole panel is 7-1/2" by 3-1/2". Although a number of stars are depicted, this set is not terribly popular as collectors do not generally like the playing tips idea. Total panels are worth more than separated cards.

		MT	NR MT	EX
Complete Set:		12.00	9.00	4.75
Common Player:		.40	.30	.15
1	Gary Carter (Catching Position)	1.00	.70	.40
2	Steve Rogers (Pitching Stance)	.50	.40	.20
3	Tim Raines (Sliding)	1.00	.70	.40
4	Andre Dawson (Batting Stance)	1.00	.70	.40
5	Terry Francona (Contact Hitting)	.40	.30	.15
6	Gary Carter (Fielding Pop Fouls)	1.00	.70	.40
7	Warren Cromartie (Fielding at First Base)			
		.40	.30	.15
8	Chris Speier (Fielding at Shortstop)			
		.40	.30	.15
9	Billy DeMars (Signals)	.40	.30	.15
10	Andre Dawson (Batting Stroke)	1.00	.70	.40
11	Terry Francona (Outfield Throws)	.40	.30	.15
12	Woodie Fryman (Holding the Runner-Left Handed)			
		.40	.30	.15
13	Gary Carter (Fielding Low Balls)	1.00	.70	.40
14	Andre Dawson (Playing Centerfield)			
		1.00	.70	.40
15	Bill Gullickson (The Slurve)	.50	.40	.20
16	Gary Carter (Catching Stance)	1.00	.70	.40
17	Scott Sanderson (Fielding as a Pitcher)			
		.40	.30	.15
18	Warren Cromartie (Handling Bad Throws)			
		.40	.30	.15
19	Gary Carter (Hitting Stride)	1.00	.70	.40
20	Ray Burris (Holding the Runner-Right Handed)			
		.40	.30	.15

GRADING GUIDE

Mint (MT): A perfect card. Well-centered with all corners sharp and square. No creases, stains, edge nicks, surface marks, yellowing or fading.

Near Mint (NM): A nearly perfect card. At first glance, a NM card appears to be perfect. May be slightly off-center. No surface marks, creases or loss of gloss.

Excellent (EX): Corners are still fairly sharp with only moderate wear. Borders may be off-center. No creases or stains on fronts or backs, but may show slight loss of surface luster.

Very Good (VG): Shows obvious handling. May have rounded corners, minor creases, major gum or wax stains. No major creases, tape marks, writing, etc.

Good (G): A well-worn card, but exhibits no intentional damage. May have major or multiple creases. Corners may be rounded well beyond card border.

1992 Donruss Triple Play

This 264-card set was released in wax pack form only by Donruss. The cards feature red borders and mark the first release of its kind by Donruss. Boyhood photos, mascots and ballparks are among the featured cards. This set was designed to give collectors an alternative product to the high end card sets. The cards are standard sized.

		MT	NR MT	EX
Complete Set:		12.00	9.00	4.75
Common Player:		.05	.04	.02
1	SkyDome	.05	.04	.02
2	Tom Foley	.05	.04	.02
3	Scott Erickson	.20	.15	.08
4	Matt Williams	.15	.11	.06
5	Dave Valle	.05	.04	.02
6	Andy Van Slyke	.08	.06	.03
7	Tom Glavine	.15	.11	.06
8	Kevin Appier	.08	.06	.03
9	Pedro Guerrero	.08	.06	.03
10	Terry Steinbach	.06	.05	.02
11	Terry Mulholland	.06	.05	.02
12	Mike Boddicker	.05	.04	.02
13	Gregg Olson	.12	.09	.05
14	Tim Burke	.05	.04	.02
15	Candy Maldonado	.05	.04	.02
16	Orlando Merced	.15	.11	.06
17	Robin Ventura	.30	.25	.12
18	Eric Anthony	.10	.08	.04
19	Greg Maddux	.12	.09	.05
20	Erik Hanson	.06	.05	.02
21	Bob Ojeda	.05	.04	.02
22	Nolan Ryan	.15	.11	.06
23	Dave Righetti	.06	.05	.02
24	Reggie Jefferson	.20	.15	.08
25	Jody Reed	.06	.05	.02
26	Awesome Action	.05	.04	.02
27	Chili Davis	.05	.04	.02
28	Hector Villanueva	.05	.04	.02
29	Cecil Fielder	.25	.20	.10
30	Hal Morris	.12	.09	.05
31	Barry Larkin	.15	.11	.06
32	Bobby Thigpen	.12	.09	.05
33	Andy Benes	.12	.09	.05
34	Harold Baines	.08	.06	.03
35	David Cone	.12	.09	.05
36	Mark Langston	.08	.06	.03
37	Bryan Harvey	.08	.06	.03
38	John Kruk	.12	.09	.05
39	Scott Sanderson	.05	.04	.02
40	Lonnie Smith	.06	.05	.02
41	Awesome Action	.05	.04	.02
42	George Bell	.08	.06	.03
43	Steve Finley	.06	.05	.02
44	Mickey Tettleton	.08	.06	.03
45	Robby Thompson	.05	.04	.02
46	Pat Kelly	.10	.08	.04
47	Marquis Grissom	.12	.09	.05
48	Tony Pena	.05	.04	.02
49	Alex Cole	.05	.04	.02
50	Steve Buechele	.05	.04	.02
51	Ivan Rodriguez	.50	.40	.20
52	John Smiley	.05	.04	.02
53	Gary Sheffield	.35	.25	.14
54	Greg Olson	.08	.06	.03
55	Ramon Martinez	.08	.06	.03
56	B.J. Surhoff	.08	.06	.03
57	Bruce Hurst	.06	.05	.02
58	Todd Stottlemyre	.05	.04	.02
59	Brett Butler	.06	.05	.02
60	Glenn Davis	.10	.08	.04
61	Awesome Action	.05	.04	.02
62	Lee Smith	.08	.06	.03
63	Rickey Henderson	.25	.20	.10
64	Fun at the Ballpark	.05	.04	.02
65	Rick Aguilera	.05	.04	.02
66	Kevin Elster	.05	.04	.02
67	Dwight Evans	.08	.06	.03
68	Andujar Cedeno	.15	.11	.06
69	Brian McRae	.15	.11	.06
70	Benito Santiago	.12	.09	.05
71	Randy Johnson	.06	.05	.02
72	Roberto Kelly	.12	.09	.05
74	Alex Fernandez	.15	.11	.06
75	Felix Jose	.15	.11	.06
76	Brian Harper	.06	.05	.02
77	Scott Sanderson	.05	.04	.02
78	Ken Caminiti	.06	.05	.02
79	Mo Vaughn	.15	.11	.06
80	Roger McDowell	.05	.04	.02
81	Robin Yount	.20	.15	.08
82	Dave Magadan	.06	.05	.02
83	Julio Franco	.12	.09	.05
84	Roberto Alomar	.15	.11	.06
85	Steve Avery	.20	.15	.08
86	Travis Fryman	.30	.25	.12
87	Fred McGriff	.15	.11	.06
88	Dave Stewart	.06	.05	.02
89	Larry Walker	.15	.11	.06
90	Chris Sabo	.15	.11	.06
91	Chuck Finley	.06	.05	.02
92	Dennis Martinez	.06	.05	.02
93	Jeff Johnson	.06	.05	.02
94	Len Dykstra	.15	.11	.06
95	Mark Whiten	.08	.06	.03
96	Wade Taylor	.08	.06	.03
97	Lance Dickson	.08	.06	.03
98	Kevin Tapani	.06	.05	.02
99	Awesome Action	.05	.04	.02
100	Milt Cuyler	.05	.04	.02
101	Willie McGee	.05	.04	.02
102	Awesome Action	.05	.04	.02
103	Albert Belle	.25	.20	.10
104	Todd Hundley	.08	.06	.03
105	Ben McDonald	.15	.11	.06
106	Doug Drabek	.12	.09	.05
107	Tim Raines	.06	.05	.02
108	Joe Carter	.12	.09	.05
109	Reggie Sanders	.50	.40	.20
110	John Olerud	.15	.11	.06
111	Darren Lewis	.15	.11	.06
112	Juan Gonzalez	.50	.40	.20
113	Awesome Action	.05	.04	.02
114	Mark Grace	.12	.09	.05
115	George Brett	.12	.09	.05
116	Barry Bonds	.20	.15	.08
117	Lou Whitaker	.06	.05	.02
118	Jose Oquendo	.05	.04	.02
119	Lee Stevens	.06	.05	.02
120	Phil Plantier	.40	.30	.15
121	Awesome Action	.05	.04	.02
122	Greg Vaughn	.12	.09	.05
123	Royce Clayton	.25	.20	.10
124	Bob Welch	.06	.05	.02
125	Juan Samuel	.05	.04	.02
126	Ron Gant	.20	.15	.08
127	Edgar Martinez	.08	.06	.03
128	Andy Ashby	.08	.06	.03
129	Jack McDowell	.08	.06	.03
130	Awesome Action	.05	.04	.02
131	Leo Gomez	.12	.09	.05
132	Checklist	.05	.04	.02
133	Phillie Mascot	.05	.04	.02
134	Bret Barbarie	.08	.06	.03
135	Kent Hrbek	.06	.05	.02
136	Hall Of Fame	.05	.04	.02
137	Omar Vizquel	.05	.04	.02
138	The Chicken	.05	.04	.02
139	Terry Pendleton	.08	.06	.03
140	Jim Eisenreich	.05	.04	.02
141	Todd Zeile	.06	.05	.02
142	Todd Van Poppel	.50	.40	.20
143	Darren Daulton	.08	.06	.03
144	Mike Macfarlane	.05	.04	.02
145	Luis Mercedes	.20	.15	.08
146	Trevor Wilson	.05	.04	.02
147	Dave Steib	.05	.04	.02
148	Andy Van Slyke	.08	.06	.03
149	Carlton Fisk	.15	.11	.06

		MT	NR MT	EX
150	Craig Biggio	.08	.06	.03
151	Joe Girardi	.05	.04	.02
152	Ken Griffey, Jr.	1.00	.70	.40
153	Jose Offerman	.08	.06	.03
154	Bobby Witt	.06	.05	.02
155	Will Clark	.35	.25	.14
156	Steve Olin	.08	.06	.03
157	Greg Harris	.05	.04	.02
158	Dale Murphy	.08	.06	.03
159	Don Mattingly	.20	.15	.08
160	Shawon Dunston	.08	.06	.03
161	Bill Gullickson	.06	.05	.02
162	Paul O'Neill	.06	.05	.02
163	Norm Charlton	.06	.05	.02
164	Bo Jackson	.30	.25	.12
165	Tony Fernandez	.06	.05	.02
166	Dave Henderson	.06	.05	.02
167	Dwight Gooden	.15	.11	.06
168	Junior Felix	.06	.05	.02
169	Lance Parrish	.06	.05	.02
170	Pat Combs	.06	.05	.02
171	Chuck Knoblauch	.50	.40	.20
172	John Smoltz	.10	.08	.04
173	Wrigley Field	.05	.04	.02
174	Andre Dawson	.12	.09	.05
175	Pete Harnisch	.05	.04	.02
176	Alan Trammell	.08	.06	.03
177	Kirk Dressendorfer	.08	.06	.03
178	Matt Nokes	.06	.05	.02
179	Wil Cordero	.25	.20	.10
180	Scott Cooper	.08	.06	.03
181	Glenallen Hill	.06	.05	.02
182	John Franco	.06	.05	.02
183	Rafael Palmeiro	.12	.09	.05
184	Jay Bell	.06	.05	.02
185	Bill Wegman	.06	.05	.02
186	Deion Sanders	.15	.11	.06
187	Darryl Strawberry	.25	.20	.10
188	Jaime Navarro	.06	.05	.02
189	Darren Jackson	.06	.05	.02
190	Eddie Zosky	.06	.05	.02
191	Mike Scioscia	.05	.04	.02
192	Chito Martinez	.15	.11	.06
193	Awesome Action	.05	.04	.02
194	Ray Lankford	.30	.25	.12
195	Dennis Eckersley	.10	.08	.04
196	Awesome Action	.05	.04	.02
197	Shane Mack	.06	.05	.02
198	Checklist	.05	.04	.02
199	Cal Ripken	.40	.30	.15
200	Jeff Bagwell	.50	.40	.20
201	David Howard	.05	.04	.02
202	Kirby Puckett	.40	.30	.15
203	Harold Reynolds	.06	.05	.02
204	Jim Abbott	.12	.09	.05
205	Mark Lewis	.08	.06	.03
206	Frank Thomas	1.25	.90	.50
207	Rex Hudler	.05	.04	.02
208	Vince Coleman	.06	.05	.02
209	Delino DeShields	.10	.08	.04
210	Luis Gonzalez	.15	.11	.06
211	Wade Boggs	.25	.20	.10
212	Orel Hershiser	.08	.06	.03
213	Cal Eldred	.25	.20	.10
214	Jose Canseco	.50	.40	.20
215	Jose Guzman	.06	.05	.02
216	Roger Clemens	.40	.30	.15
217	Dave Justice	.30	.25	.14
218	Tony Phillips	.06	.05	.02
219	Tony Gwynn	.25	.20	.10
220	Mitch Williams	.06	.05	.02
221	Bill Sampen	.05	.04	.02
222	Billy Hatcher	.05	.04	.02
223	Gary Gaetti	.06	.05	.02
224	Tim Wallach	.06	.05	.02
225	Kevin Maas	.06	.05	.02
226	Kevin Brown	.06	.05	.02
227	Sandy Alomar	.15	.11	.06
228	John Habyan	.05	.04	.02
229	Ryne Sandberg	.40	.30	.15
230	Greg Gagne	.05	.04	.02
231	Autographs	.05	.04	.02
232	Mike LaValliere	.05	.04	.02
233	Mark Gubicza	.05	.04	.02
234	Lance Parrish	.06	.05	.02
235	Carlos Baerga	.15	.11	.06
236	Howard Johnson	.12	.09	.05
237	Mike Mussina	.70	.50	.30
238	Ruben Sierra	.10	.08	.04
239	Lance Johnson	.06	.05	.02
240	Devon White	.06	.05	.02

		MT	NR MT	EX
241	Dan Wilson	.25	.20	.10
242	Kelly Gruber	.12	.09	.05
243	Brett Butler	.06	.05	.02
244	Ozzie Smith	.15	.11	.06
245	Chuck McElroy	.05	.04	.02
246	Shawn Boskie	.06	.05	.02
247	Mark Davis	.05	.04	.02
248	Bill Landrum	.05	.04	.02
249	Frank Tanana	.05	.04	.02
250	Darryl Hamilton	.08	.06	.03
251	Gary DiSarcina	.05	.04	.02
252	Mike Greenwell	.12	.09	.05
253	Cal Ripken	.15	.11	.06
254	Paul Molitor	.12	.09	.05
255	Tim Teufel	.05	.04	.02
256	Chris Hoiles	.35	.25	.14
257	Rob Dibble	.12	.09	.05
258	Sid Bream	.05	.04	.02
259	Chito Martinez	.08	.06	.03
260	Dale Murphy	.08	.06	.03
261	Greg Hibbard	.06	.05	.02
262	Mark McGwire	.25	.20	.10
263	Oriole Park	.05	.04	.02
264	Checklist	.05	.04	.02

Values quoted in this guide reflect the retail price of a card — the price a collector can expect to pay when buying a card from a dealer. The wholesale price — that which a collector can expect to receive from a dealer when selling cards — will be significantly lower, depending on desirability and condition.

Card company addresses

Collectors frequently want to know the addresses of the major baseball card manufacturers. They are:

Donruss-Leaf
2355 Waukegan Road
Bannockburn, Ill. 60015
Fleer Corp.
Executive Plaza
Suite 300
1120 Route 73
Mt. Laurel, N.J. 08054
Score
c/o Major League Marketing
25 Ford Road
Westport, Conn. 06880
Topps Gum Co.
254 36th St.
Brooklyn, N.Y. 11232
Upper Deck Co.
5909 Sea Otter Place
Carlsbad, Calif. 92008-6621

1992 Kenner statues checklist (37)

Atlanta Braves
Dave Justice $10
Tom Glavine $20

Baltimore Orioles
Cal Ripken Jr. $20

Boston Red Sox
Roger Clemens $10

California Angels
Chuck Finley $30

Chicago Cubs
Ryne Sandberg $15
George Bell $10

Chicago White Sox
Frank Thomas $30
Bo Jackson spring $15
Bo Jackson running $15

Cincinnati Reds
Rob Dibble $10
Chris Sabo $10

Cleveland Indians
Albert Belle $20

Detroit Tigers
Cecil Fielder $30

Houston Astros
Craig Biggio $15

Kansas City Royals
Brian McRae $25

Los Angeles Dodgers
Ramon Martinez $13
Darryl Strawberry $10

Milwaukee Brewers

Minnesota Twins
Scott Erickson $30

Montreal Expos
Ivan Calderon $30

New York Mets
Howard Johnson $15

New York Yankees
Kevin Maas $13

Oakland A's
Jose Canseco $10
Dave Henderson $10
Rickey Henderson $13

Philadelphia Phillies

Pittsburgh Pirates
Barry Bonds $10

St. Louis Cardinals
Felix Jose $30

San Diego Padres
Tony Gwynn $15
Fred McGriff $20

San Francisco Giants
Matt Williams $10
Will Clark $10

Seattle Mariners
Ken Griffey Jr. $15
Ken Griffey Jr. $15

Texas Rangers
Nolan Ryan $20
Juan Gonzalez $30
Ruben Sierra $20

Toronto Blue Jays
Roberto Alomar $15